SOU

Waterloo Station, London, ... Telephone: WATerloo 5100

GENERAL MANAGER: Sir E... STACE MISSENDEN, O.B.E.

DEPUTY GENERAL MANAGER: J. ELLIOT

TRAFFIC MANAGER
R. M. T. RICHARDS, O.B.E.

Superintendent of Operation
S. W. SMART, O.B.E.

Commercial Superintendent
A. E. HAMMETT

Continental Superintendent
R. H. HACKER
(Victoria Station, S.W.1, Phone WATerloo 5100)

Divisional Superintendents (Traffic):
London East: P. NUNN (Orpington, Phone 3940)
London Central: J. BRIDGER, M.B.E. (Redhill, Phone 3361)
London West: C. F. de PURY (Woking, Phone 2424)
Southern: A. E. EDWARDS (Southampton, Phone 76241)
Western: G. BISHOP (Exeter, Phone 4194)
London Dist. Freight: F. H. MARSHALL (84, Tooley St., S.E. 1, Phone WATerloo 5100)

CHIEF CIVIL ENGINEER
V. A. M. ROBERTSON, C.B.E., M.C.

CHIEF ELECTRICAL ENGINEER
C. M. COCK
(15, St. Thomas St. S.E.1, Phone WATerloo 5100)

CHIEF MECHANICAL ENGINEER
O. V. BULLEID
(Brighton Loco Works, Phone 6261)

DOCKS AND MARINE MANAGER
R. P. BIDDLE, C.B.E.
(Dock House, Canute Road, Southampton, Phone 76241)

Divisional Marine Managers:
Southampton: C. A. PRITCHARD (Phone Southampton 76241)
Portsmouth: C. T. PELLY (Phone Portsmouth 6077)
Newhaven: R. J. CARDY (Phone Newhaven 131)
Dover and Folkestone: S. H. ISAAC (Phone Dover 800)

CHIEF OFFICER FOR LABOUR AND ESTABLISHMENT
O. W. CROMWELL

CHIEF ACCOUNTANT
W J. SAWKINS
(Deepdene Hotel, Dorking, Phone 3201)

STORES SUPERINTENDENT
A. B. MACLEOD
(29, Addington St., S.E. 1, Phone WATerloo 5100)

SOLICITOR
H. L. SMEDLEY

ESTATE AND RATING SURVEYOR
A. ENDICOTT, M.B.E.
(Victoria Station, S.W. 1, Phone WATerloo 5100)

CHIEF OF POLICE
W. E. N. GROWDON

PUBLIC RELATIONS OFFICER
C. GRASEMANN

SECRETARY: Brigadier L. F S. DAWES, M.B.E.

CONTENTS

BYE-LAWS AND REGULATIONS.

General Notices, Regulations and Conditions.

Copies of the above will be found exhibited at the Company's stations or, where not so exhibited at any station, a copy can be obtained free of charge from the Booking Office at that station.

INDEX TO STATIONS, Etc.

¶ Denotes Stations at which Car Parking facilities are available.

‡ Car Parking facilities except on Race Days.

§ Through bookings are in operation from certain stations in conjunction with an associated Omnibus Company, see page 505.

* Preceding the page number (thus: *195) denotes that the Station will be found in the Train columns or in the Notes on the page indicated, and *not* in the Station column.

☞ Italic Letter References (thus *M., Tu., W., Th., F., S.*) denote Market Days.
Places printed in Italics, as *Alum Bay*, are not Railway Stations.

LONDON

The various Stations in the Metropolis and environs are detailed under their respective alphabetical headings.

Routes to London

M

See also Routes to London

CROSS-CHANNEL SERVICES

(Passports required for travel to and from the Continent)

Following Departures from VICTORIA to the CONTINENT :—

MORNING SERVICE via DOVER-CALAIS.
(Daily). For PARIS, RIVIERA, SWITZERLAND, ITALY, etc.

"GOLDEN ARROW" SERVICE via DOVER-CALAIS.
(Daily). 1st Class ALL-PULLMAN, LONDON to PARIS. Sea passage by S.S. "INVICTA."

Connecting with Simplon-Orient Express to SWITZERLAND, ITALY and the NEAR EAST, and with principal Continental trains from Paris.

MORNING SERVICE via NEWHAVEN-DIEPPE.
(Daily). For NORMANDY, PARIS, SWITZERLAND, ITALY etc.

MORNING SERVICE via DOVER-OSTEND.
(Daily). For BELGIAN COAST, BRUSSELS, ANTWERP, GERMANY, SWITZERLAND, ITALY, CZECHO-SLOVAKIA, SCANDINAVIA, etc.).

AFTERNOON SERVICE via FOLKESTONE-CALAIS.
(Daily). For PARIS, SWITZERLAND, ITALY, AUSTRIA, etc.

NIGHT SERVICE via DOVER-DUNKERQUE (Train Ferry).
(Every Night **from Dec. 1st**). Through Sleeping Cars, London to Paris.

Following Departures from WATERLOO :—

NIGHT SERVICE via SOUTHAMPTON-HAVRE.
(Every Monday). For ROUEN, PARIS, etc.

NIGHT SERVICE via SOUTHAMPTON to GUERNSEY and JERSEY.
(Every Mon., Wed. and Fri., also Thurs., March 25th, 1948, for Easter).

For Time-table of above Services, Tickets, etc., apply to CONTINENTAL ENQUIRY OFFICE, SOUTHERN RAILWAY, VICTORIA STATION, LONDON, S.W.1, or principal Travel Agencies.

NOTE.—Continental bookings effected not more than 28 days before date of travel.

SOUTHERN RAILWAY OFFICES AND AGENCIES DEALING WITH CROSS-CHANNEL TRAFFIC

CONTINENTAL DEPARTMENT ... **Victoria Station, London, S.W.1.**
(Passenger and Freight Sections)
(Telegrams: "Sudestia London."
Telephone: WATerloo 5100.)

CONTINENTAL ENQUIRY OFFICE ... **Victoria Station, London, S.W.1.**
(Telegrams: "Sudestia London."
Telephone: WATerloo 5100.)

DOVER ... ... **Marine Department, Southern Railway.**
(Telegrams: "Foremost Dover."
Telephone: Dover 800.)

FOLKESTONE ... ... **Marine Department, Southern Railway.**
(Telegrams: "Foremost Folkestone."
Telephone: Folkestone 3728.)

NEWHAVEN ... ... **Marine Department, Southern Railway.**
(Telegrams: "Foremost Newhaven, Sussex."
Telephone: Newhaven 131, Ext. 28.)

SOUTHAMPTON ... ... **Docks and Marine Department, Southern Railway.**
(Telegrams: "Foremost Southampton."
Telephone: Southampton 76241, Ext. 420.)

BÂLE ... ... **Southern Railway Office, Centralbahnplatz, 9.**
(Telegrams: "Sudest Bâle."
Telephone: Bâle 4-18-08 & 4-18-09.)

BOULOGNE ... ... **Southern Railway Office, Gare Maritime.**
(Telegrams: "Sudest Boulogne."
Telephone: Boulogne 9-37.)

BRUSSELS ... ... **Southern Railway Office, 19, Rue de la Régence.**
(Telegrams: "Sudest Brussels."
Telephone: Brussels 12-97-27; 11-53-03; 11-53-23.)

CALAIS ... ... **Southern Railway Office, Gare Maritime.**
(Telegrams: "Sudest Calais."
Telephone Calais 521.)

DIEPPE ... ... **French National Railways (S.N.C.F.), Gare Maritime.**
(Telephone: Dieppe 10-58.)

HAVRE ... ... **Southern Railway Office.**
(Telegrams: "Sudest Havre."
Telephone: Havre 72-81 & 72-82.)

OSTEND ... ... **Southern Railway Office.**
(Telegrams: "Sudest Ostend."
Telephone: Ostend 71140.)

PARIS ... ... **British Railways, 12, Boulevard de la Madeleine**
(Telegrams: "Sudest Paris."
Telephone: OPEra 56-70, 56-71 & 56-72.)

ROUBAIX ... ... **Southern Railway Agency, 118, Avenue Jean Lebas.**
(Telegrams: "Sudest Roubaix."
Telephone: Roubaix 348-51 & 363-21.)

ST. MALO ... ... **Southern Railway Office, Quai St. Vincent.**
(Telegrams: "Sudest St. Malo."
Telephone: St. Malo 75-85.)

GUERNSEY ... ... **Great Western and Southern Railways' Office, The Jetty, St. Peter Port.**
(Telegrams: "Railboats Guernsey."
Telephone: Guernsey 1900.)

JERSEY ... ... **Southern and Great Western Railways' Office, 9, Bond Street, St. Helier.**
(Telegrams: "Railboats Jersey."
Telephone: Central 14.)

The times shown hereunder are liable to alteration.

Southern and Great Western Railway Companies.

JOINT SERVICE TO AND FROM THE
CHANNEL ISLANDS

Via SOUTHAMPTON (Southern Railway) 1st and 3rd Class Rail and Steamer.

OUTWARDS — MONDAYS, WEDNESDAYS & FRIDAYS; also Thursday, March 25th, 1948 (Easter).			INWARDS — MONDAYS, WEDNESDAYS & FRIDAYS.		
London (Waterloo)	dep.	9A0 p.m.	**Jersey**	dep.	8. 0 a.m.
Basingstoke	dep.	9.58 p.m.	**Guernsey**	arr.	9.45 a.m.
Southampton Docks	arr.	10.51 p.m.		dep.	10.15 a.m.
	dep.	11.45 p.m.	Southampton Docks	arr.	4.30 p.m.
Guernsey	arr.	6.30 a.m.		dep.	5B20 p.m.
	dep.	7.15 a.m.	Basingstoke	arr.	6.15 p.m.
Jersey	arr.	9.15 a.m.	**London** (Waterloo)	arr.	7.10 p.m.

A—Refreshment Car, Waterloo-Southampton Docks. **B**—Refreshment Car, Southampton Docks-Waterloo.

Via WEYMOUTH (G.W. Railway) 1st and 3rd Class Rail and Steamer.

OUTWARDS — TUESDAYS, THURSDAYS & SATURDAYS. (Not Christmas Day)			INWARDS — TUESDAYS, THURSDAYS & SATURDAYS. (Not Christmas Day)		
London (Padd.)	dep.	6A0 p.m.C	**Jersey**	dep.	8A15 a.m.
Weymouth Quay	arr.	10A42 p.m.	**Guernsey**	arr.	10A15 a.m.
	dep.	2B0 a.m.		dep.	10A45 a.m.
Guernsey	arr.	7B0 a.m.	Weymouth Quay	arr.	3A 0 p.m
	dep.	7B30 a.m.		dep.	3A40 p.m.D
Jersey	arr.	9B30 a m.	**London** (Paddington)	arr.	8A35 p.m.

A—Not Christmas Day. **B**—Not morning of Fri., Dec. 26th. **C**—Refreshment Car, Paddington to Weymouth. **D**—Refreshment Car, Weymouth to Paddington.

FARES (liable to alteration)

	SINGLE.			RETURN. (Available 3 months.)		
	1st Cl.	3rd Cl. Rail; 1st Cl. Stmr.	3rd Cl.	1st Cl.	3rd Cl. Rail; 1st Cl. Stmr.	3rd Cl.
	£ s. d.	£ s. d.	£ s. d.	£ s. d.	£ s. d.	£ s. d.
London (Waterloo or Paddington)-Guernsey/Jersey or vice versa	3 18 9	3 8 4	2 8 6	6 2 6	5 7 1	3 16 0
Southampton/Weym'th-Guernsey/Jersey or vice versa	2 15 8	—	1 15 11	4 12 5	—	3 1 4
Guernsey-Jersey or vice versa	13 0	—	8 10	1 0 3	—	14 3

For Tickets, Reservations, etc., by S.R. Service to the Channel Islands, apply to **Continental Enquiry Office,** Victoria Station, London, S.W.1, Docks and Marine Manager, Southampton, or principal Travel Agencies.

For Tickets, Reservations etc., by G.W.R. Service to the Channel Islands, apply to Superintendent of the Line, G.W.R., Paddington Station, London, W.2, or Quay Superintendent, G.W.R., Weymouth.

For Tickets, Reservations, etc., for journeys from Jersey or Guernsey, apply to Railway Offices in the Islands (for addresses, see below).

Jersey Office: Southern and G.W. Railways, 9, Bond Street, St. Helier.

Guernsey Office: G.W. and Southern Railways, The Jetty, St. Peter Port.

Why not a *Winter* Holiday in the South of England?

The new edition of the well-known Southern Railway illustrated guide,

"WINTER SUNSHINE HOLIDAYS IN SOUTHERN ENGLAND"

(Season 1947-48)

giving up-to-date details of resorts in Southern England offering holiday attraction to the winter visitor, is now on sale, price 1/-, at Southern Railway Bookstalls and Enquiry Offices.

A handy sized booklet, of 108 pages, it contains lists of special features at coastal and inland resorts, photographs, hotel advertisements, etc.

SUMMARY OF PRINCIPAL SERVICES

NOTE.—The Summary of Trains contained in the following yellow pages are intended ONLY as a quick guide. For full service—see pages 60 to 71.

LONDON (VICTORIA OR CANNON STREET) AND KENT COAST RESORTS

DOWN	MONDAYS TO FRIDAYS											SATS.				
		A	R			R	R	R						A		R
	a.m.	a.m.	p.m.	p.m.	p.m.	p.m.	p.m.	p.m.	p.m.	p.m.	p.m.	a.m.		a.m.		a.m.
VICTORIA dep.	8 35	10 35	12 35	2 35	3 35	...	...	...	...	7 15	9 35	8 35	...	10 35	...	11 35
Cannon Street „	...	...	...	...	...	4 45	5 15	5 45	6 15	...	...	...	...	...	...	...
Whitstable & T. ar.	10 6	12 15	2 23	4 23	5 12	6 3	6 33	7 7	7 31	8 50	11 5	10 6	...	12 15	...	1 6
Herne Bay „	10 16	12 27	2 36	4 35	5 24	6 13	6 42	7 19	7 39	9 2	11 17	10 16	...	12 27	...	1 15
Birchington „	10 29	12 40	2 50	4 48	5 38	6 26	...	7 32	7 52	9 15	11 30	10 29	...	12 40	...	1 28
Westgate-on-S. „	10 35	12 45	2 56	4 54	5 43	6 31	...	7 37	7 57	9 20	11 35	10 35	...	12 45	...	1 33
Margate ... „	10 40	12 50	3 1	4 59	5 48	6 36	6 58	7 42	8 2	9 25	11 40	10 40	...	12 50	...	1 38
Broadstairs „	10 51	1 0	3 13	5 10	5 59	6 47	7 9	7 53	8 12	9 41	11 51	10 51	...	1 0	...	1 49
Dumpton Park „	10 56	1 5	3 18	5 15	6 4	6 51	7 13	7 57	8 16	9 46	11 55	10 56	...	1 5	...	1 54
RAMSGATE „	11 0	1 9	3 22	5 19	6 8	6 55	7 17	8 2	8 20	9 50	11 59	11 0	...	1 9	...	1 58

DOWN	SATURDAYS—*continued*											SUNDAYS				
	R		R						R		R			R	R	
	p.m.		p.m.	p.m.	p.m.	p.m.	p.m.		p.m.		p.m.	a.m.	a.m.	p.m.	p.m.	p.m.
VICTORIA dep.	...	...	...	1 25	2 5	3 35	6 5	...	7 15	...	9 35	9 5	9 50	12 35	3 35	8 35
Cannon Street „	12 45	...	1 15	...	...	...	...	...	...	...	...	...	...	...	...	...
Whitstable & T. ar.	2 3	...	2 35	3 7	3 48	5 12	7 48	...	8 40	...	11 5	10 36	11 32	2 26	5 18	10 16
Herne Bay „	2 15	...	2 46	3 19	4 0	5 24	8 0	...	8 51	...	11 17	10 46	11 44	2 38	5 31	10 28
Birchington „	...	...	2 58	3 32	4 13	5 38	8 13	...	9 4	...	11 30	10 59	11 57	2 51	5 46	10 41
Westgate-on-S. „	...	...	3 3	3 38	4 19	5 43	8 18	...	9 9	...	11 35	11 4	12 2	2 56	5 52	10 46
Margate ... „	2 32	...	3 8	3 44	4 24	5 48	8 23	...	9 14	...	11 40	11 10	12 7	3 1	5 57	10 51
Broadstairs „	2 44	...	3 19	3 55	4 35	5 59	8 34	...	9 25	...	11 51	11 21	12 17	3 11	6 12	11 1
Dumpton Park „	2 49	...	3 24	4 0	4 40	6 4	8 38	...	9 30	...	11 55	11 26	12 22	3 16	6 17	11 6
RAMSGATE „	2 53	...	3 28	4 4	4 44	6 8	8 42	...	9 34	...	11 59	11 30	12 26	3 20	6 21	11 10

UP	MONDAYS TO FRIDAYS												SATURDAYS			
		R	R	R	AR									R	R	AR
	a.m.	a.m.	a.m.	a.m.	a.m.	a.m.	a.m.	p.m.	p.m.		p.m.	p.m.	a.m.	a.m.	a.m.	a.m.
RAMSGATE dep	6 6	6 29	7 20	7 35	8 35	9 45	11 15	1 10	3 15	...	5 25	7 45	6 6	6 29	7 20	8 35
Dumpton Park „	6 9	6 32	7 23	7 38	8 38	9 48	11 18	1 13	3 18	...	5 28	7 48	6 9	6 32	7 23	8 38
Broadstairs „	6 14	6 36	7 27	7 42	8 42	9 52	11 22	1 17	3 23	...	5 32	7 52	6 14	6 36	7 27	8 42
Margate ... „	6 22	6 45	7 36	7 50	8 50	10 0	11 31	1 28	3 34	...	5 41	8 1	6 22	6 45	7 36	8 50
Westgate-on-S. „	6 27	6 50	7 27	7 55	8 55	10 6	11 36	1 33	3 39	...	5 46	8 6	6 27	6 50	7 27	8 55
Birchington „	6 32	6 55	7 32	8 0	...	10 11	11 41	1 38	3 44	...	5 51	8 11	6 32	6 55	7 32	...
Herne Bay „	6 47	7 9	7 52	8 12	9 9	10 24	11 55	1 51	3 58	...	6 4	8 24	6 47	7 9	7 52	9 9
Whitstable & T. „	6 58	7 20	8 1	8 22	9 17	10 35	12 7	2 2	4 10	...	6 16	8 36	6 58	7 20	8 1	9 17
Cannon Street ar.	8 28	8 54	9 19	9 36	...	...	...	...	...	...	...	...	8 28	8 54	9 19	...
VICTORIA „	...	...	...	...	10 39	12 20	2 10	3 48	6 12	...	8 13	10 28	...	...	...	10 39

UP	SATURDAYS—*continued*										SUNDAYS					
			R				R				R	R				
	a.m.	a.m.	p.m.		p.m.	p.m.	p.m.	...	p.m.	p.m.	a.m.	a.m.	p.m.	p.m.	p.m.	p.m.
RAMSGATE dep	9 55	11 30	12 24	...	1 10	1 55	3 43	...	5 26	7 45	8 15	9 40	5 5	5 14	6 30	8 5
Dumpton Park „	9 58	11 33	12 27	...	1 13	1 58	3 46	...	5 29	7 48	8 18	9 43	5 8	5 17	6 33	8 8
Broadstairs „	10 2	11 37	12 32	...	1 17	2 2	3 51	...	5 34	7 52	8 23	9 48	5 13	5 21	6 37	8 12
Margate ... „	10 10	11 46	12 43	...	1 28	2 11	4 2	...	5 43	8 1	8 32	9 57	5 22	5 30	6 46	8 21
Westgate-on-S. „	10 15	11 51	12 48	...	1 33	2 16	4 8	...	5 50	8 6	8 37	10 2	...	5 35	...	8 26
Birchington „	10 20	11 56	12 53	...	1 38	2 21	4 14	...	5 55	8 11	8 42	10 7	...	5 40	...	8 31
Herne Bay „	10 38	12 10	1 5	...	1 51	2 34	4 29	...	6 9	8 24	8 56	10 21	...	5 54	7 4	8 45
Whitstable & T. „	10 45	12 22	1 13	...	2 2	2 46	4 42	...	6 20	8 36	9 7	10 30	...	6 5	7 13	8 54
Cannon Street ar.	...	...	...	...	...	...	...	...	...	...	...	...	...	...	...	...
VICTORIA „	12 22	2 6	2 46	...	3 52	4 20	6 21	...	8 6	10 21	10 49	12 13	7 9	7 46	8 52	10 39

A—Seats in compartments may be reserved, 1/- per seat. Application, with fee, to reach Station Master before 4.0 p.m. day prioı to journey. Seats may NOT be booked by telephone.

R—Refreshment Car facilities available.

Summary of Principal Services—continued. For full services—see pages 34 to 51.

LONDON (CHARING CROSS OR CANNON ST.) AND FOLKESTONE, DOVER, DEAL, SANDWICH

DOWN		MONDAYS TO FRIDAYS											SATURDAYS			
			ARF	R			AR	R		R				ARF	R	
		a.m.	a.m.	p.m.		p.m.	p.m.	p.m.	p.m.	p.m.	p.m.	p.m.	a.m.	a.m.	p.m.	p.m.
CHARING X	dep.	9 15	11 15	1 15	...	3 15	4 15	...	...	7 15	7 34	9 15	9 15	11 15	12 55	1 15
Cannon Street ...	„	...	...	...	...	...	...	5 0	6 18	...	...	...	...	...	...	...
Folkestone C. **B**	arr.	11 10	1 6	2 50	...	5 7	5 40	6 31	7 59	8 40	9‡56	11 9	11 10	1 6	2 20	3 9
Dover Priory ...	„	11 30	1 22	3 5	...	5 28	5 56	6 46	8 18	8 55	10‡18	11 31	11 30	1 22	2 37	3 32
Martin Mill ...	„	11 47	1 36	3 20	...	5 43	6 10	7 0	8 33	9 9	...	11 47	11 47	1 36	2 52	3 47
Walmer	„	11 53	1 42	3 27	...	5 49	6 15	7 5	8 39	9 14	...	11 53	11 53	1 42	2 59	3 53
Deal	„	11 58	1 47	3 32	...	5 55	6 20	7 10	8 44	9 19	...	11 58	11 58	1 47	3 5	3 58
SANDWICH ...	„	12 7	1 56	3 42	...	6 6	6 29	7g 2	8 54	9 28	...	12 8	12 7	1 57	3 15	3g59

DOWN		SATURDAYS—*continued*							SUNDAYS							
			AR	R		R							R			
		p.m.	p.m.	p.m.		p.m.	p.m.	p.m.	a.m.	a.m.	a.m.	p.m.	p.m.	p.m.	p.m.	p.m.
CHARING X ...	dep.	3 15	4 15	6 15	...	7 15	7 34	9 15	7 15	9 15	11 10	12 15	3 15	6 15	8 15	9L 5
Folkestone C. **B**	arr.	5 12	5 40	8 15	...	8 40	9‡56	11 9	9 45	10 40	1 11	2 13	5 3	8 8	10 20	12N 4
Dover Priory ...	„	5 33	5 56	8 34	...	8 55	10‡18	11 31	10 6	10 55	1 31	2 33	5 23	8 28	10 41	12 22
Martin Mill ...	„	5 49	6 10	8 49	...	9 9	...	11 47	10 26	11 11	1 46	2 48	5 37	8 44	10 57	12 46
Walmer	„	5 56	6 15	8 55	...	9 14	...	11 53	10 32	11 17	1 52	2 54	5 43	8 50	11 3	12 52
Deal	„	6 1	6 20	9 0	...	9 19	...	11 58	10 37	11 22	1 57	2 59	5 48	8 55	11 8	12 57
SANDWICH ...	„	6 11	6 29	9 9	...	9 28	...	12 8	10 48	11 33	2 7	3 9	5 57	9 4	11g 3	...

UP		MONDAYS TO FRIDAYS											SATURDAYS			
			R	R	AR		R			ARF				R	R	AR
		a.m.	a.m.	a.m.	a.m.	a.m.	p.m.		p.m.	p.m.	p.m.	p.m.	a.m.	a.m.	a.m.	a.m.
SANDWICH ...	dep.	5 46	7 0	8 3	10 8	11k50	1 7	..	3 14	4 8	5 32	7 40	5 46	7 0	8 3	10 8
Deal	„	5 54	7 11	8 13	10 17	11 42	1 16	...	3 24	4 17	5 42	7 49	5 54	7 11	8 13	10 17
Walmer	„	5 59	7 17	8 19	10 23	11 49	1 21	...	3 29	4 23	5 48	7 54	5 59	7 17	8 19	10 23
Martin Mill ...	„	...	7 25	8 27	10 31	11 57	1 29	...	3 37	4 30	5 56	...	...	7 25	8 27	10 31
Dover Priory ...	„	6 19	7 38	8 42	10 44	12 12	1 42	...	3 50	4 43	6 12	8 13	6 19	7 38	8 42	10 44
Folkestone C. **B**	„	6 37	7 58	9 3	11 5	12 36	2 9	...	4 17	5 3	6 33	8 32	6 37	7 58	9 3	11 5
Cannon Street ...	arr.	...	9 30	...	...	...	...	...	6 54	...	...	...	...	9 30	...	...
CHARING X ...	„	8 42	...	10 38	12 30	2 55	3 46	...	...	6 30	8 41	10 58	8 42	...	10 38	12 30

UP		SATURDAYS—*continued.*						SUNDAYS								
			R		ARF					R						
		a.m.	p.m.		p.m.	p.m.	p.m.	a.m.	a.m.	a.m.	a.m.	p.m.	p.m.	p.m.	p.m.	p.m.
SANDWICH ...	dep.	11k27	1 7	...	4 8	5 32	7 40	...	8k14	10 16	11 39	4 0	4 50	...	6 27	8 4
Deal	„	11 24	1 16	...	4 17	5 42	7 49	...	8 9	10 24	11 48	4 9	4 59	...	6 36	8 13
Walmer	„	11 29	1 21	...	4 23	5 48	7 54	...	8 15	10 30	11 53	4 14	5 5	...	6 42	8 18
Martin Mill ...	„	11 37	1 29	...	4 30	5 56	...	...	8 22	10 37	12 0	4 20	5 13	...	6 49	8 26
Dover Priory ...	„	11 50	1 42	...	4 43	6 12	8 13	6 48	8 36	10 50	12 14	4 33	5 26	...	7 2	8 40
Folkestone C. **B**	„	12 10	2 9	...	5 3	6 33	8 32	7 9	9 1	11 15	12 40	4 53	5 46	6 15	7 18	9 1
CHARING X ...	arr.	2 20	3 47	...	6 30	8 41	10 58	9 28	11 6	1 24	2 39	6 56	7 20	8 17	9 5	11 1

A—Seats in compartments may be reserved, 1/- per seat. Application, with fee, to reach Station Master before 4.0 p.m. day prior to journey. Seats may NOT be booked by telephone. **B**—Station for Sandgate. **g**—Via Ashford and Minster Jc. **k**—Via Minster Jc. and Ashford. ‡—8 minutes later commencing November 29th, 1947. **L**—London Bridge Station. **ϴ**—Third class only **N**—Folkestone Junction Station. **R**—Refreshment Car facilities available. **RF**—Refreshment Car facilities London and Folkestone.

Summary of Principal Services—continued. For full service—see pages 54, 54A and 55, 158 to 194.

LONDON (CHARING CROSS, CANNON STREET OR VICTORIA) AND SEAFORD, EASTBOURNE, BEXHILL AND HASTINGS

DOWN	MONDAYS TO FRIDAYS.														
		H		**B**		**AP**	**A**	**P**	**P**	**R**	**P**	**B**		**B**	**AP**
	a.m.	a.m.	a.m.	a.m.		a.m.	a.m.	a.m.	a.m.	p.m.	p.m.	p.m.	p.m.	p.m.	p.m.
CHARING X dep.	...	...	8 25	...	...	...	10 25	...	...	12 25	...	...	2 25	...	...
Cannon Street ... „	...	...	...	...	...	...	...	...	...	...	...	...	...	...	...
VICTORIA ... „	7L 0	8 0	...	8 28	...	9 45	...	10 45	11 45	...	12 45	1 28	...	2 28	3 45
Seaford ... ... arr.	9 7	9 57	...	10 37	...	11 22	...	12 22	1 22	...	2 22	3H22	...	4H22	5 22
Eastbourne ... „	8 39	...	...	10 26	...	11 9	...	12 9	1 9	...	2 9	3 26	...	4 26	5 11
Bexhill (West) ... „	...	...	10 45	...	...	...	12 44	...	...	2 38	...	...	4 19	...	...
Bexhill (Central) „	9 1	...	...	10 54	...	11 31	...	12 31	1 31	...	2 33	3 54	...	4 54	5 32
West St. Leonards „	...	...	10 38	...	...	...	12 38	...	...	2 28	...	...	4 11	...	...
St. Leonards (WS) „	9 10	...	10 43	11 1	...	11 38	12 42	12 38	1 38	2 33	2 40	4 1	4 15	5 1	5 39
HASTINGS ... „	9 12	...	10 47	11 3	...	11 40	12 46	12 40	1 40	2 37	2 42	4 3	4 19	5 3	5 42

DOWN	MONDAYS TO FRIDAYS—*continued*																
			P	**R**	**R**		**P**			**P**	**H**		**P**		**P**	**B**	**P**
	p.m.	p.m.	p.m.	p.m.	p.m.	p.m.	p.m.	p.m.	p.m.	p.m.	p.m.	p.m.	p.m.		p.m.	p.m.	p.m.
CHARING X ... dep.	...	4 20	...	...	...	...	...	5 31	...	...	...	6 22	...	...	...	...	...
Cannon Street ... „	...	...	...	...	5 6	5 18	...	...	6 3	...	...	...	...	...	...	...	...
VICTORIA ... „	4L 0	...	4 45	5L 3	...	...	5 20	...	...	5L45	6L 5	...	6 45	...	7 45	8 28	10 25
Seaford ... ... arr.	5 38	...	6 12	6 29	...	...	6 42	...	...	7 11	7 33	...	8 23	...	9 22	10H15	11 55
Eastbourne ... „	5 41	...	6 6	6 31	...	...	6 43	...	...	7 14	7 37	...	8 8	...	9 13	10 26	11 56
Bexhill (West) ... „	...	6 10	...	...	6 46	...	...	7 29	7 42	...	...	...	...	...	...	...	...
Bexhill (Ctl.) ... „	6 8	...	6 30	...	...	...	7 6	...	...	7 37	...	...	8 30	...	9 34	...	12 18
West St. Leonards „	...	6 2	...	...	6 38	7 13	...	7 22	7 36	...	...	8 37	...	...	...	...	...
St. Leonards (WS) „	6 18	6 6	6 38	...	6 42	7 17	7 13	7 26	7 40	7 45	...	8 42	8 37	...	9 41	...	12 25
HASTINGS ... „	6 20	6 10	6 40	...	6 46	7 21	7 16	7 30	7 44	7 48	...	8 47	8 39	...	9 44	...	12 27

DOWN	SATURDAYS														
			H				**P**				**AP**		**A**		**P**
	a.m.		a.m.		a.m.		a.m.		a.m.		a.m.		a.m.		a.m.
CHARING X ... dep.	...	...	...	...	8 25	...	...	...	...	...	...	...	10 25	...	...
Cannon Street ... „	...	...	...	...	...	...	...	...	...	...	...	...	...	...	...
VICTORIA ... „	7L 0	...	8 0	...	...	...	8 45	...	9L 0	...	9 45	...	...	...	10 45
Seaford ... ... arr.	9 7	...	9 57	...	...	...	10 37	...	...	...	11 22	...	...	...	12 22
Eastbourne ... „	8 39	...	...	...	...	...	10 9	...	10 44	...	11 9	...	...	...	12 9
Bexhill (West) ... „	...	...	...	...	10 45	...	...	...	...	...	...	...	12 19	...	...
Bexhill (Central) „	9 1	...	...	...	...	...	10 31	...	11 6	...	11 31	...	...	...	12 31
West St. Leonards „	...	...	...	...	10 38	...	...	...	...	...	...	...	12 12	...	...
St. Leonards (WS) „	9 10	...	...	...	10 43	...	10 38	...	11 14	...	11 38	...	12 16	...	12 38
HASTINGS ... „	9 12	...	...	...	10 47	...	10 40	...	11 16	...	11 40	...	12 20	...	12 40

DOWN	SATURDAYS—*continued*															
	P		**R**				**P**		**R**				**P**			**P**
	a.m.		p.m.		p.m.		p.m.		p.m.		p.m.		p.m.		p.m.	p.m.
CHARING X ... dep.	...	...	...	...	12 17	...	...	...	...	...	1 30	...	...	...	2 25	...
Cannon Street ... „	...	...	12 18	...	...	...	...	...	1 2	...	...	...	...	...	...	...
VICTORIA ... „	11 45	...	...	...	...	...	12 45	...	...	...	...	...	1 45	...	...	2 45
Seaford ... ... arr.	1 22	...	...	...	...	...	2 10	...	...	...	...	...	3 22	...	...	4 22
Eastbourne ... „	1 9	...	...	...	...	...	2 11	...	...	...	...	...	3 13	...	...	4 9
Bexhill (West) ... „	...	...	1 54	...	2 27	...	...	...	2 47	...	3 47	...	...	...	4 21	...
Bexhill (Ctl.) ... „	1 31	...	...	...	...	...	2 39	...	...	...	...	...	3 35	...	...	4 31
West St. Leonards „	...	...	1 46	...	2 21	...	...	...	2 38	...	3 42	...	...	...	4 12	...
St. Leonards (WS) „	1 38	...	1 50	...	2 25	...	2 47	...	2 42	...	3 47	...	3 42	...	4 16	4 38
HASTINGS ... „	1 40	...	1 54	...	2 29	...	2 49	...	2 46	...	3 51	...	3 44	..	4 20	4 40

A—Seats in compartments may be reserved 1/- per seat. Application, with fee, to reach Station Master before 4.0 p.m. day prior to journey. Seats may NOT be booked by telephone. **B**—Change at Brighton. **H**—Change at Haywards Heath. **L**—Starts from London Bridge. **P**—Pullman Car facilities available. **R**—Refreshment Car facilities available. Pullman Car Supplementary fees between London or East Croydon and Eastbourne, Hastings, etc., 1st class 3/-, 3rd class 1/6.

Summary of Principal Services—continued.

For full service—see pages 54 to 57, 158 to 233.

LONDON (CHARING CROSS, CANNON STREET OR VICTORIA) AND SEAFORD, EASTBOURNE, BEXHILL AND HASTINGS—*continued*

DOWN	SATURDAYS—*continued*											SUNDAYS				
		AP		**P**		**H**	**B**		**P**	**B**	**P**			**B**		**P**
	p.m.	p.m.		p.m.	p.m.	p.m.	p.m.		p.m.	p.m.	p.m.	a.m.		a.m.	a.m.	a.m.
CHARING X dep.	3 25	...	...	...	5 25	...	...	...	...	...	...	...	...	...	9 25	...
VICTORIA ... „	...	3 45	...	4 45	...	5 28	6 28	...	7 45	8 28	10 25	7L40	...	8 28	...	9 45
Seaford ... ... arr.	...	5 11	...	6 22	...	7 22	8H23	...	9 22	10H15	11 55	9 23	...	10 22	...	11 22
Eastbourne ... „	...	5 11	...	6 9	...	7 27	8 26	...	9 13	10 26	11 56	9 26	...	10 26	...	11 13
Bexhill (West) „	5 16	...	...	...	7 35	...	...	...	...	...	...	...	...	...	11 15	...
Bexhill (Centl.) „	...	5 32	...	6 31	...	7 58	8 54	...	9 34	...	12 18	9 49	...	10 54	...	11 35
West St. L'ards „	5 6	...	...	...	7 15	...	...	...	...	...	...	...	...	...	11 9	...
St. L'ards (WS) „	5 11	5 39	...	6 38	7 19	8 6	9 1	...	9 41	...	12 25	9 56	...	11 1	11 13	11 42
HASTINGS „	5 14	5 42	...	6 40	7 23	8 8	9 3	...	9 44	...	12 27	10 0	...	11 3	11 17	11 44

DOWN	SUNDAYS—*continued.*															
		P		**B**	**B**	**B**	**B**		**P**	**B**	**B**	**P**	**B**		**P**	**P**
	a.m.	a.m.	a.m.	a.m.	p.m.	p.m.	p.m.	p.m.	p.m.	p.m.	p.m.	p.m.	p.m.	p.m.	p.m.	p.m.
CHARING X dep.	10 25	...	11 25	...	...	...	...	3 25	...	...	...	...	...	7 25	...	...
VICTORIA ... „	...	10 45	...	11 28	12 28	1 28	2 28	...	3 45	4 28	5 28	6 45	7 28	...	8 45	9 45
Seaford ... ... arr.	...	12 22	...	1H22	2 22	3H22	4 22	...	5 22	6 22	7H22	8 22	9H21	...	10 42	11 11
Eastbourne ... „	...	12 13	...	1 26	2 26	3 26	4 24	...	5 9	6 24	7 26	8 12	9 26	...	10 11	11 9
Bexhill (West) „	...	...	...	...	...	...	...	5 25	...	...	...	...	...	9 46	...	...
Bexhill (Centl.) „	...	12 35	...	1 54	2 54	3 54	4 54	...	5 31	6 54	7 54	8 36	9 54	...	10 33	11 31
West St. L'ards „	12 8	...	1 18	...	...	...	...	5 17	...	...	...	...	...	9 31	...	...
St. L'ards (WS) „	12 12	12 42	1 23	2 1	3 1	4 1	5 1	5 22	5 38	7 1	8 1	8 43	10 1	9 35	10 40	11 38
HASTINGS „	12 15	12 44	1 27	2 3	3 3	4 3	5 3	5 26	5 40	7 3	8 3	8 46	10 3	9 39	10 42	11 40

UP	MONDAYS TO FRIDAYS														
	H			**P**		**P**	**P**	**R**		**P**		**AP**	**AR**		**B**
	a.m.	a.m.	a.m.	a.m.	a.m.	a.m.	a.m.	a.m.	a.m.	a.m.		a.m.	a.m.		a.m.
HASTINGS dep.	...	6 37	6 58	6 53	7 27	7 35	8 4	8 10	8 25	9 5	...	10 5	10 10	...	10 46
St. L'ards (WS) „	...	6 40	7 0	6 56	7 29	7 38	8 7	8 13	8 28	9 8	...	10 8	10 13	...	10 48
West St. L'ards „	...	...	7 4	...	7 33	...	...	8 17	8 32	...	...	...	10 18	...	...
Bexhill (Centl.) „	...	6 49	...	7 3	...	7 44	8 14	...	...	9 15	...	10 15	...	...	10 55
Bexhill (West) „	...	...	7 0	...	7 30	...	...	8 13	8 30	...	...	...	10 14	...	...
Eastbourne ... „	6 53	7 12	...	7 27	...	8 6	8 36	...	...	9 36	...	10 36	...	...	11 22
Seaford ... ... „	6 53	...	...	7 25	...	8 5	8 38	...	...	9 35	...	10 25	...	...	11H25
VICTORIA ... „	8L33	8 53	...	9L 6	...	9L33	10L 2	...	...	11 3	...	12 3	...	...	1 21
Cannon Street „	...	...	8 47	...	9 9	...	...	9 49	...	...	...	...	...	...	...
CHARING X „	...	...	...	...	...	...	...	...	10 27	...	...	...	12 5	...	...

UP	MONDAYS TO FRIDAYS—*continued*														
	B	**P**	**P**		**AP**		**B**	**P**		**B**	**P**			**B**	**B**
	p.m.	p.m.	p.m.	p.m.	p.m.	...	p.m.	p.m.	p.m.	p.m.	p.m.		p.m.	p.m.	p.m.
HASTINGS dep.	11 46	1 5	2 5	2 10	3 5	...	3 45	5 5	5 10	5 45	7 5	...	7 40	7 46	8 45
St. L'ards (WS) „	11 48	1 8	2 8	2 13	3 8	...	3 47	5 8	5 13	5 47	7 8	...	7 43	7 48	8 47
West St. L'ards „	...	...	...	2 18	...	...	...	...	5 17	...	...	...	7 47	...	...
Bexhill (Centl.) „	11 55	1 15	2 15	...	3 15	...	3 54	5 15	...	5 54	7 15	...	...	7 56	8 54
Bexhill (West) „	...	...	...	2 10	...	...	...	...	5 13	...	...	...	7 35	...	...
Eastbourne ... „	12 22	1 36	2 36	...	3 36	...	4 22	5 36	...	6 23	7 36	...	...	8 22	9 22
Seaford ... ... „	12H25	1 25	2 26	...	3 25	...	4H25	5 35	...	6 25	7 20	...	...	8H25	9 26
VICTORIA ... „	2 21	3 3	4 3	...	5 2	...	6 22	7 2	...	8 25	9 3	...	...	10 22	11 21
Cannon Street „	...	...	...	...	...	...	...	...	...	...	...	...	...	...	...
CHARING X arr.	...	...	...	3 58	...	...	...	...	7 [illegible]8	...	...	...	10 3	...	...

A—Seats in compartments may be reserved 1/– per seat. Application, with fee, to reach Station Master before 4.0 p.m. day prior to journey. Seats may NOT be booked by telephone. **B**—Change at Brighton. **H**—Change at Haywards Heath. **L**—London Bridge. **P**—Pullman Car facilities available. **R**—Refreshment Car facilities available. Pullman Car supplementary fees between London or East Croydon and Eastbourne, Hastings, etc. :—1st class 3/–, 3rd class 1/6.

Summary of Principal Services—continued. For full service—see pages 55, 56 and 57, 197 to 233.

HASTINGS, BEXHILL, EASTBOURNE, SEAFORD AND LONDON (CHARING CROSS, CANNON STREET OR VICTORIA)

UP	SATURDAYS.														
	H					P		P	P		R		P		AP
	a.m.		a.m.	a.m.		a.m.	a.m.	a.m.	a.m.		a.m.		a.m.		a.m.
HASTINGS dep.	...	...	6 37	6 58	...	6 53	7 27	7 35	8 4	...	8 25	...	9 5	...	10 5
St. L'ards (WS) ,,	...	...	6 40	7 0	...	6 56	7 29	7 38	8 7	...	8 28	...	9 8	...	10 8
West St. L'ards ,,	...	...	...	7 4	...	...	7 33	...	...	...	8 32	...	...	...	...
Bexhill (Centl.) ,,	...	...	6 49	...	...	7 3	...	7 44	8 14	...	...	...	9 15	...	10 15
Bexhill (West) ,,	...	...	...	7 0	...	...	7 30	...	...	...	8 30	...	...	...	...
Eastbourne ,,	6 53	...	7 12	...	...	7 27	...	8 6	8 36	...	...	...	9 36	...	10 36
Seaford ... ,,	6 53	...	...	...	...	7 25	...	8 5	8 38	...	...	...	9 35	...	10 25
VICTORIA arr.	8L33	...	8 53	...	...	9L 6	...	9L33	10 3	...	...	...	11 3	...	12 3
Cannon Street ,,	...	...	...	8 47	...	...	9 9	...	...	...	...	...	...	...	...
CHARING X ,,	...	...	...	...	...	...	...	...	...	...	10 27	...	...	...	...

UP	SATURDAYS—*continued*													
	AR			P	P	P		P		AP		B	P	
	a.m.	a.m.		a.m.	p.m.	p.m.		p.m.	p.m.	p.m.	p.m.	p.m.	p.m.	p.m.
HASTINGS dep.	10 10	11 15	...	11 5	12 5	1 5	...	2 5	2 10	3 5	3 30	3 45	5 5	5 10
St. L'ards (WS) ,,	10 13	11 18	...	11 8	12 8	1 8	...	2 8	2 13	3 8	3 33	3 47	5 8	5 13
West St. L'ards ,,	10 18	11 22	...	...	...	...	...	...	2 18	...	3 37	...	...	5 17
Bexhill (Centl.) ,,	...	...	...	11 15	12 15	1 15	...	2 15	...	3 15	...	3 54	5 15	...
Bexhill (West) ,,	10 14	11 15	...	...	...	...	...	...	2 10	...	...	...	...	5 13
Eastbourne ... ,,	...	...	...	11 36	12 36	1 36	...	2 36	...	3 36	...	4 22	5 36	...
Seaford ... ,,	...	...	...	11 25	12 25	1 25	...	2 26	...	3 25	...	4H25	5 25	...
VICTORIA arr.	...	...	...	1 3	2 2	3 3	...	4 3	...	5 2	...	6 22	7 2	...
CHARING X ,,	12 5	1 3	...	...	...	...	...	...	3 58	...	5 19	...	...	7 38

UP	SATURDAYS—*continued*						SUNDAYS								
	B	P			B	B			P		B		B	B	B
	p.m.	p.m.	p.m.		p.m.	p.m.	a.m.	a.m.	a.m.	a.m.	a.m.	a.m.	a.m.	a.m.	p.m.
HASTINGS dep.	5 45	7 5	7 40	...	7 46	8 45	7 19	7 0	9 5	9 10	9 45	10 40	10 45	11 45	12 45
St. L'ards (WS) ,,	5 47	7 8	7 43	...	7 48	8 47	7 21	7 3	9 8	9 13	9 47	10 43	10 47	11 47	12 47
West St. L'ards ,,	...	...	7 47	...	...	...	...	7 7	...	9 17	...	10 47	...	...	...
Bexhill (Centl.) ,,	5 54	7 15	...	...	7 56	8 54	7 30	...	9 15	...	9 54	...	10 54	11 54	12 54
Bexhill (West) ,,	...	...	7 40	...	...	...	...	7 0	...	9 12	...	10 40	...	...	...
Eastbourne ,,	6 23	7 36	...	...	8 22	9 22	7 54	...	9 36	...	10 22	...	11 22	12 22	1 22
Seaford ... ,,	6 25	7 20	...	...	8H25	9 26	8 0	...	9 25	...	10 25		11H25	12 25	1H25
VICTORIA arr.	8 25	9 3	...	...	10 22	11 21	9 42	...	11 3	...	12 20	...	1 20	2 25	3 20
CHARING X ,,	...	...	10 3	...	...	...	...	9 28	...	11 31	...	1 24	...	...	...

UP	SUNDAYS—*continued*													
		B	B	P		P	P		P			B		
	p.m.	p.m.	p.m.	p.m.	p.m.	p.m.	p.m.		p.m.		p.m.	p.m.		p.m.
HASTINGS dep.	1 40	1 45	2 45	4 0	4 50	5 5	6 5	...	7 5	...	7 25	7 45	...	8 40
St. L'ards (WS) ,,	1 43	1 47	2 47	4 3	4 53	5 8	6 8	...	7 8	...	7 28	7 47	...	8 43
West St. L'ards ,,	1 47	...	...	...	4 57	...	...	...	...	...	7 32	...	...	8 47
Bexhill (Centl.) ,,	...	1 54	2 54	4 10	...	5 15	6 15	...	7 15	...	...	7 54	...	...
Bexhill (West) ,,	1 40	...	...	...	4 50	...	...	...	...	...	7 25	...	...	8 35
Eastbourne ,,	...	2 22	3 22	4 32	...	5 36	6 36	...	7 36	...	...	8 22	...	...
Seaford ... ,,	...	2 25	3H25	4 25	...	5 25	6 25	...	7 23	...	...	8 25	...	...
VICTORIA arr.	...	4 20	5 20	6 2	...	7 3	8 3	...	9 4	...	...	10 20	...	...
CHARING X ,,	4 3	...	...	...	6 47	...	...	...	...	...	9 20	...	...	11 1

A—Seats in compartments may be reserved 1/– per seat. Application, with fee, to reach Station Master before 4.0 p.m. day prior to journey. Seats may NOT be booked by telephone. **B**—Change at Brighton. **H**—Change at Haywards Heath. **L**—London Bridge. **P**—Pullman Car facilities available. **R**—Refreshment Car facilities available. Pullman Car supplementary fees between Hastings, Eastbourne, etc., and London or East Croydon :—1st class 3/-, 3rd class 1/6.

Summary of Principal Services—continued. For full service—see pages 158 to 233.

LONDON, BRIGHTON, HOVE & WORTHING (Cen.)

DOWN	WEEK-DAYS													
	E	**E**	**P SX**	**P**		**P**		**AP**		**BB** "Brighton Belle"	**P**		**PE**	**P SO**
	a.m.	a.m.	a.m.	a.m.	a.m.	a.m.		a.m.	a.m.	a.m.	a.m.	a.m.	noon	p.m.
VICTORIA ... dep.	8 0	8 28	9 0	9 25	9 28	10 0	...	10 25	10 28	11 0	11 25	11 28	12 0	*1225*
London Bridge „	...	...	...	...	...	...	...	...	...	...	...	...	...	...
Brighton ... ... arr.	9 21	9 41	10 0	...	10 41	11 0	...	...	11 41	12 0	...	12 41	1§ 0	...
Hove ... ... „	9 30	9 53	...	10 33	...	...	...	11 35	...	...	12 33	...	1 20	*1 28*
WORTHING (Ct.)	9 52	10‡12	...	10 48	...	...	...	11 50	...	...	12 48	...	1§35	*1 43*

DOWN	WEEK-DAYS—*continued*														
	E SX	**P SO**	**E SO**	**PE SO**	**PE SO**	**R SO**	**E**	**PE**		**P SO**	**E**	**BB** "Brighton Belle"	**AP**		**PE**	**SX**
	p.m.	p.m.	p.m.	p.m.	p.m.	p.m.	p.m.	p.m.		p.m.	p.m.	p.m.	p.m.	p.m.	p.m.	p.m.
VICTORIA ... dep.	1228	*12 30*	...	*1 0*	...	...	1 28	2 0	...	*2 25*	2 28	3 0	3 25	3 28	4 0	...
London Bridge „	...	...	*12 30*	...	*1 5*	*1 24*	...	...	...	...	...	...	...	...	...	4 0
Brighton ... ... arr.	1 41	*1 30*	*1 43*	*2 0*	*2 7*	...	2§41	3§ 0	...	...	3 41	4 0	...	4 43	5 0	5 17
Hove ... ... „	1 53	...	*1 53*	*2 20*	*2 20*	*2 29*	2§50	3 20	...	*3 33*	3 53	...	4 33	...	5 20	...
WORTHING (Ct.)	2 12	...	*2 12*	*2 35*	*2 35*	*2 46*	3† 5	3 35	...	*3 48*	4‡12	...	4 48	...	5 35	...

DOWN	WEEK-DAYS—*continued*															
	P SX	**E**	**PE SO**	**P SX**	**R SX**	**PE SX**	**E SO**	**SX**	**P SX**	**R SX**	**PE**	**R SX**	**E SO**	**P SX**	**P SX**	**BB** "Brighton Belle"
	p.m.	p.m.	p.m.	p.m.	p.m.	p.m.	p.m.	p.m.	p.m.	p.m.	p.m.	p.m.	p.m.	p.m.	p.m.	p.m.
VICTORIA ... dep.	4 25	4 28	*5 0*	...	...	5 25	*5 28*	...	5 35	...	6 0	...	*6 28*	6 30	6 35	7 0
London Bridge „	...	...	...	5 0	5 6	...	...	5 30	...	5 45	...	6 5	...	...	...	...
Brighton ... ... arr.	...	5 41	*6 0*	6 0	...	6 25	*6 41*	6 39	...	...	7 0	7P 7	*7 41*	7 30	...	8 0
Hove ... ... „	5 33	5 52	*6 20*	...	6 8	6 33	*6 50*	6H43	6 43	6 48	7§12	7 9	*7 53*	...	7 42	...
WORTHING (Ct.)	5 48	6 15	*6 35*	...	6 26	6 52	*7 5*	6H59	6 59	7 5	7 36	7 24	*8 12*	...	7 57	...

DOWN	WEEK-DAYS—*continued*								SUNDAYS								
	P		**PE SX**	**E**	**PX E**	**P**		**E PR**	**E**	**P**	**P**		**P**	**P**		**BB** "Brighton Belle"	**P**
	p.m.	p.m.	p.m.	p.m.	p.m.	p.m.	p.m.	p.m.	a.m.	a.m.	a.m.		a.m.	a.m.		a.m.	a.m.
VICTORIA ... dep.	7 25	7 28	8 0	8 28	9 28	1025	1028	11 0	8 28	9 0	9 25	...	10 0	1025	...	11 0	1125
London Bridge „	...	...	...	...	...	...	...	...	...	...	...	...	...	...	...	...	...
Brighton ... ... arr.	...	8 42	9 0	9 41	1041	...	1142	12 2	9 42	10 0	...	...	11 0	...	...	12 0	...
Hove ... ... „	8 33	...	9 8	9 53	1053	1131	...	12 8	9 50	...	1033	...	...	1133	...	...	1233
WORTHING (Ct.)	8 48	...	9 31	1012	1115	1147	...	1226	10 6	...	1049	...	...	1149	...	...	1249

DOWN	SUNDAYS—*continued*																
	PE	**E**	**E**	**E**	**E**	**E**		**E**	**PE**	**P**		**P**	**PE**	**P**		**PE**	**P**
	noon	p.m.	p.m.	p.m.	p.m.	p.m.		p.m.	p.m.	p.m.		p.m.	p.m.	p.m.	p.m.	p.m.	p.m.
VICTORIA ... dep.	12 0	12 28	1 28	2 28	3 28	4 28	...	5 28	6 0	7 0	...	7 25	8 0	9 25	9 28	10 0	11 0
Brighton ... ... arr.	1 0	1 40	2 40	3 40	4 40	5 42	...	6 40	7 0	8 0	...	...	9 0	...	10 42	11 0	12 0
Hove ... ... „	1 18	1 53	2 50	3 53	4 53	5 50	...	6 53	7 20	...	...	8 33	9 20	1033	...	11 8	...
WORTHING (Ct.)	1 35	2 12	3 6	4 12	5 12	6 6	...	7 12	7 35	...	...	8 51	9 35	1048	...	11 30	...

A—Seats in compartments may be reserved, 1/- per seat. Application, with fee, to reach Station Master before 4.0 p.m. day prior to journey. Seats may NOT be booked by telephone. **BB**—"Brighton Belle," First and Third Class Pullman Cars only, tickets for which may be obtained in advance upon payment of the supplementary fees. **E**—Hove and Worthing (C.) passengers change at Brighton. **H**—Change at Haywards Heath. **P**—Pullman Car facilities available. **PR**—Pullman Car facilities available on Saturdays, Refreshment Car Mondays to Fridays. **PX**—Pullman Car facilities available Mondays to Fridays. **R**—Refreshment Car facilities available. **SX**—Mondays to Fridays only. **SO**—Saturdays only. †—Seven minutes later Saturdays. ‡—Six minutes earlier Saturdays. §—4 minutes later Saturdays.

Pullman Car Supplementary Fees :—

	1st Class	3rd Class
Between London or East Croydon and Brighton, Hove, Worthing, etc. ...	3/-	1/6
Between Hove and Worthing, etc. ...	1/6	1/6

Summary of Principal Services—continued. For full service—see pages 158 to 233.

WORTHING (Cen.), HOVE, BRIGHTON and LONDON

UP	WEEK-DAYS													
	E a.m.	SX a.m.	R a.m	P a.m.	E a.m.	PB E a.m.	P SX a.m.	P a.m.	PR a.m.	P a.m.	P a.m.	P a.m.	E SX a.m.	PBE SX a.m.
WORTHING (Cen.) dep.	6 37	6 53	7 4	...	7 10	7 26	...	8 0	...	...	...	8 35	8 40	9 6
Hove ... ... ,,	6 57	7 13	7 25	...	7 30	7 49	8 7	8 15	...	...	...	8 50	8 59	9 25
Brighton ... ... ,,	7 8	...	7 19	7 40	7 45	8 0	...	...	8 20	8 35	8 43	...	9 15	9 35
London Bridge ... arr.	8 13	8 29	8 33	...	8 55	...	...	9H23	9 23	...	9 45	9 51	10 21	...
VICTORIA ... ... ,,	8 15	...	...	8 46	...	9 4	9 18	9 21	...	9 42	...	...	...	10 35

UP	WEEK-DAYS—*continued*												
	P a.m.	a.m.	P SO a.m.	P a.m.	PB E a.m.	E a.m.	PBE SO a.m.	AP p.m.	BB "Brighton Belle" p.m.	P SX p.m.	PB E p.m.	AP p.m.	PB E p.m.
WORTHING (Cen.) dep.	9 35	...	...	10 35	10 52	11 22	*11 51*	12 35	...	1 35	1 52	2 35	2 52
Hove ... ... ,,	9 50	...	...	10 50	11 16	11 45	*12 14*	12 50	...	1 50	2 15	2 50	3 16
Brighton ... ... ,,	...	10 8	*10 25*	...	11 25	12 8	*12 25*	...	1 25	...	2 25	...	3 25
London Bridge ... arr.	...	...	...	...	...	...	...	...	...	...	...	...	...
VICTORIA ... ... ,,	10 57	11 21	*11 25*	11 57	12 25	1 21	*1 25*	1 57	2 25	2 57	3 25	3 58	4 25

UP	WEEK-DAYS—*continued*													
	P SO p.m.	p.m.	PBE SX p.m.	E p.m.	BB "Brighton Belle" p.m.	P SO p.m.	PB E p.m.	PB E p.m.	P p.m.	p.m.	P SO p.m.	PR p.m.	BB "Brighton Belle" p.m.	E p.m.
WORTHING (Cen.) dep.	*3 35*	...	3 52	4 22	...	*5 35*	5 52	6 52	7 35	...	...	8 35	...	9 21
Hove ... ... ,,	*3 50*	...	4 16	4 45	...	*5 50*	6 15	7 7	7 50	...	...	8 50	...	9 43
Brighton ... ... ,,	...	4 8	4 25	5 8	5 25	...	6 25	7 25	...	8 8	*8 25*	...	9 25	10 8
VICTORIA ... ... arr.	*4 58*	5 22	5 25	6 22	6 25	*6 58*	7 25	8 25	8 57	9 22	*9 25*	9 57	10 25	11 21

UP	SUNDAYS													
	PB E a.m.	E a.m.			E a.m.	PB E a.m.		E a.m.	E a.m.		PB E p.m.	E p.m.		E p.m.
WORTHING (Cen.) dep.	6 52	7 31	...	...	8 41	9 41	...	10 41	11 41	...	12 52	1 22	...	2 22
Hove	7 14	7 47	...	...	8 59	9 59	...	10 59	11 59	...	1 15	1 45	...	2 45
Brighton	7 25	7 55	...	...	9 8	10 8	...	11 8	12 8	...	1 25	2 8	...	3 8
VICTORIA ... arr.	8 27	9 12	...	...	10 20	11 20	...	12 20	1 20	...	2 25	3 20	...	4 20

UP	SUNDAYS—*continued*													
	P p.m.	PB E p.m.	E p.m.	BB "Brighton Belle" p.m.	P p.m.	PB E p.m.	P p.m.	PB E p.m.		PB E p.m.	P p.m.		PB E p.m.	E p.m.
WORTHING (Cen.) dep.	3 35	3 52	4 22	...	5 35	5 51	6 35	6 52	...	7 49	8 35	...	8 52	9 21
Hove	3 50	4 16	4 45	...	5 50	6 15	6 50	7 16	...	8 12	8 50	...	9 15	9 43
Brighton	...	4 25	5 8	5 25	...	6 25	...	7 25	...	8 25	...	...	9 25	10 8
VICTORIA ... arr.	4 57	5 25	6 21	6 25	6 57	7 25	7 55	8 25	...	9 25	9 59	...	10 25	11 20

A—Seats in compartments may be reserved, 1/- per seat. Application, with fee, to reach Station Master before 4.0 p.m. day prior to journey. Seats may NOT be booked by telephone. **BB**—"Brighton Belle," First and Third Class Pullman Cars only, tickets for which may be obtained in advance upon payment of the supplementary fees. **E**—Worthing (C.) and Hove passengers change at Brighton. **H**—Change at Haywards Heath. **P**—Pullman Car facilities available. **PB**—Pullman Car facilities available from Brighton. **PR**—Pullman Car facilities available Saturdays, Refreshment Car Mondays to Fridays. **R**—Refreshment Car facilities available. **SO**—Saturdays only. **SX**—Mondays to Fridays only.

Pullman Car Supplementary Fees :—

	1st Class	3rd Class
Between Worthing, Hove, Brighton, etc., and London or East Croydon	3/-	1/6
Between Worthing etc., and Hove ...	1/6	1/6

Summary of Principal Services—continued.

For full service—see pages 158 to 233.

LONDON, ARUNDEL, LITTLEHAMPTON AND BOGNOR REGIS

DOWN	WEEK-DAYS														
	C		R	P	AR	AP	R	P	C	SO R	SO P		C	SO R	SO R
	a.m.		a.m.	a.m.	a.m.	a.m.	a.m.	a.m.	a.m.	p.m.	p.m.		p.m.	p.m.	p.m.
VICTORIA dep.	8 28	...	9 18	9 25	10 18	10 25	11 18	11 25	11 48	*12 18*	*12 25*	...	12 48	*1 18*	...
London Bdge. „	...	...	...	...	...	...	...	...	...	...	*12*20*	...	...	*1ⓐ8*	*1 24*
Arundel ... arr.	10 6	...	10 41	...	11 41	...	12 41	...	1 36	*1 41*	...	...	2 36	*2 41*	...
Littlehampton „	10 15	...	...	11 10	...	12 13	...	1 10	1 43	...	*2 10*	...	2 43	...	*3 11*
BOGNOR R. „	...	...	11 1	...	12 0	...	1 0	...	2 7	*2 0*	...	...	3 7	*3 0*	...

DOWN	WEEK-DAYS—*continued*														
	SO	C	SO R	SO P	C	AR	AP		SX R	SO R	SX P	SO C	SX R	SX R	SX R
	p.m.	p.m.	p.m.	p.m.	p.m.	p.m.	p.m.		p.m.	p.m.	p.m.	p.m.	p.m.	p.m.	p.m.
VICTORIA dep.	...	1 48	*2 18*	*2 25*	2 48	3 18	3 25	...	4 18	*4 18*	4 25	*4 48*	...	...	5 4
London Bdge. „	*1 40*	...	*2ⓐ8*	*2*18*	...	...	3*18	...	4ⓐ7	...	4*20	...	5 6	5 15	...
Arundel ... arr.	*3 2*	3 36	*3 41*	...	...	4 44	...	...	5 44	*5 44*	...	...	...	6 34	6 44
Littlehampton „	...	3 43	...	*4 10*	4 43	...	5 10	...	...	...	6 10	*6 44*	6 47	6†52	6 52
BOGNOR R. „	*3 18*	4 7	*4 0*	...	...	5 2	...	...	6 2	*5 59*	...	...	...	6 50	...

DOWN	WEEK-DAYS—*continued*														
	SO R	SX R	SX P	SX R	SX	SO C	SX R	SX R	SX P	SO C	R	P	C	R	P
	p.m.	p.m.	p.m.	p.m.	p.m.	p.m.	p.m.	p.m.	p.m.	p.m.	p.m.	p.m.	p.m.	p.m.	p.m.
VICTORIA dep.	*5 18*	5 30	5 35	...	...	*5 48*	...	6 18	6 35	*6 48*	7 18	7 25	7 48	9 18	10 25
London Bdge. „	...	...	...	5 45	5 48	...	6 5	...	...	...	...	...	...	...	...
Arundel ... arr.	*6 45*	6 48	...	...	7 16	*7 36*	...	7 31	...	...	8 43	...	9 36	10 43	...
Littlehampton „	...	7† 9	7 20	7 27	...	*7 43*	7 45	7†48	8 19	*8 43*	...	9 10	9 43	10F57	12 9
BOGNOR R. „	*7 0*	7 5	...	...	7 33	*8 7*	...	7 48	...	...	8 58	...	10 7	11 7	12 39

DOWN	SUNDAYS													
	E	R		P	R	P	C	P	C	E	C	E	C	E
	a.m.	a.m.		a.m.	a.m.	a.m.	a.m.	a.m.	a.m.	p.m.	p.m.	p.m.	p.m.	p.m.
VICTORIA dep.	8 28	9 18	...	9 25	10 18	10 25	10 48	11 25	11 48	12 28	12 48	1 28	1 48	2 28
Arundel ... arr.	...	10 41	...	...	11 41	...	12 36	...	1 36	...	2 36	...	3 36	...
Littlehampton „	10 33	...	...	11 10	...	12 10	12 43	1 12	1 43	2 33	2 43	3 33	3 43	4 33
BOGNOR R. „	...	11 2	...	...	12 2	...	1 8	...	2 7	...	3 7	...	4 7	...

DOWN	SUNDAYS—*continued*													
	C	R	E	C	E	C	E	C	C	R	R	C	R	P
	p.m.	p.m.	p.m.	p.m.	p.m.	p.m.	p.m.	p.m.	p.m.	p.m.	p.m.	p.m.	p.m.	p.m.
VICTORIA dep.	2 48	3 18	3 28	3 48	4 28	4 48	5 28	5 48	6 48	7 18	7 25	7 48	9 18	9 25
Arundel ... arr.	...	4 41	...	5 36	...	6 36	...	7 36	...	8 43	...	9 36	10 43	...
Littlehampton „	4 43	...	5 33	5 43	6 33	6 43	7 33	7 43	8 43	...	9 12	9 43	...	11 10
BOGNOR R. „	...	5 0	...	6 7	...	7 7	...	8 7	...	9 4	...	10 7	11 4	...

A—Seats in compartments may be reserved, 1/-. per seat. Application, with fee, to reach Station Master before 4.0 p.m. day prior to journey. Seats may NOT be booked by telephone. **C**—Change Three Bridges. **E**—Change Brighton. **F**—Change at Ford. **SO**—Saturdays only. **P**—Pullman Car facilities available. **R**—Refreshment Car facilities available. **SX**—Mondays to Fridays only. †—Change Arundel. *—Change East Croydon. ⓐ—Third Class only between London Bridge and Sutton.

Pullman Car supplementary fees between London or East Croydon and Littlehampton :—1st Class 3/-, 3rd Class 1/6.

Summary of Principal Services—continued. For full service—see pages 196 to 233.

BOGNOR REGIS, LITTLEHAMPTON, ARUNDEL and LONDON

UP	WEEK-DAYS													
	R	R		P		R		P		R SX	R	R	P	R
	a.m.	a.m.	...	a.m.		a.m.		a.m.		a.m.	a.m.	a.m.	a.m.	a.m.
BOGNOR R. dep.	6 22	7 5	...	7 20	...	7 55	...	...	...	8 28	8 55	...	...	9 55
Littlehampton „	6 39	7† 7	...	7 37	...	8† 0	...	8 9	...	8†22	8†59	8 59	9 9	9†59
Arundel... ... „	...	7 19	...	...	...	8 12	...	...	...	8 42	9 14	...	...	10 14
London Bridge arr.	8 33	8*43	...	9H23	...	9*38	...	9 51	...	9 57	...	...	...	...
VICTORIA „	...	8 37	...	9 21	...	9 34	...	...	...	...	10 31	10 42	10 57	11 32

UP	WEEK-DAYS—*continued*													
	P	AR	R SO	AP	C	R SO	P SX		C	AR	AP	P SO	C	R
	a.m.	a.m.	a.m.	p.m.	a.m.	p.m.	p.m.		p.m.	p.m.	p.m.	p.m.	p.m.	p.m.
BOGNOR R. dep.	...	10 55	*11 55*	...	11 45	*12 55*	...	...	12 45	1 55	...	...	2 45	3 55
Littlehampton „	10 9	10†59	...	12 5	...	...	1 5	...	1 9	1†59	2 9	*3 5*	3 9	3†59
Arundel... ... „	...	11 14	*12 11*	...	12 16	*1 12*	...	...	1 16	2 15	...	...	3 16	4 14
London Bridge arr.	...	...	...	...	...	...	...	...	...	...	...	...	5SX3	...
VICTORIA „	11 57	12 40	*1 40*	1 57	2 7	*2 40*	2 57	...	3 8	3 40	3 58	*4 58*	5SO7	5 43

UP	WEEK-DAYS—*continued*													
	R	P SO	C		R	P		R SO	PR	C	C			
	p.m.	p.m.	p.m.		p.m.	p.m.		p.m.	p.m.	p.m.	p.m.			
BOGNOR R. dep.	4 55	...	5 45	...	6 55	...	...	*7 55*	...	7 40	8 45	...	...	...
Littlehampton „	4†59	*5 9*	6 9	...	7† 0	7 9	...	*8† 0*	8 9	...	9 9	...	...	...
Arundel... ... „	5 14	...	6 16	...	7 13	...	...	*8 14*	...	8 6	9 16	...	...	...
London Bridge arr.	...	...	...	...	...	...	...	...	...	...	...	...	...	...
VICTORIA „	6 40	*6 58*	8 8	...	8 40	8 57	...	*9 40*	9 57	10 7	†11 7	...	...	...

UP	SUNDAYS													
	C	R			C	R	C		C	C	C		P	C
	a.m.	a.m.			a.m.	a.m.	a.m.		a.m.	p.m.	p.m.		p.m.	p.m.
BOGNOR R. dep.	6 44	7 55	...	...	8 45	9 55	10 45	...	11 45	12 45	1 45	...	...	2 45
Littlehampton „	7 6	7†59	...	...	9 9	9†59	11 9	...	12 9	1 9	2 9	...	3 5	...
Arundel... ... „	7 12	8 14	...	...	9 16	10 14	11 16	...	12 16	1 16	2 16	...	...	3 16
VICTORIA arr.	9 5	9 31	...	...	11 6	11 43	1 6	...	2 7	3 6	4 7	...	4 57	5 7

UP	SUNDAYS—*continued*												
	R	P		C	R		P	R		R		P	C
	p.m.	p.m.		p.m.	p.m.		p.m.	p.m.	...	p.m.		p.m.	p.m.
BOGNOR R. dep.	3 55	...	...	4 44	5 55	...	...	6 55	...	7 55	...	...	8 45
Littlehampton „	3†59	5 5	...	...	5†59	...	6 9	6†59	...	7†59	...	8 9	9 9
Arundel... ... „	4 14	...	...	5 16	6 14	...	...	7 14	...	8 14	...	...	9 16
VICTORIA arr.	5 44	6 57	...	7 7	7 44	...	7 55	8 43	...	9 40	...	9 59	11 4

A—Seats in compartments may be reserved, 1/-. per seat. Application, with fee, to reach Station Master before 4.0 p.m. day prior to journey. Seats may NOT be booked by telephone. C—Change Three Bridges. H—Change at Haywards Heath. SO—Saturdays only. SX—Mondays to Fridays. P—Pullman Car facilities available. PR—Pullman Car facilities available on Saturdays; Refreshment Car Mondays to Fridays. R—Refreshment Car facilities available. *—Change at East Croydon. †—Change Arundel. Pullman Car supplementary fees between Littlehampton and London or East Croydon:—1st Class 3/-, 3rd Class 1/6.

Summary of Principal Services—*continued.* For full service see pages 359 to 372.

LONDON (Waterloo) and PORTSMOUTH & ISLE OF WIGHT

DOWN		WEEK-DAYS										
			R	R	R	SO		R	R		SO	SO	R
		a.m.	a.m.	a.m.	a.m.	a.m.		a.m.	p.m.		p.m.	p.m.	p.m.
WATERLOO	dep.	5 25	7 45	8 45	9A45	10R45	...	11 45	12 45	...	1R15	1R45	2A45
Woking	„	6u 9	8u16	9u16	10u16	11u 16	...	12u16	1u16	...	1u46	2u16	3u16
Portsmouth { S'sea ...	arr.	7 45	9 20	10 20	11 20	12 20	...	1 20	2 22	...	3 1	3 21	4 21
Portsmouth { Hbr. ...	„	7 50	9 26	10 26	11 26	12 26	...	1 26	2 28	...	...	3 27	4 27
PORTSMOUTH Hbr.	dep.	8 35	9 40	10 35	11 35	12 35	...	1 35	2 35	...	...	3 35	4 35
RYDE PIER HEAD ...	arr.	9 5	10 10	11 5	12 5	1 5	...	2 5	3 5	...	...	4 5	5 5
Ryde Esplanade	arr.	9 27	10 31	11 31	12 31	1 31	...	2 31	3 31	...	...	4 31	5 31
Bembridge	„	9 53	10 53	12 18	12 53	1 53	...	2 53	3 53	...	...	4 53	5 53
Sandown	„	9 48	10 48	11 48	12 48	1 48	...	2 48	3 48	...	...	4 48	5 48
Shanklin	„	9 55	10 55	11 55	12 55	1 55	...	2 55	3 55	...	...	4 55	5 55
Ventnor	„	10 12	11 11	12 11	1 11	2 11	...	3 11	4 11	...	...	5 11	6 11
NEWPORT	„	10 6	11 6	12 6	1 6	2 6	...	3 6	4 6	...	...	5 6	6 6

DOWN		WEEK-DAYS—*continued*											
		R	SX		R	SX		R	SX	R	SO	R	R
		p.m.	p.m.		p.m.	p.m.		p.m.	p.m.	p.m.	p.m.	p.m.	p.m.
WATERLOO	dep.	3 45	4R 20	...	4 45	5R20	...	5 45	6R20	6 45	7R45	8 45	9 45
Woking	„	4u16	...	...	...	...	...	...	...	7u16	...	9u16	10u16
Portsmouth { S'Sea ...	arr.	5 20	6 1	...	6 21	7 3	...	7 22	8 2	8 22	9 20	10 21	11 21
Portsmouth { Hbr. ...	„	5 26	6 5	...	6 26	7 7	...	7 27	8 6	8 27	...	...	...
PORTSMOUTH Hbr.	dep.	5 35	...	...	6 35	...	...	7 35	...	8 40	...	...	...
RYDE PIER HEAD ...	arr.	6 5	...	...	7 5	...	...	8 5	...	9 10	...	...	...
Ryde Esplanade	arr.	6 31	...	...	7 31	...	...	8 31	...	9 31	...	...	...
Bembridge	„	6 53	...	...	7 53	...	...	8 55	...	9 53	...	...	...
Sandown	„	6 48	...	...	7 48	...	...	8 48	...	9 48	...	...	...
Shanklin	„	6 55	...	...	7 55	...	...	8 55	...	9 55	...	...	...
Ventnor	„	7 11	...	...	8 11	...	...	9 11	...	10 11	...	...	...
NEWPORT	„	7 6	...	...	8 6	...	...	9 6	...	10 6	...	...	...

DOWN		SUNDAYS											
		③	R	R	R	R		R	R	R	R	R	R
		a.m.	a.m.	a.m.	a.m.	p.m.		p.m.	p.m.	p.m.	p.m.	p.m.	p.m.
WATERLOO	dep.	3 35	8 45	9 45	10 45	12 45	...	2 45	4 45	6 45	7 45	8 45	9 45
Woking	„	4u26	9u16	10u16	11u16	1u16	...	3u16	5u16	7u16	...	...	10u16
Portsmouth { S'sea ...	arr.	5 58	10 20	11 20	12 20	2 21	...	4 20	6 20	8 20	9 21	10 21	11 21
Portsmouth { Hbr ...	„	6 5	10 26	11 26	12 26	2 26	...	4 26	6 26	8 26	9 26	...	...
PORTSMOUTH Hbr.	dep.	6 25	10 35	...	12 35	2 35	...	4 35	6 35	8 40	...	...	...
RYDE PIER HEAD ...	arr.	6 55	11 5	...	1 5	3 5	...	5 5	7 5	9 10	...	...	...
Ryde Esplanade	arr.	7 18	11 31	...	1 31	3 31	...	5 31	7 31	9 31	...	...	...
Bembridge	„	...	11 53	...	1 53	3 53	...	6 3	7 53	10 3	...	...	...
Sandown	„	7 42	11 48	...	1 48	3 48	...	5 48	7 48	9 48	...	...	...
Shanklin	„	7 49	11 55	...	1 55	3 55	...	5 55	7 55	9 55	...	...	...
Ventnor	„	8 5	12 11	...	2 11	4 11	...	6 11	8 11	10 11	...	...	...
NEWPORT	„	7 48	12 6	...	2 6	4 6	...	6 6	8 6	10 6	...	...	...

A—Seats in compartments may be reserved, 1/- per seat. Application, with fee, to reach Station Master before 4.0 p.m. day prior to the journey. Seats may NOT be booked by telephone. **R**—Refreshment Car between Waterloo and Portsmouth. **SX**—Saturdays excepted. **SO**—Saturdays only. **u**—Take up only.
③—Third class only between Waterloo and Portsmouth Hbr.

Summary of Principal Services—continued. For full service see pages 359 to 372.

PORTSMOUTH & ISLE OF WIGHT and LONDON (Waterloo)

UP	WEEK-DAYS										
	R	**R**			**SX**	**SO**					**SO**
	a.m.	a.m.	a.m.		a.m.	a.m.	a.m.	a.m.	a.m.	a.m.	p.m.
NEWPORT ... ... dep.	...	...	6 35		...	7 38	8 42	9 38	10 38	11 38	12 38
Ventnor ... ... „	...	...	6 30		...	7 40	8 40	9 42	10 42	11 42	12 42
Shanklin ... ... „	...	...	6 42		...	7 52	8 52	9 54	10 54	11 54	12 54
Sandown ... ... „	...	...	6 50		...	7 58	8 58	10 1	11 1	12 1	1 1
Bembridge ... ... „	...	...	6 45		...	7 53	8 42	9 57	10 57	11 32	12 57
Ryde Esplanade ... ... „	...	...	7 9		...	8 19	9 19	10 19	11 19	12 19	1 19
RYDE PIER HEAD ... „	...	...	7 30		...	8 35	9 35	10 35	11 35	12 35	1 35
PORTSMOUTH Hbr. arr.	...	...	8 0		...	9 5	10 5	11 5	12 5	1 5	2 5
Portsmouth Hbr. ... dep.	...	7 35	8**SXR**15	8**R**20	8**R**42	9**R**20	10**RA**20	11**R**20	12**R**20	1**RA**20	2**R**20
Portsmouth S'sea ... „	7 27	7 39	8**SX**19	8 24	8 46	9 24	10 24	11 24	12 24	1 24	2 24
Woking ... ... arr.	...	...	...	...	...	10e31	11e29	12e30	1e29	2e29	3e29
WATERLOO ... ... „	9 13	9 30	9**SX**52	10 5	10 28	11 2	12 1	1 1	2 1	3 1	4 1

UP	WEEK-DAYS—*continued*												
													SX
	p.m.		p.m.	p.m.		p.m.		p.m.		p.m.	p.m.	p.m.
NEWPORT ... ... dep.	1 38	...	2 38	3 38	...	5 38	...	6 38	...	...	7 38	...
Ventnor ... ... „	1 42	...	2 42	3 42	...	5 42	...	6 42	...	...	7 42	...
Shanklin ... ... „	1 54	...	2 54	3 54	...	5 54	...	6 54	...	...	7 54	...
Sandown ... ... „	2 1	...	3 1	4 1	...	6 1	...	7 1	...	...	8 1	...
Bembridge ... ... „	1 57	...	2 57	3 57	...	5 57	...	6 57	...	...	7 57	...
Ryde Esplanade ... ... „	2 19	...	3 19	4 19	...	6 19	...	7 19	...	...	8 19	...
RYDE PIER HEAD ... „	2 35	...	3 35	4 35	...	6 35	...	7 35	...	...	8 35	...
PORTSMOUTH Hbr. arr.	3 5	...	4 5	5 5	...	7 5	...	8 5	...	...	9 5	...
Portsmouth Hbr. ... dep.	3**R**20	...	4**R**20	5**R**20	...	7**R**20	...	8**R**20	...	...	9 20	...
Portsmouth S'sea ... „	3 24	...	4 24	5 24	...	7 24	...	8 24	...	9 0	9 30	10 0
Woking ... ... arr.	4e30	...	5e29	6e29	...	8e29	...	9e29	...	10e34	11e 4	11e34
WATERLOO ... ... „	5 3	...	6 1	7 3	...	9 1	...	10 1	...	11 16	11 46	12 6

UP	SUNDAYS												
							R		**R**	**R**		**R**	
	a.m.		a.m.	a.m.	p.m.	p.m.	p.m.	p.m.	p.m.	p.m.	p.m.	p.m.	p.m.
NEWPORT ... ... dep.	6 20	...	8 23	10 38	12 38	2 42	...	4 38	...	...	6 38	...	8 48
Ventnor ... ... „	...	...	8 30	10 30	12 30	2 30	...	4 30	...	...	6 30	...	8 30
Shanklin ... ... „	...	...	8 42	10 42	12 42	2 42	...	4 42	...	...	6 42	...	8 44
Sandown ... ... „	...	...	8 48	10 48	12 48	2 48	...	4 48	...	...	6 48	...	8 49
Bembridge ... ... „	...	...	...	...	12 42	1 57	...	4 42	...	...	6 32	...	8 42
Ryde Esplanade ... ... „	6 52	...	9 5	11 10	1 10	3 10	...	5 10	...	...	7 10	...	9 17
RYDE PIER HEAD ... „	7 30	...	9 35	11 35	1 35	3 35	...	5 35	...	...	7 35	...	9 35
PORTSMOUTH Hbr. arr.	8 0	...	10 5	12 5	2 5	4 5	...	6 5	...	...	8 5	...	10 5
Portsmouth Hbr. ... dep.	8**R**20	...	10**R**20	12**R**20	2**R**20	4**R**20	5 20	6**R**20	6 50	7 20	8**R**20	9 20	10**R**20
Portsmouth S'sea ... „	8 24	...	10 24	12 24	2 24	4 24	5 24	6 24	6 54	7 24	8 24	9 24	10 24
Woking ... ... arr.	9e29	...	11e29	1e29	3e29	5e29	6e29	7e29	7e57	8e29	9e29	10e29	11e29
WATERLOO ... ... „	10 1	...	12 1	2 1	4 1	6 1	7 1	8 1	8 30	9 1	10 1	11 1	12 1

A—Seats in compartments may be reserved, 1/- per seat. Application, with fee, to reach Station Master before 4.0 p.m. day prior to the journey. Seats may NOT be booked by telephone. **e**—Set down only.
R—Refreshment Car between Portsmouth and Waterloo. **SO**—Saturdays only. **SX**—Saturdays excepted.

Summary of Principal Services—continued.

For full service see pages 324 to 335.

LONDON (Waterloo) and SOUTHAMPTON, BOURNEMOUTH, SWANAGE, WEYMOUTH

DOWN.	WEEK-DAYS.													
	R		R	"Bournemouth Belle"	P	SO	R			R		MONDAYS TO FRIDAYS.	R	
	a.m.	a.m.	a.m.		p.m.	p.m.	p.m.	p.m.	p.m.	p.m.	p.m.		p.m.	p.m.
WATERLOO ... dep.	8 30	9 30	11 30		1.P30	*12 35*	1 30	3A20	3 30	4 35	5 30		6A30	7 30
Woking ... ... „	9u 6	10u 6	...		...	...	...	...	4u 2	...	...		...	...
Southampton Ctl. ... arr.	10 26	11 31	1 19		1 55	*2 8*	3 20	5 0	5 28	6 16	7 28		8 6	9 31
Bournemouth Ctl. ... „	11 15	12 30	2 22		2 35	*2 55*	4 20	5 45	6 26	7 2	8 31		8 51	10 51
Bournemouth W. ... „	11 34	12 43	2 34		2 47	*3 14*	4 38	6 4	6 40	7 20	8 44		9 11	11 4
Swanage ... ... „	12 37	2 38	3SX59		3SX59	*3 59*	5 21	...	...	7 59	*10*SO *2*		10 2	...
WEYMOUTH ... „	12 25	2 21	4SX18		4SX18	*4 2*	5 32	7 18	...	8 3	*10*SO*21*		10 21	...

DOWN.	SUNDAYS.													
			R	"Bournemouth Belle"	P	R								
	a.m.		a.m.		p.m.	p.m.	...	p.m.		p.m.		p.m.		p.m.
WATERLOO ... dep.	9 30	...	11 30		12P30	1 30	...	2 54	...	4 54	...	6 30	...	8 54
Woking ... ... „	10u 6	...	...		...	...	...	3u28	...	5u26	...	7u 2	...	9u26
Southampton Ctl. ... arr.	11 25	...	1 20		1 55	3 15	...	5 25	...	7 15	...	8 31	...	11T 19
Bournemouth Ctl. ... „	12 23	...	2 20		2 35	4 15	...	7 14	...	...	...	9 31	...	...
Bournemouth W. ... „	12 34	...	2 32		2 47	4 27	...	...	...	...	...	9 50	...	...
Swanage ... ... „	...	...	3 52		3 52	5 28	...	...	...	...	...	...	...	...
WEYMOUTH ... „	1 54	...	4 8		4 8	5 42	...	...	...	...	...	10 55	...	...

UP.	WEEK-DAYS.													
		R				R				"Bournemouth Belle"		R	R	
	a.m.	a.m.	a.m.	a.m.	a.m.	a.m.	p.m.	p.m.	p.m.		p.m.	p.m.	p.m.	p.m.
WEYMOUTH ... dep.	...	7 38	...	9 20	...	11 A30	...	1 25	...		2 20	...	5 20	6 30
Swanage ... ... „	...	7 47	...	9 26	...	11 36	...	1 35	...		2 42	...	4 25	6 43
Bournemouth W. ... „	7 20	8 20	8 35	10A 12	11 2	12A 20	1 5	2 20	3 5		4P34	5 5	6 20	...
Bournemouth Ctl. ... „	7 30	8 40	8 45	10 30	11 12	12 40	1 15	2 38	3 17		4 45	5 15	6 35	7 50
Southampton Ctl. ... „	8 25	9 16	9 54	11 20	12 20	1 20	2 20	3 20	4 20		5 20	6 20	7 20	8 48
Woking ... ... arr.	...	...	11e33	...	1e45	...	...	...	...		...	7e51	...	10e35
WATERLOO ... „	10 13	10 59	12 7	12 59	2 19	2 56	4 25	4 58	6 36		6 45	8 32	8 58	11 13

UP.	SUNDAYS.													
							"Bournemouth Belle"	P		R		R		
	a.m.		a.m.	...	p.m.			p.m.	...	p.m.		p.m.		p.m.
WEYMOUTH ... dep.	7 15	...	10 0	...	2 0	...		...	...	...	...	5 50	...	...
Swanage ... ... „	...	...	10 10	...	2 5	...		...	...	...	...	5 55	...	...
Bournemouth W. ... „	...	...	11 0	...	3 10	...		4P 34	...	6 5	...	...	...	6 55
Bournemouth Ctl. ... „	8 50	...	11 20	...	3 30	...		4 45	...	6 20	...	6 57	...	7 6
Southampton Ctl. ... „	9 51	...	12 20	...	4 15	...		5 20	...	7 20	...	7 45	...	8 5
Woking ... ... arr.	11e36	...	...	...	...	...		...	...	...	...	...	...	...
WATERLOO ... „	12 13	...	2 12	...	5 57	...		6 45	...	9 21	...	9 28	...	10 19

A—Seats in compartments may be reserved, 1/- per seat. Application, with fee, to reach Station Master before 4.0 p.m. day prior to the journey. Seats may NOT be booked by telephone. **e**—Set down only.
R—Refreshment car, Waterloo to Bournemouth. **SO**—Saturdays only. **SX**—Saturdays excepted.
T—Southampton Terminus. **u**—Take up only.
P—1st and 3rd class Pullman cars only between Waterloo, Southampton Central and Bournemouth, tickets for which may be obtained in advance upon payment of the undermentioned supplementary fees :—

	1st Class.		3rd Class.	
	s.	d.	s.	d.
Between Waterloo and { Southampton Central	3	6	2	0
{ Bournemouth	5	0	3	0
Between Southampton Central and Bournemouth ...	2	0	1	6

Summary of Principal Services—continued. For full Service see pages 340 to 351.

LONDON (Waterloo) AND LYME REGIS, SEATON, SIDMOUTH, EXMOUTH

DOWN	WEEK-DAYS							SUNDAYS		
		R	R “Atlantic Coast Express.”	P “Devon Belle” MONDAYS, FRIDAYS AND SATURDAYS ONLY. TO OCTOBER 27th, 1947, ONLY.	R	R	R	R	P “Devon Belle” TO OCTOBER 26th, 1947, ONLY.	R
	a.m.	a.m.	a.m.	noon	p.m.	p.m.	p.m.	a.m.	noon	p.m.
WATERLOO ... dep.	1 25	9 0	10A50	*12P 0*	12 50	2A 50	6 0	11 0	*12P 0*	4 0
Woking ... ... „	...	9u35	...	...	1u22	...	...	11u32	...	...
Lyme Regis ... ... arr.	8 56	1 18	3 11	...	5 1	7 11	10Y11	3 31	...	...
Seaton ... ... „	8 17	1 5	3 27	...	4 57	7 10	9 58	3M27	...	...
Sidmouth ... ... „	8 24	1 32	2 48	*3 43*	5 38	6 58	10 15	3 5	*3 43*	...
Exmouth ... ... „ (via Tipton St. John's)	...	2 3	3 17	...	...	7 22	10B40	...	...	...
EXMOUTH ... ... arr. (via Exeter Central)	7 10	2 0	3 12	*4C26*	5 43	...	10 46	3 27	*4 14*	8 51

UP	WEEK-DAYS							SUNDAYS			
	R	R		R “Atlantic Coast Express”	P “Devon Belle” MONDAYS, FRIDAYS AND SATURDAYS ONLY. TO OCTOBER 2.th, 1947, ONLY.		R		P “Devon Belle” TO OCTOBER 26th, 1947 ONLY.		R
	a.m.	a.m.	a.m.	p.m.	p.m.	p.m.	p.m.	a.m.	p.m.	p.m.	p.m.
EXMOUTH ... ... dep. (via Exeter Central)	...	9 50	10 45	...	*12 15*	1 30	5 15	11 0	*12 15*	2 55	4 15
Exmouth ... ... „ (via Tipton St. John's)	6 55	9 50	...	12 10	...	...	...	...	...	...	...
Sidmouth ... ... dep.	7 20	10 20	...	12 34	*1 35*	1 35	5 45	11 8	*1 35*	3 13	...
Seaton ... ... „	...	10 5	11 45	...	...	2S35	6 5	11 38	...	3T35	...
Lyme Regis ... ... „	7F20	10 0	11 34	12 29	...	2 19	6 5	11 37	...	3 50	...
Woking ... ... arr.	...	...	...	...	...	...	9e43	3e11	...	...	...
WATERLOO ... „	11 46	2 29	4 10	4 41	*5 20*	6 40	10 27	3 44	*5 20*	8 39	9 13

LONDON (Waterloo) AND BARNSTAPLE, ILFRACOMBE AND BIDEFORD

DOWN	WEEK-DAYS						SUNDAYS		
		R	R “Atlantic Coast Express”	P “Devon Belle” MONDAYS, FRIDAYS AND SATURDAYS ONLY. TO OCTOBER 27th, 1947 ONLY.	R	R	R	P “Devon Belle” TO OCTOBER 26th, 1947 ONLY.	R
	a.m.	a.m.	a.m.	noon	p.m.	p.m.	a.m.	noon	p.m.
WATERLOO ... dep	1 25	9 0	10A 50	*12P0*	12 50	2A50	11 0	*12P 0*	4 0
Woking ... ... „	...	9u35	...	...	1u22	...	11e32	...	...
Barnstaple Jc.... ... arr.	7 4	3 7	3 44	*4 49*	6 30	8 18	4 25	*4 49*	9 59
Barnstaple Town ... „	7 18	3 13	3 54	*4 54*	6 38	8 28	4 36	*4 54*	10 8
ILFRACOMBE ... „	8 0	3 52	4 36	*5 33*	7 18	9 11	5 18	*5 33*	10 48
BIDEFORD ... ... „	7 51	3 33	4 18	*5 18*	6 58	8 48	4 58	*5 18*	10 28

UP	WEEK-DAYS						SUNDAYS		
	R		R “Atlantic Coast Express”	P “Devon Belle” MONDAYS, FRIDAYS AND SATURDAYS ONLY. TO OCTOBER 27th, 1947 ONLY.		R		P “Devon Belle” TO OCTOBER 26th, 1947 ONLY.	
	a.m.		a.m.	a.m.	p.m.	p.m.	a.m.	p.m.	a.m.
BIDEFORD ... ... dep.	8 19	...	10 24	*11 53*	12 24	3 1	10 2	*12 4*	2 9
ILFRACOMBE ... ,	8A10	...	10 15	*12 0*	12A15	3 0	9 50	*12 0*	2 0
Barnstaple Town ... „	8 46	...	10 54	*12 32*	12 54	3 36	10 26	*12 32*	2 40
Barnstaple Jc.... ... „	8 54	...	11 1	*12 37*	1 3	3 45	10 33	*12 37*	2 49
Woking ... ... arr.	...	...	...	...	...	9e43	3e11	...	...
WATERLOO ... „	2 29	...	4 41	*5 20*	6 40	10 27	3 44	*5 20*	8 39

A—Seats in compartments may be reserved, 1/- per seat. Application, with fee, to reach Station Master before 4.0 p.m. day prior to the journey. Seats may NOT be booked by telephone. **B**—Tuesdays to Fridays only. **C**—4.11 p.m. on Saturdays. **e**—Set down only. **F**—By Southern National Omnibus to Axminster. Times subject to alteration. **M**—5 mins. later to October 26th, 1947. **R**—Refreshment car between Waterloo and Exeter. **S**—10 mins. later to October 27th, 1947. **T**—10 mins. later to October 26th, 1947. **u**—Take up only **Y**—Fridays and Saturdays only. By Southern National Omnibus from Axminster. Times subject to alteration. **P**—1st and 3rd Class Pullman Cars only between Waterloo, Sidmouth, Exeter Ctl., Barnstaple Jc., tickets for which may be obtained in advance upon payment of the undermentioned Supplementary fees:—

		1st Class. s. d.	3rd Class. s. d.
Between Waterloo and	Sidmouth Jct. and Exeter Ctl.	6 0	3 6
	Barnstaple Jtc. and intermediate stations to Ilfracombe ...	8 0	4 6

Summary of Principal Services—continued. For full Services see pages 340 to 351.

LONDON (Waterloo) and SALISBURY, EXETER, OKEHAMPTON, TAVISTOCK, PLYMOUTH

DOWN	WEEK-DAYS								SUNDAYS				
		R	R "Atlantic Coast Express"	P "Devon Belle" MONDAYS, FRIDAYS AND SATURDAYS ONLY. TO OCT. 27th 1947, ONLY.	R	R		R	R	P "Devon Belle" TO OCT. 26th 1947, ONLY.	R		
	a.m.	a.m.	a.m.	noon	p.m.	p.m.	p.m.	p.m.	a.m.	noon	p.m.	p.m.	p.m.
WATERLOO ... dep.	1 25	9 0	10A50	*12P0*	1250	2A50	5 0	6 0	11 0	*12P0*	4 0	7 30	9 30
Woking ... ... „	...	9u35	...	...	1u22	...	5u33	...	11u32	...	...	...	10u10
Salisbury... ... ... arr.	3 18	11 1	1233	...	2 39	4 42	7 8	7 49	12 57	...	554	9 26	11 58
Exeter Central ... „	5 13	1 24	2 29	*3 36*	4 46	6 46	...	10 6	2 55	*3 36*	818	...	...
Exeter (St. David's) „	5 25	1 37	2 39	*3 45*	4 55	6 57	...	...	3 6	*3 45*	828	...	...
Okehampton ... ... „	6 23	2 29	3 34	*4 25*	5 39	7 56	...	...	3 50	*4 25*	924	...	...
Tavistock ... ... „	6 41	2 57	4 11	...	6 16	8 28	...	...	4 20	...	10 2	...	...
Devonport ... ... „	7 31	3 28	4 38	*5 16*	6 46	8 56	...	...	4 49	*5 16*	1037	...	...
PLYMOUTH (Nth. Rd.) „	7 36	3 35	4 44	*5 25*	6 53	9 3	...	...	4 55	*5 21*	1042	...	...
„ (Friary) „	7 48	3 47	4 55	*5 36*	7 5	9 14	...	...	5 6	*5 32*	1052	...	...

UP	WEEK-DAYS											
			R	R			R	P "Devon Belle" MONDAYS, FRIDAYS AND SATURDAYS ONLY. TO OCTOBER 27th, 1947 ONLY.				R
	a.m.	a.m.	a.m.	a.m.	p.m.	a.m.	a.m.	a.m.	a.m.	p.m.	p.m.	p.m.
PLYMOUTH (Friary) dep.	...	...	...	8A15	...	...	10 0	*11 30*	11A38	...	...	3 45
„ (Nth. Rd.) „	...	...	...	8 25	...	...	10 10	*11 40*	11 47	...	...	3 55
Devonport ... ... „	...	...	...	8 30	...	...	10 17	*11 47*	11 52	...	...	4 2
Tavistock ... ... „	...	...	...	8 59	...	...	10 51	...	12 36	...	...	4 30
Okehampton ... ... „	...	...	...	9 33	...	...	11 28	*12 45*	1 14	...	...	5 0
Exeter (St. David's) „	...	...	...	10 18	...	...	12 25	*1 33*	2 17	...	...	5 40
Exeter Central ... „	...	...	7 30	10 30	...	11 20	12 40	*1 40*	2 30	...	...	5 50
Salisbury... ... ... „	6 45	8 10	9 50	12 40	1 0	2 20	3 4	...	4 50	5 15	6 20	8 15
Woking ... ... arr.	8e46	...	...	...	3e11	...	...	...	...	7e21	8e21	9e43
WATERLOO ... „	9 20	10 3	11 46	2 29	3 49	4 10	4 41	*5 20*	6 40	8 0	9 14	10 27

UP	SUNDAYS											
				R	P "Devon Belle" TO OCTOBER 26th, 1947 ONLY.			R				
	a.m.	a.m.	a.m.	a.m.	a.m.	p.m.	p.m.	p.m.				
PLYMOUTH (Friary) dep.	...	...	8 20	10 0	*11 30*	...	...	2 50	...	...	...	...
„ (Nth. Rd.) „	...	...	8 29	10 9	*11 40*	...	...	3 0	...	...	...	...
Devonport ... ... „	...	...	8 34	10 15	*11 47*	...	...	3 6	...	...	...	...
Tavistock ... ... „	...	...	9 16	10 43	...	...	...	3 39	...	...	...	...
Okehampton ... ... „	...	...	9 53	11 12	*12 45*	...	...	4 9	...	...	...	...
Exeter (St. David's) „	...	...	11 39	11 49	*1 33*	...	4 25	4 44	...	...	...	...
Exeter Central ... „	...	...	11 48	12 0	*1 40*	...	4 38	4 55	...	...	...	...
Salisbury... ... ... „	8 32	9 55	1 52	2 18	...	5 25	6 52	7 17	...	...	...	...
Woking ... ... arr.	10e45	11e57	3e11	3e38	...	6e49	...	...	...	...	...	...
WATERLOO ... „	11 21	12 30	3 44	4 10	*5 20*	7 27	8 39	9 13	...	...	...	...

A—Seats in compartments may be reserved, 1/- per seat. Application, with fee, to reach Station Master before 4.0 p.m. day prior to the journey. Seats may NOT be booked by telephone.

e—Set down only. **R**—Refreshment car Waterloo to Exeter. **u**—Take up only.

P—1st and 3rd Class Pullman Cars only, tickets for which may be obtained in advance upon payment of the undermentioned Supplementary fees :—

	1st Class s. d.	3rd Class s. d.
Between Waterloo and Exeter ...	6 0	3 6
Between Waterloo and Okehampton and intermediate stations to Plymouth (Friary) ...	8 0	4 6
Between Exeter and Plymouth (Friary) ...	3 0	1 6

Summary of Principal Services—continued. For full Services see pages 340 to 351.

LONDON (Waterloo) and BUDE, LAUNCESTON, BODMIN, PADSTOW

DOWN	WEEK-DAYS									SUNDAYS		
				"Atlantic Coast Express" R			R		R	R		
	a.m.			a.m.			p.m.		p.m.	a.m.		
WATERLOO ... dep.	1 25	...	...	10A50	...	...	12 50	...	2A50	11 0	...	...
Woking ... ... „	...	...	...	...	...	...	1u22	...	...	11u32	...	...
Bude ... ... arr.	7 58	...	...	5 9	...	...	7 0	...	9 24	5 18	...	...
Launceston ... „	8 3	...	...	4 52	...	...	6 46	...	9 7	5 14	...	...
Camelford ... ... „	9 11	...	...	5 29	...	...	7 22	...	...	...	...	...
Port Isaac Road „	9 27	...	...	5 46	...	...	7 34	...	...	...	...	...
Wadebridge ... „	9 40	...	...	6 1	...	...	7 45	...	...	...	...	...
Bodmin ... ... „	10 6	...	...	6 30	...	...	8 33	...	...	...	...	...
PADSTOW ... „	10 4	...	...	6 21	...	...	7 56	...	...	...	...	...

UP	WEEK-DAYS									SUNDAYS		
	R		"Atlantic Coast Express" R		R					R		
	a.m.		a.m.		p.m.					p.m.		
PADSTOW ... dep.	...	...	8 25	...	1 0	...	...	...	...	...	...	...
BODMIN ... ... „	...	...	7 22	...	a.m. 11 28	...	...	...	...	...	...	...
Wadebridge ... „	...	...	8 40	...	p.m. 1 14	...	...	...	...	...	...	...
Port Isaac Road „	...	...	8 55	...	1 29	...	...	...	...	...	...	...
Camelford ... ... „	...	...	9 12	...	1 47	...	...	...	...	...	...	...
Launceston ... „	8 22	...	9 55	...	2 19	...	...	...	...	2 35	...	...
Bude ... ... „	8 0	...	9 35	...	3 13	...	...	...	...	2 35	...	...
Woking ... ... arr.	...	...	...	...	9e43	...	...	...	...	...	...	...
WATERLOO ... „	2 29	...	4 41	...	10 27	...	...	...	...	9 13	...	...

A—Seats in compartments may be reserved, 1/- per seat. Application with fee to reach Station Master before 4.0 p.m. day prior to the journey. Seats may **NOT** be booked by telephone. e—Set down only.

R—Refreshment car between Waterloo and Exeter. **u**—Take up only.

"Monthly Return" and Ordinary Single Fares between LONDON and the principal S.R. towns

(These fares are liable to revision.)

London Station.	"Monthly Return" Fares. 1st	"Monthly Return" Fares. 3rd	To	Ordinary Single Fares. 1st	Ordinary Single Fares. 3rd
	s. d.	s. d.		s. d.	s. d.
X	16 6	11 0	Allhallows-on-Sea	13 4	8 0
W	76 11	51 3	Barnstaple	63 10	38 3
W	51 11	34 7	Bath	42 11	25 10
X	26 2	17 5	Bexhill West	21 4	12 9
W	80 8	53 9	Bideford	66 11	40 2
W	103 11	69 3	Bodmin	86 5	51 10
V	27 6	18 4	Bognor Regis	22 9	13 8
W	44 0	29 4	Bournemouth Central	36 5	22 0
V	21 5	14 3	Brighton and Hove	17 4	10 6
V	31 9	21 2	Broadstairs	26 4	15 11
W	93 5	62 3	Bude	77 8	46 6
W	70 2	46 9	Budleigh Salterton (via Tipton St. Johns)	58 2	35 0
W	59 11	39 11	Burnham-on-Sea	49 9	29 10
W	97 2	64 9	Camelford (for Tintagel)	80 6	48 4
W	58 6	39 0	Chard	48 8	29 4
X	34 11	23 3	Deal	28 0	16 10
W	55 8	37 1	Dorchester	46 0	27 8
X	33 0	22 0	Dover	26 3	15 9
V	26 2	17 5	Eastbourne	21 5	12 11
W	70 2	46 9	Exeter	58 5	35 0
W	72 1	48 1	Exmouth (via Tipton St. Johns)	59 8	35 9
X	29 11	19 11	Folkestone Central	24 0	14 4
X	26 2	17 5	Hastings	21 4	12 9
W	29 3	19 6	Hayling Island	24 2	14 6
V	26 2	17 5	Herne Bay	21 5	12 11
X	28 8	19 1	Hythe (Kent)	22 9	13 8
W	82 5	54 11	Ilfracombe	68 6	41 1
W	35 6	23 8	Isle of Wight (from)	28 8	17 8
W	91 8	61 1	Launceston	75 11	45 7
V	25 8	17 1	Littlehampton	20 11	12 8
W	62 3	41 6	Lyme Regis	51 6	30 10
V	30 8	20 5	Margate	25 1	15 1
W	34 11	23 3	New Forest (from)	29 11	17 4
W	80 8	53 9	Okehampton	66 11	40 2
W	104 5	69 7	Padstow	86 8	52 1
W	92 3	61 6	Plymouth	76 4	45 10
W	30 8	20 5	Portsmouth & S'thsea (via Liss)	24 11	15 1
W	59 11	39 11	Portland	49 9	29 10
V	31 9	21 2	Ramsgate	26 4	15 11
W	34 2	22 9	Salisbury	28 7	17 1
V	24 5	16 3	Seaford	20 0	12 0
W	62 9	41 10	Seaton (Devon)	51 11	31 3
W	39 2	26 1	Shanklin	31 5	19 3
V	19 0	12 8	Sheerness-on-Sea	15 0	8 11
W	68 5	45 7	Sidmouth	57 0	34 3
W	32 5	21 7	Southampton Central	26 10	16 2
W	53 8	35 9	Swanage	44 7	26 10
X	26 2	17 5	St. Leonards (W. Square)	21 1	12 8
W	87 3	58 2	Tavistock	72 6	43 6
W	82 11	55 3	Torrington	68 10	41 4
X	14 9	9 10	Tunbridge Wells Central	11 9	7 1
W	58 6	39 0	Weymouth	48 5	29 1
V	24 5	16 3	Whitstable & Tankerton	20 2	12 3
V	24 5	16 3	Worthing Central	20 5	12 3
W	51 5	34 3	Yeovil	42 6	25 5

CHILDREN 3 AND UNDER 14 YEARS, HALF-FARE.

V—Victoria. W—Waterloo. X—Charing Cross.

"MONTHLY RETURN" TICKETS.—These tickets are issued between any two stations on **ANY DAY** by **ANY TRAIN** (except Continental Boat Trains), available forward or return any day within one month (for one round trip) with break of journey at any intermediate station.

ORDINARY RETURN TICKETS at double the ordinary single fares are available by any Train other than the Folkestone and Dover Boat Express trains, and the outward and return halves are valid for three months.

LONDON, ASHFORD, HYTHE, FOLKESTONE, DOVER, DEAL, and MARGATE

Miles from Charing C.	Miles from Victoria	Down — Week Days	a.m	a.m	a.m	a.m	a.m	a.m	a.m	a.m	a.m	a.m	a.m	a.m	a.m	a.m	a.m	a.m	a.m	a.m	a.m	a.m
			Mondays only		③			Saturdays excepted						③	Via Redhill, page 246.				Saturdays excepted	Saturdays only		
		Charing Cross .... dep.																				
		Waterloo .... "																				
		Cannon Street .... "												5 8							6 22	
		London Bridge .... "			3 45									5 12	4 50						6 30	
—	—	New Cross .... "												5 19							6 38	
—	—	Victoria .... dep.																				
—	—	Holborn Viaduct .... "																6 6				
—	—	Blackfriars .... "																6 8				
—	10½	Bromley South .... "																6 33				
—	17¼	Swanley .... "																6 45				
13½	—	Orpington .... dep.												5 43							6 58	
22	—	Sevenoaks (Tub's Hill) ..			4 19									6 9							7 15	
—	—	246 East Croydon .... dep.													5 10							7 0
—	—	246 Redhill .... "													5 44							7 27
—	—	Tonbridge .... dep.			4 46									6†19	6 34						7 41	8 10
34¾	—	Paddock Wood 53			4 58										6 46						7 53	8 19
39½	—	Marden													6 55						8 1	
41¾	—	Staplehurst													7 1						8 8	
45½	—	Headcorn													7 9						8 16	
50½	—	Pluckley													7 18						8 26	
—	40	Maidstone East .... arr.																7 28				
		Maidstone East .... dep.																7 35				
—	42¾	Bearsted and Thurnham ..																7 43				
—	45	Hollingbourne																7 48				
—	47½	Harrietsham																7 54				
—	49	Lenham																7 59				
—	53	Charing																8 6				
—	55¾	Hothfield Halt, for Westwell																8 12				
56	59½	Ashford (Kent) 58 .... arr.			5 35										7 28			8 19			8 36	
—	—	Mls Ashford (Kent) .... dep.				6 15									7 36			8 24				
—	—	4¼ Wye				6 23									7 47			8 34				
—	—	9 Chilham				6 32									7 56			8 43				
—	—	11 Chartham				6 37									8 2			8 48				
—	—	14¼ Canterbury West A				6 44			6 56						8 11			8 56				
—	—	16¾ Sturry				Stop			7 2						8 19			9 2				
—	—	18¾ Chislet Colliery Halt							7 7						8 24			9 7				
—	—	20¾ Grove Ferry							7 13						8 30			9 12				
—	—	Ashford (Kent) .... dep.			5 40												7 48				8 40	
60¼	—	Smeeth			5 50												7 57					
64½	—	Westenhanger			5 59												8 7					
65½	—	Sandling Junction			6 5												8 13				8 55	
—	—	Sandling Junction .... dep.																				
66¾	—	Hythe .... arr.																				
69½	—	Shorncliffe	5 0		6 13											7 35	8 21				9 3	
70	—	Folkestone Central M arr.	5 2		6 18											7 38	8 24				9 6	
		Folkestone Central M dep.	5 3		6 21											7 39	8 26				9 8	
71	—	Folkestone Junction	5 8		6 29											7 42	8 31				9 14	
72½	—	Folkestone Warren Halt																				
77	—	Dover Marine arr.																				
		Dover Marine dep.																				
77½	—	Dover Priory 66 arr.	5 24		6 46											7 57	8 48				9 30	
		Dover Priory 66 dep.			Stop					7 8						7 59						
82½	—	Martin Mill B								7 22						8 11						
85	—	Walmer, for Kingsdown ..								7 29						8 17						
86¾	—	Deal .... arr.								7 34						8 22						
		Deal .... dep.		7 5						7 40	7 53					8 23						
91	—	Sandwich		7 12						7 50	8 0					8 31						
93	—	Richborough Castle Halt																				
*81¼	—	Minster (Thanet) .... arr.		7 21					7 22		8 8				8 39	8 39		9 21				
—	—	Minster (Thanet) .... dep		Stop					7 28						8 50							
—	—	Richboro' Castle Halt . arr.																				
—	—	Sandwich .... "							7 36						8 59							
—	—	Deal							7 44						9 7							
—	—	Walmer, for Kingsdown "																				
—	—	Minster (Thanet) .... dep.							7 25		8 12				8 40			9 22				
*85⅝	—	Ramsgate .... arr.		a.m	a.m	a.m			7 36	8 5	8 22				8 49			9 31				
		Ramsgate .... dep.		6 6	6 29	7 7	7 20	7 35	7 40	8 8		8 35	8 42		8 52			9 34	9 45	9 55		
*86¾	—	Dumpton Park D		6 9	6 32	7 10	7 23	7 38	7 45	8 13		8 38	8 45		8 57			9 39	9 48	9 58		
*88	—	Broadstairs		6 14	6 36	7 14	7 27	7 42	7 49	8 17		8 42	8 49		9 1			9 43	9 52	10 2		
*90¼	—	Margate East							7 55	8 23			8 53									
*91½	—	Margate .... arr		6 22	6 45	7 22	7 36	7 50	7 58	8 26		8 50	9 0		9 9			9 50	10 0	1010		

③ Third class only

For Notes, see page 42; for Continuation of Trains, see pages 35 to 42

For other Trains to Dover, Deal, &c., see pages 60 to 65

LONDON, ASHFORD, HYTHE, FOLKESTONE, DOVER, DEAL, and MARGATE

Down	Week Days—continued																			
	a.m	a.m	a.m	a.m	a.m	a.m	a.m	a.m	a.m	a.m	a.m	a.m	p.m	a.m	a.m	p.m	p.m	p.m	p.m	a.m
			Saturdays excepted		Saturdays excepted		Saturdays only		Saturdays only		Saturdays excepted.		Saturdays only				Saturdays only	Saturdays excepted	Saturdays only	Saturdays excepted; Refreshment Car London to Folkestone
Charing Cross..........dep.				7B23						8 25		9 15								1115
Waterloo .... "				7B25						8 27		9 17								1117
Cannon Street.......... "																				
London Bridge .... "				7B29						8 35										
New Cross.............. "				7B36																
Victoria ....dep.		7 18						8 18							9 18					
Holborn Viaduct ..... "																				
Blackfriars............ "																				
Bromley South....... "		7 35						8 35							9 35					
Swanley .... "		7 44						8 50							9 50					
Orpington............ dep.				7B58																
Sevenoaks (Tub's Hill).. "				8 23						9 8		9 50								1150
246 East Croydon ....dep.				7 39								8 45								9 46
246 Redhill .... "				8 9								9 6								1018
Tonbridge ....dep.				8 48						9 38		10 4		10 12						12 3
Paddock Wood 53				8 59						9 47				10 22						
Marden.....................														10 30						
Staplehurst..................				9 10										10 36						
Headcorn.....................				9 17										10 43						1223
Pluckley......................														10 52						
Maidstone East.... arr.		8 23						9 30							1030					
Maidstone East.... dep.		8 28						9 35							1035					
Bearsted and Thurnham....		8 35						9 42							1042					
Hollingbourne.............		8 39						9 46							1046					
Harrietsham		8 45						9 51							1052					
Lenham......................		8 50						9 56							1057					
Charing......................		8 57						10 3							11 4					
Hothfield Halt for Westwell															1110					
Ashford (Kent) 58 ......arr.		9 7		9 33				1013				1038		11 2	1117					1239
Ashford (Kent).......dep.						9 42								11 20						
Wye.........................						9 50								11 30						
Chilham						9 59								11 39						
Chartham....................						10 6								11 45						
Canterbury West A						1013								11 53						
Sturry........................						1019								11 59						
Chislet Colliery Halt.....						1024								12 4						
Grove Ferry.................						1029								12 9						
Ashford (Kent).........dep.				9 47								1047			1122					1242
Smeeth......................																				
Westenhanger..............																				
Sandling Junction..........				10 2											1136					1256
Sandling Junction....dep.																				
Hythe ....arr.																				
Shorncliffe				10 10								11 7			1143			1232		1 3
Folkestone Central M arr.				10 13								1110			1146			1234		1 6
Folkestone Central M dep.				10 15								1112			1147			1235		1 8
Folkestone Junction.......				10 20								1117			1152			1239		
Folkestone Warren Halt ..																				
Dover Marine ...... arr.																				
Dover Marine ...... dep.																				
Dover Priory 66 .... arr.				10 33								1130			12 8			1' 55		1 22
Dover Priory 66 .... dep.				10 25								1134					1215	1257		1 24
Martin Mill B...............				10 48								1147					1226	1 12		1 36
Walmer, for Kingsdown.....				10 54								1153					1232	1 18		1 42
Deal.................. arr.				11 0								1158					1238	1 23		1 47
Deal.................. dep	1015			11 2			1120				1142	1159					1239	1 24		1 48
Sandwich	1022			11 10			1127				1150	12 7					1247	1 32		1 56
Richborough Castle Halt....																				
Minster (Thanet) ..... arr.	1031					1038	1136				1159			12 19			1256	1 41		
Minster (Thanet) . dep.						1044								12 35						
Richboro' Castle Halt..arr																				
Sandwich .... "						1052								12 43						
Deal.................... "						11 0								12 50						
Walmer, for Kingsdown "														12 57						
Minster (Thanet) ......dep.						1039								12 21						
Ramsgate .... arr.				11 25		1047						1222		12 30						2 11
Ramsgate .... dep.			1115		1127	1049			11 30				1224	12 34		1 10			1 55	2 14
Dumpton Park D...........			1118		1131	1053			11 33				1227	12 39		1 13			1 58	2 19
Broadstairs			1122		1135	1057			11 37				1232	12 43		1 17			2 2	2 23
Margate East...............					1141											1 23				
Margate ....arr.			1131		1144	11 4			11 46				1243	12 50		1 28			2 11	2 30

FOR NOTES, SEE PAGE 42

For other Trains to Dover, Deal, &c., see pages 60 to 65

LONDON, ASHFORD, HYTHE, FOLKESTONE, DOVER, DEAL, and MARGATE

Week Days—*continued*

Down	a.m	p.m	a.m	p.m	a.m	a.m	p.m	a.m	p.m	p.m	p.m	p.m	p.m	p.m	p.m	p.m	p.m	p.m	p.m	p.m	p.m
Notes	Saturdays only; Refreshment Car London to Folkestone		Saturdays only	Saturdays only	Saturdays excepted	Saturdays only; Arr Tonbridge 12 43 p.m	Saturdays only	Saturdays excepted; Saturdays excepted	Saturdays excepted; Saturdays excepted	Saturdays only	Saturdays only; Refreshment Car London to Ramsgate	Saturdays only; Saturdays only	③ Saturdays only; Saturdays only	Saturdays excepted	Saturdays only	Saturdays excepted; Refreshment Car London to Margate	Saturdays only; Refreshment Car	Saturdays excepted	Saturdays only	Saturdays only	Saturdays only
Charing Cross .... dep	1115					1155		1155			1255					1 15			1 15		
Waterloo .... "	1117							1157								1 18			1 17		
Cannon Street .... "																	1 2				
London Bridge .... "						12 2		12 5													
New Cross .... "																					
Victoria .... dep			1118		1118				1218	1228											1 18
Holborn Viaduct .... "																					
Blackfriars .... "																					
Bromley South ..... "			1135		1135				1238	1247											1 35
Swanley .... "			1144		1144				1247	1 0											1 44
Orpington .... dep													1251								
Sevenoaks (Tub's Hill) "	1150							1241					1 1[illegible]								
246 East Croydon ...... dep	9 46					1146		1146											1247		
246 Redhill .... "	1018					12 6		12 6											1 4		
Tonbridge .... dep	12 3	1210				1248		1 5					1†27				1†42		2 2	2 18	
Paddock Wood 53		1218				1 0		1 19												2 28	
Marden		Stop				1 8		1 28					Stop							2 34	
Staplehurst						1 14		1 36												2 41	
Headcorn	1223					1 22		1 44												2 48	
Pluckley						1 31		1 54												2 58	
Maidstone East .... arr			122[illegible]		1223				1 26	1 40											2 23
Maidstone East .... dep				1230	1228				1 30	1 45											2 35
Bearsted and Thurnham.				1237	1235				1 37	1 52											2 42
Hollingbourne				1241	1239				1 42	1 56											2 46
Harrietsham				1247	1245				1 48	2 2											2 52
Lenham				1252	1250				1 55	2 7											2 57
Charing .... [well				1259	1257				2 1	2 13											3 4
Hothfield Halt, for West-									2 7												3 9
Ashford (Kent) 58 ...... arr	1239			1 9	1 7	1 41		2 4	2 15	2 24						2 24			2 33	3 8	3 17
Ashford (Kent) ...... dep				1 11	1 10			Stop	Stop					2 41	2 42					Stop	
Wye				1 21	1 20									2 50	2 50						
Chilham				1 30	1 29									2 59	2 59						
Chartham				1 35	1 34									3 4	3 4						
Canterbury West A				1 44	1 43									3 13	3 13						
Sturry				1 51	1 50									3 19	3 19						
Chislet Colliery Halt					1 55									3 24	3 24						
Grove Ferry				2 2	2 1									3 30	3 30						
Ashford (Kent) .... dep	1242						1 50									2 28			2 43		
Smeeth							1 58														
Westenhanger							2 5														
Sandling Junction	1256						2 9												2 58		
Sandling Junction .. dep							2 10												3 10		
Hythe .... arr							2 16												3 15		
Shorncliffe	1 3															2 47			3 6		
Folkestone Central M arr	1 6	p.m									2 20					2 50			3 9		
Folkestone Central M dep	1 8	1 14									2 22					2 52			3 11		
Folkestone Junction		1 17																	3 16		
Folkestone Warren Halt.																					
Dover Marine ...... arr																					
Dover Marine ...... dep																					
Dover Priory 66 .... arr	1 22										2 37					3 5			3 32		
Dover Priory 66 .... dep	1 24										2 39					3 7			3 34		
Martin Mill B	1 36										2 52					3 20			3 47		
Walmer for Kingsdown	1 42										2 59					3 27			3 53		
Deal .... arr	1 47								p.m		3 5					3 32			3 58	p.m	
Deal .... dep	1 48								3 10		3 7	3 18				3 34			3 59	4 20	
Sandwich	1 57								3 17		3 15	3 25				3 42			4 8	4 27	
Richborough Castle Halt ..																					
Minster (Thanet) .... arr				2 11	2 10				3 26			3 36		3 38	3 38					4 36	
Minster (Thanet) .... dep				2 28	2 14									3 50	3 50						
Richboro' Castle Halt arr																					
Sandwich .... "				2 36	2 24									3 58	3 59						
Deal .... "				2 44	2 32									4 6	4 7						
Walmer, for Kingsdown "					2 38										4 24						
Minster (Thanet) ...... dep				2 12	2 11									3 39	3 39						
Ramsgate .... arr	2 13			2 21	2 20			p.m			3 30		p.m	3 48	3 48	3 58			4 23		
Ramsgate .... dep	2 16			2 24	2 23			3 15					3 43		3 50	4 0		4 15	4 25		
Dumpton Park D	2 21			2 29	2 28			3 18					3 46		3 55	4 5		4 1[illegible]	4 29		
Broadstairs	2 25			2 33	2 32			3 23					3 51		3 59	4 9		4 22	4 33		
Margate East								3 29					3 57					4 28			
Margate .... arr	2 32			2 40	2 39			3 34					4 2		4 6	4 16		4 33	4 40		

For Notes, see page 42; for Continuation of Trains, see pages 37 to 42

LONDON, ASHFORD, HYTHE, FOLKESTONE, DOVER, DEAL, and MARGATE

For other Trains to Dover, Deal, &c., see pages 60 to 65

Down — Week Days—*continued*	p.m	p.m	p.m	p.m	p.m	p.m	p.m	p.m	p.m	p.m	p.m		p.m	p.m	p.m	p.m	p.m	p.m	p.m	p.m	p.m
	Saturdays excepted	Saturdays only	Saturdays excepted	Saturdays only	Saturdays excepted	Saturdays only	Saturdays excepted	Saturdays only	Saturdays excepted	Saturdays only				Sats. only	Saturdays excepted	Refreshment Car London to Margate	Saturdays excepted	Saturdays excepted	Saturdays excepted	Saturdays only	Refreshment Car London to Ramsgate; Saturdays excepted
Charing Cross ....dep.						2 25	2 25		3 15	3 15					3 25	4 15					
Waterloo .... "						2 27	2 27		3 17	3 17					3 29	4 17					
Cannon Street .... "																					5 0
London Bridge .... "						2 33	2 33							3 9	3 35						
New Cross .... "														3 16							
Victoria ....dep.			2 18	2 18									3 18								
Holborn Viaduct ...... "																					
Blackfriars .... "																					
Bromley South .... "			2 35	2 35									3 35								
Swanley .... "			2 44	2 44									3 50								
Orpington ....dep.														3 40							
Sevenoaks (Tub's Hill).. "						3 3	3 2		3 49	3 50				4 7	4 5						
246 East Croydon ....dep.						1 24	1 46			2 46				3 46	3 46						
246 Redhill .... "						1 50	2 10			3 6				4 5	4 15						
Tonbridge ....dep.						3 24	3 50		4 2	4 3	4z10			4 58	4 58						
Paddock Wood 53						3 33	3 59				4z19			5 8	5 9						
Marden						Stop	Stop				4z26										
Staplehurst											4z33										
Headcorn											4z39										
Pluckley											4z48										
Maidstone East ... arr.			3 23	3 23									4 30								
Maidstone East ... dep.			3 30	3 35									4 35					5 15			
Bearsted and Thurnham...			3 37	3 43									4 42					5 22			
Hollingbourne			3 41	3 48									4 46					5 27			
Harrietsham			3 47	3 54									4 52					5 32			
Lenham			3 52	3 59									4 57					5 37			
Charing			3 59	4 6									5 4					5 44			
Hothfield Halt, for Westwell													5 9								
Ashford (Kent) 58 ......arr.			4 9	4 19					4 36	4 36	4z58		5 16					5 55			6 4
Ashford (Kent) ......dep.			4 16					4 29			5 8										
Wye			4 25					4 37			5 17										
Chilham			4 34					4 45			5 26										
Chartham			4 39					4 50			5 31										
Canterbury West A			4 47					4 59			5 39										
Sturry			4 54					5 6			5 45										
Chislet Colliery Halt			4 59					5 11			5 50										
Grove Ferry			5 5					5 17			5 56										
Ashford (Kent) ....dep.					4 25				4 39	4 39							5 30				6 7
Smeeth					4 33					4 49							5 38				
Westenhanger					4 41				4 53	4 57							5 46				
Sandling Junction					4 45				4 57	5 1							5 50				6 21
Sandling Junction ....dep.									5 2	5 5											6 26
Hythe ....arr.							p.m		5 7	5 10											6 31
Shorncliffe							4 12		5 4	5 9							5 57				6 28
Folkestone Central M ... arr.							4 14		5 7	5 12						5 40	6 0				6 31
Folkestone Central M ... dep						p.m	4 15		5 9	5 14						5 42	6 1				6 33
Folkestone Junction						4 14	4 20		5 15	5 19							6 5				
Folkestone Warren Halt ..																					
Dover Marine ...... arr																					
Dover Marine ...... dep.																					
Dover Priory 66 ...... arr.						4 29	4 36		5 28	5 33						5 56	6 18				6 46
Dover Priory 66 ...... dep.						4 31	4 40		5 30	5 36						5 58					6 48
Martin Mill B						4 43	4 53		5 43	5 49						6 10					7 0
Walmer, for Kingsdown						4 49	4 59		5 49	5 56						6 15					7 5
Deal .... arr.						4 54	5 5		5 55	6 1						6 20					7 10
Deal .... dep.						4 55	5 6		5 57	6 2						6 21			6 36	6 38	7 12
Sandwich						5 3	5 15		6 6	6 11						6 29			6 43	6 45	7 20
Richborough Castle Halt																					
Minster (Thanet) ....arr.			5 13			5 12	5 24	5 27			6 4								6 52	6 54	
Minster (Thanet) ......dep.			5 48					5 48			6 7										
Richborough Castle Halt arr																					
Sandwich .... "			5 56					5 56			6 17										
Deal .... "			6 4					6 4			6 25										
Walmer, for Kingsdown "											6 32										
Minster (Thanet) ....dep.			5 14					5 27			6 5								7 0		
Ramsgate .... arr.			5 24					5 36	6 21	6 26	6 14					6 44			7 10		7 36
Ramsgate .... dep.	5 25	5 26	5 32					5 38	6 23	6 28	6 15					6z48					
Dumpton Park D	5 28	5 29	5 37					5 42	6 28	6 32	6 19					6z53					
Broadstairs	5 32	5 34	5 41					5 46	6 32	6 36	6 23					6z57					
Margate East																					
Margate ....arr.	5 41	5 43	5 48					5 53	6 39	6 44	6 30					7z4					

FOR NOTES, SEE PAGE 42

LONDON, ASHFORD, HYTHE, FOLKESTONE DOVER, DEAL, and MARGATE

Week Days—*continued*

Down	p.m	p.m	p.m	p.m	p.m	p.m	p.m	p.m	p.m	p.m	p.m	p.m	p.m	p.m	p.m	p.m	p.m	p.m	p.m	p.m	p.m
Charing Cross ....dep	..	..	..	4 30	..	..	..	..	..	..	5 25	5 31	..	..	..	..	6 15	..	..	..	..
Waterloo ...... "	..	..	..	4 32	..	..	..	..	..	..	5 27	5 33	..	..	..	..	6 17	..	..	..	..
Cannon Street ...... "	..	..	..	..	..	4 38	..	..	..	..	..	..	5 40	..	..	6 18	..	..	..	..	..
London Bridge ...... "	..	..	..	4 39	..	4 42	..	..	..	..	5 34	5 39	5 45	..	..	..	..	..	..	..	..
New Cross ...... "	..	..	..	..	..	..	..	..	..	..	Saturdays only	..	..	..	..	..	Saturdays only	..	..	..	..
Victoria ......dep.	..	..	..	..	..	Saturdays excepted	4 52	..	5 18	5 20		..	..	Saturdays only	..	..		5 53	..	..	..
Holborn Viaduct ...... "	..	..	..	..	..		..	..	..	..		..	..		..	Saturdays excepted		..	Saturdays only	Saturdays excepted	..
Blackfriars ...... "	..	..	..	..	..		..	..	..	..		..	..		..			..			..
Bromley South ...... "	..	..	..	..	..		5 11	..	5 35	5 38		..	..		..			6 12			..
Swanley ...... "	..	..	..	..	..		5 21		5 44	5 51		..	..		..			6 23			..
Orpington ......dep.	..	..	Saturdays only	..	..		..	..					..		..			..			
Sevenoaks (Tub's Hill) .. "	..	..		5 10	..	5 13	..	..			6 4	6 10	6 20		..	6 51	6 50	..			Saturdays only
246 East Croydon ......dep.	..	..		4 5	..	..		..	Saturdays only	Saturdays excepted	4 46	..	4 46	5 46	..	5 28	5 46				
246 Redhill ...... "	..	..		4 36	..	..	Saturdays excepted	..			5 5	..	5 5	[illegible] 7	..	6 7	6 7	Saturdays excepted			
Tonbridge ......dep.	..	..		5 27		5 28		..			6 30	6†25	6 37	6 54	..	7 4	7 3		..	7 12	
Paddock Wood 53	..	..		5 38		5V50		..			6 39		6 47	7 5	..	..	7 14		7 22	7 23	
Marden	..	..		5 45		5 58		..			Arr. Tonbridge, 6 15 p.m.		6 54	..	..	..			7 30	7 32	
Staplehurst	..	..		5 51	Saturdays only	6 4		..					7 0	..	..	..			7 36	7 39	
Headcorn	..	..		5 58		6 10		..					7 7	..	..	..			7 44	7 48	
Pluckley	..	..		6 7		6 19		..					7 16	..	..	..	Refreshment Car London to Ramsgate		7 53	7 57	
Maidstone East arr.	..		..	..		..	5 54	..	6 23	6 29		Saturdays excepted	Saturdays excepted	..	..	..		7 1	..	..	..
Maidstone East dep.	..		5 27	..		..	5 58	..	6 30	6 35				..	..	..		7 5	..	..	7 32
Bearsted and Thurnham	..	Saturdays excepted	5 34	..		..	6 4	..	6 37	6 42				..	..	..		7 13	..	..	7 39
Hollingbourne	..		5 38	..		..	6 9	..	6 41	6 46				..	..	..		7 18	..	..	7 44
Harrietsham	..		5 44	..		..	6 14	..	6 47	6 52	..			..	..	..		7 24	..	..	7 50
Lenham	..		5 49	..		..	6 19	..	6 52	6 57	..			..	..	..		7 29	..	..	7 55
Charing	..		5 56	..		..	6 26	..	6 59	7 4	..			..	..	..		7 36	..	..	8 1
Hothfield Halt, for Westwell	..		..	..		..	..	..	7 4	7 10	..			..	..	..		..	..	..	..
Ashford (Kent) 58 .....arr.	..		6 7	6 17	..	6 29	6 38	..	7 11	7 17	..	Stop	7 26	..	..	7 35	7 40	7 47	8 3	8 9	8 13
Ashford (Kent) ......dep.	..	6 16	..	Saturdays only	6 30	..	6 41	Saturdays excepted	..	..	..	..	..	..	..	..	..	..	..	8 14	8 18
Wye	..	..	..		6 38	..	6 51		..	..	..	..	..	..	..	..	..	..	..	8 24	8 28
Chilham	..	..	..		6 47	..	7 0		..	..	..	..	..	..	..	..	..	..	..	8 33	8 37
Chartham	..	6 30	..		6 52	..	7 5		..	..	..	..	..	..	..	..	..	..	..	8 38	8 42
Canterbury West A	..	6 38	..		7 1	..	7 13		..	..	..	..	..	..	..	..	..	..	..	8 47	8 51
Sturry	..	..	..		7 8	..	7 19		..	..	..	..	..	..	..	..	..	..	..	8 54	8 59
Chislet Colliery Halt	..	..	..		7 13	..	7 24		..	..	..	..	..	..	..	..	..	..	..	8 59	9 5
Grove Ferry	..	..	..		7 19	..	7 30		..	..	..	..	..	..	..	..	..	..	..	9 5	9 12
Ashford (Kent) ......dep.	..	..	..	6 21	..	..	..	6 39	..	..	..	..	..	..	..	7 37	7 42	7 50	..	..	..
Smeeth	..	..	..	6 31	..	..	..	6 49	..	..	..	..	..	..	..	..	7 52	7 59	..	..	..
Westenhanger	..	..	..	6 39	..	..	..	6 57	..	..	..	..	..	..	..	..	8 0	8 7	..	..	..
Sandling Junction	..	..	..	6 44	..	..	..	7 1	..	..	..	..	..	..	..	..	8 4	8 11	..	..	..
Sandling Junction ....dep.	..	..	..	..	..	..	..	..	..	..	..	..	..	..	..	..	..	..	..	..	..
Hythe ......arr.	..	..	..	..	..	..	..	..	..	..	..	..	..	..	..	..	..	..	..	..	..
Shorncliffe	..	..	..	6 51	..	..	..	7 9	..	..	..	..	..	..	Runs 10 mins later on Saturdays	7 56	8 12	8 18	..	..	..
Folkestone Central M arr.	..	..	..	6 54	..	..	..	7 12	..	..	..	..	..	..		7 59	8 15	8 21	..	..	..
Folkestone Central M dep.	..	..	..	6 56	..	..	..	7 14	..	..	..	..	..	..		8 0	8 17	8 22	..	..	..
Folkestone Junction	..	..	..	7 1	..	..	..	7 18	..	..	..	..	..	..		8 5	8 21	8 26	..	..	..
Folkestone Warren Halt ...	..	..	..	..	..	..	..	..	..	..	..	..	..	..		..	..	..	..	..	..
Dover Marine arr	..	..	..	..	..	..	..	..	..	..	..	..	..	..		..	..	..	..	..	..
Dover Marine dep.	..	..	..	..	..	..	..	..	..	..	..	..	..	..		..	..	..	..	..	..
Dover Priory 66 arr.	..	..	..	7 15	..	..	..	..	..	..	..	..	..	..		8 18	8 34	..	..	..	..
Dover Priory 66 dep.	..	..	..	7 17	..	..	..	..	..	..	..	..	..	..		8 20	8 36	..	..	..	..
Martin Mill B	..	..	..	7 30	..	..	..	..	..	..	..	..	..	..		8 33	8 49	..	..	..	..
Walmer, for Kingsdown	..	..	..	7 36	..	..	..	..	..	..	..	..	..	..		8 39	8 55	..	..	..	..
Deal arr.	..	..	..	7 41	..	..	..	..	..	..	..	..	..	..		8 44	9 0	..	..	..	..
Deal dep.	..	..	..	7 43	..	..	..	..	..	..	..	..	..	..	8 35	8 46	9 1	..	..	..	..
Sandwich	..	..	..	7 51	..	..	..	..	..	..	..	..	..	..	8 42	8 54	9 9	..	..	..	..
Richborough Castle Halt	..	..	..	..	..	..	..	..	..	..	..	..	..	..	..	..	..	..	..	..	..
Minster (Thanet) ......arr	..	6 52	..	8 0	7 28		7 38				..	..	..	..	8 51	..	..	..	..	9 14	9 21
Minster (Thanet) ....dep.	..	6 53	..	..	7 52	..	7 58	..	..	..	..	..	..	..	..	..	..	..	..	9 30	9 30
Richborough Castle Halt arr	..	..	..	..	..	..	..		..	..	..	..	..	..	..	..	..	..	..	..	..
Sandwich ...... "	..	7 2	..	..	8 0	..	8 8	..	..	..	..	..	..	..	..	..	..	..	..	9 28	9 38
Deal ...... "	..	7 11	..	..	8 8	..	8 16	..	..	..	..	..	..	..	..	..	..	..	..	9 46	9 46
Walmer, for Kingsdown "	..	7 19	..	..	..	..	..	..	..	..	..	..	..	..	..	..	..	..	..	9 54	9 54
Minster (Thanet) ......dep.	..	..	..	8 6	7 29	..	7 39	..	..	..	..	..	..	..	..	..	..	..	..	9 16	9 25
Ramsgate arr.	..	..	..	8 16	7 38	..	7 48	..	..	..	..	p.m	..	..	..	9 9	9 24	..	..	9 25	9 35
Ramsgate dep.	7 45	..	..	8 18	..	..	7 50	..	..	..	..	9 10	..	..	..	..	..	..	..	9 27	9 36
Dumpton Park D	7 48	..	..	8 22	..	..	7 55	..	..	..	..	9 13	..	..	..	..	..	..	..	9 31	9 40
Broadstairs	7 52	..	..	8 26	..	..	7 59	..	..	..	..	9 18	..	..	..	..	..	..	..	9 35	9 44
Margate East	..	..	..	..	..	..	..	..	..	..	..	..	..	..	..	..	..	..	..	..	..
Margate ......arr.	8U 1	..	..	8 33	..	..	8 6	..	..	..	..	9 27	..	..	..	..	..	..	..	9 42	9 51

For Notes, see page 42 : for Continuation of Trains, see pages 39 to 42

LONDON, ASHFORD, HYTHE, FOLKESTONE, DOVER, DEAL, and MARGATE

For other Trains to Dover, Deal, &c., see pages 60 to 65

Down	Week Days—continued												Sundays									
	p.m	p.m	p.m	p.m	p.m	p.m	p.m	p.m	p.m	p.m	a.m		a.m	a.m	a.m	a.m	a.m	a.m	a.m	a.m	a.m	a.m
Charing Cross .... dep	7 15		7 34	7 34			9 15			3	3			3			7 15					9 15
Waterloo .... "	7 17		7 37	7 37			9 17										7 17					9 17
Cannon Street.......... "																						
London Bridge......... "			7 45	7 45					9B11	1150				4 5			7 24					
New Cross .... "									9B17								7 31					
Victoria............. dep		7 20						9 18		Via Redhill, page 247								7 18				
Holborn Viaduct..... "																						
Blackfriars.......... "																						
Bromley South ..... "		7 40						9 35										7 35				
Swanley............. "		7 49						9 44										7 48				
Orpington............. dep									9B40													
Sevenoaks (Tub's Hill) "			8 17	8 17			9 49		10 6					4 51			8 1					
246 East Croydon...... dep			7Z22	7Z22			8 46			1215										7 35		
246 Redhill............ "			7 44	7 44			9 5			1248										7 59		
Tonbridge............. dep			8 34	8 34	8 50	9 35	10 3		10 30	1 30				5 24			8 20			8 47		
Paddock Wood 53					9 0	9 44	1014		10 40					5 36						8 59		
Marden..................			8 50	8 50		Stop			10 47					5 44						9 7		
Staplehurst..............			8 56	8 56					10 53											9 14		
Headcorn................			9 3	9 3					11 1								8 46			9 21		
Pluckley................	Refreshment Car London to Margate		Runs until 28th Nov., 1947, only	Commences 29th Nov., 1947					11 10					6 10			8 58			9 31		
Maidstone East ... arr		8 28						1023										8 26				
Maidstone East ... dep		8 32						1030											8 45			
Bearsted and Thurnham.		8 39						1037											8 52			
Hollingbourne...........		8 43						1042											8 57			
Harrietsham............		8 49						1048											9 3			
Lenham.................		8 54						1053											9 8			
Charing ....well		9 1						11 0											9 15			
Hothfield Halt, for West-								11 6														
Ashford (Kent) 58..... arr		9 12	9 19	9 19		p.m	1039	1113	11 20	2 7				6 21			9 8		9 26	9 41		
Ashford (Kent)...... dep						9 38			Arr. Tonbridge 10 20 p.m		2 30										9 47	
Wye.....................						9 46															9 56	
Chilham.................						9 55															10 6	
Chartham...............						10 0															1011	
Canterbury West A						10 8					2 55										1020	
Sturry..................						1014															1028	
Chislet Colliery Halt....						1019															1033	
Grove Ferry............						1024															1039	
Ashford (Kent)........ dep			9 22	9 22			1042			2 18				6 28			9 12			9 48		
Smeeth..................			9 32	9 32										6 38			9 22					
Westenhanger...........			9 40	9 40										6 46			9 30					
Sandling Junction.......			9 44	9 44			1058							6 51			9 34					
Sandling Junction .. dep											Sunday and Monday mornings excepted											
Hythe.............. arr																						
Shorncliffe...............			9 52	10 0			11 6			2 48				7 0	7 50	9 5	9 42			10 8		
Folkestone Central ... arr	8 40		9 56	10 4			11 9							7 4	7 52	9 7	9 45			1011		1040
Folkestone Central ... dep	8 42		9 58	10 6			1111							7 5	7 53	9 8	9 48			1012		1042
Folkestone Junction			10 3	1011			1115							7 12	7 56	9 11	9 52			1018		
Folkestone Warren Halt.																						
Dover Marine...... arr																						
Dover Marine...... dep																						
Dover Priory 66 ... arr	8 55		1018	1026			1131			3y8				7 28	8 13	9 28	10 6			1032		1055
Dover Priory 66 ... dep	8 57						1134			3K20				7 35	Stop	9 30	1013					1059
Martin Mill B...........	9 9						1147							7 49		9 42	1026					1111
Walmer for Kingsdown....	9 14						1153							7 55		9 48	1032					1117
Deal............... arr	9 19						1158			3K44				8 0		9 53	1037					1122
Deal............... dep	9 20						12 0							8 4		9 54	1039					1124
Sandwich................	9 28						12 8							8 14		10 2	1048					1133
Richborough Castle Halt..																						
Minster (Thanet) ..... arr						1032								8 23		1011					1048	
Minster (Thanet)..... dep																					11 0	
Richboro' Castle Halt arr																						
Sandwich............ "																					1110	
Deal................. "																					1118	
Walmer, for Kingsdown "																					1125	
Minster (Thanet)..... dep						1033								8 27		1016					1049	
Ramsgate.......... arr	9 43					1042	1223				3 20			8 37	a.m	1026	11 6				1058	1148
Ramsgate.......... dep	9 48					1046					3 29		8 15	8 43	9 40	1028					1059	1152
Dumpton Park D.........	9 53					1051							8 18	8 48	9 43	1033					11 3	1157
Broadstairs..............	9 57					1055							8 23	8 52	9 48	1037					11 7	12 1
Margate East.............																						
Margate............... arr	10 4					11 2					3 40		8 30	8 59	9 55	1044					1114	12 8

FOR NOTES, SEE PAGE 42

LONDON, ASHFORD, HYTHE, FOLKESTONE, DOVER, DEAL, and MARGATE

Sundays—*continued*

Down	a.m	a.m	a.m	a.m	p.m	a.m	p.m	a.m		p.m	p.m	p.m	p.m	p.m	p.m	p.m	p.m	p.m	p.m	p.m	p.m	p.m
Charing Cross .... dep		9 32				1110				1215				3 15								
Waterloo .... "		9 34				1113				1217				3 17								
Cannon Street .... "																						
London Bridge .... "		9 41				1120								3 23								
New Cross .... "						1128																
Victoria .... dep				9 18				1118													5 18	
Holborn Viaduct .... "																						
Blackfriars .... "																						
Bromley South .... "				9 35				1135													5 35	
Swanley .... "				9 50				1145													5 45	
Orpington .... dep						1148																
Sevenoaks (Tub's Hill) "		10 12								1249				3 52								
246 East Croydon .... dep		9 6												2 46								
246 Redhill .... "		9 41												3 10								
Tonbridge .... dep		10 25	1058			1212				1 3				4 4								
Paddock Wood 53			11 7																			
Marden																						
Staplehurst														Refreshment Car London to Margate								
Headcorn		10 47																				
Pluckley																						
Maidstone East ... arr				10 28				1223													6 23	
Maidstone East ... dep	9 46			10 36				1242													Stop	6 30
Bearsted and Thurnham	9 53			10 43		Call, Hither Green 11 34 a.m		1249														6 37
Hollingbourne	9 58			10 48				1254														6 42
Harrietsham	10 4			10 54				1 0														6 47
Lenham	10 9			10 59				1 5														6 52
Charing .... [well	1016			11 6				1 12														6 59
Hothfield Halt, for West				11 12																		
Ashford (Kent) 58 .... arr	1027	11 3		11 21		1244		1 23		1 38				4 38								7 10
Ashford (Kent) .... dep				11 50			1 6								4 48					6 32		
Wye				11 58			1 16								4 56					6 41		
Chilham				12 7			1 25								5 5					6 50		
Chartham				12 12			1 30								5 10					6 55		
Canterbury West A				12 19			1 43								5 19					7 2		
Sturry				12 26			1 49								5 25					7 7		
Chislet Colliery Halt				12 31			1 54								5 30					7 12		
Grove Ferry				12 37			1 59								5 35					7 17		
Ashford (Kent) .... dep		11 16				1246				1 41				4 40			5 18					7 12
Smeeth										1 51							5 26					
Westenhanger										1 59							5 34					
Sandling Junction		11 30				1 0				2 3							5 38					7 26
Sandling Junction .. dep																						
Hythe .... arr																						
Shorncliffe		11 37				1 8				2 10				5 0			5 47	5 58				7 33
Folkestone Central M arr		11 40				1 11				2 13				5 3			5 50	6 0				7 36
Folkestone Central M dep		11 41				1 13				2 15	3 6			5 5			5 51	6 1				7 38
Folkestone Junction		11 47				1 18				2 20	3 9			5 10			5 55	6 4	7 0			7 42
Folkestone Warren Halt																	Stop					
Dover Marine .... arr																						
Dover Marine .... dep																						
Dover Priory 66 .... arr		12 0				1 31				2 33	3 25			5 23				6 18	7 16			7 55
Dover Priory 66 .... dep		12 2				1 34				2 35	3 27			5 25				6 19				
Martin Mill B		12 14				1 46				2 48	3 39			5 37				6 31				
Walmer, for Kingsdown		12 20				1 52				2 54	3 45			5 43				6 37				
Deal .... arr		12 25				1 57				2 59	3 50			5 48				6 42				
Deal .... dep		12 26				1 59				3 1	3 51			5 49				6 43				
Sandwich		12 34				2 7				3 9	3 59			5 57				6 51				
Richborough Castle Halt																						
Minster (Thanet) .... arr				12 46		2 17	2 7				4 8				5 44			7 0		7 25		
Minster (Thanet) .... dep				12 55			3 0													7 32		
Richboro' Castle Halt arr																						
Sandwich .... "				1 6			3 10													7 41		
Deal .... "				1 13			3 18													7 48		
Walmer, for Kingsdown "				1 19			3 25															
Minster (Thanet) .... dep				12 47		2 22	2 8				4 15				5 45					7 26		
Ramsgate .... arr		12 49		12 56		2 32	2 17			3 24	4 25			6 12	5 54		p.m			7 35	p.m	
Ramsgate .... dep				12 58	2 2	2 36	2 18			3 25	4 26	5 5	5 14	6 15		6 30	7 20			7 36	8 5	
Dumpton Park D				1 2	2 5	2 41	2 22			3 29	4 30	5 8	5 17	6 20		6 33	7 23			7 41	8 8	
Broadstairs				1 6	2 10	2 45	2 26			3 33	4 34	5 13	5 21	6 24		6 37	7 28			7 45	8 12	
Margate East																						
Margate .... arr				1 13	2 17	2 52	2 23			3 40	4 41	5 20	5 28	6 31		6 44	7 35			7 52	8 19	

For Notes, see page 42; for Continuation of SUNDAY TRAINS, see page 42

For other trains to Dover, Deal, &c., see pages 60 to 65.

LONDON, ASHFORD, HYTHE, FOLKESTONE, DOVER, DEAL, and MARGATE

Down	Sundays—*continued*													
	p.m	p.m	p.m	p.m	p.m	p.m	p.m	p.m	p.m	p.m	p.m	p.m	ngt.	
Charing Cross .... dep	6 15			7 0				8 15			9 40			
Waterloo .... "	6 18			7 3				8 17			9 43			
Cannon Street .... "														
London Bridge .... "	6 25			7 10				8 23			9 49	9 5		
New Cross .... "														
Victoria .... dep						7 18				9 18				
Holborn Viaduct .... "														
Blackfriars .... "														
Bromley South .... "						7 35				9 35				
Swanley .... "						7 45				9 45				
Orpington .... dep												Via Redhill, page 248.		
Sevenoaks (Tub's Hill) "	6 57			7 44				8 53			10 21			
246 East Croydon .... dep	4 46							7 5				9 25		
246 Redhill .... "	5 5							7 43				9 50		
Tonbridge .... dep	7 10	7 28		8 1				9 6	9 22		10†36	1048		
Paddock Wood 53		7 36		8 13					9 30					
Marden		Stop		8 22					Stop		Stop			
Staplehurst				8 30										
Headcorn				8 38										
Pluckley				8 48										
Maidstone East ... arr						8 23				1023	p.m			
Maidstone East ... dep							8 30				10 37			
Bearsted and Thurnham.							8 37				10 44			
Hollingbourne							8 42				10 49			
Harrietsham							8 47				10 55			
Lenham							8 52				11 0			
Charing							8 59				11 7			
Hothfield Halt, for Westwell											11 13			
Ashford (Kent) 58 ... arr	7 42	p.m		8 58			9 10	9 38	p.m		11 20	1126		
Ashford (Kent) .... dep		7 55							9 55				12 0	
Wye		8 3							10 3					
Chilham		8 12							1012					
Chartham		8 17							10 17					
Canterbury West A		8 26							1024				1228	
Sturry		8 30							1029					
Chislet Colliery Halt									1034					
Grove Ferry		8 41							1040					
Ashford (Kent) .... dep	7 44							9 47				1131		
Smeeth								9 57						
Westenhanger								10 5						
Sandling Junction								10 9						
Sandling Junction .. dep														
Hythe .... arr														
Shorncliffe	8 5				9 5			1017				1157		
Folkestone Central M ... arr	8 8				9 6			1020						
Folkestone Central M ... dep	8 10				9 7			1021						
Folkestone Junction	8 15				9 14			1026				12 7		
Folkestone Warren Halt														
Dover Marine .... arr														
Dover Marine .... dep														
Dover Priory 66 ... arr	8 28				9 28			1041				1222		
Dover Priory 66 ... dep	8 32				9 30			1044				1233		
Martin Mill **B**	8 44				9 42			1057				1246		
Walmer for Kingsdown	8 50				9 48			11 3				1252		
Deal .... arr	8 55				9 53			11 8				1257		
Deal .... dep	8 56		8 36		9 54			11 9						
Sandwich	9 4		8 43		10 2			1118				Arr. Shorncliffe at 11 52 p.m		
Richborough Castle Halt..														
Minster (Thanet) .... arr		8 49	8 52		1011				1048					
Minster (Thanet) .... dep		9 20							1054					
Richboro Castle Halt arr														
Sandwich .... "		9 28							11 3					
Deal .... "		9 36							1110					
Walmer, for Kingsdown "		9 42							1116					
Minster (Thanet) ...... dep		8 50							1049					
Ramsgate .... arr	9 19	8 59						1133	1058				1254	
Ramsgate .... dep	9 21	9 1						1135	11 0				1256	
Dumpton Park **D**	9 26	9 5						1140	11 4					
Broadstairs	9 30	9 9						1144	11 8					
Margate East														
Margate .... arr	9 37	9 16						1152	1115				1 8	

NOTES

3 Third class only

* Mileage via Canterbury West
† Arrival time

A ¾ mile to Canterbury East Station
B Martin Mill, for St. Margaret's Bay
D Dumpton Park, for East Ramsgate
H Change at London Bridge
K Sunday and Monday mornings excepted
M Sta. for Sandgate. Frequent Omnibus Services between Folkestone Central and Folkestone Harbour by East Kent Road Car
S O or **SO** Saturdays only
S X or **SX** Saturdays excepted
U 1 minute *earlier* on Sats.
V Arr. 5 38 p.m
y Arr. 3 5 a.m on Sunday mornings
Z Dep. 7 5 p.m on Saturdays
z 2 minutes later on Saturdays

LOCAL TRAINS and Intermediate Stations

between London Sevenoaks and Tonbridge, page 124—London, Swanley and Maidstone East, page 136.

OTHER TRAINS

between London & Maidstone West, pages 53 and 72—London and Dover, page 60

Printed and Published by—Henry Blacklock & Co. Ltd., London, and Albert Square, Manchester, 2.

MARGATE, DEAL, DOVER, FOLKESTONE, HYTHE, ASHFORD, and LONDON

Miles from Margate		Up	Week Days																			
			a.m	a.m	a.m	a.m	a.m	a.m	a.m	a.m	a.m	a.m	a.m	a.m	a.m	a.m	a.m	a.m	a.m	a.m	a.m	a.m
		Margate dep.	5 12			5 30									6 7		7 3		7 55		7 30	
½		Margate East																				
3½		**Broadstairs**	5 21			5 36									6 15		7 9		8 1		7 36	
4½		Dumpton Park **D**	5 25	Mondays only		5 40									6 21		7 13		8 6		7 40	
5½		**Ramsgate** arr.	5 29			5 44									6 25		7 17		8 10		7 44	
		Ramsgate dep.	5 35			5 46	5 30									6 44	7 18		8 11		7 46	
9½		Minster (Thanet) arr.	5 44			5 54									③		7 26		8 18			
—		Walmer, for Kingsdown dep.	③												Stop				7 29			
—		**Deal** "															7 5		7 53			
—		**Sandwich** "															7 12		8 0			
—		Richborough Castle Halt "																				
—		**Minster** (Thanet) arr.															7 21		8 8			
—		**Minster** (Thanet) dep.	5 45			5 55											7 28	7 28	8 19			
2½		Richborough Castle Halt																				
14½		**Sandwich**					5 46									7 0		7 36			8 3	
18½		**Deal** arr.					5 53									7 8		7 44			8 12	
		Deal dep.		5 36			5 54									7 11					8 13	
20½		Walmer, for Kingsdown		5 40			5 59									7 17					8 19	
23½		Martin Mill **B**		5 47												7 25					8 27	
28		**Dover** Priory arr.		5 58			6 17									7 37					8 39	
		Dover Priory dep.		Stop			6 19					6 50	7 5			7 38					8 42	
28½		**Dover** Marine arr.																				
		Dover Marine dep.																				
33½		**Folkestone** Warren Halt																				
34½		**Folkestone** Junction					6 32					7 5	7 22	7 35								
35½		**Folkestone** Central **M** arr.					6 36					7 9	Stop	7 37		7 52					8 57	
		Folkestone Central **M** dep.					6 37					7 11		7 38		7 58					9 3	
36½		Shorncliffe					6 41					7 14		7 41	a.m	8 3					9 7	
—		Mls **Hythe** dep.													7 52							
-		1½ Sandling Junc 34 arr.													7 56							
40½		Sandling Junction					6 49					7 22			7 57							
41½		Westenhanger										7 26			8 0							
45½		Smeeth										7 34			8 7							
49½		**Ashford** (Kent) **34**, 58 arr.					7 2					7 43			8 15	8 22						
—	—	Mls Grove Ferry				6 4											7 37					
—	—	2 Chislet Colliery Halt	5 58			6 10											7 43					
—	—	4 Sturry				6 16											7 49					
—	—	6½ **Canterbury West A**	6 8			6 24					7 10						7 57		8 35			
—	—	9½ Chartham	Stop			6 31					7 16						8 4					
—	—	11½ Chilham				6 37					7 21						8 9					
—	—	16½ Wye [58				6 46					7 30						8 18					
—	—	20½ **Ashford** (Kent) **34** arr		a.m		6 56					7 40						8 28		8 55			
—	—	**Ashford** (Kent) dep.		6 28	6 43		7 7		7 15	7 27		8 5				8 24	8 30			9 0		9 31
—	53	Hothfield Halt, for Westwell										8 14								9 7		
—	55¾	Charing		6 39					7 25			8 20				Refreshment Car Ramsgate to London				9 12	Refreshment Car Margate to London	
—	59½	Lenham		6 46					7 31			8 28								9 20		
—	61½	Harrietsham		6 50					7 35			8 [illegible]								9 24		
—	63½	Hollingbourne		6 55					7 40			8 37								9 28		
—	66	Bearsted and Thurnham		7 0					7 45			8 42								9 33		
—	68½	Maidstone East arr.		7 6					7 51			8 48								9 39		
		Maidstone East dep.		7 11					7 54			8 57								9 49		
55	—	Pluckley			6 52					7 36												9 40
60¼	—	Headcorn			7 1					7 45							8 45					9 50
63½	—	Staplehurst			7 7					7 53							8 51					9 57
66½	—	Marden	a.m		7 13					7 59			a.m				8 57					10 3
70½	—	Paddock Wood 53	6 32		7 21			7 43		8h18			8 55				9 6					1011
76	—	Tonbridge 54, 249 arr.	6 41		7 31		7 40	7 53		8 29			9 5				9 16					1022
95½	—	249 Redhill arr.	7 37					8 39		9 39							1010					1116
106	—	249 East Croydon "	8 9					9 5		10 9							1038					1147
83½	—	**Sevenoaks** (Tub's Hill) arr.	7 6				8 4	8 15		8 48							9 38					
91½	—	**Orpington** 130, 147 "	7③27																			
—	91	Swanley 69 arr.		7 54					8 37											1028		
—	98	**Bromley South J** "		8 7					8 51			9 40								1042		
—	109	**Blackfriars** "										10 0										
—	109½	**Holborn Viaduct** "										10 2										
106½	108½	**Victoria** "		8 28					9 14											1059		
100¼	—	**New Cross** arr.	7③51																			
103¾	—	**London Bridge** "	7③57				8 32										10 9				1028	
104¼	—	**Cannon Street** "	8③0					8 47		9 24						9 30	1014					
104½	—	**Waterloo** "					8 38														1034	
105¼	—	**Charing Cross** "					8 42														1038	

For Notes, see page 51; for Continuation of Trains, see pages 44 to 51.

For other Trains from Deal, Dover, &c., see pages 66 to 71

MARGATE, DEAL, DOVER, FOLKESTONE, HYTHE, ASHFORD, and LONDON

For other Trains from Deal, Dover, &c., see pages 66 to 71

Up	Week Days—continued																					
	a.m	a.m	a.m	a.m	a.m	a.m	a.m	a.m	a.m	a.m	a.m	a.m	a.m.	a.m	a.m	a.m	a.m	p.m	p.m	a.m	p.m	p.m
Margate .... dep	8 12					8 22		9 35	10A1	10 8	10 8			1040	1042	1110				1140		
Margate East	8 14					8 26				1010	1010											
Broadstairs	8 21					8 32		9 42	10 9	1016	1016			1051	1051	1116				1146		
Dumpton Park D	8 25					8 38		9 46	1014	1020	1020			1056	1056	1120				1150		
Ramsgate ... arr	8 29					8 42		9 50	1018	1024	1024			11 0	11 0	1124				1154		
Ramsgate ... dep	8 32					Stop		9 52		1026	1026					1128	11 0			1155		
Minster (Thanet) ...... arr	8 40									1034	1035					1138				12 3		
Walmer, for Kingsdown dp	8 17																Saturdays only					
Deal ... "	8 23									1015	1015					1120				1142		
Sandwich ... "	8 31									1022	1022					1127				1150		
Richboro' Castle Halt "																						
Minster (Thanet) .... arr	8 39					a.m				1031	1031					1136				1159		
Minster (Thanet) ...... dep	8 41					8 50				1035	1036		10 44	Saturdays excepted.	Saturdays only	1139				12 4		
Richborough Castle Halt																						
Sandwich						8 59		10 8					10 52				1114					
Deal ... arr						9 7		1016					11 [illegible]				1122					
Deal ... dep						Stop		1017		Saturdays only	Saturdays excepted	Saturdays only	Stop				1124					
Walmer, for Kingsdown								1023									1129			Saturdays excepted		
Martin Mill B								1031						Stop			1137					
Dover Priory ... arr								1042									1148					
Dover Priory ... dep		8 55						1044							Stop		1150					
Dover Marine ... arr																Saturdays only						
Dover Marine ... dep																						
Folkestone Warren Halt													a.m.									
Folkestone Junction		9 8										1113	11 14				12 4					
Folkestone Central M ... arr		9 12						1059				1117	11 17				12 8					
Folkestone Central M ... dep		9 14						11 5				1119	11 19				1210					
Shorncliffe		9 17										1122	11 24				1214					
Hythe ... dep																						
Sandling Junction 34 arr																						
Sandling Junction		9 26						Refreshment Car Margate to London				1130	11 31				1222					
Westenhanger		9 30															1226					
Smeeth		9 38																				
Ashford (Kent) 34, 58. arr		9 46			Saturdays only							1143	11 44				1238		Saturdays only			Saturdays only
Grove Ferry	8 49									1044	1044		Saturdays excepted									
Chislet Colliery Halt	8 54										1049											
Sturry	9 0									1052	1055											
Canterbury West A	9 7									11 0	11 2					1157				1223	Saturdays excepted	
Chartham	9 14									11 8	1111					12 5				1230		
Chilham	9 20									1114	1117					1211				1236		
Wye ... [58	9 29									1123	1126					1220				1245		
Ashford (Kent) 34, arr	9 39					a.m				1133	1137			p.m	p.m	1230				1256		
Ashford (Kent) ... dep		9 51			1032	1058						1146	11 52	1240	12 8		1243		12 55		1 0	1 2
Hothfield Halt, for West-						11 5																1 11
Charing ... [well						1111									1218						1 12	1 16
Lenham						1119									1225						1 20	1 24
Harrietsham			Saturdays only	Saturdays excepted		1123								Saturdays excepted			Saturdays only	Saturdays excepted			1 24	1 28
Hollingbourne						1128															1 29	1 32
Bearsted and Thurnham						1133															1 34	1 37
Maidstone East ... arr						1139									1239						1 40	1 43
Maidstone East ... dep							1149								1249						1 49	1 49
Pluckley					1041	Stop								1250	Saturdays only				1 5			
Headcorn					1051							12 3	12 8	1259					1 15			
Staplehurst					1058									1 7					1 23			
Marden					11 4	p.m								1 14					1 30			
Paddock Wood 53		1019	1056	11 9	1113	12 8						1216	12 22	1 24				1 32	1 39			
Tonbridge 54, 249 ... arr		1029	11 6	1119	1123	1218						1226	12 32	1 34			1 18	1 42	1 49			
249 Redhill ... arr												1 12	1 19						2 52			
249 East Croydon ... "												1 49	1 49						3 18			
Sevenoaks (Tub's Hill) arr		1053										1245	12 53				1 40		2 11			
Orpington 130, 147 ... "			Refreshment Car from Tonbridge																			
Swanley 60 ... arr							1228								1 28						2 28	2 28
Bromley South J ... "							1242								1 42						2 42	2 42
Blackfriars ... "																						
Holborn Viaduct ... "																						
Victoria ... "							1259								1 59						2 59	2 59
New Cross ... arr																						
London Bridge ... "		1122										1 14	1 22				2 9		2 39			
Cannon Street ... "																						
Waterloo ... "		1130	12 1					1226				1 20	1 30				2 15		2 45			
Charing Cross ... "		1134	12 5					1230				1 24	1 35				2 20		2 50			

FOR NOTES, SEE PAGE 51

MARGATE, DEAL, DOVER, FOLKESTONE, HYTHE, ASHFORD, and LONDON

Week Days—*continued*

Up	a.m	p.m	p.m	p.m	p.m	p.m	p.m	p.m		p.m	p.m	p.m	p.m	p.m	p.m	p.m	p.m	p.m	p.m	p.m	p.m
Margate dep	..	..	..	..	..	12 36	1250	..	..	1 38	..	1 40	1 50	..	2 34	3 3	3 10	..	3 15	2 42	3 5
Margate East	..	..	..	..	..	..	..	..	..	..	..	..	..	..	..	..	..	..	..	..	..
Broadstairs	..	..	..	..	..	12 42	1 0	..	..	1 49	..	1 46	1 56	..	2 44	3 13	3 19	..	3 21	2 48	3 12
Dumpton Park **D**	..	..	..	..	..	12 46	1 5	..	..	1 54	..	1 50	2 0	..	2 49	3 18	3 24	..	3 25	2 52	3 16
Ramsgate arr	..	..	..	..	..	12 50	1 9	..	..	1 58	..	1 54	2 4	..	2 53	3 22	3 28	..	3 29	2 56	3 20
Ramsgate dep	1118	..	..	..	1 8	12 52	..	1SX55	..	..	..	1 59	2 6	..				..	3 30	2 58	3 28
Minster (Thanet) arr	..	..	..	..	1 14	..	..	2SX1	..	..	..	2 8	..	..				..	3 37	..	3 37
Walmer for Kingsdown dp			..	..	1232	..	..	1SX18	..		..			..				..	..		2 59
Deal "	Saturdays excepted	Saturdays only	..	..	1239	..	..	1SX24	..		..	Sats. excepted		..				..	3 10	Saturdays excepted	3 18
Sandwich "			..	..	1247	..	..	1SX32	..		..		Saturdays only	..				..	3 17		3 25
Richboro. Castle Halt "			..	..	..	..	..	..	..		..			..				..	..		..
Minster (Thanet) arr			..	..	1256	..	..	1SX41	..		..			..				..	3 26		3 36
Minster (Thanet) dep			1235	..	1 15	..	..	2[illegible]2	..			2 14		2 28			Saturdays only	..	3 38		3 38
Richborough Castle Halt			..	..		..	..	..	..			..		..				..			
Sandwich	1132		1243	..		1 7	..	..	..	Saturdays only		2 24	2 23	2 36				..		3 14	
Deal arr	1140		1250	..		1 15	..	..	..			2 32	2 31	2 44	Saturdays only	Saturdays excepted	..	..		3 22	
Deal dep	1142		1251	..		1 16	..	..	..			2 33	2 33	..			..	..		3 24	
Walmer, for Kingsdown	1149		1257	..		1 21	..	..	..			2 38	2 38	..			..	..	Saturdays excepted	3 29	Saturdays only
Martin Mill **B**	1157		1 4	..		1 29	..	..	..		Saturdays only	2 45	2 46	..	Stop	Stop	..	..		3 37	
Dover Priory arr	12 9		1 15	..	Saturdays only	1 40	..	..	..	..		2 56	2 58	..			..	..		3 48	
Dover Priory dep	1212	1 9	..	..		1 42	..	..	..	..		2 57	3 0	..	..	..	..	..		3 50	
Dover Marine arr	..	..	..	..		..	..	..	..	..		..	..	..	..	..	..	..	..	..	..
Dover Marine dep	..	..	..	..		..	..	..	..	..		..	..	..	..	..	..	..	..	..	..
Folkestone Warren Halt	..	..	..	..		..	..	..	..	..		..	..	..	..	..	..	..	..	..	..
Folkestone Junction	1230	1 26	..	..		2 2	..	..	..	..		3 15	3 16	..	..	..	..	..	..	4 11	..
Folkestone Central **M** arr	1234	Stop	..	..		2 7	..	..	..	..		3 19	3 20	..	..	..	..	..	..	4 16	..
Folkestone Central **M** dep	1236		..	..		2 9	..	..	..	..		3 20	3 22	..	..	..	..	..	..	4 17	..
Shorncliffe	1242	..	..	..	..	2 13	..	..	..	..		3 23	3 25	..	..	..	..	..	..	4 21	..
Hythe dep	.		..	..	..	..	..	..	..	..	2 55	..	..	..	..	..	..	..	..	..	..
Sandling Junction 34 arr	..		..	..	..	..	..	..	..	..	3 0	..	..	..	..	..	..	..	..	..	..
Sandling Junction	1251		..	..	..	..	..	..	..	..	Stop	..	..	..			..	..	..	4 29	..
Westenhanger	..	Saturdays only	..	..	..	..	..	..	..	..		..	..	..	Saturdays only	Saturdays excepted	..	..	..	4 33	..
Smeeth	..		..	..	..	..	..	..	..	..	..	..	..	..			..	..	..	4 41	..
Ashford (Kent) **34**, 58 arr	1 6		..	..	..	2 33	..	..	..	..	..	3 42	3 44	..			..	..	..	4 50	..
Grove Ferry	..		..	..	1 25	..	..	2SX10	..	..	..	..	..	..			..		3 47	..	3 47
Chislet Colliery Halt	..		..	..	1 31	..	..	2SX16	..	..	..	..	..	..			..		3 53	..	3 53
Sturry	..		..	..	1 37	..	..	2SX22	..	..	..	..	..	..			..		3 59	..	3 59
Canterbury West A	..		..	..	1 45	..	..	2SX30	..	..	..	..	..	..			..	Saturdays excepted.	4 8	..	4 8
Chartham	..		..	..	1 53	..	..	2SX38	..	..	..	..	..	..			..		4 16	..	4 16
Chilham	..		..	..	2 0	..	..	2SX45	..	..	..	..	..	..			..		4 22	..	4 22
Wye [58	..		..	..	2 9	..	..	2SX54	..	..	..	..	..	..			..		4 31	..	4 31
Ashford (Kent) **34**, arr	..	p.m	..	..	2 20	..	..	3SX4	..	..	..	..	..	..	p.m	p.m	..		4 42	..	4 42
Ashford (Kent) dep	1 11	2 3	..		..	2 35	..	3L9	..	..		3 56	3 58	..	4 20	4 20	..	4 28	..	4 55	..
Hothfield Halt, for Westwell	..	..	..		..		..	..	..	..		..	..	..	..	..	..	4 35	..	..	..
Charing	..	2 14	..		..		..	3 22	..	..		4 11	4 11	..	..	..	..	4 40	..	..	..
Lenham	..	2 22	..		..		..	3 29	..	..	Saturdays only	4 19	4 19	..	..	..	..	4 48	..	..	..
Harrietsham	..	2 26	..	Saturdays only	..		..	..	..	..		4 23	4 23	..	..	..	..	4 51	..	..	..
Hollingbourne	..	2 31	..		..	Refreshment Car Margate to London	..	..	..	..		4 28	4 28	..	..	..	..	4 56	..	..	..
Bearsted and Thurnham	..	2 36	..		..		..	..	..	..		4 33	4 33	..	..	..	..	5 2	..	Saturdays excepted	..
Maidstone East arr		2 42	..		..		..	3A44	..	..		4 39	4 39	..	..	..	..	5 8	..		..
Maidstone East dep		..	..		..		..	3 49	..	..		4 49		..	..	..	..	5 17	..		..
Pluckley	Saturdays excepted	..	..	..	..		..	..	..	..				..	4 29	4 30	..	..	..	..	..
Headcorn		..	..	..	..		..	..	..	..				..	4 40	4 40	..	..	..	..	..
Staplehurst		..	..	..	..		..	..	..	..			Saturdays only	..	4 47	4 48	..	..	..	..	..
Marden		..	..	..	..		..	..	..	..	p.m			..	4 53	4 56	..	..	..	..	..
Paddock Wood 53	1 42	..	..	2 46	..		..	..	..	..	3 46			..	5 2	5 6	..	..	..	..	..
Tonbridge 54, 249 arr	1 52	..	..	2 56	..	..	..	..	..	..	3 56			..	5 12	5 16	..	..	..	5 29	..
249 Redhill arr	2 52	..	..	3 43	..	..	..	..	..	..	5 16	Saturdays excepted		..	..	..	..	..	..	6 0	..
249 East Croydon "	3 18	..	..	4 4	..	..	..	..	..	..	5 50			..	..	..	..	..	..	6 27	..
Sevenoaks (Tub's Hill) arr	2 15	..	..	..	..	..	..	..	..	..	4 17		..	..	..	5 43	..	..	..		..
Orpington 130, 147 "	..	..	..	..	..	..	..	..	..	..	4S46		..	..	..	6S7	..	..	..		..
Swanley 60 arr	..	..	..	..	..	..	..	4 28	..	..	..	5 28	..	..	..	..	..	5 55	..		..
Bromley South **J** "	..	..	..	..	..	..	..	4 42	..	..	..	5 42	..	..	..	..	..	6 7	..		..
Blackfriars "	..	..	..	..	..	..	..	..	..	..	..	..	..	..	..	..	..	..	..	Via Redhill page 250	..
Holborn Viaduct "	..	..	..	..	..	..	..	..	..	..	..	..	..	..	..	..	..	..	..		..
Victoria "	..	..	..	..	..	..	..	5A0	..	..	..	5 59	..	..	..	..	..	6 24	..		..
New Cross arr	..	..	..	..	..	..	..	..	..	..	5S13	..	..	..	..	6S30	..	..	..	..	..
London Bridge "	2 45	..	..	..	..	..	..	..	..	..	5S19	..	..	..	..	6S36	..	..	..	6 47	..
Cannon Street "	..	..	..	..	..	..	..	..	..	..	..	..	..	..	..	6S40	..	..	..	6 54	..
Waterloo "	2 51	..	..	..	..	3 42	..	..	..	..	5S23	..	..	..	..	..	..	..	..	..	..
Charing Cross "	2 55	..	..	..	..	3§46	..	..	..	..	5S26	..	..	..	..	..	..	..	..	..	..

For Notes, see page 51; for Continuation of Trains, see pages 48 to 51

For other Trains from Deal, Dover, &c., see pages 66 to 71

MARGATE, DEAL, DOVER, FOLKESTONE, HYTHE, ASHFORD, and LONDON

Up	Week Days—continued																				
	p.m	p.m	p.m	p.m	p.m	p.m	p.m	p.m.	p.m	p.m	p.m	p.m	p.m	p.m	p.m	p.m	p.m	p.m	p.m	p.m	p.m
	Saturdays only; Via Redhill page 250		Refreshment Car Folkestone to London	Saturdays only	Saturdays only; Saturdays only	Saturdays excepted	Saturdays only	Arr. Headcorn 6 31 p.m.	Saturdays only	Saturdays excepted	Saturdays excepted	Saturdays only	Saturdays excepted		Saturdays excepted	Saturdays only			Saturdays only	Saturdays excepted	Saturdays excepted
Margate dep	..	..	3 35	3 46	4 14	..	..	4S024	5 15	..	4 55	..	5 2	..	..	..	5 30	5 50	6 20		6 38
Margate East	..	..	..	..	..	..	..	..	..	..	4 57	....	..	..	..	..	5 32	5 53	..		..
Broadstairs	..	..	3 43	3 55	4 20	..	..	4S035	5 21	..	5 3	..	5 10	..	..	..	5 38	5 59	6 28		6 47
Dumpton Park D	..	..	3 47	4 0	4 24	..	..	4S040	5 25	..	5 7	....	5 15	..	..	..	5 42	6 4	6 32		6 51
Ramsgate arr	..	..	3 51	4 4	4 28	..	..	4S044	5 29	..	5 11	..	5 19	..	..	..	5 46	6 8	6 36		6 55
Ramsgate dep	3 0	..	3 53		4 33	..	..		5 34	5 36	5 16	5 18	..	..	..	..	5 50		..		
Minster (Thanet) arr		..	..		4 43	..	..	Stop	5 43	5 43			..	..	..	..	5 59	Stop	..		
Walmer, for Kingsdown dep		..	..		..	..	..	..	4 49	4 59				..	..		..	..	..		
Deal "		..	..		4 20	..	..	..	4 55	5 6				..	..		..	..	..		
Sandwich "		..	..		4 27	..	..	..	5 3	5 15				..	..		..	..			
Richboro' Castle Halt "		..	..		..	..	..	..	..	..				..	..		..	..			
Minster (Thanet) arr		..	..		4 36	..		p.m.	5 12	5 24				..	..		..	..			
Minster (Thanet) dep		3 50	..		4 44	..		4 50	5 44	5 44				5 48			6 7	..		6 53	..
Richborough Castle Halt		..	..			..		..	..	..				..			..	..		..	..
Sandwich	3 14	3§58	4 8			..		4 58	..	..	5 32	5 32		5 56			6 17	..		7 2	..
Deal arr	3 22	4§ 6	4 16			..		5 6	..	..	5 40	5 40	..	6 4			6 25	..		7 11	..
Deal dep	3 24		4 17			..		5 10	..	..	5 42	5 42	..	..			6 26	..		7 12	..
Walmer, for Kingsdown	3 29	Stop	4 23			..		5 16	..	..	5 48	5 48	..	..			6 32	..		7 19	..
Martin Mill B	3 37	..	4 30	Stop		..		5 23	..	..	5 56	5 56	..	..			6 40	..	..	7 26	..
Dover Priory arr	3 48	..	4 41	..		..	..	5 35	..	..	6 8	6 8	..	..			6 52	p.m	..	7 38	..
Dover Priory dep	3 50	..	4 43	..		5 10	5 16	Stop			6 12	6 12	..	..	6 36	6 46	Stop	7 15	..	Stop	..
Dover Marine arr	..	..	..	..	..	..	..				..	....	..	..	..	..	..	..	..	..	..
Dover Marine dep	..	..	..	..	..	..	..	..			..	..	..	..	..	..	..	....	..	..	..
Folkestone Warren Halt	..	..	..	..	..	..	..	..			..	....	..	..	..	..	..	....	..	..	..
Folkestone Junction	4 11	..	..	..	..	5 27	5 30	..			6 27	6 27	..	..	6 59	6 59	..	7 32	..	..	..
Folkestone Central M arr	4 16	..	4 57	..	..	5 31	5 34	..			6 31	6 31	..	..	7 2	7 3	..	7 37	..	..	..
Folkestone Central M dep	4 17	..	5 3	..	..	5 33	5 35	..			6 33	6 33	..	..	7 3	7 4	..	7 38	..	..	..
Shorncliffe	4 20	..	..	..	..	5 37	5 38	..			6 36	6 36	..	..	7 7	7 7	..	7 42	..	..	..
Hythe dep	4 20	..	..	..	..	..	..	..	..	..	6 15	..	..	..	..	Stop	..	..	..	..	..
Sandling Junction 34 arr	4 25	..	..	..	..	..	..	..	..	....	6 20	....	..	..	..		..	....	..	..	..
Sandling Junction	4 29	..	..	..	..	5 45	5 46	..	..	..	6 44	6 44	..	..	..	..	..	..	..	..	..
Westenhanger	4 33	..	..	..	..	.	..	..	..	....	6 48	6 48	..	..	..	..	..	....	..	..	..
Smeeth	4 41	..	..	..	..	..	..	..	..	..	..	..	..	..	..	..	..	..	..	..	..
Ashford (Kent) 34, 58 arr	4 50	..	..	..	..	5 58	5 59	..	..	....	7 0	7 0	..	..	....	..	..	8 0	..	..	..
Grove Ferry	..	..	..	..	4 52		..	..	5 54	5 53	..	..	..	..	..	..	..	..	..	..	..
Chislet Colliery Halt	..	..	..	..	..		..	..	..	5 58	..	....	..	..	....	..	..	....	..	..	..
Sturry	..	..		..	5 0		..	..	6 2	6 4	..	..	..	..	..	..	..	..	..	..	..
Canterbury West A	..	..		..	5 10		..	..	6 11	6 13	..	....	..	..	....	..	..	....	..	..	..
Chartham	..	..		..	5 18		..	..	6 20	6 21	..	..	..	..	..	..	..	..	..	..	..
Chilham	..	..		..	5 24		..	..	6 26	6 27	..	....	..	..	..	..	..	....	..	..	..
Wye [58	..	..		..	5 34		..	..	6 35	6 36	..	..	..	..	..	..	..	..	..	..	..
Ashford (Kent) 34, .. arr	..	p.m		..	5 44		..	p.m	6 46	6 47	..	....	..	..	....	p.m	..	....	..	..	..
Ashford (Kent) dep	4 55	5 4		..	Stop	6 3	6 2	6 12	..		7 6	7 6	..	..	..	7 16	..	8 4	..	..	..
Hothfield Halt for Westwell		5 11		..		..	..		..	....	..	....	..	..	....	..	..	....	..	..	..
Charing		5 16		..	..	6 15	6 14		..	..	..	..	..	..	..	7 27	..	8 17	..	..	..
Lenham		5 24		..	..	6 23	6 21		..	....			..	..	....	7 35	..	8 25	..	..	..
Harrietsham		5 28		..	..	6 27	6 25		..	..			..	..	..	7 39	..	..	..	..	..
Hollingbourne		5 32		..	..	6 32	6 30		..	....			..	..	....	7 44	..	....	..	..	..
Bearsted and Thurnham		5 37		..	..	6 37	6 35		..	..			..	..	..	7 49	..	..	..	..	..
Maidstone East arr		5 43		..	..	6 43	6 41		..	....			..	..	....	7 55	..	8 39	..	..	..
Maidstone East dep		5 49	..	..	..	6 49	6 49		..	..			..	..	..	8 22	..	8 49	..	..	..
Pluckley	..	..	..	..	..	..	..	6 22	..	....			..	..	....	..	..	....	..	..	..
Headcorn	..	..	..	..	..	..	..	6 50	..	..			..	..	..	..	..	..	..	..	..
Staplehurst	..	..	..	..	..	..	..	6 59	..	....			..	..	....	..	..	....	..	..	..
Marden	..	..	..	p.m	p.m	..	..	7 6	..	..			..	..	..	..	p.m	..	..	p.m	..
Paddock Wood 53	..	..	..	5 51	7 2	..	..	7 15	..	....	..		..	..	....	..	8 5	....	..	8 38	..
Tonbridge 54, 249 arr	5 29	..	..	6 1	7 12	..		7 26	..	..	7 39	7 39	..	..	..	..	8 15	.	..	8 48	..
249 Redhill arr	6 3	..	..	6 52		..	..	..	..	....	8 21	8 21	..	..	....	..	9 16	....	..	..	..
249 East Croydon "	6 27	..	..	7 19		..	..	..	..	..	8 48	8 48	..		..	.	9 48	..	..	..	..
Sevenoaks (Tub's Hill) arr		..	..	6 55		..	..	..	..	....	7 58	7 58	..	..	....	..	8 53	....	..	9 25	..
Orpington 130, 147 "		..	..	..		..	..	..	..	..	..	..	..	..	..	..	9B20	..	..	..	..
Swanley 60 arr		6 28	..	..		7 28	7 28	..	..	....	..	....	..	..	....	9 1	..	9 28	..	..	..
Bromley South J "		6 42	..	..		7 42	7 42	..	..	..	..	..	..	..	..	9 17	..	9 42	..	..	..
Blackfriars "		..	..	..		..	..	..	..	....	..	....	..	..	....	..	..	....	..	..	..
Holborn Viaduct "		..	..	..		..	..	..	..	..	..	..	..	..	..	..	..	..	..	..	..
Victoria "		6 59	..	..		7 59	7 59	..	..	....	..	....	..	..	....	9 38	..	9 59	..	..	..
New Cross arr	..	..	..	..		..	..	..	..	..	..	..	..	..	..	..	9B44	..	..	..	..
London Bridge "	6 47	..	..	7 24		..	..	..	..	....	8 28	8 28	..	..	....	..	9B51	....	..	9 52	..
Cannon Street "	..	..	..	..		..	..	..	..	..	..	..	..	..	..	..	..	..	..	..	..
Waterloo "	..	..	6 26	7 33	..	..	..	..	..	....	8 36	8 36	..	..	....	..	9E55	....	..	9 59	..
Charing Cross "	..	..	6 30	7 38	..	..	..	..	..	..	8 41	8 41	..	..	..	..	9B57	..	..	10 3	..

FOR NOTES, SEE PAGE 51

MARGATE, DEAL, DOVER, FOLKESTONE. HYTHE, ASHFORD, and LONDON

Up	Week Days—*continued*																Sundays			
	p.m	p.m	p.m	p.m	p.m	p.m	p.m	p.m	p.m	p.m	p.m	p.m	p.m	p.m	p.m	p.m		a.m	a.m	a.m	a.m
Margate .... dep	7S018	7 8	..	..	7 44	8 3	..	8 25	8 49	9 17	9 31	..	9 55	9 55	9 28	1140	..	6 15	..	..	..
Margate East	..	..		..	..	..	..	..	..	..	..	..	..	..	..	..	..	..	..	..	..
Broadstairs	7S024	7 15	Saturdays only	..	7 53	8 12	..	8 34	9 2	9 25	9 41	..	10 2	10 2	9 34	1151	..	6 21	..	..	..
Dumpton Park D	7S028	7 19		..	7 57	8 16	..	8 38	9 6	9 30	9 46	..	10 6	10 6	9 38	1155	..	6 25	..	..	..
Ramsgate .... arr	7S032	7 23		..	8 2	8 20	..	8 42	9 10	9 34	9 50	..	1010	1010	9 42	1159	..	6 28	..	..	..
Ramsgate .... dep	7A35	7 25		7 45	Saturdays excepted		..	..	..	..	..	..	1012	1012	9 43	..	..	6 29	..	..	..
Minster (Thanet) ...... arr	7 42	..		7 52		☞	..	..	..	..	..	..	1020	1020	..	..	..	6 36	..	..	..
Walmer, for Kingsdown dp	6 15	..		..			..	Saturdays only	Saturdays excepted	Saturdays only	Saturdays excepted	..	..	..	3	..	..	..	..	..	..
Deal .... "	6L36	..		..			..					..	..	..		..	..	..	..	..	..
Sandwich .... "	6L43	..		..			..					..	..	..	..	..	..	..	..	..	..
Richboro' Castle Halt "	..	..		..		Saturdays excepted	..					..	..	..	..	..	..	..	..	..	..
Minster (Thanet) ..... arr	6L52	..	..	..			..					..	..	..	..	..	..	..	..	..	..
Minster (Thanet) ...... dep	7 43	..	7 52	7 58	..							9 30	1021	1021	..	..	..	6 37	..	..	..
Richborough Castle Halt ..	..	..	..	..	..		Saturdays excepted					..	..	..	..	..	..	..	..	..	..
Sandwich	..	7 40	8 0	8 8	..							9 38	..	..	9 58	..	..	..	..	..	..
Deal .... arr	..	7 48	8 8	8 16	..							9 46			10 6	..	..	..	..	..	..
Deal .... dep	..	7 49	..		..							9 48			10 8	..	..	..	..	..	..
Walmer, for Kingsdown ...	..	7 54	..	☞	..	Stop		..	..	..	..	9 54			1013	..	..	..	..	..	..
Martin Mill B	..	..	..		..			..	..	..	..	10 1	Saturdays excepted	Saturdays only	1020	..	..	..	..	..	..
Dover Priory ...... arr	..	8 10	..		..	..	..	..	..	..	..	10 13			1031	..	..	..	..	..	..
Dover Priory ...... dep	..	8 12	..		..	..	9 22	..	..	..	..	10 18			1038	..	..	..	6 48	..	7 35
Dover Marine ...... arr	..	..	..		..	..	..	..	..	..	..	..			..	..	..	..	..	..	..
Dover Marine ...... dep	..	..	..	Saturdays excepted	..	..	..	..	..	..	..	..			..	..	..	..	..	..	..
Folkestone Warren Halt.	..	..	..		..	..	..	..	..	..	..	..			..	..	..	..	..	..	..
Folkestone Junction	..	8 27	..		..	..	9 38	..	..	..	..	10 41			1055	..	..	..	7 4	..	7 47
Folkestone Central M arr	..	8 31	..		..	..	9 42	..	..	..	..	10 45			11 0	..	..	..	7 8	..	7 50
Folkestone Central M dep	..	8 32	..		..	..	9 45	..	..	..	..	10 46	..	..	11 2	..	..	..	7 9	..	7 51
Shorncliffe	..	8 35	..		..	..	..	..	..	..	..	10 49	..	..	..	..	..	..	7 13	..	7 54
Hythe .... dep	..	..	..		..	..	..	..	..	..	..	Stop	..	..	..	..	..	..	..	..	Stop
Sandling Junction 34 .. arr	..	..	..	Stop	..	..	..	..	..	..	..		..	..	..	..	..	..	..	..	
Sandling Junction	..	8 42	..		..	..	9 56	..	..	..	..	..	..	..	..	..	..	..	7 21	..	..
Westenhanger	..	8 46	..	..	..	..	..	..	..	..	..	..	..	..	..	..	..	..	7 25	..	..
Smeeth	..	8 54	..	..	..	..	..	..	..	..	..	..	..	..	..	..	..	..	7 33	..	..
Ashford (Kent) 34, 58. arr	..	9 3	..	..	..	..	1012	..	..	..	..	..	..	..	1124	..	..	..	7 42	..	..
Grove Ferry	7 52	..	..	..	..	..	..	..	..	..	..	..	1029	1029	..	..	..	6 46	..	..	..
Chislet Colliery Halt	7§56	..	..	..	..	..	..	..	..	..	..	..	1034	1034	..	..	..	..	..	..	..
Sturry	8 3	..	..	..	..	..	..	..	..	..	..	..	1040	1040	..	..	..	6 54	..	..	..
Canterbury West A	8 13	..	..	..	..	..	..	..	..	..	..	..	1048	1049	..	..	..	7 1	..	..	..
Chartham	8 20	..	..	..	..	..	..	..	..	..	..	..	..	1056	..	..	..	7 8	..	..	..
Chilham	8 28	..	..	..	..	..	..	..	..	..	..	..	..	11 1	..	..	..	7 14	..	..	..
Wye .... [58	8 38	..	..	..	..	..	..	..	..	..	..	..	..	1110	..	..	..	7 23	..	..	..
Ashford (Kent) 34 .. arr	8 48	..	..	p.m	..	p.m	..	..	..	..	..	..	1110	1120	..	..	..	7 33	..	..	a.m
Ashford (Kent) .... dep	Stop	9 12	..	9 20	..	9 28	..	..	..	..	..	..	..	..	1128	..	..	..	7 49	7 56	8 4
Hothfield Halt, for West-		..	..	..	..	9 35	..	..	..	..	..	..	..	..	..	..	..	..	..	..	..
Charing .... [well	..	..	..	..	..	9 41	..	..	..	..	..	..	..	..	..	..	..	..	..	8 8	..
Lenham	..	..	..	..	..	9 49	..	..	..	..	..	..	..	..	..	..	..	..	..	8 16	..
Harrietsham	..	..	..	..	..	9 53	..	..	..	..	..	..	..	..	..	..	..	..	..	8 20	..
Hollingbourne	..	..	..	..	..	9 58	..	..	..	..	..	..	..	..	..	..	..	..	..	8 25	..
Bearsted and Thurnham.	..	..	..	..	..	10 3	..	..	..	..	..	..	..	..	..	..	..	..	..	8 30	..
Maidstone East ... arr	..	..	..	..	..	10 9	..	..	..	..	..	..	..	..	..	..	..	..	..	8 36	..
Maidstone East ... dep	..	..	..	..	..	1010	..	..	..	..	..	..	..	..	..	..	..	..	..	..	..
Pluckley	..	..	..	9 29	..	..	..	..	..	..	..	..	..	..	..	..	..	..	..	..	8 13
Headcorn	..	..	..	9 38	..	..	..	..	..	..	..	..	..	..	..	..	..	..	..	..	8 22
Staplehurst	..	..	..	9 46	..	..	..	..	..	..	..	..	..	..	..	..	..	..	..	..	8 29
Marden	p.m	..	..	9 52	..	..	..	..	..	..	..	p.m	..	..	..	..	..	..	..	..	8 35
Paddock Wood 53	9 3	9 41	..	10 1	..	..	..	..	..	..	..	10 20	..	..	..	..	..	..	..	..	8 42
Tonbridge 54, 249 ...... arr	9 13	9 51	..	1011	..	..	..	..	..	..	..	10 30	..	..	12 2	..	..	..	8 23	..	8 52
249 Redhill .... arr	10 22	..	..	..	..	..	..	..	..	..	..	..	..	..	1236	..	..	..	9 17	..	9 44
249 East Croydon ...... "	10 50	..	..	..	..	..	..	..	..	..	..	..	..	..	1259	..	..	..	9 48	..	10 3
Sevenoaks (Tub's Hill) arr	..	1011	..	..	..	..	..	..	..	..	..	10 58	..	..	Via Redhill page 250	..	..	..	8 43	..	9 16
Orpington 130, 147 ..... "	..	1025	..	..	..	..	..	..	..	..	..	11 (3) 20	..	..		..	..	..	8 56		9 (3) 47
Swanley 60 .... arr	..	..	..	..	..	11 3	..	..	..	..	..	..	..	..		..	..	..	..	..	..
Bromley South J ... "	..	..	..	..	..	1120	..	..	..	..	..	..	..	..		..	..	..	..	..	..
Blackfriars .... "	..	..	..	..	..	1145	..	..	..	..	..	..	..	..		..	..	..	..	..	..
Holborn Viaduct .... "	..	..	..	..	..	1148	..	..	..	..	..	..	..	..		..	..	..	..	..	..
Victoria .... "	..	..	..	..	..	..	..	..	..	..	..	..	..	..		..	..	..	..	..	..
New Cross .... arr	..	..	..	..	..	..	..	..	..	..	..	..	..	..	..	..	..	..	..	..	..
London Bridge .... "	..	1044	..	..	..	..	..	..	..	..	..	..	..	..	1 19	..	..	..	9 15	..	9 44
Cannon Street .... "	..	..	..	..	..	..	..	..	..	..	..	..	..	..	..	..	..	..	..	..	..
Waterloo .... "	..	1053	..	..	..	..	..	..	..	..	..	..	..	..	..	..	..	..	9 23	..	9 50
Charing Cross .... "	..	1058	..	..	..	..	..	..	..	..	..	..	..	..	..	..	..	..	9 28	..	9 54

For Notes, see page 51, for Continuation of SUNDAY TRAINS, see pages 50 and 51.

MARGATE, DEAL, DOVER, FOLKESTONE, HYTHE, ASHFORD, and LONDON

Sundays—*continued*

Up	a.m.	a.m	a.m	a.m	a.m	a.m	a.m	a.m	a.m	a.m.	p.m	p.m	p.m	p.m	p.m	p.m	p.m	p.m	p.m	p.m	p.m
Margate .... dep	7A54	8 15	7 30	..	1010	9 35	1020	1110	..	..	12 7	2 10	..	3 2	3 18	4 15	4 44	4 55	..	..	..
Margate East	..	..	..	..	..	..	..	..	..	..	..	..	..	..	..	..	..	..	..	..	..
Broadstairs	8A4	8 21	7 36	..	1017	9 42	1028	1121	..	..	1217	2 17	..	3 11	3 27	4 22	4 53	5 1	..	..	..
Dumpton Park D	..	8 25	7 40	..	1021	9 47	1032	1126	..	..	1222	2 21	..	3 16	3 31	4 27	4 57	5 5	..	..	..
Ramsgate .... arr	8A13	8 29	7 44	..	1025	9 51	1036	1130	..	..	1226	2 25	..	3 21	3 35	4 31	5 1	5 9	..	..	..
Ramsgate .... dep	Stop	8 30	7 45	..	1027	10 0	..	Stop	1140	11 25	1240	2 26	2 45	Stop	3 36	4 34	..	5 11	..	..	..
Minster (Thanet) ...... arr		8 37	..	..	1034	..	..		1148	..	1248	2 33	2 54		3 45	..	..	5 20	..	..	..
Walmer, for Kingsdown dp	..	7 55	..	..	9 48	..	..	..	..	..	..	1 52	..	..	..	..	..	..	..	..	..
Deal .... "	..	8 4	..	..	9 54	..	..	..	..	..	..	1 59	..	..	..	..	..	..	..	..	..
Sandwich .... "	..	8 14	..	..	10 2	..	..	..	..	..	..	2 7	..	..	..	..	..	..	..	..	..
Richboro' Castle Halt. "	..	..	..	..	..	..	..	..	..	..	..	..	..	..	..	..	..	..	..	..	..
Minster (Thanet) ..... arr	..	8 23	..	..	1011	..	..	a.m	..	..	..	2 17	..	..	..	..	..	..	..	..	..
Minster (Thanet) ..... dep	..	8 38	..	..	1035	..	..	11 0	1149	..	1255	2 34	3 0	..	3 50	..	..	5 21	..	..	..
Richborough Castle Halt ..	..	..	..	..	..	..	..	..	..	..	..	..	..	..	..	..	..	..	..	..	..
Sandwich	..	..	8 0	..	..	1016	..	1110	..	11 39	1 6	..	3 10	..	4 0	4 50	..	..	..	..	..
Deal .... arr	..	..	8 8	..	..	1022	..	1118	..	11 47	1 13	..	3 18	..	4 8	4 58	..	..	..	..	..
Deal .... dep	..	..	8 9	..	..	1024	..	1119	..	11 48	1 14	..	3 19	..	4 9	4 59	..	..	..	..	..
Walmer, for Kingsdown ...	..	..	8 15	..	..	1030	..	1125	..	11 53	1 19	..	3 25	..	4 14	5 5	..	..	..	..	..
Martin Mill B	..	..	8 22	..	..	1037	..	1131	..	12 0	1 26	..	3 32	..	4 20	5 13	..	..	..	..	..
Dover Priory .... arr	..	..	8 34	..	..	1048	..	1143	..	12 12	1 38	..	3 44	..	4 31	5 24	..	..	..	..	..
Dover Priory .... dep	..	..	8 36	..	..	1050	..	Stop	..	12 14	2 5	..	3 46	..	4 33	5 26	..	..	..	..	6 22
Dover Marine .... arr	..	..	..	..	..	..	..	..	..	..	..	..	..	..	..	..	..	..	..	..	..
Dover Marine .... dep	..	..	..	..	..	..	..	..	..	..	..	..	..	..	..	..	..	..	..	..	..
Folkestone Warren Halt.	..	..	..	..	..	..	..	..	..	..	..	..	..	..	..	..	..	..	..	..	..
Folkestone Junction	..	..	8 54	..	..	11 8	..	..	..	12 33	2 20	..	4 3	..	4 47	..	..	..	5 55	..	6 37
Folkestone Central M ... arr	..	..	8 59	..	..	1113	..	..	..	12 38	2 24	..	4 7	..	4 51	5 40	..	..	5 58	..	6 40
Folkestone Central M ... dep	..	..	9 1	..	..	1115	..	..	..	12 40	..	..	4 9	..	4 53	5 46	..	..	6 15	..	6 41
Shorncliffe	..	..	9 5	..	..	1119	..	..	..	12 43	..	..	4 12	..	4 56	..	..	..	..	..	6 44
Hythe .... dep	..	..	..	..	..	..	..	..	..	..	..	..	..	..	..	..	..	..	..	..	Stop
Sandling Junction 34. arr	..	..	..	..	..	..	..	..	..	..	..	..	..	..	..	..	..	..	..	..	
Sandling Junction	..	..	9 13	..	..	1127	..	..	..	..	..	..	..	..	5 4	..	..	..	..	..	..
Westenhanger	..	..	9 17	..	..	..	..	..	..	..	..	..	..	..	5 8	..	..	..	..	..	..
Smeeth	..	..	..	..	..	..	..	..	..	..	..	..	..	..	5 16	..	..	..	..	..	..
Ashford (Kent) 34, 58 arr	..	..	9 30	..	..	1141	..	..	..	1 1	..	..	..	..	5 24	..	..	..	6 37	..	..
Grove Ferry	..	..	..	..	1044	..	..	..	1157	..	..	2 44	..	..	..	..	..	5 30	..	..	..
Chislet Colliery Halt	..	..	..	..	1050	..	..	..	..	..	..	2 50	..	..	..	..	..	..	..	..	..
Sturry	..	..	..	..	1056	..	..	..	12 5	..	..	2 56	..	..	..	..	..	5 39	..	..	..
Canterbury West A	..	8 56	..	..	11 3	..	..	..	1212	..	..	3 2	..	..	..	..	..	5 46	..	..	..
Chartham	..	..	..	..	1110	..	..	..	1219	..	..	3 9	..	..	..	..	..	5 54	..	..	..
Chilham	..	..	..	..	1116	..	..	..	1225	..	..	3 15	..	..	..	..	..	6 0	..	..	..
Wye	..	9 11	..	..	1125	..	..	..	1233	..	..	3 24	..	..	..	..	..	6 9	..	..	..
Ashford (Kent) 34, 58 arr	a.m	9 22	..	..	1135	..	..	a.m	1243	..	..	3 34	..	p.m	..	..	..	6 20	..	..	p.m
Ashford (Kent) .... dep	8 50	Stop	9 35	9 45	..	1144	..	1150	..	1 2	..	..	..	5 2	5 31	..	..	Stop	6 45	6 55	7 5
Hothfield Halt, for Westwell	..		..	..	..	..	..	..	..	..	..	..	..	..	..	..	..		..	..	..
Charing	9 2		..	9 56	..	..	..	12 3	..	..	..	..	..	5 14	..	..	..		..	..	7 16
Lenham	9 10		..	10 4	..	Refreshment Car Margate to London	..	1211	..	..	..	..	..	5 21	..	..	..		..	..	7 23
Harrietsham	9 14		..	10 8	..	..	..	1215	..	..	..	..	..	5 25	..	..	..		..	..	7 27
Hollingbourne	9 19		..	10 13	..	..	..	1220	..	..	..	..	..	5 30	..	..	..		..	..	7 32
Bearsted and Thurnham.	9 24		..	10 18	..	..	..	1225	..	..	..	..	..	5 35	..	..	..		..	..	7 37
Maidstone East ... arr	9 30	a.m	..	10 24	..	..	..	1231	..	..	..	..	..	5 41	..	..	..		..	..	7 43
Maidstone East ... dep	..	9 49	..	Stop	..	..	..	..	..	..	..	..	..	5 49	..	..	..		..	..	..
Pluckley	..	..	..		..	..	..	..	..	..	..	..	..	..	..	..	..	..	..	7 4	..
Headcorn	..	..	..	..	..	..	..	..	..	..	..	..	..	..	..	..	..	..	..	7 13	..
Staplehurst	..	..	..	..	..	..	..	..	..	..	..	..	..	..	..	..	..	..	..	7 20	..
Marden	..	..	..	a.m	..	..	..	..	..	..	..	..	..	..	..	..	..	p.m	..	7 26	..
Paddock Wood 53	..	..	..	10 7	..	..	..	..	..	..	..	..	..	..	..	..	..	6 29	..	7 35	..
Tonbridge 54, 249 ..... arr	..	..	10 8	10 17	..	1218	..	..	..	1 36	..	..	..	..	..	..	..	6 39	7 18	7 47	..
249 Redhill .... arr	..	..	..	11Z14	..	..	..	..	..	2 44	..	..	..	..	..	..	..	..	8 23	..	..
249 East Croydon ...... "	..	..	..	11Z49	..	..	..	..	..	3 3	..	..	..	..	..	..	..	..	8 52	..	..
Sevenoaks (Tub's Hill) arr	..	..	..	10 53	..	1239	..	..	..	1 57	..	..	..	..	..	..	..	..	7 37	..	..
Orpington 130, 147 ..... "	..	..	1038	..	..	..	..	..	..	2A18	..	..	..	..	..	..	..	..	..	8 24	..
Swanley 60 .... arr	..	1028	..	..	..	..	..	..	..	..	..	..	..	6 28	..	..	..	..	..	..	..
Bromley South J ... "	..	1042	..	..	..	..	..	..	..	..	..	..	..	6 42	..	..	..	..	..	..	..
Blackfriars .... "	..	..	..	..	..	..	..	..	..	..	..	..	..	..	..	..	..	..	..	..	..
Holborn Viaduct .... "	..	..	..	..	..	..	..	..	..	..	..	..	..	..	..	..	..	..	..	..	..
Victoria .... "	..	1059	..	..	..	..	..	..	..	..	..	..	..	7 0	..	..	..	..	..	..	..
New Cross .... arr	..	..	..	..	..	1 5	..	..	..	..	..	..	..	..	..	..	..	..	..	..	..
London Bridge .... "	..	..	1055	11 20	..	1 12	..	..	..	2 27	..	..	..	..	6 44	..	..	..	8 5	8 43	..
Cannon Street .... "	..	..	..	..	..	..	..	..	..	..	..	..	..	..	..	..	..	..	..	..	..
Waterloo .... "	..	..	11 2	11 27	..	1 20	..	..	..	2 35	..	..	..	..	6 51	7 15	..	..	8 12	8 49	..
Charing Cross .... "	..	..	11 6	11 31	..	1 24	..	..	..	2 39	..	..	..	..	6 56	7 20	..	..	8 17	8 54	..

For other Trains from Deal, Dover, &c., see pages 66 to 71

FOR NOTES, SEE PAGE 51

MARGATE, DEAL, DOVER, FOLKESTONE, HYTHE, ASHFORD, and LONDON

Sundays—continued

Up	p.m	p.m	p.m	p.m	p.m	p.m	p.m	p.m	p.m	p.m	p.m	p.m	p.m	p.m	p.m
Margate ....dep	..	5 50	..	6 12	6 50	..	..	..	..	9 55	..	9 20	..	1035	1051
Margate East	..	..	..	..	..	..	..	..	..	..	..	..	..	..	..
Broadstairs	..	5 59	..	6 19	6 57	..	..	..	..	10 2	..	9 27	..	1042	11 1
Dumpton Park **D**	..	6 3	..	6 23	7 1	..	..	..	..	10 6	..	9 31	..	1046	11 6
Ramsgate ....arr	..	6 7	..	6 27	7 5	..	..	..	..	1010	..	9 35	..	1050	1110
Ramsgate ....dep	..	6 10	..	6 29	7 6	..	..	7 50	..	1012	..	9 38	..	1054	..
Minster (Thanet) ....arr	..	..	..	..	7 13	..	..	..	..	1019	..	..	..	11 3	..
Walmer, for Kingsdown dep	..	..	..	..	6 37	..	..	..	..	9 48	..	③	..	..	..
Deal .... "	..	..	..	..	6 43	..	..	..	..	9 54	..	..	..	..	..
Sandwich .... "	..	..	..	..	6 51	..	..	..	..	10 2	..	..	..	..	..
Richborough Castle Halt "	..	..	..	..	..	..	..	..	..	..	..	..	..	..	..
Minster (Thanet) ....arr	..	..	..	..	7 0	..	..	..	..	1011	..	..	..	..	..
Minster (Thanet) ....dep	..	..	..	..	7 14	..	7 32	..	9 20	1020	..	..	1054	11 4	..
Richborough Castle Halt..	..	..	..	..	..	..	..	..	..		..	..	..	..	..
Sandwich	..	6 27	..	6 44	..	..	7 41	8 4	9 28		..	9 55	11 3	..	..
Deal ....arr	..	6 35	..	6 52	..	..	7 48	8 12	9 36		..	10 3	1110	..	..
Deal ....dep	..	6 36	..	6 53	..	..	Stop	8 13	9 37		..	10 6	1111	..	..
Walmer, for Kingsdown...	..	6 42	..	6 59	..	..		8 18	9 42		..	1012	1116	..	..
Martin Mill **B**	..	6 49	..	7 6	..	..	..	8 26	9 49		..	1019	1123	..	..
Dover Priory ....arr	..	7 0	..	7 17	..	..	..	8 37	10 0	Arr. Canterbury West 10 40 p.m	..	1030	1135	..	..
Dover Priory ....dep	..	7 2	..	7 18	..	..	..	8 40	Stop		1022	1038	..	..	..
Dover Marine ....arr	..	..	..	..	..	..	..	..	..		..	..	..	..	..
Dover Marine ....dep	..	..	..	..	..	..	..	..	..		..	..	..	..	..
Folkestone Warren Halt.	..	..	..	..	..	..	..	..	..		..	..	..	..	..
Folkestone Junction....	..	..	..	7 36	..	..	..	8 55	..		1040	1055	..	..	..
Folkestone Central **M** arr	..	7 17	..	7 41	..	..	..	8 59	..		1043	11 0	..	..	..
Folkestone Central **M** dep	..	7 18	..	7 43	..	..	..	9 1	..		1044	11 2	..	..	..
Shorncliffe	..	..	..	7 46	..	..	..	9 4	..		1047	..	..	..	..
Hythe ....dep	..	..	..	..	..	..	..	..	..		..	..	..	..	..
Sandling Junction 34 arr	..	..	..	..	..	..	..	..	..		..	..	..	..	..
Sandling Junction	..	..	..	..	..	..	..	9 12	..		1055	..	..	..	..
Westenhanger	..	..	..	..	..	..	..	..	..	..	1059	..	..	..	..
Smeeth	..	..	..	..	..	..	..	..	..	..	11 7	..	..	..	..
Ashford (Kent) **34**, 58 arr	..	..	..	8 5	..	..	..	9 25	..	..	1116	1124	..	..	..
Grove Ferry	..	..	..	..	7 22	..	..	..	..	..	..	..	..	1113	..
Chislet Colliery Halt	..	..	..	..	7 28	..	..	..	..	1032	..	..	..	1119	..
Sturry	..	..	..	..	7 34	..	..	..	..	..	..	..	..	1125	..
Canterbury West **A**	..	..	..	..	7 42	..	..	..	..	1048	..	..	..	1131	..
Chartham	..	..	..	..	7 50	..	..	..	..	..	..	..	..	..	..
Chilham	..	..	..	..	7 57	..	..	..	..	..	..	..	..	..	..
Wye [58	..	..	..	..	8 7	..	..	..	..	..	..	..	..	..	..
Ashford (Kent) **34**. arr	..	..	..	..	8 18	..	..	..	p.m	1110	..	..	..	..	..
Ashford (Kent) ....dep	..	..	..	8 6	..	8 32	..	9 30	9 46	..	..	1128	..	..	..
Hothfield Halt, for Westwell	..	..	..		..	..	..	..	..	..	..	..	..	..	..
Charing	..	..	..	Calls Hither Green 9 22 p.m	..	..	..	..	9 57	..	..	..	..	..	..
Lenham	..	..	..		..	..	..	..	10 4	..	..	..	..	..	..
Harrietsham	..	..	..		..	..	..	..	10 8	..	..	..	..	..	..
Hollingbourne	..	..	..		..	..	..	..	..	..	..	..	..	..	..
Bearsted and Thurnham.	..	..	..		..	..	..	..	1018	..	..	..	..	..	..
Maidstone East ....arr	..	..	..		..	..	..	..	1024	..	..	..	..	..	..
Maidstone East ....dep	7 49	..	..		..	..	..	..	..	..	..	..	..	..	..
Pluckley	..	..	..		..	8 41	..	..	..	..	..	..	..	..	..
Headcorn	..	..	..		..	8 51	..	..	..	..	..	..	..	..	..
Staplehurst	..	..	..		..	8 58	..	..	..	..	..	..	..	..	..
Marden	..	..	..		..	9 5	p.m	..	..	..	..	..	..	..	..
Paddock Wood 53	..	..	8 5		..	9 14	9 40	..	..	..	..	..	..	..	..
Tonbridge 54, 249 ....arr	..	8 4	8 16	8 39	..	9 24	9 50	10 3	..	..	..	12 2	..	..	..
249 Redhill ....arr	..	..	..	9 22	..	..	..	10N45		..	..	1236	..	..	..
249 East Croydon .... "	..	..	..	9 48	..	..	..	..	..	..	..	1259	..	..	..
Sevenoaks (Tub's Hill) arr	..	..	..	8 59	..	..	..	1021	..	..	..	..	..	..	..
Orpington 130, 147 .... "	..	..	..	9 20 ③	..	..	..	..	..	..	..	..	..	..	..
Swanley 63 ....arr	8 28	..	..	..	..	..	..	..	..	..	..	Via Redhill page 251	..	..	..
Bromley South J .... "	8 42	..	..	..	..	..	..	..	..	..	..		..	..	..
Blackfriars .... "	..	..	..	..	..	..	..	..	..	..	..		..	..	..
Holborn Viaduct .... "	..	..	..	..	..	..	..	..	..	..	..		..	..	..
Victoria .... "	8 59	..	..	..	..	..	..	..	..	..	..		..	..	..
New Cross ....arr	..	..	..	9 28	..	..	..	..	..	..	..	..	..	..	..
London Bridge .... "	..	8 54	..	9 35	..	..	..	1050	..	..	..	1 19	..	..	..
Cannon Street .... "	..	..	..	..	..	..	..	..	..	..	..	..	..	..	..
Waterloo .... "	..	9 0	..	9 42	..	..	..	1056	..	..	..	..	..	..	..
Charing Cross .... "	..	9 5	..	9 46	..	..	..	11 1	..	..	..	..	..	..	..

NOTES

③ Third class only

A ½ mile to Canterbury East Station

A 1 min *earlier* on Saturdays

B Martin Mill for St. Margaret's Bay

D Dumpton Park, for East Ramsgate

I Arr. 8 8 a.m

J Over ½ mile to Bromley North Station

L 2 mins later on Saturdays

M Sta. for Sandgate. Frequent Omnibus Services between Folkestone Central and Folkestone Harbour by East Kent Road Car

N Commences 28th March, 1948,

S O or **SO** Saturdays only

S X or **SX** Saturdays excepted

Y 2 mins. *earlier* on Saturdays

Z Until 21st March, 1948 only

§ 1 min. later on Saturdays.

LOCAL TRAINS and intermediate stations

between Maidstone East, Swanley and London, see page 147—Tonbridge, Sevenoaks & London page 130

OTHER TRAINS

between Dover and London see page 66–Maidstone West and London, pages 53 and 93

TONBRIDGE, PADDOCK WOOD, HAWKHURST, and MAIDSTONE WEST

Miles from Tonbridge	Down	Week Days a.m	a.m	a.m	a.m	a.m	a.m	a.m	a.m SO	a.m SX		p.m SO	p.m SO	p.m SO
	124 Charing Cross ....dep	..	..	..	7(3)23	8 25	9 15	11 15	11 55	1155	..	1 15	2 25	3 15
	124 Waterloo .... "	..	..	..	7(3)25	8 27	9 17	11 17	..	1157	..	1 17	2 27	3 17
	124 Cannon Street .... "	5(3)8	..	6 22	..	..	..	..	..	..	..	1 2	..	..
	124 London Bridge .... "	5(3)12	..	6 30	7(3)29	8 35	..	..	12 2	12 5	..	..	2 33	..
—	Tonbridge ....dep	6 34	..	8 10	8 48	9 38	1012	12 10	12 48	1 5	..	2 18	3 24	4 12
5¼	Paddock Wood ....arr	6 45	..	8 19	8 58	9 47	1021	12 18	12 59	1 17	..	2 27	3 33	4 20
—	Paddock Wood ....dep	..	7 35	..	9 7	..	..	12 24	..	..	..	2 32	..	4 24
9¼	Horsmonden	..	7 45	..	9 17	..	..	12 34	..	..	..	2 42	..	4 35
11¼	Goudhurst	..	7 54	..	9 23	..	..	12 40	..	..	..	2 48	..	4 41
15¼	Cranbrook	..	8 5	..	9 32	..	..	12 49	..	..	..	2 57	..	4 50
16¾	Hawkhurst ....arr	..	8 10	..	9 37	..	..	12 54	..	..	..	3 2	..	4 55
—	Paddock Wood ....dep	6 53	..	8 20	..	9 49	1026	12 19	1 10	1 46	..	2 32	3 34	4 27
7½	Beltring and Branbridges	6 56	..	8 25	..	9 54	1030	12 23	1 13	1 50	..	2 35	3 39	4 30
8¾	Yalding .... [Halt	7 1	..	8 29	..	9 58	1034	12 28	1 17	1 54	..	2 39	3 43	4 35
10½	Wateringbury	7 6	..	8 34	..	10 3	1039	12 32	1 22	1 59	..	2 44	3 48	4 40
11½	Teston Crossing Halt	7 9	..	8 37	..	10 6	1043	Dd	1 26	2 3	..	2 48	3 52	4 43
13½	East Farleigh	7 14	..	8 42	..	1011	1048	12 39	1 31	2 8	..	2 53	3 57	4 48
14¾	Tovil ¶	..	..	..	..	..	..	..	..	..	..	..	..	..
15½	Maidstone West 93 ....arr	7 21	..	8 49	..	1019	1055	12 46	1 38	2 15	..	3 0	4 3	4 54

Miles from Tonbridge	Down	Week Days	p.m SX	p.m SO	p.m SX	p.m SX	p.m SO	p.m SO	p.m SX	p.m	p.m			Sundays a.m	a.m	p.m	p.m	p.m
	124 Charing Cross ....dep	..	3 15	..	3 25	..	4 30	6 15	5 31	7 34	9 15	..	..	7 15	9 32	6 15	7 0	8 15
	124 Waterloo .... "	..	3 17	..	3 29	..	4 32	6 17	5 33	7 37	9 17	..	..	7 17	9 34	6 18	7 3	8 17
	124 Cannon Street .... "	..	..	..	..	4 38	..	..	6 18	..	..	..	..	..	..	..	..	..
	124 London Bridge .... "	..	..	3(3)9	3 35	4 42	4 39	..	5 39	7 45	..	..	..	7 24	9 41	6 25	7 10	8 23
—	Tonbridge ....dep	..	4 10	4 58	4 58	5 28	5 27	7 3	7 12	8 50	10 3	..	..	8 47	1058	7 28	8 1	9 22
5¼	Paddock Wood ....arr	..	4 18	5 8	5 9	5 38	5 37	7 13	7 21	9 0	1013	..	..	8 58	11 7	7 36	8 12	9 30
—	Paddock Wood ....dep	..	4 24	..	..	5 53	5 53	7 28	7 28	..	..	..	..	..	..	..	..	..
9¼	Horsmonden	..	4 35	..	..	6 3	6 3	7 38	7 38	..	..	..	..	..	..	..	..	..
11¼	Goudhurst	..	4 41	..	..	6 9	6 9	7 44	7 44	..	..	..	..	..	..	..	..	..
15¼	Cranbrook	..	4 50	..	..	6 18	6 18	7 53	7 53	..	..	..	..	..	..	..	..	..
16¾	Hawkhurst ....arr	..	4 55	..	..	6 23	6 23	7 58	7 58	..	..	..	..	..	..	..	..	..
—	Paddock Wood ....dep	..	4 27	5 9	5 11	5 42	5 48	7 20	7 29	9 1	1020	..	..	9 3	11 9	7 37	8 20	9 31
7½	Beltring and Branbridges	..	4 31	5 13	5 15	5 45	5 51	7 23	7 33	9 6	1024	..	..	9 7	1113	..	8 23	9 35
8¾	Yalding .... [Halt	..	4 35	5 17	5 19	5 49	5 55	7 27	7 37	9 10	1028	..	..	9 12	1117	7 43	8 27	9 39
10½	Wateringbury	..	4 40	5 22	5 24	5 54	6 0	7 32	7 42	9 15	1033	..	..	9 17	1122	7 49	8 33	9 45
11½	Teston Crossing Halt	..	4 44	5 26	5 28	5 57	6 4	7 36	7 45	Dd	1037	..	..	..	1126	7 53	8 37	9 49
13½	East Farleigh	..	4 49	5 31	5 33	6 2	6 9	7 41	7 51	9 22	1042	..	..	9 24	1131	7 58	8 42	9 54
14¾	Tovil ¶	..	..	..	..	..	..	..	..	..	..	..	..	..	..	..	..	..
15½	Maidstone West 93 ....arr	..	4 56	5 37	5 39	6 8	6 16	7 48	7 58	9 28	1049	..	..	9 30	1137	8 4	8 48	10 0

Miles	Up	Week Days a.m	a.m	a.m	a.m	a.m	a.m SO	a.m SX	a.m	p.m SO	p.m SX	p.m SX	p.m SO
	Maidstone West ....dep	7 17	7 37	8 25	9 39	..	1030	10 40	1140	1 0	1 4	..	2 16
¾	Tovil ¶	..	..	..	..	..	..	..	..	..	..	..	..
1¾	East Farleigh	7 21	7 41	8 31	9 43	..	1034	10 46	1146	1 5	1 10	..	2 22
2¾	Teston Crossing Halt	7 25	7 45	8 35	9 47	..	1038	10 50	1150	1 9	1 14	..	2 26
4¾	Wateringbury	7 28	7 48	8 39	9 50	..	1042	10 54	1154	1 14	1 18	..	2 32
6½	Yalding .... [Halt	7 33	7 53	8 44	9 55	..	1047	10 59	1159	1 18	1 23	..	2 36
8	Beltring and Branbridges	7 37	7 57	8 48	9 58	..	1051	11 3	12 3	1 22	1 27	..	2 40
10	Paddock Wood 34 ....arr	7 42	8 2	8 53	10 3	..	1055	11 8	12 7	1 28	1 31	..	2 45
—	Mls Hawkhurst ....dep	..	7 40	8 24	..	9 43	..	..	..	1 5	..	1 5	..
—	1½ Cranbrook	..	7 44	8 28	..	9 47	..	..	..	1 9	..	1 9	..
—	5½ Goudhurst	..	7 53	8 37	..	9 56	..	..	..	1 18	..	1 18	..
—	7½ Horsmonden	..	7 59	8 43	..	10 2	..	..	..	1 24	..	1 24	..
—	11½ Paddock Wood ....arr	..	8 10	8 54	..	1013	..	..	..	1 35	..	1 35	..
—	Paddock Wood ....dep	7 43	8 18	8 55	1011	1019	1056	11 9	12 8	1 39	1 32	1 42	2 46
15½	Tonbridge 54 ....arr	7 53	8 29	9 5	1022	1029	11 6	11 19	1218	1 49	1 42	1 52	2 56
43	130 London Bridge ....arr	..	..	10 9	1122	1122	..	..	1V22	2 39	2 45	2 45	..
43½	130 Cannon Street .... "	8 47	9 24	1014	..	..	..	..	..	..	..	..	..
44	130 Waterloo .... "	..	..	1023	1130	1130	12 1	..	1U30	2 45	2 51	2 51	..
44¾	130 Charing Cross .... "	..	..	1027	1134	1134	12 5	..	1X35	2 50	2 55	2 55	..

Miles	Up	Week Days p.m SO	p.m SX	p.m SO	p.m SX	p.m SO	p.m SO	p.m SX	p.m	p.m	p.m	p.m	p.m	Sundays a.m	a.m	p.m	p.m	p.m
	Maidstone West ....dep	3 18	4 16	4 16	5 20	5 21	6 32	6 32	..	7 38	..	8 36	9 53	8 0	9 40	6 0	7 30	9 12
¾	Tovil ¶	..	..	..	..	..	..	..	..	..	..	..	..	..	..	..	..	..
1¾	East Farleigh	3 24	4 22	4 22	5 24	5 26	6 36	6 36	..	7 42	..	8 40	9 57	8 4	9 45	6 6	7 35	9 17
2¾	Teston Crossing Halt	3 28	4 26	4 26	5 28	5 30	6 41	6 41	..	7 46	..	8 44	10 1	8 9	9 50	6 11	..	9 21
4¾	Wateringbury	3 33	4 30	4 30	5 32	5 34	6 45	6 45	..	7 50	..	8 48	10 5	8 13	9 54	6 15	7 41	9 26
6½	Yalding .... [Halt	3 37	4 35	4 35	5 37	5 39	6 51	6 50	..	7 55	..	8 52	1010	8 17	9 58	6 19	7 46	9 30
8	Beltring and Branbridges	3 41	4 39	4 39	5 41	5 43	6 55	6 55	..	7 59	..	8 56	1014	8 21	10 2	6 23	..	9 34
10	Paddock Wood 34 ....arr	3 45	4 46	4 44	5 50	5 50	7 1	7 1	..	8 4	..	9 2	1019	8 26	10 6	6 28	7 52	9 39
—	Mls Hawkhurst ....dep	3 12	..	..	5 5	5 5	..	..	6 35	..	8 7	..	..	..	..	..	..	..
—	1½ Cranbrook	3 16	..	..	5 9	5 9	..	..	6 39	..	8 11	..	..	..	..	..	..	..
—	5½ Goudhurst	3 25	..	..	5 18	5 18	..	..	6 48	..	8 20	..	..	..	..	..	..	..
—	7½ Horsmonden	3 31	..	..	5 24	5 24	..	..	6 54	..	8 26	..	..	..	..	..	..	..
—	11½ Paddock Wood ....arr	3 42	..	..	5 35	5 35	..	..	7 5	..	8 37	..	..	..	..	..	..	..
—	Paddock Wood ....dep	3 46	5 6	5 2	5 51	5 51	7 2	7 15	7 15	8 5	8 38	9 3	1020	8 42	10 7	6 29	8 5	9 40
15½	Tonbridge 54 ....arr	3 56	5 16	5 12	6 1	6 1	7 12	7 26	7 26	8 15	8 48	9 12	1030	8 52	1017	6 39	8 16	9 50
43	130 London Bridge ....arr	5(3)19	6(3)36	6L47	7 24	7 24	8 28	8 28	8 28	9(3)51	9 52	1044	1U19	9 44	1120	8 5	9 35	1050
43½	130 Cannon Street .... "	..	6(3)40	..	..	..	..	..	..	..	..	..	..	..	..	..	..	..
44	130 Waterloo .... "	5(3)23	..	..	7 33	7 33	8 36	8 36	8 36	9(3)55	9 59	1053	..	9 50	1127	8 12	9 42	1056
44¾	130 Charing Cross .... "	5(3)26	..	..	7 38	7 38	8 41	8 41	8 41	9(3)57	10 3	1058	..	9 54	1131	8 17	9 46	11 1

(3) Third class only
D Arr. 1 20 p.m on Saturdays
Dd Stops to set down on informing Guard at previous *stopping* Station
L Via Redhill page 250
SO or S0 Saturdays only
SX or SX Saturdays excepted
U Via Redhill page 250. Third class only
V 8 mins *earlier* on Sats.
X Arr. 1 24 p.m on Saturdays
¶ Station closed

LOCAL TRAINS Tonbridge and Paddock Wood, see page 34

LONDON, ORPINGTON, TUNBRIDGE WELLS, BEXHILL WEST, and HASTINGS

Down — Mondays to Fridays

Miles from Charing C.	Down		a.m (3)	a.m (3)		a.m	a.m		a.m		a.m	a.m	a.m		a.m		a.m		a.m		a.m		a.m	a.m		p.m		p.m		p.m	p.m
	Charing Cross	dep	..	..	..	..	..	..	..	..	..	..	..	..	7(3)23	..	8 25	..	1025	..	..	..	1115	..	..	1225	..	1(3)5	..	2 25	..
	Waterloo	"	..	..	..	..	..	..	..	..	..	..	..	..	7(3)25	..	8 27	..	1027	..	..	..	1117	..	..	1227	..	1(3)7	..	2 27	..
	Cannon Street	"	..	..	..	..	5(3)8	..	..	..	..	6 22	..	..	..	..	..	..	..	..	..	..	..	..	..	R	..	..	..	..	..
	London Bridge	"	3 45	..	..	..	5(3)12	..	5 45	..	..	6 30	..	..	7(3)29	..	8 35	..	1035	..	..	..	..	..	..	1234	..	1(3)11	..	2 33	..
13¾	Orpington	dep	..	..	..	..	5(3)43	..	6 8	..	..	6 58	..	..	7(3)58	..	..	..	..	..	..	..	..	..	..	..	..	1(3)41	..	..	..
22	Sevenoaks (Tub's Hill)	"	4 19	..	..	..	6 9	..	6 27	..	6(3)47	7 15	..	..	8 23	..	9 8	..	11 6	..	..	..	1150	..	..	1 5	..	2(3)15	..	3 2	..
29½	Tonbridge 53, 249	arr	4 35	..	..	..	6 19	..	6 42	..	7(3)1	7 30	..	..	8 37	..	9 20	..	1117	..	..	..	12 1	..	..	1 16	..	2(3)29	..	3 13	..
—	246 East Croydon	dep	..	..	..	..	..	..	5 10	..	..	..	7 0	..	..	..	7 39	..	9 46	..	..	..	..	1146	..	..	..	1 46	..	..	..
—	Tonbridge	dep	4 38	5 5	..	..	6 20	..	6 46	..	7 25	..	8 14	..	8 39	..	9 22	..	1119	..	1152	..	Refreshment Car	1252	..	1 18	..	2 48	..	3 17	3 35
32¼	High Brooms		..	5 14	..	..	6 29	..	6 58	..	7 33	..	8 24	..	8 48	..	..	..	1128	..	12 2	..		1 3	..	..	..	2 58	..	..	3 44
34¼	Tunbridge Wells Central		4F51	5 18	..	..	6b34	..	7 2	..	7 37	..	8 28	..	8 52	..	9 36	..	1132	..	12 6	..		1 8	..	1 30	..	3 2	..	3 30	3 48
35¼	**Tunbridge Wells West**	arr	..	..	..	..	6 48	..	..	..	7 47	..	8 34	..	9 2	..	..	..	..	..	1213	..		1 15	..	..	..	3 8	..	..	..
36¾	Frant		..	..	..	..	Thro Train, Sevenoaks to Brighton, page 234	..	7 13	..	Thro Train, Tonbridge to Brighton, page 234	..	..	..	..	..	9 45	..	1142	..	..	..		..	..	..	..	..	..	..	3 56
39½	Wadhurst		5 8	5 42	..	..		..	7 20	..		..	..	..	..	..	9 51	..	1148	..	..	..		..	..	1 43	..	..	..	..	4 2
43¾	Stonegate		5 17	Dep. Tunbridge Wells Central 5 30 a.m	..	..		..	7 29	..		..	..	..	..	..	9 58	..	1155	..	..	..		..	..	Dd	..	..	..	..	4 9
47½	Etchingham		5 24		..	..		..	7 37	..		..	..	..	..	..	10 6	..	12 4	..	..	..		..	..	1 56	..	..	..	..	4 17
49½	Robertsbridge		5 32		..	..		..	7 46	..		..	..	..	..	..	1012	..	1210	..	..	..		..	..	2 3	..	..	..	..	4 23
52¾	Mountfield Halt		..		..	..		..	7 54	..		..	..	..	..	..	1019	..	1217	..	..	..	..	..	..	2 10	..	..	..	..	4 30
55½	Battle		5 46		..	..		..	8 1	..		..	..	..	..	..	1025	..	1223	..	..	..	..	..	..	2 16	..	..	..	4 0	4 36
57½	Crowhurst		5 53		..	7 5		..	8 8	..		..	..	..	..	..	1031	..	1230	..	..	..	..	..	..	2 21	..	..	..	4 5	4 41
61	Sidley		..		..	7 11		..	8 17	..		..	..	..	..	..	1041	..	1240	..	..	..	..	..	..	2 34	..	..	..	4 15	4 51
62	Bexhill West A	arr	..		..	7 15		..	8 21	..		..	..	..	..	..	1045	..	1244	..	..	..	..	..	..	2 38	..	..	..	4 19	4 55
60¾	West St. Leonards		..		..	..		..	8 15	..		..	..	..	..	..	1038	..	1238	..	..	..	..	..	..	2 28	..	..	..	4 11	4 47
61¾	St. Leonards (Warr. Sq.) 197		6 2		..	..		..	8 19	..		..	..	..	..	..	1043	..	1242	..	..	..	..	..	..	2 33	..	..	..	4 15	4 52
62½	Hastings 58	arr	6 9		..	..		..	8 25	..		..	..	..	..	..	1047	..	1246	..	..	..	..	..	..	2 37	..	..	..	4 19	4 56

Down — Mondays to Fridays—continued

Down		p.m	p.m		p.m	p.m		p.m		p.m		p.m	p.m	p.m	p.m	p.m		p.m		p.m		p.m		p.m		p.m		p.m	p.m		p.m
Charing Cross	dep	3 25	..	..	4 20	..	..	R	..	..	..	5 31	..	..	..	..	..	6 22	..	6(3)35	..	7 34	..	..	..	..	..	9 15	..	..	1025
Waterloo	"	3 29	..	..	4 22	..	..	..	..	..	..	5 33	..	..	..	..	..	6 24	..	6(3)37	..	7 37	..	..	..	..	..	9 17	..	..	1027
Cannon Street	"	..	..	..	..	..	..	5 6	..	5 18	..	..	5 40	6 3	..	6 18	..	..	..	..	..	..	..	..	..	..	..	..	..	..	..
London Bridge	"	3 35	..	..	4 28	..	..	..	..	..	..	5 39	5 45	..	..	..	..	6 30	..	6(3)41	..	7 45	..	..	..	..	..	..	9(3)11	..	1024
Orpington	dep	..	..	..	4 48	..	..	..	..	..	..	..	..	..	..	..	..	..	..	7(3)10	..	..	..	..	..	..	..	..	9(3)40	..	..
Sevenoaks (Tub's Hill)	"	4 5	..	..	..	..	..	..	..	5 50	..	6 10	6 20	..	..	6 51	..	7 3	..	7 32	..	8 17	..	..	..	..	..	9 49	10 6	..	11 4
Tonbridge 53, 249	arr	4 20	..	..	..	..	..	..	..	6 4	..	6 25	6 35	..	..	7 2	..	7 19	..	7 46	..	8 32	..	..	..	..	..	10 1	10 20	..	1115
246 East Croydon	dep	..	..	..	..	3 46	..	..	..	4 46	..	..	..	..	5 28	..	..	..	..	6 24	..	..	..	7 22	..		..	..	8 46	.	9 46
Tonbridge	dep	4 22	4 36	..	..	5 14	..	..	..	6 6	..	6 27	..	..	6 46	..	..	7 21	..	7 48	..	..	..	8 44	..	9 20	..	..	10 21	..	1117
High Brooms		4 31	4 44	..	..	5 22	..	..	..	6 15	..	..	..	..	6 56	..	..	..	..	7 57	..	..	..	8 52	..	..	..	..	10 30	..	..
Tunbridge Wells Central		4 35	4 48	..	5 18	5 26	..	5 53	..	6 19	..	6 39	..	6 51	7 0	..	..	7 34	..	8 1	..	..	..	8 56	..	9 31	..	..	10 34	..	1129
Tunbridge Wells West	arr	..	4 54	..	..	..	..	..	..	..	..	..	..	..	7 9	..	..	..	..	8 14	..	..	..	..	..	9 37	..	..		..	..
Frant		4 42	..	..	..	5 33	..	..	..	6 26	..	..	..	..	..	..	..	7 42	..	..	..	..	..	9 3	..	Thro Train, Tonbridge to Brighton, page 238	..	..	10 43	..	..
Wadhurst		4 48	..	..	..	5 39	..	..	..	6 32	..	..	..	7 2	..	..	..	7 48	..	..	..	..	..	9 9	..		..	..	10 49	..	1140
Stonegate		..	..	..	..	5 46	..	..	..	6 39	..	..	..	..	..	..	..	7 55	..	..	..	..	..	9 16	..		..	..	..	..	..
Etchingham		..	..	..	..	5 53	..	6 14	..	6 45	..	..	..	..	..	..	..	8 1	..	..	..	..	..	9 25	..		..	..	..	..	..
Robertsbridge		..	..	..	5 41	6 0	..	..	..	6 51	..	..	..	..	..	..	..	8 8	..	..	..	..	..	9 30	..		..	..	..	..	..
Mountfield Halt		..	..	..	..	6 6	..	..	..	..	..	..	..	..	..	..	..	8 15	..	..	..	..	..	9 37	..		..	..	..	..	..
Battle		..	..	..	5 51	6 11	..	..	..	7 2	..	..	..	7 23	..	..	..	8 22	..	..	..	..	..	9 42	..		..	..	..	..	..
Crowhurst		..	..	..	5 56	6 16	..	6 32	..	7 7	..	7 16	..	7 30	..	..	..	8 30	..	..	..	..	..	9 47	..		..	..	..	..	..
Sidley		..	..	..	6 6	..	..	6 42	..	..	..	7 25	..	7 38	..	..	..	..	..	..	..	..	..	9 58	..		..	..	..	..	..
Bexhill West A	arr	..	..	..	6 10	..	..	6 46	..	..	..	7 29	..	7 42	..	..	..	..	..	..	..	..	..	10 2	..		..	..	..	..	..
West St. Leonards		..	..	..	6 2	..	..	6 38	..	7 13	..	7 22	..	7 36	..	..	..	8 37	..	..	..	..	..	9 53	..		..	..	..	..	..
St. Leonards (Warr. Sq.) 197		..	..	..	6 6	..	..	6 42	..	7 17	..	7 26	..	7 40	..	..	..	8 42	..	..	..	..	..	9 57	..		..	..	..	..	..
Hastings 58	arr	..	..	..	6 10	..	..	6 46	..	7 21	..	7 30	..	7 44	..	..	..	8 47	..	..	..	..	..	10 1	..		..	..	..	..	..

(3) Third Class only. A Over ½ mile to Bexhill Cen. Sta. b Dep. 6 42 a.m. F Dep 4 56 a.m. Dd Calls on Weds. only. Passengers wishing to alight must inform the Guard at previous stopping station. R Refreshment Car London to Hastings.

For Saturday Trains, see page 54a; Sunday Trains, page 55

LONDON, ORPINGTON, TUNBRIDGE WELLS, BEXHILL WEST, and HASTINGS

Saturdays

Down	a.m	a.m		a.m	a.m		a.m		a.m	a.m	a.m		a.m		a.m		a.m		a.m		a.m		p.m		p.m	p.m		p.m	p.m
Charing Cross .... dep	③	③	..	..	..	..	..	..	..	..	..	..	7③23	..	8 25	..	1025	..	..	..	1115	..	..	..	R	1217	..	③	R
Waterloo .... "			..	..	..	..	..	..	..	..	..	..	7③25	..	8 27	..	1027	..	..	..	1117	..	..	..	..	1220	..		..
Cannon Street .... "	..	..	..	..	5③8	..	..	..	..	6 22	..	..	..	..	..	..	..	..	..	..	..	..	..	..	1218	..	..	..	1 2
London Bridge .... "	3 45	..	..	..	5③12	..	5 45	..	..	6 30	..	..	7③29	..	8 35	..	1034	..	..	..	..	..	..	..	..	1226	..	..	..
Orpington .... dep	..	..	..	..	5③43	..	6 8	..	..	6 58	..	..	7③58	..	..	..	..	..	..	..	..	..	..	..	..	..	..	1251	..
Sevenoaks (Tub's Hill) .... "	4 19	..	..	..	6 9	..	6 27	..	6③47	7 15	..	..	8 23	..	9 8	..	11 4	..	..	..	1150	..	..	..	..	1256	..	1 16	..
Tonbridge 53, 249 .... arr	4 35	..	..	..	6 19	..	6 42	..	7③1	7 30	..	..	8 37	..	9 20	..	1115	..	..	..	12 1	..	..	..	..	1 11	..	1 27	1 42
246 East Croydon .... dep	..	..	..	..	.	..	5 10	..	..	..	7 0	..	..	..	7 39	..	9 46	..	..	..	..	..	..	..	..	46	..	..	..
Tonbridge .... dep	4 38	5 5	..	..	6 20	..	6 46	..	7 25	..	8 14	..	8 39	..	9 22	..	1116	..	1128	..	Refreshment Car	..	1238	..	..	1 13	..	..	1 43
High Brooms	..	5 14	..	..	6 29	..	6 58	..	7 33	..	8 24	..	8 48	..	..	..		..	1136	..		..	1246	..	..	..	..	..	..
Tunbridge Wells Central	4F51	5 18	..	..	6B34	..	7 2	..	7 37	..	8 29	..	8 52	..	9 36	..	1128	..	1140	..		..	1250	..	1 7	1 25	..	..	1 55
Tunbridge Wells West .. arr	..	..	..	..	6 48	..	..	..	7 47	.	8 34	..	9 2	..	..	..	..	..	.	..		..	1256	..	..	..	..	..	.
Frant	..	..	..	..	Thro Train, Sevenoaks to Brighton, page 234	..	7 13	..	Thro Train Tonbridge to Brighton, page 234	..	..	..	..	..	9 45	..	..	..	1148	..		..	..	..	..	..	..	..	..
Wadhurst	5 8	5 42	..	..		..	7 20	..		..	..	..	..	..	9 51	..	..	..	1154	..		..	..	..	..	1 36	..	..	..
Stonegate	5 17	Dep. Tunbridge Wells Central 5 30 a.m	..	..		..	7 29	..		..	..	..	..	..	9 58	..	..	..	12 1	..		..	..	..	..	1 43	..	..	..
Etchingham	5 24		..	..		..	7 37	..		..	..	..	..	..	10 6	..	..	..	12 7	..		..	..	..	..	1 49	..	..	..
Robertsbridge	5 32		..	..		..	7 46	..		..	..	..	..	..	1012	..	..	..	1213	..		..	..	..	..	1 55	..	..	..
Mountfield Halt	..		..	..		..	7 54	..		..	..	..	..	..	1019	..	..	..	1220	..		..	..	..	..	2 2	..	..	..
Battle	5 46		..	..		..	8 1	..		..	..	..	..	..	1025	..	1159	..	1226	..		..	..	..	..	2 8	..	..	..
Crowhurst	5 53		..	7 5		..	8 8	..		..	..	..	..	..	1031	..	12 6	..	1231	..		..	..	..	1 40	2 14	..	..	2 3[illegible]
Sidley	..		..	7 11		..	8 17	..		..	..	..	..	..	1041	..	1215	..	1253	..	..	..	..	..	1 50	2 23	..	..	2 43
Bexhill West A .... arr	..		..	7 15		..	8 21	..		..	..	..	..	..	1045	..	1219	..	1257	..	..	..	..	..	1 54	2 27	..	..	2 47
West St. Leonards	..		..	..		..	8 15	..		..	..	..	..	..	1038	..	1212	..	1238	..	..	..	..	..	1 46	2 21	..	..	2 38
St. Leonards (Warr. Sq.) 197 ..	6 2		..	..		..	8 19	..		..	..	..	..	..	1043	..	1216	..	1243	..	..	..	..	..	1 50	2 25	..	..	2 42
Hastings 58 .... arr	6 9		..	..		..	8 25	..		..	..	..	..	..	1047	..	1220	..	1247	..	..	..	..	..	1 54	2 29	..	..	2 46

Saturdays—*continued*

Down	p.m		p.m		p.m		p.m		p.m		p.m		p.m		p.m		p.m	p.m		p.m		p.m	p.m		p.m		p.m	p.m		p.m
Charing Cross .... dep	1 30	..	2 25	..	3 15	..	3 25	..	..	..	4 30	..	..	..	5 25	..	6 15	..	..	..	..	7 34	..	..	..	..	9 15	..	..	1025
Waterloo .... "	1 32	..	2 27	..	3 17	..	3 27	..	..	..	4 32	..	..	..	5 27	..	6 17	..	..	..	..	7 37	..	..	..	..	9 17	..	..	1027
Cannon Street .... "	..	..	..	..	..	..	..	..	..	..	..	..	..	..	..	..	..	..	..	..	..	..	..	..	..	..	..	..	..	..
London Bridge .... "	1 39	..	2 33	..	..	..	..	..	3③9	..	4 39	..	..	..	5 34	..	..	..	..	6③11	..	7 45	..	..	..	..	..	9③11	..	1034
Orpington .... dep	..	..	..	..	..	..	..	..	3③40	..	..	..	..	..	..	..	..	..	..	6③40	..	..	..	..	..	..	..	9③40	..	..
Sevenoaks (Tub's Hill) .... "	2 12	..	3 3	..	3 50	..	..	..	4 7	..	5 10	..	..	..	6 4	..	6 50	..	..	7 8	..	8 17	..	..	..	..	9 49	10 6	..	11 4
Tonbridge 53, 249 .... arr	2 27	..	3 13	..	4 1	..	..	..	4 21	..	5 25	..	..	..	6 15	..	7 1	..	..	7 22	..	8 32	..	..	..	..	10 1	10 20	..	1115
246 East Croydon .... dep	1247	..	1 24	..	..	..	..	..	2 46	..	..	..	4 5	..	4 46	..	..	5 46	..	..	..	..	7 5	..	..	..	..	8 46	..	9 46
Tonbridge .... dep	2 29	..	3 14	..	..	..	..	..	4 25	..	..	..	5 40	..	6 17	..	Refreshment Car	7 15	..	7 48	..	..	8 44	..	9 20	..	..	10 21	..	1117
High Brooms	2 39	..	..	..	..	..	..	..	4 35	..	..	..	5 48	..	..	..		7 23	..	7 57	..	..	8 52	..	.	..	..	10 30	..	..
Tunbridge Wells Central	2 43	..	3 27	..	..	..	4 20	..	4 39	..	..	..	5 52	..	6 29	..		7 27	..	8 1	..	..	8 56	..	9 31	..	..	10 34	..	1129
Tunbridge Wells West .. arr	..	..	..	..	..	..	..	..	..	..	..	..	6 0	..	..	..		..	..	8 14	..	..	..	..	9 37	..	..	..	..	..
Frant	2 51	..	..	..	..	..	..	..	4 48	..	..	..	..	..	..	..		7 36	..	..	..	..	9 3	..	Thro Train, Tonbridge to Brighton, page 238	..	..	10 43	..	..
Wadhurst	2 57	..	..	..	..	..	..	..	4 54	..	..	..	..	..	..	..		7 42	..	..	..	..	9 9	..		..	..	10 49	..	1140
Stonegate	3 4	..	..	..	..	..	..	..	5 1	..	..	..	..	..	..	..		7 49	..	..	..	..	9 16	..		..	..	..	..	..
Etchingham	3 10	..	..	..	..	..	..	..	5 9	..	..	..	..	..	..	..		7 55	..	..	..	..	9 25	..		..	..	..	..	..
Robertsbridge	3 16	..	3 51	..	..	..	..	..	5 15	..	..	..	..	..	6 52	..		8 2	..	..	..	..	9 30	..		..	..	..	..	..
Mountfield Halt	3 23	..	..	..	..	..	..	..	5 22	..	..	..	..	..	..	..		8 8	..	..	..	..	9 37	..		..	..	..	..	..
Battle	3 28	..	4 1	..	..	..	..	..	5 27	..	..	..	..	..	..	..		8 14	..	..	..	..	9 42	..		..	..	..	..	..
Crowhurst	3 34	..	4 6	..	..	..	4 58	..	5 34	..	..	..	..	..	7 8	..		8 20	..	..	..	..	9 47	..		..	..	..	..	..
Sidley	3 43	..	4 17	..	..	..	5 12	..	5 42	..	..	..	..	..	7 31	..	..	..	..	..	..	..	9 58	..		..	..	..	..	..
Bexhill West A .... arr	3 47	..	4 21	..	..	..	5 16	..	5 46	..	..	..	..	..	7 35	..	..	..	..	..	..	..	10 2	..		..	..	..	..	..
West St. Leonards	3 42	..	4 12	..	..	..	5 6	..	5 41	..	..	..	..	..	7 15	..	..	8 28	..	..	..	..	9 53	..		..	..	..	..	..
St. Leonards (Warr. Sq.) 197 ..	3 47	..	4 16	..	..	..	5 11	..	5 47	..	..	..	..	..	7 19	..	..	8 33	..	..	..	..	9 57	..		..	..	..	..	..
Hastings 58 .... arr	3 51	..	4 20	..	..	..	5 14	..	5 51	..	..	..	..	..	7 23	..	..	8 38	..	..	..	..	10 1	..		..	..	..	..	..

③ Third class only A Over ½ mile to Bexhill Central Station B Dep 5 42 a.m. F Dep 4 56 a.m.
R Refreshment Car London to Hastings

LONDON, ORPINGTON, TUNBRIDGE WELLS, BEXHILL WEST, and HASTINGS

Down — Sundays

Down	a.m	a.m	a.m	a.m		a.m		a.m	a.m		a.m	a.m		a.m		a.m	a.m			p.m	p.m	p.m		p.m	p.m	p.m	p.m		p.m		
Charing Cross ... dep	③	..	7 15	..	..	7③58	..	9 25	9 32	..	..	1025	..	9③58	..	1110	1125	Calls New Cross 11 41 a.m.	..	1215	..	..	..	3 25	6 15	..	7 25	..	..	..	..
Waterloo ... "		..	7 17	..	..	8③0	..	9 27	9 34	..	..	1027	..	10③0	..	1113	1127		..	1217	..	..	..	3 27	6 18	..	7 27	..	..	..	..
Cannon Street ... "	..	..	..	..	..	..	..	..	..	..	..	..	..	..	..	..	..		..	..	..	..	..	..	..	..	..	..	..	..	..
London Bridge ... "	4 5	..	7 24	..	..	8 ③4	..	9 33	9 41	..	..	..	..	10③4	..	1120	1134		..	..	..	..	..	3 33	6 25	..	7 33	..	..	..	..
Orpington ... dep	..	..	..	..	..	8③32	..	..	..	..	..	..	..	10③35	..	1148	..		..	..	..	..	..	..	..	..	..	..	..	..	..
Sevenoaks (Tub's Hill) ... "	4 51	..	8 1	..	..	9 2	..	10 5	1012	..	..	..	..	11 5	..	..	12 8		..	1249	1 0	..	..	4 4	6 57	..	8 6	..	..	..	..
Tonbridge 53, 249 ... arr	5 7	..	8 16	..	..	9 15	..	1016	1023	..	..	..	..	11 19	..	1210	1219		..	1 1	1 14	..	..	4 15	7 8	..	8 17	..	..	..	..
246 East Croydon ... dep	..	..	Calls New Cross 7 31 a.m	7 35	..	..	..	..	..	..	9 6	..	..	..	..	Calls New Cross 11 28 and Hither Green 11 34 a.m.	..		..	..	..	12 5	..	2 46	..	4 46	..	..	7 5	..	..
Tonbridge ... dep	5 10	..		8 55	..	9 28	..	1017	..	..	1048	..	..	11 20	..		1221		..	..	1 16	1 25	..	4 16	..	7 21	8 19	..	8 32	..	..
High Brooms ...	..	..		9 4	..	9 38	..	..	..	..	1056	..	..	11 29	..		..		..	..	1 25	1 34	..	..	..	7 29	8 29	..	8 41	..	..
Tunbridge Wells Central ...	5V26	..		9 8	..	9 42	..	1029	..	..	11 0	1121	..	11 33	..		1234		..	..	1 29	1 38	..	4 28	..	7 33	8 33	..	8 45	..	..
Tunbridge Wells West .. arr	..	..		..	..	9 48	..	..	..	..	..	..	..	11 39	..		..		..	..	1 36	..	..	..	..	7 41	..	..	8 51	..	..
Frant ...	..	..		9 17	..	..	..	..	..	..	11 7	..	..	..	..		..		..	..	..	1 45	..	..	..	..	8 42	..	Thro Train, Tonbridge to Brighton, page 238	..	..
Wadhurst ...	5 47	..		9 23	..	..	..	..	..	..	1113	..	..	..	..		..		..	..	..	1 51	..	..	..	..	8 48	..		..	..
Stonegate ...	..	..		9 31	..	..	..	..	..	..	1119	..	..	..	..		..		..	..	..	1 58	..	..	..	..	8 55	..		..	..
Etchingham ...	..	..		9 40	..	..	..	..	..	..	1125	..	..	..	..		..		..	..	..	2 4	..	4 48	..	..	9 1	..		..	..
Robertsbridge ...	6 7	..		9 48	..	..	..	..	..	..	1132	..	..	..	..		1258		..	..	..	2 10	..	4 54	..	..	9 8	..		..	..
Mountfield Halt ...	..	..		9 55	..	..	..	..	..	..	1139	..	..	..	..		..		..	..	..	2 17	..	..	..	..	9 15	..		..	..
Battle ...	..	..		10 0	..	..	..	..	..	..	1145	..	..	..	..		..		..	..	..	2 22	..	5 5	..	..	9 20	..		..	..
Crowhurst ...	6 23	7 45		10 7	..	..	..	11 2	..	..	1151	..	..	..	..		..		..	..	..	2 27	..	5 11	..	..	9 25	..		..	..
Sidley ...	..	7 51	..	1016	..	..	..	1111	..	..	12 2	..	..	..	..		..		..	..	..	2 36	..	5 21	..	..	9 42	..		..	..
Bexhill West A ... arr	6 40	7 55	..	1020	..	..	..	1115	..	..	12 6	..	..	..	..		..		..	..	..	2 40	..	5 25	..	..	9 46	..		..	..
West St. Leonards ...	..	..	..	1014	..	..	..	11 9	..	..	12 0	12 8	..	..	..	..	1 18		..	..	..	2 33	..	5 17	..	..	9 31	..		..	..
St. Leonards (Warr. Sq.) 197 ..	6 33	..	..	1018	..	..	..	1113	..	..	12 5	1212	..	..	..	..	1 23		..	..	..	2 37	..	5 22	..	..	9 35	..		..	..
Hastings 58 ... arr	6 41	..	..	1022	..	..	..	1117	..	..	12 9	1215	..	..	..	..	1 27		..	..	..	2 41	..	5 26	..	..	9 39	..		..	..

Up — Mondays to Fridays

Miles	Up	a.m	a.m	a.m	a.m	a.m		a.m	a.m	R	a.m	a.m	a.m	a.m	a.m	R	a.m		p.m	p.m	p.m	p.m		p.m	p.m	p.m		p.m	p.m	p.m
	Hastings ... dep	..	6 22	..	6 58	7 27	..	Through Train, Eridge to Tonbridge, page 239	7 40	8 10	..	..	8 25	Through Train, Eridge to Tonbridge, page 240	..	1010	1040	..	..	Through Train, Brighton to Tonbridge, page 240	..	1 20	..	2 10	..	2 48	..	..	..	..
¾	St. Leonards (Warr. Sq.) ...	..	6 25	..	7 0	7 29	..		7 43	8 13	..	..	8 28		..	1013	1043	..	..		..	1 23	..	2 13	..	2 51	..	..	..	..
1¾	West St. Leonards ...	..	6 30	..	7 4	7 33	..		7 47	8 17	..	..	8 32		..	1018	1047	..	..		..	1 27	..	2 18	..	2 55	..	..	..	..
—	Mls — Bexhill West ... dep	..	6 26	..	7 0	7 30	..		..	8 13	..	..	8 30		..	1014	1040	..	..		..	1 22	..	2 10	..	2 46	..	4 24	..	..
—	1 Sidley ...	..	6 28	..	7 2	7 32	..		..	8 15	..	..	8 32		..	1016	1042	..	..		..	1 24	..	2 12	..	2 48	..	4 26	..	..
5	Crowhurst ...	..	6 37	..	7 11	7 41	..		7 54	8 24	..	..	8 41		..	1026	1055	..	..		..	1 34	..	2 26	..	3 3	..	4 34	..	..
7	Battle ...	..	6 43	..	..	..	..		8 0	..	..	..	8 47		..	..	11 1	..	..		..	1 40	..	..	..	3 9	..	..	..	..
9¾	Mountfield Halt ...	..	6 48	..	..	..	..		..	..	..	..	..		..	..	11 6	..	..		..	1 45	..	..	..	3 15	..	..	..	..
13	Robertsbridge ...	..	6 55	..	..	..	..		8 9	..	..	..	8 56		..	1038	1113	..	..		..	1 52	..	2 38	..	3 21	..	..	..	..
15	Etchingham ...	..	7 1	..	..	7 57	..		8 15	..	..	..	9 2		..	..	1120	..	..		..	1 58	..	..	..	3 28	..	..	..	..
18¾	Stonegate ...	..	7 8	..	..	..	..		8 22	..	..	..	..		..	..	1127	..	..		..	2 5	..	..	..	3 35	..	..	..	..
23½	Wadhurst ...	6 24	7 18	..	..	..	..		8 31	8 51	..	..	9 16		..	..	1136	..	..		..	2 15	..	..	..	3 46	..	..	4 58	..
25¾	Frant ...	6 29	7 24	..	..	..	..		8 37	..	..	..	..		..	..	1142	..	..		..	2 21	..	..	..	3 52	..	..	5 3	..
—	Tunbridge Wells West ... dep	..	..	..	..	..	..	8 25	..	..	..	9 5	..	9 37	..	..	..	..	..	1 32	..	..	..	..	3 33	..	..	..	..	..
28¼	Tunbridge Wells Central ...	6 36	7 31	..	7 44	8 18	..	8 30	8 44	9 1	..	9 12	9 26	9 44	..	11 4	1150	..	..	1 40	..	2 2[illegible]	..	3 2	3 40	4 1	..	..	5 10	..
29¾	High Brooms ...	6 40	7 35	..	..	..	..	8 34	..	..	..	..	..	9 48	..	..	1154	..	..	..	..	2 32	..	..	3 45	4 6	..	..	5 14	..
33	Tonbridge 53, 249 ... arr	6 47	7 42	..	7 53	..	..	8 41	8 53	..	..	9 23	..	9 55	..	1113	12 1	..	..	1 49	..	2 39	..	..	3 52	4 14	..	..	5 21	..
53	249 East Croydon ... arr	8 9	..	..	9 5	..	..	..	10 9	..	..	1038	..	1147	..	..	1 49	..	..	3 18	..	..	..	..	5 18	..	..	..	6 27	..
—	Tonbridge ... dep	6 48	..	7 45	7 55	..	..	..	8 55	..	9 19	..	..	..	1032	1115	..	..	1235	..	1 56	..	..	..	..	4 18	..	..	..	5 24
40½	Sevenoaks (Tub's Hill) ...	7 6	..	8 4	8 15	..	..	..	9 12	..	9 38	..	9 50	..	1053	..	..	..	1253	..	2 15	..	..	..	..	..	..	..	..	5 43
40¾	Orpington 130, 147 ... arr	7③27	..	..	..	..	..	..	..	..	..	..	..	..	..	..	..	..	..	..	..	..	..	..	..	..	..	..	..	6③7
60¼	London Bridge ... arr	7③57	..	8 32	..	..	..	..	..	..	10 9	..	1017	..	1122	..	..	..	1 22	..	2 45	..	..	..	..	..	..	..	..	6③36
61½	Cannon Street ... "	8③0	..	..	8 47	9 9	..	..	9 43	9 49	1014	..	..	..	..	..	..	..	..	..	..	..	..	..	..	..	..	..	..	6③40
61¾	Waterloo ... "	..	..	8 38	..	..	..	..	..	..	..	..	1023	..	1130	12 1	..	..	1 30	..	2 51	..	..	3 54	..	5 6	..	..	..	..
62¼	Charing Cross ... "	..	..	8 42	..	..	..	..	..	..	..	..	1027	..	1134	12 5	..	..	1 35	..	2 55	..	..	3 58	..	5 10	..	..	..	..

③ Third class only. **A** Over ½ mile to Bexhill Cen. Sta. V Dep. 5 36 a.m **R** Refreshment Car Hastings to London.

For Continuation of Trains see page 56, for Sunday Trains page 57.

HASTINGS, BEXHILL WEST, TUNBRIDGE WELLS, ORPINGTON, and LONDON

Up — Mondays to Fridays—*continued*

Up	p.m	p.m	p.m	p.m Through Train, Brighton to Tonbridge, page 241	p.m	p.m	p.m	p.m	p.m	p.m Through Train, Eastbourne to Tonbridge, page 242	p.m	p.m	p.m	p.m Through Train, Brighton to Tonbridge, page 242	ngt. (3) Via Redhill page 250	
Hastings dep	..	5 10	..		..	..	..	..	7 40		..	9 10	..			..
St. Leonards (Warr. Sq.)	..	5 13	..		..	..	..	..	7 43		..	9 13	..			..
West St. Leonards	..	5 17	..		..	..	..	..	7 47		..	9 17	..		..	..
Bexhill West dep	..	5 13	..		..	7 10	..	..	7 35		..	9 5	..		..	..
Sidley	..	5 15	..		..	7 12	..	..	7 37		..	9 11	..		..	..
Crowhurst	..	5 24	..		..	7 20	..	..	7 54		..	9 24	..		..	..
Battle	..	5 30	..		..	..	..	..	8 0		..	9 30	..		..	..
Mountfield Halt	..	5 35	..		..	..	..	..	8 5		..	9 35	..		..	..
Robertsbridge	..	5 43	..		..	..	..	..	8 13		..	9 42	..		..	..
Etchingham	..	5 50	..		..	..	..	..	8 19		..	9 48	..			..
Stonegate	..	5 57	..		..	..	..	..	8 26		..	9 55	..			..
Wadhurst	..	6 7	..		..	..	..	..	8 36		..	10 5	..			..
Frant	..	6 13	..		..	..	..	..	8 42		..	1011	..			..
Tunbridge Wells West dep	5 53	..	6 29	7 0	..	..	8 6	..	..	9 5	..	..	..	10 44		..
Tunbridge Wells Central	5 59	6 21	6 35	7 6	..	..	8 12	..	8 51	9 10	..	1020	..	10 48		..
High Brooms	6 3	..	6 39	7 10	..	..	8 16	..	8 56	9 14	..	1025	..	10 52		..
Tonbridge 53, 249 arr	6 10	6 30	6 46	7 17	..	..	8 23	..	9 4	9 21	..	1032	..	10 59		..
249 East Croydon arr	7 19	..	..	8 48	..	..	9 48	..	..	1050	..	..	..	12(3)59	..	..
Tonbridge dep	..	6 34	..	..	7 41	..	..	8 34	9 8	..	9 53	..	10 38	..	12 7	..
Sevenoaks (Tub's Hill)	..	6 55	..	..	7 58	..	..	8 53	9 25	..	1011	..	10 58	..	..	..
Orpington 130, 147 arr	..	..	..	..	..	..	..	9(3)20	..	..	1025	..	11(3)20	..	..	..
London Bridge arr	..	7 24	..	..	8 28	..	..	9(3)51	9 52	..	1044	..	..	..	1 19	..
Cannon Street "	..	..	..	..	..	..	..	..	..	..	..	..	..	..	..	..
Waterloo "	..	7 33	..	..	8 36	..	..	9(3)55	9 59	..	1053	..	..	..	..	..
Charing Cross "	..	7 38	..	..	8 41	..	..	9(3)57	10 3	..	1058	..	..	..	..	..

Saturdays

Up	a.m	a.m	a.m	a.m	a.m		a.m Through Train, Eridge to Tonbridge page 239	a.m	a.m	a.m	R	a.m Through Train, Eridge to Tonbridge, page 240	a.m
Hastings dep	..	6 22	..	6 58	7 27	..		7 40	..	..	8 25		..
St. Leonards (Warr. Sq.)	..	6 25	..	7 0	7 29	..		7 43	..	..	8 28		..
West St. Leonards	..	6 30	..	7 4	7 33	..		7 47	..	..	8 32		..
Bexhill West dep	..	6 26	..	7 0	7 30	..		..	..	..	8 30		..
Sidley	..	6 28	..	7 2	7 32	..		..	..	..	8 32		..
Crowhurst	..	6 37	..	7 11	7 41	..		7 54	..	..	8 41		..
Battle	..	6 43	..	..	..	..		8 0	..	..	8 47		..
Mountfield Halt	..	6 48	..	..	..	..		..	..	..	..		..
Robertsbridge	..	6 55	..	..	..	..		8 9	..	..	8 56		..
Etchingham	..	7 1	..	..	7 57	..		8 15	..	..	9 2		..
Stonegate	..	7 8	..	..	..	..		8 22	..	..	..		..
Wadhurst	6 24	7 18	..	..	..	..		8 31	..	..	9 16		..
Frant	6 29	7 24	..	..	..	..		8 37	..	..	..		..
Tunbridge Wells West dep	..	..	..	..	..	..	8 25	..	..	9 7	..	9 37	..
Tunbridge Wells Central	6 36	7 31	..	7 44	8 18	..	8 30	8 44	..	9 12	9 26	9 44	..
High Brooms	6 40	7 35	..	..	..	..	8 34	..	..	..	..	9 48	..
Tonbridge 53, 249 arr	6 47	7 42	..	7 53	..	..	8 41	8 53	..	9 23	..	9 55	..
249 East Croydon arr	8 9	..	..	9 5	..	..	..	10 9	..	1036	..	1147	..
Tonbridge dep	6 48	..	7 45	7 55	..	..	..	8 55	9 19	..	..	..	1032
Sevenoaks (Tub's Hill)	7 6	..	8 4	8 15	..	..	..	9 12	9 38	..	9 50	..	1053
Orpington 130, 147 arr	7(3)27	..	..	..	..	..	..	..	..	..	..	..	..
London Bridge arr	7(3)57	..	8 32	..	..	..	..	..	10 9	..	1017	..	1122
Cannon Street "	8(3)10	..	..	8 47	9 9	..	..	9 43	1014	..	..	..	..
Waterloo "	..	..	8 38	..	..	..	..	..	..	..	1023	..	1130
Charing Cross "	..	..	8 42	..	..	..	..	..	..	..	1027	..	1134

Up — Saturdays—*continued*

Up	R	a.m	a.m		p.m	p.m	p.m Through Train, Brighton to Tonbridge, page 240	p.m.	p.m	p.m	p.m	p.m		p.m	p.m
Hastings dep	1010	1040	1115	..	..	..		..	1 20	2 10	..	..	..	2 56	3 30
St. Leonards (Warr. Sq.)	1013	1043	1118	..	..	..		..	1 23	2 13	..	..	..	3 0	3 33
West St. Leonards	1018	1047	1122	..	..	..		..	1 27	2 18	..	..	..	3 4	3 37
Bexhill West dep	1014	1040	1115	..	..	1225		..	1 22	2 10	..	..	..	2 58	..
Sidley	1016	1042	1117	..	..	1227		..	1 24	2 12	..	..	..	3 0	..
Crowhurst	1026	1055	1129	..	..	1235		..	1 34	2 26	..	..	..	3 11	..
Battle	..	11 1	..	..	..	..		..	1 40	..	..	..	..	3 17	..
Mountfield Halt	..	11 6	..	..	..	..		..	1 45	..	..	..	..	3 23	..
Robertsbridge	1038	1113	..	..	..	..		..	1 52	2 38	..	..	..	3 31	..
Etchingham	..	1120	..	..	..	..		..	1 58	..	..	..	..	3 37	..
Stonegate	..	1127	..	..	..	..		..	2 5	..	..	..	..	3 44	..
Wadhurst	..	1136	..	..	..	..		..	2 15	..	..	..	..	3 54	..
Frant	..	1142	..	..	..	..		..	2 21	..	..	..	..	4 0	..
Tunbridge Wells West dep	..	..	..	..	..	..	1 27	..	..	..	3 12	..	..	..	..
Tunbridge Wells Central	11 4	1150	12 5	..	..	..	1 33	..	2 28	3 2	3 16	..	..	4 9	4 18
High Brooms	..	1154	..	..	..	..	..	..	2 32	..	3 20	..	..	4 13	..
Tonbridge 53, 249 arr	1113	12 1	..	..	..	..	1 42	..	2 39	..	3 27	..	..	4 20	..
249 East Croydon arr	..	1 49	..	..	..	..	3 18	..	4 4	..	..	..	..	5 50	..
Tonbridge dep	1115	..	..	..	1228	..	..	1 50	..	..	..	4 0	..	..	..
Sevenoaks (Tub's Hill)	..	..	..	..	1245	..	..	2 11	..	..	..	4 17	..	..	..
Orpington 130, 147 arr	..	..	..	..	..	..	..	..	..	..	..	4(3)46	..	..	..
London Bridge arr	..	..	..	..	1 14	..	..	2 39	..	..	..	5(3)19	..	..	..
Cannon Street "	..	..	..	..	..	..	..	..	..	..	..	..	..	..	..
Waterloo "	12 1	..	1255	..	1 20	..	..	2 45	..	3 54	..	5(3)23	..	..	5 14
Charing Cross "	12 5	..	1 3	..	1 24	..	..	2 50	..	3 58	..	5(3)26	..	..	5 19

Up	p.m	p.m	p.m	p.m Through Train, Brighton to Tonbridge, page 241	p.m		p.m	p.m	p.m	p.m Through Train, Eastbourne to Tonbridge, page 242	p.m	p.m	p.m Through Train, Brighton to Tonbridge, page 242	ngt. (3) Via Redhill page 250
Hastings dep	..	5 10	..		..	..	..	..	7 40		..	9 10		
St. Leonards (Warr. Sq.)	..	5 13	..		..	..	..	..	7 43		..	9 12		
West St. Leonards	..	5 17	..		..	..	..	..	7 47		..	9 17		..
Bexhill West dep	4 50	5 13	..		..	..	..	..	7 40		..	9 5		..
Sidley	4 52	5 15	..		..	..	..	..	7 42		..	9 11		..
Crowhurst	5 0	5 24	..		..	..	..	..	7 54		..	9 24		..
Battle	..	5 30	..		..	..	..	..	8 0		..	9 30		..
Mountfield Halt	..	5 35	..		..	..	..	..	8 5		..	9 35		..
Robertsbridge	..	5 43	..		..	..	..	..	8 13		..	9 42		
Etchingham	..	5 50	..		..	..	..	..	8 19		..	9 48		
Stonegate	..	5 57	..		..	..	..	..	8 26		..	9 55		
Wadhurst	..	6 7	..		..	..	..	..	8 36		..	10 5		
Frant	..	6 13	..		..	..	..	..	8 42		..	10 11		
Tunbridge Wells West dep	..	..	6 29	6 55	..	..	8 6	..	..	9 5	..	..	10 44	
Tunbridge Wells Central	..	6 21	6 35	7 1	..	..	8 12	..	8 51	9 10	..	10 20	10 48	
High Brooms	..	..	6 39	7 5	..	..	8 16	..	8 56	9 14	..	10 25	10 52	
Tonbridge 53, 249 arr	..	6 30	6 46	7 12	..	..	8 23	..	9 4	9 21	..	10 32	10 59	
249 East Croydon arr	..			8 48			9 48	..	..	10 50	..	..	12(3)59	
Tonbridge dep	..	6 34	..	..	7 41	..	..	8 34	9 8	..	9 53	10 38	..	12 7
Sevenoaks (Tub's Hill)	..	6 55	..	..	7 58	..	..	8 53	9 25	..	1011	10 58	..	..
Orpington 130, 147 arr	..	..	..	..	..	..	..	9(3)20	..	..	1025	11(3)20	..	..
London Bridge arr	..	7 24	..	..	8 28	..	..	9(3)51	9 52	..	1044	..	..	1 19
Cannon Street "	..	..	..	..	..	..	..	..	..	..	..	..	..	..
Waterloo "	..	7 33	..	..	8 36	..	..	9(3)55	9 59	..	1053	..	..	..
Charing Cross "	..	7 38	..	..	8 41	..	..	9(3)57	10 3	..	1058	..	..	..

(3) Third class only. R Refreshment Car Hastings to London

For Sunday Trains, see page 57

HASTINGS, BEXHILL WEST, TUNBRIDGE WELLS, ORPINGTON, and LONDON

Up	Sundays																										
	a.m	a.m		a.m	a.m		p.m (Refreshment Car)	p.m	p.m.		p.m	p.m	p.m	p.m.		p.m (Through Train, Brighton to Tonbridge, page 243)	p.m	p.m (Through Train, Eastbourne to Tonbridge, page243)		p.m	p.m	p.m	p.m.	p.m	p.m		p.m
Hastings ......dep	7 0	..	..	9 10	10 40	..	..	..	..	..	1 40	..	4 50	..	..		..	..	..	..	6 58	7 25	..	8 40	..	..	..
St. Leonards (Warr. Sq.)	7 3	..	..	9 13	10 43	..	..	..	..	..	1 43	..	4 53	..	..		..	..	..	..	7 1	7 28	..	8 43	..	..	..
West St. Leonards	7 7	..	..	9 17	10 47	..	..	..	..	..	1 47	..	4 57	..	..		..	..	..	..	7 5	7 32	..	8 47	..	..	..
Bexhill West ......dep	7 0	..	..	9 12	10 40	..	..	..	..	..	1 40	..	4 50	..	..		..	..	..	..	7 0	7 25	..	8 35	..	..	9 22
Sidley	7 2	..	..	9 14	10 42	..	..	..	..	..	1 42	..	4 52	..	..		..	..	..	..	7 2	7 27	..	8 37	..	..	9 24
Crowhurst	7 14	..	..	9 24	10 55	..	..	..	..	..	1 56	..	5 5	..	..		..	..	..	..	7 15	7 40	..	8 54	..	..	9 32
Battle	7 20	..	..	9 30	11 1	..	..	..	..	..	2 2	..	..	..	..		..	..	..	..	7 21	..	..	9 0	..	..	..
Mountfield Halt	..	..	..	9 35	11 5	..	..	..	..	..	2 8	..	..	..	..		..	..	..	..	7 26	..	..	9 5	..	..	..
Robertsbridge	7 30	..	..	9 42	11 12	..	..	..	..	..	2 15	..	5 17	..	..		..	..	..	..	7 34	7 52	..	9 13	..	..	..
Etchingham	7 37	..	..	9 50	11 18	..	..	..	..	..	2 21	..	..	..	..		...	..	..	..	7 40	..	..	9 20	..	..	..
Stonegate	7 44	..	..	9 58	11 25	..		..	..	..	2 28	..	..	..	..		..	..	..	..	7 47	..	..	9 27	..	..	..
Wadhurst	7 54	..	..	10 8	11 35	..		..	..	..	2 38	..	..	..	..		..	..	..	..	7 57	..	..	9 37	..	..	..
Frant	8 0	..	..	10 14	11 41	..		..	..	..	2 44	..	..	..	..		..	..	..	..	8 3	..	..	9 43	..	..	..
Tunbridge Wells West ...dep	..	..				.		1 18	..	..	..	4 20	..	6 15	..	7 33	..	7 50	..	..	..	..	..	..	..	..	..
Tunbridge Wells Central	8 7	..	..	10 21	11 48	..		1 22	..	..	2 52	4 27	5 43	6 21	..	7 37	..	7 55	..	..	8 11	8 20	..	9 50	..	..	..
High Brooms	8 11	..	..	..	11 52	..		1 26	..	..	2 56	4 31	..	..	..	7 41	..	7 59	..	..	..	..	..	9 54	..	..	..
Tonbridge 53, 249 ......arr	8 18	..	..	10 30	11 59	..		1 33	..	..	3 3	4 38	5 52	6 30	..	7 48	..	8 7	..	..	8 21	..	..	10 1	..	..	..
249 East Croydon ......arr	9 48	.	..	11Z49	.	.		3 3	..	..	..	..	7 4	8 52	..	..	.	..	..	..	9 48	..	..	12③59	..	..	..
Tonbridge ......dep	..	8 25	..	10 33	12 2	..	1221	..	1 38	..	3 5	5 0	5 56	6 33	..	..	7 56	..	..	8 12	..	..	8 40	..	10 5	..	..
Sevenoaks (Tub's Hill)	..	8 43	..	10 53	12 21	..	1239	..	1 57	..	3 21	5 17	..	6 52	..	..	..	..	..	..	..	..	8 59	..	..	..	..
Orpington 130, 147 ......arr	..	8 56	..	..	12③46	..	..	..	2③18	..	3③50	5③46	..	7③14	..	..	8 24	..	..	..	..	..	9③20	..	..	..	..
London Bridge ......arr	..	9 15	..	11 20	..	..	1 12	..	2 27	..	3 51	6③18	6 37	7 22	..	..	8 43	..	..	8 54	..	9 9	9 35	..	10 50	..	..
Cannon Street ...... "	..	..	..	..	..	..	..	..	..	..	..	..	..	..	..	..	..	..	..	..	..	..	..	..	..	..	..
Waterloo ...... "	..	9 23	..	11 27	..	..	1 20	..	2 35	..	3 59	6③21	6 43	7 28	..	..	8 49	..	..	9 0	..	9 16	9 42	..	10 56	..	..
Charing Cross ...... "	..	9 28	..	11 31	..	..	1 24	..	2 39	..	4 3	6③25	6 47	7 33	..	..	8 54	..	..	9 5	.	9 20	9 46	..	11 1	..	..

③ Third class only Z Until 21st March, 1948, inclusive

LOCAL TRAINS and Intermediate Stations Tonbridge, Sevenoaks and London, page 130

OTHER TRAINS Tonbridge and London, 249—Tunbridge Wells W. and London, 239—Hastings, Bexhill Cen. and London, 197.

QUEENBOROUGH and LEYSDOWN—Third class only

Miles	Down	Week Days only													
		a.m		a.m		a.m		p.m							
	Queenborough ......dep	6 20	..	8 16	..	1055	..	4 22	..	..	..	..	..	..	..
1½	Sheerness East	6 35	..	8 21	..	11 0	..	4 27	..	..	..	..	..	..	..
2½	East Minster-on-Sea	6 42	..	8 27	..	11 6	..	4 33	..	..	..	..	..	..	..
3¼	Minster-on-Sea	6 45	..	8 31	..	1110	..	4 37	..	..	..	..	..	..	..
4¼	Brambledown Halt	6 50	..	8 35	..	1114	..	4 41	..	..	..	..	..	..	..
5½	Eastchurch	6 58	..	8 41	..	1119	..	4 47	..	..	..	..	..	..	..
7	Harty Road Halt	7 3	..	8 45	..	1124	..	4 52	..	..	..	..	..	..	..
8¼	Leysdown ......arr	7 9	..	8 52	..	1130	..	4 57	..	..	..	..	..	..	..

Miles	Up	Week Days only									
		a.m		a.m		a.m		p.m (Saturdays excepted)		p.m (Saturdays only)	
	Leysdown ......dep	7 15	..	9 5	..	1136	..	5 5	..	5 10	..
1¾	Harty Road Halt	7 20	..	9 9	..	1140	..	5 9	..	5 15	..
3¼	Eastchurch	7 25	..	9 14	..	1145	..	5 14	..	5V24	..
4½	Brambledown Halt	7 30	..	9 19	..	1150	..	5 19	..	5 31	..
5½	Minster-on-Sea	7 34	..	9 23	..	1154	..	5 23	..	5 35	..
6¼	East Minster-on Sea	7 37	..	9 26	..	1157	..	5 26	..	5 38	..
7¼	Sheerness East	7 44	..	9 33	..	12 4	..	5 33	..	5 45	..
8¾	Queenborough 66 ...arr	7 49	..	9 39	..	1210	..	5 39	..	5 49	..

V Arr. 5 20 p.m

Printed and Published by—HENRY BLACKLOCK & Co. LTD., London, and Albert Square, Manchester, 2.

LONDON, ASHFORD, LYDD TOWN, NEW ROMNEY, RYE, and ORE

Miles from Ashford	Down	Week Days a.m	a.m	a.m	a.m	a.m SX	a.m SO	a.m	a.m SO	a.m SX	a.m	p.m SX	a.m SO	p.m SO	p.m	p.m
	34 Charing Cross ..... dep	..	..	..	..	..	7Ⓣ23	9 15	..	1115	1115	..	1155	..	1 15	..
	34 Waterloo ..... "	..	..	..	..	..	7Ⓣ25	9 17	..	1117	1117	..	..	..	1y18	..
	34 Cannon Street ..... "	..	5Ⓣ8	..	..	..	..	..	..	..	..	..	..	..	1 SO 2	..
	34 London Bridge ..... "	3Ⓣ45	5Ⓣ12	..	..	..	7Ⓣ29	..	..	..	..	..	12 2	..	..	..
	34 Victoria ..... "	..	..	7 18	..	..	..	..	9 18	..	1118	..	..	..	..	..
—	Ashford (Kent) ..... dep	5 45	8 0	9 10	..	..	9 48	1045	1155	1252	1 12	..	1 50	..	2 52	..
5½	Ham Street and Orlestone	5 53	8 8	9 20	..	..	9 58	1053	..	1 1	1 20	..	..	..	3 0	..
8½	Appledore	5 59	8 14	9 26	..	..	10 4	1059	..	1 7	1 26	1 55	2 2	2 10	3 6	..
—	Appledore ..... dep	6 0	8 20	..	..	10 10	10 10	1134	..	1 9	..	..	2 3	..	..	..
11	Brookland	6 7	8 27	..	..	10 17	10 17	1140	..	1 17	..	..	2 11	..	..	..
15¼	Lydd Town	6 20	8 40	..	..	10 28	10 28	1152	..	1 29	..	..	2 23	..	..	..
18¼	Lydd-on-Sea H	6 35	8 48	..	..	10 38	10 38	12 0	..	1 37	..	..	2 31	..	..	..
20½	Greatstone-on-Sea	6 42	8 55	..	..	10 44	10 44	12 7	..	1 44	..	..	2 38	..	..	..
22	New Romney L ..... arr	6 46	8 59	..	..	10 48	10 48	1212	..	1 49	..	..	2 42	..	..	..
15¼	Rye	..	8 26	9 37	9 50	..	10 15	1110	1215	..	1 38	2 6	..	2 21	3 17	4 8
17¾	Winchelsea	..	8 31	..	9 54	..	..	1115	1220	..	..	2 11	..	2 26	3 22	4 12
19¾	Snailham Halt	..	..	..	10 0	..	..	1120	..	..	..	2 17	..	2 32	..	4 18
21½	Doleham Halt ..... [Halt	..	8 39	..	10 5	..	..	1125	..	..	..	2 22	..	2 37	..	4 22
22¾	Three Oaks and Guestling	..	8 43	..	1010	..	..	1130	..	..	..	2 27	..	2 42	..	4 27
25½	Ore	..	8 49	9 53	1016	..	..	1137	1235	..	1 54	2 34	..	2 49	..	4 34
26½	Hastings 55, 197 ..... arr	..	8 53	9 57	1020	..	10 31	1141	1239	..	1 58	2 38	..	2 53	3 38	4 38

Down	Weekdays—continued p.m	p.m	p.m	p.m SX	p.m SO	p.m	p.m	p.m	Sundays a.m	a.m	a.m	p.m	p.m
34 Charing Cross ..... dep	3 15	..	..	..	4 30	6SO15	..	7 34	7 15	9 32	1110	—	8 15
34 Waterloo ..... "	3 17	..	..	..	4 32	6SO17	..	7 37	7 17	9 34	1113	..	8 17
34 Cannon Street ..... "	..	..	..	5 0	..	6SX18	..	..	..	..	..	..	..
34 London Bridge ..... "	..	..	..	..	4 39	..	..	7 45	7 24	9 41	1120	..	8 23
34 Victoria ..... "	..	..	..	..	..	5SX53	..	7 20	7 18	9 18	..	5 18	..
Ashford (Kent) ..... dep	4 44	4 55	..	6 12	6 22	7 52	8 59	9 42	9 45	1150	1 10	7 15	9 50
Ham Street and Orlestone	4 52	..	..	6 20	6 30	8 0	..	9 50	9 53	1158	1 18	7 23	9 58
Appledore	4 57	5 6	..	6 28	6 36	8 6	..	9 58	9 59	12 4	1 24	7 29	10 4
Appledore ..... dep	4 58	..	..	6 33	6 41	8 11	..	10 9	..	..	..	..	..
Brookland	5 6	..	..	6 41	6 49	8 19	..	1017	..	..	..	..	..
Lydd Town	5 18	..	..	6 53	7 1	8 31	..	1026	..	..	..	..	..
Lydd-on-Sea H	5 26	..	..	7 1	7 9	8 39	..	1037	..	..	..	..	..
Greatstone-on-Sea	5 32	..	..	7 8	7 16	8 47	..	1044	..	..	..	..	..
New Romney L ..... arr	5 38	..	..	7 12	7 20	8 51	..	1048	..	..	..	..	..
Rye	..	5 17	6 8	6 39	6 47	8 17	9 19	1011	1011	1216	1 36	7 41	1017
Winchelsea	..	5 22	6 12	..	..	8 22	..	1016	..	1221	..	7 47	1022
Snailham Halt	..	..	6 18	..	..	..	..	..	..	..	..	..	..
Doleham Halt ..... [Halt	..	..	6 23	..	..	..	..	Bb	..	..	..	..	..
Three Oaks and Guestling	..	..	6z27	..	..	..	..	..	..	..	..	..	..
Ore	..	5 36	6 36	..	..	8 36	9 36	1032	1027	1236	..	8 3	1037
Hastings 55, 197 ..... arr	..	5 40	6 40	..	..	8 40	9 40	1037	1031	1240	1 55	8 7	1042

Ⓣ Third class only

Bb Stops to set down on informing the Guard at the previous *stopping* station

H For Dungeness
L New Romney & Littlestone-on Sea
SO or SO Saturdays only

SX or SX Saturdays excepted
y 1 minute *earlier* on Saturdays
z 1 minute later on Saturdays

For OTHER TRAINS between Ore and Hastings see page 197

ORE, RYE, NEW ROMNEY, LYDD TOWN, ASHFORD, and LONDON

Miles	Up	Week Days a.m	a.m	a.m	a.m	a.m	a.m.	a.m	a.m	p.m	p.m.	p.m SO	p.m	p.m	p.m. SX	p.m SO	p.m	p.m	p.m
—	**Hastings** dep	6 20	7 25	5 8	8 38	..	10 8	..	11 42	12 50	..	1 28	3 0	..	3 28	3 39	4 49	5 10	..
¾	**Ore** [Halt	6 23	7 28	8 12	..	..	10 11	..	11 45	12 53	..	1 31	3 3	..	3 31	3 42	4 52	5 13	..
3¼	Three Oaks and Guestling	..	..	8 20	..	..	..	..	11 53	1 2	..	1 40	3 11	..	..	..	5 0	..	..
4¾	Doleham Halt	..	..	8 25	..	..	..	..	11 58	1 6	..	1 44	3 16	..	..	..	5 4	..	..
5½	Snailham Halt	..	..	8 28	..	..	..	..	..	1 9	..	..	3 19	..	..	..	5 8	..	..
9	Winchelsea	6 38	7 44	8 34	..	..	..	..	12 5	1 15	..	1 52	3 25	..	..	..	5 13	..	..
11	Rye	6 43	7 49	8 40	8 59	..	10 27	..	12 10	1 21	..	1 57	3 30	..	3 48	3 58	5 19	5 29	..
—	Mls New Romney L dep	6 7	7 14	..	..	9 20	..	10 54	..	..	1 5	..	..	2 57	..	..	..	..	5 44
—	1½ Greatstone-on-Sea	6 11	7 18	..	..	9 24	..	10 58	..	..	1 9	..	..	3 1	..	..	..	..	5 48
—	3¾ Lydd-on-Sea H	6 18	7 25	..	..	9 31	..	11 4	..	..	1 16	..	..	3 8	..	..	..	..	5 55
—	6¼ Lydd Town	6 26	7 32	..	..	9 39	..	11 12	..	..	1 28	..	..	3 16	..	..	..	..	6 4
—	11 Brookland	6 38	7 45	..	..	9 51	..	11 24	..	..	1 41	..	..	3 29	..	..	..	..	6 17
—	13½ Appledore arr	6 45	7 52	..	..	9 59	..	11 32	..	..	1 48	..	..	3 36	..	..	..	..	6 23
17	Appledore	6 54	8 2	..	..	10 1	10 38	11 34	12 21	1 32	1 49	2 8	..	3 37	3 58	4 10	..	5 40	6 24
20	Ham Street and Orlestone	7 1	8 9	..	..	10 8	..	11 39	12 27	..	1 55	..	..	3 43	..	..	..	5 46	6 30
26	**Ashford** B 34, 43 arr	7 12	8 21	..	9 22	10 20	10 52	11 52	12 38	..	2 7	2 24	..	3 54	4 14	4 26	..	5 57	6 41
8[illegible]	43 Victoria arr	9 14	..	..	..	..	12 59	1S059	2 59	..	..	..	..	5SX39	6 24	6 59	..	7 59	..
8[illegible]	43 London Bridge "	..	10 9	..	11 22	..	1S014	..	2N45	..	..	..	..	..	6③36	6*47	..	..	8 28
81	43 Cannon Street "	9 24	9 30	..	..	..	..	..	..	..	..	..	..	..	6③40	..	..	..	..
81½	43 Waterloo "	..	..	..	11 30	..	1S020	..	2N51	..	3 42	3 42	..	..	..	..	..	..	8 36
82¼	43 Charing Cross "	..	..	..	11 34	..	1S024	..	2N55	..	3z46	3 47	..	..	..	..	..	..	8 41

Up	Week Days—continued p.m	p.m SO	p.m SX	p.m	p.m	Sundays a.m	a.m	p.m	p.m	p.m
Hastings dep	..	6 48	6 54	7 40	9 30	6 45	9 36	5 36	6 48	8 38
Ore [Halt	..	6 51	6 57	7 43	9 34	6 49	9 29	5 39	6 51	8 41
Three Oaks and Guestling	..	..	..	7 51	9 42	..	..	..	..	..
Doleham Halt	..	..	..	7 56	Bb	..	..	..	..	..
Snailham Halt	..	..	..	7 59	..	..	..	..	..	..
Winchelsea	..	7 7	7 1[illegible]	8 5	9 50	7 4	..	5 54	..	..
Rye	6 55	7 12	7 18	8 11	9 55	7 10	9 55	5 59	7 7	8 57
New Romney L dep	..	..	..	7 25	9 14	..	..	..	..	..
Greatstone-on-Sea	..	..	..	7 29	9 18	..	..	..	..	..
Lydd-on-Sea H	..	..	..	7 35	9 25	..	..	..	..	..
Lydd Town	..	..	..	7 43	9 33	..	..	..	..	..
Brookland	..	..	..	7 55	9 45	..	..	..	..	..
Appledore arr	..	..	..	8 3	9 54	..	..	..	..	..
Appledore	7 4	7 23	7 29	8 23	10 6	7 23	10 6	6 11	7 18	9 8
Ham Street and Orlestone	..	..	..	8 29	10 12	7 29	..	6 17	..	9 14
Ashford B 34, 43 arr	7 18	7 39	7 44	8 40	10 23	7 40	10 20	6 28	7 32	9 25
43 Victoria arr	..	9 59	9 59	..	..	..	..	8 59	..	..
43 London Bridge "	..	..	..	10 44	1Z19	9 15	1 12	8 5	9 35	10 50
43 Cannon Street "	..	..	..	..	..	..	..	..	..	..
43 Waterloo "	..	..	..	10 53	..	9 23	1 20	8 12	9 42	10 56
43 Charing Cross "	..	..	..	10 58	..	9 28	1 24	8 17	9 46	11 1

* Via Redhill, page 249
③ Third class only
B Ashford (Kent)
Bb Stops to set down on informing the Guard at the previous stopping Station.

H For Dungeness
L New Romney and Littlestone-on-Sea

N Arr. London Bridge 2 9, Waterloo 2 15 and Charing Cross 2 20 p.m. on Saturdays
SO or S0 Saturdays only

SX or SX Saturdays excepted
Z Via Redhill, page 250. Third class only
z 1 min. later on Saturdays

For **OTHER TRAINS** between Hastings and Ore. see page 158

For other Trains to Dover, Deal, &c., see pages 34 to 42

LONDON, SHEERNESS-ON-SEA, MARGATE, RAMSGATE, DOVER, DEAL, and SANDWICH

Week Days

Miles from Victoria	Mls frm C.Cross	DOWN	a.m	a.m	a.m	a.m	a.m	a.m	(3)		a.m	a.m		a.m	a.m	a.m	a.m	a.m (3)	a.m (3)	a.m	a.m	a.m	a.m	a.m	a.m	a.m	a.m	a.m	a.m (3)	a.m	a.m	a.m
		Victoria dep	3 H0								5 10				6 18					6 40			7 18							8 35		8 35
		Charing Cross dep	(3)						5 11		Calls Herne Hill at 5 20 a.m				Mondays only					Mondays only										Saturdays excepted		Saturdays only
	½	Waterloo "							5 13																							
	—	Cannon Street "														5 50		6 9	6 9					7 0		7 0			8 1			
—	1¾	London Bridge "	3 10						5 18							5 57		6 14	6 14					7 8		7 7			8 4			
—	5	New Cross "							5 26									6 20	6 20													
—	9½	Woolwich Arsenal dep							5 36							6 15		6 36	6 36					7 0					8 18			
—	17	Dartford "	3 41						5 59							6 34		6 57	6 57					7 38		7 38			8 35		Saturdays excepted	
—	24	Gravesend Central "	4 1						6 17							6 48		7 15	7 15					7 52		7 52			8 51			
10¾	—	Bromley South dep									5 38				6 36					7 0			7 35							8 56		8 56
17¾	—	Swanley "									5 54									7 11			7 47							8 47		8 44
—	—	Strood dep	4 16		5 24				6 31							7 5		7 28	7 29					8 14		8 15			9 5			
33¾	31½	Rochester	4 23		5 29				6 35		6 30					7 9		7 32	7 32	7 36			8 14	8 20		8 20		Saturdays only	9 9			
34½	32½	Chatham arr	4 26		5 32				6 37		6 33				7 8	7 12		7 34	7 34	7 39			8 16	8 23		8 23			9 11	9 30		9 29
		Chatham dep	4 28		5 33			5 45			6 40				7 12	7 17		7 43		Calls Herne Hill at 6 47 a.m	7 43			8 26		8 26				9 32	9 36	9 31
36	34	Gillingham (Kent)	4 36		5 37			5 49			6 48				7 17	7 24		7 48			7 48			8 33		8 33					9 43	
39	37	Rainham						5 55			6 54					7 30		7 54	Saturdays excepted		7 54			8 39		8 39						
41½	39½	Newington						6 1			7 0					7 36		8 0			8 0			8 45		8 45			Saturdays excepted			
44¾	42¾	Sittingbourne A arr	4 49					6 8			7 7					7 43		8 7			8 7			8 52		8 52					9 56	
—	—	Sittingbourne A dep	5 5	5 50				6 13			7 10					7 48		8 13			8 14			9 8				9 8			1020	
46¾	44¾	Kemsley Halt		5 56				6 18			7 15							8 22			8 22			9 13				9 13			1025	
48½	46½	Swale Halt		6 1							7 20													9 19				9 18				
50¾	48¾	Queenborough 57	5 18	6 6				6 27			7 25					7 59		8 30			8 30			9 24				9 24			1032	
52¾	50¾	Sheerness-on-Sea arr	5 26	6 15				6 33			7 33					8 12		8 37			8 37			9 30				9 30			1038	
—	—	Sittingbourne A dep	4 51	Stop							7 8					7 45						8 27		8 54		8 54					9 59	
48	46	Teynham									7 15					7 53		Saturdays only				8 33		9 1		9 1						
52	50	Faversham arr	5 3								7 24					8 2						8 42		9 10		9 10					1011	
—	—	Faversham dep	5 5								7 27						8 8							9 12		9 11						
59	57	Whitstable & Tankerton	5 19								7 41						8 18					Saturdays excepted.		9 24		9 24	Saturdays only			10 6		10 6
60½	58½	Chestfield and Swalecliffe									7 46	Saturdays excepted		Saturdays only			8 23				Saturdays excepted			9 29	Saturdays excepted	9 29						
62¾	60¾	Herne Bay [Halt	5 29								7 54						8 29							9 36		9 36				1016		1016
70¾	68¾	Birchington-on-Sea	5 46								8 8						8 42							9 49		9 49				1029		1029
72½	70½	Westgate-on-Sea	5 53								8 14						8 48							9 54		9 54				1035		1035
74	72	Margate	5 58								8 19						8 54							9 59		10 1				1040		1040
77½	75½	Broadstairs....[Ramsgate	6 15								8 32													10 9		10 9				1051		1051
78½	76½	Dumpton Park for East	6 21	a.m							8 38													1014		1014				1056		1056
79½	77½	Ramsgate arr	6 25	J							8 42													1018		1018				11 0		11 0
—	—	Faversham dep		5 10			6 12					7 35		7 35		8 11									9 18		9 18				1013	
55¼	3¼	Selling					6 20					7 41		7 41		8 19									9 24		9 26				1020	
61¼	59½	Canterbury East B		5 28		6 20	6 36					8 K6		8 5		8 33									9 37		9 40				1033	
64¾	62¾	Bekesbourne				6 25	6 44					8 12		8 12		8 39									9 43		9 46				1039	
67¾	65¾	Adisham C		5 39		6 31	6 51					8 19		8 19		8 45								Saturdays excepted	9 49	Saturdays only	9 52				1045	
68¾	66¾	Aylesham Halt [Halt				6 35	6 55					8 23		8 23		8 49									9 52		9 55				1049	
69¾	67¾	Snowdown and Nonington		5 45		6 39	6 59					8 27		8 27		8 53									9 56		9 59				1053	
71¾	69¾	Shepherd's Well		5 50		6 45	7 5					8 32		8 32		8 58									10 0		10 3				1058	
73½	71½	Stonehall and Lydden Halt				6 50	7 11					8 37		8 37		9 3									10 5		10 8				11 3	
75	73	Kearsney D		5 59		6 54	7 16					8 41		8 41		9 7									1010		1013				11 7	
77¼	75¼	Dover { Priory 43 arr		6 5		7 0	7 22					8 47		8 47		9 13									1016		1020				1113	
78½	76½	Dover { Marine "																														
79¾	77¾	Martin Mill for St Mar arr				7 22	8 11																		1048		1048				1147	
82½	80½	Walmer F [garet's Bay "				7 29	8 17																		1054		1054				1153	
84½	82½	Deal 34 "				7 34	8 22																		11 0		11 0				1158	
88½	86½	Sandwich 34 "				7 50	8 31																		1110		1110				12 7	

FOR NOTES, SEE PAGE 65

LONDON, SHEERNESS-ON-SEA, MARGATE, RAMSGATE, DOVER, DEAL, and SANDWICH

Week Days—*continued*

Down	a.m	a.m	a.m	3	a.m	p.m	a.m	p.m	a.m	p.m
Victoria .... dep	..	..	..	..	1035	..	1035	..	..	..
Charing Cross .... dep	..	9 42	..	9 50	Calls Herne Hill at 10 44 a.m	..	Calls Herne Hill 10 44 a.m	..	1042	..
Waterloo .... "	..	9 44	..	9 52		..		..	1044	..
Cannon Street .... "	..	..	..	..		..		..	..	..
London Bridge .... "	..	9 49	..	9 57		..		..	1049	..
New Cross .... "	..	..	..	10 4		..		..	..	..
Woolwich Arsenal .. dep	Saturdays only	10 2	..	..		..		..	11 2	Saturdays only
Dartford .... "		1015	..	1031		..		..	1115	
Gravesend Central .. "		1025	..	1049		..		..	1125	
Bromley South .... dep		..	..	..	1059	..	1059	..	..	
Swanley .... "		..	..	..	1047	..	1046	..	..	
Strood .... dep		1037	..	11 6	..	..	..	..	1137	
Rochester		1041	..	1110	..	..	..	..	1141	
Chatham .... arr	..	1043	..	1112	1133	..	1133	..	1144	..
Chatham .... dep	9 36	1050	..	Saturdays excepted	1134	..	1134	..	Saturdays only	12 5
Gillingham (Kent)	9 42	1054	..		..	..	..	..		12 9
Rainham	..	11 0	..		..	..	..	..		..
Newington	..	..	..		..	..	..	..		..
Sittingbourne A .... arr	9 55	11 9	..		1148	..	1148	..		1222
Sittingbourne A .... dep	1020	..	11 18		..	..	1151	..		..
Kemsley Halt	1025	..	11D23		..	..	1156	..		..
Swale Halt	..	..	11 31		..	..	..	..		..
Queenborough 57	1032	..	11 37		..	..	12 6	..		..
Sheerness-on-Sea .... arr	1038	..	11 42		..	..	1212	..		..
Sittingbourne A .... dep	9 58	1110	..	..	1149	..	1149	..	..	1223
Teynham	..	..	..	..	..	..	..	..	..	1230
Faversham .... arr	1011	1122	..	..	12 1	..	12 1	..	..	1239
Faversham .... dep	..	Saturdays excepted	..	..	12 3	Saturdays excepted	12 3	Saturdays only	..	..
Whitstable & Tankerton	..		..	..	1215		1215		..	..
Chestfield and Swalecliffe Halt	..		..	..	1220		1220		..	..
Herne Bay	..		..	..	1227		1227		..	..
Birchington-on-Sea	..		..	..	1240		1240		..	..
Westgate-on-Sea	..		..	..	1245		1245		..	..
Margate	..		..	..	1250		1250		..	..
Broadstairs	..		..	..	1 0		1 0		..	..
Dumpton Park for East Ramsgate	..		..	..	1 5		1 5		..	..
Ramsgate .... arr	..		..	..	1 9		1 9		..	..
Faversham .... dep	1013	..	..	..	Saturdays excepted	12 7	Saturdays only	12 5	..	1242
Selling	1020	..	..	..		1213		1211	..	..
Canterbury East B	1033	..	..	..		1227		1226	..	1 3
Bekesbourne	1039	..	..	..		1234		1232	..	1 9
Adisham C	1045	..	..	..		1240		1238	..	1 16
Aylesham Halt	1049	..	..	..		1244		1242	..	1 20
Snowdown & Nonington Halt	1053	..	..	..		1248		1246	..	1 24
Shepherd's Well	1058	..	..	..		1254		1252	..	1 30
Stonehall and Lydden Halt	11 3	..	..	..	..	1 0		1257	..	1 35
Kearsney D	11 7	..	..	..	..	1 4	..	1 1	..	1 39
Dover Priory 43 .... arr	1113	..	..	..	..	1 10	..	1 7	..	1 47
Dover Marine .... "	..	..	..	..	..	..	..	..	..	..
Martin Mill, for St. Margaret's Bay arr	1147	..	..	..	..	1 36	..	1 36	..	..
Walmer .... "	1153	..	..	..	..	1 42	..	1 42	..	..
Deal 34 .... "	1158	..	..	..	..	1 47	..	1 47	..	..
Sandwich 34 .... "	12 7	..	..	..	..	1 56	..	1 57	..	..

Down	3	a.m	p.m	a.m	a.m	p.m	a.m	a.m	p.m
Victoria .... dep	..	1118	..	1135	..	..	..	1150	..
Charing Cross .... dep	1050	..	..	..	1142	..	1142	Saturdays only	..
Waterloo .... "	1052	..	..	..	1144	..	1144		..
Cannon Street .... "	..	..	..	..	..	..	..		..
London Bridge .... "	1056	..	..	..	1149	..	1149		..
New Cross .... "	11 2	..	..	..	..	..	..		..
Woolwich Arsenal .. dep	..	..	Saturdays excepted	..	12 2	Saturdays excepted	12 2		..
Dartford .... "	1135	..		..	1215		1216		..
Gravesend Central .. "	1151	..		..	1225		1227		..
Bromley South .... dep	..	1135		1156	..		..	12 2	..
Swanley .... "	..	1146		1146	..		..	1221	..
Strood .... dep	12J4	..		..	1237		1238	..	Saturdays only
Rochester	12 8	..		..	1241		1242	..	
Chatham .... arr	1211	1216		1229	1243		1245	1247	
Chatham .... dep	..	Saturdays excepted	1220	1230	Saturdays excepted	1255	Saturdays only	1251	
Gillingham (Kent)	..		1225	..		1 0		1257	
Rainham	..		..	..		1 6		..	
Newington	..		..	Saturdays only		1 12		..	
Sittingbourne A .... arr	..		1238			1 19		1 9	
Sittingbourne A .... dep	..		1248			1 25		1 16	..
Kemsley Halt	..		1253			1 31		1 24	..
Swale Halt	..		1258			..		1 30	..
Queenborough 57	..		1 3			1 42		1 36	..
Sheerness-on-Sea .... arr	..		1 9			1 48		1 42	..
Sittingbourne A .... dep	..	..	1239			..	..	1 10	..
Teynham	..	..	1246	..		..	..	..	..
Faversham .... arr	..	..	1255	1253		..	..	1 22	..
Faversham .... dep	..	..	..	1254	..	..	..	..	1 30
Whitstable & Tankerton	..	..	..	1 6	..	..	..	..	1 41
Chestfield and Swalecliffe Halt	..	..	..	..	..	..	..	..	1 46
Herne Bay	..	..	..	1 15	..	..	..	..	1 53
Birchington-on-Sea	..	..	..	1 28	..	..	..	..	2 7
Westgate-on-Sea	..	..	..	1 33	..	..	..	..	2 14
Margate	..	..	..	1 38	..	..	..	..	2 19
Broadstairs	..	..	..	1 49	..	..	..	..	..
Dumpton Park for East Ramsgate	..	..	..	1 54	..	..	..	..	..
Ramsgate .... arr	..	..	..	1 58	..	..	..	..	..
Faversham .... dep	..	..	1257	Refreshment Car London to Ramsgate	..	..	..	1 25	..
Selling	..	..	..		..	..	..	1 32	..
Canterbury East B	..	..	1 14		..	..	..	1 46	..
Bekesbourne	..	..	1 20		..	..	..	1 52	..
Adisham C	..	..	1 26		..	..	..	1 58	..
Aylesham Halt	..	..	1 30		..	..	..	2 2	..
Snowdown & Nonington Halt	..	..	1 34		..	..	..	2 6	..
Shepherd's Well	..	..	1 38		..	..	..	2 11	..
Stonehall and Lydden Halt	..	..	1 43		..	..	..	2 16	..
Kearsney D	..	..	1 47		..	..	..	2 20	..
Dover Priory 43 .... arr	..	..	1 53		..	..	..	2 26	..
Dover Marine .... "	..	..	..		..	..	..	..	..
Martin Mill, for St. Margaret's Bay arr	..	..	..		..	..	..	2 52	..
Walmer .... "	..	..	..		..	..	..	2 59	..
Deal 34 .... "	..	..	..		..	..	..	3 5	..
Sandwich 34 .... "	..	..	1 ..		..	..	..	3 15	..

Down	p.m	p.m	p.m	p.m	p.m	p.m	p.m	p.m	p.m	p.m
Victoria .... dep	..	..	..	3	..	1235	..	..	..	..
Charing Cross .... dep	..	..	Saturdays only.	..	..	..	Saturdays only	..	1242	..
Waterloo .... "	..	..		..	..	Saturdays excepted		..	1244	..
Cannon Street .... "	..	1214		..	1245			..	..	1 15
London Bridge .... "	..	1217		..	Saturdays only			..	1248	Saturdays only
New Cross .... "	..	..		..				..	..	
Woolwich Arsenal .. dep	..	..		..				..	1 2	
Dartford .... "	..	..		1248				..	1 14	
Gravesend Central .. "	..	1254		4				..	1 24	
Bromley South .... dep	..	..	..	..		125[illegible]		..	..	
Swanley .... "	..	..	..	..		1250	..	..	..	
Strood .... dep	..	1 6	..	1 17		..	..	..	1 38	
Rochester	..	1 9	..	1 21		..	..	..	1 42	
Chatham .... arr	..	1 12	..	1 24	1 31	1 29	..	..	1 45	2 1
Chatham .... dep	1258	..	1 16	Saturdays only	1 32	1 31	1 45	..	Saturdays only	2 2
Gillingham (Kent)	1 2	..	1 21		Refreshment Car London to Ramsgate	1 37	1 49	..		Refreshment Car London to Ramsgate
Rainham	1 8	Saturdays only	..			..	..	..		
Newington	1 14		..			..	..	..		
Sittingbourne A .... arr	1 20		1 35			1 50	..	..		
Sittingbourne A .... dep	..		1 39			1 55	..	..		
Kemsley Halt	..		..			2 0	..	..		
Swale Halt	..		..			2 5	..	..		
Queenborough 57	..		1 51			2 10	..	..		
Sheerness-on-Sea .... arr	..		1 57			2 20	..	..		
Sittingbourne A .... dep	1 21		..	..		1 52	..	..	..	
Teynham	1 28		..	..		1 59	..	..	..	
Faversham .... arr	1 37		..	..		2 8	..	..	..	
Faversham .... dep	Saturdays only	..	..	..	..	2 10	..	Saturdays excepted	..	..
Whitstable & Tankerton		..	..	..	2 3	2 23	..		..	2 35
Chestfield and Swalecliffe Halt		..	..	..	2 8	2 28	..		..	2 40
Herne Bay		..	..	..	2 15	2 36	..		..	2 46
Birchington-on-Sea		..	..	..	..	2 50	..		..	2 58
Westgate-on-Sea		..	..	..	..	2 56	..		..	3 3
Margate		..	..	..	2 32	3 1	..		..	3 8
Broadstairs		..	..	..	2 44	3 13	..		..	3 19
Dumpton Park for East Ramsgate		..	..	..	2 49	3 18	..		..	3 24
Ramsgate .... arr		..	..	..	2 53	3 22	..		..	3 28
Faversham .... dep	..	..	..	..	..	..	..	2 18	..	..
Selling	..	..	..	..	..	Refreshment Car London to Ramsgate	..	2 24	..	..
Canterbury East B	..	..	..	..	..		..	2B50	..	..
Bekesbourne	..	..	..	..	..		..	2 55	..	..
Adisham C	..	..	..	..	..		..	3 1	..	..
Aylesham Halt	..	..	..	..	..		..	3 5	..	..
Snowdown & Nonington Halt	..	..	..	..	..		..	3 9	..	..
Shepherd's Well	..	..	..	..	..		..	3 14	..	..
Stonehall and Lydden Halt	..	..	..	..	..		..	3 19	..	..
Kearsney D	..	..	..	..	..		..	3 23	..	..
Dover Priory 43 .... arr	..	..	..	..	..		..	3 29	..	..
Dover Marine .... "	..	..	..	..	..		..	..	..	..
Martin Mill, for St. Margaret's Bay arr	..	..	..	..	..		..	..	..	..
Walmer .... "	..	..	..	..	..		..	..	..	..
Deal 34 .... "	..	..	..	..	..		..	..	..	..
Sandwich 34 .... "	..	..	..	..	..	..	..	..	..	..

For Notes, see page 65 ; for Continuation of Trains, see pages 62 to 65

For other Trains to Dover, Deal, &c., see pages 34 to 42

LONDON. SHEERNESS-ON-SEA, MARGATE, RAMSGATE, DOVER, DEAL, and SANDWICH

Week Days—*continued*

Down	p.m	p.m	p.m	p.m	p.m	p.m	p.m	(3)	p.m	p.m	p.m	p.m	(3)		p.m	p.m	p.m	p.m	p.m	p.m	p.m	p.m	p.m	p.m	p.m	p.m		p.m	p.m	p.m	p.m	p.m
	Saturdays only	Saturdays only	Saturdays excepted	Saturdays only	Saturdays excepted	Saturdays only	Saturdays only	Saturdays excepted	Saturdays only	Saturdays only	Saturdays excepted	Saturdays excepted	Saturday excepted		Saturdays only	Saturdays excepted	Saturdays excepted	Saturdays excepted	Saturdays excepted	Saturdays only	Saturdays excepted	Saturdays excepted	Saturdays excepted; Refreshment Car London to Ramsgate	Saturdays excepted	Saturdays excepted; Refreshment Car London to Ramsgate	Saturdays excepted		Saturdays only	Saturdays only	Saturdays excepted	Saturdays only	Saturdays excepted
Victoria dep		1 25					2 5				2 35				3 25	3 35						4 18									5 18	5 20
Charing Cross dep						1 42		1 50					2 50						3 42	3 42								4 42				
Waterloo						1 44		1 52					2 52						3 44	3 44								4 44				
Cannon Street																							4 45		5 15	4 32				5 22		
London Bridge						1 49		1 56					2 56						3 49	3 49						4 36		4 49		5 13		
New Cross								2 2					3 2																			
Woolwich Arsenal dep						2 2		2 2					3 14						4 2	4 2								5 2		5 17		
Dartford						2 15		2 35					3 35						4 14	4 15								5 15		5 39		
Gravesend Central						2 25		2 51					3 51						4 25	4 25								5 25		5 49		
Bromley South dep		1 52					2 28				2 56				3 56	3 56						4 35									5 35	5 38
Swanley											2 47				3 46	3 47						4 47									5 47	5 53
Strood dep						2 38		3 5					4 5						4 37	4 38	4 54							5 38		6 1		
Rochester						2 41		3 8					4 8		4 14				4 41	4 41	4 59	5 14				5 20		5 41		6 7	6 14	6 15
Chatham arr						2 43	3 1	3 11			3 29		4 10		4 29	4 29			4 44	4 44	5 3	5 16				5 23		5 44		6 11	6 16	6 17
Chatham dep	2 7					2 50	3 3				3 31				4 31	4 31		4 37		4 52	5 5					5 28		5 52		6 13	6 23	6 20
Gillingham (Kent)	2 11					2 54	3 8				3 37							4 42		4 56	5 10					5 34		5 57		6 18	6 27	6 25
Rainham	2 17																	4 48		5 2	5 16					5 40				6 24	6 33	
Newington																		4 54		5 8						5 46					6 39	6 35
Sittingbourne A arr	2 27					3 8	3 21				3 50				4 46	4 46		5 2		5 14	5 26					5 53				6 33	6 46	
Sittingbourne A dep	2 37		2 45			3 15				3 30	4 2				4 55	4 55				5 33	5 28					5 57					7 5	
Kemsley Halt	2 42		2 51			3 21				3 37	4 7				5 1	5 1				5 40	5 34					6 2		6 14			7 11	6 45
Swale Halt			2 56							3 42	4 12					5 6				5 44	5 39											
Queenborough 57	2 49		3 2			3 31				3 48	4 17				5 9	5 11				5 51	5 44					6 9		6 24			7 23	6 56
Sheerness-on-Sea arr	2 55		3 7			3 37				3 55	4 27				5 15	5 21				5 57	5 52					6 18		6 32			7 28	7 2
Sittingbourne A dep	2 28						3 22				3 51				4 47	4 47				5 15	5 29					5 55				6 34	6 48	
Teynham	2 35																			5 22						6 2				6 41	6 55	
Faversham arr	2 44	2 53					3 34				4 3				4 59	4 59				5 31	5 42		5 50			6 11				6 50	7 4	
Faversham dep		2 55					3 36					4 12			5 0	5 0				5 33			5 52			6 28						
Whitstable & Tankerton		3 7					3 48					4 23			5 12	5 12				5 46			6 3		6 33	6 39						
Chestfield and Swalecliffe Halt		3 12					3 53					4 28			5 17	5 17							6 8			6 44						
Herne Bay		3 19					4 0					4 35			5 24	5 24				5 55			6 13		6 42	6 50						
Birchington-on-Sea		3 32					4 13					4 48			5 38	5 38				6 8			6 26			7 3						
Westgate-on-Sea		3 38					4 19					4 54			5 43	5 43				6 13			6 31			7 8						
Margate		3 44					4 24					4 59			5 48	5 48				6 18			6 36		6 58	7 13						
Broadstairs		3 55					4 35					5 10			5 59	5 59				6 28			6 47		7 9							
Dumpton Park for East Ramsgate		4 0					4 40					5 15			6 4	6 4				6 32			6 51		7 13							
Ramsgate arr		4 4					4 44					5 19			6 8	6 8				6 36			6 55		7 17							
Faversham dep				2 56					3 50		4 5				5 10		5 10							5 52					6 40	6 59		
Selling				3 4					3 56		4 13				5 18		5 18							6 0					6 46	7 6		
Canterbury East B				3 17	3 45				4 10		4 26				5 32		5 32							6 14					6 59	7 20		
Bekesbourne				3 23	3 50				4 16		4 33				5 39		5 39							6 22					7 [illegible]	7 28		
Adisham C				3 29	3 56				4 22		4 39				5 45		5 45							6 28					7 11	7 34		
Aylesham Halt				3 33	4 0				4 26		4 43				5 49		5 49							6 32					7 15	7 38		
Snowdown and Nonington Halt				3 37	4 4				4 30		4 47				5 53		5 53							6 36					7 19	7 42		
Shepherd's Well				3 42	4 9				4 35		4 52				5 58		5 58							6 42					7 24	7 47		
Stonehall and Lydden Halt				3 47	4 14				4 40		4 57				6 3		6 3							6 47					7 29	7 52		
Kearsney D				3 51	4 18				4 45		5 1				6 7		6 7							6 53					7 33	7 56		
Dover Priory 43 arr				3 57	4 24				4 53		5 7				6 17		6 17							7 1					7 39	8 3		
Dover Marine																																
Martin Mill for St Margaret's Bay arr				4 43	4 53				5 49		5 43				7 30		7 0													8 33		
Walmer				4 49	4 59				5 56		5 49				7 36		7 5													8 39		
Deal 34				4 54	5 5				6 1		5 55				7 41		7 10													8 44		
Sandwich 34				5 3	5 15				6 11		6 6				7 51		7 20													8 54		

FOR NOTES, SEE PAGE 65

LONDON, SHEERNESS-ON-SEA, MARGATE, RAMSGATE, DOVER, DEAL, and SANDWICH

Week Days—continued

Down	p.m	p.m	p.m	p.m	p.m	p.m	3	p.m	p.m	p.m	p.m	p.m	p.m	p.m	p.m	3		p.m	p.m	p.m	p.m	3	p.m	p.m	p.m	p.m	p.m	p.m	p.m	3	p.m	
Victoria .... dep	..	..	..	6 5	..	..	..	..	..	7 15	..	7 15	..	..	..	..	..	8 18	..	8 18	..	..	9 18	9 18	9 35	..	..	..	..	..	..	..
Charing Cross .... dep	..	5 42	..	Saturdays only	..	..	5 50	..	6 42	..	..	Saturdays excepted	..	..	..	7 50	..	..	Saturdays excepted	Saturdays only	..	8 46	..	..	..	..	..	..	..	9 46	9 46	..
Waterloo .... "	..	5 44	..		..	..	5 52	..	6 44	..	..		..	..	..	7 52	..	..			..	8 48	..	..	..	..	..	..	..	9 48	9 48	..
Cannon Street .... "	5 45	..	6 15		6 23	..	..	..	..	..	..		..	..	..	..	..	..			..	..	..	..	..	..	..	..	..	..	..	..
London Bridge .... "		5 49	..			..	5 56	..	6 49	..	..		..	..	..	7 56	..	..			..	8 52	..	..	..	..	..	..	..	9 52	9 52	..
New Cross .... "		..	..			..	6 2	..	..	..	..		..	..	..	8 2	..	..			..	8 58	..	..	..	..	..	..	..	9 58	9 58	..
Woolwich Arsenal .. dep	Saturdays excepted	6 2			Saturdays excepted	..	6 14	Saturdays only	7 2	Saturdays only	..		..	..	..	8 14	..	..			..	9 14	..	..	..	..	..	..	Saturdays only	1014	1014	..
Dartford .... "		6 15				..	6 35		7 15		..		..	..	..	8 35	..	..			..	9Y35	..	..	..	..	..	..		1034	1034	..
Gravesend Central .. "		6 25				..	6 51		7 25		..		..	..	..	8 51	..	..			..	9 51	..	..	..	..	..	..		1051	1052	..
Bromley South .... dep		..	Saturdays excepted	6 28		..	..		..		..	7 8	..	..	..	..	..	8 35		8 35	..	..	9 35	9 35	..	..	..	..		..	..	..
Swanley .... "		..		..		..	..		..		..	7 20	..	..	..	..	..	8 47		8 46	..	..	9 47	9 47	..	..	..	..		..	..	..
Strood .... dep		6 37		..	..	..	7 4		7 37		..	..	..	Saturdays excepted	Saturdays only	9 5	..	..	..	..	..	10 5	..	..	..	..	..	..		11 5	11 5	..
Rochester		6 41		..	7 8	..	7 8		7 41		..	..	..			9 8	..	9 14	..	..	..	10 8	1014	1014	..	..	..	..		11 7	11 7	..
Chatham .... arr	6 31	6 42		7 1	7 11	..	7 11		7 43		..	8 5	..			9 11	..	9 16	..	9 16	..	1011	1016	1016	1024	..	..	..		11 9	11 9	..
Chatham .... dep	6 32	6 43		7 3	7 12	..		7 23		..	..	8 7	..				..		9 30	9 32	..	..		1017	1025	..	..	..	1032	1111	1112	..
Gillingham (Kent)	Refreshment Car London to Ramsgate	6 47		7 8	7 18	..	Saturdays only	7 27	Saturdays excepted	..	..	..	..				..		9 37	9 37	..	..	Saturdays only	1021	..	..	..	..	1036	1116	1116	..
Rainham		..	..	..	7 24	Saturdays excepted		..		..	..	..	..				..		9 43	9 43	Saturdays excepted	..		Saturdays excepted	..	..	..	Saturdays only	1042	1122	1122	..
Newington		..	..	..	7 30			..		..	..	..	..				..		9 49	9 49		..			..	..	..		1049	..	..	..
Sittingbourne A ...... arr		Saturdays excepted	..	7 21	7 38			..		..	..	8 23	..			Saturdays excepted	..	Saturdays excepted	9 56	9 56		..			1039	..	..		1055	1132	1132	..
Sittingbourne A .... dep			..	..	7 46			..		..	..	..	..	9 10	9 25		..		10 0	10 0		..			..	..	..		..	1140	1140	..
Kemsley Halt			..	..	7 51			7 43		..	..	..	..	9 15	9 32		..		10 5	10 5		..			..	..	..		..	1145	1145	..
Swale Halt			..	..	..			..		..	..	..	..	9 20	9 38		..		1010	1010		..			..	..	..		..	1150	1150	..
Queenborough 57			..	..	8 4			7 52		..	..	..	..	9 25	9 44		..		1015	1015		..			..	..	..		..	1156	1156	..
Sheerness-on-Sea .... arr			..	..	8 10			8 1		..	..	..	..	9 33	9 50		..		1022	1022		..			..	..	..		..	12 1	12 1	..
Sittingbourne A ...... dep			..	7 22	7 39	..	..	..	..	..	..	8 24	..	..	..		..		9 57	9 57	10 4	..	..	..	1040	..	..	1047	1056	1133	1134	..
Teynham		..	..	..	7 46	..	..	..	..	..	..	..	..	..	..		..		..	10 4	1011	..	..	..	..	..	..	1055	11 3	1141	1141	..
Faversham .... arr	6 55	..	..	7 34	7 55	..	..	..	..	8 27	..	8 36	..	..	..		..	..	10 9	1013	1020	..	..	..	1052	..	..	11 4	1112	1150	1150	..
Faversham .... dep	6 56	..	..	7 36	..	8 3	..	..	..	8 29	..	8 38	..	..	..	..	..	..	..	..	..	..	..	..	1053	..	..	..	..	..	Saturdays only	..
Whitstable & Tankerton	7 7	..	7 21	7 48	..	8 15	..	..	..	8 40	..	8 50	..	..	..	..	..	..	..	..	..	..	..	..	11 5	..	..	..	..	Saturdays excepted		..
Chestfield and Swalecliffe Halt	7 12	..	..	7 53	..	8 20	..	..	..	8 45	Saturdays only	8 55	Saturdays excepted	..	..	..	..	..	..	..	..	..	..	..	1110	Saturdays only	Saturdays excepted	..	..			..
Herne Bay	7 19	..	7 39	8 0	..	8 26	..	..	..	8 51		9 2		..	..	..	..	..	..	..	..	..	..	..	1117			..	..			..
Birchington-on-Sea	7 32	..	7 52	8 13	..	8 39	..	..	..	9 4		9 15		..	..	..	..	..	..	..	..	..	..	..	1130			..	..			..
Westgate-on-Sea	7 37	..	7 57	8 18	..	8 44	..	..	..	9 9		9 20		..	..	..	..	..	..	..	..	..	..	..	1135			..	..			..
Margate	7 42	..	8 2	8 23	..	8 49	..	..	..	9 14		9 25		..	..	..	..	..	..	..	..	..	..	..	1140			..	..			..
Broadstairs	7 53	..	8 12	8 34	..	9 2	..	..	..	9 25		9 41		..	..	..	..	..	..	..	..	..	..	..	1151			..	..			..
Dumpton Park for East Ramsgate	7 57	..	8 16	8 38	..	9 6	..	..	..	9 30		9 46		..	..	..	..	..	..	..	..	..	..	..	1155			..	..			..
Ramsgate .... arr	8 2	..	8 20	8 42	..	9 10	..	..	..	9 34		9 50		..	..	..	..	..	..	..	..	..	..	..	1159			..	..			..
Faversham .... dep	..	..	..	7 40	7 57	..	..	..	..	Refreshment Car London to Ramsgate	8 35	..	8 50	..	..	..	..	..	..	..	..	..	..	..	Refreshment Car. London to Ramsgate on Saturdays	1054	1055	..	..	..	..	..
Selling	..	..	..	7 46	8 4	..	..	..	..		8 41	..	8 56	..	..	..	..	..	..	..	..	..	..	..		11 1	11 1	..	..	..	..	..
Canterbury East B	..	..	..	7 59	8 16	..	..	..	..		8 54	..	9 12	..	..	..	..	..	..	..	..	..	..	..		1115	1114	..	..	..	..	..
Bekesbourne	..	..	..	8 5	8 22	..	..	..	..		9 0	..	9 18	..	..	..	..	..	..	..	..	..	..	..		1121	1121	..	..	..	..	..
Adisham C	..	..	..	8 11	8 28	..	..	..	..		9 6	..	9 24	..	..	..	..	..	..	..	..	..	..	..		1127	1127	..	..	..	..	..
Aylesham Halt	..	..	..	8 15	8 32	..	..	..	..		9 10	..	9 28	..	..	..	..	..	..	..	..	..	..	..		1131	1131	..	..	..	..	..
Snowdown and Nonington Halt	..	..	..	8 19	..	..	..	..	..		9 14	..	9 32	..	..	..	..	..	..	..	..	..	..	..		1135	1135	..	..	..	..	..
Shepherd's Well	..	..	..	8 24	8 39	..	..	..	..		9 19	..	9 37	..	..	..	..	..	..	..	..	..	..	..		1140	1140	..	..	..	..	..
Stonehall and Lydden Halt	..	..	..	..	..	..	..	..	..		9 24	..	9 42	..	..	..	..	..	..	..	..	..	..	..		1145	1145	..	..	..	..	..
Kearsney D	..	..	..	8 31	8 46	..	..	..	..		9 28	..	9 46	..	..	..	..	..	..	..	..	..	..	..		1149	1149	..	..	..	..	..
Dover { Priory 43 ...... arr	..	..	..	8 37	8 52	..	..	..	..		9 34	..	9 52	..	..	..	..	..	..	..	..	..	..	..		1155	1155	..	..	..	..	..
Dover { Marine	..	..	..	..	..	..	..	..	..		..	..	..	..	..	..	..	..	..	..	..	..	..	..		..	..	..	..	..	..	..
Martin Mill, for St Margaret's Bay arr	..	..	..	9 9	9 9	..	..	..	..	..	..	..	..	..	..	..	..	..	..	..	..	..	..	..	..	..	..	..	..	..	..	..
Walmer .... "	..	..	..	9 14	9 14	..	..	..	..	..	..	..	..	..	..	..	..	..	..	..	..	..	..	..	..	..	..	..	..	..	..	..
Deal 34 .... "	..	..	..	9 19	9 19	..	..	..	..	..	..	..	..	..	..	..	..	..	..	..	..	..	..	..	..	..	..	..	..	..	..	..
Sandwich 34 .... "	..	..	..	9 28	9 28	..	..	..	..	..	..	..	..	..	..	..	..	..	..	..	..	..	..	..	..	..	..	..	..	..	..	..

For Notes and SUNDAY TRAINS, see page 65.

For other Trains to Dover, Deal, &c., see pages 34 to 42

LONDON, SHEERNESS-ON-SEA, MARGATE, RAMSGATE, DOVER, DEAL, and SANDWICH

Down — Sundays	a.m 3	a.m	a.m	a.m	a.m	a.m	a.m	a.m	3	a.m	a.m	3	p.m	p.m	3	p.m	p.m	3	p.m	p.m	p.m	p.m	3	p.m	3	p.m
Victoria .... dep	..	7 18	..	8 5	..	9 5	..	9 18	..	..	9 50	..	1235	..	..	..	..	..	3 35	5 18	..	..	..	7 18	..	8 35
Charing Cross ...... dep	..	..	7 20	..	8 40	..	..	..	9 4	..	..	12 4	..	..	2 4	..	..	3 4	..	..	..	6 40	7 4	..	8 4	..
Waterloo ...... "	..	..	7 23	..	8 42	..	..	..	9 6	..	..	12 6	..	..	2 6	..	..	3 6	..	..	..	6 42	7 6	..	8 6	..
Cannon Street ...... "	..	..	..	..	..	..	..	..	..	..	..	..	..	..	..	..	..	..	..	..	..	..	..	..	..	..
London Bridge ...... "	5 5	..	7 29	..	8 47	..	..	..	9 10	..	..	1210	..	..	2 10	..	..	3 10	..	..	..	6 47	7 10	..	8 10	..
New Cross ...... "	..	..	7 37	..	..	..	..	..	9 16	..	..	1216	..	..	2 16	..	..	3 16	..	..	..	..	7 16	..	8 16	..
Woolwich Arsenal .. dep	..	..	7 55	..	9 0	..	..	..	9 32	..	..	1232	..	..	2 32	..	..	3 32	..	..	..	7 0	7 32	..	8 32	..
Dartford ...... "	5 38	..	8 12	..	9 13	..	..	..	9 50	..	..	1250	..	..	2 50	..	..	3 50	..	..	..	7 13	7 50	..	8 50	..
Gravesend Central .. "	5 56	..	8 25	..	9 23	..	..	..	10 6	..	..	1 6	..	..	3 6	..	..	4 6	..	..	..	7 23	8 6	..	9 6	..
Bromley South ...... dep	..	7 35	..	8 27	..	9 28	..	9 35	..	..	1012	..	1256	..	..	..	..	..	3 56	5 35	..	..	..	7 35	..	8 56
Swanley ...... "	..	7 50	..	..	..	..	..	9 46	..	..	9 46	..	..	..	..	..	..	..	3 46	5 46	..	..	..	7 46	..	..
Strood ...... dep	6 10	..	8 38	..	9 36	..	..	..	1022	..	..	1 20	..	..	3 20	..	..	4 20	..	..	..	7 36	8 20	..	9 21	..
Rochester	6 18	8 17	8 43	..	9 39	..	..	1014	1025	..	..	1 23	..	..	3 23	..	..	4 23	..	6 14	..	7 39	8 23	..	9 25	..
Chatham ...... arr	6 22	8 19	8 46	9 0	9 42	..	..	1016	1027	..	1046	1 25	1 29	..	3 25	..	..	4 25	4 29	6 16	..	7 42	8 25	8 16	9 27	9 30
Chatham ...... dep	6 24	Stop	8 47	9 2	Stop	..	1014	..	..	1030	1047	..	1 21	..	..	3 32	..	..	4 30	6 22	..	7 43	..	8 30	..	9 32
Gillingham (Kent)	6 32	..	8 53	9 8	..	..	1018	..	..	1034	1052	..	1 37	..	..	3 36	..	..	4 36	6 26	..	7 48	..	8 35	..	9 37
Rainham	6 40	..	8 59	..	..	..	..	..	..	1040	..	..	1 43	..	..	..	..	..	..	6 32	..	..	..	8 41	..	..
Newington	6 46	..	9 5	..	..	..	..	..	..	1046	..	..	1 49	..	..	..	..	..	..	..	..	..	..	8 47	..	..
Sittingbourne A ...... arr	6 53	a.m	9 12	9 22	a.m	..	..	..	..	1053	11 5	..	1 56	..	..	3 48	..	..	4 50	..	..	8 1	..	8 54	..	9 51
Sittingbourne **A** .... dep	..	7 30	..	..	9 47	..	..	..	..	..	1110	..	2 0	..	..	3 54	..	..	4 55	..	7 0	8 8	..	9 0	..	9 58
Kemsley Halt	..	7 36	..	..	9 52	..	1034	..	..	..	1115	..	2 5	..	..	3 59	..	..	5 0	..	7 5	8 13	..	9 5	..	10 3
Swale Halt	..	7 41	..	..	..	..	..	..	..	..	..	..	2 10	..	..	..	..	..	5 5	..	..	..	..	9 9	..	10 8
Queenborough 57	..	7 46	..	..	10 0	..	1042	..	..	..	1123	..	2 15	..	..	4 7	..	..	5 10	6 55	7 15	8 23	..	9 15	..	1013
Sheerness-on-Sea .... arr	..	7 52	..	..	10 5	..	1048	..	..	..	1128	..	2 20	..	..	4 12	..	..	5 16	7 1	7 21	8 33	..	9 21	..	1022
Sittingbourne A ...... dep	6 56	Stop	9 13	9 24	..	..	..	..	..	1054	11 6	..	1 57	..	..	3 49	..	..	4 51	Stop	..	..	..	8 55	..	9 51
Teynham	7 3	..	9 20	..	..	..	..	..	..	11 0	..	..	2 4	..	..	..	..	..	..	..	..	..	..	9 2	..	..
Faversham ...... arr	7 12	..	9 29	9 37	..	1024	..	..	..	11 9	1118	..	2 13	..	..	4 1	..	..	5 3	..	..	..	..	9 12	..	10 3
Faversham ...... dep	7 20	..	9 30	..	..	1025	..	..	..	..	1120	..	2 15	..	..	4 2	..	..	5 5	..	..	..	..	..	..	10 5
Whitstable & Tankerton	7 40	..	9 43	..	..	1036	..	..	..	..	1132	..	2 26	..	..	4 13	..	..	5 18	..	..	..	..	..	..	1016
Chestfield and Swalecliffe	..	..	9 49	..	..	..	..	..	..	..	1137	..	2 31	..	..	..	..	..	5 23	..	..	..	..	..	..	1021
Herne Bay ...... [Halt	7 58	..	9 55	..	..	1046	..	..	..	..	1144	..	2 38	..	..	4 21	..	..	5 31	..	..	..	..	..	..	1028
Birchington-on-Sea	8 18	..	10 8	..	..	1059	..	..	..	..	1157	..	2 51	..	..	4 34	..	..	5 46	..	..	..	..	..	..	1041
Westgate-on-Sea	8 27	..	1013	..	..	11 4	..	..	..	..	12 2	..	2 56	..	..	4 39	..	..	5 52	..	..	..	..	..	..	1046
Margate	8 33	..	1018	..	..	1110	..	..	..	..	12 7	..	3 1	..	..	4 44	..	..	5 57	..	..	..	..	..	..	1051
Broadstairs .... [Ramsgate	8 51	..	1028	..	..	1121	..	..	..	..	1217	..	3 11	..	..	4 53	..	..	6 12	..	..	..	..	..	..	11 1
Dumpton Park, for East	..	..	1032	..	..	1126	..	..	..	..	1222	..	3 16	..	..	4 57	..	..	6 17	..	..	..	..	..	..	11 6
Ramsgate ...... arr	9 4	a.m	1036	..	..	1130	..	..	..	..	1226	..	3 20	..	..	5 1	..	..	6 21	p.m	..	..	..	..	..	1110
Faversham ...... dep	..	7 18	..	9 39	..	..	..	..	..	..	1130	..	Refreshment Car, London to Ramsgate	2 16	..	4 6	..	..	Refreshment Car, London to Ramsgate	5 8	..	..	..	9 15	..	10 5
Selling	..	..	..	9 46	..	..	..	..	..	..	1136	..		2 23	..	4 13	..	..		5 16	..	..	..	9 23	..	1013
Canterbury East B	..	7 40	..	9 59	..	..	..	..	..	..	1149	..		2 35	..	4 26	..	..		5 29	..	..	..	9 36	..	1027
Bekesbourne	..	7 47	..	10 5	..	..	..	..	..	..	1155	..		2 41	..	4 32	..	..		5 36	..	..	..	9 42	..	1033
Adisham C	..	7 54	..	1011	..	..	..	..	..	..	12 1	..		2 47	..	4 38	..	..		5 42	..	..	..	9 48	..	1039
Aylesham Halt ...... [Halt	..	7 58	..	1015	..	..	..	..	..	..	12 5	..		2 51	..	4 42	..	..		5 47	..	..	..	9 52	..	1043
Snowdown and Nonington	..	8 2	..	1019	..	..	..	..	..	..	12 9	..		2 55	..	4 46	..	..		5 51	..	..	..	9 56	..	1047
Shepherd's Well	..	8 7	..	1024	..	..	..	..	..	..	1214	..		3 0	..	4 52	..	..		5 56	..	..	..	10 1	..	1052
Stonehall and Lydden Halt	..	8 12	..	..	..	..	..	..	..	..	Zz	..		..	..	..	..	..		..	..	..	..	..	..	..
Kearsney D	..	8 16	..	1031	..	..	..	..	..	..	1221	..		3 7	..	4 58	..	..		6 3	..	..	..	10 8	..	1059
Dover { Priory 43 ..... arr	..	8 22	..	1037	..	..	..	..	..	..	1227	..		3 13	..	5 4	5Y25	..		6 9	..	..	..	1014	..	11 5
Dover { Marine ...... "	..	..	..	..	..	..	..	..	..	..	..	..		..	..	..	..	..		..	..	..	..	..	..	..
Martin Mill for St Margaret's Bay arr	..	9 42	..	1111	..	..	..	..	..	..	1 46	..		3 39	..	..	5 37	..		6 31	..	..	..	11 2	..	..
Walmer ...... "	..	9 48	..	1117	..	..	..	..	..	..	1 52	..		3 45	..	..	5 43	..		6 37	..	..	..	11 8	..	..
Deal 34 ...... "	..	9 53	..	1122	..	..	..	..	..	..	1 57	..		3 50	..	..	5 48	..		6 42	..	..	..	1113	..	..
Sandwich 34 ...... "	..	10 2	..	1133	..	..	..	..	..	..	2 7	..		3 59	..	..	5 57	..		6 51	..	..	..	1123	..	..

3 Third class only

A Sittingbourne & Milton Regis
B ¾ mile to Canterbury West Sts.
B Arr. 2 36 p.m
C Station for Wingham (2¾ miles)
D Station is adjacent to River and Ewell
D 2 minutes later on Saturdays
d Departure time
I Station for Kingsdown (2 miles)
H Holborn Viaduct
J Third class only on Saturdays
J 1 minute later on Saturdays
K Arr. 7 53 a.m.
SO or S0 Saturdays only
SX or SX Saturdays excepted
Y 1 minute *earlier* on Saturdays
Zz Stops on notice being given to the Guard

For **LOCAL TRAINS** between Margate and Ramsgate, see page 43

For **OTHER TRAINS**—London and Dover, page 34

For **LOCAL TRAINS** and **intermediate Stations** between London and Gillingham, see pages 72 and 136—Dover and Sandwich, page 34

SANDWICH, DEAL, DOVER, RAMSGATE, MARGATE, SHEERNESS-ON-SEA, and LONDON

Week Days

Miles from Dover (Mar.)	Mls	Up	a.m	a.m	a.m 3	a.m	a.m 3	a.m	a.m	a.m	a.m	a.m	a.m	a.m 3	a.m	a.m	a.m	a.m	a.m	a.m	a.m	a.m	a.m	a.m	a.m	a.m 3	a.m	a.m	a.m 3	a.m	a.m	a.m Saturdays only
		Sandwich dep																			7 0											8 3
		Deal										5N36									7 11											8 13
		Walmer (for Kingsdown) F (Margaret's Bay)										5N40									7 17											8 19
		Martin Mill, for St. Margaret's										5N47									7 25											8 27
—		Dover Marine dep																														
1¾		Dover Priory		4 40					5 30			6 8				Refreshment Car Ramsgate to London				Refreshment Car Ramsgate to London	7 40									8 14	Refreshment Car Ramsgate to London	9 0
3½		Kearsney D		4 46					5 35			6 13									7 45									8 19		9 5
F		Stonehall and Lydden Halt		4 50					5 39			6 17									7 49									8 23		
6¾		Shepherd's Well		4 55					5 44			6 24									7 55									8 29		9 12
8¾		Snowdown and Nonington		5 0					5 49			6 29									8 0	Saturdays excepted								8 34		9 17
9¾		Aylesham Halt										6 32									8 3			Saturdays only						8 37		9 20
10¾		Adisham C		5 6								6 35									8 6									8 40		9 23
13¾		Bokesbourne										6 41									8 12									8 46		9 29
16¾		Canterbury East B		5 17					6 7			6 47									8 19									8 53		9 36
23½		Selling										7 0									8 32											9 49
26½		Faversham 60 arr		5 34								7 7									8 39									9 10		9 56
—	Mls	Ramsgate dep		Stop								6 6				6 29			7 7	7 20	Stop	7 35	Saturdays excepted				Saturdays excepted				8 35	8 42
—	1	Dumpton Park (for East Ramsgate)										6 9				6 32			7 10	7 23		7 38									8 38	8 45
—	2¼	Broadstairs										6 14				6 36			7 14	7 27		7 42									8 42	8 49
—	5½	Margate				5 0						6 22				6 45			7 22	7 36		7 50						Saturdays only			8 50	9 0
—	7	Westgate-on-Sea										6 27				6 50			7 27			7 55									8 55	9 6
—	8¾	Birchington-on-Sea										6 32				6 55			7 32			8 0										9 12
—	16¾	Herne Bay (Halt)				5 16						6 47				7 9			7 44	7L52		8 12	8 20	8 20							9 9	9 26
—	19	Chestfield & Swalecliffe				5 22						6 53				7 15			7 50			8 17	8 25	8 25								9 32
—	20½	Whitstable & Tankerton				5 27						6 58				7 20			7 55	8 1		8 22	8 30	8 30							9 17	9 37
—	27½	Faversham 60 arr				5 38						7 9				7 31			8 6				8 40	8 40								9 49
—		Faversham dep	4 40			5 40				6L43		7 10			7L14	7 32			8 14				8 41	8 41	Saturdays only		8 48	8 48				10 0
30½		Teynham	4 46			5 49				6 52			Calls at Blackfriars 8 54 a.m		7 24												8 56	8 56				
33¾		Sittingbourne A arr	4 55			5 56				6 59					7 31	7 43			8 26				8 52	8 52			9 3	9 3				1014
—	Mls	Sheerness-on-Sea dep				5 31				6 35						7 22			8 0			Refreshment Car Ramsgate to London	8 23	8 25					Saturdays only			9 38
—	2	Queenborough 57				5 36				6 40						7 27			8 5				8 28	8 31								9 43
—	4½	Swale Halt								6 45													8 36	8 36		Saturdays excepted						9 48
—	6	Kemsley Halt				5 47				6 49									8 13				8 40	8 40								9 52
—	c	Sittingbourne A arr				5 53				6 55						7 39			8 19				8 46	8 46								9 58
—		Sittingbourne A dep				5 57				7 0					7 32	7 44	7 54		8 27				8 53	8 53			9 4	9 4				1015
37		Newington		a.m		6 5				7 7					7 41												9 11	9 11				
39½		Rainham		5 52		6 11				7 14					7 48						a.m						9 17	9 17				
4-½		Gillingham (Kent)		5 57	6 6	6 18				7 21					7 53	7 58	8 7	8 11	8 41		8 43						9 25	9 25				1028
44½		Chatham arr			6 9	6 23				7 26		7 37				8 3		8 13			8 45		9 8	9 8			9 30	9 30				1033
		Chatham dep			6 10		6 27	6 35		7 27	7 31	7 38	7 47	7 55		8 5		8 14			8 46		9 9		9 14	9 19	9 32		9 42			1035
44¾		Rochester			6 13		6 30	6 38		7 30	7 34		7 50	7 58				8 17			8 49				9 17	9 22	9 35		9 45			
45¼		Strood arr			6 16		6 33				7 38			8 1				8 20							9 20	9 26			9 50			
60¾		Swanley 34 arr											8 19								9 11											
67¾		Bromley South I "											8 2[illegible]								9 21						1013					1111
52½		Gravesend Cen. 113 arr			6 31		6 47				7 57			8 16				8 34							9 34	9 43			10 8			
59½		Dartford 93 "			6 49		6 59							[illegible]											9 45	9 59			1024			
67¾		Woolwich Arsenal "			7 8		7 14				8 18			8SX46				8 56							9 57	1016			1046			
71½		New Cross arr			7 22		7 29																						1054			
74¾		London Bridge "			7 28		7 35	7 19			8 35	8 23						9 10							1011				11 0			
75¼		Cannon Street "			7 31		7 39				8 38	8 28				8 54		9 13		9 19		9 36	9 56						11 3			
75¾		Waterloo "						7 24																	1017							
76½		Charing Cross "						7 27																	1020							
78½		Victoria arr											8H56								9 41						1036				1039	1133

For Notes, see page 71; for Continuation of Trains, see pages 67 to 71

For other Trains from Deal, Dover, &c., see pages 43 to 51

For other trains from Deal, Dover, &c., see pages 43 to 51

SANDWICH, DEAL, DOVER, RAMSGATE, MARGATE, SHEERNESS-ON-SEA, and LONDON

Week Days—*continued*

Up	S X	a.m	a.m	a.m	a.m	a.m	a.m	a.m	a.m	a.m		p.m	p.m	p.m	a.m	a.m	a.m	a.m	p.m	p.m	p.m	a.m	p.m	a.m	p.m	p.m	p.m	p.m	p.m	p.m	p.m	p.m
Sandwich .... dep	8 3	3	3	..	..	..	..	..	..	..	..	..	..	..	10 8	..	10 8	..	..	..	..	1114	..	1132	..	..	..	..	3	..	..	..
Deal .... "	8 13			..	..	..	..	..	..	..	..	..	..	..	1017	..	1017	..	..	..	..	1124	..	1142	..	..	..	..		..	..	..
Walmer F [garet's Bay "	8 19	..	..	..	..	..	..	..	..	..	..	..	..	..	1023	..	1023	..	..	..	..	1129	..	1149	..	..	..	..	..	..	..	..
Martin Mill, for St. Mar- "	8 27	..	..	..	..	..	..	..	..	..	..	..	..	..	1031	..	1031	..	..	..	..	1137	..	1157	..	..	..	..	..	..	..	..
Dover Marine .... dep	..	..	..	..	Saturdays excepted	..	Saturdays only	..	..	..	..	..	..	..	..	Saturdays excepted	..	Saturdays only	..	..	Saturdays only	..	..	..	..	..	..	..	..	..	..	..
Dover Priory .... "	9 0	..	..	9 42		..		..	..	1015	..	..	..	..	1117		1122		..	..		1225	..	1238	..	..	..	..	..	1 8	..	..
Kearsney D	9 5	..	..	9 47		..		..	..	1021	..	..	..	..	1123		1127		..	..		1230	..	1244	..	..	..	..	..	1 13	..	..
Stonehall and Lydden Halt	....	..	..	9 52		..		..	..	1025	..	..	..	..	1127		1131		..	..		1234	..	1248	..	..	..	..	..	1 17	..	..
Shepherd's Well	9 12	..	..	9 58		..		..	..	1031	..	..	..	..	1132		1136		..	..		1239	..	1253	..	..	..	..	..	1 22	Saturdays excepted	..
Snowdown and Nonington	9 17	..	..	10 3		..		..	..	1035	..	..	..	..	1137		1141		..	..		1244	..	1258	..	..	..	..	..	1 27		..
Aylesham Halt	9 20	..	..	10 6		..		..	..	10 [illegible]	..	..	..	..	1140		1144		..	..		1247	..	1 1	..	..	..	..	..	1 30		..
Adisham C	9 23	..	..	10 9		..		..	..	1042	..	..	..	..	1143		1147		..	..		1250	..	1 4	..	..	..	..	..	1 34		..
Bekesbourne	9 29	..	..	1015		..		..	..	1048	..	..	..	..	1149		1153		..	..		1256	..	1 10	..	..	..	..	..	1 40		..
Canterbury East B	9 36	..	..	1023		..		..	..	1056	..	..	..	..	1156		12 1		..	..		1 4	..	1 16	..	..	..	..	..	1 48		..
Selling	9 49	..	..	1036		..		..	..	1110	..	..	..	..	12 9		1215		..	..		1 17	..	..	..	..	..	..	..	2 1		..
Faversham 60 .... arr	9 56	..	..	1043		..		..	..	1117	..	..	..	..	1216		1222		..	..		1 24	..	..	..	..	..	..	..	2 8		..
Ramsgate .... dep	8 45	..	..	Saturdays excepted	9 45	..	9 55	..	..	Saturdays only	..	..	..	..	Saturdays excepted.	1115	Saturdays only	1130	..	..	1224	Saturdays only	..	Saturdays excepted	..	..	..	..	..	..	1 10	..
Dumpton Park, for East [Ramsgate]	8 48	..	..		9 48	..	9 58	..	..		..	..	Saturdays only	..		1118		1133	..	..	1227		..		Saturdays excepted	..	..	Saturdays excepted	..	..	1 13	..
Broadstairs	8 52	..	..		9 52	Saturdays excepted	10 2	..	..		..	..		..		1122		1137	..	Saturdays only	1232		..			..	Saturdays only		..	..	1 17	..
Margate	9 3	..	..		10 0		1010	..	..		..	..		..		1131		1146	..		1243		..			..			..	..	1 28	..
Westgate-on-Sea	9 9	..	..		10 6		1015	..	..		..	..		..		1136		1151	..		1248		..			..			..	..	1 33	..
Birchington-on-Sea	9 15	..	..		1011		1020	..	..		..	..		..		1141		1156	..		1253		..			..			..	..	1 38	..
Herne Bay	9 29	..	..		1024		1033	Saturdays excepted.	..		..	..		..		1155		1210	..		1 5		..			..			..	..	1 51	..
Chestfield and Swalecliffe [Halt]	9 35	..	..		1030		1039		..		..	..		..		12 1		1216	..		..		..			..			..	..	1 57	..
Whitstable & Tankerton	9 40	..	..	..	1035		1045		..		..	..		..		12 7		1222	..		1 13		..			..			..	..	2 2	..
Faversham 60 .... arr	9 52	..	..	..	1046		1056		..		..	..		..		1218		1233	..				..			..			..	..	2 13	..
Faversham .... dep	10 1	..	..	..	1048	1052	1057		..	1123	..	..			..	1222	..	1235			Refreshment Car Ramsgate to London	1 28	..	..	1 28	Saturdays excepted			Saturdays excepted	..	2 17	Saturdays excepted
Teynham	....	..	..	..	..	11 2	..		..	1134	..	..			..	1232	..	..				1 38	..	..	1 38					..	..	
Sittingbourne A .... arr	1014	..	..	..	11 0	11 9	1110		..	1141	..	..			..	1239	..	1248				1 44	..	..	1 44					..	2 30	
Sheerness-on-Sea ... dep	9 38	..	..	..	1039	..	1039	1110	Saturdays excepted	11 8	..	Saturdays only	1212	Saturdays only	..	1215	..	..	Saturdays only	1237		1 10	Saturdays only	..	1 20		2 2	2 8		..	..	
Queenborough 57	9 43	..	..	..	1043	..	1043	1115		1113	..		1217		..	1220	..	..		1242		1 15		..	1 25		2 6	2 12		..	..	
Swale Halt	9 48	..	Saturdays only	..	..	..	..	..		..	..		..		..	1226	..	..		..		1 20		..	1 30		..	..		..	..	
Kemsley Halt	9 52	Saturdays excepted.		..	1051	..	1051	1125		1124	..		1224		..	1230	..	..		1252		1 25		..	1 34		2 14	2 20		..	..	
Sittingbourne A .... arr	9 58			..	1057	..	1057	..		1130	..		1230		..	1236	..	..		1258		1 31		..	1 41		..	..		..	..	
Sittingbourne A ...... dep	1015			..	11 1	1110	1111	....		1142	..		1233		..	1241	..	1249		....		1 45		..	1 45	..	..	....	..	..	2 31	..
Newington	....			..	..	1117	..	..		1150	..		..		..	1249	..	..		..		1 52		..	1 52	..	..	..	..	..	..	..
Rainham	..			..	..	1123	..	....		1156	..		....		..	1255	..	..		..		1 58		..	1 58	..	..	....	..	..	..	..
Gillingham (Kent)	1028			..	..	1130	..	1144		12 2	..		1249		..	1 1	..	1 2		..		2 5		..	2 4	2 10	2 30	2 36	2 40	..	2 45	..
Chatham .... arr	1033			..	1116	1135	1127	1149		12 7	..		1254		..	1 6	....	1 7		....	1 47	2 10		..	..	2 13	2 35	..	2 44	..	2 50	..
Chatham .... dep	1035	1046	1046	..	1118	..	1129	..	1158	1210	..	1214	..	1258	..	1 9	..	1 9	1 14	..	1 49	..	2 14	..	..	2 14	..	..	2 46	..	2 52	3 14
Rochester	..	1049	1049	..	..	..	..	..	12 0	1213	..	1217	....	1 1	..	1 13	....	..	1 17	..	..	..	2 17	..	..	2 17	..	....	2 49	..	..	3 17
Strood .... arr	....	1051	1051	..	..	..	..	..	..	..	..	1221	..	..	..	..	..	..	1 20	..	..	..	2 20	..	..	2 20	..	..	2 52	..	..	3 20
Swanley 34 .... arr	..	..	..	..	..	..	..	..	1230	....	..	....	....	1 30	..	..	....	..	....	....	..	..	..	..	..	..	..	....	..	..	..	..
Bromley South L ...... "	1114	....	....	..	1154	..	..	..	1242	1247	..	..	..	1 42	..	1 49	..	1 45	..	..	2 24	..	..	..	..		..	..	..	..	3 28	..
Gravesend Cen. 113 .. arr	Saturdays excepted.	11 6	11 5	..	..	..	..	..	..	Calls Herne Hill 1 3 p.m	..	1234	..	..	..	..	..	..	1 35	..	..	..	2 34	..	..	2 34	..	....	3 6	..	..	3 35
Dartford 93 .... "		1123	1124	..	..	..	..	..	..		..	1244	..	..	..	..	..	..	1 44	..	..	..	2 44	..	..	2 45	..	..	3 23	..	..	3 45
Woolwich Arsenal .. "		..	1144	..	..	..	..	..	..		..	1256	..	..	..	..	..	..	1 57	..	..	..	2 57	..	..	2 57	..	....	..	..	..	3 57
New Cross .... arr		1154	....	..	..	..	..	..	..		..	..	..	..	..	..	..	..	..	..	..	..	..	..	..	..	..	..	3 54	..	..	..
London Bridge ...... "		12 1	12 7	..	..	..	..	..	..		..	1 10	....	....	..	....	....	..	2 11	....	..	..	3 11	..	..	3 11	..	....	4 0	..	..	4 11
Cannon Street ...... "		....	1212	..	..	..	..	..	..		..	..	..	..	..	..	..	..	..	..	..	..	..	..	..	..	..	..	..	..	..	..
Waterloo .... "		12 5	..	..	..	..	..	..	..		..	1 14	....	....	..	....	....	..	2 16	....	..	..	3 17	..	..	3 16	..	....	4 4	..	..	4 16
Charing Cross ...... "		12 7	....	..	..	..	..	..	..		..	1 17	..	..	..	..	..	..	2 19	..	..	..	3 19	..	..	3 20	..	..	4 7	..	..	4 19
Victoria .... arr	1136	..	..	..	1220	..	1222	..	1259	1 12	..	..	..	1 59	..	2 10	..	2 6	..	..	2 46	..	..	..	..	..	..	..	..	..	3 48	..

FOR NOTES, SEE PAGE 71

SANDWICH, DEAL, DOVER, RAMSGATE, MARGATE SHEERNESS-ON-SEA, and LONDON

Week Days—*continued*

Up	p.m	p.m	p.m	p.m	p.m	p.m	p.m	p.m	p.m	p.m	p.m
Sandwich .... dep	..	..	..	..	1 7	..	..	2 23	..	2 24	..
Deal .... "	..	..	..	..	1 16	..	..	2 33	..	2 33	..
Walmer F [garet'sBay "	..	..	..	..	1 21	..	..	2 38	..	2 38	..
Martin Mill frSt.Mar "	..	..	..	..	1 29	..	..	2 46	..	2 45	..
Dover { Marine .... dep	..	..	..	..	..	..	..	..	..	..	..
Dover { Priory .... "	..	..	..	..	2 5	..	..	3 20	..	3 20	..
Kearsney D	Saturdays only	..	..	Saturdays only	2 10	..	..	3 25	..	3 25	..
Stonehall and Lydden Halt		..	..		2 14	..	..	3 29	..	3 29	..
Shepherd's Well		..	..		2 20	..	..	3 34	..	3 34	Saturdays excepted
Snowdown and Nonington		..	..		2 25	..	..	3 38	..	3 38	
Aylesham Halt .... (Halt		..	..		2 28	..	..	3 41	..	3 41	
Adisham C		..	..		2 31	..	..	3 44	..	3 44	
Bekesbourne		..	..		2 37	..	..	3 50	..	3 50	
Canterbury East B		..	..		2 44	..	..	3 57	..	3 57	
Selling		..	..		2 57	..	..	4 10	..	4 10	
Faversham 60 .... arr		..	..		3 4	..	..	4 17	..	4 17	
Ramsgate .... dep	1 10	Saturdays only	..	1 55	Saturdays only	Saturdays excepted	..	Saturdays only	..	Saturdays excepted	3 15
Dumpton Park for East	1 13		..	1 58			..		..		3 18
Broadstairs ..[Ramsgate	1 17		..	2 2			..		..		3 23
Margate	1 28		..	2 11			..		..		3 34
Westgate-on-Sea	1 33		..	2 16			..		..		3 39
Birchington-on Sea	1 38		..	2 21			..		..		3 44
Herne Bay .... Halt	1 51		..	2 34			..		..		3 58
Chestfield and Swalecliffe	1 57		..	2 40			..		..		4 4
Whitstable & Tankerton	2 2		..	2 46			..		..		4 10
Faversham 60 .... arr	2 13		..	2 57			..		..		4 21
Faversham .... dep	2 17	2 30	Saturdays only	2 59	3 8	3 20	..	4 23	..	..	4 24
Teynham	..	2 38		..	..	3 28	..	4 34	..	..	4 34
Sittingbourne A .... arr	2 30	2 44		..	3 22	3 35	..	4 40	..	..	4 41
Sheerness-on-Sea ... dep	..	..		..	2 58	3 15	Saturdays excepted	4 12	Saturdays only	..	4 12
Queenborough 57	..	..		..	3 3	3 20		4 18		..	4 17
Swale Halt	..	..		..	3 9	3 25		4 23		..	4 23
Kemsley Halt	..	..		..	3 12	3 29		4 27		..	4 27
Sittingbourne A ... arr	..	..		..	3 19	3 35		4 33		..	4 33
Sittingbourne A .... dep	2 31	2 45	..	..	3 23	3 37		4 41		..	4 42
Newington	..	2 53	..	..	..	3 44		4 48		..	..
Rainham	..	2 59	..	..	..	3 50		4 54		..	..
Gillingham (Kent)	2 45	3 6	3 10	..	3 37	3 57		5 0		..	4 58
Chatham .... arr	2 50	..	3 13	..	3 42	4 2		5 5		..	5 3
Chatham .... dep	2 52	..	3 14	..	3 43	..	4 14	..	5 14	..	5 7
Rochester	..	..	3 17	..	..	..	4 17	..	5 17	..	..
Strood .... arr	..	..	3 20	..	..	..	4 20	..	5 20	..	..
Swanley 34 .... arr	..	..	..	..	..	..	..	..	..	..	..
Bromley South L .... "	3 28	..	..	3 59	4 19	..	..	..	..	..	5 48
Gravesend Cen. 113 .. arr	..	..	3 34	..	..	..	4 35	..	5 34	..	..
Dartford 93 .... "	..	..	3 44	..	..	..	4 45	..	5 44	..	..
Woolwich Arsenal .. "	..	..	3 57	..	..	..	4 57	..	5 57	..	..
New Cross .... arr	..	..	..	..	..	..	..	..	..	..	..
London Bridge .... "	..	..	4 11	..	..	..	5 11	..	6 11	..	..
Cannon Street .... "	..	..	..	..	..	..	..	..	..	..	..
Waterloo .... "	..	..	4 17	..	..	..	5 15	..	6 18	..	..
Charing Cross .... "	..	..	4 22	..	..	..	5 19	..	6 22	..	..
Victoria .... arr	3 52	..	..	4 20	4 40	..	..	..	..	..	6 12

Up	p.m	p.m	p.m	p.m	p.m	p.m	p.m	p.m	p.m	p.m	p.m
Sandwich .... dep	..	..	3 14	..	..	..	4 8	..	4 8	..	..
Deal .... "	..	..	3 24	..	..	..	4 17	..	4 17	..	..
Walmer F [garet'sBay "	..	..	3 29	..	..	..	4 23	..	4 23	..	..
Martin Mill frSt.Mar "	..	..	3 37	..	..	..	4 30	..	4 30	..	..
Dover { Marine .... dep	..	..	..	..	..	..	..	..	..	..	..
Dover { Priory .... "	..	..	4 20	..	..	..	5 10	..	5 15	..	..
Kearsney D	..	Saturdays only	4 25	..	..	Saturdays excepted	5 15	..	5 20	..	..
Stonehall and Lydden Halt	..		..	..	..		5 19	..	5 24	..	..
Shepherd's Well	..		4 32	..	..		5 24	..	5 30	..	Saturdays excepted
Snowdown and Nonington	..		4 36	..	..		5 28	..	5 35	..	
Aylesham Halt .... (Halt	..		4 39	..	..		5 31	..	5 38	..	
Adisham C	..		4 42	..	..		5 34	..	5 41	..	
Bekesbourne	..		4 51	..	..		5 41	..	5 47	..	
Canterbury East B	..		4 58	..	..		5 49	..	5 54	..	
Selling	..		5 11	..	..		6 2	..	6 7	..	
Faversham 60 .... arr	..		5 18	..	..		6 9	..	6 14	..	
Ramsgate .... dep	..	3 43	Saturdays excepted	..	..	4 15	Saturdays excepted	..	Saturdays only	..	5 25
Dumpton Park for East	..	3 46		..	..	4 18		..		..	5 28
Broadstairs ..[Ramsgate	..	3 51		..	..	4 22		..		..	5 32
Margate	..	4 2		Saturdays only	..	4 33		..		..	5 41
Westgate-on-Sea	..	4 8			..	4 38		..		..	5 46
Birchington-on Sea	..	4 14			..	4 43		..		..	5 51
Herne Bay .... Halt	..	4 29			..	4 56		..		..	6 4
Chestfield and Swalecliffe	..	4 35			..	5 2		..		..	6 10
Whitstable & Tankerton	..	4 42			..	5 8		..		..	6 16
Faversham 60 .... arr	..	4 53			..	5 19		..		..	6 27
Faversham .... dep	..	4 55	..		..	5 23	6 11	..	6 17	..	..
Teynham	..	Refreshment Car Ramsgate to London	..		..	..	6 20	..	6 28	..	..
Sittingbourne A .... arr	..		..		..	5 36	6 26	..	6 35	..	..
Sheerness-on-Sea ... dep	Saturdays excepted		..	5 10	Saturdays only	5 9	5 40	..	..	Saturdays only	..
Queenborough 57			..	5 15		5 14	5 45	..	..		..
Swale Halt			..	5 20		5 19	..	Saturdays excepted	..		..
Kemsley Halt			..	5 24		5 23	5 52		..		..
Sittingbourne A ... arr			..	5 30		5 29	5 59		..		..
Sittingbourne A .... dep			..	5 33		5 37	6 27		6 36		..
Newington			..	..		5 45	6 34		..		..
Rainham			..	..		5 51	6 40		..		..
Gillingham (Kent)			..	5 48		5 58	6 46		6 49	6 54	..
Chatham .... arr		5 19	..	5 53		6 3	6 51		..	6 57	..
Chatham .... dep	5 14	5 21	..	..	5 58	6 18	..	6 58	..	6 58	..
Rochester	5 17	..	..	..	6 1	..	..	7 1	..	7 1	..
Strood .... arr	5 21	..	..	..	..	..	..	..	..	..	..
Swanley 34 .... arr	..	..	..	..	6 30	6 49	..	7 30	..	7 30	..
Bromley South L .... "	..	5 59	..	..	6 42	7 1	..	7 42	..	7 42	..
Gravesend Cen. 113 .. arr	5 35	..	..	..	..	Calls Herne Hill 7 17 p.m	..	..	..	..	..
Dartford 93 .... "	5 45	..	..	..	..		..	..	..	..	..
Woolwich Arsenal .. "	5 57	..	..	..	..		..	..	..	..	..
New Cross .... arr	..	..	..	..	..		..	..	..	..	..
London Bridge .... "	6 11	..	..	..	..		..	..	..	..	..
Cannon Street .... "	..	..	..	..	..		..	..	..	..	..
Waterloo .... "	6 15	..	..	..	..		..	..	..	..	..
Charing Cross .... "	6 18	..	..	..	..		..	..	..	..	..
Victoria .... arr	..	6 21	..	..	6 59	7 28	..	7 59	..	7 59	..

Up	p.m	p.m	p.m	p.m	p.m	p.m	p.m	p.m	p.m	p.m	p.m
Sandwich .... dep	..	..	..	..	..	..	5 32	..	..	..	..
Deal .... "	..	..	..	..	..	..	5 42	..	..	..	..
Walmer F [garet'sBay "	..	..	..	..	..	..	5 48	..	..	..	..
Martin Mill frSt.Mar "	..	..	..	..	..	..	5 56	..	..	..	..
Dover { Marine .... dep	..	..	..	..	..	..	..	..	..	..	..
Dover { Priory .... "	5 39	..	..	..	..	..	6 22	..	..	..	..
Kearsney D	5 44	..	..	Saturdays only	..	..	6 27	..	..	..	..
Stonehall and Lydden Halt	..	..	..		..	..	6 31	..	..	..	..
Shepherd's Well	5 52	..	..		..	..	6 37	..	..	..	..
Snowdown and Nonington	..	..	..		..	..	6 42	..	..	..	..
Aylesham Halt .... (Halt	..	..	..		..	..	6 45	..	..	..	..
Adisham C	..	..	..		..	..	6 48	..	..	..	..
Bekesbourne	..	..	..		..	..	6 54	..	..	..	..
Canterbury East B	6 9	..	..		..	..	7 0	..	..	..	..
Selling	..	..	..		..	..	..	..	..	..	..
Faversham 60 .... arr	6 29	..	..		..	..	..	..	..	..	..
Ramsgate .... dep	Saturdays excepted	..	..	5 26	..	Saturdays excepted	Saturdays excepted	Saturdays only	6 15	Saturdays excepted	..
Dumpton Park for East		..	Saturdays only	5 29	..				6 19		..
Broadstairs ..[Ramsgate		..		5 34	..				6 23		..
Margate		..		5 43	..				6 32		..
Westgate-on-Sea		..		5 50	..				6 37		..
Birchington-on Sea		..		5 55	..				6 42		..
Herne Bay .... Halt		..		6 9	..		..		6 55		..
Chestfield and Swalecliffe		..		6 15	..		..		..		..
Whitstable & Tankerton		..		6 20	..		..		7 4		..
Faversham 60 .... arr		..		6 31	..		..	..	7 15		..
Faversham .... dep	6 33	..		6 33	..	..	..	..	..	..	..
Teynham	..	..		..	..	..	..	..	..	..	..
Sittingbourne A .... arr	6 46	..		6 45	..	..	..	..	..	..	..
Sheerness-on-Sea ... dep	6 6	..	6 20	..	Saturdays only	..	..	6 [illegible]	..	7 8	..
Queenborough 57	6 11	..	6 25	..		..	..	7 [illegible]	..	7 12	..
Swale Halt	6 16	Saturdays excepted	6 30	..		..	..	..	..	..	..
Kemsley Halt	6 20		6 34	..		..	..	7 11	..	7 20	..
Sittingbourne A ... arr	6 26		6 40	..		..	..	7 [illegible]	..	7 26	..
Sittingbourne A .... dep	6 47		..	6 46		..	..	7 [illegible]	..	7 30	..
Newington	..		..	..		..	..	7 [illegible]	..	7 37	..
Rainham	..		..	..		..	..	7 [illegible]	..	7 43	..
Gillingham (Kent)	7 1		..	7 2	7 10	..	..	7 43	..	7 49	..
Chatham .... arr	7 6		..	7 7	7 13	..	..	7 48	..	7 54	..
Chatham .... dep	7 8	7 14	..	7 9	7 14	..	..	..	..	..	7 58
Rochester	..	7 17	..	..	7 17	..	..	..	..	..	8 1
Strood .... arr	..	7 20	..	..	7 20	..	..	..	..	..	..
Swanley 34 .... arr	..	..	..	..	..	..	..	..	..	..	8 30
Bromley South L .... "	7 49	..	..	7 45	..	..	..	..	..	..	8 42
Gravesend Cen. 113 .. arr	..	7 35	..	..	7 34	..	..	..	..	..	..
Dartford 93 .... "	..	7 45	..	..	7 44	..	..	..	..	..	..
Woolwich Arsenal .. "	..	7 57	..	..	7 57	..	..	..	..	..	..
New Cross .... arr	..	..	..	..	..	..	..	..	..	..	..
London Bridge .... "	..	8 11	..	..	8 11	..	..	..	..	..	..
Cannon Street .... "	..	..	..	..	..	..	..	..	..	..	..
Waterloo .... "	..	8 16	..	..	8 16	..	..	..	..	..	..
Charing Cross .... "	..	8 19	..	..	8 19	..	..	..	..	..	..
Victoria .... arr	8 13	..	..	8 6	..	..	..	..	..	..	8 59

☞ For Notes, see page 71; for Continuation of Trains, see pages 70 and 71.

For other Trains from Deal, Dover, &c., see pages 43 to 51

SANDWICH, DEAL, DOVER, RAMSGATE, MARGATE, SHEERNESS-ON-SEA, and LONDON

Up — Week Days—continued

Up	p.m	p.m	p.m (3)	p.m	p.m	p.m	p.m	p.m	p.m	p.m
Sandwich ....dep	..	..	..	6 17	..	..	6 17	..	..	..
Deal .... "	..	..	..	6 26	..	..	6 26	..	..	..
Walmer F .... "	..	..	..	6 32	..	..	6 32	..	..	..
Martin Mill, for St. Margaret's Bay "	..	..	..	6 40	..	..	6 40	..	..	..
Dover Marine ....dep	..	..	..	..	..	..	..	Saturdays excepted	..	Saturdays only
Dover Priory	..	..	..	7 0	..	..	7 30	..	7 46	
Kearsney D	..	..	..	7 5	..	..	7 35	..	7 51	
Stonehall and Lydden Halt	..	..	..	7 9	..	..	7 39	..	7 55	
Shepherd's Well	..	..	..	7 15	..	..	7 45		8 1	
Snowdown and Nonington Halt	..	..	..	7 20	..	..	7 50		8 6	
Aylesham Halt	..	..	..	7 23	..	..	7 53		8 9	
Adisham C	..	..	..	7 26	..	..	7 56		8 12	
Bekesbourne	..	..	..	7 32	..	..	8 2		8 18	
Canterbury East B	..	..	..	7 39	..	..	8 10		8 25	
Selling	..	..	..	7 52	..	..	8 23		8 38	
Faversham 60 ....arr	..	..	..	7 59	..	..	8 31		8 45	..
Ramsgate ....dep	Saturdays excepted	..	..	Saturdays only	Saturdays only	..	Saturdays excepted	7 45	Saturdays only	7 45
Dumpton Park, for East Ramsgate		..	..			..		7 48		7 48
Broadstairs		..	..			..		7 52		7 52
Margate		..	..			..		8 1		8 1
Westgate-on-Sea		..	..			..		8 6		8 6
Birchington-on-Sea		..	..			..		8 11		8 11
Herne Bay		..	..			..		8 24		8 24
Chestfield & Swalecliffe Halt		..	..			..		8 30		8 30
Whitstable & Tankerton		..	..			..		8 36		8 36
Faversham 60 ....arr		..	..			..		8 47		8 47
Faversham ....dep		..	..	..	..	..	..	8 50	..	8 50
Teynham		..	..	..	..	..	..	..	..	..
Sittingbourne A ....arr		..	..	..	..	..	..	9 3	..	9 1
Sheerness-on-Sea ....dep	7 38	Saturdays excepted	Saturdays excepted	..	7 48	Saturdays only	..	8 24	..	8 24
Queenborough 57	7 43			..	7 54		..	8 29	..	8 28
Swale Halt	..			..	..		..	..	..	..
Kemsley Halt	7 52			..	8 2		..	8 39	..	8 38
Sittingbourne A ....arr	7 59			..	8 8		..	8 45	..	8 45
Sittingbourne A ....dep	8 3			..	8 11		..	9 4	..	9 2
Newington	..			..	..		..	..	..	..
Rainham	8 16			..	8 24		..	..	..	..
Gillingham (Kent)	8 22	..		..	8 29		..	9 19	..	9 17
Chatham ....arr	8 28	..		..	8 34		..	9 24	..	9 22
Chatham ....dep	..	8 32	8 44	..	..	8 58	..	9 28	..	9 24
Rochester	..	8 35	8 48	..	..	9 1	..	..	..	..
Strood ....arr	..	..	8 51	..	..	..	..	..	..	..
Swanley 34 ....arr	..	9 4	..	..	..	9 30	..	..	..	..
Bromley South L .... "	..	9 17	..	..	..	9 42	..	10 7	..	10 0
Gravesend Cen. 113 ....arr	..	..	9 5	..	..	..	..	..	..	..
Dartford 93 .... "	..	..	9 22	..	..	..	..	..	..	..
Woolwich Arsenal .... "	..	..	..	..	..	..	..	..	..	..
New Cross ....arr	..	..	9 54	..	..	..	..	..	..	..
London Bridge .... "	..	..	10 0	..	..	..	..	..	..	..
Cannon Street .... "	..	..	..	..	..	..	..	..	..	..
Waterloo .... "	..	..	10 4	..	..	..	..	..	..	..
Charing Cross .... "	..	..	10 7	..	..	..	..	..	..	..
Victoria ....arr	..	9 38	..	..	..	9 59	..	1028	..	1021

Up	p.m (3)	p.m	p.m	p.m	p.m	p.m	p.m	p.m	
Sandwich ....dep	..	..	..	..	..	..	9 58	9 58	..
Deal .... "	..	..	..	..	..	..	10 8	10 8	..
Walmer F .... "	..	..	..	..	..	..	1013	1013	..
Martin Mill, for St. Margaret's Bay "	..	..	..	..	..	..	1020	1020	..
Dover Marine ....dep	..	..	..	..	..	..	..	..	..
Dover Priory	..	..	..	9 10	..	9 45	1040	1040	..
Kearsney D	..	..	..	9 16	..	9 51	1045	1045	..
Stonehall and Lydden Halt	..	..	..	9 20	..	9 55	1049	1049	..
Shepherd's Well	..	..	..	9 26	..	10 1	1054	1054	..
Snowdown and Nonington Halt	..	..	..	9 31	..	10 6	1059	1059	..
Aylesham Halt	..	..	..	9 34	..	10 9	11 2	11 2	..
Adisham C	..	..	..	9 37	..	1013	11 5	11 5	..
Bekesbourne	..	..	..	9 43	..	1019	..	..	..
Canterbury East B	..	..	..	9 50	..	1026	1116	1120	..
Selling	..	..	..	10 3	..	..	..	..	..
Faversham 60 ....arr	..	..	..	1010	..	1043	1133	1140	..
Ramsgate ....dep	..	Saturdays only	Saturdays excepted	..	9 10	Saturdays only	Saturdays only	Saturdays excepted	..
Dumpton Park, for East Ramsgate	..			..	9 13				..
Broadstairs	..			..	9 18				..
Margate	..			..	9 27				..
Westgate-on-Sea	..			..	9 32				..
Birchington-on-Sea	..			..	9 37				..
Herne Bay	..			..	9 50				..
Chestfield & Swalecliffe Halt	..			..	9 56				..
Whitstable & Tankerton	..			..	10 1				..
Faversham 60 ....arr	..			..	10 12				..
Faversham ....dep	Saturdays excepted	..	9 33	..	10 14	..	..	..	..
Teynham		..	9 41	..	10 24	..	..	..	..
Sittingbourne A ....arr		..	9 48	..	10 31	..	..	..	..
Sheerness-on-Sea ....dep		9 18	9 22	..	10 8	..	..	..	..
Queenborough 57		9 23	9 27	..	10 13	..	..	..	..
Swale Halt		9 28	9 33	..	10 21	..	..	..	..
Kemsley Halt		9 32	9 37	..	10 25	..	..	..	..
Sittingbourne A ....arr		9 40	9 43	..	10 31	..	..	..	..
Sittingbourne A ....dep	..	..	..	..	10 33	..	..	..	..
Newington	..	..	..	..	10 41	..	..	..	..
Rainham	..	..	..	..	10 47	..	..	..	..
Gillingham (Kent)	..	..	..	..	10 56	..	..	..	..
Chatham ....arr	..	..	..	..	11 2	..	..	..	..
Chatham ....dep	9 46	..	..	..	11 4	..	..	..	..
Rochester	9 49		..	..	11 8	..	..	..	..
Strood ....arr	9 52	..	..	..	11 12	..	..	..	..
Swanley 34 ....arr	..	..	..	..	..	..	..	..	..
Bromley South L .... "	..	..	..	..	..	..	..	..	..
Gravesend Cen. 113 ....arr	10 6	..	..	..	11L28	..	..	..	..
Dartford 93 .... "	1023	..	..	..	11 42	..	..	..	..
Woolwich Arsenal .... "	..	..	..	..	11 57	..	..	..	..
New Cross ....arr	1054	..	..	..	..	..	..	..	..
London Bridge .... "	11 1	..	..	..	12 17	..	..	..	..
Cannon Street .... "	..	..	..	..	..	..	..	..	..
Waterloo .... "	11 4	..	..	..	12 24	..	..	..	..
Charing Cross .... "	11 7	..	..	..	12 28	..	..	..	..
Victoria ....arr	..	..	..	..	..	..	..	..	..

Sundays

Up	a.m	a.m	a.m (3)	a.m	a.m	a.m (3)	a.m	a.m	a.m	a.m	a.m (3)	a.m	p.m (3)
Sandwich ....dep	..	..	..	..	..	..	..	..	8 0	..	..	..	..
Deal .... "	..	..	..	..	..	..	..	..	8 9	..	..	..	..
Walmer F .... "	..	..	..	..	..	..	..	..	8 15	..	..	..	..
Martin Mill, for St. Margaret's Bay "	..	..	..	..	..	..	..	..	8 22	..	..	..	..
Dover Marine ....dep	..	..	..	..	Refreshment Car Ramsgate to London	..	..	..	..	Refreshment Car Ramsgate to London	..	..	..
Dover Priory	..	..	..	8 15		..	..	..	9 42		..	..	..
Kearsney D	..	..	..	8 21		..	..	..	9 47		..	..	..
Stonehall and Lydden Halt	..	..	..	..		..	..	..	..		..	..	..
Shepherd's Well	..	..	..	8 29		..	..	..	9 55		..	..	..
Snowdown and Nonington Halt	..	..	..	8 35		..	..	..	10 0		..	..	..
Aylesham Halt	..	..	..	8 38		..	..	..	10 3		..	..	..
Adisham C	..	..	..	8 42		..	..	..	10 7		..	..	..
Bekesbourne	..	..	..	8 48		..	..	..	1013		..	..	..
Canterbury East B	..	..	..	8 56		..	..	..	1020		..	..	..
Selling	..	..	..	9 9		..	..	..	1033		..	..	..
Faversham 60 ....arr	..	..	..	9 16		..	..	..	1040		..	..	..
Ramsgate ....dep	..	..	..	..	8 15	..	..	..	..	9 40	..	..	..
Dumpton Park, for East Ramsgate	..	..	..	..	8 18	..	..	..	..	9 43	..	..	..
Broadstairs	..	..	..	..	8 23	..	..	..	..	9 48	..	..	..
Margate	..	..	..	..	8 32	..	..	..	..	9 57	..	..	..
Westgate-on-Sea	..	..	..	..	8 37	..	..	..	..	10 2	..	..	..
Birchington-on-Sea	..	..	..	..	8 42	..	..	..	..	10 7	..	..	..
Herne Bay	..	..	..	..	8 56	..	..	..	..	1021	..	..	..
Chestfield & Swalecliffe Halt	..	..	..	..	9 2	..	..	..	..	..	..	..	..
Whitstable & Tankerton	..	..	..	..	9 7	..	..	..	..	1030	..	..	..
Faversham 60 ....arr	..	..	..	..	9 18	..	..	..	..	1041	..	..	..
Faversham ....dep	7 15	..	..	..	9 20	..	1010	..	..	104[illegible]	..	..	..
Teynham	..	..	..	..	..	..	1019	..	..	..	..	..	..
Sittingbourne A ....arr	7 26	..	..	..	9 33	..	1024	..	..	1057	..	..	..
Sheerness-on-Sea ....dep	7 4	..	..	..	8 50	..	..	..	..	1021	..	1130	..
Queenborough 57	7 8	..	..	..	8 55	..	..	..	..	1025	..	1135	..
Swale Halt	7 13	..	..	..	..	..	..	..	..	..	..	..	..
Kemsley Halt	7 18	..	..	..	9 [illegible]	..	..	..	..	1033	..	1143	..
Sittingbourne A ....arr	7 24	..	..	..	9 8	..	..	..	..	1041	..	1149	..
Sittingbourne A ....dep	7 27	..	..	..	9 34	..	1025	..	..	1058	..	1153	..
Newington	7 34	..	..	..	..	..	1032	..	..	..	..	12 2	..
Rainham	7 40	..	..	..	..	..	1038	..	..	..	..	12 8	..
Gillingham (Kent)	7 46	..	..	..	..	..	1044	..	..	..	..	1214	..
Chatham ....arr	7 51	..	..	..	9 50	..	1049	..	..	1113	..	1219	..
Chatham ....dep	..	7 58	8 1	..	9 52	1024	..	1058	..	1114	1124	..	1224
Rochester	..	8 1	8 4	..	..	1027	..	11 1	..	..	1127	..	1227
Strood ....arr	..	..	8 7	..	..	1031	..	11 4	..	..	1131	..	1231
Swanley 34 ....arr	..	8 30	..	..	1030	..	..	..	..	..	..	..	..
Bromley South L .... "	..	8 43	..	..	1028	..	..	..	..	1150	..	..	..
Gravesend Cen. 113 ....arr	..	..	8 20	..	..	1031	..	1118	..	..	1144	..	1244
Dartford 93 .... "	..	..	8 36	..	..	11 2	..	1128	..	..	12 2	..	1 2
Woolwich Arsenal .... "	..	..	8 54	..	..	1120	..	1140	..	..	1220	..	1 20
New Cross ....arr	..	..	..	..	..	1136	..	..	..	..	1236	..	1 36
London Bridge .... "	..	..	9 14	..	..	1142	..	1154	..	..	1242	..	1 42
Cannon Street .... "	..	..	..	..	..	..	..	..	..	..	..	..	..
Waterloo .... "	..	..	9 17	..	..	1146	..	1159	..	..	1246	..	1 46
Charing Cross .... "	..	..	9 20	..	..	1149	..	12 2	..	..	1249	..	1 49
Victoria ....arr	..	8 59	..	..	1049	..	..	..	..	1213	..	..	..

FOR NOTES, SEE PAGE 71

SANDWICH, DEAL, DOVER, RAMSGATE, MARGATE, SHEERNESS-ON-SEA, and LONDON

Sundays—*continued*

Up	a.m	p.m	p.m	p.m	p.m	p.m	p.m	p.m	p.m	p.m	p.m	p.m	p.m	p.m	p.m	p.m	p.m	p.m	p.m	p.m	p.m	p.m	p.m	p.m	p.m	
Sandwich dep	1139		1 6		③			4 0			4 50	③			③	6 44		③			③	8 4				
Deal "	1148		1 14					4 9			4 59					6 53						8 13				
Walmer F [garet's Bay "	1153		1 19					4 14			5 5					6 59						8 18				
Martin Mill, fr St. Mar- "	12 0		1 26					4 20			5 13					7 6						8 26				
Dover { Marine dep																										
Dover { Priory "	1 8		2 0					5 4			5 44					7 23						9 5		9 50		
Kearsney D	1 13		2 5					5 9			5 49					7 29						9 11		9 55		
Stonehall and Lydden Halt																										
Shepherd's Well	1 21		2 13					5 18								7 37						9 20		10 4		
Snowdown and Nonington	1 26		2 18					5 23								7 42						9 25		10 9		
Aylesham Halt [Halt	1 29		2 21					5 26								7 46						9 28		1013		
Adisham C	1 32		2 24					5 29								7 51						9 31		1016		
Bekesbourne	1 38		2 30					5 35								7 57						9 37		1022		
Canterbury East B	1 45		2 37					5 42			6 10					8 6						9 45		1029		
Selling	1 58		2 50					5 55								8 19										
Faversham 60 arr	2 5		2 57					6 2			6 28					8 27						10 2		1046		
Ramsgate dep				2 2			5 5		5 14				6 30				7 20		8 5							
Dumpton Park, for East				2 5			5 8		5 17				6 33				7 23		8 8							
Broadstairs [Ramsgate				2 10			5 13		5 21				6 37				7 28		8 12							
Margate				2 19			5 22		5 30				6 46				7 37		8 21							
Westgate-on-Sea				2 25					5 35								7 42		8 26							
Birchington-on-Sea				2 30					5 40								7 47		8 31							
Herne Bay [Halt				2 44					5 54				7 4				8 1		8 45							
Chestfield & Swalecliffe				2 50					6 0								8 7									
Whitstable & Tankerton				2 56					6 5				7 13				8 12		8 54							
Faversham 60 arr				3 7					6 16				7 24				8 23		9 5							
Faversham dep	2 8			3 9					6 17		6 32		7 25			8 31	8 40		9 6							
Teynham				3 18													8 48									
Sittingbourne A arr	2 20			3 25							6 45					8 44	8 54		9 19							
Sheerness-on-Sea dep	1 32			3 0		4 25					6 10			7 44		8 17				9 23			1010		1035	
Queenborough 57	1 36			3 4		4 29					6 14			7 49		8 22				9 27			1015		1040	
Swale Halt						4 34																	1021			
Kemsley Halt	1 46			3 12		4 39					6 22			7 56		8 32				9 37			1026		1049	
Sittingbourne A arr	1 52			3 18		4 45					6 28					8 29				9 43			1032		1054	
Sittingbourne A dep	2 21			3 26							6 46					8 45	8 55		9 20				1038			
Newington	2 28			3 34													9 2									
Rainham	2 34			3 40													9 8									
Gillingham (Kent)	2 41			3 46							7 1			8 13		9 1	9 14	9 20	9 36				1053			
Chatham arr	2 46			3 51					6 42		7 6		7 50	8 18		9 6		9 23	9 41				1058			
Chatham dep		2 58		3 58	4 24				6 44	6 58	7 7	7 24	7 51		8 24	9 8		9 24	9 42		1024					
Rochester		3 1		4 1	4 27					7 1		7 27			8 27			9 27			1027					
Strood arr		3 4			4 31					7 4		7 31			8 31			9 31			1031					
Swanley 34 arr				4 30									8 30						1030							
Bromley South L "				4 43					7 23		7 44		8 28			9 45			1018							
Gravesend Cen. 113 arr		3 18			4 44					7 18		7 44			8 44			9 44			1044					
Dartford 93 "		3 28			5 2					7 28		8 2			9 2			10 2			11 2					
Woolwich Arsenal "		3 40			5 20					7 40		8 20			9 20			1020			1120					
New Cross arr					5 36							8 36			9 36			1036			1136					
London Bridge "		3 56			5 42					7 54		8 42			9 42			1042			1142					
Cannon Street "																										
Waterloo "		4 1			5 46					8 0		8 47			9 46			1046			1146					
Charing Cross "		4 5			5 49					8 3		8 50			9 49			1049			1149					
Victoria arr				5 3			7 9		7 46		8 6		8 52			10 5			1039							

NOTES

③ Third class only

A Sittingbourne and Milton Regis
B ½ mile to Canterbury West Station
C Station for Wingham (2½ miles)
D Station is adjacent to River and Ewell
F Station for Kingsdown (2 miles)
H Holborn Viaduct
L Over ½ mile to Bromley North Station
L 1 min. later on Sats.
N Mondays only
S O or **SO** Saturdays only
S X or **SX** Saturdays excepted

LOCAL TRAINS BETWEEN — PAGE
Ramsgate and Margate 34

LOCAL TRAINS and **Intermediate Stations**
Sandwich and Dover .. 43
Gillingham, and London 93, 147

OTHER TRAINS
Dover and London .. 43

LONDON, WOOLWICH, DARTFORD, GRAVESEND CENTRAL, MAIDSTONE WEST, CHATHAM, and GILLINGHAM (Kent)

Mls	Down	Week Days — a.m.																															
—	Charing Cross....dep	③								③	5 0		5 4	5 11		③	5 24		③			5 51			③	5 56	6 4						6 21
¾	Waterloo........ "										5 2		5 6	5 13			5 26					5 53				5 58	6 6						6 23
—	Cannon Street.... "									5 2								5 21		5 37			5 50	5 55	6 0				6 9		6 16	6 18	
1½	London Bridge... "	3 10								5 6	5 8		5 11	5 18			5 30	5 25	5 35	5 41		5 57	5 57	5 59	6 4	6 3	6 11		6 14		6 19	6 21	6 28
—	Holborn Viaduct dep	3 0		③			③				③		③	③			③	③		③		③		③		③	③		③		③	③	③
—	Blackfriars..... "																																
—	Elephant and Castle.																																
—	Peckham Rye......																																
5	Deptford..........																									6 9							6 34
5½	Greenwich........									5 14								5 34								6 11							6 36
6½	Maze Hill A......									5 17								5 38								6 14							6 38
7	Westcombe Park..									5 19								5 42								6 17							6 41
5	New Cross.........										5 15		5 18	5 26			5 37		5 42	5 48		6 3		6 5	6 10		6 17		6 20		6 25	6 27	
5½	St. John's.........												5 21	5 28										6 8					6 23			6 29	
6	Lewisham.........												5 24	5 30					5 45	5 51				6 10			6 20		6 25			6 31	
7	Blackheath........												5 26	5 33					5 47	5 54				6 12			6 23		6 27			6 34	
7½	Charlton..........									5 22			5 30					5 45		5 58						6 19			6 31				6 43
8¾	Woolwich Dockyard.									5 24			5 33							6 0									6 34				6 46
9½	Woolwich Arsenal...									5 28			5 36					5 52		6 3			6 15			6 23			6 37				6 48
10	Plumstead.........									5 31			5 39					5 55		6 6						6 26			6 39				6 51
11½	Abbey Wood........									5 34			5 43			5 51		6 0		6 9						6 29			6 42				6 55
13	Belvedere.........									5 37			5 46			5 54		6 4		6 12						6 32			6 46				6 58
14½	Erith..............									5 40			5 49			5 57		6 8		6 16						6 36			6 50				7 1
8	Kidbrooke.........													5 35					5 50					6 15			6 26					6 37	
9	Eltham (Well Hall).													5 38					5 53					6 18			6 28					6 40	
9½	Eltham Park........													5 40					5 55					6 20			6 30					6 42	
10¼	Falconwood........													5 43					5 57					6 23			6 33					6 45	
11¼	Welling...........													5 46					6 0					6 26			6 35					6 48	
12¾	Bexleyheath.......													5 49					6 4					6 30			6 38					6 51	
14	Barnehurst........													5 53					6 8					6 33			6 41					6 55	
7	Hither Green......										5 21						5 42					6 8			6 15						6 30		
7¾	Lee, for Burnt Ash..										5 25						5 44					6 10			6 17						6 32		
9¼	Mottingham.......										5 28						5 47					6 13			6 20						6 35		
10¼	New Eltham.......										5 32						5 50					6 16			6 23						6 38		
12	Sidcup............										5 36						5 53					6 19			6 29						6 41		
12¾	Albany Park.......										5 40						5 56					6 22			6 32						6 43		
13¾	Bexley............										5 43						5 59					6 25			6 35						6 46		
15¼	Crayford..........										5 46						6 3					6 28			6 39						6 50		
15½	Slades Green......			4 54						5 43			5 52			6 0		6 12		6 19						6 39			6 53				7 5
17	Dartford..........	3 41		4 59			5 30			5 48	5 51		5 56	5 59		6 4	6 7	6 16	6 14	6 23		6 32	6 34	6 40	6 45	6 44	6 47		6 57		6 55	7 2	7 9
19	Stone Crossing Halt..						5 34							6 4						6 28				6 45					7 2				
19¾	Greenhithe........			5 4			5 36							6 6						6 30				6 47					7 4				
20¾	Swanscombe Halt....						5 40							6 9						6 33				6 50					7 7				
21¾	Northfleet.........	3 53		5 9			5 43							6 12						6 36				6 53					7 10				
24	Gravesend Cen. arr	3 59		5 13			5 47				6 3			6 17				6 27		6 40			6 46	6 57					7 14				
	Gravesend Cen. dep	4 1									6 4			6 18						6 41			6 48						7 15				
28½	Higham............										6 12			6 25						6 49			6 57						7 23				
31½	Strood.......... arr	4 14									6 16			6 30						6 54			7 4						7 27				
—	Strood......... dep		4 33		5 29			5 55				6 24			6 41						7 0		7 13							7 34			
33	Cuxton...........		4 37		5 33			5 59				6 28			6 45						7 4		7 17							7 38			
35¼	Halling...........		4 41		5 36			6 2				6 31			6 48						7 7		7 20							7 41			
36¼	Snodland..........		4 45		5 39			6 5				6 34			6 51						7 10		7 23							7 44			
38	New Hythe.........		4 49		5 42			6 8				6 37			6 54						7 13		7 26							7 47			
39	Aylesford.........		4 52		5 45			6 11				6 40			6 57						7 16		7 29							7 50			
42	Maidstone Barracks				5 50			6 16				6 45			7 2						7 21		7 34							7 55			
42½	" West arr		4 59		5 52			6 18				6 47			7 4						7 23		7 36							7 57			
—	Strood.......... dep	4 16				5 24			6 10		6 17			6 31						6 55			7 5						7 28				
31¾	Rochester.........	4 23				5 29			6 13		6 21			6 35						6 59			7 9						7 32				
32¼	Chatham 60........	4 26				5 32			6 16		6 24			6 37						7 1			7 ⌊12						7 34				
34	Gillingham (Kent) arr	4 34				5 37			6 21		6 32			6 42						7 6			7 23						7 39				

A Maze Hill, for National Maritime Museum.

⌊ Dep. 5 mins. later.

③ Third class only

LONDON, WOOLWICH, DARTFORD, GRAVESEND CENTRAL, MAIDSTONE WEST, CHATHAM, and GILLINGHAM (Kent)

Week Days—*continued* (a.m.)

Down																																
Charing Cross .... dep	6 30	..	..	..	..	6 40	6 49	..	..	..	..	..	..	..	..	7 11	..	..	7 20	3	..	7 28	..	7 34	7 42	..	..	..	3	..	..	..
Waterloo .... "	6 32	..	..	..	..	6 42	6 51	..	..	..	..	..	..	..	..	7 13	..	..	7 22		..	7 30	..	7 36	7 44	..	..	..		..	..	..
Cannon Street .... "	..	..	6 36	..	..	..	..	6 55	6 52	6 58	..	7 0	..	7 4	7 11	..	..	7 17	..	..	7 26	..	7 35	..	..	7 41	7 44	..	..	7 48	7 54	7 57
London Bridge .... "	6 36	6 34	6 39	..	..	6 46	6 55	6 58	6 55	7 1	..	7 7	..	7 7	7 14	7 17	..	7 20	7 26	..	7 29	7 34	7 37	7 40	7 49	7 44	7 47	..	..	7 51	7 57	7 59
Holborn Viaduct dp	3	3	3	..	..	3	3	3	3	3	..	..	..	3	3	3	3	3	3	..	3	3	3	3	..	3	3	..	7 41	3	3	3
Blackfriars .... "				..	..						..	..	..							7 21					..			..	7 42			
Elephant and Castle	..	..	..	..	..	..	..	..	..	..	..	..	..	..	..	..	..	..	..	7 24	..	..	..	..	..	..	..	..	7 45	..	..	..
Peckham Rye	..	..	..	..	..	..	..	..	..	..	..	..	..	..	..	..	..	..	..	7 31	..	..	..	..	..	..	..	..	7 52	..	..	..
Deptford	..	..	6 45	..	..	..	..	7 4	..	..	..	..	..	..	..	..	..	..	..	..	7 35	..	..	..	..	..	..	..	..	7 57	..	..
Greenwich	..	..	6 47	..	..	..	..	7 6	..	..	..	..	..	..	..	..	..	..	..	..	7 37	..	..	..	..	..	..	..	..	7 59	..	..
Maze Hill A	..	..	6 50	..	..	..	..	7 8	..	..	..	..	..	..	..	..	..	..	..	..	7 39	..	..	..	..	..	..	..	..	8 2	..	..
Westcombe Park	..	..	6 52	..	..	..	..	7 11	..	..	..	..	..	..	..	..	..	..	..	..	7 42	..	..	..	..	..	..	..	..	8 4	..	..
New Cross	6 43	6 40	..	..	..	6 52	7 2	..	7 1	7 8	..	..	..	7 13	7 20	7 23	..	7 26	7 32	..	..	7 40	7 43	7 46	..	7 49	7 54	..	..	..	8 3	8 5
St. John's	6 45	..	..	..	..	6 55	..	..	..	7 10	..	..	..	..	..	..	..	..	..	..	..	..	..	..	..	7 52	..	..	..	..	..	..
Lewisham	..	6 44	..	..	..	6 57	..	..	7 5	7 12	..	..	..	7 16	..	7 26	..	7 29	..	7 36	..	7 43	..	7 49	..	7 54	..	..	7 58	..	..	8 9
Blackheath	..	6 47	..	..	..	7 1	..	..	7 7	7 15	..	..	..	7 19	..	7 28	..	7 31	..	..	..	7 45	..	7 51	..	7 57	..	..	8 1	..	..	8 11
Charlton	..	..	6 55	..	..	7 5	..	7 13	..	7 19	..	..	..	..	..	7 32	..	..	..	..	7 44	..	..	..	..	8 2	..	..	..	8 7	..	..
Woolwich Dockyard	..	..	6 57	..	..	7 8	..	7 16	..	7 21	..	..	..	..	..	7 35	..	..	..	..	7 47	..	..	..	..	..	..	..	..	8 9	..	..
Woolwich Arsenal	..	..	7 0	..	..	7 11	..	7 19	..	7 25	..	..	..	..	..	7 37	..	..	..	..	7 50	..	..	..	8 2	8 6	..	..	..	8 12	..	..
Plumstead	..	..	7 3	..	..	7 14	..	7 23	..	7 28	..	..	..	..	..	7 39	..	..	..	..	7 52	..	..	..	..	8 8	..	..	..	8 14	..	..
Abbey Wood	..	..	7 6	..	..	7 18	..	7 26	..	7 32	..	..	..	..	..	7 43	..	..	..	..	7 56	..	..	..	..	..	..	..	..	8 17	..	..
Belvedere	..	..	7 9	..	..	7 21	..	7 29	..	7 35	..	..	..	..	..	7 46	..	..	..	..	7 59	..	..	..	..	..	..	..	..	8 20	..	..
Erith	..	..	7 12	..	..	7 24	..	7 33	..	7 38	..	..	..	..	..	7 49	..	..	..	..	8 2	..	..	..	8 10	8 15	..	..	..	8 24	..	..
Kidbrooke	..	6 51	..	..	..	..	..	..	7 10	..	..	..	..	7 22	..	..	..	7 34	..	..	..	7 48	..	7 54	..	..	..	..	8 4	..	..	8 14
Eltham (Well Hall)	..	6 57	..	..	..	..	..	..	7 13	..	..	..	..	7 25	..	..	..	7 37	..	..	..	7 51	..	7 56	..	..	..	..	8 7	..	..	8 17
Eltham Park	..	7 1	..	..	..	..	..	..	7 16	..	..	..	..	7 27	..	..	..	7 39	..	..	..	7 53	..	7 58	..	..	..	..	8 9	..	..	8 19
Falconwood	..	7 4	..	..	..	..	..	..	7 19	..	..	..	..	7 29	..	..	..	7 42	..	..	..	7 55	..	8 1	..	..	..	..	8 11	..	..	8 21
Welling	..	7 8	..	..	..	..	..	..	7 22	..	..	..	..	7 32	..	..	..	7 44	..	..	..	7 58	..	8 3	..	..	..	..	8 14	..	..	8 24
Bexleyheath	..	7 14	..	..	..	..	..	..	7 25	..	..	..	..	7 35	..	..	..	7 47	..	..	..	8 1	..	8 6	..	..	..	..	8 17	..	..	8 27
Barnehurst	..	7 19	..	..	..	..	..	..	7 28	..	..	..	..	7 38	..	..	..	7 50	..	..	..	8 4	..	8 10	..	..	..	..	8 20	..	..	8 20
Hither Green	6 49	..	..	..	..	..	7 6	..	..	..	..	..	..	..	7 25	..	..	..	..	7 40	..	..	7 48	..	..	..	7 59	..	..	..	8 8	..
Lee, for Burnt Ash	6 51	..	..	..	..	..	7 8	..	..	..	..	..	..	..	7 27	..	..	..	7 37	7 42	..	..	..	..	..	..	8 1	..	..	..	..	..
Mottingham	6 55	..	..	..	..	..	7 12	..	..	..	..	..	..	..	7 31	..	..	..	7 41	7 45	..	..	..	..	..	..	8 4	..	..	..	..	..
New Eltham	6 58	..	..	..	..	..	7 14	..	..	..	..	..	..	..	7 34	..	..	..	7 43	7 48	..	..	7 53	..	..	..	8 7	..	..	..	8 14	..
Sidcup	7 1	..	..	..	..	..	7 17	..	..	..	..	..	..	..	7 37	..	..	..	7 46	7 51	..	..	7 56	..	..	..	8 10	..	..	..	8 17	..
Albany Park	7 3	..	..	..	..	..	7 19	..	..	..	..	..	..	..	7 40	..	..	..	..	7 53	..	..	..	..	..	..	8 12	..	..	..	..	..
Bexley	7 6	..	..	..	..	..	7 23	..	..	..	..	..	..	..	7 43	..	..	..	7 50	7 56	..	..	8 0	..	..	..	8 15	..	..	..	..	..
Crayford	7 9	..	..	..	..	..	7 26	..	..	..	..	..	..	..	7 46	..	..	..	7 54	7 59	..	..	8 4	..	..	..	8 18	..	..	..	8 23	..
Slades Green	..	7 25	7 15	..	..	7 27	..	7 37	..	7 41	..	..	..	..	..	7 52	..	..	..	..	8 6	..	..	..	..	..	..	..	..	8 27	..	..
Dartford	7 13	..	7 20	..	..	..	7 30	7 41	7 34	..	..	7 38	..	7 44	7 51	7 55	..	..	7 59	8 4	..	8 10	..	..	8 16	..	8 22	..	8 26	8 31	..	8 36
Stone Crossing Halt	..	..	7 24	..	..	..	..	..	..	..	..	..	..	7 48	..	7 59	..	..	..	..	..	..	..	..	..	..	..	..	..	..	..	..
Greenhithe	..	..	7 26	..	..	..	..	..	..	..	..	..	..	7 50	..	8 1	..	..	..	..	..	..	..	..	..	..	..	..	..	..	..	..
Swanscombe Halt	..	..	7 30	..	..	..	..	..	..	..	..	..	..	7 53	..	8 5	..	..	..	..	..	..	..	..	..	..	..	..	..	..	..	..
Northfleet	..	..	7 32	..	..	..	..	..	..	..	..	..	..	7 56	..	8 8	..	..	..	..	..	..	..	..	..	..	..	..	..	..	..	..
Gravesend Cen. arr	..	..	7 35	..	..	..	..	..	..	..	..	7 50	..	8 0	..	8 12	..	..	..	..	..	..	..	..	8 25	..	..	..	..	..	..	..
Gravesend Cen. dep	..	..	7 36	..	..	..	..	..	..	..	..	7 52	..	..	..	8 13	..	..	..	..	..	..	..	..	8 26	..	..	..	..	..	..	..
Higham	..	..	7 44	..	..	..	..	..	..	..	..	8 3	..	..	..	8 21	3	..	..	..	..	..	..	..	..	..	..	..	..	..	..	..
Strood .... arr	..	..	7 49	..	..	..	..	..	..	..	..	8 11	..	..	..	8 26		..	..	..	..	..	..	..	8 37	..	..	..	..	..	..	..
Strood .... dep	..	..	..	7 56	..	..	..	..	..	..	..	..	8 22	..	..	..	Mondays to Fridays	..	..	..	..	..	..	..	8 40	..	..	..	..	..	..	..
Cuxton	..	..	..	8 0	..	..	..	..	..	..	..	..	8 26	..	..	..		..	..	..	..	..	..	..	8 44	..	..	..	..	..	..	..
Halling	..	..	..	8 3	..	..	..	..	..	..	..	..	8 29	..	..	..		..	..	..	..	..	..	..	8 47	..	..	..	..	..	..	..
Snodland	..	..	..	8 6	..	..	..	..	..	..	..	..	8 32	..	..	..		..	..	..	..	..	..	..	8 50	..	..	..	..	..	..	..
New Hythe	..	..	..	8 9	..	..	..	..	..	..	..	..	8 35	..	..	..		..	..	..	..	..	..	..	8 53	..	..	..	..	..	..	..
Aylesford	..	..	..	8 12	..	..	..	..	..	..	..	..	8 38	..	..	..		..	..	..	..	..	..	..	8 56	..	..	..	..	..	..	..
Maidstone Barracks	..	..	..	8 17	..	..	..	..	..	..	..	..	8 43	..	..	..		..	..	..	..	..	..	..	9 1	..	..	..	..	..	..	..
" West arr	..	..	..	8 19	..	..	..	..	..	..	..	..	8 45	..	..	..		..	..	..	..	..	..	..	9 3	..	..	..	..	..	..	..
Strood .... dep	..	..	7 50	..	..	..	..	..	..	..	..	8 14	..	..	..	..	8 27	..	..	..	..	..	..	..	8 38	..	..	..	..	..	..	..
Rochester	..	..	7 53	..	..	..	..	..	..	..	..	8 20	..	..	..	..	8 30	..	..	..	..	..	..	..	8 41	..	..	..	..	..	..	..
Chatham 60	..	..	7 56	..	..	..	..	..	..	..	..	8‖23	..	..	..	..	8 32	..	..	..	..	..	..	..	8 44	..	..	..	..	..	..	..
Gillingham (Kent) arr	..	..	8 1	..	..	..	..	..	..	..	..	8 32	..	..	..	..	8 37	..	..	..	..	..	..	..	8 52	..	..	..	..	..	..	..

A Maze Hill, for National Maritime Museum. ‖ Dep. 3 mins. later

3 Third class only

LONDON, WOOLWICH, DARTFORD, GRAVESEND CENTRAL, MAIDSTONE WEST, CHATHAM and GILLINGHAM (Kent)

Down	a.m.														Week Days—continued												a.m.					
Charing Cross dep			7 59				3				8 9					8 17				3				8 40	8 42		8 44					8 52
Waterloo			8 1								8 11					8 19								8 42	8 44		8 46					8 54
Cannon Street		8 1							8 9				8 17					8 23			8 30	8 36						8 52			8 55	
London Bridge		8 4	8 5						8 12		8 15		8 21		8 23	8 23		8 26			8 33	8 39		8 47	8 49		8 51	8 55			8 58	8 59
Holborn Viaduct dp		3	3				8 3		3		3		3		3	3		3		8 25	3	3		3			3	3			3	3
Blackfriars							8 5													8 26												
Elephant and Castle																				8 29												
Peckham Rye							8 15													8 36												
Deptford									8 17						Mondays to Fridays						8 38										9 3	
Greenwich									8 19												8 40										9 5	
Maze Hill A									8 22												8 43										9 8	
Westcombe Park									8 24												8 45										9 10	
New Cross			8 13								8 21											8 45		8 54			8 57	9 1				9 5
St. John's											8 24													8 56								9 8
Lewisham							8 20				8 26		8 29							8 41		8 48					9 0	9 5				
Blackheath							8 23				8 28		8 32									8 51					9 3	9 8				
Charlton		8 13									8 32							8 35			8 48						9 7				9 13	
Woolwich Dockyard		8 16																8 38									9 9					
Woolwich Arsenal		8 18							8 30		8 36							8 41			8 51				9 2		9 13				9 17	
Plumstead		8 20							8 33		8 38							8 43			8 53						9 16				9 19	
Abbey Wood									8 36		8 41										8 57						9 19					
Belvedere									8 39		8 44										9 0						9 22					
Erith		8 28							8 42		8 47										9 3						9 25					
Kidbrooke							8 26						8 35									8 54						9 11				
Eltham (Well Hall)							8 28						8 37									8 56						9 13				
Eltham Park													8 39									8 59						9 16				
Falconwood													8 42									9 1						9 18				
Welling							8 33						8 44									9 4						9 21				
Bexleyheath													8 47									9 7						9 25				
Barnehurst							8 39						8 50									9 11						9 28				
Hither Green			8 18													8 33				8 45				9 0								9 12
Lee, for Burnt Ash			8 20													8 35				8 47				9 2								9 14
Mottingham			8 23													8 39				8 50				9 6								9 17
New Eltham			8 26													8 41				8 53				9 8								9 20
Sidcup			8 29												8 37	8 44				8 56				9 11								9 23
Albany Park			8 32													8 47								9 14								9 26
Bexley			8 35													8 50								9 17								9 29
Crayford			8 38												8 43	8 53				9 1				9 22								9 33
Slades Green		8 31							8 45		8 50										9 6						9 29					
Dartford		8 35	8 44						8 50		8 54					8 57				9 5	9 10	9 18		9 27	9 15		9 33	9 35				9 38
Stone Crossing Halt		8 39									8 58																	9 39				
Greenhithe		8 41									9 0																	9 41				
Swanscombe Halt		8 44									9 3																	9 45				
Northfleet		8 47									9 6																	9 47				
Gravesend Cen. arr		8 50									9 10														9 24			9 51				
Gravesend Cen. dep		8 51																							9 25			9 52				
Higham		8 59																										10 0				
Strood arr		9 4																							9 36			10 5				
Strood dep		9 10																							9 40					1010		
Cuxton		9 14																							9 44					1014		
Halling		9 17																							9 47					1017		
Snodland		9 20																							9 50					1020		
New Hythe		9 23																							9 53					1023		
Aylesford		9 26																							9 56					1026		
Maidstone Barracks		9 31																							10 1					1031		
" West arr		9 33																							10 3					1033		
Strood dep		9 5																							9 37			10 6				
Rochester		9 9																							9 40			10 10				
Chatham 60		9 11																							9 43			10†B25				
Gillingham (Kent) arr		9 16																							9 47			10B30				

A Maze Hill, for National Maritime Museum B Dep. Chatham 10 14 and arr. Gillingham 10 19 a.m. on Sats. † Arr. 10 13 a.m.

3 Third class only

LONDON, WOOLWICH, DARTFORD, GRAVESEND CENTRAL, MAIDSTONE WEST, CHATHAM, and GILLINGHAM (Kent)

Week Days—*continued* — a.m.

Down																																
Charing Cross....dep	..	..	9 3	..	..	..	..	..	9 13	..	3	..	9 23	9 25	..	9 28	..	9 42	..	..	9 40	3	9 46	..	9 47	9 50	..	..	9 53	9 55	..	10 2
Waterloo ......"	..	..	9 5	..	..	..	..	..	9 15	..		..	9 25	9 27	..	9 30	..	9 44	..	..	9 42		9 48	..	9 49	9 52	..	..	9 55	9 57	..	10 4
Cannon Street...."	9 1	9 3	..	9 8	9 10	9 10	9 12	9 15	..	9 21	..	9 24	..	..	9 29	..	..	..	9 38	9 39	..	9 45	..	9 49	..	..	..	..	..	..	10 5	..
London Bridge...."	9 4	9 6	9 10	9 11	9 13	9 13	9 15	9 18	9 20	9 24	..	9 27	9 29	9 31	9 32	9 35	..	9 49	9 41	9 42	9 46	9 47	9 52	9 52	9 54	9 57	..	..	9 59	10 1	10 8	10 8
Holborn Viaduct dep	3	3	3	3	3	3	3	3	3	3	..	3	3	3	3	3	..	..	3	3	3	..	3	3	3	3	..	..	3	3	3	3
Blackfriars ...."											9 21						..	..				..					..	..				
Elephant and Castle	..	..	..	..	..	..	..	..	..	..	9 24	..	..	..	..	..	..	..	..	..	..	..	..	..	..	..	..	..	..	..	..	..
Peckham Rye.......	..	..	..	..	..	..	..	..	..	..	9 31	..	..	..	..	..	..	..	..	..	..	..	..	..	..	..	..	..	..	..	..	..
Deptford.........	..	..	..	..	..	..	..	9 24	..	..	..	9 33	..	..	9 38	..	..	..	..	..	..	..	..	..	..	..	..	..	10 6	..	..	..
Greenwich........	..	..	..	..	9 20	9 20	..	9 26	..	..	..	9 35	..	..	9 40	..	..	..	..	..	..	..	..	..	..	..	..	..	10 8	..	..	..
Maze Hill A......	..	..	..	..	9 22	9 22	..	9 29	..	..	..	9 38	..	..	9 42	..	..	..	..	..	..	..	..	..	..	..	..	..	10 10	..	..	..
Westcombe Park..	..	..	9 19	9 19	9 25	9 25	..	9 31	..	..	..	9 41	..	..	9 45	..	..	..	..	..	..	..	..	..	..	..	..	..	10 13	..	..	..
New Cross...........	9 9	9 12	..	..	..	..	9 20	..	9 26	9 30	..	..	9 37	9 38	..	9 43	..	..	9 47	9 47	9 52	9 53	9 58	9 58	10 1	10 4	..	..	..	10 8	1015	1015
St. John's..........	..	..	..	..	..	..	..	..	9 29	..	..	..	9 39	9 40	..	..	..	..	9 49	9 50	9 55	..	10 0	10 0	10 3	..	..	..	..	..	1017	1017
Lewisham...........	9 13	9 15	..	..	..	..	9 23	..	..	9 33	9 36	..	9 41	9 42	..	9 46	..	..	9 52	9 52	..	9 56	10 3	10 3	Saturdays only	Mondays to Fridays	..	..	..	10 12	1019	1019
Blackheath..........	9 16	Saturdays only	..	..	..	..	9 26	..	..	9 36	9 40	..	Mondays to Fridays	Saturdays only	..	9 49	..	..	9 55	9 55	..	9 59	10 5	10 5			..	..	..	10 15	1022	1022
Charlton............	..		9 22	9 22	9 27	9 27	..	9 34	..	9 40	..	9 44			9 47	..	..	..	..	..	..	10 3	10 9	10 9			..	..	10 15	..	..	..
Woolwich Dockyard.	..		9 24	9 24	9 30	9 30	..	9 36	..	9 42	..	9 46			9 50	..	..	..	..	..	..	10 5	1012	1012			..	..	10 18	..	..	..
Woolwich Arsenal...	..		9 27	9 27	9 32	9 33	..	9 39	..	9 45	..	9 49			9 52	..	..	10 2	..	..	..	10 8	1015	1015			..	..	10 21	..	..	..
Plumstead...........	..		9 29	9 29	9 36	9 35	..	9 41	..	9 47	..	9 51			9 54	..	..	..	..	..	..	1010	1017	1017			..	..	10 24	..	..	..
Abbey Wood..........	..		9 32	9 32	..	9 38	..	..	..	9 50	..	9 55			..	..	..	..	..	..	..	1013	1021	1021			..	..	10 28	..	..	..
Belvedere...........	..		9 35	9 35	..	9 41	..	..	..	9 53	..	9 58			..	..	..	..	..	..	..	1016	1024	1024			..	..	10 31	..	..	..
Erith...............	..		9 38	9 38	..	9 44	..	9 48	..	9 56	..	10 1			..	..	..	..	..	..	..	1019	1027	1027			..	..	10 34	..	..	..
Kidbrooke..........	9 19	..	Saturdays only	Mondays to Fridays	Mondays to Fridays	Saturdays only	9 29	Mondays to Fridays	..	..	9 43	..			..	..	..	..	9 58	9 58	..	Mondays to Fridays	Mondays to Fridays	Saturdays only			..	..	..	10 18	1025	1025
Eltham (Well Hall)..	9 21	..					9 31		..	..	9 45	..			..	9 53	..	..	10 0	10 0	..						..	..	..	10 20	1027	1027
Eltham Park........	9 23	..					9 33		..	..	9 47	Mondays to Fridays			Saturdays only	9 55	..	..	10 2	10 2	..						..	..	..	10 22	1029	1029
Falconwood.........	9 26	..					9 36		..	..	9 50					9 58	..	..	10 5	10 5	..						..	..	..	10 25	1032	1032
Welling............	9 28	..					9 38		..	..	9 52					10 0	..	..	10 7	10 7	..						..	..	..	10 27	1034	1034
Bexleyheath........	9 31	..					9 41		..	..	9 55					10 3	..	..	1010	1010	..						..	..	..	10 30	1037	1037
Barnehurst.........	9 34	..					9 45		..	..	9 59					10 6	..	..	1013	1013	..						..	..	..	10 33	1040	1040
Hither Green	..	9 18					..		9 32	..	..		9 45	9 45		..	..	..	Mondays to Fridays	Saturdays only	9 59				10 6	10 8	..	..	..	Mondays to Fridays	Mondays to Fridays	Saturdays only
Lee, for Burnt Ash..	..	9 20					..		9 34	..	..		9 47	9 47		..	..	..			10 1				10 8	10 10	..	..	..			
Mottingham.........	..	9 24					..		9 38	..	..		9 51	9 51		..	..	..			10 4				1012	10 14	..	..	..			
New Eltham.........	..	9 26					..		9 40	..	..		9 53	9 53		..	..	..			10 7				1014	10 16	..	..	..			
Sidcup.............	..	9 30					..		9 43	..	..		9 56	9 56		..	..	..			1010				1017	10 19	..	..	..			
Albany Park........	..	9 33					..		9 47	..	..		9 59	9 59		..	..	..			1012				1020	10 22	..	..	..			
Bexley.............	..	9 36					..		9 50	..	..		10 2	10 2		..	..	..			1015				1023	10 25	..	..	..			
Crayford...........	..	9 39					..		9 56	..	..		10 5	10 5		..	..	..			1018				1027	10 28	..	..	..			
Slades Green........	9 40	..	9 42	9 42	..	9 47	..	9 51	..	10 0	..	10 6	..	..	10 4	..	..	..	..	..	..	1023	1030	1030	..	..	..	..	10 37	10 38	..	..
Dartford............	..	9 43	9 46	9 46	..	9 52	9 52	..	10 1	10 7	..	..	10 9	10 9	..	1012	..	10 15	1020	1019	1023	..	..	..	1031	10 31	..	..	10 43	..	1046	1047
Stone Crossing Halt..	..	..	..	9 50	..	..	..	..	10 5	..	..	..	..	..	..	..	..	..	..	1024	..	..	..	..	1035	10 35	..	..	..	..	..	..
Greenhithe.........	..	..	..	9 52	..	..	..	..	10 7	..	..	..	..	..	..	..	..	..	..	1026	..	..	..	..	1037	10 37	..	..	..	..	..	..
Swanscombe Halt.....	..	..	..	9 55	..	..	..	..	1010	..	..	..	..	..	..	..	..	..	..	1030	..	..	..	..	1041	10 41	..	..	..	..	..	..
Northfleet..........	..	..	..	9 58	..	..	..	..	1013	..	..	..	..	..	..	..	..	..	..	1032	..	..	..	..	1043	10 43	..	..	..	..	..	..
Gravesend Cen. arr	..	..	..	10 2	..	..	..	..	1017	..	..	..	..	..	..	..	..	10 24	..	1037	..	..	..	..	1048	10 48	..	..	..	..	..	..
Gravesend Cen. dep	..	..	..	..	..	..	..	..	..	..	..	..	..	..	..	..	..	10 25	..	..	..	..	..	..	..	10 49	..	..	..	..	..	..
Higham..............	..	..	..	..	..	..	..	..	..	..	..	..	..	..	..	..	..	..	..	..	..	..	..	..	..	10 57	..	..	..	..	..	..
Strood .... arr	..	..	..	..	..	..	..	..	..	..	..	..	..	..	..	..	..	10 36	..	..	..	..	..	..	..	11 5	..	..	..	..	..	..
Strood .... dep	..	..	..	..	..	..	..	..	..	..	..	..	..	..	..	..	..	10 40	..	..	..	..	..	..	..	..	1110	..	..	..	..	..
Cuxton..............	..	..	..	..	..	..	..	..	..	..	..	..	..	..	..	..	..	10 44	..	..	..	..	..	..	..	..	1114	..	..	..	..	..
Halling.............	..	..	..	..	..	..	..	..	..	..	..	..	..	..	..	..	..	10 47	..	..	..	..	..	..	..	..	1117	..	..	..	..	..
Snodland............	..	..	..	..	..	..	..	..	..	..	..	..	..	..	..	..	..	10 50	..	..	..	..	..	..	..	..	1120	..	..	..	..	..
New Hythe...........	..	..	..	..	..	..	..	..	..	..	..	..	..	..	..	..	..	10 53	..	..	..	..	..	..	..	..	1123	..	..	..	..	..
Aylesford...........	..	..	..	..	..	..	..	..	..	..	..	..	..	..	..	..	..	10 56	..	..	..	..	..	..	..	..	1126	..	..	..	..	..
Maidstone Barracks	..	..	..	..	..	..	..	..	..	..	..	..	..	..	..	..	..	11 1	..	..	..	..	..	..	..	..	1131	..	..	..	..	..
" West arr	..	..	..	..	..	..	..	..	..	..	..	..	..	..	..	..	..	11 3	..	..	..	..	..	..	..	..	1133	..	..	..	..	..
Strood.......... dep	..	..	..	..	..	..	..	..	..	..	..	..	..	..	..	..	..	10 37	..	..	..	..	..	..	..	11 6	..	..	..	..	..	..
Rochester...........	..	..	..	..	..	..	..	..	..	..	..	..	..	..	..	..	..	10 41	..	..	..	..	..	..	..	11 10	..	..	..	..	..	..
Chatham 60	..	..	..	..	..	..	..	..	..	..	..	..	..	..	..	..	..	10 43	..	..	..	..	..	..	..	11 12	..	..	..	..	..	..
Gillingham (Kent) arr	..	..	..	..	..	..	..	..	..	..	..	..	..	..	..	..	..	10 48	..	..	..	..	..	..	..	11 17	..	..	..	..	..	..

A Maze Hill, for National Maritime Museum

3 Third class only

LONDON, WOOLWICH, DARTFORD, GRAVESEND CENTRAL, MAIDSTONE WEST, CHATHAM and GILLINGHAM (Kent)

Mondays to Fridays

Down	a.m																
Charing Cross....dep	10 5	1010	..	1020	1028	..	1040	1046	1050	1110	1120	1128	1142	1140	1146	1150	1210
Waterloo .... "	10 7	1012	..	1022	1030	..	1042	1048	1052	1112	1122	1130	1144	1142	1148	1152	1212
Cannon Street.... "	..	..	..	..	..	..	..	..	..	..	..	..	..	..	..	..	..
London Bridge.... "	1011	1016	1024	1026	1034	..	1046	1052	1056	1116	1126	1134	1149	1146	1152	1156	1216
Holborn Viaduct dp	③	③	③	③	③	..	③	③	③	③	③	③	..	③	③	③	③
Blackfriars.... "						..							..				
Elephant and Castle	..	..	..	..	..	..	..	..	..	..	..	..	..	..	..	..	..
Peckham Rye........	..	..	..	..	..	..	..	..	..	..	..	..	..	..	..	..	..
Deptford..........	1017	..	..	..	1039	..	..	..	..	..	..	1139	..	..	..	..	..
Greenwich	1019	..	1030	..	1041	..	..	..	..	..	..	1141	..	..	..	..	..
Maze Hill A......	1021	..	1033	..	1044	..	..	..	..	..	..	1144	..	..	..	..	..
Westcombe Park..	1024	..	1036	..	1046	..	..	..	..	..	..	1146	..	..	..	..	..
New Cross.........	..	1023	..	1032	..	..	1052	1058	11 2	1123	1132	..	..	1152	1158	12 2	1223
St. John's.........	..	1025	..	1035	..	..	1054	11 0	11 5	1125	1135	..	..	1154	12 0	12 5	1225
Lewisham	..	1027	..	1037	..	..	1056	11 3	11 7	1127	1137	..	..	1156	12 3	12 7	1227
Blackheath.........	..	..	..	1039	..	..	..	11 5	11 9	..	1139	..	..	..	12 5	12 9	..
Charlton...........	1026	..	1038	..	1049	..	..	11 9	..	..	..	1149	..	..	12 9	..	..
Woolwich Dockyard.	1029	..	..	..	1051	..	..	1112	..	..	..	1151	..	..	1212	..	..
Woolwich Arsenal..	1032	..	1044	..	1054	..	..	1114	..	..	..	1154	12 2	..	1214	..	..
Plumstead..........	1034	..	1047	..	1056	..	..	1116	..	..	..	1156	..	..	1216	..	..
Abbey Wood.........	..	..	1050	..	1059	..	..	1120	..	..	..	1159	..	..	1220	..	..
Belvedere..........	..	..	1053	..	11 2	..	..	1123	..	..	..	12 2	..	..	1223	..	..
Erith..............	..	..	1057	..	11 5	..	..	1126	..	..	..	12 5	..	..	1226	..	..
Kidbrooke	..	..	..	1042	..	..	..	..	1112	..	1142	..	..	..	..	1212	..
Eltham (Well Hall)..	..	..	..	1045	..	..	..	..	1115	..	1145	..	..	..	..	1215	..
Eltham Park.......	..	..	..	1047	..	..	..	..	1117	..	1147	..	..	..	..	1217	..
Falconwood.........	..	..	..	1049	..	..	..	..	1119	..	1149	..	..	..	..	1219	..
Welling	..	..	..	1052	..	..	..	..	1122	..	1152	..	..	..	..	1222	..
Bexleyheath........	..	..	..	1055	..	..	..	..	1125	..	1155	..	..	..	..	1225	..
Barnehurst.........	..	..	..	1058	..	..	..	..	1129	..	1158	..	..	..	..	1229	..
Hither Green.......	..	1030	..	..	..	..	1059	..	..	1130	..	..	..	1159	..	..	1230
Lee, for Burnt Ash.	..	1032	..	..	..	..	11 1	..	..	1132	..	..	..	12 1	..	..	1232
Mottingham.........	..	1036	..	..	..	..	11 5	..	..	1136	..	..	..	12 5	..	..	1236
New Eltham.........	..	1038	..	..	..	..	11 7	..	..	1138	..	..	..	12 7	..	..	1238
Sidcup.............	..	1041	..	..	..	..	1110	..	..	1141	..	..	..	1210	..	..	1241
Albany Park........	..	1044	..	..	..	..	1113	..	..	1144	..	..	..	1213	..	..	1244
Bexley.............	..	1047	..	..	..	..	1116	..	..	1147	..	..	..	1216	..	..	1247
Crayford...........	..	1050	..	..	..	..	1119	..	..	1150	..	..	..	1219	..	..	1250
Slades Green.......	..	..	11 0	..	11 8	..	..	1129	..	..	..	12 8	..	..	1229	..	..
Dartford...........	..	1054	..	11 4	1112	..	1123	1133	1135	1154	12 4	1212	1215	1223	1233	1235	1254
Stone Crossing Halt..	..	..	..	..	..	..	..	..	1139	—	..	..	..	..	..	1239	—
Greenhithe.........	..	..	..	..	..	..	..	..	1141	Stop	..	..	..	..	..	1241	Stop
Swanscombe Halt.....	..	..	..	..	..	..	..	..	1144	..	..	..	..	..	..	1244	..
Northfleet..........	..	..	..	..	..	..	..	..	1147	..	..	..	..	..	..	1247	..
Gravesend Cen. arr	..	..	..	..	..	..	..	..	1151	..	..	..	1224	..	..	1251	..
Gravesend Cen. dep	..	..	..	..	..	..	..	..	1152	..	..	..	1225	..	..	1252	..
Higham..............	..	..	..	..	..	..	..	..	1159	..	..	..	..	..	..	1259	..
Strood.......... arr	..	..	..	..	..	..	..	..	12 4	p.m	..	..	1237	..	..	1 4	p.m
Strood.......... dep	..	..	..	..	..	..	..	..	..	1210	..	..	1240	..	..	..	1 10
Cuxton..............	..	..	..	..	..	..	..	..	..	1214	..	..	1244	..	..	..	1 14
Halling.............	..	..	..	..	..	..	..	..	..	1217	..	..	1247	..	..	..	1 17
Snodland............	..	..	..	..	..	..	..	..	..	1220	..	..	1250	..	..	..	1 20
New Hythe...........	..	..	..	..	..	..	..	..	..	1223	..	..	1253	..	..	..	1 23
Aylesford	..	..	..	..	..	..	..	..	..	1226	..	..	1256	..	..	..	1 26
Maidstone Barracks	..	..	..	..	..	..	..	..	..	1231	..	..	1 1	..	..	..	1 31
" West arr	..	..	..	..	..	..	..	..	..	1233	..	..	1 3	..	..	..	1 33
Strood............ dep	..	..	..	..	..	..	..	..	12 5	..	..	..	1238	..	..	1 5	..
Rochester...........	..	..	..	..	..	..	..	..	12 8	..	..	..	1241	..	..	1 8	..
Chatham 60..........	..	..	..	..	..	..	..	..	1212	..	..	..	1243	..	..	1 10	..
Gillingham (Kent) arr	..	..	..	..	..	..	..	..	1217	..	..	..	1248	..	..	1 15	..

Down					p.m											
Charing Cross....dep	1220	1228	..	..	1240	1246	1250	1 10	1 20	1 28	1 42	1 40	1 46	1 56	2 10	2 20
Waterloo .... "	1222	1230	..	..	1242	1248	1252	1 12	1 22	1 30	1 44	1 42	1 48	1 52	2 12	2 22
Cannon Street.... "	..	..	..	..	..	..	..	..	..	..	..	..	..	..	..	..
London Bridge.... "	1226	1234	..	..	1246	1252	1256	1 16	1 26	1 34	1 49	1 46	1 52	1 56	2 16	2 26
Holborn Viaduct dp	③	③	..	..	③	③	③	③	③	③	..	③	③	③	③	③
Blackfriars.... "			..	..							..					
Elephant and Castle	..	..	..	..	..	..	..	..	..	..	..	..	..	..	..	..
Peckham Rye........	..	..	..	..	..	..	..	..	..	..	..	..	..	..	..	..
Deptford..........	..	1239	..	..	..	..	..	..	..	1 39	..	..	..	..	..	..
Greenwich	..	1241	..	..	..	..	..	..	..	1 41	..	..	..	..	..	..
Maze Hill A......	..	1244	..	..	..	..	..	..	..	1 44	..	..	..	..	..	..
Westcombe Park..	..	1246	..	..	..	..	..	..	..	1 46	..	..	..	..	..	..
New Cross.........	1232	..	..	..	1252	1258	1 2	1 23	1 32	..	..	1 52	1 58	2 2	2 23	2 32
St. John's.........	1235	..	..	..	1254	1 0	1 5	1 25	1 35	..	..	1 54	2 0	2 5	2 25	2 35
Lewisham	1237	..	..	..	1256	1 3	1 7	1 27	1 37	..	..	1 56	2 3	2 7	2 27	2 37
Blackheath.........	1239	..	..	..	..	1 5	1 9	..	1 39	..	..	..	2 5	2 9	..	2 39
Charlton...........	..	1249	..	..	..	1 9	..	..	..	1 49	..	..	2 9	..	..	..
Woolwich Dockyard.	..	1251	..	..	..	1 12	..	..	..	1 51	..	..	2 12	..	..	..
Woolwich Arsenal..	..	1254	..	..	..	1 14	..	..	..	1 54	2 2	..	2 14	..	..	..
Plumstead..........	..	1256	..	..	..	1 16	..	..	..	1 56	..	..	2 16	..	..	..
Abbey Wood.........	..	1259	..	..	..	1 20	..	..	..	1 59	..	..	2 20	..	..	..
Belvedere..........	..	1 2	..	..	..	1 23	..	..	..	2 2	..	..	2 23	..	..	..
Erith..............	..	1 5	..	..	..	1 26	..	..	..	2 5	..	..	2 26	..	..	..
Kidbrooke	1242	..	..	..	..	..	1 12	..	1 42	..	..	..	..	2 12	..	2 42
Eltham (Well Hall)..	1245	..	..	..	..	..	1 15	..	1 45	..	..	..	..	2 15	..	2 45
Eltham Park.......	1247	..	..	..	..	..	1 17	..	1 47	..	..	..	..	2 17	..	2 47
Falconwood.........	1249	..	..	..	..	..	1 19	..	1 49	..	..	..	..	2 19	..	2 49
Welling	1252	..	..	..	..	..	1 22	..	1 52	..	..	..	..	2 22	..	2 52
Bexleyheath........	1255	..	..	..	..	..	1 25	..	1 55	..	..	..	..	2 25	..	2 55
Barnehurst.........	1258	..	..	..	..	..	1 29	..	1 58	..	..	..	..	2 29	..	2 58
Hither Green.......	..	..	..	..	1259	..	..	1 30	..	..	..	1 59	..	..	2 30	..
Lee, for Burnt Ash.	..	..	..	..	1 1	..	..	1 32	..	..	..	2 1	..	..	2 32	..
Mottingham.........	..	..	..	..	1 5	..	..	1 36	..	..	..	2 5	..	..	2 36	..
New Eltham.........	..	..	..	..	1 7	..	..	1 38	..	..	..	2 7	..	..	2 38	..
Sidcup.............	..	..	..	..	1 10	..	..	1 41	..	..	..	2 10	..	..	2 41	..
Albany Park........	..	..	..	..	1 13	..	..	1 44	..	..	..	2 13	..	..	2 44	..
Bexley.............	..	..	..	..	1 16	..	..	1 47	..	..	..	2 16	..	..	2 47	..
Crayford...........	..	..	..	..	1 19	..	..	1 50	..	..	..	2 19	..	..	2 50	..
Slades Green.......	..	1 8	..	..	..	1 29	..	..	..	2 8	..	..	2 29	..	..	..
Dartford...........	1 4	1 12	..	..	1 23	1 33	1 35	1 54	2 4	2 12	2 15	2 23	2 33	2 35	2 55	3 4
Stone Crossing Halt..	..	..	..	..	..	..	1 39	—	2 8	..	..	..	..	2 39	—	..
Greenhithe.........	..	..	..	..	..	..	1 41	Stop	2 10	..	..	..	..	2 41	Stop	..
Swanscombe Halt.....	..	..	..	..	..	..	1 44	..	2 13	..	..	..	..	2 44	..	..
Northfleet..........	..	..	..	..	..	..	1 47	..	2 16	..	..	..	..	2 47	..	..
Gravesend Cen. arr	..	..	..	..	..	..	1 51	..	2 20	..	2 24	..	..	2 51	..	..
Gravesend Cen. dep	..	..	..	..	..	..	1 52	..	..	..	2 25	..	..	2 52	..	..
Higham..............	..	..	..	..	..	..	1 59	..	..	..	..	..	..	2 59	..	..
Strood.......... arr	..	..	..	..	..	..	2 4	p.m	..	..	2 37	..	..	3 4	p.m	..
Strood.......... dep	..	..	..	1 40	..	..	..	2 10	..	..	2 40	..	..	..	3 10	..
Cuxton..............	..	..	..	1 44	..	..	..	2 14	..	..	2 44	..	..	..	3 14	..
Halling.............	..	..	..	1 47	..	..	..	2 17	..	..	2 47	..	..	..	3 17	..
Snodland............	..	..	..	1 50	..	..	..	2 20	..	..	2 50	..	..	..	3 20	..
New Hythe...........	..	..	..	1 53	..	..	..	2 23	..	..	2 53	..	..	..	3 23	..
Aylesford	..	..	..	1 56	..	..	..	2 26	..	..	2 56	..	..	..	3 26	..
Maidstone Barracks	..	..	..	2 1	..	..	..	2 31	..	..	3 1	..	..	..	3 31	..
" West arr	..	..	..	2 3	..	..	..	2 33	..	..	3 3	..	..	..	3 33	..
Strood............ dep	..	..	..	..	..	..	2 5	..	..	..	2 38	..	..	3 5	..	..
Rochester...........	..	..	..	..	..	..	2 8	..	..	..	2 41	..	..	3 8	..	..
Chatham 60..........	..	..	..	..	..	..	2 10	..	..	..	2 43	..	..	3 10	..	..
Gillingham (Kent) arr	..	..	..	..	..	..	2 15	..	..	..	2 48	..	..	3 15	..	..

A Maze Hill, for National Maritime Museum

③ Third class only

LONDON, WOOLWICH, DARTFORD, GRAVESEND CENTRAL, MAIDSTONE WEST, CHATHAM, and GILLINGHAM (Kent)

Mondays to Fridays—continued (p.m.)

Down																																
Charing Cross .... dep	2 28	..	2 40	2 46	2 50	3 10	..	..	3 20	3 27	..	3 42	3 40	3 44	3 50	..	3 54	..	4 3	..	..	..	..	..	4 23	..	..	4 33	..	4 42	..	..
Waterloo .... "	2 30	..	2 42	2 48	2 52	3 12	..	..	3 22	3 29	..	3 44	3 42	3 46	3 52	..	3 56	..	4 5	..	..	..	..	..	4 25	..	..	4 35	..	4 44	..	..
Cannon Street .... "	..	..	..	..	..	..	..	..	..	..	3 32	..	..	..	..	3 55	..	4 4	..	4 14	4 11	4 18	4 21	..	..	4 32	4 35	..	4 39	..	4 47	4 51
London Bridge ... "	2 34	..	2 46	2 52	2 56	3 16	..	..	3 26	3 33	3 35	3 49	3 46	3 50	3 56	3 58	4 0	4 7	4 9	4 17	4 14	4 21	4 24	..	4 29	4 36	4 38	4 39	4 42	4 49	4 50	4 54
Holborn Viaduct dep	3	..	3	3	3	3	..	..	3	3	3	..	3	3	3	3	3	3	3	..	3	3	3	..	3	..	3	3	3	..	3	3
Blackfriars .... "	..	..	..	..	..	..	..	..	..	..	..	..	..	..	..	..	..	..	..	..	..	..	..	..	..	..	..	..	..	..	..	..
Elephant and Castle	..	..	..	..	..	..	..	..	..	..	..	..	..	..	..	..	..	..	..	..	..	..	..	..	..	..	..	..	..	..	..	..
Peckham Rye	..	..	..	..	..	..	..	..	..	..	..	..	..	..	..	..	..	..	..	..	..	..	..	..	..	..	..	..	..	..	..	..
Deptford	2 39	..	..	..	..	..	..	..	..	3 39	..	..	..	..	..	..	4 6	..	..	..	..	..	4 29	..	..	..	4 44	..	..	..	..	..
Greenwich	2 41	..	..	..	..	..	..	..	..	3 41	..	..	..	..	..	..	4 8	..	..	..	..	..	4 31	..	..	..	4 46	..	..	..	..	..
Maze Hill A	2 44	..	..	..	..	..	..	..	..	3 44	..	..	..	..	..	..	4 10	..	..	..	..	..	4 34	..	..	..	4 48	..	..	..	..	..
Westcombe Park ..	2 46	..	..	..	..	..	..	..	..	3 46	..	..	..	..	..	..	4 13	..	..	..	..	..	4 36	..	..	..	4 51	..	..	..	..	..
New Cross	..	..	2 52	2 58	3 2	3 23	..	..	3 32	..	3 42	..	3 52	3 56	4 2	4 5	..	4 13	4 15	..	4 20	4 28	..	..	4 35	..	..	4 45	4 48	..	4 56	5 0
St. John's	..	..	2 54	3 0	3 5	3 25	..	..	3 35	..	3 45	..	..	3 58	4 5	4 7	..	..	4 18	..	..	4 30	..	..	..	..	..	..	..	..	..	5 3
Lewisham	..	..	2 56	3 3	3 7	3 27	..	..	3 37	..	3 47	..	..	4 0	4 7	4 9	..	..	4 20	..	4 23	4 32	..	..	..	..	..	4 48	..	..	4 59	5 5
Blackheath	..	..	..	3 5	3 9	..	..	..	3 39	..	3 50	..	..	4 3	4 9	..	..	..	4 22	..	4 25	4 35	..	..	..	..	..	4 51	..	..	5 1	5 7
Charlton	2 49	..	..	3 9	..	..	..	—	..	3 49	..	..	..	4 7	..	..	4 15	..	..	..	4 29	..	4 39	..	..	..	4 53	..	..	..	5 5	..
Woolwich Dockyard	2 51	..	..	3 12	..	..	..	—	..	3 51	..	..	..	4 9	..	..	4 18	..	..	..	..	..	4 41	..	..	..	4 56	..	..	..	5 8	..
Woolwich Arsenal	2 54	..	..	3 14	..	..	..	..	..	3 54	..	4 2	..	4 12	..	..	4 21	..	..	4 29	4 33	..	4 44	..	..	..	4 58	..	..	5 4	5 10	..
Plumstead	2 56	..	..	3 16	..	..	..	..	..	3 56	..	..	..	4 14	..	..	4 23	..	..	..	4 35	..	4 46	..	..	..	5 0	..	..	..	5 12	..
Abbey Wood	2 59	..	..	3 20	..	..	..	..	..	3 59	..	..	..	4 17	..	..	4 26	..	..	..	4 38	..	4 49	..	..	..	..	..	..	..	5 16	..
Belvedere	3 2	..	..	3 23	..	..	..	..	..	4 2	..	..	..	4 20	..	..	4 29	..	..	..	4 41	..	4 52	..	..	..	..	..	..	..	5 19	..
Erith	3 5	..	..	3 26	..	..	..	..	..	4 5	..	..	..	4 23	..	..	4 32	..	..	4 37	4 44	..	4 55	..	..	..	5 7	..	..	5 12	5 22	..
Kidbrooke	..	..	..	..	3 12	..	..	..	3 42	..	3 53	..	..	..	4 12	..	..	..	4 25	..	..	4 38	..	..	..	..	..	4 54	..	..	..	5 10
Eltham (Well Hall)	..	..	..	..	3 15	..	..	..	3 45	..	3 56	..	..	..	4 15	..	..	..	4 28	..	..	4 41	..	..	..	..	..	4 56	..	..	..	5 13
Eltham Park	..	..	..	..	3 17	..	..	..	3 47	..	3 58	..	..	..	4 17	..	..	..	4 30	..	..	4 43	..	..	..	..	..	4 58	..	..	..	5 15
Falconwood	..	..	..	..	3 19	..	..	..	3 49	..	4 0	..	..	..	4 19	..	..	..	4 32	..	..	4 45	..	..	..	..	..	5 1	..	..	..	5 17
Welling	..	..	..	..	3 22	..	..	..	3 52	..	4 3	..	..	..	4 22	..	..	..	4 35	..	..	4 48	..	..	..	..	..	5 3	..	..	..	5 20
Bexleyheath	..	..	..	..	3 25	..	..	..	3 55	..	4 6	..	..	..	4 25	..	..	..	4 38	..	..	4 51	..	..	..	..	..	5 6	..	..	..	5 23
Barnehurst	..	..	..	..	3 29	..	..	..	3 58	..	4 12	..	..	..	4 28	..	..	..	4 41	..	..	4 54	..	..	..	..	..	5 9	..	..	..	5 26
Hither Green	..	..	2 59	..	..	3 30	..	..	..	..	..	..	3 56	..	..	4 12	..	4 17	..	..	..	..	..	..	4 40	..	..	..	4 53	..	..	..
Lee, for Burnt Ash	..	..	3 1	..	..	3 32	..	..	..	..	..	..	3 58	..	..	4 14	..	4 19	..	..	..	..	..	..	4 42	..	..	..	4 55	..	..	..
Mottingham	..	..	3 5	..	..	3 36	..	..	..	..	..	..	4 2	..	..	4 18	..	4 23	..	..	..	..	..	..	4 45	..	..	..	4 59	..	..	..
New Eltham	..	..	3 7	..	..	3 38	..	..	..	..	..	..	4 4	..	..	4 20	..	4 25	..	..	..	..	..	..	4 48	..	..	..	5 1	..	..	..
Sidcup	..	..	3 10	..	..	3 41	..	..	..	..	..	..	4 7	..	..	4 23	..	4 28	..	..	..	..	..	..	4 51	..	..	..	5 4	..	..	..
Albany Park	..	..	3 13	..	..	3 44	..	..	..	..	..	..	4 10	..	..	4 26	..	4 31	..	..	..	..	..	..	4 53	..	..	..	5 7	..	..	..
Bexley	..	..	3 16	..	..	3 47	..	..	..	..	..	..	4 13	..	..	4 29	..	4 34	..	..	..	..	..	..	4 56	..	..	..	5 10	..	..	..
Crayford	..	..	3 19	..	..	3 50	..	..	..	..	..	..	4 18	..	..	4 32	..	4 38	..	..	..	..	..	..	4 59	..	..	..	5 13	..	..	..
Slades Green	3 8	..	..	3 29	..	..	..	..	..	4 8	..	..	..	4 26	..	..	4 36	..	..	..	4 47	..	4 58	..	..	..	5 10	5 14	..	..	5 25	..
Dartford	3 12	..	3 23	3 33	3 35	3 54	..	..	4 4	4 12	4 18	4 15	4 23	4 30	4 34	4 36	..	..	4 47	4 43	4 51	5 0	5 2	..	5 5	..	5 14	..	5 18	5 21	5 28	5 32
Stone Crossing Halt	..	..	3 27	..	3 39	..	..	..	..	..	4 22	..	..	4 34	..	..	..	..	Stop	..	4 55	..	5 7	..	..	..	..	..	..	..	5 32	..
Greenhithe	..	..	3 29	..	3 41	3 59	..	..	..	..	4 24	..	..	4 36	..	..	..	..	..	..	4 57	..	5 9	..	..	..	..	..	..	..	5 34	..
Swanscombe Halt	..	..	3 32	..	3 44	..	..	..	..	..	4 27	..	..	4 39	..	..	..	..	..	..	5 1	..	5 12	..	..	..	..	..	..	..	5 38	..
Northfleet	..	..	3 35	..	3 47	4 4	..	..	..	..	4 30	..	..	4 42	..	..	..	..	..	..	5 3	..	5 15	..	..	..	..	..	..	..	5 40	..
Gravesend Cen. arr	..	..	3 39	..	3 51	4 8	..	..	..	..	4 34	4 24	..	4 46	..	..	..	..	..	4 53	5 8	..	5 18	..	..	..	..	..	..	5 29	5 45	..
Gravesend Cen. dep	..	..	..	..	3 52	..	..	..	..	..	..	4 25	..	..	..	..	..	..	..	4 54	..	..	5 19	..	..	..	..	..	..	5 30	..	..
Higham	..	..	..	..	3 59	..	..	..	..	..	..	..	..	..	..	..	..	..	..	5 1	..	..	5 27	..	..	..	..	..	..	..	..	..
Strood .... arr	..	..	..	..	4 4	..	..	..	..	..	..	4 37	..	..	..	..	..	..	p.m.	5 7	..	..	5 32	..	..	..	..	..	..	5 41	..	..
Strood .... dep	..	..	..	..	..	..	4 10	..	..	..	..	4 40	..	..	..	..	..	..	4 52	5 12	..	..	..	5 40	..	..	..	..	..	5 46	..	..
Cuxton	..	..	..	..	..	..	4 14	..	..	..	..	4 44	..	..	..	..	..	..	4 56	5 16	..	..	..	5 44	..	..	..	..	..	5 50	..	..
Halling	..	..	..	..	..	..	4 17	..	..	..	..	4 47	..	..	..	..	..	..	4 59	5 19	..	..	..	5 47	..	..	..	..	..	5 53	..	..
Snodland	..	..	..	..	..	..	4 20	..	..	..	..	4 50	..	..	..	..	..	..	5 2	5 22	..	..	..	5 50	..	..	..	..	..	5 56	..	..
New Hythe	..	..	..	..	..	..	4 23	..	..	..	..	4 53	..	..	..	..	..	..	5 5	5 25	..	..	..	5 53	..	..	..	..	..	6 4	..	..
Aylesford	..	..	..	..	..	..	4 26	..	..	..	..	4 56	..	..	..	..	..	..	5 8	5 28	..	..	..	5 56	..	..	..	..	..	6 7	..	..
Maidstone Barracks	..	..	..	..	..	..	4 31	..	..	..	..	5 1	..	..	..	..	..	..	5 13	5 33	..	..	..	6 1	..	..	..	..	..	6 12	..	..
" West arr	..	..	..	..	..	..	4 33	..	..	..	..	5 3	..	..	..	..	..	..	5 15	5 35	..	..	..	6 3	..	..	..	..	..	6 14	..	..
Strood .... dep	..	..	..	..	4 5	..	..	..	..	..	..	4 38	..	..	..	..	..	..	..	5 8	..	..	5 33	..	..	..	..	..	..	5 42	..	..
Rochester	..	..	..	..	4 8	..	..	..	..	..	..	4 41	..	..	..	..	..	..	..	5 11	..	..	5 36	..	..	5 20	..	..	..	5 45	..	..
Chatham 60	..	..	..	..	4 10	..	..	..	..	..	..	4 43	..	..	..	..	..	..	..	5 13	..	..	5 38	..	..	5 [23	..	..	..	5 47	..	..
Gillingham (Kent) arr	..	..	..	..	4 15	..	..	..	..	..	..	4 48	..	..	..	..	..	..	..	5 17	..	..	5 42	..	..	5 34	..	..	..	5 52	..	..

A Maze Hill, for National Maritime Museum. [Dep 5 mins later. For Saturday Trains, see page 82: SUNDAY TRAINS, page 88

3 Third class only

LONDON, WOOLWICH, DARTFORD, GRAVESEND CENTRAL, MAIDSTONE WEST, CHATHAM, and GILLINGHAM (Kent)

Mondays to Fridays—*continued*

Down	p.m.																										p.m.						
Charing Cross....dep	4 48	4 51	..	..	..	5 4	5 6	5 12	..	5 17	..	..	..	5 25	..	..	..	5 30	5 42	..	..	..	..	..	5 45	..	5 47	..	..	..	5 55	..	..
Waterloo .... "	4 50	4 53	..	..	..	5 6	5 8	5 14	..	5 19	..	..	..	5 27	..	..	..	5 32	5 44	..	..	..	..	..	5 47	..	5 49	..	..	..	5 57	..	..
Cannon Street.... "	..	..	5 10	③	5 3	..	..	..	5 12	..	5 22	5 22	5 26	..	③	③	5 32	..	..	5 42	5 40	..	③	5 45	..	5 50	..	③	5 53	5 57	..	6 0	6 23
London Bridge... "	4 54	4 57	5 13		5 6	5 10	5 12	5 19	5 15	5 23	..	5 25	5 29	5 31			5 35	5 36	5 49	5 45	5 43	..		..	5 51	5 53	5 53		5 56	6 0	6 1	6 3	..
Holborn Viaduct dep	③	③	..	5 0	③	③	③	③	③	③	..	③	③	③	5 20	5 23	③	③	..	③	③	..	5 40	..	③	③	③	..	③	③	③	③	..
Blackfriars .... "			..	5 1							..				5 21	5 24			..			..	5 41	..				5 48					..
Elephant and Castle	..	..	..	5 4	..	..	..	..	..	..	..	..	..	..	5 24	5 27	..	..	..	..	..	..	5 44	..	..	..	..	5 51	..	..	..	..	..
Peckham Rye.......	..	..	..	5 11	..	..	..	..	..	..	..	..	..	..	5 31	5 34	..	..	..	..	..	..	5 51	..	..	..	..	5 58	..	..	..	..	..
Deptford..........	..	5 2	..	..	..	..	..	..	5 21	..	..	..	..	5 37	..	..	..	..	..	..	..	..	..	..	..	5 59	..	..	..	..	6 8	..	..
Greenwich	..	5 4	..	..	..	..	..	..	5 23	..	..	..	..	5 39	..	..	..	..	..	..	..	..	..	..	..	6 1	..	..	..	..	6 10	..	..
Maze Hill A.......	..	5 7	..	..	..	..	..	..	5 25	..	..	..	..	5 41	..	..	..	..	..	..	..	..	..	..	..	6 3	..	..	..	..	6 12	..	..
Westcombe Park..	..	5 9	..	..	..	..	..	..	5 28	..	..	..	..	5 45	..	..	..	..	..	..	..	..	..	..	..	6 6	..	..	..	..	6 15	..	..
New Cross.........	5 0	..	..	..	5 12	..	5 18	..	..	5 29	..	5 31	5 34	..	..	..	5 41	..	..	..	5 49	..	..	..	..	..	5 59	..	6 2	6 6	..	6 9	..
St. John's.........	5 2	..	..	..	..	5 17	..	..	..	5 32	..	..	..	..	..	..	..	5 43	..	..	..	..	..	..	..	..	..	..	6 4	..	..	..	..
Lewisham..........	..	..	..	5 16	..	5 19	5 22	..	..	..	..	..	5 37	..	5 36	5 40	..	5 45	..	..	..	..	5 56	..	6 0	..	..	6 3	6 6	..	..	6 12	..
Blackheath........	..	..	..	5 18	..	5 21	5 24	..	..	..	..	5 35	5 40	..	..	5 43	..	5 48	..	..	5 53	..	..	..	6 2	..	..	6 6	6 9	..	..	6 14	..
Charlton	..	5 12	..	..	..	5 25	..	..	5 30	..	..	..	5 44	5 48	..	..	..	..	..	..	..	..	..	..	..	6 8	..	..	6 13	..	6 17	..	..
Woolwich Dockyard.	..	5 14	..	..	..	5 28	..	..	5 33	..	..	..	..	5 50	..	..	..	..	..	..	..	..	..	..	..	..	..	..	6 15	..	6 20	..	..
Woolwich Arsenal...	..	5 17	..	..	..	5 30	..	..	5 35	..	..	..	5 47	5 53	..	..	..	..	6 2	..	..	..	..	..	..	6 12	..	..	6 18	..	6 22	..	..
Plumstead	..	5 19	..	..	..	5 32	..	..	5 37	..	..	..	5 50	5 55	..	..	..	..	..	..	..	..	..	..	..	6 14	..	..	6 20	..	6 25	..	..
Abbey Wood........	..	5 22	..	..	..	5 36	..	..	5 41	..	..	..	..	5 58	..	..	..	..	..	..	..	..	..	..	..	6 17	..	..	6 23	..	..	..	..
Belvedere	..	5 25	..	..	..	5 39	..	..	5 44	..	..	..	..	6 1	..	..	..	..	..	..	..	..	..	..	..	6 20	..	..	6 26	..	..	..	..
Erith..............	..	5 28	..	..	..	5 42	..	..	5 47	..	..	..	..	6 4	..	..	..	..	..	..	..	..	..	..	..	6 23	..	..	6 29	..	..	..	..
Kidbrooke..........	..	..	..	5 21	..	..	5 27	..	..	..	..	5 38	..	..	..	5 46	..	5 51	..	..	5 56	..	..	..	6 5	..	..	6 9	..	..	..	6 17	..
Eltham (Well Hall).	..	..	..	5 24	..	..	5 30	..	..	..	..	5 41	..	..	..	5 48	..	5 53	..	..	5 59	..	..	..	6 8	..	..	6 12	..	..	..	6 20	..
Eltham Park........	..	..	..	5 26	..	..	5 32	..	..	..	..	5 43	..	..	..	5 50	..	5 55	..	..	6 2	..	..	..	6 10	..	..	6 15	..	..	..	6 22	..
Falconwood........	..	..	..	5 28	..	..	5 35	..	..	..	..	5 45	..	..	..	5 53	..	5 58	..	..	6 4	..	..	..	6 12	..	..	6 18	..	..	..	6 24	..
Welling	..	..	..	5 31	..	..	5 38	..	..	..	..	5 48	..	..	..	5 55	..	6 1	..	..	6 7	..	..	..	6 15	..	..	6 21	..	..	..	6 27	..
Bexleyheath........	..	..	..	5 34	..	..	5 41	..	..	..	..	5 51	..	..	..	5 58	..	6 4	..	..	6 10	..	..	..	6 18	..	..	6 25	..	..	..	6 30	..
Barnehurst.........	..	..	..	5 37	..	..	5 45	..	..	..	..	5 54	..	..	..	6 1	..	6 7	..	..	6 13	..	..	..	6 22	..	..	6 28	..	..	..	6 33	..
Hither Green.......	5 6	..	..	..	5 17	..	..	..	..	5 35	..	..	..	..	5 40	..	5 46	..	..	..	..	..	5 59	..	..	..	6 4	..	..	6 11	..	..	..
Lee, for Burnt Ash.	5 8	..	..	..	5 19	..	..	..	..	5 37	..	..	..	..	5 42	..	5 48	..	..	..	..	..	6 1	..	..	..	6 6	..	..	6 13	..	..	..
Mottingham	5 11	..	..	..	5 22	..	..	..	..	5 41	..	..	..	..	5 46	..	5 52	..	..	..	..	..	6 5	..	..	..	6 10	..	..	6 17	..	..	..
New Eltham........	5 14	..	..	..	5 25	..	..	5 32	..	5 43	..	..	..	..	5 49	..	5 54	..	..	6 0	..	..	6 7	..	..	..	6 13	..	..	6 19	..	..	..
Sidcup	5 17	..	..	..	5 28	..	..	5 35	..	5 46	..	..	..	..	5 52	..	5 57	..	..	6 3	..	..	6 10	..	..	..	6 16	..	..	6 22	..	..	..
Albany Park........	5 19	..	..	..	5 30	..	..	5 37	..	5 49	..	..	..	..	5 54	..	6 0	..	..	6 6	..	..	6 13	..	..	..	6 19	..	..	6 25	..	..	..
Bexley	5 22	..	..	..	5 33	..	..	..	..	5 52	..	..	..	..	5 57	..	6 3	..	..	6 9	..	..	6 16	..	..	..	6 22	..	..	6 28	..	..	..
Crayford	5 25	..	..	..	5 37	..	..	..	..	5 55	..	..	..	..	6 0	..	..	..	..	6 14	..	..	6 19	..	..	..	6 25	..	..	6 31	..	..	..
Slades Green.......	..	5 31	..	..	..	5 45	..	..	5 51	..	..	6 0	..	6 7	..	..	..	6 16	..	..	..	..	..	..	..	6 27	..	..	6 32	..	..	6 40	..
Dartford...........	..	5 35	5 39	..	5 42	5 49	5 52	5 45	..	5 59	..	..	..	6 11	6 4	6 7	..	..	6 15	6 20	6 21	..	6 24	..	..	..	6 30	6 34	6 37	..	..	..	..
Stone Crossing Halt..	..	..	..	..	..	..	..	5 49	..	6 3	..	..	..	..	..	..	..	..	..	..	6 25	..	..	..	..	..	6 34	..	..	..	..	..	..
Greenhithe.........	..	..	..	..	..	..	..	5 51	..	6 5	..	..	..	..	..	..	..	..	..	..	6 27	..	..	..	..	..	6 36	..	..	..	..	..	..
Swanscombe Halt....	..	..	..	..	..	..	..	5 55	..	6 8	..	..	..	..	..	..	..	..	..	..	6 31	..	..	..	..	..	6 40	..	..	..	..	..	..
Northfleet.........	..	..	..	..	..	..	..	5 57	..	6 11	..	..	..	..	..	..	..	..	..	..	6 33	..	..	..	..	..	6 42	..	..	..	..	..	..
Gravesend Cen. arr	..	..	5 48	..	..	..	..	6 1	..	6 15	..	..	..	..	..	..	..	..	6 24	..	6 36	..	..	..	..	..	6 47	..	..	..	..	..	..
Gravesend Cen. dep	..	..	5 49	..	..	..	..	6 2	..	..	..	..	..	..	..	..	..	..	6 25	..	6 37	..	..	..	..	..	..	..	..	..	..	..	..
Higham.............	..	..	..	..	..	..	..	6 10	..	..	..	..	..	..	..	..	..	..	..	..	6 45	..	..	..	..	..	..	..	..	..	..	..	..
Strood .... arr	..	..	6 0	..	..	..	..	6 15	..	..	..	..	..	..	..	..	..	..	6 36	..	6 50	..	..	..	..	..	..	..	..	..	..	..	..
Strood .... dep	..	..	6 10	..	..	..	..	..	..	..	..	..	..	..	..	..	..	..	6 40	..	..	6 55	..	..	..	..	..	..	..	..	..	..	..
Cuxton.............	..	..	6 14	..	..	..	..	..	..	..	..	..	..	..	..	..	..	..	6 44	..	..	6 59	..	..	..	..	..	..	..	..	..	..	..
Halling............	..	..	6 17	..	..	..	..	..	..	..	..	..	..	..	..	..	..	..	6 47	..	..	7 2	..	..	..	..	..	..	..	..	..	..	..
Snodland...........	..	..	6 20	..	..	..	..	..	..	..	..	..	..	..	..	..	..	..	6 50	..	..	7 5	..	..	..	..	..	..	..	..	..	..	..
New Hythe..........	..	..	6 23	..	..	..	..	..	..	..	..	..	..	..	..	..	..	..	6 53	..	..	7 8	..	..	..	..	..	..	..	..	..	..	..
Aylesford	..	..	6 26	..	..	..	..	..	..	..	..	..	..	..	..	..	..	..	6 56	..	..	7 11	..	..	..	..	..	..	..	..	..	..	..
Maidstone Barracks	..	..	6 31	..	..	..	..	..	..	..	..	..	..	..	..	..	..	..	7 1	..	..	7 16	..	..	..	..	..	..	..	..	..	..	..
" West arr	..	..	6 33	..	..	..	..	..	..	..	..	..	..	..	..	..	..	..	7 3	..	..	7 18	..	..	..	..	..	..	..	..	..	..	..
Strood .... dep	..	..	6 1	..	..	..	..	6 16	..	..	..	..	..	..	..	..	..	..	6 37	..	6 51	..	..	..	..	..	..	..	..	..	..	..	..
Rochester	..	..	6 5	..	..	..	..	6 21	..	..	6 7	..	..	..	..	..	..	..	6 41	..	6 54	..	..	..	..	..	..	..	..	..	..	..	7 8
Chatham 60.........	..	..	6 7	..	..	..	..	6 23	..	..	6 11	..	..	..	..	..	..	..	6 43	..	6†57	..	..	6 31	..	..	..	..	..	..	..	..	7 11
Gillingham (Kent) arr	..	..	6 11	..	..	..	..	6 28	..	..	6 18	..	..	..	..	..	..	..	6 47	..	7 7	..	..	..	..	..	..	..	..	..	..	..	7 17

A Maze Hill, for National Maritime Museum † Dep 7 3 p.m.

③ Third class only

LONDON, WOOLWICH, DARTFORD, GRAVESEND CENTRAL, MAIDSTONE WEST, CHATHAM, and GILLINGHAM (Kent)

Mondays to Fridays—*continued* (p.m.)

Down																																	
Charing Cross .... dep	5 58	6 10	6 1	..	3	..	..	6 13	3	6 16	..	..	3	6 26	6 28	6 31	3	6 42	..	..	3	6 44	6 50	..	..	6 54	..	..	7 10	7 20	..	7 28	..
Waterloo .... "	6 0	6 12	6 3	..		..	..	6 15		6 18	..	..		6 28	6 30	6 33		6 44	..	..		6 46	6 52	..	..	6 56	..	..	7 12	7 22	..	7 30	..
Cannon Street.... "	..	..	..	..	..	6 9	6 15	..	..	..	6 19	6 25	..	..	..	..	..	..	6 40	6 44	..	..	..	..	6 56	..	7 6	7 17	..	..	7 25	..	7 34
London Bridge ... "	6 4	6 16	6 7	..	..	6 12	6 18	6 19	..	6 22	6 22	6 28	..	6 32	6 34	6 37	..	6 49	6 43	6 47	..	6 50	6 56	..	6 59	7 0	7 9	7 20	7 16	7 26	7 28	7 34	7 37
Holborn Viaduct dep	3	..	3	..	6 1	3	3	3	..	3	3	3	6 20	3	3	3	..	..	3	3	6 41	3	3	..	3	3	3	3	3	3	3	3	3
Blackfriars .... "		..		..	6 2				6 10				6 21				6 28	..			6 42			..									
Elephant and Castle	..	..	..	..	6 5	..	..	..	6 13	..	..	..	6 24	..	..	..	6 31	..	..	..	6 45	..	..	..	..	..	..	..	..	..	..	..	..
Peckham Rye	..	..	..	..	6 12	..	..	..	6 20	..	..	..	6 31	..	..	..	6 38	..	..	..	6 52	..	..	..	..	..	..	..	..	..	..	..	..
Deptford	..	..	..	..	..	..	6 24	..	..	..	..	..	..	..	6 40	..	..	..	..	..	..	..	..	..	..	7 6	..	7 26	..	..	..	7 39	..
Greenwich	..	..	..	..	..	..	6 26	..	..	..	..	..	..	..	6 42	..	..	..	..	..	..	..	..	..	..	7 8	..	7 28	..	..	..	7 41	..
Maze Hill A	..	..	..	..	..	..	6 28	..	..	..	..	..	..	..	6 45	..	..	..	..	..	..	..	..	..	..	7 11	..	7 30	..	..	..	7 44	..
Westcombe Park ..	..	..	..	..	..	..	6 31	..	..	..	..	..	..	..	6 47	..	..	..	..	..	..	..	..	..	..	7 13	..	7 33	..	..	..	7 46	..
New Cross	6 11	..	6 14	..	..	6 19	..	..	..	..	6 28	..	..	..	..	6 44	..	..	6 49	6 53	..	6 56	7 2	..	7 5	..	7 15	..	7 23	7 32	7 35	..	7 43
St. John's	6 13	..	..	..	..	6 21	..	..	..	..	6 30	..	..	..	..	..	..	..	..	..	..	..	7 5	..	7 7	..	7 17	..	7 25	7 35	7 37	..	7 46
Lewisham	..	..	6 17	..	6 17	6 23	..	..	6 28	..	6 32	..	6 41	..	..	..	6 46	..	..	6 56	6 59	6 59	..	..	7 9	..	7 19	..	7 27	7 37	..	..	7 48
Blackheath	..	..	6 20	..	..	6 26	..	..	6 31	..	6 35	..	..	6 42	..	..	6 49	..	..	6 59	..	7 1	..	..	7 12	..	7 22	..	..	7 39	..	..	7 50
Charlton	..	..	..	..	..	6 30	6 33	..	..	..	..	..	..	..	6 50	..	..	..	..	7 4	..	..	..	..	..	7 16	7 26	7 35	..	..	..	7 49	..
Woolwich Dockyard.	..	..	..	..	..	..	6 36	..	..	..	..	..	..	..	..	..	..	..	..	7 6	..	..	..	..	..	7 18	7 29	7 38	..	..	..	7 51	..
Woolwich Arsenal ...	..	..	..	..	..	6 33	6 38	..	..	..	..	..	..	..	6 53	..	..	7 2	..	7 9	..	..	..	..	..	7 21	7 31	7 40	..	..	..	7 54	..
Plumstead	..	..	..	..	..	6 35	6 40	..	..	..	..	..	..	..	6 55	..	..	..	..	7 11	..	..	..	..	..	7 23	7 34	7 42	..	..	..	7 56	..
Abbey Wood	..	..	..	..	..	6 39	6 44	..	..	..	..	..	..	..	6 59	..	..	..	..	7 14	..	..	..	..	..	7 26	7 37	7 46	..	..	..	7 59	..
Belvedere	..	..	..	..	..	6 42	6 47	..	..	..	..	..	..	..	7 2	..	..	..	..	7 17	..	..	..	..	..	7 29	7 40	7 49	..	..	..	8 2	..
Erith	..	..	..	..	..	6 45	6 50	..	..	..	..	..	..	..	7 5	..	..	..	..	7 20	..	..	..	..	..	7 32	7 43	7 52	..	..	..	8 5	..
Kidbrooke	..	..	6 23	..	..	..	..	..	6 34	..	6 39	..	..	6 45	..	..	6 52	..	..	..	..	7 4	..	..	7 15	..	..	..	..	7 42	..	..	7 53
Eltham (Well Hall).	..	..	6 26	..	..	..	..	..	6 37	..	6 42	..	..	6 48	..	..	6 55	..	..	..	..	7 7	..	..	7 17	..	..	..	..	7 45	..	..	7 56
Eltham Park	..	..	6 28	..	..	..	..	6 34	6 39	..	6 44	..	..	6 50	..	..	6 57	..	..	..	..	7 9	..	..	7 19	..	..	..	..	7 47	..	..	7 58
Falconwood	..	..	6 31	..	..	..	..	6 37	6 42	..	6 47	..	..	6 52	..	..	7 0	..	..	..	..	7 11	..	..	7 22	..	..	..	..	7 49	..	..	8 0
Welling	..	..	6 34	..	..	..	..	6 39	6 44	..	6 50	..	..	6 55	..	..	7 3	..	..	..	..	7 14	..	..	7 24	..	..	..	..	7 52	..	..	8 3
Bexleyheath	..	..	6 37	..	..	..	..	6 42	6 47	..	6 53	..	..	6 58	..	..	7 6	..	..	..	..	7 17	..	..	7 27	..	..	..	..	7 55	..	..	8 6
Barnehurst	..	..	6 40	..	..	..	..	6 45	6 51	..	6 56	..	..	7 1	..	..	7 10	..	..	..	..	7 22	..	..	7 30	..	..	..	..	7 58	..	..	8 9
Hither Green	6 17	..	..	..	6 21	..	..	..	..	..	..	6 37	6 44	..	..	6 48	..	..	6 53	..	7 2	..	7 8	..	..	..	..	..	7 30	..	7 40	..	..
Lee, for Burnt Ash.	6 19	..	..	..	6 23	..	..	..	..	6 34	..	6 39	6 46	..	..	6 50	..	..	6 55	..	7 4	..	7 10	..	..	..	..	..	7 32	..	7 42	..	..
Mottingham	6 22	..	..	..	6 27	..	..	..	..	..	..	6 43	6 49	..	..	6 54	..	..	6 59	..	7 7	..	7 13	..	..	..	..	..	7 36	..	7 46	..	..
New Eltham	6 25	..	..	..	6 30	..	..	..	..	6 38	..	6 45	6 52	..	..	6 57	..	..	7 2	..	7 10	..	7 16	..	..	..	..	..	7 38	..	7 48	..	..
Sidcup	6 28	..	..	..	6 34	..	..	..	..	6 41	..	6 48	6 55	..	..	7 0	..	..	7 5	..	7 13	..	7 19	..	..	..	..	..	7 41	..	7 51	..	..
Albany Park	6 30	..	..	..	6 37	..	..	..	..	6 44	..	6 51	6 57	..	..	7 3	..	..	7 8	..	7 15	..	7 21	..	..	..	..	..	7 44	..	7 55	..	..
Bexley	6 33	..	..	..	6 40	..	..	..	..	6 47	..	6 54	7 0	..	..	7 6	..	..	7 11	..	7 18	..	7 24	..	..	..	..	..	7 47	..	7 57	..	..
Crayford	6 36	..	..	..	6 43	..	..	..	..	6 49	..	6 57	7 3	..	..	7 9	..	..	7 15	..	7 21	..	7 28	..	..	..	..	..	7 50	..	8 2	..	..
Slades Green	..	..	..	..	..	6 48	6 54	..	..	..	7 8	..	..	..	7 8	..	..	..	..	7 24	..	..	..	..	..	7 36	7 46	7 55	..	..	..	8 8	8 15
Dartford	6 41	6 43	6 50	..	6 47	..	7 0	6 52	..	6 56	..	7 2	7 9	7 7	7 13	..	..	7 15	7 21	..	7 25	7 30	7 33	..	7 36	7 40	..	..	7 54	8 4	8 5	8 12	..
Stone Crossing Halt.	..	..	6 54	..	..	..	..	..	..	..	..	7 6	..	..	..	..	..	..	7 25	..	..	..	7 37	..	..	..	..	..	7 58	..	..	..	..
Greenhithe	..	..	6 56	..	..	..	..	..	..	..	..	7 8	..	..	..	..	..	..	7 27	..	..	..	7 39	..	..	..	..	..	8 0	..	..	..	..
Swanscombe Halt	..	..	6 59	..	..	..	..	..	..	..	..	7 12	..	..	..	..	..	..	7 30	..	..	..	7 43	..	..	..	..	..	8 3	..	..	..	..
Northfleet	..	..	7 2	..	..	..	..	..	..	..	..	7 14	..	..	..	..	..	..	7 33	..	..	..	7 45	..	..	..	..	..	8 6	..	..	..	..
Gravesend Cen. arr	..	6 52	7 5	..	..	..	..	..	..	..	..	7 19	..	..	..	..	..	7 24	7 37	..	..	..	7 49	..	..	..	..	..	8 9	..	..	..	..
Gravesend Cen. dep	..	6 53	7 6	..	..	..	..	..	..	..	..	..	..	..	..	..	..	7 25	..	..	..	..	7 50	..	..	..	..	..	8 10	..	..	..	..
Higham	..	7 1	7 14	..	..	..	..	..	..	..	..	..	..	..	..	..	..	..	..	..	..	..	7 58	..	..	..	..	..	8 18	..	..	..	..
Strood .... arr	..	7 6	7 19	..	..	..	..	..	..	..	..	..	..	..	..	..	..	7 36	..	..	..	..	8 4	..	..	..	..	..	8 23	..	..	..	..
Strood .... dep	..	..	..	7 22	..	..	..	..	..	..	..	..	..	..	..	..	..	7 40	..	..	..	..	..	8 10	..	..	..	..	..	..	..	..	..
Cuxton	..	..	..	7 26	..	..	..	..	..	..	..	..	..	..	..	..	..	7 44	..	..	..	..	..	8 14	..	..	..	..	..	..	..	..	..
Halling	..	..	..	7 29	..	..	..	..	..	..	..	..	..	..	..	..	..	7 47	..	..	..	..	..	8 17	..	..	..	..	..	..	..	..	..
Snodland	..	..	..	7 32	..	..	..	..	..	..	..	..	..	..	..	..	..	7 50	..	..	..	..	..	8 20	..	..	..	..	..	..	..	..	..
New Hythe	..	..	..	7 35	..	..	..	..	..	..	..	..	..	..	..	..	..	7 53	..	..	..	..	..	8 23	..	..	..	..	..	..	..	..	..
Aylesford	..	..	..	7 38	..	..	..	..	..	..	..	..	..	..	..	..	..	7 56	..	..	..	..	..	8 26	..	..	..	..	..	..	..	..	..
Maidstone Barracks	..	..	..	7 43	..	..	..	..	..	..	..	..	..	..	..	..	..	8 1	..	..	..	..	..	8 31	..	..	..	..	..	..	..	..	..
" West arr	..	..	..	7 45	..	..	..	..	..	..	..	..	..	..	..	..	..	8 3	..	..	..	..	..	8 33	..	..	..	..	..	..	..	..	..
Strood .... dep	..	7 7	7 20	..	..	..	..	..	..	..	..	..	..	..	..	..	..	7 37	..	..	..	..	8 6	..	..	..	..	..	8 24	..	..	..	..
Rochester	..	7 12	7 22	..	..	..	..	..	..	..	..	..	..	..	..	..	..	7 41	..	..	..	..	8 11	..	..	..	..	..	8 29	..	..	..	..
Chatham 60	..	7 18	7 24	..	..	..	..	..	..	..	..	..	..	..	..	..	..	7 43	..	..	..	..	8 13	..	..	..	..	..	8 31	..	..	..	..
Gillingham (Kent) arr	..	7 22	7 29	..	..	..	..	..	..	..	..	..	..	..	..	..	..	7 47	..	..	..	..	8 19	..	..	..	..	..	8 36	..	..	..	..

A Maze Hill, for National Maritime Museum

For Saturday Trains, see page 82; SUNDAY TRAINS, page 88

3 Third class only

LONDON, WOOLWICH, DARTFORD, GRAVESEND CENTRAL, MAIDSTONE WEST, CHATHAM, and GILLINGHAM (Kent)

Mondays to Fridays—*continued.*

Down	p.m.																						p.m.									ngt.
Charing Cross....dep	7 40	..	7 46	7 50	8 10	..	..	8 28	8 30	8 40	8 42	8 46	9 0	9 10	9 28	9 30	9 40	..	9 46	10 0	1010	1028	1030	1040	1046	11 0	1110	1116	1132	1142	1148	1253
Waterloo .... "	7 42	..	7 48	7 52	8 12	..	..	8 30	8 32	8 42	8 44	8 48	9 2	9 12	9 30	9 32	9 42	..	9 48	10 2	1012	1030	1032	1042	1048	11 2	1112	1118	1134	1144	1150	1255
Cannon Street ... "	..	..	..	..	..	..	..	..	..	..	..	..	..	..	..	..	..	..	..	..	..	..	..	..	..	..	..	..	..	..	..	1 3
London Bridge... "	7 46	..	7 52	7 56	8 16	..	..	8 34	8 38	8 46	8 49	8 52	9 6	9 16	9 34	9 36	9 43	..	9 52	10 6	1016	1034	1038	1046	1052	11 6	1116	1122	1138	1148	1154	1 7
Holborn Viaduct dp	3	..	3	3	3	..	..	3	3	3	..	3	3	3	3	3	3	..	3	3	3	3	3	3	3	3	3	3	3	3	3	3
Blackfriars ...... "		..				..	..				..							..														
Elephant and Castle	..	..	..	..	..	..	..	..	..	..	..	..	..	..	..	..	..	..	..	..	..	..	..	..	..	..	..	..	..	..	..	..
Peckham Rye........	..	..	..	..	..	..	..	..	..	..	..	..	..	..	..	..	..	..	..	..	..	..	..	..	..	..	..	..	..	..	..	..
Deptford..........	..	..	..	..	..	..	..	8 39	..	..	..	..	..	..	9 39	..	..	..	..	..	..	1039	..	..	..	..	..	..	1144	..	..	..
Greenwich.........	..	..	..	..	..	..	..	8 41	..	..	..	..	..	..	9 41	..	..	..	..	..	..	1041	..	..	..	..	..	..	1146	..	..	..
Maze Hill A.......	..	..	..	..	..	..	..	8 44	..	..	..	..	..	..	9 44	..	..	..	..	..	..	1044	..	..	..	..	..	..	1148	..	..	..
Westcombe Park..	..	..	..	..	..	..	..	8 46	..	..	..	..	..	..	9 46	..	..	..	..	..	..	1046	..	..	..	..	..	..	1151	..	..	..
New Cross..........	7 52	..	7 58	8 2	8 23	..	..	..	8 42	8 53	..	8 58	9 12	9 23	..	9 42	9 53	..	9 58	1012	1023	..	1042	1053	1058	1112	1123	1128	..	1153	12 0	1 13
St. John's..........	7 54	..	8 0	8 5	8 25	..	..	..	8 45	8 55	..	9 0	9 15	9 25	..	9 45	9 55	..	10 0	1015	1025	..	1045	1055	11 0	1115	1125	1130	..	..	12 2	1 16
Lewisham	7 57	..	8 3	8 7	8 27	..	..	..	8 47	8 57	..	9 3	9 17	9 27	..	9 47	9 57	..	10 3	1017	1027	..	1047	1057	11 3	1117	1127	1132	..	1156	..	1 18
Blackheath..........	..	..	8 5	8 9	..	..	..	..	8 49	..	..	9 5	9 19	..	..	9 49	..	..	10 5	1019	..	..	1049	..	11 5	1119	..	1135	..	1159	..	1 21
Charlton	..	..	8 9	..	..	..	..	8 49	..	..	..	9 9	..	..	9 49	..	..	..	10 9	..	..	1049	..	..	11 9	..	..	1139	1153	..	..	1 25
Woolwich Dockyard.	..	..	8 12	..	..	..	..	8 51	..	..	..	9 12	..	..	9 51	..	..	..	10 12	..	..	1051	..	..	1112	..	..	1141	1156	..	..	1 27
Woolwich Arsenal...	..	..	8 14	..	..	..	..	8 54	..	..	9 4	9 14	..	..	9 54	..	..	..	10 14	..	..	1054	..	..	1114	..	..	1144	1158	..	..	1 30
Plumstead..........	..	..	8 16	..	..	..	..	8 56	..	..	..	9 16	..	..	9 56	..	..	..	10 16	..	..	1056	..	..	1116	..	..	1146	12 0	..	..	1 33
Abbey Wood..........	..	..	8 20	..	..	..	..	8 59	..	..	..	9 20	..	..	9 59	..	..	..	10 20	..	..	1059	..	..	1120	..	..	1149	12 4	..	..	1 37
Belvedere	..	..	8 23	..	..	..	..	9 2	..	..	..	9 23	..	..	10 2	..	..	..	10 23	..	..	11 2	..	..	1123	..	..	1152	12 7	..	..	1 40
Erith..............	..	..	8 26	..	..	..	..	9 5	..	..	..	9 26	..	..	10 5	..	..	..	10 26	..	..	11 5	..	..	1126	..	..	1155	1210	..	..	1 43
Kidbrooke..........	..	..	..	8 12	..	..	..	..	8 52	..	..	..	9 22	..	..	9 52	..	..	..	1022	..	..	1052	..	..	1122	..	..	..	12 2	..	..
Eltham (Well Hall)..	..	..	..	8 15	..	..	..	..	8 55	..	..	..	9 25	..	..	9 55	..	..	..	1025	..	..	1055	..	..	1125	..	..	..	12 4	..	..
Eltham Park........	..	..	..	8 17	..	..	..	..	8 57	..	..	..	9 27	..	..	9 57	..	..	..	1027	..	..	1057	..	..	1127	..	..	..	12 6	..	..
Falconwood..........	..	..	..	8 19	..	..	..	..	8 59	..	..	..	9 29	..	..	9 59	..	..	..	1029	..	..	1059	..	..	1129	..	..	..	12 9	..	..
Welling	..	..	..	8 22	..	..	..	..	9 2	..	..	..	9 32	..	..	10 2	..	..	..	1032	..	..	11 2	..	..	1132	..	..	..	1211	..	..
Bexleyheath........	..	..	..	8 25	..	..	..	..	9 5	..	..	..	9 35	..	..	10 5	..	..	..	1035	..	..	11 5	..	..	1135	..	..	..	1214	..	..
Barnehurst..........	..	..	..	8 29	..	..	..	..	9 9	..	..	..	9 38	..	..	10 9	..	..	..	1038	..	..	11 9	..	..	1138	..	..	..	1217	..	..
Hither Green........	8 0	..	..	..	8 30	..	..	..	..	9 0	..	..	..	9 30	..	..	10 0	..	..	..	1030	..	..	11 0	..	..	1130	..	..	..	12 6	..
Lee, for Burnt Ash.	8 2	..	..	..	8 32	..	..	..	..	9 2	..	..	..	9 32	..	..	10 2	..	..	..	1032	..	..	11 2	..	..	1132	..	..	..	12 8	..
Mottingham	8 5	..	..	..	8 36	..	..	..	..	9 6	..	..	..	9 36	..	..	10 6	..	..	..	1036	..	..	11 6	..	..	1136	..	..	..	1211	..
New Eltham.........	8 8	..	..	..	8 38	..	..	..	..	9 8	..	..	..	9 38	..	..	10 8	..	..	..	1038	..	..	11 8	..	..	1138	..	..	..	1214	..
Sidcup	8 11	..	..	..	8 41	..	..	..	..	9 11	..	..	..	9 41	..	..	1011	..	..	..	1041	..	..	1111	..	..	1141	..	..	..	1217	..
Albany Park.........	8 13	..	..	..	8 44	..	..	..	..	9 14	..	..	..	9 44	..	..	1014	..	..	..	1044	..	..	1114	..	..	1144	..	..	..	1219	..
Bexley	8 16	..	..	..	8 47	..	..	..	..	9 17	..	..	..	9 47	..	..	1017	..	..	..	1047	..	..	1117	..	..	1147	..	..	..	1222	..
Crayford	8 19	..	..	..	8 50	..	..	..	..	9 20	..	..	..	9 50	..	..	1020	..	..	..	1050	..	..	1120	..	..	1150	..	..	..	1225	..
Slades Green........	..	..	8 29	..	..	..	..	9 8	..	..	..	9 29	..	..	10 8	..	..	..	10 29	..	..	11 8	..	..	1129	..	..	1158	1213	..	..	1 46
Dartford...........	8 23	..	8 33	8 35	8 54	..	..	9 12	9 15	9 24	9 18	9 34	9 44	9 54	1012	1015	1024	..	10 34	1044	1054	1112	1115	1124	1134	1144	1154	12 2	1217	1225	1229	1 50
Stone Crossing Halt..	8 27	..	..	8 39	..	..	..	..	..	..	..	9 39	—	..	..	..	..	..	10 39	..	—	..	—	..	1139	—	..	..	..	..	..	..
Greenhithe	8 29	..	..	8 41	..	..	..	..	..	..	..	9 41	Stop	..	..	..	..	..	10 41	..	Stop	..	Stop	..	1141	Stop	..	..	..	1231	..	..
Swanscombe Halt.....	8 32	..	..	8 44	..	..	..	..	..	..	..	9 44	..	..	..	..	..	..	10 44	..	..	..	..	..	1144	..	..	..	..	..	..	..
Northfleet..........	8 35	..	..	8 47	..	..	..	..	..	..	..	9 47	..	..	..	..	..	..	10 47	..	..	..	..	..	1147	..	..	..	..	1236	..	..
Gravesend Cen. arr	8 39	..	..	8 51	..	..	..	..	..	..	9 27	9 51	..	..	..	..	..	..	10 51	..	p.m	..	..	..	1151	..	..	..	..	1239	..	..
Gravesend Cen. dep	..	..	..	8 52	..	..	..	..	..	..	9 28	9 52	..	..	..	..	..	..	10 52	..	11 0	..	..	..	1152	..	..	..	..	1240	..	..
Higham..............	..	..	..	8 59	..	..	..	..	..	..	..	9 59	..	..	..	..	..	..	10 59	..	11 8	..	..	..	1159	..	..	..	..	..	..	..
Strood .... arr	..	..	..	9 4	..	..	..	..	..	..	9 39	10 4	p.m	..	..	..	..	..	11 4	..	1115	..	p.m	..	12 4	ngt.	..	..	..	1252	..	..
Strood .... dep	..	8 40	..	..	..	9 10	..	..	..	..	9 42	..	1010	..	..	..	..	..	..	..	..	..	1110	..	..	1210	..	..	..	..	..	..
Cuxton	..	8 44	..	..	..	9 14	..	..	..	..	9 46	..	1014	..	..	..	..	..	..	..	..	..	1114	..	..	1214	..	..	..	..	..	..
Halling	..	8 47	..	..	..	9 17	..	..	..	..	9 49	..	1017	..	..	..	..	..	..	..	..	..	1117	..	..	1217	..	..	..	..	..	..
Snodland............	..	8 50	..	..	..	9 20	..	..	..	..	9 52	..	1020	..	..	..	..	..	..	..	..	..	1120	..	..	1220	..	..	..	..	..	..
New Hythe...........	..	8 53	..	..	..	9 23	..	..	..	..	9 55	..	1023	..	..	..	..	..	..	..	..	..	1123	..	..	1223	..	..	..	..	..	..
Aylesford	..	8 56	..	..	..	9 26	..	..	..	..	9 58	..	1026	..	..	..	..	..	..	..	..	..	1126	..	..	1225	..	..	..	..	..	..
Maidstone Barracks	..	9 1	..	..	..	9 31	..	..	..	..	10 3	..	1031	..	..	..	..	..	..	..	..	..	1131	..	..	1231	..	..	..	..	..	..
" West arr	..	9 3	..	..	..	9 33	..	..	..	..	10 5	..	1033	..	..	..	..	..	..	..	..	..	1133	..	..	1233	..	..	..	..	..	..
Strood .... dep	..	..	..	9 5	..	..	..	..	..	..	9 40	10 5	..	..	..	..	..	..	11 5	..	1116	..	..	..	12 5	..	..	..	..	1253	..	..
Rochester...........	..	..	..	9 8	..	..	..	..	..	..	9 43	10 7	..	..	..	..	..	..	11 7	..	1120	..	..	..	12 7	..	..	..	..	..	..	..
Chatham 60..........	..	..	..	9 10	..	..	..	..	..	..	9 46	1010	..	..	..	..	..	..	11 9	..	1123	..	..	..	1210	..	..	..	..	1258	..	..
Gillingham (Kent) arr	..	..	..	9 15	..	..	..	..	..	..	9 50	1015	..	..	..	..	..	..	..	..	1129	..	..	..	1215	..	..	..	..	1 2	..	..

A Maze Hill, for National Maritime Museum.

3 Third class only

LONDON, WOOLWICH, DARTFORD, GRAVESEND CENTRAL, MAIDSTONE WEST, CHATHAM, and GILLINGHAM (Kent)

Down	a.m.															Saturdays												a.m.					
Charing Cross....dep		1010			1020		1028			1042	1040				1050			10 58	1110				1120		1128	1142	1140			1146		1152	
Waterloo........ "		1012			1022		1030			1044	1042				1052			11 0	1112				1122		1130	1144	1142			1148		1154	
Cannon Street.... "	10 8		1015			1028			1034				1047								1114								1143		1152		
London Bridge... "	10 11	1017	1018		1026	1031	1034		1037	1049	1046		1050		1056			11 4	1116		1117		1126		1134	1149	1146		1146	1152	1155	1158	3
	3	3			3	3	3		3		3		3		3			3	3		3		3		3		3		3	3	3	3	
Holborn Viaduct dp																																	1159
Blackfriars... "																																	12 1
Elephant and Castle																																	12 4
Peckham Rye......																																	1211
Deptford..........							1039											11 9							1139						12 1		
Greenwich........							1041											11 11							1141						12 3		
Maze Hill A......							1044											11 14							1144						12 5		
Westcombe Park..							1046											11 16							1146						12 8		
New Cross..........	10 17	1023			1032	1038			1042		1052		1056		11 2				1122		1123		1132				1152		1152	1159		12 5	
St. John's..........	10 20				1035	1040			1045				1058		11 5						1125		1135						1154				
Lewisham..........	10 22	1026			1037	1042			1047				11 0		11 7						1127		1137						1156	12 2			1215
Blackheath........		1029			1039				1050				11 3		11 9						1130		1139						1159	12 4			
Charlton..........		1033					1049						11 7					11 19			1134				1149				12 3		1210		
Woolwich Dockyard.		1035					1051						11 9					11 21			1136				1151				12 5				
Woolwich Arsenal...		1038	1032				1054			11 2			1112					11 24			1139				1154	12 2			12 8		1214		
Plumstead..........		1040					1056						1114					11 26			1141				1156				1210		1216		
Abbey Wood........		1043					1059						1117					11 29			1144				1159				1213		1219		
Belvedere..........		1046					11 2						1120					11 32			1147				12 2				1216		1222		
Erith..............		1049					11 5						1123					11 35			1150				12 5	1210			1219		1225		
Kidbrooke..........					1042				1053						1112								1142							12 7			
Eltham (Well Hall).					1045				1056						1115								1145							1210			
Eltham Park........					1047				1058						1117								1147							1212			
Falconwood........					1049				11 0						1119								1149							1214			
Welling............					1052				11 3						1122								1152							1217			
Bexleyheath........					1055				11 6						1125								1155							1220			
Barnehurst..........					1058				1110						1128								1158							1223			
Hither Green........	10 25					1045					1056								1127								1157					12 9	1218
Lee, for Burnt Ash..	10 28					1047					1058								1129								1159					1211	1220
Mottingham........	10 31					1051					11 2								1133								12 3					1215	1224
New Eltham........	10 34					1053					11 4								1135								12 6					1217	1226
Sidcup..............	10 37					1056					11 7								1138								12 9					1220	1229
Albany Park........	10 39					1059					1110								1141								1212					1223	1232
Bexley..............	10 42					11 2					1113								1144								1215					1226	1235
Crayford............	10 45					11 5					1116								1147								1218					1229	1238
Slades Green........		1053					11 8						1126					11 38			1153				12 8				1222		1228		
Dartford............	10 50	1058			11 4	11 9	1112		1118	1115	1120		1130		1135			11 42	1152		1158		12 4		1212	1216	1221		1226	1229	1232		1242
Stone Crossing Halt..	10 54										1124				1139						12 4						1225						
Greenhithe..........	10 56										1126				1141						12 7						1227			1234			
Swanscombe Halt.....	10 59										1129				1144						1210						1231						
Northfleet..........	11 2										1132				1147						1213						1233			1238			
Gravesend Cen. arr	11 6		1053							1124	1136				1151						1217					1226	1237			1244			
Gravesend Cen. dep	11 7		1054							1125					1152											1227	1238						
Higham..............	11 15														1159												1247						
Strood........... arr	11 19		11 5							1136					12 4	p.m.								p.m.		1237	1252	p.m.					
Strood.......... dep			1110							1143						1213								1225		1241		1257					
Cuxton..............			1114							1147						1217								1229		1245		1 1					
Halling..............			1117							1150						1220								1232		1248		1 4					
Snodland............			1120							1153						1223								1235		1251		1 7					
New Hythe..........			1123							1156						1226								1238		1254		1 10					
Aylesford..........			1126							1159						1229								1241		1257		1 13					
Maidstone Barracks			1131							12 4						1234								1246		1 2		1 18					
" West arr			1133							12 6						1236								1248		1 4		1 20					
Strood............ dep	11 20		11 6							1137					12 5											1238	1254						
Rochester..........			11 9							1141					12 8											1242	1258						
Chatham 60..........	11 24		1111							1143					1210											1244	1 0						
Gillingham (Kent) arr	11 29		1117							1148					1215											1249	1 6						

A Maze Hill, for National Maritime Museum

For SUNDAY TRAINS, see page 88

3 Third class only

LONDON, WOOLWICH, DARTFORD, GRAVESEND CENTRAL, MAIDSTONE WEST, CHATHAM, and GILLINGHAM (Kent).

Saturdays—*continued*

Down	noon							p.m.																				p.m.				
Charing Cross.... dep	12 0							1213			1217				1225		1227							1242				1239			1246	
Waterloo .... "	12 2							1215			1219				1227		1229							1244				1241			1248	
Cannon Street.... "		1214		1210			12 9		1219					1224				1232			12 37		1245		1240				1247			1250
London Bridge... "	12 6	1217		1213			1212	1219	1222		1223	3		1227	1231		1233	1235		3	12 40			1248	1243			1246	1250		1252	1253
Holborn Viaduct dep	3			3			3	3	3		3			3	3		3	3		12 28	3				3			3	3		3	3
Blackfriars.... "												1221								12 30												
Elephant and Castle												1224								12 33												
Peckham Rye........												1231								12 40												
Deptford..........								1226							1237																	1259
Greenwich								1228							1239																	1 1
Maze Hill A......								1230							1241																	1 3
Westcombe Park..								1233							1244						12 48											1 6
New Cross..........	1213			1219			1218		1228					1232			1239	1241							1249			1254				
St. John's..........							1221		1230									1243							1251							
Lewisham..........	1216						1223		1232			1239						1245		12 47					1253			1257				
Blackheath..........	1219						1225		1235			1241						1248							1256			1259				
Charlton..........							1229	1235							1246						12 51				1 1							1 8
Woolwich Dockyard.							1232								1249						12 53				1 4							
Woolwich Arsenal..							1234	1239							1251						12 56			1 1	1 6							1 12
Plumstead..........							1236	1241							1253						12 58				1 8							1 14
Abbey Wood..........							1240	1244							1257										1 12							1 17
Belvedere..........							1243	1247							1 0										1 15							1 20
Erith..........							1246	1250							1 3										1 18							1 23
Kidbrooke..........	1222								1238			1244						1251														
Eltham (Well Hall)..	1224								1240			1247						1253										1 4				
Eltham Park..........	1226								1242			1249						1255										1 6				
Falconwood..........	1229								1245			1251						1258														
Welling	1231								1247			1254						1 0										1 9				
Bexleyheath..........	1234								1250			1257						1 3										1 12				
Barnehurst..........	1238								1253			1 0						1 7										1 15				
Hither Green..........				1223										1237			1244			12 50												
Lee, for Burnt Ash.				1225										1239			1246			12 52											1 3	
Mottingham..........				1229							1236			1242			1250			12 56											1 7	
New Eltham..........				1232							1238			1245			1252			12 59									1 4		1 10	
Sidcup..........				1235							1241			1248			1255			1 2									1 7		1 13	
Albany Park..........				1238							1244			1250			1258			1 4									1 10		1 16	
Bexley..........				1241							1247			1253			1 1			1 7									1 13		1 19	
Crayford..........				1244							1250			1258			1 4			1 11									1 16		1 22	
Slades Green..........							1249	1254							1 6										1 21			1 21				1 27
Dartford..........				1248				1258	1 0		1254	1 6		1 3			1 10			1 17				1 14	1 25				1 20		1 26	
Stone Crossing Halt..				1252					1 4																				1 24			
Greenhithe..........				1254					1 6																				1 26			
Swanscombe Halt.....				1258					1 10																				1 29			
Northfleet..........				1 0					1 12																				1 32			
Gravesend Cen. arr		1253		1 3					1 17															1 23					1 36			
Gravesend Cen. dep		1254		1 4																				1 24					1 37			
Higham..........				1 12																				1 32					1 45			
Strood.......... arr		1 5		1 17																				1 37					1 49			
Strood.......... dep		1 10			1 21																			1 41		1 55						
Cuxton..........		1 14			1 25																			1 45		1 59						
Halling..........		1 17			1 28																			1 48		2 2						
Snodland..........		1 20			1 31																			1 51		2 5						
New Hythe..........		1 23			1 34																			1 54		2 8						
Aylesford..........		1 26			1 37																			1 57		2 11						
Maidstone Barracks		1 31			1 42																			2 2		2 16						
" West arr		1 33			1 44																			2 4		2 18						
Strood.......... dep		1 6		1 18																				1 38					1 50			
Rochester..........		1 9		1 21																				1 42					1 54			
Chatham 60..........		1 11		1 23																			1 31	1 44					1 56			
Gillingham (Kent) arr		1 16		1 29																				1 49					2 0			

A Maze Hill, for National Maritime Museum

LONDON, WOOLWICH, DARTFORD, GRAVESEND CENTRAL, MAIDSTONE WEST, CHATHAM, and GILLINGHAM (Kent)

p.m. — **Saturdays**—*continued* — p.m.

Down																																	
Charing Cross ....dep.			1251									1 5	1 13		1 18				1 23		1 27	1 29		1 42				1 38			1 47	1 53	
Waterloo .... "			1253									1 7	1 15		1 20				1 25		1 29	1 31		1 44				1 40			1 49	1 55	
Cannon Street.... "				1256	1257	1 6		1 8	1 15					1 19		1 21	1 23	1 25					1 35				1 40		1 45				
London Bridge... "	3	3	1257	1259	1 0	1 9	3	1 11				1 11	1 20	1 22	1 24	1 24	1 26	1 28	1 29	3	1 33	1 35	1 38	1 49		3	1 43	1 44	1 48		1 53	1 59	
Holborn Viaduct dep		1247	3	3	3	3	1 0	3				3	3	3	3		3	3	3	1 21	3	3	3			1 27	3	3	3		3	3	
Blackfriars .... "	1242	1249					1 2													1 23						1 29							
Elephant and Castle	1245	1252					1 6													1 26						1 32							
Peckham Rye.......	1253	1259					1 13													1 34						1 39							
Deptford..........								1 17														1 41										2 5	
Greenwich			1 5					1 19														1 43										2 7	
Maze Hill A.......			1 7					1 22														1 46										2 9	
Westcombe Park..								1 24														1 48										2 12	
New Cross.........				1 6	1 6	1 15							1 26	1 28					1 35				1 44				1 49	1 50	1 54		1 59		
St. John's.........				1 8	1 8	1 17						1 19		1 31			1 33										1 51				2 2		
Lewisham.........	1259	1 4			1 10		1 18					1 21	1 30	1 33				1 36		1 41	1 41					1 46	1 53		1 57		2 4		
Blackheath........	1 2				1 13		1 20					1 24	1 32	1 35				1 38			1 44					1 49			1 59		2 6		
Charlton..........			1 11					1 27						1 39								1 51							2 4			2 14	
Woolwich Dockyard.			1 14					1 29						1 42								1 53							2 6			2 17	
Woolwich Arsenal...			1 16					1 32						1 44		1 37						1 56		2 2					2 9			2 19	
Plumstead.........			1 19					1 34						1 46								1 58							2 11			2 21	
Abbey Wood.......			1 22											1 50															2 14			2 25	
Belvedere.........			1 25											1 53															2 17			2 28	
Erith..............			1 28					1 40						1 56															2 20			2 31	
Kidbrooke.........	1 5				1 16		1 23					1 28	1 35					1 41								1 52	1 57				2 9		
Eltham (Well Hall).	1 8				1 19		1 26					1 31	1 38					1 44			1 49					1 54	2 0				2 12		
Eltham Park.......	1 10				1 21		1 28					1 33	1 40					1 46			1 51					1 56	2 2				2 14		
Falconwood........	1 13				1 24		1 30					1 36	1 42					1 48			1 54					1 59	2 5				2 16		
Welling	1 15				1 26		1 33					1 38	1 45					1 51			1 56					2 2	2 7				2 19		
Bexleyheath.......	1 18				1 29		1 36					1 41	1 48					1 54			1 59					2 5	2 10				2 23		
Barnehurst........	1 22				1 33		1 39					1 45	1 51					1 57			2 3					2 8	2 14				2 26		
Hither Green.......		1 7		1 12		1 21											1 36		1 40	1 45			1 48					1 55					
Lee, for Burnt Ash.		1 9		1 15		1 23													1 42	1 47			1 51					1 57					
Mottingham........		1 13		1 19		1 27													1 46	1 51			1 55					2 1					
New Eltham........		1 16		1 22		1 29											1 42		1 48	1 53			1 58					2 4					
Sidcup		1 20		1 26		1 32									1 38		1 44		1 51	1 56			2 1					2 7					
Albany Park........		1 22		1 29											1 41		1 47			1 59			2 4					2 10					
Bexley		1 25		1 32		1 37									1 44		1 50		1 55	2 2			2 7					2 13					
Crayford..........		1 27		1 35		1 40									1 48		1 53		1 59	2 5			2 11					2 16					
Slades Green.......			1 31											1 59															2 24			2 34	
Dartford...........	1 30	1 34	1 35	1 39		1 44	1 48							2 3	1 54	1 50	1 57		2 4	2 9				2 15		2 18		2 20	2 28		2 33	2 37	
Stone Crossing Halt..			1 39												1 58				2 8									2 24				2 41	
Greenhithe.........			1 41												2 0				2 10									2 26				2 43	
Swanscombe Halt....			1 45												2 3				2 13									2 30				2 47	
Northfleet.........			1 47												2 6				2 16									2 32				2 49	
Gravesend Cen. arr			1 52												2 10	1 59			2 20					2 25				2 37				2 53	
Gravesend Cen. dep																2 0								2 26								2 54	
Higham.............																																3 2	
Strood........... arr																2 11								2 37								3 6	
Strood.......... dep																2 15									2 40								3 10
Cuxton.............																2 19									2 44								3 14
Halling............																2 22									2 47								3 17
Snodland...........																2 25									2 50								3 20
New Hythe.........																2 28									2 53								3 23
Aylesford..........																2 31									2 56								3 26
Maidstone Barracks																2 36									3 1								3 31
" West arr																2 38									3 3								3 33
Strood........... dep																2 12								2 38								3 7	
Rochester																2 17								2 41								3 11	
Chatham 60.........									2 1	2 7						2 19								2 43								3 13	
Gillingham (Kent) arr										2 11						2 24								2 47								3 18	

A Maze Hill, for National Maritime Museum

For SUNDAY TRAINS, see page 88.

3 Third class only

LONDON, WOOLWICH, DARTFORD, GRAVESEND CENTRAL, MAIDSTONE WEST, CHATHAM, and GILLINGHAM (Kent)

Saturdays—*continued.* (p.m)

Down																																	
Charing Cross .... dep	1 59	2 5	..	..	2 14	..	2 20	..	2 28	2 42	..	2 40	..	..	2 50	2 58	..	3 10	..	3 20	3 28	..	3 42	3 40	3 46	..	3 50	4 10	..	..	4 20	4 28	4 42
Waterloo .... "	2 1	2 7	..	..	2 16	..	2 22	..	2 30	2 44	..	2 42	..	..	2 52	3 0	..	3 12	..	3 22	3 30	..	3 44	3 42	3 48	..	3 52	4 12	..	..	4 22	4 30	4 44
Cannon Street .... "	..	..	..	2 11	..	..	..	..	..	..	..	..	2 47	..	..	..	..	..	..	..	..	..	..	..	..	..	..	..	..	..	..	..	..
London Bridge ... "	2 5	2 11	..	2 14	2 20	..	2 26	..	2 34	2 49	..	2 46	2 50	..	2 56	3 4	..	3 16	..	3 26	3 34	..	3 49	3 46	3 52	..	3 56	4 16	..	..	4 26	4 34	4 49
Holborn Viaduct dep	③	③	..	③	③	..	③	..	③	..	..	③	③	..	③	③	..	③	..	③	③	..	..	③	③	..	③	③	..	..	③	③	..
Blackfriars ..... "	..	..	..	..	..	..	..	..	..	..	..	..	..	..	..	..	..	..	..	..	..	..	..	..	..	..	..	..	..	..	..	..	..
Elephant and Castle	..	..	..	..	..	..	..	..	..	..	..	..	..	..	..	..	..	..	..	..	..	..	..	..	..	..	..	..	..	..	..	..	..
Peckham Rye	..	..	..	..	..	..	..	..	..	..	..	..	..	..	..	..	..	..	..	..	..	..	..	..	..	..	..	..	..	..	..	..	..
Deptford	..	..	..	..	..	..	..	..	2 39	..	..	..	..	..	..	3 9	..	..	..	..	3 39	..	..	..	..	..	..	..	..	..	..	4 39	..
Greenwich	..	..	..	..	..	..	..	..	2 41	..	..	..	..	..	..	3 11	..	..	..	..	3 41	..	..	..	..	..	..	..	..	..	..	4 41	..
Maze Hill A	..	..	..	..	..	..	..	..	2 44	..	..	..	..	..	..	3 14	..	..	..	..	3 44	..	..	..	..	..	..	..	..	..	..	4 44	..
Westcombe Park ..	..	..	..	..	..	..	..	..	2 46	..	..	..	..	..	..	3 16	..	..	..	..	3 46	..	..	..	..	..	..	..	..	..	..	4 46	..
New Cross	2 11	2 17	..	2 20	2 26	..	2 32	..	..	..	..	2 52	2 56	..	3 2	..	..	3 23	..	3 32	..	..	..	3 53	3 58	..	4 2	4 23	..	..	4 32	..	..
St. John's	..	2 19	..	2 22	2 28	..	2 35	..	..	..	..	..	2 58	..	3 5	..	..	3 25	..	3 35	..	..	..	3 55	4 0	..	4 5	4 25	..	..	4 35	..	..
Lewisham	..	2 21	..	2 24	..	..	2 37	..	..	..	..	2 55	3 0	..	3 7	..	..	3 27	..	3 37	..	..	..	3 57	4 3	..	4 7	4 27	..	..	4 37	..	..
Blackheath	..	2 24	..	2 27	..	..	2 39	..	..	..	..	..	3 3	..	3 9	..	..	..	..	3 39	..	..	..	..	4 5	..	4 9	..	..	..	4 39	..	..
Charlton	..	..	..	2 31	..	..	..	..	2 49	..	..	..	3 7	..	..	3 19	..	..	..	..	3 49	..	..	..	4 9	..	..	..	..	..	..	4 49	..
Woolwich Dockyard.	..	..	..	2 33	..	..	..	..	2 51	..	..	..	3 9	..	..	3 21	..	..	..	..	3 51	..	..	..	4 12	..	..	..	..	..	..	4 51	..
Woolwich Arsenal ..	..	..	..	2 37	..	..	..	..	2 54	3 2	..	..	3 12	..	..	3 24	..	..	..	..	3 54	..	4 2	..	4 14	..	..	..	..	..	..	4 54	5 2
Plumstead	..	..	..	2 40	..	..	..	..	2 56	..	..	..	3 14	..	..	3 26	..	..	..	..	3 56	..	..	..	4 16	..	..	..	..	..	..	4 56	..
Abbey Wood	..	..	..	2 43	..	..	..	..	2 59	..	..	..	3 17	..	..	3 29	..	..	..	..	3 59	..	..	..	4 20	..	..	..	..	..	..	4 59	..
Belvedere	..	..	..	2 46	..	..	..	..	3 2	..	..	..	3 20	..	..	3 32	..	..	..	..	4 2	..	..	..	4 23	..	..	..	..	..	..	5 2	..
Erith	..	..	..	2 49	..	..	..	..	3 5	..	..	..	3 23	..	..	3 35	..	..	..	..	4 5	..	..	..	4 26	..	..	..	..	..	..	5 5	..
Kidbrooke	..	2 27	..	..	..	..	2 42	..	..	..	..	..	..	..	3 12	..	..	..	..	3 42	..	..	..	..	..	..	4 12	..	..	..	4 42	..	..
Eltham (Well Hall) ..	..	2 30	..	..	..	..	2 45	..	..	..	..	..	..	..	3 15	..	..	..	..	3 45	..	..	..	..	..	..	4 15	..	..	..	4 45	..	..
Eltham Park	..	2 32	..	..	..	..	2 47	..	..	..	..	..	..	..	3 17	..	..	..	..	3 47	..	..	..	..	..	..	4 17	..	..	..	4 47	..	..
Falconwood	..	2 34	..	..	..	..	2 49	..	..	..	..	..	..	..	3 19	..	..	..	..	3 49	..	..	..	..	..	..	4 19	..	..	..	4 49	..	..
Welling	..	2 37	..	..	..	..	2 52	..	..	..	..	..	..	..	3 22	..	..	..	..	3 52	..	..	..	..	..	..	4 22	..	..	..	4 52	..	..
Bexleyheath	..	2 40	..	..	..	..	2 55	..	..	..	..	..	..	..	3 25	..	..	..	..	3 55	..	..	..	..	..	..	4 25	..	..	..	4 55	..	..
Barnehurst	..	2 43	..	..	..	..	2 58	..	..	..	..	..	..	..	3 29	..	..	..	..	3 58	..	..	..	..	..	..	4 28	..	..	..	4 58	..	..
Hither Green	2 15	..	..	..	2 32	..	..	..	..	..	..	2 58	..	..	..	..	..	3 30	..	..	..	..	..	4 0	..	..	..	4 30	..	..	..	..	..
Lee, for Burnt Ash.	2 17	..	..	..	2 34	..	..	..	..	..	..	3 0	..	..	..	..	..	3 32	..	..	..	..	..	4 2	..	..	..	4 32	..	..	..	..	..
Mottingham	2 21	..	..	..	2 37	..	..	..	..	..	..	3 3	..	..	..	..	..	3 36	..	..	..	..	..	4 6	..	..	..	4 36	..	..	..	..	..
New Eltham	2 23	..	..	..	2 40	..	..	..	..	..	..	3 6	..	..	..	..	..	3 38	..	..	..	..	..	4 8	..	..	..	4 38	..	..	..	..	..
Sidcup	2 26	..	..	..	2 43	..	..	..	..	..	..	3 9	..	..	..	..	..	3 41	..	..	..	..	..	4 11	..	..	..	4 41	..	..	..	..	..
Albany Park	2 29	..	..	..	2 45	..	..	..	..	..	..	3 11	..	..	..	..	..	3 44	..	..	..	..	..	4 14	..	..	..	4 44	..	..	..	..	..
Bexley	2 32	..	..	..	2 48	..	..	..	..	..	..	3 14	..	..	..	..	..	3 47	..	..	..	..	..	4 17	..	..	..	4 47	..	..	..	..	..
Crayford	2 35	..	..	..	2 51	..	..	..	..	..	..	3 17	..	..	..	..	..	3 50	..	..	..	..	..	4 20	..	..	..	4 50	..	..	..	..	..
Slades Green	..	..	..	2 52	..	..	..	..	3 8	..	..	..	3 26	..	..	3 38	..	..	..	..	4 8	..	..	..	4 29	..	..	..	..	..	..	5 8	..
Dartford	2 40	..	..	2 57	2 55	..	3 4	..	3 12	3 15	..	3 21	3 30	..	3 35	3 42	..	3 54	..	4 4	4 12	..	4 15	4 24	4 33	..	4 35	4 54	..	..	5 4	5 12	5 15
Stone Crossing Halt ..	..	..	..	..	..	..	..	..	..	..	..	3 25	..	..	3 39	..	..	..	..	..	..	..	..	..	..	..	4 39	..	..	..	..	..	..
Greenhithe	..	..	..	..	..	..	..	..	..	..	..	3 27	..	..	3 41	..	..	..	..	..	..	..	..	..	..	..	4 41	..	..	..	..	..	..
Swanscombe Halt	..	..	..	..	..	..	..	..	..	..	..	3 30	..	..	3 44	..	..	..	..	..	..	..	..	..	..	..	4 44	..	..	..	..	..	..
Northfleet	..	..	..	..	..	..	..	..	..	..	..	3 33	..	..	3 47	..	..	..	..	..	..	..	..	..	..	..	4 47	..	..	..	..	..	..
Gravesend Cen arr	..	..	..	..	..	..	..	..	..	3 24	..	3 37	..	..	3 51	..	..	..	..	..	..	..	4 24	..	..	..	4 51	..	..	..	..	..	5 25
Gravesend Cen dep	..	..	..	..	..	..	..	..	..	3 25	..	..	..	..	3 52	..	..	..	..	..	..	..	4 25	..	..	..	4 52	..	..	..	..	..	5 26
Higham	..	..	..	..	..	..	..	..	..	..	..	..	..	..	3 59	..	..	..	..	..	..	..	..	..	..	..	4 59	..	..	..	..	..	..
Strood .... arr	..	..	..	..	..	..	..	..	..	3 36	..	..	..	..	4 5	..	..	..	..	..	..	..	4 37	..	..	..	5 4	..	..	..	..	..	5 37
Strood .... dep	..	..	..	..	..	..	..	..	..	3 40	..	..	..	..	..	..	..	..	4 10	..	..	..	4 40	..	..	..	..	..	5 12	..	..	..	5 40
Cuxton	..	..	..	..	..	..	..	..	..	3 44	..	..	..	..	..	..	..	..	4 14	..	..	..	4 44	..	..	..	..	..	5 16	..	..	..	5 44
Halling	..	..	..	..	..	..	..	..	..	3 47	..	..	..	..	..	..	..	..	4 17	..	..	..	4 47	..	..	..	..	..	5 19	..	..	..	5 47
Snodland	..	..	..	..	..	..	..	..	..	3 50	..	..	..	..	..	..	..	..	4 20	..	..	..	4 50	..	..	..	..	..	5 22	..	..	..	5 50
New Hythe	..	..	..	..	..	..	..	..	..	3 53	..	..	..	..	..	..	..	..	4 23	..	..	..	4 53	..	..	..	..	..	5 25	..	..	..	5 53
Aylesford	..	..	..	..	..	..	..	..	..	3 56	..	..	..	..	..	..	..	..	4 26	..	..	..	4 56	..	..	..	..	..	5 28	..	..	..	5 56
Maidstone Barracks	..	..	..	..	..	..	..	..	..	4 1	..	..	..	..	..	..	..	..	4 31	..	..	..	5 1	..	..	..	..	..	5 33	..	..	..	6 1
" West arr	..	..	..	..	..	..	..	..	..	4 3	..	..	..	..	..	..	..	..	4 33	..	..	..	5 3	..	..	..	..	..	5 35	..	..	..	6 3
Strood .... dep	..	..	..	..	..	..	..	..	..	3 37	..	..	..	..	4 6	..	..	..	..	..	..	..	4 38	..	..	..	5 5	..	..	..	..	..	5 38
Rochester	..	..	..	..	..	..	..	..	..	3 41	..	..	..	..	4 10	..	..	..	..	..	..	..	4 41	..	..	..	5 8	..	..	..	..	..	5 41
Chatham 60	..	..	..	..	..	..	..	..	..	3 43	..	..	..	..	4 12	..	..	..	..	..	..	..	4 44	..	..	..	5 11	..	..	..	..	..	5 44
Gillingham (Kent) arr	..	..	..	..	..	..	..	..	..	3 49	..	..	..	..	4 17	..	..	..	..	..	..	..	4 48	..	..	..	5 15	..	..	..	..	..	5 48

A Maze Hill, for National Maritime Museum.

③ Third class only

LONDON, WOOLWICH, DARTFORD, GRAVESEND CENTRAL, MAIDSTONE WEST, CHATHAM, and GILLINGHAM (Kent).

Saturdays—*continued* (p.m.)

Down																																	
Charing Cross....dep	4 40	4 46	..	4 50	5 10	..	5 20	5 28	..	5 40	5 46	5 50	..	6 10	..	..	6 20	6 28	..	6 40	6 42	..	6 46	6 50	7 10	..	..	7 20	7 28	..	7 40	7 46	7 50
Waterloo "	4 42	4 48	..	4 52	5 12	..	5 22	5 30	..	5 42	5 48	5 52	..	6 12	..	..	6 22	6 30	..	6 42	6 44	..	6 48	6 52	7 12	..	..	7 22	7 30	..	7 42	7 48	7 52
Cannon Street.... "	..	..	..	..	..	..	..	..	..	..	..	..	..	..	..	..	..	..	..	..	..	..	..	..	..	..	..	..	..	..	..	..	..
London Bridge ... "	4 46	4 52	..	4 56	5 16	..	5 26	5 34	..	5 46	5 52	5 56	..	6 16	..	..	6 26	6 34	..	6 46	6 49	..	6 52	6 56	7 16	..	..	7 26	7 34	..	7 46	7 52	7 56
Holborn Viaduct dep	3	3	..	3	3	..	3	3	..	3	3	3	..	3	..	..	3	3	..	3	..	..	3	3	3	..	..	3	3	..	3	3	3
Blackfriars .... "	..	..	..	..	..	..	..	..	..	..	..	..	..	..	..	..	..	..	..	..	..	..	..	..	..	..	..	..	..	..	..	..	..
Elephant and Castle	..	..	..	..	..	..	..	..	..	..	..	..	..	..	..	..	..	..	..	..	..	..	..	..	..	..	..	..	..	..	..	..	..
Peckham Rye.......	..	..	..	..	..	..	..	..	..	..	..	..	..	..	..	..	..	..	..	..	..	..	..	..	..	..	..	..	..	..	..	..	..
Deptford.........	..	..	..	..	..	..	..	5 39	..	..	..	..	..	..	..	..	..	6 39	..	..	..	..	..	..	..	..	..	..	7 39	..	..	..	..
Greenwich	..	..	..	..	..	..	..	5 41	..	..	..	..	..	..	..	..	..	6 41	..	..	..	..	..	..	..	..	..	..	7 41	..	..	..	..
Maze Hill A.......	..	..	..	..	..	..	..	5 44	..	..	..	..	..	..	..	..	..	6 44	..	..	..	..	..	..	..	..	..	..	7 44	..	..	..	..
Westcombe Park..	..	..	..	..	..	..	..	5 46	..	..	..	..	..	..	..	..	..	6 46	..	..	..	..	..	..	..	..	..	..	7 46	..	..	..	..
New Cross.........	4 53	4 58	..	5 2	5 23	..	5 32	..	..	5 53	5 58	6 2	..	6 23	..	..	6 32	..	..	6 53	..	..	6 58	7 2	7 23	..	..	7 32	..	..	7 53	7 58	8 2
St. John's.........	4 55	5 0	..	5 5	5 25	..	5 35	..	..	5 55	6 0	6 5	..	6 25	..	..	6 35	..	..	6 55	..	..	7 0	7 5	7 25	..	..	7 35	..	..	7 55	8 0	8 5
Lewisham.........	4 57	5 3	..	5 7	5 27	..	5 37	..	..	5 57	6 3	6 7	..	6 27	..	..	6 37	..	..	6 57	..	..	7 3	7 7	7 27	..	..	7 37	..	..	7 57	8 3	8 7
Blackheath.........	..	5 5	..	5 9	..	..	5 39	..	..	..	6 5	6 9	..	..	..	..	6 39	..	..	..	..	..	7 5	7 9	..	..	..	7 39	..	..	..	8 5	8 9
Charlton.........	..	5 9	..	..	..	..	..	5 49	..	..	6 9	..	..	..	..	..	..	6 49	..	..	..	..	7 9	..	..	..	..	..	7 49	..	..	8 9	..
Woolwich Dockyard	..	5 12	..	..	..	..	..	5 51	..	..	6 12	..	..	..	..	..	..	6 51	..	..	..	..	7 12	..	..	..	..	..	7 51	..	..	8 12	..
Woolwich Arsenal...	..	5 14	..	..	..	..	..	5 54	..	..	6 14	..	..	..	..	..	..	6 54	..	..	7 2	..	7 14	..	..	..	..	..	7 54	..	..	8 14	..
Plumstead.........	..	5 16	..	..	..	..	..	5 56	..	..	6 16	..	..	..	..	..	..	6 56	..	..	..	..	7 16	..	..	..	..	..	7 56	..	..	8 16	..
Abbey Wood.........	..	5 20	..	..	..	..	..	5 59	..	..	6 20	..	..	..	..	..	..	6 59	..	..	..	..	7 20	..	..	..	..	..	7 59	..	..	8 20	..
Belvedere.........	..	5 23	..	..	..	..	..	6 2	..	..	6 23	..	..	..	..	..	..	7 2	..	..	..	..	7 23	..	..	..	..	..	8 2	..	..	8 23	..
Erith.........	..	5 26	..	..	..	..	..	6 5	..	..	6 26	..	..	..	..	..	..	7 5	..	..	..	..	7 26	..	..	..	..	..	8 5	..	..	8 26	..
Kidbrooke.........	..	..	..	5 12	..	..	5 42	..	..	..	..	6 12	..	..	..	..	6 42	..	..	..	..	..	..	7 12	..	..	..	7 42	..	..	..	..	8 12
Eltham (Well Hall).	..	..	..	5 15	..	..	5 45	..	..	..	..	6 15	..	..	..	..	6 45	..	..	..	..	..	..	7 15	..	..	..	7 45	..	..	..	..	8 15
Eltham Park.........	..	..	..	5 17	..	..	5 47	..	..	..	..	6 17	..	..	..	..	6 47	..	..	..	..	..	..	7 17	..	..	..	7 47	..	..	..	..	8 17
Falconwood.........	..	..	..	5 19	..	..	5 49	..	..	..	..	6 19	..	..	..	..	6 49	..	..	..	..	..	..	7 19	..	..	..	7 49	..	..	..	..	8 19
Welling.........	..	..	..	5 22	..	..	5 52	..	..	..	..	6 22	..	..	..	..	6 52	..	..	..	..	..	..	7 22	..	..	..	7 52	..	..	..	..	8 22
Bexleyheath.........	..	..	..	5 25	..	..	5 55	..	..	..	..	6 25	..	..	..	..	6 55	..	..	..	..	..	..	7 25	..	..	..	7 55	..	..	..	..	8 25
Barnehurst.........	..	..	..	5 29	..	..	5 58	..	..	..	..	6 29	..	..	..	..	6 58	..	..	..	..	..	..	7 29	..	..	..	7 58	..	..	..	..	8 29
Hither Green.........	5 0	..	..	..	5 30	..	..	..	..	6 0	..	..	..	6 30	..	..	..	..	..	7 0	..	..	..	..	7 30	..	..	..	..	..	8 0	..	..
Lee, for Burnt Ash.	5 2	..	..	..	5 32	..	..	..	..	6 2	..	..	..	6 32	..	..	..	..	..	7 2	..	..	..	..	7 32	..	..	..	..	..	8 2	..	..
Mottingham.........	5 6	..	..	..	5 36	..	..	..	..	6 6	..	..	..	6 36	..	..	..	..	..	7 6	..	..	..	..	7 36	..	..	..	..	..	8 6	..	..
New Eltham.........	5 8	..	..	..	5 38	..	..	..	..	6 8	..	..	..	6 38	..	..	..	..	..	7 8	..	..	..	..	7 38	..	..	..	..	..	8 8	..	..
Sidcup.........	5 11	..	..	..	5 41	..	..	..	..	6 11	..	..	..	6 41	..	..	..	..	..	7 11	..	..	..	..	7 41	..	..	..	..	..	8 11	..	..
Albany Park.........	5 14	..	..	..	5 44	..	..	..	..	6 14	..	..	..	6 44	..	..	..	..	..	7 14	..	..	..	..	7 44	..	..	..	..	..	8 14	..	..
Bexley.........	5 17	..	..	..	5 47	..	..	..	..	6 17	..	..	..	6 47	..	..	..	..	..	7 17	..	..	..	..	7 47	..	..	..	..	..	8 17	..	..
Crayford.........	5 20	..	..	..	5 50	..	..	..	..	6 20	..	..	..	6 50	..	..	..	..	..	7 20	..	..	..	..	7 50	..	..	..	..	..	8 20	..	..
Slades Green.........	..	5 29	..	..	..	..	..	6 8	..	..	6 29	..	..	..	..	..	..	7 8	..	..	..	..	7 29	..	..	..	..	..	8 8	..	..	8 29	..
Dartford.........	5 24	5 33	..	5 35	5 54	..	6 4	6 12	..	6 24	6 33	6 35	..	6 54	..	..	7 4	7 12	..	7 24	7 15	..	7 33	7 35	7 54	..	..	8 4	8 12	..	8 24	8 33	8 35
Stone Crossing Halt..	..	..	..	5 39	..	..	..	..	..	..	..	6 39	..	..	..	..	..	..	..	..	..	..	..	7 39	..	..	..	..	..	..	..	..	8 39
Greenhithe.........	..	..	..	5 41	..	..	..	..	..	..	..	6 41	..	..	..	..	..	..	..	..	..	..	..	7 41	..	..	..	..	..	..	..	..	8 41
Swanscombe Halt.....	..	..	..	5 44	..	..	..	..	..	..	..	6 44	..	..	..	..	..	..	..	..	..	..	..	7 44	..	..	..	..	..	..	..	..	8 44
Northfleet.........	..	..	..	5 47	..	..	..	..	..	..	..	6 47	..	..	..	..	..	..	..	..	..	..	..	7 47	..	..	..	..	..	..	..	..	8 47
Gravesend Cen. arr	..	..	..	5 51	..	..	..	..	..	..	..	6 51	..	..	..	..	..	..	..	..	7 25	..	..	7 51	..	..	..	..	..	..	..	..	8 51
Gravesend Cen. dep	..	..	..	5 52	..	..	..	..	..	..	..	6 52	..	..	..	..	..	..	..	..	7 26	..	..	7 52	..	..	..	..	..	..	..	..	8 52
Higham.........	..	..	..	5 59	..	..	..	..	..	..	..	6 59	..	..	..	..	..	..	..	..	..	..	..	7 59	..	..	..	..	..	..	..	..	8 59
Strood......... arr	..	..	..	6 4	..	..	..	..	..	..	..	7 4	..	..	..	..	..	..	..	..	7 37	..	..	8 4	..	..	..	..	..	..	..	..	9 4
Strood......... dep	..	..	..	..	..	6 10	..	..	..	..	..	..	7 10	..	..	..	..	..	..	..	7 40	..	..	..	..	..	8 10	..	..	..	..	..	..
Cuxton.........	..	..	..	..	..	6 14	..	..	..	..	..	..	7 14	..	..	..	..	..	..	..	7 44	..	..	..	..	..	8 14	..	..	..	..	..	..
Halling.........	..	..	..	..	..	6 17	..	..	..	..	..	..	7 17	..	..	..	..	..	..	..	7 47	..	..	..	..	..	8 17	..	..	..	..	..	..
Snodland.........	..	..	..	..	..	6 20	..	..	..	..	..	..	7 20	..	..	..	..	..	..	..	7 50	..	..	..	..	..	8 20	..	..	..	..	..	..
New Hythe.........	..	..	..	..	..	6 23	..	..	..	..	..	..	7 23	..	..	..	..	..	..	..	7 53	..	..	..	..	..	8 23	..	..	..	..	..	..
Aylesford.........	..	..	..	..	..	6 26	..	..	..	..	..	..	7 26	..	..	..	..	..	..	..	7 56	..	..	..	..	..	8 26	..	..	..	..	..	..
Maidstone Barracks	..	..	..	..	..	6 31	..	..	..	..	..	..	7 31	..	..	..	..	..	..	..	8 1	..	..	..	..	..	8 31	..	..	..	..	..	..
" West arr	..	..	..	..	..	6 33	..	..	..	..	..	..	7 33	..	..	..	..	..	..	..	8 3	..	..	..	..	..	8 33	..	..	..	..	..	..
Strood......... dep	..	..	..	6 5	..	..	..	..	..	..	..	7 5	..	..	..	..	..	..	..	..	7 38	..	..	8 5	..	..	..	..	..	..	..	..	9 5
Rochester.........	..	..	..	6 8	..	..	..	..	..	..	..	7 8	..	..	..	..	..	..	..	..	7 41	..	..	8 8	..	..	..	..	..	..	..	..	9 8
Chatham 60.........	..	..	..	6 11	..	..	..	..	..	..	..	7 11	..	..	..	..	..	..	..	..	7 44	..	..	8 11	..	..	..	..	..	..	..	..	9 11
Gillingham (Kent) arr	..	..	..	6 15	..	..	..	..	..	..	..	7 15	..	..	..	..	..	..	..	..	7 48	..	..	8 15	..	..	..	..	..	..	..	..	9 15

A Maze Hill, for National Maritime Museum.

For SUNDAY TRAINS, see page 88

3 Third class only.

LONDON, WOOLWICH, DARTFORD, GRAVESEND CENTRAL, MAIDSTONE WEST, CHATHAM, and GILLINGHAM (Kent)

Saturdays—*continued*

Down	p.m																														ngt.
Charing Cross .... dep	8 10	..	8 28	8 30	8 40	8 42	8 46	..	9 0	9 10	9 28	9 30	9 40	..	9 46	..	..	10 0	1010	1028	1030	1040	..	1046	..	11 0	1110	1116	1132	1142	11 48	1253
Waterloo .... "	8 12	..	8 30	8 32	8 42	8 44	8 48	..	9 2	9 12	9 30	9 32	9 42	..	9 48	..	..	10 2	1012	1030	1032	1042	..	1048	..	11 2	1112	1118	1134	1144	11 50	1255
Cannon Street .... "	..	..	..	..	..	..	..	..	..	..	..	..	..	..	..	..	..	..	..	..	..	..	..	..	..	..	..	..	..	..	..	1 3
London Bridge ... "	8 16	..	8 34	8 36	8 46	8 49	8 52	..	9 6	9 16	9 34	9 36	9 46	..	9 52	..	..	10 6	1016	1034	1036	1046	..	1052	..	11 6	1116	1122	1138	1148	11 54	1 7
Holborn Viaduct dp	3	..	3	3	3	..	3	..	3	3	3	3	3	..	3	..	..	3	3	3	3	3	..	3	..	3	3	3	3	3	3	3
Blackfriars .... "	..	..	..	..	..	..	..	..	..	..	..	..	..	..	..	..	..	..	..	..	..	..	..	..	..	..	..	..	..	..	..	..
Elephant and Castle	..	..	..	..	..	..	..	..	..	..	..	..	..	..	..	..	..	..	..	..	..	..	..	..	..	..	..	..	..	..	..	..
Peckham Rye	..	..	..	..	..	..	..	..	..	..	..	..	..	..	..	..	..	..	..	..	..	..	..	..	..	..	..	..	..	..	..	..
Deptford	..	..	8 39	..	..	..	..	..	..	..	9 39	..	..	..	..	..	..	..	..	1039	..	..	..	..	..	..	..	..	1144	..	..	..
Greenwich	..	..	8 41	..	..	..	..	..	..	..	9 41	..	..	..	..	..	..	..	..	1041	..	..	..	..	..	..	..	..	1146	..	..	..
Maze Hill A	..	..	8 44	..	..	..	..	..	..	..	9 44	..	..	..	..	..	..	..	..	1044	..	..	..	..	..	..	..	..	1148	..	..	..
Westcombe Park ..	..	..	8 46	..	..	..	..	..	..	..	9 46	..	..	..	..	..	..	..	..	1046	..	..	..	..	..	..	..	..	1151	..	..	..
New Cross	8 23	..	..	8 42	8 53	..	8 58	..	9 12	9 23	..	9 42	9 53	..	9 58	..	..	1012	1023	..	1042	1053	..	1058	..	11 12	1123	1128	..	1153	12 0	1 13
St. John's	8 25	..	..	8 45	8 55	..	9 0	..	9 15	9 25	..	9 45	9 55	..	10 0	..	..	1015	1025	..	1045	1055	..	11 0	..	11 15	1125	1130	..	..	12 2	1 16
Lewisham	8 27	..	..	8 47	8 57	..	9 3	..	9 17	9 27	..	9 47	9 57	..	10 3	..	..	1017	1027	..	1047	1057	..	11 3	..	11 17	1127	1132	..	1156	..	1 18
Blackheath	..	..	..	8 49	..	..	9 5	..	9 19	..	..	9 49	..	..	10 5	..	..	1019	..	..	1049	..	..	11 5	..	11 19	..	1135	..	1159	..	1 21
Charlton	..	..	8 49	..	..	..	9 9	..	..	..	9 49	..	..	..	10 9	..	..	..	..	1049	..	..	..	11 9	..	..	..	1139	1153	..	..	1 25
Woolwich Dockyard	..	..	8 51	..	..	..	9 12	..	..	..	9 51	..	..	..	1012	..	..	..	..	1051	..	..	..	1112	..	..	..	1141	1156	..	..	1 27
Woolwich Arsenal ..	..	..	8 54	..	..	9 4	9 14	..	..	..	9 54	..	..	..	1014	..	..	..	..	1054	..	..	..	1114	..	..	..	1144	1158	..	..	1 30
Plumstead	..	..	8 56	..	..	..	9 16	..	..	..	9 56	..	..	..	1016	..	..	..	..	1056	..	..	..	1116	..	..	..	1146	12 0	..	..	1 33
Abbey Wood	..	..	8 59	..	..	..	9 20	..	..	..	9 59	..	..	..	1020	..	..	..	..	1059	..	..	..	1120	..	..	..	1149	12 4	..	..	1 37
Belvedere	..	..	9 2	..	..	..	9 23	..	..	..	10 2	..	..	..	1023	..	..	..	..	11 2	..	..	..	1123	..	..	..	1152	12 7	..	..	1 40
Erith	..	..	9 5	..	..	..	9 26	..	..	..	10 5	..	..	..	1026	..	..	..	..	11 5	..	..	..	1126	..	..	..	1155	1210	..	..	1 43
Kidbrooke	..	..	..	8 52	..	..	..	..	9 22	..	..	9 52	..	..	..	..	..	1022	..	..	1052	..	..	..	..	11 22	..	..	..	12 2	..	..
Eltham (Well Hall) ..	..	..	..	8 55	..	..	..	..	9 25	..	..	9 55	..	..	..	..	..	1025	..	..	1055	..	..	..	..	11 25	..	..	..	12 4	..	..
Eltham Park	..	..	..	8 57	..	..	..	..	9 27	..	..	9 57	..	..	..	..	..	1027	..	..	1057	..	..	..	..	11 27	..	..	..	12 6	..	..
Falconwood	..	..	..	8 59	..	..	..	..	9 29	..	..	9 59	..	..	..	..	..	1029	..	..	1059	..	..	..	..	11 29	..	..	..	12 9	..	..
Welling	..	..	..	9 2	..	..	..	..	9 32	..	..	10 2	..	..	..	..	..	1032	..	..	11 2	..	..	..	..	11 32	..	..	..	1211	..	..
Bexleyheath	..	..	..	9 5	..	..	..	..	9 35	..	..	10 5	..	..	..	..	..	1035	..	..	11 5	..	..	..	..	11 35	..	..	..	1214	..	..
Barnehurst	..	..	..	9 9	..	..	..	..	9 38	..	..	10 9	..	..	..	..	..	1038	..	..	11 9	..	..	..	..	11 38	..	..	..	1217	..	..
Hither Green	8 30	..	..	..	9 0	..	..	..	..	9 30	..	..	10 0	..	..	..	..	..	1030	..	..	11 0	..	..	..	..	1130	..	..	..	12 6	..
Lee, for Burnt Ash	8 32	..	..	..	9 2	..	..	..	..	9 32	..	..	10 2	..	..	..	..	..	1032	..	..	11 2	..	..	..	..	1132	..	..	..	12 8	..
Mottingham	8 36	..	..	..	9 6	..	..	..	..	9 36	..	..	10 6	..	..	..	..	..	1036	..	..	11 6	..	..	..	..	1136	..	..	..	12 11	..
New Eltham	8 38	..	..	..	9 8	..	..	..	..	9 38	..	..	10 8	..	..	..	..	..	1038	..	..	11 8	..	..	..	..	1138	..	..	..	12 14	..
Sidcup	8 41	..	..	..	9 11	..	..	..	..	9 41	..	..	1011	..	..	..	..	..	1041	..	..	1111	..	..	..	..	1141	..	..	..	12 17	..
Albany Park	8 44	..	..	..	9 14	..	..	..	..	9 44	..	..	1014	..	..	..	..	..	1044	..	..	1114	..	..	..	..	1144	..	..	..	12 19	..
Bexley	8 47	..	..	..	9 17	..	..	..	..	9 47	..	..	1017	..	..	..	..	..	1047	..	..	1117	..	..	..	..	1147	..	..	..	12 22	..
Crayford	8 50	..	..	..	9 20	..	..	..	..	9 50	..	..	1020	..	..	..	..	..	1050	..	..	1120	..	..	..	..	1150	..	..	..	12 25	..
Slades Green*	..	..	9 8	..	..	..	9 29	..	..	..	10 8	..	..	..	1029	..	..	..	..	11 8	..	..	..	1129	..	..	..	1158	1213	..	..	1 46
Dartford	8 54	..	9 12	9 15	9 24	9 18	9 34	..	9 44	9 54	1012	1015	1024	..	1034	..	..	1044	1054	1112	1115	1124	..	1134	..	11 44	1154	12 2	1217	1225	12 29	1 50
Stone Crossing Halt ..	..	..	..	..	..	..	9 39	..	..	..	..	..	..	..	1039	..	..	..	..	..	..	..	..	1139	..	..	..	..	..	..	..	..
Greenhithe	..	..	..	..	..	..	9 41	..	..	..	..	..	..	..	1041	..	..	..	..	..	..	..	..	1141	..	..	..	..	..	1231	..	..
Swanscombe Halt ...	..	..	..	..	..	..	9 44	..	..	..	..	..	..	..	1044	..	..	..	..	..	..	..	..	1144	..	..	..	..	..	..	..	..
Northfleet	..	..	..	..	..	..	9 47	..	..	..	..	..	..	..	1047	..	..	..	..	..	..	..	..	1147	..	..	..	..	..	1236	..	..
Gravesend Cen. arr	..	..	..	..	..	9 27	9 51	..	..	..	..	..	..	..	1051	..	..	..	..	..	..	..	..	1151	..	..	..	..	..	1239	..	..
Gravesend Cen. dep	..	..	..	..	..	9 28	9 52	..	..	..	..	..	..	..	1052	..	11 0	..	..	..	..	..	..	1152	..	..	..	..	..	1240	..	..
Higham	..	..	..	..	..	..	9 59	..	..	..	..	..	..	..	1059	..	11 8	..	..	..	..	..	..	1159	..	..	..	..	..	..	..	..
Strood .... arr	..	..	..	..	..	9 39	10 4	..	..	..	..	..	..	..	11 4	..	1115	..	..	..	..	..	..	12 4	..	..	..	..	..	1252	..	..
Strood .... dep	..	9 10	..	..	..	9 42	..	10 10	..	..	..	..	..	..	..	11 10	..	..	..	..	..	..	..	..	1210	..	..	..	..	..	..	..
Cuxton	..	9 14	..	..	..	9 46	..	10 14	..	..	..	..	..	..	..	11 14	..	..	..	..	..	..	..	..	1214	..	..	..	..	..	..	..
Halling	..	9 17	..	..	..	9 49	..	10 17	..	..	..	..	..	..	..	11 17	..	..	..	..	..	..	..	..	1217	..	..	..	..	..	..	..
Snodland	..	9 20	..	..	..	9 52	..	10 20	..	..	..	..	..	..	..	11 20	..	..	..	..	..	..	..	..	1220	..	..	..	..	..	..	..
New Hythe	..	9 23	..	..	..	9 55	..	10 23	..	..	..	..	..	..	..	11 23	..	..	..	..	..	..	..	..	1223	..	..	..	..	..	..	..
Aylesford	..	9 26	..	..	..	9 58	..	10 26	..	..	..	..	..	..	..	11 26	..	..	..	..	..	..	..	..	1225	..	..	..	..	..	..	..
Maidstone Barracks	..	9 31	..	..	..	10 3	..	10 31	..	..	..	..	..	..	..	11 31	..	..	..	..	..	..	..	..	1231	..	..	..	..	..	..	..
" West arr	..	9 33	..	..	..	10 5	..	10 33	..	..	..	..	..	..	..	11 33	..	..	..	..	..	..	..	..	1233	..	..	..	..	..	..	..
Strood .... dep	..	..	..	..	..	9 40	10 5	..	..	..	..	..	..	..	11 5	..	1116	..	..	..	..	..	..	12 5	..	..	..	..	..	1253	..	..
Rochester	..	..	..	..	..	9 43	10 7	..	..	..	..	..	..	..	11 7	..	1120	..	..	..	..	..	..	12 7	..	..	..	..	..	..	..	..
Chatham 60	..	..	..	..	..	9 46	1010	..	..	..	..	..	..	..	11 9	..	1123	..	..	..	..	..	..	1210	..	..	..	..	..	1258	..	..
Gillingham (Kent) arr	..	..	..	..	..	9 50	1015	..	..	..	..	..	..	..	..	..	1129	..	..	..	..	..	..	1215	..	..	..	..	..	1 2	..	..

A Maze Hill, for National Maritime Museum

For SUNDAY TRAINS, see page 88

3 Third class only

LONDON, WOOLWICH, DARTFORD, GRAVESEND CENTRAL, MAIDSTONE WEST CHATHAM, and GILLINGHAM (Kent)

Sundays

Down	a.m															
Charing Cross....dep	..	..	..	6 18	6 21	..	6 40	6 46	7 1	7 4	7 18	7 20	..	..	7 44	7 55
Waterloo .... "	..	..	..	6 20	6 23	..	6 42	6 48	7 3	7 6	7 20	7 23	..	..	7 46	7 57
Cannon Street.... "	..	..	..	..	..	..	..	..	..	..	..	..	..	..	..	..
London Bridge.... "	5 5	..	..	6 24	6 27	6 39	6 46	6 53	7 7	7 10	7 23	7 29	7 36	..	7 50	8 1
Holborn Viaduct dep	3	..	3	3	3	3	3	3	3	3	3	..	3	..	3	3
Blackfriars .... "		..										..		..		
Elephant and Castle	..	..	..	..	..	..	..	..	..	..	..	..	..	..	..	..
Peckham Rye.......	..	..	..	..	..	..	..	..	..	..	..	..	..	..	..	..
Deptford..........	..	..	..	..	..	..	..	..	..	..	7 29	..	..	..	7 56	..
Greenwich	..	..	..	..	..	..	..	..	..	..	7 31	..	..	..	7 58	..
Maze Hill A.......	..	..	..	..	..	..	..	..	..	..	7 34	..	..	..	8 0	..
Westcombe Park..	..	..	..	..	..	..	..	..	..	..	7 36	..	..	..	8 3	..
New Cross.........	..	..	..	6 30	6 33	6 45	6 52	6 59	7 13	7 16	..	7 37	7 41	..	..	8 7
St. John's.........	..	..	..	6 32	6 35	6 47	6 55	7 2	7 15	7 18	..	..	7 44	..	..	8 9
Lewisham.........	..	..	..	6 34	6 37	6 50	6 57	..	7 17	7 20	..	7 41	7 46	..	..	8 11
Blackheath........	..	..	..	..	6 40	6 52	6 59	..	7 20	7 23	..	..	7 49	..	..	..
Charlton..........	..	..	..	..	6 44	..	7 2	..	..	7 27	7 39	..	..	..	8 5	..
Woolwich Dockyard.	..	..	..	..	6 46	..	7 6	..	..	7 29	7 41	..	..	..	8 8	..
Woolwich Arsenal ..	..	..	..	..	6 49	..	7 8	..	..	7 32	7 44	7 55	..	..	8 10	..
Plumstead.........	..	..	..	..	6 52	..	7 10	..	..	7 34	7 46	..	..	..	8 12	..
Abbey Wood........	..	..	..	..	6 55	..	7 14	..	..	7 37	7 49	..	..	..	8 16	..
Belvedere.........	..	..	..	..	6 58	..	7 17	..	..	7 40	7 52	..	..	..	8 19	..
Erith..............	..	..	6 20	..	7 1	..	7 20	..	..	7 43	7 55	..	..	..	8 22	..
Kidbrooke	..	..	..	..	..	6 55	..	..	7 23	..	..	Through Train to Ramsgate see page 65	7 52	..	..	..
Eltham (Well Hall) .	..	..	..	..	..	6 58	..	..	7 25	..	..		7 54	..	..	..
Eltham Park........	..	..	..	..	..	7 0	..	..	7 27	..	..		7 56	..	..	..
Falconwood........	..	..	..	..	..	7 2	..	..	7 30	..	..		7 59	..	..	..
Welling	..	..	..	..	..	7 5	..	..	7 32	..	..		8 1	..	..	..
Bexleyheath........	..	..	..	..	..	7 8	..	..	7 35	..	..		8 4	..	..	..
Barnehurst.........	..	..	..	..	..	7 11	..	..	7 38	..	..		8 7	..	..	..
Hither Green.......	..	..	..	6 38	..	..	..	7 5	..	..	..		..	..	..	8 14
Lee, for Burnt Ash..	..	..	..	6 40	..	..	..	7 7	..	..	..		..	..	..	8 16
Mottingham	..	..	..	6 44	..	..	..	7 11	..	..	..		..	..	..	8 20
New Eltham........	..	..	..	6 46	..	..	..	7 13	..	..	..		..	..	..	8 22
Sidcup............	..	..	..	6 49	..	..	..	7 16	..	..	..		..	..	..	8 25
Albany Park	..	..	..	6 52	..	..	..	7 19	..	..	..		..	..	..	8 28
Bexley.............	..	..	..	6 55	..	..	..	7 22	..	..	..		..	..	..	8 31
Crayford...........	..	..	..	6 58	..	..	..	7 25	..	..	..		..	..	..	8 34
Slades Green.......	..	..	6 23	..	7 4	..	7 23	..	..	7 46	7 58	..	..	..	8 25	..
Dartford...........	5F38	..	6 26	7 2	7 8	7 17	7 27	7 29	7 44	7 F0	8 2	8 12	8 14	..	8 29	8 38
Stone Crossing Halt...	..	..	6 30	..	..	..	..	7 34	..	7 54	..	..	..	..	..	..
Greenhithe.........	..	..	6 32	..	..	..	..	7 36	..	7 56	..	..	..	..	..	..
Swanscombe Halt.....	..	..	6 36	..	..	..	..	7 39	..	7 59	..	..	..	..	..	..
Northfleet.........	5 49	..	6 38	..	..	..	..	7 42	..	8 2	..	..	..	..	..	..
Gravesend Cen. arr	5 55	..	6 42	..	..	..	..	7 47	..	8 5	..	8 24	..	..	..	..
Gravesend Cen. dep	5 56	..	6 43	..	..	..	..	7 48	..	8 6	..	8 25	..	..	..	..
Higham.............	..	..	6 50	..	..	..	..	7 54	..	8 14	..	..	..	..	..	..
Strood.........arr	6 9	..	6 55	..	..	..	..	8 0	..	8 19	..	8 37	..	..	..	..
Strood..........dep	..	633	..	..	..	..	..	..	..	..	..	8 46	..	..	..	..
Cuxton.............	..	637	..	..	..	..	..	..	..	..	..	8 50	..	..	..	..
Halling............	..	641	..	..	..	..	..	..	..	..	..	8 53	..	..	..	..
Snodland...........	..	645	..	..	..	..	..	..	..	..	..	8 56	..	..	..	..
New Hythe..........	..	649	..	..	..	..	..	..	..	..	..	8 59	..	..	..	..
Aylesford..........	..	652	..	..	..	..	..	..	..	..	..	9 2	..	..	..	..
Maidstone Barracks	..	658	..	..	..	..	..	..	..	..	..	9 7	..	..	..	..
" West arr	..	7 1	..	..	..	..	..	..	..	..	..	9 9	..	..	..	..
Strood..........dep	6 10	..	6 56	..	..	..	..	8 1	..	8 20	..	8 38	..	..	..	..
Rochester..........	6 18	..	6 59	..	..	..	..	8 4	..	8 23	..	8 43	..	..	..	..
Chatham 60.........	6H24	..	7 0	..	..	..	..	8 6	..	8 25	..	8 46	..	..	..	..
Gillingham (Kent) arr	6 30	..	7 4	..	..	..	..	8 11	..	8 30	..	8 53	..	..	..	..

Down	Sundays—a.m																
Charing Cross....dep	8 1	8 4	8 25	8 32	8 40	8 44	..	8 55	9 1	9 4	9 25	9 32	9 44	9 55	10 1	10 4	1025
Waterloo .... "	8 3	8 6	8 27	8 34	8 42	8 46	..	8 57	9 3	9 6	9 27	9 34	9 46	9 57	10 3	10 6	1027
Cannon Street.... "	..	..	..	..	..	..	..	..	..	..	..	..	..	..	..	..	..
London Bridge.... "	8 7	8 10	8 31	8 38	8 47	8 50	..	9 1	9 7	9 10	9 31	9 38	9 50	10 1	10 7	10 10	1031
Holborn Viaduct dep	3	3	3	3	..	3	..	3	3	3	3	3	3	3	3	3	3
Blackfriars .... "					..		..										
Elephant and Castle	..	..	..	..	..	..	..	..	..	..	..	..	..	..	..	..	..
Peckham Rye.......	..	..	..	..	..	..	..	..	..	..	..	..	..	..	..	..	..
Deptford..........	..	..	..	..	..	8 56	..	..	..	..	..	..	9 56	..	..	..	..
Greenwich	..	..	..	..	..	8 58	..	..	..	..	..	..	9 58	..	..	..	..
Maze Hill A.......	..	..	..	..	..	9 0	..	..	..	..	..	..	10 0	..	..	..	..
Westcombe Park..	..	..	..	..	..	9 3	..	..	..	..	..	..	10 3	..	..	..	..
New Cross.........	8 13	8 16	8 37	8 44	..	..	..	9 7	9 13	9 16	9 37	9 44	..	10 7	1013	10 16	1037
St. John's.........	8 15	8 18	8 39	8 46	..	..	..	9 9	9 15	9 18	9 39	9 46	..	10 9	1015	10 18	1039
Lewisham.........	8 17	8 20	8 41	8 48	..	..	..	9 11	9 17	9 20	9 41	9 48	..	1011	1017	10 20	1041
Blackheath........	8 20	8 23	..	8 51	..	..	..	..	9 20	9 23	..	9 51	..	..	1020	10 23	..
Charlton..........	..	8 27	..	..	..	9 5	..	..	..	9 27	..	..	10 5	..	..	10 27	..
Woolwich Dockyard.	..	8 29	..	..	..	9 8	..	..	..	9 29	..	..	10 8	..	..	10 29	..
Woolwich Arsenal ..	..	8 32	..	..	9 0	9 10	..	..	..	9 32	..	..	1010	..	..	10 32	..
Plumstead.........	..	8 34	..	..	..	9 12	..	..	..	9 34	..	..	1012	..	..	10 34	..
Abbey Wood........	..	8 37	..	..	..	9 16	..	..	..	9 37	..	..	1016	..	..	10 37	..
Belvedere.........	..	8 40	..	..	..	9 19	..	..	..	9 40	..	..	1019	..	..	10 40	..
Erith..............	..	8 43	..	..	..	9 22	..	..	..	9 43	..	..	1022	..	..	10 43	..
Kidbrooke	8 23	..	..	8 54	..	..	..	..	9 23	..	..	9 54	..	..	1023	..	..
Eltham (Well Hall) .	8 25	..	..	8 56	..	..	..	..	9 25	..	..	9 56	..	..	1025	..	..
Eltham Park........	8 27	..	..	8 58	..	..	..	..	9 27	..	..	9 58	..	..	1027	..	..
Falconwood........	8 30	..	..	9 1	..	..	..	..	9 30	..	..	10 1	..	..	1030	..	..
Welling	8 32	..	..	9 3	..	..	..	..	9 32	..	..	10 3	..	..	1032	..	..
Bexleyheath........	8 35	..	..	9 6	..	..	..	..	9 35	..	..	10 6	..	..	1035	..	..
Barnehurst.........	8 38	..	..	9 9	..	..	..	..	9 38	..	..	10 9	..	..	1038	..	..
Hither Green.......	..	..	8 44	..	..	..	..	9 14	..	..	9 44	..	..	1014	..	..	1044
Lee, for Burnt Ash..	..	..	8 46	..	..	..	..	9 16	..	..	9 46	..	..	1016	..	..	1046
Mottingham	..	..	8 50	..	..	..	..	9 20	..	..	9 50	..	..	1020	..	..	1050
New Eltham........	..	..	8 52	..	..	..	..	9 22	..	..	9 52	..	..	1022	..	..	1052
Sidcup............	..	..	8 55	..	..	..	..	9 25	..	..	9 55	..	..	1025	..	..	1055
Albany Park	..	..	8 58	..	..	..	..	9 28	..	..	9 58	..	..	1028	..	..	1058
Bexley.............	..	..	9 1	..	..	..	..	9 31	..	..	10 1	..	..	1031	..	..	11 1
Crayford...........	..	..	9 4	..	..	..	..	9 34	..	..	10 4	..	..	1034	..	..	11 4
Slades Green.......	..	8 46	..	..	..	9 25	..	..	..	9 46	..	..	1025	..	..	10 46	..
Dartford...........	8 44	8 50	9 8	9 16	9 13	9 29	..	9 38	9 44	9 50	10 8	1016	1029	1038	1044	10 50	11 8
Stone Crossing Halt...	..	8 54	..	..	..	..	..	..	..	9 54	Stop	..	..	..	..	10 54	..
Greenhithe.........	..	8 56	..	..	..	..	..	..	..	9 56	..	..	..	..	..	10 56	..
Swanscombe Halt.....	..	8 59	..	..	..	..	..	..	..	9 59	..	..	..	..	..	10 59	..
Northfleet.........	..	9 2	..	..	..	..	..	..	..	10 2	..	..	..	..	..	11 2	..
Gravesend Cen. arr	..	9 5	..	..	9 23	..	..	..	..	10 5	..	..	..	..	..	11 5	..
Gravesend Cen. dep	..	9 6	..	..	9 24	..	..	..	..	10 6	..	..	..	..	..	11 6	..
Higham.............	..	9 14	..	..	..	..	..	..	..	10 14	..	..	..	..	..	11 14	..
Strood.........arr	..	9 20	..	..	9 35	..	..	..	..	10 19	a.m	..	..	..	..	11 19	..
Strood..........dep	..	..	..	..	9 38	..	..	..	..	..	1038	..	..	..	..	..	..
Cuxton.............	..	..	..	..	9 42	..	..	..	..	..	1042	..	..	..	..	..	..
Halling............	..	..	..	..	9 45	..	..	..	..	..	1045	..	..	..	..	..	..
Snodland...........	..	..	..	..	9 48	..	..	..	..	..	1048	..	..	..	..	..	..
New Hythe..........	..	..	..	..	9 51	..	..	..	..	..	1051	..	..	..	..	..	..
Aylesford..........	..	..	..	..	9 54	..	..	..	..	..	1054	..	..	..	..	..	..
Maidstone Barracks	..	..	..	..	9 59	..	..	..	..	..	1059	..	..	..	..	..	..
" West arr	..	..	..	..	10 1	..	..	..	..	..	11 1	..	..	..	..	..	..
Strood..........dep	..	9 22	..	..	9 36	..	..	..	..	10 21	..	..	..	..	..	11 20	..
Rochester..........	..	9 26	..	..	9 39	..	..	..	..	10 25	..	..	..	..	..	11 23	..
Chatham 60.........	..	9 28	..	..	9 42	..	..	..	..	10B33	..	..	..	..	..	11B31	..
Gillingham (Kent) arr	..	9 32	..	..	9 46	..	..	..	..	10 38	..	..	..	..	..	11 36	..

A Maze Hill, for National Maritime Museum B Arr 6 mins *earlier* F Arr 4 mins *earlier* H Arr 2 mins *earlier*

3 Third class only

LONDON, WOOLWICH, DARTFORD, GRAVESEND CENTRAL, MAIDSTONE WEST, CHATHAM, and GILLINGHAM (Kent)

Down	Sundays—continued a.m.										p.m.																						
Charing Cross .... dep	1032	1040	1044	1055	11 1	11 4	1125	1132	1144	1155	12 1	12 4	1225	1232	1240	1244	1255	1 1	1 4	1 25	1 32	1 44	1 55	2 1	2 4	2 25	2 32	2 40	2 44	2 55	3 1	3 4	..
Waterloo .... "	1034	1042	1046	1057	11 3	11 6	1127	1134	1146	1157	12 3	12 6	1227	1234	1242	1246	1257	1 3	1 6	1 27	1 34	1 46	1 57	2 3	2 6	2 27	2 34	2 42	2 46	2 57	3 3	3 6	..
Cannon Street .... "	..	..	..	..	..	..	..	..	..	..	..	..	..	..	..	..	..	..	..	..	..	..	..	..	..	..	..	..	..	..	..	..	..
London Bridge .... "	1038	1047	1030	11 1	11 7	1110	1131	1138	1150	12 1	12 7	1210	1231	1238	1247	1250	1 1	1 7	1 10	1 31	1 38	1 50	2 1	2 7	2 10	2 31	2 38	2 47	2 50	3 1	3 7	3 10	..
Holborn Viaduct dp	3	..	3	3	3	3	3	3	3	3	3	3	3	3	..	3	3	3	3	3	3	3	3	3	3	3	3	..	3	3	3	3	..
Blackfriars .... "		..													..													..					..
Elephant and Castle	..	..	..	..	..	..	..	..	..	..	..	..	..	..	..	..	..	..	..	..	..	..	..	..	..	..	..	..	..	..	..	..	..
Peckham Rye	..	..	..	..	..	..	..	..	..	..	..	..	..	..	..	..	..	..	..	..	..	..	..	..	..	..	..	..	..	..	..	..	..
Deptford	..	..	1056	..	..	..	..	..	1156	..	..	..	..	..	..	1256	..	..	..	..	..	1 56	..	..	..	..	..	..	2 56	..	..	..	..
Greenwich	..	..	1058	..	..	..	..	..	1158	..	..	..	..	..	..	1258	..	..	..	..	..	1 58	..	..	..	..	..	..	2 58	..	..	..	..
Maze Hill A	..	..	11 0	..	..	..	..	..	12 0	..	..	..	..	..	..	1 0	..	..	..	..	..	2 0	..	..	..	..	..	..	3 0	..	..	..	..
Westcombe Park	..	..	11 3	..	..	..	..	..	12 3	..	..	..	..	..	..	1 3	..	..	..	..	..	2 3	..	..	..	..	..	..	3 3	..	..	..	..
New Cross	1044	..	..	11 7	1113	1116	1137	1144	..	12 7	1213	1216	1237	1244	..	..	1 7	1 13	1 16	1 37	1 44	..	2 7	2 13	2 16	2 37	2 44	..	..	3 7	3 13	3 16	..
St. John's	1046	..	..	11 9	1115	1118	1139	1146	..	12 9	1215	1218	1239	1246	..	..	1 9	1 15	1 18	1 39	1 46	..	2 9	2 15	2 18	2 39	2 46	..	..	3 9	3 15	3 18	..
Lewisham	1048	..	..	1111	1117	1120	1141	1148	..	1211	1217	1220	1241	1248	..	..	1 11	1 17	1 20	1 41	1 48	..	2 11	2 17	2 20	2 41	2 48	..	..	3 11	3 17	3 20	..
Blackheath	1051	..	..	..	1120	1123	..	1151	..	..	1220	1223	..	1251	..	..	..	1 20	1 23	..	1 51	..	..	2 20	2 23	..	2 51	..	..	..	3 20	3 23	..
Charlton	..	..	11 5	..	..	1127	..	..	12 5	..	..	1227	..	..	..	1 5	..	..	1 27	..	..	2 5	..	..	2 27	..	..	..	3 5	..	..	3 27	..
Woolwich Dockyard.	..	..	11 8	..	..	1129	..	..	12 8	..	..	1229	..	..	..	1 8	..	..	1 29	..	..	2 8	..	..	2 29	..	..	..	3 8	..	..	3 29	..
Woolwich Arsenal ..	..	11 0	1110	..	..	1132	..	..	1210	..	..	1232	..	..	1 0	1 10	..	..	1 32	..	..	2 10	..	..	2 32	..	..	3 0	3 10	..	..	3 32	..
Plumstead	..	..	1112	..	..	1134	..	..	1212	..	..	1234	..	..	..	1 12	..	..	1 34	..	..	2 12	..	..	2 34	..	..	..	3 12	..	..	3 34	..
Abbey Wood	..	..	1116	..	..	1137	..	..	1216	..	..	1237	..	..	..	1 16	..	..	1 37	..	..	2 16	..	..	2 37	..	..	..	3 16	..	..	3 37	..
Belvedere	..	..	1119	..	..	1140	..	..	1219	..	..	1240	..	..	..	1 19	..	..	1 40	..	..	2 19	..	..	2 40	..	..	..	3 19	..	..	3 40	..
Erith	..	..	1122	..	..	1143	..	..	1222	..	..	1243	..	..	..	1 22	..	..	1 43	..	..	2 22	..	..	2 43	..	..	..	3 22	..	..	3 43	..
Kidbrooke	1054	..	..	..	1123	..	..	1154	..	..	1223	..	..	1254	..	..	..	1 23	..	..	1 54	..	..	2 23	..	..	2 54	..	..	..	3 23	..	..
Eltham (Well Hall)..	1056	..	..	..	1125	..	..	1156	..	..	1225	..	..	1256	..	..	..	1 25	..	..	1 56	..	..	2 25	..	..	2 56	..	..	..	3 25	..	..
Eltham Park	1058	..	..	..	1127	..	..	1158	..	..	1227	..	..	1258	..	..	..	1 27	..	..	1 58	..	..	2 27	..	..	2 58	..	..	..	3 27	..	..
Falconwood	11 1	..	..	..	1130	..	..	12 1	..	..	1230	..	..	1 1	..	..	..	1 30	..	..	2 1	..	..	2 30	..	..	3 1	..	..	..	3 30	..	..
Welling	11 3	..	..	..	1132	..	..	12 3	..	..	1232	..	..	1 3	..	..	..	1 32	..	..	2 3	..	..	2 32	..	..	3 3	..	..	..	3 32	..	..
Bexleyheath	11 6	..	..	..	1135	..	..	12 6	..	..	1235	..	..	1 6	..	..	..	1 35	..	..	2 6	..	..	2 35	..	..	3 6	..	..	..	3 35	..	..
Barnehurst	11 9	..	..	..	1138	..	..	12 9	..	..	1238	..	..	1 9	..	..	..	1 38	..	..	2 9	..	..	2 38	..	..	3 9	..	..	..	3 38	..	..
Hither Green	..	..	..	1114	..	..	1144	..	..	1214	..	..	1244	..	..	..	1 14	..	..	1 44	..	..	2 14	..	..	2 44	..	..	..	3 14	..	..	..
Lee, for Burnt Ash.	..	..	..	1116	..	..	1146	..	..	1216	..	..	1246	..	..	..	1 16	..	..	1 46	..	..	2 16	..	..	2 46	..	..	..	3 16	..	..	..
Mottingham	..	..	..	1120	..	..	1150	..	..	1220	..	..	1250	..	..	..	1 20	..	..	1 50	..	..	2 20	..	..	2 50	..	..	..	3 20	..	..	..
New Eltham	..	..	..	1122	..	..	1152	..	..	1222	..	..	1252	..	..	..	1 22	..	..	1 52	..	..	2 22	..	..	2 52	..	..	..	3 22	..	..	..
Sidcup	..	..	..	1125	..	..	1155	..	..	1225	..	..	1255	..	..	..	1 25	..	..	1 55	..	..	2 25	..	..	2 55	..	..	..	3 25	..	..	..
Albany Park	..	..	..	1128	..	..	1158	..	..	1228	..	..	1258	..	..	..	1 28	..	..	1 58	..	..	2 28	..	..	2 58	..	..	..	3 28	..	..	..
Bexley	..	..	..	1131	..	..	12 1	..	..	1231	..	..	1 1	..	..	..	1 31	..	..	2 1	..	..	2 31	..	..	3 1	..	..	..	3 31	..	..	..
Crayford	..	..	..	1134	..	..	12 4	..	..	1234	..	..	1 4	..	..	..	1 34	..	..	2 4	..	..	2 34	..	..	3 4	..	..	..	3 34	..	..	..
Slades Green	..	..	1125	..	..	1146	..	..	1225	..	..	1246	..	..	..	1 25	..	..	1 46	..	..	2 25	..	..	2 46	..	..	..	3 25	..	..	3 46	..
Dartford	1116	1113	1129	1138	1144	1150	12 8	1216	1229	1238	1244	1250	1 8	1 16	1 13	1 29	1 38	1 44	1 50	2 8	2 16	2 29	2 38	2 44	2 50	3 8	3 16	3 13	3 29	3 38	3 44	3 50	..
Stone Crossing Halt..	..	..	..	..	..	1154	—	..	..	..	..	1254	..	..	..	..	..	..	1 54	—	..	..	..	..	2 54	..	..	..	..	..	..	3 54	..
Greenhithe	..	..	..	..	..	1156	Stop	..	..	..	..	1256	..	..	..	..	..	..	1 56	Stop	..	..	..	..	2 56	..	..	..	..	..	..	3 56	..
Swanscombe Halt	..	..	..	..	..	1159	..	..	..	..	..	1259	..	..	..	..	..	..	1 59	..	..	..	..	..	2 59	..	..	..	..	..	..	3 59	..
Northfleet	..	..	..	..	..	12 2	..	..	..	..	..	1 2	..	..	..	..	..	..	2 2	..	..	..	..	..	3 2	..	..	..	..	..	..	4 2	..
Gravesend Cen. arr	..	1123	..	..	..	12 5	..	..	..	..	..	1 5	..	..	1 23	..	..	..	2 5	..	..	..	..	..	3 5	..	..	3 23	..	..	..	4 5	..
Gravesend Cen. dep	..	1124	..	..	..	12 6	..	..	..	..	..	1 6	..	..	1 24	..	..	..	2 6	..	..	..	..	..	3 6	..	..	3 24	..	..	..	4 6	..
Higham	..	..	..	..	..	1214	..	..	..	..	..	1 14	..	..	..	..	..	..	2 14	..	..	..	..	..	3 14	..	..	..	..	..	..	4 14	..
Strood .... arr	..	1135	..	..	..	1219	p.m	..	..	..	..	1 19	..	..	1 35	..	..	..	2 19	p.m	..	..	..	..	3 19	..	..	3 35	..	..	..	4 19	..
Strood .... dep	..	1138	..	..	..	..	1238	..	..	..	..	..	..	..	1 38	..	..	..	..	2 38	..	..	..	..	..	..	..	3 38	..	..	..	..	4 38
Cuxton	..	1142	..	..	..	..	1242	..	..	..	..	..	..	..	1 42	..	..	..	..	2 42	..	..	..	..	..	..	..	3 42	..	..	..	..	4 42
Halling	..	1145	..	..	..	..	1245	..	..	..	..	..	..	..	1 45	..	..	..	..	2 45	..	..	..	..	..	..	..	3 45	..	..	..	..	4 45
Snodland	..	1148	..	..	..	..	1248	..	..	..	..	..	..	..	1 48	..	..	..	..	2 48	..	..	..	..	..	..	..	3 48	..	..	..	..	4 48
New Hythe	..	1151	..	..	..	..	1251	..	..	..	..	..	..	..	1 51	..	..	..	..	2 51	..	..	..	..	..	..	..	3 51	..	..	..	..	4 51
Aylesford	..	1154	..	..	..	..	1254	..	..	..	..	..	..	..	1 54	..	..	..	..	2 54	..	..	..	..	..	..	..	3 54	..	..	..	..	4 54
Maidstone Barracks	..	1159	..	..	..	..	1259	..	..	..	..	..	..	..	1 59	..	..	..	..	2 59	..	..	..	..	..	..	..	3 59	..	..	..	..	4 59
" West arr	..	12 1	..	..	..	..	1 1	..	..	..	..	..	..	..	2 1	..	..	..	..	3 1	..	..	..	..	..	..	..	4 1	..	..	..	..	5 1
Strood .... dep	..	1136	..	..	..	1220	..	..	..	..	..	1 20	..	..	1 36	..	..	..	2 20	..	..	..	..	..	3 20	..	..	3 36	..	..	..	4 20	..
Rochester	..	1139	..	..	..	1223	..	..	..	..	..	1 23	..	..	1 39	..	..	..	2 23	..	..	..	..	..	3 23	..	..	3 39	..	..	..	4 23	..
Chatham 60	..	1141	..	..	..	1225	..	..	..	..	..	1 25	..	..	1 41	..	..	..	2 25	..	..	..	..	..	3 25	..	..	3 41	..	..	..	4 25	..
Gillingham (Kent) arr	..	1146	..	..	..	1230	..	..	..	..	..	1 30	..	..	1 46	..	..	..	2 30	..	..	..	..	..	3 30	..	..	3 46	..	..	..	4 30	..

A Maze Hill, for National Maritime Museum

3 Third class only

LONDON, WOOLWICH, DARTFORD, GRAVESEND CENTRAL, MAIDSTONE WEST, CHATHAM, and GILLINGHAM (Kent)

Sundays — *continued*

Down	p.m.										
Charing Cross .... dep	3 25	3 32	3 44	3 55	4 1	4 4	4 25	4 32	4 40	4 44	4 55
Waterloo .... "	3 27	3 34	3 46	3 57	4 3	4 6	4 27	4 34	4 42	4 46	4 57
Cannon Street .... "	..	..	..	..	..	..	..	..	..	..	..
London Bridge ... "	3 31	3 38	3 50	4 1	4 7	4 10	4 31	4 38	4 47	4 50	5 1
Holborn Viaduct dp	③	③	③	③	③	③	③	③	..	③	③
Blackfriars ..... "									..		
Elephant and Castle	..	..	..	..	..	..	..	..	..	..	..
Peckham Rye	..	..	..	..	..	..	..	..	..	..	..
Deptford	..	..	3 56	..	..	..	..	..	..	4 56	..
Greenwich	..	..	3 58	..	..	..	..	..	..	4 58	..
Maze Hill A	..	..	4 0	..	..	..	..	..	..	5 0	..
Westcombe Park ..	..	..	4 3	..	..	..	..	..	..	5 3	..
New Cross	3 37	3 44	..	4 7	4 13	4 16	4 37	4 44	..	..	5 7
St. John's	3 39	3 46	..	4 9	4 15	4 18	4 39	4 46	..	..	5 9
Lewisham	3 41	3 48	..	4 11	4 17	4 20	4 41	4 48	..	..	5 11
Blackheath	..	3 51	..	..	4 20	4 23	..	4 51	..	..	..
Charlton	..	..	4 5	..	..	4 27	..	..	..	5 5	..
Woolwich Dockyard.	..	..	4 8	..	..	4 29	..	..	..	5 8	..
Woolwich Arsenal ...	..	..	4 10	..	..	4 32	..	..	5 0	5 10	..
Plumstead	..	..	4 12	..	..	4 34	..	..	..	5 12	..
Abbey Wood	..	..	4 16	..	..	4 37	..	..	..	5 16	..
Belvedere	..	..	4 19	..	..	4 40	..	..	..	5 19	..
Erith	..	..	4 22	..	..	4 43	..	..	..	5 22	..
Kidbrooke	..	3 54	..	..	4 23	..	..	4 54	..	..	..
Eltham (Well Hall) .	..	3 56	..	..	4 25	..	..	4 56	..	..	..
Eltham Park	..	3 58	..	..	4 27	..	..	4 58	..	..	..
Falconwood	..	4 1	..	..	4 30	..	..	5 1	..	..	..
Welling	..	4 3	..	..	4 32	..	..	5 3	..	..	..
Bexleyheath	..	4 6	..	..	4 35	..	..	5 6	..	..	..
Barnehurst	..	4 9	..	..	4 38	..	..	5 9	..	..	..
Hither Green	3 44	..	..	4 14	..	..	4 44	..	..	..	5 14
Lee, for Burnt Ash..	3 46	..	..	4 16	..	..	4 46	..	..	..	5 16
Mottingham	3 50	..	..	4 20	..	..	4 50	..	..	..	5 20
New Eltham	3 52	..	..	4 22	..	..	4 52	..	..	..	5 22
Sidcup	3 55	..	..	4 25	..	..	4 55	..	..	..	5 25
Albany Park	3 58	..	..	4 28	..	..	4 58	..	..	..	5 28
Bexley	4 1	..	..	4 31	..	..	5 1	..	..	..	5 31
Crayford	4 4	..	..	4 34	..	..	5 4	..	..	..	5 34
Slades Green	..	..	4 25	..	..	4 46	..	..	..	5 25	..
Dartford	4 8	4 16	4 29	4 38	4 44	4 50	5 8	5 16	5 13	5 29	5 38
Stone Crossing Halt..	..	..	..	..	..	4 54	..	..	..	..	..
Greenhithe	..	..	..	..	..	4 56	..	..	..	..	..
Swanscombe Halt	..	..	..	..	..	4 59	..	..	..	..	..
Northfleet	..	..	..	..	..	5 2	..	..	..	..	..
Gravesend Cen. arr	..	..	..	..	..	5 5	..	..	5 23	..	..
Gravesend Cen. dep	..	..	..	..	..	5 6	..	..	5 24	..	..
Higham	..	..	..	..	..	5 14	..	..	..	..	..
Strood .... arr	..	..	..	..	..	5 19	..	..	5 35	..	..
Strood .... dep	..	..	..	..	..	..	..	..	5 38	..	..
Cuxton	..	..	..	..	..	..	..	..	5 42	..	..
Halling	..	..	..	..	..	..	..	..	5 45	..	..
Snodland	..	..	..	..	..	..	..	..	5 48	..	..
New Hythe	..	..	..	..	..	..	..	..	5 51	..	..
Aylesford	..	..	..	..	..	..	..	..	5 54	..	..
Maidstone Barracks	..	..	..	..	..	..	..	..	5 59	..	..
" West arr	..	..	..	..	..	..	..	..	6 1	..	..
Strood .... dep	..	..	..	..	..	5 20	..	..	5 36	..	..
Rochester	..	..	..	..	..	5 23	..	..	5 39	..	..
Chatham 60	..	..	..	..	..	5 25	..	..	5 41	..	..
Gillingham (Kent) arr	..	..	..	..	..	5 30	..	..	5 46	..	..

Down	p.m.										
Charing Cross .... dep	5 1	5 4	..	5 25	5 32	5 44	5 55	6 1	6 4	6 25	6 32
Waterloo .... "	5 3	5 6	..	5 27	5 34	5 46	5 57	6 3	6 6	6 27	6 34
Cannon Street .... "	..	..	..	..	..	..	..	..	..	..	..
London Bridge ... "	5 7	5 10	..	5 31	5 38	5 50	6 1	6 7	6 10	6 31	6 38
Holborn Viaduct dp	③	③	..	③	③	③	③	③	③	③	③
Blackfriars ..... "			..								
Elephant and Castle	..	..	..	..	..	..	..	..	..	..	..
Peckham Rye	..	..	..	..	..	..	..	..	..	..	..
Deptford	..	..	..	..	..	5 56	..	..	..	..	..
Greenwich	..	..	..	..	..	5 58	..	..	..	..	..
Maze Hill A	..	..	..	..	..	6 0	..	..	..	..	..
Westcombe Park ..	..	..	..	..	..	6 3	..	..	..	..	..
New Cross	5 13	5 16	..	5 37	5 44	..	6 7	6 13	6 16	6 37	6 44
St. John's	5 15	5 18	..	5 39	5 46	..	6 9	6 15	6 18	6 39	6 46
Lewisham	5 17	5 20	..	5 41	5 48	..	6 11	6 17	6 20	6 41	6 48
Blackheath	5 20	5 23	..	..	5 51	..	..	6 20	6 23	..	6 51
Charlton	..	5 27	..	..	..	6 5	..	..	6 27	..	..
Woolwich Dockyard.	..	5 29	..	..	..	6 8	..	..	6 29	..	..
Woolwich Arsenal ...	..	5 32	..	..	..	6 10	..	..	6 32	..	..
Plumstead	..	5 34	..	..	..	6 12	..	..	6 34	..	..
Abbey Wood	..	5 37	..	..	..	6 16	..	..	6 37	..	..
Belvedere	..	5 40	..	..	..	6 19	..	..	6 40	..	..
Erith	..	5 43	..	..	..	6 22	..	..	6 43	..	..
Kidbrooke	5 23	..	..	..	5 54	..	..	6 23	..	..	6 54
Eltham (Well Hall) .	5 25	..	..	..	5 56	..	..	6 25	..	..	6 56
Eltham Park	5 27	..	..	..	5 58	..	..	6 27	..	..	6 58
Falconwood	5 30	..	..	..	6 1	..	..	6 30	..	..	7 1
Welling	5 32	..	..	..	6 3	..	..	6 32	..	..	7 3
Bexleyheath	5 35	..	..	..	6 6	..	..	6 35	..	..	7 6
Barnehurst	5 38	..	..	..	6 9	..	..	6 38	..	..	7 9
Hither Green	..	..	..	5 44	..	..	6 14	..	..	6 44	..
Lee, for Burnt Ash..	..	..	..	5 46	..	..	6 16	..	..	6 46	..
Mottingham	..	..	..	5 50	..	..	6 20	..	..	6 50	..
New Eltham	..	..	..	5 52	..	..	6 22	..	..	6 52	..
Sidcup	..	..	..	5 55	..	..	6 25	..	..	6 55	..
Albany Park	..	..	..	5 58	..	..	6 28	..	..	6 58	..
Bexley	..	..	..	6 1	..	..	6 31	..	..	7 1	..
Crayford	..	..	..	6 4	..	..	6 34	..	..	7 4	..
Slades Green	..	5 46	..	..	..	6 25	..	..	6 46	..	..
Dartford	5 44	5 50	..	6 8	6 16	6 29	6 38	6 44	6 50	7 8	7 16
Stone Crossing Halt..	..	5 54	..	..	..	..	..	..	6 54	..	..
Greenhithe	..	5 56	..	..	..	..	..	..	6 56	..	..
Swanscombe Halt	..	5 59	..	..	..	..	..	..	6 59	..	..
Northfleet	..	6 2	..	..	..	..	..	..	7 2	..	..
Gravesend Cen. arr	..	6 5	..	..	..	..	..	..	7 5	..	..
Gravesend Cen. dep	..	6 6	..	..	..	..	..	..	7 6	..	..
Higham	..	6 14	..	..	..	..	..	..	7 14	..	..
Strood .... arr	..	6 19	..	..	..	..	..	..	7 19	..	..
Strood .... dep	..	..	6 38	..	..	..	..	..	..	..	..
Cuxton	..	..	6 42	..	..	..	..	..	..	..	..
Halling	..	..	6 45	..	..	..	..	..	..	..	..
Snodland	..	..	6 48	..	..	..	..	..	..	..	..
New Hythe	..	..	6 51	..	..	..	..	..	..	..	..
Aylesford	..	..	6 54	..	..	..	..	..	..	..	..
Maidstone Barracks	..	..	6 59	..	..	..	..	..	..	..	..
" West arr	..	..	7 1	..	..	..	..	..	..	..	..
Strood .... dep	..	6 20	..	..	..	..	..	..	7 20	..	..
Rochester	..	6 23	..	..	..	..	..	..	7 23	..	..
Chatham 60	..	6 25	..	..	..	..	..	..	7 25	..	..
Gillingham (Kent) arr	..	6 30	..	..	..	..	..	..	7 30	..	..

Down	p.m.										
Charing Cross .... dep	6 40	6 44	6 55	7 1	7 4	..	7 25	7 32	7 44	7 55	8 1
Waterloo .... "	6 42	6 46	6 57	7 3	7 6	..	7 27	7 34	7 46	7 57	8 3
Cannon Street .... "	..	..	..	..	..	..	..	..	..	..	..
London Bridge ... "	6 47	6 50	7 1	7 7	7 10	..	7 31	7 38	7 50	8 1	8 7
Holborn Viaduct dp	..	③	③	③	③	..	③	③	③	③	③
Blackfriars ..... "	..					..					
Elephant and Castle	..	..	..	..	..	..	..	..	..	..	..
Peckham Rye	..	..	..	..	..	..	..	..	..	..	..
Deptford	..	6 56	..	..	..	..	..	..	7 56	..	..
Greenwich	..	6 58	..	..	..	..	..	..	7 58	..	..
Maze Hill A	..	7 0	..	..	..	..	..	..	8 0	..	..
Westcombe Park ..	..	7 3	..	..	..	..	..	..	8 3	..	..
New Cross	..	..	7 7	7 13	7 16	..	7 37	7 44	..	8 7	8 13
St. John's	..	..	7 9	7 15	7 18	..	7 39	7 46	..	8 9	8 15
Lewisham	..	..	7 11	7 17	7 20	..	7 41	7 48	..	8 11	8 17
Blackheath	..	..	..	7 20	7 23	..	..	7 51	..	..	8 20
Charlton	..	7 5	..	..	7 27	..	..	..	8 5	..	..
Woolwich Dockyard.	..	7 8	..	..	7 29	..	..	..	8 8	..	..
Woolwich Arsenal ...	7 0	7 10	..	..	7 32	..	..	..	8 10	..	..
Plumstead	..	7 12	..	..	7 34	..	..	..	8 12	..	..
Abbey Wood	..	7 16	..	..	7 37	..	..	..	8 16	..	..
Belvedere	..	7 19	..	..	7 40	..	..	..	8 19	..	..
Erith	..	7 22	..	..	7 43	..	..	..	8 22	..	..
Kidbrooke	..	..	..	7 23	..	..	..	7 54	..	..	8 23
Eltham (Well Hall) .	..	..	..	7 25	..	..	..	7 56	..	..	8 25
Eltham Park	..	..	..	7 27	..	..	..	7 58	..	..	8 27
Falconwood	..	..	..	7 30	..	..	..	8 1	..	..	8 30
Welling	..	..	..	7 32	..	..	..	8 3	..	..	8 32
Bexleyheath	..	..	..	7 25	..	..	..	8 6	..	..	8 35
Barnehurst	..	..	..	7 38	..	..	..	8 9	..	..	8 38
Hither Green	..	..	7 14	..	..	..	7 44	..	..	8 14	..
Lee, for Burnt Ash..	..	..	7 16	..	..	..	7 46	..	..	8 16	..
Mottingham	..	..	7 20	..	..	..	7 50	..	..	8 20	..
New Eltham	..	..	7 22	..	..	..	7 52	..	..	8 22	..
Sidcup	..	..	7 25	..	..	..	7 55	..	..	8 25	..
Albany Park	..	..	7 28	..	..	..	7 58	..	..	8 28	..
Bexley	..	..	7 31	..	..	..	8 1	..	..	8 31	..
Crayford	..	..	7 34	..	..	..	8 4	..	..	8 34	..
Slades Green	..	7 25	..	..	7 46	..	..	..	8 25	..	..
Dartford	7 13	7 29	7 38	7 44	7 50	..	8 8	8 16	8 29	8 38	8 44
Stone Crossing Halt..	..	..	..	..	7 54	..	..	..	..	..	..
Greenhithe	..	..	..	..	7 56	..	..	..	..	..	..
Swanscombe Halt	..	..	..	..	7 59	..	..	..	..	..	..
Northfleet	..	..	..	..	8 2	..	..	..	..	..	..
Gravesend Cen. arr	7 23	..	..	..	8 5	..	..	..	..	..	..
Gravesend Cen. dep	7 24	..	..	..	8 6	..	..	..	..	..	..
Higham	..	..	..	..	8 14	..	..	..	..	..	..
Strood .... arr	7 35	..	..	..	8 19	..	..	..	..	..	..
Strood .... dep	7 38	..	..	..	..	8 38	..	..	..	..	..
Cuxton	7 42	..	..	..	..	8 42	..	..	..	..	..
Halling	7 45	..	..	..	..	8 45	..	..	..	..	..
Snodland	7 48	..	..	..	..	8 48	..	..	..	..	..
New Hythe	7 51	..	..	..	..	8 51	..	..	..	..	..
Aylesford	7 54	..	..	..	..	8 54	..	..	..	..	..
Maidstone Barracks	7 59	..	..	..	..	8 59	..	..	..	..	..
" West arr	8 1	..	..	..	..	9 1	..	..	..	..	..
Strood .... dep	7 36	..	..	..	8 20	..	..	..	..	..	..
Rochester	7 39	..	..	..	8 23	..	..	..	..	..	..
Chatham 60	7F46	..	..	..	8 25	..	..	..	..	..	..
Gillingham (Kent) arr	7 51	..	..	..	8 30	..	..	..	..	..	..

A Maze Hill, for National Maritime Museum. F Arr 4 minutes *earlier*.

③ Third class only

LONDON, WOOLWICH, DARTFORD, GRAVESEND CENTRAL, MAIDSTONE WEST, CHATHAM, and GILLINGHAM (Kent)

Down	p.m								Sundays — continued.												p.m				ngt.
Charing Cross .... dep	8 4	8 25	8 32	[illegible]	8 44	8 55	9 1	9 4	..	9 25	9 32	9 44	9 55	10 1	10 4	1025	1032	1040	1044	1055	11 1	11 4	1118	1125	1132	1253
Waterloo .... "	8 6	8 27	8 34	8 42	8 46	8 57	9 3	9 6	..	9 27	9 34	9 46	9 57	10 3	10 6	1027	1034	1042	1046	1057	11 3	11 6	1120	1127	1134	1255
Cannon Street .... "	..	..	..	..	..	..	..	..	..	..	..	..	..	..	..	..	..	..	..	..	..	..	..	..	..	1 2
London Bridge .... "	8 10	8 31	8 38	8 47	8 50	9 1	9 7	9 10	..	9 31	9 38	9 50	10 1	10 7	1010	1031	1038	1047	1050	11 1	11 7	1110	1124	1131	1138	1 7
Holborn Viaduct dep	3	3	3	..	3	3	3	3	..	3	3	3	3	3	3	3	3	..	3	3	3	3	3	3	3	3
Blackfriars .... "				..					..									..								
Elephant and Castle	..	..	..	..	..	..	..	..	..	..	..	..	..	..	..	..	..	..	..	..	..	..	..	..	..	..
Peckham Rye	..	..	..	..	..	..	..	..	..	..	..	..	..	..	..	..	..	..	..	..	..	..	..	..	..	..
Deptford	..	..	..	..	8 56	..	..	..	..	..	..	9 56	..	..	..	..	..	..	1056	..	..	..	1130	..	..	..
Greenwich	..	..	..	..	8 58	..	..	..	..	..	..	9 58	..	..	..	..	..	..	1058	..	..	..	1132	..	..	..
Maze Hill A	..	..	..	..	9 0	..	..	..	..	..	..	10 0	..	..	..	..	..	..	11 0	..	..	..	1134	..	..	..
Westcombe Park	..	..	..	..	9 3	..	..	..	..	..	..	10 3	..	..	..	..	..	..	11 3	..	..	..	1137	..	..	..
New Cross	8 16	8 37	8 44	..	..	9 7	9 13	9 16	..	9 37	9 44	..	10 7	1013	1016	1037	1044	..	..	11 7	1113	1116	..	1137	1144	1 13
St. John's	8 18	8 39	8 46	..	..	9 9	9 15	9 18	..	9 39	9 46	..	10 9	1015	1018	1039	1046	..	..	11 9	1115	1118	..	1139	1146	1 16
Lewisham	8 20	8 41	8 48	..	..	9 11	9 17	9 20	..	9 41	9 48	..	1011	1017	1020	1041	1048	..	..	1111	1117	1120	..	1141	1148	1 18
Blackheath	8 23	..	8 51	..	..	..	9 20	9 23	..	..	9 51	..	..	1020	1023	..	1051	..	..	..	1120	1123	..	..	1151	1 21
Charlton	8 27	..	..	..	9 5	..	..	9 27	..	..	..	10 5	..	..	1027	..	..	..	11 5	..	..	1127	1139	..	..	1 25
Woolwich Dockyard	8 29	..	..	..	9 8	..	..	9 29	..	..	..	10 8	..	..	1029	..	..	..	11 8	..	..	1129	1142	..	..	1 27
Woolwich Arsenal	8 32	..	..	9 0	9 10	..	..	9 32	..	..	..	1010	..	..	1032	..	..	11 0	1110	..	..	1132	1144	..	..	1 30
Plumstead	8 34	..	..	..	9 12	..	..	9 34	..	..	..	1012	..	..	1034	..	..	..	1112	..	..	1134	1146	..	..	1 33
Abbey Wood	8 37	..	..	..	9 16	..	..	9 37	..	..	..	1016	..	..	1037	..	..	..	1116	..	..	1137	1150	..	..	1 37
Belvedere	8 40	..	..	..	9 19	..	..	9 40	..	..	..	1019	..	..	1040	..	..	..	1119	..	..	1140	1153	..	..	1 40
Erith	8 43	..	..	..	9 22	..	..	9 43	..	..	..	1022	..	..	1043	..	..	..	1122	..	..	1143	1156	..	..	1 43
Kidbrooke	..	..	8 54	..	..	..	9 23	..	..	..	9 54	..	..	1023	..	..	1054	..	..	..	1123	..	..	..	1154	..
Eltham (Well Hall)	..	..	8 56	..	..	..	9 25	..	..	..	9 56	..	..	1025	..	..	1056	..	..	..	1125	..	..	..	1156	..
Eltham Park	..	..	8 58	..	..	..	9 27	..	..	..	9 58	..	..	1027	..	..	1058	..	..	..	1127	..	..	..	1158	..
Falconwood	..	..	9 1	..	..	..	9 30	..	..	..	10 1	..	..	1030	..	..	11 1	..	..	..	1130	..	..	..	12 1	..
Welling	..	..	9 3	..	..	..	9 32	..	..	..	10 3	..	..	1032	..	..	11 3	..	..	..	1132	..	..	..	12 3	..
Bexleyheath	..	..	9 6	..	..	..	9 35	..	..	..	10 6	..	..	1035	..	..	11 6	..	..	..	1135	..	..	..	12 6	..
Barnehurst	..	..	9 9	..	..	..	9 38	..	..	..	10 9	..	..	1038	..	..	11 9	..	..	..	1138	..	..	..	12 9	..
Hither Green	..	8 44	..	..	..	9 14	..	..	..	9 44	..	..	1014	..	..	1044	..	..	..	1114	..	..	..	1144	..	..
Lee, for Burnt Ash	..	8 46	..	..	..	9 16	..	..	..	9 46	..	..	1016	..	..	1046	..	..	..	1116	..	..	..	1146	..	..
Mottingham	..	8 50	..	..	..	9 20	..	..	..	9 50	..	..	1020	..	..	1050	..	..	..	1120	..	..	..	1150	..	..
New Eltham	..	8 52	..	..	..	9 22	..	..	..	9 52	..	..	1022	..	..	1052	..	..	..	1122	..	..	..	1152	..	..
Sidcup	..	8 55	..	..	..	9 25	..	..	..	9 55	..	..	1025	..	..	1055	..	..	..	1125	..	..	..	1155	..	..
Albany Park	..	8 58	..	..	..	9 28	..	..	..	9 58	..	..	1028	..	..	1058	..	..	..	1128	..	..	..	1158	..	..
Bexley	..	9 1	..	..	..	9 31	..	..	..	10 1	..	..	1031	..	..	11 1	..	..	..	1131	..	..	..	12 1	..	..
Crayford	..	9 4	..	..	..	9 34	..	..	..	10 4	..	..	1034	..	..	11 4	..	..	..	1134	..	..	..	12 4	..	..
Slades Green	8 46	..	..	..	9 25	..	..	9 46	..	..	..	1025	..	..	1046	..	..	..	1125	..	..	1146	1159	..	..	1 46
Dartford	8 50	9 8	9 16	9 13	9 29	9 38	9 44	9 50	..	10 8	1016	1029	1038	1044	1050	11 8	1116	1113	1129	1138	1144	1150	12 3	12 8	1216	1 50
Stone Crossing Halt	8 54	..	..	..	..	..	..	9 54	..	..	..	..	..	..	1054	..	..	..	..	..	..	1154	..	..	..	..
Greenhithe	8 56	..	..	..	..	..	..	9 56	..	..	..	..	..	..	1056	..	..	..	..	..	..	1156	..	..	..	..
Swanscombe Halt	8 59	..	..	..	..	..	..	9 59	..	..	..	..	..	..	1059	..	..	..	..	..	..	1159	..	..	..	..
Northfleet	9 2	..	..	..	..	..	..	10 2	..	..	..	..	..	..	11 2	..	..	..	..	..	..	12 2	..	..	..	..
Gravesend Cen. arr	9 5	..	..	9 23	..	..	..	10 5	..	..	..	..	..	..	11 5	..	..	1123	..	..	..	12 6	..	..	..	..
Gravesend Cen. dep	9 6	..	..	9 24	..	..	..	10 6	..	..	..	..	..	..	11 6	..	..	1124	..	..	..	12 7	..	..	..	..
Higham	9 14	..	..	..	..	..	..	1014	..	..	..	..	..	..	1114	..	..	..	..	..	..	1214	..	..	..	..
Strood .... arr	9 20	..	..	9 35	..	..	..	1019	..	..	..	..	..	..	1119	..	..	1135	..	..	..	1219	..	..	..	..
Strood .... dep	..	..	..	9 38	..	..	..	..	1038	..	..	..	..	..	..	..	..	1138	..	..	..	..	..	..	..	..
Cuxton	..	..	..	9 42	..	..	..	..	1042	..	..	..	..	..	..	..	..	1142	..	..	..	..	..	..	..	..
Halling	..	..	..	9 45	..	..	..	..	1045	..	..	..	..	..	..	..	..	1145	..	..	..	..	..	..	..	..
Snodland	..	..	..	9 48	..	..	..	..	1048	..	..	..	..	..	..	..	..	1148	..	..	..	..	..	..	..	..
New Hythe	..	..	..	9 51	..	..	..	..	1051	..	..	..	..	..	..	..	..	1151	..	..	..	..	..	..	..	..
Aylesford	..	..	..	9 54	..	..	..	..	1054	..	..	..	..	..	..	..	..	1154	..	..	..	..	..	..	..	..
Maidstone Barracks	..	..	..	9 59	..	..	..	..	1059	..	..	..	..	..	..	..	..	1159	..	..	..	..	..	..	..	..
" West arr	..	..	..	10 1	..	..	..	..	11 1	..	..	..	..	..	..	..	..	12 1	..	..	..	..	..	..	..	..
Strood .... dep	9 21	..	..	9 36	..	..	..	1025	..	..	..	..	..	..	1120	..	..	1136	..	..	..	1220	..	..	..	..
Rochester	9 25	..	..	9 42	..	..	..	1029	..	..	..	..	..	..	1123	..	..	1139	..	..	..	1223	..	..	..	..
Chatham 69	9F38	..	..	9 45	..	..	..	1031	..	..	..	..	..	..	1125	..	..	1141	..	..	..	1225	..	..	..	..
Gillingham (Kent) arr	9 41	..	..	9 50	..	..	..	1036	..	..	..	..	..	..	1130	..	..	1146	..	..	..	1230	..	..	..	..

A Maze Hill, for National Maritime Museum F Arr. 9 27 p.m

3 Third class only

OTHER TRAINS

BETWEEN — PAGE

GILLINGHAM (Kent), CHATHAM, MAIDSTONE WEST, GRAVESEND CENTRAL, DARTFORD, WOOLWICH, and LONDON

Mls		Up	Week Days a.m																															a.m
—		Gillingham (Kent) dep				4 0							4 50		5 15				5 40								5 52						6 6	
1¾		Chatham				4 3							4 54		5 18				5 44								5 56						6 10	
2½		Rochester				4 6									5 21				5 47								5 59						6 13	
2¾		Strood 72 arr				4 8							5 1		5 24				5 50								6 2						6 16	
	Ml	Maidstone West dp	3	3	3	3	3	3	3	3	3	4 34	3	3	3	3	3	3	3	3	3	3	3	3	3	5 36	3	3	3	3	3	5 50	3	3
—	½	" Barracks																								5 38						5 52		
—	3½	Aylesford										4 39														5 43						5 57		
—	4½	New Hythe										4 42														5 46						6 0		
—	5¾	Snodland										4 45														5 49						6 3		
—	7½	Halling										4 48														5 52						6 6		
—	9	Cuxton										4 51														5 55						6 9		
—	11½	Strood 72 arr										4 56														6 0						6 14		
—		Strood dep				4 9							5 2														6 3						6 17	
5½		Higham											5 8														6 9						6 23	
10		Gravesend arr				4 20							5 17														6 17						6 31	
		Central dep				4 21											5 25			5 42				6 4			6 19						6 32	
12½		Northfleet				4 26											5 29			5 46				6 8			6 24						6 37	
13½		Swanscombe Halt															5 31			5 48				6 10			6 26						6 39	
14½		Greenhithe				4 30											5 34			5 51				6 13			6 29						6 42	
15		Stone Crossing Halt															5 37			5 54				6 16			6 32						6 45	
17		Dartford		4 5		4 36	4 46		5 2	5 13	5 16			5 23		5 38	5 41	5 46		5 59	6 4	6 10	6 17	6 20			6 36	6 39	6 41		6 46		6 49	6 53
18½		Slades Green	3 55				4 50	5 0	5 6					5 27			5 45			6 5				6 24	6 26		6 40			6 48			6 53	
—	Mls	Crayford		4 8		4 41					5 20							5 50			6 7		6 24						6 45		6 52			
—	1½	Bexley		4 11		4 44					5 23							5 53			6 10		6 27						6 48		6 56			
—	2½	Albany Park		4 14		4 47					5 26							5 56			6 13		6 30						6 51		6 59			
—	3½	Sidcup		4 17		4 49					5 28							5 58			6 16		6 33						6 53		7 2			
—	5	New Eltham		4 20		4 52					5 31							6 1			6 19		6 36						6 56		7 5			
—	5¾	Mottingham		4 22		4 55					5 34							6 4			6 21		6 38						6 59		7 8			
—	7½	Lee, for Burnt Ash		4 26		4 58					5 37							6 7			6 25		6 42						7 2		7 12			
—	8½	Hither Green 124		4 28		5 0					5 39							6 10			6 27		6 44						7 4		7 14			
—	Mls	Barnehurst			4 10			5 4		5 19						5 48						6 16			6 34			6 45						7 0
—	1½	Bexleyheath			4 13			5 7		5 22						5 51						6 19			6 37			6 48						7 3
—	2½	Welling			4 16			5 10		5 25						5 54						6 22			6 40			6 51						7 6
—	3½	Falconwood			4 19			5 12		5 27						5 56						6 24			6 42			6 53						7 8
—	4½	Eltham Park			4 22			5 15		5 30						5 59						6 27			6 45			6 55						7 11
—	5	Eltham (Well Hall)			4 24			5 17		5 32						6 1						6 29			6 47			6 58						7 13
—	6	Kidbrooke			4 26			5 20		5 35						6 4						6 32			6 49			7 1						7 16
19½		Erith	3 58				4 53		5 9					5 30			5 48			6 8				6 27			6 43			6 51			6 56	
21¼		Belvedere	4 1				4 56		5 13					5 33			5 51			6 11				6 30			6 46			6 54			6 59	
22¼		Abbey Wood	4 4				4 59		5 16					5 36			5 54			6 14				6 33			6 49			6 57			7 2	
24¼		Plumstead	4 7				5 2		5 20					5 39			5 57			6 18				6 36			6 52			7 0			7 5	
25		Woolwich Arsenal	4 11				5 4		5 22					5 41			5 59			6 20				6 38			6 54			7 3			7 8	
25½		Woolwich Dockyard	4 13				5 7		5 25					5 44			6 2			6 22				6 41			6 57			7 6				
26¼		Charlton	4 16				5 9		5 27					5 46			6 4			6 25				6 43			6 59			7 8			7 12	
27¾		Blackheath	4 20		4 29		5 13	5 23		5 38				5 50		6 7						6 35		6 47	6 52			7 4						7 20
28¼		Lewisham 114	4 22		4 32		5 16	5 25		5 41				5 53		6 10						6 38		6 50	6 55			7 7					7 17	7 23
28¾		St. John's 124	4 24		4 34	5 4					5 43			5 55				6 14				6 40	6 47						7 8				7 19	7 25
29½		New Cross	4 27	4 33	4 36	5 6	5 19	5 28		5 44	5 45			5 58		6 13		6 16			6 32	6 42	6 50	6 53	6 58			7 10	7 10		7 18		7 22	7 27
—	Mls	Westcombe Park							5 30								6 7			6 27							7 2			7 11				
—	½	Maze Hill A							5 32								6 9			6 30							7 4			7 13				
—	1½	Greenwich							5 35								6 12			6 32							7 7			7 17				
—	2	Deptford															6 14			6 34							7 9			7 19				
—		Peckham Rye																																
—		Elephant and Castle																																
—		Blackfriars arr																																
—		Holborn Viaduct "																																
32½		London Bridge arr	4 33	4 40	4 42	5 12	5 26	5 34	5 42	5 50	5 52			6 4		6 19	6 20	6 22		6 41	6 38	6 49	6 56	6 59	7 4		7 15	7 17	7 17	7 25	7 24		7 28	7 33
32¾		Cannon Street "		4 48			5 29	5 39	5 45					6 8		6 22					6 42	6 52	6 59	7 3			7 19	7 20			7 27		7 31	
33½		Waterloo "	4 37		4 47	5 17				5 54	5 56						6 24	6 26		6 45					7 8				7 20	7 29				7 37
34		Charing Cross "	4 39		4 50	5 19				5 56	5 58						6 26	6 28		6 47					7 10				7 23	7 32				7 39

A Maze Hill, for National Maritime Museum

3 Third class only

GILLINGHAM (Kent), CHATHAM, MAIDSTONE WEST, GRAVESEND CENTRAL, DARTFORD, WOOLWICH, and LONDON

Week Days—*continued*

Up	a.m																																
Gillingham (Kent) dep		6 24		6 32													6 46				6 56		7 8							7 18	7 27		
Chatham		6 27		6 35													6 50				7 0		7 12							7 22	7 31	7 37	
Rochester		6 30		6 38													6 52				7 3		7 15							7 25	7 34		
Strood 72 arr		6 33															6 56				7 6		7 19							7 28	7 38		
Maidstone West dep	6 7	3	3		3	3	3	3	3	3	3	3	3	3	3	6 24	3	3	3	6 41	3	3	6 55	3	3	3	3	3	7 3	3	7 16		3
" Barracks	6 9															6 26				6 43			6 57						7 5		7 18		
Aylesford	6 14															6 31				6 48			7 2						7 10		7 23		
New Hythe	6 18															6 34				6 51			7 5						7 13		7 26		
Snodland	6 21															6 37				6 54			7 8						7 16		7 29		
Halling	6 24															6 40				6 57			7 11						7 19		7 32		
Cuxton	6 27															6 43				7 0			7 14						7 22		7 35		
Strood 72 arr	6 32															6 48				7 5			7 20						7 27		7 39		
Strood dep	Stop	6 34														Stop	6 57				7 7		7 22						Stop	7 29	7 42		
Higham		6 40															7 3				7 13									7 34			
Gravesend Central arr		6 47															7 11				7 21		7 34							7 42	7 56		
Gravesend Central dep		6 48									6 59			7 8			7 12				7 23		7 35							7 44	7 57		
Northfleet											7 3			7 12			7 16				7 28									7 50			
Swanscombe Halt	a.m										7 5						7 19				7 30								a.m	7 52			
Greenhithe	3										7 8			7 16		a.m	7 22				7 33								3	7 55			
Stone Crossing Halt											7 11					3	7 25				7 36									7 58			
Dartford	6 56	7 0	7 3					7 9	7 11		7 15		7 20	7 23	7 27		7 30		7 35		7 41		7 45	7 50	7 48	7 53		7 56	8 0	8 2			
Slades Green						7 9	7 0	7 13				7 26				7 27	7 33	7 34				7 41			7 51		7 57						
Crayford	6 59		7 7						7 14				7 23		7 31				7 38		7 44			7 53				8 0		8 6			8 11
Bexley	7 3		7 10						7 17				7 26		7 34				7 41		7 47			7 57				8 3		8 9			8 14
Albany Park	7 7		7 13						7 20				7 29		7 37				7 44		7 50			8 0				8 6		8 12			8 17
Sidcup	7 10		7 16						7 23				7 32		7 40				7 47		7 53			8 3				8 9		8 15			8 20
New Eltham	7 13		7 20						7 26				7 35		7 43				7 50		7 56			8 6				8 12		8 18			8 23
Mottingham	7 16		7 22						7 28				7 37		7 46				7 52		7 59			8 9				8 15		8 20			8 25
Lee, for Burnt Ash	7 20		7 26						7 32				7 41		7 49				7 56		8 2			8 13				8 18		8 24			8 29
Hither Green 124	7 22								7 34				7 43		7 52				7 58		8 4			8 15				8 21					
Barnehurst					7 5		7 14			7 21				7 29		7 34		7 39				7 50				7 59			8 6				
Bexleyheath					7 8		7 17			7 24				7 33		7 38		7 43				7 53				8 2			8 9				
Welling					7 11		7 20			7 27				7 37		7 41		7 46				7 56				8 5			8 12				
Falconwood					7 14		7 23			7 29						7 43		7 49				7 59				8 7			8 14				
Eltham Park					7 17		7 26			7 32								7 51				8 1				8 10			8 17				
Eltham (Well Hall)					7 19		7 29			7 34								7 53				8 3				8 12			8 19				
Kidbrooke					7 23		7 32											7 56				8 6				8 14			8 22				
Erith		7 5				7 12		7 16			7 21	7 30					7 36								7 54		8 0						
Belvedere						7 15		7 19			7 24	7 34					7 39								7 57		8 3						
Abbey Wood						7 18		7 22			7 27	7 37					7 42								8 0		8 6						
Plumstead		7 12				7 21		7 26			7 31	7 40					7 46								8 4		8 10						
Woolwich Arsenal		7 14				7 23		7 28			7 33	7 42					7 48						7 57		8 6		8 12				8 18		
Woolwich Dockyard		7 17						7 30			7 35						7 51								8 9		8 14						
Charlton		7 19				7 27		7 33			7 38	7 46					7 53								8 11		8 17						
Blackheath		7 23			7 27	7 31	7 35				7 42							7 59				8 8				8 17	8 21		8 25				
Lewisham 114	7 26	7 26			7 31	7 34	7 38			7 41	7 44		7 46					8 1	8 2			8 11				8 20	8 23	8 25	8 27				
St. John's 124										7 43											8 8	8 13		8 19									
New Cross		7 29	7 31		7 34	7 37	7 41		7 39	7 46	7 48				7 57			8 5			8 10	8 15		8 21			8 26		8 30				8 35
Westcombe Park								7 35				7 48					7 56								8 14								
Maze Hill A								7 38									7 58								8 17								
Greenwich								7 40				7 52					8 1								8 20								
Deptford								7 42									8 3								8 22								
Peckham Rye	7 30												7 50						8 6							8 26		8 30					
Elephant and Castle	7 37												7 57						8 14							8 33		8 37					
Blackfriars arr	7 41												7 59						8 18							8 37		8 41					
Holborn Viaduct "	7 43												8 0						8 20							8 39		8 43					
London Bridge arr		7 35	7 38	7 19	7 40	7 44	7 47	7 49	7 45	7 53	7 55	7 59		7 58	8 3	7 59	8 9	8 11			8 16	8 23	8 13	8 28	8 29		8 32		8 37	8 36	8 35	8 23	8 43
Cannon Street "		7 39	7 41				7 50	7 53		7 56		8 0				8 0		8 14			8 20	8 25			8 33				8 40		8 38	8 28	8 46
Waterloo "				7 24	7 44	7 48			7 50		7 58			7 59	8 7		8 13						8 17	8 32			8 36			8 40			
Charing Cross "				7 27	7 46	7 51			7 53		8 0			8 0	8 10		8 16						8 20	8 34			8 39			8 42			

A Maze Hill, for National Maritime Museum.

3 Third class only

GILLINGHAM (Kent), CHATHAM, MAIDSTONE WEST, GRAVESEND CENTRAL, DARTFORD, WOOLWICH, and LONDON

Week Days—continued (a.m.)

Up																																		
Gillingham (Kent) dep									SX	SO					7 50	758	8 11		SX		SO	SX				SX				8 21	8 21	8 37	SX	SX
Chatham															7 55	8 5	8 15													8 26	8 26	8 43		9 9
Rochester															7 58		8 17													8 29	8 29	8 45		
Strood 72 arr															8 1		8 20													8 32	8 32	8 48		
Maidstone West dep	3	3	3	3	3	3	725	3	3	3	3		3	736	3		7 54	3	3	3	3	3	3	3	3	3		3	8 6	3	3		3	
Barracks							727							738			7 56												8 8					
Aylesford							732							743			8 1												813	SX	SO			
New Hythe							735							746			8 4												816					
Snodland							738							749			8 7												819					
Halling							741							752			8 10												822					
Cuxton							744							755			8 13												825					
Strood 72 arr							749							8 0			8 18												830					
Strood dep															8 2		8 22													8 35	8 35	8 52		
Higham															8 8															8 41	8 41			
Gravesend Central arr															8 16		8 33													8 49	8 49	9 4		
Gravesend Central dep								8 7							8 18		8 34													8 51	8 51	9 5		
Northfleet								8 11							8 23															8 57	8 57			
Swanscombe Halt								8 13							8 25															8 59	8 59			
Greenhithe								8 16							8 28															9 2	9 2			
Stone Crossing Halt								8 19							8 31															9 5	9 5			
Dartford		8 11		8 15		8 20		8 23	8 27	8 27			8 32		8 35				8 39		8 40		8 42	8 51		8 58		9 7		9 9	9 10	9 14		
Slades Green	8 7	8 15							8 30	8 30										8 40				8 55										
Crayford				8 18		8 24					8 30								8 42		8 49	8 49				9 1		9 10						
Bexley				8 21		8 28					8 33								8 46		8 52	8 52				9 4		9 13						
Albany Park				8 24							8 36				8 42				8 49		8 55	8 55				9 7		9 16						
Sidcup				8 27		8 32					8 38				8 45				8 51		8 57	8 57				9 10		9 19						
New Eltham				8 30		8 35					8 41				8 48				8 54		9 0	9 0				9 13		9 22						
Mottingham				8 32		8 38					8 44								8 57		9 3	9 3				9 15		9 24						
Lee, for Burnt Ash				8 36		8 41					8 47								9 0		9 6	9 6				9 19		9 28						
Hither Green 124				8 39		8 43					8 50								9 2		9 8	9 8				9 21								
Barnehurst	8 11		8 18		8 23			8 30					8 38							8 45			8 50		8 59					9 17	9 17			
Bexleyheath	8 15		8 21		8 27			8 33					8 41							8 48			8 54		9 2					9 20	9 20			
Welling	8 18		8 25		8 30			8 36					8 44							8 51			8 57		9 5					9 23	9 23			
Falconwood	8 20		8 27		8 33								8 46							8 53			8 59		9 8					9 25	9 25			
Eltham Park	8 23		8 30		8 35			8 40					8 49							8 56			9 2		9 10					9 28	9 28			
Eltham (Well Hall)	8 25		8 32		8 27			8 42					8 51							8 58			9 4		9 12					9 30	9 30			
Kidbrooke	8 28		8 35		8 40								8 54							9 1			9 7		9 15					9 32	9 32			
Erith		8 18							8 33	8 33														8 58										
Belvedere		8 21							8 36	8 36														9 1										
Abbey Wood		8 24							8 39	8 39														9 4									SX	
Plumstead		8 27							8 43	8 43								8 49						9 8									9 29	
Woolwich Arsenal		8 29							8 46	8 46							8 56	8 51						9 10									9 31	
Woolwich Dockyard		8 32																8 53						9 13									9 33	
Charlton		8 34							8 49	8 49								8 56						9 15									9 36	
Blackheath	8 31		8 38		8 43			8 47					8 57					9 1		9 4			9 9		9 18					9 35	9 36			
Lewisham 114	8 34		8 41	8 42	8 45			8 49					9 0					9 4	9 6	9 7					9 20					9 38	9 38			
St. John's 124	8 36		8 44															9 6		9 9						9 25				9 40	9 40			
New Cross			8 46			8 48		8 52										9 9		9 11	9 13	9 13	9 14		9 24	9 27				9 43	9 43			
Westcombe Park		8 37							8 52	8 52														9 18									9 38	
Maze Hill A		8 39							8 54	8 54														9 21									9 41	
Greenwich		8 42							8 57	8 57														9 23									9 43	
Deptford		8 44							8 59	8 59														9 25									9 45	
Peckham Rye				8 47	8 52								9 6						9 12															
Elephant and Castle				8 54	9 0								9 14						9 20															
Blackfriars arr				8 58	9 4								9 17						9 23															
Holborn Viaduct "													9 20																					
London Bridge arr	8 44	8 51	8 53			8 55		8 58	9 6	9 5	9 0				9 3		9 10	9 15		9 17	9 19	9 19	9 20	9 32	9 30	9 35		9 38		9 49	9 49	9 41	9 51	
Cannon Street "			8 57							9 10	9 3					854	9 13	9 19					9 24	9 37						9 53	9 52		9 55	9 58
Waterloo "	8 48	8 56				8 59		9 2	9 10						9 7					9 21	9 23	9 23			9 34	9 40		9 43				9 45		
Charing Cross "	8 51	8 59				9 1		9 5	9 13						9 11					9 24	9 27	9 26			9 36	9 42		9 46				9 48		

A Maze Hill, for National Maritime Museum. S O Saturdays only S X Saturdays excepted

3 Third class only.

GILLINGHAM (Kent), CHATHAM, MAIDSTONE WEST, GRAVESEND CENTRAL, DARTFORD, WOOLWICH, and LONDON

Up	a.m.												Mondays to Fridays									a.m.							p.m.				
Gillingham (Kent) dep									9 15				1010						1042								1142		1210				
Chatham									9 19				1014						1046								1146		1214				
Rochester									9 22				1017						1049								1149		1217				
Strood 72 arr									9 25				1020						1051								1151		1220				
Maidstone West dep	3	3	3		3	3	3	9 4	3	3	3	3	9 54	3	3	3	3	1026	3	3		3	3	3	3	1126	3	3	1154	3	3	3	3
" Barracks								9 6					9 56					1028								1128			1156				
Aylesford								9 11					10 1					1033								1133			12 1				
New Hythe								9 14					10 4					1036								1136			12 4				
Snodland								9 17					10 7					1039								1139			12 7				
Halling								9 20					1010					1042								1142			1210				
Cuxton								9 24					1014					1045								1145			1214				
Strood 72 arr								9 28					1018					1050								1150			1218				
Strood dep									9 29				1022						1052								1152		1222				
Higham									9 34										1058								1158						
Gravesend arr									9 42				1034						11 5								12 5		1234				
Central dep			9 16						9 43			1012	1035				11 0		11 6								12 6		1235				
Northfleet			9 20						9 47			1016					11 4		1110								1210						
Swanscombe Halt			9 22						9 49			1018					11 6		1113								1213						
Greenhithe			9 25						9 52			1021					11 9		1116								1216						
Stone Crossing Halt			9 28						9 55			1024					1112		1118						p.m.		1218						
Dartford	9 18	9 25	9 32		9 50	9 48	9 57		9 59	1018	1023	1029	1045	1050	1057	1059	1118		1123	1129		1150	1157	1159	1218		1223	1229	1245	1250	1257	1259	1 18
Slades Green	9 21					9 51	10 1			1021					11 1		1121						12 1		1221						1 1		1 21
Crayford		9 28			9 53						1026			1053					1126			1153					1226			1253			
Bexley		9 31			9 56						1029			1056					1129			1156					1229			1256			
Albany Park		9 34			9 59						1032			1059					1132			1159					1232			1259			
Sidcup		9 37			10 2						1035			11 2					1135			12 2					1235			1 2			
New Eltham		9 40			10 5						1038			11 5					1138			12 5					1238			1 5			
Mottingham		9 42			10 7						1040			11 7					1140			12 7					1240			1 7			
Lee, for Burnt Ash		9 46			1011						1044			1111					1144			1211					1244			1 11			
Hither Green 124		9 48			1013						1046			1113					1146			1213					1246			1 13			
Barnehurst			9 38						10 5			1035				11 5				1135				12 5				1235				1 5	
Bexleyheath			9 41						10 8			1038				11 8				1138				12 8				1238				1 8	
Welling			9 44						1011			1041				1111				1141				1211				1241				1 11	
Falconwood			9 46						1013			1043				1113				1143				1213				1243				1 13	
Eltham Park			9 49						1016			1046				1116				1146				1216				1246				1 16	
Eltham (Well Hall)			9 51						1018			1048				1118				1148				1218				1248				1 18	
Kidbrooke			9 53						1020			1050				1120				1150				1220				1250				1 20	
Erith	9 25					9 54	10 4			1024					11 4		1124						12 4		1224						1 4		1 24
Belvedere	9 28					9 57	10 7			1027					11 7		1127						12 7		1227						1 7		1 27
Abbey Wood	9 31					10 0	1010			1030					1110		1130						1210		1230						1 10		1 30
Plumstead	9 35					10 4	1014			1034					1114		1134						1214		1234						1 14		1 34
Woolwich Arsenal	9 37					10 6	1016			1036			1057		1116		1136						1216		1236				1257		1 16		1 36
Woolwich Dockyard	9 39					10 9	1019			1038					1119		1138						1219		1238						1 19		1 38
Charlton	9 42					1011	1021			1041					1121		1141						1221		1241						1 21		1 41
Blackheath	9 46		9 56			1015			1023	1045		1053				1123	1145			1153				1223	1245			1253				1 23	1 45
Lewisham 114	9 49	9 51	9 59		1016	1018			1026	1047	1050	1056		1116		1126	1147		1150	1156		1216		1226	1247		1250	1256		1 16		1 26	1 47
St. John's 124	9 51	9 53	10 1		1018	1021			1028	1049	1052	1058		1118		1128	1149		1152	1158		1218		1228	1249		1252	1258		1 18		1 28	1 49
New Cross	9 53	9 56	10 3		1021	1023			1030	1052	1054	11 0		1121		1130	1152		1154	12 0		1221		1230	1252		1254	1 0		1 21		1 30	1 52
Westcombe Park							1024								1124								1224								1 24		
Maze Hill A							1026								1126								1226								1 26		
Greenwich							1029								1129								1229								1 29		
Deptford							1031								1131								1231								1 31		
Peckham Rye																																	
Elephant and Castle																																	
Blackfriars arr																																	
Holborn Viaduct "																																	
London Bridge arr	10 0	10 3	10 9		1027	1030	1039		1036	1058	11 1	11 6	1111	1127	1128	1138	1158		12 1	12 6		1228	1239	1236	1258		1 1	1 6	1 11	1 27	1 39	1 36	1 58
Cannon Street "																																	
Waterloo "	10 3	10 6	1014		1031		1043		1040	11 2	11 5	1116	1117	1131	1143	1140	12 2		12 5	1210		1231	1243	1240	1 2		1 5	1 10	1 17	1 31	1 43	1 40	2 2
Charing Cross "	10 6	10 9	1016		1034		1046		1043	11 5	11 7	1118	1122	1134	1146	1143	12 5		12 7	1213		1234	1246	1243	1 5		1 7	1 13	1 19	1 34	1 46	1 43	2 5

A Maze Hill, for National Maritime Museum.

3 Third class only

GILLINGHAM (Kent), CHATHAM, MAIDSTONE WEST, GRAVESEND CENTRAL, DARTFORD, WOOLWICH, and LONDON.

p.m. — Mondays to Fridays—continued — p.m.

Up																																	
Gillingham (Kent) dep	..	1242	..	..	..	..	..	..	1 42	..	..	2 10	..	..	..	..	2 18	..	..	..	..	2 41	..	..	..	..	3 10	..	..	..	3 18	..	..
Chatham	..	1246	..	..	..	..	..	..	1 46	..	..	2 14	..	..	..	..	2 22	..	..	..	..	2 46	..	..	..	..	3 14	..	..	..	3 22	..	..
Rochester	..	1249	..	..	..	..	..	..	1 49	..	..	2 17	..	..	..	..	2 25	..	..	..	..	2 49	..	..	..	..	3 17	..	..	..	3 25	..	..
Strood 72 arr	..	1251	..	..	..	..	..	..	1 51	..	..	2 20	..	..	..	..	2 27	..	..	..	..	2 51	..	..	..	..	3 20	..	..	..	3 29	..	..
Maidstone West dep	1226	**3**	**3**	**3**	**3**	**3**	**3**	1 26	**3**	**3**	..	1 54	**3**	**3**	**3**	**3**	**3**	**3**	**3**	**3**	2 26	**3**	**3**	**3**	**3**	**3**	2 54	**3**	**3**	**3**	**3**	**3**	**3**
" Barracks	1228							1 28			..	1 56									2 28						2 56						
Aylesford	1233	..	..	..	..	..	..	1 33	..	..	..	2 1	..	..	..	..	..	..	..	..	2 33	..	..	..	..	..	3 1	..	..	..	..	..	..
New Hythe	1236	..	..	..	..	..	..	1 36	..	..	..	2 4	..	..	..	..	..	..	..	..	2 36	..	..	..	..	..	3 4	..	..	..	..	..	..
Snodland	1239	..	..	..	..	..	..	1 39	..	..	..	2 7	..	..	..	..	..	..	..	..	2 39	..	..	..	..	..	3 7	..	..	..	..	..	..
Halling	1242	..	..	..	..	..	..	1 42	..	..	..	2 10	..	..	..	..	..	..	..	..	2 42	..	..	..	..	..	3 10	..	..	..	..	..	..
Cuxton	1245	..	..	..	..	..	..	1 45	..	..	..	2 14	..	..	..	..	..	..	..	..	2 45	..	..	..	..	..	3 13	..	..	..	..	..	..
Strood 72 arr	1250	..	..	..	..	..	..	1 50	..	..	..	2 18	..	..	..	..	..	..	..	..	2 50	..	..	..	..	..	3 18	..	..	..	..	..	..
Strood dep	..	1252	..	..	..	..	..	..	1 52	..	..	2 22	..	..	..	..	2 28	..	..	..	—	2 52	..	..	..	..	3 22	..	..	..	3 30	..	..
Higham	..	1258	..	..	..	..	..	..	1 58	..	..	..	..	..	..	..	2 34	..	..	..	Stop	2 58	..	..	..	..	..	..	..	..	..	..	..
Gravesend Central arr	..	1 5	..	..	..	..	..	..	2 5	..	..	2 34	..	..	..	..	2 42	..	..	..	..	3 5	..	..	..	..	3 34	..	..	..	3 39	..	..
Gravesend Central dep	..	1 6	..	..	..	..	..	..	2 6	..	..	2 35	..	..	..	..	2 43	..	..	..	..	3 6	..	..	..	..	3 35	..	..	..	3 40	..	..
Northfleet	..	1 10	..	..	..	..	..	..	2 10	..	..	..	..	..	..	..	2 47	..	..	..	..	3 10	..	..	..	..	..	..	..	..	..	..	..
Swanscombe Halt	..	1 13	..	..	..	..	..	..	2 13	..	..	..	..	..	..	..	2 49	..	..	..	p.m.	3 13	..	..	..	..	..	..	..	..	..	..	..
Greenhithe	..	1 16	..	..	..	..	..	..	2 16	..	..	..	..	..	..	..	2 52	..	..	..	**3**	3 16	..	..	..	..	..	..	..	..	..	..	..
Stone Crossing Halt	..	1 18	..	..	..	..	..	..	2 18	..	..	..	..	..	..	..	2 55	..	..	..		3 18	..	..	..	..	..	..	..	..	..	..	..
Dartford	..	1 23	1 29	1 50	1 57	1 59	2 18	..	2 23	2 29	..	2 45	2 42	2 50	2 53	2 57	2 59	3 9	..	3 16	3 18	3 24	..	..	..	3 36	3 45	3 47	..	..	3 50	3 57	4 1
Slades Green	..	..	..	..	2 1	..	2 21	..	..	..	..	..	..	..	..	3 1	..	..	3 10	..	3 21	..	3 22	3 26	3 33	..	..	..	..	..	3 53	..	..
Crayford	..	1 26	..	1 53	..	..	..	..	2 26	..	..	..	..	2 53	..	..	..	3 13	..	..	..	3 28	..	..	..	..	..	3 50	..	..	..	4 0	..
Bexley	..	1 29	..	1 56	..	..	..	..	2 29	..	..	..	..	2 56	..	..	..	3 16	..	..	..	3 31	..	..	..	..	..	3 53	..	..	..	4 3	..
Albany Park	..	1 32	..	1 59	..	..	..	..	2 32	..	..	..	..	2 59	..	..	..	3 19	..	..	..	3 34	..	..	..	..	..	3 56	..	..	..	4 6	..
Sidcup	..	1 35	..	2 2	..	..	..	..	2 35	..	..	..	..	3 2	..	..	..	3 22	..	..	..	3 36	..	..	..	..	..	3 59	..	..	..	4 9	..
New Eltham	..	1 38	..	2 5	..	..	..	..	2 38	..	..	..	..	3 5	..	..	..	3 25	..	..	..	3 39	..	..	..	..	..	4 2	..	..	..	4 12	..
Mottingham	..	1 40	..	2 7	..	..	..	..	2 40	..	..	..	..	3 7	..	..	..	3 27	..	..	..	3 42	..	..	..	..	..	4 4	..	..	..	4 14	..
Lee, for Burnt Ash	..	1 44	..	2 11	..	..	..	..	2 44	..	..	..	..	3 11	..	..	..	3 31	..	..	..	3 45	..	..	..	..	..	4 8	..	..	..	4 18	..
Hither Green 124	..	1 46	..	2 13	..	..	..	..	2 46	..	..	..	..	3 13	..	..	..	3 33	..	..	..	3 47	..	..	..	..	..	4 10	..	..	..	4 20	..
Barnehurst	..	..	1 35	..	..	2 5	..	..	..	2 35	..	..	2 51	..	..	..	3 5	..	..	3 22	..	..	3 35	..	..	3 45	..	..	..	3 54	..	..	4 7
Bexleyheath	..	..	1 38	..	..	2 8	..	..	..	2 38	..	..	2 55	..	..	..	3 8	..	..	3 25	..	..	3 38	..	..	3 48	..	..	..	3 58	..	..	4 10
Welling	..	..	1 41	..	..	2 11	..	..	..	2 41	..	..	2 58	..	..	..	3 11	..	..	3 28	..	..	3 41	..	..	3 51	..	..	..	4 1	..	..	4 13
Falconwood	..	..	1 43	..	..	2 13	..	..	..	2 43	..	..	3 1	..	..	..	3 13	..	..	3 31	..	..	3 43	..	..	3 55	..	..	..	4 3	..	..	4 16
Eltham Park	..	..	1 46	..	..	2 16	..	..	..	2 46	..	..	3 3	..	..	..	3 16	..	..	3 33	..	..	3 46	..	..	3 57	..	..	..	4 6	..	..	4 18
Eltham (Well Hall)	..	..	1 48	..	..	2 18	..	..	..	2 48	..	..	3 5	..	..	..	3 18	..	..	3 35	..	..	3 48	..	..	3 59	..	..	..	4 8	..	..	4 20
Kidbrooke	..	..	1 50	..	..	2 20	..	..	..	2 50	..	..	3 8	..	..	..	3 20	..	..	3 38	..	..	3 50	..	..	4 2	..	..	..	4 10	..	..	4 23
Erith	..	..	..	..	2 4	..	2 24	..	..	..	..	..	..	..	2 58	3 4	..	..	..	..	3 24	..	..	3 29	3 37	..	..	..	..	..	3 56	..	..
Belvedere	..	..	..	..	2 7	..	2 27	..	..	..	..	..	..	..	..	3 7	..	..	..	..	3 27	..	..	3 32	..	..	..	..	..	..	3 59	..	..
Abbey Wood	..	..	..	..	2 10	..	2 30	..	..	..	..	..	..	..	..	3 10	..	..	..	..	3 30	..	..	3 35	..	..	..	..	..	..	4 2	..	..
Plumstead	..	..	..	..	2 14	..	2 34	..	..	..	..	..	..	..	..	3 14	..	..	3 20	..	3 34	..	..	3 38	3 43	..	..	..	4 0	..	4 6	..	..
Woolwich Arsenal	..	..	..	..	2 16	..	2 36	..	..	..	..	2 57	..	..	3 9	3 16	..	..	3 28	..	3 36	..	..	3 41	3 46	..	3 57	..	4 2	..	4 8	..	..
Woolwich Dockyard	..	..	..	..	2 19	..	2 38	..	..	..	..	..	..	..	..	3 19	..	..	..	..	3 38	..	..	..	3 49	..	..	..	4 4	..	4 10	..	..
Charlton	..	..	..	..	2 21	..	2 41	..	..	..	..	..	..	..	3 14	3 21	..	..	3 32	..	3 41	..	..	3 46	3 51	..	..	..	4 7	..	4 13	..	..
Blackheath	..	..	1 53	..	..	2 23	2 45	..	..	2 53	..	..	3 11	..	..	..	3 23	..	..	3 41	3 45	..	3 53	3 50	..	4 5	..	..	..	4 13	4 17	..	4 26
Lewisham 114	..	1 50	1 56	2 16	..	2 26	2 47	..	2 50	2 56	..	..	3 14	3 16	..	..	3 26	..	..	3 44	3 47	3 51	3 56	3 53	..	4 7	..	..	..	4 16	4 20	..	4 28
St. John's 124	..	1 52	1 58	2 18	..	2 28	2 49	..	2 52	2 58	..	..	..	3 18	..	..	3 28	..	..	3 46	3 49	..	3 58	..	..	..	..	..	..	4 18	..	4 23	..
New Cross	..	1 54	2 0	2 21	..	2 30	2 52	..	2 54	3 0	..	..	3 17	3 21	..	..	3 30	3 37	..	3 48	3 52	3 54	4 0	3 57	..	..	..	4 14	..	4 20	4 23	4 26	4 31
Westcombe Park	..	..	..	..	2 24	..	..	..	..	..	..	..	..	..	..	3 24	..	..	3 35	..	..	..	..	..	3 54	..	..	..	4 10	..	..	..	..
Maze Hill A	..	..	..	..	2 26	..	..	..	..	..	..	..	..	..	3 18	3 26	..	..	3 37	..	..	..	..	..	3 56	..	..	..	4 12	..	..	..	..
Greenwich	..	..	..	..	2 29	..	..	..	..	..	..	..	..	..	3 23	3 29	..	..	3 40	..	..	..	..	..	3 59	..	..	..	4 15	..	..	..	..
Deptford	..	..	..	..	2 31	..	..	..	..	..	..	..	..	..	..	3 31	..	..	3 42	..	..	..	..	..	4 1	..	..	..	..	..	..	..	..
Peckham Rye	..	..	..	..	..	..	..	..	..	..	..	..	..	..	..	..	..	..	..	..	..	..	..	..	..	..	..	..	..	..	..	..	..
Elephant and Castle	..	..	..	..	..	..	..	..	..	..	..	..	..	..	..	..	..	..	..	..	..	..	..	..	..	..	..	..	..	..	..	..	..
Blackfriars arr	..	..	..	..	..	..	..	..	..	..	..	..	..	..	..	..	..	..	..	..	..	..	..	..	..	..	..	..	..	..	..	..	..
Holborn Viaduct "	..	..	..	..	..	..	..	..	..	..	..	..	..	..	..	..	..	..	..	..	..	..	..	..	..	..	..	..	..	..	..	..	..
London Bridge arr	..	2 1	2 6	2 27	2 39	2 36	2 58	..	3 1	3 6	..	3 11	3 23	3 27	3 31	3 39	3 36	3 44	3 49	3 55	3 58	4 0	4 6	4 3	4 8	4 16	4 12	4 21	4 22	4 27	4 29	4 32	4 38
Cannon Street "	..	..	..	..	..	..	..	..	..	..	..	..	3 27	..	3 37	..	..	..	3 54	..	4 2	..	4 10	..	4 12	4 20	..	..	4 25	4 31	..	4 37	4 41
Waterloo "	..	2 5	2 10	2 31	2 43	2 40	3 2	..	3 5	3 10	..	3 17	..	3 31	..	3 43	3 40	3 48	..	3 59	..	4 4	..	4 8	..	..	4 16	4 25	..	..	4 33	..	..
Charing Cross "	..	2 7	2 13	2 34	2 46	2 43	3 5	..	3 7	3 13	..	3 19	..	3 34	..	3 46	3 43	3 51	..	4 2	..	4 7	..	4 11	..	..	4 19	4 27	..	..	4 35	..	..

A Maze Hill, for National Maritime Museum

For Saturday Trains, see page 101; SUNDAY TRAINS, page 107

3 Third class only

GILLINGHAM (Kent), CHATHAM, MAIDSTONE WEST, GRAVESEND CENTRAL, DARTFORD, WOOLWICH, and LONDON

Mondays to Fridays—*continued* (p.m)

Up																																
Gillingham (Kent) dep	..	..	..	..	..	..	..	3 42	..	..	..	..	..	4 10	..	..	..	..	..	..	..	..	..	..	..	..	..	4 40	..	..	..	..	..
Chatham	..	..	..	..	..	..	..	3 46	..	..	..	..	..	4 14	..	..	..	..	..	..	..	..	..	..	..	..	..	4 44	..	..	..	..	..
Rochester	..	..	..	..	..	..	..	3 49	..	..	..	..	..	4 17	..	..	..	..	..	..	..	..	..	..	..	..	..	4 47	..	..	..	..	..
Strood 72 arr	..	..	..	..	..	..	..	3 51	..	..	..	..	..	4 20	..	..	..	..	..	..	..	..	..	..	..	..	..	4 49	..	..	..	..	..
Maidstone West dep	③	③	③	③	③	③	3 26	③	..	③	③	③	③	3 54	③	③	③	③	③	③	③	③	③	③	③	③	4 22	③	③	③	③	③	③
" Barracks							3 28		..					3 56													4 24						
Aylesford	..	..	..	..	..	..	3 33	..	..	..	..	..	..	4 1	..	..	..	..	..	..	..	..	..	..	..	..	4 29	..	..	..	..	..	..
New Hythe	..	..	..	..	..	..	3 36	..	..	..	..	..	..	4 4	..	..	..	..	..	..	..	..	..	..	..	..	4 32	..	..	..	..	..	..
Snodland	..	..	..	..	..	..	3 39	..	..	..	..	..	..	4 7	..	..	..	..	..	..	..	..	..	..	..	..	4 35	..	..	..	..	..	..
Halling	..	..	..	..	..	..	3 42	..	..	..	..	..	..	4 10	..	..	..	..	..	..	..	..	..	..	..	..	4 38	..	..	..	..	..	..
Cuxton	..	..	..	..	..	..	3 45	..	..	..	..	..	..	4 13	..	..	..	..	..	..	..	..	..	..	..	..	4 41	..	..	..	..	..	..
Strood 72 arr	..	..	..	..	..	..	3 50	..	..	..	..	..	..	4 18	..	..	..	..	..	..	..	..	..	..	..	..	4 46	..	..	..	..	..	..
Strood dep	..	..	..	..	..	..	Stop	3 52	..	..	..	..	..	4 22	..	..	..	..	..	..	..	..	..	..	..	..	Stop	4 50	..	..	..	..	..
Higham	..	..	..	..	..	..		3 59	..	..	..	..	..	..	..	..	..	..	..	..	..	..	..	..	..	..		4 56	..	..	..	..	..
Gravesend Central arr	..	..	..	..	..	..	..	4 7	..	..	..	..	..	4 34	..	..	..	..	..	..	..	..	..	..	..	..	..	5 3	..	..	..	..	..
Gravesend Central dep	..	..	..	3 56	..	..	..	4 9	..	..	..	..	4 21	4 35	..	..	..	..	..	..	4 41	4 52	..	..	..	..	..	5 5	..	..	..	5 18	..
Northfleet	..	..	..	4 0	..	..	..	4 15	..	..	..	..	4 25	..	..	..	..	..	..	..	4 45	4 56	..	..	..	..	..	5 11	..	..	..	5 22	..
Swanscombe Halt	..	..	..	4 3	..	..	..	4 17	..	..	..	..	4 27	..	..	..	..	..	..	..	4 47	..	..	..	..	..	..	5 13	..	..	..	5 24	..
Greenhithe	..	..	..	4 5	..	..	..	4 20	..	..	..	..	4 30	..	..	..	..	..	..	..	4 50	5 0	..	..	..	..	..	5 16	..	..	..	5 27	..
Stone Crossing Halt	..	..	..	4 8	..	..	..	4 23	..	..	..	..	4 33	..	..	..	..	..	..	..	4 53	..	..	..	..	..	p.m	5 19	..	..	..	5 31	..
Dartford	..	4 10	..	4 12	..	4 20	..	4 27	..	..	4 32	..	4 38	4 45	4 47	..	4 52	..	4 55	..	4 59	5 5	5 8	5 14	..	5 19	③	5 23	5 26	..	..	5 35	5 40
Slades Green	..	..	4 10	..	4 17	4 23	..	..	..	..	..	..	..	..	..	4 51	4 56	..	..	5 4	..	5 8	..	..	5 17	..		5 26	..	5 31	..	5 39	..
Crayford	..	..	..	4 16	..	..	..	4 32	..	..	..	4 46	..	..	4 51	..	..	..	5 0	..	5 9	..	..	5 18	..	..	5 32	..	..	..	..	..	5 44
Bexley	..	..	..	4 19	..	..	..	4 35	..	..	..	..	..	..	4 55	..	..	..	5 4	..	5 12	..	..	5 21	..	..	5 35	..	..	..	..	..	5 47
Albany Park	..	..	..	4 22	..	..	..	4 38	..	..	..	..	..	..	4 58	..	..	..	5 7	..	..	..	..	5 24	..	..	5 38	..	..	..	..	..	..
Sidcup	..	..	..	4 24	..	..	..	4 40	..	..	..	4 52	..	..	5 1	..	..	..	5 10	..	5 16	..	..	5 27	..	..	5 40	..	..	..	..	..	5 51
New Eltham	..	..	..	4 27	..	..	..	4 43	..	..	..	..	..	..	5 4	..	..	..	5 13	..	5 19	..	..	5 30	..	..	5 43	..	..	..	..	..	5 54
Mottingham	..	..	..	4 30	..	..	..	4 46	..	..	..	4 56	..	..	5 6	..	..	..	5 15	..	5 22	..	..	5 32	..	..	5 46	..	..	..	..	..	5 57
Lee, for Burnt Ash	..	..	..	4 33	..	..	..	4 49	..	..	..	..	..	..	5 10	..	..	..	5 19	..	5 26	..	..	5 36	..	..	5 50	..	..	..	..	..	6 0
Hither Green 124	..	..	..	4 35	..	..	..	4 51	..	..	..	5 1	..	..	5 12	..	..	..	5 21	..	5 29	..	..	5 38	..	..	..	..	..	..	..	..	6 2
Barnehurst	..	4 17	..	..	..	..	..	..	..	4 33	4 40	..	4 47	..	..	..	..	5 2	..	..	..	..	5 14	..	..	5 25	..	..	5 33	..	5 43	..	..
Bexleyheath	..	4 21	..	..	..	..	..	..	..	4 36	4 45	..	4 50	..	..	..	..	5 5	..	..	..	..	5 18	..	..	5 28	..	..	5 36	..	5 46	..	..
Welling	..	4 24	..	..	..	..	..	..	..	4 39	4 48	..	4 53	..	..	..	..	5 8	..	..	..	..	5 21	..	..	5 31	..	..	5 39	..	5 49	..	..
Falconwood	..	4 26	..	..	..	..	..	..	..	4 41	4 50	..	4 57	..	..	..	..	5 10	..	..	..	..	5 23	..	..	5 33	..	..	5 41	..	..	..	..
Eltham Park	..	4 29	..	..	..	..	..	..	..	4 44	4 53	..	4 59	..	..	..	..	5 13	..	..	..	..	5 26	..	..	5 36	..	..	5 44	..	..	..	..
Eltham (Well Hall)	..	4 31	..	..	..	..	..	..	..	4 46	4 55	..	5 1	..	..	..	..	5 15	..	..	..	..	5 28	..	..	5 38	..	..	5 46	..	5 53	..	..
Kidbrooke	..	4 34	..	..	..	..	..	..	..	4 48	4 58	..	5 4	..	..	..	..	5 17	..	..	..	..	5 31	..	..	5 40	..	..	5 49	..	..	..	..
Erith	..	..	4 13	..	4 20	4 26	p.m	..	..	..	..	..	..	..	..	4 54	4 59	..	..	5 7	..	5 11	..	..	5 21	..	..	5 29	..	5 34	..	5 42	..
Belvedere	..	..	4 17	..	4 23	4 29	③	..	..	..	..	..	..	..	..	4 57	5 2	..	..	..	..	5 14	..	..	5 24	..	..	5 32	..	5 37	..	5 45	..
Abbey Wood	..	..	4 21	..	4 26	4 32		..	..	..	..	..	..	..	..	5 0	5 5	..	..	..	..	5 17	..	..	5 27	..	..	5 35	..	5 40	..	5 48	..
Plumstead	4 18	..	4 25	..	4 29	4 36	4 41	..	..	..	..	..	..	..	..	5 3	5 8	..	..	5 15	..	5 21	..	..	5 30	..	..	5 39	..	5 43	..	5 52	..
Woolwich Arsenal	4 20	..	4 27	..	4 32	4 38	4 43	..	..	..	..	..	..	4 57	..	5 5	5 10	..	..	5 17	..	5 23	..	..	5 32	..	..	5 41	..	5 46	..	5 54	..
Woolwich Dockyard	4 23	..	4 30	..	4 34	4 40	..	..	..	..	..	..	..	..	..	5 8	..	..	..	5 19	..	5 25	..	..	..	..	..	5 43	..	5 49	..	..	..
Charlton	4 26	..	4 33	..	4 37	4 43	4 46	..	..	..	..	..	..	..	..	5 10	5 14	..	..	5 22	..	5 28	..	..	5 36	..	..	5 46	..	5 51	..	5 57	..
Blackheath	..	4 36	..	..	4 41	..	..	..	..	4 51	5 1	..	5 7	..	..	5 14	..	5 20	..	..	..	..	5 33	..	5 40	5 43	..	..	5 52	..	5 58	6 1	..
Lewisham 114	..	4 39	..	..	4 44	..	..	..	..	4 54	5 4	5 5	5 9	..	..	5 17	..	5 23	..	..	..	..	5 36	..	5 42	5 46	..	..	5 55	..	6 1	6 4	6 6
St. John's 124	..	..	..	4 38	4 46	..	..	4 55	..	..	..	..	5 11	..	..	..	..	..	..	..	..	..	5 38	..	..	5 48	..	..	..	..	..	..	..
New Cross	..	4 42	..	4 41	4 48	..	..	4 57	..	..	5 8	..	5 14	..	5 16	5 20	..	..	5 25	..	5 34	..	..	5 42	5 45	5 50	5 55	..	5 59	..	..	6 7	..
Westcombe Park	4 28	..	4 36	..	..	4 45	4 49	..	..	..	..	..	..	..	..	..	5 16	..	..	5 24	..	5 30	..	..	..	..	..	5 48	..	5 54	..	..	..
Maze Hill A	4 31	..	4 39	..	..	..	4 51	..	..	..	..	..	..	..	..	..	5 19	..	..	..	..	5 33	..	..	..	..	..	5 51	..	5 56	..	..	..
Greenwich	4 33	..	4 42	..	..	..	4 54	..	..	..	..	..	..	..	..	..	5 21	..	..	5 28	..	5 35	..	..	..	..	..	5 53	..	5 59	..	..	..
Deptford	4 35	..	..	..	..	..	4 56	..	..	..	..	..	..	..	..	..	5 23	..	..	..	..	5 37	..	..	..	..	..	5 55	..	..	..	..	..
Peckham Rye	..	..	..	..	..	..	..	..	..	5 3	..	5 12	..	..	..	..	..	5 32	..	..	..	..	..	..	..	..	..	..	..	..	6 7	..	6 11
Elephant and Castle	..	..	..	..	..	..	..	..	..	5 10	..	..	..	..	..	..	..	..	..	..	..	..	..	..	..	..	..	..	..	..	6 14	..	6 17
Blackfriars arr	..	..	..	..	..	..	..	..	..	5 14	..	5 22	..	..	..	..	..	5 43	..	..	..	..	..	..	..	..	..	..	..	..	6 17	..	6 21
Holborn Viaduct "	..	..	..	..	..	..	..	..	..	5 16	..	5 24	..	..	..	..	..	5 45	..	..	..	..	..	..	..	..	..	..	..	..	6 20	..	..
London Bridge arr.	4 42	4 48	4 51	4 47	4 54	4 58	5 2	5 4	..	..	5 14	..	5 20	5 11	5 23	5 26	5 30	..	5 32	5 36	5 40	5 43	5 46	5 48	5 51	5 57	6 1	6 2	6 5	6 7	..	6 13	..
Cannon Street "	4 45	..	4 55	..	4 58	..	5 5	5 9	..	..	5 18	..	..	..	5 26	5 30	..	..	5 35	..	..	5 49	..	..	5 56	..	..	6 7	6 9	..	..	6 17	..
Waterloo "	..	4 52	..	4 50	..	5 2	..	..	..	..	..	..	5 24	5 15	..	..	5 34	..	..	5 40	5 44	..	5 49	5 52	..	6 0	6 5	..	..	6 10	..	..	..
Charing Cross "	..	4 55	..	4 53	..	5 4	..	..	..	..	..	..	5 27	5 19	..	..	5 36	..	..	5 43	5 47	..	5 52	5 55	..	6 3	6 8	..	..	6 13	..	..	..

A Maze Hill, for National Maritime Museum

③ Third class only

GILLINGHAM (Kent), CHATHAM, MAIDSTONE WEST, GRAVESEND CENTRAL, DARTFORD, WOOLWICH and LONDON

Up — Mondays to Fridays—continued (p.m)

Up	p.m										
Gillingham (Kent) dep	..	5 10	..	..	..	..	..	..	..	..	..
Chatham	..	5 14	..	..	..	..	..	..	..	..	..
Rochester	..	5 17	..	..	..	..	..	..	..	..	..
Strood72 arr	..	5 21	..	..	..	..	..	..	..	..	..
Maidstone West dep	3	4 54	3	3	3	3	5 7	3	3	3	3
.. Barracks	..	4 56	..	..	..	..	5 9	..	..	..	..
Aylesford	..	5 1	..	..	..	..	5 14	..	..	..	..
New Hythe	..	5 4	..	..	..	..	5 17	..	..	..	..
Snodland	..	5 7	..	..	..	..	5 20	..	..	..	..
Halling	..	5 10	..	..	..	..	5 23	..	..	..	..
Cuxton	..	5 13	..	..	..	..	5 26	..	..	..	..
Strood 72 arr	..	5 18	..	..	..	..	5 31	..	..	..	..
Strood dep	..	5 22	..	..	..	..	Stop	..	..	..	..
Higham	..	..	..	..	..	..	..	..	..	..	..
Gravesend Central arr	..	5 34	..	..	..	..	..	..	..	..	..
Gravesend Central dep	..	5 35	..	..	..	..	..	..	..	5 53	..
Northfleet	..	..	..	..	..	..	..	..	..	5 57	..
Swanscombe Halt	..	..	..	..	..	..	..	..	..	5 59	..
Greenhithe	..	..	..	..	..	..	..	..	..	6 2	..
Stone Crossing Halt	..	..	..	..	..	..	..	..	..	6 5	..
Dartford	5 38	5 45	..	5 50	..	5 54	p.m	6 0	..	6 9	6 12
Slades Green	..	..	..	..	5 53	5 57	3	..	6 8	6 14	..
Crayford	..	..	..	5 53	..	..	..	..	..	..	6 17
Bexley	..	..	..	5 56	..	..	6 10	..	..	..	6 20
Albany Park	..	..	..	6 0	..	..	..	..	..	..	6 23
Sidcup	..	..	..	6 4	..	..	6 14	..	..	..	6 26
New Eltham	..	..	..	6 7	..	..	..	..	..	..	6 29
Mottingham	..	..	..	6 9	..	..	..	..	..	..	6 32
Lee for Burnt Ash	..	..	..	6 13	..	..	..	..	..	..	6 36
Hither Green 124	..	..	..	6 15	..	..	..	..	..	..	6 38
Barnehurst	5 46	..	..	..	5 58	..	..	6 7	..	..	..
Bexleyheath	5 50	..	..	..	6 1	..	..	6 11	..	..	..
Welling	5 54	..	..	..	6 4	..	..	6 14	..	..	..
Falconwood	5 56	..	..	..	6 7	..	..	6 16	..	..	..
Eltham Park	5 59	..	..	..	6 9	..	..	6 19	..	..	..
Eltham (Well Hall)	6 1	..	..	..	6 11	..	..	6 21	..	..	..
Kidbrooke	6 3	..	..	..	6 14	..	..	6 23	..	..	..
Erith	..	..	..	..	..	6 0	..	..	6 11	6 17	..
Belvedere	..	..	..	..	..	6 3	..	..	6 14	6 20	..
Abbey Wood	..	..	..	..	..	..	..	..	6 17	6 23	..
Plumstead	..	..	6 2	..	..	6 8	..	..	6 20	6 26	..
Woolwich Arsenal	..	5 57	6 4	..	..	6 10	..	..	6 22	6 28	..
Woolwich Dockyard	..	..	..	..	..	6 13	..	..	6 25	..	..
Charlton	..	..	6 7	..	..	6 15	..	..	6 27	6 32	..
Blackheath	6 7	..	..	..	6 17	6 19	..	6 26	..	6 36	..
Lewisham 114	6 9	..	..	..	6 19	6 22	..	6 29	..	6 40	..
St. John's 124	..	..	..	6 18	..	..	..	..	..	..	6 42
New Cross	6 12	..	..	6 20	6 22	6 25	..	6 33	..	6 44	6 44
Westcombe Park	..	..	6 9	..	..	..	..	..	6 30	..	..
Maze Hill A	..	..	6 12	..	..	..	..	..	6 32	..	..
Greenwich	..	..	6 14	..	..	..	..	..	6 35	..	..
Deptford	..	..	6 16	..	..	..	..	..	6 37	..	..
Peckham Rye	..	..	..	..	..	..	6 27	..	..	..	..
Elephant and Castle	..	..	..	..	..	..	6 35	..	..	..	..
Blackfriars arr	..	..	..	..	..	..	6 38	..	..	..	..
Holborn Viaduct "	..	..	..	..	..	..	..	..	..	..	..
London Bridge arr	6 20	6 11	6 23	6 26	6 28	6 32	..	6 39	6 44	6 50	6 51
Cannon Street "	..	..	..	..	6 32	6 35	..	..	..	..	..
Waterloo "	6 23	6 15	6 27	6 30	..	..	..	6 43	6 48	6 54	6 55
Charing Cross "	6 26	6 18	6 30	6 32	..	..	..	6 45	6 51	6 56	6 59

Up	Mondays to Fridays—continued										
Gillingham (Kent) dep	..	..	..	..	5 50	..	..	..	..	..	..
Chatham	..	..	..	..	5 54	..	..	..	..	..	..
Rochester	..	..	..	..	5 57	..	..	..	..	..	..
Strood72 arr	..	..	..	..	6 0	..	..	..	..	..	..
Maidstone West dep	3	3	3	5 27	3	5 54	3	3	3	3	3
.. Barracks	..	..	..	5 29	..	5 56	..	..	..	..	..
Aylesford	..	..	..	5 34	..	6 1	..	..	..	..	..
New Hythe	..	..	..	5 37	..	6 4	..	..	..	..	..
Snodland	..	..	..	5 40	..	6 7	..	..	..	..	..
Halling	..	..	..	5 43	..	6 10	..	..	..	..	..
Cuxton	..	..	..	5 46	..	6 13	..	..	..	..	..
Strood 72 arr	..	..	..	5 51	..	6 18	..	..	..	..	..
Strood dep	..	..	..	Stop	6 1	..	..	..	..	..	..
Higham	..	..	..	..	6 6	..	..	..	..	..	..
Gravesend Central arr	..	..	..	..	6 13	..	..	..	..	..	..
Gravesend Central dep	..	..	..	..	6 14	..	..	..	..	..	..
Northfleet	..	..	..	..	6 18	..	..	..	..	..	..
Swanscombe Halt	..	..	..	..	6 21	..	..	..	..	..	..
Greenhithe	..	..	..	..	6 24	..	..	..	..	..	..
Stone Crossing Halt	..	..	..	..	6 26	..	..	..	..	..	..
Dartford	6 16	..	6 25	..	6 31	..	..	..	6 40	6 50	6 53
Slades Green	..	6 21	..	..	6 35	..	..	6 32	..	..	..
Crayford	..	..	6 29	..	..	..	6 40	..	..	6 53	..
Bexley	..	..	6 33	..	..	..	6 43	..	..	6 56	..
Albany Park	..	..	6 36	..	..	..	6 46	..	..	6 59	..
Sidcup	..	..	6 39	..	..	..	6 48	..	..	7 2	..
New Eltham	..	..	6 42	..	..	..	6 51	..	..	7 5	..
Mottingham	..	..	6 45	..	..	..	6 54	..	..	7 7	..
Lee for Burnt Ash	..	..	6 48	p.m	..	..	6 57	..	..	7 11	..
Hither Green 124	..	..	6 50	3	..	..	6 59	..	..	7 13	..
Barnehurst	6 22	..	..	6 35	..	..	..	6 43	6 47	..	..
Bexleyheath	6 26	..	..	6 38	..	..	..	6 46	6 52	..	..
Welling	6 29	..	..	6 41	..	..	..	6 49	6 57	..	..
Falconwood	6 31	..	..	6 43	..	..	..	6 51	7 0	..	..
Eltham Park	6 34	..	..	6 46	..	..	..	6 56	7 3	..	..
Eltham (Well Hall)	6 36	..	..	6 48	..	..	..	6 58	7 5	..	..
Kidbrooke	6 39	..	..	6 50	..	..	..	7 1	7 8	..	..
Erith	..	6 24	..	..	6 38	..	..	..	..	..	6 58
Belvedere	..	6 27	..	..	6 41	..	..	..	..	..	..
Abbey Wood	..	6 30	..	..	6 44	..	..	..	..	..	..
Plumstead	..	6 33	..	..	6 48	..	..	..	..	..	7 5
Woolwich Arsenal	..	6 35	..	..	6 51	..	..	..	..	..	7 7
Woolwich Dockyard	..	6 38	..	..	6 53	..	..	..	..	..	7 10
Charlton	..	6 41	..	..	6 56	..	..	..	..	..	7 12
Blackheath	6 42	6 45	..	6 53	7 0	..	..	7 3	7 11	..	7 16
Lewisham 114	6 44	6 47	..	6 56	7 3	..	..	7 6	7 14	7 16	7 19
St. John's 124	..	..	..	6 58	..	..	..	..	..	7 18	7 21
New Cross	6 47	6 50	6 55	7 0	7 7	..	7 4	..	7 17	7 21	7 23
Westcombe Park	..	..	..	..	..	..	..	..	..	..	..
Maze Hill A	..	..	..	..	..	..	..	..	..	..	..
Greenwich	..	..	..	..	..	..	..	..	..	..	..
Deptford	..	..	..	..	..	..	..	..	..	..	..
Peckham Rye	..	..	..	..	..	..	..	7 11	..	..	..
Elephant and Castle	..	..	..	..	..	..	..	7 17	..	..	..
Blackfriars arr	..	..	..	..	..	..	..	7 21	..	..	..
Holborn Viaduct "	..	..	..	..	..	..	..	..	..	..	..
London Bridge arr	6 53	6 56	7 2	7 6	7 14	..	7 10	..	7 23	7 27	7 30
Cannon Street "	6 57	7 0	7 4	..	7 17	..	7 14	..	7 29	..	..
Waterloo "	..	..	..	7 10	..	..	..	..	..	7 31	7 34
Charing Cross "	..	..	..	7 13	..	..	..	..	..	7 34	7 36

Up	p.m										
Gillingham (Kent) dep	..	..	..	..	..	..	..	6 42	..	..	7 10
Chatham	..	..	..	..	..	..	..	6 46	..	..	7 14
Rochester	..	..	..	..	..	..	..	6 49	..	..	7 17
Strood72 arr	..	..	..	..	..	..	..	6 51	..	..	7 20
Maidstone West dep	3	3	6 13	3	3	3	6 26	3	3	3	6 54
.. Barracks	..	..	6 15	..	..	..	6 28	..	..	..	6 56
Aylesford	..	..	6 19	..	..	..	6 33	..	..	..	7 1
New Hythe	..	..	6 22	..	..	..	6 36	..	..	..	7 4
Snodland	..	..	6 26	..	..	..	6 39	..	..	..	7 7
Halling	..	..	6 29	..	..	..	6 42	..	..	..	7 10
Cuxton	..	..	6 32	..	..	..	6 45	..	..	..	7 13
Strood 72 arr	..	..	6 37	..	..	..	6 50	..	..	..	7 18
Strood dep	..	..	..	..	..	..	..	6 52	..	..	7 22
Higham	..	..	..	..	..	..	..	6 58	..	..	..
Gravesend Central arr	..	..	..	..	..	..	..	7 5	..	..	7 34
Gravesend Central dep	..	6 40	..	..	..	..	..	7 6	7 0	..	7 35
Northfleet	..	6 44	..	..	..	..	..	7 10	7 4	..	..
Swanscombe Halt	..	6 46	..	..	..	..	..	7 13	7 6	..	..
Greenhithe	..	6 49	..	..	..	..	..	7 16	7 9	..	..
Stone Crossing Halt	..	6 52	..	..	..	..	..	7 18	7 12	..	..
Dartford	6 59	6 57	..	7 6	..	7 14	..	7 23	7 18	7 29	7 45
Slades Green	..	7 1	..	..	..	..	..	..	7 21	..	..
Crayford	..	..	..	7 11	7 17	..	..	7 26	..	..	..
Bexley	..	..	..	7 14	7 20	..	..	7 29	..	..	..
Albany Park	..	..	..	7 17	7 23	..	..	7 32	..	..	..
Sidcup	..	..	..	7 20	7 25	..	..	7 35	..	..	..
New Eltham	..	..	..	7 23	7 28	..	..	7 38	..	..	..
Mottingham	..	..	..	7 25	7 31	..	..	7 40	..	..	..
Lee for Burnt Ash	..	..	..	7 29	..	..	..	7 44	..	..	..
Hither Green 124	..	..	..	7 31	7 35	..	..	7 46	..	..	..
Barnehurst	7 5	..	..	..	..	7 20	..	..	..	7 35	..
Bexleyheath	7 8	..	..	..	..	7 23	..	..	..	7 38	..
Welling	7 11	..	..	..	..	7 27	..	..	..	7 41	..
Falconwood	7 13	..	..	..	..	7 31	..	..	..	7 43	..
Eltham Park	7 16	..	..	..	..	7 33	..	..	..	7 46	..
Eltham (Well Hall)	7 18	..	..	..	..	7 35	..	..	..	7 48	..
Kidbrooke	7 20	..	..	..	..	7 38	..	..	..	7 50	..
Erith	..	7 4	..	..	..	..	..	..	7 24	..	..
Belvedere	..	7 7	..	..	..	..	..	..	7 27	..	..
Abbey Wood	..	7 10	..	..	..	..	..	..	7 30	..	..
Plumstead	..	7 14	..	..	..	..	..	..	7 34	..	..
Woolwich Arsenal	..	7 16	..	..	..	..	..	..	7 36	..	7 57
Woolwich Dockyard	..	7 19	..	..	..	..	..	..	7 38	..	..
Charlton	..	7 21	..	..	..	..	..	..	7 41	..	..
Blackheath	7 23	..	..	..	..	7 41	..	..	7 45	7 53	..
Lewisham 114	7 26	..	..	..	..	7 43	..	7 50	7 47	7 56	..
St. John's 124	7 28	..	..	7 34	7 39	..	..	7 52	7 49	7 58	..
New Cross	7 30	..	..	7 37	7 41	7 46	..	7 54	7 52	8 0	..
Westcombe Park	..	7 24	..	..	..	..	..	..	..	..	..
Maze Hill A	..	7 26	..	..	..	..	..	..	..	..	..
Greenwich	..	7 29	..	..	..	..	..	..	..	..	..
Deptford	..	7 31	..	..	..	..	..	..	..	..	..
Peckham Rye	..	..	..	..	..	..	..	..	..	..	..
Elephant and Castle	..	..	..	..	..	..	..	..	..	..	..
Blackfriars arr	..	..	..	..	..	..	..	..	..	..	..
Holborn Viaduct "	..	..	..	..	..	..	..	..	..	..	..
London Bridge arr	7 36	7 39	..	7 44	7 47	7 52	..	8 1	7 58	8 7	8 11
Cannon Street "	..	..	..	..	7 51	7 57	..	..	..	..	..
Waterloo "	7 40	7 43	..	7 48	..	..	..	8 5	8 2	8 11	8 17
Charing Cross "	7 43	7 46	..	7 52	..	..	..	8 7	8 5	8 13	8 19

A Maze Hill, for National Maritime Museum. **For Saturday Trains, see page 101; SUNDAY TRAINS, page 107**

3 Third class only

GILLINGHAM (Kent), CHATHAM, MAIDSTONE WEST, GRAVESEND CENTRAL, DARTFORD, WOOLWICH, and LONDON

Mondays to Fridays—continued. (p.m.)

Up	3	3		3	3	3		3	3		3	3	3	3		3	3	3	3	3		3		3	3	3	3	3	3		3	3		
Gillingham (Kent) dep	..	..	..	7 18	..	..	..	7 34	..	..	..	..	..	..	..	8 40	..	..	..	..	..	..	..	9 42	..	..	9 58	..	..	..	..	..	1056	..
Chatham	..	..	..	7 22	..	..	..	7 39	..	..	..	..	..	..	..	8 44	..	..	..	..	..	..	..	9 46	..	..	10 2	..	..	..	..	..	11 4	..
Rochester	..	..	..	7 26	..	..	..	7 45	..	..	..	..	..	..	..	8 48	..	..	..	..	..	..	..	9 49	..	..	10 7	..	..	..	..	..	11 8	..
Strood 72 arr	..	..	..	7 29	..	..	..	7 49	..	..	..	..	..	..	..	8 51	..	..	..	..	..	..	..	9 51	..	..	1011	..	..	..	..	..	1112	..
Maidstone West dep	..	..	..	..	..	..	7 26	..	..	..	..	..	..	..	8 26	..	..	..	..	..	..	..	926	..	..	..	..	..	..	10 9	..	..	..	1117
" Barracks	..	..	..	..	..	..	7 28	..	..	..	..	..	..	..	8 28	..	..	..	..	..	..	..	928	..	..	..	..	..	..	1011	..	..	..	1119
Aylesford	..	..	..	..	..	..	7 33	..	..	..	..	..	..	..	8 33	..	..	..	..	..	..	..	933	..	..	..	..	..	..	1016	..	..	..	1124
New Hythe	..	..	..	..	..	..	7 36	..	..	..	..	..	..	..	8 36	..	..	..	..	..	..	..	936	..	..	..	..	..	..	1019	..	..	..	1127
Snodland	..	..	..	..	..	..	7 39	..	..	..	..	..	..	..	8 39	..	..	..	..	..	..	..	939	..	..	..	..	..	..	1022	..	..	..	1130
Halling	..	..	..	..	..	..	7 42	..	..	..	..	..	..	..	8 42	..	..	..	..	..	..	..	942	..	..	..	..	..	..	1026	..	..	..	1133
Cuxton	..	..	..	..	..	..	7 45	..	..	..	..	..	..	..	8 45	..	..	..	..	..	..	..	945	..	..	..	..	..	..	1028	..	..	..	1136
Strood 72 arr	..	..	..	..	..	..	7 50	..	..	..	..	..	..	..	8 50	..	..	..	..	..	..	..	950	..	..	..	..	..	..	1033	..	..	..	1141
Strood dep	..	..	..	7 30	..	..	..	7 52	..	..	..	..	..	..	..	8 52	..	..	..	..	..	..	..	9 52	..	..	1013	..	..	..	..	..	1113	..
Higham	..	..	..	7 36	..	..	..	7 58	..	..	..	..	..	..	..	8 58	..	..	..	..	..	..	..	9 58	..	..	1020	..	..	..	..	..	1120	..
Gravesend Central arr	..	..	..	7 44	..	..	..	8 5	..	..	..	..	..	..	..	9 5	..	..	..	..	..	..	..	10 5	..	..	1026	..	..	..	..	..	1128	..
Gravesend Central dep	..	..	..	7 45	..	..	..	8 6	..	..	..	8 40	..	..	..	9 6	..	..	..	..	..	..	..	10 6	..	..	1027	..	..	..	..	..	1129	..
Northfleet	..	..	..	7 49	..	..	..	8 10	..	..	..	8 44	..	..	..	9 10	..	..	..	..	..	..	..	1010	..	..	1032	..	..	..	..	..	..	..
Swanscombe Halt	..	..	..	..	..	..	..	8 13	..	..	..	8 46	..	..	..	9 13	..	..	..	..	..	..	..	1013	..	..	1034	..	..	..	..	..	..	..
Greenhithe	..	..	..	7 52	..	..	..	8 16	..	..	..	8 49	..	..	..	9 16	..	..	..	..	..	..	..	1016	..	..	1037	..	..	..	..	..	..	..
Stone Crossing Halt	..	..	..	..	..	..	..	8 18	..	..	..	8 52	..	..	..	9 18	..	..	..	..	..	..	..	1018	..	..	1040	..	..	..	..	..	..	..
Dartford	7 34	7 50	..	7 57	7 59	8 18	..	8 23	8 29	..	8 50	8 57	8 59	9 18	..	9 23	9 29	9 50	9 57	9 59	..	1018	..	1023	1029	1035	1045	1050	1058	..	1112	1116	1142	..
Slades Green	7 37	..	..	8 1	..	8 21	..	..	..	..	..	9 1	..	9 21	..	..	..	..	10 1	..	..	1021	..	..	..	1039	..	..	11 1	..	..	..	..	..
Crayford	..	7 53	..	..	..	..	..	8 26	..	..	8 53	..	..	..	..	9 26	..	9 53	..	..	..	..	..	1026	..	..	..	1053	..	..	..	1119	..	..
Bexley	..	7 56	..	..	..	..	..	8 29	..	..	8 56	..	..	..	..	9 29	..	9 56	..	..	..	..	..	1029	..	..	..	1056	..	..	..	1122	..	..
Albany Park	..	7 59	..	..	..	..	..	8 32	..	..	8 59	..	..	..	..	9 32	..	9 59	..	..	..	..	..	1032	..	..	..	1059	..	..	..	1125	..	..
Sidcup	..	8 2	..	..	..	..	..	8 35	..	..	9 2	..	..	..	..	9 35	..	10 2	..	..	..	..	..	1035	..	..	..	11 2	..	..	..	1128	..	..
New Eltham	..	8 5	..	..	..	..	..	8 38	..	..	9 5	..	..	..	..	9 38	..	10 5	..	..	..	..	..	1038	..	..	..	11 5	..	..	..	1131	..	..
Mottingham	..	8 7	..	..	..	..	..	8 40	..	..	9 7	..	..	..	..	9 40	..	10 7	..	..	..	..	..	1040	..	..	..	11 7	..	..	..	1133	..	..
Lee, for Burnt Ash	..	8 11	..	..	..	..	..	8 44	..	..	9 11	..	..	..	..	9 44	..	1011	..	..	..	..	..	1044	..	..	..	1111	..	..	..	1137	..	..
Hither Green 124	..	8 13	..	..	..	..	..	8 46	..	..	9 13	..	..	..	..	9 46	..	1013	..	..	..	..	..	1046	..	..	..	1113	..	..	..	1139	..	..
Barnehurst	..	..	..	..	8 5	..	..	..	8 35	..	..	..	9 5	..	..	..	9 35	..	..	10 5	..	..	..	..	1035	..	1051	..	..	..	1118	..	..	..
Bexleyheath	..	..	..	..	8 8	..	..	..	8 38	..	..	..	9 8	..	..	..	9 38	..	..	10 8	..	..	..	..	1038	..	1054	..	..	..	1121	..	..	..
Welling	..	..	..	..	8 11	..	..	..	8 41	..	..	..	9 11	..	..	..	9 41	..	..	1011	..	..	..	..	1041	..	1057	..	..	..	1124	..	..	..
Falconwood	..	..	..	..	8 13	..	..	..	8 43	..	..	..	9 13	..	..	..	9 43	..	..	1013	..	..	..	..	1043	..	1059	..	..	..	1127	..	..	..
Eltham Park	..	..	..	..	8 16	..	..	..	8 46	..	..	..	9 16	..	..	..	9 46	..	..	1016	..	..	..	..	1046	..	11 2	..	..	..	1129	..	..	..
Eltham (Well Hall)	..	..	..	..	8 18	..	..	..	8 48	..	..	..	9 18	..	..	..	9 48	..	..	1018	..	..	..	..	1048	..	11 4	..	..	..	1131	..	..	..
Kidbrooke	..	..	..	..	8 20	..	..	..	8 50	..	..	..	9 20	..	..	..	9 50	..	..	1020	..	..	..	..	1050	..	11 6	..	..	..	1134	..	..	..
Erith	7 40	..	..	8 4	..	8 24	..	..	..	..	..	9 4	..	9 24	..	..	..	..	10 4	..	..	1024	..	..	..	1042	..	..	11 4	..	..	..	..	..
Belvedere	7 43	..	..	8 7	..	8 27	..	..	..	..	..	9 7	..	9 27	..	..	..	..	10 7	..	..	1027	..	..	..	1045	..	..	11 7	..	..	..	..	..
Abbey Wood	7 46	..	..	8 10	..	8 30	..	..	..	..	..	9 10	..	9 30	..	..	..	..	1010	..	..	1030	..	..	..	1048	..	..	1110	..	..	..	..	..
Plumstead	7 50	..	..	8 14	..	8 34	..	..	..	..	..	9 14	..	9 34	..	..	..	..	1014	..	..	1034	..	..	..	1051	..	..	1114	..	..	..	..	..
Woolwich Arsenal	7 52	..	..	8 16	..	8 36	..	..	..	..	..	9 16	..	9 36	..	..	..	..	1016	..	..	1036	..	..	..	1053	..	..	1116	..	..	..	..	..
Woolwich Dockyard	7 54	..	..	8 19	..	8 38	..	..	..	..	..	9 19	..	9 38	..	..	..	..	1019	..	..	1038	..	..	..	1056	..	..	1119	..	..	..	1157	..
Charlton	7 57	..	..	8 21	..	8 41	..	..	..	..	..	9 21	..	9 41	..	..	..	..	1021	..	..	1041	..	..	..	1058	..	..	1122	..	..	..	..	..
Blackheath	8 1	..	..	..	8 23	8 45	..	..	8 53	..	..	..	9 23	9 45	..	..	9 53	..	..	1023	..	1045	..	..	1053	..	11 9	..	1126	..	1137	..	..	..
Lewisham 114	8 4	8 16	..	..	8 26	8 47	..	8 50	8 56	..	9 16	..	9 26	4 47	..	9 50	9 56	1016	..	1026	..	1047	..	1050	1056	..	1112	1116	1129	..	1139	..	..	..
St. John's 124	8 7	8 18	..	..	8 28	8 49	..	8 52	8 58	..	9 18	..	9 28	9 49	..	9 52	9 58	1018	..	1028	..	1049	..	1052	1058	..	1114	1118	1131	..	1141	1142	..	..
New Cross	8 9	8 21	..	..	8 30	8 52	..	8 54	9 0	..	9 21	..	9 30	9 52	..	9 54	10 0	1021	..	1030	..	1052	..	1054	11 0	..	1116	1121	1133	..	1144	1145	..	..
Westcombe Park	..	..	..	8 24	..	..	..	..	..	..	..	9 24	..	..	..	..	..	..	1024	..	..	..	..	..	..	11 1	..	..	..	..	..	..	..	..
Maze Hill A	..	..	..	8 26	..	..	..	..	..	..	..	9 26	..	..	..	..	..	..	1026	..	..	..	..	..	..	11 3	..	..	..	..	..	..	..	..
Greenwich	..	..	..	8 29	..	..	..	..	..	..	..	9 29	..	..	..	..	..	..	1029	..	..	..	..	..	..	11 6	..	..	..	..	..	..	..	..
Deptford	..	..	..	8 31	..	..	..	..	..	..	..	9 31	..	..	..	..	..	..	1031	..	..	..	..	..	..	11 8	..	..	..	..	..	..	..	..
Peckham Rye	..	..	..	..	..	..	..	..	..	..	..	..	..	..	..	..	..	..	..	..	..	..	..	..	..	..	..	..	..	..	..	..	..	..
Elephant and Castle	..	..	..	..	..	..	..	..	..	..	..	..	..	..	..	..	..	..	..	..	..	..	..	..	..	..	..	..	..	..	..	..	..	..
Blackfriars arr	..	..	..	..	..	..	..	..	..	..	..	..	..	..	..	..	..	..	..	..	..	..	..	..	..	..	..	..	..	..	..	..	..	..
Holborn Viaduct "	..	..	..	..	..	..	..	..	..	..	..	..	..	..	..	..	..	..	..	..	..	..	..	..	..	..	..	..	..	..	..	..	..	..
London Bridge arr	8 15	8 27	..	8 38	8 36	8 58	..	9 1	9 6	..	9 27	9 38	9 36	9 58	..	10 1	10 6	1027	1039	1036	..	1058	..	11 1	11 6	1114	1123	1127	1140	..	1150	1151	1217	..
Cannon Street "	..	..	..	..	..	..	..	..	..	..	..	..	..	..	..	..	..	..	..	..	..	..	..	..	..	..	..	..	..	..	..	..	..	..
Waterloo "	..	8 31	..	8 43	8 40	9 2	..	9 5	9 10	..	9 32	9 42	9 40	10 2	..	10 5	1010	1032	1043	1040	..	11 2	..	11 5	1110	..	1130	1132	1144	..	1154	..	1224	..
Charing Cross "	..	8 34	..	8 46	8 43	9 5	..	9 7	9 13	..	9 35	9 46	9 43	10 5	..	10 7	1013	1035	1046	1043	..	11 5	..	11 7	1113	..	1132	1135	1147	..	1157	..	1228	..

A Maze Hill, for National Maritime Museum

3 Third class only

GILLINGHAM (Kent), CHATHAM, MAIDSTONE WEST, GRAVESEND CENTRAL, DARTFORD, WOOLWICH, and LONDON

Up	a.m													Saturdays													a.m						
Gillingham (Kent) dep							9 10							9 38				10 8									1040						11 7
Chatham							9 14							9 42				1014									1046						1111
Rochester							9 17							9 45				1017									1049						1114
Strood 72 arr							9 20							9 49				1020									1051						1117
Maidstone West dep	3	3	3	3	3	3	8 54	3	3	3	3	3	9 26	3	3	3	3	9 54	3		3	3	3	3	3	1026	3	3	3	3	3	3	1054
" Barracks							8 56						9 28					9 56								1028							1056
Aylesford							9 1						9 33					10 1								1033							11 1
New Hythe							9 4						9 36					10 4								1036							11 4
Snodland							9 7						9 39					10 7								1039							11 7
Halling							9 10						9 42					1010								1042							1110
Cuxton							9 13						9 45					1013								1045							1113
Strood 72 arr							9 18						9 50					1018								1050							1120
Strood dep			9 0				9 22						Stop	9 51				1022									1052						1122
Higham			9 5											9 58													1058						
Gravesend Central arr			9 12				9 33							10 7				1034									11 5						1134
Gravesend Central dep			9 13		9 20		9 34							10 8		1023		1035				1052					11 7				1122		1135
Northfleet			9 18		9 24									1012		1027						1056					1112				1126		
Swanscombe Halt					9 26								a.m	1015		1029						1058					1115				1128		
Greenhithe			9 22		9 29								3	1018		1032						11 1					1118				1131		
Stone Crossing Halt					9 32									1020		1035						11 4					1120				1134		
Dartford	9 18	9 24	9 28	9 30	9 36	9 42	9 45	9 48	9 59	9 57	10 6	1016	1018	1024	1027	1039	1042	1045	1054		1057	11 9		1116	1118		1125	1127		1132	1138	1141	1145
Slades Green	9 21		9 32					9 51		10 0			1021		1031						11 1		1117		1121		1128		1131	1135			
Crayford				9 33		9 47					10 9			1028		1042			1058			1112						1132				1144	
Bexley				9 36		9 51					1012			1031		1045			11 1			1115						1136				1147	
Albany Park				9 39		9 54					1015			1034		1048			11 4			1118						1139				1150	
Sidcup				9 42		9 57					1018			1036		1051			11 6			1121						1142				1153	
New Eltham				9 45		10 0					1021			1039		1054			11 9			1124						1145				1156	
Mottingham				9 47		10 2					1023			1042		1056			1112			1126						1148				1158	
Lee, for Burnt Ash				9 51		10 6					1027			1045		11 0			1115			1130						1151				12 2	
Hither Green 124				9 53		10 8					1029			1047		11 2			1117			1132						1153				12 4	
Barnehurst		9 30			9 43				10 5			1022					1051							1122					1135		1144		
Bexleyheath		9 33			9 46				10 8			1025					1055							1125					1138		1147		
Welling		9 36			9 49				1011			1028					1058							1128					1141		1150		
Falconwood		9 39			9 51				1013			1031					11 1							1131					1143		1152		
Eltham Park		9 41			9 54				1016			1033					11 3							1133					1146		1155		
Eltham (Well Hall)		9 43			9 56				1018			1035					11 5							1135					1148		1157		
Kidbrooke		9 46			9 58				1020			1038					11 8							1138					1150		12 0		
Erith	9 25		9 35					9 54		10 4			1024		1034						11 4		1120		1124		1132			1138			
Belvedere	9 28		9 38					9 57		10 7			1027		1037						11 7				1127		1135			1141			
Abbey Wood	9 31		9 41					10 0		1010			1030		1040						1110		1125		1130		1138			1144			
Plumstead	9 35		9 44					10 4		1014			1034		1043						1114		1128		1134		1142			1148			
Woolwich Arsenal	9 37		9 46				9 56	10 6		1016			1036		1045			1057			1116		1131		1136		1144			1150			1157
Woolwich Dockyard	9 39		9 50					10 8		1019			1038		1049						1119				1138		1147						
Charlton	9 42		9 52					1011		1021			1041		1051						1121				1141		1149			1153			
Blackheath	9 46	9 49			10 1			1015	1023			1041	1045				1111							1141	1145				1153	1157	12 3		
Lewisham 114	9 49	9 51			10 4			1017	1026		1032	1044	1047	1051			1114		1121					1144	1147				1156	12 0	12 5		
St. John's 124	9 51	9 53			10 6	1011			1028		1034	1046	1049											1146	1149					12 2	12 7		
New Cross	9 53	9 56		9 57	10 9	1014		1020	1030		1037	1049	1052	1054		11 7	1117		1124			1137		1148	1152			1158		12 5	1210	12 8	
Westcombe Park			9 55							1024					1054						1124						1152						
Maze Hill A			9 57							1026					1056						1126						1154						
Greenwich			10 0							1029					1059						1129						1157						
Deptford			10 2							1031					11 1						1131						1159						
Peckham Rye																													12 6				
Elephant and Castle																													1213				
Blackfriars arr																													1216				
Holborn Viaduct "																																	
London Bridge arr	10 0	10 2	10 9	10 3	1015	1020	1011	1027	1037	1038	1043	1055	1058	11 0	11 8	1113	1123	1110	1131		1138	1143	1146	1154	1158		12 7	12 4		1212	1216	1214	1211
Cannon Street "			1015	10 7	1019			1031	1040				11 1	11 3					1135				1150		12 2		1212			1216	1221		
Waterloo "	10 3	10 5				1023	1017			1042	1047	1059			1112	1117	1126	1114			1142	1147		1158				12 8				1218	1215
Charing Cross "	10 6	10 8				1026	1020			1045	1050	11 2			1116	1120	1130	1118			1145	1150		12 1				1211				1221	1219

A Maze Hill, for National Maritime Museum

For SUNDAY TRAINS, see page 107

3 Third class only

GILLINGHAM (Kent), CHATHAM, MAIDSTONE WEST, GRAVESEND CENTRAL, DARTFORD, WOOLWICH, and LONDON

Saturdays—continued

Up	a.m.																									p.m.							
Gillingham (Kent) dep														1140								1210											1240
Chatham														1146								1214											1246
Rochester														1149								1217											1249
Strood 72 arr														1151								1221											1251
Maidstone West dep	3	3	3	3	3	3		3	3	3	3	3	1126	3	3	3	3	3		3	3	1154	3		3	12 6	3	3	3	3	3	1226	3
Barracks													1128									1156				12 8						1228	
Aylesford													1133									12 1				1213						1233	
New Hythe													1136									12 4				1216						1236	
Snodland													1139									12 7				1219						1239	
Halling													1142									1210				1222						1242	
Cuxton													1145									1213				1225						1245	
Strood 72 arr													1150									1218				1230						1250	
Strood dep														1152								1222				Stop							1252
Higham														1158																			1258
Gravesend Central arr														12 5								1233											1 5
Gravesend Central dep					1145									12 7							1224	1234						1249					1 7
Northfleet					1149									1212							1228							1253					1 12
Swanscombe Halt					1151									1215							1230							1255					1 15
Greenhithe					1154									1218							1233							1258					1 18
Stone Crossing Halt					1157			p.m	p.m		p.m			1220							1236							1 1					1 20
Dartford	1148		1153		12 1	p.m		12 9	1213	p.m	1219	p.m		1224		1227	1233			1238	1240	1244	12 47				1 3	1 5	1 0	1 12			1 24
Slades Green	1151			1158		12 4		1212		1219		1226					1236								1251				1 3				
Crayford			1156		12 5						1224				1236						1250							1 9					1 28
Bexley			12 0		12 8						1228				1239					1243	1254									1 17			1 31
Albany Park			12 3		1211						1231									1246	1257							1 13					1 34
Sidcup			12 6		1213						1234				1243					1249	1 0							1 16		1 21			1 36
New Eltham			12 9		1216						1237									1252	1 3									1 24			1 39
Mottingham			1212		1219						1239									1254	1 6									1 27			1 42
Lee, for Burnt Ash			1215		1223						1243									1258	1 9									1 30			1 45
Hither Green 124			1217		1225						1245				1250						1 11									1 32			1 47
Barnehurst									1219					1230				1245							1255		1 9				1 19		
Bexleyheath									1222					1233				1248							1258		1 12				1 22		
Welling									1225					1236				1251							1 1		1 15				1 25		
Falconwood									1227					1239				1253							1 4		1 18				1 28		
Eltham Park									1230					1241				1256							1 6		1 20				1 30		
Eltham (Well Hall)									1232					1243				1258							1 8		1 22				1 32		
Kidbrooke									1234					1246				1 1							1 11		1 25				1 35		
Erith	1155			12 1		12 7		1216		1222						1234	1239						12 52			p.m			1 6				
Belvedere	1158			12 4		1210		1219		1225						1237	1242						12 55			3			1 9				
Abbey Wood	12 1	non		12 7		1213		1222		1228						1240	1245						12 58						1 12				
Plumstead	12 4	12 0		1211		1217		1226		1231		1234				1243	1249						1 2			1 7			1 16				
Woolwich Arsenal	12 6	12 2		1213		1219		1228		1233		1237				1245	1251					1256	1 4			1 9			1 18				
Woolwich Dockyard		12 4				1221				1236							1254									1 12			1 20				
Charlton		12 7		1216		1224				1238						1249	1256						1 7			1 14			1 23				
Blackheath		1213				1228		1234	1237					1249			1 0	1 4							1 14	1 18	1 28				1 38		
Lewisham 114		1216				1230		1237	1240			1247		1251	1254		1 3	1 6							1 16	1 21	1 30				1 40		
St. John's 124						1232																											
New Cross		1219	1222		1231	1235		1240	1243		1249	1250		1254			1 7	1 9			1 16						1 33	1 28		1 37	1 43		1 52
Westcombe Park				1219						1241						1252							1 10						1 25				
Maze Hill A				1221						1243													1 12						1 28				
Greenwich				1224						1246													1 15						1 30				
Deptford				1226						1248													1 17										
Peckham Rye															1 2										1 27								
Elephant and Castle															1 10										1 34								
Blackfriars arr															1 13										1 37								
Holborn Viaduct "															1 16										1 39								
London Bridge arr	1221	1226	1228	1232	1237	1241		1246	1249	1256	1256	1259		1 0		1 2	1 13	1 16		1 8	1 22	1 10	1 23			1 29	1 40	1 34	1 38	1 44	1 50		1 58
Cannon Street "	1224	1230		1237		1245		1249	1252		1 0	1 2				1 6					1 25		1 26							1 47			
Waterloo "			1232		1242					1259				1 4			1 17	1 20		1 12		1 14				1 33	1 44	1 37	1 41		1 53		2 4
Charing Cross "			1235		1246					1 2				1 7			1 20	1 23		1 15		1 17				1 36	1 47	1 40	1 44		1 56		2 7

A Maze Hill for National Maritime Museum

GILLINGHAM (Kent), CHATHAM, MAIDSTONE WEST, GRAVESEND CENTRAL, DARTFORD, WOOLWICH, and LONDON

Saturdays—continued

Up	p.m																										p.m						
Gillingham (Kent) dep								1 10												1 40		2 10							2 42			3 10	
Chatham								1 14												1 44		2 14							2 46			3 14	
Rochester								1 17												1 47		2 17							2 49			3 17	
Strood 72 arr								1 20												1 50		2 20							2 51			3 20	
Maidstone West dep	3	3	3	3	3	3	1241	1254	3	3	3	1 9	3	3	3	3	3	3	1 26	3	3	1 54	3	3	3	3	2 26		3	3	2 54		3
" Barracks							1243	1256				1 11							1 28			1 56					2 28				2 56		
Aylesford							1248	1 1				1 16							1 33			2 1					2 33				3 1		
New Hythe							1251	1 4				1 19							1 36			2 4					2 36				3 4		
Snodland							1254	1 7				1 22							1 39			2 7					2 39				3 7		
Halling							1257	1 10				1 25							1 42			2 10					2 42				3 10		
Cuxton							1 0	1 13				1 28							1 45			2 13					2 45				3 13		
Strood 72 arr							1 5	1 18				1 33							1 50			2 18					2 50				3 18		
Strood dep								1 22												1 51		2 22							2 52			3 22	
Higham																				1 58									2 58				
Gravesend arr								1 34												2 5		2 34							3 5			3 34	
Central dep					1 23			1 35										1 59		2 6		2 35			2 43				3 6			3 35	
Northfleet					1 27													2 3		2 10					2 47				3 10				
Swanscombe Halt					1 29													2 5		2 13					2 49				3 13				
Greenhithe					1 32													2 8		2 16					2 52				3 16				
Stone Crossing Halt					1 35													2 11		2 19					2 55				3 18				
Dartford	1 22	1 28	1 30		1 39			1 45	1 48	1 54	1 56		1 59		2 10			2 17		2 23	2 29	2 45	2 50	2 57	2 59	3 18			3 23	3 29		3 45	3 50
Slades Green	1 25	1 31		1 36					1 51		1 59			2 4				2 21						3 1		3 21							
Crayford					1 42					1 58					2 13	2 19				2 26			2 53						3 26				3 53
Bexley					1 45					2 1					2 16	2 22				2 29			2 56						3 29				3 56
Albany Park					1 48					2 4					2 19	2 25				2 32			2 59						3 32				3 59
Sidcup					1 51					2 6					2 22	2 27				2 35			3 2						3 35				4 2
New Eltham					1 54					2 9					2 25	2 30				2 38			3 5						3 38				4 5
Mottingham					1 56					2 12					2 27	2 33				2 40			3 7						3 40				4 7
Lee, for Burnt Ash					2 0					2 15					2 31	2 36				2 44			3 11						3 44				4 11
Hither Green 124					2 2					2 17					2 33	2 38				2 46			3 13						3 46				4 13
Barnehurst			1 36	1 42		1 53							2 5				2 24				2 35				3 5					3 35			
Bexleyheath			1 39	1 46		1 56							2 8				2 27				2 38				3 8					3 38			
Welling			1 42	1 49		1 59							2 11				2 30				2 41				3 11					3 41			
Falconwood			1 44	1 51		2 1							2 13								2 43				3 13					3 43			
Eltham Park			1 47	1 54		2 4							2 16				2 33				2 46				3 16					3 46			
Eltham (Well Hall)			1 49	1 56		2 6							2 18				2 35				2 48				3 18					3 48			
Kidbrooke			1 51	1 58		2 8							2 20				2 38				2 50				3 20					3 50			
Erith	1 28	1 34							1 54		2 2			2 8				2 24						3 4		3 24							
Belvedere	1 31	1 37							1 57		2 5			2 11				2 27						3 7		3 27							
Abbey Wood	1 34	1 40							2 0		2 8			2 14				2 30						3 10		3 30							
Plumstead	1 38	1 44							2 4		2 12			2 18				2 34						3 14		3 34							
Woolwich Arsenal	1 40	1 46						1 57	2 6		2 15							2 36				2 57		3 16		3 36						3 57	
Woolwich Dockyard	1 42	1 49							2 8		2 19							2 38						3 19		3 38							
Charlton	1 45	1 51							2 11		2 21							2 41						3 21		3 41							
Blackheath	1 49		1 54	2 1		2 11			2 15				2 23				2 41	2 45			2 53				3 23	3 45				3 53			
Lewisham 114	1 53		1 57	2 4		2 14			2 17	2 21			2 26			2 42	2 44	2 47		2 50	2 56		3 16		3 26	3 47			3 50	3 56			4 16
St. John's 124	1 55												2 28				2 46	2 49		2 52	2 58		3 18		3 28	3 49			3 52	3 58			4 18
New Cross	1 58		2 0		2 6	2 17			2 20	2 24			2 30		2 38		2 49	2 52		2 54	3 0		3 21		3 30	3 52			3 54	4 0			4 21
Westcombe Park		1 54									2 24													3 24									
Maze Hill **A**		1 56									2 26													3 26									
Greenwich		1 59									2 30													3 29									
Deptford		2 1									2 32													3 31									
Peckham Rye				2 12												2 47																	
Elephant and Castle				2 20												2 56																	
Blackfriars arr				2 23												2 59																	
Holborn Viaduct "				2 25																													
London Bridge arr	2 5	2 8	2 6		2 13	2 23		2 11	2 27	2 31	2 39		2 36		2 44		2 55	2 58		3 1	3 6	3 11	3 27	3 39	3 36	3 58			4 1	4 6		4 11	4 27
Cannon Street "			2 9							2 35			2 40					3 2		3 6													
Waterloo "	2 8	2 12			2 18	2 27		2 16	2 31		2 43				2 47		3 0				3 10	3 17	3 31	3 43	3 40	4 2			4 5	4 10		4 17	4 31
Charing Cross "	2 12	2 15			2 21	2 30		2 19	2 35		2 46				2 50		3 3				3 13	3 19	3 34	3 46	3 43	4 5			4 9	4 13		4 19	4 34

A Maze Hill, for National Maritime Museum

For SUNDAY TRAINS, see page 107

3 Third class only

GILLINGHAM (Kent), CHATHAM, MAIDSTONE WEST, GRAVESEND CENTRAL, DARTFORD, WOOLWICH, and LONDON

Saturdays—*continued*

Up	p.m										
Gillingham (Kent) dep	..	..	..	..	3 33	..	..	..	..	..	..
Chatham	..	..	..	..	3‖46	..	..	..	..	..	..
Rochester	..	..	..	..	3 49	..	..	..	..	..	..
Strood 72 arr	..	..	..	..	3 51	..	..	..	..	..	..
Maidstone West dep	3	3	3	3 26	3	..	3	3	3	3	3
" Barracks				3 28		..					
Aylesford	..	..	..	3 33	..	..	..	..	..	..	..
New Hythe	..	..	..	3 36	..	..	..	..	..	..	..
Snodland	..	..	..	3 39	..	..	..	..	..	..	..
Halling	..	..	..	3 42	..	..	..	..	..	..	..
Cuxton	..	..	..	3 45	..	..	..	..	..	..	..
Strood 72 arr	..	..	..	3 50	..	..	..	..	..	..	..
Strood dep	..	..	..	..	3 52	..	..	..	..	..	..
Higham	..	..	..	..	3 58	..	..	..	..	..	..
Gravesend Central arr	..	..	..	..	4 5	..	..	..	..	..	..
Gravesend Central dep	..	3 45	..	..	4 6	..	..	..	..	..	..
Northfleet	..	3 49	..	..	4 10	..	..	..	..	..	..
Swanscombe Halt	..	..	..	..	4 13	..	..	..	..	..	..
Greenhithe	..	3 53	..	..	4 16	..	..	..	..	..	..
Stone Crossing Halt	..	..	..	..	4 18	..	..	..	..	..	..
Dartford	3 57	3 59	4 18	..	4 23	..	4 29	4 50	4 57	4 59	5 18
Slades Green	4 1	..	4 21	..	..	..	..	..	5 1	..	5 21
Crayford	..	..	..	..	4 26	..	..	4 53	..	..	..
Bexley	..	..	..	..	4 29	..	..	4 56	..	..	..
Albany Park	..	..	..	..	4 32	..	..	4 59	..	..	..
Sidcup	..	..	..	..	4 35	..	..	5 2	..	..	..
New Eltham	..	..	..	..	4 38	..	..	5 5	..	..	..
Mottingham	..	..	..	..	4 40	..	..	5 7	..	..	..
Lee, for Burnt Ash	..	..	..	..	4 44	..	..	5 11	..	..	..
Hither Green 124	..	..	..	..	4 46	..	..	5 13	..	..	..
Barnehurst	..	4 5	..	..	..	..	4 35	..	..	5 5	..
Bexleyheath	..	4 8	..	..	..	..	4 38	..	..	5 8	..
Welling	..	4 11	..	..	..	..	4 41	..	..	5 11	..
Falconwood	..	4 13	..	..	..	..	4 43	..	..	5 13	..
Eltham Park	..	4 16	..	..	..	..	4 46	..	..	5 16	..
Eltham Well Hall	..	4 18	..	..	..	..	4 48	..	..	5 18	..
Kidbrooke	..	4 20	..	..	..	..	4 50	..	..	5 20	..
Erith	4 4	..	4 24	..	..	..	..	..	5 4	..	5 24
Belvedere	4 7	..	4 27	..	..	..	..	..	5 7	..	5 27
Abbey Wood	4 10	..	4 30	..	..	..	..	..	5 10	..	5 30
Plumstead	4 14	..	4 34	..	..	..	..	..	5 14	..	5 34
Woolwich Arsenal	16	..	4 36	..	..	..	..	..	5 16	..	5 36
Woolwich Dockyard	4 19	..	4 38	..	..	..	..	..	5 19	..	5 38
Charlton	4 21	..	4 41	..	..	..	..	..	5 21	..	5 41
Blackheath	..	4 23	4 45	..	..	..	4 53	..	..	5 23	5 45
Lewisham 114	..	4 26	4 47	..	4 50	..	4 56	5 16	..	5 26	5 47
St. John's 124	..	4 28	4 49	..	4 52	..	4 58	5 18	..	5 28	5 49
New Cross	..	4 30	4 52	..	4 54	..	5 0	5 21	..	5 30	5 52
Westcombe Park	4 24	..	..	..	..	..	..	..	5 24	..	..
Maze Hill A	4 26	..	..	..	..	..	..	..	5 26	..	..
Greenwich	4 29	..	..	..	..	..	..	..	5 29	..	..
Deptford	4 31	..	..	..	..	..	..	..	5 31	..	..
Peckham Rye	..	..	..	..	..	..	..	..	..	..	..
Elephant and Castle	..	..	..	..	..	..	..	..	..	..	..
Blackfriars arr	..	..	..	..	..	..	..	..	..	..	..
Holborn Viaduct "	..	..	..	..	..	..	..	..	..	..	..
London Bridge arr	4 39	4 36	4 58	..	5 1	..	5 6	5 27	5 39	5 36	5 58
Cannon Street "	..	..	..	..	..	..	..	..	..	..	..
Waterloo "	4 43	4 40	5 2	..	5 5	..	5 10	5 30	5 43	5 40	6 2
Charing Cross "	4 46	4 43	5 5	..	5 7	..	5 13	5 33	5 45	5 43	6 5

Up	p.m										
Gillingham (Kent) dep	..	..	4 42	..	5 10	..	..	..	..	..	..
Chatham	..	..	4 46	..	5 14	..	..	..	..	..	..
Rochester	..	..	4 49	..	5 17	..	..	..	..	..	..
Strood 72 arr	..	..	4 51	..	5 20	..	..	..	..	..	..
Maidstone West dep	..	4 26	3	3	4 54	3	..	3	3	3	5 26
" Barracks	..	4 28			4 56		..				5 28
Aylesford	..	4 23	..	..	5 1	..	..	..	..	..	5 33
New Hythe	..	4 36	..	..	5 4	..	..	..	..	..	5 36
Snodland	..	4 39	..	..	5 7	..	..	..	..	..	5 39
Halling	..	4 42	..	..	5 10	..	..	..	..	..	5 42
Cuxton	..	4 45	..	..	5 13	..	..	..	..	..	5 45
Strood 72 arr	..	4 50	..	..	5 18	..	..	..	..	..	5 50
Strood dep	..	..	4 52	..	5 22	..	..	..	..	..	..
Higham	..	..	4 58	..	..	..	..	..	..	..	..
Gravesend Central arr	..	..	5 5	..	5 34	..	..	..	..	..	..
Gravesend Central dep	..	..	5 6	..	5 35	..	..	..	..	..	..
Northfleet	..	..	5 10	..	..	..	..	..	..	..	..
Swanscombe Halt	..	..	5 13	..	..	..	..	..	..	..	..
Greenhithe	..	..	5 16	..	..	..	..	..	..	..	..
Stone Crossing Halt	..	..	5 18	..	..	..	..	..	..	..	..
Dartford	..	..	5 23	5 29	5 45	5 50	..	5 57	5 59	6 18	..
Slades Green	..	..	..	..	..	..	..	6 1	..	6 21	..
Crayford	..	..	5 26	..	..	5 53	..	..	..	..	..
Bexley	..	..	5 29	..	..	5 56	..	..	..	..	..
Albany Park	..	..	5 32	..	..	5 59	..	..	..	..	..
Sidcup	..	..	5 35	..	..	6 2	..	..	..	..	..
New Eltham	..	..	5 38	..	..	6 5	..	..	..	..	..
Mottingham	..	..	5 40	..	..	6 7	..	..	..	..	..
Lee, for Burnt Ash	..	..	5 44	..	..	6 11	..	..	..	..	..
Hither Green 124	..	..	5 46	..	..	6 13	..	..	..	..	..
Barnehurst	..	..	..	5 35	..	..	..	..	6 5	..	..
Bexleyheath	..	..	..	5 38	..	..	..	..	6 8	..	..
Welling	..	..	..	5 41	..	..	..	..	6 11	..	..
Falconwood	..	..	..	5 43	..	..	..	..	6 13	..	..
Eltham Park	..	..	..	5 46	..	..	..	..	6 16	..	..
Eltham Well Hall	..	..	..	5 48	..	..	..	..	6 18	..	..
Kidbrooke	..	..	..	5 50	..	..	..	..	6 20	..	..
Erith	..	..	..	..	..	..	..	6 4	..	6 24	..
Belvedere	..	..	..	..	..	..	..	6 7	..	6 27	..
Abbey Wood	..	..	..	..	..	..	..	6 10	..	6 30	..
Plumstead	..	..	..	..	..	..	..	6 14	..	6 34	..
Woolwich Arsenal	..	..	..	..	5 57	..	..	6 16	..	6 36	..
Woolwich Dockyard	..	..	..	..	..	..	..	6 19	..	6 38	..
Charlton	..	..	..	..	..	..	..	6 21	..	6 41	..
Blackheath	..	..	..	5 53	..	..	..	..	6 23	6 45	..
Lewisham 114	..	..	5 50	5 56	..	6 16	..	..	6 26	6 47	..
St. John's 124	..	..	5 52	5 58	..	6 18	..	..	6 28	6 49	..
New Cross	..	..	5 54	6 0	..	6 21	..	..	6 30	6 52	..
Westcombe Park	..	..	..	..	..	..	..	6 24	..	..	..
Maze Hill A	..	..	..	..	..	..	..	6 26	..	..	..
Greenwich	..	..	..	..	..	..	..	6 29	..	..	..
Deptford	..	..	..	..	..	..	..	6 31	..	..	..
Peckham Rye	..	..	..	..	..	..	..	..	..	..	..
Elephant and Castle	..	..	..	..	..	..	..	..	..	..	..
Blackfriars arr	..	..	..	..	..	..	..	..	..	..	..
Holborn Viaduct "	..	..	..	..	..	..	..	..	..	..	..
London Bridge arr	..	..	6 1	6 6	6 11	6 27	..	6 38	6 36	6 58	..
Cannon Street "	..	..	..	..	..	..	..	..	..	..	..
Waterloo "	..	..	6 5	6 10	6 17	6 31	..	6 42	6 40	7 2	..
Charing Cross "	..	..	6 7	6 13	6 19	6 34	..	6 46	6 43	7 5	..

Up	p.m										
Gillingham (Kent) dep	5 42	..	..	..	..	..	..	..	6 42	..	7 10
Chatham	5 46	..	..	..	..	..	..	..	6 46	..	7 14
Rochester	5 49	..	..	..	..	..	..	..	6 49	..	7 17
Strood 72 arr	5 51	..	..	..	..	..	..	..	6 50	..	7 20
Maidstone West dep	3	3	3	..	3	3	3	6 26	3	3	6 54
" Barracks				..				6 28			6 56
Aylesford	..	..	..	..	..	..	..	6 33	..	..	7 1
New Hythe	..	..	..	..	..	..	..	6 36	..	..	7 4
Snodland	..	..	..	..	..	..	..	6 39	..	..	7 7
Halling	..	..	..	..	..	..	..	6 42	..	..	7 10
Cuxton	..	..	..	..	..	..	..	6 45	..	..	7 13
Strood 72 arr	..	..	..	..	..	..	..	6 50	..	..	7 18
Strood dep	5 52	..	..	..	..	..	..	..	6 52	..	7 22
Higham	5 58	..	..	..	..	..	..	..	6 58	..	..
Gravesend Central arr	6 5	..	..	..	..	..	..	..	7 5	..	7 34
Gravesend Central dep	6 6	..	..	..	..	..	..	..	7 6	..	7 35
Northfleet	6 10	..	..	..	..	..	..	..	7 10	..	..
Swanscombe Halt	6 13	..	..	..	..	..	..	..	7 13	..	..
Greenhithe	6 16	..	..	..	..	..	..	..	7 16	..	..
Stone Crossing Halt	6 18	..	..	..	..	..	..	..	7 18	..	..
Dartford	6 23	6 29	6 50	..	6 57	6 59	7 18	..	7 23	7 29	7 45
Slades Green	..	..	..	..	7 1	..	7 21	..	..	..	..
Crayford	6 26	..	6 53	..	..	..	..	..	7 26	..	..
Bexley	6 29	..	6 56	..	..	..	..	..	7 29	..	..
Albany Park	6 32	..	6 59	..	..	..	..	..	7 32	..	..
Sidcup	6 35	..	7 2	..	..	..	..	..	7 35	..	..
New Eltham	6 38	..	7 5	..	..	..	..	..	7 38	..	..
Mottingham	6 40	..	7 7	..	..	..	..	..	7 40	..	..
Lee, for Burnt Ash	6 44	..	7 11	..	..	..	..	..	7 44	..	..
Hither Green 124	6 46	..	7 13	..	..	..	..	..	7 46	..	..
Barnehurst	..	6 35	..	..	..	7 5	..	..	..	7 35	..
Bexleyheath	..	6 38	..	..	..	7 8	..	..	..	7 38	..
Welling	..	6 41	..	..	..	7 11	..	..	..	7 41	..
Falconwood	..	6 43	..	..	..	7 13	..	..	..	7 43	..
Eltham Park	..	6 46	..	..	..	7 16	..	..	..	7 46	..
Eltham Well Hall	..	6 48	..	..	..	7 18	..	..	..	7 48	..
Kidbrooke	..	6 50	..	..	..	7 20	..	..	..	7 50	..
Erith	..	..	..	..	7 4	..	7 24	..	..	..	..
Belvedere	..	..	..	..	7 7	..	7 27	..	..	..	..
Abbey Wood	..	..	..	..	7 10	..	7 30	..	..	..	..
Plumstead	..	..	..	..	7 14	..	7 34	..	..	..	..
Woolwich Arsenal	..	..	..	..	7 16	..	7 36	..	..	..	7 57
Woolwich Dockyard	..	..	..	..	7 19	..	7 38	..	..	..	..
Charlton	..	..	..	..	7 21	..	7 41	..	..	..	..
Blackheath	..	6 53	..	..	..	7 23	7 45	..	..	7 53	..
Lewisham 114	6 50	6 56	7 16	..	..	7 26	7 47	..	7 50	7 56	..
St. John's 124	6 52	6 58	7 18	..	..	7 28	7 49	..	7 52	7 58	..
New Cross	6 54	7 0	7 21	..	..	7 30	7 52	..	7 54	8 0	..
Westcombe Park	..	..	..	..	7 24	..	..	..	..	..	..
Maze Hill A	..	..	..	..	7 26	..	..	..	..	..	..
Greenwich	..	..	..	..	7 29	..	..	..	..	..	..
Deptford	..	..	..	..	7 31	..	..	..	..	..	..
Peckham Rye	..	..	..	..	..	..	..	..	..	..	..
Elephant and Castle	..	..	..	..	..	..	..	..	..	..	..
Blackfriars arr	..	..	..	..	..	..	..	..	..	..	..
Holborn Viaduct "	..	..	..	..	..	..	..	..	..	..	..
London Bridge arr	7 1	7 6	7 27	..	7 38	7 36	7 58	..	8 1	8 7	8 11
Cannon Street "	..	..	..	..	..	..	..	..	..	..	..
Waterloo "	7 5	7 10	7 31	..	7 43	7 40	8 2	..	8 5	8 11	8 17
Charing Cross "	7 7	7 13	7 34	..	7 46	7 43	8 5	..	8 7	8 13	8 19

A Maze Hill, for National Maritime Museum ‖ Arr. 3 36 p.m

GILLINGHAM (Kent), CHATHAM, MAIDSTONE WEST, GRAVESEND CENTRAL, DARTFORD, WOOLWICH, and LONDON

Saturdays—*continued*

Up	p.m.																					p.m.										
Gillingham (Kent) dep	..	..	..	..	..	7 34	..	..	..	..	..	..	..	8 40	..	..	..	..	..	..	..	9 42	..	..	..	..	..	..	..	1040	1056	..
Chatham	..	..	..	..	..	7 39	..	..	..	..	..	..	..	8 44	..	..	..	..	..	..	..	9 46	..	..	..	..	..	..	..	1044	11 4	..
Rochester	..	..	..	..	..	7 45	..	..	..	..	..	..	..	8 48	..	..	..	..	..	..	..	9 49	..	..	..	..	..	..	..	1047	11 8	..
Strood 72 arr	..	..	..	..	..	7 49	..	..	..	..	..	..	..	8 51	..	..	..	..	..	..	..	9 51	..	..	..	..	..	..	..	1049	1112	..
Maidstone West dep	3	3	3	3	7 26	3	3	..	3	3	3	3	8 26	3	3	3	3	3	3	9 26	..	3	3	3	3	3	3	3	10 9	3	..	1117
" Barracks	..	..	..	..	7 28	..	..	..	..	..	..	..	8 28	..	..	..	..	..	..	9 28	..	..	..	..	..	..	..	..	1011	..	..	1119
Aylesford	..	..	..	..	7 33	..	..	..	..	..	..	..	8 33	..	..	..	..	..	..	9 33	..	..	..	..	..	..	..	..	1016	..	..	1124
New Hythe	..	..	..	..	7 36	..	..	..	..	..	..	..	8 36	..	..	..	..	..	..	9 36	..	..	..	..	..	..	..	..	1019	..	..	1127
Snodland	..	..	..	..	7 39	..	..	..	..	..	..	..	8 39	..	..	..	..	..	..	9 39	..	..	..	..	..	..	..	..	1022	..	..	1130
Halling	..	..	..	..	7 42	..	..	..	..	..	..	..	8 42	..	..	..	..	..	..	9 42	..	..	..	..	..	..	..	..	1026	..	..	1133
Cuxton	..	..	..	..	7 45	..	..	..	..	..	..	..	8 45	..	..	..	..	..	..	9 45	..	..	..	..	..	..	..	..	1028	..	..	1136
Strood 72 arr	..	..	..	..	7 50	..	..	..	..	..	..	..	8 50	..	..	..	..	..	..	9 50	..	..	..	..	..	..	..	..	1033	..	..	1141
Strood dep	..	..	..	..	..	7 52	..	..	..	..	..	..	..	8 52	..	..	..	..	..	..	..	9 52	..	..	..	..	..	..	..	1050	1113	..
Higham	..	..	..	..	..	7 58	..	..	..	..	..	..	..	8 58	..	..	..	..	..	..	..	9 58	..	..	..	..	..	..	..	1056	1120	..
Gravesend Central arr	..	..	..	..	..	8 5	..	..	..	..	..	..	..	9 5	..	..	..	..	..	..	..	10 5	..	..	..	..	..	..	..	11 3	1128	..
Gravesend Central dep	..	..	..	..	..	8 6	..	..	..	..	..	..	..	9 6	..	..	..	..	..	..	..	10 6	..	..	..	..	..	..	..	11 4	1129	..
Northfleet	..	..	..	..	..	8 10	..	..	..	..	..	..	..	9 10	..	..	..	..	..	..	..	1010	..	..	..	..	..	..	..	11 8	..	..
Swanscombe Halt	..	..	..	..	..	8 13	..	..	..	..	..	..	..	9 13	..	..	..	..	..	..	..	1013	..	..	..	..	..	..	..	1110	..	..
Greenhithe	..	..	..	..	..	8 16	..	..	..	..	..	..	..	9 16	..	..	..	..	..	..	..	1016	..	..	..	..	..	..	..	1113	..	..
Stone Crossing Halt	..	..	..	..	..	8 18	..	..	..	..	..	..	..	9 18	..	..	..	..	..	..	..	1018	..	..	..	..	..	..	..	1116	..	..
Dartford	7 50	7 57	7 59	8 18	..	8 23	8 29	..	8 50	8 57	8 59	9 18	..	9 23	9 29	9 50	9 57	9 59	1018	..	..	1023	1029	1035	1045	1050	1112	11 16	..	1121	1142	..
Slades Green	..	8 1	..	8 21	..	..	..	..	..	9 1	..	9 21	..	..	..	..	10 1	..	1021	..	..	..	..	1039	..	..	..	..	..	1125	..	..
Crayford	7 53	..	..	..	..	8 26	..	..	8 53	..	..	..	..	9 26	..	9 53	..	..	..	..	..	1026	..	..	..	1053	..	11 19	..	..	..	..
Bexley	7 56	..	..	..	..	8 29	..	..	8 56	..	..	..	..	9 29	..	9 56	..	..	..	..	..	1029	..	..	..	1056	..	11 22	..	..	..	..
Albany Park	7 59	..	..	..	..	8 32	..	..	8 59	..	..	..	..	9 32	..	9 59	..	..	..	..	..	1032	..	..	..	1059	..	11 25	..	..	..	..
Sidcup	8 2	..	..	..	..	8 35	..	..	9 2	..	..	..	..	9 35	..	10 2	..	..	..	..	..	1035	..	..	..	11 2	..	11 28	..	..	..	..
New Eltham	8 5	..	..	..	..	8 38	..	..	9 5	..	..	..	..	9 38	..	10 5	..	..	..	..	..	1038	..	..	..	11 5	..	11 31	..	..	..	..
Mottingham	8 7	..	..	..	..	8 40	..	..	9 7	..	..	..	..	9 40	..	10 7	..	..	..	..	..	1040	..	..	..	11 7	..	11 33	..	..	..	..
Lee, for Burnt Ash	8 11	..	..	..	..	8 44	..	..	9 11	..	..	..	..	9 44	..	1011	..	..	..	..	..	1044	..	..	..	1111	..	11 37	..	..	..	..
Hither Green 124	8 13	..	..	..	..	8 46	..	..	9 13	..	..	..	..	9 46	..	1013	..	..	..	..	..	1046	..	..	..	1113	..	11 39	..	..	..	..
Barnehurst	..	..	8 5	..	..	..	8 35	..	..	..	9 5	..	..	..	9 35	..	..	10 5	..	..	..	..	1035	..	1051	..	1118	..	..	..	..	..
Bexleyheath	..	..	8 8	..	..	..	8 38	..	..	..	9 8	..	..	..	9 38	..	..	10 8	..	..	..	..	1038	..	1054	..	1121	..	..	..	..	..
Welling	..	..	8 11	..	..	..	8 41	..	..	..	9 11	..	..	..	9 41	..	..	1011	..	..	..	..	1041	..	1057	..	1124	..	..	..	..	..
Falconwood	..	..	8 13	..	..	..	8 43	..	..	..	9 13	..	..	..	9 43	..	..	1013	..	..	..	..	1043	..	1059	..	1127	..	..	..	..	..
Eltham Park	..	..	8 16	..	..	..	8 46	..	..	..	9 16	..	..	..	9 46	..	..	1016	..	..	..	..	1046	..	11 2	..	1129	..	..	..	..	..
Eltham (Well Hall)	..	..	8 18	..	..	..	8 48	..	..	..	9 18	..	..	..	9 48	..	..	1018	..	..	..	..	1048	..	11 4	..	1131	..	..	..	..	..
Kidbrooke	..	..	8 20	..	..	..	8 50	..	..	..	9 20	..	..	..	9 50	..	..	1020	..	..	..	..	1050	..	11 6	..	1134	..	..	..	..	..
Erith	..	8 4	..	8 24	..	..	..	..	..	9 4	..	9 24	..	..	..	..	10 4	..	1024	..	..	..	..	1042	..	..	..	..	..	1128	..	..
Belvedere	..	8 7	..	8 27	..	..	..	..	..	9 7	..	9 27	..	..	..	..	10 7	..	1027	..	..	..	..	1045	..	..	..	..	..	1131	..	..
Abbey Wood	..	8 10	..	8 30	..	..	..	..	..	9 10	..	9 30	..	..	..	..	1010	..	1030	..	..	..	..	1048	..	..	..	..	..	1134	..	..
Plumstead	..	8 14	..	8 34	..	..	..	..	..	9 14	..	9 34	..	..	..	..	1014	..	1034	..	..	..	..	1051	..	..	..	..	..	1138	..	..
Woolwich Arsenal	..	8 16	..	8 36	..	..	..	..	..	9 16	..	9 36	..	..	..	..	1016	..	1036	..	..	..	..	1053	..	..	..	..	..	1141	1157	..
Woolwich Dockyard	..	8 19	..	8 38	..	..	..	..	..	9 19	..	9 38	..	..	..	..	1019	..	1038	..	..	..	..	1056	..	..	..	..	..	1143	..	..
Charlton	..	8 21	..	8 41	..	..	..	..	..	9 21	..	9 41	..	..	..	..	1021	..	1041	..	..	..	..	1058	..	..	..	..	..	1146	..	..
Blackheath	..	..	8 23	8 45	..	..	8 53	..	..	..	9 23	9 45	..	..	9 53	..	..	1023	1045	..	..	..	1053	..	11 9	..	1137	..	..	1150	..	..
Lewisham 114	8 16	..	8 26	8 47	..	8 50	8 56	..	9 16	..	9 26	9 47	..	9 50	9 56	1016	..	1026	1047	..	..	1050	1056	..	1112	1116	1139	..	..	1153	..	..
St. John's 124	8 18	..	8 28	8 49	..	8 52	8 58	..	9 18	..	9 28	9 49	..	9 52	9 58	1018	..	1028	1049	..	..	1052	1058	..	1114	1118	1141	11 42	..	1155	..	..
New Cross	8 21	..	8 30	8 52	..	8 54	9 0	..	9 21	..	9 30	9 52	..	9 54	10 0	1021	..	1030	1052	..	..	1054	11 0	..	1116	1121	1144	11 45	..	1157	..	..
Westcombe Park	..	8 24	..	..	..	..	..	..	..	9 24	..	..	..	..	..	..	1024	..	..	..	..	..	..	11 1	..	..	..	..	..	..	..	..
Maze Hill A	..	8 26	..	..	..	..	..	..	..	9 26	..	..	..	..	..	..	1026	..	..	..	..	..	..	11 3	..	..	..	..	..	..	..	..
Greenwich	..	8 29	..	..	..	..	..	..	..	9 29	..	..	..	..	..	..	1029	..	..	..	..	..	..	11 6	..	..	..	..	..	..	..	..
Deptford	..	8 31	..	..	..	..	..	..	..	9 31	..	..	..	..	..	..	1031	..	..	..	..	..	..	11 8	..	..	..	..	..	..	..	..
Peckham Rye	..	..	..	..	..	..	..	..	..	..	..	..	..	..	..	..	..	..	..	..	..	..	..	..	..	..	..	..	..	..	..	..
Elephant and Castle	..	..	..	..	..	..	..	..	..	..	..	..	..	..	..	..	..	..	..	..	..	..	..	..	..	..	..	..	..	..	..	..
Blackfriars .... arr	..	..	..	..	..	..	..	..	..	..	..	..	..	..	..	..	..	..	..	..	..	..	..	..	..	..	..	..	..	..	..	..
Holborn Viaduct "	..	..	..	..	..	..	..	..	..	..	..	..	..	..	..	..	..	..	..	..	..	..	..	..	..	..	..	..	..	..	..	..
London Bridge arr	8 27	8 38	8 36	8 58	..	9 1	9 6	..	9 27	9 38	9 36	9 58	..	10 1	10 6	1027	1039	1036	1058	..	..	11 1	11 6	1114	1123	1127	1150	11 51	..	12 3	1217	..
Cannon Street "	..	..	..	..	..	..	..	..	..	..	..	..	..	..	..	..	..	..	..	..	..	..	..	..	..	..	..	..	..	..	..	..
Waterloo "	8 31	8 43	8 40	9 2	..	9 5	9 10	..	9 32	9 42	9 40	10 2	..	10 5	1010	1032	1043	1040	11 2	..	..	11 5	1110	1119	1130	1132	1154	..	..	12 7	1224	..
Charing Cross "	8 34	8 46	8 43	9 5	..	9 7	9 13	..	9 35	9 46	9 43	10 5	..	10 7	1013	1035	1046	1043	11 5	..	..	11 7	1113	1122	1132	1135	1157	..	..	12 9	1228	..

A Maze Hill, for National Maritime Museum

For SUNDAY TRAINS, see page 107

3 Third class only

GILLINGHAM (Kent), CHATHAM, MAIDSTONE WEST, GRAVESEND CENTRAL, DARTFORD, WOOLWICH, and LONDON

Up					a.m.												Sundays												a.m.				
Gillingham (Kent) dep					5 50						6 20						6 54						7 20						7 58				
Chatham					5 54						6 24						6 58						7 24						8 1				
Rochester					5 57						6 27						7 1						7 27						8 4				
Strood 72 arr					6 0						6 29						7 4						7 29						8 6				
Maidstone West dep	3	3	3				3		3	3	3		3		3		6 39	3	3	3	3		3		3		3		3		3		3
" Barracks																	6 40																
Aylesford																	6 45																
New Hythe																	6 48																
Snodland																	6 51																
Halling																	6 54																
Cuxton																	6 57																
Strood 72 arr																	7 2																
Strood dep					6 1						6 30						7 5						7 30						8 7				
Higham					6 8						6 36												7 36						8 12				
Gravesend Central arr					6 17						6 42						7 16						7 44						8 19				
Gravesend Central dep									6 25		6 43						7 17						7 45						8 20				
Northfleet									6 29		6 48												7 50						8 24				
Swanscombe Halt									6 31		6 50												7 52						8 26				
Greenhithe									6 34		6 53												7 55						8 29				
Stone Crossing Halt									6 37		6 56												7 58						8 32				
Dartford			6 12				6 43		6 41	6 48	7 1		7 8		7 12		7 28	7 32	7 41	7 43	7 52		8 2		8 12		8 16		8 36		8 44		8 52
Slades Green		5 40	6 15						6 45		7 5							7 35	7 45				8 5						8 39				
Crayford							6 46								7 15					7 46					8 15						8 47		
Bexley							6 49								7 18					7 49					8 18						8 50		
Albany Park							6 52								7 21					7 52					8 21						8 53		
Sidcup							6 54								7 24					7 55					8 24						8 56		
New Eltham							6 57								7 27					7 58					8 27						8 59		
Mottingham							7 0								7 30					8 0					8 30						9 2		
Lee, for Burnt Ash							7 3								7 33					8 4					8 33						9 5		
Hither Green 124							7 5								7 35					8 6					8 35						9 7		
Barnehurst										6 52			7 14								7 58						8 22						8 58
Bexleyheath										6 55			7 17								8 1						8 25						9 1
Welling										6 58			7 20								8 4						8 28						9 4
Falconwood										7 0			7 23								8 6						8 30						9 6
Eltham Park										7 3			7 25								8 9						8 33						9 9
Eltham (Well Hall)										7 5			7 27								8 11						8 35						9 11
Kidbrooke										7 7			7 30								8 13						8 37						9 13
Erith		5 43	6 18						6 48		7 8							7 38	7 48				8 8						8 42				
Belvedere		5 46	6 21						6 51		7 11							7 41	7 51				8 11						8 45				
Abbey Wood		5 49	6 24						6 54		7 14							7 44	7 54				8 14						8 48				
Plumstead		5 52	6 28						6 58		7 18							7 48	7 58				8 18						8 52				
Woolwich Arsenal		5 55	6 30						7 0		7 20						7 40	7 50	8 0				8 20						8 54				
Woolwich Dockyard		5 57	6 32						7 3		7 22							7 53	8 3				8 22						8 56				
Charlton		6 0	6 35						7 5		7 25							7 55	8 5				8 25						8 59				
Blackheath	5 4	6 4								7 10	7 29		7 33					7 59			8 16		8 29				8 40						9 16
Lewisham 114	5 7	6 6								7 13	7 31		7 35		7 39			8 2		8 9	8 19		8 31		8 39		8 43				9 11		9 19
St. John's 121	5 9	6 9					7 9			7 15	7 33		7 37		7 41			8 4		8 11	8 21		8 33		8 41		8 45				9 13		9 21
New Cross	5 11	6 11					7 11			7 17	7 36		7 40		7 43			8 7		8 14	8 23		8 36		8 43		8 47				9 15		9 23
Westcombe Park			6 37						7 8										8 8										9 1				
Maze Hill A			6 40						7 10										8 10										9 4				
Greenwich			6 42						7 13										8 13										9 6				
Deptford			6 44						7 15										8 15										9 8				
Peckham Rye																																	
Elephant and Castle																																	
Blackfriars arr																																	
Holborn Viaduct "																																	
London Bridge arr	5 17	6 17	6 51				7 17		7 21	7 23	7 42		7 46		7 49		7 55	8 13	8 21	8 20	8 29		8 42		8 49		8 53		9 14		9 22		9 29
Cannon Street "																																	
Waterloo "	5 21	6 20	6 54				7 22		7 24		7 45		7 49		7 53		7 59	8 16	8 24		8 32		8 46		8 53		8 57		9 17		9 26		9 33
Charing Cross "	5 24	6 23	6 57				7 25		7 27		7 47		7 52		7 56		8 2	8 19	8 27		8 35		8 49		8 57		9 0		9 20		9 29		9 36

A Maze Hill, for National Maritime Museum

GILLINGHAM (Kent), CHATHAM, MAIDSTONE WEST, GRAVESEND CENTRAL, DARTFORD, WOOLWICH, and LONDON

Up	a.m.												Sundays—continued														a.m.					
Gillingham (Kent) dep	..	8 20	..	..	..	..	8 54	..	..	..	..	..	9 20	..	..	..	..	..	..	..	..	..	1020	..	..	..	1054	..	..	..	..	1120
Chatham	..	8 24	..	..	..	..	8 58	..	..	..	..	..	9 24	..	..	..	..	..	..	..	..	..	1024	..	..	..	1058	..	..	..	..	1124
Rochester	..	8 27	..	..	..	..	9 1	..	..	..	..	..	9 27	..	..	..	..	..	..	..	..	..	1027	..	..	..	11 1	..	..	..	..	1127
Strood 72 arr	..	8 29	..	..	..	..	9 4	..	..	..	..	..	9 29	..	..	..	..	..	..	..	..	..	1029	..	..	..	11 4	..	..	..	..	1129
Maidstone West dep	7 39	3	3	..	3	..	8 39	..	3	..	3	3	3	..	3	..	3	..	3	3	3	9 39	3	3	..	3	1039	..	3	3	3	3
" Barracks	7 40			..		..	8 40	..		..				..		..		..				9 40			..		1040	..				
Aylesford	7 45	..	..	..	..	..	8 45	..	..	..	..	..	..	..	..	..	..	..	..	..	..	9 45	..	..	..	..	1045	..	..	..	..	..
New Hythe	7 48	..	..	..	..	..	8 48	..	..	..	..	..	..	..	..	..	..	..	..	..	..	9 48	..	..	..	..	1048	..	..	..	..	..
Snodland	7 51	..	..	..	..	..	8 51	..	..	..	..	..	..	..	..	..	..	..	..	..	..	9 51	..	..	..	..	1051	..	..	..	..	..
Halling	7 54	..	..	..	..	..	8 54	..	..	..	..	..	..	..	..	..	..	..	..	..	..	9 54	..	..	..	..	1054	..	..	..	..	..
Cuxton	7 57	..	..	..	..	..	8 57	..	..	..	..	..	..	..	..	..	..	..	..	..	..	9 57	..	..	..	..	1057	..	..	..	..	..
Strood 72 arr	8 2	..	..	..	..	..	9 2	..	..	..	..	..	..	..	..	..	..	..	..	..	..	10 2	..	..	..	..	11 2	..	..	..	..	..
Strood dep	..	8 30	..	..	..	..	9 5	..	..	..	..	..	9 30	..	..	..	..	..	..	..	..	..	1030	..	..	..	11 5	..	..	..	..	1130
Higham	..	8 36	..	..	..	..	..	..	..	..	..	..	9 36	..	..	..	..	..	..	..	..	..	1036	..	..	..	..	..	..	..	..	1136
Gravesend Central arr	..	8 44	..	..	..	..	9 17	..	..	..	..	..	9 44	..	..	..	..	..	..	..	..	..	1044	..	..	..	1117	..	..	..	..	1144
Gravesend Central dep	..	8 45	..	..	..	..	9 18	..	..	..	..	..	9 45	..	..	..	..	..	..	..	..	..	1045	..	..	..	1118	..	..	..	..	1145
Northfleet	..	8 50	..	..	..	..	..	..	..	..	..	..	9 50	..	..	..	..	..	..	..	..	..	1050	..	..	..	..	..	..	..	..	1150
Swanscombe Halt	..	8 52	..	..	..	..	..	..	..	..	..	..	9 52	..	..	..	..	..	..	..	..	..	1052	..	..	..	..	..	..	..	..	1152
Greenhithe	..	8 55	..	..	..	..	..	..	..	..	..	..	9 55	..	..	..	..	..	..	..	..	..	1055	..	..	..	..	..	..	..	..	1155
Stone Crossing Halt	..	8 58	..	..	..	..	..	..	..	..	..	..	9 58	..	..	..	..	..	..	..	..	..	1058	..	..	..	..	..	..	..	..	1158
Dartford	..	9 2	9 12	..	9 16	..	9 28	..	9 36	..	9 44	9 52	10 2	..	1012	..	1016	..	1036	1044	1052	..	11 2	1112	..	1116	1128	..	1136	1144	1152	12 2
Slades Green	..	9 5	..	..	..	..	..	..	9 39	..	..	..	10 5	..	..	..	..	..	1039	..	..	..	11 5	..	..	..	..	..	1139	..	..	12 5
Crayford	..	..	9 15	..	..	..	..	..	..	..	9 47	..	..	..	1015	..	..	..	..	1047	..	..	..	1115	..	..	..	..	..	1147	..	..
Bexley	..	..	9 18	..	..	..	..	..	..	..	9 50	..	..	..	1018	..	..	..	..	1050	..	..	..	1118	..	..	..	..	..	1150	..	..
Albany Park	..	..	9 21	..	..	..	..	..	..	..	9 53	..	..	..	1021	..	..	..	..	1053	..	..	..	1121	..	..	..	..	..	1153	..	..
Sidcup	..	..	9 24	..	..	..	..	..	..	..	9 56	..	..	..	1024	..	..	..	..	1056	..	..	..	1124	..	..	..	..	..	1156	..	..
New Eltham	..	..	9 27	..	..	..	..	..	..	..	9 59	..	..	..	1027	..	..	..	..	1059	..	..	..	1127	..	..	..	..	..	1159	..	..
Mottingham	..	..	9 30	..	..	..	..	..	..	..	10 2	..	..	..	1030	..	..	..	..	11 2	..	..	..	1130	..	..	..	..	..	12 2	..	..
Lee, for Burnt Ash	..	..	9 33	..	..	..	..	..	..	..	10 5	..	..	..	1033	..	..	..	..	11 5	..	..	..	1133	..	..	..	..	..	12 5	..	..
Hither Green 124	..	..	9 35	..	..	..	..	..	..	..	10 7	..	..	..	1035	..	..	..	..	11 7	..	..	..	1135	..	..	..	..	..	12 7	..	..
Barnehurst	..	..	..	..	9 22	..	..	..	..	..	..	9 58	..	..	..	..	1022	..	..	..	1058	..	..	..	..	1122	..	..	..	..	1158	..
Bexleyheath	..	..	..	..	9 25	..	..	..	..	..	..	10 1	..	..	..	..	1025	..	..	..	11 1	..	..	..	..	1125	..	..	..	..	12 1	..
Welling	..	..	..	..	9 28	..	..	..	..	..	..	10 4	..	..	..	..	1028	..	..	..	11 4	..	..	..	..	1128	..	..	..	..	12 4	..
Falconwood	..	..	..	..	9 30	..	..	..	..	..	..	10 6	..	..	..	..	1030	..	..	..	11 6	..	..	..	..	1130	..	..	..	..	12 6	..
Eltham Park	..	..	..	..	9 33	..	..	..	..	..	..	10 9	..	..	..	..	1033	..	..	..	11 9	..	..	..	..	1133	..	..	..	..	12 9	..
Eltham (Well Hall)	..	..	..	..	9 35	..	..	..	..	..	..	1011	..	..	..	..	1035	..	..	..	1111	..	..	..	..	1135	..	..	..	..	1211	..
Kidbrooke	..	..	..	..	9 37	..	..	..	..	..	..	1013	..	..	..	..	1037	..	..	..	1113	..	..	..	..	1137	..	..	..	..	1213	..
Erith	..	9 8	..	..	..	..	..	..	9 42	..	..	..	10 8	..	..	..	..	..	1042	..	..	..	11 8	..	..	..	..	..	1142	..	..	12 8
Belvedere	..	9 11	..	..	..	..	..	..	9 45	..	..	..	1011	..	..	..	..	..	1045	..	..	..	1111	..	..	..	..	..	1145	..	..	1211
Abbey Wood	..	9 14	..	..	..	..	..	..	9 48	..	..	..	1014	..	..	..	..	..	1048	..	..	..	1114	..	..	..	..	..	1148	..	..	1214
Plumstead	..	9 18	..	..	..	..	..	..	9 52	..	..	..	1018	..	..	..	..	..	1052	..	..	..	1118	..	..	..	..	..	1152	..	..	1218
Woolwich Arsenal	..	9 20	..	..	..	..	9 39	..	9 54	..	..	..	1020	..	..	..	..	..	1054	..	..	..	1120	..	..	..	1140	..	1154	..	..	1220
Woolwich Dockyard	..	9 22	..	..	..	..	..	..	9 56	..	..	..	1022	..	..	..	..	..	1056	..	..	..	1122	..	..	..	..	..	1156	..	..	1222
Charlton	..	9 25	..	..	..	..	..	..	9 59	..	..	..	1025	..	..	..	..	..	1059	..	..	..	1125	..	..	..	..	..	1159	..	..	1225
Blackheath	..	9 29	..	..	9 40	..	..	..	..	..	..	1016	1029	..	..	..	1040	..	..	..	1116	..	1129	..	..	1140	..	..	..	..	1216	1229
Lewisham 114	..	9 31	9 39	..	9 43	..	..	..	..	..	1011	1019	1031	..	1039	..	1043	..	..	1111	1119	..	1131	1139	..	1143	..	..	..	1211	1219	1231
St. John's 124	..	9 33	9 41	..	9 45	..	..	..	..	..	1013	1021	1033	..	1041	..	1045	..	..	1113	1121	..	1133	1141	..	1145	..	..	..	1213	1221	1233
New Cross	..	9 36	9 43	..	9 47	..	..	..	..	..	1015	1023	1036	..	1043	..	1047	..	..	1115	1123	..	1136	1143	..	1147	..	..	..	1215	1223	1236
Westcombe Park	..	..	..	..	..	..	..	..	10 1	..	..	..	..	..	..	..	..	..	11 1	..	..	..	..	..	..	..	..	..	12 1	..	..	..
Maze Hill A	..	..	..	..	..	..	..	..	10 4	..	..	..	..	..	..	..	..	..	11 4	..	..	..	..	..	..	..	..	..	12 4	..	..	..
Greenwich	..	..	..	..	..	..	..	..	10 6	..	..	..	..	..	..	..	..	..	11 6	..	..	..	..	..	..	..	..	..	12 6	..	..	..
Deptford	..	..	..	..	..	..	..	..	10 8	..	..	..	..	..	..	..	..	..	11 8	..	..	..	..	..	..	..	..	..	12 8	..	..	..
Peckham Rye	..	..	..	..	..	..	..	..	..	..	..	..	..	..	..	..	..	..	..	..	..	..	..	..	..	..	..	..	..	..	..	..
Elephant and Castle	..	..	..	..	..	..	..	..	..	..	..	..	..	..	..	..	..	..	..	..	..	..	..	..	..	..	..	..	..	..	..	..
Blackfriars .... arr	..	..	..	..	..	..	..	..	..	..	..	..	..	..	..	..	..	..	..	..	..	..	..	..	..	..	..	..	..	..	..	..
Holborn Viaduct "	..	..	..	..	..	..	..	..	..	..	..	..	..	..	..	..	..	..	..	..	..	..	..	..	..	..	..	..	..	..	..	..
London Bridge .... arr	..	9 42	9 49	..	9 53	..	9 54	..	1014	..	1021	1029	1042	..	1049	..	1053	..	1114	1121	1129	..	1142	1149	..	1153	1154	..	1214	1221	1229	1242
Cannon Street .... "	..	..	..	..	..	..	..	..	..	..	..	..	..	..	..	..	..	..	..	..	..	..	..	..	..	..	..	..	..	..	..	..
Waterloo .... "	..	9 46	9 54	..	9 57	..	9 59	..	1018	..	1025	1033	1046	..	1053	..	1057	..	1117	1125	1133	..	1146	1153	..	1159	1159	..	1218	1225	1233	1246
Charing Cross .... "	..	9 49	9 57	..	10 0	..	10 2	..	1020	..	1028	1036	1049	..	1057	..	11 0	..	1120	1128	1136	..	1149	1157	..	12 2	12 2	..	1220	1228	1236	1249

A Maze Hill, for National Maritime Museum

3 Third class only

GILLINGHAM (Kent), CHATHAM, MAIDSTONE WEST, GRAVESEND CENTRAL, DARTFORD, WOOLWICH, and LONDON

Up	p.m.														Sundays—continued													p.m.					
Gillingham (Kent) dep									1220				1254							1 20									2 20				2 54
Chatham									1224				1258							1 24									2 24				2 58
Rochester									1227				1 1							1 27									2 27				3 1
Strood 72 arr									1229				1 4							1 29									2 29				3 4
Maidstone West dep	(3)		(3)		(3)	(3)	(3)	1139	(3)		(3)	(3)	1239		(3)		(3)	(3)		(3)		(3)		(3)	(3)	(3)	(3)	1 39	(3)	(3)		(3)	2 39
" Barracks								1140					1240															1 40					2 40
Aylesford								1145					1245															1 45					2 45
New Hythe								1148					1248															1 48					2 48
Snodland								1151					1251															1 51					2 51
Halling								1154					1254															1 54					2 54
Cuxton								1157					1257															1 57					2 57
Strood 72 arr								12 2					1 2															2 2					3 2
Strood dep									1230				1 5							1 30									2 30				3 5
Higham									1236											1 36									2 36				
Gravesend Central arr									1244				1 17							1 44									2 44				3 17
Gravesend Central dep									1245				1 18							1 45									2 45				3 18
Northfleet									1250											1 50									2 50				
Swanscombe Halt									1252											1 52									2 52				
Greenhithe									1255											1 55									2 55				
Stone Crossing Halt									1258											1 58									2 58				
Dartford	1212		1216		1236	1244	1252		1 2		1 12	1 16	1 28		1 36		1 44	1 52		2 2		2 12		2 16	2 36	2 44	2 52		3 2	3 12		3 16	3 28
Slades Green					1239				1 5						1 39					2 5					2 39				3 5				
Crayford	1215					1247					1 15						1 47					2 15				2 47				3 15			
Bexley	1218					1250					1 18						1 50					2 18				2 50				3 18			
Albany Park	1221					1253					1 21						1 53					2 21				2 53				3 21			
Sidcup	1224					1256					1 24						1 56					2 24				2 56				3 24			
New Eltham	1227					1259					1 27						1 59					2 27				2 59				3 27			
Mottingham	1230					1 2					1 30						2 2					2 30				3 2				3 30			
Lee, for Burnt Ash	1233					1 5					1 33						2 5					2 33				3 5				3 33			
Hither Green 124	1235					1 7					1 35						2 7					2 35				3 7				3 35			
Barnehurst			1222				1258					1 22						1 58						2 22			2 58					3 22	
Bexleyheath			1225				1 1					1 25						2 1						2 25			3 1					3 25	
Welling			1228				1 4					1 28						2 4						2 28			3 4					3 28	
Falconwood			1230				1 6					1 30						2 6						2 30			3 6					3 30	
Eltham Park			1233				1 9					1 33						2 9						2 33			3 9					3 33	
Eltham (Well Hall)			1235				1 11					1 35						2 11						2 35			3 11					3 35	
Kidbrooke			1237				1 13					1 37						2 13						2 37			3 13					3 37	
Erith					1242				1 8						1 42					2 8					2 42				3 8				
Belvedere					1245				1 11						1 45					2 11					2 45				3 11				
Abbey Wood					1248				1 14						1 48					2 14					2 48				3 14				
Plumstead					1252				1 18						1 52					2 18					2 52				3 18				
Woolwich Arsenal					1254				1 20				1 40		1 54					2 20					2 54				3 20				3 40
Woolwich Dockyard					1256				1 22						1 56					2 22					2 56				3 22				
Charlton					1259				1 25						1 59					2 25					2 59				3 25				
Blackheath			1240				1 16		1 29			1 40						2 16		2 29				2 40			3 16		3 29			3 40	
Lewisham 114	1239		1243			1 11	1 19		1 31		1 39	1 43					2 11	2 19		2 31		2 39		2 43		3 11	3 19		3 31	3 39		3 43	
St. John's 124	1241		1245			1 13	1 21		1 33		1 41	1 45					2 13	2 21		2 33		2 41		2 45		3 13	3 21		3 33	3 41		3 45	
New Cross	1243		1247			1 15	1 23		1 36		1 43	1 47					2 15	2 23		2 36		2 43		2 47		3 15	3 23		3 36	3 43		3 47	
Westcombe Park					1 1										2 1										3 1								
Maze Hill A					1 4										2 4										3 4								
Greenwich					1 6										2 6										3 6								
Deptford					1 8										2 8										3 8								
Peckham Rye																																	
Elephant and Castle																																	
Blackfriars arr																																	
Holborn Viaduct "																																	
London Bridge arr	1249		1253		1 14	1 21	1 29		1 42		1 49	1 53	1 54		2 14		2 21	2 29		2 42		2 49		2 53	3 14	3 21	3 29		3 42	3 49		3 53	3 56
Cannon Street "																																	
Waterloo "	1254		1257		1 17	1 25	1 33		1 46		1 54	1 57	1 59		2 17		2 25	2 33		2 46		2 53		2 57	3 17	3 25	3 33		3 46	3 54		3 58	4 1
Charing Cross "	1257		1 0		1 20	1 28	1 36		1 49		1 57	2 0	2 2		2 20		2 28	2 36		2 49		2 57		3 0	3 20	3 28	3 36		3 49	3 57		4 0	4 4

A Maze Hill, for National Maritime Museum

(3) Third class only

GILLINGHAM (Kent), CHATHAM, MAIDSTONE WEST, GRAVESEND CENTRAL, DARTFORD, WOOLWICH, and LONDON

Up — **Sundays**—*continued* — p.m

Up	p.m															
Gillingham (Kent) dep				3 20							4 20			4 54		
Chatham				3 24							4 24			4 58		
Rochester				3 27							4 27			5 1		
Strood 72 arr				3 29							4 29			5 4		
Maidstone West dep	3	3	3	3	3	3	3	3	3	3 39	3	3	3	4 39	3	3
" Barracks										3 40				4 40		
Aylesford										3 45				4 45		
New Hythe										3 48				4 48		
Snodland										3 51				4 51		
Halling										3 54				4 54		
Cuxton										3 57				4 57		
Strood 72 arr										4 2				5 2		
Strood dep				3 30							4 30			5 5		
Higham				3 36							4 36					
Gravesend Central arr				3 44							4 44			5 17		
Gravesend Central dep				3 45							4 45			5 18		
Northfleet				3 50							4 50					
Swanscombe Halt				3 52							4 52					
Greenhithe				3 55							4 55					
Stone Crossing Halt				3 58							4 58					
Dartford	3 36	3 44	3 52	4 2	4 12	4 16	4 36	4 44	4 52		5 2	5 12	5 16	5 28	5 36	5 44
Slades Green	3 39			4 5			4 39				5 5				5 39	
Crayford		3 47			4 15			4 47				5 15				5 47
Bexley		3 50			4 18			4 50				5 18				5 50
Albany Park		3 53			4 21			4 53				5 21				5 53
Sidcup		3 56			4 24			4 56				5 24				5 56
New Eltham		3 59			4 27			4 59				5 27				5 59
Mottingham		4 2			4 30			5 2				5 30				6 2
Lee, for Burnt Ash		4 5			4 33			5 5				5 33				6 5
Hither Green 124		4 7			4 35			5 7				5 35				6 7
Barnehurst			3 58			4 22			4 58				5 22			
Bexleyheath			4 1			4 25			5 1				5 25			
Welling			4 4			4 28			5 4				5 28			
Falconwood			4 6			4 30			5 6				5 30			
Eltham Park			4 9			4 33			5 9				5 33			
Eltham (Well Hall)			4 11			4 35			5 11				5 35			
Kidbrooke			4 13			4 37			5 13				5 37			
Erith	3 42			4 8			4 42				5 8				5 42	
Belvedere	3 45			4 11			4 45				5 11				5 45	
Abbey Wood	3 48			4 14			4 48				5 14				5 48	
Plumstead	3 52			4 18			4 52				5 18				5 52	
Woolwich Arsenal	3 54			4 20			4 54				5 20			5 39	5 54	
Woolwich Dockyard	3 56			4 22			4 56				5 22				5 56	
Charlton	3 59			4 25			4 59				5 25				5 59	
Blackheath			4 16	4 29		4 40			5 16		5 29		5 40			
Lewisham 114		4 11	4 19	4 31	4 39	4 43		5 11	5 19		5 31	5 39	5 43			6 11
St. John's 124		4 13	4 21	4 33	4 41	4 45		5 13	5 21		5 33	5 41	5 45			6 13
New Cross		4 15	4 23	4 36	4 43	4 47		5 15	5 23		5 36	5 43	5 47			6 15
Westcombe Park	4 1						5 1								6 1	
Maze Hill **A**	4 4						5 4								6 4	
Greenwich	4 6						5 6								6 6	
Deptford	4 8						5 8								6 8	
Peckham Rye																
Elephant and Castle																
Blackfriars arr																
Holborn Viaduct "																
London Bridge arr	4 14	4 21	4 29	4 42	4 49	4 53	5 14	5 21	5 29		5 42	5 49	5 53	5 54	6 14	6 21
Cannon Street "																
Waterloo "	4 17	4 25	4 33	4 46	4 54	4 57	5 17	5 25	5 33		5 46	5 54	5 57	5 59	6 18	6 25
Charing Cross "	4 20	4 28	4 36	4 49	4 57	5 0	5 20	5 28	5 36		5 49	5 57	6 0	6 2	6 21	6 28

Up	p.m															
Gillingham (Kent) dep		5 20								6 20			6 54			
Chatham		5 24								6 24			6 58			
Rochester		5 27								6 27			7 1			
Strood 72 arr		5 29								6 29			7 4			
Maidstone West dep	3	3	3	3		3	3	3	5 39	3	3	3	6 39	3	3	3
" Barracks									5 40				6 40			
Aylesford									5 45				6 45			
New Hythe									5 48				6 48			
Snodland									5 51				6 51			
Halling									5 54				6 54			
Cuxton									5 57				6 57			
Strood 72 arr									6 2				7 2			
Strood dep		5 30								6 30			7 5			
Higham		5 36								6 36						
Gravesend Central arr		5 44								6 44			7 17			
Gravesend Central dep		5 45								6 45			7 18			
Northfleet		5 50								6 50						
Swanscombe Halt		5 52								6 52						
Greenhithe		5 55								6 55						
Stone Crossing Halt		5 58								6 58						
Dartford	5 52	6 2	6 12	6 16		6 36	6 44	6 52		7 2	7 12	7 16	7 28	7 36	7 44	7 52
Slades Green		6 5				6 39				7 5				7 39		
Crayford			6 15				6 47				7 15				7 47	
Bexley			6 18				6 50				7 18				7 50	
Albany Park			6 21				6 53				7 21				7 53	
Sidcup			6 24				6 56				7 24				7 56	
New Eltham			6 27				6 59				7 27				7 59	
Mottingham			6 30				7 2				7 30				8 2	
Lee, for Burnt Ash			6 33				7 5				7 33				8 5	
Hither Green 124			6 35				7 7				7 35				8 7	
Barnehurst	5 58			6 22				6 58				7 22				7 58
Bexleyheath	6 1			6 25				7 1				7 25				8 1
Welling	6 4			6 28				7 4				7 28				8 4
Falconwood	6 6			6 30				7 6				7 30				8 6
Eltham Park	6 9			6 33				7 9				7 33				8 9
Eltham (Well Hall)	6 11			6 35				7 11				7 35				8 11
Kidbrooke	6 13			6 37				7 13				7 37				8 13
Erith		6 8				6 42				7 8				7 42		
Belvedere		6 11				6 45				7 11				7 45		
Abbey Wood		6 14				6 48				7 14				7 48		
Plumstead		6 18				6 52				7 18				7 52		
Woolwich Arsenal		6 20				6 54				7 20			7 39	7 54		
Woolwich Dockyard		6 22				6 56				7 22				7 56		
Charlton		6 25				6 59				7 25				7 59		
Blackheath	6 16	6 29		6 40				7 16		7 29		7 40				8 16
Lewisham 114	6 19	6 31	6 39	6 43			7 11	7 19		7 31	7 39	7 43			8 11	8 19
St. John's 124	6 21	6 33	6 41	6 45			7 13	7 21		7 33	7 41	7 45			8 13	8 21
New Cross	6 23	6 36	6 43	6 47			7 15	7 23		7 36	7 43	7 47			8 15	8 23
Westcombe Park						7 1								8 1		
Maze Hill **A**						7 4								8 4		
Greenwich						7 6								8 6		
Deptford						7 8								8 8		
Peckham Rye																
Elephant and Castle																
Blackfriars arr																
Holborn Viaduct "																
London Bridge arr	6 29	6 42	6 49	6 53		7 14	7 22	7 29		7 42	7 50	7 53	7 54	8 15	8 22	8 29
Cannon Street "																
Waterloo "	6 33	6 46	6 54	6 57		7 17	7 25	7 33		7 46	7 54	7 57	8 0	8 19	8 26	8 33
Charing Cross "	6 36	6 49	6 57	7 0		7 20	7 28	7 36		7 49	7 57	8 0	8 3	8 22	8 29	8 36

A Maze Hill, for National Maritime Museum

3 Third class only

GILLINGHAM (Kent), CHATHAM, MAIDSTONE WEST, GRAVESEND CENTRAL, DARTFORD, WOOLWICH, and LONDON

Sundays—continued (p.m)

Up	p.m																									
Gillingham (Kent) dep	7 20	..	..	..	..	..	..	8 20	..	..	8 57	..	..	..	..	9 20	..	..	..	..	..	..	1020	..	..	1058
Chatham	7 24	..	..	..	..	..	..	8 24	..	..	9 1	..	..	..	..	9 24	..	..	..	..	..	..	1024	..	..	11 1
Rochester	7 27	..	..	..	..	..	..	8 27	..	..	9 4	..	..	..	..	9 27	..	..	..	..	..	..	1027	..	..	11 4
Strood 72 arr	7 29	..	..	..	..	..	..	8 29	..	..	9 8	..	..	..	..	9 29	..	..	..	..	..	..	1029	..	..	11 6
Maidstone West dep	3	3	3	3	3	3	7 39	3	3	3	8 39	3	3	..	3	3	3	3	3	3	3	10 2	3	3	3	3
" Barracks							7 40				8 40			..								10 3				
Aylesford	..	..	..	..	..	..	7 45	..	..	..	8 45	..	..	..	..	..	..	..	..	..	..	10 8	..	..	..	..
New Hythe	..	..	..	..	..	..	7 48	..	..	..	8 48	..	..	..	..	..	..	..	..	..	..	1011	..	..	..	..
Snodland	..	..	..	..	..	..	7 51	..	..	..	8 51	..	..	..	..	..	..	..	..	..	..	1014	..	..	..	..
Halling	..	..	..	..	..	..	7 54	..	..	..	8 54	..	..	..	..	..	..	..	..	..	..	1017	..	..	..	..
Cuxton	..	..	..	..	..	..	7 57	..	..	..	8 57	..	..	..	..	..	..	..	..	..	..	1020	..	..	..	..
Strood 72 arr	..	..	..	..	..	..	8 2	..	..	..	9 2	..	..	..	..	..	..	..	..	..	..	1025	..	..	..	..
Strood dep	7 30	..	..	..	..	..	..	8 30	..	..	9 9	..	..	..	..	9 30	..	..	..	..	..	..	1030	..	..	11 7
Higham	7 36	..	..	..	..	..	..	8 36	..	..	..	..	..	..	..	9 36	..	..	..	..	..	..	1036	..	..	1113
Gravesend Central arr	7 44	..	..	..	..	..	..	8 44	..	..	9 21	..	..	..	..	9 44	..	..	..	..	..	..	1044	..	..	1119
Gravesend Central dep	7 45	..	..	..	..	..	..	8 45	..	..	9 22	..	..	..	..	9 45	..	..	..	..	..	..	1045	..	..	1120
Northfleet	7 50	..	..	..	..	..	..	8 50	..	..	..	..	..	..	..	9 50	..	..	..	..	..	..	1050	..	..	1124
Swanscombe Halt	7 52	..	..	..	..	..	..	8 52	..	..	..	..	..	..	..	9 52	..	..	..	..	..	..	1052	..	..	..
Greenhithe	7 55	..	..	..	..	..	..	8 55	..	..	..	..	..	..	..	9 55	..	..	..	..	..	..	1055	..	..	1128
Stone Crossing Halt	7 58	..	..	..	..	..	..	8 58	..	..	..	..	..	..	..	9 58	..	..	..	..	..	..	1058	..	..	..
Dartford	8 2	8 12	8 16	8 36	8 44	8 52	..	9 2	9 12	9 16	9 32	9 36	9 44	..	9 52	10 2	1012	1016	1032	1040	1044	..	11 2	11 6	1112	1134
Slades Green	8 5	..	..	8 39	..	..	..	9 5	..	..	..	9 39	..	..	..	10 5	..	..	1035	1044	..	..	11 5	..	..	1138
Crayford	..	8 15	..	..	8 47	..	..	..	9 15	..	..	..	9 47	..	..	..	1015	..	..	..	1047	..	..	..	1115	..
Bexley	..	8 18	..	..	8 50	..	..	..	9 18	..	..	..	9 50	..	..	..	1018	..	..	..	1050	..	..	..	1118	..
Albany Park	..	8 21	..	..	8 53	..	..	..	9 21	..	..	..	9 53	..	..	..	1021	..	..	..	1053	..	..	..	1121	..
Sidcup	..	8 24	..	..	8 56	..	..	..	9 24	..	..	..	9 56	..	..	..	1024	..	..	..	1056	..	..	..	1124	..
New Eltham	..	8 27	..	..	8 59	..	..	..	9 27	..	..	..	9 59	..	..	..	1027	..	..	..	1059	..	..	..	1127	..
Mottingham	..	8 30	..	..	9 2	..	..	..	9 30	..	..	..	10 2	..	..	..	1030	..	..	..	11 2	..	..	..	1130	..
Lee, for Burnt Ash	..	8 34	..	..	9 5	..	..	..	9 33	..	..	..	10 5	..	..	..	1033	..	..	..	11 5	..	..	..	1133	..
Hither Green 124	..	8 37	..	..	9 7	..	..	..	9 35	..	..	..	10 7	..	..	..	1035	..	..	..	11 7	..	..	..	1135	..
Barnehurst	..	..	8 22	..	..	8 58	..	..	..	9 22	..	..	..	..	9 58	..	..	1022	..	..	..	..	..	1113	..	..
Bexleyheath	..	..	8 25	..	..	9 1	..	..	..	9 25	..	..	..	..	10 1	..	..	1025	..	..	..	..	..	1117	..	..
Welling	..	..	8 28	..	..	9 4	..	..	..	9 28	..	..	..	..	10 4	..	..	1028	..	..	..	..	..	1120	..	..
Falconwood	..	..	8 30	..	..	9 6	..	..	..	9 30	..	..	..	..	10 6	..	..	1030	..	..	..	..	..	1123	..	..
Eltham Park	..	..	8 33	..	..	9 9	..	..	..	9 33	..	..	..	..	10 9	..	..	1033	..	..	..	..	..	1125	..	..
Eltham (Well Hall)	..	..	8 35	..	..	9 11	..	..	..	9 35	..	..	..	..	1011	..	..	1035	..	..	..	..	..	1127	..	..
Kidbrooke	..	..	8 37	..	..	9 13	..	..	..	9 37	..	..	..	..	1013	..	..	1037	..	..	..	..	..	1130	..	..
Erith	8 8	..	..	8 42	..	..	..	9 8	..	..	..	9 42	..	..	..	10 8	..	..	1038	1048	..	..	11 8	..	..	..
Belvedere	8 11	..	..	8 45	..	..	..	9 11	..	..	..	9 45	..	..	..	1011	..	..	1041	1051	..	..	1111	..	..	..
Abbey Wood	8 14	..	..	8 48	..	..	..	9 14	..	..	..	9 48	..	..	..	1014	..	..	1044	1054	..	..	1114	..	..	..
Plumstead	8 18	..	..	8 52	..	..	..	9 18	..	..	..	9 52	..	..	..	1018	..	..	1048	1058	..	..	1118	..	..	..
Woolwich Arsenal	8 20	..	..	8 54	..	..	..	9 20	..	..	9 44	9 54	..	..	..	1020	..	..	1050	11 0	..	..	1120	..	..	..
Woolwich Dockyard	8 22	..	..	8 56	..	..	..	9 22	..	..	..	9 56	..	..	..	1022	..	..	1052	11 2	..	..	1122	..	..	..
Charlton	8 25	..	..	8 59	..	..	..	9 25	..	..	..	9 59	..	..	..	1025	..	..	1055	11 5	..	..	1125	..	..	..
Blackheath	8 29	..	8 40	..	..	9 16	..	9 29	..	9 40	..	..	..	..	1016	1029	..	1040	1059	..	..	..	1129	1133	..	..
Lewisham 114	8 31	8 40	8 43	..	9 11	9 19	..	9 31	9 39	9 43	..	..	1011	..	1019	1031	1039	1043	11 1	..	1111	..	1131	1135	1138	..
St. John's 124	8 33	8 42	8 45	..	9 13	9 21	..	9 33	9 41	9 45	..	..	1013	..	1021	1033	1041	1045	11 3	..	1113	..	1133	1137	1140	..
New Cross	8 36	8 45	8 47	..	9 15	9 23	..	9 36	9 43	9 48	..	..	1015	..	1023	1036	1043	1047	11 6	..	1115	..	1136	1140	1143	..
Westcombe Park	..	..	..	9 1	..	..	..	..	..	..	..	10 1	..	..	..	..	..	..	..	11 7	..	..	..	..	..	..
Maze Hill A	..	..	..	9 4	..	..	..	..	..	..	..	10 4	..	..	..	..	..	..	..	1110	..	..	..	..	..	..
Greenwich	..	..	..	9 6	..	..	..	..	..	..	..	10 6	..	..	..	..	..	..	..	1112	..	..	..	..	..	..
Deptford	..	..	..	9 8	..	..	..	..	..	..	..	10 8	..	..	..	..	..	..	..	1114	..	..	..	..	..	..
Peckham Rye	..	..	..	..	..	..	..	..	..	..	..	..	..	..	..	..	..	..	..	..	..	..	..	..	..	..
Elephant and Castle	..	..	..	..	..	..	..	..	..	..	..	..	..	..	..	..	..	..	..	..	..	..	..	..	..	..
Blackfriars arr	..	..	..	..	..	..	..	..	..	..	..	..	..	..	..	..	..	..	..	..	..	..	..	..	..	..
Holborn Viaduct "	..	..	..	..	..	..	..	..	..	..	..	..	..	..	..	..	..	..	..	..	..	..	..	..	..	..
London Bridge arr	8 42	8 51	8 53	9 14	9 21	9 29	..	9 42	9 49	9 54	10 0	1014	1021	..	1029	1042	1050	1053	1112	1120	1121	..	1142	1146	1149	..
Cannon Street "	..	..	..	..	..	..	..	..	..	..	..	..	..	..	..	..	..	..	..	..	..	..	..	..	..	..
Waterloo "	8 47	8 55	8 57	9 17	9 25	9 33	..	9 46	9 54	9 59	10 5	1017	1025	..	1033	1046	1054	1057	1116	1124	1125	..	1146	1150	1153	..
Charing Cross "	8 50	8 58	9 0	9 20	9 28	9 36	..	9 49	9 57	10 1	10 8	1020	1028	..	1036	1049	1057	11 0	1119	1127	1128	..	1149	1153	1156	..

A Maze Hill, for National Maritime Museum

OTHER TRAINS

BETWEEN	PAGE
Gillingham and London	147
Maidstone East and London	43
Maidstone West and London	53
Hither Green and London	130
Lewisham and London	119, 130

LONDON, GRAVESEND CENTRAL, and ALLHALLOWS-ON-SEA

Miles from Gravesend	Down	Week Days a.m	a.m	a.m		a.m	a.m		a.m SO	a m SX	.	noon SO		p.m SO	p.m SX		p m SO	p.m SX		p.m SO
	72 Charing Cross...dep	..	5③24	..	..	7 42	9 42	..	11 42	11③50	..	12③ 0	..	1③18	1 42	..	1 42	3③10	..	3 42
	72 Waterloo .... "	..	5③26	..	..	7 44	9 44	..	11 44	11③52	..	12③ 2	..	1③20	1 44	..	1 44	3③12	..	3 44
	72 Cannon Street .. "	..	5③21	..	..	8③1	9[③24	..	11③14	..	..	12 14	..	1 21	..	..	1③35	..	..	..
	72 London Bridge.. "	3③10	5③25	..	..	8③4	9 49	..	11 49	11③56	..	12③13	..	1 24	1 49	..	1 49	3③16	..	3 49
—	Gravesend Central..dep	5 30	6 36	..	..	9 0	10 31	..	12 33	1 0	..	1 10	..	2 17	2 35	..	2 45	4 14	..	4 32
1¼	Denton Halt..............	..	6 39	..	..	9 3	10 34	..	..	..	..	..	..	..	2 38	..	2 48	4 17	..	4 35
3½	Uralite Halt..............	5 38	6 45	..	..	9 9	10 40	..	12 41	1 8	..	1 18	..	2 25	2 44	..	2 54	4 23	..	4 41
5¾	Cliffe.....................	5 42	6 49	..	..	9 13	10 45	..	12 45	1 11	..	1 22	..	2 29	2 48	..	2 58	4 27	..	4 45
8¼	High Halstow Halt......	..	6 55	..	..	9 19	10 51	..	12 51	1 17	..	1 27	..	..	2 54	..	3 4	4 33	..	4 51
9½	Sharnal Street **B**	5 49	6 57	..	..	9 21	10 53	..	12 53	1 19	..	1 30	..	2 36	2 57	..	3 6	4 35	..	4 53
10¼	Beluncle Halt	..	7 1	..	..	9 25	10 57	..	12 57	..	..	..	..	..	3 5	..	3 10	4 39	..	4 57
12½	Middle Stoke Halt......	..	7 6	..	..	9 30	11 2	..	1 2	..	..	..	..	..	3 10	..	3 15	4 44	..	5 2
13	Stoke Junction Halt....	5 56	7 9	7 51	..	9 32	11 4	..	1 4	1 26	..	1 37	..	2 43	3 12	..	3 17	4 46	..	5 4
14¾	Allhallows-on-Sea. arr	6 0	..	7 57	..	9 37	11 8	..	1 8	1 31	..	1 42	..	2 48	3 16	..	3 21	..	..	5 8
14½	Grain Crossing Ht.dp.	..	7 14	..	..	..	..	..	..	..	..	..	..	..	..	..	..	4 49	..	..
15¾	Port Victoria..... arr	..	7 17	..	..	..	..	..	..	..	..	..	..	..	..	..	..	4 53	..	..

Down	Week Days—*continued* p.m SX	p.m SO	p.m SX		p.m SX		p.m SO	p.m SX	p.m SO				Sundays a.m	a.m	a.m		p.m	p.m	p.m
72 Charing Cross... dep	4 42	4③50	5③12	..	6 42	..	6③50	7③40	8 42	..	..	..	..	8③ 4	10③ 4	..	1③ 4	3③ 4	6③ 4
72 Waterloo .... "	4 44	4③52	5③14	..	6 44	..	6③52	7③42	8 44	..	..	..	..	8③ 6	10③ 6	..	1③ 6	3③ 6	6③ 6
72 Cannon Street... "	4③39	..	5 10	..	6③40	..	..	7③34	..	..	..	..	..	..	..	..	..	..	..
72 London Bridge.. "	4 49	4③56	5③19	..	6 49	..	6③56	7③46	8 49	..	..	..	4③35	8③10	10③10	..	1③10	3③10	6③10
Gravesend Central..dep	5 39	6 4	6 8	..	7 45	..	8 2	8 46	9 33	..	..	..	7 0	9 13	11 12	..	2 12	4 12	7 12
Denton Halt............	..	6 7	..	..	..	..	8 5	..	9 36	..	..	..	7 3	9 16	11 15	..	2 15	4 15	7 15
Uralite Halt............	5 48	6 13	6 16	..	7 53	..	8 11	8 54	9 42	..	..	..	7 9	9 22	11 21	..	2 21	4 21	7 21
Cliffe.....................	5 52	6 17	6 20	..	7 57	..	8 15	8 58	9 46	..	..	..	7 13	9 26	11 25	..	2 25	4 25	7 25
High Halstow Halt......	5 58	6 23	6 26	..	8 3	..	8 21	9 4	9 52	..	..	..	7 19	9 32	11 31	..	2 31	4 31	7 31
Sharnal Street **B**	6 0	6 25	6 28	..	8 5	..	8 23	9 6	9 54	..	..	..	7 21	9 34	11 33	..	2 33	4 33	7 33
Beluncle Halt	6 4	6 29	..	..	..	..	8 27	9 12	9 58	..	..	..	7 25	9 38	11 37	..	2 37	4 37	7 37
Middle Stoke Halt......	6 9	6 34	6 34	..	..	..	8 32	9 16	10 3	..	..	..	7 30	9 43	11 42	..	2 42	4 42	7 42
Stoke Junction Halt....	6 11	6 36	6 37	..	8 14	..	8 34	9 18	10 5	..	..	..	7 32	9 45	11 44	..	2 44	4 44	7 44
Allhallows-on-Sea. arr	6 16	6 41	6 42	..	8 18	..	8 39	9 23	10 10	..	..	..	7 37	9 50	11 49	..	2 49	4 49	7 49
Grain Crossing Ht.dp.	..	..	..	..	..	..	..	..	..	..	..	..	..	..	..	..	..	..	..
Port Victoria..... arr	..	..	..	..	..	..	..	..	..	..	..	..	..	..	..	..	..	..	..

Miles	Up	Week Days a.m	a.m	a.m	a.m		a.m SO	a.m SX	a.m SX	a.m SO		p.m SO	p.m SX	p.m SO	p.m SO	p.m SX	p.m SO	p.m SX	p.m SO
	Port Victoria.....dep	..	..	7 40	..	..	..	..	..	..	..	12 32	..	..	..	..	..	5 5	..
1¼	Grain Crossing Halt,,	..	..	7 44	..	..	..	..	..	..	..	12 35	..	..	..	..	..	5 8	..
—	Allhallows-on-Sea. dep	6 5	7 14	..	8 3	..	9 48	9 48	1120	11 45	..	..	1 40	1 40	2 18	3 22	3 45	..	5 17
2¾	Stoke Junction Halt....	6 9	7 18	7 49	8 7	..	9 52	9 52	1124	11 49	..	12 39	1 43	1 43	2 22	3 26	3 49	5 11	5 21
3¼	Middle Stoke Halt......	6 12	7 21	..	8 10	..	9 56	9 56	1127	11 52	..	12 42	..	..	2 25	3 29	3 52	5 14	5 24
5¼	Beluncle Halt	..	7 26	..	8 15	..	10 1	10 1	1132	11 57	..	12 47	..	..	2 30	3 34	3 57	5 19	5 29
6½	Sharnal Street **B**	6 17	7 29	..	8 18	..	10 4	10 4	1135	12 0	..	12 50	1 50	1 50	2 34	3 37	4 0	5 22	5 32
7½	High Halstow Halt......	6 21	7 33	..	8 22	..	10 9	10 9	..	..	..	12 59	1 54	1 54	..	3 41	4 4	5 26	5 36
10	Cliffe.....................	6 26	7 37	..	8 26	..	10 13	10 13	1141	12 6	..	1 3	1 58	1 58	2 43	3 45	4 8	5 30	5 40
12½	Uralite Halt............	6 31	7 42	..	8 31	..	10 19	10 19	1146	12 11	..	1 8	2 3	2 3	2 48	3 50	4 13	5 35	5 45
14½	Denton Halt............	..	..	..	8 37	..	10 26	10 26	1152	12 17	..	1 14	2 9	2 9	2 54	3 57	4 20	..	5 51
15¾	Gravesend Central. arr	6 39	7 50	..	8 40	..	10 29	10 29	1155	12 20	..	1 17	2 12	2 12	2 57	4 0	4 23	5 43	5 54
38	93 London Bridge.. arr	7③35	8 35	..	9 41	..	11 10	11 11	1③1	1 10	..	2③13	3 11	3 11	4③1	5③ 4	6 31	6③50	7③1
38½	93 Cannon Street.. "	7③39	8 38	..	9③53	..	11③35	..	..	1③26	..	2③35	3③27	..	..	5③ 9	..	6③57	..
39	93 Waterloo .... .. "	7③48	8③56	..	9 45	..	11 14	11 17	1③5	1 14	..	2③18	3 17	3 17	4③5	5 15	6 35	6③54	7③5
39½	93 Charing Cross... "	7③51	8③59	..	9 48	..	11 18	11 22	1③7	1 17	..	2③21	3 19	3 19	4③9	5 19	6 37	6③56	7③7

Up	Week Days—*contd* p.m	p.m	p.m SX	p.m SO		Sundays a.m	a.m		noon	p.m	p.m	p.m
Port Victoria.... dep.	..	..	..	..	..	..	..	..	..	..	..	..
Grain Crossing Halt,,	..	..	..	..	..	..	..	..	..	..	..	..
Allhallows-on-Sea. dep	6 50	8 52	9 39	10 15	..	8 2	10 0	..	12 0	2 56	4 56	8 20
Stoke Junction Halt....	6 54	8 56	9 43	10 19	..	8 6	10 4	..	12 4	3 0	5 0	8 24
Middle Stoke Halt......	6 57	9 0	9 46	10 22	..	8 9	10 7	..	12 7	3 3	5 3	8 27
Beluncle Halt	7 2	9 4	9 51	10 27	..	8 14	10 12	..	12 12	3 8	5 8	8 32
Sharnal Street **B**	7 5	9 6	9 54	10 30	..	8 17	10 15	..	12 15	3 11	5 11	8 35
High Halstow Halt......	7 9	..	9 58	10 34	..	8 21	10 19	..	12 19	3 15	5 15	8 39
Cliffe.....................	7 13	9 14	10 2	10 38	..	8 25	10 23	..	12 23	3 19	5 19	8 43
Uralite Halt............	..	9 19	..	..	..	8 30	10 28	..	12 28	3 24	5 24	8 48
Denton Halt............	..	..	..	10 48	..	8 36	10 34	..	12 34	3 30	5 30	8 54
Gravesend Central..arr	7 26	9 26	10 14	10 51	..	8 39	10 37	..	12 37	3 34	5 34	8 59
93 London Bridge.. arr	8 11	11③1	11 23	12③3	..	9③42	11③42	..	1③42	4③42	6③42	10 0
93 Cannon Street .. "	..	..	..	..	..	..	..	..	..	..	..	..
93 Waterloo .... "	8 17	11③5	11 30	12③7	..	9③46	11③46	..	1③46	4③46	6③46	10 5
93 Charing Cross... "	8 19	11③7	11 32	12③9	..	9③49	11③49	..	1③49	4③49	6③49	10 8

NOTES.

③ Third class only

B Sta for Hoo and St. Mary's Hoo (2 miles).

SO Sats. only

SX Sats. excepted.

[5 mins. later on Sats.

Printed and Published by—
HENRY BLACKLOCK & Co. LTD.,
London, and
Albert Square, Manchester, 2.

LONDON, NEW BECKENHAM, HAYES, ADDISCOMBE (CROYDON), and SANDERSTEAD

3—All Trains on this page are Third class only

Mls	Down	a.m.										Week Days											a.m. S X
—	Charing Cross ...... dep						5 9				5 36				6 1						6 38		
¾	Waterloo						5 11				5 38				6 3						6 40		
—	Cannon Street			4 50					5 30				5 48				6 14		6 23				6 45
1½	London Bridge			4 53			5 16		5 33		5 43		5 50		6 7		6 18		6 26		6 44		6 48
4½	New Cross			5 1			5 23		5 40		5 50		5 58		6 13		6 24		6 33		6 50		6 54
5½	St. John's						5 25				5 53		6 0		6 15		6 26						
6	Lewisham						5 28				5 55		6 3		6 17		6 28		6 37		6 53		
6¾	Lady Well			5 6			5 30		5 45		5 58		6 5		6 19		6 30		6 40				6 58
7½	Catford Bridge			5 8			5 33		5 47		6 1		6 7		6 22		6 33		6 43		6 56		7 1
9	Lower Sydenham			5 11			5 37		5 50		6 4		6 10		6 25		6 36		6 47				7 4
9½	New Beckenham			5 13			5 39		5 52		6 6		6 12		6 27		6 38		6 49				7 6
10½	Clock House			5 16			5 41		5 55		6 9		6 15		6 29		6 40		6 51		7 1		7 8
11	Elmer's End			5 18			5 43		5 58		6 12		6 17		6 31		6 42		6 53		7 3		7 10
—	Elmer's End ...... dep	4 44			5 20				5 58				6 17				6 42				7 3		
12½	Eden Park				5 23				6 2				6 21				6 46				7 7		
13½	West Wickham				5 25				6 4				6 23				6 48				7 9		
14½	Hayes A .... arr	4 50			5 29				6 8				6 27				6 52				7 13		
12	Woodside (Surrey)			5 20			5 46				6 14				6 34				6 56				7 13
13	Addiscombe C .... arr			5 23			5 50																7 16
12¾	Bingham Road										6 17				6 37				6 59				
13¾	Coombe Road										6 20				6 40				7 2				
14¼	Selsdon										6 22				6 42				7 6				
15	Sanderstead 234 .... arr										6 24				6 44				7 10				

Down	a.m.								Saturdays only				Week Days										a.m.
Charing Cross ...... dep		6 54	6 58			7 15					7 36		7 38		7 48		7 52				8 1		8 5
Waterloo		6 56	7 0			7 17					7 38		7 40		7 50		7 54				8 3		8 7
Cannon Street	6 46				7 8			7 24		7 34									7 59				
London Bridge	6 49	7 0	7 4		7 11	7 20		7 26		7 36	7 43		7 45		7 54		7 58		8 2		8 7		8 12
New Cross	6 56	7 6	7 11		7 18	7 27		7 32		7 43			7 52		8 0				8 8		8 13		8 19
St. John's	7 0							7 35											8 10		8 16		
Lewisham	7 2				7 21					7 46			7 55		8 3				8 12				8 22
Lady Well	7 4		7 15		7 23	7 31		7 38			7 52		7 57				8 8						
Catford Bridge	7 6	7 13	7 18		7 25	7 34		7 41		7 50	7 55		8 0		8 6		8 11		8 16		8 21		8 25
Lower Sydenham	7 9	7 16	7 21		7 28	7 37		7 44		7 53	7 58		8 3		8 9		8 14		8 19				8 28
New Beckenham	7 11	7 18	7 23			7 39		7 46		7 55			8 5		8 11				8 21		8 25		8 30
Clock House	7 14	7 21	7 25			7 41		7 48		7 57			8 7		8 14		8 17		8 23		8 27		
Elmer's End	7 16	7 23	7 27		7 33	7 43		7 50		7 59	8 3		8 9		8 16		8 19		8 25		8 29		8 33
Elmer's End ...... dep	7 16		7 27			7 43			7 55	7 59			8 9		8 16						8 29		
Eden Park	7 19		7 31			7 47				8 3			8 13		8 19						8 33		
West Wickham	7 22		7 33			7 49				8 5			8 15		8 22						8 35		
Hayes A .... arr	7 25		7 37			7 53			8 1	8 9			8 19		8 26						8 39		
Woodside (Surrey)		7 25			7 35			7 53			8 5						8 22		8 28				8 36
Addiscombe C .... arr					7 38						8 8								8 32				
Bingham Road		7 28						7 55									8 24						8 38
Coombe Road		7 31						7 58									8 27						8 41
Selsdon		7 33						8 0									8 29						8 44
Sanderstead 234 .... arr		7 35						8 2															8 47

Down	a.m.								Mondays to Fridays														a.m.
Charing Cross ...... dep				8 33	8 31			8 49	8 58	9 0	9 8			9 33	9 38		10 0	10 7		1037	11 7		1137
Waterloo				8 35	8 33			8 51	9 0	9 2	9 10			9 35	9 40		10 2	10 9		1039	11 9		1139
Cannon Street	8 14	8 20	8 25			8 44	8 50					9 25	9 31										
London Bridge	8 17	8 23	8 28	8 39	8 36	8 47	8 52	8 57	9 4	9 8	9 14	9 28	9 34	9 40	9 44		10 6	1012		1042	1112		1142
New Cross	8 23		8 35		8 43	8 53	8 59	9 3		9 15	9 20	9 34	9 40	9 46	9 50		1012	1019		1049	1119		1149
St. John's		8 30										9 37	9 43		9 53		1014	1021		1051	1121		1151
Lewisham		8 32			8 47	8 56	9 2			9 18		9 39	9 45		9 56			1023		1053	1123		1153
Lady Well	8 28	8 34			8 50			9 8	9 14		9 25		9 47	9 51	9 58		1018	1025		1055	1125		1155
Catford Bridge	8 30	8 36	8 41		8 52	8 59	9 5	9 10	9 16	9 21		9 42	9 49	9 53	10 0		1020	1028		1058	1128		1158
Lower Sydenham	8 33	8 39	8 44	8 52	8 56		9 8	9 13	9 20	9 24	9 29	9 45	9 52	9 57	10 3		1023	1031		11 1	1131		12 1
New Beckenham			8 46	8 54	8 58		9 10	9 15	9 22	9 26	9 31	9 47	9 54	9 59	10 5		1025	1033		11 3	1133		12 3
Clock House	8 37	8 43	8 48	8 56	9 0	9 4	9 13	9 18	9 24	9 29	9 34	9 50	9 57		10 8			1035		11 5	1135		12 5
Elmer's End	8 39	8 45	8 51	8 58	9 2	9 6	9 15	9 20	9 26	9 31	9 36	9 52	9 59		1010			1037		11 9	1137		12 9
Elmer's End ...... dep	8 39	8 45		8 58			9 15			9 31		9 52			1010				1040	11 9		1140	12 9
Eden Park	8 42	8 48		9 2			9 18			9 34		9 55			1013				1042	1112		1143	1212
West Wickham	8 45	8 52		9 4			9 21			9 37		9 58			1016				1046	1115		1146	1215
Hayes A .... arr	8 48	8 56		9 8			9 24			9 40		10 1			1019				1049	1118		1149	1218
Woodside (Surrey)			8 54		9 5	9 9		9 22	9 30		9 38		10 1					1040			1140		
Addiscombe C .... arr			8 57			9 12		9 25			9 41		10 4										
Bingham Road					9 7				9 32									1042			1142		
Coombe Road					9 10				9 35									1045			1145		
Selsdon					9 12				9 37									1047			1147		
Sanderstead 234 .... arr					9 14				9 40									1049			1149		

For Notes, see page 118

LONDON, NEW BECKENHAM, HAYES, ADDISCOMBE (CROYDON), and SANDERSTEAD

3—All Trains on this page are Third class only

Mondays to Fridays—*continued.* — p.m

Down	p.m																						
Charing Cross ..dep	12 7	..	1237	1 7	..	1 37	..	2 7	..	2 37	3 7	..	3 37	..	3 57	4 10	..	..	..	4 28	4 38	..	..	..
Waterloo	12 9	..	1239	1 9	..	1 39	..	2 9	..	2 39	3 9	..	3 39	..	3 59	4 12	..	..	..	4 30	4 40	..	..	..
Cannon Street	..	..	..	..	..	..	..	..	..	..	..	..	..	3 51	..	..	4 21	4 28	..	..	..	4 42	..	4 49
London Bridge	1212	..	1242	1 12	..	1 42	..	2 12	..	2 42	3 13	..	3 42	3 53	4 2	4 16	4 24	4 30	..	4 33	4 43	4 46	..	4 51
New Cross	1219	..	1249	1 19	..	1 49	..	2 19	..	2 49	3 20	..	3 49	4 0	4 9	4 22	4 31	4 37	..	4 40	4 50	4 53	..	4 58
St. John's	1221	..	1251	1 21	..	1 51	..	2 21	..	2 51	3 22	..	..	4 2	..	..	..	..	..	4 43	..	4 55	..	..
Lewisham	1223	..	1253	1 23	..	1 53	..	2 23	..	2 53	3 24	..	3 52	4 5	4 12	4 25	4 34	4 41	..	..	..	..	..	5 1
Lady Well	1225	..	1255	1 25	..	1 55	..	2 25	..	2 55	3 26	..	3 54	4 7	4 14	4 27	..	4 43	..	4 46	..	4 59	..	5 3
Catford Bridge	1228	..	1258	1 28	..	1 58	..	2 28	..	2 58	3 29	..	3 56	4 9	4 16	4 30	4 37	4 45	..	4 49	4 56	5 1	..	5 5
Lower Sydenham	1231	..	1 1	1 31	..	2 1	..	2 31	..	3 1	3 32	..	3 59	4 12	4 19	4 33	4 40	4 48	..	4 52	4 59	5 4	..	5 8
New Beckenham	1233	..	1 3	1 33	..	2 3	..	2 33	..	3 3	3 34	..	4 1	4 14	4 21	4 35	4 42	4 50	..	4 54	..	5 6	..	5 10
Clock House	1235	..	1 5	1 35	..	2 5	..	2 35	..	3 5	3 36	..	4 4	4 17	4 24	4 37	4 44	4 53	..	4 57	5 2	5 9	..	5 13
Elmer's End	1237	..	1 9	1 37	..	2 9	..	2 37	..	3 9	3 38	..	4 6	4 19	4 26	4 39	4 46	4 55	..	4 59	5 4	5 11	..	5 15
Elmer's End...dep.	..	1240	1 9	..	1 40	2 9	..	..	2 40	3 9	..	3 40	4 6	4 19	..	..	4 46	..	..	4 59	..	5 11	..	..
Eden Park	..	1243	1 12	..	1 43	2 12	..	..	2 43	3 12	..	3 43	4 9	4 22	..	..	4 50	..	..	5 2	..	5 14	..	..
West Wickham	..	1246	1 15	..	1 46	2 15	..	..	2 46	3 15	..	3 46	4 12	4 25	..	..	4 52	..	..	5 5	..	5 17	..	..
Hayes A ......arr.	..	1249	1 18	..	1 49	2 18	..	..	2 49	3 18	..	3 49	4 15	4 28	..	..	4 56	..	..	5 8	..	5 20	..	..
Woodside (Surrey)	1240	..	..	1 40	..	..	..	2 40	..	..	3 41	..	..	..	4 29	4 42	..	4 58	..	..	5 7	..	..	5 17
Addiscombe C arr.	..	..	..	..	..	..	..	..	..	..	..	..	..	..	..	4 45	..	..	..	..	5 10	..	..	..
Bingham Road	1242	..	..	1 42	..	..	..	2 42	..	..	3 43	..	..	..	4 31	..	..	5 0	..	..	..	..	..	5 19
Coombe Road	1245	..	..	1 45	..	..	..	2 45	..	..	3 46	..	..	..	4 34	..	..	5 3	..	..	..	..	..	5 22
Selsdon	1247	..	..	1 47	..	..	..	2 47	..	..	3 48	..	..	..	4 36	..	..	5 5	..	..	..	..	..	5 25
Sanderstead 234 arr.	1249	..	..	1 49	..	..	..	2 49	..	..	3 50	..	..	..	4 38	..	..	5 8	..	..	..	..	..	..

Mondays to Fridays — p.m

Down	p.m																						
Charing Cross...dep.	4 58	..	5 11	..	..	5 22	5 27	..	..	..	5 49	5 51	..	..	6 4	..	6 8	6 20	6 22	..	..	6 48	6 57	7 7
Waterloo	5 0	..	5 13	..	..	5 24	5 29	..	..	..	5 51	5 53	..	..	6 6	..	6 10	6 22	6 24	..	..	6 50	6 59	7 9
Cannon Street	..	5 6	..	5 19	5 24	..	..	5 35	..	5 48	..	..	6 3	..	..	..	..	..	..	6 32	6 37	..	..	..
London Bridge	5 4	5 8	5 16	5 21	5 26	5 28	5 33	5 38	..	5 50	5 54	5 57	6 5	..	6 9	..	6 14	6 26	6 29	6 34	6 39	6 53	7 2	7 13
New Cross	..	5 15	..	..	5 32	5 35	..	5 44	..	..	..	6 4	..	..	6 16	..	6 21	..	6 35	6 41	6 46	7 0	7 9	7 19
St. John's	..	..	..	..	..	..	5 40	..	..	5 58	..	..	..	..	..	..	..	..	..	..	6 48	..	..	7 21
Lewisham	..	..	..	5 29	..	..	..	5 47	..	..	..	6 8	..	..	..	..	6 25	..	6 38	..	6 51	..	7 12	7 23
Lady Well	5 13	5 19	5 26	..	..	5 39	5 44	5 50	..	..	6 4	6 10	..	..	6 20	..	6 27	..	6 40	6 46	6 53	7 5	7 14	7 25
Catford Bridge	5 16	5 22	5 28	5 32	..	5 42	5 46	5 52	..	6 3	6 7	6 12	6 16	..	6 22	..	6 30	6 39	6 43	6 49	6 55	7 7	7 16	7 28
Lower Sydenham	5 19	..	5 31	5 35	..	5 45	5 49	5 55	..	..	6 10	6 15	6 19	..	6 25	..	6 33	..	6 46	6 52	6 58	7 10	7 19	7 31
New Beckenham	5 21	5 25	5 33	5 37	5 41	..	5 51	5 57	..	6 6	6 12	6 17	..	..	6 27	..	6 35	..	6 48	6 54	7 0	7 12	7 21	7 33
Clock House	5 23	5 28	5 36	5 40	5 44	5 48	5 54	6 0	..	6 9	6 14	6 20	6 23	..	6 30	..	6 38	6 44	6 50	6 56	7 3	7 15	7 24	7 35
Elmer's End	5 25	5 30	5 38	5 42	5 46	5 50	5 56	6 2	..	6 11	6 16	6 22	6 25	..	6 32	..	6 40	6 46	6 52	6 58	7 5	7 17	7 26	7 37
Elmer's End...dep.	5 25	..	..	5 42	..	5 50	..	6 2	..	..	6 16	..	6 25	..	6 32	..	..	6 46	..	6 58	..	7 17	..	..
Eden Park	5 29	..	..	5 45	..	5 54	..	6 5	..	..	6 20	..	6 28	..	6 35	..	..	6 49	..	7 2	..	7 20	..	..
West Wickham	5 31	..	..	5 48	..	5 56	..	6 8	..	..	6 22	..	6 31	..	6 38	..	..	6 52	..	7 4	..	7 23	..	..
Hayes A ......arr.	5 35	..	..	5 51	..	6 0	..	6 12	..	..	6 26	..	6 34	..	6 41	..	..	6 55	..	7 8	..	7 26	..	..
Woodside (Surrey)	..	5 32	5 40	..	5 48	..	5 58	..	..	6 13	..	6 24	..	..	..	..	6 42	..	6 55	..	7 7	..	7 28	7 40
Addiscombe C arr.	..	..	5 43	..	..	..	6 1	..	..	..	..	6 27	..	..	..	..	..	..	6 58	..	7 10	..	7 31	7 43
Bingham Road	..	5 34	..	..	5 50	..	..	..	..	6 15	..	..	..	..	..	..	6 41	..	..	..	..	..	..	..
Coombe Road	..	5 37	..	..	5 53	..	..	..	..	6 18	..	..	..	..	..	..	6 47	..	..	..	..	..	..	..
Selsdon	..	5 39	..	..	5 55	..	..	..	..	6 20	..	..	..	..	..	..	6F55	..	..	..	..	..	..	..
Sanderstead 234 arr.	..	5 42	..	..	5 58	..	..	..	..	6 23	..	..	..	..	..	..	6 59	..	..	..	..	..	..	..

Mondays to Fridays — p.m

Down	p.m																				ngt.	ngt.	
Charing Cross .dep.	..	..	7 38	..	..	8 7	..	8 37	..	9 7	..	9 37	..	10 7	..	1037	..	11 7	..	..	1144	..	..	..
Waterloo	..	..	7 40	..	..	8 9	..	8 39	..	9 9	..	9 39	..	10 9	..	1039	..	11 9	..	..	1146	..	..	..
Cannon Street	7 16	..	..	..	..	..	..	..	..	..	..	..	..	..	..	..	..	..	..	..	..	..	..	..
London Bridge	7 19	..	7 43	..	..	8 12	..	8 42	..	9 12	..	9 42	..	1012	..	1042	..	1112	..	..	1149	..	..	..
New Cross	7 26	..	7 50	..	..	8 19	..	8 49	..	9 19	..	9 49	..	1019	..	1049	..	1119	..	..	1155	..	..	..
St. John's	7 28	..	7 52	..	..	8 21	..	8 51	..	9 21	..	9 51	..	1021	..	1051	..	1121	..	..	1158	..	..	..
Lewisham	7 30	..	7 54	..	..	8 23	..	8 53	..	9 23	..	9 53	..	1023	..	1053	..	1123	..	..	12 0	..	..	..
Lady Well	7 32	..	7 56	..	..	8 25	..	8 55	..	9 25	..	9 55	..	1025	..	1055	..	1125	..	..	12 2	..	..	..
Catford Bridge	7 35	..	7 59	..	..	8 28	..	8 58	..	9 28	..	9 58	..	1028	..	1058	..	1128	..	..	12 4	..	..	..
Lower Sydenham	7 38	..	8 2	..	..	8 31	..	9 1	..	9 31	..	10 1	..	1031	..	11 1	..	1131	..	..	12 7	..	..	..
New Beckenham	7 40	..	8 4	..	..	8 33	..	9 3	..	9 33	..	10 3	..	1033	..	11 3	..	1133	..	..	12 9	..	..	..
Clock House	..	..	8 6	..	..	8 35	..	9 5	..	9 35	..	10 5	..	1035	..	11 5	..	1135	..	..	1212	..	..	..
Elmer's End	..	..	8 8	..	8 30	8 37	8 41	9 7	9 11	9 37	9 41	10 7	1011	1037	1041	11 7	1111	1137	..	..	1214	..	1238	..
Elmer's End...dep.	..	7 43	..	8 13	..	8 37	..	9 7	..	9 37	..	10 7	..	1037	..	11 7	..	..	1140	..	..	1216	..	..
Eden Park	..	7 46	..	8 16	..	8 41	..	9 11	..	9 41	..	1011	..	1041	..	1111	..	..	1143	..	..	1219	..	..
West Wickham	..	7 48	..	8 19	..	8 43	..	9 13	..	9 43	..	1013	..	1043	..	1113	..	..	1146	..	..	1221	..	..
Hayes A ......arr.	..	7 52	..	8 22	..	8 47	..	9 17	..	9 47	..	1017	..	1047	..	1117	..	..	1149	..	..	1224	..	..
Woodside (Surrey)	..	..	8 11	..	8 32	..	8 43	..	9 13	..	9 43	..	1013	..	1043	..	1113	1140	..	..	1216	..	1240	..
Addiscombe C arr.	..	..	8 14	..	8 35	..	8 46	..	9 16	..	9 46	..	1016	..	1046	..	1116	1143	..	..	1219	..	1243	..
Bingham Road	..	..	..	..	..	..	..	..	..	..	..	..	..	..	..	..	..	..	..	..	..	..	..	..
Coombe Road	..	..	..	..	..	..	..	..	..	..	..	..	..	..	..	..	..	..	..	..	..	..	..	..
Selsdon	..	..	..	..	..	..	..	..	..	..	..	..	..	..	..	..	..	..	..	..	..	..	..	..
Sanderstead 234 arr.	..	..	..	..	..	..	..	..	..	..	..	..	..	..	..	..	..	..	..	..	..	..	..	..

For Notes, see page 118   **For SATURDAY Trains, see page 116**

LONDON, NEW BECKENHAM, HAYES, ADDISCOMBE (CROYDON), and SANDERSTEAD

3—All Trains on this page are Third class only

Down	a.m. — Saturdays — a.m.																						
Charing Cross ......dep	..	..	8 33	8 31	..	..	8 49	8 58	9 0	..	..	..	..	..	9 35	..	9 50	9 58	10 8	..	..	1037	..
Waterloo	..	..	8 35	8 33	..	..	8 51	9 0	9 2	..	..	..	..	..	9 37	..	9 52	10 0	1010	..	..	1039	..
Cannon Street	8 14	..	..	..	8 44	8 50	..	..	..	..	9 14	..	..	9 32	..	..	..	..	..	..	1025	..	..
London Bridge	8 16	..	8 39	8 36	8 47	8 52	8 57	9 4	9 8	..	9 16	..	..	9 34	9 42	..	9 57	10 4	1013	..	1028	1042	..
New Cross	8 23	..	..	8 43	8 53	8 59	9 3	..	9 15	..	9 23	..	..	9 40	9 49	..	10 4	1010	1020	..	1035	1049	..
St. John's	..	..	..	..	..	..	..	..	..	..	..	..	..	9 43	..	..	..	..	..	..	..	..	..
Lewisham	..	..	..	8 47	8 56	9 2	..	..	9 18	..	9 26	..	..	9 45	..	..	..	1013	..	..	..	1052	..
Lady Well	8 28	..	..	8 50	..	..	9 8	9 14	..	..	9 28	..	..	9 47	9 53	..	..	1015	1024	..	1039	1054	..
Catford Bridge	8 30	..	..	8 52	8 59	9 5	9 10	9 16	9 21	..	9 31	..	..	9 51	9 56	..	1010	1018	1027	..	1042	1056	..
Lower Sydenham	8 33	..	8 52	8 56	..	9 8	9 13	9 20	9 24	..	9 34	..	..	9 54	9 59	..	..	1021	1030	..	1045	1059	..
New Beckenham	..	..	8 54	8 58	..	9 10	9 15	9 22	9 26	..	9 36	..	..	9 56	10 1	..	1014	1023	1032	..	1047	11 1	..
Clock House	8 37	..	8 56	9 0	9 4	9 13	9 18	9 24	9 29	..	9 38	..	..	9 59	10 3	..	1017	1026	1034	..	1049	11 4	..
Elmer's End	8 39	..	8 58	9 2	9 6	9 15	9 20	9 26	9 31	..	9 41	..	9 58	10 1	10 5	..	1019	1028	1036	..	1052	11 6	..
Elmer's End ......dep	8 39	..	8 58	..	..	9 15	..	..	9 31	..	..	..	..	..	10 5	..	..	1028	..	..	..	..	11 8
Eden Park	8 42	..	9 2	..	..	9 18	..	..	9 34	..	..	..	..	..	10 9	..	..	1031	..	..	..	..	1111
West Wickham	8 45	..	9 4	..	..	9 21	..	..	9 37	..	..	..	..	..	1011	..	..	1034	..	..	..	..	1114
Hayes A ......arr	8 48	..	9 8	..	..	9 24	..	..	9 40	..	..	..	..	..	1015	..	..	1037	..	..	..	..	1117
Woodside (Surrey)	..	..	..	9 5	9 9	..	9 22	9 30	..	..	9 44	..	10 0	10 3	..	..	1021	..	1040	..	1054	11 8	..
Addiscombe C ....arr	..	..	..	..	9 12	..	9 25	..	..	..	9 47	..	10 3	..	..	..	..	..	..	..	1057	..	..
Bingham Road	..	..	..	9 7	..	..	..	9 32	..	..	..	..	..	10 5	..	..	1023	..	1043	..	..	1110	..
Coombe Road	..	..	..	9 10	..	..	..	9 35	..	..	..	..	..	10 8	..	..	1026	..	1046	..	..	1113	..
Selsdon	..	..	..	9 12	..	..	..	9 37	..	..	..	..	..	1010	..	..	1028	..	1048	..	..	1115	..
Sanderstead 234 ....arr	..	..	..	9 14	..	..	..	9 40	..	..	..	..	..	1013	..	..	1031	..	1050	..	..	1118	..

Down	a.m. — Saturdays — p.m.																						
Charing Cross ......dep	1052	..	11 7	..	..	..	1122	1136	..	..	..	..	12 3	12 9	..	..	..	..	1229	..	1233	..	..
Waterloo	1054	..	11 9	..	..	..	1124	1138	..	..	..	..	12 5	1211	..	..	..	..	1231	..	1235	..	..
Cannon Street	..	..	..	..	1120	..	..	..	..	1147	1155	..	..	..	..	1212	..	1221	..	..	..	..	1243
London Bridge	1058	..	1112	..	1122	..	1128	1141	..	1149	1157	..	12 8	1214	..	1214	..	1223	1235	..	1239	..	1245
New Cross	11 5	..	1119	..	1128	..	1135	1148	..	1155	12 4	..	1215	1221	..	1221	..	1230	1242	..	1246	..	1252
St. John's	..	..	..	..	..	..	..	..	..	..	12 6	..	1218	..	..	1224	..	..	..	..	..	..	..
Lewisham	..	..	1122	..	1132	..	..	1152	..	..	12 8	..	1220	..	..	1226	..	1234	..	..	1249	..	..
Lady Well	11 9	..	1124	..	1134	..	1140	1154	..	1159	1210	..	..	1225	..	1228	..	1236	1247	..	1251	..	1257
Catford Bridge	1112	..	1126	..	1136	..	1143	1156	..	12 2	1213	..	1223	..	..	1231	..	1238	1249	..	1254	..	1259
Lower Sydenham	1115	..	1129	..	1139	..	1146	1159	..	12 5	1216	..	..	1229	..	1234	..	1241	1252	..	1257	..	1 2
New Beckenham	1117	..	1131	..	1141	..	1148	12 1	..	12 7	1218	..	..	1231	..	1236	..	1243	1254	..	1259	..	1 4
Clock House	1119	..	1134	..	1144	..	1151	12 4	..	12 9	1220	..	1228	1234	..	1238	..	1246	1257	..	1 1	..	1 7
Elmer's End	1121	..	1136	..	1146	..	1153	12 6	..	1211	1222	..	1230	1236	..	1240	..	1248	1259	..	1 3	..	1 9
Elmer's End ......dep	1121	..	..	..	1146	..	..	12 6	..	..	1222	..	..	1236	..	..	..	1248	..	..	1 3	..	..
Eden Park	1125	..	..	..	1149	..	..	12 9	..	..	1226	..	..	1239	..	..	..	1251	..	..	1 7	..	..
West Wickham	1127	..	..	..	1152	..	..	1212	..	..	1228	..	..	1242	..	..	..	1254	..	..	1 9	..	..
Hayes A ......arr	1131	..	..	..	1155	..	..	1215	..	..	1232	..	..	1245	..	..	..	1257	..	..	1 13	..	..
Woodside (Surrey)	..	..	1139	..	..	..	1155	..	..	1214	..	..	1233	..	..	1243	..	..	1 2	..	..	..	1 11
Addiscombe C ....arr	..	..	..	..	..	..	..	..	..	..	..	..	1236	..	..	..	..	..	1 5	..	..	..	..
Bingham Road	..	..	1141	..	..	..	1157	..	..	1216	..	..	..	..	..	1245	..	..	..	..	..	..	1 13
Coombe Road	..	..	1144	..	..	..	12 0	..	..	1219	..	..	..	..	..	1248	..	..	..	..	..	..	1 16
Selsdon	..	..	1146	..	..	..	12 2	..	..	1221	..	..	..	..	..	1250	..	..	..	..	..	..	1 18
Sanderstead 234 ....arr	..	..	1148	..	..	..	12 5	..	..	1223	..	..	..	..	..	1252	..	..	..	..	..	..	1 21

Down	p.m. — Saturdays — p.m.																						
Charing Cross ......dep	..	..	1249	..	1257	1 8	..	..	1 11	..	..	..	..	..	1 33	..	1 40	.	..	..	2 2	..	2 7
Waterloo	..	..	1251	..	1259	1 10	..	..	1 13	..	..	..	..	..	1 35	..	1 42	..	..	..	2 4	..	2 9
Cannon Street	1249	..	..	..	..	..	1 11	..	..	..	1 25	..	1 31	..	..	..	..	.	1 53	1 59	..	..	..
London Bridge	1251	..	1254	..	1 3	1 14	1 13	..	1 18	..	1 28	..	1 34	..	1 39	..	1 45	..	1 55	2 1	2 7	..	2 13
New Cross	1258	..	..	..	1 10	..	1 20	..	..	..	1 35	..	1 41	..	1 45	..	1 52	.	2 2	2 8	2 14	..	2 19
St. John's	..	..	1 2	..	1 12	..	..	..	..	..	..	..	..	..	..	..	..	..	2 4	..	2 16	..	..
Lewisham	1 1	..	..	..	1 14	..	1 23	..	1 27	..	..	..	1 44	..	..	..	1 55	.	2 6	2 11	..	..	..
Lady Well	1 3	..	1 6	..	1 16	..	1 26	..	1 30	..	..	..	1 46	..	1 50	..	1 57	..	2 8	2 13	2 20	..	2 25
Catford Bridge	1 6	..	1 9	..	1 19	1 25	1 28	..	1 32	..	1 41	..	1 48	..	1 52	..	1 59	.	2 11	2 15	2 22	..	2 28
Lower Sydenham	..	..	1 12	..	1 22	..	1 31	..	1 36	..	1 44	..	1 51	..	1 55	..	2 2	..	2 14	2 18	2 25	..	2 31
New Beckenham	1 10	..	..	..	1 24	..	1 33	..	1 38	..	1 46	..	1 53	..	1 57	..	2 4	.	2 16	2 20	2 27	..	2 33
Clock House	1 13	..	1 16	..	1 26	1 30	1 36	..	1 40	..	1 49	..	1 56	..	2 0	..	2 7	.	2 18	2 23	2 30	..	2 35
Elmer's End	1 15	..	1 18	..	1 28	1 32	1 38	..	1 42	..	1 51	..	1 58	..	2 2	..	2 9	..	2 20	2 25	2 32	..	2 37
Elmer's End ......dep	1 15	..	..	..	1 28	..	..	..	1 42	..	..	..	1 58	..	..	..	2 9	.	..	2 25	..	..	2 37
Eden Park	1 18	..	..	..	1 32	..	..	..	1 46	..	..	..	2 1	..	..	..	2 12	..	..	2 28	..	..	2 41
West Wickham	1 21	..	..	..	1 34	..	..	..	1 48	..	..	..	2 4	..	..	..	2 15	.	..	2 31	..	..	2 43
Hayes A ......arr	1 24	..	..	..	1 38	..	..	..	1 52	..	..	..	2 7	..	..	..	2 18	..	..	2 34	..	..	2 47
Woodside (Surrey)	..	..	1 21	..	..	1 35	1 40	..	..	..	1 53	..	..	..	2 4	..	..	.	2 23	..	2 34	..	..
Addiscombe C ....arr	..	..	1 24	..	..	1 38	..	..	..	..	1 56	..	..	..	..	..	..	..	2 26	..	..	..	..
Bingham Road	..	..	..	..	..	..	1 43	..	..	..	..	..	..	..	2 6	..	..	.	..	..	2 36	..	..
Coombe Road	..	..	..	..	..	..	1 46	..	..	..	..	..	..	..	2 9	..	..	..	..	..	2 39	..	..
Selsdon	..	..	..	..	..	..	1 48	..	..	..	..	..	..	..	2 11	..	..	.	..	..	2 41	..	..
Sanderstead 234 ....arr	..	..	..	..	..	..	1 51	..	..	..	..	..	..	..	2 14	..	..	..	..	..	2 44	..	..

For Notes, see page 118

LONDON, NEW BECKENHAM, HAYES, ADDISCOMBE (CROYDON), and SANDERSTEAD

3–All Trains on this page are Third class only

Down	p.m. — Saturdays—continued — p.m.																						
Charing Cross..dep.	..	..	2 37	..	..	..	3 7	..	..	3 37	..	4 7	..	..	4 37	..	..	5 7	..	..	5 37	..	6 7	..
Waterloo	..	..	2 39	..	..	..	3 9	..	..	3 39	..	4 9	..	..	4 39	..	..	5 9	..	..	5 39	..	6 9	..
Cannon Street	2 20	2 27	..	..	2 56	3 4	..	..	..	..	..	..	..	..	..	..	..	..	..	..	..	..	..	..
London Bridge	2 22	2 30	2 42	..	2 59	3 6	3 12	..	..	3 42	..	4 12	..	..	4 42	..	..	5 12	..	..	5 42	..	6 12	..
New Cross	2 28	..	2 49	..	3 5	3 13	3 19	..	..	3 49	..	4 19	..	..	4 49	..	..	5 19	..	..	5 49	..	6 19	..
St. John's	2 31	..	..	..	3 7	3 15	3 21	..	..	3 51	..	4 21	..	..	4 51	..	..	5 21	..	..	5 51	..	6 21	..
Lewisham	2 33	..	2 52	..	3 9	3 17	3 23	..	..	3 53	..	4 23	..	..	4 53	..	..	5 23	..	..	5 53	..	6 23	..
Lady Well	2 35	2 40	2 54	..	3 11	3 19	3 25	..	..	3 55	..	4 25	..	..	4 55	..	..	5 25	..	..	5 55	..	6 25	..
Catford Bridge	2 37	2 42	2 56	..	3 14	3 22	3 28	..	..	3 58	..	4 28	..	..	4 58	..	..	5 28	..	..	5 58	..	6 28	..
Lower Sydenham	2 40	2 45	2 59	..	3 17	3 25	3 31	..	..	4 1	..	4 31	..	..	5 1	..	..	5 31	..	..	6 1	..	6 31	..
New Beckenham	2 42	2 47	3 1	..	3 19	3 27	3 33	..	..	4 3	..	4 33	..	..	5 3	..	..	5 33	..	..	6 3	..	6 33	..
Clock House	2 45	2 50	3 4	..	3 21	..	3 35	..	..	4 5	..	4 35	..	..	5 5	..	..	5 35	..	..	6 5	..	6 35	..
Elmer's End	2 47	2 52	3 6	..	3 23	..	3 37	3 42	..	4 7	4 11	4 37	4 41	..	5 7	5 11	..	5 37	5 41	..	6 7	6 11	6 37	6 41
Elmer's End..dep.	..	2 52	..	3 9	..	..	3 37	..	..	4 7	..	4 37	..	..	5 7	..	..	5 37	..	..	6 7	..	6 37	..
Eden Park	..	2 55	..	3 12	..	..	3 41	..	..	4 11	..	4 41	..	..	5 11	..	..	5 41	..	..	6 11	..	6 41	..
West Wickham	..	2 58	..	3 15	..	..	3 43	..	..	4 13	..	4 43	..	..	5 13	..	..	5 43	..	..	6 13	..	6 43	..
Hayes A .....arr.	..	3 1	..	3 18	..	..	3 47	..	..	4 17	..	4 47	..	..	5 17	..	..	5 47	..	..	6 17	..	6 47	..
Woodside (Surrey)	2 49	..	3 8	..	3 26	..	..	3 44	..	..	4 13	..	4 43	..	..	5 13	..	..	5 43	..	..	6 13	..	6 43
Addiscombe C ar.	2 52	..	..	..	3 29	..	..	3 47	..	..	4 16	..	4 46	..	..	5 16	..	..	5 46	..	..	6 16	..	6 46
Bingham Road	..	..	3 10	..	..	..	..	..	..	..	..	..	..	..	..	..	..	..	..	..	..	..	..	..
Coombe Road	..	..	3 13	..	..	..	..	..	..	..	..	..	..	..	..	..	..	..	..	..	..	..	..	..
Selsdon	..	..	3 15	..	..	..	..	..	..	..	..	..	..	..	..	..	..	..	..	..	..	..	..	..
Sanderstead 234 arr	..	..	3 18	..	..	..	..	..	..	..	..	..	..	..	..	..	..	..	..	..	..	..	..	..

Down	p.m. — Saturdays — p.m.																						
																					ngt.	ngt.	
Charing Cross..dep.	6 37	..	7 7	..	7 38	..	8 7	..	8 37	..	9 7	..	9 37	..	10 7	..	1037	..	11 7	..	1144	..	..	..
Waterloo	6 39	..	7 9	..	7 40	..	8 9	..	8 39	..	9 9	..	9 39	..	10 9	..	1039	..	11 9	..	1146	..	..	..
Cannon Street	..	..	..	..	..	..	..	..	..	..	..	..	..	..	..	..	..	..	..	..	..	..	..	..
London Bridge	6 42	..	7 12	..	7 43	..	8 12	..	8 43	..	9 12	..	9 42	..	1012	..	1042	..	1112	..	1149	..	..	..
New Cross	6 49	..	7 19	..	7 50	..	8 19	..	8 49	..	9 19	..	9 49	..	1019	..	1049	..	1119	..	1155	..	..	..
St. John's	6 51	..	7 21	..	7 52	..	8 21	..	8 51	..	9 21	..	9 51	..	1021	..	1051	..	1121	..	1158	..	..	..
Lewisham	6 53	..	7 23	..	7 54	..	8 23	..	8 53	..	9 23	..	9 53	..	1023	..	1053	..	1123	..	12 0	..	..	..
Lady Well	6 55	..	7 25	..	7 56	..	8 25	..	8 55	..	9 25	..	9 55	..	1025	..	1055	..	1125	..	12 2	..	..	..
Catford Bridge	6 58	..	7 28	..	7 59	..	8 28	..	8 58	..	9 28	..	9 58	..	1028	..	1058	..	1128	..	12 4	..	..	..
Lower Sydenham	7 1	..	7 31	..	8 2	..	8 31	..	9 1	..	9 31	..	10 1	..	1031	..	11 1	..	1131	..	12 7	..	..	..
New Beckenham	7 3	..	7 33	..	8 4	..	8 33	..	9 3	..	9 33	..	10 3	..	1033	..	11 3	..	1133	..	12 9	..	..	..
Clock House	7 5	..	7 35	..	8 6	..	8 35	..	9 5	..	9 35	..	10 5	..	1035	..	11 5	..	1135	..	1212	..	..	..
Elmer's End	7 7	7 11	7 37	7 41	8 8	8 11	8 37	8 41	9 7	9 11	9 37	9 41	10 7	1011	1037	1041	11 7	1111	1127	..	1214	..	1238	..
Elmer's End..dep.	7 7	..	7 37	..	8 8	..	8 37	..	9 7	..	9 37	..	10 7	..	1037	..	11 7	..	..	1140	..	1216	..	..
Eden Park	7 11	..	7 41	..	8 12	..	8 41	..	9 11	..	9 41	..	1011	..	1041	..	1111	..	..	1143	..	1219	..	..
West Wickham	7 13	..	7 43	..	8 14	..	8 43	..	9 13	..	9 43	..	1013	..	1043	..	1113	..	..	1146	..	1221	..	..
Hayes A .....arr.	7 17	..	7 47	..	8 18	..	8 47	..	9 17	..	9 47	..	1017	..	1047	..	1117	..	..	1149	..	1224	..	..
Woodside (Surrey)	..	7 13	..	7 43	..	8 13	..	8 43	..	9 13	..	9 43	..	1013	..	1043	..	1113	1140	..	1216	..	1240	..
Addiscombe C ar.	..	7 16	..	7 46	..	8 16	..	8 46	..	9 16	..	9 46	..	1016	..	1046	..	1116	1143	..	1219	..	1243	..
Bingham Road	..	..	..	..	..	..	..	..	..	..	..	..	..	..	..	..	..	..	..	..	..	..	..	..
Coombe Road	..	..	..	..	..	..	..	..	..	..	..	..	..	..	..	..	..	..	..	..	..	..	..	..
Selsdon	..	..	..	..	..	..	..	..	..	..	..	..	..	..	..	..	..	..	..	..	..	..	..	..
Sanderstead 234 arr	..	..	..	..	..	..	..	..	..	..	..	..	..	..	..	..	..	..	..	..	..	..	..	..

Down	a.m. — Sundays — a.m.																						
Charing Cross..dep	..	7 8	..	..	7 38	..	8 8	..	..	8 38	..	9 8	..	9 38	..	..	10 8	..	1038	..	11 8	..	..	1138
Waterloo	..	7 10	..	..	7 40	..	8 10	..	..	8 40	..	9 10	..	9 40	..	..	1010	..	1040	..	1110	..	..	1140
Cannon Street	..	..	..	..	..	..	..	..	..	..	..	..	..	..	..	..	..	..	..	..	..	..	..	..
London Bridge	..	7 14	..	..	7 44	..	8 14	..	..	8 44	..	9 14	..	9 44	..	..	1014	..	1044	..	1114	..	..	1144
New Cross	..	7 21	..	..	7 50	..	8 20	..	..	8 50	..	9 20	..	9 50	..	..	1020	..	1050	..	1120	..	..	1150
St John's	..	7 23	..	..	7 52	..	8 22	..	..	8 52	..	9 22	..	9 52	..	..	1022	..	1052	..	1122	..	..	1152
Lewisham	..	7 25	..	..	7 54	..	8 24	..	..	8 54	..	9 24	..	9 54	..	..	1024	..	1054	..	1124	..	..	1154
Lady Well	..	7 27	..	..	7 56	..	8 26	..	..	8 56	..	9 26	..	9 56	..	..	1026	..	1056	..	1126	..	..	1156
Catford Bridge	..	7 30	..	..	7 59	..	8 29	..	..	8 59	..	9 29	..	9 59	..	..	1029	..	1059	..	1129	..	..	1159
Lower Sydenham	..	7 33	..	..	8 2	..	8 32	..	..	9 2	..	9 32	..	10 2	..	..	1032	..	11 2	..	1132	..	..	12 2
New Beckenham	..	7 35	..	..	8 4	..	8 34	..	..	9 4	..	9 34	..	10 4	..	..	1034	..	11 4	..	1134	..	..	12 4
Clock House	..	7 37	..	..	8 6	..	8 36	..	..	9 6	..	9 36	..	10 6	..	..	1036	..	11 6	..	1136	..	..	12 6
Elmer's End	..	7 39	7 45	..	8 8	8 13	8 38	8 43	..	9 8	9 13	9 38	9 43	10 8	1013	..	1038	1043	11 8	1113	1138	1143	..	12 8
Elmer's End..dep.	7 13	7 39	..	..	8 8	..	8 38	..	..	9 8	..	9 38	..	10 8	..	..	1038	..	11 8	..	1138	..	..	12 8
Eden Park	7 16	7 42	..	..	8 11	..	8 41	..	..	9 11	..	9 41	..	1011	..	..	1041	..	1111	..	1141	..	..	1211
West Wickham	7 18	7 45	..	..	8 14	..	8 44	..	..	9 14	..	9 44	..	1014	..	..	1044	..	1114	..	1144	..	..	1214
Hayes A .....arr.	7 22	7 48	..	..	8 17	..	8 47	..	..	9 17	..	9 47	..	1017	..	..	1047	..	1117	..	1147	..	..	1217
Woodside (Surrey)	..	..	7 47	..	..	8 15	..	8 45	..	..	9 15	..	9 45	..	1015	..	..	1045	..	1115	..	1145	..	..
Addiscombe C ar.	..	..	7 50	..	..	8 18	..	8 48	..	..	9 18	..	9 48	..	1018	..	..	1048	..	1118	..	1148	..	..
Bingham Road	..	..	..	..	..	..	..	..	..	..	..	..	..	..	..	..	..	..	..	..	..	..	..	..
Coombe Road	..	..	..	..	..	..	..	..	..	..	..	..	..	..	..	..	..	..	..	..	..	..	..	..
Selsdon	..	..	..	..	..	..	..	..	..	..	..	..	..	..	..	..	..	..	..	..	..	..	..	..
Sanderstead 234 arr	..	..	..	..	..	..	..	..	..	..	..	..	..	..	..	..	..	..	..	..	..	..	..	..

For Notes and Continuation of SUNDAY TRAINS, see page 118

LONDON, NEW BECKENHAM, HAYES, ADDISCOMBE (CROYDON), and SANDERSTEAD

3 –All Trains on this page are Third class only

Down	p.m. — Sundays *continued* — p.m.																						
Charing Cross ......dep.		12 8		1238			1 8		1 38			2 8			2 38		3 8			3 38		4 8	
Waterloo		1210		1240			1 10		1 40			2 10			2 40		3 10			3 40		4 10	
Cannon Street																							
London Bridge		1214		1244			1 14		1 44			2 14			2 44		3 14			3 44		4 14	
New Cross		1220		1250			1 20		1 50			2 20			2 50		3 20			3 50		4 20	
St. John's		1222		1252			1 22		1 52			2 22			2 52		3 22			3 52		4 22	
Lewisham		1224		1254			1 24		1 54			2 24			2 54		3 24			3 54		4 24	
Lady Well		1226		1256			1 26		1 56			2 26			2 56		3 26			3 56		4 26	
Catford Bridge		1229		1259			1 29		1 59			2 29			2 59		3 29			3 59		4 29	
Lower Sydenham		1232		1 2			1 32		2 2			2 32			3 2		3 32			4 2		4 32	
New Beckenham		1234		1 4			1 34		2 4			2 34			3 4		3 34			4 4		4 34	
Clock House		1236		1 6			1 36		2 6			2 36			3 6		3 36			4 6		4 36	
Elmer's End	1213	1238	1243	1 8	1 13		1 38	1 43	2 8		2 13	2 38	2 43		3 8	3 13	3 38	3 43		4 8	4 13	4 38	4 43
Elmer's End ......dep.		1238		1 8			1 38		2 8			2 38			3 8		3 38			4 8		4 38	
Eden Park		1241		1 11			1 41		2 11			2 41			3 11		3 41			4 11		4 41	
West Wickham		1244		1 14			1 44		2 14			2 44			3 14		3 44			4 14		4 44	
Hayes A ......arr.		1247		1 17			1 47		2 17			2 47			3 17		3 47			4 17		4 47	
Woodside (Surrey)	1215		1245		1 15			1 45			2 15		2 45			3 15		3 45			4 15		4 45
Addiscombe C ....arr.	1218		1248		1 18			1 48			2 18		2 48			3 18		3 48			4 18		4 48
Bingham Road																							
Coombe Road																							
Selsdon																							
Sanderstead 234....arr.																							

Down	p.m. — Sundays — p.m.																							
Charing Cross ......dep.	4 38			5 8			5 38			6 8			6 38		7 8		7 38		8 8			8 38		9 8
Waterloo	4 40			5 10			5 40			6 10			6 40		7 10		7 40		8 10			8 40		9 10
Cannon Street																								
London Bridge	4 44			5 14			5 44			6 14			6 44		7 14		7 44		8 14			8 44		9 14
New Cross	4 50			5 20			5 50			6 20			6 50		7 20		7 50		8 20			8 50		9 20
St. John's	4 52			5 22			5 52			6 22			6 52		7 22		7 52		8 22			8 52		9 22
Lewisham	4 54			5 24			5 54			6 24			6 54		7 24		7 54		8 24			8 54		9 24
Lady Well	4 56			5 26			5 56			6 26			6 56		7 26		7 56		8 26			8 56		9 26
Catford Bridge	4 59			5 29			5 59			6 29			6 59		7 29		7 59		8 29			8 59		9 29
Lower Sydenham	5 2			5 32			6 2			6 32			7 2		7 32		8 2		8 32			9 2		9 32
New Beckenham	5 4			5 34			6 4			6 34			7 4		7 34		8 4		8 34			9 4		9 34
Clock House	5 6			5 36			6 6			6 36			7 6		7 36		8 6		8 36			9 6		9 36
Elmer's End	5 8		5 13	5 38		5 43	6 8		6 13	6 38		6 43	7 8	7 13	7 38	7 43	8 8	8 13	8 38		8 43	9 8	9 13	9 38
Elmer's End ......dep.	5 8			5 38			6 8			6 38			7 8		7 38		8 8		8 38			9 8		9 38
Eden Park	5 11			5 41			6 11			6 41			7 11		7 41		8 11		8 41			9 11		9 41
West Wickham	5 14			5 44			6 14			6 44			7 14		7 44		8 14		8 44			9 14		9 44
Hayes A ......arr.	5 17			5 47			6 17			6 47			7 17		7 47		8 17		8 47			9 17		9 47
Woodside (Surrey)			5 15			5 45			6 15			6 45		7 15		7 45		8 15			8 45		9 15	
Addiscombe C ....arr.			5 18			5 48			6 18			6 48		7 18		7 48		8 18			8 48		9 18	
Bingham Road																								
Coombe Road																								
Selsdon																								
Sanderstead 234....arr.																								

Down	p.m. — Sundays — p.m.													
Charing Cross ......dep.		9 38			10 8		1038			11 8			1138		
Waterloo		9 40			1010		1040			1110			1140		
Cannon Street															
London Bridge		9 44			1014		1044			1114			1144		
New Cross		9 50			1020		1050			1120			1150		
St John's		9 52			1022		1052			1122			1152		
Lewisham		9 54			1024		1054			1124			1154		
Lady Well		9 56			1026		1056			1126			1156		
Catford Bridge		9 59			1029		1059			1129			1159		
Lower Sydenham		10 2			1032		11 2			1132			12 2		
New Beckenham		10 4			1034		11 4			1134			12 4		
Clock House		10 6			1036		11 6			1136			12 6		
Elmer's End	9 43	10 8	1013		1038	1043	11 8		1113	1138			12 8	mdt	
Elmer's End ......dep.		10 8			1038		11 8				1140			1210	
Eden Park		1011			1041		1111				1143			1213	
West Wickham		1014			1044		1114				1145			1215	
Hayes A ......arr.		1017			1047		1117				1149			1219	
Woodside (Surrey)	9 45		1015			1045			1115	1141			1211		
Addiscombe C ....arr.	9 48		1018			1048			1118	1143			1214		
Bingham Road															
Coombe Road															
Selsdon															
Sanderstead 234....arr.															

NOTES

3 Third class only.
A Station for Keston (1¼ miles).
C Addiscombe (Croydon).
F Arrives 5 mins. *earlier*
SX Saturdays excepted

OTHER TRAINS

between

London and Lewisham, pages 72 and 124—London & Sanderstead, 234.

SANDERSTEAD, ADDISCOMBE (CROYDON), HAYES, NEW BECKENHAM, and LONDON

3—All Trains on this page are Third class only

Miles	Up	Week Days a.m.																					
																			SX				
	Sanderstead dep.																						6 32
¾	Selsdon																						6 34
1¼	Coombe Road																						6 36
2¼	Bingham Road																						6 38
—	Addiscombe C. dep.	4 3	4 25		4 35			5 2		5 25		5 40			5 58				6 12	6 26			
3	Woodside (Surrey)	4 5	4 27		4 37			5 4		5 27		5 42			6 0				6 14	6 28			6 41
—	Mls Hayes dep.						4 56						5 45				6 0					6 30	
—	1¼ West Wickham						4 58						5 47				6 2					6 32	
—	2 Eden Park						5 1						5 50				6 5					6 35	
—	3½ Elmer's End arr.						5 5						5 53				6 8					6 38	
4	Elmer's End	4 7	4 30		4 40			5 6		5 29		5 44	5 53		6 2		6 8		6 16	6 30		6 38	6 44
4¾	Clock House	4 9			4 42			5 8		5 31		5 46	5 55		6 4		6 10		6 18	6 32		6 40	6 46
5½	New Beckenham	4 12			4 44			5 11	5 20	5 34		5 49	5 58		6 7		6 13		6 21	6 35		6 43	6 48
6	Lower Sydenham	4 14			4 46			5 13	5 22	5 36		5 51	6 0		6 9		6 15		6 23	6 37		6 45	6 50
7½	Catford Bridge	4 17			4 49			5 16	5 25	5 39		5 54	6 3		6 12		6 18		6 26	6 40		6 48	6 53
8¼	Lady Well	4 19			4 52			5 18	5 27	5 41		5 56	6 5		6 14		6 20		6 28	6 42		6 50	6 56
9	Lewisham 72								5 29	5 43		5 58	6 7		6 16		6 22		6 30	6 44		6 52	6 58
9½	St. John's 124	4 23						5 21	5 31	45		6 0			6 18		6 24		6 32				
10½	New Cross	4 25			4 56			5 24	5 34	5 48		6 3	6 10		6 21		6 27		6 35	6 47		6 55	7 1
13¼	London Bridge	4 32			5 2			5 30	5 39	5 54		6 9	6 16		6 27		6 33		6 41	6 53		7 2	7 7
14	Cannon Street	4 38			5 5			5 33		5 58			6 20				6 38		6 45			7 6	7 11
14¼	Waterloo								5 43			6 12			6 30					6 57			
15	Charing Cross arr.								5 46			6 15			6 33					7 0			

Up	Week Days a.m.																						
															SX	SO							
Sanderstead dep.					6 58							7 26							7 51				
Selsdon					7 0							7 28							7 53				
Coombe Road					7 2							7 30							7 55				
Bingham Road					7 4							7 32							7 57				
Addiscombe C. dep.	6 51									7 26					7 45	7 45							8 13
Woodside (Surrey)	6 53				7 7					7 28		7 35			7 47	7 47			8 0				8 15
Hayes dep.			6 52				7 8		7 19					7 33			7 44				8 0		
West Wickham			6 54				7 10		7 21					7 35			7 46				8 2		
Eden Park			6 57				7 13		7 24					7 38			7 49				8 5		
Elmer's End arr.			7 0				7 16		7 27					7 41			7 52				8 8		
Elmer's End	6 55		7 0		7 9		7 16		7 27	7 31				7 41	7 49	7 50	7 52		8 2		8 8		8 17
Clock House	6 57		7 2		7 11		7 18		7 29	7 33				7 43	7 51		7 55		8 4		8 10		
New Beckenham	7 0		7 5		7 14		7 21							7 46	7 54		7 57		8 7				8 20
Lower Sydenham	7 2		7 7		7 16		7 23							7 48	7 56		7 59				8 14		8 22
Catford Bridge	7 5		7 10		7 19		7 26		7 34	7 38				7 51	7 59		8 2		8 11		8 17		8 25
Lady Well	7 7		7 12		7 21					7 41				7 53	8 1		8 5		8 13		8 20		8 28
Lewisham 72	7 10													7 56			8 8		8 15				8 30
St. John's 124	7 12								7 40					7 58	8 5		8 10						
New Cross	7 15		7 16		7 26		7 31		7 42	7 45		7 48		8 0	8 7		8 13		8 19		8 23		8 33
London Bridge	7 21		7 23		7 32		7 37		7 48	7 51		7 54		8 6	8 14		8 19		8 25		8 29		8 40
Cannon Street					7 35					7 54					8 18								8 43
Waterloo	7 24		7 26				7 41		7 52			7 57		8 10			8 22		8 29		8 33		
Charing Cross arr.	7 27		7 30				7 43		7 55			8 0		8 13			8 25		8 31		8 36		

Up	Week Days a.m.																						
												SX	SX	SO									
Sanderstead dep.			8 18												8 53								9 21
Selsdon			8 20								8 39				8 55								9 23
Coombe Road			8 22								8 41				8 57								9 25
Bingham Road			8 24								8 43				8 59								9 27
Addiscombe C. dep.							8 37												9 18				
Woodside (Surrey)			8 27				8 39				8 46				9 2				9 20				9 30
Hayes dep.	8 14				8 28				8 36			8 43	8 52	8 50			9 0				9 20		
West Wickham	8 16				8 30				8 38			8 45	8 54	8 52			9 2				9 22		
Eden Park	8 19				8 33				8 41			8 48	8 57	8 55			9 5				9 25		
Elmer's End arr.	8 22				8 36				8 45			8 52	9 0	8 58			9 8				9 28		
Elmer's End	8 22		8 30		8 36		8 41		8 45		8 49	8 52	9 0	8 58	9 4		9 8		9 22		9 28		9 32
Clock House	8 24		8 32		8 38		8 43		8 47		8 51	8 54		9 0	9 6		9 10		9 24		9 30		9 34
New Beckenham	8 27				8 41		8 46		8 49			8 56		9 3	9 9		9 13		9 27		9 33		9 37
Lower Sydenham	8 29				8 43				8 51			8 58	9 5	9 5			9 15		9 29		9 35		9 39
Catford Bridge	8 32				8 46		8 50				8 57	9 1	9 8	9 8	9 13		9 18		9 32		9 38		9 42
Lady Well	8 34		8 38				8 52		8 56			9 4	9 10	9 10			9 21		9 34		9 40		9 44
Lewisham 72	8 37								8 58				9 12	9 12	9 16				9 36		9 42		9 46
St John's 124							8 55						9 14	9 14									9 48
New Cross	8 40				8 53				9 1			9 8	9 17	9 17	9 19		9 25		9 39		9 45		9 51
London Bridge	8 46		8 48		8 59		9 3		9 8		9 9	9 14	9 23	9 23	9 25		9 31		9 46		9 51		9 57
Cannon Street	8 50				9 2		9 7		9 11						9 29				9 50				10 0
Waterloo			8 51								9 12	9 19	9 28	9 28			9 35				9 55		
Charing Cross arr.			8 55								9 15	9 22	9 31	9 31			9 38				9 58		

For Notes, see page 123

SANDERSTEAD, ADDISCOMBE (CROYDON), HAYES, NEW BECKENHAM, and LONDON

3–All Trains on this page are Third class only

Up	a.m. — Mondays to Fridays — p.m.																						
Sanderstead dep				9 56				1058				1158					1258				1 58		
Selsdon				9 58				11 0				12 0					1 0				2 0		
Coombe Road				10 0				11 2				12 2					1 2				2 2		
Bingham Road				10 2				11 4				12 4					1 4				2 4		
Addiscombe C dep																							
Woodside (Surrey)				10 5				11 7				12 7					1 7				2 7		
Hayes dep	9 31	9 55			1031		1057			1131	1157			1231		1257			1 31	1 57			2 31
West Wickham	9 33	9 57			1033		1059			1133	1159			1238		1259			1 33	1 59			2 33
Eden Park	9 36	10 0			1036		11 2			1136	12 2			1236		1 2			1 36	2 2			2 36
Elmer's End arr	9 40	10 4			1039		11 6			1139	12 6			1239		1 6			1 39	2 6			2 39
Elmer's End	9 40			10 7	1039			11 9		1139		12 9		1239			1 9		1 39		2 9		2 39
Clock House	9 42			10 9	1041			1111		1141		1211		1241			1 11		1 41		2 11		2 41
New Beckenham	9 44			1012	1044			1114		1144		1214		1244			1 14		1 44		2 14		2 44
Lower Sydenham	9 46			1014	1046			1116		1146		1216		1246			1 16		1 46		2 16		2 46
Catford Bridge	9 49			1017	1049			1119		1149		1219		1249			1 19		1 49		2 19		2 49
Lady Well	9 52			1019	1051			1121		1151		1221		1251			1 21		1 51		2 21		2 51
Lewisham 72	9 54			1021	1053			1123		1153		1223		1253			1 23		1 53		2 23		2 53
St. John's 124	9 56			1023	1055			1125		1155		1225		1255			1 25		1 55		2 25		2 55
New Cross	9 58			1026	1058			1128		1158		1228		1258			1 28		1 58		2 28		2 58
London Bridge	10 4			1032	11 4			1134		12 4		1234		1 4			1 34		2 4		2 34		3 4
Cannon Street																							
Waterloo	10 9			1035	11 8			1137		12 8		1237		1 8			1 37		2 8		2 37		3 8
Charing Cross arr	1012			1038	1111			1140		1211		1240		1 11			1 40		2 11		2 40		3 11

Up	p.m. — Mondays to Fridays — p.m.																						
Sanderstead dep			2 58							4 10							4 44						5 16
Selsdon			3 0							4 12							4 48						5 18
Coombe Road			3 2							4 14							4 52						5 20
Bingham Road			3 4							4 16							4 55						5 22
Addiscombe C dep	2 48			3 15			4 1				4 22	4 30						5 0		5 15			
Woodside (Surrey)	2 50		3 7	3 17			4 3			4 19	4 24	4 32					4 57	5 2		5 17			5 25
Hayes dep		2 57			3 17	3 49			4 9					4 33		4 43			5 2		5 15		
West Wickham		2 59			3 19	3 51			4 11					4 35		4 45			5 4		5 17		
Eden Park		3 2			3 22	3 54			4 14					4 38		4 48			5 7		5 20		
Elmer's End arr		3 6			3 25	3 57			4 17					4 41		4 51			5 10		5 23		
Elmer's End	2 52		3 9	3 19	3 25	3 57	4 5		4 17	4 21	4 26	4 34		4 41		4 51	5 0	5 4	5 10	5 19	5 23		5 27
Clock House	2 54		3 11	3 21	3 27	3 59	4 7		4 19	4 23	4 29	4 36		4 43		4 53	5 2	5 6	5 12	5 21	5 25		5 29
New Beckenham	2 57		3 14	3 24	3 30	4 2	4 10	4 16	4 22	4 26	4 31	4 39		4 46	4 51		5 4	5 9	5 15		5 28		
Lower Sydenham	3 0		3 16	3 26	3 32	4 4	4 12	4 18	4 24	4 28	4 33	4 42		4 48	4 53	4 57	5 6	5 11	5 17	5 24			5 33
Catford Bridge	3 4		3 19	3 29	3 35	4 7	4 15	4 21	4 27	4 31	4 36	4 45		4 51	4 56	5 0	5 9	5 14	5 20	5 27	5 32		5 36
Lady Well	3 6		3 21	3 31	3 37	4 9	4 17	4 24	4 29		4 39	4 47		4 54		5 2	5 12		5 22		5 34		
Lewisham 72	3 8		3 23	3 33		4 11				4 34		4 49		4 57	4 59				5 25	5 31			
St. John's 124			3 25	3 35		4 13			4 33	4 36		4 51				5 6		5 18					
New Cross	3 11		3 28	3 38	3 41	4 16	4 21		4 35	4 38		4 54		5 0	5 3	5 8	5 16	5 21		5 34	5 38		
London Bridge	3 17		3 34	3 44	3 47	4 23	4 27	4 34	4 42	4 44	4 49	5 0		5 7	5 10	5 14	5 22	5 27	5 34	5 40	5 44		5 47
Cannen Street	3 21			3 48			4 31			4 48	4 53	5 3			5 15				5 38	5 43	5 49		5 52
Waterloo			3 37		3 51	4 27		4 39	4 45					5 12		5 18	5 27	5 30					
Charing Cross arr			3 40		3 54	4 30		4 42	4 48					5 15		5 21	5 30	5 33					

Up	p.m. — Mondays to Fridays — p.m.																						
Sanderstead dep.					5 47				6 12			6 30											
Selsdon		5 31			5 49				6 14			6 32											
Coombe Road		5 33			5 51				6 16			6 34											
Bingham Road		5 35			5 53				6 18			6 36											
Addiscombe C dep				5 48			6 8								7 2					7 32		8 2	
Woodside (Surrey)		5 38		5 50	5 56		6 10		6 21			6 39			7 4					7 34		8 4	
Hayes dep	5 27		5 40			6 0		6 9		6 18	6 31			6 42			7 1		7 30				8 0
West Wickham	5 29		5 42			6 2		6 11		6 20	6 33			6 44			7 3		7 32				8 2
Eden Park	5 32		5 45			6 5		6 14		6 23	6 36			6 47			7 6		7 35				8 5
Elmer's End arr	5 35		5 48			6 8		6 17		6 26	6 39			6 50			7 9		7 38				8 8
Elmer's End	5 35	5 40	5 48	5 52	5 58	6 8	6 12	6 17	6 23	6 26	6 39	6 42		6 50	7 7		7 9		7 38	7 37		8 7	8 8
Clock House	5 37	5 42		5 54	6 0	6 11		6 19		6 28	6 41	6 45		6 52			7 11		7 40				8 10
New Beckenham	5 40	5 45		5 57			6 16	6 22		6 31	6 44	6 47		6 55			7 14		7 43				8 13
Lower Sydenham	5 42	5 47	5 53	5 59	6 4	6 14	6 18	6 24	6 28		6 46	6 50		6 58			7 16		7 46				8 16
Catford Bridge	5 45	5 50	5 55	6 2	6 7	6 17	6 21	6 27	6 31	6 34	6 49	6 54		7 1			7 19		7 49				8 19
Lady Well	5 47	5 52			6 9			6 29	6 33		6 51	6 56		7 3			7 21		7 51				8 21
Lewisham 72	5 50				6 11		6 24			6 37	6 53						7 23		7 53				8 23
St. John's 124		5 55	6 0					6 32			6 55			7 6			7 25		7 55				
New Cross	5 53	5 58	6 2		6 15	6 24	6 27	6 35	6 37	6 40	6 58	7 0		7 9			7 28		7 58				8 26
London Bridge	5 59	6 4	6 8	6 12	6 21	6 30	6 34	6 41	6 44	6 48	7 4	7 6		7 15			7 33		8 4				8 32
Cannon Street					6 26		6 37		6 47	6 51		7 11											
Waterloo	6 3	6 7	6 12	6 16		6 34		6 45			7 8			7 20			7 37						8 37
Charing Cross arr.	6 6	6 11	6 15	6 20		6 36		6 48			7 11			7 23			7 40						8 40

For Notes, see page 123 For SATURDAY TRAINS, see page 121

SANDERSTEAD, ADDISCOMBE (CROYDON), HAYES, NEW BECKENHAM, and LONDON

3—All Trains on this page are Third class only

Up	p.m.							**Mondays to Fridays**—*continued*										p.m.					ngt.
Sanderstead dep.																							
Selsdon																							
Coombe Road																							
Bingham Road																							
Addiscombe C dep.			8 32			9 2			9 32			10 2			1032				11 8			1138	
Woodside (Surrey)			8 34			9 4			9 34			10 4			1034				1110			1140	
Hayes dep.	8 15			8 30			9 1			9 31			10 1			1031		11 0			1127		1227
West Wickham	8 17			8 32			9 3			9 33			10 3			1033		11 2			1129		
Eden Park	8 20			8 35			9 6			9 36			10 6			1036		11 5			1132		
Elmer's End arr.	8 24			8 38			9 9			9 39			10 9			1039		11 9			1136		1233
Elmer's End			8 37	8 38		9 7	9 9		9 37	9 39		10 7	10 9		1037	1039			1112			1142	
Clock House				8 40			9 11			9 41			1011			1041			1114			1144	
New Beckenham				8 43			9 14			9 44			1014			1044			1117			1147	
Lower Sydenham				8 46			9 16			9 46			1016			1046			1119			1149	
Catford Bridge				8 49			9 19			9 49			1019			1049			1122			1152	
Lady Well				8 51			9 21			9 51			1021			1051			1124			1154	
Lewisham 72				8 53			9 23			9 53			1023			1053			1126			1156	
St. John's 124				8 55						9 55						1055			1128			1158	
New Cross				8 58			9 26			9 58			1026			1058			1131			12 1	
London Bridge				9 4			9 33			10 4			1032			11 4			1137			12 7	
Cannon Street																							
Waterloo				9 8			9 36			10 8			1036			11 8			1141			1210	
Charing Cross arr.				9 11			9 39			1011			1039			1111			1144			1213	

Up	a.m.							**Saturdays**										a.m.					
Sanderstead dep.					9 55			1028			1044				1111							1146	
Selsdon					9 59			1030			1046				1113							1148	
Coombe Road					10 2			1032			1048				1115							1150	
Bingham Road					10 4			1034			1050				1118							1152	
Addiscombe C dep		9 49																1136					
Woodside (Surrey)		9 51			10 7			1037			1053				1120			1138				1155	
Hayes dep.	9 33		9 51				1027						11 0				1127			1140			1156
West Wickham	9 35		9 53				1029						11 2				1129			1142			1158
Eden Park	9 38		9 56				1032						11 5				1132			1145			12 1
Elmer's End arr.	9 41		9 59				1036						11 8				1135			1148			12 4
Elmer's End	9 41	9 54	9 59		10 9			1039			1055		11 8		1123		1135	1140		1148		1157	12 4
Clock House	9 43		10 1		1011			1041			1057		1110		1125		1137	1142		1150		1159	12 6
New Beckenham	9 46		10 4		1014			1044			11 0		1113		1127		1140	1145		1153		12 2	12 9
Lower Sydenham	9 48		10 6		1016			1046			11 2		1116		1129		1142	1147		1155		12 4	1211
Catford Bridge	9 51		10 9		1019			1049			11 5		1119		1132		1145	1150		1158		12 7	1214
Lady Well	9 53		1011		1021			1051			11 8		1121		1135		1148	1152		12 0		12 9	1217
Lewisham 72	9 55				1023			1053					1123				1150	1154		12 2			1219
St. John's 124					1025						1111		1125				1152			12 4			1221
New Cross	9 58		1015		1028			1057			1114		1128		1140		1154	1158		12 7		1214	1224
London Bridge	10 4		1022		1034			11 3			1120		1134		1146		12 0	12 5		1214		1220	1230
Cannon Street			1025															12 8		1218			1234
Waterloo	10 8				1037			11 7			1123		1137		1150		12 4					1224	
Charing Cross arr.	1012				1040			1110			1126		1140		1153		12 7					1227	

Up	p.m.							**Saturdays**										p.m.					
Sanderstead dep			12 3		1217		1233					1258					1 30				1 58		
Selsdon			12 7		1219		1235					1 0					1 32				2 0		
Coombe Road			1210		1221		1237					1 2					1 34				2 2		
Bingham Road			1212		1223		1239					1 4					1 36				2 4		
Addiscombe C dep.	12 4			1219					1250					1 15				1 44				2 13	
Woodside (Surrey)	12 6		1215	1221	1226		1242		1252			1 7		1 17			1 39	1 46			2 7	2 15	
Hayes dep.		12 5				1224		1241			1252		1 5		1 20	1 29			1 47	1 57			2 15
West Wickham		12 7				1226		1243			1254		1 7		1 22	1 31			1 49	1 59			2 18
Eden Park		1210				1229		1246			1257		1 10		1 25	1 34			1 52	2 2			2 21
Elmer's End arr.		1213				1232		1249			1 0		1 13		1 28	1 37			1 55	2 5			2 24
Elmer's End	12 8	1213	1217	1223	1228	1232		1249	1254		1 0	1 9	1 13	1 19	1 28	1 37	1 41	1 48	1 55	2 5	2 9	2 17	2 24
Clock House	1210	1215	1219	1225	1230	1234	1245		1256		1 2		1 15	1 21	1 30		1 43	1 50	1 57	2 7	2 11	2 19	2 26
New Beckenham	1213	1218	1222	1228		1237	1248	1253	1259				1 18	1 24	1 33		1 46	1 53	2 0		2 14	2 22	2 29
Lower Sydenham	1215	1220	1224	1230	1234	1239	1250		1 1		1 6	1 13	1 20	1 26	1 35		1 48	1 55	2 2	2 11	2 16	2 24	2 31
Catford Bridge	1218	1223	1227	1233	1237	1242	1253	1257	1 4			1 16		1 29	1 38	1 43	1 51	1 58	2 5	2 14	2 19	2 27	2 34
Lady Well	1220		1230	1235	1239				1 6			1 19		1 31		1 46		2 0	2 7	2 16	2 21	2 29	2 36
Lewisham 72		1226			1241			1 0	1 8		1 11		1 25	1 33				2 2			2 23	2 31	2 38
St. John's 124	1223				1243		1257	1 2							1 42			2 4	2 10	2 19	2 25	2 33	2 40
New Cross	1226	1229	1234	1240	1246			1 5	1 11		1 14	1 23	1 28	1 36	1 45	1 50	1 57	2 7	2 13	2 22	2 28	2 36	2 43
London Bridge	1232	1235	1240	1246	1252	1253	1 5	1 12	1 18		1 20	1 30	1 35	1 42	1 51	1 56	2 3	2 13	2 19	2 28	2 34	2 41	2 49
Cannon Street		1239			1256			1 15	1 21			1 34	1 38		1 54		2 6	2 17		2 32		2 45	
Waterloo	1236		1244	1250		1256	1 9				1 24			1 46		2 0			2 23		2 38		2 53
Charing Cross arr.	1239		1248	1252		1 0	1 13				1 27			1 49		2 2			2 26		2 42		2 55

For Notes, see page 123; for SUNDAY TRAINS, see pages 122 and 123

SANDERSTEAD, ADDISCOMBE (CROYDON), HAYES, NEW BECKENHAM, and LONDON

3—All Trains on this page are Third class only

Up	p.m. Saturdays—*continued* p.m.																						
Sanderstead ....dep	2 28	..	..	..	..	3 28	..	..	..	..	..	..	..	..	..	..	..	..	..	..	..	..	..
Selsdon	2 30	..	..	..	..	3 30	..	..	..	..	..	..	..	..	..	..	..	..	..	..	..	..	..
Coombe Road	2 32	..	..	..	..	3 32	..	..	..	..	..	..	..	..	..	..	..	..	..	..	..	..	..
Bingham Road	2 34	..	..	..	..	3 34	..	..	..	..	..	..	..	..	..	..	..	..	..	..	..	..	..
Addiscombe C ....dep	..	3 2	..	..	..	..	..	..	4 2	..	4 32	..	5 2	..	5 32	..	..	6 2	..	6 32	..	7 2	..
Woodside (Surrey)	2 37	3 4	..	..	..	3 37	..	..	4 4	..	4 34	..	5 4	..	5 34	..	..	6 4	..	6 34	..	7 4	..
Hayes ....dep	..	..	3 1	..	3 27	..	..	..	..	4 1	..	4 31	..	5 1	..	5 31	..	..	6 1	..	6 31	..	7 1
West Wickham	..	..	3 3	..	3 29	..	..	..	..	4 3	..	4 33	..	5 3	..	5 33	..	..	6 3	..	6 33	..	7 3
Eden Park	..	..	3 6	..	3 32	..	..	..	..	4 6	..	4 36	..	5 6	..	5 36	..	..	6 6	..	6 36	..	7 6
Elmer's End ......arr	..	..	3 9	..	3 36	..	..	..	..	4 9	..	4 39	..	5 9	..	5 39	..	..	6 9	..	6 39	..	7 9
Elmer's End	2 39	3 7	3 9	..	..	2 39	..	..	4 7	4 9	4 37	4 39	5 7	5 9	5 37	5 39	..	6 7	6 9	6 37	6 39	7 7	7 9
Clock House	2 41	..	3 11	..	..	3 41	..	..	..	4 11	..	4 41	..	5 11	..	5 41	..	..	6 11	..	6 41	..	7 11
New Beckenham	2 44	..	3 14	..	..	3 44	..	..	..	4 14	..	4 44	..	5 14	..	5 44	..	..	6 14	..	6 44	..	7 14
Lower Sydenham	2 46	..	3 16	..	..	3 46	..	..	..	4 16	..	4 46	..	5 16	..	5 46	..	..	6 16	..	6 46	..	7 16
Catford Bridge	2 49	..	3 19	..	..	3 49	..	..	..	4 19	..	4 49	..	5 19	..	5 49	..	..	6 19	..	6 49	..	7 19
Lady Well	2 51	..	3 21	..	..	3 51	..	..	..	4 21	..	4 51	..	5 21	..	5 51	..	..	6 21	..	6 51	..	7 21
Lewisham 72	2 53	..	3 23	..	..	3 53	..	..	..	4 23	..	4 53	..	5 23	..	5 53	..	..	6 23	..	6 53	..	7 23
St. John's 124	2 55	..	..	..	..	3 55	..	..	..	..	..	4 55	..	..	..	5 56	..	..	..	..	6 55	..	..
New Cross	2 58	..	3 26	..	..	3 58	..	..	..	4 26	..	4 58	..	5 26	..	5 58	..	..	6 26	..	6 58	..	7 26
London Bridge	3 4	..	3 32	..	..	4 4	..	..	..	4 32	..	5 4	..	5 32	..	6 4	..	..	6 32	..	7 4	..	7 32
Cannon Street	..	..	..	..	..	..	..	..	..	..	..	..	..	..	..	..	..	..	..	..	..	..	..
Waterloo	3 8	..	3 36	..	..	4 8	..	..	..	4 36	..	5 8	..	5 36	..	6 8	..	..	6 36	..	7 8	..	7 36
Charing Cross ......arr	3 11	..	3 39	..	..	4 11	..	..	..	4 39	..	5 11	..	5 39	..	6 11	..	..	6 39	..	7 11	..	7 39

Up	p.m. Saturdays p.m.																						
Sanderstead ....dep	..	..	..	..	..	..	..	..	..	..	..	..	..	..	..	..	..	..	..	..	..	..	ugt.
Selsdon	..	..	..	..	..	..	..	..	..	..	..	..	..	..	..	..	..	..	..	..	..	..	..
Coombe Road	..	..	..	..	..	..	..	..	..	..	..	..	..	..	..	..	..	..	..	..	..	..	..
Bingham Road	..	..	..	..	..	..	..	..	..	..	..	..	..	..	..	..	..	..	..	..	..	..	..
Addiscombe C ....dep	..	7 32	8 2	..	8 32	..	9 2	..	9 32	..	..	..	10 2	..	..	1032	..	..	11 8	..	..	1138	..
Woodside (Surrey)	..	7 34	8 4	..	8 34	..	9 4	..	9 34	..	..	..	10 4	..	..	1034	..	..	1110	..	..	1140	..
Hayes ....dep	7 30	..	..	8 0	..	8 30	..	9 1	..	..	9 31	..	..	10 1	..	..	1031	11 0	..	..	1127	..	1227
West Wickham	7 32	..	..	8 2	..	8 32	..	9 3	..	..	9 33	..	..	10 3	..	..	1033	11 2	..	..	1129	..	..
Eden Park	7 35	..	..	8 5	..	8 35	..	9 6	..	..	9 36	..	..	10 6	..	..	1036	11 5	..	..	1132	..	..
Elmer's End ......arr	7 38	..	..	8 8	..	8 38	..	9 9	..	..	9 39	..	..	10 9	..	..	1039	11 9	..	..	1136	..	1233
Elmer's End	7 38	7 37	8 7	8 8	8 37	8 38	9 7	9 9	9 37	..	9 39	..	10 7	10 9	..	1037	1039	..	1112	..	..	1142	..
Clock House	7 40	..	..	8 10	..	8 40	..	9 11	..	..	9 41	..	..	1011	..	..	1041	..	1114	..	..	1144	..
New Beckenham	7 43	..	..	8 13	..	8 43	..	9 14	..	..	9 44	..	..	1014	..	..	1044	..	1117	..	..	1147	..
Lower Sydenham	7 46	..	..	8 16	..	8 46	..	9 16	..	..	9 46	..	..	1016	..	..	1046	..	1119	..	..	1149	..
Catford Bridge	7 49	..	..	8 19	..	8 49	..	9 19	..	..	9 49	..	..	1019	..	..	1049	..	1122	..	..	1152	..
Lady Well	7 51	..	..	8 21	..	8 51	..	9 21	..	..	9 51	..	..	1021	..	..	1051	..	1124	..	..	1154	..
Lewisham 72	7 53	..	..	8 23	..	8 53	..	9 23	..	..	9 53	..	..	1023	..	..	1053	..	1126	..	..	1156	..
St. John's 124	7 55	..	..	..	..	8 55	..	..	..	..	9 55	..	..	..	..	..	1055	..	1128	..	..	1158	..
New Cross	7 58	..	..	8 26	..	8 58	..	9 26	..	..	9 58	..	..	1026	..	..	1058	..	1131	..	..	12 1	..
London Bridge	8 5	..	..	8 32	..	9 4	..	9 32	..	..	10 4	..	..	1032	..	..	11 4	..	1137	..	..	12 7	..
Cannon Street	..	..	..	..	..	..	..	..	..	..	..	..	..	..	..	..	..	..	..	..	..	..	..
Waterloo	8 10	..	..	8 37	..	9 8	..	9 36	..	..	10 8	..	..	1036	..	..	11 8	..	1141	..	..	1210	..
Charing Cross ......arr	8 13	..	..	8 40	..	9 11	..	9 39	..	..	1011	..	..	1039	..	..	1111	..	1144	..	..	1213	..

Up	a.m. Sundays a.m.																						
Sanderstead ....dep.	..	..	..	..	..	..	..	..	..	..	..	..	..	..	..	..	..	..	..	..	..	..	..
Selsdon	..	..	..	..	..	..	..	..	..	..	..	..	..	..	..	..	..	..	..	..	..	..	..
Coombe Road	..	..	..	..	..	..	..	..	..	..	..	..	..	..	..	..	..	..	..	..	..	..	..
Bingham Road	..	..	..	..	..	..	..	..	..	..	..	..	..	..	..	..	..	..	..	..	..	..	..
Addiscombe C ....dep.	..	6 37	..	7 7	..	..	7 37	8 2	..	..	8 32	..	9 2	..	..	9 32	..	10 2	..	..	1032	..	11 2
Woodside (Surrey)	..	6 39	..	7 9	..	..	7 39	8 4	..	..	8 34	..	9 4	..	..	9 34	..	10 4	..	..	1034	..	11 4
Hayes ....dep.	6 30	..	..	..	..	7 26	..	..	8 3	..	..	8 33	..	9 3	..	..	9 33	..	10 3	..	..	1033	..
West Wickham	6 32	..	..	..	..	7 28	..	..	8 5	..	..	8 35	..	9 5	..	..	9 35	..	10 5	..	..	1035	..
Eden Park	6 35	..	..	..	..	7 31	..	..	8 8	..	..	8 38	..	9 8	..	..	9 38	..	10 8	..	..	1038	..
Elmer's End ......arr.	6 39	..	..	..	..	7 35	..	..	8 11	..	..	8 41	..	9 11	..	..	9 41	..	1011	..	..	1041	..
Elmer's End	..	6 41	..	7 11	..	..	7 41	8 7	8 11	..	8 37	8 41	9 7	9 11	..	9 37	9 41	10 7	1011	..	1037	1041	11 7
Clock House	..	6 43	..	7 13	..	..	7 43	..	8 13	..	..	8 43	..	9 13	..	..	9 43	..	1013	..	..	1043	..
New Beckenham	..	6 46	..	7 16	..	..	7 46	..	8 16	..	..	8 46	..	9 16	..	..	9 46	..	1016	..	..	1046	..
Lower Sydenham	..	6 48	..	7 18	..	..	7 48	..	8 18	..	..	8 48	..	9 18	..	..	9 48	..	1018	..	..	1048	..
Catford Bridge	..	6 51	..	7 21	..	..	7 51	..	8 21	..	..	8 51	..	9 21	..	..	9 51	..	1021	..	..	1051	..
Lady Well	..	6 53	..	7 23	..	..	7 53	..	8 23	..	..	8 53	..	9 23	..	..	9 53	..	1023	..	..	1053	..
Lewisham 72	..	6 55	..	7 26	..	..	7 55	..	8 26	..	..	8 56	..	9 26	..	..	9 56	..	1026	..	..	1056	..
St. John's 124	..	..	..	7 28	..	..	7 57	..	8 28	..	..	8 58	..	9 28	..	..	9 58	..	1028	..	..	1058	..
New Cross	..	6 58	..	7 30	..	..	8 0	..	8 30	..	..	9 0	..	9 30	..	..	10 0	..	1030	..	..	11 0	..
London Bridge	..	7 4	..	7 36	..	..	8 6	..	8 36	..	..	9 6	..	9 36	..	..	10 6	..	1036	..	..	11 6	..
Cannon Street	..	..	..	..	..	..	..	..	..	..	..	..	..	..	..	..	..	..	..	..	..	..	..
Waterloo	..	7 7	..	7 39	..	..	8 9	..	8 40	..	..	9 10	..	9 40	..	..	1010	..	1040	..	..	1110	..
Charing Cross ......arr.	..	7 10	..	7 42	..	..	8 12	..	8 43	..	..	9 13	..	9 43	..	..	1013	..	1043	..	..	1113	..

For Notes, see page 123

SANDERSTEAD, ADDISCOMBE (CROYDON), HAYES, NEW BECKENHAM, and LONDON

3—All Trains on this page are Third class only

Up	a.m	a.m	a.m	a.m	p.m	p.m	p.m	p.m	p.m	p.m	p.m	p.m	p.m	p.m	p.m	p.m	p.m	p.m	p.m	p.m	p.m	p.m	p.m
	Sundays—*continued.*																						
Sanderstead ....dep.	..	..	..	..	..	..	..	..	..	..	..	..	..	..	..	..	..	..	..	..	..	..	..
Selsdon	..	..	..	..	..	..	..	..	..	..	..	..	..	..	..	..	..	..	..	..	..	..	..
Coombe Road	..	..	..	..	..	..	..	..	..	..	..	..	..	..	..	..	..	..	..	..	..	..	..
Bingham Road	..	..	..	..	..	..	..	..	..	..	..	..	..	..	..	..	..	..	..	..	..	..	..
Addiscombe C ....dep.	..	1132	..	..	12 2	..	1232	..	..	1 2	..	1 32	..	..	2 2	..	..	2 32	..	..	3 2	..	3 32
Woodside (Surrey)	..	1134	..	..	12 4	..	1234	..	..	1 4	..	1 34	..	..	2 4	..	..	2 34	..	..	3 4	..	3 34
Hayes ....dep.	11 3	..	1133	..	..	12 3	..	1233	..	..	1 3	..	1 33	..	..	2 3	..	..	2 33	..	..	3 3	..
West Wickham	11 5	..	1135	..	..	12 5	..	1235	..	..	1 5	..	1 35	..	..	2 5	..	..	2 35	..	..	3 5	..
Eden Park	11 8	..	1138	..	..	12 8	..	1238	..	..	1 8	..	1 38	..	..	2 8	..	..	2 38	..	..	3 8	..
Elmer's End ......arr.	1111	..	1141	..	..	1211	..	1241	..	..	1 11	..	1 41	..	..	2 11	..	..	2 41	..	..	3 11	..
Elmer's End	1111	1137	1141	..	12 7	1211	1237	1241	..	1 7	1 11	1 37	1 41	..	2 7	2 11	..	2 37	2 41	..	3 7	3 11	3 37
Clock House	1113	..	1143	..	..	1213	..	1243	..	..	1 13	..	1 43	..	..	2 13	..	..	2 43	..	..	3 13	..
New Beckenham	1116	..	1146	..	..	1216	..	1246	..	..	1 16	..	1 46	..	..	2 16	..	..	2 46	..	..	3 16	..
Lower Sydenham	1118	..	1148	..	..	1218	..	1248	..	..	1 18	..	1 48	..	..	2 18	..	..	2 48	..	..	3 18	..
Catford Bridge	1121	..	1151	..	..	1221	..	1251	..	..	1 21	..	1 51	..	..	2 21	..	..	2 51	..	..	3 21	..
Lady Well	1123	..	1153	..	..	1223	..	1253	..	..	1 23	..	1 53	..	..	2 23	..	..	2 53	..	..	3 23	..
Lewisham 72	1126	..	1156	..	..	1226	..	1256	..	..	1 26	..	1 56	..	..	2 26	..	..	2 56	..	..	3 26	..
St. John's **124**	1128	..	1158	..	..	1228	..	1258	..	..	1 28	..	1 58	..	..	2 28	..	..	2 58	..	..	3 28	..
New Cross	1130	..	12 0	..	..	1230	..	1 0	..	..	1 30	..	2 0	..	..	2 30	..	..	3 0	..	..	3 30	..
London Bridge	1136	..	12 6	..	..	1236	..	1 6	..	..	1 36	..	2 6	..	..	2 36	..	..	3 6	..	..	3 36	..
Cannon Street	..	..	..	..	..	..	..	..	..	..	..	..	..	..	..	..	..	..	..	..	..	..	..
Waterloo	1140	..	1210	..	..	1240	..	1 10	..	..	1 40	..	2 10	..	..	2 40	..	..	3 10	..	..	3 40	..
Charing Cross ....arr.	1143	..	1213	..	..	1243	..	1 13	..	..	1 43	..	2 13	..	..	2 43	..	..	3 13	..	..	3 43	..

Up	p.m											**Sundays**							p.m				
Sanderstead ....dep.	..	..	..	..	..	..	..	..	..	..	..	..	..	..	..	..	..	..	..	..	..	..	..
Selsdon	..	..	..	..	..	..	..	..	..	..	..	..	..	..	..	..	..	..	..	..	..	..	..
Coombe Road	..	..	..	..	..	..	..	..	..	..	..	..	..	..	..	..	..	..	..	..	..	..	..
Bingham Road	..	..	..	..	..	..	..	..	..	..	..	..	..	..	..	..	..	..	..	..	..	..	..
Addiscombe C ....dep.	..	4 2	..	4 32	..	..	5 2	..	5 32	..	..	6 2	..	6 32	..	7 2	..	..	7 32	..	8 2	..	8 32
Woodside (Surrey)	..	4 4	..	4 34	..	..	5 4	..	5 34	..	..	6 4	..	6 34	..	7 4	..	..	7 34	..	8 4	..	8 34
Hayes ....dep.	3 33	..	4 3	..	4 33	..	..	5 3	..	5 33	..	..	6 3	..	6 33	..	7 3	..	..	7 33	..	8 3	..
West Wickham	3 35	..	4 5	..	4 35	..	..	5 5	..	5 35	..	..	6 5	..	6 35	..	7 5	..	..	7 35	..	8 5	..
Eden Park	3 38	..	4 8	..	4 38	..	..	5 8	..	5 38	..	..	6 8	..	6 38	..	7 8	..	..	7 38	..	8 8	..
Elmer's End ......arr.	3 41	..	4 11	..	4 41	..	..	5 11	..	5 41	..	..	6 11	..	6 41	..	7 11	..	..	7 41	..	8 11	..
Elmer's End	3 41	4 7	4 11	4 37	4 41	..	5 7	5 11	5 37	5 41	..	6 7	6 11	6 37	6 41	7 7	7 11	..	7 37	7 41	8 7	8 11	8 37
Clock House	3 43	..	4 13	..	4 43	..	..	5 13	..	5 43	..	..	6 13	..	6 43	..	7 13	..	..	7 43	..	8 13	..
New Beckenham	3 46	..	4 16	..	4 46	..	..	5 16	..	5 46	..	..	6 16	..	6 46	..	7 16	..	..	7 46	..	8 16	..
Lower Sydenham	3 48	..	4 18	..	4 48	..	..	5 18	..	5 48	..	..	6 18	..	6 48	..	7 18	..	..	7 48	..	8 18	..
Catford Bridge	3 51	..	4 21	..	4 51	..	..	5 21	..	5 51	..	..	6 21	..	6 51	..	7 21	..	..	7 51	..	8 21	..
Lady Well	3 53	..	4 23	..	4 53	..	..	5 23	..	5 53	..	..	6 23	..	6 53	..	7 23	..	..	7 53	..	8 23	..
Lewisham 72	3 56	..	4 26	..	4 56	..	..	5 26	..	5 56	..	..	6 26	..	6 56	..	7 26	..	..	7 56	..	8 26	..
St. John's **124**	3 58	..	4 28	..	4 58	..	..	5 28	..	5 58	..	..	6 28	..	6 58	..	7 28	..	..	7 58	..	8 28	..
New Cross	4 0	..	4 30	..	5 0	..	..	5 30	..	6 0	..	..	6 30	..	7 0	..	7 30	..	..	8 0	..	8 30	..
London Bridge	4 6	..	4 36	..	5 6	..	..	5 36	..	6 6	..	..	6 36	..	7 6	..	7 36	..	..	8 6	..	8 36	..
Cannon Street	..	..	..	..	..	..	..	..	..	..	..	..	..	..	..	..	..	..	..	..	..	..	..
Waterloo	4 10	..	4 40	..	5 10	..	..	5 40	..	6 10	..	..	6 40	..	7 10	..	7 40	..	..	8 10	..	8 40	..
Charing Cross ......arr.	4 13	..	4 43	..	5 13	..	..	5 43	..	6 13	..	..	6 43	..	7 13	..	7 43	..	..	8 13	..	8 43	..

Up	p.m					**Sundays**					p.m				
Sanderstead ....dep	..	..	..	..	..	..	..	..	..	..	..	..	..	..	..
Selsdon	..	..	..	..	..	..	..	..	..	..	..	..	..	..	..
Coombe Road	..	..	..	..	..	..	..	..	..	..	..	..	..	..	..
Bingham Road	..	..	..	..	..	..	..	..	..	..	..	..	..	..	..
Addiscombe C ....dep.	..	9 2	..	9 32	..	10 2	..	1032	..	11 2	..	..	..	..	..
Woodside (Surrey)	..	9 4	..	9 34	..	10 4	..	1034	..	11 4	..	..	..	..	..
Hayes ....dep.	8 33	..	9 3	..	9 33	..	10 3	..	1033	..	11 3	1126	1156	..	..
West Wickham	8 35	..	9 5	..	9 35	..	10 5	..	1035	..	11 5	1128	1158	..	..
Eden Park	8 38	..	9 8	..	9 38	..	10 8	..	1038	..	11 8	1131	12 1	..	..
Elmer's End ......arr.	8 41	..	9 11	..	9 41	..	1011	..	1041	..	1111	1135	12 5	..	..
Elmer's End	8 41	9 7	9 11	9 37	9 41	10 7	1011	1037	1041	11 7	1111	..	..	..	..
Clock House	8 43	..	9 13	..	9 43	..	1013	..	1043	..	1113	..	..	..	..
New Beckenham	8 46	..	9 16	..	9 46	..	1016	..	1046	..	1116	..	..	..	..
Lower Sydenham	8 48	..	9 18	..	9 48	..	1018	..	1048	..	1118	..	..	..	..
Catford Bridge	8 51	..	9 21	..	9 51	..	1021	..	1051	..	1121	..	..	..	..
Lady Well	8 53	..	9 23	..	9 53	..	1023	..	1053	..	1123	..	..	..	..
Lewisham 72	8 56	..	9 26	..	9 56	..	1026	..	1056	..	1126	..	..	..	..
St. John's **124**	8 58	..	9 28	..	9 58	..	1028	..	1058	..	1128	..	..	..	..
New Cross	9 0	..	9 30	..	10 0	..	1030	..	11 0	..	1130	..	..	..	..
London Bridge	9 6	..	9 36	..	10 6	..	1036	..	11 6	..	1136	..	..	..	..
Cannon Street	..	..	..	..	..	..	..	..	..	..	..	..	..	..	..
Waterloo	9 10	..	9 40	..	1010	..	1040	..	1110	..	1140	..	..	..	..
Charing Cross ......arr.	9 13	..	9 43	..	1013	..	1043	..	1113	..	1143	..	..	..	..

NOTES

3 Third class only

C Addiscombe (Croydon)

S O Saturdays only

S X Saturdays excepted

OTHER TRAINS
between
Sanderstead and London, page 239—Lewisham and London, 93 and 130

For Saturday Trains, see page 126; for SUNDAY TRAINS, pages 128 and 129

LONDON, BROMLEY NORTH, ORPINGTON, DUNTON GREEN, WESTERHAM, SEVENOAKS, and TONBRIDGE

Mondays to Fridays — a.m

Miles	Down	3	3	3	3	3			3	3	3		3	3		3
	Charing Cross ......dep.													6 15		
½	Waterloo													6 17		
—	Cannon Street				5 8								6 6		6 22	6 31
1½	London Bridge	1 7	3 45		5 11			5 45		5 48			6 10	6 21	6 30	6 34
5	New Cross	1 13			5 19					5 53			6 16	6 28	6 38	6 41
5½	St. John's	1 16								5 56			6 19	6 30		6 44
6	Lewisham															
7	Hither Green	1 19			5 24					5 59			6 23	6 34		6 47
9	Grove Park	1 23		4 30	5 29	5 32				6 3	6 12		6 26	6 37		6 51
10½	Sundridge Park	1 26				5 35					6 15			6 40		6 54
10¾	Bromley North A arr.	1 28		4 35		5 37					6 17			6 43		6 56
10½	Elmstead Woods	Except Monday mornings. Dep. Holborn Viaduct 1 0 and Blackfriars 1 2 a.m.			5 33					6 6			6 29			
11½	Chislehurst				5 36					6 9			6 32			
12½	Petts Wood				5 39					6 14			6 36			
13½	Orpington 34				5 43			6 7		6 17			6 39		6 57	
15½	Chelsfield				5 47								6 45			
16½	Knockholt				5 50								6 48			
20½	Dunton Green				5 56			6 21					6 55			
—	Dunton Green ....dep.								6 34							
21½	Chevening Halt								6 36							
23½	Brasted								6 41							
25½	Westerham ......arr.								6 45							
22	Sevenoaks arr.		4 16		6 0			6 26					6 59		7 13	
	(Tub's Hill) dep.		4 19				6 9	6 27				6 47			7 15	
27	Hildenborough		4 29					6 36				6 55			7 24	
29½	Tonbridge 249 .....arr.		4 35				6 19	6 42				7 1			7 30	

Miles	Down	3	3	3	3	3	3	3	3	3	3	3	3	3	3	3
	Charing Cross ......dep.	6 35			7 8	7 23			7 41	7 45	7 54	7 56			8 13	
½	Waterloo	6 37			7 10	7 25			7 43	7 47	7 56	7 58			8 15	
—	Cannon Street		6 48	6 56				7 32					8 2	8 7		
1½	London Bridge	6 41	6 51	6 59	7 15	7 29		7 34	7 47	7 51	8 1	8 3	8 5	8 10	8 18	
5	New Cross	6 47	6 57	7 5	7 21	7 36		7 41	7 53	7 57	8 7	8 10		8 17	8 25	
5½	St. John's	6 49		7 7					7 56	8 0						
6	Lewisham															
7	Hither Green	6 53	7 2	7 12	7 26	7 41		7 45	7 59	8 3		8 14	8 14	8 21	8 29	
9	Grove Park	6 56	7 5	7 16	7 30	7 44		7 49	8 3	8 7		8 18	8 17	8 25	8 33	
10½	Sundridge Park		7 8		7 32			7 52		8 10		8 21				
10¾	Bromley North A arr.		7 11		7 35			7 54		8 12		8 23				
10½	Elmstead Woods	6 59	Stop	7 19		7 47			8 6				8 21			
11½	Chislehurst	7 2		7 22		7 50			8 8		8 16		8 24	8 29	8 38	
12½	Petts Wood	7 5		7 25		7 53			8 12		8 20		8 29	8 32	8 41	
13½	Orpington 34	7 9		7 29		7 57			8 15		8 23		8 31	8 37	8 44	
15½	Chelsfield	7 14	a.m	7 33		8 2			Stop				8 36	8 41	8 49	
16½	Knockholt	7 17	3	7 36		8 5								8 44	8 52	
20½	Dunton Green	7 23		7 42		8 11								8 50	8 58	
—	Dunton Green ....dep.		7 26				8 14									9 1
21½	Chevening Halt		7 28				8 16									9 3
23½	Brasted		7 33				8 21									9 8
25½	Westerham ......arr.		7 37				8 25									9 12
22	Sevenoaks arr.	7 26		7 45		8 15			a.m					8 54	9 2	
	(Tub's Hill) dep.								8 23							
27	Hildenborough								8 31							
29½	Tonbridge 249 .....arr.								8 37							

Mondays to Fridays — a.m

Down	3	3	3		3	3	3	3	3	3	3		3	3		3
Charing Cross ......dep.	8 20		8 25	8 25	8 36	8 47		9 3	9 6		9 10	9 15	9 19	9 21		9 35
Waterloo	8 22		8 27	8 27	8 38	8 49		9 5	9 8		9 12	9 17	9 21	9 22		9 37
Cannon Street		8 25					8 57									
London Bridge	8 25	8 28	8 31	8 35	8 42	8 53	9 0	9 9	9 12		9 17		9 25	9 27		9 42
New Cross	8 32	8 34			8 49	9 0	9 6		9 18		9 23		9 31	9 34		9 48
St John's		8 37														9 50
Lewisham		8 39														
Hither Green	8 37	8 42			8 53		9 11	9 18	9 23		9 27		9 36	9 39		9 54
Grove Park	8 41	8 45			8 57	9 6	9 14	9 22	9 28		9 31		9 39	9 42		9 57
Sundridge Park	8 44				9 0		9 17		9 32				9 42			
Bromley North A arr.	8 46				9 2		9 20		9 34				9 45			
Elmstead Woods		8 48						9 25			9 34					10 0
Chislehurst		8 51				9 11		9 27			9 36			9 47		10 3
Petts Wood		8 54				9 14		9 31			9 40			9 50		10 7
Orpington 34		8 57	8 52			9 17		9 34			9 44			9 54		1010
Chelsfield		9 2				9 22					9 48					1015
Knockholt						9 25					9 51					1018
Dunton Green						9 31					9 57					1024
Dunton Green ... dep.										9 35						
Chevening Halt										9 37						
Brasted										9 42						
Westerham ......arr.										9 46						
Sevenoaks arr.				9 7		9 35					10 0	9 49				1027
(Tub's Hill) dep.				9 8								9 50			1018	
Hildenborough															1026	
Tonbridge, 249 ....arr.				9 20								10 2			1032	

Down	3	3	3	3	3		3	3	3		3	3	3	3	3	
Charing Cross ......dep.		9 44	10 3			1025	1035			1115	11 5		1135			1155
Waterloo		9 46	10 5			1027	1037			1117	11 7		1137			1157
Cannon Street				1016												
London Bridge		9 50	10 9	1019		1035	1041				11 11		1141			12 5
New Cross		9 57	10 16	1028			1047				11 17		1147			
St John's			10 18	1031			1050				11 20		1150			
Lewisham				1033												
Hither Green		10 2	10 22	1037			1053				11 23		1153		p.m	
Grove Park	10 2	10 6	10 25	1043	1032		1057		11 2		11 27	1132	1157		12 2	
Sundridge Park	10 5	1010			1035				11 5			1135			12 5	
Bromley North A arr.	10 7	1013			1037				11 7			1137			12 7	
Elmstead Woods	Stop		10 28	1049			11 0				11 30		12 0			
Chislehurst			10 31	1052			11 3				11 33		12 3			
Petts Wood			10 34	1058			11 7				11 37		12 7			
Orpington 34			10C41	11 1			1110				11 40		1210			
Chelsfield	a.m		10 45				1115				11 45		1215			
Knockholt	3		10 48				1118				11 48		1218			
Dunton Green			10 54				1124				11 54		1224			
Dunton Green ... dep.	1025							1127						1227		
Chevening Halt	1027							1129						1229		
Brasted	1032							1134						1234		
Westerham ......arr.	1036							1138						1238		
Sevenoaks arr.			10 57			11 5	1127			1149	11 57		1227			1240
(Tub's Hill) dep.						11 6				1150						1241
Hildenborough																1252
Tonbridge, 249 ....arr.						1117				12 1						1257

A Over ½ mile to Bromley South Station   C Arr. 3 mins. *earlier*

3 Third class only

For Saturday Trains, see page 126; for SUNDAY TRAINS, pages 128 and 129

LONDON, BROMLEY NORTH, ORPINGTON, DUNTON GREEN, WESTERHAM, SEVENOAKS, and TONBRIDGE

p.m — Mondays to Fridays—*continued* — p.m

Down	3	3		3	3		3	3	3		3	3	3	3	3			3	3	3		3	3		3	3	3	3	3	3	3	
Charing Cross......dep.	12 5		1225	1235				1 5			1 35			2 5		2 25		2 35			3 15	3 5		3 25	3 35		3 46				4 13	4 20
Waterloo	12 7		1227	1237				1 7			1 37			2 7		2 27		2 37			3 17	3 7		3 29	3 37		3 48				4 15	4 23
Cannon Street																												4 8	4 9			
London Bridge	12 11		1234	1241				1 11			1 41			2 11		2 33		2 41				3 11		3 34	3 41		3 52	4 10	4 12		4 19	4 28
New Cross	12 17			1247				1 17			1 47			2 17				2 47				3 17			3 47		3 58	4 16	4 19		4 25	
St John's	12 20			1250				1 20			1 50			2 20				2 50				3 20			3 50		4 0					
Lewisham																																
Hither Green	12 23			1253				1 23			1 53			2 23				2 53				3 23			3 53		4 3	4 21	4 23		4 29	
Grove Park	12 27	1232		1257			1 2	1 27	1 32		1 57		2 2	2 27	2 32			2 57		3 2		3 27	3 32		3 57		4 7	4 24	4 27		4 33	
Sundridge Park		1235					1 5		1 35				2 5		2 35					3 5			3 35				4 10	4 27			4 36	
Bromley North A arr.		1237					1 7		1 37				2 7		2 37					3 7			3 37				4 12	4 30			4 38	
Elmstead Woods	12 30			1 0				1 30			2 0			2 30				3 0				3 30			4 0				4 30			
Chislehurst	12 33			1 3				1 33			2 3			2 33				3 3				3 33			4 3				4 32			
Petts Wood	12 37			1 7				1 37			2 7			2 37				3 7				3 37			4 7				4 36			
Orpington 34	12 40			1 10				1 40			2 10			2 40				3 10				3 40			4 10				4 59			4 47
Chelsfield	12 45			1 15				1 45			2 15			2 45				3 15				3 45			4 15				4 43			
Knockholt	12 48			1 18				1 48			2 18			2 48				3 18				3 48			4 18				4 46			
Dunton Green	12 54			1 24				1 54		2 12	2 24			2 54				3 24				3 54			4 24				4 52			
Dunton Green....dep					1 27							2 27							3 27							4 27				4 57		
Chevening Halt					1 29							2 29							3 29							4 29				4 59		
Brasted					1 34							2 34							3 34							4 34				5 4		
Westerham......arr.					1 38							2 38							3 38							4 38				5 8		
Sevenoaks (Tub's Hill) arr.	12 57		1 4	1 27				1 57		2 14	2 27			2 57		3 1		3 27			3 48	3 57		4 4	4 27				4 56			
Sevenoaks (Tub's Hill) dep.			1 5							2 15						3 2					3 49			4 5								
Hildenborough										2 23														4 14								
Tonbridge 249.....arr.			1 16							2 29						3 13					4 0			4 20								

p.m — Mondays to Fridays — p.m

Down	3		3	3	3	3		3	3	3		3	3			3	3	3	3	3	3	3			3	3	3	3	3		3	3	3
Charing Cross......dep.			4 31		4 44	4 53			5 8					5 31		5 34		5 40				6 6		6 22		6 18		6 35	6 37				6 59
Waterloo			4 33		4 46	4 55			5 10					5 33		5 36		5 42				6 8		6 24		6 20		6 37	6 39				7 1
Cannon Street	4 28	4 38						5 0		5 17	5 18		5 30		5 41				5 53	5 56	6 5		6 18				6 28				6 51		
London Bridge	4 31	4 42	4 37		4 50	4 59		5 3	5 14	5 20			5 32	5 39	5 45	5 40		5 46	5 56	5 59	6 8	6 11		6 30		6 24	6 30	6 41	6 44		6 54		7 5
New Cross	4 37		4 43		4 56	5 5		5 9		5 27			5 38					5 53	6 2	6 5		6 18				6 30	6 38	6 47	6 51		7 0		7 11
St John's					4 59			5 12																			6 40	6 50	6 53		7 2		7 14
Lewisham																																	
Hither Green	4 42		4 48		5 2	5 10		5 15	5 23	5 31			5 43			5 50		5 57	6 7	6 9		6 23				6 35	6 44	6 53	6 57		7 6		7 17
Grove Park	4 46		4 52		5 6	5 14		5 20	5 27	5 35			5 46			5 53		6 1	6 10	6 13		6 26				6 39	6 47	6 57	7 0		7 9	7 11	7 21
Sundridge Park	4 49				5 9			5 23	5 30				5 49					6 4	6 13			6 29					6 50		7 3			7 14	7 24
Bromley North A arr.	4 51				5 11			5 25	5 32				5 52					6 6	6 16			6 32					6 53		7 6			7 16	7 26
Elmstead Woods			4 55			5 17				5 38						5 56				6 16						6 42		7 0			7 12	Stop	
Chislehurst			4 57			5 20				5 40						5 59				6 18	6 23					6 44		7 3			7 15		
Petts Wood			5 2			5 23				5 44						6 2				6 23	6 26					6 48		7 7			7 19		
Orpington 34			5 5			5 26				5 47						6 6				6 26	6 30					6 51		7 10			7 22		
Chelsfield			5 9			5 31				5 51						6 11					6 34					6 56		7 15			7 27	p.m	
Knockholt			5 12			5 34				5 54					6 8	6 14					6 37					6 59		7 18			7 30	3	
Dunton Green			5 18			5 40				6 0					6 15	6 20					6 43			6 58		7 5		7 24			7 36		
Dunton Green....dep				5 27								6 3					6 23								7 0							7 40	
Chevening Halt				5 29								6 5					6 25								7 2							7 42	
Brasted				5 34								6 10					6 30								7 7							7 47	
Westerham......arr.				5 38								6 14					6 34								7 11							7 51	
Sevenoaks (Tub's Hill) arr.		5 12	5 22			5 44				6 4	5 49			6 9	6 19	6 24					6 46		6 50	7 3		7 8		7 27			7 39		
Sevenoaks (Tub's Hill) dep.		5 13									5 50			6 10	6 20								6 51	7 4						7 32			
Hildenborough		5 21									5 59			6 19	6 29									7 13						7 40			
Tonbridge 249.....arr.		5 27									6 4			6 25	6 35								7 2	7 19						7 46			

A Over ½ mile to Bromley South Station

3 Third class only

For SUNDAY TRAINS, see pages 128 and 129

LONDON, BROMLEY NORTH, ORPINGTON, DUNTON GREEN, WESTERHAM, SEVENOAKS, and TONBRIDGE

Mondays to Fridays—continued (p.m.)

Down	3	3	3		3	3	3	3		3	3	3	3	3			3	3	3	3	3	3		3	3		3	3		3	3	3
Charing Cross dep	7 5			7 34		7 35		8 5			8 35		9 5		9 15			9 25		10 5			1025	1025			11 3			1138		
Waterloo	7 7			7 37		7 37		8 7			8 37		9 7		9 18			9 37		10 7			1027	1037			11 5			1140		
Cannon Street			7 20																													
London Bridge	7 11		7 23	7 45		7 41		8 11			8 41		9 11					9 41		10 11			1034	1041			11 9			1144		1150
New Cross	7 17		7 29			7 47		8 17			8 47		9 17					9 47		10 17				1047			1115			1150		
St. John's	7 20					7 50		8 20			8 50		9 20					9 50		10 20				1049			1118					
Lewisham																																
Hither Green	7 23		7 33			7 53		8 23			8 53		9 23					9 53		10 23				1053			1122			1154		
Grove Park	7 27	7 32	7 37			7 57	8 2	8 27	8 32		8 57	9 2	9 27	9 32				9 57	10 2	10 27	1032			1057	11 2		1126	1132		1158	12 2	
Sundridge Park		7 35					8 5		8 35			9 5		9 35					10 5		1035				11 5			1135			12 5	
Bromley North A arr		7 37					8 7		8 37			9 7		9 37					10 7		1037				11 7			1137			12 7	
Elmstead Woods	7 30					8 0		8 30			9 0		9 30					10 0		10 30				11 0			1129			12 1		Via Redhill, see page 247
Chislehurst	7 33		7 43			8 3		8 33			9 3		9 33					10 3		10 33				11 2			1132			12 5		
Petts Wood	7 37		7 46			8 7		8 37			9 7		9 37					10 7		10 37				11 6			1135			12 9		
Orpington 34	7 40		7 50			8 10		8 39			9 10		9 40					1010		10 40				11 9			1139			1212		
Chelsfield	7 45					8 15		8 45			9 15		9 45					1015		10 45				1114			1144			1217		
Knockholt	7 48					8 18		8 48			9 18		9 48					1018		10 48				1117			1147			1220		
Dunton Green	7 54					8 24		8 54			9 24		9 54					1024		10 54				1123			1153		1157	1226		
Dunton Green dep					8 10					9 0							10 0					11 0										
Chevening Halt					8 12					9 2							10 2					11 2										
Brasted					8 17					9 7							10 7					11 7										
Westerham arr					8 21					9 11							1011					1111										
Sevenoaks (Tub's Hill) arr	7 57			8 16		8 27		8 57			9 27		9 57		9 49			1027		10 57			11 3	1126			1156		12 0	1229		
Sevenoaks (Tub's Hill) dep				8 17											9 50	10 6							11 4			1130			12 1			
Hildenborough				8 26												1014										1138			1210			
Tonbridge 249 arr				8 32											10 1	1020							1115			1145			1216			1 19

Saturdays (a.m.)

Down	3	3	3	3		3		3	3	3		3	3			3	3	3	3		3	3	3		3		3	3	3	3	3	3
Charing Cross dep													6 15				6 35						7 8		7 23			7 41	7 45	7 54	7 56	
Waterloo													6 17				6 37						7 10		7 25			7 43	7 47	7 56	7 58	
Cannon Street				5 8								6 6			6 22	6 31			6 48		6 56						7 32					8 2
London Bridge	1 7	3 45		5 12			5 45		5 48			6 10	6 21		6 30	6 34	6 41		6 51		6 59		7 15		7 29		7 34	7 46	7 51	8 0	8 3	8 5
New Cross	1 13			5 19					5 53			6 16	6 28		6 38	6 41	6 47		6 57		7 5		7 21		7 36		7 41	7 53	7 57	8 7	8 10	
St. John's	1 16								5 56			6 19	6 30			6 44	6 49				7 7							7 56	8 0			
Lewisham																																
Hither Green	1 19			5 24					5 59			6 23	6 34			6 47	6 53		7 2		7 12		7 26		7 41		7 45	7 59	8 3		8 14	8 14
Grove Park	1 23		4 30	5 29		5 32			6 3	6 12		6 26	6 37			6 51	6 56		7 5		7 16		7 30		7 44		7 49	8 3	8 7		8 18	8 18
Sundridge Park	1 26					5 35				6 15			6 40			6 54			7 8				7 33				7 52		8 10		8 21	
Bromley North A arr	1 28		4 35			5 37				6 17			6 43			6 56			7 11				7 35				7 54		8 12		8 23	
Elmstead Woods	Dep Holborn Viaduct 1 0 and Blackfriars 1 2 a.m			5 33					6 6			6 29					6 59				7 19				7 47			8 6				8 21
Chislehurst				5 36					6 9			6 32					7 2				7 22				7 50			8 8		8 16		8 24
Petts Wood				5 39					6 14			6 36					7 5				7 25				7 53			8 12		8 20		8 29
Orpington 34				5 43			6 7		6 17			6 39			6 57		7 9				7 29				7 57			8 15		8 25		8 31
Chelsfield				5 47								6 45					7 14				7 33				8 2							8 36
Knockholt				5 50								6 48					7 17				7 36				8 5							
Dunton Green				5 56			6 21					6 55					7 23				7 42				8 11							
Dunton Green dep								6 34										7 26				8 14										
Chevening Halt								6 36										7 28				8 16										
Brasted								6 41										7 33				8 21										
Westerham arr								6 45										7 37				8 25										
Sevenoaks (Tub's Hill) arr		4 16		6 0			6 26					6 59			7 13		7 26				7 45				8 15							
Sevenoaks (Tub's Hill) dep		4 19			6 9		6 27				6 47				7 15											8 23						
Hildenborough		4 29					6 36				6 55				7 24											8 31						
Tonbridge 249 arr		4 35			6 19		6 42				7 1				7 30											8 37						

A Over ½ mile to Bromley South Station

3 Third class only

For SUNDAY TRAINS, see pages 128 and 129

LONDON, BROMLEY NORTH, ORPINGTON, DUNTON GREEN, WESTERHAM, SEVENOAKS and TONBRIDGE

Saturdays—continued

Down (a.m.)	3	3	3	3	3	3		3	3	3	3	3	3		3	3	
Charing Cross dep.	..	81 3	..	8 20	..	8 25	8 25	8 36	8 47	..	..	9 6	9 10	915	9 19	..	..
Waterloo	..	8 15	..	8 22	..	8 27	8 27	8 38	8 49	..	..	9 8	9 12	917	9 21	..	..
Cannon Street	8 7	..	..	..	8 25	..	..	..	..	..	8 57	..	..	..	..	9 24	..
London Bridge	8 10	8 18	..	8 25	8 28	8 31	8 35	8 42	8 52	..	9 0	9 12	9 16	..	9 26	9 27	..
New Cross	8 17	8 25	..	8 32	8 34	..	..	8 49	9 0	..	9 6	9 18	9 23	..	..	9 34	..
St John's	..	..	..	..	8 37	..	..	..	..	..	..	..	..	..	..	..	..
Lewisham	..	..	..	..	8 39	..	..	..	..	..	..	..	..	..	..	..	..
Hither Green	8 21	8 29	..	8 37	8 42	..	..	8 53	..	..	9 11	9 23	9 27	..	9 36	9 39	..
Grove Park	8 25	8 33	..	8 41	8 45	..	..	8 57	9 6	..	9 14	9 28	9 31	..	9 40	9 42	..
Sundridge Park	..	..	..	8 44	..	..	..	9 0	..	..	9 17	9 32	..	..	9 43	..	..
Bromley North A arr.	..	..	..	8 46	..	..	..	9 2	..	..	9 20	9 34	..	..	9 45	..	..
Elmstead Woods	..	..	..	..	8 48	..	..	..	..	..	..	..	9 34	..	..	9 45	..
Chislehurst	8 29	8 38	..	..	8 51	..	..	..	9 11	..	..	..	9 36	..	..	9 48	..
Petts Wood	8 32	8 41	..	..	8 54	..	..	..	9 14	..	..	..	9 40	..	..	9 51	..
Orpington 34	8 36	8 45	..	..	8 57	8 52	..	..	9 17	..	..	..	9 44	..	..	9 55	..
Chelsfield	8 41	8 49	..	..	9 2	..	..	..	9 22	..	..	..	9 48	..	..	..	..
Knockholt	8 44	8 52	..	..	..	..	..	..	9 25	..	..	..	9 51	..	..	..	..
Dunton Green	8 50	8 58	..	..	..	..	..	..	9 31	..	..	..	9 57	..	..	..	..
Dunton Green dep.	..	..	9 1	..	..	..	..	..	..	9 35	..	..	..	..	..	..	..
Chevening Halt	..	..	9 3	..	..	..	..	..	..	9 37	..	..	..	..	..	..	..
Brasted	..	..	9 8	..	..	..	..	..	..	9 42	..	..	..	..	..	..	..
Westerham arr.	..	..	9 12	..	..	..	..	..	..	9 46	..	..	..	..	..	..	..
Sevenoaks (Tub's Hill) arr.	8 54	9 2	..	..	..	..	9 7	..	9 35	..	..	..	10 0	949	..	..	..
Sevenoaks (Tub's Hill) dep.	..	..	..	..	..	..	9 8	..	..	..	..	..	..	950	..	..	1018
Hildenborough	..	..	..	..	..	..	..	..	..	..	..	..	..	..	..	..	1026
Tonbridge 249 arr.	..	..	..	..	..	..	9 20	..	..	..	..	..	..	102	..	..	1032

Down (a.m.)	3	3		3	3	3	3		3	3	3	3		3	3	3
Charing Cross dep.	9 33	..	..	..	9 44	..	1018	1025	1033	..	..	..	1115	..	..	..
Waterloo	9 35	..	..	..	9 46	..	1020	1027	1035	..	..	..	1117	..	..	..
Cannon Street	..	9 47	..	..	..	10 3	..	..	..	..	..	1050	..	11 6	..	..
London Bridge	9 39	9 50	..	..	9 50	10 6	1024	1034	1038	..	..	1053	..	11 9	..	..
New Cross	9 46	9 55	..	..	9 56	1012	1030	..	1045	..	..	1059	..	11 15	..	..
St John's	..	9 58	..	..	..	1015	..	..	1047	..	..	11 1	..	11 17	..	..
Lewisham	..	..	..	..	..	..	..	..	..	..	..	..	..	..	..	..
Hither Green	9 50	10 1	..	..	10 1	1019	1034	..	1052	..	..	11 5	..	11 22	..	..
Grove Park	9 54	..	..	..	10 5	1022	1038	..	1055	11 2	..	11 8	..	11 27	1132	..
Sundridge Park	..	..	..	..	10 8	..	1041	..	..	11 5	..	..	..	..	1135	..
Bromley North A arr.	..	..	..	..	1011	..	1043	..	..	11 7	..	..	..	..	1137	..
Elmstead Woods	9 57	..	..	..	..	1025	..	..	1058	..	..	1111	..	11 31	..	..
Chislehurst	9 59	..	..	..	..	1028	..	..	11 0	..	..	1114	..	11 33	..	..
Petts Wood	10 3	1010	..	..	..	1031	..	..	11 4	..	..	1117	..	11 37	..	..
Orpington 34	10 7	1013	..	..	..	1035	..	..	11 7	..	..	1121	..	11 40	..	..
Chelsfield	1012	..	..	..	..	1039	..	..	1112	..	..	..	..	11 44	..	..
Knockholt	1015	..	..	..	..	1043	..	..	1115	..	..	..	..	11 47	..	..
Dunton Green	1021	..	..	..	..	1049	..	..	1121	..	..	..	..	11 53	..	non
Dunton Green dep.	..	..	..	1025	..	..	..	..	..	..	1127	..	..	..	..	12 0
Chevening Halt	..	..	..	1027	..	..	..	..	..	..	1129	..	..	..	..	12 2
Brasted	..	..	..	1032	..	..	..	..	..	..	1134	..	..	..	..	12 7
Westerham arr.	..	..	..	1036	..	..	..	..	..	..	1138	..	..	..	..	1211
Sevenoaks (Tub's Hill) arr.	1025	..	..	..	..	1052	..	11 3	1125	..	..	..	1149	11 57	..	..
Sevenoaks (Tub's Hill) dep.	..	..	..	..	..	..	..	11 4	..	..	..	..	1150	..	..	..
Hildenborough	..	..	..	..	..	..	..	..	..	..	..	..	..	..	..	..
Tonbridge 249 arr.	..	..	..	..	..	..	..	1115	..	..	..	..	12 1	..	..	..

Saturdays

Down (a.m. / p.m.)	3		3	3	3		3		3	3		3	3	3	3	3
Charing Cross dep.	1133	..	..	11 50	..	1155	..	1217	1222	..	..	1231	..	..	1244	..
Waterloo	1135	..	..	11 52	..	..	..	1220	1224	..	..	1233	..	..	1246	..
Cannon Street	..	..	..	..	..	..	12 2	..	..	1226	..	..	..	1240	..	1253
London Bridge	1139	..	..	11 55	..	12 2	12 5	1226	1228	1229	..	1237	..	1242	1250	1256
New Cross	1145	..	..	12 2	..	..	1211	..	1235	..	..	1244	..	1249	1256	1 3
St John's	1147	..	..	..	..	..	..	..	..	..	..	..	..	..	..	1 6
Lewisham	..	..	..	..	..	..	..	..	..	..	..	..	..	..	..	..
Hither Green	1152	..	p.m	12 7	..	..	1216	..	1239	..	..	1248	..	1253	1 1	1 10
Grove Park	1156	..	12 2	12 10	..	..	1219	..	1243	..	..	1252	..	1257	1 5	1 13
Sundridge Park	..	..	12 5	..	..	..	1222	..	1246	..	..	..	..	1 0	1 8	..
Bromley North A arr.	..	..	12 7	..	..	..	1225	..	1248	..	..	..	..	1 2	1 10	..
Elmstead Woods	1159	..	..	12 13	..	..	..	..	..	..	..	1255	..	..	..	1 16
Chislehurst	12 1	..	..	12 16	..	..	..	..	..	1245	..	1257	..	..	..	1 19
Petts Wood	12 5	..	..	12 19	..	..	..	..	..	1248	..	1 1	..	..	..	1 22
Orpington 34	12 8	..	..	12B28	..	..	..	..	..	1250	..	1 4	..	..	..	1 26
Chelsfield	1213	..	..	12 32	..	..	..	..	..	1255	..	1 9	..	..	..	..
Knockholt	1216	..	..	12 35	..	..	..	..	..	1258	..	1 12	..	..	..	..
Dunton Green	1222	..	..	12 41	p.m	..	..	..	..	1 4	1 13	1 18	..	..	..	..
Dunton Green dep.	..	..	..	..	1240	..	..	..	..	..	..	..	1 21	..	..	..
Chevening Halt	..	..	..	..	1242	..	..	..	..	..	..	..	1 23	..	..	..
Brasted	..	..	..	..	1247	..	..	..	..	..	..	..	1 28	..	..	..
Westerham arr.	..	..	..	..	1251	..	..	..	..	..	..	..	1 32	..	..	..
Sevenoaks (Tub's Hill) arr.	1225	..	..	12 45	..	..	..	1255	..	1 8	1 15	1 22	..	..	..	..
Sevenoaks (Tub's Hill) dep.	..	..	..	..	..	..	..	1256	..	..	1 16	..	..	..	..	..
Hildenborough	..	..	..	..	..	..	..	1 5	..	..	..	..	..	..	..	..
Tonbridge 249 arr.	..	..	..	..	..	1243	..	1 11	..	..	1 27	..	..	..	..	..

Down (p.m.)		3	3	3		3	3	3			3	3		3	3	3
Charing Cross dep.	..	..	1 2	..	1 15	1 20	..	1 25	1 30	..	..	..	..	1 56	..	..
Waterloo	..	..	1 4	..	1 17	1 22	..	1 27	1 32	..	..	..	..	1 58	..	..
Cannon Street	1 2	1 4	..	1 7	..	..	..	..	..	..	1 38	1 44	..	..	..	2 5
London Bridge	..	1 6	1 8	1 10	..	1 26	..	1 31	1 39	..	1 40	1 46	..	2 2	..	2 7
New Cross	..	..	1 15	1 17	..	..	..	1 38	..	..	1 46	1 53	..	2 8	..	2 14
St John's	..	..	..	..	..	..	..	..	..	..	..	1 55	..	..	..	2 16
Lewisham	..	..	..	..	..	..	..	..	..	..	..	..	..	..	..	..
Hither Green	..	..	1 19	1 22	..	..	..	1 42	..	..	1 51	1 59	..	2 12	..	2 20
Grove Park	..	..	1 23	1 26	..	..	..	1 46	..	..	1 54	2 2	..	2 16	..	2 23
Sundridge Park	..	..	..	1 29	..	..	..	1 49	..	..	..	2 5	..	..	..	2 26
Bromley North A arr.	..	..	..	1 31	..	..	..	1 51	..	..	..	2 8	..	..	..	2 29
Elmstead Woods	..	..	1 26	..	..	..	..	..	..	..	1 57	..	..	2 19	..	..
Chislehurst	..	..	1 29	..	..	..	..	..	..	..	2 0	..	..	2 21	..	..
Petts Wood	..	1 26	1 32	..	..	1 42	..	..	..	..	2 4	..	..	2 25	..	..
Orpington 34	..	1 30	1 36	..	..	1 45	..	..	..	..	2 8	..	..	2 29	..	..
Chelsfield	..	1 34	..	..	..	1 49	..	..	..	..	2 12	..	..	2 33	..	..
Knockholt	..	1 37	..	..	..	1 52	..	..	..	..	2 15	..	..	2 36	..	..
Dunton Green	..	1 43	..	..	..	1 58	..	..	..	..	2 21	..	..	2 42	..	..
Dunton Green dep.	..	..	..	..	..	..	2 2	..	..	..	..	..	..	..	2 45	..
Chevening Halt	..	..	..	..	..	..	2 4	..	..	..	..	..	..	..	2 47	..
Brasted	..	..	..	..	..	..	2 9	..	..	..	..	..	..	..	2 52	..
Westerham arr.	..	..	..	..	..	..	2 13	..	..	..	..	..	..	..	2 56	..
Sevenoaks (Tub's Hill) arr.	..	1 47	..	..	..	2 2	..	..	2 11	..	2 24	..	..	2 45	..	..
Sevenoaks (Tub's Hill) dep.	..	..	..	..	..	..	..	..	2 12	..	..	..	..	..	..	..
Hildenborough	..	..	..	..	..	..	..	..	2 21	..	..	..	..	..	..	..
Tonbridge 249 arr.	1 42	..	..	..	2 0	..	..	..	2 27	..	..	..	..	..	..	..

A Over ½ mile to Bromley South Station. B Arr. 4 minutes *earlier*.

3 Third class only

For SUNDAY TRAINS, see pages 128 and 129

LONDON, BROMLEY NORTH, ORPINGTON, DUNTON GREEN, WESTERHAM, SEVENOAKS, and TONBRIDGE

Saturdays—*continued* (p.m)

Down	3	3		3		3		3	3		3		3	3	3	
Charing Cross ......dep.	2 10	2 18	2 25	2 33	..	2 48	..	3 3	..	3 15	..	..	3 35	..	4 5	4 30
Waterloo	2 12	2 20	2 27	2 35	..	2 50	..	3 5	..	3 17	..	..	3 37	..	4 7	4 32
Cannon Street	..	..	..	..	..	..	..	..	..	..	..	..	..	..	..	..
London Bridge	2 16	2 23	2 33	2 38	..	2 53	..	3 9	..	..	..	..	3 41	..	4 11	4 39
New Cross	2 22	2 30	..	2 45	..	3 0	..	3 16	..	..	..	..	3 47	..	4 17	..
St John's	..	..	..	2 47	..	..	..	3 19	..	..	..	..	3 50	..	4 20	..
Lewisham	..	..	..	..	..	..	..	..	..	..	..	..	..	..	..	..
Hither Green	2 26	2 34	..	2 51	..	3 4	..	3 23	..	..	..	..	3 53	..	4 23	..
Grove Park	2 30	2 38	..	2 55	..	3 8	..	3 27	3 32	..	..	..	3 57	4 2	4 27	..
Sundridge Park	..	2 41	..	..	..	3 11	..	..	3 35	..	..	..	..	4 5	..	..
Bromley North A arr.	..	2 43	..	..	..	3 13	..	..	3 37	..	..	..	..	4 7	..	..
Elmstead Woods	2 33	..	..	2 58	..	..	..	3 30	..	..	..	..	4 0	..	4 30	..
Chislehurst	2 35	..	..	3 0	..	..	..	3 33	..	..	..	..	4 3	..	4 33	..
Petts Wood	2 39	..	..	3 4	..	..	..	3 37	..	..	..	..	4 7	..	4 37	..
Orpington 34	2 41	..	..	3 7	..	..	..	3 40	..	..	..	..	4 10	..	4 40	..
Chelsfield	2 46	..	..	3 12	..	..	..	3 45	..	..	..	..	4 15	..	4 45	..
Knockholt	2 49	..	..	3 15	..	..	..	3 48	..	..	..	..	4 18	..	4 48	..
Dunton Green	2 55	..	..	3 21	..	..	..	3 54	..	..	..	..	4 24	..	4 54	..
Dunton Green .. dep.	..	..	..	..	..	..	..	..	..	..	4 0	..	..	..	..	..
Chevening Halt	..	..	..	..	..	..	..	..	..	..	4 2	..	..	..	..	..
Brasted	..	..	..	..	..	..	..	..	..	..	4 7	..	..	..	..	..
Westerham ......arr.	..	..	..	..	..	..	..	..	..	..	4 11	..	..	..	..	..
Sevenoaks (Tub's Hill) arr.	2 58	..	3 2	3 25	..	..	..	3 57	..	3 49	..	..	4 27	..	4 57	5 9
Sevenoaks (Tub's Hill) dep.	..	..	3 3	..	..	..	..	..	..	3 50	..	4 7	..	..	..	5 10
Hildenborough	..	..	..	..	..	..	..	..	..	..	..	4 15	..	..	..	5 19
Tonbridge 249 ....arr.	..	..	3 13	..	..	..	..	..	..	4 1	..	4 21	..	..	..	5 25

Down	3	3	3	3	3	3	3		3	3	3	3	3			3
Charing Cross ......dep.	..	..	4 35	..	5 5	..	..	5 25	5 35	..	6 5	..	..	6 15	..	6 35
Waterloo	..	..	4 37	..	5 7	..	..	5 27	5 37	..	6 7	..	..	6 17	..	6 37
Cannon Street	..	..	..	..	..	..	..	..	..	..	..	..	..	..	..	..
London Bridge	..	..	4 41	..	5 11	..	..	5 34	5 41	..	6 11	..	..	..	..	6 41
New Cross	..	..	4 47	..	5 17	..	..	..	5 47	..	6 17	..	..	..	..	6 47
St John's	..	..	4 50	..	5 20	..	..	..	5 50	..	6 20	..	..	..	..	6 50
Lewisham	..	..	..	..	..	..	..	..	..	..	..	..	..	..	..	..
Hither Green	..	..	4 53	..	5 23	..	..	..	5 53	..	6 23	..	..	..	..	6 53
Grove Park	..	4 32	4 57	5 2	5 27	..	5 32	..	5 57	6 2	6 27	..	6 32	..	..	6 57
Sundridge Park	..	4 35	..	5 5	..	..	5 35	..	..	6 5	..	..	6 35	..	..	..
Bromley North A arr.	..	4 37	..	5 7	..	..	5 37	..	..	6 7	..	..	6 37	..	..	..
Elmstead Woods	..	..	5 0	..	5 30	..	..	..	6 0	..	6 30	..	..	..	..	7 0
Chislehurst	..	..	5 3	..	5 33	..	..	..	6 3	..	6 33	..	..	..	..	7 3
Petts Wood	..	..	5 7	..	5 37	..	..	..	6 7	..	6 37	..	..	..	..	7 7
Orpington 34	..	..	5 10	..	5 40	..	..	..	6 10	..	6 40	..	..	..	..	7 10
Chelsfield	..	..	5 15	..	5 45	..	..	..	6 15	..	6 45	..	..	..	..	7 15
Knockholt	..	..	5 18	..	5 48	..	..	..	6 18	..	6 48	..	..	..	..	7 18
Dunton Green	..	..	5 24	..	5 54	..	..	..	6 24	..	6 54	..	..	..	..	7 24
Dunton Green .. dep.	5 0	..	..	..	..	6 0	..	..	..	..	..	7 0	..	..	..	..
Chevening Halt	5 2	..	..	..	..	6 2	..	..	..	..	..	7 2	..	..	..	..
Brasted	5 7	..	..	..	..	6 7	..	..	..	..	..	7 7	..	..	..	..
Westerham ......arr.	5 11	..	..	..	..	6 11	..	..	..	..	..	7 11	..	..	..	..
Sevenoaks (Tub's Hill) arr.	..	..	5 27	..	5 57	..	..	6 3	6 27	..	6 57	..	..	6 49	..	7 27
Sevenoaks (Tub's Hill) dep.	..	..	..	..	..	..	..	6 4	..	..	..	..	..	6 50	7 8	..
Hildenborough	..	..	..	..	..	..	..	..	..	..	..	..	..	..	7 16	..
Tonbridge 249 ....arr.	..	..	..	..	..	..	..	6 15	..	..	..	..	..	7 1	7 22	..

Saturdays (p.m)

Down	3	3	3	3		3	3		3	3	3	3	3	3		
Charing Cross ......dep.	..	7 5	..	..	734	7 35	..	..	8 5	..	..	8 35	..	9 5	9 15	..
Waterloo	..	7 7	..	..	736	7 37	..	..	8 7	..	..	8 37	..	9 7	9 18	..
Cannon Street	..	..	..	..	..	..	..	..	..	..	..	..	..	..	..	..
London Bridge	..	7 11	..	..	745	7 41	..	..	8 11	..	..	8 41	..	9 11	..	..
New Cross	..	7 17	..	..	..	7 47	..	..	8 17	..	..	8 47	..	9 17	..	..
St John's	..	7 20	..	..	..	7 50	..	..	8 29	..	..	8 50	..	9 20	..	..
Lewisham	..	..	..	..	..	..	..	..	..	..	..	..	..	..	..	..
Hither Green	..	7 23	..	..	..	7 53	..	..	8 23	..	..	8 53	..	9 23	..	..
Grove Park	7 2	7 27	..	7 32	..	7 57	8 2	..	8 27	8 32	..	8 57	9 2	9 27	..	..
Sundridge Park	7 5	..	..	7 35	..	..	8 5	..	..	8 35	..	..	9 5	..	..	..
Bromley North A arr.	7 7	..	..	7 37	..	..	8 7	..	..	8 37	..	..	9 7	..	..	..
Elmstead Woods	..	7 30	..	..	..	8 0	..	..	8 30	..	..	9 0	..	9 30	..	..
Chislehurst	..	7 33	..	..	..	8 3	..	..	8 33	..	..	9 3	..	9 33	..	..
Petts Wood	..	7 37	..	..	..	8 7	..	..	8 37	..	..	9 7	..	9 37	..	..
Orpington 34	..	7 40	..	..	..	8 10	..	..	8 40	..	..	9 10	..	9 40	..	..
Chelsfield	..	7 45	..	..	..	8 15	..	..	8 45	..	..	9 15	..	9 45	..	..
Knockholt	..	7 48	..	..	..	8 18	..	..	8 48	..	..	9 18	..	9 48	..	..
Dunton Green	..	7 54	..	..	..	8 24	..	..	8 54	..	..	9 24	..	9 54	..	..
Dunton Green .. dep.	..	..	8 0	..	..	..	..	..	..	..	9 0	..	..	..	..	..
Chevening Halt	..	..	3 2	..	..	..	..	..	..	..	9 2	..	..	..	..	..
Brasted	..	..	8 7	..	..	..	..	..	..	..	9 7	..	..	..	..	..
Westerham ......arr.	..	..	8 11	..	..	..	..	..	..	..	9 11	..	..	..	..	..
Sevenoaks (Tub's Hill) arr.	..	7 57	..	..	816	8 27	..	..	8 57	..	..	9 27	..	9 57	9 49	..
Sevenoaks (Tub's Hill) dep.	..	..	..	..	817	..	..	..	..	..	..	..	..	..	9 50	10 6
Hildenborough	..	..	..	..	826	..	..	..	..	..	..	..	..	..	..	1014
Tonbridge 249 ....arr.	..	..	..	..	832	..	..	..	..	..	..	..	..	..	10 1	1020

Down	3	3	3	3	3	3	3		3		3	3	3		3	3	3
Charing Cross ......dep.	..	..	9 35	..	10 5	..	..	1025	1035	..	..	11 3	..	..	1138	..	..
Waterloo	..	..	9 37	..	10 7	..	..	1027	1037	..	..	11 5	..	..	1140	..	..
Cannon Street	..	..	..	..	..	..	..	..	..	..	..	..	..	..	..	..	..
London Bridge	..	..	9 41	..	1011	..	..	1034	1041	..	..	11 9	..	..	1144	..	1150
New Cross	..	..	9 47	..	1017	..	..	..	1047	..	..	1115	..	..	1150	..	..
St John's	..	..	9 50	..	1029	..	..	..	1050	..	..	1118	..	..	..	..	..
Lewisham	..	..	..	..	..	..	..	..	..	..	..	..	..	..	..	..	..
Hither Green	..	..	9 53	..	1023	..	..	..	1053	..	..	1122	..	..	1154	ngt	..
Grove Park	9 32	..	9 57	10 2	1027	..	1032	..	1057	..	11 2	1126	1132	..	1158	12 2	..
Sundridge Park	9 35	..	..	10 5	..	..	1035	..	..	..	11 5	..	1135	..	..	12 5	..
Bromley North A arr.	9 37	..	..	10 7	..	..	1037	..	..	..	11 7	..	1137	..	..	12 7	..
Elmstead Woods	..	..	10 0	..	1030	..	..	..	11 0	..	..	1129	..	..	12 1	..	Via Redhill see page 247
Chislehurst	..	..	10 3	..	1033	..	..	..	11 3	..	..	1132	..	..	12 5	..	
Petts Wood	..	..	10 7	..	1037	..	..	..	11 7	..	..	1135	..	..	12 9	..	
Orpington 34	..	..	1010	..	1040	..	..	..	1110	..	..	1139	..	..	1212	..	
Chelsfield	..	..	1015	..	1045	..	..	..	1115	..	..	1144	..	..	1217	..	
Knockholt	..	..	1018	..	1048	..	..	..	1118	..	..	1147	..	..	1220	..	
Dunton Green	..	..	1024	..	1054	..	..	..	1124	..	..	1153	..	1157	1226	..	
Dunton Green .. dep.	..	10 0	..	..	..	11 0	..	..	..	..	..	..	..	..	..	..	..
Chevening Halt	..	10 2	..	..	..	11 2	..	..	..	..	..	..	..	..	..	..	..
Brasted	..	10 7	..	..	..	11 7	..	..	..	..	..	..	..	..	..	..	..
Westerham ......arr.	..	1011	..	..	..	1111	..	..	..	..	..	..	..	..	..	..	..
Sevenoaks (Tub's Hill) arr.	..	..	1027	..	1057	..	..	11 3	1127	..	..	1156	..	1159	1229	..	..
Sevenoaks (Tub's Hill) dep.	..	..	..	..	..	..	..	11 4	..	1130	..	..	..	12 0	..	..	..
Hildenborough	..	..	..	..	..	..	..	..	..	1138	..	..	..	1210	..	..	..
Tonbridge 249 ....arr.	..	..	..	..	..	..	..	1115	..	1145	..	..	..	1216	..	..	1 19

A Over ½ mile to Bromley South Station.

3 Third class only

LONDON, BROMLEY NORTH, ORPINGTON, DUNTON GREEN, WESTERHAM, SEVENOAKS, and TONBRIDGE

Down — Sundays — a.m.

Down	3	3	3	3	3			3	3	3	3	3		3	3	
Charing Cross .... dep	..	..	6 10	6 58	..	7 15	..	..	7 30	..	7 58	..	..	..	8 30	..
Waterloo	..	..	6 12	7 0	..	7 18	..	..	7 32	..	8 0	..	..	..	8 32	..
Cannon Street	..	..	..	..	..	..	..	..	..	..	..	..	..	..	..	..
London Bridge	1 7	4 5	6 16	7 4	..	7 24	..	..	7 36	..	8 4	..	..	..	8 36	..
New Cross	1 13	..	6 22	7 10	..	7 31	..	..	7 42	..	8 10	..	..	..	8 42	..
St. John's	1 16	..	6 24	7 12	..	..	..	..	7 44	..	8 12	..	..	..	8 44	..
Lewisham	..	..	..	..	..	..	..	..	..	..	..	..	..	..	..	..
Hither Green	1 19	..	6 28	7 16	..	..	..	..	7 48	..	8 16	..	..	..	8 48	..
Grove Park	1 23	..	6 32	7 19	..	..	..	7 32	7 51	8 0	8 19	8 30	..	..	8 51	..
Sundridge Park	1 26	..	6 35	..	..	..	..	7 35	..	8 3	..	8 33	..	..	..	..
Bromley North A ... arr	1 28	..	6 27	..	..	..	..	7 37	..	8 5	..	8 35	..	..	..	..
Elmstead Woods	Dep. Holborn Viaduct 1 0 and Blackfriars 1 2 a.m.	..	..	7 22	..	..	..	..	7 54	..	8 22	..	..	..	8 54	..
Chislehurst		..	..	7 25	..	..	..	..	7 57	..	8 25	..	..	..	8 57	..
Petts Wood		..	..	7 28	..	..	..	..	8 0	..	8 28	..	..	..	9 0	..
Orpington 34		..	..	7H35	..	..	..	..	8 3	..	8 32	..	..	..	9 3	..
Chelsfield		..	..	7 39	..	..	..	..	8 7	..	8 36	..	..	..	9 7	..
Knockholt		..	..	7 42	..	..	..	..	8 10	..	8 39	..	..	..	9 10	..
Dunton Green		..	..	7 48	..	..	..	..	8 16	..	8 45	..	..	..	9 16	..
Dunton Green ...... dep		..	..	..	7 55	..	..	..	..	..	..	..	..	8 55	..	..
Chevening Halt		..	..	..	7 57	..	..	..	..	..	..	..	..	8 57	..	..
Brasted		..	..	..	8 2	..	..	..	..	..	..	..	..	9 2	..	..
Westerham ...... arr		..	..	..	8 6	..	..	..	..	..	..	..	..	9 6	..	..
Sevenoaks (Tub's Hill) arr		4 48	..	7 51	..	8 0	..	..	8 20	..	8 48	..	..	..	9 20	..
Sevenoaks (Tub's Hill) dep		4 51	..	..	..	8 1	..	..	..	..	..	..	9 2	..	..	..
Hildenborough		..	..	..	..	8 10	..	..	..	..	..	..	9 9	..	..	..
Tonbridge 249 ...... arr		5 7	..	..	..	8 16	..	..	..	..	..	..	9 15	..	..	..

Down	3	3	3	3					3	3		3	3	3		3
Charing Cross .... dep	..	8 58	..	..	..	9 25	..	9 32	9 30	..	..	9 58	..	..	..	1030
Waterloo	..	9 0	..	..	..	9 27	..	9 35	9 32	..	..	10 0	..	..	..	1032
Cannon Street	..	..	..	..	..	..	..	..	..	..	..	..	..	..	..	..
London Bridge	..	9 4	..	..	..	9 33	..	9 41	9 36	..	..	10 4	..	..	..	1036
New Cross	..	9 10	..	..	..	..	..	..	9 42	..	..	10 10	..	..	..	1042
St. John's	..	9 12	..	..	..	..	..	..	9 44	..	..	10 12	..	..	..	1044
Lewisham	..	..	..	..	..	..	..	..	..	..	..	..	..	..	..	..
Hither Green	..	9 16	..	..	..	..	..	..	9 48	..	..	10 16	..	..	..	1048
Grove Park	9 0	9 19	9 30	..	..	..	..	..	9 51	10 0	..	10 19	1030	..	..	1051
Sundridge Park	9 3	..	9 33	..	..	..	..	..	..	10 3	..	..	1033	..	..	..
Bromley North A ... arr	9 5	..	9 35	..	..	..	..	..	..	10 5	..	..	1035	..	..	..
Elmstead Woods	..	9 22	..	..	..	..	..	..	9 54	..	..	10 22	..	..	..	1054
Chislehurst	..	9 25	..	..	..	..	..	..	9 57	..	..	10 25	..	..	..	1057
Petts Wood	..	9 28	..	..	..	..	..	..	10 1	..	..	10 28	..	..	..	11 0
Orpington 34	..	9J39	..	..	..	..	..	..	10 3	..	..	10C35	..	..	..	11 3
Chelsfield	..	9 43	..	..	..	..	..	..	10 8	..	..	10 39	..	..	..	11 7
Knockholt	..	9 46	..	..	..	..	..	..	1011	..	..	10 42	..	..	..	1110
Dunton Green	..	9 52	..	..	..	..	..	..	1017	..	..	10 48	..	..	..	1116
Dunton Green ...... dep	..	..	..	9 55	..	..	..	..	..	..	..	..	..	1055	..	..
Chevening Halt	..	..	..	9 57	..	..	..	..	..	..	..	..	..	1057	..	..
Brasted	..	..	..	10 2	..	..	..	..	..	..	..	..	..	11 2	..	..
Westerham ...... arr	..	..	..	10 6	..	..	..	..	..	..	..	..	..	11 6	..	..
Sevenoaks (Tub's Hill) arr	..	9 56	..	..	..	10 4	..	1011	1020	..	..	10 51	..	..	..	1120
Sevenoaks (Tub's Hill) dep	..	..	..	..	..	10 5	..	1012	..	..	..	..	..	..	11 5	..
Hildenborough	..	..	..	..	..	..	..	..	..	..	..	..	..	..	1113	..
Tonbridge 249 ...... arr	..	..	..	..	..	1016	..	1023	..	..	..	..	..	..	1119	..

Down — Sundays — a.m. / p.m.

Down	3	3	3		3			3	3	3				3	3	
Charing Cross .... dep	..	10 58	..	..	..	1110	1125	1130	..	11 58	..	1215	..	..	..	..
Waterloo	..	11 0	..	..	..	1113	1127	1132	..	12 0	..	1217	..	..	..	..
Cannon Street	..	..	..	..	..	..	..	..	..	..	..	..	..	..	..	..
London Bridge	..	11 4	..	..	..	1120	1134	1136	..	12 4	..	..	..	..	..	..
New Cross	..	11 10	..	..	..	1128	1141	1144	..	12 10	..	..	..	..	..	..
St. John's	..	11 12	..	..	..	..	..	1146	..	12 12	..	..	..	..	..	..
Lewisham	..	..	..	..	..	..	..	..	..	..	..	..	..	..	..	..
Hither Green	..	11 16	..	..	..	1134	..	1150	non	12 16	..	..	..	..	..	..
Grove Park	11 0	11 19	1130	..	..	..	..	1153	12 0	12 19	..	..	..	1230	..	..
Sundridge Park	11 3	..	1133	..	..	..	..	..	12 3	..	..	..	..	1233	..	..
Bromley North A ... arr	11 5	..	1135	..	..	..	..	..	12 5	..	..	..	..	1235	..	..
Elmstead Woods	..	11 22	..	..	..	..	..	1156	..	12 22	..	..	..	..	..	..
Chislehurst	..	11 25	..	..	..	..	..	1159	..	12 25	..	..	..	..	..	..
Petts Wood	..	11 28	..	..	..	..	..	12 2	..	12 28	..	..	..	..	..	..
Orpington 34	..	11 31	..	..	..	1147	..	12 4	..	12K38	..	..	..	..	..	..
Chelsfield	..	11 36	..	..	..	..	..	12 9	..	12 41	..	..	..	..	..	..
Knockholt	..	11 39	..	..	..	..	..	1212	..	12 44	..	..	..	..	..	..
Dunton Green	..	11 45	..	..	..	..	..	1218	..	12 50	..	..	..	..	..	..
Dunton Green ...... dep	..	..	..	..	1155	..	..	..	..	..	..	..	..	..	1255	..
Chevening Halt	..	..	..	..	1157	..	..	..	..	..	..	..	..	..	1257	..
Brasted	..	..	..	..	12 2	..	..	..	..	..	..	..	..	..	1 2	..
Westerham ...... arr	..	..	..	..	12 6	..	..	..	..	..	..	..	..	..	1 6	..
Sevenoaks (Tub's Hill) arr	..	11 48	..	..	..	..	12 7	1221	..	12 54	..	1248	..	..	..	..
Sevenoaks (Tub's Hill) dep	..	..	..	..	..	..	12 8	..	..	..	..	1249	1 0	..	..	..
Hildenborough	..	..	..	..	..	..	..	..	..	..	..	..	1 8	..	..	..
Tonbridge 249 ...... arr	..	..	..	..	..	1210	1219	..	..	..	..	1 1	1 14	..	..	..

Down	3	3	3	3		3	3	3	3	3	3	3	3	3	3	3
Charing Cross .... dep	1230	..	1258	..	..	..	1 30	..	1 58	..	..	2 30	..	2 58	..	..
Waterloo	1232	..	1 0	..	..	..	1 32	..	2 0	..	..	2 32	..	3 0	..	..
Cannon Street	..	..	..	..	..	..	..	..	..	..	..	..	..	..	..	..
London Bridge	1236	..	1 4	..	..	..	1 36	..	2 4	..	..	2 36	..	3 4	..	..
New Cross	1242	..	1 10	..	..	..	1 42	..	2 10	..	..	2 42	..	3 10	..	..
St. John's	1244	..	1 12	..	..	..	1 44	..	2 12	..	..	2 44	..	3 12	..	..
Lewisham	..	..	..	..	..	..	..	..	..	..	..	..	..	..	..	..
Hither Green	1248	..	1 16	..	..	..	1 48	..	2 16	..	..	2 48	..	3 16	..	..
Grove Park	1251	1 0	1 19	1 30	..	..	1 51	2 0	2 19	2 30	..	2 51	3 0	3 19	3 30	..
Sundridge Park	..	1 3	..	1 33	..	..	..	2 3	..	2 33	..	..	3 3	..	3 33	..
Bromley North A ... arr	..	1 5	..	1 35	..	..	..	2 5	..	2 35	..	..	3 5	..	3 35	..
Elmstead Woods	1254	..	1 22	..	..	..	1 54	..	2 22	..	..	2 54	..	3 22	..	..
Chislehurst	1257	..	1 25	..	..	..	1 57	..	2 25	..	..	2 57	..	3 25	..	..
Petts Wood	1 0	..	1 28	..	..	..	2 0	..	2 28	..	..	3 0	..	3 28	..	..
Orpington 34	1 3	..	1 31	..	..	..	2 3	..	2 31	..	..	3 3	..	3 31	..	..
Chelsfield	1 7	..	1 36	..	..	..	2 7	..	2 36	..	..	3 7	..	3 36	..	..
Knockholt	1 10	..	1 39	..	..	..	2 10	..	2 39	..	..	3 10	..	3 39	..	..
Dunton Green	1 16	..	1 45	..	..	..	2 16	..	2 45	..	..	3 16	..	3 45	..	..
Dunton Green ...... dep	..	..	..	..	..	1 55	..	..	..	..	2 55	..	..	..	..	3 55
Chevening Halt	..	..	..	..	..	1 57	..	..	..	..	2 57	..	..	..	..	3 57
Brasted	..	..	..	..	..	2 2	..	..	..	..	3 2	..	..	..	..	4 2
Westerham ...... arr	..	..	..	..	..	2 6	..	..	..	..	3 6	..	..	..	..	4 6
Sevenoaks (Tub's Hill) arr	1 20	..	1 48	..	..	..	2 20	..	2 48	..	..	3 20	..	3 48	..	..
Sevenoaks (Tub's Hill) dep	..	..	..	..	..	..	..	..	..	..	..	..	..	..	..	..
Hildenborough	..	..	..	..	..	..	..	..	..	..	..	..	..	..	..	..
Tonbridge 249 ...... arr	..	..	..	..	..	..	..	..	..	..	..	..	..	..	..	..

A Over ½ mile to Bromley South Station. C Arr. 3 mins. *earlier*. H Arr. 4 mins *earlier*. J Arr. 7 mins *earlier*. K Arr. 6 mins *earlier*

3 Third class only.

LONDON, BROMLEY NORTH ORPINGTON, DUNTON GREEN, WESTERHAM, SEVENOAKS, and TONBRIDGE

Sundays—*continued* (p.m.)

Down			3	3	3	3	3	3		3	3	3	3	3		3	3	3	3		3	3		3	3		3	3	3	3	3	3
Charing Cross dep	3 15	3 25	3 30	..	3 58	..	..	4 30	..	..	4 58	..	..	5 30	..	..	5 58	..	..	6 15	6 30	..	7 0	6 58	..	7 25	..	7 30	..	7 58	..	..
Waterloo	3 17	3 27	3 32	..	4 0	..	..	4 32	..	..	5 0	..	..	5 32	..	..	6 0	..	..	6 18	6 32	..	7 3	7 0	..	7 27	..	7 32	..	8 0	..	..
Cannon Street	..	..	..	..	..	..	..	..	..	..	..	..	..	..	..	..	..	..	..	..	..	..	..	..	..	..	..	..	..	..	..	..
London Bridge	3 23	3 33	3 36	..	4 4	..	..	4 36	..	..	5 4	..	..	5 36	..	..	6 4	..	..	6 25	6 36	..	7 10	7 4	..	7 33	..	7 36	..	8 4	..	..
New Cross	..	..	3 42	..	4 10	..	..	4 42	..	..	5 10	..	..	5 42	..	..	6 10	..	..	..	6 42	..	..	7 10	..	..	..	7 43	..	8 10	..	..
St. John's	..	..	3 44	..	4 12	..	..	4 44	..	..	5 12	..	..	5 44	..	..	6 12	..	..	..	6 44	..	..	7 12	..	..	..	7 45	..	8 12	..	..
Lewisham	..	..	..	..	..	..	..	..	..	..	..	..	..	..	..	..	..	..	..	..	..	..	..	..	..	..	..	..	..	..	..	..
Hither Green	..	..	3 48	..	4 16	..	..	4 48	..	..	5 16	..	..	5 48	..	..	6 16	..	..	..	6 48	..	..	7 16	..	..	..	7 49	..	8 16	..	..
Grove Park	..	..	3 51	4 0	4 19	..	4 30	4 51	..	5 0	5 19	5 30	..	5 51	..	6 0	6 19	6 30	..	..	6 51	7 0	..	7 19	7 30	..	..	7 52	8 0	8 19	8 30	..
Sundridge Park	..	..	..	4 3	..	..	4 33	..	..	5 3	..	5 33	..	..	..	6 3	..	6 33	..	..	..	7 3	..	..	7 33	..	..	..	8 3	..	8 33	..
Bromley North A arr	..	..	..	4 5	..	..	4 35	..	..	5 5	..	5 35	..	..	..	6 5	..	6 35	..	..	..	7 5	..	..	7 35	..	..	..	8 5	..	8 35	..
Elmstead Woods	..	..	3 54	..	4 22	..	..	4 54	..	..	5 22	..	..	5 54	..	..	6 22	..	..	..	6 54	..	..	7 22	..	..	..	7 55	..	8 22	..	..
Chislehurst	..	..	3 57	..	4 25	..	..	4 57	..	..	5 25	..	..	5 57	..	..	6 25	..	..	..	6 57	..	..	7 25	..	..	..	7 58	..	8 25	..	..
Petts Wood	..	..	4 0	..	4 28	..	..	5 0	..	..	5 28	..	..	6 0	..	..	6 28	..	..	..	7 0	..	..	7 29	..	..	..	8 1	..	8 28	..	..
Orpington 34	..	..	4 3	..	4 31	..	..	5 3	..	..	5 31	..	..	6 3	..	..	6C35	..	..	..	7 3	..	..	7 32	..	..	..	8 4	..	8 31	..	..
Chelsfield	..	..	4 7	..	4 36	..	..	5 7	..	..	5 36	..	..	6 7	..	..	6 39	..	..	..	7 7	..	..	7 37	..	..	..	8 8	..	8 36	..	..
Knockholt	..	..	4 10	..	4 39	..	..	5 10	..	..	5 39	..	..	6 10	..	..	6 42	..	..	..	7 10	..	..	7 40	..	..	..	8 11	..	8 39	..	..
Dunton Green	..	..	4 16	..	4 45	..	..	5 16	..	..	5 45	..	..	6 16	..	..	6 48	..	..	..	7 16	..	..	7 46	..	..	..	8 17	..	8 45	..	..
Dunton Green dep	..	..	..	..	..	4 55	..	..	..	..	..	..	5 55	..	..	..	..	..	6 55	..	..	..	..	..	..	..	7 55	..	..	..	..	8 55
Chevening Halt	..	..	..	..	..	4 57	..	..	..	..	..	..	5 57	..	..	..	..	..	6 57	..	..	..	..	..	..	..	7 57	..	..	..	..	8 57
Brasted	..	..	..	..	..	5 2	..	..	..	..	..	..	6 2	..	..	..	..	..	7 2	..	..	..	..	..	..	..	8 2	..	..	..	..	9 2
Westerham arr	..	..	..	..	..	5 6	..	..	..	..	..	..	6 6	..	..	..	..	..	7 6	..	..	..	..	..	..	..	8 6	..	..	..	..	9 6
Sevenoaks arr	3 51	4 3	4 20	..	4 48	..	..	5 20	..	..	5 48	..	..	6 20	..	..	6 51	..	..	6 56	7 20	..	7 43	7 49	..	8 5	..	8 21	..	8 48	..	..
(Tub's Hill) dep	3 52	4 4	..	..	..	..	..	..	..	..	..	..	..	..	..	..	..	..	..	6 57	..	..	7 44	..	..	8 6	..	..	..	..	..	..
Hildenborough	..	..	..	..	..	..	..	..	..	..	..	..	..	..	..	..	..	..	..	..	..	..	7 53	..	..	..	..	..	..	..	..	..
Tonbridge 249 arr	4 3	4 15	..	..	..	..	..	..	..	..	..	..	..	..	..	..	..	..	..	7 8	..	..	7 59	..	..	8 17	..	..	..	..	..	..

Sundays (p.m.)

Down		3	3			3	3		3	3			3	3		3	3		3		3	3	3	3	
Charing Cross dep	8 15	8 30	..	..	..	8 58	..	..	..	9 30	9 40	..	..	9 58	..	..	1030	..	..	..	10 58	..	1134	..	..
Waterloo	8 17	8 32	..	..	..	9 0	..	..	..	9 32	9 43	..	..	10 0	..	..	1032	..	..	..	11 0	..	1136	..	..
Cannon Street	..	..	..	..	..	..	..	..	..	..	..	..	..	..	..	..	..	..	..	..	..	..	..	..	..
London Bridge	8 23	8 36	..	9 5	..	9 4	..	..	..	9 36	9 49	..	..	10 4	..	..	1036	..	..	..	11 4	..	1140	..	..
New Cross	..	8 42	..	..	..	9 10	..	..	..	9 42	..	..	..	10 10	..	..	1042	..	..	..	11 10	..	1146	..	..
St. John's	..	8 44	..	..	..	9 12	..	..	..	9 44	..	..	..	10 12	..	..	1044	..	..	..	11 12	..	1149	..	..
Lewisham	..	..	..	..	..	..	..	..	..	..	..	..	..	..	..	..	..	..	..	..	..	..	..	..	..
Hither Green	..	8 48	..	..	..	9 16	..	..	..	9 48	..	..	..	10 16	..	..	1048	..	..	..	11 16	..	1153	ngt	..
Grove Park	..	8 51	9 0	..	..	9 19	9 3[illegible]	..	..	9 51	..	..	10 0	10 19	..	1030	1051	..	11 0	..	11 19	1130	1156	12 0	..
Sundridge Park	..	..	9 3	Through Train (via Redhill), see page 248	..	..	9 33	..	..	..	..	..	10 3	..	..	1033	..	..	11 3	..	..	1133	..	12 3	..
Bromley North A arr	..	..	9 5		..	..	9 35	..	..	..	..	..	10 5	..	..	1035	..	..	11 5	..	..	1135	..	12 5	..
Elmstead Woods	..	8 54	..		..	9 22	..	..	..	9 54	..	..	..	10 22	..	..	1054	..	..	..	11 22	..	1159	..	..
Chislehurst	..	8 57	..		..	9 25	..	..	..	9 57	..	..	..	10 25	..	..	1057	..	..	..	11 25	..	12 2	..	..
Petts Wood	..	9 0	..		..	9 28	..	..	..	10 0	..	..	..	10 28	..	..	11 0	..	..	..	11 28	..	12 6	..	..
Orpington 34	..	9 3	..		..	9 31	..	..	..	10H8	..	..	..	10 31	..	..	11 8	..	..	..	11C38	..	1210	..	..
Chelsfield	..	9 7	..		..	9 36	..	..	..	1012	..	..	..	10 36	..	..	11 8	..	..	..	11 42	..	..	..	..
Knockholt	..	9 10	..		..	9 39	..	..	..	1015	..	..	..	10 39	..	..	1111	..	..	..	11 45	..	..	..	..
Dunton Green	..	9 16	..		..	9 45	..	..	..	1021	..	..	..	10 45	..	..	1117	..	..	..	11 51	..	..	..	..
Dunton Green dep	..	..	..		..	..	..	..	9 55	..	..	..	..	..	..	..	..	..	..	..	..	..	..	..	..
Chevening Halt	..	..	..		..	..	..	..	9 57	..	..	..	..	..	..	..	..	..	..	..	..	..	..	..	..
Brasted	..	..	..		..	..	..	..	10 2	..	..	..	..	..	..	..	..	..	..	..	..	..	..	..	..
Westerham arr	..	..	..		..	..	..	..	10 6	..	..	..	..	..	..	..	..	..	..	..	..	..	..	..	..
Sevenoaks arr	8 52	9 20	..		..	9 48	..	..	..	1025	1020	..	..	10 48	..	..	1121	..	..	..	11 54	..	..	..	..
(Tub's Hill) dep	8 53	..	..		..	..	..	..	..	..	1021	..	..	..	..	..	..	..	..	1132	..	..	..	..	..
Hildenborough	..	..	..		..	..	..	..	..	..	1030	..	..	..	..	..	..	..	..	1140	..	..	..	..	..
Tonbridge 249 arr	9 4	..	..	1033	..	..	..	..	..	..	1036	..	..	..	..	..	..	..	..	1146	..	..	..	..	..

A Over ½ mile to Bromley South Station. C Arr. 3 mins. *earlier*. H Arr. 4 mins. *earlier*.

OTHER TRAINS

London & Lewisham 72, 114
London and Hither Green 72
London and Bromley S. 136
London and Orpington 136
London and Sevenoaks 136
London and Tonbridge 246

3 Third class only.

For Saturday Trains, see page 132: for SUNDAY TRAINS, pages 134 and 135

TONBRIDGE, SEVENOAKS, WESTERHAM, DUNTON GREEN, ORPINGTON, BROMLEY NORTH, and LONDON

Up — Mondays to Fridays — a.m

Miles	Up	3	3	3	3	3	3	3	3	3	3	3	3	3	3		3
	Tonbridge dep		Arr. Blackfriars 3 55 and Holborn Viaduct 3 57 a.m		Arr. Blackfriars 4 50 and Holborn Viaduct 4 52 a.m											6 5	
2¼	Hildenborough															6 11	
7½	Sevenoaks (Tub's Hill) arr															6 22	
—	Sevenoaks (Tub's Hill) dep									5 42		6 0					
—	Mls Westerham dep																6 16
—	1½ Brasted																6 19
—	3½ Chevening Halt																6 24
—	4½ Dunton Green arr.																6 27
9	Dunton Green									5 45		6 3					
13	Knockholt									5 52		6 10					
14½	Chelsfield									5 54		6 12					
15¾	Orpington	3 20			4 18		5 10		5 37	6 0		6 18		6 30			
17	Petts Wood	3 23			4 21		5 13		5 40	6 4		6 22		6 33			
18½	Chislehurst				4 24		5 16		5 43	6 7		6 25		6 36			
19½	Elmstead Woods						5 18		5 45	6 9		6 27		6 38			
—	Mls Bromley North dep		3 30	4 18		5 15		5 43			6 16		6 28		6 49		
—	½ Sundridge Park					5 16		5 44			6 17		6 29		6 50		
20½	Grove Park	3 29	3 35	4 23	4 28	5 20	5 21	5 48	5 49	6 13	6 20	6 30	6 32	6 41	6 53		
22½	Hither Green		3 38		4 32		5 25		5 52	6 16	6 24	6 34	6 36	6 45	6 57		
23½	Lewisham																
24	St John's		3 42						5 56	6 20		6 37		6 48	7 0		
24½	New Cross		3 44		4 37		5 29		5 58	6 22	6 29	6 40	6 40	6 51	7 3		
27½	London Bridge		3 50		4 43		5 35		6 4	6 28	6 35	6 46	6 47	6 57	7 9		
28½	Cannon Street						5 39			6 33			6 50				
28¾	Waterloo								6 8		6 39	6 49		7 1	7 13		
29½	Charing Cross arr.								6 10		6 41	6 52		7 3	7 15		

Miles	Up	3	3	3	3	3		3	3	3	3		3		3	3
	Tonbridge dep						648					710		7 23		
2¼	Hildenborough						654					716		7 28		
7½	Sevenoaks (Tub's Hill) arr						7 6					728		7 38		
—	Sevenoaks (Tub's Hill) dep	6 26		6 44					7 11				7 34	7 39		
—	Mls Westerham dep							6 59								
—	1½ Brasted							7 2								
—	3½ Chevening Halt							7 7								
—	4½ Dunton Green arr.							7 10								
9	Dunton Green	6 29		6 47					7 14				7 37	7 43		
13	Knockholt	6 36		6 54					7 21				7 45			
14½	Chelsfield	6 38		6 56					7 23				7 47			
15¾	Orpington	6 44		7 2		7 18			7 29				7 53		8 2	
17	Petts Wood	6 48		7 6		7 21			7 33				7 57		8 5	
18½	Chislehurst	6 51		7 9		7 24			7 36				8 0		8 8	
19½	Elmstead Woods	6 53		7 11		7 26			7 38				8 2		8 10	
—	Mls Bromley North dep		7 8		7 21					7 40	7 58					8 20
—	½ Sundridge Park		7 9		7 22					7 41	7 59					8 21
20½	Grove Park	6 56	7 12	7 15	7 26	7 29			7 41	7 45	8 2		8 6		8 13	8 24
22½	Hither Green	7 0	7 16	7 19	7 30	7 33			7 45	7 48	8 6		8 9		8 17	8 28
23½	Lewisham															
24	St John's	7 4			7 33	7 37				7 52						
24½	New Cross	7 6	7 20	7 23	7 36	7 39			7 51	7 54	8 11		8 14			8 32
27½	London Bridge	7 12	7 26	7 29	7 42	7 46			7 57	8 1	8 17		8 20		8 26	8 39
28½	Cannon Street		7 30			7 49			8 0	8 4	8 20				8 30	
28¾	Waterloo	7 16		7 33	7 47								8 24			8 43
29½	Charing Cross arr.	7 18		7 36	7 49								8 27			8 46

Up — Mondays to Fridays — a.m

Up	3	3			3	3		3	3	3	3		3	3	3	
Tonbridge dep.			745	7 57												8 31
Hildenborough			752	8 3												8 37
Sevenoaks (Tub's Hill) arr			8 4	8 15												8 48
Sevenoaks (Tub's Hill) dep		7 57	8 5	8 16					8 22					8 43		8 49
Westerham dep	7 46														8 38	
Brasted	7 49														8 41	
Chevening Halt	7 54														8 46	
Dunton Green arr.	7 57														8 49	
Dunton Green		8 0							8 25					8 46		8 53
Knockholt		8 7							8 32					8 53		9 2
Chelsfield		8 9							8 34		8 43			8 55		
Orpington		8 14			8 22			8 35	8 38		8 46			9 1		
Petts Wood		8 18			8 26			8 38			8 49			9 5		
Chislehurst		8 21			8 29			8 41			8 52			9 8		
Elmstead Woods		8 23			8 31			8 43			8 55			9 10		
Bromley North dep.						8 31				8 53			9 9			
Sundridge Park						8 32				8 54			9 10			
Grove Park		8 26				8 35		8 46		8 58	8 58		9 13	9 13		
Hither Green		8 30			8 36	8 39		8 50		9 1	9 1			9 17		
Lewisham																
St John's																
New Cross		8 35				8 44		8 55		9 6	9 6			9 21		
London Bridge		8 41	832		8 48	8 50		9 1	8 56	9 12	9 12		9 24	9 28		
Cannon Street				8 47	8 52	8 54			9 0		9 16		9 28	9 32		9 24
Waterloo		8 45	838					9 6		9 16						
Charing Cross arr.		8 48	842					9 8		9 18						

Up	3	3		3	3	3	3			3	3	3	3	3		3	3
Tonbridge dep.			8 55					9 19							1032		
Hildenborough								9 26							1040		
Sevenoaks (Tub's Hill) arr			9 11					9 37	9 49						1052		
Sevenoaks (Tub's Hill) dep			9 12				9 32	9 38	9 50			10 7		1034	1053		
Westerham dep						9 16					9 51						1054
Brasted						9 19					9 57						1057
Chevening Halt						9 24					10 2						11 2
Dunton Green arr.						9 27					10 5						11 5
Dunton Green							9 35					1010		1037			
Knockholt							9 42	9 48				1017		1044			
Chelsfield	9 8						9 44					1019		1046			
Orpington	9 11			9 34			9 49					1022		1052			
Petts Wood	9 15			9 37			9 53					1025		1056			
Chislehurst	9 18			9 40			9 56					1028		1059			
Elmstead Woods	9 20			9 43			9 58					1030		11 2			
Bromley North dep.		9 26			9 50					1021			1051			1121	
Sundridge Park		9 27			9 51					1022			1052			1122	
Grove Park	9 23	9 30		9 46	9 55		10 1			1026		1033	1056	11 5		1126	
Hither Green	9 27	9 34		9 50			10 5					1038		11 8			
Lewisham																	
St John's							10 8					1042		1112			
New Cross	9 31	9 38		9 54			1011					1044		1114			
London Bridge	9 37	9 44		10 1			1017	10 9	1017			1051		1121	1122		
Cannon Street			9 43	10 4				1014									
Waterloo	9 41	9 48					1021		1023			1055		1125	1129		
Charing Cross arr.	9 44	9 50					1026		1027			1057		1127	1134		

3 Third class only

For Saturday Trains, see page 132; for SUNDAY TRAINS, see pages 134 and 135

TONBRIDGE, SEVENOAKS, WESTERHAM, DUNTON GREEN, ORPINGTON, BROMLEY NORTH, and LONDON

Up — Mondays to Fridays—continued

Up	a.m. 3	a.m.	a.m. 3	a.m. 3	p.m. 3	p.m. 3	p.m. 3	p.m. 3	p.m. 3	p.m.	p.m. 3	p.m. 3	p.m. 3	p.m. 3	p.m. 3	p.m. 3	p.m. 3
Tonbridge dep.		1115								1235				1 5			
Hildenborough														1 11			
Sevenoaks (Tub's Hill) arr.										1252				1 22			
Sevenoaks (Tub's Hill) dep.	11 4			1134			12 4		1234	1253			1 4	1 23		1 34	
Westerham dep.						1154						1254					
Brasted						1157						1257					
Chevening Halt						12 2						1 2					
Dunton Green arr.						12 5						1 5					
Dunton Green	11 7			1137			12 7		1237				1 7	1 27		1 37	
Knockholt	1114			1144			1214		1244				1 14			1 44	
Chelsfield	1116			1146			1216		1246				1 16			1 46	
Orpington	1122			1151			1221		1251				1 22			1 51	
Petts Wood	1126			1155			1225		1255				1 26			1 55	
Chislehurst	1129			1158			1228		1258				1 29			1 58	
Elmstead Woods	1132			12 0			1230		1 0				1 32			2 0	
Bromley North dep.			1151		1221			1251			1 21				1 51		2 21
Sundridge Park			1152		1222			1252			1 22				1 52		2 22
Grove Park	1135		1156	12 4	1226		1233	1256	1 4		1 26		1 35		1 56	2 4	2 26
Hither Green	1138			12 8			1238		1 8				1 38			2 8	
Lewisham																	
St. John's	1142			1211			1242		1 12				1 42			2 12	
New Cross	1144			1214			1244		1 14				1 44			2 14	
London Bridge	1151			1220			1250		1 21	1 22			1 51			2 21	
Cannon Street																	
Waterloo	1155	12 1		1224			1254		1 25	1 30			1 55			2 25	
Charing Cross arr.	1157	12 5		1227			1257		1 27	1 35			1 57			2 27	

Up	p.m. 3	p.m. 3	p.m.	p.m. 3	p.m. 3	p.m. 3	p.m. 3	p.m. 3	p.m. 3	p.m. 3	p.m. 3	p.m. 3	p.m.	p.m. 3	p.m. 3	p.m. 3
Tonbridge dep.			1 56										322			
Hildenborough			2 4										327			
Sevenoaks (Tub's Hill) arr.			2 15										339			
Sevenoaks (Tub's Hill) dep.		2 4	2 16		2 34				3 0			3 32				
Westerham dep.	1 54							2 50								3 54
Brasted	1 57							2 53								3 57
Chevening Halt	2 2							2 58								4 2
Dunton Green arr.	2 5							3 1								4 5
Dunton Green		2 7			2 37				3 3			3 35				
Knockholt		2 14			2 44				3 10			3 42				
Chelsfield		2 16			2 46				3 12			3 44				
Orpington		2 22			2 52				3 B22	3 30		3 C51				
Petts Wood		2 26			2 56				3 26	3 33		3 55				
Chislehurst		2 29			2 59				3 29	3 36		3 58				
Elmstead Woods		2 32			3 2				3 32	3 38		4 0				
Bromley North dep.				2 51		3 13	3 23				3 43			3 55	4 19	
Sundridge Park				2 52		3 14	3 24				3 44			3 56	4 20	
Grove Park		2 35		2 56	3 5	3 17	3 28		3 35	3 41	3 47	4 3		3 59	4 23	
Hither Green		2 38			3 8	3 21			3 38	3 45	3 51	4 7		4 3	4 27	
Lewisham																
St. John's		2 42			3 12				3 42					4 6	4 30	
New Cross		2 44			3 14	3 25			3 44		3 55	4 11		4 9	4 33	
London Bridge		2 51	2 45		3 21	3 31			3 51	3 54	4 1	4 18		4 16	4 39	
Cannon Street										3 58	4 6			4 20		
Waterloo		2 55	2 51		3 25	3 35			3 56			4 22			4 43	
Charing Cross arr.		2 57	2 55		3 27	3 37			3 58			4 24			4 46	

Up — Mondays to Fridays

Up	p.m. 3	p.m. 3	p.m. 3	p.m. 3	p.m. 3	p.m. 3	p.m.	p.m. 3	p.m. 3	p.m. 3	p.m.	p.m. 3	p.m. 3	p.m. 3	p.m. 3	p.m. 3
Tonbridge dep.							4 18				4 39					
Hildenborough											4 44					
Sevenoaks (Tub's Hill) arr.											4 56					
Sevenoaks (Tub's Hill) dep.	4 3							4 38				5 3				
Westerham dep.																4 42
Brasted																4 45
Chevening Halt																4 50
Dunton Green arr.																4 53
Dunton Green	4 6							4 41				5 6				
Knockholt	4 12							4 47				5 12				
Chelsfield	4 15							4 50				5 15				
Orpington	4 20		4 40		4 50			4 55	5 8			5 C22	5 29			
Petts Wood	4 23		4 43		4 53			4 59	5 11			5 26	5 32			
Chislehurst	4 26		4 46		4 56			5 2	5 14							
Elmstead Woods	4 28				4 59				5 17							
Bromley North dep.		4 36		4 48		4 58				5 19				5 34	5 42	
Sundridge Park		4 37		4 49		4 59				5 20				5 35		
Grove Park	4 31	4 40	4 50	4 52	5 1	5 2			5 20	5 23				5 38		
Hither Green		4 44	4 54	4 56	5 5	5 6		5 8	5 24	5 27				5 42		
Lewisham																
St John's					5 8								5 42			
New Cross	4 38	4 49	4 58	5 1	5 11	5 10		5 13	5 29	5 31			5 45		5 52	
London Bridge	4 44	4 56	5 4	5 7	5 17	5 16		5 20	5 35	5 38		5 42	5 51	5 53	5 58	
Cannon Street					5 21			5 25				5 45		5 56	6 2	
Waterloo	4 48	5 0	5 8	5 11		5 21	5 6		5 39	5 43			5 55			
Charing Cross arr.	4 51	5 2	5 11	5 14		5 24	5 10		5 41	5 46			5 57			

Up	p.m. 3	p.m. 3	p.m. 3	p.m. 3	p.m. 3	p.m.	p.m. 3	p.m. 3	p.m. 3	p.m.	p.m. 3	p.m. 3	p.m. 3	p.m. 3	p.m. 3	p.m. 3
Tonbridge dep.		5 0				5 24				5 32				6 1		
Hildenborough		5 5				5 31				Through Train via Redhill, page 249				6 9		
Sevenoaks (Tub's Hill) arr.		5 16				5 43								6 21		
Sevenoaks (Tub's Hill) dep.	5 12	5 17		5 33					5 51						6 34	
Westerham dep.			5 12					5 42								
Brasted			5 15					5 45								
Chevening Halt			5 20					5 50								
Dunton Green arr.			5 23					5 53								
Dunton Green	5 15	5 21		5 36					5 54						6 37	
Knockholt	5 22			5 43					6 1						6 44	
Chelsfield	5 24			5 45					6 3						6 46	
Orpington	5 30			5 49					6 9			6 34			6 51	
Petts Wood	5 33			5 52					6 13			6 37			6 55	
Chislehurst	5 36			5 55					6 16			6 41			6 58	
Elmstead Woods	5 38								6 19						7 0	
Bromley North dep.					5 57		6 14				6 28		6 45			7 2
Sundridge Park					5 58		6 15				6 29		6 46			7 3
Grove Park	5 41				6 1		6 18		6 22		6 32		6 49		7 4	7 7
Hither Green	5 45				6 5		6 22		6 25		6 36		6 53		7 8	
Lewisham																
St John's															7 11	
New Cross	5 49			6 4	6 9		6 26		6 30		6 40		6 57		7 14	
London Bridge	5 55			6 10	6 15		6 33		6 36	6 47	6 46	6 56	7 4		7 20	
Cannon Street	5 59			6 13					6 40							
Waterloo					6 19		6 37				6 51	7 0	7 8		7 24	
Charing Cross arr.					6 22		6 39				6 54	7 2	7 10		7 27	

B Arr. 7 mins. *earlier* C Arr. 3 mins. *earlier*

3 Third class only

For SUNDAY TRAINS, see pages 134 and 135

TONBRIDGE, SEVENOAKS, WESTERHAM, DUNTON GREEN, ORPINGTON, BROMLEY NORTH, and LONDON

Mondays to Fridays—*continued* (p.m)

Up		3	3	3	3	3	3			3	3	3	3	3	3	
Tonbridge dep	6 34								7 41				8 34			9 8
Hildenborough	6 42												8 41			
Sevenoaks arr	6 54								7 58				8 53			9 24
(Tub's Hill) dep	6 55			6 59		7 34			7 59	8 4		8 34			9 4	9 25
Westerham dep			6 40		7 23						7 55			8 40		
Brasted			6 43		7 26						7 58			8 43		
Chevening Halt			6 48		7 31						8 3			8 48		
Dunton Green arr			6 51		7 34						8 6			8 51		
Dunton Green			Stop	7 2	Stop	7 37				8 7	Stop	8 37		Stop	9 7	
Knockholt				7 9		7 44				8 14		8 44			9 14	
Chelsfield				7 11		7 46				8 16		8 46			9 16	
Orpington				7 ▮22		7 51				8 21		8 51			9 21	
Petts Wood			p.m	7 26	p.m	7 55				8 25	p.m	8 55		p.m	9 25	
Chislehurst			3	7 29	3	7 58				8 29	3	8 58		3	9 28	
Elmstead Woods				7 31		8 0				8 32		9 0			9 30	
Bromley North dep		7 18	7 23		7 51		8 21				8 51			9 21		
Sundridge Park		7 19	7 24		7 52		8 22				8 52			9 22		
Grove Park		7 22	7 28	7 34	7 56	8 3	8 26			8 35	8 56	9 3		9 26	9 33	
Hither Green		7 26		7 38		8 7				8 38		9 7			9 38	
Lewisham																
St. John's		7 30		7 42		8 11				8 42		9 11			9 42	
New Cross		7 32		7 44		8 13				8 44		9 13			9 44	
London Bridge	7 24	7 38		7 50		8 19			8 28	8 51		9 19			9 51	9 52
Cannon Street		7 44														
Waterloo	7 33			7 55		8 23			8 36	8 55		9 23			9 55	9 59
Charing Cross arr	7 38			7 57		8 26			8 41	8 57		9 26			9 57	10 3

Up	3	3		3	3	3	3	3	3		3	3	3	3	3	3
Tonbridge dep			9 53								1038					12 7
Hildenborough			9 59								1045					
Sevenoaks arr			1011								1058					
(Tub's Hill) dep		9 34	1012		10 4		1034						11 4		1140	
Westerham dep				9 45								1040		1130		Through Train via Redhill, page 250
Brasted				9 48								1043		1133		
Chevening Halt				9 53								1048		1138		
Dunton Green arr				9 56								1051		1141		
Dunton Green		9 37		Stop	10 7		1037						11 7		1143	
Knockholt		9 44			1014		1044						1114		1150	
Chelsfield		9 46			1016		1046						1116		1152	
Orpington		9 51	1025		1023		1051						1120		1156	
Petts Wood		9 55		p.m	1027		1055									
Chislehurst		9 58		3	1030		1058									
Elmstead Woods		10 0			1032		11 0									
Bromley North dep	9 51			1021		1051		1121	1142							
Sundridge Park	9 52			1022		1052		1122	1143							
Grove Park	9 56	10 4		1026	1035	1056	11 4	1126	1147							
Hither Green		10 8		—	1039		11 8									
Lewisham																
St. John's		1012			1042		1112									
New Cross		1014			1045		1114									
London Bridge		1020	1044		1051		1120									1 19
Cannon Street																
Waterloo		1024	1053		1056		1124									
Charing Cross arr		1027	1058		1059		1127									

Saturdays (a.m)

Up	3	3	3	3	3	3		3	3	3	3		3	3	3	3
Tonbridge dep																
Hildenborough																
Sevenoaks arr																
(Tub's Hill) dep										5 42			6 0			
Westerham dep		Arr. Blackfriars 3 55 and Holborn Viaduct 3 57 a.m		Arr. Blackfriars 4 49 and Holborn Viaduct 4 52 a.m												
Brasted																
Chevening Halt																
Dunton Green arr																
Dunton Green										5 45			6 3			
Knockholt										5 52			6 10			
Chelsfield										5 54			6 12			
Orpington	3 20			4 18		5 10			5 37	6 0			6 18		6 30	
Petts Wood	3 23			4 21		5 13			5 40	6 4			6 22		6 33	
Chislehurst				4 24		5 16			5 43	6 7			6 25		6 36	
Elmstead Woods						5 18			5 45	6 9			6 27		6 38	
Bromley North dep		3 30	4 18		5 15			5 43			6 16			6 28		6 49
Sundridge Park					5 16			5 44			6 17			6 29		6 50
Grove Park	3 29	3 35	4 23	4 28	5 20	5 21		5 48	5 49	6 13	6 20		6 30	6 32	6 41	6 53
Hither Green		3 38		4 32		5 25			5 52	6 16	6 24		6 34	6 36	6 45	6 57
Lewisham																
St. John's		3 42							5 56	6 20			6 37		6 48	7 0
New Cross		3 44		4 37		5 29			5 58	6 22	6 29		6 40	6 40	6 51	7 3
London Bridge		3 50		4 43		5 35			6 4	6 28	6 35		6 46	6 47	6 57	7 9
Cannon Street						5 39				6 33				6 50		
Waterloo									6 8		6 39		6 50		7 1	7 13
Charing Cross arr									6 10		6 41		6 52		7 3	7 15

Up		3	3		3	3	3	3			3	3	3	3	
Tonbridge dep	6 5									6 48					7 10
Hildenborough	6 11									6 54					7 16
Sevenoaks arr	6 22									7 6					7 28
(Tub's Hill) dep			6 26			6 44						7 11			
Westerham dep		6 16	—								6 59				
Brasted		6 19									7 2				
Chevening Halt		6 24									7 7				
Dunton Green arr		6 27									7 10				
Dunton Green			6 29			6 47						7 14			
Knockholt			6 36			6 54						7 21			
Chelsfield			6 38			6 56						7 23			
Orpington			6 44			7 2		7 18				7 29			
Petts Wood			6 48			7 6		7 21				7 33			
Chislehurst			6 51			7 9		7 24				7 36			
Elmstead Woods			6 53			7 11		7 26				7 38			
Bromley North dep					7 8		7 21						7 40	7 58	
Sundridge Park					7 9		7 22						7 41	7 59	
Grove Park			6 56		7 12	7 15	7 26	7 29				7 41	7 44	8 2	
Hither Green			7 0		7 16	7 19	7 30	7 33				7 45	7 48	8 6	
Lewisham															
St. John's			7 4				7 33	7 37					7 52		
New Cross			7 6		7 20	7 23	7 36	7 39				7 51	7 54	8 11	
London Bridge			7 12		7 26	7 29	7 42	7 46				7 57	8 1	8 17	
Cannon Street					7 30			7 49				8 0	8 4	8 20	
Waterloo			7 16			7 33	7 47								
Charing Cross arr			7 18			7 36	7 49								

3 Third class only

▮ Arr 7 mins earlier

For SUNDAY TRAINS, see pages 134 and 135

TONBRIDGE, SEVENOAKS, WESTERHAM, DUNTON GREEN, ORPINGTON, BROMLEY NORTH, and LONDON

Up — Saturdays—continued (a.m)

Up	3		3	3	3			3	3	3	3	3	3	3		3	3	3		3	3	3		3		3	3	3	3	3	3	
Tonbridge dep		7 23				7 45	7 57								8 31				8 55				9 19									1032
Hildenborough		7 28				7 52	8 3								8 37								9 26									1040
Sevenoaks (Tub's Hill) arr		7 38				8 4	8 14								8 48				9 11				9 37		9 49							1052
Sevenoaks (Tub's Hill) dep	7 34	7 39			7 57	8 5	8 15				8 22				8 49		8 43		9 12				9 38	9 32	9 50				10 7		10 34	1053
Westerham dep				7 46										8 38								9 16						9 54				
Brasted				7 49										8 41								9 19						9 57				
Chevening Halt				7 54										8 46								9 24						10 2				
Dunton Green arr				7 57										8 49								9 27						10 5				
Dunton Green	7 37	7 43			8 0						8 25				8 53		8 46							9 35					10 10		10 37	
Knockholt	7 45				8 7						8 32				9 2		8 53						9 48	9 42					10 17		10 44	
Chelsfield	7 47				8 9						8 34	8 43					8 55	9 8						9 44					10 19		10 46	
Orpington	7 53				8 14			8 22		8 35	8 38	8 46					9 1	9 11						9 49		10 0			10 24		10§53	
Petts Wood	7 57				8 18			8 26		8 38		8 49					9 5	9 15						9 53		10 3			10 28		10 56	
Chislehurst	8 0				8 21			8 29		8 41		8 52					9 8	9 18						9 56		10 6			10 31		10 59	
Elmstead Woods	8 2				8 23			8 31		8 43		8 55					9 10	9 20						9 58		10 8			10 33		11 2	
Bromley North dep			8 20						8 31				8 53			9 9				9 26	9 48						1021			1051		
Sundridge Park			8 21						8 32				8 54			9 10				9 27	9 49						1022			1052		
Grove Park	8 6		8 24		8 26				8 35	8 46		8 58	8 58			9 13	9 13	9 23		9 30	9 52			10 1		1011	1026		10 36	1055	11 5	
Hither Green	8 9		8 28		8 30			8 36	8 39	8 50		9 1	9 1				9 17	9 27		9 34	9 56			10 5		1015			10 40		11 8	
Lewisham																																
St John's																								10 8					10 44		11 12	
New Cross	8 14		8 32		8 35				8 44	8 55		9 6	9 6				9 21	9 31		9 38	10 1			1011		1020			10 46		11 14	
London Bridge	8 20		8 39		8 41	8 32		8 48	8 50	9 1	8 56	9 12	9 12			9 24	9 28	9 37		9 44	10 7		10 9	1017	1017	1026			10 52		11 21	1122
Cannon Street							8 47	8 52	8 54		9 0	9 16			9 24	9 28	9 32		9 43				1015									
Waterloo	8 24		8 42		8 45	8 38				9 6			9 15					9 41		9 48	1011			1021	1023	1029			10 56		11 25	1130
Charing Cross arr	8 27		8 46		8 48	8 42				9 8			9 18					9 44		9 50	1015			1024	1027	1032			10 59		11 28	1134

Up — Saturdays (a.m / p.m)

Up	3	3	3	3		3	3	3	3	3	3	3	3	3	3	a.m	3	3	3		3	3	3	3		3	3	3			3	3
Tonbridge dep					1115											1159				1228									1 0	1 22		
Hildenborough																12 5													1 6			
Sevenoaks (Tub's Hill) arr.																1216				1244									1 18	1 39		
Sevenoaks (Tub's Hill) dep.			11 4			1120		1134				a.m	1211			1217				1245	1234		1251					1 13		1 40		1 34
Westerham dep.		1054										1145					1219										1 3					
Brasted		1057										1148					1222										1 6					
Chevening Halt		11 2										1153					1227										1 11					
Dunton Green arr.		11 5										1156					1230										1 14					
Dunton Green			11 7					1137				Stop	1214			1221					1237		1254					1 16				1 37
Knockholt			11 14			1129		1144					1221								1244		1 1					1 23				1 44
Chelsfield			11 16			1131		1146					1223								1246		1 3					1 25				1 46
Orpington			11§23	1128		1135		1151	12 2		1217		1228	1233				1246			1251		1 8					1§32				1§53
Petts Wood			11 26	1131		1138		1155	12 5		1220		1231	1236				1249			1254		1 12					1 36				1 56
Chislehurst			11 29	1134		1141		1158			1223	3		1239							1257		1 15					1 39				1 59
Elmstead Woods			11 32			1143		12 1			1226	p.m		1241							1 0		1 17					1 41				2 2
Bromley North dep.	1121						1148			1216		1225			1243				1253			1 6		1 17		1 35					1 57	
Sundridge Park	1122						1149			1217		1226			1244				1254			1 7		1 18		1 36					1 58	
Grove Park	1126		11 36			1146	1152	12 4		1220	1229	1229		1244	1247				1257		1 3	1 10		1 21		1 39		1 44			2 1	2 5
Hither Green			11 39	1141		1150	1156	12 8		1224	1232	1233		1248	1251				1 1		1 7	1 14		1 25		1 43		1 48			2 5	2 8
Lewisham																																
St John's			11 43																					1 29								2 12
New Cross			11 46	1145		1154	12 0		1216	1228	1237	1237		1252	1255			1 0			1 12	1 18	1 25	1 31		1 47		1 53			2 9	2 14
London Bridge			11 52	1151		12 1	12 7	1218	1223	1235	1243	1243	1248	1259	1 2			1 7	1 11	1 14	1 18	1 24	1 31	1 38		1 53		1 59		2 9	2 16	2 20
Cannon Street			11 56			12 5				1239	1247		1253	1 2				1 16	1 15				1 35	1 43							2 19	
Waterloo				1155	12 1		1211	1222	1227			1248			1 6					1 20	1 22	1 28				1 57		2 3		2 15		2 25
Charing Cross arr.				1158	12 5		1214	1224	1231			1251			1 9					1 24	1 25	1 31				1 59		2 5		2 20		2 28

3 Third class only

§ Arr. 3 minutes earlier

For SUNDAY TRAINS, see pages 134 and 135

TONBRIDGE, SEVENOAKS, WESTERHAM, DUNTON GREEN, ORPINGTON, BROMLEY NORTH, and LONDON

Saturdays—continued (p.m)

Up	3	3	3		3	3	3	3	3	3	3	3		3	3	3
Tonbridge ... dep				1 51									3 22			
Hildenborough				1 58									3 27			
Sevenoaks (Tub's Hill) arr.				2 10									3 39			
Sevenoaks (Tub's Hill) dep.			2 4	2 11			2 34		3 4		3 34				4 4	
Westerham ... dep.		1 45			2 23							3 40				
Brasted		1 48			2 26							3 43				
Chevening Halt		1 53			2 31							3 48				
Dunton Green ... arr.		1 56			2 34							3 51				
Dunton Green			2 7				2 37		2 7		3 37				4 7	
Knockholt			2 14				2 44		3 14		3 44				4 14	
Chelsfield			2 16				2 46		3 16		3 46				4 16	
Orpington			2 22				2 52		3 21		3 51				4 21	
Petts Wood			2 26				2 55		3 25		3 55				4 25	
Chislehurst			2 29				2 58		3 28		3 58				4 28	
Elmstead Woods			2 31				3 0		3 30		4 0				4 30	
Bromley North ... dep.	2 18					2 55		3 21		3 51				4 21		4 51
Sundridge Park	2 19					2 56		3 22		3 52				4 22		4 52
Grove Park	2 22		2 34			2 59	3 4	3 26	3 34	3 56	4 3			4 26	4 34	4 56
Hither Green	2 26		2 40			3 3	3 8		3 38		4 7				4 38	
Lewisham																
St John's			2 43				3 12		3 42		4 10				4 42	
New Cross	2 30		2 46			3 7	3 14		3 44		4 13				4 44	
London Bridge	2 37		2 52	2 39		3 14	3 20		3 50		4 19				4 51	
Cannon Street	2 40					3 19										
Waterloo			2 57	2 45			3 24		3 55		4 23				4 55	
Charing Cross ... arr.			3 0	2 50			3 27		3 58		4 26				4 57	

Up		3	3	3	3		3	3		3	3	3	3	3	3	
Tonbridge ... dep	4 0					5 5			5 33							6 34
Hildenborough	4 5					5 10										6 42
Sevenoaks (Tub's Hill) arr.	4 17					5 20										6 54
Sevenoaks (Tub's Hill) dep.		4 30			5 4	5 21		5 34				6 4		6 34		6 55
Westerham ... dep.				4 40					Through Train via Redhill, page 249		5 40					
Brasted				4 43							5 43					
Chevening Halt				4 48							5 48					
Dunton Green ... arr.				4 51							5 51					
Dunton Green		4 33			5 7	5 25		5 37				6 7		6 37		
Knockholt		4 40			5 14			5 44				6 14		6 44		
Chelsfield		4 42			5 16			5 46				6 16		6 46		
Orpington		4A51			5 21			5 51				6 21		6 51		
Petts Wood		4 55			5 25			5 55				6 25		6 55		
Chislehurst		4 58			5 28			5 58				6 28		6 58		
Elmstead Woods		5 0			5 30			6 0				6 30		7 0		
Bromley North ... dep.			5 21				5 51			6 21			6 51		7 21	
Sundridge Park			5 22				5 52			6 22			6 52		7 22	
Grove Park		5 3	5 26		5 34		5 56	6 4		6 26		6 34	6 56	7 3	7 26	
Hither Green		5 7			5 38			6 8				6 38		7 7		
Lewisham																
St John's		5 10			5 42			6 12				6 42		7 10		
New Cross		5 13			5 44			6 14				6 44		7 13		
London Bridge		5 19			5 51			6 20	6 47			6 51		7 19		7 24
Cannon Street																
Waterloo		5 23			5 54			6 24				6 54		7 23		7 34
Charing Cross ... arr.		5 26			5 57			6 28				6 57		7 26		7 38

Saturdays (p.m)

Up	3	3	3	3	3		3		3	3	3	3		3		3
Tonbridge ... dep.						7 41							8 34		9 8	
Hildenborough													8 41			
Sevenoaks (Tub's Hill) arr.						7 58							8 53		9 24	
Sevenoaks (Tub's Hill) dep		6 59		7 34		7 59			8 4		8 34			9 4	9 25	
Westerham ... dep.	6 40						7 40					8 40				
Brasted	6 43						7 43					8 43				
Chevening Halt	6 48						7 48					8 48				
Dunton Green ... arr.	6 51						7 51					8 51				
Dunton Green		7 2		7 37					8 7		8 37	Stop		9 7		
Knockholt		7 9		7 44					8 14		8 44			9 14		
Chelsfield		7 11		7 46					8 16		8 46			9 16		
Orpington		7A20		7 51					8 21		8 51			9 21		
Petts Wood		7 26		7 55					8 25		8 55	p.m		9 25		
Chislehurst		7 29		7 58					8 29		8 58	3		9 28		
Elmstead Woods		7 31		8 0					8 32		9 0			9 30		
Bromley North ... dep.			7 51		8 21					8 51		9 21				9 51
Sundridge Park			7 52		8 22					8 52		9 22				9 52
Grove Park		7 34	7 56	8 3	8 26				8 35	8 56	9 3	9 26		9 33		9 56
Hither Green		7 38		8 7					8 38		9 7			9 38		
Lewisham																
St John's		7 42		8 11					8 42		9 11			9 42		
New Cross		7 44		8 13					8 44		9 13			9 44		
London Bridge		7 50		8 19		8 28			8 51		9 19			9 51	9 52	
Cannon Street																
Waterloo		7 54		8 23		8 36			8 55		9 23			9 55	9 59	
Charing Cross ... arr.		7 57		8 26		8 41			8 57		9 26			9 57	10 3	

Up	3	3	3	3			3	3	3		3	3	3	3	3	3
Tonbridge ... dep.					9 53					1038						12 7
Hildenborough					9 59					1045						
Sevenoaks (Tub's Hill) arr.					1011					1058						
Sevenoaks (Tub's Hill) dep	9 34			10 4	1012			1034				11 4			1140	
Westerham ... dep.		9 45							10 40					1130		Through Train via Redhill, page 250
Brasted		9 48							10 43					1133		
Chevening Halt		9 53							10 48					1138		
Dunton Green ... arr.		9 56							10 51					1141		
Dunton Green	9 37			10 7				1037				11 7			1143	
Knockholt	9 44			10 14				1044				1114			1150	
Chelsfield	9 46			10 16				1046				1116			1152	
Orpington	9 51			10‖23	1025			1051				1120			1156	
Petts Wood	9 55			10 27				1055								
Chislehurst	9 58			10 30				1058								
Elmstead Woods	10 0			10 32				11 0								
Bromley North ... dep.			1021				1051				1121		1142			
Sundridge Park			1022				1052				1122		1143			
Grove Park	10 4		1026	10 35			1056	11 4			1126		1147			
Hither Green	10 8			10 39				11 8								
Lewisham																
St John's	1012			10 42				1112								
New Cross	1014			10 45				1114								
London Bridge	1020			10 51	1044			1120								1 19
Cannon Street																
Waterloo	1024			10 56	1053			1124								
Charing Cross ... arr.	1027			10 59	1058			1127								

3 Third class only. A Arr. 5 mins. earlier ‖ Arr. 3 mins. earlier.

TONBRIDGE, SEVENOAKS, WESTERHAM, DUNTON GREEN, ORPINGTON, BROMLEY NORTH, and LONDON

Sundays — a.m.

Up	3	3	3	3		3	3		3	3	3		3	3	3		3		3		3	3		3	3		3		3	3	3	
Tonbridge dep	..	..	..	..	..	..	..	7 5	..	..	..	..	..	..	..	8 25	..	..	..	8 58	..	..	..	..	..	..	..	1011	..	..	..	1033
Hildenborough	..	..	..	..	..	..	..	7 11	..	..	..	..	..	..	..	—	..	..	..	9 4	..	..	..	..	..	..	..	..	..	..	..	1041
Sevenoaks arr	..	..	..	..	..	..	..	7 23	..	..	..	..	..	..	..	8 42	..	..	..	9 15	..	..	..	..	..	..	..	..	..	..	..	1052
(Tub's Hill) dep	..	..	6 30	..	..	7 2	..	..	7 30	..	8 2	..	..	..	8 30	8 43	..	..	9 2	9 16	..	..	..	9 30	..	..	10 2	..	..	..	1030	1053
Westerham dep	..	..	..	..	..	..	..	..	..	..	..	..	8 17	..	..	..	..	..	..	..	9 17	..	..	..	..	..	..	..	1017	..	..	..
Brasted	..	..	..	..	..	..	..	..	..	..	..	..	8 20	..	..	..	..	..	..	..	9 20	..	..	..	..	..	..	..	1020	..	..	..
Chevening Halt	..	..	..	..	..	..	..	..	..	..	..	..	8 25	..	..	..	..	..	..	..	9 25	..	..	..	..	..	..	..	1025	..	..	..
Dunton Green arr	..	..	..	..	..	..	..	..	..	..	..	..	8 28	..	..	..	..	..	..	..	9 28	..	..	..	..	..	..	..	1028	..	..	..
Dunton Green	..	..	6 33	..	..	7 5	..	..	7 33	..	8 5	..	..	..	8 33	..	..	..	9 5	..	..	..	..	9 33	..	..	10 5	..	..	..	1033	..
Knockholt	..	..	6 40	..	..	7 12	..	..	7 40	..	8 12	..	..	..	8 40	..	..	..	9 12	..	..	..	..	9 40	..	..	1012	..	..	..	1040	..
Chelsfield	..	..	6 42	..	..	7 14	..	..	7 42	..	8 14	..	..	..	8 42	..	..	..	9 14	..	..	..	..	9 42	..	..	1014	..	..	..	1042	..
Orpington	..	..	6 48	..	..	7 19	..	..	7 48	..	8 19	..	..	..	8 48	8 56	..	..	9 20	..	..	..	..	9 48	..	..	1019	1038	..	..	1048	..
Petts Wood	..	..	6 52	..	..	7 23	..	..	7 52	..	8 23	..	..	..	8 52	..	..	..	9 24	..	..	..	..	9 52	..	..	1023	..	..	..	1052	..
Chislehurst	..	..	6 56	..	..	7 26	..	..	7 56	..	8 26	..	..	..	8 56	..	..	..	9 27	..	..	..	..	9 56	..	..	1026	..	..	..	1056	..
Elmstead Woods	..	..	6 58	..	..	7 28	..	..	7 58	..	8 28	..	..	..	8 58	..	..	..	9 29	..	..	..	..	9 58	..	..	1028	..	..	..	1058	..
Bromley North dep	6 32	6 51	..	7 21	..	..	7 51	..	..	8 21	..	..	..	8 51	..	..	9 21	..	..	..	..	9 51	..	..	1021	..	..	..	..	1051	..	..
Sundridge Park	6 33	6 52	..	7 22	..	..	7 52	..	..	8 22	..	..	..	8 52	..	..	9 22	..	..	..	..	9 52	..	..	1022	..	..	..	..	1052	..	..
Grove Park	6 37	6 56	7 1	7 26	..	7 31	7 56	..	8 1	8 26	8 31	..	..	8 56	9 1	..	9 26	..	9 32	..	..	9 56	..	10 1	1026	..	1031	..	..	1056	11 1	..
Hither Green	6 40	..	7 5	..	..	7 35	..	..	8 5	..	8 35	..	..	..	9 5	..	..	..	9 36	..	..	..	..	10 5	..	..	1034	..	..	..	11 5	..
Lewisham	..	..	..	..	..	..	..	..	..	..	..	..	..	..	..	..	..	..	..	..	..	..	..	..	..	..	..	..	..	..	..	..
St. John's	6 44	..	7 9	..	..	7 38	..	..	8 9	..	8 38	..	..	..	9 9	..	..	..	9 39	..	..	..	..	10 9	..	..	1038	..	..	..	11 9	..
New Cross	6 46	..	7 11	..	..	7 41	..	..	8 11	..	8 41	..	..	..	9 11	..	..	..	9 42	..	..	..	..	1011	..	..	1041	..	..	..	1111	..
London Bridge	6 52	..	7 17	..	..	7 47	..	..	8 17	..	8 46	..	..	..	9 17	9 16	..	..	9 48	9 44	..	..	..	1018	..	..	1046	1055	..	..	1118	1120
Cannon Street	..	..	..	..	..	..	..	..	..	..	..	..	..	..	..	..	..	..	..	—	..	..	..	..	..	..	..	..	..	..	..	..
Waterloo	6 56	..	7 20	..	..	7 50	..	..	8 20	..	8 50	..	..	..	9 20	9 23	..	..	9 51	9 50	..	..	..	1021	..	..	1050	11 1	..	..	1121	1127
Charing Cross arr	6 59	..	7 23	..	..	7 53	..	..	8 23	..	8 53	..	..	..	9 23	9 28	..	..	9 54	9 54	..	..	..	1025	..	..	1053	11 6	..	..	1125	1131

Sundays — a.m. / p.m.

Up	3	3	3	3	3		3	3			3	3	3			3	3	3	3		3		3	3		3	3	3	3	3		3
Tonbridge dep	..	..	..	..	..	..	..	..	12 2	..	..	..	..	1221	..	..	..	..	..	..	..	1 38	..	..	..	..	..	..	..	..	3 5	..
Hildenborough	..	..	..	..	..	..	..	..	1210	..	..	..	..	..	..	..	..	..	..	..	..	1 44	..	..	..	..	..	..	..	..	..	..
Sevenoaks arr	..	..	..	..	..	..	..	..	1221	..	..	..	..	1239	..	..	..	..	..	..	..	1 56	..	..	..	..	..	..	..	..	3 20	..
(Tub's Hill) dep	..	11 2	..	..	1130	..	..	12 2	..	..	..	..	1230	1240	..	..	1 2	..	..	..	1 30	1 57	..	2 2	..	..	..	2 30	..	3 2	3 21	..
Westerham dep	..	..	1117	..	..	..	..	..	..	..	1217	..	..	..	..	..	..	1 17	..	..	..	..	..	..	..	2 17	..	..	..	..	..	3 17
Brasted	..	..	1120	..	..	..	..	..	..	..	1220	..	..	..	..	..	..	1 20	..	..	..	..	..	..	..	2 20	..	..	..	..	..	3 20
Chevening Halt	..	..	1125	..	..	..	..	..	..	..	1225	..	..	..	..	..	..	1 25	..	..	..	..	..	..	..	2 25	..	..	..	..	..	3 25
Dunton Green arr	..	..	1128	..	..	..	..	..	..	..	1228	..	..	..	..	..	..	1 28	..	..	..	..	..	..	..	2 28	..	..	..	..	..	3 28
Dunton Green	..	11 5	..	..	1133	..	..	12 5	..	..	..	..	1233	..	..	..	1 5	..	..	..	1 33	..	..	2 5	..	..	..	2 33	..	3 5	..	..
Knockholt	..	1112	..	..	1140	..	..	1212	..	..	..	..	1240	..	..	..	1 12	..	..	..	1 40	..	..	2 12	..	..	..	2 40	..	3 12	..	..
Chelsfield	..	1114	..	..	1142	..	..	1214	..	..	..	..	1242	..	..	..	1 14	..	..	..	1 42	..	..	2 14	..	..	..	2 42	..	3 14	..	..
Orpington	..	1121	..	..	1148	..	..	1219	..	..	..	..	1248	..	..	..	1 19	..	..	..	1 48	..	..	2 19	..	..	..	2 48	..	3 19	..	..
Petts Wood	..	1125	..	..	1152	..	..	1223	..	..	..	..	1252	..	..	..	1 23	..	..	..	1 52	..	..	2 23	..	..	..	2 52	..	3 23	..	..
Chislehurst	..	1128	..	..	1156	..	..	1226	..	..	..	..	1256	..	..	..	1 26	..	..	..	1 56	..	..	2 26	..	..	..	2 56	..	3 26	..	..
Elmstead Woods	..	1130	..	..	1158	..	..	1228	..	..	..	..	1258	..	..	..	1 28	..	..	..	1 58	..	..	2 28	..	..	..	2 58	..	3 28	..	..
Bromley North dep	1121	..	..	1151	..	..	1221	..	..	..	..	1251	..	..	..	1 21	..	..	1 51	..	..	..	2 21	..	..	..	2 51	..	3 21	..	..	..
Sundridge Park	1122	..	..	1152	..	..	1222	..	..	..	..	1252	..	..	..	1 22	..	..	1 52	..	..	..	2 22	..	..	..	2 52	..	3 22	..	..	..
Grove Park	1126	1133	..	1156	12 1	..	1226	1231	..	..	..	1256	1 1	..	..	1 26	1 31	..	1 56	..	2 1	..	2 26	2 31	..	..	2 56	3 1	3 26	3 31	..	..
Hither Green	..	1137	..	..	12 5	..	..	1235	..	..	..	..	1 5	..	..	..	1 35	..	..	..	2 5	..	..	2 35	..	..	..	3 5	..	3 35	..	..
Lewisham	..	..	..	..	..	..	..	..	..	..	..	..	..	..	..	..	..	..	..	..	..	..	..	..	..	..	..	..	..	..	..	..
St. John's	..	1140	..	..	12 9	..	..	1238	..	..	..	..	1 9	..	..	..	1 38	..	..	..	2 9	..	..	2 38	..	..	..	3 9	..	3 38	..	..
New Cross	..	1143	..	..	1211	..	..	1241	..	..	..	..	1 11	1 5	..	..	1 41	..	..	..	2 11	..	..	2 41	..	..	..	3 11	..	3 41	..	..
London Bridge	..	1149	..	..	1218	..	..	1246	..	..	..	..	1 18	1 12	..	..	1 46	..	..	..	2 18	2 27	..	2 46	..	..	..	3 18	..	3 46	3 51	..
Cannon Street	..	..	..	..	..	..	..	..	..	..	..	..	..	..	..	..	..	..	..	..	..	..	..	..	..	..	..	..	..	..	..	..
Waterloo	..	1152	..	..	1221	..	..	1250	..	..	..	..	1 21	1 20	..	..	1 50	..	..	..	2 21	2 35	..	2 50	..	..	..	3 21	..	3 50	3 59	..
Charing Cross arr	..	1155	..	..	1225	..	..	1253	..	..	..	..	1 25	1 24	..	..	1 53	..	..	..	2 25	2 39	..	2 53	..	..	..	3 25	..	3 53	4 3	..

3 Third class only

TONBRIDGE, SEVENOAKS, WESTERHAM, DUNTON GREEN, ORPINGTON, BROMLEY NORTH, and LONDON

Up — p.m — **Sundays**—*continued* — p.m

Up	3	3	3	3		3	3	3	3		3	3		3		3
Tonbridge ... dep	..	..	..	..	..	..	..	..	..	..	..	..	5 0	..	..	..
Hildenborough	..	..	..	..	..	..	..	..	..	..	..	..	5 5	..	..	..
Sevenoaks arr	..	..	..	..	..	..	..	..	..	..	..	..	5 17	..	..	..
(Tub's Hill) dep	..	3 34	..	4 2	..	..	..	4 30	..	..	5 2	..	..	..	..	5 30
Westerham ... dep	..	..	..	..	..	4 17	..	..	..	..	..	5 17	..	..	..	..
Brasted	..	..	..	..	..	4 20	..	..	..	..	..	5 20	..	..	..	..
Chevening Halt	..	..	..	..	..	4 25	..	..	..	..	..	5 25	..	..	..	..
Dunton Green ... arr	..	..	..	..	..	4 28	..	..	..	..	..	5 28	..	..	..	..
Dunton Green	..	3 37	..	4 5	..	..	..	4 33	..	..	5 5	..	..	..	..	5 33
Knockholt	..	3 44	..	4 12	..	..	..	4 40	..	..	5 12	..	..	..	..	5 40
Chelsfield	..	3 46	..	4 14	..	..	..	4 42	..	..	5 14	..	..	..	..	5 42
Orpington	..	3 50	..	4 19	..	..	..	4 48	..	..	5 19	..	..	..	..	5 48
Petts Wood	..	3 53	..	4 23	..	..	..	4 52	..	..	5 23	..	..	..	..	5 52
Chislehurst	..	3 56	..	4 26	..	..	..	4 56	..	..	5 26	..	..	..	..	5 56
Elmstead Woods	..	3 59	..	4 28	..	..	..	4 58	..	..	5 28	..	..	..	..	5 58
Bromley North ... dep	3 51	..	4 21	..	..	..	4 51	..	5 21	..	..	..	..	5 51	..	..
Sundridge Park	3 52	..	4 22	..	..	..	4 52	..	5 22	..	..	..	..	5 52	..	..
Grove Park	3 56	4 2	4 26	4 31	..	..	4 56	5 1	5 26	..	5 31	..	..	5 56	..	6 1
Hither Green	..	4 5	..	4 35	..	..	..	5 5	..	..	5 35	..	..	..	..	6 5
Lewisham	..	..	..	..	..	..	..	..	..	..	..	..	..	..	..	..
St. John's	..	4 9	..	4 38	..	..	..	5 9	..	..	5 38	..	..	..	..	6 9
New Cross	..	4 11	..	4 41	..	..	..	5 11	..	..	5 41	..	..	..	..	6 11
London Bridge	..	4 18	..	4 46	..	..	..	5 18	..	..	5 46	..	..	..	..	6 18
Cannon Street	..	..	..	..	..	..	..	..	..	..	..	..	..	..	..	..
Waterloo	..	4 21	..	4 50	..	..	..	5 21	..	..	5 50	..	..	..	..	6 21
Charing Cross ... arr	..	4 25	..	4 53	..	..	..	5 25	..	..	5 53	..	..	..	..	6 25

Up		3	3		3	3	3	3		3	3		3	3		3
Tonbridge ... dep	5 56	..	..	..	..	..	..	..	6 33	..	..	..	..	..	7 20	..
Hildenborough	..	..	..	..	..	..	..	..	6 40	..	..	..	..	..	..	..
Sevenoaks arr	..	..	..	..	..	..	..	..	6 52	..	..	..	..	..	7 36	..
(Tub's Hill) dep	..	..	5 57	..	..	..	6 28	..	6 53	6 58	..	..	..	7 30	7 37	..
Westerham ... dep	..	..	..	..	..	6 17	..	..	..	..	7 17	..	..	..	..	..
Brasted	..	..	..	..	..	6 20	..	..	..	..	7 20	..	..	..	..	..
Chevening Halt	..	..	..	..	..	6 25	..	..	..	..	7 25	..	..	..	..	..
Dunton Green ... arr	..	..	..	..	..	6 28	..	..	..	..	7 28	..	..	..	..	..
Dunton Green	..	..	6 0	..	..	..	6 31	..	..	7 1	..	..	..	7 33	..	..
Knockholt	..	..	6 7	..	..	..	6 38	..	..	7 8	..	..	..	7 40	..	..
Chelsfield	..	..	6 9	..	..	..	6 40	..	..	7 10	..	..	..	7 42	..	..
Orpington	..	..	6J21	..	..	..	6A48	..	..	7h19	..	..	..	7 48	..	..
Petts Wood	..	..	6 25	..	..	..	6 52	..	..	7 23	..	..	..	7 52	..	..
Chislehurst	..	..	6 28	..	..	..	6 56	..	..	7 26	..	..	..	7 56	..	..
Elmstead Woods	..	..	6 30	..	..	..	6 58	..	..	7 28	..	..	..	7 58	..	..
Bromley North ... dep	..	6 21	..	..	6 51	..	..	7 21	..	..	..	..	7 51	..	..	8 21
Sundridge Park	..	6 22	..	..	6 52	..	..	7 22	..	..	..	..	7 52	..	..	8 22
Grove Park	..	6 26	6 33	..	6 56	..	7 1	7 26	..	7 31	..	..	7 56	8 1	..	8 26
Hither Green	..	..	6 37	..	..	..	7 5	..	..	7 35	..	..	..	8 5	..	..
Lewisham	..	..	..	..	..	..	..	..	..	..	..	..	..	..	..	..
St. John's	..	..	6 40	..	..	..	7 9	..	..	7 38	..	..	..	8 9	..	..
New Cross	..	..	6 43	..	..	..	7 11	..	..	7 41	..	..	..	8 11	..	..
London Bridge	6 37	..	6 48	..	..	..	7 18	..	7 22	7 46	..	..	..	8 18	8 5	..
Cannon Street	..	..	..	..	..	..	..	..	..	..	..	..	..	..	..	..
Waterloo	6 43	..	6 52	..	..	..	7 21	..	7 28	7 50	..	..	..	8 22	8 12	..
Charing Cross ... arr	6 47	..	6 55	..	..	..	7 25	..	7 33	7 53	..	..	..	8 25	8 17	..

Up — p.m — **Sundays** — p.m

Up	3			3	3	3		3	3	3		3	3	3	3		3	3	3	3	3	3	
Tonbridge ... dep	..	7 56	8 12	..	..	..	8 41	..	..	..	..	..	..	..	..	10 5	..	..	..	12 7	..	..	..
Hildenborough	..	..	..	..	..	..	8 47	..	..	..	..	..	..	..	..	..	..	..	..	..	..	..	..
Sevenoaks arr	..	..	..	..	..	..	8 58	..	..	..	..	..	..	..	..	1020	..	..	..	..	..	..	..
(Tub's Hill) dep	8 0	..	..	..	..	8 32	8 59	..	9 4	..	..	..	9 30	..	10 0	1021	..	1030	1110	..	..	..	..
Westerham ... dep	..	..	..	8 17	..	..	..	..	..	9 17	..	..	..	..	..	..	..	..	..	..	..	..	..
Brasted	..	..	..	8 20	..	..	..	..	..	9 20	..	..	..	..	..	..	..	..	..	..	..	..	..
Chevening Halt	..	..	..	8 25	..	..	..	..	..	9 25	..	..	..	..	..	..	..	..	..	..	..	..	..
Dunton Green ... arr	..	..	..	8 28	..	..	..	..	..	9 28	..	..	..	..	..	..	..	..	..	..	..	..	..
Dunton Green	8 3	..	..	..	..	8 35	..	..	9 7	..	..	..	9 33	..	10 3	..	..	1033	1113	Through Train (via Redhill), see page 250	..	..	..
Knockholt	8 10	..	..	..	..	8 42	..	..	9 14	..	..	..	9 40	..	1010	..	..	1040	1120		..	..	..
Chelsfield	8 12	..	..	..	..	8 44	..	..	9 16	..	..	..	9 42	..	1012	..	..	1042	1122		..	..	..
Orpington	8 19	8 24	..	..	..	8 49	..	..	9 22	..	..	..	9 48	..	1017	..	..	1048	1126		..	..	..
Petts Wood	8 23	..	..	..	..	8 52	..	..	9 25	..	..	..	9 52	..	1021	..	..	1052	..		..	..	..
Chislehurst	8 26	..	..	..	..	8 56	..	..	9 28	..	..	..	9 56	..	1024	..	..	1056	..		..	..	..
Elmstead Woods	8 28	..	..	..	..	8 58	..	..	9 30	..	..	..	9 58	..	1028	..	..	1058	..		..	..	..
Bromley North ... dep	..	..	..	..	8 51	..	..	9 21	..	..	..	9 51	..	1021	..	..	1051	..	..		1121	1151	..
Sundridge Park	..	..	..	..	8 52	..	..	9 22	..	..	..	9 52	..	1022	..	..	1052	..	..		1122	1152	..
Grove Park	8 31	..	..	..	8 56	9 1	..	9 26	9 33	..	..	9 56	10 1	1026	1029	..	1056	11 1	..		1126	1156	..
Hither Green	8 35	..	..	..	..	9 5	9 22	..	9 37	..	..	..	10 5	..	1033	..	..	11 5	..		..	..	..
Lewisham	..	..	..	..	..	..	..	..	..	..	..	..	..	..	..	..	..	..	..		..	..	..
St. John's	8 38	..	..	..	..	9 9	..	..	9 40	..	..	..	10 9	..	1037	..	..	11 9	..		..	..	..
New Cross	8 41	..	..	..	..	9 11	9 28	..	9 43	..	..	..	1011	..	1039	..	..	1111	..		..	..	..
London Bridge	8 46	8 43	8 54	..	..	9 18	9 35	..	9 49	..	..	..	1017	..	1045	1050	..	1117	..	1 19	..	..	..
Cannon Street	..	..	..	..	..	..	..	..	..	..	..	..	..	..	..	..	..	..	..	..	..	..	..
Waterloo	8 50	8 49	9 0	..	..	9 21	9 42	..	9 52	..	..	..	1021	..	1050	1056	..	1120	..	..	..	..	..
Charing Cross ... arr	8 53	8 54	9 5	..	..	9 25	9 46	..	9 55	..	..	..	1025	..	1053	11 1	..	1123	..	..	..	..	..

3 Third class only
A 4 mins. *earlier*
h Arr. 5 minutes *earlier*
J Arr. 6 15 p.m.

OTHER TRAINS

BETWEEN	PAGE
Tonbridge and London	249
Sevenoaks and London	147
Orpington and London	147
Bromley South & London	147
Hither Green and London	93
Lewisham and London	93, 119

LONDON, CRYSTAL PALACE (H.L.), ORPINGTON, SEVENOAKS, MAIDSTONE EAST, GRAVESEND WEST STREET, CHATHAM and GILLINGHAM (Kent)

Week Days — a.m.

Miles	Miles	Down	3	3	3	3	3	3	3		3	3		3	3		3			3	3	3	3	3	3		3			3		3	3
—	—	Victoria .... dep	..	..	..	..	4 52	..	..	5 10	..	..	..	..	5 44	..	..	..	6 18	..	..	6 24	..	..	..	..	..	6 40	..	6 44	..	..	..
3½	—	Brixton	..	..	..	..	..	..	..	..	..	..	..	..	5 49	..	..	..	..	..	..	6 29	..	..	..	..	..	..	..	6 49	..	..	..
—	—	Holborn Viaduct. dep	1 20	1 51	..	3 15	..	4 50	5 0	..	..	..	..	5 34	..	..	5 51	6 6	..	6 11	6 14	..	6 25	6 31	6 34	..	..	..	..	..	..	6 46	6 51
—	¼	Blackfriars ...... "	1 22	1 53	2 20	3 17	..	4 52	5 2	..	5 30	..	..	5 35	..	..	5 52	6 8	..	6 12	6 15	..	6 26	6 32	6 35	..	6 37	..	..	..	..	6 47	6 52
—	1½	Elephant and Castle	1 25	1 56	2 23	3 20	..	4 55	5 5	..	5 33	..	..	5 38	..	..	5 55	..	..	6 15	6 18	..	6 29	6 35	6 38	..	6 40	..	..	..	..	6 50	6 55
—	3½	Loughborough Junc.	1 29	..	2 27	3 24	..	4 59	..	..	5 37	..	..	5 43	..	..	..	..	..	..	6 23	..	6 34	..	6 43	..	..	..	..	..	..	6 55	..
—	4½	Denmark Hill	..	..	..	..	..	..	5 11	..	..	..	..	..	..	..	6 2	..	..	6 22	..	..	..	6 42	..	..	6 45	..	..	..	..	..	7 2
—	5	Peckham Rye	..	2 3	..	..	..	..	5 13	..	..	..	..	..	..	..	6 4	..	..	6 24	..	..	..	6 44	..	..	6 47	..	..	..	..	..	7 4
—	6	Nunhead	..	2 6	..	..	..	..	5 15	..	..	..	..	..	..	..	6 6	..	..	6 26	..	..	..	6 46	..	..	6 50	..	..	..	..	..	7 6
—	7½	Honor Oak	..	..	..	..	..	..	..	..	..	..	..	..	..	..	..	..	..	..	..	..	..	..	..	..	6 53	..	..	..	..	..	..
—	8¼	Lordship Lane A	..	..	..	..	..	..	..	..	..	..	..	..	..	..	..	..	..	..	..	..	..	..	..	..	6 56	..	..	..	..	..	..
—	9	Upper Sydenham	..	..	..	..	..	..	..	..	..	..	..	..	..	..	..	..	..	..	..	..	..	..	..	..	6 58	..	..	..	..	..	..
—	9¾	Crystal Palace B arr	..	..	..	..	..	..	..	..	..	..	..	..	..	..	..	..	Mondays only	..	..	..	..	..	..	..	7 1	Mondays only	..	..	..	..	..
—	7	Crofton Park	..	2 9	..	..	..	..	5 18	..	..	..	..	..	..	..	6 9	..		6 29	..	..	..	6 49	..	..	..		..	..	..	..	7 9
—	8	Catford	..	2 12	..	..	..	..	5 21	..	..	..	..	..	..	..	6 12	..		6 32	..	..	..	6 52	..	..	..		..	..	..	..	7 12
—	8¾	Bellingham	..	2 14	..	..	..	..	5 23	..	..	..	..	..	..	..	6 14	..		6 34	..	..	..	6 54	..	..	..		..	..	..	..	7 14
—	9½	Beckenham Hill	..	..	..	..	..	..	5 25	..	..	..	..	..	..	..	6 16	..	..	6 36	..	..	..	6 56	..	..	..		..	..	..	..	7 16
—	10¼	Ravensbourne	..	..	..	..	..	..	5 27	..	..	..	..	..	..	..	6 18	..	..	6 38	..	..	..	6 58	..	..	..	..	..	..	..	..	7 18
4	4½	Herne Hill	1 32	..	2 30	3 27	5 0	5 2	..	5 20	5 40	..	..	5 45	5 51	..	..	..	..	..	6 25	6 31	6 36	..	6 45	..	..	6 47	..	6 51	..	6 57	..
5	5¼	West Dulwich	1 35	..	2 32	3 30	..	5 5	..	..	..	..	..	..	5 53	..	..	..	..	..	..	6 33	6 38	..	..	..	..	..	..	6 53	..	6 59	..
5½	6¼	Sydenham Hill	..	..	..	..	..	5 7	..	..	..	..	..	..	5 55	..	..	..	..	..	..	6 35	6 40	..	..	..	..	..	..	6 55	..	7 1	..
7½	7¾	Penge East C	1 40	..	2 37	3 35	..	5 11	..	..	..	..	..	..	5 58	..	..	..	..	..	..	6 38	6 43	..	..	..	..	..	..	6 58	..	7 4	..
7½	8½	Kent House	1 42	..	2 39	3 37	..	5 13	..	..	..	..	..	..	6 0	..	..	..	..	..	..	6 40	6 45	..	..	..	..	..	..	7 0	..	7 6	..
8½	9¼	Beckenham Junction	1 45	..	2 42	3 39	..	5 16	..	..	..	..	..	..	6 2	..	..	6 27	..	..	..	6 42	6 47	..	..	..	..	..	..	7 2	..	7 8	..
10	11	Shortlands	1 49	2 19	2 45	3 42	..	5 21	5 28	..	..	..	..	..	6 5	..	6 19	..	..	6 39	..	6 45	6 50	6 59	..	..	..	..	..	7 5	..	7 11	7 19
10½	12	Bromley South D	1 52	2 22	2 47	3 44	..	5R24	5 31	5 38	..	5 52	..	..	6 8	..	6 22	6 33	6 36	6 42	..	6 47	6 52	7 2	..	..	..	7 0	..	7 7	..	7 14	7 22
12	13	Bickley	1 56	2 26	2 50	3 48	..	5 29	5 35	..	..	5 55	..	..	6 11	..	6 25	..	..	6 45	..	6 50	6 56	7 5	..	..	..	..	..	7 10	..	7 17	7 25
13½	14¾	Petts Wood	2 0	2 30	2 54	3 52	..	5 33	..	..	..	5 59	..	..	..	..	6 29	..	..	..	..	6 54	7 1	..	..	..	..	..	..	7 14	..	7 21	..
15	16	Orpington .... arr	2 3	2 33	2 57	3 55	..	5 36	..	..	..	6 2	..	..	..	..	6 32	..	..	..	..	6 57	7 4	..	..	..	..	..	..	7 17	..	7 24	..
14¾	15¾	St. Mary Cray	..	..	..	..	..	..	5 40	..	..	..	..	..	6 16	..	..	..	..	6 50	..	..	..	7 10	..	..	..	..	..	..	..	..	7 30
17½	18¾	Swanley 34, 60	..	..	..	..	..	..	5 45	5K54	..	..	6 5	..	6 21	6 27	..	6R46	..	6 55	..	..	..	7 15	..	..	..	7 10	7 22	..	..	..	7 35
19½	20¾	Lullingstone	..	..	..	..	..	..	..	..	..	..	..	..	..	..	..	..	..	..	..	..	..	..	..	..	..	..	..	..	..	..	..
20½	21¾	Eynsford	..	..	..	..	..	..	5 50	..	..	..	..	..	6 27	..	..	..	..	7 1	..	..	..	7 22	..	..	..	..	..	..	..	..	7 42
22¼	23½	Shoreham (Kent)	..	..	..	..	..	..	5 55	..	..	..	..	..	6 31	..	..	..	..	7 5	..	..	..	7 27	..	..	..	..	..	..	..	..	7 47
24	25	Otford	..	..	..	..	..	..	5 58	..	..	..	6 14	..	6 34	..	..	6 57	..	7 8	..	..	..	7 30	..	..	..	..	..	..	..	..	7 50
25½	26¼	Seven- oaks { Bat & Ball	..	..	..	..	..	..	6 1	..	..	..	..	..	6 38	..	..	..	..	7 12	..	..	..	7 33	..	..	..	..	..	..	..	..	7 53
26½	27½	Seven- oaks { Tub's H. ar	..	..	..	..	..	6c0	6 4	..	..	6c26	..	..	6 41	..	6c59	..	..	7 15	..	..	7c26	7 36	..	..	..	..	..	..	..	7c45	7 56
27	28	Kemsing	..	..	..	..	..	..	..	..	..	..	6 20	..	..	..	..	..	..	..	..	..	..	..	..	..	..	..	..	..	..	..	..
29½	30½	Wrotham & Boro' Gr'n	..	..	..	..	..	..	..	..	..	..	6 26	..	..	..	..	7 9	..	..	..	..	..	..	..	..	..	..	..	..	..	..	..
34½	35½	Malling	..	..	..	..	..	..	..	..	..	..	6 34	..	..	..	..	7 19	..	..	..	..	..	..	..	..	..	..	..	..	..	..	..
35½	36½	East Malling Halt	..	..	..	..	..	..	..	..	..	..	6 37	..	..	..	..	..	..	..	..	..	..	..	..	..	..	..	..	..	..	..	..
37½	38½	Barming	..	..	..	..	..	..	..	..	..	..	6 42	..	..	..	..	..	..	..	..	..	..	..	..	..	..	..	..	..	..	..	..
40	41	Maidstone East .. arr	..	..	..	..	..	..	..	..	..	..	6 47	..	..	..	..	7 28	..	..	..	..	..	..	..	..	..	..	..	..	..	..	..
20½	21¼	Farningham Road F	..	..	..	..	..	..	..	6 0	..	..	..	..	..	6 32	..	..	..	..	..	..	..	..	..	..	..	..	7 27	..	..	..	..
23½	24½	Longfield Halt G	..	..	..	..	..	..	..	..	..	..	..	..	..	6 38	..	..	..	..	..	..	..	..	..	..	..	..	7 33	..	..	..	..
25	26½	Southfleet (Springh'd)	..	..	..	..	..	..	..	..	..	..	..	..	..	6 42	..	..	..	..	..	..	..	..	..	..	..	..	7 37	..	..	..	..
27½	28½	Gravesend West St ar	..	..	..	..	..	..	..	..	..	..	..	..	..	6 48	..	..	..	..	..	..	..	..	..	..	..	..	7 43	..	..	..	..
23½	24½	Fawkham, for Hartley &	..	..	..	..	..	..	..	6 7	..	..	..	..	..	..	..	..	..	..	..	..	..	..	..	..	..	..	..	..	..	..	..
26	27½	Meopham .....[Longfield	..	..	..	..	..	..	..	6 13	..	..	..	..	..	..	..	..	..	..	..	..	..	..	..	..	..	..	..	..	..	..	..
27	28½	Sole Street	..	..	..	..	..	..	..	6 17	..	..	..	..	..	..	..	..	..	..	..	..	..	..	..	..	..	..	..	..	..	..	..
33½	35	Rochester	..	..	..	..	..	..	..	6 30	..	..	..	..	..	..	..	..	..	..	..	..	..	..	..	..	..	7 36	..	..	..	..	..
34½	35½	Chatham	..	..	..	..	..	..	..	6 33	..	..	..	..	..	..	..	..	7 8	..	..	..	..	..	..	..	..	7 39	..	..	..	..	..
36	37½	Gillingham (Kent) .. arr	..	..	..	..	..	..	..	6 44	..	..	..	..	..	..	..	..	7 17	..	..	..	..	..	..	..	..	7 47	..	..	..	..	..

3 Third class only. R 1 minute later on Sats. c Change at Orpington. K Arr 5 52 a.m. R Arr. 3 mins. *earlier*

For Other Notes, see page 80

For Other Notes, see page 146

LONDON, CRYSTAL PALACE (H.L.), ORPINGTON, SEVENOAKS, MAIDSTONE EAST, GRAVESEND WEST STREET, CHATHAM, and GILLINGHAM (Kent).

Week Days—*continued* (a.m.)

Down	3	3	3			3	3	3	3	SO 3	3	3	3		3	SX 3
Victoria ... dep	..	..	7 4	7 18	..	..	..	..	..	..	7 24	..	..	..	..	7 39
Brixton	..	..	7 9	..	..	..	..	..	..	..	7 29	..	..	..	..	7 44
Holborn Viaduct ... dep	6 54	..	..	..	..	7 4	7 11	7 14	..	7 18	..	7 31	..	..	7 34	..
Blackfriars ... "	6 55	6 57	..	..	..	7 5	7 12	7 15	7 17	7 19	..	7 32	7 37	..	7 35	..
Elephant and Castle	6 58	7 0	..	..	..	7 9	7 15	7 18	7 20	7 22	..	7 35	7 40	..	7 38	..
Loughborough Junc.	7 3	..	..	..	..	7 13	..	7 23	..	..	..	..	..	..	7 43	..
Denmark Hill	..	7 5	..	..	..	..	7 22	..	7 25	..	..	7 42	7 45	..	..	..
Peckham Rye	..	7 7	..	..	..	..	7 24	..	7 27	..	..	7 44	7 47	..	..	..
Nunhead	..	7 10	..	..	..	..	7 26	..	7 30	..	..	7 46	7 50	..	..	..
Honor Oak	..	7 13	..	..	..	..	..	..	7 33	..	..	..	7 53	..	..	..
Lordship Lane **A**	..	7 16	..	..	..	..	..	..	7 36	..	..	..	7 56	..	..	..
Upper Sydenham	..	7 18	..	..	..	..	..	..	7 38	..	..	..	7 58	..	..	..
Crystal Palace B ... arr	..	7 21	..	..	..	..	..	..	7 41	..	..	..	8 1	..	..	..
Crofton Park	..	..	..	..	..	..	7 29	..	..	..	..	7 49	..	..	..	..
Catford	..	..	..	..	..	..	7 32	..	..	..	..	7 52	..	..	..	..
Bellingham	..	..	..	..	..	..	7 34	..	..	..	..	7 54	..	..	..	..
Beckenham Hill	..	..	..	..	..	..	7 36	..	..	..	..	7 56	..	..	..	..
Ravensbourne	..	..	..	..	..	..	7 38	..	..	..	..	7 58	..	..	..	..
Herne Hill	7 5	..	7 11	..	..	7 16	..	7 26	..	7 28	7 31	..	..	..	7 45	7 47
West Dulwich	..	..	7 13	..	..	7 18	..	..	..	..	7 34	..	..	..	..	..
Sydenham Hill	..	..	7 15	..	..	7 20	..	..	..	..	7 36	..	..	..	..	..
Penge East **C**	..	..	7 18	..	..	7 23	..	..	..	..	7 39	..	..	..	..	..
Kent House	..	..	7 20	..	..	7d31	..	..	..	..	7 41	..	..	..	..	..
Beckenham Junction	..	..	7 22	..	..	7 33	..	..	..	7 37	7 43	..	..	..	..	7 54
Shortlands	..	..	7 25	..	..	..	7 39	..	..	7 40	7 46	7 59	..	..	..	..
Bromley South D	..	..	7 27	7 35	..	7 38	7 42	..	..	7 43	7 50	8 2	..	..	..	7 59
Bickley	..	..	7 30	..	..	7 42	7 45	..	..	7 46	7 54	8 5	..	..	..	8 3
Petts Wood	..	..	7 34	..	..	7 46	..	..	..	7 51	7 57	..	..	..	..	8 8
Orpington ... arr	..	..	7 37	..	..	7 49	..	..	..	7 54	8 0	..	..	..	..	8 12
St. Mary Cray	..	..	..	..	..	..	7 50	..	..	..	..	8 10	..	..	..	..
Swanley 34, 60	..	..	..	7B43	7 47	..	7 55	..	..	..	..	8 15	..	828	..	..
Lullingstone	..	..	..	..	..	..	..	..	..	..	..	..	..	..	..	..
Eynsford	..	..	..	..	..	..	8 1	..	..	..	..	8 22	..	..	..	..
Shoreham (Kent)	..	..	..	..	..	..	8 5	..	..	..	..	8 27	..	..	..	..
Otford	..	..	..	7 55	..	..	8 8	..	..	..	..	8 30	..	..	..	..
Sevenoaks Bat & Ball	..	..	..	..	..	..	8 12	..	..	..	..	8 33	..	..	..	..
Sevenoaks Tub's Hill arr	..	..	..	..	..	..	8 15	..	..	8c15	..	8 38	..	..	..	..
Kemsing	..	..	..	8 1	..	..	..	..	..	..	..	..	..	..	..	..
Wrotham & Boro' Green	..	..	..	8 5	..	..	..	..	..	..	..	..	..	..	..	..
Malling	..	..	..	8 12	..	..	..	..	..	..	..	..	..	..	..	..
East Malling Halt	..	..	..	8 15	..	..	..	..	..	..	..	..	..	..	..	..
Barming	..	..	..	8 19	..	..	..	..	..	..	..	..	..	..	..	..
Maidstone East ... arr	..	..	..	8 23	..	..	..	..	..	..	..	..	..	..	..	..
Farningham Road **F**	..	..	..	..	7 51	..	..	..	..	..	..	..	..	833	..	..
Longfield Halt **G**	..	..	..	..	..	..	..	..	..	..	..	..	..	839	..	..
Southfleet (Springhead	..	..	..	..	..	..	..	..	..	..	..	..	..	843	..	..
Gravesend West St. arr	..	..	..	..	..	..	..	..	..	..	..	..	..	849	..	..
Fawkham, for Hartley and	..	..	..	..	7 56	..	..	..	..	..	..	..	..	..	..	..
Meopham ... [Longfield	..	..	..	..	8 1	..	..	..	..	..	..	..	..	..	..	..
Sole Street	..	..	..	..	8 3	..	..	..	..	..	..	..	..	..	..	..
Rochester	..	..	..	..	8 14	..	..	..	..	..	..	..	..	..	..	..
Chatham	..	..	..	..	8C17	..	..	..	..	..	..	..	..	..	..	..
Gillingham (Kent) ... arr	..	..	..	..	8 23	..	..	..	..	..	..	..	..	..	..	..

Down	3	SX 3	SO 3	SX 3	SX 3	3	SX 3	SO 3	SO 3	3	SX 3	SX	SX	SO	SO	SO 3
Victoria ... dep	7 44	..	..	..	..	..	..	..	..	8 4	..	8 18	..	8 18	..	..
Brixton	7 49	..	..	..	..	..	..	..	..	8 9	..	..	..	..	..	..
Holborn Viaduct ... dep	..	7 44	..	..	7 49	7 51	..	7 53	..	7SX57	8 5	..	..	..	..	8 7
Blackfriars ... "	..	7 45	7 47	7 49	7 50	7 52	7 55	7 55	8 0	7SX58	8 7	..	..	..	..	8 9
Elephant and Castle	..	7 48	7 50	7 52	7 53	7C56	..	7 58	8 3	..	..	..	..	..	..	8 11
Loughborough Junc.	..	7 53	..	..	7 58	..	..	8 3	..	..	..	..	..	..	..	..
Denmark Hill	..	..	7 56	7 58	..	8 2	..	..	8 8	..	..	..	..	..	..	8 17
Peckham Rye	..	..	7 58	8 0	..	8 4	..	..	8 10	..	8 17	..	..	..	..	8 19
Nunhead	..	..	8 0	8 2	..	8 6	..	..	8 13	..	8 20	..	..	..	..	8 22
Honor Oak	..	..	8 4	8 6	..	..	..	..	..	..	..	..	..	..	..	..
Lordship Lane **A**	..	..	8 6	8 8	..	..	..	..	..	..	..	..	..	..	..	..
Upper Sydenham	..	..	8 9	8 11	..	..	..	..	..	..	..	..	..	..	..	..
Crystal Palace B ... arr	..	..	8 11	8 13	..	..	..	..	8 22	..	..	..	..	..	..	..
Crofton Park	..	..	..	..	..	8 9	..	..	..	..	..	..	..	..	..	..
Catford	..	..	..	..	..	8 12	..	..	..	..	..	..	..	..	..	..
Bellingham	..	..	..	..	..	8 14	..	..	..	..	8 25	..	..	..	..	8 27
Beckenham Hill	..	..	..	..	..	8 16	..	..	..	..	..	..	..	..	..	8 29
Ravensbourne	..	..	..	..	..	8 18	..	..	..	..	..	..	..	..	..	8 31
Herne Hill	7 51	7 55	..	..	8 0	..	8 3	8 6	..	8 11	..	..	..	..	..	..
West Dulwich	7 53	7 58	..	..	..	..	..	..	..	8 13	..	..	..	..	..	..
Sydenham Hill	7 55	8 0	..	..	8 4	..	..	..	..	8 15	..	..	..	..	..	..
Penge East **C**	7 58	8 3	..	..	8 7	..	..	..	..	8 18	..	..	..	..	..	..
Kent House	8 0	8 5	..	..	..	..	..	..	..	8 20	..	..	..	..	..	..
Beckenham Junction	8 2	8 7	..	..	8 10	..	..	..	..	8 22	..	..	..	..	..	..
Shortlands	8 5	..	..	..	8 13	8 19	..	..	..	8 25	..	..	..	..	..	8 32
Bromley South D	8B7	8 12	..	..	8 16	8 22	..	..	..	8 27	..	8 35	..	8 35	..	8 35
Bickley	8B10	8 15	..	..	8 20	8 25	..	..	..	8 30	..	..	..	..	..	8 38
Petts Wood	8B14	..	..	..	..	..	..	..	..	8 34	..	..	..	..	..	..
Orpington ... arr	8B17	..	..	..	..	..	..	..	..	8 37	..	..	..	..	..	..
St. Mary Cray	..	..	..	..	..	8 30	..	..	..	..	..	..	..	..	..	..
Swanley 34, 60	..	..	..	..	..	8 35	..	..	..	..	..	8A50	8 47	8 44	851	..
Lullingstone	..	..	..	..	..	..	..	..	..	..	..	..	..	..	..	..
Eynsford	..	..	..	..	..	8 42	..	..	..	..	..	..	..	..	..	..
Shoreham (Kent)	..	..	..	..	..	8 47	..	..	..	..	..	..	..	..	..	..
Otford	..	..	..	..	..	8 50	..	..	..	..	..	9 2	..	..	9 3	..
Sevenoaks Bat & Ball	..	..	..	..	..	8C54	..	..	..	..	..	..	..	..	..	..
Sevenoaks Tub's Hill arr	8c54	..	..	..	..	8C57	..	..	..	9c2	..	..	..	..	..	..
Kemsing	..	..	..	..	..	..	..	..	..	..	..	9 8	..	..	9 9	..
Wrotham & Boro' Green	..	..	..	..	..	..	..	..	..	..	..	9 12	..	..	913	..
Malling	..	..	..	..	..	..	..	..	..	..	..	9 19	..	..	920	..
East Malling Halt	..	..	..	..	..	..	..	..	..	..	..	9 22	..	..	922	..
Barming	..	..	..	..	..	..	..	..	..	..	..	9 26	..	..	927	..
Maidstone East ... arr	..	..	..	..	..	..	..	..	..	..	..	9 30	..	..	930	..
Farningham Road **F**	..	..	..	..	..	..	..	..	..	..	..	..	8 51	8 51	..	..
Longfield Halt **G**	..	..	..	..	..	..	..	..	..	..	..	..	..	..	..	..
Southfleet (Springhead	..	..	..	..	..	..	..	..	..	..	..	..	..	..	..	..
Gravesend West St. arr	..	..	..	..	..	..	..	..	..	..	..	..	..	..	..	..
Fawkham, for Hartley and	..	..	..	..	..	..	..	..	..	..	..	..	8 56	8 56	..	..
Meopham ... [Longfield	..	..	..	..	..	..	..	..	..	..	..	..	9 1	9 1	..	..
Sole Street	..	..	..	..	..	..	..	..	..	..	..	..	9 3	9 3	..	..
Rochester	..	..	..	..	..	..	..	..	..	..	..	..	9 14	9 14	..	..
Chatham	..	..	..	..	..	..	..	..	..	..	..	..	9 16	9 16	..	..
Gillingham (Kent) ... arr	..	..	..	..	..	..	..	..	..	..	..	..	9 21	9 21	..	..

3 Third class only. A Arr. 8 44 a.m. B 1 min. later on Sats. H 2 mins. *earlier* on Sats. C 1 min. *earlier* on Sats. SO or SO Saturdays only. c Change at Orpington. SX or SX Saturdays excepted. d Arr. 7 25 a.m.

For Other Notes, see page 146.

LONDON, CRYSTAL PALACE (H.L.) ORPINGTON, SEVENOAKS, MAIDSTONE EAST, GRAVESEND WEST STREET, CHATHAM, and GILLINGHAM (Kent)

Week Days—continued (a.m.)

Down				SO		SX	SX	SO					SO		SX	SX			SO	SX			SX	SO			SX	SO			
	3	3			3		3	3	3	3	3	3	3	3	3	3	3	3	3	3	3	3	3	3						3	3
Victoria dep				8 35	8 24	8 25					8 40			8 44							9 4					9 18					
Brixton					8 29						8 45			8 49							9 9										
Holborn Viaduct dep	8 11				8 14		8 30	8 30	8 34			8C42	8 44		8 47	8 50	8SO50		8 58	8 57	8 54	9SX0		9 3						9SX4	9SO11
Blackfriars "	8B12	8K17			8 15		8 32	8 32	8 35	8 37		8C43	8 46		8 49	8 52	8C53	8 57	9 0	8 59	8 55	9F2	9 4	9 4						9F6	9H11
Elephant and Castle	8 16	8C20			8 18		8 36	8 36	8 38	8 40		8SO45				8 55	8C56	9 0		9 3	8 58	9F5	9 7							9F9	9B15
Loughborough Junc.					8 23				8 43				8 52		8 56				9 8		9B2	9H10									
Denmark Hill	8 22	8 25					8 42	8 42		8 45							9 2	9 5		9 10			9 13							9H16	9 22
Peckham Rye	8 24	8 27					8 44	8 44		8 47							9 4	9 7		9 12			9 15							9B19	9 24
Nunhead	8 26	8 30					8 46	8 47		8B50							9 6	9 10		9 15			9 18	9 14						9B21	9 26
Honor Oak		8 33								8 54										9 18				9 18						9H24	
Lordship Lane A		8 36								8 57										9 21				9 20							
Upper Sydenham		8 38								8 59										9 23				9 23							
Crystal Palace B arr		8 41								9 2								9 18		9 26				9 26						9B31	
Crofton Park	8 29						8 49	8 49									9 9														9 29
Catford	8 32						8 52	8 52									9 12														9 32
Bellingham	8 34						8 54	8 54									9 14														9 34
Beckenham Hill	8 36						8 56	8 56									9 16														9 36
Ravensbourne	8 38						8 58	8 58									9 18														9 38
Herne Hill					8 31				8 45		8 47	8 50		8 52		9 1					9 11	9H13									
West Dulwich					8 33									8 55							9 13										
Sydenham Hill					8 35									8 57							9 15										
Penge East C					8 38							8 56		9B0		9 7					9 18										
Kent House					8 40									9B2							9 20										
Beckenham Junction					8 42							9 0		9 5		9 10					9 22										
Shortlands	8 39				8 45		8 59	8 59				9SO3		9 9			9 19				9 25										9 39
Bromley South D	8 42			8 56	8 48	8 56	9 2	9 2				9B4		9 11		9 15	9 22				9 27					9 35					9 42
Bickley	8 45				8 53		9 5	9 5			9 0	9B8		9 14		9 18	9 25				9 30		9 29								9 45
Petts Wood					8 58						9SO4			9 19		9 22					9 34										
Orpington arr					9 1						9SO8			9C23		9 25					9 37										
St. Mary Cray	8 50						9 10	9 10									9 30														9 50
Swanley 34, 60	8 55						9 15	9 14									9 35									9J46	9 50	9 51			9 55
Lullingstone																															
Eynsford							9 20	9 19									9 42														10C2
Shoreham (Kent)							9 25	9 24									9 47														10K7
Otford							9 29	9 29									9 50										10 2	10 2			10K10
Sevenoaks { Bat & Ball							9 34	9 38									9 53														10C13
Sevenoaks { Tub's H. arr					9c35		9 38	9 43			9SOc35						9 56				10c0										10C16
Kemsing																											10 8	10 8			
Wrotham & Boro' Gr'n																											1012	1012			
Malling																											1019	1019			
East Malling Halt																											1022	1023			
Barming																											1024	1026			
Maidstone East arr																											1030	1030			
Farningham Road F																										9 51					
Longfield Halt G																															
Southfleet (Springh'd)																															
Gravesend West St arr																															
Fawkham, for Hartley & Longfield																										9 56					
Meopham																										10 1					
Sole Street																										10 3					
Rochester																										1014					
Chatham				9 29		9 30																				1016					
Gillingham (Kent) arr				9 42		9 42																				1027					

3 Third class only. B 1 minute later on Sats. J Arr. 9 44 a.m. C 1 minute *earlier* on Sats. K 2 minutes *earlier* on Saturdays. c Change at Orpington. F 3 minutes later on Sats. H 2 minutes later on Sats. SO or SO Saturdays only. SX or SX Saturdays excepted.

For Other Notes, see page 146

LONDON, CRYSTAL PALACE (H.L.), ORPINGTON, SEVENOAKS, MAIDSTONE EAST, GRAVESEND WEST STREET, CHATHAM and GILLINGHAM (Kent).

Mondays to Fridays — a.m

Down	3	3	3	3		3	3	3		3	3	3		3	3	3	3				3	3	3		3	3	3		3		
Victoria ... dep	..	..	9 24	..	..	..	..	..	..	..	..	9 44	..	..	..	..	10 4	..	..	10 18	..	10 24	..	1035	..	..	..	..	11 4	1118	..
Brixton	..	..	9 29	..	..	..	..	..	..	..	..	9 49	..	..	..	..	10 9	..	..	..	..	10 29	..	..	..	..	..	..	11 9	..	..
Holborn Viaduct ... dep	9 14	..	9 11	9 18	..	9 23	9 25	..	..	9 30	..	9 40	..	..	9 51	..	9 54	..	..	..	1011	10 14	..	..	1031	..	1051	..	10 43	..	..
Blackfriars ... "	9 16	9 17	9 13	9 20	..	9 24	9 26	9 27	..	9 32	9 37	9 41	..	9 43	9 52	9 57	9 55	..	..	..	1012	10 15	..	..	1032	..	1052	..	10 44	..	..
Elephant and Castle	9 19	9 20	9 16	9 23	..	9 27	9 29	..	..	9 35	9 40	9 44	..	9 46	9 55	10 0	9 58	..	..	..	1016	10 18	..	..	1036	..	1055	..	10 47	..	..
Loughborough Junc.	9 24	..	9 20	9 29	..	..	9 34	..	..	..	..	9 49	..	..	..	..	10 3	..	..	..	..	10 23	..	..	..	..	..	..	10 52	..	..
Denmark Hill	..	9 25	..	..	..	..	..	..	..	9 42	9 45	..	..	9 52	10 2	10 5	..	..	..	..	1022	..	..	..	1042	..	11 2	..	..	..	..
Peckham Rye	..	9 27	..	..	..	9 34	..	9 37	..	9 44	9 47	..	..	9 54	10 4	10 7	..	..	..	..	1024	..	..	..	1044	..	11 4	..	..	..	..
Nunhead	..	9 30	..	..	..	9 36	..	9 40	..	9 46	9 50	..	..	9 56	10 6	1010	..	..	..	..	1026	..	1034	..	1046	1054	11 6	..	..	..	..
Honor Oak	..	9 33	..	..	..	..	..	..	..	..	9 53	..	..	..	..	1013	..	..	..	..	..	..	1037	..	..	1057	..	..	..	..	..
Lordship Lane **A**	..	9 36	..	..	..	..	..	..	..	..	9 56	..	..	..	..	1016	..	..	..	..	..	..	1040	..	..	11 0	..	..	..	..	..
Upper Sydenham	..	9 38	..	..	..	..	..	..	..	..	9 58	..	..	..	..	1018	..	..	..	..	..	..	1042	..	..	11 2	..	..	..	..	..
Crystal Palace B ... arr	..	9 41	..	..	..	9 46	..	..	..	..	10 1	..	..	..	..	1021	..	..	..	..	..	..	1045	..	..	11 5	..	..	..	..	..
Crofton Park	..	..	..	..	..	..	..	9 42	..	9 49	..	..	..	9 59	10 9	..	..	..	..	..	1029	..	..	..	1049	..	11 9	..	..	..	..
Catford	..	..	..	..	..	..	..	9 45	..	9 52	..	..	..	10 2	1012	..	..	..	..	..	1032	..	..	..	1052	..	1112	..	..	..	..
Bellingham	..	..	..	..	..	..	..	9 47	..	9 54	..	..	..	10 4	1014	..	..	..	..	..	1034	..	..	..	1054	..	1114	..	..	..	..
Beckenham Hill	..	..	..	..	..	..	..	..	..	9 56	..	..	..	..	1016	..	..	..	..	..	1036	..	..	..	1056	..	1116	..	..	..	..
Ravensbourne	..	..	..	..	..	..	..	..	..	9 58	..	..	..	..	1018	..	..	..	..	..	1038	..	..	..	1058	..	1118	..	..	..	..
Herne Hill	..	..	9 31	9 32	..	..	..	..	..	..	..	9 51	..	..	..	..	1011	..	..	..	..	10 31	..	1044	..	..	..	..	11 11	..	..
West Dulwich	..	..	9 33	..	..	..	..	..	..	..	..	9 53	..	..	..	..	1013	..	..	..	..	10 33	..	..	..	..	..	..	11 13	..	..
Sydenham Hill	..	..	9 35	..	..	..	..	..	..	..	..	9 55	..	..	..	..	1015	..	..	..	..	10 35	..	..	..	..	..	..	11 15	..	..
Penge East **C**	..	..	9 38	..	..	..	..	..	..	..	..	9 58	..	..	..	..	1018	..	..	..	..	10 38	..	..	..	..	..	..	11 18	..	..
Kent House	..	..	9 40	..	..	..	..	..	..	..	..	10 0	..	..	..	..	1020	..	..	..	..	10 40	..	..	..	..	..	..	11 20	..	..
Beckenham Junction	..	..	9 42	..	..	..	..	..	..	..	..	10 2	..	..	..	..	1022	..	..	..	..	10 42	..	..	..	..	..	..	11 22	..	..
Shortlands	..	..	9 45	..	..	..	..	9 51	..	9 59	..	10 5	..	10 8	1019	..	1025	..	..	..	1039	10 45	..	..	1059	..	1119	..	11 25	..	..
Bromley South D	..	..	9 47	..	..	..	..	9 53	..	10 2	..	10 7	..	10 10	1022	..	1027	..	..	10 35	1042	10 47	..	1059	11 3	..	1122	..	11 27	1135	..
Bickley	..	..	9 50	..	..	..	..	9 56	..	10 5	..	1010	..	10 13	1025	..	1031	..	..	..	1045	10 50	..	..	11 7	..	1125	..	11 30	..	..
Petts Wood	..	..	9 54	..	..	..	..	10 0	..	..	..	1014	..	10 17	..	..	1035	..	..	..	..	10 54	..	..	1111	..	..	..	11 34	..	..
Orpington ... arr	..	..	9 57	..	..	..	..	10 3	..	..	..	1017	..	10 20	..	..	1039	..	..	..	..	10 57	..	..	1114	..	..	..	11 37	..	..
St. Mary Cray	..	..	..	..	..	..	..	..	..	1010	..	..	..	..	1030	..	..	..	..	..	1050	..	..	..	..	..	1130	..	..	..	..
Swanley 34, 60	..	..	..	..	..	..	..	..	..	1015	..	..	..	..	1035	..	..	..	1047	10ß50	1054	..	..	..	..	..	1134	..	..	1143	1147
Lullingstone	..	..	..	..	..	..	..	..	..	..	..	..	..	..	..	..	..	..	..	..	..	..	..	..	..	..	..	..	..	..	..
Eynsford	..	..	..	..	..	..	..	..	..	1022	..	..	..	..	1042	..	..	..	..	..	11 1	..	..	..	..	..	1142	..	..	..	..
Shoreham (Kent)	..	..	..	..	..	..	..	..	..	1027	..	..	..	..	1047	..	..	..	..	..	11 5	..	..	..	..	..	1147	..	..	..	..
Otford	..	..	..	..	..	..	..	..	..	1030	..	..	..	..	1050	..	..	..	..	11 2	11 8	..	..	..	..	..	1150	..	..	1155	..
Seven-oaks { Bat & Ball	..	..	..	..	..	..	..	..	..	1033	..	..	..	..	1053	..	..	..	..	..	1112	..	..	..	..	..	1153	..	..	..	..
Seven-oaks { Tub's H. arr	..	..	..	..	..	..	..	10c27	..	1036	..	..	..	..	1056	..	..	..	..	..	1115	11c27	..	..	..	..	1156	..	11c57	..	..
Kemsing	..	..	..	..	..	..	..	..	..	..	..	..	..	..	..	..	..	..	..	11 8	..	..	..	..	..	..	..	..	..	12 1	..
Wrotham & Boro' Green	..	..	..	..	..	..	..	..	..	..	..	..	..	..	..	..	..	..	..	11 12	..	..	..	..	..	..	..	..	..	12 5	..
Malling	..	..	..	..	..	..	..	..	..	..	..	..	..	..	..	..	..	..	..	11 19	..	..	..	..	..	..	..	..	..	1212	..
East Malling Halt	..	..	..	..	..	..	..	..	..	..	..	..	..	..	..	..	..	..	..	11 22	..	..	..	..	..	..	..	..	..	1215	..
Barming	..	..	..	..	..	..	..	..	..	..	..	..	..	..	..	..	..	..	..	11 24	..	..	..	..	..	..	..	..	..	1219	..
Maidstone East ... arr	..	..	..	..	..	..	..	..	..	..	..	..	..	..	..	..	..	..	..	11 30	..	..	..	..	..	..	..	..	..	1223	..
Farningham Road **F**	..	..	..	..	..	..	..	..	..	..	..	..	..	..	..	..	..	..	1051	..	..	..	..	..	..	..	..	..	..	..	1151
Longfield Halt **G**	..	..	..	..	..	..	..	..	..	..	..	..	..	..	..	..	..	..	..	..	..	..	..	..	..	..	..	..	..	..	..
Southfleet (Springhead)	..	..	..	..	..	..	..	..	..	..	..	..	..	..	..	..	..	..	..	..	..	..	..	..	..	..	..	..	..	..	..
Gravesend West St. .. arr	..	..	..	..	..	..	..	..	..	..	..	..	..	..	..	..	..	..	..	..	..	..	..	..	..	..	..	..	..	..	..
Fawkham, for Hartley and [Longfield	..	..	..	..	..	..	..	..	..	..	..	..	..	..	..	..	..	..	1056	..	..	..	..	..	..	..	..	..	..	..	1156
Meopham	..	..	..	..	..	..	..	..	..	..	..	..	..	..	..	..	..	..	11 1	..	..	..	..	..	..	..	..	..	..	..	12 1
Sole Street	..	..	..	..	..	..	..	..	..	..	..	..	..	..	..	..	..	..	11 3	..	..	..	..	..	..	..	..	..	..	..	12 3
Rochester	..	..	..	..	..	..	..	..	..	..	..	..	..	..	..	..	..	..	1114	..	..	..	..	..	..	..	..	..	..	..	1214
Chatham	..	..	..	..	..	..	..	..	..	..	..	..	..	..	..	..	..	..	1116	..	..	..	..	1133	..	..	..	..	..	..	1216
Gillingham (Kent) ... arr	..	..	..	..	..	..	..	..	..	..	..	..	..	..	..	..	..	..	1121	..	..	..	..	..	..	..	..	..	..	..	1221

3 Third class only. ß Arr 6 mins *earlier* c Change at Orpington. **For Other Notes, see page 146.**

For Saturday Trains, see pages 140a to 142a: for SUNDAY TRAINS, see pages, 143 to 146.

LONDON, CRYSTAL PALACE (H.L.), ORPINGTON, SEVENOAKS, MAIDSTONE EAST, GRAVESEND WEST STREET, CHATHAM and GILLINGHAM (Kent).

Mondays to Fridays—continued

Down	a.m.					p.m.																				p.m.					
	3	3	3	3		3			3		3	3	3		3			3	3	3	3	3					3			3	3	3
Victoria .... dep	11 24	..	..	..	..	12 4	1218	..	1224	1235	..	..	..	..	1 4	1 18	..	1 24	..	..	..	2 4	..	2 18	..	..	2 24	2 35	..	..	..	..
Brixton	11 29	..	..	..	..	12 9	..	..	1229	..	..	..	..	..	1 9	..	..	1 29	..	..	..	2 9	..	..	..	..	2 29	..	..	..	..	..
Holborn Viaduct. dep	11 14	1131	..	1151	..	11 43	..	..	1214	..	1231	..	1251	..	1243	..	..	1 14	1 31	..	1 51	1 43	..	..	..	..	2 14	..	..	2 31	..	2 51
Blackfriars ...... "	11 15	1132	..	1152	..	11 44	..	..	1215	..	1232	..	1252	..	1244	..	..	1 15	1 32	..	1 52	1 44	..	..	..	..	2 15	..	..	2 32	..	2 52
Elephant and Castle	11 18	1135	..	1155	..	11 47	..	..	1218	..	1235	..	1255	..	1247	..	..	1 18	1 35	..	1 55	1 47	..	..	..	..	2 18	..	..	2 35	..	2 55
Loughborough Junc.	11 23	..	..	..	..	11 52	..	..	1223	..	..	..	..	..	1252	..	..	1 23	..	..	..	1 52	..	..	..	..	2 23	..	..	..	..	..
Denmark Hill	..	1142	..	12 2	..	..	..	..	..	..	1242	..	1 2	..	..	..	..	..	1 42	..	2 2	..	..	..	..	..	..	..	..	2 42	..	3 2
Peckham Rye	..	1144	..	12 4	..	..	..	..	..	..	1244	..	1 4	..	..	..	..	..	1 44	..	2 4	..	..	..	..	..	..	..	..	2 44	..	3 4
Nunhead	..	1146	1154	12 6	..	..	..	..	..	..	1246	1254	1 6	..	..	..	..	..	1 46	1 54	2 6	..	..	..	..	..	..	..	..	2 46	2 54	3 6
Honor Oak	..	..	1157	..	..	..	..	..	..	..	..	1257	..	..	..	..	..	..	..	1 57	..	..	..	..	..	..	..	..	..	..	2 57	..
Lordship Lane A	..	..	12 0	..	..	..	..	..	..	..	..	1 0	..	..	..	..	..	..	..	2 0	..	..	..	..	..	..	..	..	..	..	3 0	..
Upper Sydenham	..	..	12 2	..	..	..	..	..	..	..	..	1 2	..	..	..	..	..	..	..	2 2	..	..	..	..	..	..	..	..	..	..	3 2	..
Crystal Palace B. arr	..	..	12 5	..	..	..	..	..	..	..	..	1 5	..	..	..	..	..	..	..	2 5	..	..	..	..	..	..	..	..	..	..	3 5	..
Crofton Park	..	1149	..	12 9	..	..	..	..	..	..	1249	..	1 9	..	..	..	..	..	1 49	..	2 9	..	..	..	..	..	..	..	..	2 49	..	3 9
Catford	..	1152	..	1212	..	..	..	..	..	..	1252	..	1 12	..	..	..	..	..	1 52	..	2 12	..	..	..	..	..	..	..	..	2 52	..	3 12
Bellingham	..	1154	..	1214	..	..	..	..	..	..	1254	..	1 14	..	..	..	..	..	1 54	..	2 14	..	..	..	..	..	..	..	..	2 54	..	3 14
Beckenham Hill	..	1156	..	1216	..	..	..	..	..	..	1256	..	1 16	..	..	..	..	..	1 56	..	2 16	..	..	..	..	..	..	..	..	2 56	..	3 16
Ravensbourne	..	1158	..	1218	..	..	..	..	..	..	1258	..	1 18	..	..	..	..	..	1 58	..	2 18	..	..	..	..	..	..	..	..	2 58	..	3 18
Herne Hill	11 31	..	..	..	..	12 11	..	..	1231	..	..	..	..	..	1 11	..	..	1 31	..	..	..	2 11	..	..	..	..	2 31	..	..	..	..	..
West Dulwich	11 33	..	..	..	..	12 13	..	..	1233	..	..	..	..	..	1 13	..	..	1 33	..	..	..	2 13	..	..	..	..	2 33	..	..	..	..	..
Sydenham Hill	11 35	..	..	..	..	12 15	..	..	1235	..	..	..	..	..	1 15	..	..	1 35	..	..	..	2 15	..	..	..	..	2 35	..	..	..	..	..
Penge East C	11 38	..	..	..	..	12 18	..	..	1238	..	..	..	..	..	1 18	..	..	1 38	..	..	..	2 18	..	..	..	..	2 38	..	..	..	..	..
Kent House	11 40	..	..	..	..	12 20	..	..	1240	..	..	..	..	..	1 20	..	..	1 40	..	..	..	2 20	..	..	..	..	2 40	..	..	..	..	..
Beckenham Junction	11 42	..	..	..	..	12 22	..	..	1242	..	..	..	..	..	1 22	..	..	1 42	..	..	..	2 22	..	..	..	..	2 42	..	..	..	..	..
Shortlands	11 45	1159	..	1219	..	12 25	..	..	1245	..	1259	..	1 19	..	1 25	..	..	1 45	1 59	..	2 19	2 25	..	..	..	..	2 45	..	..	2 59	..	3 19
Bromley South D	11 47	12 2	..	1222	..	12 27	1238	..	1247	1256	1 2	..	1 22	..	1 27	1 35	..	1 47	2 2	..	2 22	2 27	..	2 35	..	..	2 48	2 56	..	3 2	..	3 22
Bickley	11 51	12 5	..	1225	..	12 30	..	..	1250	..	1 5	..	1 25	..	1 30	..	..	1 50	2 5	..	2 25	2 30	..	..	..	..	2 55	..	..	3 5	..	3 25
Petts Wood	11 55	..	..	..	..	12 34	..	..	1255	..	..	..	..	..	1 34	..	..	1 54	..	..	..	2 34	..	..	..	..	3 0	..	..	..	..	..
Orpington ...... arr	11 58	..	..	..	..	12 37	..	..	1258	..	..	..	..	..	1 37	..	..	1 57	..	..	..	2 37	..	..	..	..	3 4	..	..	..	..	..
St. Mary Cray	..	1210	..	1230	..	..	..	..	..	..	1 10	..	1 30	..	..	..	..	..	2 10	..	2 30	..	..	..	..	..	..	..	..	3 10	..	3 30
Swanley 34, 60	..	1214	..	1234	..	..	1246	1250	..	..	1 14	..	1 34	..	..	1 43	1 47	..	2 14	..	2 34	..	..	2 43	2 47	..	..	..	..	3 14	..	3 34
Lullingstone	..	..	..	..	..	..	..	..	..	..	..	..	..	..	..	..	..	..	..	..	..	..	..	..	..	..	..	..	..	..	..	..
Eynsford	..	1221	..	1241	..	..	..	..	..	..	1 21	..	1 41	..	..	..	..	..	2 21	..	2 41	..	..	..	..	..	..	..	..	3 21	..	3 41
Shoreham (Kent)	..	1225	..	1245	..	..	..	..	..	..	1 25	..	1 46	..	..	..	..	..	2 25	..	2 45	..	..	..	..	..	..	..	..	3 25	..	3 45
Otford	..	1228	..	1248	..	..	1258	..	..	..	1 28	..	1 49	..	..	1 55	..	..	2 28	..	2 48	..	..	2 55	..	..	..	..	..	3 28	..	3 48
Sevenoaks { Bat & Ball	..	1232	..	1252	..	..	..	..	..	..	1 32	..	1 52	..	..	..	..	..	2 32	..	2 52	..	..	..	..	..	..	..	..	3 32	..	3 52
Sevenoaks { Tub's H. arr	12c27	1235	..	1255	..	12c57	..	..	1c27	..	1 35	..	1 55	..	1c57	..	..	2c27	2 35	..	2 55	2c57	..	..	..	..	3c27	..	..	3 35	..	3 55
Kemsing	..	..	..	..	..	..	1 4	..	..	..	..	..	..	..	..	2 1	..	..	..	..	..	..	..	3 1	..	..	..	..	..	..	..	..
Wrotham & Boro' Gr'n	..	..	..	..	..	..	1 8	..	..	..	..	..	..	..	..	2 5	..	..	..	..	..	..	..	3 5	..	..	..	..	..	..	..	..
Malling	..	..	..	..	..	..	1 15	..	..	..	..	..	..	..	..	2 12	..	..	..	..	..	..	..	3 12	..	..	..	..	..	..	..	..
East Malling Halt	..	..	..	..	..	..	1 18	..	..	..	..	..	..	..	..	2 15	..	..	..	..	..	..	..	3 15	..	..	..	..	..	..	..	..
Barming	..	..	..	..	..	..	1 22	..	..	..	..	..	..	..	..	2 19	..	..	..	..	..	..	..	3 19	..	..	..	..	..	..	..	..
Maidstone East .. arr	..	..	..	..	..	..	1 26	..	..	..	..	..	..	..	..	2 23	..	..	..	..	..	..	..	3 23	..	..	..	..	..	..	..	..
Farningham Road F	..	..	..	..	..	..	..	1254	..	..	..	..	..	..	..	..	1 51	..	..	..	..	..	..	..	2 51	..	..	..	..	..	..	..
Longfield Halt G	..	..	..	..	..	..	..	..	..	..	..	..	..	..	..	..	..	..	..	..	..	..	..	..	..	..	..	..	..	..	..	..
Southfleet (Springh'd).	..	..	..	..	..	..	..	..	..	..	..	..	..	..	..	..	..	..	..	..	..	..	..	..	..	..	..	..	..	..	..	..
Gravesend West St ar	..	..	..	..	..	..	..	..	..	..	..	..	..	..	..	..	..	..	..	..	..	..	..	..	..	..	..	..	..	..	..	..
Fawkham for Hartley & [Longfield	..	..	..	..	..	..	..	1259	..	..	..	..	..	..	..	..	1 56	..	..	..	..	..	..	..	2 56	..	..	..	..	..	..	..
Meopham	..	..	..	..	..	..	..	1 4	..	..	..	..	..	..	..	..	2 1	..	..	..	..	..	..	..	3 1	..	..	..	..	..	..	..
Sole Street	..	..	..	..	..	..	..	1 6	..	..	..	..	..	..	..	..	2 3	..	..	..	..	..	..	..	3 3	..	..	..	..	..	..	..
Rochester	..	..	..	..	..	..	..	1 17	..	..	..	..	..	..	..	..	2 14	..	..	..	..	..	..	..	3 14	..	..	..	..	..	..	..
Chatham	..	..	..	..	..	..	..	1 19	..	1 29	..	..	..	..	..	..	2 16	..	..	..	..	..	..	..	3 16	..	..	3 29	..	..	..	..
Gillingham (Kent).. arr	..	..	..	..	..	..	..	1 24	..	1 36	..	..	..	..	..	..	2 21	..	..	..	..	..	..	..	3 21	..	..	3 36	..	..	..	..

3 Third class only.

c Change at Orpington.

For Other Notes, see page 146.

For Saturday Trains, see pages 140a to 142a: for SUNDAY TRAINS, see pages 143 to 146

LONDON, CRYSTAL PALACE (H.L.), ORPINGTON, SEVENOAKS, MAIDSTONE EAST, GRAVESEND WEST STREET, CHATHAM, and GILLINGHAM (Kent)

Mondays to Fridays—*continued* (p.m)

Down	3			3		3	3		3	3			3	3		3	3	3			3	3	3	3		3		3		3	3	3
Victoria dep	3 4	3 18	..	3 24	3 35	..	..	..	..	4 4	4 18	..	..	..	..	..	4 20	..	..	..	..	4 34	..	..	..	4 44	4 52	..	..	..	..	..
Brixton	3 9	..	..	3 29	..	..	..	..	..	4 9	..	..	..	..	..	..	4 25	..	..	..	..	4 39	..	..	..	4 49	..	..	..	..	..	..
Holborn Viaduct dep	2 43	..	..	3 14	..	3 31	..	..	3 51	3 43	..	..	4 4	4 11	..	..	4 14	4 27	..	4 40	4 31	..	4 34	..	..	..	..	4 45	..	4 51	..	4 57
Blackfriars "	2 44	..	..	3 15	..	3 32	..	..	3 52	3 44	..	..	4 5	4 12	..	4 17	4 15	4 28	..	4 41	4 32	..	4 35	4 37	..	..	..	4 46	..	4 52	4 57	4 58
Elephant and Castle	2 47	..	..	3 18	..	3 35	..	..	3 55	3 47	..	..	4 8	4 15	..	4 20	4 18	4 32	..	..	4 35	..	4 38	4 40	..	..	..	4 49	..	4 56	5 0	5 1
Loughborough Junc.	2 52	..	..	3 23	..	..	..	..	..	3 52	..	..	..	..	..	..	4 23	4 37	..	..	..	..	4 43	..	..	..	..	4 54	..	..	..	..
Denmark Hill	..	..	..	..	..	3 42	..	..	4 2	..	..	..	..	4 22	..	4 25	..	..	..	..	4 42	..	..	4 45	..	..	..	..	..	5 2	5 5	..
Peckham Rye	..	..	..	..	..	3 44	..	..	4 4	..	..	..	..	4 24	..	4 27	..	..	..	..	4 44	..	..	4 47	..	..	..	..	..	5 4	5 7	..
Nunhead	..	..	..	..	..	3 46	3 54	..	4 6	..	..	..	..	4 26	..	4 30	..	..	..	..	4 46	..	..	4 50	..	..	..	..	..	5 6	5 10	..
Honor Oak	..	..	..	..	..	..	3 57	..	..	..	..	..	..	..	..	4 33	..	..	..	..	..	..	..	4 53	..	..	..	..	..	..	5 13	..
Lordship Lane **A**	..	..	..	..	..	..	4 0	..	..	..	..	..	..	..	..	4 36	..	..	..	..	..	..	..	4 56	..	..	..	..	..	..	5 16	..
Upper Sydenham	..	..	..	..	..	..	4 2	..	..	..	..	..	..	..	..	4 38	..	..	..	..	..	..	..	4 58	..	..	..	..	..	..	5 18	..
Crystal Palace B arr	..	..	..	..	..	..	4 5	..	..	..	..	..	..	..	..	4 41	..	..	..	..	..	..	..	5 1	..	..	..	..	..	..	5 21	..
Crofton Park	..	..	..	..	..	3 49	..	..	4 9	..	..	..	..	4 29	..	..	..	..	..	..	4 49	..	..	..	..	..	..	..	..	5 9	..	..
Catford	..	..	..	..	..	3 52	..	..	4 12	..	..	..	..	4 32	..	..	..	..	..	..	4 52	..	..	..	..	..	..	..	..	5 12	..	..
Bellingham	..	..	..	..	..	3 54	..	..	4 14	..	..	..	..	4 34	..	..	..	..	..	..	4 54	..	..	..	..	..	..	..	..	5 14	..	..
Beckenham Hill	..	..	..	..	..	3 56	..	..	4 16	..	..	..	..	4 36	..	..	..	..	..	..	4 56	..	..	..	..	..	..	..	..	5 16	..	..
Ravensbourne	..	..	..	..	..	3 58	..	..	4 18	..	..	..	..	4 38	..	..	..	..	..	..	4 58	..	..	..	..	..	..	..	..	5 18	..	..
Herne Hill	3 11	..	..	3 31	..	..	..	..	..	4 11	..	..	4 15	..	..	..	4 27	4 39	..	..	..	4 41	4 45	..	..	4 51	..	4 56	..	..	..	5 8
West Dulwich	3 13	..	..	3 33	..	..	..	..	..	4 13	..	..	4 17	..	..	..	4 30	4 42	..	..	..	..	..	..	..	4 54	..	4 59	..	..	..	5 10
Sydenham Hill	3 15	..	..	3 35	..	..	..	..	..	4 15	..	..	4 19	..	..	..	4 32	4 44	..	..	..	..	..	..	..	4 56	..	5 1	..	..	..	..
Penge East C	3 18	..	..	3 38	..	..	..	..	..	4 18	..	..	..	..	..	..	4 35	4 47	..	..	..	..	..	..	..	4 59	..	5 4	..	..	..	5 15
Kent House	3 20	..	..	3 40	..	..	..	..	..	4 20	..	..	4K30	..	..	..	4 37	4 49	..	..	..	..	..	..	..	5 1	..	5 6	..	..	..	5 17
Beckenham Junction	3 22	..	..	3 42	..	..	..	..	..	4 22	..	..	4 33	..	..	..	4 39	4 51	..	..	..	..	..	..	..	5 3	..	5 8	..	..	..	5 19
Shortlands	3 25	..	..	3 45	..	3 59	..	..	4 19	4 25	..	..	4 36	4 39	..	..	4 43	4 54	..	..	4 59	..	..	..	..	5 6	..	5 11	..	5 19	..	5 23
Bromley South D	3 27	3 35	..	3 47	3 56	4 2	..	..	4 22	4 27	4 35	..	4 38	4 42	..	..	4 45	4 56	..	5 1	5 2	..	..	..	..	5 10	5 11	5 14	..	5 22	..	5 26
Bickley	3 30	..	..	3 50	..	4 5	..	..	4 25	4 30	..	..	4 41	4 45	..	..	4 48	4 59	..	..	5 5	..	..	..	..	5 14	..	5 17	..	5 25	..	5 29
Petts Wood	3 34	..	..	3 54	..	..	..	..	..	4 34	..	..	4 44	..	..	..	4 52	5 3	..	..	..	..	..	..	..	5 17	..	..	..	..	..	..
Orpington arr	3 37	..	..	3 57	..	..	..	..	..	4 37	..	..	4 48	..	..	..	4 55	5 7	..	..	..	..	..	..	..	5 21	..	..	..	..	..	..
St. Mary Cray	..	..	..	..	..	4 10	..	..	4 30	..	..	..	..	4 50	..	..	..	..	..	..	5 11	..	..	..	..	..	..	..	..	5 30	..	..
Swanley 34, 60	..	3 43	3 47	..	..	4 14	..	..	4 34	..	4 44	4 47	..	4 55	..	..	..	..	..	5 11	5 15	..	..	..	..	..	5 21	..	..	5 34	..	..
Lullingstone	..	..	..	..	..	..	..	..	..	..	..	..	..	..	..	..	..	..	..	..	..	..	..	..	..	..	..	..	..	..	..	..
Eynsford	..	..	..	..	..	4 21	..	..	4 41	..	..	..	..	5 2	..	..	..	..	..	..	5 20	..	..	..	..	..	..	..	..	5 42	..	..
Shoreham (Kent)	..	..	..	..	..	4 25	..	..	4 45	..	..	..	..	5 7	..	..	..	..	..	..	5 25	..	..	..	..	..	..	..	..	5 47	..	..
Otford	..	4 2	..	..	..	4 28	..	..	4 48	..	4 55	..	..	5 10	..	..	..	..	..	..	5 28	..	..	..	..	..	..	..	..	5 50	..	..
Sevenoaks { Bat & Ball	..	..	..	..	..	4 32	..	..	4 52	..	..	..	..	5 13	..	..	..	..	..	..	5 31	..	..	..	..	..	..	..	..	5 53	..	..
Sevenoaks { Tub's H. ar	3c57	..	..	4c27	..	4 35	..	..	4 55	4c56	..	..	..	5 16	..	..	5c22	..	..	..	5 34	..	..	..	..	5c44	..	..	..	5 56	..	..
Kemsing	..	4 8	..	..	..	..	..	..	..	..	5 1	..	..	..	..	..	..	..	..	..	..	..	..	..	..	..	..	..	..	..	..	..
Wrotham & Boro' Gr'n	..	4 12	..	..	..	..	..	..	..	..	5 5	..	..	..	..	..	..	..	..	..	..	..	..	..	..	..	5 40	..	..	..	..	..
Malling	..	4 19	..	..	..	..	..	..	..	..	5 12	..	..	..	..	..	..	..	..	..	..	..	..	..	..	..	5 47	..	..	..	..	..
East Malling Halt	..	4 22	..	..	..	..	..	..	..	..	5 15	..	..	..	..	..	..	..	..	..	..	..	..	..	..	..	..	..	..	..	..	..
Barming	..	4 24	..	..	..	..	..	..	..	..	5 19	..	..	..	..	..	..	..	..	..	..	..	..	..	..	..	..	..	..	..	..	..
Maidstone East arr	..	4 30	..	..	..	..	..	..	..	..	5 23	..	..	..	..	..	..	..	..	..	..	..	..	..	..	..	5 54	..	..	..	..	..
Farningham Road **F**	..	..	3 51	..	..	..	..	..	..	..	..	4 51	..	..	..	..	..	..	..	5 16	..	..	..	..	5 22	..	..	..	..	..	..	..
Longfield Halt **G**	..	..	..	..	..	..	..	..	..	..	..	..	..	..	..	..	..	..	..	..	..	..	..	..	5 27	..	..	..	..	..	..	..
Southfleet (Springh'd)	..	..	..	..	..	..	..	..	..	..	..	..	..	..	..	..	..	..	..	..	..	..	..	..	5 31	..	..	..	..	..	..	..
Gravesend West St ar	..	..	..	..	..	..	..	..	..	..	..	..	..	..	..	..	..	..	..	..	..	..	..	..	5 37	..	..	..	..	..	..	..
Fawkham (for Hartley &	..	..	3 56	..	..	..	..	..	..	..	..	4 56	..	..	..	..	..	..	..	5 21	..	..	..	..	..	..	..	..	..	..	..	..
Meopham [Longfield	..	..	4 1	..	..	..	..	..	..	..	..	5 1	..	..	..	..	..	..	..	5 26	..	..	..	..	..	..	..	..	..	..	..	..
Sole Street	..	..	4 3	..	..	..	..	..	..	..	..	5 3	..	..	..	..	..	..	..	5 28	..	..	..	..	..	..	..	..	..	..	..	..
Rochester	..	..	4 14	..	..	..	..	..	..	..	..	5 14	..	..	..	..	..	..	..	5 39	..	..	..	..	..	..	..	..	..	..	..	..
Chatham	..	..	4 16	..	4 29	..	..	..	..	..	..	5 16	..	..	..	..	..	..	..	5 41	..	..	..	..	..	..	..	..	..	..	..	..
Gillingham (Kent) arr	..	..	4 21	..	..	..	..	..	..	..	..	5 21	..	..	..	..	..	..	..	5 46	..	..	..	..	..	..	..	..	..	..	..	..

3 Third class only   c Change at Orpington   K Arr. 4 25 p.m   **For Other Notes, see page 146**

For Saturday Trains, see pages 140a to 142a; for SUNDAY TRAINS, see pages 143 to 146

LONDON, CRYSTAL PALACE (H.L.), ORPINGTON, SEVENOAKS, MAIDSTONE EAST, GRAVESEND WEST STREET, CHATHAM, and GILLINGHAM (Kent)

Down — p.m — **Mondays to Fridays**—*continued* — p.m

Down	3		3			3		3	3	3	3		3	3	3	3
Victoria .... dep	5 4	..	..	5 20	..	..	..	..	..	5 24	..	..	5 35	..	..	..
Brixton	5 9	..	..	..	..	..	..	..	..	5 30	..	..	5 [illegible]	..	..	..
Holborn Viaduct. dep	4 54	..	5 4	..	..	5 11	..	..	5 17	..	5 27	..	..	5 31	5 34	..
Blackfriars ...... "	4 55	..	5 5	..	..	5 12	..	5 17	5 18	..	5 28	..	..	5 32	5 35	5 37
Elephant and Castle	4 58	..	5 8	..	..	5 15	..	5 20	5 22	..	5 31	..	..	5 35	5 38	5 40
Loughborough Junc.	5 3	..	5 13	..	..	..	..	..	5 27	..	5 36	..	..	..	5 43	..
Denmark Hill	..	..	..	..	..	5 22	..	5 25	..	..	..	..	..	5 41	..	5 45
Peckham Rye	..	..	..	..	..	5 24	..	5 27	..	..	..	..	..	5 44	..	5 47
Nunhead	..	..	..	..	..	5 26	..	5 30	..	..	..	..	..	5 46	..	5 50
Honor Oak	..	..	..	..	..	..	..	5 33	..	..	..	..	..	..	..	5 53
Lordship Lane **A**	..	..	..	..	..	..	..	5 36	..	..	..	..	..	..	..	5 56
Upper Sydenham	..	..	..	..	..	..	..	5 38	..	..	..	..	..	..	..	5 58
Crystal Palace B arr	..	..	..	..	..	..	..	5 41	..	..	..	..	..	..	..	6 1
Crofton Park	..	..	..	..	..	5 29	..	..	..	..	..	..	..	5 49	..	..
Catford	..	..	..	..	..	5 32	..	..	..	..	..	..	..	5 52	..	..
Bellingham	..	..	..	..	..	5 34	..	..	..	..	..	..	..	5 54	..	..
Beckenham Hill	..	..	..	..	..	5 36	..	..	..	..	..	..	..	5 56	..	..
Ravensbourne	..	..	..	..	..	5 38	..	..	..	..	..	..	..	5 58	..	..
Herne Hill	5 11	..	5 15	..	..	..	..	..	5 30	5 32	5 38	..	5 43	..	5 46	..
West Dulwich	5 14	..	5 18	..	..	..	..	..	5 32	5 35	5 41	..	5 45	..	..	..
Sydenham Hill	..	..	5 20	..	..	..	..	..	..	5 38	5 43	..	5 47	..	..	..
Penge East **C**	5 19	..	5 24	..	..	..	..	..	5 37	5 41	5 46	..	5 50	..	..	..
Kent House	5 21	..	5 26	..	..	..	..	..	5 39	5 43	5 48	..	5 52	..	..	..
Beckenham Junction	5 23	..	5 28	..	..	..	..	..	5 41	5 45	5 50	..	5 54	..	..	..
Shortlands	5 27	..	5 31	..	..	5 39	..	..	5 44	5 48	5 53	..	5 57	5 59	..	..
Bromley South D	5 30	..	5 33	5 38	..	5 42	..	..	5 46	5 51	5 55	..	6 0	6 2	..	..
Bickley	5 34	..	5 37	..	..	5 45	..	..	5 49	5 54	6 0	..	6 3	6 5	..	..
Petts Wood	5 38	..	..	..	..	..	..	..	5 52	..	6 6	..	..	..	..	..
Orpington ...... arr	5 41	..	..	..	..	..	..	..	5 56	..	6 9	..	..	..	..	..
St. Mary Cray	..	..	..	5 45	..	5 50	..	..	..	..	..	..	..	6 10	..	..
Swanley 34, 60	..	..	..	5 51	5 53	5 55	..	..	..	..	..	..	..	6 15	..	..
Lullingstone	..	..	..	..	..	..	..	..	..	..	..	..	..	..	..	..
Eynsford	..	..	..	..	..	6 2	..	..	..	..	..	..	..	6 23	..	..
Shoreham (Kent)	..	..	..	..	..	6 7	..	..	..	..	..	..	..	6 27	..	..
Otford	..	..	..	6 1	..	6 10	..	..	..	..	..	..	..	6 30	..	..
Sevenoaks Bat & Ball	..	..	..	..	..	6 13	..	..	..	..	..	..	..	6 34	..	..
Sevenoaks Tub'sH. arr	6c 4	..	..	..	..	6 16	..	..	6c24	..	..	..	..	6 37	..	..
Kemsing	..	..	..	6 7	..	..	..	..	..	..	..	..	..	..	..	..
Wrotham & Boro' Gr'n	..	..	..	6 12	..	..	..	..	..	..	..	..	..	..	..	..
Malling	..	..	..	6 19	..	..	..	..	..	..	..	..	..	..	..	..
East Malling Halt	..	..	..	6 21	..	..	..	..	..	..	..	..	..	..	..	..
Barming	..	..	..	6 25	..	..	..	..	..	..	..	..	..	..	..	..
Maidstone East .. arr	..	..	..	6 29	..	..	..	..	..	..	..	..	..	..	..	..
Farningham Road **F**	..	..	..	..	..	..	..	..	..	..	..	..	..	..	..	..
Longfield Halt **G**	..	..	..	..	..	..	..	..	..	..	..	..	..	..	..	..
Southfleet (Springh'd)	..	..	..	..	..	..	..	..	..	..	..	..	..	..	..	..
Gravesend West St ar	..	..	..	..	..	..	..	..	..	..	..	..	..	..	..	..
Fawkham for Hartley & [Longfield	..	..	..	..	6 1	..	..	..	..	..	..	..	..	..	..	..
Meopham	..	..	..	..	..	..	..	..	..	..	..	..	..	..	..	..
Sole Street	..	..	..	..	..	..	..	..	..	..	..	..	..	..	..	..
Rochester	..	..	..	..	6 15	..	..	..	..	..	..	..	..	..	..	..
Chatham	..	..	..	..	6 17	..	..	..	..	..	..	..	..	..	..	..
Gillingham (Kent) .. arr	..	..	..	..	6 21	..	..	..	..	..	..	..	..	..	..	..

Down			3		3	3		3	3	3	3		3	3	3	3
Victoria .... dep	..	..	5 44	5 53	..	..	..	..	..	6 4	..	6 18	..	..	..	..
Brixton	..	..	5 49	..	..	..	..	..	..	6 9	..	..	..	..	..	..
Holborn Viaduct. dep	..	5 43	..	..	5 47	5 51	..	..	5 57	..	6 4	..	6 11	6 14	..	6 17
Blackfriars ...... "	..	5 44	..	..	5 48	5 52	..	5 57	5 58	..	6 5	..	6 12	6 15	6 17	6 18
Elephant and Castle	..	..	..	..	5 51	5 55	..	6 0	6 1	..	6 8	..	6 16	6 19	6 20	6 22
Loughborough Junc.	..	..	..	..	5 56	..	..	..	6 6	..	6 13	..	..	6 23	..	..
Denmark Hill	..	..	..	..	..	6 2	..	6 5	..	..	..	..	6 22	..	6 25	..
Peckham Rye	..	..	..	..	..	6 4	..	6 7	..	..	..	..	6 24	..	6 27	..
Nunhead	..	..	..	..	..	6 6	..	6 10	..	..	..	..	6 26	..	6 30	..
Honor Oak	..	..	..	..	..	..	..	6 14	..	..	..	..	..	..	6 33	..
Lordship Lane **A**	..	..	..	..	..	..	..	6 16	..	..	..	..	..	..	6 36	..
Upper Sydenham	..	..	..	..	..	..	..	6 19	..	..	..	..	..	..	6 38	..
Crystal Palace B arr	..	..	..	..	..	..	..	6 21	..	..	..	..	..	..	6 41	..
Crofton Park	..	..	..	..	..	6 9	..	..	..	..	..	..	6 29	..	Stop	..
Catford	..	..	..	..	..	6 12	..	..	..	..	..	..	6 32	..	..	..
Bellingham	..	..	..	..	..	6 14	..	..	..	..	..	..	6 34	..	..	..
Beckenham Hill	..	..	..	..	..	6 16	..	..	..	..	..	..	6 36	..	..	..
Ravensbourne	..	..	..	..	..	6 18	..	..	..	..	..	..	6 38	..	..	..
Herne Hill	..	..	5 51	..	5 58	..	..	..	6 8	6 11	6 16	..	..	6 26	..	6 28
West Dulwich	..	..	5 53	..	6 1	..	..	..	6 11	6 15	6 18	..	..	..	..	6 31
Sydenham Hill	..	..	5 55	..	6 3	..	..	..	6 13	..	6 21	..	..	..	..	..
Penge East **C**	..	..	5 58	..	6 6	..	..	..	6 16	6 20	6 24	..	..	..	..	6 35
Kent House	..	..	6 0	..	6 8	..	..	..	6 18	6 22	..	..	..	..	..	6 37
Beckenham Junction	..	..	6 2	..	6 10	..	..	..	6 20	6 24	6 28	..	..	..	..	6 39
Shortlands	..	..	6 5	..	6 13	6 19	..	..	6 23	6 27	6 31	..	6 39	..	..	6 43
Bromley South D	..	6 7	6 7	6 12	6 15	6 22	..	..	6 25	6 29	6 34	6 36	6 42	..	..	6 45
Bickley	..	..	6 10	..	6 18	6 25	..	..	6 28	6 33	6 38	..	6 45	..	..	6 48
Petts Wood	..	..	6 14	..	..	..	..	..	6 31	6 37	6 43	..	..	..	..	6 51
Orpington ...... arr	..	..	6 17	..	..	..	..	..	6 35	6 41	6 46	..	..	..	..	6 54
St. Mary Cray	..	..	..	6 18	..	6 30	..	..	..	..	..	..	6 50	..	p.m	..
Swanley 34, 60	..	6 18	..	6 22	..	6 35	..	..	..	..	..	6 44	6 55	..	7 13	..
Lullingstone	..	..	..	..	..	..	..	..	..	..	..	..	..	..	..	..
Eynsford	..	..	..	6 28	..	6 42	..	..	..	..	..	..	7 2	..	..	..
Shoreham (Kent)	..	..	..	6 32	..	6 47	..	..	..	..	..	..	7 7	..	..	..
Otford	..	..	..	6 35	..	6 50	..	..	..	..	..	6 55	7 10	..	..	..
Sevenoaks Bat & Ball	..	..	..	..	..	6 53	..	..	..	..	..	..	7 13	..	..	..
Sevenoaks Tub'sH. arr	..	..	6c46	..	..	6 56	..	..	..	..	7c8	..	7 16	..	..	..
Kemsing	..	..	..	6 41	..	..	..	..	..	..	..	7 1	..	..	..	..
Wrotham & Boro' Gr'n	..	..	..	6 45	..	..	..	..	..	..	..	7 5	..	..	..	..
Malling	..	..	..	6 52	..	..	..	..	..	..	..	7 12	..	..	..	..
East Malling Halt	..	..	..	6 54	..	..	..	..	..	..	..	7 15	..	..	..	..
Barming	..	..	..	..	..	..	..	..	..	..	..	7 19	..	..	..	..
Maidstone East .. arr	..	..	..	7 1	..	..	..	..	..	..	..	7 23	..	..	..	..
Farningham Road **F**	..	6 24	..	..	..	..	..	..	..	..	..	..	..	..	7 18	..
Longfield Halt **G**	..	..	..	..	..	..	..	..	..	..	..	..	..	..	7 25	..
Southfleet (Springh'd)	..	..	..	..	..	..	..	..	..	..	..	..	..	..	7 29	..
Gravesend West St ar	..	..	..	..	..	..	..	..	..	..	..	..	..	..	7 34	..
Fawkham for Hartley & [Longfield	..	6 29	..	..	..	..	..	..	..	..	..	..	..	..	..	..
Meopham	..	6 34	..	..	..	..	..	..	..	..	..	..	..	..	..	..
Sole Street	..	6 36	..	..	..	..	..	..	..	..	..	..	..	..	..	..
Rochester	..	6 47	..	..	..	..	..	..	..	..	..	..	..	..	..	..
Chatham	..	6 49	..	..	..	..	..	..	..	..	..	..	..	..	..	..
Gillingham (Kent) .. arr	..	6 54	..	..	..	..	..	..	..	..	..	..	..	..	..	..

3 Third class only   c Change at Orpington   **For Other Notes, see page 146.**

For Saturday Trains, see pages 140a to 142a: for SUNDAY TRAINS, see pages 143 to 146

LONDON, CRYSTAL PALACE (H.L.), ORPINGTON, SEVENOAKS, MAIDSTONE EAST, GRAVESEND WEST STREET, CHATHAM and GILLINGHAM (Kent).

Mondays to Fridays—*continued* (p.m)

Down		3	3	3		3	3			3		3	3	3	3		3				3		3	3	3	3		3				3
Victoria .... dep	..	6 24	..	..	..	..	..	6 50	..	6 44	..	..	..	..	..	..	7 4	7 15	7 20	..	7 24	..	..	..	..	..	..	8 4	8 18	..	..	8 24
Brixton	..	6 29	..	..	..	..	..	..	..	6 49	..	..	..	..	..	..	7 9	..	..	..	7 29	..	..	..	..	..	..	8 9	..	..	..	8 29
Holborn Viaduct. dep	6 24	..	6 27	6 31	..	..	6 38	..	..	..	..	..	6 51	6 54	..	..	..	..	..	..	7 14	..	..	7 31	..	7 51	..	7 43	..	..	..	8 14
Blackfriars ...... "	6 25	..	6 28	6 32	..	6 37	6 39	..	..	..	..	6 50	6 53	6 55	..	..	..	..	..	..	7 15	..	7 27	7 32	..	7 52	..	7 44	..	..	..	8 15
Elephant and Castle..	..	..	6 31	6 36	..	6 40	6 42	..	..	..	..	6 52	6 56	6 58	..	..	..	..	..	..	7 18	..	7 30	7 36	..	7 55	..	7 47	..	..	..	8 18
Loughborough Junc...	..	..	6 36	..	..	..	6 47	..	..	..	..	6 57	..	7 3	..	..	..	..	..	..	7 23	..	..	..	..	..	..	7 52	..	..	..	8 23
Denmark Hill..........	..	..	..	6 42	..	6 45	..	..	..	..	..	..	7 2	..	..	..	..	..	..	..	..	..	7 35	7 42	..	8 1	..	..	..	..	..	..
Peckham Rye..........	..	..	..	6 44	..	6 47	..	..	..	..	..	..	7 4	..	..	..	..	..	..	..	..	..	7 37	7 44	..	8 4	..	..	..	..	..	..
Nunhead..............	..	..	..	6 46	..	6 50	..	..	..	..	..	..	7 6	..	7 10	..	..	..	..	..	..	..	7 40	7 46	7 54	8 6	..	..	..	..	..	..
Honor Oak...........	..	..	..	..	..	6 53	..	..	..	..	..	..	..	..	7 13	..	..	..	..	..	..	..	7 43	..	7 57	..	..	..	..	..	..	..
Lordship Lane **A**.....	..	..	..	..	..	6 56	..	..	..	..	..	..	..	..	7 16	..	..	..	..	..	..	..	7 46	..	8 0	..	..	..	..	..	..	..
Upper Sydenham......	..	..	..	..	..	6 58	..	..	..	..	..	..	..	..	7 18	..	..	..	..	..	..	..	7 48	..	8 2	..	..	..	..	..	..	..
Crystal Palace **B** arr	..	..	..	..	..	7 1	..	..	..	..	..	..	..	..	7 21	..	..	..	..	..	..	..	7 51	..	8 5	..	..	..	..	..	..	..
Crofton Park.........	..	..	..	6 49	..	..	..	..	..	..	..	..	7 9	..	..	..	..	..	..	..	..	..	..	7 49	..	8 9	..	..	..	..	..	..
Catford	..	..	..	6 52	..	..	..	..	..	..	..	..	7 12	..	..	..	..	..	..	..	..	..	..	7 52	..	8 12	..	..	..	..	..	..
Bellingham	..	..	..	6 54	..	..	..	..	..	..	..	..	7 14	..	..	..	..	..	..	..	..	..	..	7 54	..	8 14	..	..	..	..	..	..
Beckenham Hill.......	..	..	..	6 56	..	..	..	..	..	..	..	..	7 16	..	..	..	..	..	..	..	..	..	..	7 56	..	8 16	..	..	..	..	..	..
Ravensbourne.........	..	..	..	6 58	..	..	..	..	..	..	..	..	7 18	..	..	..	..	..	..	..	..	..	..	7 58	..	8 18	..	..	..	..	..	..
Herne Hill...........	..	6 32	6 38	..	..	..	6 49	..	..	6 51	..	6 59	..	7 5	..	..	7 11	..	..	..	7 31	..	..	..	..	..	..	8 11	..	..	..	8 31
West Dulwich.........	..	6 34	6 41	..	..	..	..	..	..	6 55	..	7 2	..	..	..	..	7 13	..	..	..	7 33	..	..	..	..	..	..	8 13	..	..	..	8 33
Sydenham Hill........	..	6 37	6 43	..	..	..	..	..	..	6 57	..	7 4	..	..	..	..	7 15	..	..	..	7 35	..	..	..	..	..	..	8 15	..	..	..	8 35
Penge East **C**........	..	6 40	6 46	..	..	..	..	..	..	7 0	..	7 7	..	..	..	..	7 18	..	..	..	7 38	..	..	..	..	..	..	8 18	..	..	..	8 38
Kent House...........	..	6 42	6 48	..	..	..	..	..	..	7 2	..	7 9	..	..	..	..	7 20	..	..	..	7 40	..	..	..	..	..	..	8 20	..	..	..	8 40
Beckenham Junction...	..	6 44	6 50	..	..	..	..	..	..	7 5	..	7 11	..	..	..	..	7 22	..	..	..	7 42	..	..	..	..	..	..	8 22	..	..	..	8 42
Shortlands	..	6 47	6 53	6 59	..	..	..	..	..	7 8	..	7 14	7 19	..	..	..	7 25	..	..	..	7 45	..	..	7 59	..	8 19	..	8 25	..	..	..	8 45
Bromley South **D**......	6 47	6 50	6 55	7 2	..	..	..	7 8	..	7 10	..	7 16	7 22	..	..	..	7 27	..	7 40	..	7 47	..	..	8 2	..	8 22	..	8 27	8 35	..	..	8 47
Bickley	..	6 53	6 59	7 5	..	..	..	..	..	7 13	..	7 19	7 25	..	..	..	7 30	..	..	..	7 50	..	..	8 5	..	8 25	..	8 30	..	..	..	8 53
Petts Wood..........	..	6 58	..	..	..	..	..	..	..	7 16	..	7 22	..	..	..	..	7 34	..	..	..	7 54	..	..	..	..	..	..	8 34	..	..	..	8 58
Orpington......... arr	..	7 3	..	..	..	..	..	..	..	7 19	..	7 26	..	..	..	..	7 37	..	..	..	7 57	..	..	..	..	..	..	8 37	..	..	..	9 1
St. Mary Cray........	..	..	..	7 10	..	..	..	..	..	..	..	..	7 30	..	..	..	..	..	..	..	..	..	..	8 10	..	8 30	..	..	..	..	..	..
Swanley 54, 60.......	6 58	..	..	7 14	..	..	..	7 18	7 21	..	..	..	7 35	..	..	..	..	..	7 49	7 52	..	..	..	8 15	..	8 35	..	..	8 44	8 47	..	..
Lullingstone.........	..	..	..	..	..	..	..	..	..	..	..	..	..	..	..	..	..	..	..	..	..	..	..	..	..	..	..	..	..	..	..	..
Eynsford	..	..	..	7 19	..	..	..	..	..	..	..	..	7 42	..	..	..	..	..	..	..	..	..	..	8 22	..	8 41	..	..	..	..	..	..
Shoreham (Kent)......	..	..	..	7 24	..	..	..	..	..	..	..	..	7 47	..	..	..	..	..	..	..	..	..	..	8 27	..	8 45	..	..	..	..	..	..
Otford...............	..	..	..	7 27	..	..	..	7 30	..	..	..	..	7 50	..	..	..	..	..	8 0	..	..	..	..	8 30	..	8 48	..	..	8 55	..	..	..
Sevenoaks { Bat & Ball..	..	..	..	7 30	..	..	..	..	..	..	..	..	7 53	..	..	..	..	..	..	..	..	..	..	8 33	..	8 52	..	..	..	..	..	..
Sevenoaks { Tub's H. arr	..	7c27	..	7 33	..	..	..	..	..	7c39	..	..	7 56	..	..	..	7c57	..	..	..	8c27	..	..	8 36	..	8 55	..	8c57	..	..	..	9c27
Kemsing	..	..	..	..	..	..	..	7 36	..	..	..	..	..	..	..	..	..	..	8 6	..	..	..	..	..	..	..	..	..	9 1	..	..	..
Wrotham & Boro' Gr'n	..	..	..	..	..	..	..	7 40	..	..	..	..	..	..	..	..	..	..	8 10	..	..	..	..	..	..	..	..	..	9 5	..	..	..
Malling..............	..	..	..	..	..	..	..	7 47	..	..	..	..	..	..	..	..	..	..	8 17	..	..	..	..	..	..	..	..	..	9 12	..	..	..
East Malling Halt....	..	..	..	..	..	..	..	7 50	..	..	..	..	..	..	..	..	..	..	8 20	..	..	..	..	..	..	..	..	..	9 15	..	..	..
Barming	..	..	..	..	..	..	..	7 54	..	..	..	..	..	..	..	..	..	..	8 24	..	..	..	..	..	..	..	..	..	9 19	..	..	..
Maidstone East.. arr	..	..	..	..	..	..	..	7 58	..	..	..	..	..	..	..	..	..	..	8 28	..	..	..	..	..	..	..	..	..	9 23	..	..	..
Farningham Road **F**...	7 3	..	..	..	..	..	..	..	..	..	..	..	..	..	..	..	..	..	..	7 56	..	..	..	..	..	..	..	..	..	8 51	..	..
Longfield Halt **G**.....	..	..	..	..	..	..	..	..	..	..	..	..	..	..	..	..	..	..	..	..	..	..	..	..	..	..	..	..	..	..	..	..
Southfleet (Springh'd).	..	..	..	..	..	..	..	..	..	..	..	..	..	..	..	..	..	..	..	..	..	..	..	..	..	..	..	..	..	..	..	..
Gravesend West St ar	..	..	..	..	..	..	..	..	..	..	..	..	..	..	..	..	..	..	..	..	..	..	..	..	..	..	..	..	..	..	..	..
Fawkham for Hartley &	7 8	..	..	..	..	..	..	..	..	..	..	..	..	..	..	..	..	..	..	8 1	..	..	..	..	..	..	..	..	..	8 56	..	..
Meopham ..... [Longfield	7 13	..	..	..	..	..	..	..	..	..	..	..	..	..	..	..	..	..	..	8 6	..	..	..	..	..	..	..	..	..	9 1	..	..
Sole Street...........	7 15	..	..	..	..	..	..	..	..	..	..	..	..	..	..	..	..	..	..	8 8	..	..	..	..	..	..	..	..	..	9 3	..	..
Rochester	7 26	..	..	..	..	..	..	..	7 44	..	..	..	..	..	..	..	..	..	..	8 19	..	..	..	..	..	..	..	..	..	9 14	..	..
Chatham..............	7 28	..	..	..	..	..	..	..	7 46	..	..	..	..	..	..	..	..	8 5	..	8 21	..	..	..	..	..	..	..	..	..	9 16	..	..
Gillingham (Kent).. arr	7 33	..	..	..	..	..	..	..	7 51	..	..	..	..	..	..	..	..	..	..	8 26	..	..	..	..	..	..	..	..	..	9 21	..	..

3 Third class only   c Change at Orpington

For Other Notes, see page 146

For Saturday Trains, see pages 140a to 142a; for SUNDAY TRAINS, see pages 143 to 146

LONDON, CRYSTAL PALACE (H.L.), ORPINGTON, SEVENOAKS, MAIDSTONE EAST, GRAVESEND WEST STREET, CHATHAM, and GILLINGHAM (Kent)

Mondays to Fridays—*continued* (p.m)

Down	3		3	3	3		3			3	3	3		3	3				3	3	3	3		3	3	3	3	3	3	3	3
Victoria dep	..	..	..	..	..	..	9 4	9 18	..	9 24	..	..	9 35	..	10 4	..	1018	..	10 24	..	..	..	..	11 4	..	..	11 30	..	..	..	..
Brixton	..	..	..	..	..	..	9 9	..	..	9 29	..	..	..	..	10 9	..	..	..	10 29	..	..	..	..	11 9	..	..	11 35	..	ngt.	ngt.	..
Holborn Viaduct dep	..	..	8 31	..	8 51	..	8 43	..	..	9 14	9 31	..	..	9 51	9 43	..	..	..	10 14	1031	..	1051	..	10 43	1114	11 25	..	..	1215	1221	..
Blackfriars "	8 27	..	8 32	..	8 52	..	8 44	..	..	9 15	9 32	..	..	9 52	9 44	..	..	..	10 15	1032	..	1052	..	10 44	1115	11 26	..	..	1216	1222	..
Elephant and Castle	8 30	..	8 35	..	8 55	..	8 47	..	..	9 19	9 35	..	..	9 55	9 47	..	..	..	10 18	1035	..	1055	..	10 47	1118	11 29	..	..	1220	1225	..
Loughborough Junc.	..	..	..	..	..	..	8 52	..	..	9 23	..	..	..	..	9 52	..	..	..	10 23	..	..	..	..	10 52	1123	..	..	..	..	1230	..
Denmark Hill	8 36	..	8 42	..	9 2	..	..	..	..	..	9 42	..	..	10 2	..	..	..	..	..	1042	..	11 2	..	..	..	11 36	..	..	1226	..	..
Peckham Rye	8 38	..	8 44	..	9 4	..	..	..	..	..	9 44	..	..	10 4	..	..	..	..	..	1044	..	11 4	..	..	..	11 38	..	..	1228	..	..
Nunhead	8 41	..	8 46	8 54	9 6	..	..	..	..	..	9 46	9 54	..	10 6	..	..	..	..	..	1046	1054	11 6	..	..	..	11 40	..	1154	1230	..	..
Honor Oak	8 44	..	..	8 57	..	..	..	..	..	..	..	9 57	..	..	..	..	..	..	..	..	1057	..	..	..	..	..	..	1157	..	..	..
Lordship Lane A	8 47	..	..	9 0	..	..	..	..	..	..	..	10 0	..	..	..	..	..	..	..	..	11 0	..	..	..	..	..	..	12 0	..	..	..
Upper Sydenham	8 49	..	..	9 2	..	..	..	..	..	..	..	10 2	..	..	..	..	..	..	..	..	11 2	..	..	..	..	..	..	12 2	..	..	..
Crystal Palace B arr	8 52	..	..	9 5	..	..	..	..	..	..	..	10 5	..	..	..	..	..	..	..	..	11 5	..	..	..	..	..	..	12 5	..	..	..
Crofton Park	..	..	8 49	..	9 9	..	..	..	..	..	9 49	..	..	10 9	..	..	..	..	..	1049	..	11 9	..	..	..	11 43	..	..	1233	..	..
Catford	..	..	8 52	..	9 12	..	..	..	..	..	9 52	..	..	1012	..	..	..	..	..	1052	..	1112	..	..	..	11 46	..	..	1236	..	..
Bellingham	..	..	8 54	..	9 14	..	..	..	..	..	9 54	..	..	1014	..	..	..	..	..	1054	..	1114	..	..	..	11 48	..	..	1238	..	..
Beckenham Hill	..	..	8 56	..	9 16	..	..	..	..	..	9 56	..	..	1016	..	..	..	..	..	1056	..	1116	..	..	..	11 50	..	..	1240	..	..
Ravensbourne	..	..	8 58	..	9 18	..	..	..	..	..	9 58	..	..	1018	..	..	..	..	..	1058	..	1118	..	..	..	11 52	..	..	..	..	ngt.
Herne Hill	..	..	..	..	..	..	9 11	..	..	9 31	..	..	..	..	10 11	..	..	..	10 31	..	..	..	..	11 11	1126	..	11 37	..	..	1233	1235
West Dulwich	..	..	..	..	..	..	9 13	..	..	9 33	..	..	..	..	10 13	..	..	..	10 33	..	..	..	..	11 13	..	..	11 39	..	..	..	1237
Sydenham Hill	..	..	..	..	..	..	9 15	..	..	9 35	..	..	..	..	10 15	..	..	..	10 35	..	..	..	..	11 15	..	..	11 41	..	..	..	1240
Penge East C	..	..	..	..	..	..	9 18	..	..	9 38	..	..	..	..	10 18	..	..	..	10 38	..	..	..	..	11 18	..	..	11 44	..	..	..	1243
Kent House	..	..	..	..	..	..	9 20	..	..	9 40	..	..	..	..	10 20	..	..	..	10 40	..	..	..	..	11 20	..	..	11 46	..	..	..	1245
Beckenham Junction	..	..	..	..	..	..	9 22	..	..	9 42	..	..	..	..	10 22	..	..	..	10 42	..	..	..	..	11 22	..	..	11 48	..	..	..	1248
Shortlands	..	..	8 59	..	9 19	..	9 25	..	..	9 45	9 59	..	..	1019	10 25	..	..	..	10 45	1059	..	1119	..	11 25	..	11 53	11 51	..	1243	..	..
Bromley South D	..	..	9 2	..	9 22	..	9 27	9 35	..	9 47	10 2	..	..	1022	10 27	..	1035	..	10 47	11 2	..	1122	..	11 27	..	11 57	11L57	..	1246	..	..
Bickley	..	..	9 5	..	9 25	..	9 30	..	..	9 50	10 5	..	..	1025	10 30	..	..	..	10 50	11 5	..	1125	..	11 30	..	12 1	12 1	..	1249	..	..
Petts Wood	..	..	..	..	..	..	9 34	..	..	9 54	..	..	..	..	10 34	..	..	..	10 54	..	..	..	..	11 34	..	..	12 5	..	1253	..	..
Orpington arr	..	..	..	..	..	..	9 37	..	..	9 57	..	..	..	..	10 37	..	..	..	10 57	..	..	..	..	11 37	..	..	12 8	..	1256	..	..
St. Mary Cray	..	..	9 10	..	9 30	..	..	..	..	..	1010	..	..	1030	..	..	..	..	..	1110	..	1130	..	..	..	12 6	..	..	..	..	..
Swanley 34, 60	..	..	9 14	..	9 34	..	..	9 44	9 47	..	1014	..	..	1034	..	..	1044	1047	..	1114	..	1134	..	..	..	12 10	..	..	..	..	..
Lullingstone	..	..	..	..	..	..	..	..	..	..	..	..	..	..	..	..	..	..	..	..	..	..	..	..	..	..	..	..	..	..	..
Eynsford	..	..	9 21	..	9 41	..	..	..	..	..	1021	..	..	1041	..	..	..	..	..	1121	..	1141	..	..	..	12 17	..	..	..	..	..
Shoreham (Kent)	..	..	9 25	..	9 45	..	..	..	..	..	1025	..	..	1045	..	..	..	..	..	1125	..	1145	..	..	..	12 21	..	..	..	..	..
Otford	..	..	9 28	..	9 48	..	..	9 55	..	..	1028	..	..	1048	..	..	1055	..	..	1128	..	1148	..	..	..	12 24	..	..	..	..	..
Sevenoaks Bat & Ball	..	..	9 32	..	9 52	..	..	..	..	..	1032	..	..	1052	..	..	..	..	..	1132	..	1152	..	..	..	12 28	..	..	..	..	..
Sevenoaks Tub's H. ar	..	..	9 35	..	9 55	..	9c57	..	..	10c27	1035	..	..	1035	10c57	..	..	..	11c26	1135	..	1155	..	11c56	..	12 31	12c29	..	..	..	..
Kemsing	..	..	..	..	..	..	..	10 1	..	..	..	..	..	..	..	..	11 1	..	..	..	..	..	..	..	..	..	..	..	..	..	..
Wrotham & Boro' Gr'n	..	..	..	..	..	..	..	10 5	..	..	..	..	..	..	..	..	11 5	..	..	..	..	..	..	..	..	..	..	..	..	..	..
Malling	..	..	..	..	..	..	..	1012	..	..	..	..	..	..	..	..	1112	..	..	..	..	..	..	..	..	..	..	..	..	..	..
East Malling Halt	..	..	..	..	..	..	..	1015	..	..	..	..	..	..	..	..	1115	..	..	..	..	..	..	..	..	..	..	..	..	..	..
Barming	..	..	..	..	..	..	..	1019	..	..	..	..	..	..	..	..	1119	..	..	..	..	..	..	..	..	..	..	..	..	..	..
Maidstone East arr	..	..	..	..	..	..	..	1023	..	..	..	..	..	..	..	..	1123	..	..	..	..	..	..	..	..	..	..	..	..	..	..
Farningham Road F	..	..	..	..	..	..	..	..	9 51	..	..	..	..	..	..	..	..	1051	..	..	..	..	..	..	..	..	..	..	..	..	..
Longfield Halt G	..	..	..	..	..	..	..	..	..	..	..	..	..	..	..	..	..	..	..	..	..	..	..	..	..	..	..	..	..	..	..
Southfleet (Springh'd)	..	..	..	..	..	..	..	..	..	..	..	..	..	..	..	..	..	..	..	..	..	..	..	..	..	..	..	..	..	..	..
Gravesend West St ar	..	..	..	..	..	..	..	..	..	..	..	..	..	..	..	..	..	..	..	..	..	..	..	..	..	..	..	..	..	..	..
Fawkham for Hartley &	..	..	..	..	..	..	..	..	9 56	..	..	..	..	..	..	..	..	1056	..	..	..	..	..	..	..	..	..	..	..	..	..
Meopham ....[Longfield	..	..	..	..	..	..	..	..	10 1	..	..	..	..	..	..	..	..	11 1	..	..	..	..	..	..	..	..	..	..	..	..	..
Sole Street	..	..	..	..	..	..	..	..	10 3	..	..	..	..	..	..	..	..	11 3	..	..	..	..	..	..	..	..	..	..	..	..	..
Rochester	..	..	..	..	..	..	..	..	1014	..	..	..	..	..	..	..	..	1114	..	..	..	..	..	..	..	..	..	..	..	..	..
Chatham	..	..	..	..	..	..	..	..	1016	..	..	..	1024	..	..	..	..	1116	..	..	..	..	..	..	..	..	..	..	..	..	..
Gillingham (Kent) arr	..	..	..	..	..	..	..	..	1021	..	..	..	..	..	..	..	..	1121	..	..	..	..	..	..	..	..	..	..	..	..	..

3 Third class only c Change at Orpington L Arr 11 54 p.m

For Other Notes, see page 146

For Saturday Trains, see pages 140a to 142a: for SUNDAY TRAINS, see pages 143 to 146

LONDON, CRYSTAL PALACE (H.L.), ORPINGTON, SEVENOAKS, MAIDSTONE EAST, GRAVESEND WEST STREET, CHATHAM and GILLINGHAM (Kent)

Down — Saturdays — a.m

Down	3		3		3	3	3		3	3	3	3	3			
Victoria ..... dep	..	..	9 24	..	..	..	..	..	9 44	..	..	..	10 4	10 18	..	..
Brixton	..	..	9 29	..	..	..	..	..	9 49	..	..	..	10 9	..	..	..
Holborn Viaduct. dep	..	..	9 18	..	9 29	..	..	..	9 38	..	9 51	..	9 59	..	..	..
Blackfriars ..... "	9 17	..	9 20	..	9 31	9 33	9 37	..	9 39	9 49	9 52	9 57	10 0	..	..	..
Elephant and Castle	9 20	..	9 23	..	9 34	9 36	9 40	..	9 42	9 52	9 56	10 0	10 3	..	..	..
Loughborough Junc.	..	..	9 28	..	9 40	..	..	..	9 47	..	..	..	10 8	..	..	..
Denmark Hill	9 25	..	..	..	..	9 42	9 45	..	..	9 57	10 2	10 5	..	..	..	..
Peckham Rye	9 27	..	..	..	..	9 44	9 47	..	..	9 59	10 4	10 7	..	..	..	..
Nunhead	9 30	..	..	..	..	9 46	9 50	..	..	10 2	10 6	1010	..	..	..	..
Honor Oak	9 33	..	..	..	..	..	9 53	..	..	10 5	..	1013	..	..	..	..
Lordship Lane **A**	9 36	..	..	..	..	..	9 56	..	..	10 8	..	1016	..	..	..	..
Upper Sydenham	9 38	..	..	..	..	..	9 58	..	..	1010	..	1018	..	..	..	..
Crystal Palace **B** arr	9 41	..	..	..	..	..	10 1	..	..	1013	..	1021	..	..	..	..
Crofton Park	..	..	..	..	..	9 49	..	..	..	..	10 9	..	..	..	..	..
Catford	..	..	..	..	..	9 52	..	..	..	..	10 12	..	..	..	..	..
Bellingham	..	..	..	..	..	9 54	..	..	..	..	10 14	..	..	..	..	..
Beckenham Hill	..	..	..	..	..	9 56	..	..	..	..	10 16	..	..	..	..	..
Ravensbourne	..	..	..	..	..	9 58	..	..	..	..	10 18	..	..	..	..	..
Herne Hill	..	..	9 31	..	9 42	..	..	..	9 51	..	..	..	1011	..	..	..
West Dulwich	..	..	9 34	..	9 45	..	..	..	9 53	..	..	..	1013	..	..	..
Sydenham Hill	..	..	9 36	..	9 47	..	..	..	9 55	..	..	..	1015	..	..	..
Penge East **C**	..	..	9 39	..	9 50	..	..	..	9 58	..	..	..	1018	..	..	..
Kent House	..	..	9 41	..	9 52	..	..	..	10 0	..	..	..	1020	..	..	..
Beckenham Junction	..	..	9 43	..	9 54	..	..	..	10 2	..	..	..	1022	..	..	..
Shortlands	..	..	9 46	..	9 57	9 59	..	..	10 5	..	10 19	..	1025	..	..	..
Bromley South **D**	..	..	9 49	..	10 0	10 2	..	..	10 8	..	10 22	..	1028	10 35	..	..
Bickley	..	..	9 52	..	10 3	10 5	..	..	10 10	..	10 25	..	1033	..	..	..
Petts Wood	..	..	9 56	..	..	..	..	..	10 14	..	10 29	..	1038	..	..	..
Orpington ..... arr	..	..	9 59	..	..	..	..	..	10 17	..	10 32	..	1042	..	..	..
St. Mary Cray	..	..	..	..	..	1010	..	..	..	..	..	..	..	..	..	..
Swanley 34, 60	..	..	..	..	..	1015	..	..	..	..	..	..	..	10R47	1051	..
Lullingstone	..	..	..	..	..	..	..	..	..	..	..	..	..	..	..	..
Eynsford	..	..	..	..	..	1022	..	..	..	..	..	..	..	..	..	..
Shoreham (Kent)	..	..	..	..	..	1027	..	..	..	..	..	..	..	..	..	..
Otford	..	..	..	..	..	1030	..	..	..	..	..	..	..	..	11 1	..
Seven- oaks { Bat & Ball.	..	..	..	..	..	1033	..	..	..	..	..	..	..	..	..	..
Seven- oaks { Tub's H. arr	..	..	10c25	..	..	1036	..	..	..	..	10c52	..	..	..	..	..
Kemsing	..	..	..	..	..	..	..	..	..	..	..	..	..	..	11 7	..
Wrotham & Boro' Gr'n	..	..	..	..	..	..	..	..	..	..	..	..	..	..	1111	..
Malling	..	..	..	..	..	..	..	..	..	..	..	..	..	..	1118	..
East Malling Halt	..	..	..	..	..	..	..	..	..	..	..	..	..	..	1121	..
Barming	..	..	..	..	..	..	..	..	..	..	..	..	..	..	1125	..
Maidstone East .. arr	..	..	..	..	..	..	..	..	..	..	..	..	..	..	1129	..
Farningham Road **F**	..	..	..	..	..	..	..	..	..	..	..	..	..	10 51	..	..
Longfield Halt **G**	..	..	..	..	..	..	..	..	..	..	..	..	..	..	..	..
Southfleet (Springh'd)	..	..	..	..	..	..	..	..	..	..	..	..	..	..	..	..
Gravesend West St arr	..	..	..	..	..	..	..	..	..	..	..	..	..	..	..	..
Fawkham for Hartley &	..	..	..	..	..	..	..	..	..	..	..	..	..	10 56	..	..
Meopham ..... Longfield	..	..	..	..	..	..	..	..	..	..	..	..	..	11 1	..	..
Sole Street	..	..	..	..	..	..	..	..	..	..	..	..	..	11 3	..	..
Rochester	..	..	..	..	..	..	..	..	..	..	..	..	..	11 14	..	..
Chatham	..	..	..	..	..	..	..	..	..	..	..	..	..	11 16	..	..
Gillingham (Kent) .. arr.	..	..	..	..	..	..	..	..	..	..	..	..	..	11 21	..	..

Down	3	3	3		3	3		3		3	3	3			3
Victoria ..... dep	..	..	10 24	1035	..	..	..	10 44	..	..	..	11 4	1118	..	..
Brixton	..	..	10 29	..	..	..	..	10 49	..	..	..	11 9	..	..	..
Holborn Viaduct. dep	1011	..	10 19	..	10 31	..	..	10 39	..	1051	..	10 59	..	..	1111
Blackfriars ..... "	1013	1017	10 20	..	10 32	1037	..	10 40	..	1052	1057	11 0	..	..	1113
Elephant and Castle	1016	1020	10 23	..	10 36	1040	..	10 43	..	1056	11 0	11 3	..	..	1116
Loughborough Junc.	..	..	10 28	..	..	..	..	10 48	..	..	..	11 8	..	..	..
Denmark Hill	1022	1025	..	..	10 42	1045	..	..	..	11 2	11 5	..	..	..	1122
Peckham Rye	1024	1027	..	..	10 44	1047	..	..	..	11 4	11 7	..	..	..	1124
Nunhead	1026	1030	..	..	10 46	1050	..	..	..	11 6	1110	..	..	..	1126
Honor Oak	..	1033	..	..	..	1053	..	..	..	..	1113	..	..	..	..
Lordship Lane **A**	..	1036	..	..	..	1056	..	..	..	..	1116	..	..	..	..
Upper Sydenham	..	1038	..	..	..	1058	..	..	..	..	1118	..	..	..	..
Crystal Palace **B** arr	..	1041	..	..	..	11 1	..	..	..	..	1121	..	..	..	..
Crofton Park	1029	..	..	..	10 49	..	..	..	..	11 9	..	..	..	..	1129
Catford	1032	..	..	..	10 52	..	..	..	..	1112	..	..	..	..	1132
Bellingham	1034	..	..	..	10 54	..	..	..	..	1114	..	..	..	..	1134
Beckenham Hill	1036	..	..	..	10 56	..	..	..	..	1116	..	..	..	..	1136
Ravensbourne	1038	..	..	..	10 58	..	..	..	..	1118	..	..	..	..	1138
Herne Hill	..	..	10 31	1044	..	..	..	10 51	..	..	..	11 11	..	..	..
West Dulwich	..	..	10 33	..	..	..	..	10 53	..	..	..	11 13	..	..	..
Sydenham Hill	..	..	10 35	..	..	..	..	10 55	..	..	..	11 15	..	..	..
Penge East **C**	..	..	10 38	..	..	..	..	10 58	..	..	..	11 18	..	..	..
Kent House	..	..	10 40	..	..	..	..	11 0	..	..	..	11 20	..	..	..
Beckenham Junction	..	..	10 42	..	..	..	..	11 2	..	..	..	11 22	..	..	..
Shortlands	1039	..	10 45	..	10 59	..	..	11 5	..	1119	..	11 25	..	..	1139
Bromley South **D**	1042	..	10 47	1059	11 2	..	..	11 7	..	1122	..	11 27	1135	..	1142
Bickley	1045	..	10 50	..	11 5	..	..	11 10	..	1125	..	11 30	..	..	1145
Petts Wood	..	..	10 54	..	..	..	..	11 14	..	..	..	11 34	..	..	..
Orpington ..... arr	..	..	10 57	..	..	..	..	11 17	..	..	..	11 37	..	..	..
St. Mary Cray	1050	..	..	..	11 12	..	..	..	..	1130	..	..	..	..	1150
Swanley 34, 60	1054	..	..	..	11 17	..	..	..	..	1135	..	..	1144	1147	1155
Lullingstone	..	..	..	..	..	..	..	..	..	..	..	..	..	..	..
Eynsford	11 1	..	..	..	11 23	..	..	..	..	1142	..	..	..	..	12 2
Shoreham (Kent)	11 5	..	..	..	11 28	..	..	..	..	1147	..	..	..	..	12 7
Otford	11 8	..	..	..	11 31	..	..	..	..	1150	..	..	1155	..	1210
Seven- oaks { Bat & Ball.	1112	..	..	..	11 34	..	..	..	..	1153	..	..	..	..	1213
Seven- oaks { Tub's H. arr	1115	..	11c25	..	11 37	..	..	..	..	1156	..	11c57	..	..	1216
Kemsing	..	..	..	..	..	..	..	..	..	..	..	..	12 1	..	..
Wrotham & Boro' Gr'n	..	..	..	..	..	..	..	..	..	..	..	..	12 5	..	..
Malling	..	..	..	..	..	..	..	..	..	..	..	..	1212	..	..
East Malling Halt	..	..	..	..	..	..	..	..	..	..	..	..	1215	..	..
Barming	..	..	..	..	..	..	..	..	..	..	..	..	1219	..	..
Maidstone East .. arr	..	..	..	..	..	..	..	..	..	..	..	..	1223	..	..
Farningham Road **F**	..	..	..	..	..	..	..	..	..	..	..	..	..	1151	..
Longfield Halt **G**	..	..	..	..	..	..	..	..	..	..	..	..	..	..	..
Southfleet (Springh'd)	..	..	..	..	..	..	..	..	..	..	..	..	..	..	..
Gravesend West St arr	..	..	..	..	..	..	..	..	..	..	..	..	..	..	..
Fawkham for Hartley &	..	..	..	..	..	..	..	..	..	..	..	..	..	1156	..
Meopham ..... Longfield	..	..	..	..	..	..	..	..	..	..	..	..	..	12 1	..
Sole Street	..	..	..	..	..	..	..	..	..	..	..	..	..	12 3	..
Rochester	..	..	..	..	..	..	..	..	..	..	..	..	..	1214	..
Chatham	..	..	..	1133	..	..	..	..	..	..	..	..	..	1216	..
Gillingham (Kent) .. arr.	..	..	..	..	..	..	..	..	..	..	..	..	..	1221	..

3 Third class only   c Change at Orpington   R Arrive 3 minutes *earlier*   For Other Notes, see page 146

For SUNDAY TRAINS, see pages 143 to 146

LONDON, CRYSTAL PALACE (H.L.), ORPINGTON, SEVENOAKS, MAIDSTONE EAST, GRAVESEND WEST STREET, CHATHAM, and GILLINGHAM (Kent)

a.m — p.m — Saturdays—*continued* — p.m

Down	3	3			3	3	3		3	3	3	3		3	3		3	3	3	3	3	3	3	3		3	3			3	3	3
Victoria dep	..	11 24	1135	..	..	..	11 44	1150	..	..	12 4	..	..	..	..	1228	1224	..	..	..	1244	..	..	..	..	1 4	..	1 18	..	..	..	1 21
Brixton	..	11 29	..	..	..	..	11 49	..	..	..	12 9	..	..	..	..	..	1229	..	..	..	1249	..	..	..	..	1 9	..	..	..	..	..	1 26
Holborn Viaduct. dep	..	11 19	..	..	1131	..	11 39	..	1151	..	..	12 5	1220	1211	..	..	1214	1225	1231	..	1234	1245	1251	..	..	1254	1 3	..	..	1 11	..	1 14
Blackfriars	1117	11 21	..	..	1132	1137	11 40	..	1152	1157	1159	12 6	1222	1212	1217	..	1215	1226	1232	1237	1235	1246	1252	1257	..	1255	1 4	..	..	1 13	1 17	1 15
Elephant and Castle	1120	11 24	..	..	1135	1140	11 43	..	1156	12 0	12 2	12 9	..	1215	1220	..	1218	1229	1236	1240	1238	1249	1255	1 0	..	1258	1 7	..	..	1 16	1 20	1 18
Loughborough Junc.	..	11 28	..	..	..	..	11 48	..	..	..	12 7	1214	..	..	..	..	1223	1234	..	..	1243	1254	..	..	..	1 3	1 12	..	..	..	..	1 23
Denmark Hill	1125	..	..	..	1142	1145	..	..	12 2	12 5	..	..	..	1222	1225	..	..	..	1242	1245	..	..	1 2	1 5	..	..	Arr Kent House 1 26 p.m	..	..	1 22	1 25	..
Peckham Rye	1127	..	..	..	1144	1147	..	..	12 4	12 7	..	..	..	1224	1227	..	..	..	1244	1247	..	..	1 4	1 7	..	..		..	..	1 24	1 27	..
Nunhead	1130	..	..	..	1146	1150	..	..	12 6	1210	..	..	..	1226	1230	..	..	..	1246	1250	..	..	1 6	1 10	..	..		..	..	1 26	1 30	..
Honor Oak	1133	..	..	..	..	1153	..	..	..	1213	..	..	..	..	1234	..	..	..	..	1253	..	..	..	1 13	..	..		..	..	..	1 33	..
Lordship Lane A	1136	..	..	..	..	1156	..	..	..	1216	..	..	..	..	1236	..	..	..	..	1256	..	..	..	1 16	..	..		..	..	..	1 36	..
Upper Sydenham	1138	..	..	..	..	1158	..	..	..	1218	..	..	..	..	1239	..	..	..	..	1258	..	..	..	1 18	..	..		..	..	..	1 38	..
Crystal Palace B arr	1141	..	..	..	..	12 1	..	..	..	1221	..	..	..	..	1241	..	..	..	..	1 1	..	..	..	1 21	..	..		..	..	..	1 41	..
Crofton Park	..	..	..	..	1149	..	..	..	12 9	..	..	..	..	1229	..	..	..	..	1249	..	..	..	1 9	..	..	..		..	..	1 29	..	..
Catford	..	..	..	..	1152	..	..	..	1212	..	..	..	..	1232	..	..	..	..	1252	..	..	..	1 12	..	..	..		..	..	1 32	..	..
Bellingham	..	..	..	..	1154	..	..	..	1214	..	..	..	..	1234	..	..	..	..	1254	..	..	..	1 14	..	..	..		..	..	1 34	..	..
Beckenham Hill	..	..	..	..	1156	..	..	..	1216	..	..	..	..	1236	..	..	..	..	1256	..	..	..	1 16	..	..	..		..	..	1 36	..	..
Ravensbourne	..	..	..	..	1158	..	..	..	1218	..	..	..	..	1238	..	..	..	..	1258	..	..	..	1 18	..	..	..		..	..	1 38	..	..
Herne Hill	..	11 31	..	..	..	..	11 51	..	..	..	1211	1216	..	..	..	..	1231	1236	..	..	1252	1256	..	..	..	1 11	1 15	..	..	..	..	1 28
West Dulwich	..	11 33	..	..	..	..	11 53	..	..	..	1213	1219	..	..	..	..	1234	1239	..	..	1254	1259	..	..	..	1 13	1 18	..	..	..	..	1 30
Sydenham Hill	..	11 35	..	..	..	..	11 55	..	..	..	1215	1221	..	..	..	..	1236	1242	..	..	1257	1 1	..	..	..	..	1 20	..	..	..	..	1 32
Penge East C	..	11 38	..	..	..	..	11 58	..	..	..	1218	1224	..	..	..	..	1239	1246	..	..	1 0	1 4	..	..	..	1 18	1 23	..	..	..	..	1 35
Kent House	..	11 40	..	..	..	..	12 0	..	..	..	1220	1226	..	..	..	..	1241	1248	..	..	1 2	1 6	..	..	..	1 20	1 30	..	..	..	..	1 37
Beckenham Junction	..	11 42	..	..	..	..	12 2	..	..	..	1222	1228	..	..	..	..	1243	1250	..	..	1 4	1 8	..	..	..	1 22	1 33	..	..	..	..	1 40
Shortlands	..	11 45	..	..	1159	..	12 5	..	1219	..	1225	1231	..	1239	..	..	1246	1254	1259	..	1 7	1 11	1 19	..	..	1 25	1 36	..	..	1 39	..	1 43
Bromley South D	..	11 48	1156	..	12 2	..	12 7	..	1222	..	1227	1233	1240	1242	..	1247	1248	1256	1 2	..	1 10	1‡21	1 22	..	..	1 27	1 39	1 35	..	1 42	..	1 46
Bickley	..	11 51	..	..	12 5	..	12 10	..	1225	..	1230	1237	..	1245	..	..	1251	1 0	1 5	..	1 13	1 26	1 25	..	..	1 31	1 42	..	..	1 45	..	1 51
Petts Wood	..	11 55	..	..	..	..	12 14	..	..	..	1234	1243	..	..	..	..	1255	1 6	..	..	1 17	1 30	..	..	..	1 37	1 46	..	..	..	..	1 57
Orpington arr	..	11 58	..	..	..	..	12 17	..	..	..	1237	1246	..	..	..	..	1258	1 9	..	..	1 20	1 33	..	..	..	1 40	1 49	..	..	..	..	2 0
St. Mary Cray	..	..	..	..	1210	..	..	..	1230	..	..	..	..	..	..	1253	..	..	1 10	..	..	..	1 30	..	..	..	..	..	..	1 50	..	..
Swanley 3', 60	..	..	..	..	1215	..	..	1220	1234	..	..	..	1249	1252	..	1258	..	..	1 15	..	..	..	1 35	..	..	..	..	1 44	1 47	1 55	..	..
Lullingstone	..	..	..	..	..	..	..	..	..	..	..	..	..	..	..	..	..	..	..	..	..	..	..	..	..	..	..	..	..	..	..	..
Eynsford	..	..	..	..	1222	..	..	..	1239	..	..	..	..	1259	..	1 6	..	..	1 22	..	..	..	1 42	..	..	..	..	..	..	2 2	..	..
Shoreham (Kent)	..	..	..	..	1227	..	..	..	1244	..	..	..	..	1 3	..	1 10	..	..	1 27	..	..	..	1 47	..	..	..	..	..	..	2 7	..	..
Otford	..	..	..	..	1230	..	..	..	1247	..	..	..	..	1 6	..	1 13	..	..	1 30	..	..	..	1 50	..	..	..	..	1 55	..	2 10	..	..
Sevenoaks { Bat & Ball	..	..	..	..	1233	..	..	..	1250	..	..	..	..	1 12	..	..	..	..	1 33	..	..	..	1 53	..	..	..	..	..	..	2 13	..	..
Sevenoaks { Tub's H. arr	..	12c25	..	..	1236	..	12c45	..	1253	..	..	1 c 8	..	1 15	..	..	1c22	..	1 36	..	1c47	..	1 56	..	..	2 c 2	..	..	..	2 16	..	2c24
Kemsing	..	..	..	..	..	..	..	..	..	..	..	..	..		..	1 18	..	..	..	..	..	..	..	..	..	..	..	2 1	..	..	..	..
Wrotham & Boro' Gr'n	..	..	..	..	..	..	..	..	..	..	..	..	..	Stop	..	1 23	..	..	..	..	..	..	..	..	..	..	..	2 5	..	..	..	..
Malling	..	..	..	..	..	..	..	..	..	..	..	..	..	..	..	1 30	..	..	..	..	..	..	..	..	..	..	..	2 12	..	..	..	..
East Malling Halt	..	..	..	..	..	..	..	..	..	..	..	..	..	..	..	1 32	..	..	..	..	..	..	..	..	..	..	..	2 15	..	..	..	..
Barming	..	..	..	..	..	..	..	..	..	..	..	..	..	..	..	1 36	..	..	..	..	..	..	..	..	..	..	..	2 19	..	..	..	..
Maidstone East arr	..	..	..	..	..	..	..	..	..	..	..	..	..	p.m	..	1 40	..	..	..	..	..	..	..	..	..	..	..	2 23	..	..	..	..
Farningham Road F	..	..	..	..	..	..	..	..	..	..	..	..	1254	1 8	..	..	..	..	..	..	..	..	..	..	..	..	..	..	1 51	..	..	..
Longfield Halt G	..	..	..	..	..	..	..	..	..	..	..	..	..	1 14	..	..	..	..	..	..	..	..	..	..	..	..	..	..	..	..	..	..
Southfleet (Springh'd)	..	..	..	..	..	..	..	..	..	..	..	..	..	1 18	..	..	..	..	..	..	..	..	..	..	..	..	..	..	..	..	..	..
Gravesend West St arr	..	..	..	..	..	..	..	..	..	..	..	..	..	1 23	..	..	..	..	..	..	..	..	..	..	..	..	..	..	..	..	..	..
Fawkham, for Hartley &	..	..	..	..	..	..	..	..	..	..	..	..	1259	..	..	..	..	..	..	..	..	..	..	..	..	..	..	..	1 56	..	..	..
Meopham [Longfield	..	..	..	..	..	..	..	..	..	..	..	..	1 4	..	..	..	..	..	..	..	..	..	..	..	..	..	..	..	2 1	..	..	..
Sole Street	..	..	..	..	..	..	..	..	..	..	..	..	1 6	..	..	..	..	..	..	..	..	..	..	..	..	..	..	..	2 3	..	..	..
Rochester	..	..	..	..	..	..	..	..	..	..	..	..	1 17	..	..	..	..	..	..	..	..	..	..	..	..	..	..	..	2 14	..	..	..
Chatham	..	..	1229	..	..	..	..	1247	..	..	..	..	1 19	..	..	..	..	..	..	..	..	..	..	..	..	..	..	..	2 16	..	..	..
Gillingham (Kent) arr	..	..	..	..	..	..	..	1257	..	..	..	..	1 24	..	..	..	..	..	..	..	..	..	..	..	..	..	..	..	2 21	..	..	..

3 Third class only   c Change at Orpington   ‡ Arr. 1 14 p.m   **For Other Notes, see page 146**

For SUNDAY TRAINS, see pages 143 to 146

LONDON, CRYSTAL PALACE (H.L.), ORPINGTON, SEVENOAKS, MAIDSTONE EAST, GRAVESEND WEST STREET, CHATHAM and GILLINGHAM (Kent)

Saturdays—*continued* (p.m.)

Down		3	3		3	3	3	3		3					3	3	3	3	3	3	3		3			3		3	3		3	3
Victoria .... dep	1 40	..	..	..	1 44	..	..	..	..	2 4	2 5	2 18	..	..	..	2 24	..	..	..	..	..	..	3 4	3 18	..	..	..	..	3 24	3 35	..	..
Brixton	..	..	..	..	1 49	..	..	..	..	2 9	..	..	..	..	..	2 29	..	..	..	..	..	..	3 9	..	..	..	..	..	3 29	..	..	..
Holborn Viaduct dep	..	1 31	..	1 40	1 34	1 45	1 51	..	..	1 54	..	..	..	..	2 11	2 14	..	2 31	2 38	2 51	..	..	2 43	..	..	3 11	..	..	3 14	..	3 31	..
Blackfriars ...... "	..	1 32	1 37	1 42	1 35	1 46	1 52	1 57	..	1 55	..	..	..	..	2 12	2 15	..	2 32	2 39	2 52	..	..	2 44	..	..	3 12	..	3 16	3 15	..	3 32	..
Elephant and Castle..	..	1 36	1 40	..	1 38	1 49	1 55	2 0	..	1 58	..	..	..	..	2 15	2 18	..	2 35	2 42	2 55	..	..	2 47	..	..	3 15	..	3 19	3 18	..	3 35	..
Loughborough Junc...	..	..	..	..	1 43	1 54	..	..	..	2 3	..	..	..	..	..	2 23	..	..	..	..	..	..	2 52	..	..	..	..	..	3 23	..	..	..
Denmark Hill	..	1 42	1 45	..	..	..	2 2	2 5	..	..	..	..	..	..	2 22	..	..	2 42	2 49	3 2	..	..	..	..	..	3 22	..	3 26	..	..	3 42	..
Peckham Rye	..	1 44	1 47	..	..	..	2 4	2 7	..	..	..	..	..	..	2 24	..	..	2 44	2 51	3 4	..	..	..	..	..	3 24	..	3 28	..	..	3 44	..
Nunhead	..	1 46	1 50	..	..	..	2 6	2 10	..	..	..	..	..	..	2 26	..	2 34	2 46	2 53	3 6	3 14	..	..	..	..	3 26	..	3 30	..	..	3 46	3 54
Honor Oak	..	..	1 53	..	..	..	..	2 13	..	..	..	..	..	..	..	..	2 37	..	2 57	..	3 17	..	..	..	..	..	..	3 34	..	..	..	3 57
Lordship Lane **A**	..	..	1 56	..	..	..	..	2 16	..	..	..	..	..	..	..	..	2 40	..	3 0	..	3 20	..	..	..	..	..	..	3 36	..	..	..	4 0
Upper Sydenham	..	..	1 58	..	..	..	..	2 18	..	..	..	..	..	..	..	..	2 42	..	3 2	..	3 22	..	..	..	..	..	..	3 39	..	..	..	4 2
Crystal Palace **B** arr	..	..	2 1	..	..	..	..	2 21	..	..	..	..	..	..	..	..	2 45	..	3 5	..	3 25	..	..	..	..	..	..	3 41	..	..	..	4 5
Crofton Park	..	1 49	..	..	..	..	2 9		..	..	..	..	..	..	2 29	..	..	2 49	..	3 9	..	..	..	..	..	3 29	..	..	..	..	3 49	..
Catford	..	1 52	..	..	..	..	2 12	Stop	..	..	..	..	..	..	2 32	..	..	2 52	..	3 12	..	..	..	..	..	3 32	..	..	..	..	3 52	..
Bellingham	..	1 54	..	..	..	..	2 14	..	..	..	..	..	..	..	2 34	..	..	2 54	..	3 14	..	..	..	..	..	3 34	..	..	..	..	3 54	..
Beckenham Hill	..	1 56	..	..	..	..	2 16	..	..	..	..	..	..	..	2 36	..	..	2 56	..	3 16	..	..	..	..	..	3 36	..	..	..	..	3 56	..
Ravensbourne	..	1 58	..	..	..	..	2 18	..	..	..	..	..	..	..	2 38	..	..	2 58	..	3 18	..	..	..	..	..	3 38	..	..	..	..	3 58	..
Herne Hill	..	..	..	..	1 51	1 56	..	..	..	2 11	..	..	..	..	..	2 31	..	..	..	..	..	..	3 11	..	..	..	..	..	3 31	..	..	..
West Dulwich	..	..	..	..	1 53	1 59	..	..	..	2 13	..	..	..	..	..	2 33	..	..	..	..	..	..	3 13	..	..	..	..	..	3 33	..	..	..
Sydenham Hill	..	..	..	..	1 55	2 1	..	..	..	2 15	..	..	..	..	..	2 35	..	..	..	..	..	..	3 15	..	..	..	..	..	3 35	..	..	..
Penge East **C**	..	..	..	..	1 58	2 4	..	..	..	2 18	..	..	..	..	..	2 38	..	..	..	..	..	..	3 18	..	..	..	..	..	3 38	..	..	..
Kent House	..	..	..	..	2 0	2 6	..	..	..	2 20	..	..	..	..	..	2 40	..	..	..	..	..	..	3 20	..	..	..	..	..	3 40	..	..	..
Beckenham Junction	..	..	..	..	2 2	2 8	..	..	..	2 22	..	..	..	..	..	2 42	..	..	..	..	..	..	3 22	..	..	..	..	..	3 42	..	..	..
Shortlands	..	1 59	..	..	2 5	2 11	2 19	..	..	2 25	..	..	..	..	2 39	2 45	..	2 59	..	3 19	..	..	3 25	..	..	3 39	..	..	3 45	..	3 59	..
Bromley South **D**	1 57	2 2	..	2 1	2 8	2 13	2 22	..	..	2 27	2 28	2 35	..	..	2 42	2 48	..	3 2	..	3 22	..	..	3 27	3 35	..	3 42	..	..	3 47	3 56	4 2	..
Bickley	..	2 5	..	..	2 10	2 16	2 25	..	..	2 30	..	..	..	..	2 45	2F55	..	3 5	..	3 25	..	..	3 30	..	..	3 45	..	..	3 50	..	4 5	..
Petts Wood	..	..	..	..	2 14	..	..	..	..	2 34	..	..	..	..	..	3 1	..	..	..	..	..	..	3 34	..	..	..	..	..	3 54	..	..	..
Orpington ...... arr.	..	..	..	..	2 17	..	..	..	..	2 37	..	..	..	..	..	3 4	..	..	..	..	..	..	3 37	..	..	..	..	..	3 57	..	..	..
St. Mary Cray	..	2 10	..	2 7	..	..	2 30	..	..	..	..	..	..	..	2 50	..	..	3 10	..	3 30	..	..	..	..	..	3 50	..	..	..	..	4 10	..
Swanley 34, 60	2 7	2 15	..	2 11	..	..	2 35	..	..	..	..	2 44	2 47	..	2 55	..	..	3 15	..	3 35	..	..	..	3 46	3 51	3 55	..	..	..	..	4 14	..
Lullingstone	..	..	..	..	..	..	..	..	..	..	..	..	..	..	..	..	..	..	..	..	..	..	..	..	..	..	..	..	..	..	..	..
Eynsford	..	2 20	..	..	..	..	2 40	..	..	..	..	..	..	..	3 2	..	..	..	..	3 42	..	..	..	..	..	..	..	..	..	..	4 21	..
Shoreham (Kent)	..	2 25	..	..	..	..	2 45	..	..	..	..	..	..	..	3 7	..	..	..	..	3 47	..	..	..	..	..	..	..	..	..	..	4 25	..
Otford	..	2 28	..	2 22	..	..	2 48	..	..	..	..	2 55	..	..	3 10	..	..	..	..	3 50	..	..	..	..	4 1	..	..	..	..	..	4 28	..
Seven- oaks { Bat & Ball..	..	2 31	..	..	..	..	2 51	..	..	..	..	..	..	..	3 13	..	..	..	..	3 53	..	..	..	..	..	..	..	..	..	..	4 32	..
Seven- oaks { Tub's H. ar	..	2 34	..	..	2c45	..	2 54	..	..	2c58	..	..	..	..	3 16	3c25	..	..	..	3 56	..	..	3c57	..	..	..	..	..	4c27	..	4 35	..
Kemsing	..	..	..	2 28	..	..	..	..	..	..	..	3 1	..	..	..	..	..	..	..	..	..	..	..	..	4 7	..	..	..	..	..	..	..
Wrotham & Boro' Gr'n	..	..	..	2 22	..	..	..	..	..	..	..	3 5	..	..	..	..	..	..	..	..	..	..	..	..	4 11	..	..	..	..	..	..	..
Malling	..	..	..	2 39	..	..	..	..	..	..	..	3 12	..	..	..	..	..	..	..	..	..	..	..	..	4 18	..	..	..	..	..	..	..
East Malling Halt	..	..	..	2 42	..	..	..	..	..	..	..	3 15	..	..	..	..	..	..	..	..	..	..	..	..	4 21	..	..	..	..	..	..	..
Barming	..	..	..	2 46	..	..	..	..	..	..	..	3 19	..	..	..	..	..	..	..	..	..	..	..	..	4 25	..	..	..	..	..	..	..
Maidstone East .. arr	..	..	..	2 50	..	..	..	p.m	..	..	..	3 23	..	..	..	..	..	..	..	..	..	..	..	..	4 29	..	..	..	..	..	..	..
Farningham Road **F**	2 12	..	..	..	..	..	..	2 18	..	..	..	..	2 51	..	..	..	..	..	..	..	..	..	..	3 51	..	..	3 58	..	..	..	..	..
Longfield Halt **G**	..	..	..	..	..	..	..	2 24	..	..	..	..	..	..	..	..	..	..	..	..	..	..	..	..	..	..	4 4	..	..	..	..	..
Southfleet (Springh'd)	..	..	..	..	..	..	..	2 28	..	..	..	..	..	..	..	..	..	..	..	..	..	..	..	..	..	..	4 8	..	..	..	..	..
Gravesend West St ar	..	..	..	..	..	..	..	2 33	..	..	..	..	..	..	..	..	..	..	..	..	..	..	..	..	..	..	4 13	..	..	..	..	..
Fawkham for Hartley &	2 17	..	..	..	..	..	..	..	..	..	..	..	2 56	..	..	..	..	..	..	..	..	..	..	3 56	..	..	..	..	..	..	..	..
Meopham ..... Longfield	2 22	..	..	..	..	..	..	..	..	..	..	..	3 1	..	..	..	..	..	..	..	..	..	..	4 1	..	..	..	..	..	..	..	..
Sole Street	2 24	..	..	..	..	..	..	..	..	..	..	..	3 3	..	..	..	..	..	..	..	..	..	..	4 3	..	..	..	..	..	..	..	..
Rochester	2 35	..	..	..	..	..	..	..	..	..	..	..	3 14	..	..	..	..	..	..	..	..	..	..	4 14	..	..	..	..	..	..	..	..
Chatham	2 37	..	..	..	..	..	..	..	..	..	3 1	..	3 16	..	..	..	..	..	..	..	..	..	..	4 16	..	..	..	..	..	4 29	..	..
Gillingham (Kent) .. arr	2 42	..	..	..	..	..	..	..	..	..	3 8	..	3 21	..	..	..	..	..	..	..	..	..	..	4 21	..	..	..	..	..	..	..	..

3 Third class only

c Change at Orpington.

F Arr. 2 52 p.m

For Other Notes, see page 146

For SUNDAY TRAINS, see pages 143 to 146

LONDON, CRYSTAL PALACE (H.L.), ORPINGTON, SEVENOAKS, MAIDSTONE EAST, GRAVESEND WEST STREET, CHATHAM and GILLINGHAM (Kent)

Down — Saturdays—*continued* — p.m.

Down	3	3		3		3	3	3
Victoria dep		4 4		4 24				
Brixton		4 9		4 29				
Holborn Viaduct dep	3 51	3 43		4 14		4 31		4 51
Blackfriars "	3 52	3 44		4 15		4 32		4 52
Elephant and Castle	3 55	3 47		4 18		4 35		4 55
Loughborough Junc.		3 52		4 23				
Denmark Hill	4 2					4 42		5 2
Peckham Rye	4 4					4 44		5 4
Nunhead	4 6					4 46	4 54	5 6
Honor Oak							4 57	
Lordship Lane **A**							5 0	
Upper Sydenham							5 2	
Crystal Palace B arr							5 5	
Crofton Park	4 9					4 49		5 9
Catford	4 12					4 52		5 12
Bellingham	4 14					4 54		5 14
Beckenham Hill	4 16					4 56		5 16
Ravensbourne	4 18					4 58		5 18
Herne Hill		4 11		4 31				
West Dulwich		4 13		4 33				
Sydenham Hill		4 15		4 35				
Penge East C		4 18		4 38				
Kent House		4 20		4 40				
Beckenham Junction		4 22		4 42				
Shortlands	4 19	4 25		4 45		4 59		5 19
Bromley South D	4 22	4 27		4 47		5 2		5 22
Bickley	4 25	4 30		4 50		5 5		5 25
Petts Wood		4 34		4 54				
Orpington arr		4 37		4 57				
St. Mary Cray	4 30					5 10		5 30
Swanley 34, 60	4 35					5 14		5 34
Lullingstone								
Eynsford	4 42					5 21		5 41
Shoreham (Kent)	4 47					5 25		5 45
Otford	4 50					5 28		5 48
Sevenoaks { Bat & Ball	4 53					5 32		5 52
Sevenoaks { Tub's H. arr	4 56	4c57		5c27		5 35		5 55
Kemsing								
Wrotham & Boro' Gr'n								Stop
Malling								
East Malling Halt								
Barming								
Maidstone East arr								p.m
Farningham Road **F**								5 13
Longfield Halt **G**								5 19
Southfleet (Springh'd)								5 23
Gravesend West St arr								5 28
Fawkham for Hartley & Longfield								
Meopham								
Sole Street								
Rochester								
Chatham								
Gillingham (Kent) arr								

Down	3				3	3	3	
Victoria dep	5 4		5 18		5 24			
Brixton	5 9				5 29			
Holborn Viaduct dep	4 43				5 14	5 31		
Blackfriars "	4 44				5 15	5 32		
Elephant and Castle	4 47				5 18	5 35		
Loughborough Junc.	4 52				5 23			
Denmark Hill						5 42		
Peckham Rye						5 44		
Nunhead						5 46	5 54	
Honor Oak							5 57	
Lordship Lane **A**							6 0	
Upper Sydenham							6 2	
Crystal Palace B arr							6 5	
Crofton Park						5 49		
Catford						5 52		
Bellingham						5 54		
Beckenham Hill						5 56		
Ravensbourne						5 58		
Herne Hill	5 11				5 31			
West Dulwich	5 13				5 33			
Sydenham Hill	5 15				5 35			
Penge East C	5 18				5 38			
Kent House	5 20				5 40			
Beckenham Junction	5 22				5 42			
Shortlands	5 25				5 45	5 59		
Bromley South D	5 27		5 35		5 47	6 2		
Bickley	5 30				5 50	6 5		
Petts Wood	5 34				5 54			
Orpington arr	5 37				5 57			
St. Mary Cray						6 10		
Swanley 34, 60			5 44	5 47		6 14		
Lullingstone								
Eynsford						6 21		
Shoreham (Kent)						6 25		
Otford			5 55			6 28		
Sevenoaks { Bat & Ball						6 32		
Sevenoaks { Tub's H. arr	5c57				6c27	6 35		
Kemsing			6 1					
Wrotham & Boro' Gr'n			6 5					
Malling			6 12					
East Malling Halt			6 15					
Barming			6 19					
Maidstone East arr			6 23					
Farningham Road **F**				5 51				
Longfield Halt **G**								
Southfleet (Springh'd)								
Gravesend West St arr								
Fawkham for Hartley & Longfield				5 56				
Meopham				6 1				
Sole Street				6 3				
Rochester				6 14				
Chatham				6 16				
Gillingham (Kent) arr				6 21				

Down	3	3			3	3	3	3
Victoria dep		6 4	6 5		6 24			
Brixton		6 9			6 29			
Holborn Viaduct dep	5 51	5 43			6 14	6 31		6 51
Blackfriars "	5 52	5 44			6 15	6 32		6 52
Elephant and Castle	5 55	5 47			6 18	6 35		6 55
Loughborough Junc.		5 52			6 23			
Denmark Hill	6 2					6 42		7 2
Peckham Rye	6 4					6 44		7 4
Nunhead	6 6					6 46	6 54	7 6
Honor Oak							6 57	
Lordship Lane **A**							7 0	
Upper Sydenham							7 2	
Crystal Palace B arr							7 5	
Crofton Park	6 9					6 49		7 9
Catford	6 12					6 52	Stop	7 12
Bellingham	6 14					6 54		7 14
Beckenham Hill	6 16					6 56		7 16
Ravensbourne	6 18					6 58		7 18
Herne Hill		6 11			6 31			
West Dulwich		6 13			6 33			
Sydenham Hill		6 15			6 35			
Penge East C		6 18			6 38			
Kent House		6 20			6 40			
Beckenham Junction		6 22			6 42			
Shortlands	6 19	6 25			6 45	6 59		7 19
Bromley South D	6 22	6 27	6 28		6 47	7 2		7 22
Bickley	6 25	6 30			6 50	7 5		7 25
Petts Wood		6 34			6 54			
Orpington arr		6 37			6 57			
St. Mary Cray	6 30					7 10		7 30
Swanley 34, 60	6 34					7 15		7 34
Lullingstone								
Eynsford	6 41					7 21		7 42
Shoreham (Kent)	6 45					7 25		7 47
Otford	6 48					7 28		7 50
Sevenoaks { Bat & Ball	6 52					7 32		7 53
Sevenoaks { Tub's H. arr	6 55	6c57			7c27	7 35		7 56
Kemsing								
Wrotham & Boro' Gr'n								
Malling								
East Malling Halt								
Barming								
Maidstone East arr							p.m	
Farningham Road **F**							6 56	
Longfield Halt **G**							7 2	
Southfleet (Springh'd)							7 6	
Gravesend West St arr							7 11	
Fawkham for Hartley & Longfield								
Meopham								
Sole Street								
Rochester								
Chatham			7 1					
Gillingham (Kent) arr			7 8					

Down		3			3	3	3	3
Victoria dep		7 4	7 20		7 24			
Brixton		7 9			7 29			
Holborn Viaduct dep		6 43			7 14	7 31		7 51
Blackfriars "		6 44			7 15	7 32		7 52
Elephant and Castle		6 47			7 18	7 35		7 55
Loughborough Junc.		6 52			7 23			
Denmark Hill						7 42		8 2
Peckham Rye						7 44		8 4
Nunhead						7 46	7 54	8 6
Honor Oak							7 57	
Lordship Lane **A**							8 0	
Upper Sydenham							8 2	
Crystal Palace B arr							8 5	
Crofton Park						7 49		8 9
Catford						7 52		8 12
Bellingham						7 54		8 14
Beckenham Hill						7 56		8 16
Ravensbourne						7 58		8 18
Herne Hill		7 11			7 31			
West Dulwich		7 13			7 33			
Sydenham Hill		7 15			7 35			
Penge East C		7 18			7 38			
Kent House		7 20			7 40			
Beckenham Junction		7 22			7 42			
Shortlands		7 25			7 45	7 59		8 19
Bromley South D		7 27	7 40		7 47	8 2		8 22
Bickley		7 30			7 50	8 5		8 25
Petts Wood		7 34			7 54			
Orpington arr		7 37			7 57			
St. Mary Cray						8 10		8 30
Swanley 34, 60			7 49	7 52		8 15		8 34
Lullingstone								
Eynsford						8 21		8 41
Shoreham (Kent)						8 25		8 45
Otford			8 0			8 28		8 48
Sevenoaks { Bat & Ball						8 32		8 52
Sevenoaks { Tub's H. arr		7c57			8c27	8 35		8 55
Kemsing			8 6					
Wrotham & Boro' Gr'n			8 10		Stop			
Malling			8 17					
East Malling Halt			8 20					
Barming			8 24					
Maidstone East arr			8 28		p.m			
Farningham Road **F**				7 56	8 3			
Longfield Halt **G**					8 9			
Southfleet (Springh'd)					8 13			
Gravesend West St arr					8 18			
Fawkham for Hartley & Longfield				8 1				
Meopham				8 6				
Sole Street				8 8				
Rochester				8 19				
Chatham				8 21				
Gillingham (Kent) arr				8 26				

3 Thirdclass only *c* Change at Orpington

For Other Notes, see page 146

For SUNDAY TRAINS, see pages 143 to 146

LONDON, CRYSTAL PALACE (H.L.), ORPINGTON, SEVENOAKS, MAIDSTONE EAST, GRAVESEND WEST STREET, CHATHAM and GILLINGHAM (Kent)

Saturdays—continued

Down	3			3	3	3		3	3			3		3		3	3	3			3	3	3	3	3	3	3	3	3	3	
	p.m																				p.m										
Victoria .... dep	8 4	8 18		8 24					9 4	9 18		9 24	9 35					10 4	1018		10 24				11 4	11 30					
Brixton	8 9			8 29					9 9			9 29						10 9			10 29				11 9	11 35			ngt.	ngt.	
Holborn Viaduct. dep	7 43			8 14	8 31			8 51	8 43			9 14		9 31			9 51	9 43			10 14	1031		1051	10 43	11 14	11 25		1215	1221	
Blackfriars ...... "	7 44			8 15	8 32			8 52	8 44			9 15		9 32			9 52	9 44			10 15	1032		1052	10 44	11 15	11 26		1216	1222	
Elephant and Castle..	7 47			8 18	8 35			8 55	8 47			9 18		9 35			9 55	9 47			10 18	1035		1055	10 47	11 18	11 29		1220	1225	
Loughborough Junc...	7 52			8 23					8 52			9 23						9 52			10 23				10 52	11 23				1230	
Denmark Hill					8 42			9 2						9 42			10 2					1042		11 2			11 36		1226		
Peckham Rye					8 44			9 4						9 44			10 4					1044		11 4			11 38		1228		
Nunhead					8 46	8 54		9 6						9 46		9 54	10 6					1046	1054	11 6			11 40	1154	1230		
Honor Oak						8 57										9 57							1057					1157			
Lordship Lane **A**						9 0										10 0							11 0					12 0			
Upper Sydenham						9 2										10 2							11 2					12 2			
Crystal Palace B arr						9 5										10 5							11 5					12 5			
Crofton Park					8 49			9 9						9 49			10 9					1049		11 9			11 43		1233		
Catford					8 52			9 12						9 52			1012					1052		1112			11 46		1236		
Bellingham					8 54			9 14						9 54			1014					1054		1114			11 48		1238		
Beckenham Hill					8 56			9 16						9 56			1016					1056		1116			11 50		1240		
Ravensbourne					8 58			9 18						9 58			1018					1058		1118			11 52				
Herne Hill	8 11			8 31					9 11			9 31						10 11			10 31				11 11	11 37				1235	
West Dulwich	8 13			8 33					9 13			9 33						10 13			10 33				11 13	11 39				1237	
Sydenham Hill	8 15			8 35					9 15			9 35						10 15			10 35				11 15	11 41				1239	
Penge East C	8 18			8 38					9 18			9 38						10 18			10 38				11 18	11 44				1242	
Kent House	8 20			8 40					9 20			9 40						10 20			10 40				11 20	11 46				1244	
Beckenham Junction ...	8 22			8 42					9 22			9 42						10 22			10 42				11 22	11 48				1248	
Shortlands	8 25			8 45	8 59			9 19	9 25			9 45		9 59			1019	10 25			10 45	1059		1119	11 25	11 51	11 53		1243		
Bromley South D	8 27	8 35		8 47	9 2			9 22	9 27	9 35		9 47		10 2			1022	10 27	1035		10 47	11 2		1122	11 27	11F57	11 57		1246		
Bickley	8 30			8 53	9 5			9 25	9 30			9 50		10 5			1025	10 30			10 50	11 5		1125	11 30	12 1	12 1		1249		
Petts Wood	8 34			8 58					9 34			9 54						10 34			10 54				11 34	12 5			1253		
Orpington .... arr	8 37			9 1					9 37			9 57						10 37			10 57				11 37	12 8			1256		
St. Mary Cray					9 10			9 30						1010			1030					1110		1130			12 6				
Swanley 34, 60		8 45	8 47		9 14		9 12	9 34		9 44	9 47			1014			1034		1044	1047		1114		1134			12 10				
Lullingstone																															
Eynsford					9 21			9 41						1021			1041					1121		1141			12 17				
Shoreham (Kent)					9 25			9 45						1025			1045					1125		1145			12 21				
Otford		8 55			9 28			9 48		9 55				1028			1048		1055			1128		1148			12 24				
Seven-oaks Bat & Ball..					9 32			9 52						1032			1052					1132		1152			12 28				
Seven-oaks Tub's H. arr	8c57			9c27	9 35			9 55	9c57			10c27		1035			1055	10c57			11c27	1135		1155	11c56	12c29	12 31				
Kemsing		9 1								10 1									11 1												
Wrotham & Boro' Gr'n		9 5								10 5									11 5												
Malling		9 12								1012									1112												
East Malling Halt		9 15								1015									1115												
Barming		9 19								1019									1119												
Maidstone East .. arr		9 23								1023									1123												
Farningham Road **F** ...			8 51				9 17				9 51									1051											
Longfield Halt **G**							9 23																								
Southfleet (Springh'd).							9 27																								
Gravesend West Star							9 32																								
Fawkham (for Hartley &			8 56								9 56									1056											
Meopham ..... Longfield)			9 1								10 1									11 1											
Sole Street			9 3								10 3									11 3											
Rochester			9 14								1014									1114											
Chatham			9 16								1016		1024							1116											
Gillingham (Kent) .. arr			9 21								1021									1121											

3 Third class only

c Change at Orpington

For Other Notes see page 146

F Arr. 11 54 p.m

For SUNDAY TRAINS, see pages 143 to 146

LONDON, CRYSTAL PALACE (H.L.), ORPINGTON, SEVENOAKS, MAIDSTONE EAST GRAVESEND WEST STREET, CHATHAM, and GILLINGHAM (Kent)

Sundays

Down	a.m. 3	3	3	3			3	3	3	3		3	3	3	3	3
Victoria dep	6 10	6 54	..	..	7 18	..	..	..	..	8 4	8 5	..	8 24	..	..	..
Brixton	6 15	6 59	..	..	..	..	..	..	..	8 9	..	..	8 29	..	..	..
Holborn Viaduct dep	6 8	6 48	6 51	..	..	..	..	7 51	..	7 47	..	8 6	8 17	8 31	..	8 51
Blackfriars "	6 9	6 49	6 52	..	..	..	..	7 52	..	7 48	..	8 7	8 18	8 32	..	8 52
Elephant and Castle	6 12	6 52	6 55	..	..	..	..	7 55	..	7 51	..	8 10	8 21	8 35	..	8 55
Loughborough Junc.	6 17	6 57	..	..	..	..	..	..	..	7 56	..	8 15	8 26	..	..	..
Denmark Hill	..	..	7 1	..	..	..	..	8 1	..	..	..	..	..	8 42	..	9 1
Peckham Rye	..	..	7 3	..	..	..	..	8 3	..	..	..	..	..	8 44	..	9 3
Nunhead	..	..	7 6	7 15	..	..	7 32	8 6	8 15	..	..	..	..	8 46	8 51	9 6
Honor Oak	..	..	..	7 18	..	..	7 35	..	8 18	..	..	..	..	..	8 54	..
Lordship Lane **A**	..	..	..	7 21	..	..	7 38	..	8 21	..	..	..	..	..	8 57	..
Upper Sydenham	..	..	..	7 23	..	..	7 40	..	8 23	..	..	..	..	..	8 59	..
Crystal Palace B arr	..	..	..	7 26	..	..	7 43	..	8 26	..	..	..	..	..	9 2	..
Crofton Park	..	..	7 9	..	..	..	..	8 9	..	..	..	..	..	8 49	..	9 9
Catford	..	..	7 11	..	..	..	..	8 11	..	..	..	..	..	8 52	..	9 11
Bellingham	..	..	7 13	..	..	..	..	8 13	..	..	..	..	..	8 54	..	9 13
Beckenham Hill	..	..	7 15	..	..	..	..	8 15	..	..	..	..	..	8 56	..	9 15
Ravensbourne	..	..	7 17	..	..	..	..	8 17	..	..	..	..	..	8 58	..	9 17
Herne Hill	6 19	7 2	..	..	..	..	..	..	..	8 11	..	8 17	8 31	..	..	..
West Dulwich	6 22	7 4	..	..	..	..	..	..	..	8 13	..	8 20	8 33	..	..	..
Sydenham Hill	6 24	7 7	..	..	..	..	..	..	..	8 15	..	8 22	8 35	..	..	..
Penge East **C**	6 27	7 10	..	..	..	..	..	..	..	8 18	..	8 25	8 38	..	..	..
Kent House	6 29	7 12	..	..	..	..	..	..	..	8 20	..	8 27	8 40	..	..	..
Beckenham Junction	6 31	7 15	..	..	..	..	..	..	..	8 22	..	8 29	8 42	..	..	..
Shortlands	6 34	7 18	7 19	..	..	..	..	8 19	..	8 25	..	8 32	8 45	8 59	..	9 19
Bromley South D	6 36	7‡23	7 22	..	7 35	..	..	8 22	..	8 27	8 27	8 35	8 47	9 2	..	9 22
Bickley	6 39	7 26	7 25	..	..	..	..	8 25	..	8 30	..	8 39	8 50	9 5	..	9 25
Petts Wood	6 42	7 31	..	..	..	..	..	..	..	8 34	..	8 43	8 54	..	..	..
Orpington arr.	6 46	7 34	..	..	..	..	..	..	..	8 37	..	8 47	8 57	..	..	..
St. Mary Cray	..	..	7 30	..	..	..	..	8 30	..	..	..	..	..	9 10	..	9 30
Swanley 34, 60	..	..	7 34	..	7 47	7 50	..	8 34	..	..	..	..	..	9 14	..	9 34
Lullingstone	..	..	..	..	..	..	..	..	..	..	..	..	..	..	..	..
Eynsford	..	..	7 41	..	..	..	..	8 41	..	..	..	..	..	9 21	..	9 41
Shoreham (Kent)	..	..	7 45	..	..	..	..	8 45	..	..	..	..	..	9 25	..	9 45
Otford	..	..	7 48	..	7 58	..	..	8 48	..	..	..	..	..	9 28	..	9 48
Sevenoaks Bat & Ball	..	..	7 52	..	..	..	..	8 52	..	..	..	..	..	9 32	..	9 51
Sevenoaks Tub's H. ar	..	7c51	7 55	..	..	..	..	8 55	..	..	..	..	9c20	9 35	..	9 54
Kemsing	..	..	..	..	8 4	..	..	..	..	..	..	..	..	..	..	..
Wrotham & Boro' Gr'n	..	..	..	..	8 8	..	..	..	..	..	..	..	..	..	..	..
Malling	..	..	..	..	8 15	..	..	..	..	..	..	..	..	..	..	..
East Malling Halt	..	..	..	..	8 18	..	..	..	..	..	..	..	..	..	..	..
Barming	..	..	..	..	8 22	..	..	..	..	..	..	..	..	..	..	..
Maidstone East arr	..	..	..	..	8 26	..	..	..	..	..	..	..	..	..	..	..
Farningham Road **F**	..	..	..	..	..	7 54	..	..	..	..	..	..	..	..	..	..
Longfield Halt **G**	..	..	..	..	..	..	..	..	..	..	..	..	..	..	..	..
Southfleet (Springh'd)	..	..	..	..	..	..	..	..	..	..	..	..	..	..	..	..
Gravesend West St ar	..	..	..	..	..	..	..	..	..	..	..	..	..	..	..	..
Fawkham for Hartley & [Longfield	..	..	..	..	..	7 59	..	..	..	..	..	..	..	..	..	..
Meopham	..	..	..	..	..	8 4	..	..	..	..	..	..	..	..	..	..
Sole Street	..	..	..	..	..	8 6	..	..	..	..	..	..	..	..	..	..
Rochester	..	..	..	..	..	8 17	..	..	..	..	..	..	..	..	..	..
Chatham	..	..	..	..	..	8 19	..	..	..	..	9 0	..	..	..	..	..
Gillingham (Kent)	..	..	..	..	..	8 24	..	..	..	..	9 7	..	..	..	..	..

Down	a.m. 3			3	3	3	3		3	3	3	3	3	3	3	3
Victoria dep	9 4	9 18	..	..	9 24	..	..	9 50	..	..	10 4	10 24	..	..	..	11 4
Brixton	9 9	..	..	..	9 29	..	..	..	..	..	10 9	10 29	..	..	..	11 9
Holborn Viaduct dep	8 47	..	..	..	9 17	9 31	..	..	9 51	..	9 47	10 17	1031	..	1051	1047
Blackfriars "	8 48	..	..	..	9 18	9 32	..	..	9 52	..	9 48	10 18	1032	..	1052	1048
Elephant and Castle	8 51	..	..	..	9 21	9 35	..	..	9 55	..	9 51	10 21	1035	..	1055	1051
Loughborough Junc.	8 56	..	..	..	9 26	..	..	..	..	..	9 56	10 26	..	..	..	1056
Denmark Hill	..	..	..	..	..	9 42	..	..	10 1	..	..	..	1042	..	11 1	..
Peckham Rye	..	..	..	..	..	9 44	..	..	10 3	..	..	..	1044	..	11 3	..
Nunhead	..	..	..	9 15	..	9 46	9 51	..	10 6	1015	..	..	1046	1051	11 6	..
Honor Oak	..	..	..	9 18	..	..	9 54	..	..	1018	..	..	..	1054	..	..
Lordship Lane **A**	..	..	..	9 21	..	..	9 57	..	..	1021	..	..	..	1057	..	..
Upper Sydenham	..	..	..	9 23	..	..	9 59	..	..	1023	..	..	..	1059	..	..
Crystal Palace B arr	..	..	..	9 26	..	..	10 2	..	..	1026	..	..	..	11 2	..	..
Crofton Park	..	..	..	..	..	9 49	..	..	10 9	..	..	..	1049	..	11 9	..
Catford	..	..	..	..	..	9 52	..	..	1011	..	..	..	1052	..	1111	..
Bellingham	..	..	..	..	..	9 54	..	..	1013	..	..	..	1054	..	1113	..
Beckenham Hill	..	..	..	..	..	9 56	..	..	1015	..	..	..	1056	..	1115	..
Ravensbourne	..	..	..	..	..	9 58	..	..	1017	..	..	..	1058	..	1117	..
Herne Hill	9 11	..	..	..	9 31	..	..	..	..	..	10 11	10 31	..	..	..	1111
West Dulwich	9 13	..	..	..	9 33	..	..	..	..	..	10 13	10 33	..	..	..	1113
Sydenham Hill	9 15	..	..	..	9 35	..	..	..	..	..	10 15	10 35	..	..	..	1115
Penge East **C**	9 18	..	..	..	9 38	..	..	..	..	..	10 18	10 38	..	..	..	1118
Kent House	9 20	..	..	..	9 40	..	..	..	..	..	10 20	10 40	..	..	..	1120
Beckenham Junction	9 22	..	..	..	9 42	..	..	..	..	..	10 22	10 42	..	..	..	1122
Shortlands	9 25	..	..	..	9 45	9 59	..	..	1019	..	10 25	10 45	1059	..	1119	1125
Bromley South D	9 27	9 35	..	..	9 47	10 2	..	1012	1022	..	10 27	10 47	11 2	..	1122	1127
Bickley	9 30	..	..	..	9 50	10 5	..	..	1025	..	10 30	10 50	11 5	..	1125	1130
Petts Wood	9 34	..	..	..	9 54	..	..	..	..	..	10 34	10 54	..	..	..	1134
Orpington arr.	9 37	..	..	..	9 57	..	..	..	..	..	10 37	10 57	..	..	..	1137
St. Mary Cray	..	..	..	..	..	1010	..	..	1030	..	..	..	1110	..	1130	..
Swanley 34, 60	..	9 44	9 50	..	..	1014	..	..	1034	..	..	..	1114	..	1134	..
Lullingstone	..	..	..	..	..	..	..	..	..	..	..	..	..	..	..	..
Eynsford	..	..	..	..	..	1021	..	..	1041	..	..	..	1121	..	1141	..
Shoreham (Kent)	..	..	..	..	..	1025	..	..	1045	..	..	..	1125	..	1145	..
Otford	..	..	10 0	..	..	1028	..	..	1048	..	..	..	1128	..	1148	..
Sevenoaks Bat & Ball	..	..	..	..	..	1032	..	..	1052	..	..	..	1132	..	1152	..
Sevenoaks Tub's H. ar	..	..	..	..	10c20	1035	..	..	1055	..	..	11c20	1135	..	1155	..
Kemsing	..	..	10 6	..	..	..	..	..	..	..	..	..	..	..	..	..
Wrotham & Boro' Gr'n	..	..	1011	..	..	..	..	..	..	..	..	..	..	..	..	..
Malling	..	..	1018	..	..	..	..	..	..	..	..	..	..	..	..	..
East Malling Halt	..	..	1020	..	..	..	..	..	..	..	..	..	..	..	..	..
Barming	..	..	1024	..	..	..	..	..	..	..	..	..	..	..	..	..
Maidstone East arr	..	..	1028	..	..	..	..	..	..	..	..	..	..	..	..	..
Farningham Road **F**	..	9 51	..	..	..	..	..	..	..	..	..	..	..	..	..	..
Longfield Halt **G**	..	..	..	..	..	..	..	..	..	..	..	..	..	..	..	..
Southfleet (Springh'd)	..	..	..	..	..	..	..	..	..	..	..	..	..	..	..	..
Gravesend West St ar	..	..	..	..	..	..	..	..	..	..	..	..	..	..	..	..
Fawkham for Hartley & [Longfield	..	9 56	..	..	..	..	..	..	..	..	..	..	..	..	..	..
Meopham	..	10 1	..	..	..	..	..	..	..	..	..	..	..	..	..	..
Sole Street	..	10 3	..	..	..	..	..	..	..	..	..	..	..	..	..	..
Rochester	..	1014	..	..	..	..	..	..	..	..	..	..	..	..	..	..
Chatham	..	1016	..	..	..	..	..	1046	..	..	..	..	..	..	..	..
Gillingham (Kent)	..	1021	..	..	..	..	..	1052	..	..	..	..	..	..	..	..

3 Third class only

c Change at Orpington

‡ Arr 2 minutes *earlier*

For Other Notes see page 146

LONDON, CRYSTAL PALACE (H.L.), ORPINGTON, SEVENOAKS, MAIDSTONE EAST, GRAVESEND WEST STREET, CHATHAM, and GILLINGHAM (Kent)

Sundays—*continued*

Down	a.m							p.m									p.m															
			3	3	3	3	3	3	3	3		3	3	3	3		3	3	3	3	3	3	3		3	3	3	3	3		3	3
Victoria dep	1118	..	..	11 24	..	..	..	12 4	..	1224	1235	..	..	..	1 4	1 18	..	1 24	..	..	..	..	2 4	..	2 24	..	..	..	3 4	3 18	..	3 24
Brixton	..	..	..	11 29	..	..	..	12 9	..	1229	..	..	..	..	1 9	..	..	1 29	..	..	..	..	2 9	..	2 29	..	..	..	3 9	..	..	3 29
Holborn Viaduct dep	.	..	..	11 17	1131	..	1151	11 47	..	1217	..	1231	..	1251	1247	..	..	1 17	1 31	..	1 51	..	1 47	.	2 17	2 31	..	2 51	2 47	..	..	3 17
Blackfriars "	..	..	..	11 18	1132	..	1152	11 48	..	1218	..	1232	..	1252	1248	..	..	1 18	1 32	..	1 52	..	1 48	..	2 18	2 32	..	2 52	2 48	..	..	3 18
Elephant and Castle	..	..	..	11 21	1135	..	1155	11 51	..	1221	..	1235	..	1255	1251	..	..	1 21	1 35	..	1 55	..	1 51	..	2 21	2 35	..	2 55	2 51	..	..	3 21
Loughborough Junc.	..	..	..	11 26	..	..	..	11 56	..	1226	..	..	..	..	1256	..	..	1 26	..	..	..	..	1 56	..	2 26	..	..	..	2 56	..	..	3 26
Denmark Hill	..	..	..	..	1142	..	12 1	..	..	..	..	1242	..	1 1	..	..	..	..	1 42	..	2 1	..	..	..	Arrives Bickley at 2 51 p.m	2 42	..	3 1	..	..	..	..
Peckham Rye	..	..	..	..	1144	..	12 3	..	..	..	..	1244	..	1 3	..	..	..	..	1 44	..	2 3	..	..	..		2 44	..	3 3	..	..	..	..
Nunhead	..	..	1115	..	1146	1151	12 6	..	1215	..	..	1246	1251	1 6	..	..	1 15	..	1 46	1 51	2 6	2 15	..	..		2 46	2 51	3 6	..	..	3 15	..
Honor Oak	..	..	1118	..	..	1154	..	..	1218	..	..	..	1254	..	..	..	1 18	..	..	1 54	..	2 18	..	..		..	2 54	..	..	..	3 18	..
Lordship Lane A	..	..	1121	..	..	1157	..	..	1221	..	..	..	1257	..	..	..	1 21	..	..	1 57	..	2 21	..	..		..	2 57	..	..	..	3 21	..
Upper Sydenham	..	..	1123	..	..	1159	..	..	1223	..	..	..	1259	..	..	..	1 23	..	..	1 59	..	2 23	..	..		..	2 59	..	..	..	3 23	..
Crystal Palace B arr	..	..	1126	..	..	12 2	..	..	1226	..	..	..	1 2	..	..	..	1 26	..	..	2 2	..	2 26	..	..		..	3 2	..	..	..	3 26	..
Crofton Park	..	..	..	..	1149	..	12 9	..	..	..	..	1249	..	1 9	..	..	Stop	..	1 49	..	2 9	..	..	..		2 49	..	3 9	..	..	Stop	..
Catford	..	..	..	..	1152	..	1211	..	..	..	..	1252	..	1 11	..	..		..	1 52	..	2 11	..	..	..		2 52	..	3 11	..	..		..
Bellingham	..	..	..	..	1154	..	1213	..	..	..	..	1254	..	1 13	..	..	..	..	1 54	..	2 13	..	..	..		2 54	..	3 13	..	..	..	..
Beckenham Hill	..	..	..	..	1156	..	1215	..	..	..	..	1256	..	1 15	..	..	..	..	1 56	..	2 15	..	..	..		2 56	..	3 15	..	..	..	..
Ravensbourne	..	..	..	..	1158	..	1217	..	..	..	..	1258	..	1 17	..	..	..	..	1 58	..	2 17	..	..	..		2 58	..	3 17	..	..	..	..
Herne Hill	..	..	..	11 31	..	..	..	12 11	..	1231	..	..	..	..	1 11	..	..	1 31	..	..	..	..	2 11	..	2 31	..	..	..	3 11	..	..	3 31
West Dulwich	..	..	..	11 33	..	..	..	12 13	..	1233	..	..	..	..	1 13	..	..	1 33	..	..	..	..	2 13	..	2 33	..	..	..	3 13	..	..	3 33
Sydenham Hill	..	..	..	11 35	..	..	..	12 15	..	1235	..	..	..	..	1 15	..	..	1 35	..	..	..	..	2 15	..	2 35	..	..	..	3 15	..	..	3 35
Penge East C	..	..	..	11 38	..	..	..	12 18	..	1238	..	..	..	..	1 18	..	..	1 38	..	..	..	..	2 18	..	2 38	..	..	..	3 18	..	..	3 38
Kent House	..	..	..	11 40	..	..	..	12 20	..	1240	..	..	..	..	1 20	..	..	1 40	..	..	..	..	2 20	..	2 40	..	..	..	3 20	..	..	3 40
Beckenham Junction	..	..	..	11 42	..	..	..	12 22	..	1242	..	..	..	..	1 22	..	..	1 42	..	..	..	..	2 22	..	2 42	..	..	..	3 22	..	..	3 42
Shortlands	..	..	..	11 45	1159	..	1219	12 25	..	1245	..	1259	..	1 19	1 25	..	..	1 45	1 59	..	2 19	..	2 25	..	2 45	2 59	..	3 19	3 25	..	..	3 45
Bromley South D	1135	..	..	11 47	12 2	..	1222	12 27	..	1247	1256	1 2	..	1 22	1 27	1 35	..	1 47	2 2	..	2 22	..	2 27	..	2 48	3 2	..	3 22	3 27	3 35	..	3 47
Bickley	..	..	..	11 50	12 5	..	1225	12 30	..	1250	..	1 5	..	1 25	1 30	..	..	1 50	2 5	..	2 25	..	2 30	..	2 54	3 5	..	3 25	3 30	..	..	3 50
Petts Wood	..	..	..	11 54	..	..	..	12 34	..	1254	..	..	..	..	1 34	..	..	1 54	..	..	..	..	2 34	..	2 59	..	..	..	3 34	..	..	3 54
Orpington arr	..	..	..	11 57	..	..	..	12 37	..	1257	..	..	..	..	1 37	..	..	1 57	..	..	..	..	2 37	..	3 2	..	..	..	3 27	..	..	3 57
St. Mary Cray	..	..	..	..	1210	..	1230	..	..	..	..	1 10	..	1 30	..	..	p.m	..	2 10	..	2 30	..	.	..	..	3 10	..	3 30	.	..	p.m	..
Swanley 34, 60	1144	1147	..	..	1214	..	1234	..	..	..	..	1 14	..	1 34	..	1 44	1 47	..	2 14	..	2 34	..	..	..	..	3 14	..	3 34	..	3B44	3 47	..
Lullingstone	..	..	..	..	..	..	..	..	..	..	..	..	..	..	..	..	..	..	..	..	..	..	..	..	..	..	..	..	..	..	..	..
Eynsford	..	..	..	..	1221	..	1241	..	..	..	..	1 21	..	1 41	..	..	..	..	2 21	..	2 41	..	..	..	..	3 21	..	3 41	..	..	..	..
Shoreham (Kent)	..	..	..	..	1225	..	1245	..	..	..	..	1 25	..	1 45	..	..	..	..	2 25	..	2 45	..	..	..	..	3 25	..	3 45	..	..	..	..
Otford	1155	..	..	..	1228	..	1248	..	..	..	..	1 28	..	1 48	..	1 55	..	..	2 28	..	2 48	..	..	..	..	3 28	..	3 48	..	..	..	..
Sevenoaks { Bat & Ball	..	..	..	..	1232	..	1252	..	..	..	..	1 32	..	1 52	..	..	..	..	2 32	..	2 52	..	..	..	..	3 32	..	3 52	..	..	..	..
Sevenoaks { Tub's H. arr	..	..	..	12c21	1235	..	1255	..	..	1c20	..	1 35	..	1 55	..	..	..	2c20	2 35	..	2 55	..	..	..	3c20	3 35	..	3 55	..	..	..	4c20
Kemsing	12 1	..	..	..	..	..	..	..	..	..	..	..	..	..	..	2 1	..	..	..	..	..	..	..	..	..	..	..	..	..	4 8	..	..
Wrotham & Boro' Gr'n	12 5	..	..	..	..	..	..	..	..	..	..	..	..	..	..	2 5	..	..	..	..	..	..	..	..	..	..	..	..	..	4 12	..	..
Malling	1212	..	..	..	..	..	..	..	..	..	..	..	..	..	..	2 12	..	..	..	..	..	..	..	..	..	..	..	..	..	4 19	..	..
East Malling Halt	1215	..	..	..	..	..	..	..	..	..	..	..	..	..	..	2 15	..	..	..	..	..	..	..	..	..	..	..	..	..	4 22	..	..
Barming	1219	..	..	..	..	..	..	..	..	..	..	..	..	..	..	2 19	..	..	..	..	..	..	..	..	..	..	..	..	..	4 24	..	..
Maidstone East arr	1223	..	..	..	..	..	..	..	..	..	..	..	..	..	..	2 23	..	..	..	..	..	..	..	..	..	..	..	..	..	4 30	..	..
Farningham Road F	..	1151	..	..	..	..	..	..	..	..	..	..	..	..	..	..	1 51	..	..	..	..	..	..	..	..	..	..	..	..	..	3 51	..
Longfield Halt G	..	..	..	..	..	..	..	..	..	..	..	..	..	..	..	..	..	..	..	..	..	..	..	..	..	..	..	..	..	..	..	..
Southfleet (Springh'd)	..	..	..	..	..	..	..	..	..	..	..	..	..	..	..	..	..	..	..	..	..	..	..	..	..	..	..	..	..	..	..	..
Gravesend West St arr	..	..	..	..	..	..	..	..	..	..	..	..	..	..	..	..	..	..	..	..	..	..	..	..	..	..	..	..	..	..	..	..
Fawkham (for Hartley & Longfield)	..	1156	..	..	..	..	..	..	..	..	..	..	..	..	..	..	1 56	..	..	..	..	..	..	..	..	..	..	..	..	..	3 56	..
Meopham	..	12 1	..	..	..	..	..	..	..	..	..	..	..	..	..	..	2 1	..	..	..	..	..	..	..	..	..	..	..	..	..	4 1	..
Sole Street	..	12 3	..	..	..	..	..	..	..	..	..	..	..	..	..	..	2 3	..	..	..	..	..	..	..	..	..	..	..	..	..	4 3	..
Rochester	..	1214	..	..	..	..	..	..	..	..	..	..	..	..	..	..	2 14	..	..	..	..	..	..	..	..	..	..	..	..	..	4 14	..
Chatham	..	1216	..	..	..	..	..	..	..	..	1 29	..	..	..	..	..	2 16	..	..	..	..	..	..	..	..	..	..	..	..	..	4 16	..
Gillingham (Kent) arr	..	1221	..	..	..	..	..	..	..	..	1 36	..	..	..	..	..	2 22	..	..	..	..	..	..	..	..	..	..	..	..	..	4 21	..

3 Third class only. B Depart 6 mins. later. c Change at Orpington. **For Other Notes, see page 146**

LONDON, CRYSTAL PALACE (H.L.), ORPINGTON, SEVENOAKS, MAIDSTONE EAST, GRAVESEND WEST STREET, CHATHAM, and GILLINGHAM (Kent)

Down — Sundays—*continued* — p.m

Down		3	3	3	3	3	3	3	3	3	3	
Victoria .... dep	3 35	..	..	..	..	4 4	4 24	..	..	..	5 4	5 18
Brixton	..	..	..	..	..	4 9	4 29	..	..	..	5 9	..
Holborn Viaduct. dep	..	3 31	..	3 51	..	3 47	4 17	4 31	..	4 51	4 47	..
Blackfriars ...... "	..	3 32	..	3 52	..	3 48	4 18	4 32	..	4 52	4 48	..
Elephant and Castle	..	3 35	..	3 55	..	3 51	4 21	4 35	..	4 55	4 51	..
Loughborough Junc.	..	..	..	..	..	3 56	4 26	..	..	..	4 56	..
Denmark Hill	..	3 42	..	4 1	..	..	..	4 42	..	5 1	..	..
Peckham Rye	..	3 44	..	4 3	..	..	..	4 44	..	5 3	..	..
Nunhead	..	3 46	3 51	4 6	4 15	..	..	4 46	4 51	5 6	..	..
Honor Oak	..	..	3 54	..	4 18	..	..	..	4 54	..	..	..
Lordship Lane **A**	..	..	3 57	..	4 21	..	..	..	4 57	..	..	..
Upper Sydenham	..	..	3 59	..	4 23	..	..	..	4 59	..	..	..
Crystal Palace **B** arr	..	..	4 2	..	4 26	..	..	..	5 2	..	..	..
Crofton Park	..	3 49	..	4 9	..	..	..	4 49	..	5 9	..	..
Catford	..	3 52	..	4 11	..	..	..	4 52	..	5 11	..	..
Bellingham	..	3 54	..	4 13	..	..	..	4 54	..	5 13	..	..
Beckenham Hill	..	3 56	..	4 15	..	..	..	4 56	..	5 15	..	..
Ravensbourne	..	3 58	..	4 17	..	..	..	4 58	..	5 17	..	..
Herne Hill	..	..	..	..	..	4 11	4 31	..	..	..	5 11	..
West Dulwich	..	..	..	..	..	4 13	4 33	..	..	..	5 13	..
Sydenham Hill	..	..	..	..	..	4 15	4 35	..	..	..	5 15	..
Penge East **C**	..	..	..	..	..	4 18	4 38	..	..	..	5 18	..
Kent House	..	..	..	..	..	4 20	4 40	..	..	..	5 20	..
Beckenham Junction	..	..	..	..	..	4 22	4 42	..	..	..	5 22	..
Shortlands	..	3 59	..	4 19	..	4 25	4 45	4 59	..	5 19	5 25	..
Bromley South **D**	3 56	4 2	..	4 22	..	4 27	4 47	5 2	..	5 22	5 27	5 35
Bickley	..	4 5	..	4 25	..	4 30	4 50	5 5	..	5 25	5 30	..
Petts Wood	..	..	..	..	..	4 34	4 54	..	..	..	5 34	..
Orpington ...... arr	..	..	..	..	..	4 37	4 57	..	..	..	5 37	..
St. Mary Cray	..	4 10	..	4 30	..	..	..	5 10	..	5 30	..	..
Swanley 34, 60	..	4 14	..	4 34	..	..	..	5 14	..	5 34	..	5 44
Lullingstone	..	..	..	..	..	..	..	..	..	..	..	..
Eynsford	..	4 21	..	4 41	..	..	..	5 21	..	5 41	..	..
Shoreham (Kent)	..	4 25	..	4 45	..	..	..	5 25	..	5 45	..	..
Otford	..	4 28	..	4 48	..	..	..	5 28	..	5 48	..	5 55
Seven- oaks { Bat & Ball	..	4 32	..	4 52	..	..	..	5 32	..	5 52	..	..
Seven- oaks { Tub's H. ar	..	4 35	..	4 55	..	..	5c20	5 35	..	5 55	..	..
Kemsing	..	..	..	..	..	..	..	..	..	..	..	6 1
Wrotham & Boro' Gr'n	..	..	..	..	..	..	..	..	..	..	..	6 5
Malling	..	..	..	..	..	..	..	..	..	..	..	6 12
East Malling Halt	..	..	..	..	..	..	..	..	..	..	..	6 15
Barming	..	..	..	..	..	..	..	..	..	..	..	6 19
Maidstone East .. arr	..	..	..	..	..	..	..	..	..	..	..	6 23
Farningham Road **F**	..	..	..	..	..	..	..	..	..	..	..	..
Longfield Halt **G**	..	..	..	..	..	..	..	..	..	..	..	..
Southfleet (Springh'd)	..	..	..	..	..	..	..	..	..	..	..	..
Gravesend West St ar	..	..	..	..	..	..	..	..	..	..	..	..
Fawkham for Hartley &	..	..	..	..	..	..	..	..	..	..	..	..
Meopham ..... [Longfield	..	..	..	..	..	..	..	..	..	..	..	..
Sole Street	..	..	..	..	..	..	..	..	..	..	..	..
Rochester	..	..	..	..	..	..	..	..	..	..	..	..
Chatham	4 29	..	..	..	..	..	..	..	..	..	..	..
Gillingham (Kent) .. arr	4 35	..	..	..	..	..	..	..	..	..	..	..

Down	3	3	3	3		3	3	3	3	3	3	3	3
Victoria .... dep	..	5 24	..	..	..	..	..	6 4	6 24	..	..	..	7 4
Brixton	..	5 29	..	..	..	..	..	6 9	6 29	..	..	..	7 9
Holborn Viaduct. dep	..	5 17	5 31	..	..	5 51	..	5 47	6 17	6 31	..	6 51	6 47
Blackfriars ...... "	..	5 18	5 32	..	..	5 52	..	5 48	6 18	6 32	..	6 52	6 48
Elephant and Castle	..	5 21	5 35	..	..	5 55	..	5 51	6 21	6 35	..	6 55	6 51
Loughborough Junc.	..	5 26	..	..	..	..	..	5 56	6 26	..	..	..	6 56
Denmark Hill	..	..	5 42	..	..	6 1	..	..	..	6 42	..	7 1	..
Peckham Rye	..	..	5 44	..	..	6 3	..	..	..	6 44	..	7 3	..
Nunhead	5 15	..	5 46	5 51	..	6 6	6 15	..	..	6 46	6 51	7 6	..
Honor Oak	5 18	..	..	5 54	..	..	6 18	..	..	..	6 54	..	..
Lordship Lane **A**	5 21	..	..	5 57	..	..	6 21	..	..	..	6 57	..	..
Upper Sydenham	5 23	..	..	5 59	..	..	6 23	..	..	..	6 59	..	..
Crystal Palace **B** arr	5 26	..	..	6 2	..	..	6 26	..	..	..	7 2	..	..
Crofton Park	Stop	..	5 49	..	..	6 9	..	..	..	6 49	..	7 9	..
Catford	..	..	5 52	..	..	6 11	..	..	..	6 52	..	7 11	..
Bellingham	..	..	5 54	..	..	6 13	..	..	..	6 54	..	7 13	..
Beckenham Hill	..	..	5 56	..	..	6 15	..	..	..	6 56	..	7 15	..
Ravensbourne	..	..	5 58	..	..	6 17	..	..	..	6 58	..	7 17	..
Herne Hill	..	5 31	..	..	..	..	..	6 11	6 31	..	..	..	7 11
West Dulwich	..	5 33	..	..	..	..	..	6 13	6 33	..	..	..	7 13
Sydenham Hill	..	5 35	..	..	..	..	..	6 15	6 35	..	..	..	7 15
Penge East **C**	..	5 38	..	..	..	..	..	6 18	6 38	..	..	..	7 18
Kent House	..	5 40	..	..	..	..	..	6 20	6 40	..	..	..	7 20
Beckenham Junction	..	5 42	..	..	..	..	..	6 22	6 42	..	..	..	7 22
Shortlands	..	5 45	5 59	..	..	6 19	..	6 25	6 45	6 59	..	7 19	7 25
Bromley South **D**	..	5 47	6 2	..	..	6 22	..	6 27	6 47	7 2	..	7 22	7 27
Bickley	..	5 50	6 5	..	..	6 25	..	6 30	6 50	7 5	..	7 25	7 30
Petts Wood	..	5 54	..	..	..	..	..	6 34	6 54	..	..	..	7 34
Orpington ...... arr	..	5 57	..	..	..	..	..	6 37	6 57	..	..	..	7 37
St. Mary Cray	p.m	..	6 10	..	..	6 30	..	..	..	7 10	..	7 30	..
Swanley 34, 60	5 47	..	6 14	..	..	6 34	..	..	..	7 14	..	7 34	..
Lullingstone	..	..	..	..	..	..	..	..	..	..	..	..	..
Eynsford	..	..	6 21	..	..	6 41	..	..	..	7 21	..	7 41	..
Shoreham (Kent)	..	..	6 25	..	..	6 45	..	..	..	7 25	..	7 45	..
Otford	..	..	6 28	..	..	6 48	..	..	..	7 28	..	7 48	..
Seven- oaks { Bat & Ball	..	..	6 32	..	..	6 52	..	..	..	7 32	..	7 52	..
Seven- oaks { Tub's H. ar	..	6c20	6 35	..	..	6 55	..	..	7c20	7 35	..	7 55	..
Kemsing	..	..	..	..	..	..	..	..	..	..	..	..	..
Wrotham & Boro' Gr'n	..	..	..	..	..	..	..	..	..	..	..	..	..
Malling	..	..	..	..	..	..	..	..	..	..	..	..	..
East Malling Halt	..	..	..	..	..	..	..	..	..	..	..	..	..
Barming	..	..	..	..	..	..	..	..	..	..	..	..	..
Maidstone East .. arr	..	..	..	..	..	..	..	..	..	..	..	..	..
Farningham Road **F**	5 51	..	..	..	..	..	..	..	..	..	..	..	..
Longfield Halt **G**	..	..	..	..	..	..	..	..	..	..	..	..	..
Southfleet (Springh'd)	..	..	..	..	..	..	..	..	..	..	..	..	..
Gravesend West St ar	..	..	..	..	..	..	..	..	..	..	..	..	..
Fawkham for Hartley &	5 56	..	..	..	..	..	..	..	..	..	..	..	..
Meopham ..... [Longfield	6 1	..	..	..	..	..	..	..	..	..	..	..	..
Sole Street	6 3	..	..	..	..	..	..	..	..	..	..	..	..
Rochester	6 14	..	..	..	..	..	..	..	..	..	..	..	..
Chatham	6 16	..	..	..	..	..	..	..	..	..	..	..	..
Gillingham (Kent) .. arr	6 22	..	..	..	..	..	..	..	..	..	..	..	..

Down		3	3	3	3	3	3
Victoria .... dep	7 18	..	7 24	..	..	..	8 4
Brixton	..	..	7 29	..	..	..	8 9
Holborn Viaduct. dep	..	..	7 17	7 31	..	7 51	7 47
Blackfriars ...... "	..	..	7 18	7 32	..	7 52	7 48
Elephant and Castle	..	..	7 21	7 35	..	7 55	7 51
Loughborough Junc.	..	..	7 26	..	..	..	7 56
Denmark Hill	..	..	..	7 42	..	8 1	..
Peckham Rye	..	..	..	7 44	..	8 3	..
Nunhead	..	7 15	..	7 46	7 51	8 6	..
Honor Oak	..	7 18	..	..	7 54	..	..
Lordship Lane **A**	..	7 21	..	..	7 57	..	..
Upper Sydenham	..	7 23	..	..	7 59	..	..
Crystal Palace **B** arr	..	7 26	..	..	8 2	..	..
Crofton Park	..	Stop	..	7 49	..	8 9	..
Catford	..	..	..	7 52	..	8 11	..
Bellingham	..	..	..	7 54	..	8 13	..
Beckenham Hill	..	..	..	7 56	..	8 15	..
Ravensbourne	..	..	..	7 58	..	8 17	..
Herne Hill	..	..	7 31	..	..	..	8 11
West Dulwich	..	..	7 33	..	..	..	8 13
Sydenham Hill	..	..	7 35	..	..	..	8 15
Penge East **C**	..	..	7 38	..	..	..	8 18
Kent House	..	..	7 40	..	..	..	8 20
Beckenham Junction	..	..	7 42	..	..	..	8 22
Shortlands	..	..	7 45	7 59	..	8 19	8 25
Bromley South **D**	7 35	..	7 47	8 2	..	8 22	8 27
Bickley	..	..	7 50	8 5	..	8 25	8 30
Petts Wood	..	..	7 54	..	..	..	8 34
Orpington ...... arr	..	..	7 57	..	..	..	8 37
St. Mary Cray	..	p.m	..	8 10	..	8 30	..
Swanley 34, 60	7 44	7 47	..	8 14	..	8 34	..
Lullingstone	..	..	..	..	..	..	..
Eynsford	..	..	..	8 21	..	8 41	..
Shoreham (Kent)	..	..	..	8 25	..	8 45	..
Otford	7 55	..	..	8 28	..	8 48	..
Seven- oaks { Bat & Ball	..	..	..	8 32	..	8 52	..
Seven- oaks { Tub's H. ar	..	..	8c21	8 35	..	8 55	..
Kemsing	8 1	..	..	..	..	..	..
Wrotham & Boro' Gr'n	8 5	..	..	..	..	..	..
Malling	8 12	..	..	..	..	..	..
East Malling Halt	8 15	..	..	..	..	..	..
Barming	8 19	..	..	..	..	..	..
Maidstone East .. arr	8 23	..	..	..	..	..	..
Farningham Road **F**	..	7 51	..	..	..	..	..
Longfield Halt **G**	..	..	..	..	..	..	..
Southfleet (Springh'd)	..	..	..	..	..	..	..
Gravesend West St ar	..	..	..	..	..	..	..
Fawkham for Hartley &	..	7 56	..	..	..	..	..
Meopham ..... [Longfield	..	8 1	..	..	..	..	..
Sole Street	..	8 3	..	..	..	..	..
Rochester	..	8 14	..	..	..	..	..
Chatham	..	8 16	..	..	..	..	..
Gillingham (Kent) .. arr	..	8 21	..	..	..	..	..

3 Third class only c Change at Orpington

For Other Notes, see page 146

LONDON, CRYSTAL PALACE (H.L.), ORPINGTON, SEVENOAKS. MAIDSTONE EAST, GRAVESEND WEST STREET, CHATHAM, and GILLINGHAM (Kent)

Sundays—*continued* (p.m)

Down	3	3	3		3		3	3	3			3	3	3	3	3	3			3	3	3	3	3	3	3	3
Victoria .... dep	..	8 24	..	835	..	..	..	..	9 4	9 18	..	9 24	..	..	..	..	10 4	1018	..	10 24	..	..	..	..	11 4	..	1130
Brixton	..	8 29	..	..	..	..	..	..	9 9	..	..	9 29	..	..	..	..	10 9	..	..	10 29	..	..	..	..	11 9	..	1135
Holborn Viaduct. dep	..	8 17	8 31	..	..	..	8 51	..	8 47	..	..	9 17	9 31	..	9 51	..	9 47	..	..	10 17	1031	..	1051	..	1047	11 25	..
Blackfriars ...... "	..	8 18	8 32	..	..	..	8 52	..	8 48	..	..	9 18	9 32	..	9 52	..	9 48	..	..	10 18	1032	..	1052	..	1048	11 26	..
Elephant and Castle..	..	8 21	8 35	..	..	..	8 55	..	8 51	..	..	9 21	9 35	..	9 55	..	9 51	..	..	10 21	1035	..	1055	..	1051	11 29	..
Loughborough Junc...	..	8 26	..	..	..	..	..	..	8 56	..	..	9 26	..	..	..	..	9 56	..	..	10 26	..	..	..	..	1056	..	..
Denmark Hill........	..	..	8 42	..	..	..	9 1	..	..	..	..	..	9 42	..	10 1	..	..	..	..	..	1042	..	11 1	..	..	11 36	..
Peckham Rye........	..	..	8 44	..	..	..	9 3	..	..	..	..	..	9 44	..	10 3	..	..	..	..	..	1044	..	11 3	..	..	11 38	..
Nunhead........	8 15	..	8 46	..	8 51	..	9 6	9 15	..	..	..	..	9 46	9 51	10 6	1015	..	..	..	..	1046	1051	11 6	1115	..	11 40	..
Honor Oak........	8 18	..	..	..	8 54	..	..	9 18	..	..	..	..	..	9 54	..	1018	..	..	..	..	..	1054	..	1118	..	..	..
Lordship Lane **A**.....	8 21	..	..	..	8 57	..	..	9 21	..	..	..	..	..	9 57	..	1021	..	..	..	..	..	1057	..	1121	..	..	..
Upper Sydenham......	8 23	..	..	..	8 59	..	..	9 23	..	..	..	..	..	9 59	..	1023	..	..	..	..	..	1059	..	1123	..	..	..
Crystal Palace B arr	8 26	..	..	..	9 2	..	..	9 26	..	..	..	..	..	10 2	..	1026	..	..	..	..	..	11 2	..	1126	..	..	..
Crofton Park........	..	..	8 49	..	..	..	9 9	..	..	..	..	..	9 49	..	10 9	..	..	..	..	..	1049	..	11 9	..	..	11 43	..
Catford........	..	..	8 52	..	..	..	9 11	..	..	..	..	..	9 52	..	1011	..	..	..	..	..	1052	..	1111	..	..	11 46	..
Bellingham	..	..	8 54	..	..	..	9 13	..	..	..	..	..	9 54	..	1013	..	..	..	..	..	1054	..	1113	..	..	11 48	..
Beckenham Hill	..	..	8 56	..	..	..	9 15	..	..	..	..	..	9 56	..	1015	..	..	..	..	..	1056	..	1115	..	..	11 50	..
Ravensbourne........	..	..	8 58	..	..	..	9 17	..	..	..	..	..	9 58	..	1017	..	..	..	..	..	1058	..	1117	..	..	11 52	..
Herne Hill........	..	8 31	..	..	..	..	..	..	9 11	..	..	9 31	..	..	..	..	1011	..	..	10 31	..	..	..	..	1111	..	1138
West Dulwich........	..	8 33	..	..	..	..	..	..	9 13	..	..	9 33	..	..	..	..	1013	..	..	10 32	..	..	..	..	1113	..	1140
Sydenham Hill........	..	8 35	..	..	..	..	..	..	9 15	..	..	9 35	..	..	..	..	1015	..	..	10 35	..	..	..	..	1115	..	1143
Penge East **C**........	..	8 38	..	..	..	..	..	..	9 18	..	..	9 38	..	..	..	..	1018	..	..	10 38	..	..	..	..	1118	..	1146
Kent House........	..	8 40	..	..	..	..	..	..	9 20	..	..	9 40	..	..	..	..	1020	..	..	10 40	..	..	..	..	1120	..	1148
Beckenham Junction...	..	8 42	..	..	..	..	..	..	9 22	..	..	9 42	..	..	..	..	1022	..	..	10 42	..	..	..	..	1122	..	1151
Shortlands........	..	8 45	8 59	..	..	..	9 19	..	9 25	..	..	9 45	9 59	..	1019	..	1025	..	..	10 45	1059	..	1119	..	1125	11 53	1154
Bromley South D	..	8 47	9 2	856	..	..	9 22	..	9 27	9 35	..	9 47	10 2	..	1022	..	1027	1035	..	10 47	11 2	..	1122	..	1127	11‡58	1157
Bickley........	..	8 50	9 5	..	..	..	9 25	..	9 30	..	..	9 50	10 5	..	1025	..	1030	..	..	10 50	11 5	..	1125	..	1130	12 1	12 1
Petts Wood........	..	8 54	..	..	..	..	..	..	9 34	..	..	9 54	..	..	..	..	1034	..	..	10 54	..	..	..	..	1134	..	12 5
Orpington........ arr	..	8 57	..	..	..	..	..	..	9 37	..	..	9 57	..	..	..	..	1037	..	..	10 57	..	..	..	..	1137	..	12 8
St. Mary Cray........	..	..	9 10	..	..	..	9 30	..	..	..	..	..	1010	..	1030	..	..	..	..	..	1110	..	1130	..	..	12 6	..
Swanley 34, 60........	..	..	9 15	..	..	..	9 34	..	..	9 44	9 47	..	1014	..	1034	..	..	1044	1047	..	1114	..	1134	..	..	12 10	..
Lullingstone	..	..	..	..	..	..	..	..	..	..	..	..	..	..	..	..	..	..	..	..	..	..	..	..	..	..	..
Eynsford........	..	..	9 21	..	..	..	9 41	..	..	..	..	..	1021	..	1041	..	..	..	..	..	1121	..	1141	..	..	12 17	..
Shoreham (Kent)......	..	..	9 25	..	..	..	9 45	..	..	..	..	..	1025	..	1045	..	..	..	..	..	1125	..	1145	..	..	12 21	..
Otford........	..	..	9 28	..	..	..	9 48	..	..	9 55	..	..	1028	..	1048	..	..	1055	..	..	1128	..	1148	..	..	12 24	..
Seven- { Bat & Ball .	..	..	9 32	..	..	..	9 52	..	..	..	..	..	1032	..	1052	..	..	..	..	..	1132	..	1152	..	..	12 28	..
oaks { Tub's H. ar	..	9c20	9 35	..	..	..	9 55	..	..	..	..	10c25	1035	..	1055	..	..	..	..	11c21	1135	..	1155	..	..	12 31	..
Kemsing........	..	..	..	..	..	..	..	..	..	10 1	..	..	..	..	..	..	..	11 1	..	..	..	..	..	..	..	..	..
Wrotham & Boro' Gr'n	..	..	..	..	..	..	..	..	..	10 5	..	..	..	..	..	..	..	11 5	..	..	..	..	..	..	..	..	..
Malling........	..	..	..	..	..	..	..	..	..	1012	..	..	..	..	..	..	..	1112	..	..	..	..	..	..	..	..	..
East Malling Halt....	..	..	..	..	..	..	..	..	..	1015	..	..	..	..	..	..	..	1115	..	..	..	..	..	..	..	..	..
Barming........	..	..	..	..	..	..	..	..	..	1019	..	..	..	..	..	..	..	1119	..	..	..	..	..	..	..	..	..
Maidstone East.. arr	..	..	..	..	..	..	..	..	..	1023	..	..	..	..	..	..	..	1123	..	..	..	..	..	..	..	..	..
Farningham Road **F**....	..	..	..	..	..	..	..	..	..	..	9 51	..	..	..	..	..	..	..	1051	..	..	..	..	..	..	..	..
Longfield Halt **G**.....	..	..	..	..	..	..	..	..	..	..	..	..	..	..	..	..	..	..	..	..	..	..	..	..	..	..	..
Southfleet (Springh'd).	..	..	..	..	..	..	..	..	..	..	..	..	..	..	..	..	..	..	..	..	..	..	..	..	..	..	..
Gravesend West St ar	..	..	..	..	..	..	..	..	..	..	..	..	..	..	..	..	..	..	..	..	..	..	..	..	..	..	..
Fawkham for Hartley &	..	..	..	..	..	..	..	..	..	..	9 56	..	..	..	..	..	..	..	1056	..	..	..	..	..	..	..	..
Meopham.....[Longfield	..	..	..	..	..	..	..	..	..	..	10 1	..	..	..	..	..	..	..	11 1	..	..	..	..	..	..	..	..
Sole Street........	..	..	..	..	..	..	..	..	..	..	10 3	..	..	..	..	..	..	..	11 3	..	..	..	..	..	..	..	..
Rochester........	..	..	..	..	..	..	..	..	..	..	1014	..	..	..	..	..	..	..	1114	..	..	..	..	..	..	..	..
Chatham........	..	..	..	932	..	..	..	..	..	..	1016	..	..	..	..	..	..	..	1116	..	..	..	..	..	..	..	..
Gillingham (Kent).. arr	..	..	..	937	..	..	..	..	..	..	1021	..	..	..	..	..	..	..	1121	..	..	..	..	..	..	..	..

3 Third class only

A Station for Forest Hill

B Crystal Palace (H.L.) and Upper Norwood; nearly ¼ mile to Low Level Station.

C Under ¼ mile to Penge West Station

c Change at Orpington

D Over ¼ mile to Bromley North Station

F Farningham Road and Sutton-at-Hone

G Halt for Pinden and Westwood

‡ Arr. 2 minutes *earlier*.

OTHER TRAINS

BETWEEN	PAGE
London & Herne Hill	320
London and Beckenham Junc.	255
London and Bromley North	124
London & Sevenoaks	124
London, Gravesend, Maidstone, and Gillingham (Kent)	72

GILLINGHAM (Kent), CHATHAM, GRAVESEND WEST STREET, MAIDSTONE EAST, SEVENOAKS, ORPINGTON, CRYSTAL PALACE (H.L.) and LONDON

Week Days — a.m.

Mls	Miles from Maidstone E	Miles from Sevenoaks (T.H.)	Up	3	3		3	3	3	3	3		3		3	3		3	3	3		3	3	3		3	3	3		3		3	3
			Gillingham (Kent) .. dep																														
1½			Chatham	..	..	..	..	..	..	..	..	..	..	..	..	..	..	..	..	..	..	..	..	..	..	..	..	..	..	..	..	..	..
2¼			Rochester	..	..	..	..	..	..	..	..	..	..	..	..	..	..	..	..	..	..	..	..	..	..	..	..	..	..	..	..	..	..
9¼			Sole Street	..	..	..	..	..	..	..	..	..	..	..	..	..	..	..	..	..	..	..	..	..	..	..	..	..	..	..	..	..	..
10			Meopham ......[Longfield	..	..	..	..	..	..	..	..	..	..	..	..	..	..	..	..	..	..	..	..	..	..	..	..	..	..	..	..	..	..
12¾			Fawkham, for Hartley &	..	..	..	..	..	..	..	..	..	..	..	..	..	..	..	..	..	..	..	..	..	..	..	..	..	..	..	..	..	..
—			Mls — Gravesend W. St dp	..	..	..	..	..	..	..	..	..	..	..	..	..	..	..	..	..	..	..	..	..	..	..	..	..	..	..	..	..	..
—			2¼ Southfl't (Springh'd)	..	..	..	..	..	..	..	..	..	..	..	..	..	..	..	..	..	..	..	..	..	..	..	..	..	..	..	..	..	..
—			4 Longfield Halt **G**	..	..	..	..	..	..	..	..	..	..	..	..	..	..	..	..	..	..	..	..	..	..	..	..	..	..	..	..	..	..
15¼	—	—	Farningham Road **F**	..	..	..	..	..	..	..	..	..	..	..	..	..	..	..	..	..	..	..	..	..	..	..	..	..	..	..	..	..	..
—			**Maidstone East** ..dep	..	..	..	..	..	..	..	..	..	..	..	..	..	..	..	..	..	..	..	..	..	..	..	..	..	..	..	..	..	..
—	2¼		Barming	..	..	..	..	..	..	..	..	..	..	..	..	..	..	..	..	..	..	..	..	..	..	..	..	..	..	..	..	..	..
—	4¼		East Malling Halt	..	..	..	..	..	..	..	..	..	..	..	..	..	..	..	..	..	..	..	..	..	..	..	..	..	..	..	..	..	..
—	5¼		Malling	..	..	..	..	..	..	..	..	..	..	..	..	..	..	..	..	..	..	..	..	..	..	..	..	..	..	..	..	..	..
—	10½		Wrotham & Boro' Gr'n	..	..	..	..	..	..	..	..	..	..	..	..	..	..	..	..	..	..	..	..	..	..	..	..	..	..	..	..	..	..
—	13		Kemsing	..	..	..	..	..	..	..	..	..	..	..	..	..	..	..	..	..	..	..	..	..	..	..	..	..	..	..	..	..	..
—	—	—	Sevenoaks { Tub's H. dp	..	..	..	..	..	..	..	..	..	..	..	..	..	..	..	..	5c42	..	..	..	6e0	..	..	6 1	..	..	..	..	..	..
—	—	1	Sevenoaks { Bat & Ball	..	..	..	..	..	..	..	..	..	..	..	..	..	..	..	..	..	..	..	..	..	..	..	6 4	..	..	..	..	..	..
—	16	2½	Otford	..	..	..	..	..	..	..	..	..	..	..	..	..	..	..	..	..	..	..	..	..	..	..	6 7	..	..	..	..	..	..
—	17½	4½	Shoreham (Kent)	..	..	..	..	..	..	..	..	..	..	..	..	..	..	..	..	..	..	..	..	..	..	..	6 10	..	..	..	..	..	..
—	19¾	6¼	Eynsford	..	..	..	..	..	..	..	..	..	..	..	..	..	..	..	..	..	..	..	..	..	..	..	6 15	..	..	..	..	..	..
—	20½	7	Lullingstone	..	..	..	..	..	..	..	..	..	..	..	..	..	..	..	..	..	..	..	..	..	..	..	..	..	..	..	..	..	..
18½	22½	9	**Swanley** 60	..	..	..	..	..	5 7	..	..	..	..	..	..	5 45	..	..	..	..	..	6 5	..	..	..	..	6 24	..	..	..	..	..	..
21¼	25½	12	St. Mary Cray	..	..	..	..	..	5 12	..	..	..	..	..	..	5 50	..	..	..	..	..	6 10	..	..	..	..	6 30	..	..	..	..	..	..
—	—	—	— **Orpington** ..... dep	4 0	4 8	..	5 0	5 7	..	..	5 22	..	..	..	5 43	..	..	..	6 0	6 7	..	..	..	6 20	..	6 25	..	..	..	..	..	6 40	6 46
—	—	—	1½ Petts Wood	4 3	4 11	..	5 3	5 10	..	..	5 25	..	..	..	5 46	..	..	..	6 3	6 10	..	..	..	6 23	..	6 28	..	..	..	..	..	6 43	6 49
24	28	14¾	Bickley	4 6	4 1[illegible]	..	5 6	5 13	5 16	..	5 28	..	..	..	5 49	5 54	..	..	6 7	6 13	..	6 14	..	6 27	..	6 31	6 34	..	..	..	..	6 47	6 52
25½	29½	16¼	**Bromley South D**	4 9	4 18	..	5 9	5 16	5 19	..	5 31	..	..	..	5 52	5 57	..	..	6 10	6 16	..	6 17	..	6 30	..	6 34	6 37	..	..	..	..	6 51	6 56
26	30	16¾	Shortlands	4 12	4 20	..	5 12	5 19	5 22	..	5 34	..	..	..	5 55	6 0	..	..	6 14	6 19	..	6 20	..	6 33	..	6 37	6 40	..	..	..	..	6 54	6 58
27½	31½	—	Beckenham Junction	..	4 23	..	5 15	5 22	..	..	5 37	..	..	..	5 58	..	..	..	6 17	6 22	..	..	..	6 36	..	6 40	..	..	..	..	..	6 57	7 1
28½	32½	—	Kent House	..	4 25	..	5 17	5 24	..	..	5 39	..	..	..	6 0	..	..	..	6 19	6 24	..	..	..	6 38	..	6 42	..	..	..	..	..	6 59	7 3
28¾	32¾	—	Penge East **C**	..	4 27	..	5 19	5 26	..	..	5 41	..	..	..	6 2	..	..	..	6 21	6 26	..	..	..	6 40	..	6 44	..	..	..	..	..	7 1	7 5
30½	34½	—	Sydenham Hill	..	4 30	..	5 22	5 29	..	..	5 44	..	..	..	6 5	..	..	..	6 24	6 29	..	..	..	6 43	..	6 47	..	..	..	..	..	7 4	7 8
31	35	—	West Dulwich	..	4 32	..	5 24	5 31	..	..	5 46	..	..	..	6 7	..	..	..	6 26	6 31	..	..	..	6 45	..	6 49	..	..	..	..	..	7 6	7 11
32	36	—	Herne Hill	..	4 35	..	5 26	5§33	..	5 42	5 48	..	..	..	6 9	..	..	..	6 28	6 33	..	..	..	6 47	..	6§52	..	..	..	..	..	7 8	7 13
—	—	17½	Ravensbourne	..	..	..	..	..	5 24	..	..	..	..	..	..	6 2	..	..	..	..	..	6 22	..	..	..	..	6 42	..	..	..	..	..	..
—	—	18½	Beckenham Hill	..	..	..	..	..	5 26	..	..	..	..	..	..	6 4	..	..	..	..	..	6 24	..	..	..	..	6 44	..	..	..	..	..	..
—	—	19	Bellingham	4 17	..	..	..	..	5 28	..	..	..	..	..	..	6 6	..	..	..	..	..	6 26	..	..	..	..	6 46	..	..	..	..	..	..
—	—	20	**Catford**	4 19	..	..	..	..	5 30	..	..	..	..	..	..	6 8	..	..	..	..	..	6 28	..	..	..	..	6 48	..	..	..	..	..	..
—	—	20¾	Crofton Park	4 21	..	..	..	..	5 32	..	..	..	..	..	..	6 10	..	..	..	..	..	6 30	..	..	..	..	6 50	..	..	..	..	..	..
—	—	—	— **Crystal Palace B** dp	..	..	..	..	..	..	..	..	..	5 46	..	..	..	..	6 6	..	..	..	..	6 26	..	..	..	..	6 46	..	6 56	..	..	..
—	—	—	¾ Upper Sydenham	..	..	..	..	..	..	..	..	..	5 48	..	..	..	..	6 8	..	..	..	..	6 28	..	..	..	..	6 48	..	..	..	..	..
—	—	—	1½ Lordship Lane **A**	..	..	..	..	..	..	..	..	..	5 50	..	..	..	..	6 10	..	..	..	..	6 30	..	..	..	..	6 50	..	..	..	..	..
—	—	—	2¼ Honor Oak	..	..	..	..	..	..	..	..	..	5 53	..	..	..	..	6 13	..	..	..	..	6 33	..	..	..	..	6 53	..	..	..	..	..
—	—	22	Nunhead	4 24	..	..	..	..	5 35	..	..	..	5 56	..	..	6 13	..	6 16	..	..	..	6 33	6 36	..	..	..	6 53	6 56	..	7 2	..	..	..
—	—	22¾	Peckham Rye	4 26	..	..	..	..	5 37	..	..	..	5 59	..	..	6 15	..	6 19	..	..	..	6 35	6 39	..	..	..	6 55	6 59	..	7 5	..	..	..
—	—	23½	Denmark Hill	..	..	..	..	..	5 40	..	..	..	6 1	..	..	6 18	..	6 21	..	..	..	6 38	6 41	..	..	..	6 58	7 1	..	7 7	..	..	..
33	37	—	Loughborough Junc.	..	4 37	..	5 29	..	..	5 45	5 51	..	..	..	6 12	..	..	..	..	6 36	..	..	..	..	..	6 54	..	..	..	..	..	..	7 16
35	39	26½	Elephant and Castle	4 34	4 42	..	5 33	..	5 46	5 50	5 56	..	6 7	..	6 16	6 24	..	6 27	..	6 40	..	6 43	6 47	..	..	6 59	7 4	7 7	..	7 13	..	..	7 20
36½	40½	27½	**Blackfriars** ...... arr	4§38	4 45	..	5 36	..	5 49	5 53	5 59	..	6 10	..	6 19	6 27	..	6 30	..	6 43	..	6§46	6 50	..	..	7 2	7 7	7 10	..	7 16	..	..	7§23
36½	40½	27¾	**Holborn Viaduct.** "	4 40	4 47	..	5 39	..	..	5 56	6 1	..	..	..	6 22	6 29	..	..	..	6 46	..	6 49	..	..	..	7 4	7 9	..	..	..	..	..	7 28
32¼	36¼	—	Brixton	..	4 38	..	5 33	..	..	..	5 51	..	..	..	..	..	..	..	6 31	..	..	..	..	6 50	..	..	..	..	..	..	..	7 11	..
36	40	28	**Victoria** .... arr	..	4 45	..	5 39	..	..	..	5 57	..	..	..	..	..	..	..	6 37	..	..	..	..	6 56	..	..	..	..	..	..	..	7 16	..

3 Third class only

§ 1 min. later on Sats. § 1 minute *earlier* on Sats. e Change at Orpington.

For Other Notes, see page 157

GILLINGHAM (Kent), CHATHAM, GRAVESEND WEST STREET, MAIDSTONE EAST, SEVENOAKS, ORPINGTON, CRYSTAL PALACE (H.L.) and LONDON

Week Days—*continued* (a.m)

Up	3	3				3		3		3	3	3		3	3	3
Gillingham (Kent) dep	..	..	..	6 15	..	..	..	..	..	..	..	..	..	..	..	..
Chatham	..	..	..	6 18	..	..	..	..	..	..	..	..	..	..	..	..
Rochester	..	..	..	6 21	..	..	..	..	..	..	..	..	..	..	..	..
Sole Street	..	..	..	6 33	..	..	..	..	..	..	..	..	..	..	..	..
Meopham [Longfield	..	..	..	6 36	..	..	..	..	..	..	..	..	..	..	..	..
Fawkham, for Hartley and	..	..	..	6 40	..	..	..	..	..	..	..	..	..	..	..	..
Gravesend West St. dep	..	..	..	3	..	..	..	..	..	..	..	..	6 55	..	..	..
Southfleet (Springhead)	..	..	..		..	..	..	..	..	..	..	..	7 0	..	..	..
Longfield Halt G	..	..	..	..	..	..	..	..	..	..	..	..	7B4	..	..	..
Farningham Road F	..	..	..	6 45	..	..	..	..	..	..	..	..	7 10	..	..	..
Maidstone East dep	..	..	..	..	..	..	..	..	..	..	..	..	..	..	..	..
Barming	..	..	..	..	..	..	..	..	..	..	..	..	..	..	..	..
East Malling Halt	..	..	..	..	..	..	..	..	..	..	..	..	..	..	..	..
Malling	..	..	..	..	..	..	..	..	..	..	..	..	..	..	..	..
Wrotham and Boro' Green	..	..	..	..	..	..	..	..	..	..	..	..	..	..	..	..
Kemsing	..	..	..	..	..	..	..	..	..	..	..	..	..	..	..	..
Seven-oaks { Tub's H. dep	6 21	..	..	..	..	6c26	..	..	..	6 41	..	..	..	6c44	6 53	..
Seven-oaks { Bat & Ball	6 24	..	..	..	..	..	..	..	..	6 44	..	..	..	..	6 56	..
Otford	6 27	..	..	..	..	..	..	..	..	6 47	..	..	..	..	6 59	..
Shoreham (Kent)	6 30	..	..	..	..	..	..	..	..	6 50	..	..	..	..	7 2	..
Eynsford	6 35	..	..	..	..	..	..	..	..	6 55	..	..	..	..	7 7	..
Lullingstone	..	..	..	..	..	..	..	..	..	..	..	..	..	..	..	..
Swanley 60	6 44	..	..	6B52	..	..	..	..	..	7 4	..	..	7 16	..	7 16	..
St. Mary Cray	6 50	..	..	6 58	..	..	..	..	..	7 10	..	..	..	..	7 22	..
Orpington dep	..	..	..	..	..	7 0	..	..	..	..	..	..	..	7 16	..	7 21
Petts Wood	..	..	..	..	..	7 3	..	..	..	..	..	..	..	7 19	..	7 24
Bickley	6 54	..	..	7 2	..	7 7	..	7 15	..	7 14	..	..	..	7 22	7 26	7 27
Bromley South D	6 57	..	..	7 5	..	7 11	..	7 18	..	7 17	..	..	..	7 25	7B30	7 30
Shortlands	7 0	..	..	7 7	..	7 14	..	7 20	..	7 20	..	..	..	7 28	7 34	7 33
Beckenham Junction	..	..	..	7 10	..	7 17	..	7 23	..	..	..	..	..	7 31	..	7 36
Kent House	..	..	..	7 12	..	7 19	..	7 25	..	..	..	..	..	7 33	..	7 38
Penge East C	..	..	..	7 14	..	7 21	..	7 27	..	..	..	..	..	7 35	..	7 40
Sydenham Hill	..	..	..	7 18	..	7 24	..	7 30	..	..	..	..	..	7 38	..	7 43
West Dulwich	..	..	..	7 20	..	7 26	..	7 32	..	..	..	..	..	7 40	..	7 45
Herne Hill	..	..	..	7 22	..	7 29	..	7 35	..	..	7 41	..	..	7 42	..	7 48
Ravensbourne	7 2	..	..	..	..	..	..	..	..	7 22	..	..	..	..	7 36	..
Beckenham Hill	7 4	..	..	..	..	..	..	..	..	7 24	..	..	..	..	7 38	..
Bellingham	7 6	..	..	..	..	..	..	..	..	7 26	..	..	..	..	7 40	..
Catford	7 8	..	..	..	..	..	..	..	..	7 28	..	..	..	..	7 42	..
Crofton Park	7 10	..	..	..	..	..	..	..	..	7 30	..	..	..	..	7 44	..
Crystal Palace B dep	..	7 6	..	..	..	..	..	..	..	..	..	7 26	..	..	..	..
Upper Sydenham	..	7 8	..	..	..	..	..	..	..	..	..	7 28	..	..	..	..
Lordship Lane A	..	7 10	..	..	..	..	..	..	..	..	..	7 30	..	..	..	..
Honor Oak	..	7 13	..	..	..	..	..	..	..	..	..	7 33	..	..	..	..
Nunhead	7 13	7 16	..	..	..	..	..	..	..	7 33	..	7 36	..	..	..	..
Peckham Rye	7 15	7 19	..	..	..	..	..	..	..	7 35	..	7 39	..	..	..	..
Denmark Hill	7 18	7 21	..	..	..	..	..	..	..	7 37	..	7 41	..	..	..	..
Loughborough Junction	..	..	..	..	..	..	..	..	..	..	7 43	..	..	7B45	..	..
Elephant and Castle	7 23	7 27	..	..	..	..	..	7 40	..	7 43	7 48	7 47	..	7 51	7 54	..
Blackfriars arr	7B26	7 30	..	..	..	..	..	7 43	..	7B46	7 51	7 50	..	7 54	7 57	..
Holborn Viaduct "	7 29	..	..	..	..	..	..	7 46	..	7 49	7 53	..	..	7 56	7 59	..
Brixton	..	..	..	7 24	..	7 31	..	..	..	..	..	..	..	..	..	7 50
Victoria arr	..	..	..	7 30	..	7 37	..	..	..	..	..	..	..	..	..	7 56

Up	3		3	3		3	3		3	3	3	3			3	3
Gillingham (Kent) dep	..	..	..	..	..	..	..	..	..	..	..	..	7 13	..	..	..
Chatham	..	..	..	..	..	..	..	..	..	..	..	..	7 18	..	..	..
Rochester	..	..	..	..	..	..	..	..	..	..	..	..	7 22	..	..	..
Sole Street	..	..	..	..	..	..	..	..	..	..	..	..	7 33	..	..	..
Meopham [Longfield	..	..	..	..	..	..	..	..	..	..	..	..	7 36	..	..	..
Fawkham, for Hartley and	..	..	..	..	..	..	..	..	..	..	..	..	7 40	..	..	..
Gravesend West St. dep	..	..	..	..	..	..	..	..	..	..	..	..	..	..	..	..
Southfleet (Springhead)	..	..	..	..	..	..	..	..	..	..	..	..	..	..	..	..
Longfield Halt G	..	..	..	..	..	..	..	..	..	..	..	..	..	..	..	..
Farningham Road F	..	..	..	..	..	..	..	..	..	..	..	..	7 46	..	..	..
Maidstone East dep	..	..	..	..	..	..	..	..	..	..	..	..	..	7 11	..	..
Barming	..	..	..	..	..	..	..	..	..	..	..	..	..	7 16	..	..
East Malling Halt	..	..	..	..	..	..	..	..	..	..	..	..	..	7 19	..	..
Malling	..	..	..	..	..	..	..	..	..	..	..	..	..	7 22	..	..
Wrotham and Boro' Green	..	..	..	..	..	..	..	..	..	..	..	..	..	7 31	..	..
Kemsing	..	..	..	..	..	..	..	..	..	..	..	..	..	7 35	..	..
Seven-oaks { Tub's H. dep	..	..	..	..	..	7c11	..	..	7 21	..	..	..	..	..	7c34	..
Seven-oaks { Bat & Ball	..	..	..	..	..	..	..	..	7 24	..	..	..	..	..	..	..
Otford	..	..	..	..	..	..	..	..	7 27	..	..	..	..	7 41	..	..
Shoreham (Kent)	..	..	..	..	..	..	..	..	7 30	..	..	..	..	7 44	..	..
Eynsford	..	..	..	..	..	..	..	..	7 35	..	..	..	..	7 49	..	..
Lullingstone	..	..	..	..	..	..	..	..	..	..	..	..	..	..	..	..
Swanley 60	..	..	..	..	..	..	..	..	7B44	..	..	..	7 52	7 55	..	..
St. Mary Cray	..	..	..	..	..	..	S X	..	7 50	..	..	..	..	8 1	..	..
Orpington dep	7 26	..	..	..	..	7 42	7 47	..	..	7 51	..	..	..	..	8 0	8 7
Petts Wood	7 29	..	..	..	..	7 45	7 50	..	..	7 54	..	..	..	..	8 3	8 10
Bickley	7 33	..	7 34	..	..	7 48	7 54	..	7 54	7 58	..	..	..	..	8 7	8 13
Bromley South D	7 36	..	7 37	..	..	7 51	7 56	..	7 57	8 1	..	..	..	8 8	8 10	8 16
Shortlands	7 38	..	7 40	..	..	7 54	7 59	..	8 0	8 3	..	..	..	8 10	8 13	8 19
Beckenham Junction	7 42	..	..	..	..	7 57	8 2	..	..	8 6	..	..	..	..	8 16	8 22
Kent House	7 44	..	..	..	..	7 59	8 4	..	..	8 8	..	..	..	..	8 18	8 24
Penge East C	7 46	..	..	..	..	8 1	8 6	..	..	8 10	..	..	..	..	8 20	8 26
Sydenham Hill	7 49	..	..	..	..	8 4	8 9	..	..	8 13	..	..	..	..	8 23	8 29
West Dulwich	7 51	..	..	..	..	8 6	8 11	..	..	8 15	..	..	..	..	8 25	8 31
Herne Hill	7 53	..	..	..	..	8 8	8 13	..	..	8 18	..	8 24	..	..	8 28	8 33
Ravensbourne	..	..	7 42	..	..	..	..	..	8 2	..	..	..	..	..	..	..
Beckenham Hill	..	..	7 44	..	..	..	..	..	8 4	..	..	..	..	..	..	..
Bellingham	..	..	7 46	..	..	..	..	..	8 6	..	..	..	..	..	..	..
Catford	..	..	7 48	..	..	..	..	..	8 8	..	..	..	..	..	..	..
Crofton Park	..	..	7 50	..	..	..	..	..	8 10	..	..	..	..	..	..	..
Crystal Palace B dep	..	..	..	7 46	..	..	..	..	..	..	8 6	..	..	..	..	..
Upper Sydenham	..	..	..	7 48	..	..	..	..	..	..	8 8	..	..	..	..	..
Lordship Lane A	..	..	..	7 50	..	..	..	..	..	..	8 10	..	..	..	..	..
Honor Oak	..	..	..	7 53	..	..	..	..	..	..	8 13	..	..	..	..	..
Nunhead	..	..	7 53	7 56	..	..	..	..	8 13	..	8 16	..	..	..	..	..
Peckham Rye	..	..	7 55	7 59	..	..	..	..	8 15	..	8 19	..	..	..	..	..
Denmark Hill	..	..	7 58	8 1	..	..	..	..	8 18	..	8 21	..	..	..	..	..
Loughborough Junction	7 56	..	..	..	..	..	8 16	..	..	..	..	8 27	..	..	..	..
Elephant and Castle	8 0	..	8 4	8 7	..	..	8 20	..	8 23	..	8 27	8 32	..	..	..	8 40
Blackfriars arr	8 4	..	8 7	8 10	..	..	8 23	..	8B26	..	8 30	8 35	..	..	..	8 43
Holborn Viaduct "	8 7	..	8 9	..	..	..	8 26	..	8 29	..	..	8 37	..	..	..	8 46
Brixton	..	..	..	..	..	8 11	..	..	..	8 20	..	..	..	..	8 30	..
Victoria arr	..	..	..	..	..	8 17	..	..	..	8 26	..	..	..	8 28	8 36	..

3 Third class only   B 1 min later on Sats.   c Change at Orpington   SX Saturdays excepted   For Other Notes, see page 157

GILLINGHAM (Kent), CHATHAM, GRAVESEND WEST STREET, MAIDSTONE EAST, SEVENOAKS, ORPINGTON, CRYSTAL PALACE (H.L.) and LONDON

Week Days—continued (a.m.)

Up	3	3			3	3	3	3		3	3		3	3	3	3		3	3		3		3		3		3			3	3	3
Gillingham (Kent) .. dep	..	..	..	..	..	..	..	..	..	..	..	7 43	..	..	..	..	..	..	..	..	..	8 15	..	..	..	..	..	..	8 43	..	..	..
Chatham	..	..	..	..	..	..	..	..	..	..	..	7 47	..	..	..	..	..	..	..	..	..	8 19	..	..	..	..	..	..	8 46	..	..	..
Rochester	..	..	..	..	..	..	..	..	..	..	..	7 50	..	..	..	..	..	..	..	..	..	8 22	..	..	..	..	..	..	8 49	..	..	..
Sole Street	..	..	..	..	..	..	..	..	..	..	..	8 1	..	..	..	..	..	..	..	..	..	8 33	..	..	..	..	..	8 49	..	..	..	..
Meopham ..... [Longfield	..	..	..	..	..	..	..	..	..	..	..	8 4	..	..	..	..	..	..	..	..	..	8 36	..	..	..	..	..	8 51	..	..	..	..
Fawkham, for Hartley &	..	..	..	..	..	..	..	..	..	..	..	8 9	..	..	..	..	..	..	..	..	..	8 40	..	..	..	..	..	8 56	..	..	..	..
Gravesend West St dp	..	..	7 50	..	..	..	..	..	..	..	..	..	..	..	..	..	..	..	..	..	..	..	..	..	..	..	..	..	..	..	..	..
Southfleet (Springh'd).	..	..	7 55	..	..	..	..	..	..	..	..	..	..	..	..	..	..	..	..	..	..	..	..	..	..	..	..	..	..	..	..	..
Longfield Halt G	..	..	7B59	..	..	..	..	..	..	..	..	..	..	..	..	..	..	..	..	..	..	..	..	..	..	..	..	..	..	..	..	..
Farningham Road F	..	..	8 5	..	..	..	..	..	..	..	..	8 13	..	..	..	..	..	..	..	..	..	8 45	..	..	..	..	..	9 0	..	..	..	..
Maidstone East .. dep.	..	..	..	7 40	..	..	..	..	..	..	..	..	..	..	..	..	7 54	..	..	..	..	..	..	..	..	8 20	..	..	..	..	..	..
Barming	..	..	..	..	..	..	..	..	..	..	..	..	..	..	..	..	7 59	..	..	..	..	..	..	..	..	8 25	..	..	..	..	..	..
East Malling Halt	..	..	..	..	..	..	..	..	..	..	..	..	..	..	..	..	8 2	..	..	..	..	..	..	..	..	8 28	..	..	..	..	..	..
Malling	..	..	..	..	..	..	..	..	..	..	..	..	..	..	..	..	8 5	..	..	..	..	..	..	..	..	8 31	..	..	..	..	..	..
Wrotham & Boro' Gr'n	..	..	..	..	..	..	..	..	..	..	..	..	..	..	..	..	8 14	..	..	..	..	..	..	..	..	8 40	..	..	..	..	..	..
Kemsing	..	..	..	..	..	..	..	..	..	..	..	..	..	..	..	..	8 18	..	..	..	..	..	..	..	..	8 44	..	..	..	..	..	..
Sevenoaks { Tub's H. dp	..	7 42	..	..	..	..	..	..	..	7c57	..	..	..	8 1	..	..	..	8c22	..	..	8 20	..	..	..	8c43	..	..	..	..	..	..	..
Sevenoaks { Bat & Ball..	..	7 45	..	..	..	..	..	..	..	..	..	..	..	8 4	..	..	..	..	..	..	8 25	..	..	..	..	..	..	..	..	..	..	..
Otford	..	7 48	..	8 2	..	..	..	..	..	..	..	..	..	8 7	..	..	8 24	..	..	..	8 29	..	..	..	..	8 50	..	..	..	..	..	..
Shoreham (Kent)	..	7 51	..	8 5	..	..	..	..	..	..	..	..	..	8 10	..	..	8 27	..	..	..	8 32	..	..	..	..	8 53	..	..	..	..	..	..
Eynsford	..	7 56	..	8 10	..	..	..	..	..	..	..	..	..	8 15	..	..	8 31	..	..	..	8 37	..	..	..	..	8 57	..	..	..	..	..	..
Lullingstone	..	..	..	..	..	..	..	..	..	..	..	..	..	..	..	..	..	..	..	..	..	..	..	..	..	..	..	..	..	..	..	..
Swanley 60	..	8 4	8 11	8 15	..	..	..	..	..	..	..	8 20	..	8 24	..	..	8 39	..	..	..	8 44	8 52	..	..	..	..	9 4	9 6	9 11	..	..	..
St. Mary Cray	..	8 10	..	8 20	..	..	..	..	..	..	..	..	..	8 30	..	..	8 44	..	..	..	8 50	..	..	..	..	..	9 9	..	..	..	..	..
Orpington .... dep	..	..	..	..	..	..	..	..	..	8 20	..	..	..	..	8 31	..	..	8 43	..	..	..	..	..	..	9 0	..	..	..	..	..	..	..
Petts Wood	..	..	..	..	..	..	..	..	..	8 23	..	..	SX	..	8 34	..	..	8 46	..	..	..	..	..	..	9 3	..	..	..	..	..	..	..
Bickley	..	8 14	..	..	..	..	..	8 23	..	8 26	..	..	8 33	8 34	8 38	..	..	8 49	8 53	..	8 54	..	..	..	9 8	..	9 14	..	..	..	..	..
Bromley South D	..	8 17	..	..	..	..	..	8 26	..	8 30	..	8 30	8 36	8 37	8 41	..	8 51	8 52	8 56	..	8 57	9 3	..	..	9 11	9 12	9 17	..	9 21	..	..	..
Shortlands	..	8 20	..	..	..	..	..	8 29	..	8 32	..	8 34	8 38	8 40	8 43	..	..	8 55	8 59	..	9 0	..	..	..	9 14	..	9 20	..	..	..	..	..
Beckenham Junction	..	..	..	..	..	..	..	8 32	..	8 36	..	..	8 41	..	8 46	..	..	8 58	9 2	..	..	..	..	..	9 17	..	..	..	..	..	..	..
Kent House	..	..	..	..	..	..	..	8 34	..	8 38	..	..	8 43	..	8 48	..	..	9 0	9 4	..	..	..	..	..	9 19	..	..	..	..	..	..	..
Penge East C	..	..	..	..	..	..	..	8 36	..	8 40	..	..	8 45	..	8 50	..	..	9 2	9 6	..	..	..	..	..	9 21	..	..	..	..	..	..	..
Sydenham Hill	..	..	..	..	..	..	..	8 39	..	8 43	..	..	8 48	..	8 53	..	..	9 5	..	..	..	..	..	..	9 24	..	..	..	..	..	..	..
West Dulwich	..	..	..	..	..	..	..	8 41	..	8 45	SX	..	8 50	..	8 55	..	..	9 7	9 10	..	..	..	..	..	9 26	..	..	..	..	SX	..	..
Herne Hill	..	..	..	8 38	8 39	8 43	..	8 45	..	8 48	8 48	..	8 53	..	8 58	..	..	9 9	9 13	..	..	..	..	..	9 28	..	..	..	..	9 40	..	9 41
Ravensbourne	..	8 22	..	..	..	..	..	..	..	..	..	..	..	8 42	..	..	..	..	..	..	9 2	..	..	..	..	..	9 22	..	..	..	..	..
Beckenham Hill	..	8 24	..	..	..	..	SX	..	..	..	..	..	..	8 44	..	..	..	..	..	..	9 4	..	..	..	..	..	9 24	..	..	..	..	..
Bellingham	..	8 26	..	..	..	..	8 32	..	..	..	..	..	..	8 46	..	..	..	..	..	..	9 6	..	..	..	..	..	9 26	..	..	..	..	..
Catford	..	8 28	..	..	..	..	8 34	..	..	..	..	..	..	8 48	..	..	..	..	..	..	9 8	..	..	..	..	..	9 28	..	..	..	..	..
Crofton Park	..	8 30	..	..	..	..	8 36	..	..	..	..	..	..	8 50	..	..	..	..	..	..	9 10	..	..	..	..	..	9 30	..	..	..	..	..
Crystal Palace B dep	8 20	..	..	..	..	..	..	..	..	..	..	..	..	..	..	8 46	..	..	..	..	..	..	9 6	..	..	..	..	..	..	..	9 26	..
Upper Sydenham	8 22	..	..	..	..	..	..	..	..	..	..	..	..	..	..	8 48	..	..	..	..	..	..	9 8	..	..	..	..	..	..	..	9 28	..
Lordship Lane A	8 24	..	..	..	..	..	..	..	..	..	..	..	..	..	..	8 50	..	..	..	..	..	..	9 10	..	..	..	..	..	..	..	9 30	..
Honor Oak	8 27	..	..	..	..	..	..	..	..	..	..	..	..	..	..	8 53	..	..	..	..	..	..	9 13	..	..	..	..	..	..	..	9 33	..
Nunhead	8 30	8 33	..	..	..	..	..	..	..	..	..	..	..	8 53	..	8 56	..	..	..	..	9 13	..	9 16	..	..	..	9 33	..	..	..	9 36	..
Peckham Rye	8 32	8 36	..	..	..	..	..	..	..	..	..	..	..	8 55	..	8 59	..	..	..	..	9 15	..	9 19	..	..	..	9 35	..	..	..	9 39	..
Denmark Hill	8 35	8 38	..	..	..	..	..	..	..	..	..	..	..	8 58	..	9 1	..	..	..	..	9 18	..	9 21	..	..	..	9 38	..	..	..	9 41	..
Loughborough Junc.	..	..	..	..	8 41	..	..	8SO48	..	..	8 51	..	8 55	..	9 0	..	..	..	9 15	..	..	..	..	..	9 33	..	..	..	..	..	..	9 43
Elephant and Castle..	8 41	8 44	..	..	8 46	8 49	..	8 53	..	..	8 56	..	9 0	9 4	9 5	9 7	..	..	9 20	..	9 24	..	9 27	..	9 37	..	9 43	..	..	..	9 47	9 48
Blackfriars ...... arr	8 44	8 47	..	..	8 49	8 52	8 52	8 56	..	..	8 59	8 54	9 3	9 7	9 8	9 10	..	..	9 23	..	9 27	9 25	9 30	..	9B40	9 33	9 46	..	..	..	9 50	9 51
Holborn Viaduct. "	..	8 49	..	..	..	8 54	..	8 59	..	..	9 2	8 56	9 6	..	9 11	..	..	..	9 25	..	..	9 27	..	..	9SX43	9 35	9 49	..	..	..	..	9 53
Brixton	..	..	..	..	..	..	..	..	..	8 51	..	..	..	..	..	..	..	9 11	..	..	..	..	..	..	9 30	..	..	..	..	9 42	..	..
Victoria .... arr	..	..	..	8 46	..	..	..	..	..	8 57	..	..	..	..	..	..	9 14	9 17	..	..	..	..	..	..	9 36	..	..	..	9 40	9 48	..	..

3 Third class only

B 1 min. later on Sats.

SX Saturdays excepted

C 1 min. *earlier* on Sats.

c Change at Orpington.

SO Saturdays only.

For Other Notes, see page 157

GILLINGHAM (Kent), CHATHAM, GRAVESEND WEST STREET, MAIDSTONE EAST, SEVENOAKS, ORPINGTON, CRYSTAL PALACE (H.L.) and LONDON

Up — Mondays to Fridays — a.m.

Up	3	3			3	3		3		3	3			3	3	3
Gillingham (Kent) ..... dep	..	..	..	..	..	..	..	..	..	..	..	9 25	..	..	..	..
Chatham	..	..	..	..	..	..	..	..	..	..	..	9 32	..	..	..	..
Rochester	..	..	..	..	..	..	..	..	..	..	..	9 35	..	..	..	..
Sole Street	..	..	..	..	..	..	..	..	..	..	..	..	..	..	..	..
Meopham .... [Longfield	..	..	..	..	..	..	..	..	..	..	..	..	..	..	..	..
Fawkham, for Hartley and	..	..	..	..	..	..	..	..	..	..	..	..	..	..	..	..
Gravesend West St. dep	..	..	..	..	..	..	..	..	..	..	..	..	..	..	..	..
Southfleet (Springhead)	..	..	..	..	..	..	..	..	..	..	..	..	..	..	..	..
Longfield Halt G	..	..	..	..	..	..	..	..	..	..	..	..	..	..	..	..
Farningham Road F	..	..	..	..	..	..	..	..	..	..	..	..	..	..	..	..
Maidstone East ..... dep	..	..	8 57	..	..	..	..	..	..	..	..	..	..	..	..	..
Barming	..	..	..	..	..	..	..	..	..	..	..	..	..	..	..	..
East Malling Halt	..	..	..	..	..	..	..	..	..	..	..	..	..	..	..	..
Malling	..	..	9 5	..	..	..	..	..	..	..	..	..	..	..	..	..
Wrotham and Boro' Green	..	..	9 14	..	..	..	..	..	..	..	..	..	..	..	..	..
Kemsing	..	..	9 18	..	..	..	..	..	..	..	..	..	..	..	..	..
Sevenoaks { Tub's H. ... dep	..	9 2	..	..	..	..	..	..	..	9 24	..	..	..	9c32	..	10 2
Sevenoaks { Bat & Ball	..	9 5	..	..	..	..	..	..	..	9 27	..	..	..	..	..	10 5
Otford	..	9 8	9 23	..	..	..	..	..	..	9 32	..	..	..	..	..	10 9
Shoreham (Kent)	..	9 11	..	..	..	..	..	..	..	9 35	..	..	..	..	..	1012
Eynsford	..	9 16	..	..	..	..	..	..	..	9 40	..	..	..	..	..	1017
Lullingstone	..	..	..	..	..	..	..	..	..	..	..	..	..	..	..	..
Swanley 60	..	9 24	..	..	..	..	..	..	..	9 45	..	..	..	..	..	1024
St. Mary Cray	..	9 30	..	..	..	..	..	..	..	9 50	..	..	..	..	..	1030
Orpington .... dep	9 16	..	..	..	9 43	..	..	..	..	..	..	..	..	1023	..	..
Petts Wood	9 19	..	..	..	9 46	..	..	..	..	..	..	..	..	1026	..	..
Bickley	9 27	9 34	..	..	9 49	..	..	..	..	9 54	..	..	..	1029	..	1034
Bromley South D	9 31	9 37	9 41	..	9 52	..	..	..	..	9 57	..	1013	..	1032	..	1037
Shortlands	9 34	9 40	..	..	9 55	..	..	..	..	10 0	..	..	..	1035	..	1040
Beckenham Junction	9 37	..	..	..	9 58	..	..	..	..	..	..	..	..	1038	..	..
Kent House	9 39	..	..	..	10 0	..	..	..	..	..	..	..	..	1040	..	..
Penge East C	9 41	..	..	..	10 2	..	..	..	..	..	..	..	..	1042	..	..
Sydenham Hill	9 44	..	..	..	10 5	..	..	..	..	..	..	..	..	1045	..	..
West Dulwich	9 46	..	..	..	10 7	..	..	..	..	..	..	..	..	1047	..	..
Herne Hill	9 48	..	9 52	9 55	10 9	..	..	1013	..	..	..	..	..	1049	..	..
Ravensbourne	..	9 42	..	..	..	..	..	..	..	10 2	..	..	..	..	..	1042
Beckenham Hill	..	9 44	..	..	..	..	..	..	..	10 4	..	..	..	..	..	1044
Bellingham	..	9 46	..	..	..	..	..	..	..	10 6	..	..	..	..	..	1046
Catford	..	9 48	..	..	..	..	..	..	..	10 8	..	..	..	..	..	1048
Crofton Park	..	9 50	..	..	..	..	..	..	..	1010	..	..	..	..	..	1050
Crystal Palace B ... dep	..	..	..	..	..	9 46	..	..	..	..	1016	..	..	..	1036	..
Upper Sydenham	..	..	..	..	..	9 48	..	..	..	..	1018	..	..	..	1038	..
Lordship Lane A	..	..	..	..	..	9 50	..	..	..	..	1020	..	..	..	1040	..
Honor Oak	..	..	..	..	..	9 53	..	..	..	..	1023	..	..	..	1043	..
Nunhead	..	9 53	..	..	..	9 56	..	..	..	1013	1027	..	..	..	1047	1053
Peckham Rye	..	9 55	..	..	..	9 59	..	..	..	1015	..	..	..	..	..	1055
Denmark Hill	..	9 58	..	..	..	10 1	..	..	..	1018	..	..	..	..	..	1058
Loughborough Junction	..	..	..	..	..	..	..	1015	..	..	..	..	..	..	..	..
Elephant and Castle	..	10 4	..	..	..	10 7	..	1020	..	1023	..	..	..	..	..	11 3
Blackfriars .... arr	..	10 7	10 0	..	..	1010	..	1023	..	1026	..	..	..	..	..	11 6
Holborn Viaduct .... "	..	10 9	10 2	..	..	..	..	1025	..	1029	..	..	..	..	..	11 9
Brixton	9 50	..	..	9 57	1011	..	..	..	..	..	..	..	..	1051	..	..
Victoria .... arr	9 56	..	..	10 3	1017	..	..	..	..	..	..	1036	..	1057	..	..

Up			3		3	3		3	3	3	3			3		3
Gillingham (Kent) ..... dep	..	9 54	..	..	..	..	1028	..	..	..	..	..	1054	..	..	..
Chatham	..	9 58	..	..	..	..	1035	..	..	..	..	..	1058	..	1118	..
Rochester	..	10 1	..	..	..	..	..	..	..	..	..	..	11 1	..	..	..
Sole Street	..	1012	..	..	..	..	..	..	..	..	..	..	1112	..	..	..
Meopham .... [Longfield	..	1015	..	..	..	..	..	..	..	..	..	..	1115	..	..	..
Fawkham, for Hartley and	..	1019	..	..	..	..	..	..	..	..	..	..	1119	..	..	..
Gravesend West St. dep	..	..	..	..	..	..	..	..	..	..	..	..	..	..	..	..
Southfleet (Springhead)	..	..	..	..	..	..	..	..	..	..	..	..	..	..	..	..
Longfield Halt G	..	..	..	..	..	..	..	..	..	..	..	..	..	..	..	..
Farningham Road F	..	1024	..	..	..	..	..	..	..	..	..	..	1124	..	..	..
Maidstone East ..... dep	9 49	..	..	..	..	..	..	..	..	..	..	1049	..	..	..	..
Barming	9 54	..	..	..	..	..	..	..	..	..	..	1054	..	..	..	..
East Malling Halt	9 57	..	..	..	..	..	..	..	..	..	..	1057	..	..	..	..
Malling	10 0	..	..	..	..	..	..	..	..	..	..	11 0	..	..	..	..
Wrotham and Boro' Green	10 9	..	..	..	..	..	..	..	..	..	..	11 9	..	..	..	..
Kemsing	1013	..	..	..	..	..	..	..	..	..	..	1113	..	..	..	..
Sevenoaks { Tub's H. ... dep	..	..	10c7	..	1024	..	..	10c34	..	11 2	..	..	..	11c4	..	11 24
Sevenoaks { Bat & Ball	..	..	..	..	1027	..	..	..	..	11 5	..	..	..	..	..	11 27
Otford	1019	..	..	..	1030	..	..	..	..	11 8	..	1119	..	..	..	11 30
Shoreham (Kent)	..	..	..	..	1033	..	..	..	..	1111	..	..	..	..	..	11 33
Eynsford	..	..	..	..	1038	..	..	..	..	1116	..	..	..	..	..	11 38
Lullingstone	..	..	..	..	..	..	..	..	..	..	..	..	..	..	..	..
Swanley 60	1028	1032	..	..	1044	..	..	..	..	1124	..	1128	1131	..	..	11§47
St. Mary Cray	..	..	..	..	1050	..	..	..	..	1130	..	..	..	..	..	11 53
Orpington .... dep	..	..	1043	..	..	..	..	11 23	..	..	..	..	..	1143	..	..
Petts Wood	..	..	1046	..	..	..	..	11 26	..	..	..	..	..	1146	..	..
Bickley	..	..	1049	..	1054	..	..	11 29	..	1134	..	..	..	1149	..	11 57
Bromley South D	..	1042	1052	..	1057	..	1115	11 32	..	1137	..	..	1143	1152	1156	12 0
Shortlands	..	..	1055	..	11 0	..	..	11 35	..	1140	..	..	..	1155	..	12 3
Beckenham Junction	..	..	1058	..	..	..	..	11 38	..	..	..	..	..	1158	..	..
Kent House	..	..	11 0	..	..	..	..	11 40	..	..	..	..	..	12 0	..	..
Penge East C	..	..	11 2	..	..	..	..	11 42	..	..	..	..	..	12 2	..	..
Sydenham Hill	..	..	11 5	..	..	..	..	11 45	..	..	..	..	..	12 5	..	..
West Dulwich	..	..	11 7	..	..	..	..	11 47	..	..	..	..	..	12 7	..	..
Herne Hill	..	..	11 9	..	..	1129	..	11 49	..	..	p.m. 12 2	..	..	12 9	..	..
Ravensbourne	..	..	..	..	11 2	..	..	..	..	1142	..	..	..	..	..	12 5
Beckenham Hill	..	..	..	..	11 4	..	..	..	..	1144	..	..	..	..	..	12 7
Bellingham	..	..	..	..	11 6	..	..	..	..	1146	..	..	..	..	..	12 9
Catford	..	..	..	..	11 8	..	..	..	..	1148	..	..	..	..	..	12 11
Crofton Park	..	..	..	..	1110	..	..	..	..	1150	..	..	..	..	..	12 13
Crystal Palace B ... dep	..	..	..	..	..	..	..	..	1136	..	..	..	..	..	..	..
Upper Sydenham	..	..	..	..	..	..	..	..	1138	..	..	..	..	..	..	..
Lordship Lane A	..	..	..	..	..	..	..	..	1140	..	..	..	..	..	..	..
Honor Oak	..	..	..	..	..	..	..	..	1143	..	..	..	..	..	..	..
Nunhead	..	..	..	..	1113	..	..	..	1147	1153	..	..	..	..	..	12 16
Peckham Rye	..	..	..	..	1115	..	..	..	..	1155	..	..	..	..	..	12 18
Denmark Hill	..	..	..	..	1118	..	..	..	..	1158	..	..	..	..	..	12 21
Loughborough Junction	..	..	..	..	..	1131	..	..	..	..	12 5	..	..	..	..	..
Elephant and Castle	..	..	..	..	1123	1136	..	..	..	12 3	1210	..	..	..	..	12 26
Blackfriars .... arr	..	..	..	..	1126	1139	..	..	..	12 6	1213	..	..	..	..	12 29
Holborn Viaduct .... "	..	..	..	..	1129	1141	..	..	..	12 9	1215	..	..	..	..	12 32
Brixton	..	..	1111	..	..	..	..	11 51	..	..	..	..	..	1211	..	..
Victoria .... arr	..	1059	1117	..	..	..	1136	11 57	..	..	..	..	1159	1217	1220	..

3 Third class only. c Change at Orpington. § Arr. 4 mins. *earlier*

For Other Notes, see page 157.
For Saturday Trains, see pages 151a to 153a; for SUNDAY TRAINS, see pages 154 to 157

GILLINGHAM (Kent), CHATHAM, GRAVESEND WEST STREET, MAIDSTONE EAST, SEVENOAKS, ORPINGTON, CRYSTAL PALACE (H.L.) and LONDON

p.m. — Mondays to Fridays—continued — p.m.

Up	3	3	3	3		a.m	3	3	3	3	3		3				3		3	3	3	3	3	3			3	3	3	3	3	
Gillingham (Kent) .. dep						1154									1254	1 1										1 54						245
Chatham						1158									1258	1 8										1 58						252
Rochester						12 1									1 1	1 13										2 1						
SoleStreet						1212									1 12											2 12						
Meopham .....[Longfield						1215									1 15											2 15						
Fawkham, for Hartley &						1219									1 19											2 19						
Gravesend West St dp																																
Southfleet (Springh'd).																																
Longfield Halt G																																
Farningham Road F					a.m	1224									1 24											2 24						
Maidstone East .. dep					1149									1249											1 49							
Barming					1154									1254											1 54							
East Malling Halt					1157									1257											1 57							
Malling					12 0									1 0											2 0							
Wrotham & Boro' Gr'n					12 9									1 9											2 9							
Kemsing					1213									1 13											2 13							
Sevenoaks Tub's H. dp		12c4		12 2					1224		12c34		1 2						1c 4	1 24		2c 4		2 2				2 24	2c34			
Sevenoaks Bat & Ball				12 5					1227				1 5							1 27				2 5				2 27				
Otford				12 8	1219				1230				1 8	1 19						1 30				2 8	2 19			2 30				
Shoreham (Kent)				1211					1233				1 11							1 33				2 11				2 33				
Eynsford				1216					1238				1 16							1 38				2 16				2 38				
Lullingstone																																
Swanley 60				1224	1228	1232			1244				1 24	1 28	1 31					1 44				2 24	2 28	2 31		2 44				
St. Mary Cray				1230					1250				1 30							1 50				2 30	Stop			2 50				
Orpington .. dep		1223						12 43			1 23								1 43			2 23					2 43		2 58	3 5	3 13	
Petts Wood		1226						12 46			1 26								1 46			2 26					2 46		3 1	3 8	3 16	
Bickley		1229		1234				12 49	1254		1 29		1 34						1 49	1 54		2 29		2 34			2 49	2 54	3 4	3 11	3 20	
Bromley South D		1232		1237		1242		12 52	1257		1 32		1 37		1 42	1 50			1 52	1 57		2 32		2 37		2 42	2 52	2 57	3 7	3 14	3 23	328
Shortlands		1235		1240				12 55	1 0		1 35		1 40						1 55	2 0		2 35		2 40			2 55	3 0	3 10	3 17	3 25	
Beckenham Junction		1238						12 58			1 38								1 58			2 38					2 58		3 13	3 20		
Kent House		1240						1 0			1 40								2 0			2 40					3 0		3 15	3 22		
Penge East C		1242						1 2			1 42								2 2			2 42			p.m		3 2		3 17	3 24		
Sydenham Hill		1245						1 5			1 45								2 5			2 45			3		3 5		3 20	3 27		
West Dulwich		1247						1 7			1 47								2 7			2 47					3 7		3 22	3 29		
Herne Hill	1228	1249					1 2	1 9		1 28	1 49				1 53		2 3		2 9		2 28	2 49			3 2		3 9		3 24	3 31		
Ravensbourne				1242					1 2				1 42							2 2				2 42				3 2			3 27	
Beckenham Hill				1244					1 4				1 44							2 4				2 44				3 4			3 29	
Bellingham				1246					1 6				1 46							2 6				2 46				3 6			3 31	
Catford				1248					1 8				1 48							2 8				2 48				3 8			3 33	
Crofton Park				1250					1 10				1 50							2 10				2 50				3 10			3 35	
Crystal Palace B dep			1236									1 36											2 36									
Upper Sydenham			1238									1 38											2 38									
Lordship Lane A			1240									1 40											2 40									
Honor Oak			1243									1 43											2 43									
Nunhead			1247	1253					1 13			1 47	1 53							2 13			2 47	2 53				3 13			3 39	
Peckham Rye				1255					1 15				1 55							2 15				2 55				3 15			3 42	
Denmark Hill				1258					1 18				1 58							2 18				2 58				3 18			3 45	
Loughborough Junc.	1230						1 5			1 30							2 6				2 30				3 5				3 31	3 34		
Elephant and Castle	1235			1 3			1 10		1 23	1 35			2 3				2 10			2 23	2 35			3 3	3 10			3 23	3 35	3 39	3 51	
Blackfriars .. arr	1238			1 6			1 13		1 26	1 38			2 6				2 13			2 26	2 38			3 6	3 13			3 26	3 38	3 42	3 54	
Holborn Viaduct "	1240			1 9			1 15		1 29	1 40			2 9				2 16			2 29	2 40			3 9	3 15			3 29	3 41	3 45	3 56	
Brixton		1251						1 11			1 51								2 11			2 51					3 11		3 26			
Victoria .. arr		1257				1259		1 17			1 57				2 0	2 10			2 17			2 57				2 59	3 17		3 32			348

3 Third class only

c Change at Orpington.

For Other Notes, see page 157

For Saturday Trains, see pages 151a to 153a; for SUNDAY TRAINS, see pages 154 to 157

GILLINGHAM (Kent), CHATHAM, GRAVESEND WEST STREET, MAIDSTONE EAST, SEVENOAKS, ORPINGTON, CRYSTAL PALACE, (H.L) and LONDON

Mondays to Fridays—continued (p.m)

Up	3	3	3			3	3	3	3	3	3		3	3	3	3		3	3	3	3		3	3			3	3	3	3	3	3	3
Gillingham (Kent) .. dep	..	..	..	..	2 54	..	..	..	..	..	..	..	..	..	..	..	..	..	..	..	..	..	..	..	..	3 54	..	..	..	..	..	..	..
Chatham	..	..	..	..	2 58	..	..	..	..	..	..	..	..	..	..	..	..	..	..	..	..	..	..	..	..	3 58	..	..	..	..	..	..	..
Rochester	..	..	..	..	3 1	..	..	..	..	..	..	..	..	..	..	..	..	..	..	..	..	..	..	..	..	4 1	..	..	..	..	..	..	..
Sole Street	..	..	..	..	3 12	..	..	..	..	..	..	..	..	..	..	..	..	..	..	..	..	..	..	..	..	4 12	..	..	..	..	..	..	..
Meopham .....[Longfield	..	..	..	..	3 15	..	..	..	..	..	..	..	..	..	..	..	..	..	..	..	..	..	..	..	..	4 15	..	..	..	..	..	..	..
Fawkham for Hartley &	..	..	..	..	3 19	..	..	..	..	..	..	..	..	..	..	..	..	..	..	..	..	..	..	..	..	4 19	..	..	..	..	..	..	..
Gravesend West St dp	..	..	..	..	..	..	..	..	..	..	..	..	..	..	..	..	..	..	..	..	..	..	..	..	..	..	..	..	..	..	..	..	..
Southfleet (Springh'd)	..	..	..	..	..	..	..	..	..	..	..	..	..	..	..	..	..	..	..	..	..	..	..	..	..	..	..	..	..	..	..	..	..
Longfield Halt G	..	..	..	..	..	..	..	..	..	..	..	..	..	..	..	..	..	..	..	..	..	..	..	..	..	..	..	..	..	..	..	..	..
Farningham Road F	..	..	..	..	3 24	..	..	..	..	..	..	..	..	..	..	..	..	..	..	..	..	..	..	..	..	4 24	..	..	..	..	..	..	..
Maidstone East .. dep	..	..	..	2 49	..	..	..	..	..	..	..	..	..	..	..	..	..	..	..	..	..	..	..	..	3 49	..	..	..	..	..	..	..	..
Barming	..	..	..	2 54	..	..	..	..	..	..	..	..	..	..	..	..	..	..	..	..	..	..	..	..	3 54	..	..	..	..	..	..	..	..
East Malling Halt	..	..	..	2 57	..	..	..	..	..	..	..	..	..	..	..	..	..	..	..	..	..	..	..	..	3 57	..	..	..	..	..	..	..	..
Malling	..	..	..	3 0	..	..	..	..	..	..	..	..	..	..	..	..	..	..	..	..	..	..	..	..	4 0	..	..	..	..	..	..	..	..
Wrotham & Boro' Gr'n	..	..	..	3 9	..	..	..	..	..	..	..	..	..	..	..	..	..	..	..	..	..	..	..	..	4 9	..	..	..	..	..	..	..	..
Kemsing	..	..	..	3 13	..	..	..	..	..	..	..	..	..	..	..	..	..	..	..	..	..	..	..	..	4 13	..	..	..	..	..	..	..	..
Sevenoaks { Tub's H. dp	..	..	3 2	..	..	..	..	3c0	..	3 24	..	..	..	3c32	..	3 41	..	..	..	..	..	..	4c 3	4 1	..	..	..	..	..	..	4 21	..	4c38
Sevenoaks { Bat & Ball	..	..	3 5	..	..	..	..	..	..	3 27	..	..	..	..	..	3 44	..	..	..	..	..	..	..	4 4	..	..	..	..	..	..	4 24	..	..
Otford	..	..	3 8	3 19	..	..	..	..	..	3 30	..	..	..	..	..	3 47	..	..	..	..	..	..	..	4 7	4 19	..	..	..	..	..	4 27	..	..
Shoreham (Kent)	..	..	3 11	..	..	..	..	..	..	3 33	..	..	..	..	..	3 50	..	..	..	..	..	..	..	4 10	..	..	..	..	..	..	4 30	..	..
Eynsford	..	..	3 16	..	..	..	..	..	..	3 38	..	..	..	..	..	3 55	..	..	..	..	..	..	..	4 15	..	..	..	..	..	..	4 35	..	..
Lullingstone	..	..	..	..	..	..	..	..	..	..	..	..	..	..	..	..	..	..	..	..	..	..	..	..	..	..	..	..	..	..	..	..	..
Swanley 63	..	..	3 24	3 28	3 31	..	..	..	..	3 44	..	..	..	..	..	4 4	..	..	..	..	..	..	..	4 24	4 28	4 31	..	..	..	..	4 44	..	..
St. Mary Cray	..	..	3 30	..	..	..	..	..	..	3 50	..	..	..	..	..	4 10	..	..	..	..	..	..	..	4 30	..	..	..	..	..	..	4 50	..	..
Orpington .... dep	3 18	..	..	..	..	..	..	3 43	..	..	..	..	..	4 0	..	..	..	..	..	4 15	..	..	4 23	..	..	..	..	..	4 40	..	..	..	5 0
Petts Wood	3 21	..	..	..	..	..	..	3 46	..	..	..	..	..	4 3	..	..	..	..	..	4 18	..	..	4 26	..	..	..	..	..	4 43	..	..	..	5 3
Bickley	3 29	..	3 34	..	..	..	..	3 49	3 51	3 54	..	..	..	4 6	4 5	4 14	..	..	..	4 22	..	..	4 29	4 34	..	..	..	..	4 46	..	4 54	..	5 6
Bromley South D	3 32	..	3 37	..	3 42	..	..	3 52	3 54	3 57	..	..	..	4 9	4 8	4 17	..	..	..	4 25	..	..	4 32	4 37	..	4 42	..	..	4 49	..	4 57	..	5 9
Shortlands	3 35	..	3 40	..	..	..	..	3 55	..	4 0	..	..	..	4 12	4 11	4 20	..	..	..	4 28	..	..	4 35	4 40	..	..	..	..	4 52	..	5 0	..	5 12
Beckenham Junction	3 38	..	..	..	..	..	..	3 58	..	..	..	..	..	4 15	..	..	..	..	..	4 31	..	..	4 38	..	..	..	..	..	4 56	..	..	..	5 15
Kent House	3 40	..	..	..	..	..	..	4 0	..	..	..	..	..	4 17	..	..	..	..	..	4 33	..	..	4 40	..	..	..	..	..	4 58	..	..	..	5 17
Penge East C	3 42	..	..	..	..	..	..	4 2	..	..	..	..	..	4 19	..	..	..	..	..	4 35	..	..	4 42	..	..	..	..	..	5 0	..	..	..	5 19
Sydenham Hill	3 45	..	..	..	..	..	..	4 5	..	..	..	..	..	4 22	..	..	..	..	..	4 38	..	..	4 45	..	..	..	..	..	5 3	..	..	..	5 22
West Dulwich	3 47	..	..	..	..	..	..	4 7	..	..	..	..	..	4 25	..	..	..	..	..	4 41	..	..	4 47	..	..	..	..	..	5 5	..	..	..	5 24
Herne Hill	3 49	..	..	..	..	..	4 2	4 9	..	..	..	..	4 23	4 27	..	..	..	4 42	..	4 44	..	..	4 49	..	..	..	..	..	5 7	..	..	5 19	5 27
Ravensbourne	..	..	3 42	..	..	..	..	..	..	4 2	..	..	..	..	4 13	4 22	..	..	..	..	..	..	..	4 42	..	..	..	..	..	..	5 2	..	..
Beckenham Hill	..	..	3 44	..	..	..	..	..	..	4 4	..	..	..	..	4 15	4 24	..	..	..	..	..	..	..	4 44	..	..	..	..	..	..	5 4	..	..
Bellingham	..	..	3 46	..	..	..	..	..	4 0	4 6	..	..	..	..	4 17	4 26	..	..	..	..	..	..	..	4 46	..	..	..	..	..	..	5 6	..	..
Catford	..	..	3 48	..	..	..	..	..	4 2	4 8	..	..	..	..	4 19	4 28	..	..	..	..	..	..	..	4 48	..	..	..	..	..	..	5 8	—	..
Crofton Park	..	..	3 50	..	..	..	..	..	..	4 10	..	..	..	..	4 21	4 30	..	..	..	..	..	..	..	4 50	..	..	..	..	..	..	5 10	..	..
Crystal Palace B dep	..	3 36	..	..	..	3 46	..	..	..	..	4 6	..	..	..	..	..	..	..	4 26	..	4 36	..	..	..	..	..	4 46	..	..	..	..	..	..
Upper Sydenham	..	3 38	..	..	..	3 48	..	..	..	..	4 8	..	..	..	..	..	..	..	4 28	..	..	..	..	..	..	..	4 48	..	..	..	..	..	..
Lordship Lane A	..	3 40	..	..	..	3 50	..	..	..	..	4 10	..	..	..	..	..	..	..	4 30	..	..	..	..	..	..	..	4 50	..	..	..	..	..	..
Honor Oak	..	3 43	..	..	..	3 53	..	..	..	..	4 13	..	..	..	..	..	..	..	4 33	..	..	..	..	..	..	..	4 53	..	..	..	..	..	..
Nunhead	..	3 47	3 53	..	..	3 56	..	..	4 6	4 13	4 16	..	..	..	4 24	4 33	..	..	4 36	..	4 44	..	..	4 53	..	..	4 56	..	..	..	5 13	..	..
Peckham Rye	..	..	3 55	..	..	3 59	..	..	4 9	4 15	4 19	..	..	..	4 26	4 35	..	..	4 39	..	4 46	..	..	4 55	..	..	4 59	..	..	..	5 15	..	..
Denmark Hill	..	..	3 58	..	..	4 1	..	..	4 12	4 18	4 21	..	..	..	4 29	4 38	..	..	4 41	..	4 49	..	..	4 58	..	..	5 1	..	..	..	5 18	..	..
Loughborough Junc.	..	..	..	..	..	..	4 5	..	..	..	..	..	4 26	..	..	..	..	..	..	4 47	..	..	4 55	..	..	..	..	5 7	..	5 17	..	5 21	..
Elephant and Castle	..	..	4 4	..	..	4 7	4 9	..	4 18	4 23	4 27	..	4 32	..	4 35	4 43	..	4 47	4 47	4 51	4 54	..	5 0	5 3	..	..	5 7	5 12	..	5 21	5 24	5 26	..
Blackfriars ...... arr	..	..	4 7	..	..	4 10	4 13	..	4 21	4 26	4 31	..	4 35	..	4 39	4 46	..	4 50	4 50	4 54	4 57	..	5 3	5 6	..	..	5 10	5 16	..	5 24	5 27	5 30	..
Holborn Viaduct. "	..	..	4 9	..	..	..	4 16	..	4 23	4 29	4 34	..	4 37	..	4 42	4 49	..	4 53	..	4 57	4 59	..	5 6	5 9	..	..	..	5 19	..	5 27	5 29	5 33	..
Brixton	3 51	..	..	..	..	..	..	4 11	..	..	..	..	..	4 29	..	..	..	..	..	..	..	..	4 51	..	..	..	..	..	5 9	..	..	..	5 29
Victoria .... arr	3 57	..	..	..	3 59	..	..	4 17	..	..	..	..	..	4 35	..	..	..	..	..	..	..	..	4 57	..	..	4 59	..	..	5 15	..	..	..	5 35

3 Third class only

c Change at Orpington

For Other Notes, see page 157

For Saturday Trains, see pages 151a to 153a; for SUNDAY TRAINS, see pages 154 to 157

GILLINGHAM (Kent), CHATHAM, GRAVESEND WEST STREET, MAIDSTONE EAST, SEVENOAKS, ORPINGTON, CRYSTAL PALACE (H.L.) and LONDON

Mondays to Fridays—continued (p.m.)

Up	3	3	3	..	3	3	3	3	..	3	..	3	3	3	..		..	3		3	3	3	..	3	..	3	3	..	3	3	..	3	3
Gillingham (Kent) .. dep	..	..	..	..	..	..	..	..	..	..	..	..	..	..	..	4 54	..	..	4 58	..	..	..	..	..	..	..	..	..	..	..	..	..	..
Chatham	..	..	..	..	..	..	..	..	..	..	..	..	..	..	..	4 58	..	..	5 7	..	..	..	..	..	..	..	..	..	..	..	..	..	..
Rochester	..	..	..	..	..	..	..	..	..	..	..	..	..	..	..	5 1	..	..	..	..	..	..	..	..	..	..	..	..	..	..	..	..	..
Sole Street	..	..	..	..	..	..	..	..	..	..	..	..	..	..	..	5 12	..	..	..	..	..	..	..	..	..	..	..	..	..	..	..	..	..
Meopham ..... [Longfield	..	..	..	..	..	..	..	..	..	..	..	..	..	..	..	5 15	..	..	..	..	..	..	..	..	..	..	..	..	..	..	..	..	..
Fawkham, for Hartley &	..	..	..	..	..	..	..	..	..	..	..	..	..	..	..	5 19	..	..	..	..	..	..	..	..	..	..	..	..	..	..	..	..	..
Gravesend West St dp	..	..	..	..	..	..	..	..	4 50	..	..	..	..	..	..	..	..	..	..	..	..	..	..	..	..	..	..	..	..	..	..	..	..
Southfleet (Springh'd).	..	..	..	..	..	..	..	..	4 55	..	..	..	..	..	..	..	..	..	..	..	..	..	..	..	..	..	..	..	..	..	..	..	..
Longfield Halt **G**	..	..	..	..	..	..	..	..	4 59	..	..	..	..	..	..	..	..	..	..	..	..	..	..	..	..	..	..	..	..	..	..	..	..
Farningham Road **F**	..	..	..	..	..	..	..	..	5 5	..	..	..	..	..	..	5 24	..	..	..	..	..	..	..	..	..	..	..	..	..	..	..	..	..
Maidstone East .. dep	..	..	..	..	..	..	..	..	..	..	..	..	..	..	4 49	..	..	..	..	..	..	..	..	..	5 17	..	..	..	..	..	..	..	..
Barming	..	..	..	..	..	..	..	..	..	..	..	..	..	..	4 54	..	..	..	..	..	..	..	..	..	5 22	..	..	..	..	..	..	..	..
East Malling Halt	..	..	..	..	..	..	..	..	..	..	..	..	..	..	4 57	..	..	..	..	..	..	..	..	..	5 25	..	..	..	..	..	..	..	..
Malling	..	..	..	..	..	..	..	..	..	..	..	..	..	..	5 0	..	..	..	..	..	..	..	..	..	5 28	..	..	..	..	..	..	..	..
Wrotham & Boro' Gr'n	..	..	..	..	..	..	..	..	..	..	..	..	..	..	5 9	..	..	..	..	..	..	..	..	..	5 37	..	..	..	..	..	..	..	..
Kemsing	..	..	..	..	..	..	..	..	..	..	..	..	..	..	5 13	..	..	..	..	..	..	..	..	..	5 41	..	..	..	..	..	..	..	..
Sevenoaks Tub's H. dp	..	..	4 41	..	..	..	..	..	..	..	..	..	..	5 1	..	..	..	..	..	..	5c12	5 21	..	..	..	..	5c33	..	..	5 44	..	..	5c51
Sevenoaks Bat & Ball	..	..	4 44	..	..	..	..	..	..	..	..	..	..	5 4	..	..	..	..	..	..	..	5 24	..	..	..	..	..	..	..	5 47	..	..	..
Otford	..	..	4 47	..	..	..	..	..	..	..	..	..	..	5 7	5 19	..	..	..	..	..	..	5 27	..	..	5 47	..	..	..	..	5 51	..	..	..
Shoreham (Kent)	..	..	4 50	..	..	..	..	..	..	..	..	..	..	5 10	..	..	..	..	..	..	..	5 30	..	..	..	..	..	..	..	5 54	..	..	..
Eynsford	..	..	4 55	..	..	..	..	..	..	..	..	..	..	5 15	..	..	..	..	..	..	..	5 35	..	..	..	..	..	..	..	5 58	..	..	..
Lullingstone	..	..	..	..	..	..	..	..	..	..	..	..	..	..	..	..	..	..	..	..	..	..	..	..	..	..	..	..	..	..	..	..	..
Swanley 6J	..	..	5 4	..	..	..	..	..	..	..	..	..	..	5 24	5 28	5 31	..	..	..	..	..	5 44	..	..	5 57	..	..	..	..	6 5	..	..	..
St. Mary Cray	..	..	5 10	..	..	..	..	..	..	..	..	..	..	5 30	..	..	..	..	..	..	..	5 50	..	..	..	..	..	..	..	6 10	..	..	..
Orpington .. dep	5 4	..	..	..	..	..	5 15	..	..	..	..	..	..	..	..	..	..	..	..	..	5 45	..	..	..	..	..	6 2	..	..	..	..	..	6 21
Petts Wood	5 7	..	..	..	..	..	5 18	..	..	..	..	..	..	..	..	..	..	..	..	..	5 48	..	..	..	..	..	6 5	..	..	..	..	..	6 24
Bickley	5 10	..	5 14	..	..	..	5 21	5 22	..	5 31	..	..	5 36	5 34	..	..	..	..	..	5 49	5 53	5 54	..	..	..	6 2	6 8	..	6 12	6 14	..	..	6 30
Bromley South D	5 13	..	5 17	..	..	..	5 24	5 25	..	5 34	..	..	5 39	5 37	5 40	5 43	..	..	5 49	5 52	5 57	5 57	..	..	6 7	6 5	6 11	..	6 15	6 17	..	..	6 34
Shortlands	..	..	5 20	..	..	..	5 27	5 28	..	..	..	..	..	5 40	..	..	..	..	..	5 54	5 59	6 0	..	..	..	6 8	6 14	..	6 17	6 20	..	..	6 37
Beckenham Junction	..	..	..	..	..	..	5 30	..	..	..	..	..	5 43	..	..	..	..	..	..	5 57	6 3	..	..	..	..	..	6 17	..	..	..	..	..	6 40
Kent House	..	..	..	..	..	..	5 32	..	..	..	..	..	..	..	..	..	..	..	..	5 59	..	..	..	..	..	..	6 19	..	..	..	..	..	6 42
Penge East **C**	..	..	..	..	..	..	5 34	..	..	..	..	..	..	..	..	..	..	..	..	6 1	6 7	..	..	..	..	..	6 21	..	..	..	..	..	6 44
Sydenham Hill	..	..	..	..	..	..	5 37	..	..	..	..	..	..	..	..	..	..	..	..	6 4	..	..	..	..	..	..	6 24	..	..	..	..	..	6 47
West Dulwich	..	..	..	..	..	..	5 39	..	..	..	..	..	..	..	..	..	..	..	..	6 6	6 11	..	..	..	..	..	6 26	..	..	..	..	..	6 49
Herne Hill	..	..	..	..	5 41	..	5 42	..	..	..	..	..	5 50	..	..	..	..	..	..	6 9	6 14	..	..	..	..	..	6 29	..	..	..	..	6 42	6 51
Ravensbourne	..	..	5 22	..	..	..	..	5 30	..	..	..	..	..	5 42	..	..	..	..	..	..	..	6 2	..	..	..	..	..	..	..	6 22	..	..	..
Beckenham Hill	..	..	5 24	..	..	..	..	5 32	..	..	..	..	..	5 44	..	..	..	..	..	..	..	6 4	..	..	..	..	..	..	..	6 24	..	..	..
Bellingham	..	..	5 26	..	..	..	..	5 34	..	..	..	..	..	5 46	..	..	..	..	..	..	..	6 6	..	..	..	6 14	..	..	6 22	6 26	..	..	..
Catford	..	..	5 28	..	..	..	..	5 36	..	..	..	..	..	5 48	..	..	..	..	..	..	..	6 8	..	..	..	6 16	..	..	6 24	6 28	..	..	..
Crofton Park	..	..	5 30	..	..	..	..	5 38	..	..	..	..	..	5 50	..	..	..	..	..	..	..	6 10	..	..	..	..	..	..	..	6 30	..	..	..
Crystal Palace B dep	..	5 16	..	..	..	..	..	..	..	..	..	5 36	..	..	..	..	..	5 46	..	..	..	..	..	6 6	..	..	..	..	..	..	..	..	..
Upper Sydenham	..	5 18	..	..	..	..	..	..	..	..	..	5 38	..	..	..	..	..	5 48	..	..	..	..	..	6 8	..	..	..	..	..	..	..	..	..
Lordship Lane **A**	..	5 20	..	..	..	..	..	..	..	..	..	5 40	..	..	..	..	..	5 50	..	..	..	..	..	6 10	..	..	..	..	..	..	..	..	..
Honor Oak	..	5 23	..	..	..	..	..	..	..	..	..	5 43	..	..	..	..	..	5 53	..	..	..	..	..	6 13	..	..	..	..	..	..	..	..	..
Nunhead	5 23	5 26	5 33	..	..	..	..	5 41	..	..	..	5 47	..	5 53	..	..	..	5 56	..	..	..	6 13	..	6 16	..	6 20	..	..	6 28	6 33	..	..	..
Peckham Rye	5 26	5 29	5 35	..	..	..	..	5 43	..	5 47	..	5 50	..	5 55	..	..	..	5 59	..	..	..	6 15	..	6 19	..	6 22	..	..	6 30	6 35	..	..	..
Denmark Hill	5 28	5 31	5 38	..	..	..	..	..	..	..	..	5 52	..	5 58	..	..	..	6 1	..	..	..	6 18	..	6 21	..	6 25	..	..	6 33	6 38	..	..	..
Loughborough Junc.	..	..	..	..	5 43	5 49	..	..	..	..	..	..	5 54	..	..	..	..	..	..	..	6 16	..	..	..	..	..	..	..	..	..	..	6 44	..
Elephant and Castle	5 34	5 37	5 43	..	5 47	5 53	..	5 50	..	5 56	..	..	6 0	6 4	..	..	..	6 7	..	..	6 21	6 24	..	6 27	..	..	..	..	6 39	6 43	..	6 48	..
Blackfriars .. arr	5 38	5 40	5 46	..	5 50	5 57	..	5 53	..	6 0	..	6 0	6 3	6 7	..	..	..	6 10	..	..	6 24	6 27	..	6 30	..	6 33	..	..	6 42	6 47	..	6 51	..
Holborn Viaduct. "	5 41	..	5 49	..	5 53	5 59	..	5 56	..	6 3	..	..	6 6	6 9	..	..	..	..	..	..	6 26	6 30	..	..	..	6 35	..	..	6 45	6 49	..	6 54	..
Brixton	..	..	..	..	..	..	5 44	..	..	..	..	..	..	..	..	..	..	..	..	6 11	..	..	..	..	..	..	6 31	..	..	..	..	..	6 53
Victoria .. arr	..	..	..	..	..	..	5 50	..	..	..	..	..	..	..	5 59	6 3	..	..	6 13	6 17	..	..	..	..	6 24	..	6 37	..	..	..	..	..	6 59

3 Third class only.

c Change at Orpington.

For Other Notes, see page 157

For Saturday Trains, see pages 151a to 153a; for SUNDAY TRAINS, see pages 154 to 157.

GILLINGHAM (Kent), CHATHAM, GRAVESEND WEST STREET, MAIDSTONE EAST, SEVENOAKS, ORPINGTON, CRYSTAL PALACE (H.L.), and LONDON

Up — p.m. — Mondays to Fridays—*continued* — p.m.

Up	3			3	3	3	3	3		3	3	3		3		3			3		3	3	3		3	3	3	3	3			3
Gillingham (Kent).. dep	..	..	5 54	..	..	..	..	..	..	..	..	..	..	..	..	..	..	6 54	..	7 1	..	..	..	..	..	..	..	..	..	..	7 54	..
Chatham	..	..	5 58	..	..	..	..	..	6 18	..	..	..	..	..	..	..	..	6 58	..	7 7	..	..	..	..	..	..	..	..	..	..	7 58	..
Rochester	..	..	6 1	..	..	..	..	..	..	..	..	..	..	..	..	..	..	7 1	..	..	..	..	..	..	..	..	..	..	..	..	8 1	..
Sole Street	..	..	6 12	..	..	..	..	..	..	..	..	..	..	..	..	..	..	7 12	..	..	..	..	..	..	..	..	..	..	..	..	8 12	..
Meopham .....[Longfield	..	..	6 15	..	..	..	..	..	..	..	..	..	..	..	..	..	..	7 15	..	..	..	..	..	..	..	..	..	..	..	..	8 15	..
Fawkham for Hartley &	..	..	6 19	..	..	..	..	..	..	..	..	..	..	..	..	..	..	7 18	..	..	..	..	..	..	..	..	..	..	..	..	8 19	..
Gravesend West St dp	..	..	..	..	..	..	..	..	..	..	..	..	..	..	6 42	..	..	..	..	..	..	..	..	7 55	..	..	..	..	..	..	..	..
Southfleet (Springh'd).	..	..	..	..	..	..	..	..	..	..	..	..	..	..	6 47	..	..	..	..	..	..	..	..	8 0	..	..	..	..	..	..	..	..
Longfield Halt **G**	..	..	..	..	..	..	..	..	..	..	..	..	..	..	6 51	..	..	..	..	..	..	..	..	8 5	..	..	..	..	..	..	..	..
Farningham Road **F**	..	..	6 24	..	..	..	..	..	..	..	..	..	..	..	6 58	..	..	7 24	..	..	..	..	..	8 12	..	..	..	..	..	..	8 24	..
Maidstone East.. dep	..	5 49	..	..	..	..	..	..	..	..	..	..	6 12	..	..	..	6 49	..	..	..	..	..	..	..	..	..	..	..	..	7 49	..	..
Barming	..	5 54	..	..	..	..	..	..	..	..	..	..	6 17	..	..	..	6 54	..	..	..	..	..	..	..	..	..	..	..	..	7 54	..	..
East Malling Halt	..	5 57	..	..	..	..	..	..	..	..	..	..	6 20	..	..	..	6 57	..	..	..	..	..	..	..	..	..	..	..	..	7 57	..	..
Malling	..	6 0	..	..	..	..	..	..	..	..	..	..	6 23	..	..	..	7 0	..	..	..	..	..	..	..	..	..	..	..	..	8 0	..	..
Wrotham & Boro' Gr'n	..	6 9	..	..	..	..	..	..	..	..	..	..	6 33	..	..	..	7 9	..	..	..	..	..	..	..	..	..	..	..	..	8 9	..	..
Kemsing	..	6 13	..	..	..	..	..	..	..	..	..	..	6 38	..	..	..	7 13	..	..	..	..	..	..	..	..	..	..	..	..	8 13	..	..
Sevenoaks Tub's H. dp	6 1	..	..	..	..	..	..	6 24	..	6c34	..	6c59	..	..	..	7 2	..	..	..	..	..	7 24	..	..	7c34	7 40	..	8 2	..	..	..	8c4
Sevenoaks Bat & Ball..	6 4	..	..	..	..	..	..	6 27	..	..	..	..	..	..	..	7 5	..	..	..	..	..	7 27	..	..	..	7 43	..	8 5	..	..	..	..
Otford	6 7	6 19	..	..	..	..	..	6 30	..	..	..	..	6 44	..	..	7 8	7 19	..	..	..	..	7 30	..	..	..	7 46	..	8 9	..	8 19	..	..
Shoreham (Kent)	6 10	..	..	..	..	..	..	6 33	..	..	..	..	..	..	..	7 11	..	..	..	..	..	7 33	..	..	..	7 49	..	8 12	..	..	..	..
Eynsford	6 15	..	..	..	..	..	..	6 38	..	..	..	..	..	..	..	7 16	..	..	..	..	..	7 38	..	..	..	7 54	..	8 16	..	..	..	..
Lullingstone	..	..	..	..	..	..	..	..	..	..	..	..	..	..	..	..	..	..	..	..	..	..	..	..	..	..	..	..	..	..	..	..
Swanley 60	6 24	6 28	6 31	..	..	..	..	6 44	6 50	..	..	..	6 53	..	7 3	7H24	7 28	7 32	..	..	..	7 44	..	8 17	..	7 59	..	8 24	..	8 28	8 32	..
St. Mary Cray	6 30	..	..	..	..	..	..	6 50	..	..	..	..	..	..	..	7 30	..	..	..	..	..	7 50	..	..	..	..	..	8 30	..	..	..	..
Orpington .... dep	..	..	..	..	..	6 43	..	..	..	6 55	..	7 18	..	..	..	..	..	..	..	..	7 43	..	..	..	8 18	..	..	..	..	..	..	8 43
Petts Wood	..	..	..	..	..	6 46	..	..	..	6 58	..	7 21	..	..	..	..	..	..	..	..	7 46	..	..	..	8 21	..	..	..	..	..	..	8 46
Bickley	6 34	..	..	..	..	6 49	..	6 54	..	7 1	..	7 28	..	..	..	7 34	..	..	..	..	7 49	7 54	..	..	8 28	..	..	8 34	..	..	..	8 49
Bromley South D	6 37	..	6 43	..	..	6 52	..	6 57	7 2	7 5	..	7 32	..	..	..	7 37	..	7 43	..	7 50	7 52	7 57	..	..	8 32	..	..	8 37	..	..	8 43	8 52
Shortlands	6 40	..	..	..	..	6 55	..	7 0	..	7 8	..	7 35	..	..	..	7 40	..	..	..	..	7 55	8 0	..	..	8 35	..	..	8 40	..	..	..	8 55
Beckenham Junction	..	..	..	..	..	6 58	..	..	..	7 11	..	7 38	..	..	..	..	..	..	..	..	7 58	..	..	..	8 38	..	..	..	..	..	..	8 58
Kent House	..	..	..	..	..	7 0	..	..	..	7 13	..	7 40	..	..	..	..	..	..	..	..	8 0	..	..	..	8 40	..	..	..	..	..	..	9 0
Penge East C	..	..	..	..	..	7 2	..	..	..	7 15	..	7 42	..	..	..	..	..	..	..	..	8 2	..	..	..	8 42	..	..	..	..	..	..	9 2
Sydenham Hill	..	..	..	..	..	7 5	..	..	..	7 18	..	7 45	..	..	..	..	..	..	..	..	8 5	..	..	..	8 45	..	..	..	..	..	..	9 5
West Dulwich	..	..	..	..	..	7 7	..	..	..	7 21	..	7 47	..	..	..	..	..	..	..	..	8 7	..	..	..	8 47	..	..	..	..	..	..	9 7
Herne Hill	..	..	..	7 1	7 4	7 9	..	..	7 19	7 24	7 27	7 49	..	..	..	..	..	..	8 3	..	8 9	..	8 28	..	8 49	..	..	..	9 3	..	..	9 9
Ravensbourne	6 42	..	..	..	..	..	..	7 2	..	..	..	..	..	..	..	7 42	..	..	..	..	..	8 2	..	..	..	..	..	8 42	..	..	..	..
Beckenham Hill	6 44	..	..	..	..	..	..	7 4	..	..	..	..	..	..	..	7 44	..	..	..	..	..	8 4	..	..	..	..	..	8 44	..	..	..	..
Bellingham	6 46	..	..	..	..	..	..	7 6	..	..	..	..	..	..	..	7 46	..	..	..	..	..	8 6	..	..	..	..	..	8 46	..	..	..	..
Catford	6 48	..	..	..	..	..	..	7 8	..	..	..	..	..	..	..	7 48	..	..	..	..	..	8 8	..	..	..	..	..	8 48	..	..	..	..
Crofton Park	6 50	..	..	..	..	..	..	7 10	..	..	..	..	..	..	..	7 50	..	..	..	..	..	8 10	..	..	..	..	..	8 50	..	..	..	..
Crystal Palace B dep	..	..	..	..	..	..	6 54	..	..	..	..	..	..	7 36	..	..	..	..	..	..	..	..	..	..	..	..	8 36	..	..	..	..	..
Upper Sydenham	..	..	..	..	..	..	6 56	..	..	..	..	..	..	7 38	..	..	..	..	..	..	..	..	..	..	..	..	8 38	..	..	..	..	..
Lordship Lane **A**	..	..	..	..	..	..	6 58	..	..	..	..	..	..	7 40	..	..	..	..	..	..	..	..	..	..	..	..	8 40	..	..	..	..	..
Honor Oak	..	..	..	..	..	..	7 1	..	..	..	..	..	..	7 43	..	..	..	..	..	..	..	..	..	..	..	..	8 43	..	..	..	..	..
Nunhead	6 53	..	..	..	..	..	7 5	7 13	..	..	..	..	..	7 47	..	7 53	..	..	..	..	..	8 13	..	..	..	..	8 46	8 53	..	..	..	..
Peckham Rye	6 55	..	..	..	..	..	..	7 15	..	..	..	..	..	..	..	7 55	..	..	..	..	..	8 15	..	..	..	..	..	8 55	..	..	..	..
Denmark Hill	6 58	..	..	..	..	..	..	7 18	..	..	..	..	..	..	..	7 58	..	..	..	..	..	8 18	..	..	..	..	..	8 58	..	..	..	..
Loughborough Junc	..	..	..	7 3	..	..	..	..	..	7 26	7 30	..	..	..	..	..	..	..	8 5	..	..	..	8 30	..	..	..	..	..	9 5	..	..	..
Elephant and Castle..	7 4	..	..	7 8	..	..	..	7 23	..	7 31	7 35	..	..	..	..	8 3	..	..	8 10	..	..	8 23	8 35	..	..	..	..	9 3	9 10	..	..	..
Blackfriars ...... arr	7 7	..	..	7 11	..	..	..	7 26	..	7 33	7 38	..	..	..	..	8 7	..	..	8 13	..	..	8 26	8 38	..	..	..	..	9 6	9 13	..	..	..
Holborn Viaduct "	7 9	..	..	7 13	..	..	..	7 29	..	..	7 40	..	..	..	..	8 9	..	..	8 15	..	..	8 28	8 40	..	..	..	..	9 9	9 15	..	..	..
Brixton	..	..	..	..	7 6	7 11	..	..	..	..	..	7 51	..	..	..	..	..	..	..	..	8 11	..	..	..	8 51	..	..	..	..	..	..	9 11
Victoria .... arr	..	..	7 1	..	7 12	7 17	..	..	7 28	..	..	7 57	..	..	..	..	..	7 59	..	8 13	8 17	..	..	..	8 57	..	..	..	..	..	8 59	9 17

3 Third class only. c Change at Orpington. H Arr. 3 mins. *earlier*

For Other Notes, see page 157.
For Saturday Trains, see pages 151a to 153a; for SUNDAY TRAINS, see pages 154 to 157

GILLINGHAM (Kent) CHATHAM, GRAVESEND WEST STREET, MAIDSTONE EAST, SEVENOAKS, ORPINGTON, CRYSTAL PALACE (H.L.) and LONDON

Up — Mondays to Fridays—*continued* — p.m

Up	3	3		3		3	3	3			3	3			3	3	3		3	3			3		3		3			3	3	
Gillingham (Kent) .. dep			8 28		..				..	8 54			9 19	..				..			9 54	..		..		..		..	..			..
Chatham	..	..	8 32	..	..	..	..	..	..	8 58	..	..	9 28	..	..	..	..	..	..	..	9 58	..	..	..	..	..	..	..	..	..	..	..
Rochester	..	..	8 35	..	..	..	..	..	..	9 1	..	..	..	..	..	..	..	..	..	..	10 1	..	..	..	..	..	..	..	..	..	..	..
Sole Street	..	..	8 46	..	..	..	..	..	..	9 12	..	..	..	..	..	..	..	..	..	..	1012	..	..	..	..	..	..	..	..	..	..	..
Meopham .....[Longfield	..	..	8 49	..	..	..	..	..	..	9 15	..	..	..	..	..	..	..	..	..	..	1015	..	..	..	..	..	..	..	..	..	..	..
Fawkham, for Hartley &	..	..	8 53	..	..	..	..	..	..	9 19	..	..	..	..	..	..	..	..	..	..	1019	..	..	..	..	..	..	..	..	..	..	..
Gravesend West St dp	..	..	3	..	..	..	..	..	..	..	..	..	..	..	..	..	..	..	..	..	..	..	..	..	..	..	..	..	..	..	..	..
Southfleet (Springh'd).	..	..		..	..	..	..	..	..	..	..	..	..	..	..	..	..	..	..	..	..	..	..	..	..	..	..	..	..	..	..	..
Longfield Halt G	..	..	..	..	..	..	..	..	..	..	..	..	..	..	..	..	..	..	..	..	..	..	..	..	..	..	..	..	..	..	..	..
Farningham Road F	..	..	8 58	..	..	..	..	..	..	9 24	..	..	..	..	..	..	..	..	..	..	1024	..	..	..	..	..	..	..	..	..	..	..
Maidstone East .. dep.	..	..	..	8 22	..	..	..	..	8 49	..	..	..	..	..	..	..	..	..	..	..	..	9 49	..	..	..	..	..	..	1010	..	..	..
Barming	..	..	..	8 27	..	..	..	..	8 54	..	..	..	..	..	..	..	..	..	..	..	..	9 54	..	..	..	..	..	..	1017	..	..	..
East Malling Halt	..	..	..	8 30	..	..	..	..	8 57	..	..	..	..	..	..	..	..	..	..	..	..	9 57	..	..	..	..	..	..	1021	..	..	..
Malling	..	..	..	8 33	..	..	..	..	9 0	..	..	..	..	..	..	..	..	..	..	..	..	10 0	..	..	..	..	..	..	1025	..	..	..
Wrotham & Boro' Gr'n	..	..	..	8 42	..	..	..	..	9 9	..	..	..	..	..	..	..	..	..	..	..	..	10 9	..	..	..	..	..	..	1038	..	..	..
Kemsing	..	..	..	8 46	..	..	..	..	9 13	..	..	..	..	..	..	..	..	..	..	..	..	10 13	..	..	..	..	..	..	..	..	..	..
Seven-oaks { Tub's H. dp	8 24	..	..	..	..	9c4	..	9 2	..	..	..	..	..	..	9 24	..	9c34	..	..	10 2	..	..	..	..	1026	..	10c34	..	..	..	11 2	..
Seven-oaks { Bat & Ball..	8 27	..	..	..	..	..	..	9 5	..	..	..	..	..	..	9 27	..	..	..	..	10 5	..	..	..	..	1029	..	..	..	..	..	11 5	..
Otford	8 30	..	..	8 52	..	..	..	9 8	9 19	..	..	..	..	..	9 30	..	..	..	..	10 8	..	10 19	..	..	1032	..	..	..	1051	..	11 8	..
Shoreham (Kent)	8 33	..	..	..	..	..	..	9 11	..	..	..	..	..	..	9 33	..	..	..	..	10 11	..	..	..	..	1035	..	..	..	..	..	1111	..
Eynsford	8 38	..	..	..	..	..	..	9 16	..	..	..	..	..	..	9 38	..	..	..	..	10 15	..	..	..	..	1040	..	..	..	..	..	1116	..
Lullingstone	..	..	..	..	..	..	..	..	..	..	..	..	..	..	..	..	..	..	..	..	..	..	..	..	..	..	..	..	..	..	..	..
Swanley 60	8 44	..	9 4	9 D6	..	..	..	9 24	9 28	9 32	..	..	..	..	9 44	..	..	..	..	10‡24	1030	10‡32	..	..	1045	..	..	..	11 6	..	1124	..
St. Mary Cray	8 50	..	..	..	..	..	..	9 30	..	..	..	..	..	..	9 50	..	..	..	..	10 30	..	..	..	..	1050	..	..	..	..	..	1130	..
Orpington .... dep	..	..	..	..	..	9 23	..	..	..	..	..	9 43	..	..	..	..	10 18	..	..	..	..	..	..	..	..	..	10 55	..	..	..	..	..
Petts Wood	..	..	..	..	..	9 26	..	..	..	..	..	9 46	..	..	..	..	10 21	..	..	..	..	..	..	..	..	..	10 58	..	..	..	..	..
Bickley	8 54	..	..	..	..	9 29	..	9 34	..	..	..	9 49	..	..	9 54	..	10‡29	..	..	10 34	..	..	..	..	1054	..	11 1	..	..	..	1134	..
Bromley South D	8 57	..	..	9 17	..	9 32	..	9 37	..	9 42	..	9 52	10 7	..	9 57	..	10 32	..	..	10 37	..	10 42	..	..	1057	..	11 5	..	1121	..	1137	..
Shortlands	9 0	..	..	..	..	9 35	..	9 40	..	..	..	9 55	..	..	10 0	..	10 35	..	..	10 40	..	..	..	..	11 0	..	11 7	..		..	1140	..
Beckenham Junction	..	..	..	..	..	9 38	..	..	..	..	..	9 58	..	..	..	..	10 38	..	..	..	..	..	..	..	11 4	..	11 11	..		..	..	..
Kent House	..	..	..	..	..	9 40	..	..	..	..	..	10 0	..	..	..	..	10 40	..	..	..	..	..	..	..	..	..	11 13	..	Arr. Swanley 11 3 p.m	..	..	..
Penge East C	..	..	..	..	..	9 42	..	..	..	..	..	10 2	..	..	..	..	10 42	..	..	..	..	..	..	..	..	..	11 15	..		..	..	..
Sydenham Hill	..	..	..	..	..	9 45	..	..	..	..	..	10 5	..	..	..	..	10 45	..	..	..	..	..	..	..	..	..	11 19	..		..	..	..
West Dulwich	..	..	..	..	..	9 47	..	..	..	..	..	10 7	..	..	..	..	10 47	..	..	..	..	..	..	..	..	..	11 21	..		..	..	..
Herne Hill	..	9 27	..	..	..	9 49	..	..	..	..	10 3	10 9	..	..	..	1028	10 49	..	..	..	..	..	11 3	..	..	..	11 24	..		..	..	..
Ravensbourne	9 2	..	..	..	..	..	..	9 42	..	..	..	..	..	..	10 2	..	..	..	..	10 42	..	..	..	..	..	..	..	..		..	1142	..
Beckenham Hill	9 4	..	..	..	..	..	..	9 44	..	..	..	..	..	..	10 4	..	..	..	..	10 44	..	..	..	..	..	..	..	..		..	1144	..
Bellingham	9 6	..	..	..	..	..	..	9 46	..	..	..	..	..	..	10 6	..	..	..	..	10 46	..	..	..	..	..	..	..	..		..	1146	..
Catford	9 8	..	..	..	..	..	..	9 48	..	..	..	..	..	..	10 8	..	..	..	..	10 48	..	..	..	..	..	..	..	..		..	1148	..
Crofton Park	9 10	..	..	..	..	..	..	9 50	..	..	..	..	..	..	1010	..	..	..	..	10 50	..	..	..	..	..	..	..	..		..	1150	..
Crystal Palace B dep	..	..	..	..	..	..	9 36	..	..	..	..	..	..	..	..	..	..	..	1036	..	..	..	..	..	..	..	..	..	..	1136	..	..
Upper Sydenham	..	..	..	..	..	..	9 38	..	..	..	..	..	..	..	..	..	..	..	1038	..	..	..	..	..	..	..	..	..	..	1138	..	..
Lordship Lane A	..	..	..	..	..	..	9 40	..	..	..	..	..	..	..	..	..	..	..	1040	..	..	..	..	..	..	..	..	..	..	1140	..	..
Honor Oak	..	..	..	..	..	..	9 43	..	..	..	..	..	..	..	..	..	..	..	1043	..	..	..	..	..	..	..	..	..	..	1143	..	..
Nunhead	9 13	..	..	..	..	..	9 47	9 53	..	..	..	..	..	..	1013	..	..	..	1047	10 53	..	..	..	..	..	..	..	..	..	1147	1153	..
Peckham Rye	9 15	..	..	..	..	..	..	9 55	..	..	..	..	..	..	1015	..	..	..	..	10 55	..	..	..	..	..	..	..	..	..	..	1155	..
Denmark Hill	9 18	..	..	..	..	..	..	9 58	..	..	..	..	..	..	1018	..	..	..	..	10 58	..	..	..	..	..	..	..	..	..	..	1158	..
Loughborough Junc.	..	9 30	..	..	..	..	..	..	..	..	10 5	..	..	..	..	1030	..	..	..	..	..	..	11 5	..	..	..	11 31	..	..	..	..	..
Elephant and Castle..	9 23	9 35	..	..	..	..	..	10 3	..	..	1010	..	..	..	1023	1035	..	..	..	11 3	..	..	1110	..	..	..	11 36	..	..	..	12 3	..
Blackfriars ...... arr	9 26	9 38	..	..	..	..	..	10 6	..	..	1013	..	..	..	1026	1038	..	..	..	11 6	..	..	1113	..	..	..	11 39	..	1145	..	12 6	..
Holborn Viaduct. "	9 29	9 40	..	..	..	..	..	10 9	..	..	1015	..	..	..	1029	1040	..	..	..	11 9	..	..	1115	..	..	..	11 41	..	1148	..	12 9	..
Brixton	..	..	..	..	..	9 51	..	..	..	..	..	1011	..	..	..	..	10 51	..	..	..	..	..	..	..	..	..	11 26	..	..	..	..	..
Victoria .... arr	..	..	..	9 38	..	9 57	..	..	..	9 59	..	1017	1028	..	..	..	10 57	..	..	..	..	10 59	..	..	..	..	11 32	..	..	..	..	..

3 Third class only. *c* Change at Orpington. D Arr. 5 mins. *earlier* ‡ Arr. 4 mins. *earlier*. **For Other Notes, see page 157.**

For Saturday Trains see pages 151a to 153a: For SUNDAY TRAINS, see pages 154 to 157

GILLINGHAM (Kent), CHATHAM, GRAVESEND WEST STREET, MAIDSTONE EAST, SEVENOAKS, ORPINGTON, CRYSTAL PALACE (H.L.) and LONDON

Saturdays — a.m

Up	3	3		3	3	3	3		3	3	3	3	3	3		
Gillingham (Kent) .. dep	..	..	..	..	..	..	..	9 14	..	..	..	..	..	..	..	9 54
Chatham	..	..	..	..	..	..	..	9 17	..	..	..	..	..	..	..	9 58
Rochester	..	..	..	..	..	..	..	9 20	..	..	..	..	..	..	..	10 1
Sole Street	..	..	..	..	..	..	..	9 32	..	..	..	..	..	..	..	1012
Meopham	..	..	..	..	..	..	..	9 34	..	..	..	..	..	..	..	1015
Fawkham, for Hartley & Longfield	..	..	..	..	..	..	..	9 39	..	..	..	..	..	..	..	1019
Gravesend West St dp	..	..	..	..	..	..	..	..	..	..	..	..	..	..	..	..
Southfleet (Springh'd)	..	..	..	..	..	..	..	..	..	..	..	..	..	..	..	..
Longfield Halt G	..	..	..	..	..	..	..	..	..	..	..	..	..	..	..	..
Farningham Road F	..	..	..	..	..	..	..	9 43	..	..	..	..	..	..	..	1024
Maidstone East .. dep	..	..	8 57	..	..	..	..	..	..	..	..	..	..	..	9 49	..
Barming	..	..	..	..	..	..	..	..	..	..	..	..	..	..	9 54	..
East Malling Halt	..	..	..	..	..	..	..	..	..	..	..	..	..	..	9 57	..
Malling	..	..	9 5	..	..	..	..	..	..	..	..	..	..	..	10 0	..
Wrotham & Boro' Gr'n	..	..	9 14	..	..	..	..	..	..	..	..	..	..	..	10 9	..
Kemsing	..	..	9 18	..	..	..	..	..	..	..	..	..	..	..	1013	..
Sevenoaks { Tub's H. dp	8c43	9 2	..	..	..	..	9 24	..	..	9c32	9 41	..	..	10 2	..	..
Sevenoaks { Bat & Ball	..	9 5	..	..	..	..	9 27	..	..	..	9 44	..	..	10 5	..	..
Otford	..	9 8	9 23	..	..	..	9 32	..	..	..	9 47	..	..	10 9	1019	..
Shoreham (Kent)	..	9 11	..	..	..	..	9 35	..	..	..	9 50	..	..	10 12	..	..
Eynsford	..	9 16	..	..	..	..	9 40	..	..	..	9 55	..	..	10 16	..	..
Lullingstone	..	..	..	..	..	..	..	..	..	..	..	..	..	..	..	..
Swanley 60	..	9 24	..	..	..	..	9 45	9 51	..	..	10 4	..	..	10H25	1028	1032
St. Mary Cray	..	9 30	..	..	..	..	9 50	..	..	..	1010	..	..	10 30	Stop	..
Orpington .. dep	9 16	..	..	..	..	9 40	..	..	..	9 55	..	..	1020	..	..	..
Petts Wood	9 19	..	..	..	..	9 43	..	..	..	9 58	..	..	1023	..	..	..
Bickley	9H27	9 34	..	..	9 41	9 46	9 54	..	..	10H5	1014	..	1026	10 34	..	..
Bromley South D	9 31	9 37	9 41	..	9 44	9 49	9 57	10 2	..	10 9	1017	..	1029	10 37	..	1043
Shortlands	9 34	9 40	..	..	9 47	9 52	10 0	..	..	1012	1020	..	1032	10 40	..	..
Beckenham Junction	9 37	..	..	..	9 50	9 55	..	..	..	1015	..	..	1035	..	..	..
Kent House	9 39	..	..	..	9 53	9 58	..	..	..	1017	..	..	1037	..	..	..
Penge East C	9 41	..	..	..	9 55	10 0	..	..	..	1019	..	..	1039	..	..	..
Sydenham Hill	9 44	..	..	..	9 58	10 3	..	..	..	1022	..	..	1043	..	..	..
West Dulwich	9 46	..	..	..	10 1	10 6	..	..	..	1024	..	..	1045	..	..	..
Herne Hill	9 48	..	9 52	..	10 4	10 8	..	..	..	1026	..	..	1047	..	..	..
Ravensbourne	..	9 42	..	..	..	..	10 2	..	..	..	1022	..	..	10 42	..	..
Beckenham Hill	..	9 44	..	..	..	..	10 4	..	..	..	1024	..	..	10 44	..	..
Bellingham	..	9 46	..	..	..	..	10 6	..	..	..	1026	..	..	10 46	a.m	..
Catford	..	9 48	..	..	..	..	10 8	..	..	..	1028	..	..	10 48	3	..
Crofton Park	..	9 50	..	..	..	..	1010	..	..	..	1030	..	..	10 50		..
Crystal Palace B dep	..	..	..	9 46	..	..	..	..	10 6	..	..	1026	..	..	1046	..
Upper Sydenham	..	..	..	9 48	..	..	..	..	10 8	..	..	1028	..	..	1048	..
Lordship Lane A	..	..	..	9 50	..	..	..	..	1010	..	..	1030	..	..	1050	..
Honor Oak	..	..	..	9 53	..	..	..	..	1013	..	..	1033	..	..	1053	..
Nunhead	..	9 53	..	9 56	..	..	1013	..	1016	..	1033	1036	..	10 53	1056	..
Peckham Rye	..	9 55	..	9 59	..	..	1015	..	1019	..	1036	1039	..	10 55	1059	..
Denmark Hill	..	9 58	..	10 1	..	..	1018	..	1021	..	1038	1041	..	10 58	11 1	..
Loughborough Junc.	9 57	..	..	..	10 7	1011	..	..	..	1035	..	..	1055	..	..	..
Elephant and Castle	10 2	10 4	..	10 7	1011	1016	1023	..	1027	1040	1043	1047	11 0	11 3	11 7	..
Blackfriars .. arr	10 5	10 7	10 0	1010	1015	1019	1027	1022	1030	1043	1047	1050	11 3	11 7	1110	..
Holborn Viaduct "	10 7	10 9	10 2	..	1017	1021	1029	1024	..	1045	1049	..	11 5	11 9	..	..
Brixton	9 50	..	..	..	..	1011	..	..	..	1028	..	..	1049	..	..	..
Victoria .. arr	9 56	..	..	..	..	1017	..	..	..	1034	..	..	1055	..	..	1059

Up	3	3			3	3	3	3	3	3	3			3	3	
Gillingham (Kent) .. dep	..	..	..	1028	..	..	..	..	..	..	..	..	1054	..	..	..
Chatham	..	..	..	1035	..	..	..	..	..	..	..	..	1058	..	..	1129
Rochester	..	..	..	..	..	..	..	..	..	..	..	..	11 1	..	..	..
Sole Street	..	..	..	..	..	..	..	..	..	..	..	..	1112	..	..	..
Meopham	..	..	..	..	..	..	..	..	..	..	..	..	1115	..	..	..
Fawkham, for Hartley & Longfield	..	..	..	..	..	..	..	..	..	..	..	..	1119	..	..	..
Gravesend West St dp	..	..	..	..	..	..	..	..	..	..	..	..	..	..	..	..
Southfleet (Springh'd)	..	..	..	..	..	..	..	..	..	..	..	..	..	..	..	..
Longfield Halt G	..	..	..	..	..	..	..	..	..	..	..	..	..	..	..	..
Farningham Road F	..	..	..	..	..	..	..	..	..	..	..	..	1124	..	..	..
Maidstone East .. dep	..	..	..	..	..	..	..	..	..	..	..	1049	..	..	..	..
Barming	..	..	..	..	..	..	..	..	..	..	..	1054	..	..	..	..
East Malling Halt	..	..	..	..	..	..	..	..	..	..	..	1057	..	..	..	..
Malling	..	..	..	..	..	..	..	..	..	..	..	11 0	..	..	..	..
Wrotham & Boro' Gr'n	..	..	..	..	..	..	..	..	..	..	..	11 9	..	..	..	..
Kemsing	..	..	..	..	..	..	..	..	..	..	..	1113	..	..	..	..
Sevenoaks { Tub's H. dp	10c7	..	..	..	..	10c34	1041	..	..	..	11 3	..	..	11c20	..	..
Sevenoaks { Bat & Ball	..	..	..	..	..	..	1044	..	..	..	11 6	..	..	..	..	..
Otford	..	..	..	..	..	..	1047	..	..	..	11 9	1119	..	..	..	..
Shoreham (Kent)	..	..	..	..	..	..	1050	..	..	..	11 12	..	..	..	..	..
Eynsford	..	..	..	..	..	..	1055	..	..	..	11 17	..	..	..	..	..
Lullingstone	..	..	..	..	..	..	..	..	..	..	..	..	..	..	..	..
Swanley 60	..	..	..	..	..	..	11H5	..	..	..	11H25	1128	1132	..	..	..
St. Mary Cray	..	..	..	..	..	..	1110	..	..	..	11 30	Stop	..	..	..	..
Orpington .. dep	1040	..	..	..	..	11 0	..	..	..	1118	..	..	..	11 40	..	..
Petts Wood	1043	..	..	..	..	11 3	..	..	..	1121	..	..	..	11 43	..	..
Bickley	1046	1055	..	..	..	11 6	1114	..	..	1126	11 34	..	..	11 48	..	..
Bromley South D	1049	1057	..	1111	..	11 9	1117	..	..	1129	11 37	..	1142	11 51	..	..
Shortlands	1052	11 0	..	..	..	11 12	1120	..	..	1132	11 40	..	..	11 54	..	..
Beckenham Junction	1055	..	..	..	..	11 15	..	..	..	1135	..	..	..	11 57	..	..
Kent House	1057	..	..	..	..	11 17	..	..	..	1137	..	..	..	11 59	..	..
Penge East C	1059	..	..	..	..	11 19	..	..	..	1139	..	..	..	12 1	..	..
Sydenham Hill	11 3	..	..	..	..	11 22	..	..	..	1143	..	..	..	12 4	..	..
West Dulwich	11 5	..	..	..	..	11 24	..	..	..	1145	..	..	..	12 6	..	..
Herne Hill	11 7	..	..	..	..	11 27	..	..	..	1147	..	..	..	12 8	..	..
Ravensbourne	..	11 2	..	..	..	..	1122	..	..	..	11 42	..	..	..	..	..
Beckenham Hill	..	11 4	..	..	..	..	1124	..	..	..	11 44	..	..	..	..	..
Bellingham	..	11 6	..	..	..	..	1126	..	..	..	11 46	a.m	..	..	..	..
Catford	..	11 8	..	..	..	..	1128	..	..	..	11 48	3	..	..	..	..
Crofton Park	..	1110	..	..	..	..	1130	..	..	..	11 50		..	..	..	..
Crystal Palace B dep	..	..	..	..	11 6	..	..	1126	..	..	..	1146	..	..	1157	..
Upper Sydenham	..	..	..	..	11 8	..	..	1128	..	..	..	1148	..	..	1159	..
Lordship Lane A	..	..	..	..	1110	..	..	1130	..	..	..	1150	..	..	12 1	..
Honor Oak	..	..	..	..	1113	..	..	1133	..	..	..	1153	..	..	12 4	..
Nunhead	..	1113	..	..	1116	..	1133	1136	..	..	11 53	1156	..	..	12 7	..
Peckham Rye	..	1115	..	..	1119	..	1135	1139	..	..	11 55	1159	..	..	1210	..
Denmark Hill	..	1118	..	..	1121	..	1138	1141	..	..	11 58	12 1	..	..	1212	..
Loughborough Junc.	1115	..	..	..	..	11 35	..	..	1149	1155	..	..	..	12 15	..	..
Elephant and Castle	1120	1123	..	..	1127	11 40	1143	1147	1153	12 0	12 3	12 7	..	12 20	1218	..
Blackfriars .. arr	1123	1127	..	..	1130	11 43	1147	1150	1156	12 3	12 7	1210	..	12 24	1221	..
Holborn Viaduct "	1125	1129	..	..	..	11 45	1149	..	1158	12 5	12 9	..	..	12 26	1223	..
Brixton	11 9	..	..	..	..	11 31	..	..	..	1149	..	..	..	12 11	..	..
Victoria .. arr	1115	..	..	1133	..	11 37	..	..	..	1155	..	..	1159	12 17	..	1222

3 Third class only

c Change at Orpington

H Arr. 3 mins. *earlier*.

For Other Notes, see page 157

For SUNDAY TRAINS, see pages 154 to 157

GILLINGHAM (Kent), CHATHAM, GRAVESEND WEST STREET, MAIDSTONE EAST, SEVENOAKS, ORPINGTON, CRYSTAL PALACE (H.L.) and LONDON

Saturdays—*continued* (a.m … p.m)

Up	3	3	3	3	3	3	3	3	3	3	3	3		a.m		3	3	3	3	3		3	3	3		3	3	3			
Gillingham (Kent).. dep													..	1153	12 2										..				..	..	1254
Chatham	..	..	..	..	..	..	..	..	..	..	..	..	..	1158	12 9	..	..	..	..	..	..	..	..	..	..	..	..	..	..	..	1258
Rochester	..	..	..	..	..	..	..	..	..	..	..	..	..	12 1	1213	..	..	..	..	..	..	..	..	..	..	..	..	..	..	..	1 1
Sole Street	..	..	..	..	..	..	..	..	..	..	..	..	..	1212	..	..	..	..	..	..	..	..	..	..	..	..	..	..	..	..	1 12
Meopham .....[Longfield	..	..	..	..	..	..	..	..	..	..	..	..	..	1215	..	..	..	..	..	..	..	..	..	..	..	..	..	..	..	..	1 15
Fawkham, for Hartley &	..	..	..	..	..	..	..	..	..	..	..	..	..	1219	..	..	..	..	..	..	..	..	..	..	..	..	..	..	..	..	1 19
Gravesend West St dp	..	..	..	..	..	..	..	..	..	..	..	..	..	..	..	..	..	..	..	..	..	..	..	..	..	..	..	..	1248	..	..
Southfleet (Springh'd).	..	..	..	..	..	..	..	..	..	..	..	..	..	..	..	..	..	..	..	..	..	..	..	..	..	..	..	..	1253	..	..
Longfield Halt G	..	..	..	..	..	..	..	..	..	..	..	..	..	..	..	..	..	..	..	..	..	..	..	..	..	..	..	..	1258	..	..
Farningham Road F	..	..	..	..	..	..	..	..	..	..	..	..	a.m	1224	..	..	..	..	..	..	..	..	..	..	..	..	..	..	1 3	..	1 24
Maidstone East..dep.	..	..	..	..	..	..	..	..	..	..	..	..	1149	..	..	..	..	..	..	..	..	..	..	..	..	..	..	..	—	1249	..
Barming	..	..	..	..	..	..	..	..	..	..	..	..	1154	..	..	..	..	..	..	..	..	..	..	..	..	..	..	..	Stop	1254	..
East Malling Halt	..	..	..	..	..	..	..	..	..	..	..	..	1157	..	..	..	..	..	..	..	..	..	..	..	..	..	..	..	..	1257	..
Malling	..	..	..	..	..	..	..	..	..	..	..	..	12 0	..	..	..	..	..	..	..	..	..	..	..	..	..	..	..	p.m	1 0	..
Wrotham & Boro' Gr'n	..	..	..	..	..	..	..	..	..	..	..	..	12 9	..	..	..	..	..	..	..	..	..	..	..	..	..	..	..	3	1 9	..
Kemsing	..	..	..	..	..	..	..	..	..	..	..	p.m	1213	..	..	..	..	..	..	..	..	..	..	..	..	..	..	..		1 13	..
Seven-oaks { Tub's H. dp	11 21	..	..	..	11c34	1143	..	..	..	..	..	12 1	..	..	..	..	12c11	12 21	..	..	..	12c34	..	1241	..	..	12c51	..	1 3	..	..
Seven-oaks { Bat & Ball..	11 24	..	..	..	..	1146	..	..	..	..	..	12 4	..	..	..	..	..	12 24	..	..	..	..	..	1244	..	..	..	..	1 6	..	..
Otford	11 27	..	..	..	..	1149	..	..	..	..	..	12 7	1219	..	..	..	..	12 27	..	..	..	..	..	1247	..	..	..	..	1 9	1 19	..
Shoreham (Kent)	11 30	..	..	..	..	1152	..	..	..	..	..	12 10	..	..	..	..	..	12 30	..	..	..	..	..	1250	..	..	..	..	1 12	..	..
Eynsford	11 35	..	..	..	..	1157	..	..	..	..	..	12 15	..	..	..	..	..	12 35	..	..	..	..	..	1255	..	..	..	..	1 17	..	..
Lullingstone	..	..	..	..	..	..	..	..	..	..	..	..	..	..	..	..	..	..	..	..	..	..	..	..	..	..	..	..	..	..	..
Swanley 60	11H45	..	..	..	..	12H5	..	..	..	..	..	12H25	1228	1232	..	..	..	12H45	..	..	..	..	..	1H5	..	..	..	..	1H25	1 28	1 32
St. Mary Cray	11 50	..	..	..	..	1210	..	p.m	..	p.m	..	12 30	—	..	..	..	..	12 50	..	..	..	..	..	1 10	..	..	..	..	1 30	..	..
Orpington.......... dep	..	..	..	..	12 0	..	..	1212	..	1220	..	..	Stop	..	..	..	12 40	..	..	..	..	1 0	..	..	..	..	1 20	1 23	..	..	..
Petts Wood	..	..	..	..	12 3	..	..	1215	..	1223	p.m		..	..	..	..	12 43	..	..	..	..	1 3	..	..	..	..	1 23	..	..	..	..
Bickley	11 54	..	..	..	12 6	1214	..	1219	..	1226	1229	12 34	..	..	..	..	12 46	12 54	..	..	..	1 6	..	1 14	..	..	1 26	..	1 34	..	..
Bromley South D	11 57	..	..	..	12 9	1217	..	1222	..	1229	1232	12 37	..	1242	1247	..	12 49	12 57	..	..	..	1 9	..	1 17	..	..	1 29	1 31	1 37	..	1 42
Shortlands	12 0	..	..	..	12 12	1220	..	1224	..	1232	..	12 40	..	..	..	..	12 52	1 0	..	..	..	1 12	..	1 20	..	..	1 32	..	1 40	..	..
Beckenham Junction	..	..	..	..	12 15	..	..	1227	..	1235	..	..	..	..	..	..	12 55	..	..	..	..	1 15	..	..	..	..	1 35	..	..	..	..
Kent House	..	..	..	..	12 17	..	..	1229	..	1237	..	..	..	..	..	..	12 57	..	..	..	..	1 18	..	..	..	..	1 38	..	..	..	..
Penge East C	..	..	..	..	12 19	..	..	1231	..	1239	..	..	..	..	..	..	1 0	..	..	..	..	1 20	..	..	..	..	1 40	..	..	..	..
Sydenham Hill	..	..	..	..	12 23	..	..	1234	..	1243	..	..	..	..	..	..	1 3	..	..	..	..	1 23	..	..	..	..	1 43	..	..	..	..
West Dulwich	..	..	..	..	12 25	..	..	1236	p.m	1245	..	..	..	..	..	..	1 5	..	..	..	..	1 26	..	..	..	..	1 45	..	..	..	..
Herne Hill	..	..	..	..	12 27	..	..	1239	1242	1247	..	..	..	..	1 3	..	1 7	..	1 21	..	..	1 28	1 41	..	..	..	1 47	..	..	..	..
Ravensbourne	12 2	..	..	..	..	1222	..	..	..	..	..	12 42	..	..	..	..	..	1 2	..	..	..	..	..	1 22	..	..	..	..	1 42	..	..
Beckenham Hill	12 4	..	..	..	..	1224	..	..	..	..	..	12 44	..	..	..	..	..	1 4	..	..	..	..	..	1 24	..	..	..	..	1 44	..	..
Bellingham	12 6	..	..	..	..	1226	..	..	..	..	1240	12 46	p.m	..	..	..	..	1 6	..	..	..	..	..	1 26	..	..	..	..	1 46	..	..
Catford	12 8	..	..	..	..	1228	..	..	..	..	1242	12 48	3	..	..	..	..	1 8	..	..	..	..	..	1 28	..	..	..	1 39	1 48	..	..
Crofton Park	12 10	p.m	..	p.m	..	1230	p.m	..	..	..	..	12 50		..	..	..	..	1 10	..	..	..	..	..	1 30	..	..	..	..	1 50	..	..
Crystal Palace B dep	..	12 6	..	1216	..	..	1226	..	..	..	..	..	1246	..	..	1258	..	..	..	1 6	..	..	..	..	..	1 26	..	..	..	..	..
Upper Sydenham	..	12 8	..	1218	..	..	1228	..	..	..	..	..	1248	..	..	1 0	..	..	..	1 8	..	..	..	..	..	1 28	..	..	..	..	..
Lordship Lane A	..	1210	..	1220	..	..	1230	..	..	..	..	..	1250	..	..	1 2	..	..	..	1 10	..	..	..	..	..	1 30	..	..	..	..	..
Honor Oak	..	1213	..	1223	..	..	1233	..	..	..	..	..	1253	..	..	1 5	..	..	..	1 13	..	..	..	..	..	1 33	..	..	..	..	..
Nunhead	12 13	1216	..	1226	..	1233	1236	..	..	..	1248	12 53	1256	..	..	1 8	..	1 13	..	1 16	..	..	..	1 33	..	1 36	..	1 44	1 53	..	..
Peckham Rye	12 15	1219	..	..	..	1235	1239	..	..	..	1251	12 55	1259	..	..	..	..	1 15	..	1 19	..	..	..	1 35	..	1 39	..	1 47	1 55	..	..
Denmark Hill	12 18	1221	p.m	1230	..	1237	1241	..	..	..	1254	12 58	1 1	..	..	..	..	1 17	..	1 21	..	..	..	1 38	..	1 41	..	1 49	1 58	..	..
Loughborough Junc.	..	..	1226	..	..	..	..	1241	1245	1 3	..	..	..	..	..	..	..	..	1 23	..	..	..	1 43	..	..	..	2 3	..	..	..	..
Elephant and Castle..	12 23	1228	1231	1236	12 39	1243	1247	1246	1249	1 8	1 0	1 3	1 7	..	..	1 17	..	1 23	1 28	1 28	..	..	1 48	1 43	..	1 47	2 8	1 55	2 3	..	..
Blackfriars ...... arr	12 27	1232	1234	1239	12 42	1246	1250	1249	1252	1 11	1 3	1 7	1 10	..	..	1 21	..	1 27	1 31	1 32	..	..	1 51	1 47	..	1 50	2 11	1 59	2 7	..	..
Holborn Viaduct. "	12 30	..	1236	1241	12 44	1248	..	1251	1255	1 13	1 5	1 9	..	..	..	1 23	..	1 29	1 33	..	..	..	1 53	1 49	..	..	2 13	..	2 9	..	..
Brixton	..	..	..	..	12 29	..	..	..	..	1249	..	..	..	..	..	..	1 9	..	..	..	..	1 31	..	..	..	..	1 49	..	..	..	..
Victoria.......... arr	..	..	..	..	12 35	..	..	..	..	1255	..	..	..	1259	1 12	..	1 15	..	..	..	..	1 37	..	..	..	..	1 55	..	..	..	1 59

3 Third class only

c Change at Orpington

H Arr. 3 minutes *earlier*

For Other Notes, see page 157   **For SUNDAY TRAINS, see pages 154 to 157**

GILLINGHAM (Kent) CHATHAM, GRAVESEND WEST STREET, MAIDSTONE EAST, SEVENOAKS, ORPINGTON, CRYSTAL PALACE (H.L.) and LONDON

Saturdays—*continued.* (p.m.)

Up			3	3		3	3	3	3			3	3	3		3			3		3	3	3		3	3	3	3	3		3	3	
Gillingham (Kent).. dep	1 2																	1 54						2 45									337
Chatham	1 9									1 49								1 58						2 52									343
Rochester																		2 1															
Sole Street																		2 12															
Meopham .....[Longfield																		2 15															
Fawkham. for Hartley &																		2 19															
Gravesend West St dp															1 48															3 4			
Southfleet (Springh'd).															1 53															3 9			
Longfield Halt G															1 58															3 14			
Farningham Road F															2 3			2 24												3 19			
Maidstone East.. dep																	1 49																
Barming																	1 54																
East Malling Halt																	1 57																
Malling																	2 0																
Wrotham & Boro' Gr'n																	2 9																
Kemsing																	2 13																
Seven-oaks { Tub's H. dp			1c13	1 20			1c34		1 41				2 2						2c4		2 24		2 44		2c34		3 2		3c4		3 26		
Seven-oaks { Bat & Ball				1 23					1 44				2 5								2 27		2 47				3 5				3 29		
Otford				1 27					1 47				2 9				2 19				2 31		2 51				3 9				3 32		
Shoreham (Kent)				1 30					1 50				2 12								2 34		2 54				3 12				3 35		
Eynsford				1 35					1 55				2 16								2 38		2 58				3 16				3 40		
Lullingstone																																	
Swanley 60				1 42					2 4				2 24				2 28	2 32			2 44		3 4				3 24				3 44		
St. Mary Cray				1 47					2 10				2 30								2 50		3 10				3 30				3 50		
Orpington.......... dep			1 43				2 0					2 18							2 43						3 18				3 43				
Petts Wood			1 46				2 3					2 21							2 46						3 21				3 46				
Bickley			1 49	1 53			2 6		2 14			2 27	2 34						2 49		2 54		3 14		3‖28		3 34		3 49		3 54		
Bromley South D	1 46		1 52	1 57			2 9		2 17	2 25		2 31	2 37					2 42	2 52		2 57		3 17	3 29	3 32		3 37		3 52		3 57		420
Shortlands			1 55	2 0			2 12		2 20			2 35	2 40						2 55		3 0		3 20		3 35		3 40		3 55		4 0		
Beckenham Junction			1 58				2 15					2 38							2 58						3 38				3 58				
Kent House			2 0				2 17					2 40							3 0						3 40				4 0				
Penge East C			2 2				2 19					2 42							3 2						3 42				4 2				
Sydenham Hill			2 5				2 22					2 45							3 5						3 45				4 5				
West Dulwich			2 7				2 24					2 47							3 7						3 47				4 7				
Herne Hill			2 9			2 21	2 26					2 49				3 3			3 9			3 29			3 49			4 3	4 9			4 28	
Ravensbourne				2 2					2 22				2 42								3 2		3 22				3 42				4 2		
Beckenham Hill				2 4					2 24				2 44								3 4		3 24				3 44				4 4		
Bellingham				2 6					2 26				2 46								3 6		3 26				3 46				4 6		
Catford				2 8					2 28				2 48								3 8		3 28				3 48				4 8		
Crofton Park				2 10					2 30				2 50								3 10		3 30				3 50				4 10		
Crystal Palace B dep								2 16						2 56												3 36							
Upper Sydenham								2 18						2 58												3 38							
Lordship Lane A								2 20						3 0												3 40							
Honor Oak								2 23						3 3												3 43							
Nunhead				2 13				2 27	2 33				2 53	3 7							3 13		3 33			3 47	3 53				4 13		
Peckham Rye				2 15					2 35				2 55								3 15		3 35				3 55				4 15		
Denmark Hill				2 18					2 38				2 58								3 18		3 38				3 58				4 18		
Loughborough Junc.						2 23	2 47									3 5						3 31						4 5				4 31	
Elephant and Castle				2 23		2 28	2 51		2 44				3 3			3 10					3 23	3 36	3 43				4 3	4 10			4 23	4 35	
Blackfriars ...... arr				2 27		2 31	2 54		2 47				3 6			3 13					3 26	3 39	3 46				4 6	4 13			4 26	4 38	
Holborn Viaduct. "				2 29		2 33	2 57		2 49				3 9			3 15					3 29	3 41					4 9	4 15			4 29	4 41	
Brixton			2 11				2 28					2 51							3 11						3 51				4 11				
Victoria........... arr	2 6		2 17				2 34			2 46		2 57						2 59	3 17					3 52	3 57				4 17				440

3 Third class only

c Change at Orpington

‖ Arr. 3 mins. *earlier*.

For Other Notes, see page 157 **For SUNDAY TRAINS, see pages 154 to 157**

GILLINGHAM (Kent), CHATHAM, GRAVESEND WEST STREET, MAIDSTONE EAST, SEVENOAKS, ORPINGTON, CRYSTAL PALACE (H.L.) and LONDON

Saturdays—*continued* (p.m.)

Up	3	3	3			3	3	3	3		3	3	3			3	3		3		3		3		3	3	3	3		3		3	
Gillingham (Kent) .. dep	..	..	..	3 54	..	..	..	..	..	..	..	..	..	..	..	..	..	..	..	..	..	..	..	5 54	..	..	..	..	6 54	..	7 2	..	..
Chatham	..	..	..	3 58	..	..	..	..	..	..	..	..	..	..	..	..	..	5 21	..	..	..	..	..	5 58	..	..	..	..	6 58	..	7 9	..	..
Rochester	..	..	..	4 1	..	..	..	..	..	..	..	..	..	..	..	..	..	..	..	..	..	..	..	6 1	..	..	..	..	7 1	..	..	..	..
Sole Street	..	..	..	4 12	..	..	..	..	..	..	..	..	..	..	..	..	..	..	..	..	..	..	..	6 12	..	..	..	..	7 12	..	..	..	..
Meopham ..... [Longfield	..	..	..	4 15	..	..	..	..	..	..	..	..	..	..	..	..	..	..	..	..	..	..	..	6 15	..	..	..	..	7 15	..	..	..	..
Fawkham for Hartley &	..	..	..	4 19	..	..	..	..	..	..	..	..	..	..	..	..	..	..	..	..	..	..	..	6 19	..	..	..	..	7 19	..	..	..	..
Gravesend West St dp	..	..	..	..	..	..	..	..	..	..	..	..	..	4 46	..	..	..	..	..	6 3	..	..	..	..	..	..	..	..	..	..	..	..	..
Southfleet (Springh'd).	..	..	..	..	..	..	..	..	..	..	..	..	..	4 51	..	..	..	..	..	6 8	..	..	..	..	..	..	..	..	..	..	..	..	..
Longfield Halt G	..	..	..	..	..	..	..	..	..	..	..	..	..	4 56	..	..	..	..	..	6 13	..	..	..	..	..	..	..	..	..	..	..	..	..
Farningham Road F	..	..	..	4 24	..	..	..	..	..	..	..	..	..	5 1	..	..	..	..	..	6 18	..	..	..	6 24	..	..	..	..	7 24	..	..	..	..
Maidstone East .. dep.	..	..	..	..	3 49	..	..	..	..	..	..	..	..	..	..	..	..	..	..	..	..	5 49	..	..	..	..	..	..	..	..	..	..	6 49
Barming	..	..	..	..	3 54	..	..	..	..	..	..	..	..	..	..	..	..	..	..	Stop	..	5 54	..	..	..	..	..	..	..	..	..	..	6 54
East Malling Halt	..	..	..	..	3 57	..	..	..	..	..	..	..	..	..	..	..	..	..	..	..	..	5 57	..	..	..	..	..	..	..	..	..	..	6 57
Malling	..	..	..	..	4 0	..	..	..	..	..	..	..	..	..	..	..	..	..	..	p.m	..	6 0	..	..	..	..	..	..	..	..	..	..	7 0
Wrotham & Boro' Gr'n	..	..	..	..	4 9	..	..	..	..	..	..	..	..	..	..	..	..	..	..	3	..	6 9	..	..	..	..	..	..	..	..	..	..	7 9
Kemsing	..	..	..	..	4 13	..	..	..	..	..	..	..	..	..	..	..	..	..	..		..	6 13	..	..	..	..	..	..	..	..	..	..	7 13
Sevenoaks { Tub's H. dp	3c34	..	4 2	..	..	4c4	..	4 24	..	..	5 2	5c4	..	..	..	..	5 24	..	..	5c34	6 2	..	..	..	6c4	..	6 24	6c59	..	..	..	7 2	..
Sevenoaks { Bat & Ball	..	..	4 5	..	..	..	..	4 27	..	..	5 5	..	..	..	..	..	5 27	..	..	..	6 5	..	..	..	..	..	6 27	..	..	..	..	7 5	..
Otford	..	..	4 9	..	4 19	..	..	4 31	..	..	5 9	..	..	..	..	..	5 31	..	..	..	6 9	6 19	..	..	..	..	6 31	..	..	..	..	7 9	7 19
Shoreham (Kent)	..	..	4 12	..	..	..	..	4 34	..	..	5 12	..	..	..	..	..	5 34	..	..	..	6 12	..	..	..	..	..	6 34	..	..	..	..	7 12	..
Eynsford	..	..	4 16	..	..	..	..	4 38	..	..	5 16	..	..	..	..	..	5 38	..	..	..	6 16	..	..	..	..	..	6 38	..	..	..	..	7 16	..
Lullingstone	..	..	..	..	..	..	..	..	..	..	..	..	..	..	..	..	..	..	..	..	..	..	..	..	..	..	..	..	..	..	..	..	..
Swanley 60	..	..	4 24	4 30	4§32	..	..	4 44	..	..	5 24	..	..	..	..	..	5 44	..	..	..	6 24	6 28	..	6 32	..	..	6 44	..	7 32	..	..	7 24	7 28
St. Mary Cray	..	..	4 30		..	..	..	4 50	..	..	5 30	..	..	..	..	..	5 50	..	..	..	6 30	..	..	..	..	..	6 50	..	..	..	..	7 30	..
Orpington .... dep	4 23	..	..	..	..	4 43	..	..	..	..	..	5 23	..	..	..	5 43	..	..	..	6 21	..	..	..	..	6 43	..	..	7 18	..	..	..	..	..
Petts Wood	4 26	..	..	..	..	4 46	..	..	..	..	..	5 26	..	..	..	5 46	..	..	..	6 24	..	..	..	..	6 46	..	..	7 21	..	..	..	..	..
Bickley	4 29	..	4 34	..	..	4 49	..	4 54	..	..	5 34	5 29	..	..	..	5 49	5 54	..	..	6 30	6 34	..	..	..	6 49	..	6 54	7 28	..	..	..	7 34	..
Bromley South D	4 32	..	4 37	..	4 42	4 52	..	4 57	..	..	5 37	5 32	..	..	..	5 52	5 57	6 0	..	6 34	6 37	..	..	6 43	6 52	..	6 57	7 32	7 42	..	746	7 37	..
Shortlands	4 35	..	4 40	..	..	4 55	..	5 0	..	..	5 40	5 35	..	..	..	5 55	6 0	..	..	6 37	6 40	..	..	..	6 55	..	7 0	7 35	..	..	..	7 40	..
Beckenham Junction	4 38	..	..	..	..	4 58	..	..	..	..	..	5 38	..	..	..	5 58	..	..	..	6 40	..	..	..	..	6 58	..	..	7 38	..	..	..	..	..
Kent House	4 40	..	..	..	..	5 0	..	..	..	..	..	5 40	..	..	..	6 0	..	..	..	6 42	..	..	..	..	7 0	..	..	7 40	..	..	..	..	..
Penge East C	4 42	..	..	..	..	5 2	..	..	..	..	..	5 42	..	..	..	6 2	..	..	..	6 44	..	..	..	..	7 2	..	..	7 42	..	..	..	..	..
Sydenham Hill	4 45	..	..	..	..	5 5	..	..	..	..	..	5 45	..	..	..	6 5	..	..	..	6 47	..	..	..	..	7 5	..	..	7 45	..	..	..	..	..
West Dulwich	4 47	..	..	..	..	5 7	..	..	..	..	..	5 47	..	..	..	6 7	..	..	..	6 49	..	..	..	..	7 7	..	..	7 47	..	..	..	..	..
Herne Hill	4 49	..	..	..	..	5 9	5 28	..	..	..	..	5 49	6 3	..	..	6 9	..	..	..	6 51	..	..	7 4	..	7 9	7 30	..	7 49	..	..	..	..	..
Ravensbourne	..	..	4 42	..	..	..	..	5 2	..	..	5 42	..	..	..	..	..	6 2	..	..	..	6 42	..	..	..	..	..	7 2	..	..	..	..	7 42	..
Beckenham Hill	..	..	4 44	..	..	..	..	5 4	..	..	5 44	..	..	..	..	..	6 4	..	..	..	6 44	..	..	..	..	..	7 4	..	..	..	..	7 44	..
Bellingham	..	..	4 46	..	..	..	..	5 6	..	..	5 46	..	..	..	..	..	6 6	..	..	..	6 46	..	..	..	..	..	7 6	..	..	..	..	7 46	..
Catford	..	..	4 48	..	..	..	..	5 8	..	..	5 48	..	..	..	..	..	6 8	..	..	..	6 48	..	..	..	..	..	7 8	..	..	..	..	7 48	..
Crofton Park	..	..	4 50	..	..	..	..	5 10	..	..	5 50	..	..	..	..	..	6 10	..	..	..	6 50	..	..	..	..	..	7 10	..	..	..	..	7 50	..
Crystal Palace B dep	..	4 36	..	..	..	..	..	..	5 36	..	..	..	..	..	..	..	..	..	6 36	..	..	..	..	..	..	..	..	..	..	7 36	..	..	..
Upper Sydenham	..	4 38	..	..	..	..	..	..	5 38	..	..	..	..	..	..	..	..	..	6 38	..	..	..	..	..	..	..	..	..	..	7 38	..	..	..
Lordship Lane A	..	4 40	..	..	..	..	..	..	5 40	..	..	..	..	..	..	..	..	..	6 40	..	..	..	..	..	..	..	..	..	..	7 40	..	..	..
Honor Oak	..	4 43	..	..	..	..	..	..	5 43	..	..	..	..	..	..	..	..	..	6 43	..	..	..	..	..	..	..	..	..	..	7 43	..	..	..
Nunhead	..	4 47	4 53	..	..	..	..	5 13	5 47	..	5 53	..	..	..	..	..	6 13	..	6 47	..	6 53	..	..	..	..	..	7 13	..	..	7 47	..	7 53	..
Peckham Rye	..	..	4 55	..	..	..	..	5 15	..	..	5 55	..	..	..	..	..	6 15	..	..	..	6 55	..	..	..	..	..	7 15	..	..	..	..	7 55	..
Denmark Hill	..	..	4 58	..	..	..	..	5 18	..	..	5 58	..	..	..	..	..	6 18	..	..	..	6 58	..	..	..	..	..	7 18	..	..	..	..	7 58	..
Loughborough Junc.	5 6	..	..	..	..	..	5 31	..	..	..	..	..	6 5	..	..	6 31	..	..	..	..	..	..	7 7	..	..	7 33	..	8 5	..	..	..	..	..
Elephant and Castle	5 10	..	5 3	..	..	..	5 36	5 24	..	..	6 3	..	6 10	..	..	6 36	6 23	..	..	..	7 3	..	7 11	..	..	7 38	7 23	8 10	..	..	..	8 3	..
Blackfriars ...... arr	5 13	..	5 6	..	..	..	5 39	5 27	..	..	6 6	..	6 13	..	..	6 39	6 26	..	..	..	7 6	..	7 14	..	..	7 41	7 26	8 13	..	..	..	8 7	..
Holborn Viaduct "	5 16	..	5 9	..	..	..	5 41	5 30	..	..	6 9	..	6 15	..	..	6 41	6 29	..	..	..	7 9	..	7 17	..	..	7 43	7 29	8 15	..	..	..	8 9	..
Brixton	4 51	..	..	..	..	5 11	..	..	..	..	..	5 51	..	..	..	6 11	..	..	..	6 53	..	..	..	..	7 11	..	..	7 51	..	..	..	..	..
Victoria .... arr	4 57	..	..	..	4 59	5 17	..	..	..	..	..	5 57	..	..	..	6 17	..	6 21	..	6 59	..	..	..	7 1	7 17	..	..	7 57	7 59	..	8 6	..	..

3 Third class only c Change at Orpington § Arr. 4 mins. *earlier*

For Other Notes, see page 157 **For SUNDAY TRAINS, see pages 154 to 157**

GILLINGHAM (Kent), CHATHAM, GRAVESEND WEST STREET, MAIDSTONE EAST, SEVENOAKS, ORPINGTON, CRYSTAL PALACE (H.L.) and LONDON

Up — p.m. — **Saturdays**—*continued* — p.m.

Up	3	3	3		3		3			3	3
Gillingham (Kent) .. dep	..	..	..	..	..	..	..	..	754	..	..
Chatham	..	..	..	..	..	..	..	..	758	..	..
Rochester	..	..	..	..	..	..	..	..	8 1	..	..
Sole Street	..	..	..	..	..	..	..	..	812	..	..
Meopham ..... {Longfield	..	..	..	..	..	..	..	..	815	..	..
Fawkham, for Hartley &	..	..	..	..	..	..	..	..	819	..	..
Gravesend West St dp	..	..	..	..	..	7 25	..	..	..	..	..
Southfleet (Springh'd).	..	..	..	..	..	7 30	..	..	..	..	..
Longfield Halt G	..	..	..	..	..	7 35	..	..	..	..	..
Farningham Road F	..	..	..	..	..	7 40	..	..	824	..	..
Maidstone East .. dep.	..	..	..	..	..	..	..	7 49	..	..	..
Barming	..	..	..	..	..	Stop	..	7 54	..	..	..
East Malling Halt	..	..	..	..	..	..	..	7 57	..	..	..
Malling	..	..	..	..	..	..	..	8 0	..	..	..
Wrotham & Boro' Gr'n	..	..	..	..	..	..	..	8 9	..	..	..
Kemsing	..	..	..	..	..	..	..	8 13	..	..	..
Seven- oaks {Tub's H. dp	..	..	7 24	..	7c34	..	8 2	..	..	8c4	8 24
{Bat & Ball	..	..	7 27	..	..	..	8 5	..	..	..	8 27
Otford	..	..	7 31	..	..	..	8 9	8 19	..	..	8 31
Shoreham (Kent)	..	..	7 34	..	..	..	8 12	..	..	..	8 34
Eynsford	..	..	7 38	..	..	..	8 16	..	..	..	8 38
Lullingstone	..	..	..	..	..	..	..	..	..	..	..
Swanley 60	..	..	7 44	..	..	..	8 24	8 28	832	..	8 44
St. Mary Cray	..	..	7 50	..	..	..	8 30	..	..	..	8 50
Orpington .. dep	7 43	..	..	..	8 18	..	..	..	..	8 43	..
Petts Wood	7 46	..	..	..	8 21	..	..	..	..	8 46	..
Bickley	7 49	..	7 54	..	8‖28	..	8 34	..	..	8 43	8 54
Bromley South D	7 52	..	7 57	..	8 32	..	8 37	..	842	8 52	8 57
Shortlands	7 55	..	8 0	..	8 35	..	8 40	..	..	8 55	9 0
Beckenham Junction	7 58	..	..	..	8 38	..	..	..	..	8 58	..
Kent House	8 0	..	..	..	8 40	..	..	..	..	9 0	..
Penge East C	8 2	..	..	..	8 42	..	..	..	..	9 2	..
Sydenham Hill	8 5	..	..	..	8 45	..	..	..	..	9 5	..
West Dulwich	8 7	..	..	..	8 47	..	..	..	..	9 7	..
Herne Hill	8 9	8 28	..	..	8 49	..	..	..	..	9 9	..
Ravensbourne	..	..	8 2	..	..	..	8 42	..	..	..	9 2
Beckenham Hill	..	..	8 4	..	..	..	8 44	..	..	..	9 4
Bellingham	..	..	8 6	..	..	..	8 46	..	..	..	9 6
Catford	..	..	8 8	..	..	p.m	8 48	..	..	..	9 8
Crofton Park	..	..	8 10	..	..	3	8 50	..	..	..	9 10
Crystal Palace B dep	..	..	..	..	..	8 36	..	..	..	..	..
Upper Sydenham	..	..	..	..	..	8 38	..	..	..	..	..
Lordship Lane A	..	..	..	..	..	8 40	..	..	..	..	..
Honor Oak	..	..	..	..	..	8 43	..	..	..	..	..
Nunhead	..	..	8 13	..	..	8 47	8 53	..	..	..	9 13
Peckham Rye	..	..	8 15	..	..	..	8 55	..	..	..	9 15
Denmark Hill	..	..	8 18	..	..	..	8 58	..	..	..	9 18
Loughborough Junc.	..	8 30	..	..	9 5	..	..	..	..	..	..
Elephant and Castle	..	8 35	8 23	..	9 10	..	9 3	..	..	..	9 23
Blackfriars ...... arr	..	8 38	8 26	..	9 13	..	9 6	..	..	..	9 26
Holborn Viaduct. "	..	8 40	8 29	..	9 15	..	9 9	..	..	..	9 29
Brixton	8 11	..	..	..	8 51	..	..	..	..	9 11	..
Victoria ...... arr	8 17	..	..	..	8 57	..	..	..	859	9 17	..

Up				3	3				3		3
Gillingham (Kent) .. dep	8 28	..	..	..	..	..	..	854	..	9 17	..
Chatham	8 32	..	..	..	..	..	..	858	..	9 24	..
Rochester	8 35	..	..	..	..	..	..	9 1	..	..	..
Sole Street	8 46	..	..	..	..	..	..	912	..	..	..
Meopham ..... {Longfield	8 49	..	..	..	..	..	..	915	..	..	..
Fawkham, for Hartley &	8 53	..	..	..	..	..	..	919	..	..	..
Gravesend West St dp	..	8 35	..	..	..	..	..	..	..	..	..
Southfleet (Springh'd).	..	8 40	..	..	..	..	..	..	..	..	..
Longfield Halt G	..	8 45	..	..	..	..	..	..	..	..	..
Farningham Road F	8 58	8 50	..	..	..	..	..	924	..	..	..
Maidstone East .. dep.	..	..	8 22	..	..	..	8 49	..	..	..	..
Barming	..	..	8 27	..	..	..	8 54	..	..	..	..
East Malling Halt	..	..	8 30	..	..	..	8 57	..	..	..	..
Malling	..	..	8 33	..	..	..	9 0	..	..	..	..
Wrotham & Boro' Gr'n	..	..	8 42	..	..	..	9 9	..	..	..	..
Kemsing	..	..	8 46	..	..	..	9-13	..	..	..	..
Seven- oaks {Tub's H. dp	..	..	..	8c34	9 2	..	..	..	9c4	..	9 24
{Bat & Ball	..	..	..	..	9 5	..	..	..	..	..	9 27
Otford	..	..	8 52	..	9 9	..	9 19	..	..	..	9 31
Shoreham (Kent)	..	..	..	..	9 12	..	..	..	..	..	9 34
Eynsford	..	..	..	..	9 16	..	..	..	..	..	9 38
Lullingstone	..	..	..	..	..	..	..	..	..	..	..
Swanley 60	9 4	8 56	9§5	..	9 24	..	9 28	932	..	..	9 44
St. Mary Cray	..	..	..	..	9 30	..	..	..	..	..	9 50
Orpington .. dep	Stop	Stop	..	9 23	..	..	Stop	..	9 43	..	..
Petts Wood	..	..	..	9 26	..	..	..	..	9 46	..	..
Bickley	..	..	..	9 29	9 34	..	..	..	9 49	..	9 54
Bromley South D	..	..	9 17	9 32	9 37	..	..	942	9 52	10 0	9 57
Shortlands	..	..	..	9 35	9 40	..	..	..	9 55	..	10 0
Beckenham Junction	..	..	..	9 38	..	..	..	..	9 58	..	..
Kent House	..	..	..	9 40	..	..	..	..	10 0	..	..
Penge East C	..	p.m	..	9 42	..	..	p.m	..	10 2	..	..
Sydenham Hill	..	3	..	9 45	..	..	3	..	10 5	..	..
West Dulwich	..	..	..	9 47	..	..	..	..	10 7	..	..
Herne Hill	..	9 27	..	9 49	..	..	10 3	..	10 9	..	..
Ravensbourne	..	..	..	..	9 42	..	..	..	..	..	10 2
Beckenham Hill	..	..	..	..	9 44	..	..	..	..	..	10 4
Bellingham	..	..	..	..	9 46	..	..	..	..	..	10 6
Catford	p.m	..	..	..	9 48	..	..	..	..	..	10 8
Crofton Park	3	..	..	..	9 50	..	..	..	..	..	1010
Crystal Palace B dep	9 36	..	..	..	..	..	..	..	..	..	..
Upper Sydenham	9 38	..	..	..	..	..	..	..	..	..	..
Lordship Lane A	9 40	..	..	..	..	..	..	..	..	..	..
Honor Oak	9 43	..	..	..	..	..	..	..	..	..	..
Nunhead	9 47	..	..	..	9 53	..	..	..	..	..	1013
Peckham Rye	..	..	..	..	9 55	..	..	..	..	..	1015
Denmark Hill	..	..	..	..	9 58	..	..	..	..	..	1018
Loughborough Junc.	..	9 30	..	..	..	..	10 5	..	..	..	..
Elephant and Castle	..	9 35	..	..	10 3	..	1010	..	..	..	1023
Blackfriars ...... arr	..	9 38	..	..	10 6	..	1013	..	..	..	1026
Holborn Viaduct. "	..	9 40	..	..	10 9	..	1015	..	..	..	1029
Brixton	..	..	..	9 51	..	..	..	..	1011	..	..
Victoria ...... arr	..	..	9 37	9 57	..	..	..	959	1017	1021	..

Up		3		3			3	3		3	3
Gillingham (Kent) .. dep	..	..	..	..	..	9 54	..	..	..	..	..
Chatham	..	..	..	..	..	9 58	..	..	..	..	..
Rochester	..	..	..	..	..	10 1	..	..	..	..	..
Sole Street	..	..	..	..	..	1012	..	..	..	..	..
Meopham ..... {Longfield	..	..	..	..	..	1015	..	..	..	..	..
Fawkham, for Hartley &	..	..	..	..	..	1019	..	..	..	..	..
Gravesend West St dp	..	..	9 50	..	..	..	..	..	..	..	..
Southfleet (Springh'd).	..	..	9 55	..	..	..	..	..	..	..	..
Longfield Halt G	..	..	10 1	..	..	..	..	..	..	..	..
Farningham Road F	..	..	10 7	..	..	1024	..	..	..	..	..
Maidstone East .. dep.	..	..	..	..	9 49	..	..	..	1010	..	..
Barming	..	..	..	..	9 54	..	..	..	1017	..	..
East Malling Halt	..	..	..	..	9 57	..	..	..	1021	..	..
Malling	..	..	..	..	10 0	..	..	..	1025	..	..
Wrotham & Boro' Gr'n	..	..	..	..	10 9	..	..	..	1038	..	..
Kemsing	..	..	..	..	1013	..	..	..	..	..	..
Seven- oaks {Tub's H. dp	..	9c34	..	10 2	..	..	10 24	10c34	..	..	11 2
{Bat & Ball	..	..	..	10 5	..	..	10 27	..	..	..	11 5
Otford	..	..	..	10 9	1019	..	10 31	..	1051	..	11 9
Shoreham (Kent)	..	..	..	1012	..	..	10 34	..	..	..	1112
Eynsford	..	..	..	1016	..	..	1038	..	..	..	1116
Lullingstone	..	..	..	..	..	..	..	..	..	..	..
Swanley 60	1012	..	1012	1024	1028	1032	10 44	..	11§7	..	1124
St. Mary Cray	1018	..	..	1030	..	..	10 50	..	..	..	1130
Orpington .. dep	Stop	1018	Stop	..	..	..	..	10 55	..	..	..
Petts Wood	..	1021	..	..	..	..	..	10 58	..	..	..
Bickley	..	10§29	..	1034	..	..	1054	11 1	..	..	1134
Bromley South D	..	1032	..	1037	..	1042	1057	11 5	1121	..	1137
Shortlands	..	1035	..	1040	..	..	11 0	11 7	..	..	1140
Beckenham Junction	..	1038	..	..	..	..	..	11 11	..	..	..
Kent House	..	1040	..	..	..	..	..	11 13	..	..	..
Penge East C	p.m	1042	..	..	..	..	..	11 15	..	..	..
Sydenham Hill	3	1045	..	..	..	..	..	11 19	..	..	..
West Dulwich	..	1047	..	..	..	..	..	11 21	..	..	..
Herne Hill	1028	1049	..	..	..	..	..	11 24	..	..	..
Ravensbourne	..	..	..	1042	..	..	11 2	..	..	..	1142
Beckenham Hill	..	..	..	1044	..	..	11 4	..	..	..	1144
Bellingham	..	..	..	1046	..	..	11 6	..	..	..	1146
Catford	..	..	p.m	1048	..	..	11 8	..	..	..	1148
Crofton Park	..	..	3	1050	..	..	1110	..	..	..	1150
Crystal Palace B dep	..	..	1036	..	..	..	..	..	..	1136	..
Upper Sydenham	..	..	1038	..	..	..	..	..	..	1138	..
Lordship Lane A	..	..	1040	..	..	..	..	..	..	1140	..
Honor Oak	..	..	1043	..	..	..	..	..	..	1143	..
Nunhead	..	..	1047	1053	..	..	1113	..	..	1147	1153
Peckham Rye	..	..	..	1055	..	..	1115	..	..	..	1155
Denmark Hill	..	..	..	1058	..	..	1118	..	..	..	1158
Loughborough Junc.	1030	11 5	..	..	..	..	..	11 31	..	..	..
Elephant and Castle	1035	1110	..	11 3	..	..	1123	11 36	..	..	12 3
Blackfriars ...... arr	1038	1113	..	11 6	..	..	1126	11 39	1145	..	12 6
Holborn Viaduct. "	1040	1115	..	11 9	..	..	1129	11 41	1148	..	12 9
Brixton	..	1051	..	..	..	..	..	11 26	..	..	..
Victoria ...... arr	..	1057	..	..	..	1059	..	11 32	..	..	..

3 Third class only — c Change at Orpington — ‖ Arr. 3 mins. *earlier* — § Arr 4 mins. *earlier*

For Other Notes, see page 157. **For SUNDAY TRAINS, see pages 154 to 157.**

GILLINGHAM (Kent), CHATHAM, GRAVESEND WEST STREET, MAIDSTONE EAST, SEVENOAKS, ORPINGTON, CRYSTAL PALACE (H.L.) and LONDON

Sundays — a.m.

Up	3	3	3	3	3	3	3	3	3	3	3	3	3	3	3	3			3	3	3	3	3	3	3	3	3	3		3			3
Gillingham (Kent) .. dep																		754														9 54	
Chatham																		758											9 51			9 58	
Rochester																		8 1														10 1	
Sole Street																		812														1012	
Meopham ...... [Longfield																		815														1015	
Fawkham, for Hartley &																		819														1019	
Gravesend West St dep																																	
Southfleet (Springh'd)																																	
Longfield Halt G																																	
Farningham Road F																		824														1024	
Maidstone East .. dep																	7 49														9 49		
Barming																	7 54														9 54		
East Malling Halt																	7 57														9 57		
Malling																	8 0														10 0		
Wrotham & Boro' Gr'n																	8 9														10 9		
Kemsing																	8 13														1013		
Sevenoaks { Tub's H. dp						6c30				7c2			7 24		7 44	8c2					8 24	8 44			9c2	9 24		9 44		10c2			
Sevenoaks { Bat & Ball													7 27		7 47						8 27	8 47				9 27		9 47					
Otford													7 30		7 51		8 19				8 30	8 51				9 30		9 51			1019		
Shoreham (Kent)													7 33		7 54						8 33	8 54				9 33		9 54					
Eynsford													7 38		7 58						8 38	8 58				9 38		9 58					
Lullingstone																																	
Swanley 60							6 58						7 45		8 5		8 28	832			8 45	9 5				9 45		10 5			1028	1032	
St Mary Cray							7 3						7 50		8 10						8 50	9 10				9 50		1010					
Orpington .... dep	5 18		6 13			7 0				7 23		7 43				8 23	Stop		8 43				9 23		9 43					1023	Stop		1043
Petts Wood	5 21		6 16			7 3				7 26		7 46				8 26			8 46				9 26		9 46					1026			1046
Bickley	5 24		6 19			7 6	7 7			7 29		7 49	7 54		8 14	8 29			8 49		8 54	9 14	9 29		9 49	9 54		1014		1029			1049
Bromley South D	5 27		6 22			7 10	7 11			7 32		7 52	7 57		8 17	8 32		842	8 52		8 57	9 17	9 32		9 52	9 57		1017	1029	1032		1042	1052
Shortlands	5 30		6 25			7 14	7 14			7 35		7 55	8 0		8 20	8 35			8 55		9 0	9 20	9 35		9 55	10 0		1020		1035			1055
Beckenham Junction	5 33		6 28			7 17				7 38		7 58				8 38			8 58				9 38		9 58					1038			1058
Kent House	5 35		6 30			7 19				7 40		8 0				8 40			9 0				9 40		10 0					1040			11 0
Penge East C	5 37		6 32			7 21				7 42		8 2				8 42			9 2				9 42		10 2					1042			11 2
Sydenham Hill	5 40		6 35			7 24				7 45		8 5				8 45			9 5				9 45		10 5					1045			11 5
West Dulwich	5 42		6 37			7 26				7 47		8 7				8 47			9 7				9 47		10 7					1047			11 7
Herne Hill	5 45	6 25	6 39		7 24	7 28		7 39		7 49		8 9				8 49			9 9				9 49		10 9					1049			11 9
Ravensbourne							7 16						8 2		8 22						9 2	9 22				10 2		1022					
Beckenham Hill							7 18						8 4		8 24						9 4	9 24				10 4		1024					
Bellingham							7 20						8 6		8 26		a.m				9 6	9 26				10 6		1026			a.m		
Catford							7 22						8 8		8 28		3				9 8	9 28				10 8		1028			3		
Crofton Park							7 24						8 10		8 30						9 10	9 30				1010		1030					
Crystal Palace B dep				6 50					7 10		7 56			8 14			8 56			9 14				9 56			1014				1056		
Upper Sydenham				6 52					7 12		7 58			8 16			8 58			9 16				9 58			1016				1058		
Lordship Lane A				6 54					7 14		8 0			8 18			9 0			9 18				10 0			1018				11 0		
Honor Oak				6 57					7 17		8 3			8 21			9 3			9 21				10 3			1021				11 3		
Nunhead				7 1			7 27		7 21		8 7		8 13	8 25	8 33		9 7			9 25	9 13	9 33		10 7		1013	1025	1033			11 7		
Peckham Rye							7 30						8 15		8 35						9 15	9 35				1015		1035					
Denmark Hill							7 32						8 17		8 37						9 17	9 37				1017		1037					
Loughborough Junc.	5 48	6 27			7 27			7 42				8 14				8 53			9 14				9 53		1014					1053			1114
Elephant and Castle	5 53	6 32			7 32		7 39	7 47				8 18	8 23		8 43	8 58			9 18		9 23	9 43	9 58		1018	1023		1043		1058			1118
Blackfriars ...... arr	5 56	6 35			7 35		7 42	7 50				8 21	8 26		8 46	9 1			9 21		9 26	9 46	10 1		1021	1026		1046		11 1			1121
Holborn Viaduct. "	5 58	6 37			7 37		7 44	7 52				8 24	8 29		8 49	9 3			9 24		9 29	9 49	10 3		1024	1029		1049		11 3			1124
Brixton	5 47		6 41			7 30				7 51		8 11				8 51			9 11				9 51		1011					1051			1111
Victoria .... arr	5 53		6 47			7 36				7 57		8 17				8 57		9 3	9 17				9 57		1017				1049	1057		1059	1117

3 Third class only

c Change at Orpington

For Other Notes, see page 157

GILLINGHAM (Kent), CHATHAM, GRAVESEND WEST STREET, MAIDSTONE EAST, SEVENOAKS, ORPINGTON, CRYSTAL PALACE (H.L.), and LONDON

a.m — **Sundays**—*continued* — p.m

Up	3	3	3	3		3	3	3	3		3	3			3	3
Gillingham (Kent)..dep	..	..	..	..	..	..	..	..	..	..	..	..	..	1154	..	..
Chatham	..	..	..	..	1114	..	..	..	..	..	..	..	..	1158	..	..
Rochester	..	..	..	..	..	..	..	..	..	..	..	..	..	12 1	..	..
Sole Street	..	..	..	..	..	..	..	..	..	..	..	..	..	1212	..	..
Meopham......[Longfield	..	..	..	..	..	..	..	..	..	..	..	..	..	1215	..	..
Fawkham for Hartley &	..	..	..	..	..	..	..	..	..	..	..	..	..	1219	..	..
Gravesend West St dp	..	..	..	..	..	..	..	..	..	..	..	..	..	..	..	..
Southfleet (Springh'd)	..	..	..	..	..	..	..	..	..	..	..	..	..	..	..	..
Longfield Halt G	..	..	..	..	..	..	..	..	..	..	..	..	..	..	..	..
Farningham Road F	..	..	..	..	..	..	..	..	..	..	..	..	..	1224	..	..
Maidstone East..dep	..	..	..	..	..	..	..	..	..	..	..	..	1149	..	..	..
Barming	..	..	..	..	..	..	..	..	..	..	..	..	1154	..	..	..
East Malling Halt	..	..	..	..	..	..	..	..	..	..	..	..	1157	..	..	..
Malling	..	..	..	..	..	..	..	..	..	..	..	..	12 0	..	..	..
Wrotham & Boro' Gr'n	..	..	..	..	..	..	..	..	..	..	..	..	12 9	..	..	..
Kemsing	..	..	..	..	..	..	..	..	..	..	..	p.m	1213	..	..	..
Sevenoaks { Tub's H. dp	..	1024	1044	11c2	..	..	..	1124	..	..	1144	12c2	..	..	..	1224
Sevenoaks { Bat & Ball	..	1027	1047	..	..	..	..	1127	..	..	1147	..	..	..	..	1227
Otford	..	1030	1050	..	..	..	..	1130	..	..	1151	..	1219	..	..	1230
Shoreham (Kent)	..	1033	1053	..	..	..	..	1133	..	..	1154	..	..	..	..	1233
Eynsford	..	1038	1058	..	..	..	..	1138	..	..	1158	..	..	..	..	1238
Lullingstone	..	..	..	..	..	..	..	..	..	..	..	..	..	..	..	..
Swanley 60	..	1045	11 5	..	..	..	..	1145	..	..	12 5	..	1228	1232	..	1245
St. Mary Cray	..	1050	1110	..	..	..	..	1150	..	..	1210	..	Stop	..	..	1250
Orpington.........dep	..	..	..	1123	..	..	11 43	..	..	..	..	1223	..	..	12 43	..
Petts Wood	..	..	..	1126	..	..	11 46	..	..	..	..	1226	..	..	12 46	..
Bickley	..	1054	1114	1129	..	..	11 49	1154	..	..	1214	1229	..	..	12 49	1254
Bromley South D	..	1057	1117	1132	1151	..	11 52	1157	..	..	1217	1232	..	1242	12 52	1257
Shortlands	..	11 0	1120	1135	..	..	11 55	12 0	..	..	1220	1235	..	..	12 55	1 0
Beckenham Junction	..	..	..	1138	..	..	11 58	..	..	..	..	1238	..	..	12 58	..
Kent House	..	..	..	1140	..	..	12 0	..	..	..	..	1240	..	..	1 0	..
Penge East C	..	..	..	1142	..	..	12 2	..	..	..	..	1242	..	..	1 2	..
Sydenham Hill	..	..	..	1145	..	..	12 5	..	..	..	..	1245	..	..	1 5	..
West Dulwich	..	..	..	1147	..	..	12 7	..	..	..	..	1247	..	..	1 7	..
Herne Hill	..	..	..	1149	..	..	12 9	..	..	..	..	1249	..	..	1 9	..
Ravensbourne	..	11 2	1122	..	..	..	..	12 2	..	..	1222	..	..	..	..	1 2
Beckenham Hill	..	11 4	1124	..	..	..	..	12 4	..	..	1224	..	..	..	..	1 4
Bellingham	..	11 6	1126	..	..	..	..	12 6	..	..	1226	..	p.m	..	..	1 6
Catford	..	11 8	1128	..	..	..	..	12 8	..	..	1228	..	..	..	..	1 8
Crofton Park	..	1110	1130	..	..	..	..	1210	p.m	..	1230	..	3	..	..	1 10
Crystal Palace B dep	1114	..	..	..	..	1156	..	..	1214	..	..	..	1256	..	..	..
Upper Sydenham	1116	..	..	..	..	1158	..	..	1216	..	..	..	1258	..	..	..
Lordship Lane A	1118	..	..	..	..	12 0	..	..	1218	..	..	..	1 0	..	..	..
Honor Oak	1121	..	..	..	..	12 3	..	..	1221	..	..	..	1 3	..	..	..
Nunhead	1125	1113	1133	..	..	12 7	..	1213	1225	..	1233	..	1 7	..	..	1 13
Peckham Rye	..	1115	1135	..	..	..	..	1215	..	..	1235	..	..	..	..	1 15
Denmark Hill	..	1117	1137	..	..	..	..	1217	..	..	1237	..	..	..	..	1 17
Loughborough Junc.	..	..	..	1153	..	..	12 14	..	..	..	..	1253	..	..	1 14	..
Elephant and Castle	..	1123	1143	1158	..	..	12 18	1223	..	..	1243	1258	..	..	1 18	1 23
Blackfriars......arr	..	1126	1146	12 1	..	..	12 21	1226	..	..	1246	1 1	..	..	1 21	1 26
Holborn Viaduct. "	..	1129	1149	12 3	..	..	12 24	1229	..	..	1249	1 3	..	..	1 24	1 29
Brixton	..	..	..	1151	..	..	12 11	..	..	..	..	1251	..	..	1 11	..
Victoria..........arr	..	..	..	1157	1213	..	12 17	..	..	..	..	1257	..	1259	1 17	..

Up	3	3	3	3	3	3	3	3	3			3	3	3	3	3
Gillingham (Kent)..dep	..	..	..	..	..	..	..	..	..	..	1 54	..	..	..	..	..
Chatham	..	..	..	..	..	..	..	..	..	..	1 58	..	..	..	..	..
Rochester	..	..	..	..	..	..	..	..	..	..	2 1	..	..	..	..	..
Sole Street	..	..	..	..	..	..	..	..	..	..	2 12	..	..	..	..	..
Meopham......[Longfield	..	..	..	..	..	..	..	..	..	..	2 15	..	..	..	..	..
Fawkham for Hartley &	..	..	..	..	..	..	..	..	..	..	2 19	..	..	..	..	..
Gravesend West St dp	..	..	..	..	..	..	..	..	..	..	..	..	..	..	..	..
Southfleet (Springh'd)	..	..	..	..	..	..	..	..	..	..	..	..	..	..	..	..
Longfield Halt G	..	..	..	..	..	..	..	..	..	..	..	..	..	..	..	..
Farningham Road F	..	..	..	..	..	..	..	..	..	..	2 24	..	..	..	..	..
Maidstone East..dep	..	..	..	..	..	..	..	..	..	1 49	..	..	..	..	..	..
Barming	..	..	..	..	..	..	..	..	..	1 54	..	..	..	..	..	..
East Malling Halt	..	..	..	..	..	..	..	..	..	1 57	..	..	..	..	..	..
Malling	..	..	..	..	..	..	..	..	..	2 0	..	..	..	..	..	..
Wrotham & Boro' Gr'n	..	..	..	..	..	..	..	..	..	2 9	..	..	..	..	..	..
Kemsing	..	..	..	..	..	..	..	..	..	2 13	..	..	..	..	..	..
Sevenoaks { Tub's H. dp	..	1244	1 c 2	..	..	1 24	..	1 44	2 c 2	..	..	..	2 24	..	2 44	3 c 2
Sevenoaks { Bat & Ball	..	1247	..	..	..	1 27	..	1 47	..	..	..	..	2 27	..	2 47	..
Otford	..	1251	..	..	..	1 30	..	1 51	..	2 19	..	..	2 30	..	2 51	..
Shoreham (Kent)	..	1254	..	..	..	1 33	..	1 54	..	..	..	..	2 33	..	2 54	..
Eynsford	..	1258	..	..	..	1 38	..	1 58	..	..	..	..	2 38	..	2 58	..
Lullingstone	..	..	..	..	..	..	..	..	..	..	..	..	..	..	..	..
Swanley 60	..	1 5	..	..	..	1 45	..	2 5	..	2 28	2 32	..	2 45	..	3 5	..
St. Mary Cray	..	1 10	..	..	..	1 50	..	2 10	..	Stop	..	..	2 50	..	3 10	..
Orpington.........dep	..	..	1 23	..	1 43	..	..	..	2 23	..	..	2 43	..	..	..	3 23
Petts Wood	..	..	1 26	..	1 46	..	..	..	2 26	..	..	2 46	..	..	..	3 26
Bickley	..	1 14	1 29	..	1 49	1 54	..	2 14	2 29	..	..	2 49	2 55	..	3 14	3 29
Bromley South D	..	1 17	1 32	..	1 52	1 57	..	2 17	2 32	..	2 42	2 52	2 58	..	3 17	3 32
Shortlands	..	1 20	1 35	..	1 55	2 0	..	2 20	2 35	..	..	2 55	3 1	..	3 20	3 35
Beckenham Junction	..	..	1 38	..	1 58	..	..	..	2 38	..	..	2 58	..	..	..	3 38
Kent House	..	..	1 40	..	2 0	..	..	..	2 40	..	..	3 0	..	..	..	3 40
Penge East C	..	..	1 42	..	2 2	..	..	..	2 42	..	..	3 2	..	..	..	3 42
Sydenham Hill	..	..	1 45	..	2 5	..	..	..	2 45	..	..	3 5	..	..	..	3 45
West Dulwich	..	..	1 47	..	2 7	..	..	..	2 47	..	..	3 7	..	..	..	3 47
Herne Hill	..	..	1 49	..	2 9	..	..	..	2 49	..	..	3 9	..	..	..	3 49
Ravensbourne	..	1 22	..	..	..	2 2	..	2 22	..	..	..	..	3 3	..	3 22	..
Beckenham Hill	..	1 24	..	..	..	2 4	..	2 24	..	..	..	..	3 5	..	3 24	..
Bellingham	..	1 26	..	..	..	2 6	..	2 26	..	p.m	..	..	3 7	..	3 26	..
Catford	..	1 28	..	..	..	2 8	..	2 28	..	..	..	..	3 9	..	3 28	..
Crofton Park	..	1 30	..	..	..	2 10	..	2 30	..	3	..	..	3 11	..	3 30	..
Crystal Palace B dep	1 14	..	..	1 56	..	..	2 14	..	..	2 56	..	..	..	3 14	..	..
Upper Sydenham	1 16	..	..	1 58	..	..	2 16	..	..	2 58	..	..	..	3 16	..	..
Lordship Lane A	1 18	..	..	2 0	..	..	2 18	..	..	3 0	..	..	..	3 18	..	..
Honor Oak	1 21	..	..	2 3	..	..	2 21	..	..	3 3	..	..	..	3 21	..	..
Nunhead	1 25	1 33	..	2 7	..	2 13	2 25	2 33	..	3 7	..	..	3 14	3 25	3 33	..
Peckham Rye	..	1 35	..	..	..	2 15	..	2 35	..	..	..	..	3 16	..	3 35	..
Denmark Hill	..	1 37	..	..	..	2 17	..	2 37	..	..	..	..	3 18	..	3 37	..
Loughborough Junc.	..	..	1 53	..	2 14	..	..	..	2 53	..	..	3 17	..	..	..	3 53
Elephant and Castle	..	1 43	1 58	..	2 18	2 23	..	2 43	2 58	..	..	3 21	3 24	..	3 43	3 58
Blackfriars......arr	..	1 46	2 1	..	2 21	2 26	..	2 46	3 1	..	..	3 24	3 27	..	3 46	4 1
Holborn Viaduct. "	..	1 49	2 3	..	2 24	2 29	..	2 49	3 3	..	..	3 27	3 30	..	3 49	4 3
Brixton	..	..	1 51	..	2 11	..	..	..	2 51	..	..	3 11	..	..	..	3 51
Victoria..........arr	..	..	1 57	..	2 17	..	..	..	2 57	..	2 59	3 17	..	..	..	3 57

3 Third class only   c Change at Orpington

For Other Notes, see page 157

GILLINGHAM (Kent), CHATHAM, GRAVESEND WEST STREET, MAIDSTONE EAST, SEVENOAKS, ORPINGTON, CRYSTAL PALACE (H.L.) and LONDON

p.m — Sundays—continued — p.m

Up	3	3	3	3	3	..	3	..	..	3	3	3	3	3	3	3	3	3	3	3	..	..	3	3	3	3	..	3	..	3	3	3	3
Gillingham (Kent)..dep	..	..	..	..	..	..	..	..	3 54	..	..	..	..	..	..	..	..	..	..	..	..	5 54	..	..	..	..	..	..	7 1	..	..	..	..
Chatham	..	..	..	..	..	..	..	..	3 58	..	..	..	..	..	..	..	..	..	..	..	..	5 58	..	..	..	..	6 44	..	7 7	..	..	..	..
Rochester	..	..	..	..	..	..	..	..	4 1	..	..	..	..	..	..	..	..	..	..	..	..	6 1	..	..	..	..	..	..	..	..	..	..	..
Sole Street	..	..	..	..	..	..	..	..	4 12	..	..	..	..	..	..	..	..	..	..	..	..	6 12	..	..	..	..	..	..	..	..	..	..	..
Meopham .....[Longfield	..	..	..	..	..	..	..	..	4 15	..	..	..	..	..	..	..	..	..	..	..	..	6 15	..	..	..	..	..	..	..	..	..	..	..
Fawkham, for Hartley &	..	..	..	..	..	..	..	..	4 19	..	..	..	..	..	..	..	..	..	..	..	..	6 19	..	..	..	..	..	..	..	..	..	..	..
Gravesend West St dp	..	..	..	..	..	..	..	..	..	..	..	..	..	..	..	..	..	..	..	..	..	..	..	..	..	..	..	..	..	..	..	..	..
Southfleet (Springh'd).	..	..	..	..	..	..	..	..	..	..	..	..	..	..	..	..	..	..	..	..	..	..	..	..	..	..	..	..	..	..	..	..	..
Longfield Halt G	..	..	..	..	..	..	..	..	..	..	..	..	..	..	..	..	..	..	..	..	..	..	..	..	..	..	..	..	..	..	..	..	..
Farningham Road F	..	..	..	..	..	..	..	..	4 24	..	..	..	..	..	..	..	..	..	..	..	..	6 24	..	..	..	..	..	..	..	..	..	..	..
Maidstone East..dep.	..	..	..	..	..	..	..	3 49	..	..	..	..	..	..	..	..	..	..	..	..	5 49	..	..	..	..	..	..	..	..	..	..	..	..
Barming	..	..	..	..	..	..	..	3 54	..	..	..	..	..	..	..	..	..	..	..	..	5 54	..	..	..	..	..	..	..	..	..	..	..	..
East Malling Halt	..	..	..	..	..	..	..	3 57	..	..	..	..	..	..	..	..	..	..	..	..	5 57	..	..	..	..	..	..	..	..	..	..	..	..
Malling	..	..	..	..	..	..	..	4 0	..	..	..	..	..	..	..	..	..	..	..	..	6 0	..	..	..	..	..	..	..	..	..	..	..	..
Wrotham & Boro' Gr'n	..	..	..	..	..	..	..	4 9	..	..	..	..	..	..	..	..	..	..	..	..	6 9	..	..	..	..	..	..	..	..	..	..	..	..
Kemsing	..	..	..	..	..	..	..	4 13	..	..	..	..	..	..	..	..	..	..	..	..	6 13	..	..	..	..	..	..	..	..	..	..	..	..
Seven- { Tub's H. dp	..	..	3 24	..	3 44	..	4c2	..	..	..	4 24	..	4 44	5 c 2	..	..	5 24	..	5 44	5c57	..	..	..	6 24	..	6 44	..	6c58	..	..	..	7 24	..
oaks { Bat & Ball	..	..	3 27	..	3 47	..	..	..	..	..	4 27	..	4 47	..	..	..	5 27	..	5 47	..	..	..	..	6 27	..	6 47	..	..	..	..	..	7 27	..
Otford	..	..	3 30	..	3 51	..	..	4 19	..	..	4 30	..	4 51	..	..	..	5 30	..	5 51	..	6 19	..	..	6 30	..	6 51	..	..	..	..	..	7 30	..
Shoreham (Kent)	..	..	3 33	..	3 54	..	..	..	..	..	4 33	..	4 54	..	..	..	5 33	..	5 54	..	..	..	..	6 33	..	6 54	..	..	..	..	..	7 33	..
Eynsford	..	..	3 38	..	3 58	..	..	..	..	..	4 38	..	4 58	..	..	..	5 38	..	5 58	..	..	..	..	6 38	..	6 58	..	..	..	..	..	7 38	..
Lullingstone	..	..	..	..	..	..	..	..	..	..	..	..	..	..	..	..	..	..	..	..	..	..	..	..	..	..	..	..	..	..	..	..	..
Swanley 69	..	..	3 45	..	4 5	..	..	4 28	4 32	..	4 45	..	5 5	..	..	..	5 45	..	6 5	..	6 28	6 32	..	6 45	..	7 5	..	..	..	..	..	7 45	..
St. Mary Cray	..	..	3 50	..	4 10	..	..	Stop	..	..	4 50	..	5 10	..	..	..	5 50	..	6 10	..	Stop	..	..	6 50	..	7 10	..	..	..	..	..	7 50	..
Orpington dep	..	3 43	..	..	..	..	4 23	..	..	4 43	..	..	..	5 23	..	5 43	..	..	..	6 23	..	..	6 43	..	..	..	..	7 23	..	..	7 43	..	..
Petts Wood	..	3 46	..	..	..	..	4 26	..	..	4 46	..	..	..	5 26	..	5 46	..	..	..	6 26	..	..	6 46	..	..	..	..	7 26	..	..	7 46	..	..
Bickley	..	3 49	3 54	..	4 14	..	4 29	..	..	4 49	4 54	..	5 14	5 29	..	5 49	5 54	..	6 14	6 29	..	..	6 49	6 54	..	7 14	..	7 29	..	..	7 49	7 54	..
Bromley South D	..	3 52	3 57	..	4 17	..	4 32	..	4 42	4 52	4 57	..	5 17	5 32	..	5 52	5 57	..	6 17	6 32	..	6 42	6 52	6 57	..	7 17	7 25	7 32	745	..	7 52	7 57	..
Shortlands	..	3 55	4 0	..	4 20	..	4 35	..	..	4 55	5 0	..	5 20	5 35	..	5 55	6 0	..	6 20	6 35	..	..	6 55	7 0	..	7 20	..	7 35	..	..	7 55	8 0	..
Beckenham Junction	..	3 58	..	..	..	..	4 38	..	..	4 58	..	..	..	5 38	..	5 58	..	..	..	6 38	..	..	6 58	..	..	..	..	7 38	..	..	7 58	..	..
Kent House	..	4 0	..	..	..	..	4 40	..	..	5 0	..	..	..	5 40	..	6 0	..	..	..	6 40	..	..	7 0	..	..	..	..	7 40	..	..	8 0	..	..
Penge East C	..	4 2	..	..	..	..	4 42	..	..	5 2	..	..	..	5 42	..	6 2	..	..	..	6 42	..	..	7 2	..	..	..	..	7 42	..	..	8 2	..	..
Sydenham Hill	..	4 5	..	..	..	..	4 45	..	..	5 5	..	..	..	5 45	..	6 5	..	..	..	6 45	..	..	7 5	..	..	..	..	7 45	..	..	8 5	..	..
West Dulwich	..	4 7	..	..	..	..	4 47	..	..	5 7	..	..	..	5 47	..	6 7	..	..	..	6 47	..	..	7 7	..	..	..	..	7 47	..	..	8 7	..	..
Herne Hill	..	4 9	..	..	..	..	4 49	..	..	5 9	..	..	..	5 49	..	6 9	..	..	..	6 49	..	..	7 9	..	..	..	..	7 49	..	..	8 9	..	..
Ravensbourne	..	..	4 2	..	4 22	..	..	..	..	..	5 2	..	5 22	..	..	..	6 2	..	6 22	..	..	..	..	7 2	..	7 22	..	..	..	..	..	8 2	..
Beckenham Hill	..	..	4 4	..	4 24	..	..	..	..	..	5 4	..	5 24	..	..	..	6 4	..	6 24	..	..	..	..	7 4	..	7 24	..	..	..	..	..	8 4	..
Bellingham	..	..	4 6	..	4 26	..	..	p.m	..	..	5 6	..	5 26	..	..	..	6 6	..	6 26	..	p.m	..	..	7 6	..	7 26	..	..	..	..	..	8 6	..
Catford	..	..	4 8	..	4 28	..	..	3	..	..	5 8	..	5 28	..	..	..	6 8	..	6 28	..	3	..	..	7 8	..	7 28	..	..	..	..	..	8 8	..
Crofton Park	..	..	4 10	..	4 30	..	..	..	..	..	5 10	..	5 30	..	..	..	6 10	..	6 30	..	..	..	..	7 10	..	7 30	..	..	..	..	..	8 10	..
Crystal Palace B dep	3 56	..	..	4 14	..	..	..	4 56	..	..	..	5 14	..	..	5 56	..	..	6 14	..	..	6 56	..	..	..	7 14	..	..	..	..	7 56	..	..	8 14
Upper Sydenham	3 58	..	..	4 16	..	..	..	4 58	..	..	..	5 16	..	..	5 58	..	..	6 16	..	..	6 58	..	..	..	7 16	..	..	..	..	7 58	..	..	8 16
Lordship Lane A	4 0	..	..	4 18	..	..	..	5 0	..	..	..	5 18	..	..	6 0	..	..	6 18	..	..	7 0	..	..	..	7 18	..	..	..	..	8 0	..	..	8 18
Honor Oak	4 3	..	..	4 21	..	..	..	5 3	..	..	..	5 21	..	..	6 3	..	..	6 21	..	..	7 3	..	..	..	7 21	..	..	..	..	8 3	..	..	8 21
Nunhead	4 7	..	4 13	4 25	4 33	..	..	5 7	..	..	5 13	5 25	5 33	..	6 7	..	6 13	6 25	6 33	..	7 7	..	..	7 13	7 25	7 33	..	..	..	8 7	..	8 13	8 25
Peckham Rye	..	..	4 15	..	4 35	..	..	..	..	..	5 15	..	5 35	..	..	..	6 15	..	6 35	..	..	..	..	7 15	..	7 35	..	..	..	..	..	8 15	..
Denmark Hill	..	..	4 17	..	4 37	..	..	..	..	..	5 17	..	5 37	..	..	..	6 17	..	6 37	..	..	..	..	7 17	..	7 37	..	..	..	..	..	8 17	..
Loughborough Junc	..	4 14	..	..	..	..	4 53	..	..	5 14	..	..	..	5 53	..	6 14	..	..	..	6 53	..	..	7 14	..	..	..	..	7 53	..	..	8 14	..	..
Elephant and Castle	..	4 18	4 23	..	4 43	..	4 58	..	..	5 18	5 23	..	5 43	5 58	..	6 18	6 23	..	6 43	6 58	..	..	7 18	7 23	..	7 43	..	7 58	..	..	8 18	8 23	..
Blackfriars ...... arr	..	4 21	4 26	..	4 46	..	5 1	..	..	5 21	5 26	..	5 46	6 1	..	6 21	6 26	..	6 46	7 1	..	..	7 21	7 26	..	7 46	..	8 1	..	..	8 21	8 26	..
Holborn Viaduct. "	..	4 24	4 29	..	4 49	..	5 3	..	..	5 24	5 29	..	5 49	6 3	..	6 24	6 29	..	6 49	7 3	..	..	7 24	7 29	..	7 49	..	8 3	..	..	8 24	8 29	..
Brixton	..	4 11	..	..	..	..	4 51	..	..	5 11	..	..	..	5 51	..	6 11	..	..	..	6 51	..	..	7 11	..	..	..	..	7 51	..	..	8 11	..	..
Victoria .... arr	..	4 17	..	..	..	..	4 57	..	5 3	5 17	..	..	..	5 57	..	6 17	..	..	..	6 57	..	7 3	7 17	..	..	..	7 46	7 57	8 6	..	8 17	..	..

3 Third class only c Change at Orpington.

For Other Notes, see page 157

GILLINGHAM (Kent), CHATHAM, GRAVESEND WEST STREET, MAIDSTONE EAST, SEVENOAKS, ORPINGTON, CRYSTAL PALACE (H.L.) and LONDON

Sundays—*continued* (p.m)

Up.	3	3				3	3	3	3				3			3	3	3		3	3	3			3	3	3
Gillingham (Kent).. dep	..	..	..	..	754	..	..	..	..	..	..	..	..	8 54	9 0	..	..	..	9 36	..	..	..	..	9 54	..	..	..
Chatham	..	..	751	..	758	..	..	..	..	..	..	..	..	8 58	9 7	..	..	..	9 42	..	..	..	..	9 58	..	..	..
Rochester	..	..	..	..	8 1	..	..	..	..	..	..	..	..	9 1	..	..	..	..	..	..	..	..	..	10 1	..	..	..
Sole Street	..	..	..	..	812	..	..	..	..	..	..	..	..	9 12	..	..	..	..	..	..	..	..	..	1012	..	..	..
Meopham.....[Longfield	..	..	..	..	815	..	..	..	..	..	..	..	..	9 15	..	..	..	..	..	..	..	..	..	1015	..	..	..
Fawkham, for Hartley &	..	..	..	..	819	..	..	..	..	..	..	..	..	9 19	..	..	..	..	..	..	..	..	..	1019	..	..	..
Gravesend West St dp	..	..	..	..	..	..	..	..	..	..	..	..	..	..	..	..	..	..	..	..	..	..	..	..	..	..	..
Southfleet (Springh'd).	..	..	..	..	..	..	..	..	..	..	..	..	..	..	..	..	..	..	..	..	..	..	..	..	..	..	..
Longfield Halt G	..	..	..	..	..	..	..	..	..	..	..	..	..	..	..	..	..	..	..	..	..	..	..	..	..	..	..
Farningham Road F	..	..	..	..	824	..	..	..	..	..	..	..	..	9 24	..	..	..	..	..	..	..	..	..	1024	..	..	..
Maidstone East.. dep	..	..	..	7 49	..	..	..	..	..	..	8 49	..	..	..	..	..	..	..	..	..	..	..	9 49	..	..	..	..
Barming	..	..	..	7 54	..	..	..	..	..	..	8 54	..	..	..	..	..	..	..	..	..	..	..	9 54	..	..	..	..
East Malling Halt	..	..	..	7 57	..	..	..	..	..	..	8 57	..	..	..	..	..	..	..	..	..	..	..	9 57	..	..	..	..
Malling	..	..	..	8 0	..	..	..	..	..	..	9 0	..	..	..	..	..	..	..	..	..	..	..	10 0	..	..	..	..
Wrotham & Boro' Gr'n	..	..	..	8 9	..	..	..	..	..	..	9 9	..	..	..	..	..	..	..	..	..	..	..	10 9	..	..	..	..
Kemsing	..	..	..	8 13	..	..	..	..	..	..	9 13	..	..	..	..	..	..	..	..	..	..	..	1013	..	..	..	..
Seven- Tub's H. dp	7 44	7c30	..	..	..	8c0	8 24	..	8 44	..	..	..	..	..	..	..	9c4	9 24	..	..	9 56	10c0	..	..	1024	10c30	1044
oaks Bat & Ball..	7 47	..	..	..	..	..	8 27	..	8 47	..	..	..	..	..	..	..	..	9 27	..	..	9 59	..	..	..	1027	..	1047
Otford	7 51	..	..	8 19	..	..	8 30	..	8 51	..	9 19	..	..	..	..	..	..	9 30	..	..	10 2	..	1019	..	1030	..	1051
Shoreham (Kent)	7 54	..	..	..	..	..	8 33	..	8 54	..	..	..	..	..	..	..	..	9 33	..	..	10 5	..	..	..	1033	..	1054
Eynsford	7 58	..	..	..	..	..	8 38	..	8 58	..	..	..	..	..	..	..	..	9 38	..	..	10 10	..	..	..	1038	..	1058
Lullingstone	..	..	..	..	..	..	..	..	..	..	..	..	..	..	..	..	..	..	..	..	..	..	..	..	..	..	..
Swanley 60	8 5	..	..	8 28	832	..	8 45	..	9 5	..	9 28	..	..	9 32	..	..	..	9 45	..	..	10 16	..	1028	1032	1045	..	11 5
St. Mary Cray	8 10	..	..		..	..	8 50	..	9 10	..	..	..	..	..	..	..	..	9 50	..	..	10 21	..	..	..		..	1110
Orpington........ dep	..	8 17	..	Stop	..	8 43	..	..	..	..	..	..	9 23	..	..	..	9 43	..	..	..	..	1023	..	..	Stop	10 48	..
Petts Wood	..	8 20	..	..	..	8 46	..	..	..	..	..	..	9 26	..	..	..	9 46	..	..	..	..	1026	..	..	..	10 51	..
Bickley	8 14	8 24	..	..	..	8 49	8 54	..	9 14	..	..	..	9 29	..	..	..	9 49	9 54	..	..	10 25	1029	..	..	..	10 54	1114
Bromley South D	8 17	8 29	829	..	842	8 52	8 57	..	9 17	..	..	..	9 32	9 42	945	..	9 52	9 57	1018	..	10 30	1032	..	1042	..	10‡59	1117
Shortlands	8 20	8 32	..	..	..	8 55	9 0	..	9 20	..	..	..	9 35	..	..	..	9 55	10 0	..	..	10 33	1035	..	..	..	11 2	1120
Beckenham Junction	..	8 35	..	..	..	8 58	..	..	..	..	..	..	9 38	..	..	..	9 58	..	..	..	..	1038	..	..	..	11 5	..
Kent House	..	8 37	..	..	..	9 0	..	..	..	..	..	..	9 40	..	..	..	10 0	..	..	..	..	1040	..	..	..	11 8	..
Penge East C	..	8 39	..	..	..	9 2	..	..	..	..	..	..	9 42	..	..	..	10 2	..	..	..	..	1042	..	..	..	11 10	..
Sydenham Hill	..	8 42	..	..	..	9 5	..	..	..	..	..	..	9 45	..	..	..	10 5	..	..	..	..	1045	..	..	..	11 13	..
West Dulwich	..	8 44	..	..	..	9 7	..	..	..	..	..	..	9 47	..	..	..	10 7	..	..	..	..	1047	..	..	..	11 16	..
Herne Hill	..	8 46	..	..	..	9 9	..	..	..	..	..	..	9 49	..	..	..	10 9	..	..	..	..	1049	..	..	..	11 18	..
Ravensbourne	8 22	..	..	..	..	..	9 2	..	9 22	..	..	..	..	..	..	..	..	10 2	..	..	10 35	..	..	..	..	..	1122
Beckenham Hill	8 24	..	..	..	..	..	9 4	..	9 24	..	..	..	..	..	..	..	..	10 4	..	..	10 37	..	..	..	..	..	1124
Bellingham	8 26	..	..	p.m	..	..	9 6	..	9 26	..	..	..	..	..	..	..	..	10 6	..	..	10 39	..	..	..	p.m.	..	1126
Catford	8 28	..	..	3	..	..	9 8	..	9 28	..	..	..	..	..	..	..	..	10 8	..	..	10 41	..	..	..	3	..	1128
Crofton Park	8 30	..	..		..	..	9 10	..	9 30	..	..	..	..	..	..	..	..	1010	..	..	10 43	..	..	..		..	1130
Crystal Palace B dep	..	..	..	8 56	..	..	..	9 14	..	..	..	..	..	..	..	9 56	..	..	..	1030	..	..	..	..	1050	..	..
Upper Sydenham	..	..	..	8 58	..	..	..	9 16	..	..	..	..	..	..	..	9 58	..	..	..	1032	..	..	..	..	1052	..	..
Lordship Lane A	..	..	..	9 0	..	..	..	9 18	..	..	..	..	..	..	..	10 0	..	..	..	1034	..	..	..	..	1054	..	..
Honor Oak	..	..	..	9 3	..	..	..	9 21	..	..	..	..	..	..	..	10 3	..	..	..	1037	..	..	..	..	1057	..	..
Nunhead	8 33	..	..	9 7	..	..	9 13	9 25	9 33	..	..	..	..	..	..	10 7	..	1013	..	1041	10 46	..	..	..	11 1	..	1133
Peckham Rye	8 35	..	..	..	..	..	9 15	..	9 35	..	..	..	..	..	..	..	..	1015	..	..	10 49	..	..	..	..	..	1135
Denmark Hill	8 37	..	..	..	..	..	9 17	..	9 37	..	..	..	..	..	..	..	..	1017	..	..	10 51	..	..	..	..	..	1137
Loughborough Junc.	..	8 53	..	..	..	9 14	..	..	..	..	..	..	9 53	..	..	..	1014	..	..	..	..	1056	..	..	..	..	..
Elephant and Castle	8 43	8 58	..	..	..	9 18	9 23	..	9 43	..	..	..	9 58	..	..	..	1018	1023	..	..	10 57	11 1	..	..	..	..	1143
Blackfriars...... arr	8 46	9 1	..	..	..	9 21	9 26	..	9 46	..	..	..	10 1	..	..	..	1021	1026	..	..	11 0	11 4	..	..	..	..	1146
Holborn Viaduct. "	8 49	9 3	..	..	..	9 24	9 29	..	9 49	..	..	..	10 3	..	..	..	1024	1029	..	..	11 2	11 6	..	..	..	..	1149
Brixton	..	8 48	..	..	..	9 11	..	..	..	..	..	..	9 51	..	..	..	1011	..	..	..	..	1051	..	..	..	11 21	..
Victoria.......... arr	..	8 54	854	..	859	9 17	..	..	..	..	..	..	9 57	10 0	105	..	1017	..	1039	..	..	1057	..	1059	..	11 27	..

3 Third class only

A For Forest Hill
B Crystal Palace (High Level) and Upper Norwood; nearly ¼ mile to Low Level Station
C Under ½ mile to Penge West Station
c Change at Orpington
D Over ½ mile to Bromley North Station
F Farningham Road and Sutton-at-Hone
G Halt for Pinden and Westwood
‡ Arr 2 minutes *earlier*

OTHER TRAINS

BETWEEN	PAGE
Gillingham (Kent), Gravesend, Maidstone and London	93
Sevenoaks and London	130
Bromley North and London	130
Beckenham Junction and London	285
Herne Hill and London	322

For SERVICES from LONDON (Waterloo) to PORTSMOUTH and ISLE OF WIGHT, see pages 359 to 365

From LONDON to THE SOUTH COAST—Week Days

Miles from London Bridge	Miles from London Bridge	Miles from London Bridge	Station	1	2	3	4	5	6	7	8	9	10	11	12	13	14
				a.m	a.m	a.m	a.m	a.m	a.m	a.m	a.m	a.m	a.m	a.m	a.m	a.m	a.m
			VICTORIA .... dep.	..	③	..	..	..	..	..	..	..	..	..	..	..	..
			Clapham Junction .... "	..		..	..	..	..	..	..	..	..	..	..	..	..
			LONDON BRIDGE... dep.	..	3 25	..	..	..	..	..	..	..	..	..	..	..	..
			New Cross Gate ..... "	..	..	..	..	..	..	..	..	..	..	..	..	..	..
			Norwood Junction B "	..	..	..	..	..	..	..	..	..	..	..	..	..	..
10¼	10¼	—	East Croydon .... dep.	..	..	..	..	..	..	..	..	..	..	..	..	..	..
13¼	13¼	—	Purley	..	..	..	..	..	..	..	..	..	..	..	..	..	..
15	15	—	Coulsdon South	..	..	..	..	..	..	..	..	..	..	..	..	..	..
18¾	18¾	—	Merstham	..	..	..	..	..	..	..	..	..	..	..	..	..	..
20¾	20¾	—	Redhill 246	..	3N58	..	..	..	..	..	..	..	..	..	..	..	..
21½	21½	—	Earlswood	..	..	..	..	..	..	..	..	..	..	..	..	..	..
23½	23½	—	Salfords	..	..	..	..	..	..	..	..	..	..	..	..	..	..
25¾	25¾	—	Horley	..	..	..	..	..	..	..	..	..	..	..	..	..	..
27	27	—	Gatwick Airport	..	..	..	..	..	..	..	..	..	..	..	..	..	..
29½	29½	—	Three Bridges (*below*) 234.	..	4N12	..	..	..	..	..	..	..	..	..	..	..	..
33¾	33¾	—	Balcombe	..	..	..	..	..	..	..	..	..	..	..	..	..	..
—	—	—	Horsted Keynes ...... dep.	..	..	..	..	..	..	..	..	..	..	..	..	..	..
—	—	—	Ardingly	..	..	..	..	..	..	..	..	..	..	..	..	..	..
37½	37½	—	Haywards Heath C 239 ...	..	4N26	..	..	..	..	..	..	..	..	..	..	..	..
40¼	—	—	Wivelsfield (*below*)	..	..	..	..	..	..	..	..	..	..	..	..	..	..
41½	—	—	Burgess Hill	..	..	..	..	..	..	..	..	..	..	..	..	..	..
43¾	—	—	Hassocks D	..	..	..	..	..	..	..	..	..	..	..	..	..	..
49¼	—	—	Preston Park	..	..	..	..	..	..	..	..	..	..	..	..	..	..
50½	—	—	Brighton (*below*) .... arr.	..	4 47	..	..	..	..	..	..	..	..	..	..	..	..
—	—	—	Haywards Heath ... dep.	..	..	..	..	..	..	..	..	..	..	..	..	..	..
—	40½	—	Wivelsfield (*above*)	..	..	..	..	..	..	..	..	..	..	..	..	..	..
—	44½	—	Plumpton	..	..	..	..	..	..	..	..	..	..	..	..	..	..
—	47½	—	Cooksbridge	..	..	..	..	..	..	..	..	..	..	..	..	..	..
—	50	—	Lewes 239 .... arr.	..	..	..	..	..	..	..	..	..	..	..	..	..	..
—	—	—	Brighton .... dep	..	5 0	..	..	..	..	..	..	..	..	6 15	6 34	..	..
51½	—	—	London Rd. (Brighton)	..	..	..	..	..	..	..	..	..	..	6 18	6 36	..	..
54	—	—	Falmer	..	..	..	..	..	..	..	..	..	..	..	6 40	..	..
58½	—	—	Lewes .... arr.	..	5N16	..	..	..	..	..	..	..	..	6 36	6 48	..	..
—	—	—	Lewes .... dep.	..	..	..	..	..	..	..	..	..	..	Stop	6 49	..	..
62	53½	—	Southease and Rodmell	..	..	..	..	..	..	..	..	..	..		6 54	..	..
64½	56½	—	Newhaven Town. [Halt	..	..	..	..	..	..	..	..	..	..	..	6 59	..	..
65	56¾	—	" Harbour	..	..	..	..	..	..	..	..	..	..	..	7 0	..	..
66¼	58	—	Bishopstone	..	..	..	..	..	..	..	..	..	..	..	7 5	..	..
67¼	59	—	Seaford .... arr.	..	..	..	..	..	..	..	..	..	..	..	7 8	..	..
—	—	—	Lewes .... dep	..	..	..	..	..	..	..	..	..	..	..	Stop	..	..
61½	53	—	Glynde	..	..	..	..	..	..	..	..	..	..	..		..	..
66	57½	—	Berwick	..	5N30	..	..	..	..	..	..	..	..	..	..	..	..
70	61½	—	Polegate 239	..	5 39	..	..	..	..	..	..	..	6 30	a.m	a.m	7 8	..
72½	63¾	—	Hampden Park F	..	5 44	..	..	..	..	..	..	..	6 33	6 37	7 5	7 13	7 19
74½	65½	—	Eastbourne .... arr.	..	5 49	..	..	..	..	..	..	..	6 37	6 41	7 9	7 18	7 23
			Eastbourne .... dep.	..	Stop	..	..	..	..	..	..	6 25	Stop	Stop	Stop	7 29	Stop
—	—	—	Hampden Park F	..		..	..	..	..	..	..	6 28				7 32	
73½	65	—	Pevensey and Westham....	..	..	..	..	..	..	..	..	6 35	..	..	..	7 39	..
74½	65¾	—	Pevensey Bay Halt	..	..	..	..	..	..	..	..	..	..	..	..	7 41	..
76¼	67¾	—	Norman's Bay Halt	..	..	..	..	..	..	..	..	..	..	..	..	7 44	..
78	69½	—	Cooden Beach	..	..	..	..	..	..	..	..	6 43	..	..	..	7 48	..
79½	71	—	Collington Halt	..	..	..	..	..	..	..	..	..	..	..	..	7 51	..
80½	71¾	—	Bexhill (Central) G	..	..	..	..	..	..	..	..	6 47	..	..	..	7 54	..
83	74½	—	St. Leonards (W.M.)	..	..	..	..	..	..	..	..	6 52	..	..	..	7 58	..
84	75½	—	" (W.S.)	..	..	..	..	..	..	..	..	6 55	..	..	..	8 1	..
84¾	76½	—	Hastings 56, 59	..	..	..	..	..	..	..	..	6 57	..	..	..	8 4	..
85¾	77½	—	Ore .... arr.	..	..	..	..	..	..	..	..	7 2	..	..	..	8 6	..

Station	15	16	17	18	19	20	21	22	23	24	25	26	27	28
	a.m	a.m	a.m	a.m	a.m	a.m	a.m	a.m	a.m	a.m	a.m	a.m	a.m	a.m
VICTORIA .... dep.	5③14	..	5*20	..	..	..	..	..	..	..	..	6‡15	..	6 40
Clapham Junction .... "	5③21	..	5*28	..	..	..	..	..	..	..	..	6‡21	..	6 47
LONDON BRIDGE... dep.	5 10	..	5 25	..	..	..	..	..	6 16	..	..	6 28	..	6③35
New Cross Gate ..... "	..	..	5 31	..	..	..	..	..	6 21	..	..	③	..	..
Norwood Junction B "	..	..	5 40	..	..	..	..	..	6 29	..	..		..	6③49
East Croydon .... dep.	..	..	5 45	..	..	..	..	..	6 35	..	..	..	..	7 0
Purley	..	..	5 51	..	..	..	..	..	6 40	..	..	..	..	7 5
Coulsdon South	..	..	5 56	..	..	..	..	..	6 44	..	..	..	..	7 9
Merstham	..	..	6 3	..	..	..	..	..	6 50	..	..	..	..	7 15
Redhill 246	..	..	6 8	..	..	..	..	..	6 57	..	..	..	7 8	7 23
Earlswood	..	..	6 11	..	..	..	..	..	6 59	..	..	..	7 11	7 25
Salfords	..	..	6 14	..	..	..	..	..	7 3	..	..	..	7 15	7 29
Horley	..	..	6 19	..	..	..	..	..	7 7	..	..	.	7 20	7 34
Gatwick Airport	..	..	6 22	..	..	..	..	..	7 10	..	..	..	7 25	7 37
Three Bridges (*below*) 234.	..	..	6 27	..	..	..	..	..	7c17	..	..	..	7 29	7‖45
Balcombe	..	..	6 34	..	..	..	..	..	7 23	..	..	..	..	7 52
Horsted Keynes ...... dep.	..	..	..	..	..	..	..	7 20	..	7 20	..	..	..	..
Ardingly	..	..	..	..	..	..	..	7 24	..	7 24	..	..	..	..
Haywards Heath C 239 ...	..	..	6 41	..	..	..	7 0	7 28	7 30	7 28	..	..	..	7 59
Wivelsfield (*below*)	..	..	6 46	..	..	..	7 5	Stop	7 34	..	..	..	..	8 4
Burgess Hill	..	..	6 49	..	..	..	7 7		7 37	..	..	..	..	8 7
Hassocks D	..	..	6 53	..	..	..	7 12	..	7 41	..	..	..	..	8 11
Preston Park	..	..	7 1	..	..	..	7 20	..	7 49	..	8 13	..	..	8 19
Brighton (*below*) .... arr.	..	..	7 4	..	..	..	7 23	..	7 52	..	8 16	..	..	8 23
Haywards Heath ... dep.	..	..	Stop	..	..	..	Stop	..	Stop	7 34	Stop	..	..	Stop
Wivelsfield (*above*)	..	..		..	..	..		..		7 38		..	..	
Plumpton	..	..	..	..	..	..	..	..	..	7 44	..	..	..	..
Cooksbridge	..	..	..	..	..	..	..	..	..	7 49	..	..	..	..
Lewes 239 .... arr.	..	..	a.m	..	..	..	..	..	..	7 55	a.m	..	..	..
Brighton .... dep	..	..	6 58	7 7	..	7 14	..	..	..	Stop	7 44	..	..	..
London Rd. (Brighton)	..	..	7 1	7 10	..	7 16	..	..	..		7 46	..	..	..
Falmer	..	..	..	..	..	7 20	..	..	..	..	7 50	..	..	..
Lewes .... arr.	..	..	7 18	7 24	..	7 27	a.m	..	..	..	7 57	..	..	a.m
Lewes .... dep.	..	..	Stop	Stop	..	..	7 32	..	..	..	..	..	..	8 6
Southease and Rodmell	..	..			..	..	7 37	..	..	..	..	..	..	8 11
Newhaven Town. [Halt	..	..	..	..	..	..	7 42	..	..	..	..	..	..	8 16
" Harbour	..	..	..	..	..	..	7 43	..	..	..	..	..	..	8 17
Bishopstone	..	..	..	..	..	..	7 48	..	..	..	..	..	..	8 22
Seaford .... arr.	..	..	..	..	..	..	7 51	..	..	..	..	..	..	8 25
Lewes .... dep	..	..	..	..	..	7 29	Stop	..	..	..	7 59	..	..	Stop
Glynde	..	..	..	..	..	7 34		..	..	..	8 4	..	..	
Berwick	..	..	..	..	..	7 40	..	..	..	..	8 10	..	..	a.m
Polegate 239	..	..	a.m	..	7 40	7 47	..	..	a.m	..	8 17	..	..	8 24
Hampden Park F	..	..	7 42	..	7 45	7 50	..	..	8 15	..	8 20	..	..	8 30
Eastbourne .... arr.	..	..	7 46	..	7 50	7 54	..	..	8 19	..	8 24	..	..	8 35
Eastbourne .... dep.	..	..	Stop	..	Stop	7 57	..	..	..	..	8 27	..	..	Stop
Hampden Park F	..	..		..		8 0	..	..	..	..	8 30	..	..	
Pevensey and Westham....	..	..	..	..	..	8 7	..	..	..	..	8 37	..	..	..
Pevensey Bay Halt	..	..	..	..	..	8 9	..	..	..	..	8 39	..	..	..
Norman's Bay Halt	..	..	..	..	..	8 12	..	..	..	..	8 42	..	..	..
Cooden Beach	..	..	..	..	..	8 16	..	..	..	..	8 46	..	..	..
Collington Halt	..	..	..	..	..	8 19	..	..	..	..	8 49	..	..	..
Bexhill (Central) G	..	..	..	..	..	8 22	..	..	..	..	8 52	..	..	..
St. Leonards (W.M.)	..	..	..	..	..	8 26	..	..	..	..	8 56	..	..	..
" (W.S.)	..	..	..	..	..	8 29	..	..	..	..	8 59	..	..	..
Hastings 56, 59	..	..	..	..	..	8 31	..	..	..	..	9 1	..	..	..
Ore .... arr.	..	..	..	a.m	..	8 35	..	..	..	..	9 4	..	..	..

Miles	Miles	Miles	Station	1	2	3	4	5	6	7	8	9	10	11	12	13	14	15	16	17	18	19	20	21	22	23	24	25	26	27	28
—	—	—	**Three Bridges** *(above)* dep.	..	..	..	..	..	..	..	..	..	..	..	..	..	..	..	..	..	6 47	..	..	..	..	..	..	..	..	7 31	..
—	30¼	—	Crawley	..	..	..	..	..	..	..	..	Stop	..	..	..	Stop	..	..	..	..	6 51	..	..	..	..	..	..	Stop	..	7 35	..
—	31¼	—	Ifield	..	..	..	..	..	..	..	..	..	..	..	..	..	..	..	..	..	6 53	..	..	..	..	..	..	..	..	7 37	..
—	34½	—	Fay Gate	..	..	..	..	..	..	..	..	..	..	..	..	..	..	..	..	..	6 58	..	..	..	..	..	..	..	..	7 42	..
—	36¼	—	Littlehaven Halt	..	..	..	..	..	..	..	..	..	..	..	..	..	..	..	..	..	7 2	..	..	..	..	..	..	..	..	7 46	..
—	37¼	—	**Horsham** 244, 245 arr.	..	..	..	..	..	..	..	..	..	..	..	..	..	..	..	..	..	7 4	..	..	..	..	..	..	..	..	7 49	..
—	—	13¾	**Sutton** dep.	..	..	..	..	..	..	..	..	..	..	..	..	..	..	5 54	..	..	..	..	..	..	..	..	..	..	6 57	..	..
—	—	25½	Dorking North **H**	..	..	..	..	..	..	..	..	..	..	..	..	..	..	6 36	..	..	..	..	..	..	..	..	..	..	7 25	..	..
—	—	39	**Horsham** 244, 245 arr.	..	..	..	..	..	..	..	..	..	..	..	..	..	..	7 7	..	..	..	..	..	..	..	..	..	..	7 49	..	..
			Horsham dep.	..	..	..	..	..	..	..	..	..	..	..	..	..	..	..	..	..	7 5	..	..	..	..	..	..	..	..	7 52	..
—	40½	41½	Christ's Hospital, West Horsham	..	..	..	..	..	..	..	..	..	..	..	..	..	..	Stop	..	..	7 9	..	..	..	..	..	..	..	..	7 56	..
—	45	46½	Billingshurst	..	..	..	..	..	..	..	..	..	..	..	..	..	..	..	..	..	7 16	..	..	..	..	..	..	..	Stop	8 3	..
—	50	51½	Pulborough **J** 374	..	..	..	..	..	..	..	..	..	..	..	..	..	..	..	..	..	7 23	..	..	..	..	..	..	..	..	8 10	..
—	54¾	56	Amberley	..	..	..	..	..	..	..	..	..	..	..	..	..	..	..	..	..	7 31	..	..	..	..	..	..	..	..	8 17	..
—	58¾	59½	Arundel	..	a.m	..	..	..	..	..	..	a.m	a.m	a.m	..	..	a.m	a.m	..	a.m	7 36	a.m	..	a.m	a.m	..	a.m	a.m	a.m	8 23	..
—	—	—	**Brighton** dep.	..	4 55	..	5 33	..	..	5 50	6 3	6 17	6 30	6 33	..	..	6 47	6 50	..	7 7	..	7 21	..	7 33	7 47	..	7 57	8 6	8 4	..	..
51½	—	—	Holland Road Halt	..	..	..	..	..	..	..	6 5	..	..	6 35	..	..	..	6 52	..	..	..	..	..	7 35	..	..	..	..	8 6	..	..
52	—	—	**Hove**	..	4 59	..	5 36	..	..	5 53	6 7	6 20	6 34	6 39	..	..	6 50	6 54	..	7 10	..	7 24	..	7 37	7 50	..	8 0	8 4	8 8	..	..
52½	—	—	Aldrington Halt	..	..	..	5 38	..	..	5 55	6 9	..	..	6 41	..	..	..	6 56	..	..	..	7 26	..	7 39	7 52	..	8 2	..	8 10	..	..
53½	—	—	Portslade and West Hove	..	5 2	..	5 41	..	..	5 58	6 12	..	6 38	6 44	..	..	..	6 59	..	..	..	7 29	..	7 42	..	..	8 5	8 8	8 13	..	..
54	—	—	Fishersgate Halt	..	..	..	5 43	..	..	..	6 14	..	..	6 46	..	..	..	7 1	..	..	..	..	..	7 44	..	..	..	..	8 15	..	..
55	—	—	Southwick	..	5 6	..	5 45	..	..	6 1	6 17	..	6 42	6 48	..	..	..	7 4	..	..	..	7 32	..	7 47	..	..	8 8	8 12	8 18	..	..
56½	—	—	Shoreham-by-Sea **K**	..	5 9	..	5 49	..	..	6 4	6 20	6 27	6 46	6 52	..	..	6 57	7 7	..	7 17	..	7 35	..	7 50	7 59	..	8 11	8 16	8 21	..	..
58¾	—	—	Lancing	..	5 14	..	5 53	..	..	6 8	6 24	..	Stop	6 57	..	..	..	7 12	..	7 22	..	7 39	..	7 54	..	..	8 16	Stop	8 25	..	..
60½	—	—	Ham Bridge Halt **N**	..	..	..	5 56	..	..	..	6 27	..	..	7 0	..	..	..	7 15	..	..	..	..	..	7 57	..	..	..	..	8 28	..	..
61	—	—	**Worthing Central**	..	5 19	..	5 58	..	..	6 12	6 30	6 35	..	7 3	..	..	7 11	7 18	..	7 27	..	7 43	..	8 0	8 6	..	8 20	..	8 31	..	..
62	—	—	West Worthing **U**	..	5 22	..	6 1	..	..	6 14	6 32	6 38	..	7 5	..	..	7 13	7 20	..	7 29	..	7 45	..	8 2	8 8	..	8 23	..	8 33	..	..
62¾	—	—	Durrington-on-Sea	..	..	..	..	..	..	6 16	..	..	..	..	..	..	7 15	..	..	..	..	7 47	..	..	8 10	..	..	..	..	..	..
63½	—	—	Goring-by-Sea	..	5 27	..	Stop	..	..	6 19	Stop	6 41	..	Stop	..	..	7 17	Stop	..	7 33	..	7 50	..	Stop	8 13	..	Stop	..	Stop	..	..
66	—	—	Angmering **L**	..	5 32	..	a.m	..	..	6 23	a.m	6 46	..	a.m	a.m	..	7 22	a.m	..	7 38	..	7 54	..	..	8 17	..	a.m	a.m	..	..	..
—	—	—	**Ford** (Sussex) dep.	5 43	..	..	5 50	..	6 2	..	6 32	..	..	6 55	7 24	..	..	7 30	..	..	7 44	..	..	..	..	..	8 14	8 30	..	..	..
71½	61¼	63	**Littlehampton** arr.	5 47	5 47	..	5 55	..	6 6	6 33	6 37	6 59	a.m	6 59	7 28	a.m	7 31	7 35	..	..	7 50	8 4	..	a.m	8 25	..	8 19	8 35	..	8 30	..
			Littlehampton dep.	Stop	5 30	5 53	..	..	Stop	6 36	..	6 36	6 58	Stop	..	7 20	7 34	..	..	7 34	7 56	..	..	8 18	8 18	..	..	..	..	8 33	..
70½	60¾	62	**Ford** (Sussex)	..	5 40	5 57	..	..	..	6 40	..	6 53	7 2	a.m	..	7 24	7 38	..	..	7 45	8 0	..	..	8 22	8 24	..	..	..	a.m	8 37	a.m
73	63½	64¾	**Barnham** arr.	..	5 45	..	..	6d10	..	6 45	..	6 58	7 7	7d31	..	7 28	7 42	..	..	7 50	8 6	..	..	..	8 29	..	..	..	8d33	8 42	8d50
76½	67	68¾	**Bognor Regis** arr.	a.m	6 16	..	..	6 16	a.m	6 51	..	7 14	7 14	7 37	..	7 37	7 49	..	..	8 12	8 12	..	..	..	8 39	..	..	..	8 39	8 56	8 56
			Bognor Regis dep.	5 25	5 38	..	..	..	6 22	Stop	..	6 42	..	..	..	7 20	..	..	..	7 35	..	..	..	..	8K14	..	..	..	..	..	..
—	—	—	**Barnham** dep.	5 33	5 46	..	..	..	6 32	..	..	6 58	..	..	..	7 28	..	..	..	7 50	..	..	..	..	8 29	..	..	..	..	8 42	..
79½	69½	71	Chichester **Z**	5 44	5 56	..	..	..	6 42	..	..	7 8	..	..	..	7 37	..	..	..	8 2	..	..	..	..	8 38	..	..	..	..	8 58	..
80¾	71¼	72½	Fishbourne Halt	5 47	..	..	..	..	6 45	..	..	7 11	..	..	..	7 40	..	..	..	8 5	..	..	..	..	8 41	..	..	..	..	..	..
82	72½	73¾	Bosham	5 50	6 2	..	..	..	6 49	..	..	7 14	..	..	..	7 43	..	..	..	8 8	..	..	..	..	8 44	..	..	..	..	9 3	..
83¾	74½	75½	Nutbourne Halt	5 55	..	..	..	..	6 52	..	..	7 17	..	..	..	7 47	..	..	..	8 12	..	..	..	..	8 47	..	..	..	..	..	..
84¾	75½	76½	Southbourne Halt	5 58	..	..	..	..	6 56	..	..	7 20	..	..	..	7 49	..	..	..	8 14	..	..	..	..	8 50	..	..	..	..	..	..
86½	76¾	78	Emsworth	6 1	6 9	..	..	..	6 59	..	..	7 23	..	..	..	7 52	..	..	..	8 18	..	..	..	..	8 53	..	..	..	..	9 10	..
87½	78	79¼	Warblington Halt	6 4	..	..	..	..	..	..	..	7 26	..	..	..	7 55	..	..	..	8 21	..	..	..	..	8 56	..	..	..	..	..	..
88	78½	79¾	Havant 244, 366	6 7	6 13	..	..	..	7 3	..	..	7 28	..	..	..	7 57	..	..	..	8 24	..	..	..	..	8 58	..	..	..	..	9 14	..
92½	83	84½	244 **Hayling Island** arr.	6 45	6 45	..	..	..	7 35	..	..	..	..	..	..	8 29	..	..	..	..	..	..	..	..	9 22	..	..	..	..	..	..
88¾	79½	80½	Bedhampton Halt	6 9	6 15	..	..	..	7 5	..	..	..	..	..	..	7 59	..	..	..	..	..	..	..	..	9 0	..	..	..	..	..	..
92½	82¾	84	Hilsea Halt	6 14	6 22	..	..	..	7 10	..	..	7 34	..	..	..	8 4	..	..	..	..	..	..	..	..	9 5	..	..	..	..	..	..
94½	85	86½	Fratton 380	6 18	6 26	..	..	..	7 15	..	..	7 38	..	..	..	8 8	..	..	..	8 34	..	..	..	..	9 9	..	..	..	..	9 23	..
95½	85¾	87	**Portsmouth & Southsea** arr.	6 21	6 29	..	..	..	7 18	a.m	..	7 41	..	..	..	8 11	..	..	..	8 37	..	..	..	..	9 12	..	..	..	..	9 26	..
96	86½	87¾	**Portsmouth Harbour** "	6 25	6 33	..	..	..	..	7d40	..	7 45	..	..	..	..	..	..	8d35	8 41	..	..	..	..	9 16	..	..	..	..	9 31	..
100	90½	91¾	500 Ryde Pier (Boat) arr.	..	..	..	..	..	..	8 10	..	..	..	..	..	..	..	..	9 5	..	..	..	..	..	..	..	..	..	..	1010	..
106½	97	98¾	Page 359 Sandown "	..	..	..	..	..	..	8 57	..	..	..	..	..	..	..	..	9 48	..	..	..	..	..	..	..	..	..	..	1048	..
108½	99	100¼	Page 359 Shanklin "	..	..	..	..	..	..	9 5	..	..	..	..	..	..	..	..	9 55	..	..	..	..	..	..	..	..	..	..	1055	..
112½	103	104¼	Page 359 Ventnor "	..	..	..	..	..	..	9 21	..	..	..	..	..	..	..	..	1012	..	..	..	..	..	..	..	..	..	..	1111	..
110	100½	101½	Page 359 Newport "	..	..	..	..	..	..	8 56	..	..	..	..	..	..	..	..	10 6	..	..	..	..	..	..	..	..	..	..	11 6	..
114½	104¾	106	Page 359 Cowes "	..	..	..	..	..	..	9 11	..	..	..	..	..	..	..	..	1030	..	..	..	..	..	..	..	..	..	..	1120	..
120	110½	111¾	Page 359 Yarmouth "	..	..	..	..	..	..	9 33	..	..	..	..	..	..	..	..	..	..	..	..	..	..	..	..	..	..	..	1140	..

E Third class only * Change at East Croydon. ‡ Change at Sutton. Third Class only. ‖ Arr. 4 mins. *earlier* *c* Arr. 3 mins. *earlier.* *d* Departure time.
K Dep. 8 4 a.m. on Saturdays **N** Calls only to set down passengers.

For Other Notes, see page 195.

For SERVICES from LONDON (Waterloo) to PORTSMOUTH and ISLE OF WIGHT, see pages 359 to 365

From LONDON to THE SOUTH COAST—Week Days—continued

Station	a.m	a.m	a.m	a.m	a.m	a.m	a.m	a.m	a.m	a.m	a.m	a.m	a.m	a.m	a.m
									Saturdays excepted						
VICTORIA ....dep.	6*40	..	..	..	..	..	..	..	..	..	..	..	7 47	..	8 0
Clapham Junction..... "	6*47	..	..	..	..	..	..	..	..	..	..	..	7 52	..	8 5
LONDON BRIDGE...dep.	7 0	..	..	..	..	7 20	..	..	..	..	..	..	7Ⓑ35	..	7Ⓑ55
New Cross Gate..... "	7 5	..	..	..	..	..	..	..	..	..	..	..	..	..	8Ⓑ 0
Norwood Junction **B** "	..	..	..	..	..	7 32	..	..	..	..	..	..	7Ⓑ48	..	8Ⓑ 8
East Croydon ....dep.	7 17	..	..	..	..	7 39	..	..		..	..	..	8 5	..	8 20
Purley..................	..	..	..	..	..	7 44	..	..		..	..	..	8 10	..	8 26
Coulsdon South..........	..	..	..	..	..	7 48	..	..		..	..	..	8 14	..	..
Merstham	..	..	..	..	..	7 54	..	..		..	..	..	8 20	..	..
Redhill 246	7 32	..	..	..	..	8 2	..	..		..	..	..	8 27	..	8 37
Earlswood................	..	..	..	..	..	8 4	..	..		..	..	..	8 29	..	..
Salfords...................	..	..	..	..	..	8 8	..	..		..	..	..	8 33	..	..
Horley	..	..	..	..	..	8 12	..	..		..	..	..	8 37	..	..
Gatwick Airport	7 40	..	..	..	..	8 15	..	..		..	..	..	8 40	..	8 45
Three Bridges *(below)* 234	..	..	..	..	..	8 19	..	..		..	..	..	8 45	..	..
Balcombe..................	..	..	..	..	..	8 26	..	..		..	..	..	8 53	..	..
Horsted Keynes......dep.	..	..	..	7 58	..	..	8 30	8 30		..	..	..	..	..	..
Ardingly	..	..	..	8 2	..	..	8 34	8 34		..	..	..	..	..	..
Haywards Heath **C** 239 ..	7 54	..	..	8 6	8 18	8 32	8 38	8 38	8 44	..	..	..	9c 2	..	8 58
Wivelsfield *(below)*..........	..	..	..	Stop	8 22	8 36	..	Stop	8 48	..	..	..	9 6	..	..
Burgess Hill...............	..	..	..		8 25	8 39	..		8 51	..	..	..	9 9	..	..
Hassocks **D**...............	..	..	..	..	8 29	8 44	..	..	8 55	..	..	..	9 13	..	..
Preston Park..............	..	..	..	..	8 33	8 52	..	..	9 3	..	..	..	9 21	..	9 15
Brighton *(below)*.......arr.	..	..	..	..	8 41	8 55	..	..	9 6	..	..	..	9 24	..	9 19
Haywards Heath ...dep.	7 54	..	..	..	Stop	Stop	8 40	..	Stop	..	..	..	Stop	..	Stop
Wivelsfield *(above)*.......	..	..	..	..			8 45	..		..	..	..	..	..	..
Plumpton	8 3	..	..	..	..	..	8 52	..	..	..	..	..	..	..	..
Cooksbridge	8 8	..	..	..	..	..	8 57	..	..	..	..	..	..	..	..
Lewes 239...........arr.	8 13	..	..	..	a.m	..	9 3	..	..	..	..	..	a.m	..	..
Brighton ....dep.	..	..	8 0	..	8 14	..	..	..	..	8 44	8 48	..	9 14	..	..
London Road (Brighton) ..	..	..	..	..	8 16	..	..	..	..	8 46	8 51	..	9 16	..	..
Falmer	..	..	..	..	8 20	..	..	..	..	8 50	..	..	9 20	..	..
Lewes ....arr.	..	..	8 16	..	8 28	a.m	..	..	..	8 58	9 6	..	9 28	..	..
Lewes ....dep.	..	..	Stop	..	..	8 48	9 4	..	..	..	Stop	..	..	..	..
Southease and Rodmell	..	..		..	..	8 53	..	..	..	..		..	..	..	..
Newhaven Town ...[Halt	..	..	..	..	..	8 58	9 12	..	..	..	..	..	..	..	..
" Harbour	..	..	..	..	..	8 59	9 13	..	..	..	..	..	..	..	..
Bishopstone	..	..	..	..	..	9 4	9 18	..	..	..	..	..	..	..	..
Seaford ....arr.	..	..	..	..	..	9 7	9 21	..	..	..	..	..	..	..	..
Lewes..................dep.	8 15	..	..	..	8 29	Stop	Stop	..	..	8 59	..	..	9 29	..	..
Glynde	..	..	..	..	8 34			..	..	9 4	..	..	9 34	..	..
Berwick	..	..	..	..	8 40	a.m	..	..	..	9 10	..	..	9 40	..	..
Polegate 239	8 32	..	..	a.m	8 47	8 52	..	a.m	..	9 17	a.m	..	9 47	..	..
Hampden Park **F**.........	8 35	..	..	8 45	8 50	8 56	..	9 15	..	9 20	9 45	..	9 50	..	..
Eastbourne .... arr.	8 39	..	..	8 49	8 54	9 1	..	9 19	..	9 24	9 49	..	9 54	..	..
Eastbourne .... dep.	8 42	..	..	Stop	8 57	Stop	..	Stop	..	9 27	..	..	9 57	..	..
Hampden Park **F**.........	8 45	..	..		9 0		..		..	9 30	..	..	10 0	..	..
Pevensey and Westham ...	8 51	..	..	..	9 7	..	..	..	..	9 37	..	..	10 7	..	..
Pevensey Bay Halt.......	..	..	..	..	9 9	..	..	..	..	9 39	..	..	10 9	..	..
Norman's Bay Halt........	..	..	..	..	9 12	..	..	..	..	9 42	..	..	10 12	..	..
Cooden Beach..............	8 57	..	..	..	9 16	..	..	..	..	9 46	..	..	10 16	..	..
Collington Halt...........	..	..	..	..	9 19	..	..	..	..	9 49	..	..	10 19	..	..
Bexhill (Central) **G**.......	9 1	..	..	..	9 22	..	..	..	..	9 52	..	..	10 22	..	..
St. Leonards (W.M.)	9 7	..	..	..	9 26	..	..	..	..	9 56	..	..	10 26	..	..
" (W.S.).......	9 10	..	..	..	9 29	..	..	..	..	9 59	..	..	10 29	..	..
Hastings 56, 59............	9 12	..	..	..	9 31	..	..	..	..	10 1	..	..	10 31	..	..
Ore.....................arr.	9 15	..	..	..	9 34	..	..	..	..	10 4	..	..	10 34	..	..
	1	2	3	4	5	6	7	8	9	10	11	12	13	14	15

Station	a.m	a.m	a.m	a.m	a.m P	a.m	a.m	a.m	a.m		a.m	a.m	a.m	a.m	a.m P
					Saturdays only								Sats. only		Saturdays excepted
VICTORIA ....dep.	..	..	8*0	8 28	8 45	..	..	..	..	..	8b48	8b48	..	..	9 0
Clapham Junction..... "	..	—	8*5	8 33	..	..	..	..	..	..	..	..	..	..	..
LONDON BRIDGE...dep.	..	..	8 18	8*18	8Ⓑ35	..	..	..	..	..	8 48	9 0	9 0	..	..
New Cross Gate..... "	..	..	..	..	..	..	..	..	..	..	..	9 5	9 5	..	..
Norwood Junction **B** "	..	..	8 30	8*30	8Ⓑ49	..	..	..	..	..	9 2	9 14	9 14	..	..
East Croydon ....dep.	..	..	8 35	8 44	9 1	..	..	..	..	..	9 8	9 18	9 18	..	
Purley..................	..	..	8 40	..		..	..	..	..	..	9 13	..		..	
Coulsdon South..........	..	..	8 44	..		..	..	..	..	..	9 17	..		..	
Merstham	..	..	8 50	..		..	..	..	..	..	9 23	..		..	
Redhill 246	..	..	8 57	9 1		..	..	..	..	..	9 31	..		..	
Earlswood................	..	..	8 59	..		..	..	..	..	..	9 34	..		..	
Salfords...................	..	..	9 3	..		..	..	..	..	..	9 37	..		..	
Horley	..	..	9 7	..		..	..	..	..	..	9 41	9 38	9 38	..	
Gatwick Airport	..	..	9 10	..		..	..	..	..	..	9 44	..	..	..	
Three Bridges *(below)* 234	..	..	9 15	9 12		..	..	..	..	..	9 48	9 44	9 44	..	
Balcombe..................	..	..	9 21	..		..	..	..	..	..	9 55	..	..	..	
Horsted Keynes......dep.	8 56	9 21	..	..	..	..	..	..	..	..	..	..	..	..	
Ardingly	9 1	9 25	..	..	..	..	..	..	..	..	..	..	..	..	
Haywards Heath **C** 239 ..	9 6	9 30	9c30	9 23	9 32	..	..	..	..	..	10 1	9y56	9 54	..	..
Wivelsfield *(below)*..........	..	Stop	9 34	..	..	..	..	..	..	..	10 5	..	..	..	..
Burgess Hill...............	..		9 37	..	..	..	..	..	..	..	10 8	..	..	..	..
Hassocks **D**...............	..	..	9 41	..	..	..	..	..	..	..	10 12	..	..	..	..
Preston Park..............	..	..	9 49	9 37	..	..	..	..	..	..	10 20	10 11	..	..	..
Brighton *(below)*.......arr.	..	..	9 52	9 41	..	..	..	..	..	..	10 23	10 14	..	..	10 0
Haywards Heath ...dep.	9 12	..	Stop	..	9 33	..	..	..	..	..	Stop	Stop	10 4	..	..
Wivelsfield *(above)*.......	9 16	..		..	..	..	..	..	..	..			..	..	..
Plumpton	9 22	..	..	..	..	..	..	..	..	..	..	..	..	..	..
Cooksbridge	9 27	..	..	..	..	..	..	..	..	..	..	..	..	..	..
Lewes 239...........arr.	9 33	..	..	..	9 48	..	..	..	..	..	..	..	1021	..	..
Brighton ....dep.	..	..	..	..	..	..	9 46	..	10 3	..	..	..	Saturdays only	..	..
London Road (Brighton) ..	..	..	..	..	..	..	9 48	..	10 5	..	..	..		..	..
Falmer	..	..	..	..	..	..	9 52	..	10 9	..	..	..		..	..
Lewes ....arr.	..	..	..	..	..	..	10 0	..	1017	..	..	..		..	..
Lewes ....dep.	9 38	..	..	..	..	..	..	..	1018	..	..	..		..	..
Southease and Rodmell	9 43	..	..	..	..	..	..	..	1023	..	..	..		..	..
Newhaven Town ...[Halt	9 48	..	..	..	..	..	..	..	1028	..	..	..		..	..
" Harbour	9 49	..	..	—	..	..	..	..	1029	..	..	..		..	..
Bishopstone	9 54	..	..	..	..	..	..	..	1034	..	..	..		..	..
Seaford ....arr.	9 57	..	..	..	..	..	..	..	1037	..	..	..		..	..
Lewes..................dep.	Stop	..	..	..	9 50	..	10 1	..	Stop	..	..	..	1021	..	..
Glynde		..	..	..	..	..	10 6	..		..	..	..	..	..	..
Berwick	..	a.m	..	..	..	..	10 12	..	..	..	..	..	..	..	..
Polegate 239	..	9 51	..	..	..	..	10 19	1028	..	..	..	..	1037	..	..
Hampden Park **F**.........	..	9 57	..	..	..	1015	10 22	1033	..	..	..	..	..	..	..
Eastbourne .... arr.	..	10 2	..	..	10 9	1019	10 26	1038	..	..	..	..	1044	..	..
Eastbourne .... dep.	..	Stop	..	..	10 13	Stop	10 29	Stop	..	..	..	..	1047	..	..
Hampden Park **F**.........	..		..	..	..		10 32		—	..	..	..	..	..	..
Pevensey and Westham ...	..	..	..	..	..	..	10 39	..	..	..	..	..	1055	..	..
Pevensey Bay Halt.......	..	..	..	..	..	..	10 41	..	..	..	..	..	..	..	..
Norman's Bay Halt........	..	..	..	..	..	..	10 44	..	..	..	..	..	..	..	..
Cooden Beach..............	..	..	..	..	10 26	..	10 48	..	..	..	..	..	11 1	..	..
Collington Halt...........	..	..	..	..	..	..	10 51	..	..	..	..	..	..	..	..
Bexhill (Central) **G**.......	..	..	..	..	10 31	..	10 54	..	..	..	..	..	11 6	..	..
St. Leonards (W.M.)	..	..	..	..	..	..	10 58	..	..	..	..	..	1111	..	..
" (W.S.).......	..	..	..	..	10 38	..	11 1	..	..	..	..	..	1114	..	..
Hastings 56, 59............	..	..	..	..	10 40	..	11 3	..	..	..	..	..	1116	..	..
Ore.....................arr.	..	..	..	..	10 45	..	11 6	a.m	..	..	..	..	1120	..	..
	16	17	18	19	20	21	22	23	24	25	26	27	28	29	30

Station	1	2	3	4	5	6	7	8	9	10	11	12	13	14	15	16	17	18	19	20	21	22	23	24	25	26	27	28	29	30
Three Bridges (*above*) dep.	..	7 48	..	..	Stop	..	..	..	..	..	..	8 32	Stop	8 47	..	..	..	..	..	..	..	Stop	9 17	..	..	..	..	..	9 47	..
Crawley	..	7 51	..	..	..	..	..	..	..	..	..	8 35	..	8 51	..	..	..	..	..	..	..	..	9 21	..	..	..	..	..	9 51	..
Ifield	..	7 54	..	..	..	..	..	..	..	..	..	8 38	..	8 53	..	..	..	..	..	..	..	..	9 23	..	..	..	..	..	9 53	..
Fay Gate	..	7 58	..	..	..	..	..	..	..	..	..	8 42	..	8 58	..	..	..	..	..	..	..	..	9 28	..	..	..	..	..	9 58	..
Littlehaven Halt	..	8 2	..	..	..	..	..	..	..	..	..	8 46	..	9 2	..	..	..	..	..	..	..	..	9 32	..	..	..	..	..	10 2	..
Horsham 244, 245 arr.	..	8 5	..	..	..	..	..	..	..	..	..	8 49	..	9 5	..	..	..	..	..	..	..	..	9 35	..	..	..	..	..	10 5	..
Sutton dep.	..	..	..	..	..	..	..	..	..	..	..	Stop	..	..	..	..	..	..	..	..	..	..	..	..	..	..	..	..	..	..
Dorking North **H**	..	..	..	..	..	..	..	..	..	..	..	..	..	..	..	..	..	..	..	..	..	..	..	..	..	..	..	..	..	..
Horsham 244, 245 arr.	..	..	..	..	..	..	..	..	..	..	..	..	..	..	..	..	..	..	..	..	..	..	..	..	..	..	..	..	..	..
Horsham 244, 245 dep.	..	8 5	..	..	..	..	..	..	..	..	..	..	..	9 5	..	..	..	..	..	..	..	..	9 35	..	..	..	..	..	10 5	..
Christ's Hospital, West Horsham	..	8 9	..	..	..	..	..	..	..	..	..	..	..	9 9	..	..	..	..	..	..	..	..	9 39	..	..	..	..	..	10 9	..
Billingshurst	..	8 16	..	..	..	..	..	..	..	..	..	..	..	9 16	..	..	..	..	..	..	..	..	9 46	..	..	..	..	..	10 16	..
Pulborough **J** 374	..	8 23	..	..	..	..	..	..	..	..	..	..	..	9 23	..	..	..	..	..	..	..	..	9 53	..	..	..	..	..	10 23	..
Amberley	..	8 31	..	..	..	..	..	..	..	..	..	..	..	9 30	..	..	..	..	..	..	..	..	10 1	..	..	..	..	..	10 31	..
Arundel	..	8 36	a.m	a.m	a.m	a.m	a.m	..	..	..	..	a.m	..	9 36	a.m	a.m	a.m	a.m	..	..	..	a.m	10 6	..	..	a.m	a.m	..	10 36	..
Brighton dep.	..	..	8 17	8 20	8 33	8 47	8 50	..	..	..	..	9 3	..	..	9 17	9 20	9 27	9 30	..	..	..	9 47	..	..	..	9 50	10 3	..	..	..
Holland Road Halt	..	..	..	..	8 35	..	..	..	..	..	..	9 5	..	..	..	..	..	..	..	..	..	..	..	..	..	..	10 5	..	..	..
Hove	..	..	8 20	8 23	8 37	8 50	8 53	..	..	..	..	9 7	..	..	9 20	9 23	9 30	9 34	..	..	..	9 50	..	..	..	9 53	10 7	..	..	..
Aldrington Halt	..	..	..	8 25	8 39	..	8 55	..	..	..	..	9 9	..	..	..	9 25	..	..	..	..	..	..	..	..	..	9 55	10 9	..	..	..
Portslade and West Hove	..	..	..	8 28	8 42	..	8 58	..	..	..	..	9 12	..	..	..	9 28	9 33	9 38	..	..	..	..	..	..	..	9 58	10 12	..	..	..
Fishersgate Halt	..	..	..	..	8 44	..	..	..	..	..	..	9 14	..	..	..	..	9 35	..	..	..	..	..	..	..	..	..	10 14	..	..	..
Southwick	..	..	..	8 31	8 47	..	9 1	..	Saturdays excepted	..	..	9 17	..	..	..	9 31	9 38	..	..	..	..	..	..	..	..	10 1	10 17	..	..	..
Shoreham-by-Sea **K**	..	..	8 27	8 34	8 50	8 57	9 6	..		..	..	9 20	..	..	9 27	9 34	9 41	9 44	..	..	..	9 57	..	..	..	10 4	10 20	..	..	..
Lancing	..	..	..	8 38	8 55	..	9 10	..		..	..	9 25	..	..	..	9 38	9 46	..	..	..	..	..	..	..	..	10 9	10 25	..	..	..
Ham Bridge Halt **N**	..	..	..	..	8 58	..	..	..		..	..	9 28	..	..	..	..	9 49	..	..	..	..	..	..	..	..	..	10 28	..	..	..
Worthing Central	..	..	8 34	8 42	9 1	9 6	9 14	..		..	..	9 31	..	..	9 34	9 42	9 52	..	..	..	..	10 6	..	..	..	10 13	10 31	..	..	..
West Worthing **U**	..	..	8 36	8 45	9 3	..	9 16	..		..	..	9 33	..	..	9 36	9 45	9 54	..	..	..	..	Saturdays only	..	..	..	10 15	10 33	..	..	..
Durrington-on-Sea	..	..	8 38	..	..	..	9 18	..		..	..	Stop	..	..	9 38	..	..	..	..	..	..		..	..	..	10 17	Stop	..	..	..
Goring-by-Sea	..	..	8 41	..	..	..	9 21	..		..	..	..	..	..	9 41	..	..	..	..	..	..		..	..	..	10 20	..	..	..	..
Angmering **L**	..	..	8 45	..	..	..	9 25	..		..	..	..	..	..	9 45	..	..	..	..	..	a.m		..	..	..	10 24	..	..	..	..
Ford (Sussex) dep.	..	..	..	..	..	..	..	..		..	..	..	..	..	..	..	..	..	..	..	9 52		..	..	..	..	..	..	..	..
Littlehampton arr.	..	8 43	..	..	..	..	9 34	..		..	..	..	..	9 43	..	..	..	..	..	..	9 57		1015	..	..	10 34	..	..	10 43	..
Littlehampton dep.	..	8 46	8 46	..	..	..	..	..		..	..	..	..	9 46	9 46	..	..	..	..	..	..		..	..	..	..	..	..	10 46	..
Ford (Sussex)	..	8a50	8 52	..	..	..	..	a.m	a.m	..	..	..	..	9a50	9 52	..	..	..	..	..	..		..	..	..	..	a.m	..	10a50	..
Barnham arr.	..	9d1	8 57	..	..	9 22	..	9d25	9d36	..	..	..	..	10 2	9 57	..	..	..	..	..	..	10 22	..	..	..	..	10d36	..	11 1	..
Bognor Regis arr.	..	9 7	9 7	..	..	9 31	..	9 31	9 42	..	..	..	..	10 8	10 8	..	..	..	..	..	..	10 42	..	..	..	..	10 42	..	11 7	..
Bognor Regis dep.	..	..	8 40	..	..	9SX10	..	..	..	..	..	..	..	..	9 40	..	..	..	..	..	..	10 10	..	..	..	..	..	..	..	..
Barnham dep.	..	..	8 57	..	..	9 22	..	..	..	..	..	a.m	..	..	9 57	..	..	..	..	..	..	10 23	..	a.m	..	..	..	..	..	..
Chichester **Z**	..	..	9 6	..	..	9 32	..	..	..	..	..	9 37	..	..	10 7	..	..	..	..	..	..	10 33	..	1037	..	..	..	..	..	..
Fishbourne Halt	..	..	9 9	..	..	..	..	..	..	..	..	9 40	..	..	10 10	..	..	..	..	..	..	..	..	1040	..	..	..	..	..	..
Bosham	..	..	9 12	..	..	..	..	..	..	..	..	9 43	..	..	10 13	..	..	..	..	..	..	..	..	1043	..	..	..	..	..	..
Nutbourne Halt	..	..	9 16	..	..	..	..	..	..	..	..	9 46	..	..	10 16	..	..	..	..	..	..	..	..	1046	..	..	..	..	..	..
Southbourne Halt	..	..	9 18	..	..	..	..	..	..	..	..	9 49	..	..	10 19	..	..	..	..	..	..	..	..	1049	..	..	..	..	..	..
Emsworth	..	..	9 21	..	..	..	..	..	..	..	..	9 52	..	..	10 22	..	..	..	..	..	..	..	..	1052	..	..	..	..	..	..
Warblington Halt	..	..	9 24	..	..	..	..	..	..	..	..	9 55	..	..	10 25	..	..	..	..	..	..	..	..	1055	..	..	..	..	..	..
Havant 244, 366	..	..	9 27	..	..	9 45	..	..	..	..	..	9 57	..	..	10 27	..	..	..	..	..	..	10 42	..	1057	..	..	..	..	..	..
244 Hayling Island arr.	..	..	..	..	..	..	..	..	..	..	..	1032	..	..	..	..	..	..	..	..	..	..	..	..	..	..	..	..	..	..
Bedhampton Halt	..	..	..	..	..	..	..	..	..	..	..	9 59	..	..	..	..	..	..	..	..	..	..	..	1059	..	..	..	..	..	..
Hilsea Halt	..	..	..	..	..	..	..	..	..	..	..	..	..	..	..	..	..	..	..	..	..	..	..	..	..	..	..	..	..	..
Fratton 380	..	..	9 36	..	..	9 54	..	..	..	..	..	10 7	a.m	..	10 36	..	..	..	..	..	..	10 54	..	11 7	..	..	..	..	..	..
Portsmouth & Southsea arr	..	..	9 38	..	..	9 56	..	..	..	..	..	1010	10d20	..	10 38	..	..	..	..	..	..	10 56	..	1110	..	..	..	..	..	..
Portsmouth Harbour "	..	..	9 42	..	..	10 0	..	..	..	..	..	..	10 26	..	10 42	..	..	..	..	..	..	11 0	..	..	..	..	..	..	..	..
500 RYDE PIER (Boat) arr.	..	..	..	..	..	..	..	..	..	..	..	..	11 5	..	..	..	..	..	..	..	..	..	..	..	..	..	..	..	..	..
Page 359 SANDOWN "	..	..	..	..	..	..	..	..	..	..	..	..	11 48	..	..	..	..	..	..	..	..	..	..	..	..	..	..	..	..	..
Page 359 SHANKLIN "	..	..	..	..	..	..	..	..	..	..	..	..	11 55	..	..	..	..	..	..	..	..	..	..	..	..	..	..	..	..	..
Page 359 VENTNOR "	..	..	..	..	..	..	..	..	..	..	..	..	12 11	..	..	..	..	..	..	..	..	..	..	..	..	..	..	..	..	..
Page 359 NEWPORT "	..	..	..	..	..	..	..	..	..	..	..	..	12 6	..	..	..	..	..	..	..	..	..	..	..	..	..	..	..	..	..
Page 359 COWES "	..	..	..	..	..	..	..	..	..	..	..	..	12 20	..	..	..	..	..	..	..	..	..	..	..	..	..	..	..	..	..
Page 359 YARMOUTH "	..	..	..	..	..	..	..	..	..	..	..	..	1 10	..	..	..	..	..	..	..	..	..	..	..	..	..	..	..	..	..

3 Third class only. • Change at East Croydon. *a* Dep. 5 mins. later. *b* Third class only. 4 mins. *earlier* on Sats. *c* Arr. 3 mins. *earlier* *d* Departure time

P Pullman Car facilities available. **SX** Sats. excepted. *y* Arr. 2 mins. *earlier*

For Other Notes, see page 195

For SERVICES from LONDON (Waterloo) to PORTSMOUTH and ISLE OF WIGHT, see pages 359 to 363

From LONDON to THE SOUTH COAST—Week Days—*continued*

Station	1	2	3	4	5	6	7	8	9	10	11	12	13	14
	a.m RB	a.m	a.m	a.m	a.m P	a.m Saturdays only	a.m	a.m P	a.m	a.m	a.m	a.m	a.m P	a.m
VICTORIA .... dep	9 18	..	..	9*18	9 25	..	9 28	9 45	..	..	..	9 48	10 0	..
Clapham Junction .... "	..	..	..	..	..	..	9 33	..	..	..	..	9 53	..	..
LONDON BRIDGE .. dep	9 15	..	..	9 18	9*18	..	9*18	9 36	..	..	..	9 36	..	..
New Cross Gate ..... "	9* 5	..	..	..	..	..	..	..	..	..	..	..	..	..
Norwood Junction **B** "	9*14	..	..	9 31	9*31	..	9*31	..	..	..	..	..	..	..
East Croydon .... dep	9 34	..	..	9 36	9 42	..	9 46	10 1	..	..	..	10 5	..	..
Purley	..	..	..	9 42	..	..	..	..	..	..	..	10 11	..	..
Coulsdon South	..	..	..	9 45	..	..	..	..	..	..	..	10 14	..	..
Merstham	..	..	..	9 51	..	..	..	..	..	..	..	10 20	..	..
Redhill 246	9 49	..	..	9 57	..	..	10 1	..	..	..	..	10 27	..	..
Earlswood	..	..	..	10 0	..	..	..	..	..	..	..	10 30	..	..
Salfords	..	..	..	10 3	..	..	..	..	..	..	..	10 33	..	..
Horley	..	..	..	10 7	..	..	..	..	..	..	..	10 37	..	..
Gatwick Airport	..	..	..	1010	..	..	1010	..	..	..	..	10 40	..	..
Three Bridges (*below*). 234	10 0	..	..	1015	..	..	..	..	..	..	..	10y46	..	..
Balcombe	..	..	..	1022	..	..	..	..	..	..	..	10 52	..	..
Horsted Keynes ..... dep	..	..	..	..	..	..	..	..	..	..	..	..	..	..
Ardingly	..	..	..	..	..	..	..	..	..	..	..	..	..	..
Haywards Heath **C** 239 ...	..	..	..	1029	10 14	..	1023	10 32	..	..	..	10 59	..	..
Wivelsfield (*below*)	..	..	..	1033	Through Train, Victoria to Littlehampton	..	..	..	..	..	..	11 3	..	..
Burgess Hill	..	..	..	1036		..	..	..	..	..	..	11 6	..	..
Hassocks **D**	..	..	..	1040		..	..	..	..	..	..	11 10	..	..
Preston Park	..	..	..	1048		..	1037	..	..	..	..	11 18	..	..
Brighton (*below*) ...... arr	..	..	..	1051		..	1041	..	..	..	..	11 21	11 0	..
Haywards Heath ... dep	..	..	..	Stop		..	Stop	10 33	1035	..	..	Stop	..	..
Wivelsfield (*above*)	..	..	..	..		..	..	..	1039	..	..	..	..	..
Plumpton	..	..	..	..		..	..	..	1045	..	..	..	..	..
Cooksbridge	..	..	..	..		..	..	..	1050	..	..	..	..	..
Lewes 239 .... arr	..	..	..	a.m		..	..	10 48	1055	..	..	..	..	..
Brighton .... dep	..	..	1014	1018		1031	..	..	..	1046	10 50	..	..	..
London Road (Brighton) ...	..	..	1016	1021		1033	..	..	..	1048	..	..	..	..
Falmer	..	..	1020	..		1037	..	..	..	1052	..	..	..	..
Lewes .... arr	..	..	1028	1036		1045	..	..	..	11 0	11 6	..	..	..
Lewes .... dep	..	..	..	Stop	..	1046	..	..	11 4	..	Stop	..	..	..
Southease and Rodmell	..	..	..	..	..	1051	..	..	11 9	..	..	..	..	..
Newhaven Town ...[Halt	..	..	..	..	..	1056	..	..	1114	..	..	..	..	..
" Harbour	..	..	..	..	..	1057	..	..	1115	..	..	..	..	..
Bishopstone	..	..	..	..	..	11 2	..	..	1120	..	..	..	..	..
Seaford .... arr	..	..	..	..	..	11 5	..	..	1122	..	..	..	..	..
Lewes .... dep	Through Train Victoria to Bognor Regis	..	1029	..	..	Stop	..	10 50	Stop	11 1	..	..	..	..
Glynde		..	1034	..	..	..	..	..	..	11 6	..	..	..	..
Berwick		..	1040	..	..	..	..	..	..	1112	..	a.m	..	..
Polegate 239		..	1047	..	..	..	..	..	a.m	1119	..	11*27	..	..
Hampden Park **F**		10 45	1050	..	..	..	..	..	1115	1122	..	11 32	..	..
Eastbourne .... arr		10 49	1054	..	..	..	..	11 9	1119	1126	..	11 37	..	..
Eastbourne .... dep		..	1057	..	..	..	..	11 13	Stop	1129	..	Stop	..	..
Hampden Park **F**		..	11 0	..	..	..	..	..	..	1132	..	..	..	..
Pevensey and Westham		..	11 7	..	..	..	..	..	..	1139	..	..	..	..
Pevensey Bay Halt		..	11 9	..	..	..	..	..	..	1141	..	..	..	..
Norman's Bay Halt		..	1112	..	..	..	..	..	..	1144	..	..	..	..
Cooden Beach		..	1116	..	..	..	..	11 26	..	1148	..	..	..	..
Collington Halt		..	1119	..	..	..	..	..	..	1151	..	..	..	..
Bexhill (Central) **G**		..	1122	..	..	..	..	11 31	..	1154	..	..	..	..
St. Leonards (W.M.)		..	1126	..	..	..	..	..	..	1158	..	..	..	..
" (W.S.)		..	1129	..	..	..	..	11 38	..	12 1	..	..	..	..
Hastings 56, 59		..	1131	..	..	..	..	11 40	..	12 3	..	..	..	..
Ore .... arr		..	1134	..	..	..	..	11 49	a.m	12 6	..	..	..	..

Station	15	16	17	18	19	20	21	22	23	24	25	26	27	28
		a.m RB	a.m	a.m	a.m	a.m	a.m	a.m Saturdays only	a.m	a.m P	a.m	a.m	a.m P	a.m Saturdays only
VICTORIA .... dep	..	10 18	..	..	..	..	..	..	..	10 25	..	10 28	10 45	..
Clapham Junction .... "	..	..	..	..	..	..	..	..	..	..	..	10 34	..	..
LONDON BRIDGE .. dep	..	10 18	..	..	..	..	10 16	..	..	10*16	..	10*16	10 36	..
New Cross Gate ..... "	..	..	..	..	..	..	..	..	..	..	..	..	..	..
Norwood Junction **B** "	..	..	..	..	..	..	10 28	..	..	10*28	..	10*28	10 48	..
East Croydon .... dep	..	..	..	..	..	..	10 32	..	..	10 41	..	10 46	11 1	..
Purley	..	..	..	..	..	..	10 38	..	..	..	..	..	..	..
Coulsdon South	..	..	..	..	..	..	10 41	..	..	..	..	..	..	..
Merstham	..	..	..	..	..	..	10 47	..	..	..	..	..	..	..
Redhill 246	..	..	..	..	..	..	10 55	..	..	..	..	11 1	..	..
Earlswood	..	..	..	..	..	..	10 58	..	..	..	..	..	..	..
Salfords	..	..	..	..	..	..	11 2	..	..	..	..	..	..	..
Horley	..	..	..	..	..	..	11 6	..	..	..	..	..	..	..
Gatwick Airport	..	..	..	..	..	..	11 9	..	..	..	..	11 16	..	..
Three Bridges (*below*). 234	..	..	..	..	..	..	11y15	..	..	..	..	..	..	..
Balcombe	..	..	..	..	..	..	11 22	..	..	..	..	..	..	..
Horsted Keynes ..... dep	..	..	..	..	..	..	..	..	..	..	..	..	..	..
Ardingly	..	..	..	..	..	..	..	..	..	..	..	..	..	..
Haywards Heath **C** 239 ...	..	..	..	..	..	..	11 28	..	..	11 14	..	11 23	11 32	..
Wivelsfield (*below*)	..	Through Train Victoria to Bognor Regis	..	..	..	..	11 33	..	..	Through Train Victoria to Littlehampton	..	..	..	..
Burgess Hill	..		..	..	..	..	11 35	..	..		..	..	..	..
Hassocks **D**	..		..	..	..	..	11 39	..	..		..	..	..	..
Preston Park	..		..	..	..	..	11 47	..	..		..	11 37	..	..
Brighton (*below*) ...... arr	..		..	..	..	..	11 51	..	..		..	11 41	..	..
Haywards Heath ... dep	..		..	..	..	..	Stop	..	..		..	..	11 33	1135
Wivelsfield (*above*)	..		..	..	..	..	..	..	..		..	..	..	1139
Plumpton	..		..	..	..	..	..	..	..		..	..	..	1145
Cooksbridge	..		..	..	..	..	..	..	..		..	..	..	1150
Lewes 239 .... arr	..		..	..	..	..	..	..	..		..	..	11 48	1155
Brighton .... dep	..		..	..	..	1114	..	1131	..		..	..	..	..
London Road (Brighton) ...	..		..	..	..	1116	..	1133	..		..	..	..	..
Falmer	..		..	..	..	1120	..	1137	..		..	..	..	..
Lewes .... arr	..		..	..	..	1128	..	1145	..		..	..	..	..
Lewes .... dep	..	..	..	..	..	..	..	1146	..	..	..	..	..	..
Southease and Rodmell	..	..	..	..	..	..	..	1151	..	..	..	..	..	..
Newhaven Town ...[Halt	..	..	..	..	..	..	..	1156	..	..	..	..	..	..
" Harbour	..	..	..	..	..	..	..	1157	..	..	..	..	..	..
Bishopstone	..	..	..	..	..	..	..	12 2	..	..	..	..	..	..
Seaford .... arr	..	..	..	..	..	..	..	12 5	..	..	..	..	..	..
Lewes .... dep	..	..	..	..	..	1129	..	..	..	..	..	..	11 50	..
Glynde	..	..	..	..	..	1134	..	..	..	..	..	..	..	..
Berwick	..	..	..	..	..	1140	..	..	..	..	..	..	..	..
Polegate 239	..	..	..	..	..	1147	a.m	..	..	..	..	..	..	..
Hampden Park **F**	..	..	..	..	..	1150	11 53	..	..	..	..	..	..	..
Eastbourne .... arr	..	..	..	..	..	1154	11 57	..	..	..	..	..	12 9	..
Eastbourne .... dep	..	..	..	..	..	1157	..	..	..	..	..	..	12 13	..
Hampden Park **F**	..	..	..	..	..	12 0	..	..	..	..	..	..	..	..
Pevensey and Westham	..	..	..	..	..	12 7	..	..	..	..	..	..	..	..
Pevensey Bay Halt	..	..	..	..	..	12 9	..	..	..	..	..	..	..	..
Norman's Bay Halt	..	..	..	..	..	1212	..	..	..	..	..	..	..	..
Cooden Beach	..	..	..	..	..	1216	..	..	..	..	..	..	12 26	..
Collington Halt	..	..	..	..	..	1219	..	..	..	..	..	..	..	..
Bexhill (Central) **G**	..	..	..	..	..	1222	..	..	..	..	..	..	12 31	..
St. Leonards (W.M.)	..	..	..	..	..	1226	..	..	..	..	..	..	..	..
" (W.S.)	..	..	..	..	..	1229	..	..	..	..	..	..	12 38	..
Hastings 56, 59	..	..	..	..	..	1231	..	..	..	..	..	..	12 40	..
Ore .... arr	..	..	..	..	..	1234	..	..	..	..	..	..	12 45	..

Station	1	2	3	4	5	6	7	8	9	10	11	12	13	14	15	16	17	18	19	20	21	22	23	24	25	26	27	28
Three Bridges (above). dep.	10 2	..		..	..	..	..	..	1017		..	..	..	..	..	..	..	10 47	..		..	..	..	..	..	..	..	..
Crawley	..	..	Stop	..	..	..	..	..	1021	Stop	..	..	..	..	..	..	..	10 51	..	Stop	..	..	..	..	..	..	..	..
Ifield	..	..	..	..	..	..	..	..	1023	..	..	..	..	..	..	..	Saturdays only ☞	10 53	..	..	..	..	..	..	..	..	..	..
Fay Gate	..	..	..	..	..	..	..	..	1028	..	..	..	..	..	..	..		10 58	..	..	..	..	..	..	..	..	..	..
Littlehaven Halt	..	..	..	..	..	..	..	..	1032	..	..	..	..	..	..	..		11 2	..	..	..	..	..	..	..	..	..	..
Horsham 244, 245 arr.	10 13	..	..	..	..	..	..	..	1035	..	..	..	..	..	..	..		11 5	..	..	..	..	..	..	..	..	..	..
Sutton dep.	..	..	..	..	..	..	..	..	..	..	..	..	..	..	..	10 39		..	..	..	..	..	..	..	..	..	..	..
Dorking North H	..	..	..	..	..	..	..	..	..	..	..	..	..	..	..	10 56		..	..	..	..	..	..	..	..	..	..	..
Horsham 244, 245 arr.	..	..	..	..	..	..	..	..	..	..	..	..	..	..	..	11 13		..	..	..	..	..	..	..	..	..	..	..
Horsham 244, 245 dep.	10 15	..	..	..	..	..	..	..	1035	..	..	..	..	..	..	11 15		11 5	..	..	..	..	..	..	..	..	..	..
Christ's Hospital, West Horsham	..	..	..	..	..	..	..	..	1039	..	..	..	..	..	..	..		11 9	..	..	..	..	..	..	..	..	..	..
Billingshurst	..	..	..	..	..	..	..	..	1046	..	..	..	..	..	..	..		11 16	..	..	..	..	..	..	..	..	..	..
Pulborough J 374	10 30	..	..	..	..	..	..	..	1053	..	..	..	..	..	..	11 30		11 23	..	..	..	..	..	..	..	..	..	..
Amberley	..	..	..	..	..	..	..	..	11 1	..	..	..	..	..	..	..		11 30	..	..	..	..	..	..	..	..	..	..
Arundel	10 41	..	a.m	a.m	..	a.m	..	..	11 6	a.m	..	a.m	..	..	..	11 41		11 36	..	a.m	..	..	..	..	..	..	..	..
Brighton dep.	RB	..	1017	1020	P	1033	..	..	..	1046	..	10 49	..	11 0	..	RB	11 3	..	1117	1120	..	..	11 30	P	1133	..	..	..
Holland Road Halt	..	..	..	..	..	1035	..	..	..	..	..	..	..	..	..	..	11 5	..	..	..	..	..	R	..	1135	..	..	..
Hove	..	..	1020	1023	10 33	1037	..	..	..	1049	..	10 52	..	Saturdays only	..	..	11 7	..	1120	1123	..	..	..	11 35	1138	..	..	..
Aldrington Halt	..	..	..	1025	..	1039	..	..	..	..	..	10 54	..		..	..	11 9	..	..	1125	..	..	..	..	1140	..	..	..
Portslade and West Hove	..	..	..	1028	..	1042	..	..	..	..	..	10 57	..		..	..	11 12	..	..	1128	..	..	..	..	1143	..	..	..
Fishersgate Halt	..	..	..	..	..	1044	..	..	..	..	..	..	..		..	..	11 14	..	..	..	..	..	..	..	1145	..	..	..
Southwick	..	..	..	1031	..	1047	..	..	..	..	..	11 0	..		..	..	11 17	..	..	1131	..	..	..	..	1148	..	..	..
Shoreham-by-Sea K	..	..	1027	1034	10 40	1050	..	..	..	1056	..	11 3	..		..	..	11 20	..	1127	1134	..	..	..	11 42	1151	..	..	..
Lancing	..	..	..	1038	..	1055	..	..	..	..	..	11 7	..		..	..	11 25	..	..	1138	..	..	..	..	1156	..	..	..
Ham Bridge Halt N	..	..	..	..	..	1058	..	..	..	..	..	..	..		..	..	11 28	..	..	..	..	..	..	..	1159	..	..	..
Worthing Central	..	..	1035	1042	10 48	11 1	..	..	..	11 6	..	11 11	..	11U18	..	..	11 31	..	1135	1142	..	..	11U47	11 51	12 2	..	..	..
West Worthing U	..	..	1037	1045	10 51	11 3	..	..	..	..	..	11 13	..	..	..	..	11 33	..	1137	1145	..	..	..	11 53	12 4	..	..	..
Durrington-on-Sea	..	..	..		10 53	..	..	..	..	..	..	11 15	..	..	..	..		..	..		..	..	..	11 55	..	..	..	..
Goring-by-Sea	..	..	1041	Stop	10 56	..	..	..	..	..	..	11 18	..	..	..	..	Stop	..	1141	Stop	..	..	..	11 58	..	..	..	..
Angmering L	..	..	1045	a.m	11 0	..	..	..	..	..	..	11 22	..	..	..	..		..	1145	p.m	..	..	..	12 2	..	..	..	..
Ford (Sussex) dep.	..	..	..	1052	..	..	..	..	..	..	..	..	..	..	..	..	..	..	..	12 2	..	..	..	..	..	..	..	..
Littlehampton arr.	10 57	..	..	1057	11 10	..	..	..	1113	..	..	11 32	..	..	..	..	..	11 43	12 7	12 7	..	..	..	12 13	..	..	..	..
Littlehampton dep.	..	..	1046	..	..	..	..	..	..	..	..	Stop	..	..	..	..	..	11 46	1146	..	..	..	11 46	..	..	..	..	..
Ford (Sussex)	10 46	..	1052	..	..	..	..	..	..	..	a.m		..	..	..	..	..	11a50	1152	..	..	..	..	..	..	..	..	..
Barnham arr.	10 51	..	1057	..	..	..	..	..	..	1122	11d36		..	11 37	..	11 49	..	12 1	1157	..	..	..	12 5	..	..	..	..	..
Bognor Regis arr.	11 1	..	11 7	..	..	..	..	..	..	1142	11 42	..	..	..	..	12 0	..	12 7	12 7	..	..	..	..	..	..	..	..	..
Bognor Regis dep.	10 40	..	1040	..	..	..	..	..	..	1110	..	..	..	11 10	..	..	..	..	1145	..	..	..	11 45	..	..	..	..	..
Barnham dep.	10 53	..	1057	..	..	..	..	..	..	1122	..	a.m	..	11 37	..	11 52	..	..	1157	..	..	..	12 6	..	..	..	..	..
Chichester Z	11 2	..	11 7	..	..	..	..	..	..	1132	..	11 37	..	11 48	..	12 2	Saturdays only ☞	..	12 7	..	..	..	12 18	..	..	..	..	..
Fishbourne Halt	..	..	1110	..	..	..	..	..	..	..	..	11 40	..	Through Train to Cardiff pages 380 and 493	..	..		..	1210	..	..	..	Through Train to Plymouth, pages 380 and 342	..	..	..	..	..
Bosham	..	..	1113	..	..	..	..	..	..	..	..	11 43	..		..	..		..	1213	..	..	..		..	..	..	..	..
Nutbourne Halt	..	..	1116	..	..	..	..	..	..	..	..	11 46	..		..	..		..	1216	..	..	..		..	..	..	..	..
Southbourne Halt	..	..	1119	..	..	..	..	..	..	..	..	11 49	..		..	..		..	1219	..	..	..		..	..	..	..	..
Emsworth	..	..	1122	..	..	..	..	..	..	..	..	11 52	..		..	12 11		..	1222	..	..	..		..	..	..	..	..
Warblington Halt	..	..	1125	..	..	..	..	..	..	..	..	11 55	..		..	..		..	1225	..	..	..		..	..	..	..	..
Havant 244, 366	11 15	..	1127	..	..	..	..	..	..	1145	..	11 57	..		..	12 15		..	1227	..	..	..		..	..	..	..	..
244 Hayling Island arr.	..	..	..	..	..	..	..	..	..	..	..	..	..		..	..		..	1 3	..	..	..		..	..	..	..	..
Bedhampton Halt	..	..	..	..	..	..	..	..	..	..	..	11 59	..		..	..		..	..	..	..	..		..	..	..	..	..
Hilsea Halt	..	..	..	..	..	..	..	..	..	..	..	..	..		..	..		..	..	..	..	..		..	..	..	..	..
Fratton 380	11 23	..	1136	..	..	..	..	..	..	1154	..	12 7	..		..	12 23		..	1236	..	..	..		..	..	..	..	..
Portsmouth & Southsea arr	11 27	..	1138	..	..	..	..	..	..	1156	..	12 10	..		..	12 27	p.m	..	1238	..	..	..		..	..	..	..	..
Portsmouth Harbour "	11 31	..	1142	..	..	..	..	..	..	12 0	..	..	..		..	12 31	12d35	..	1242	..	..	..		..	..	..	..	..
500 Ryde Pier (Boat) arr.	12 5	..	..	..	..	..	..	..	..	..	..	..	..		..	..	1 5	..	..	..	..	..		..	..	..	..	..
Page 359 Sandown "	12 48	..	..	..	..	..	..	..	..	..	..	..	..		..	..	1 48	..	..	..	..	..		..	..	..	..	..
Shanklin "	12 55	..	..	..	..	..	..	..	..	..	..	..	..		..	..	1 55	..	..	..	..	..		..	..	..	..	..
Ventnor "	1 12	..	..	..	..	..	..	..	..	..	..	..	..	..	..	..	2 11	..	..	..	..	..	..	..	..	..	..	..
Newport "	1 6	..	..	..	..	..	..	..	..	..	..	..	..	..	..	..	2 6	..	..	..	..	..	..	..	..	..	..	..
Cowes "	1 20	..	..	..	..	..	..	..	..	..	..	..	..	..	..	..	2 20	..	..	..	..	..	..	..	..	..	..	..
Yarmouth "	3SX10	..	..	..	..	..	..	..	..	..	..	..	..	..	..	..	3 10	..	..	..	..	..	..	..	..	..	..	..

3 Third class only. * Change at East Croydon. a Dep. 5 mins. later. d Departure time. P Pullman Car facilities available
R Refreshment Car facilities available. RB Refreshment Car facilities available between London and Bognor Regis. SX Saturdays excepted.
U Calls to take up only. y Arr. 2 mins. earlier.

For Other Notes, see page 195

For SERVICES from LONDON (Waterloo) to PORTSMOUTH and ISLE OF WIGHT, see pages 359 to 365

From LONDON to THE SOUTH COAST—Week Days—*continued*

	1	2	3	4	5	6	7	8	9	10	11	12	13	14
	p.m	a.m	a.m	p.m	a.m	a.m	a.m	p.m	p.m	p.m	a.m RB	p.m	a.m	p.m
VICTORIA dep.	..	..	..	..	10 48	..	11 0	..	..	..	1118	..	11*8	..
Clapham Junction "	..	..	..	..	10 53	..		..	..	..	..	..	..	..
LONDON BRIDGE dep.	..	..	..	..	10ⓑ36	..	Brighton Belle 1st and 3rd class Pullman Cars only	..	..	..	..	..	1118	..
New Cross Gate "	..	..	..	..	..	..		..	..	..	..	..	..	..
Norwood Junction B "	..	..	..	..	10ⓑ48	..		..	..	..	..	..	1130	..
East Croydon dep.	..	..	..	..	11 5	..		..	..	..	Through Train, Victoria to Bognor Regis	..	1135	..
Purley	..	..	..	..	11 11	..		..	..	..		..	1140	..
Coulsdon South	..	..	..	..	11 14	..		..	..	..		..	1144	..
Merstham	..	..	..	..	11 20	..		..	..	..		..	1150	..
Redhill 246	..	..	..	..	11 27	..		..	..	..		..	1157	..
Earlswood	..	..	..	..	11 30	..		..	..	..		..	12 0	..
Salfords	..	..	..	..	11 33	..		..	..	..		..	12 3	..
Horley	..	..	..	..	11 37	..		..	..	..		..	12 7	..
Gatwick Airport	..	..	..	..	11 40	..		..	..	..		..	1210	..
Three Bridges *(below)* 234	..	..	..	..	11y46	..		..	..	..		..	1215	..
Balcombe	..	..	..	..	11 52	..		..	..	..		..	1222	..
Horsted Keynes dep.	..	..	..	..	..	..		..	..	..		12 16	..	..
Ardingly	..	..	..	..	..	..		..	..	..		12 20	..	..
Haywards Heath ℂ.239	..	..	..	..	11 59	..		..	..	..	..	12 24	1228	..
Wivelsfield *(below)*	..	..	..	..	12 3	..		..	..	..	..	Stop	1232	..
Burgess Hill	..	..	..	..	12 6	..		..	..	..	..		1235	..
Hassocks D	..	..	..	..	12 10	..		..	..	..	..	..	1239	..
Preston Park	..	..	..	..	12 18	..		..	..	..	..	..	1247	..
Brighton *(below)* arr.	..	..	..	..	12 21	..	12 0	..	..	..	..	..	1250	..
Haywards Heath dep.	..	..	..	..	Stop	..	..	..	..	..	..	..	..	..
Wivelsfield *(above)*	..	..	..	..		..	..	..	..	..	..	..	..	..
Plumpton	..	..	..	..	..	..	..	..	..	..	..	..	..	..
Cooksbridge	..	..	..	..	..	..	..	..	..	..	..	..	..	..
Lewes 239 arr.	..	..	..	..	..	..	..	..	..	..	..	..	..	..
Brighton dep.	..	1146	..	..	..	..	..	12 5	..	1214	..	..	..	..
London Road (Brighton)	..	1148	..	..	..	..	..	12 8	..	1216	..	..	..	..
Falmer	..	1152	..	..	..	..	..	..	..	1220	..	..	..	..
Lewes arr.	..	12 0	..	..	..	..	..	1223	..	1228	..	..	..	..
Lewes dep.	..	..	..	12 4	..	..	..	Stop	..	..	..	..	..	..
Southease and Rodmell	..	..	..	12 9	..	..	..		..	..	..	..	..	..
Newhaven Town [Halt	..	..	..	1214	..	..	..	..	..	..	..	..	..	..
" Harbour	..	..	..	1215	..	..	..	..	..	..	..	..	..	..
Bishopstone	..	..	..	1220	..	..	..	..	..	..	..	..	..	..
Seaford arr.	..	..	..	1222	..	..	..	..	..	..	..	..	..	..
Lewes dep.	..	12 1	..	Stop	..	..	..	..	..	1229	..	..	..	..
Glynde	..	12 6	..		..	..	..	..	..	1234	..	..	..	..
Berwick	..	1212	..	..	..	..	..	..	..	1240	..	..	..	..
Polegate 239	..	1219	..	..	..	..	..	p.m	..	1248	..	..	..	..
Hampden Park F	12 15	1222	..	..	..	..	..	1245	..	1251	..	..	..	..
Eastbourne arr.	12 19	1226	..	..	..	..	..	1249	..	1255	..	..	..	..
Eastbourne dep.	Stop	1229	..	..	..	..	..	..	..	1259	..	..	..	..
Hampden Park F		1232	..	..	..	..	..	..	..	1 2	..	..	..	..
Pevensey and Westham	..	1239	..	..	..	..	..	..	..	1 9	..	..	..	..
Pevensey Bay Halt	..	1241	..	..	..	..	..	..	..	1 11	..	..	..	..
Norman's Bay Halt	..	1244	..	..	..	..	..	..	..	1 14	..	..	..	..
Cooden Beach	..	1248	..	..	..	..	..	..	..	1 18	..	..	..	..
Collington Halt	..	1251	..	..	..	..	..	..	..	1 21	..	..	..	..
Bexhill (Central) G	..	1254	..	..	..	..	..	..	..	1 24	..	..	..	..
St. Leonards (W.M.)	..	1258	..	..	..	..	..	..	..	1 28	..	..	..	..
" (W.S.)	..	1 1	..	..	..	..	..	..	..	1 31	..	..	..	..
Hastings 56, 59	..	1 3	..	..	..	..	..	..	..	1 33	..	..	..	..
Ore arr.	a.m	1 6	..	..	..	..	..	..	..	1 36	..	..	..	..

	15	16	17	18	19	20	21	22	23	24	25	26	27	28
	p.m.	a.m P	p.m	a.m	p.m	a.m P	p.m	p.m	a.m	noon P	non P		p.m RB	p.m
VICTORIA dep.	..	11 25	..	11 28	..	11 45	..	..	11 48	12 0	12 0	..	12 18	..
Clapham Junction "	..	..	..	11 34	..	..	..	..	11 53	..	..	..	..	..
LONDON BRIDGE dep.	..	11*18	..	11*18	..	11ⓑt31			11tⓑ31	11ⓑ55	..	..	12*15	..
New Cross Gate "	..	..	..	..	..	..	..	..	..	..	..	..	..	..
Norwood Junction B "	..	11*30	..	11*30	..	11ⓑt44			11tⓑ44	12ⓑ7	..	..	..	..
East Croydon dep.	..	11 42	..	11 46	..	12 1	..	..	12 5	12 16	..	..	12 34	..
Purley	..	..	..	..	..	..	..	..	12 11	Saturdays only	Saturdays excepted	..	Saturdays only	..
Coulsdon South	..	..	..	..	..	..	..	..	12 14			..		..
Merstham	..	..	..	..	..	..	..	..	12 20			..		..
Redhill 246	..	..	..	12 1	..	..	..	..	12 27			..		..
Earlswood	..	..	..	..	..	..	..	..	12 30			..		..
Salfords	..	..	..	..	..	..	..	..	12 33			..		..
Horley	..	..	..	..	..	..	..	..	12 37			..		..
Gatwick Airport	..	..	..	12 10	..	..	..	..	12 40			..		..
Three Bridges *(below)* 234	..	..	..	..	..	..	..	..	12y46			..	12 57	..
Balcombe	..	..	..	..	..	..	..	..	12 53		..	..	..	..
Horsted Keynes dep.	..	..	Saturdays only ☞	..	..	12 16	1216	..	..	..	..	..	..	..
Ardingly	..	..		..	..	12 20	1220	..	..	..	..	..	..	..
Haywards Heath ℂ.239	..	12 14		12 23	..	12 32	1224	..	1 0	12 48	..	..	Through Train, Victoria to Bognor Regis.	..
Wivelsfield *(below)*	..	..		..	..	..	..	..	1 4	..	..	..		..
Burgess Hill	..	..		..	..	..	..	..	1 7	..	..	..		..
Hassocks D	..	..		..	..	..	..	..	1 11	..	..	..		..
Preston Park	..	..		12 37	..	..	..	..	1 19	..	..	..		..
Brighton *(below)* arr.	..	..		12 41	..	..	..	..	1 22	1 3	1 0	..		..
Haywards Heath dep.	..	Through Train, Victoria to Littlehampton		Stop	..	12 33	1235	..	..	Stop	Stop	..		..
Wivelsfield *(above)*	..				..	..	1239	..	..			..		..
Plumpton	..			..	..	..	1245	..	..	..	..	..		..
Cooksbridge	..			..	..	..	1250	..	..	..	..	..		..
Lewes 239 arr.	..			..	..	12 48	1255	..	..	..	..	..		..
Brighton dep.	..		1231	..	..	..	Stop	1245	..	..	..	..		..
London Road (Brighton)	..		1233	..	..	..		1247	..	..	..	..		..
Falmer	..		1237	..	..	..	..	1251	..	..	..	..		..
Lewes arr.	..		1245	..	..	..	..	1259	..	..	p.m	..		..
Lewes dep.	..		1246	..	..	..	..	..	..	..	1 4	..	..	..
Southease and Rodmell	..		1251	..	..	..	..	..	..	..	1 9	..	..	..
Newhaven Town [Halt	..		1256	..	..	..	..	..	..	..	1 14	..	..	..
" Harbour	..		1257	..	..	..	..	..	..	..	1 15	..	..	..
Bishopstone	..		1 2	..	..	..	..	..	..	..	1 20	..	..	..
Seaford arr.	..		1 5	..	..	..	..	..	..	..	1 22	..	..	..
Lewes dep.	..	..	Stop	..	..	12 50	..	1 0	..	..	Stop	..	..	..
Glynde	..	..		..	..	..	..	1 5	..	..		..	..	..
Berwick	..	..	..	..	..	..	..	1 11	..	..	..	..	..	..
Polegate 239	..	..	..	..	..	..	p.m	1 17	..	..	..	..	..	1 24
Hampden Park F	..	..	..	..	..	..	1 15	1 20	..	..	..	..	..	1 30
Eastbourne arr.	..	..	..	..	..	1 9	1 19	1 24	..	..	..	..	..	1 35
Eastbourne dep.	..	..	..	..	..	1 13	Stop	1 27	..	..	..	..	..	Stop
Hampden Park F	..	..	..	..	..	..		1 30	..	..	..	..	..	
Pevensey and Westham	..	..	..	..	..	..	..	1 37	..	..	..	..	..	..
Pevensey Bay Halt	..	..	..	..	..	..	..	1 39	..	..	..	..	..	..
Norman's Bay Halt	..	..	..	..	..	..	..	1 42	..	..	..	..	..	..
Cooden Beach	..	..	..	..	..	1 26	..	1 46	..	..	..	..	..	..
Collington Halt	..	..	..	..	..	..	..	1 49	..	..	..	..	..	..
Bexhill (Central) G	..	..	..	..	..	1 31	..	1 52	..	..	..	..	..	..
St. Leonards (W.M.)	..	..	..	..	..	..	..	1 56	..	..	..	..	..	..
" (W.S.)	..	..	..	..	..	1 38	..	1 59	..	..	..	..	..	..
Hastings 56, 59	..	..	..	..	..	1 40	..	2 1	..	..	..	..	..	..
Ore arr.	..	..	..	p.m.	..	1 48	..	2 4	..	..	..	..	..	..

Station	1	2	3	4	5	6	7	8	9	10	11	12	13	14
Three Bridges (*above*)..dep.	11 17	—	..	..	..	11 47	..	..	..	..	..	..	..	..
Crawley	11 21	Stop	..	..	..	11 51	..	..	..	..	..	..	..	..
Ifield	11 23	..	..	..	..	11 53	..	..	..	..	..	..	..	..
Fay Gate	11 28	..	..	..	..	11 58	..	..	..	..	..	..	..	..
Littlehaven Halt	11 32	..	..	..	..	12 2	..	..	..	..	..	..	..	..
Horsham 244, 245 ...... arr.	11 35	..	..	..	..	12 5	..	..	..	..	..	..	..	..
Sutton ......dep.	..	..	..	..	..	..	..	..	..	..	1139	..	..	..
Dorking North **H**	..	..	..	..	..	..	..	..	..	..	1156	..	..	..
Horsham 244, 245 ..... arr.	..	..	..	..	..	..	..	..	..	..	1213	..	..	..
Horsham 244, 245 ..... dep.	11 35	..	..	..	..	12 5	..	..	..	..	1215	..	..	..
Christ's Hospital, West Horsham	11 39	..	..	..	..	12 9	..	..	..	..	..	..	..	..
Billingshurst	11 46	..	..	..	..	12 16	..	..	..	..	..	..	..	..
Pulborough **J** 374	11 53	..	..	..	..	12 23	..	..	..	..	1230	..	..	..
Amberley	12 1	..	..	..	..	12 21	..	..	..	..	..	..	..	..
Arundel	12 8	a.m	..	..	p.m	12 36	..	..	..	..	1241	p.m	..	..
Brighton ......dep.	..	1147	11 50	..	12 3	..	..	..	1212	..	**RB**	12 17	..	1220
Holland Road Halt	..	..	..	..	12 5	..	..	..	..	..	..	..	..	..
Hove	..	1150	11 53	..	12 7	..	..	..	1216	..	..	12 20	..	1223
Aldrington Halt	..	..	11 55	..	12 9	..	..	..	..	..	..	..	..	1225
Portslade and West Hove	..	..	11 58	**Saturdays only**	12 12	..	..	..	..	..	..	..	..	1228
Fishersgate Halt	..	..	..		12 14	..	..	..	..	..	..	..	..	..
Southwick	..	..	12 1		12 17	..	..	..	..	..	..	..	..	1231
Shoreham-by-Sea **K**	..	1157	12 4		12 20	..	..	..	1224	..	..	12 27	..	1234
Lancing	..	..	12 8		12 25	..	..	..	..	..	..	..	..	1238
Ham Bridge Halt **N**	..	..	..		12 28	..	..	..	..	..	..	..	..	..
Worthing Central	..	12 6	12 12		12 31	..	..	..	..	..	..	12 35	..	1242
West Worthing U	..	**Saturdays only**	12 14		12 33	..	..	..	..	..	..	12 37	..	1245
Durrington-on-Sea	..		12 16		— Stop	..	..	..	..	..	..	..	..	..
Goring-by-Sea	..		12 19			..	..	..	..	..	..	12 41	..	..
Angmering ¶	..		12 23		..	..	..	..	..	..	..	12 45	..	..
Ford (Sussex) ......dep.	..		..		..	..	..	..	..	..	..	..	..	..
Littlehampton .... arr.	12 15		12 33		..	12 43	..	..	..	..	..	..	..	..
Littlehampton .... dep.	..		..		..	12 46	..	..	..	..	..	12 46	..	..
Ford (Sussex)	..		..	p.m	..	12a50	..	..	..	..	..	12 52	..	..
Barnham ......arr.	..	1222	..	12d26	..	1 1	..	..	..	..	1249	12 57	..	..
Bognor Regis ..... arr	..	1232	..	1232	..	1 7	..	..	..	..	1 0	1 7	..	..
Bognor Regis ..... dep.	..	1210	..	..	..	..	..	..	..	..	..	12 45	..	..
Barnham ......dep	..	1222	..	..	p.m	..	..	..	..	..	1252	12 57	..	..
Chichester **Z**	..	1232	..	..	12 37	..	..	..	..	..	1 2	1 7	..	..
Fishbourne Halt	..	..	..	..	12 40	..	..	..	..	..	..	1 10	..	..
Bosham	..	..	..	..	12 43	..	..	..	..	..	..	1 13	..	..
Nutbourne Halt	..	..	..	..	12 46	..	..	..	..	..	..	1 16	..	..
Southbourne Halt	..	..	..	..	12 49	..	..	..	..	..	..	1 19	..	..
Emsworth	..	..	..	..	12 52	..	..	..	..	..	..	1 22	..	..
Warblington Halt	..	..	..	..	12 55	..	..	..	..	..	..	1 25	..	..
Havant 244, 366	..	1245	..	..	12 57	..	..	..	..	..	1 15	1 27	..	..
244 Hayling Island ....arr.	..	1 3	..	..	..	..	..	..	..	..	..	1 47	..	..
Bedhampton Halt	..	..	..	..	12 59	..	..	..	..	..	..	..	..	..
Hilse Halt	..	..	..	..	..	..	..	..	..	..	..	..	..	..
Fratton 380	..	1254	..	..	1 7	..	..	..	..	..	1 23	1 36	..	..
Portsmouth & Southsea arr	..	1257	..	..	1 10	..	..	..	..	..	1 27	1 38	..	..
Portsmouth Harbour .. "	..	1 1	..	..	..	..	..	..	..	..	1 31	1 42	..	..
500 Ryde Pier (Boat) .. arr.	..	..	..	..	..	..	..	..	..	..	2 5	..	..	..
Sandown (Page 359) "	..	..	..	..	..	..	..	..	..	..	2 48	..	..	..
Shanklin "	..	..	..	..	..	..	..	..	..	..	2 55	..	..	..
Ventnor "	..	..	..	..	..	..	..	..	..	..	3 12	..	..	..
Newport "	..	..	..	..	..	..	..	..	..	..	3 6	..	..	..
Cowes "	..	..	..	..	..	..	..	..	..	..	3 20	..	..	..
Yarmouth "	..	..	..	..	..	..	..	..	..	..	..	..	..	..

Station	15	16	17	18	19	20	21	22	23	24	25	26	27	28
Three Bridges (*above*)..dep.	..	..	..	12 17	..	..	..	—	..	..	1247	..	12 59	..
Crawley	..	..	..	12 21	..	..	..	Stop	..	..	1251	..	1 3	..
Ifield	..	..	..	12 23	..	..	..	..	..	..	1253	..	..	..
Fay Gate	..	..	..	12 28	..	..	..	..	..	..	1258	..	..	..
Littlehaven Halt	..	..	..	12 32	..	..	..	..	..	..	1 2	..	..	..
Horsham 244, 245 ...... arr.	..	..	..	12 34	..	..	..	..	..	..	1 5	..	1 13	..
Sutton ......dep.	..	..	..	..	..	..	..	..	..	..	..	..	..	..
Dorking North **H**	..	..	..	..	..	..	..	..	..	..	..	..	..	..
Horsham 244, 245 ..... arr.	..	..	..	..	..	..	..	..	..	..	..	..	..	..
Horsham 244, 245 ..... dep.	..	..	..	12 35	..	..	..	..	..	..	1 5	..	1 15	..
Christ's Hospital, West Horsham	..	..	..	12 39	..	..	..	..	..	..	1 9	..	..	..
Billingshurst	..	..	..	12 46	..	..	..	..	..	..	1 16	..	..	..
Pulborough **J** 374	..	..	..	12 53	..	..	..	..	..	..	1 23	..	1 30	..
Amberley	..	..	..	1 1	..	..	..	..	..	..	1 31	..	..	..
Arundel	..	..	p.m	1 8	..	..	p.m	p.m	..	..	1 36	..	1 41	..
Brighton ......dep.	..	**P**	1233	..	1247	..	1250	1 3	..	..	..	..	**RB**	..
Holland Road Halt	..	..	1235	..	..	..	..	1 5	..	..	..	..	..	..
Hove	..	12 33	1237	..	1250	..	1253	1 7	..	..	..	..	**Saturdays only**	..
Aldrington Halt	..	..	1229	..	..	..	1255	1 9	..	..	..	..		..
Portslade and West Hove	..	..	1242	..	..	..	1257	1 12	..	**Saturdays only**	..	..		..
Fishersgate Halt	..	..	1244	..	..	..	1259	1 14	..		..	..		..
Southwick	..	..	1247	..	..	..	1 1	1 17	..		..	..		..
Shoreham-by-Sea **K**	..	12 40	1250	..	1257	..	1 5	1 20	..		..	..		..
Lancing	..	..	1255	..	..	..	1 9	1 25	..		..	..		..
Ham Bridge Halt **N**	..	..	1258	..	..	..	..	1 28	..		..	..		..
Worthing Central	..	12 48	1 1	..	1 6	..	1 13	1 31	..		..	..		..
West Worthing U	..	12 51	1 3	..	**Saturdays only**	..	1 15	1 33	..		..	..		..
Durrington-on-Sea	..	12 53	..	..		..	1 17	—	..		..	..	..	..
Goring-by-Sea	..	12 56	..	..		..	1 19	Stop	..		..	..	..	..
Angmering ¶	..	1 0	..	..		..	1 24	..	..		..	..	..	..
Ford (Sussex) ......dep.	1 2	..	..	..		..	..	..	..		..	..	..	..
Littlehampton .... arr.	1 7	1 10	..	1 15		..	1 33	..	..		1 43	..	..	..
Littlehampton .... dep.	..	..	..	..		..	..	..	..		1 46	..	..	..
Ford (Sussex)	..	..	..	..		..	..	..	..	p.m	1a50	..	..	..
Barnham ......arr.	..	..	..	..	1 22	..	..	..	..	1d25	2 1	..	1 49	..
Bognor Regis ..... arr	..	..	..	..	1 31	..	..	..	..	1 31	2 7	..	2 0	..
Bognor Regis ..... dep.	..	..	..	..	1 10	..	..	..	..	..	..	..	1 40	..
Barnham ......dep	..	..	..	..	1 22	..	..	p.m	..	..	..	..	1 52	..
Chichester **Z**	..	..	..	..	1 32	..	..	1 37	..	..	..	..	2 2	..
Fishbourne Halt	..	..	..	..	..	..	..	1 40	..	..	..	..	..	..
Bosham	..	..	..	..	..	..	..	1 43	..	..	..	..	..	..
Nutbourne Halt	..	..	..	..	..	..	..	1 46	..	..	..	..	..	..
Southbourne Halt	..	..	..	..	..	..	..	1 49	..	..	..	..	..	..
Emsworth	..	..	..	..	..	..	..	1 52	..	..	..	..	..	..
Warblington Halt	..	..	..	..	..	..	..	1 55	..	..	..	..	..	..
Havant 244, 366	..	..	..	..	1 45	..	..	1 57	..	..	..	..	2 15	..
244 Hayling Island ....arr.	..	..	..	..	..	..	..	..	..	..	..	..	2 33	..
Bedhampton Halt	..	..	..	..	..	..	..	1 59	..	..	..	..	..	..
Hilse Halt	..	..	..	..	..	..	..	..	..	..	..	..	..	..
Fratton 380	..	..	..	..	1 54	..	..	2 7	..	..	..	..	2 24	..
Portsmouth & Southsea arr	..	..	..	..	1 56	..	..	2 10	..	..	..	..	2 28	p.m
Portsmouth Harbour .. "	..	..	..	..	2 0	..	..	..	..	..	..	..	2 32	2d35
500 Ryde Pier (Boat) .. arr.	..	..	..	..	..	..	..	..	..	..	..	..	..	3 5
Sandown (Page 359) "	..	..	..	..	..	..	..	..	..	..	..	..	..	3 48
Shanklin "	..	..	..	..	..	..	..	..	..	..	..	..	..	3 55
Ventnor "	..	..	..	..	..	..	..	..	..	..	..	..	..	4 11
Newport "	..	..	..	..	..	..	..	..	..	..	..	..	..	4 6
Cowes "	..	..	..	..	..	..	..	..	..	..	..	..	..	4 20
Yarmouth "	..	..	..	..	..	..	..	..	..	..	..	..	..	4 40

¶ Third class only. * Change at East Croydon. *a* Dep. 5 mins. later. *d* Departure time. **P** Pullman Car facilities available.
RB Refreshment Car facilities available between London and Bognor Regis. *t* 4 mins. later on Sats. *y* Arr 2 mins. *earlier*

For Other Notes, see page 195

For SERVICES from LONDON (Waterloo) to PORTSMOUTH and ISLE OF WIGHT, see pages 359 to 365

From LONDON to THE SOUTH COAST—Week Days—*continued*

	p.m	p.m	p.m	p.m	p.m	p.m	p.m.	p.m	p.m	p.m	p.m	p.m	p.m	p.m	p.m	p.m	p.m	p.m	p.m	p.m	p.m	p.m	p.m	p.m	p.m	p.m	p.m	p.m	p.m	p.m
									P			P			P	P						P	P		RB					R
VICTORIA ....dep.	..	..	..	..	..	..	12*3	..	12 25	..	1228	1230	12*25		12 45	12 45	..	..	..	..	12 48	1 0	..	..	1 18	..	..	..	..	..
Clapham Junction .... "	..	..	..	..	..	..	..	..	..	..	1234	..	..	..	..	..	..	..	..	..	12U53	..	..	..	..	..	..	..	..	..
LONDON BRIDGE ..dep.	..	..	..	..	..	1215	12 18	..	12*20		12*18	..	1230		12B31	12B35	..	..	..	..	12B t31	..	1 5	..	1B 8	..	..	..	1 9	1 24
New Cross Gate ..... "	..	..	..	..	..	..	..	..	..	..	..	..	..	..	..	..	..	..	..	..	..	..	..	..	..	..	..	..	..	..
Norwood Junction B "	..	..	..	..	..	..	12 30	..	..		12*30	..	..		12B43	..	..	..	..	..	12B SX43		..	..	..	..	..	..	..	..
East Croydon ....dep.	..	..	..	..	..	1230	12 36	..	12U40	..	1246	Saturdays only	1247	..	1 1	1U0	..	..	..	..	1 5	Saturdays only	1U20	..	Saturdays only	..	..	..	1 24	Saturdays only
Purley	..	..	..	..	..	1236	12 41	..	Saturdays only	..	..		..	..	Saturdays excepted	Saturdays only	..	..	..	..	1 11		Saturdays only	..		..	..	..	..	
Coulsdon South	..	..	..	..	..	1240	12 45	..		..	..		..	..			..	..	..	..	1 14			..		..	..	..	1 31	
Merstham	..	..	..	..	..	1246	12 51	..		..	..		..	..			..	..	..	..	1 20			..		..	..	..	1 37	
Redhill 246	..	..	..	..	..	1255	12 57	..		..	1 1		1 2	..			..	..	..	..	1 27			..		..	..	..	1 43	
Earlswood	..	..	..	..	..	1257	1 0	..		..	..		Sats. only	..			..	..	..	..	1 30			..		..	..	..	1 46	
Salfords	..	..	..	..	..	1 1	1 3	..		..	..			..			..	..	..	..	1 33			..		..	..	..	1 49	
Horley	..	..	..	..	..	1 5	1 7	..		..	..			..			..	..	..	..	1 37			..		..	..	..	1 53	1 55
Gatwick Airport	..	..	..	..	..	1 8	1 10	..		..	1 10	..		..			..	..	..	..	1 40			..		..	..	..	1 56	..
Three Bridges (*below*) 234.	..	..	..	..	..	1y15	1 15	..		..	..	..	1 13	..			..	..	..	..	1y46		1 43	..		..	..	..	2y2	..
Balcombe	..	..	..	..	..	1 22	1 22	..		..	..	..	..	..			..	..	..	..	1 52		..	..		..	..	..	2 8	..
Horsted Keynes ....dep	..	..	..	..	1 16	..	..	..	..	..	..	..	..	1 16	..	..	..	..	..	..	..	..	..	..	..	..	..	..	..	..
Ardingly	..	..	..	..	1 20	..	..	..	..	..	..	..	..	1 20	..	..	..	..	..	..	..	..	..	..	..	..	..	..	..	..
Haywards Heath C 239...	..	..	..	..	1 24	1 28	1 28	..	1 11	..	1 23	..	1 25	1 24	1 32	1 32	..	..	..	..	1 59	..	..	..		..	..	..	2 14	2 10
Wivelsfield (*below*)	..	..	..	..		1 32	1 32	..	Through Train Victoria to Littlehampton	..	..	..	..	..	..	..	..	..	..	..	2 3	..	..	..	Through Train, Victoria to Bognor Regis	..	..	..	2 19	..
Burgess Hill	..	..	..	..	Stop	1 35	1 35	..		..	..	..	..	..	..	..	..	..	..	..	2 6	..	..	..		..	..	..	2 21	..
Hassocks D	..	..	..	..		1 39	1 39	..		..	..	..	..	..	..	..	..	..	..	..	2 10	..	..	..		..	..	..	2 25	..
Preston Park	..	..	..	..	..	1 47	1 47	..		..	1 37	..	1 40	..	..	..	..	..	..	..	2 18	..	..	..		..	..	..	2 33	2 24
Brighton (*below*) ....arr.	..	..	..	..	..	1 50	1 50	..		..	1 41	1 30	1 43	..	..	..	..	..	..	..	2 21	2 0	2 7	..		..	..	..	2 37	..
Haywards Heath ...dep.	..	..	..	..	..	Saturdays only	Saturdays excepted.	..		..		Stop	Stop	..	1 33	1 33	..	1 35	..	..	..	Stop	..	..		..	..	..	Saturdays only	..
Wivelsfield (*above*)	..	..	..	..	..			..		..		..	..	..	..	..	..	1 39	..	..	..	..	..	..		..	..	..		..
Plumpton	..	..	..	..	..			..		..		..	..	..	..	..	..	1x45	..	..	..	..	..	..		..	..	..		..
Cooksbridge	..	..	..	..	..			..		..	☞	..	..	..	..	..	..	1b50	..	..	..	..	..	..		..	..	..		..
Lewes 239 ....arr.	..	..	..	..	..			..		..		..	..	..	1 48	1 48	..	1b55	..	..	..	..	..	..		..	..	..		..
Brighton ....dep.	..	..	..	1 14	..		..	1 20		..		..	..	..	..	..	..	Stop	1 46	..	..	..	..	..		2 14	..	..		..
London Road (Brighton)...	..	..	..	1 16	..		..	1 23		..	Saturdays excepted.	..	..	..	..	..	..		1 48	..	..	..	..	..		2 16	..	..		Through Train. London Bridge to Littlehampton.
Falmer	..	..	..	1 21	..		..	..		..		..	..	..	..	..	..	..	1 52	..	..	..	..	..		2 21	..	..		
Lewes ....arr.	..	..	..	1 28	..		..	1 38		..		..	..	..	..	..	..	..	2 0	..	..	..	..	..		2 28	..	..		
Lewes ....dep.	..	..	..	..	..	..	..	Stop	..	..		..	..	..	..	1 54	6 minutes later on Saturdays	..	..	2 4	..	..	..	..	..	..	..	..	..	
Southease and Rodmell	..	..	..	..	..	..	..	..	..	..		..	..	..	..	..		..	..	2 9	..	..	..	..	..	..	..	..	..	
Newhaven Town ...[Halt	..	..	..	..	..	..	..	..	..	..		..	..	..	..	2 4		..	..	2 14	..	..	..	..	..	..	..	..	..	
" Harbour	..	..	..	..	..	..	..	..	..	..		..	..	..	..	2 6		..	..	2 15	..	..	..	..	..	..	..	..	..	
Bishopstone	..	..	..	..	..	..	..	..	..	..	Stop	..	..	..	..	..		..	..	2 20	..	..	..	..	..	..	..	..	..	
Seaford ....arr.	..	..	..	..	..	..	..	..	..	..		..	..	..	..	2 10		..	..	2 22	..	..	..	..	..	..	..	..	..	
Lewes ....dep.	..	..	..	1 29	..	..	..	..	..	..	..	..	..	..	1 50	1 52		..	2 1	..	..	..	..	..	..	2 29	..	..	..	
Glynde	..	..	..	1 34	..	..	..	..	..	..	..	..	..	..	..	..		..	2 6	..	..	..	..	..	..	2 34	..	..	..	
Berwick	..	..	..	1 40	..	..	..	p.m	..	..	..	..	..	..	..	..		..	2 12	..	..	..	..	..	..	2 40	..	..	..	
Polegate 239	..	..	..	1 47	..	..	..	1 49	..	..	..	..	..	..	..	..	2 7	p.m	2 19	..	..	..	..	..	..	2 47	..	..	..	
Hampden Park F	..	..	1 45	1 50	..	..	..	1 54	..	..	..	..	..	..	..	..	2 11	2 15	2 22	..	..	..	..	2 45	..	2 50	..	..	..	
Eastbourne ....arr.	..	..	1 49	1 54	..	..	..	1 59	..	..	..	..	..	..	2 9	2 11	2 16	2 19	2 26	..	..	..	..	2 49	..	2 54	..	..	..	
Eastbourne ....dep.	..	..	..	1 57	..	..	..	Stop	..	..	..	..	..	..	2 13	2 16	..	Stop	2 29	..	..	..	..	Stop	..	2 57	..	..	..	
Hampden Park F	..	..	..	2 0	..	..	..		..	..	..	..	..	..	..	..	..		2 32	..	..	..	..		..	3 0	..	..	..	
Pevensey and Westham....	..	..	..	2 6	..	..	..	..	..	..	..	..	..	..	..	2 26	..	..	2 39	..	..	..	..	..	..	3 7	..	..	..	
Pevensey Bay Halt	..	..	..	2 8	..	..	..	..	..	..	..	..	..	..	..	..	..	..	2 41	..	..	..	..	..	..	3 9	..	..	..	
Norman's Bay Halt	..	..	..	2 11	..	..	..	..	..	..	..	..	..	..	..	..	..	..	2 44	..	..	..	..	..	..	3 12	..	..	..	..
Cooden Beach	..	..	..	2 15	..	..	..	..	..	..	..	..	..	..	2 27	2 33	..	..	2 48	..	..	..	..	..	..	3 16	..	..	..	..
Collington Halt	..	..	..	2 18	..	..	..	..	..	..	..	..	..	..	..	..	..	..	2 51	..	..	..	..	..	..	3 19	..	..	..	..
Bexhill (Central) G	..	..	..	2 21	..	..	..	..	..	..	..	..	..	..	2 33	2 39	..	..	2 54	..	..	..	..	..	..	3 24	..	..	..	..
St. Leonards (W.M.)	..	..	..	2 27	..	..	..	..	..	..	..	..	..	..	..	..	..	..	2 59	..	..	..	..	..	..	3 28	..	..	..	..
" (W.S.)	..	..	..	2 30	..	..	..	..	..	..	..	..	..	..	2 40	2 47	..	..	3 2	..	..	..	..	..	..	3 31	..	..	..	..
Hastings 56, 59	..	..	..	2 32	..	..	..	..	..	..	..	..	..	..	2 42	2 49	..	..	3 3	..	..	..	..	..	..	3 33	..	..	..	..
Ore ....arr.	..	..	..	2 35	..	..	..	..	..	..	..	p.m	..	..	2 50	2 53	..	..	3 6	..	..	..	..	p.m	..	3 36	..	..	..	..
	1	2	3	4	5	6	7	8	9	10	11	12	13	14	15	16	17	18	19	20	21	22	23	24	25	26	27	28	29	30

Station	1	2	3	4	5	6	7	8	9	10	11	12	13	14	15	16	17	18	19	20	21	22	23	24	25	26	27	28	29	30
Three Bridges (*above*)..dep.	..	..	..	..	..	..	..	..	..	..	..	1 17	..	..	..	..	..	..	..	..	..	..	..	1 47	..	..	..	..	..	..
Crawley	..	..	..	..	..	..	..	..	..	..	..	1 21	..	..	..	..	..	..	..	..	..	..	..	1 51	..	Stop	..	..	..	..
Ifield	..	..	..	..	..	..	..	..	..	..	..	1 23	..	..	..	..	..	..	..	..	..	..	..	1 53	..	..	..	..	..	..
Fay Gate	..	..	..	..	..	..	..	..	..	..	..	1 28	..	..	..	..	..	..	..	..	..	..	..	1 58	..	..	..	..	..	..
Littlehaven Halt	..	..	..	..	..	..	..	..	..	..	..	1 32	..	..	..	..	..	..	..	..	..	..	..	2 2	..	..	..	..	..	..
Horsham 244, 245 ......arr.	..	..	..	..	..	..	..	..	..	..	..	1 35	..	..	..	..	..	..	..	..	..	..	..	2 5	..	..	..	..	..	..
Sutton ......dep.	Saturdays excepted	Saturdays only	..	..	Saturdays excepted ☞	..	..	..	Saturdays only	Saturdays only	Saturdays excepted ☞	..	Saturdays only ☞	..	..	..	..	..	..	..	..	..	..	..	1 39	..	..	..	..	Saturdays only
Dorking North **H**			..	..		..	..	..				..		..	..	..	..	..	..	..	..	..	..	..	1 56	..	..	..	..	
Horsham 244, 245 ... arr.			..	..		..	..	..				..		..	..	..	..	..	..	..	..	..	..	..	2 13	..	..	..	..	
Horsham 244, 245 ... dep.			..	..		..	..	..				1 35		..	..	..	..	..	..	..	..	..	..	2 5	2 15	..	..	..	..	
Christ's Hospital, West [Horsham			..	..		..	..	..				1 39		..	..	..	..	..	..	..	..	..	..	2 9	..	..	..	..	..	
Billingshurst			..	..		..	..	..				1 46		..	..	..	..	..	..	..	..	..	..	2 16	..	..	..	..	..	
Pulborough **J** 374			..	..		..	..	..				1 53		..	..	..	..	..	..	..	..	..	..	2 23	2 30	..	..	..	..	
Amberley			..	..		..	..	..				2 1		..	..	..	..	..	..	..	..	..	..	2 31	..	..	..	..	..	
Arundel			..	..	p.m	..	..	..			p.m	2 6	p.m	..	..	..	..	p.m	..	..	..	p.m	..	2 36	2 41	..	..	..	..	
Brighton ......dep.	1 16	1 17	..	..	1 20	..	..	..	**P**	1 28	1 33	..	1 35	..	..	..	..	1 50	..	..	..	2 3	..	..	**RB** Saturdays only	..	2 17	2 20	..	**R**
Holland Road Halt	..	..	..	..	..	..	..	..	..	1 30	1 35	..	..	..	..	..	..	..	..	..	..	2 5	..	..		..	..	..	..	..
Hove	1 19	1 20	..	..	1 23	..	..	..	1 29	1 32	1 37	..	1 39	..	..	..	..	1 53	..	..	..	2 7	..	..		..	2 20	2 23	..	2 29
Aldrington Halt	..	..	..	..	1 25	..	..	..	..	1 34	1 39	..	..	..	..	..	..	1 55	..	..	..	2 9	..	..		..	..	..	..	..
Portslade and West Hove	..	1 23	..	..	1 28	..	..	..	..	1 37	1 42	..	1 42	..	..	..	..	1 58	..	..	..	2 12	..	..		..	..	2 26	..	..
Fishersgate Halt	..	..	..	..	..	..	..	..	..	1 39	1 44	..	..	..	..	..	..	..	..	..	..	2 14	..	..		..	..	..	..	..
Southwick	1 24	1 26	..	..	1 31	..	..	..	..	1 42	1 47	..	..	..	..	..	..	2 1	..	..	..	2 17	..	..		..	..	2 29	..	..
Shoreham-by-Sea **K**	1 28	1 28	..	..	1 34	..	..	..	1 36	1 45	1 50	..	1 48	..	..	..	..	2 4	..	..	..	2 20	..	..		..	2 27	2 33	..	2 37
Lancing	..	1 34	..	..	1 38	..	..	..	..	1 50	1 55	..	..	..	..	..	..	2 8	..	..	..	2 25	..	..		..	..	2 37	..	..
Ham Bridge Halt **N**	..	..	..	..	..	..	..	..	..	1 53	1 58	..	..	..	..	..	..	..	..	..	..	2 28	..	..		..	..	..	..	..
Worthing Central	1 35	1 38	..	..	1 42	..	..	..	1 46	1 56	2 1	..	..	..	..	..	..	2 12	..	..	..	2 31	..	..		..	2 35	2 41	..	2 46
West Worthing **U**	1 37	1 40	..	..	1 45	..	..	..	1 49	1 58	2 3	..	..	..	..	..	..	2 14	..	..	..	2 33	..	..		..	2 37	2 43	..	2 50
Durrington-on-Sea	..	..	..	..	..	..	..	..	1 52	..	..	..	..	..	..	..	..	2 16	..	..	..	..	..	..		..	..	..	..	2 53
Goring-by-Sea	1 41	..	..	..	..	..	..	..	1 55	..	..	..	..	..	..	..	..	2 19	..	..	..	..	..	..		..	2 41	Stop	..	2 57
Angmering **L**	1 45	..	..	..	..	..	..	p.m	2 0	..	..	..	..	..	..	..	..	2 23	..	..	..	..	..	..		..	2 45	p.m	..	3 2
Ford (Sussex) ......dep.	..	..	..	..	..	..	..	1 52	..	..	..	..	..	..	..	..	..	..	..	..	..	..	..	..		..	..	3 2	..	..
Littlehampton ... arr.	..	..	..	..	..	..	..	1 57	2 10	..	..	2 13	..	..	..	..	..	2 33	..	..	..	..	..	2 43	..	..	3 7	3 7	..	3 11
Littlehampton ... dep.	1 46	1 46	..	..	..	..	..	..	..	..	..	..	..	..	..	..	..	Stop	..	..	..	..	..	2 46	..	..	2 46	..	..	..
Ford (Sussex)	1 52	1 52	..	..	..	..	..	..	..	..	..	..	..	..	..	..	..		..	..	..	..	..	2*a*50	..	..	2 52	..	..	..
Barnham ......arr.	1 57	1 57	..	..	..	..	..	..	..	..	..	..	..	..	..	..	..	..	..	..	..	..	..	3 1	2 49	..	2 57	..	..	..
Bognor Regis ... arr.	2 7	2 7	..	..	..	..	..	..	..	..	..	..	..	..	..	..	..	..	..	..	..	..	..	3 7	3 0	..	3 7	..	..	..
Bognor Regis ... dep.	1 40	1 40	..	..	..	..	..	..	..	..	..	..	..	..	..	..	..	..	..	..	..	..	..	..	..	..	2 45	..	..	..
Barnham ......dep.	1 57	1 57	..	..	..	..	..	..	..	..	..	..	..	..	..	..	..	p.m	..	..	..	..	..	..	2 52	..	2 57	..	..	..
Chichester **Z**	2 7	2 7	..	..	..	..	..	..	..	..	..	..	..	..	..	..	..	2 37	..	..	..	..	..	..	3 2	..	3 7	..	..	..
Fishbourne Halt	2 10	2 10	..	..	..	..	..	..	..	..	..	..	..	..	..	..	..	2 40	..	..	..	..	..	..	..	..	3 10	..	..	..
Bosham	2 13	2 13	..	..	..	..	..	..	..	..	..	..	..	..	..	..	..	2 43	..	..	..	..	..	..	..	..	3 13	..	..	..
Nutbourne Halt	2 16	2 16	..	..	..	..	..	..	..	..	..	..	..	..	..	..	..	2 46	..	..	..	..	..	..	..	..	3 16	..	..	..
Southbourne Halt	2 19	2 19	..	..	..	..	..	..	..	..	..	..	..	..	..	..	..	2 49	..	..	..	..	..	..	..	..	3 19	..	..	..
Emsworth	2 22	2 22	..	..	..	..	..	..	..	..	..	..	..	..	..	..	..	2 52	..	..	..	..	..	..	..	..	3 22	..	..	..
Warblington Halt	2 25	2 25	..	..	..	..	..	..	..	..	..	..	..	..	..	..	..	2 55	..	..	..	..	..	..	..	..	3 25	..	..	..
Havant 244, 366	2 27	2 27	..	..	..	..	..	..	..	..	..	..	..	..	..	..	..	2 57	..	..	..	..	..	..	3 15	..	3 27	..	..	..
244 Hayling Island ....arr.	..	..	..	..	..	..	..	..	..	..	..	..	..	..	..	..	..	..	..	..	..	..	..	..	..	..	..	..	..	..
Bedhampton Halt	..	..	..	..	..	..	..	..	..	..	..	..	..	..	..	..	..	2 59	..	..	..	..	..	..	..	..	..	..	..	..
Hilsea Halt	..	..	..	..	..	..	..	..	..	..	..	..	..	..	..	..	..	..	..	..	..	..	..	..	..	..	..	..	..	..
Fratton 380	2 36	2 36	..	..	..	..	..	..	..	..	..	..	..	..	..	..	..	3 7	..	..	..	..	..	..	3 23	..	3 36	..	..	..
Portsmouth & Southsea arr.	2 38	2 38	..	..	..	..	..	..	..	..	..	..	..	..	..	..	..	3 10	..	..	..	..	..	..	3 27	p.m	3 38	..	..	..
Portsmouth Harbour .. "	2 42	2 42	..	..	..	..	..	..	..	..	..	..	..	..	..	..	..	..	..	..	..	..	..	..	3 31	3*d*35	3 42	..	..	..
500 Ryde Pier (Boat) .. arr.	..	..	..	..	..	..	..	..	..	..	..	..	..	..	..	..	..	..	..	..	..	..	..	..	..	4 5	..	..	..	..
Page 359 Sandown "	..	..	..	..	..	..	..	..	..	..	..	..	..	..	..	..	..	..	..	..	..	..	..	..	..	4 48	..	..	..	..
Shanklin "	..	..	..	..	..	..	..	..	..	..	..	..	..	..	..	..	..	..	..	..	..	..	..	..	..	4 55	..	..	..	..
Ventnor "	..	..	..	..	..	..	..	..	..	..	..	..	..	..	..	..	..	..	..	..	..	..	..	..	..	5 11	..	..	..	..
Newport "	..	..	..	..	..	..	..	..	..	..	..	..	..	..	..	..	..	..	..	..	..	..	..	..	..	5 6	..	..	..	..
Cowes "	..	..	..	..	..	..	..	..	..	..	..	..	..	..	..	..	..	..	..	..	..	..	..	..	..	5 20	..	..	..	..
Yarmouth "	..	..	..	..	..	..	..	..	..	..	..	..	..	..	..	..	..	..	..	..	..	..	..	..	..	5 45	..	..	..	..

3 Third class only. * Change at East Croydon. *a* Dep. 5 mins. later. *b* 2 mins. later on Sats. *d* Departure time.
P Pullman Car facilities available. **R** Refreshment Car facilities available. **RB** Refreshment Car facilities available between London and Bognor Regis.
SX Saturdays excepted. *t* Dep. 12 47 p.m on Sats. **U** Stops to take up only. *z* 1 min. later on Sats. *y* Arr. 2 mins. earlier.

For SERVICES from LONDON (Waterloo) to PORTSMOUTH and ISLE OF WIGHT, see pages 359 to 365

From LONDON to THE SOUTH COAST—Week Days—*continued*

	p.m	p.m	p.m	p.m	p.m	p.m	p.m	p.m	p.m	p.m	p.m	p.m	p.m	p.m	p.m	p.m	p.m	p.m	p.m	p.m	p.m	p.m	p.m	p.m	p.m	p.m	p.m	p.m	p.m	p.m	p.m
										P							P	P	KB					P					P		
VICTORIA dep.	..	..	..	1 28	..	1 28	1*28	..	1*28	1 45	..	..	..	..	..	1 48	2 0	2 A 0	2 18	..	..	..	..	2 25	2 28	..	..	..	2 45	..	..
Clapham Junction "	..	..	..	1 34	..	1‖34	1*‖34	..	1*‖34	..	..	..	..	..	..	1‖53	..	..	..	..	..	..	..	..	2‖34	..	..	..	..	..	..
LONDON BRIDGE dep.	..	..	1 18	1*18	..	1 S 16	1 40	..	1 32	1*42	..	..	..	..	..	1t S 31	..	1 S 55	2 S 8	..	..	2 18	..	2*18	2*18	..	..	..	..	..	..
New Cross Gate "	..	..	..	..	..	..	..	..	..	..	..	..	..	..	..	..	..	..	..	..	..	..	..	..	..	..	..	..	..	..	..
Norwood Junction **B** "	..	..	1 30	1*30	..	..	..	..	..	..	..	..	..	..	..	1SX S 43	..	..	..	..	..	2 30	..	2*30	2*30	..	..	..	..	..	..
East Croydon dep.	..	..	1 35	1 46	..	1 46	1 55	..	1 48	2 1	..	..	..	..	..	2 5	..	2 16	..	..	..	2 35	..	2 42	2 46	..	..	..	3 1	..	..
Purley	..	..	1 40	..	..	..	Saturdays only	..	1 54	..	..	..	..	..	..	2 11	..	..	..	..	..	2 40	..	..	..	..	..	..	..	..	..
Coulsdon South	..	..	1 44	..	..	..		..	1 57	..	..	..	..	..	..	2 14	..	..	..	..	..	2 44	..	..	..	..	..	..	..	..	..
Merstham	..	..	1 50	..	..	..		..	2 3	Saturdays only	..	..	..	..	..	2 20	Saturdays excepted	Saturdays only	Saturdays only	..	..	2 50	..	Saturdays only	..	..	..	..	Saturdays only	..	..
Redhill 246	..	..	1 57	2 1	..	2 1		..	2 10		..	..	..	..	..	2 27				..	..	2 57	..		3 1	..	..	..		..	..
Earlswood	..	..	1 59	..	..	..		..	2 12		..	..	..	..	..	2 30				..	..	2 59	..		..	..	..	..		..	..
Salfords	..	..	2 3	..	..	..		..	2 16		..	..	..	..	..	2 33				..	..	3 3	..		..	..	..	..		..	..
Horley	..	..	2 7	..	..	2 9		..	2 20		..	..	..	..	..	2 37				..	..	3 7	..		..	..	..	..		..	..
Gatwick Airport	..	..	2 10	2 10	..	2 12		..	2 23		..	..	..	..	..	2 40				..	..	3 10	..		3 10	..	..	..		..	..
Three Bridges (*below*) 234	..	..	2 15	..	..	..	2 18	..	2 28		..	..	..	..	..	2y46				..	..	3 15	..		..	..	..	..		..	..
Balcombe	..	..	2 22	..	..	2 21	..	..	2 34	..	..	..	..	..	..	2 52	..	..	..	..	..	3 21	..	..	..	..	..	..	..	..	..
Horsted Keynes dep.	..	..	2 16	..	2 16	..	..	..	..	..	2 16	..	..	..	..	..	..	..	..	..	3 16	..	..	..	..	..	..	..	..	3 16	..
Ardingly	..	..	2 20	..	2 20	..	..	..	..	..	2 20	..	..	..	..	..	..	..	..	..	3 20	..	..	..	..	..	..	..	..	3 20	..
Haywards Heath C 239	..	..	2 28	2 23	2 24	2 27	..	..	2‖50	2 32	2 24	..	..	..	..	2 59	..	2 48	..	..	3 24	3 28	..	3 14	3 23	..	..	..	3 32	3 24	..
Wivelsfield (*below*)	..	..	2 32	..	Stop	..	..	..	2 54	..	..	..	..	..	..	3 3	..	..	..	..	Stop	3 32	..	..	..	..	..	..	..	..	..
Burgess Hill	..	..	2 35	..	..	..	..	..	2 57	..	..	..	..	..	..	3 6	..	..	..	..	..	3 35	..	..	..	..	..	..	..	..	..
Hassocks **D**	..	..	2 39	..	..	..	..	..	3 1	..	..	..	..	..	..	3 10	..	..	..	..	..	3 39	..	..	..	..	..	..	..	..	..
Preston Park	..	..	2 47	2 37	..	2 42	..	..	3 9	..	..	..	..	..	..	3 18	..	..	..	..	..	3 47	..	..	3 37	..	..	..	..	..	..
Brighton (*below*) arr.	..	..	2 50	2 41	..	2 45	..	..	3 12	..	..	..	..	..	..	3 21	3 0	3 3	..	..	..	3 50	..	..	3 41	..	..	..	..	..	..
Haywards Heath dep.	..	..	Saturdays excepted	Saturdays excepted	..	..	..	..		2 33	2 35	..	..	..	..	Stop	Stop	..	Through Train, Victoria to Bognor Regis.	..	..	Stop	..	Through Train, Victoria to Littlehampton.	Stop	..	..	..	3 33	3 35	..
Wivelsfield (*above*)	..	..			..	Saturdays only	..	..		..	2 39	..	..	..	..	..	..	..		..	..	..	..		..	..	..	..	..	3 39	..
Plumpton	..	..			..		..	..		..	2 45	..	..	..	..	..	..	..		..	..	..	..		..	..	..	..	..	3 45	..
Cooksbridge	..	..			..		..	..		..	2 50	..	..	..	..	..	..	..		..	..	..	..		..	..	..	..	..	3 50	..
Lewes 239 arr.	..	..			..		..	..		2 53	2 57	..	..	..	..	..	..	..		..	..	..	..		..	..	..	..	3 48	3 57	..
Brighton dep.	..	Saturdays excepted			..		Through Train, London Bridge to Bognor Regis.	..	Saturdays only	..	..	2 46	..	..	3 5	..	..	..		..	..	..	..		..	3 14	..	3 31	..	Stop	3 46
London Road (Brighton)	..				..			..		..	..	2 48	..	..	3 8	..	..	..		..	..	..	..		..	3 16	..	3 33	..	..	3 48
Falmer	..				..			..		..	..	2 52	..	..	..	..	..	..		..	..	..	..		..	3 21	..	3 37	..	..	3 52
Lewes arr	..		..	..	..			..		..	..	3 0	..	..	3 24	..	..	..		..	..	..	..		..	3 28	..	3 45	..	..	4 0
Lewes dep	..		..	..	..	..		..		..	..	..	3 4	..	Stop	..	..	..		..	..	..	..		..	..	..	3 46	..	..	..
Southease and Rodmell	..		..	..	..	..		..		..	..	..	3 9	..	..	..	..	..		..	..	..	..		..	..	..	3 51	..	..	..
Newhaven Town [Halt	..		..	..	..	..		..		..	..	..	3 14	..	..	..	..	..		..	..	..	..		..	..	..	3 56	..	..	..
" Harbour	..		..	..	..	..		..		..	..	..	3 15	..	..	..	..	..		..	..	..	..		..	..	..	3 57	..	..	..
Bishopstone	..		..	..	..	..		..	Stop	..	..	..	3 20	..	..	..	..	..		..	..	..	..		..	..	..	4 2	..	..	..
Seaford arr	..		..	..	..	..		..	..	..	..	..	3 22	..	..	..	..	..	..	..	..	..	..	..	..	..	..	4 5	..	..	..
Lewes dep	..		..	..	..	..		..	..	2 54	..	3 1	..	..	..	..	..	..	..	..	..	..	..	..	..	3 29	..	Stop	3 50	..	4 1
Glynde	..		..	..	..	..		..	..	..	..	3 6	..	..	..	..	..	..	..	..	..	..	..	..	..	3 34	..	..	..	..	4 6
Berwick	..		..	..	..	..		..	p.m	..	..	3 12	..	..	..	..	..	..	..	..	..	p.m	..	..	..	3 40	..	..	..	..	4 12
Polegate 239	..	3 6	..	..	p.m	..		..	3 12	..	..	3 19	..	..	..	..	..	..	..	..	..	3 37	..	..	p.m	3 47	..	..	..	p.m	4 19
Hampden Park **F**	..	3 11	..	..	3 15	..		..	3 18	..	..	3 22	..	..	..	..	..	..	..	..	..	3 41	..	..	3 45	3 50	..	..	..	4 15	4 22
Eastbourne arr.	..	3 16	..	..	3 19	..		..	3 23	3 13	..	3 26	..	..	..	..	..	..	..	..	..	3 46	..	..	3 49	3 54	..	..	4 9	4 19	4 26
Eastbourne dep.	..	Stop	..	..	Stop	..	..	..		3 17	..	3 29	..	..	..	..	..	..	..	..	..	Stop	..	..	Stop	3 57	..	..	4 13	..	4 29
Hampden Park **F**	..	..	..	..	..	..	..	..		..	..	3 32	..	..	..	..	..	..	..	..	..	..	..	..	..	4 0	..	..	..	..	4 32
Pevensey and Westham	..	..	..	..	..	..	..	..		..	..	3 39	..	..	..	..	..	..	..	..	..	..	..	..	..	4 7	..	..	..	..	4 39
Pevensey Bay Halt	..	..	..	..	..	..	..	..	Saturdays only	..	..	3 41	..	..	..	..	..	..	..	..	..	..	..	..	..	4 9	..	..	..	..	4 41
Norman's Bay Halt	..	..	..	..	..	..	..	..		..	..	3 44	..	..	..	..	..	..	..	..	..	..	..	..	..	4 12	..	..	..	..	4 44
Cooden Beach	..	..	..	..	..	..	..	..		3 30	..	3 48	..	..	..	..	..	..	..	..	..	..	..	..	..	4 16	..	..	4 26	..	4 48
Collington Halt	..	..	..	..	..	..	..	..		..	..	3 51	..	..	..	..	..	..	..	..	..	..	..	..	..	4 19	..	..	..	..	4 51
Bexhill (Central) **G**	..	..	..	..	..	..	..	..		3 35	..	3 54	..	..	..	..	..	..	..	..	..	..	..	..	..	4 23	..	..	4 31	..	4 54
St. Leonards (W.M.)	..	..	..	..	..	..	..	..		..	..	3 58	..	..	..	..	..	..	..	..	..	..	..	..	..	4 28	..	..	..	..	4 58
" (W.S.)	..	..	..	..	..	..	..	..		3 42	..	4 1	..	..	..	..	..	..	..	..	..	..	..	..	..	4 31	..	..	4 38	..	5 1
Hastings 56, 59	..	..	..	..	..	..	..	..		3 44	..	4 3	..	..	..	..	..	..	..	..	..	..	..	..	..	4 33	..	..	4 40	..	5 3
Ore arr.	..	..	..	..	p.m	..	..	..		3 47	..	4 6	..	..	..	..	p.m	..	..	..	..	..	..	..	..	4 36	..	..	4 45	..	5 6
	1	2	3	4	5	6	7	8	9	10	11	12	13	14	15	16	17	18	19	20	21	22	23	24	25	26	27	28	29	30	31

Station	1	2	3	4	5	6	7	8	9	10	11	12	13	14	15	16
Three Bridges (above) ..dep.		Saturdays excepted			2 17		2 19	2 24								
Crawley					2 21		2 23	2 27				Stop				
Ifield					2 23			2 30								
Fay Gate					2 28			2 34								
Littlehaven Halt					2 32			2 38								
Horsham 244, 245 ......arr.					2 35		2 32	2 41								
Sutton ......dep.	Saturdays only							Saturdays only								
Dorking North H																
Horsham 244, 245 ... arr.																
dep.		☞			2 35		2 34									
Christ's Hospital, West Horsham					2 39											
Billingshurst					2 46											
Pulborough J 374					2 53		2 48									
Amberley					3 1		2 56									
Arundel		p.m			3 6		3 2					p.m			p.m	
Brighton ......dep.	2 28	2 33										2 47		2 50	3 3	
Holland Road Halt	2 30	2 35													3 5	
Hove	2 32	2 37										2 50		2 53	3 7	
Aldrington Halt	2 34	2 39												2 55	3 9	
Portslade and West Hove	2 37	2 42			Saturdays excepted									2 58	3 12	
Fishersgate Halt	2 39	2 44					Saturdays only								3 14	
Southwick	2 42	2 47												3 1	3 17	
Shoreham-by-Sea K	2 45	2 50										2 57		3 4	3 20	
Lancing	2 50	2 55												3 8	3 25	
Ham Bridge Halt N	2 53	2 58													3 28	
Worthing Central	2 56	3 1										3 5		3 12	3 31	
West Worthing U	2 58	3 3												3 14	3 33	
Durrington-on-Sea														3 16	Stop	
Goring-by-Sea														3 19		
Angmering L														3 23		
Ford (Sussex) ......dep.																
Littlehampton ... arr.					3 13									3 33		
dep.																
Ford (Sussex)															p.m	
Barnham ......arr.							3 10					3 21			3kd26	
Bognor Regis ... arr.							3 18								3k32	
dep.												3 10				
Barnham ......dep.												3 22				p.m
Chichester Z												3 32				3 37
Fishbourne Halt																3 40
Bosham																3 43
Nutbourne Halt																3 46
Southbourne Halt																3 49
Emsworth																3 52
Warblington Halt																3 55
Havant 244, 366												3 45				3 57
244 Hayling Island ....arr.																
Bedhampton Halt																3 59
Hilsea Halt																
Fratton 380												3 54				4 7
Portsmouth & Southsea arr												3 56				4 10
Portsmouth Harbour .. "												4 0				
500 Ryde Pier (Boat) .. arr.																
(Page 359) Sandown ... "																
Shanklin ... "																
Ventnor ... "																
Newport ... "																
Cowes ... "																
Yarmouth ... "																

Station	17	18	19	20	21	22	23	24	25	26	27	28	29	30	31
Three Bridges (above) ..dep.	2 47										3 17				
Crawley	2 51										3 21				Stop
Ifield	2 53										3 23				
Fay Gate	2 58										3 28				
Littlehaven Halt	3 2										3 32				
Horsham 244, 245 ......arr.	3 5										3 35				
Sutton ......dep.			2 39					Saturdays only							
Dorking North H			2 56												
Horsham 244, 245 ... arr.			3 13												
dep.	3 5		3 15								3 35				
Christ's Hospital, West Horsham	3 9										3 39				
Billingshurst	3 16										3 46				
Pulborough J 374	3 23		3 30								3 53				
Amberley	3 31										4 1				
Arundel	3 36		3 41		p.m				p.m		4 6	p.m			p.m
Brighton ......dep.			RB		3 17		3 20	P	3 33			3 47			3 50
Holland Road Halt									3 35						
Hove					3 20		3 23	3 33	3 37			3 50			3 53
Aldrington Halt			Saturdays only				3 25		3 39						3 55
Portslade and West Hove							3 28		3 42						3 58
Fishersgate Halt									3 44						
Southwick							3 31		3 47						4 1
Shoreham-by-Sea K					3 27		3 34	3 40	3 50			3 57			4 4
Lancing							3 38		3 55						4 8
Ham Bridge Halt N									3 58						
Worthing Central					3 35		3 42	3 48	4 1			4 6			4 12
West Worthing U					3 37		3 45	3 51	4 3						4 14
Durrington-on-Sea								3 53							4 16
Goring-by-Sea					3 41		Stop	3 56				Saturdays only			4 19
Angmering L					3 45	p.m		4 0							4 23
Ford (Sussex) ......dep.						3 52									
Littlehampton ... arr.	3 43					3 57		4 10			4 18				4 33
dep.	3 46				3 46										
Ford (Sussex)	3a50				3 52		p.m								Stop
Barnham ......arr.	4 1		3 49		3 57		4d22					4 22			
Bognor Regis ... arr.	4 7		4 0		4 7		4 31					4 31			
dep.			3 40		3 40							4 10			
Barnham ......dep.			3 52		3 57							4 22			p.m
Chichester Z			4 2		4 7							4 32			4 37
Fishbourne Halt					4 10										4 40
Bosham					4 13										4 43
Nutbourne Halt					4 16										4 46
Southbourne Halt					4 19										4 49
Emsworth					4 22										4 52
Warblington Halt					4 25										4 55
Havant 244, 366			4 15		4 27							4 45			4 57
244 Hayling Island ....arr.					4 55										
Bedhampton Halt															4 59
Hilsea Halt															5SX4
Fratton 380			4 23		4 38							4 54			5 7
Portsmouth & Southsea arr			4 26		4 40							4 56			5 11
Portsmouth Harbour .. "			4 30	4d35	4 44							5 0			
500 Ryde Pier (Boat) .. arr.				5 5											
(Page 359) Sandown ... "				5 48											
Shanklin ... "				5 55											
Ventnor ... "				6 11											
Newport ... "				6 6											
Cowes ... "				6 20											
Yarmouth ... "				6 40											

E Third class only. * Change at East Croydon. ‖ Arr. 2 40 p.m A Local Passengers between Victoria and East Croydon not conveyed. a Dep. 5 mins. later
d Departure time. k 10 mins. later on Saturdays. P Pullman Car facilities available. RB Refreshment Car facilities available between London and Bognor Regis. SX Saturdays excepted. t 11 mins. later on Saturdays. U Calls to take up only. y Arr. 2 mins. earlier.

For SERVICES from LONDON (Waterloo) to PORTSMOUTH and ISLE OF WIGHT, see pages 359 to 365

From LONDON to THE SOUTH COAST—Week Days—*continued*

Week Days—*continued*

Station	1	2	3	4	5	6	7	8	9	10	11	12	13	14	15
	p.m	p.m	p.m	p.m	p.m	p.m	p.m	p.m	p.m	p.m	p.m	p.m	p.m	p.m	p.m
						RB				P				P	
VICTORIA .... dep.	2 48	..	3 0	..	..	3 18	..	..	3*18	3 25	..	..	3 28	3 45	..
Clapham Junction ..... "	2‖53	..	..	..	..	..	..	..	..	..	..	..	3 34	..	..
LONDON BRIDGE ... dep.	2▣SX31	..	Brighton Belle 1st and 3rd class Pullman Cars only	..	..	..	..	..	3 18	3*18	..	..	3*18	3▣31	..
New Cross Gate ..... "	..	..		..	..	..	..	..	..	..	..	..	..	..	..
Norwood Junction B "	2▣SX43	..		..	..	..	..	..	3 30	3*30	..	..	3*30	3▣43	..
East Croydon .... dep.	3 5	..		..	..	3 34	..	..	3 36	3 42	..	..	3 46	4 1	..
Purley	3 11	..		..	..	..	..	..	3 41	..	..	..	..	..	..
Coulsdon South	3 14	..		..	..	..	..	..	3 45	..	..	..	..	..	..
Merstham	3 20	..		..	..	..	..	..	3 51	..	..	..	..	..	..
Redhill 246	3 27	..		..	..	3 49	..	..	3 57	..	..	..	4 1	..	..
Earlswood	3 30	..		..	..	..	..	..	3 59	..	..	..	..	..	..
Salfords	3 33	..		..	..	..	..	..	4 3	..	..	..	..	..	..
Horley	3 37	..		..	..	..	..	..	4 7	..	..	..	..	..	..
Gatwick Airport	3 40	..		..	..	..	..	..	4 10	..	..	..	4 10	..	..
Three Bridges (*below*) 234	3y46	..		..	..	4 0	..	..	4 15	..	..	..	..	..	..
Balcombe	3 52	..		..	..	..	..	..	4 21	..	..	..	..	..	..
Horsted Keynes ...... dep.	..	..		..	..	Through Train, Victoria to Bognor Regis.	..	..	4 17	..	Saturdays excepted	..	..	4 17	..
Ardingly	..	..		..	..		..	..	4 21	..		..	..	4 21	..
Haywards Heath C 239 ...	3 59	..		..	..		..	..	4 28	4 14		..	4 23	4 32	..
Wivelsfield (*below*)	4 3	..		..	..		..	..	4 32	Through Train, Victoria to Littlehampton.		..	..	..	..
Burgess Hill	4 6	..		..	..		..	..	4 35			..	..	..	..
Hassocks D	4 10	..		..	..		..	..	4 39			..	4 31	..	..
Preston Park	4 18	..		..	..		..	..	4 47			..	4 40	..	..
Brighton (*below*) ...... arr.	4 21	..	4 0	..	..		..	..	4 50			..	4 43	..	..
Haywards Heath ... dep.	..	..	..	..	..		..	..	Stop		4 17	..	..	4 33	..
Wivelsfield (*above*)	..	..	..	..	..		..	..	..		..	..	..	..	..
Plumpton	..	..	..	..	..		..	..	..		..	..	..	..	..
Cooksbridge	..	..	..	..	..		..	..	..		..	..	..	..	..
Lewes 239 ...... arr.	..	..	..	..	..		..	..	..		4 33	..	..	4 48	..
Brighton .... dep.	..	..	..	..	..	..	4 14	..	..		..	4 28	..	..	4 36
London Road (Brighton) ...	..	..	..	..	..	..	4 16	..	..		..	4 30	..	..	..
Falmer	..	..	..	..	..	..	4 21	..	..		..	4 34	..	..	..
Lewes .... arr.	..	..	..	..	..	..	4 28	..	..		..	4 42	..	..	4 52
Lewes .... dep.	..	4 4	..	..	..	..	..	..	..	..	4 34	4 46	..	..	..
Southease and Rodmell ..	..	4 9	..	..	..	..	..	..	..	..	..	4 51	..	..	..
Newhaven Town ....[Halt	..	4 14	..	..	..	..	..	..	..	..	4 43	4 56	..	..	..
" Harbour	..	4 15	..	..	..	..	..	..	..	..	..	4 57	..	..	..
Bishopstone	..	4 20	..	..	..	..	..	..	..	..	..	5 2	..	..	..
Seaford .... arr.	..	4 22	..	..	..	..	..	..	..	..	4 49	5 5	..	..	..
Lewes .... dep.	..	Stop	..	..	..	..	4 29	..	..	..	..	Stop	..	4 50	..
Glynde	..	..	..	..	..	..	4 34	..	..	..	..	..	..	..	..
Berwick	..	..	..	..	..	..	4 40	..	..	..	..	..	..	..	..
Pelegate 239	..	..	..	..	..	..	4 46	..	..	..	..	..	..	5 4	..
Hampden Park F	..	..	..	..	4 45	..	4 50	..	..	..	..	..	..	..	..
Eastbourne .... arr.	..	..	..	..	4 49	..	4 54	..	..	..	..	..	..	5 11	..
Eastbourne .... dep.	..	..	..	..	Stop	..	4 57	..	..	..	..	..	..	5 14	..
Hampden Park F	..	..	..	..	..	..	5 0	..	..	..	..	..	..	..	..
Pevensey and Westham	..	..	..	..	..	..	5 7	..	..	..	..	..	..	..	..
Pevensey Bay Halt	..	..	..	..	..	..	5 9	..	..	..	..	..	..	..	..
Norman's Bay Halt	..	..	..	..	..	..	5 12	..	..	..	..	..	..	..	..
Cooden Beach	..	..	..	..	..	..	5 16	..	..	..	..	..	..	5 28	..
Collington Halt	..	..	..	..	..	..	5 19	..	..	..	..	..	..	..	..
Bexhill (Central) G	..	..	..	..	..	..	5 22	..	..	..	..	..	..	5 32	..
St. Leonards (W.M.)	..	..	..	..	..	..	5 26	..	..	..	..	..	..	..	..
" (W.S.)	..	..	..	..	..	..	5 29	..	..	..	..	..	..	5 39	..
Hastings 56, 59	..	..	..	..	..	..	5 31	..	..	..	..	..	..	5 42	..
Ore .... arr.	..	..	..	..	p.m	..	5 34	..	..	..	..	p.m	..	5 45	..

Station	16	17	18	19	20	21	22	23	24	25	26	27	28	29	30
	p.m	p.m	p.m	p.m	p.m	p.m	p.m	p.m	p.m	p.m	p.m	p.m	p.m	p.m	p.m
		R	P						SX			RB	R		
VICTORIA .... dep.	..	3 45	4 0	..	..	3 48	3 48	..	3*48	3*48	..	4 18	4 18	..	..
Clapham Junction ..... "	..	..	..	..	..	3 53	3 53	..	3*53	3*53	..	..	..	..	..
LONDON BRIDGE ... dep.	..	3▣31	..	..	..	3▣31	3▣31	..	4 0	4 0	..	4▣7	Saturdays only	..	..
New Cross Gate ..... "	..	..	..	..	..	..	..	..	..	..	..	..		..	..
Norwood Junction B "	..	3▣43	..	..	..	3▣43	3▣43	..	..	..	..	..		..	..
East Croydon .... dep.	..	4 1	..	..	..	4 5	4 5	..	4 17	4 17	..	Saturdays excepted		..	..
Purley	..	Saturdays only	..	..	..	4 11	4 11	..	..	..	..			..	..
Coulsdon South	..		..	..	..	4 14	4 14	..	..	..	..			..	..
Merstham	..		..	..	..	4 20	4 20	..	..	..	..			..	..
Redhill 246	..		..	..	..	4 27	4 27	..	4 32	4 32	..			..	..
Earlswood	..		..	..	..	4 29	4 29	..	..	..	..			..	..
Salfords	..		..	..	..	4 33	4 33	..	..	..	..			..	..
Horley	..		..	..	..	4 37	4 37	..	4 40	4 40	..		..	..	..
Gatwick Airport	..		..	..	..	4 40	4 40	..	..	..	..		..	..	..
Three Bridges (*below*) 234	..		..	..	..	4c47	4c47	..	4 45	4 45	..		..	..	..
Balcombe	..		..	..	..	4 54	4 54	..	..	..	..		..	..	..
Horsted Keynes ...... dep.	4 17	4 17	..	..	4 45	..	..	..	..	..	..	..	..	..	..
Ardingly	4 21	4 21	..	..	4 50	..	..	..	..	..	..	..	..	..	..
Haywards Heath C 239 ...	4 25	4 32	..	..	4 56	5 1	5 5	..	4 55	4 56	..	..	Through Train. Victoria to Bognor Regis	..	..
Wivelsfield (*below*)	..	..	..	..	Stop	5 5	5 9	..	Sats. except	..	..	..		..	..
Burgess Hill	..	..	..	..	..	5 8	5 12	..		5 2	..	..		..	..
Hassocks D	..	..	..	..	..	5 12	5 16	..		5 6	..	..		..	..
Preston Park	..	..	..	..	..	5 20	5 24	..		5 14	..	..		..	..
Brighton (*below*) ...... arr.	..	..	5 0	..	..	5 23	5 27	..		5 17	..	..		..	..
Haywards Heath ... dep.	4 35	4 33	Stop	..	..	} ☞ Saturdays only	Saturdays excepted	..	4 59	Saturdays excepted	..	Through Train Victoria to Bognor Regis		..	..
Wivelsfield (*above*)	4 39	..	..	..	..			..	..		..			..	..
Plumpton	4 45	..	..	..	..			..	..		..			..	..
Cooksbridge	4 50	..	..	..	..			..	..		..			..	..
Lewes 239 ...... arr.	4 57	4 48	..	..	..			..	5 15		..			..	..
Brighton .... dep.	Stop	..	..	4 46	..			..	..		..			5 14	5 18
London Road (Brighton) ...	..	..	..	4 48	..			..	..		..			5 16	5 21
Falmer	..	..	..	4 52	..			..	..		..			5 21	..
Lewes .... arr.	..	..	..	5 0	p.m			..	..		..			5 28	5 36
Lewes .... dep.	..	4 55	..	..	5 4		..	..	5 19	..	..		..	..	Stop
Southease and Rodmell ..	..	..	..	..	5 9		..	..	..	..	..		..	..	..
Newhaven Town ....[Halt	..	5 4	..	..	5 14		..	..	5 30	..	..		..	..	..
" Harbour	..	5 6	..	..	5 15		..	..	..	..	..		..	..	..
Bishopstone	..	..	..	..	5 20		..	..	5 35	..	..		..	..	..
Seaford .... arr.	..	5 11	..	..	5 22		..	..	5 38	..	..		..	..	..
Lewes .... dep.	..	..	..	5 1	Stop	..	..	..	5 16	..	..	..	..	5 29	..
Glynde	..	..	..	5 6	..	..	..	..	..	..	..	..	..	5 34	..
Berwick	..	..	..	5 12	..	..	..	..	..	..	..	..	..	5 40	p.m
Pelegate 239	p.m	..	..	5 19	..	..	..	..	5 33	..	..	..	..	5 47	5 51
Hampden Park F	5 15	..	..	5 22	..	..	..	5 45	5 37	..	..	..	..	5 50	5 56
Eastbourne .... arr.	5 19	..	..	5 26	..	..	..	5 49	5 41	..	..	..	..	5 54	6 1
Eastbourne .... dep.	Stop	..	..	5 29	..	..	..	Stop	5 45	..	..	..	..	5 59	Stop
Hampden Park F	..	..	..	5 32	..	..	..	..	..	..	..	..	..	6 2	..
Pevensey and Westham	..	..	..	5 39	..	..	..	..	5 53	..	..	..	..	6 9	..
Pevensey Bay Halt	..	..	..	5 41	..	..	..	..	..	..	..	..	..	6 11	..
Norman's Bay Halt	..	..	..	5 44	..	..	..	..	..	..	..	..	..	6 14	..
Cooden Beach	..	..	..	5 48	..	..	..	..	6 0	..	..	..	..	6 18	..
Collington Halt	..	..	..	5 51	..	..	..	..	..	..	..	..	..	6 21	..
Bexhill (Central) G	..	..	..	5 54	..	..	..	..	6 8	..	..	..	..	6 23	..
St. Leonards (W.M.)	..	..	..	5 58	..	..	..	..	6 13	..	..	..	..	6 29	..
" (W.S.)	..	..	..	6 1	..	..	..	..	6 18	..	..	..	..	6 32	..
Hastings 56, 59	..	..	..	6 3	..	..	..	..	6 20	..	..	..	..	6 34	..
Ore .... arr.	..	..	..	6 6	..	..	..	..	6 23	..	..	..	..	6 37	..

	1	2	3	4	5	6	7	8	9	10	11	12	13	14	15	16	17	18	19	20	21	22	23	24	25	26	27	28	29	30
Three Bridges (above) dep.	..	..	..	..	3 47	4 1	..	..	..	..	..	4 17	..		..	..	..	..		..	..	..	..	..	..	4 47	..	..		..
Crawley	..	..	..	..	3 51	..	..	..	..	..	..	4 21	..	Stop	..	..	..	..	Stop	..	..	..	..	..	..	4 51	..	..	Stop	..
Ifield	..	..	..	..	3 53	..	..	..	..	..	..	4 23	..	..	..	..	..	..	..	..	..	..	..	..	..	4 53	..	..	..	..
Fay Gate	..	..	..	..	3 58	..	..	..	..	..	..	4 28	..	..	..	..	..	..	..	..	..	..	..	..	..	4 58	..	..	..	..
Littlehaven Halt	..	..	..	..	4 2	..	..	..	..	..	..	4 32	..	..	..	..	..	..	..	..	..	..	..	..	..	5 2	..	..	..	..
Horsham 244, 245 arr.	..	..	..	..	4 5	4 13	..	..	..	..	..	4 35	..	..	..	..	..	..	..	..	..	..	..	..	..	5 5	..	..	..	..
Sutton dep.	..	..	..	..	..	..	..	..	..	..	..	..	..	..	..	..	..	..	..	..	..	..	..	..	..	..	4 39	4 39	..	..
Dorking North M	..	..	..	..	..	..	..	..	..	..	..	..	..	..	..	..	..	..	..	..	..	..	..	..	..	..	4 56	4 56	..	..
Horsham 244, 245 arr.	..	..	..	..	..	..	..	..	..	..	..	.	..	..	..	..	..	..	..	..	..	..	..	..	..	..	5 13	5 13	..	..
Horsham 244, 245 dep.	..	..	..	..	4 5	4 15	..	..	..	..	..	4 35	..	..	..	..	..	..	..	..	..	..	..	..	..	5 5	5 15	5 15	..	..
Christ's Hospital, West Horsham	..	..	..	..	4 9	..	..	..	..	..	..	4 39	..	..	..	..	..	..	..	..	..	..	..	..	..	5 9	..	..	..	..
Billingshurst	..	..	..	..	4 16	..	..	..	..	..	..	4 46	..	..	..	..	..	..	..	..	..	..	..	..	..	5 16	5 25	5 25	..	..
Pulborough J 374	..	..	..	..	4 23	4 32	..	..	..	..	..	4 53	..	..	..	..	..	..	..	..	..	..	..	..	..	5 23	5 32	5 32	..	..
Amberley	..	..	..	..	4 31	..	..	..	..	..	..	5 1	..	..	..	..	..	..	..	..	..	..	..	..	..	5 31	..	..	..	..
Arundel	..	p.m	..	..	4 36	4 44	..	..	p.m	..	..	5 6	..	p.m	..	..	..	p.m	p.m	..	..	..	p.m	..	..	5 36	5 44	5 44	..	p.m
Brighton dep.	..	3 57	..	4 3	..	RB	..	4 16	4 18	P	..	..	..	4 33	..	..	..	4 49	4 58		..	..	5 3	..	..	..	RB	R	..	5 17
Holland Road Halt	..	..	..	4 5	..	..	..	..	4 20	..	..	..	..	4 35	..	..	..	4 51	..		..	..	5 5	..	..	..	..	..	..	..
Hove	..	4 1	..	4 7	..	..	..	4 19	4 22	4 33	..	..	..	4 37	..	..	..	4 53	5 2	Saturdays excepted	..	..	5 7	..	..	..	..	..	..	5 20
Aldrington Halt	..	..	..	4 9	..	..	..	..	..	..	..	..	..	4 39	..		..	4 55			..	..	5 9	..	..	..	..	..	..	..
Portslade and West Hove	..	4 5	..	4 12	..	..	..	..	4 26	..	..	..	..	4 42	..		..	4 58	5 5		..	..	5 12	..	..	..	..	..	..	..
Fishersgate Halt	..	..	..	4 14	..	..	..	..	..	..	..	..	..	4 44	..		..	..	..		..	..	5 14	..	..	..	..	..	..	..
Southwick	..	4 8	..	4 17	..	..	..	..	4 29	..	..	..	..	4 47	..	Saturdays only	..	5 1	5 9		..	..	5 17	..	..	..	..	..	..	..
Shoreham-by-Sea K	..	4 12	..	4 20	..	..	..	4 27	4 32	4 40	..	..	..	4 50	..		..	5 4	5 12		..	..	5 20	..	..	..	..	..	..	5 27
Lancing	..	..	..	4 25	..	..	..	..	4 37	..	..	..	..	4 55	..		..	5 8	..		..	..	5 25	..	..	..	..	..	..	..
Ham Bridge Halt N	..	..	..	4 28	..	..	..	..	..	..	..	..	..	4 58	..		..	..	..		..	..	5 28	..	..	..			..	..
Worthing Central	..	..	..	4 31	..	..	..	4 35	4 41	4 48	..	..	..	5 1	..		..	5 12	..		..	..	5 31	..	..	..	Saturdays excepted	Saturdays only	..	5 35
West Worthing U	..	..	..	4 33	..	..	..	4 37	4 44	4 51	..	..	..	5 3	..		..	5 14	..		..	..	5 33	..	..	..			..	5 37
Durrington-on-Sea	..	..	..	..	..	..	..	..		4 53	..	..	..	..	..		..	5 16	..		..	..		..	..	..			..	..
Goring-by-Sea	..	..	..	..	..	..	..	4 41	Stop	4 56	..	..	..	..	..		..	5 19	..		..	..	Stop	..	..	..			..	5 41
Angmering L	..	..	..	..	..	..	..	4 45	p.m	5 0	..	..	..	..	..		..	5 23	..	p.m	..	..	..	..	..	..			..	5 45
Ford (Sussex) dep.	..	..	..	..	..	..	..	..	4 52	..	..	..	..	..	..		..	..	..	5 41	..	..	..	..	..	..			..	..
Littlehampton arr.	..	..	..	..	4 43	..	..	..	4 57	5 10	..	5 13	..	..	..		..	5 33	..	5 46	..	..	..	..	..	5 43			..	6 7
Littlehampton dep.	..	..	..	..	4 46	..	..	4 46	..	..	..	..	..	..	..			5SX36	..	..	..	..	..	..	..	5 46	5 36	..	..	5 46
Ford (Sussex)	..	..	..	..	4a51	..	..	4 52	..	..	..	..	..	..	..	p.m		5SX40	..	..	..	..	..	..	..	5a51	..	..	..	5 52
Barnham arr.	..	..	..	..	5 2	4 52	..	4 57	..	..	..	..	..	..	..	5d36		5SX45	..	..	..	..	..	..	..	6 2	5 52	5 52	..	5 57
Bognor Regis arr.	..	..	..	..	5 9	5 2	..	5 9	..	..	..	..	..	..	..	5 42		5SX51	..	..	..	..	..	..	..	6 9	6 2	5 59	..	6 9
Bognor Regis dep.	..	..	..	..	..	4 40	..	4 40	..	..	..	..	..	..	..	..	..	..	..	..	..	..	..	..	..	..	5 45	..	..	5 45
Barnham dep.	..	..	..	..	..	4 53	..	4 57	..	..	..	..	..	..	..	..	..	..	..	..	..	..	p.m	..	..	..	5 53	..	..	5 57
Chichester Z	..	..	..	..	..	5 3	..	5 7	..	..	..	..	..	..	..	..	..	..	..	..	..	..	5 37	..	..	..	6 3	..	..	6 7
Fishbourne Halt	..	..	..	..	..	..	..	5 10	..	..	..	..	..	..	..	..	..	..	..	..	..	..	5 40	..	..	..	..	..	..	6 10
Bosham	..	..	..	..	..	5 8	..	5 13	..	..	..	..	..	..	..	..	..	..	..	..	..	..	5 43	..	..	..	..	..	..	6 13
Nutbourne Halt	..	..	..	..	..	..	..	5 16	..	..	..	..	..	..	..	..	..	..	..	..	..	..	5 46	..	..	..	..	..	..	6 16
Southbourne Halt	..	..	..	..	..	..	..	5 19	..	..	..	..	..	..	..	..	..	..	..	..	..	..	5 49	..	..	..	..	..	..	6 19
Emsworth	..	..	..	..	..	..	..	5 22	..	..	..	..	..	..	..	..	..	..	..	..	..	..	5 52	..	..	..	6 12	..	..	6 22
Warblington Halt	..	..	..	..	..	..	..	5 25	..	..	..	..	..	..	..	..	..	..	..	..	..	..	5 55	..	..	..	..	..	..	6 25
Havant 244, 366	..	..	..	..	..	5 16	..	5 27	..	..	..	..	..	..	..	..	..	..	..	..	..	..	5 57	..	..	..	6 16	..	..	6 27
244 Hayling Island arr.	..	..	..	..	..	..	..	5 46	..	..	..	..	..	..	..	..	..	..	..	..	..	..	..	..	..	..	6 33	..		6SO47
Bedhampton Halt	..	..	..	..	..	..	..	..	..	..	..	..	..	..	..	..	..	..	..	..	..	..	5 59	..	..	..	..	..	..	..
Hilsea Halt	..	..	..	..	..	..	..	..	..	..	..	..	..	..	..	..	..	..	..	..	..	..	6SX4	..	..	..	..	..		6SX33
Fratton 380	..	..	..	..	..	5 24	..	5 36	..	..	..	..	..	..	..	..	..	..	..	..	..	..	6 7	..	..	..	6 24	..	..	6 36
Portsmouth & Southsea arr	..	..	..	..	..	5 27	..	5 38	..	..	..	..	..	..	..	..	..	..	..	..	..	..	6 11	..	..	..	6 27	..	p.m	6 39
Portsmouth Harbour "	..	..	..	..	..	5 31	..	5 42	..	..	..	..	..	..	..	..	..	..	..	..	..	..	..	..	..	..	6 31	..	6d35	6 44
50J Ryde Pier (Boat) arr.	..	..	..	..	..	6 5	..	..	..	..	..	..	..	..	..	..	..	..	..	..	..	..	..	..	..	..	..	..	7 5	..
Page 359 Sandown "	..	..	..	..	..	6 48	..	..	..	..	..	..	..	..	..	..	..	..	..	..	..	..	..	..	..	..	..	..	7 48	..
Page 359 Shanklin "	..	..	..	..	..	6 55	..	..	..	..	..	..	..	..	..	..	..	..	..	..	..	..	..	..	..	..	..	..	7 55	..
Page 359 Ventnor "	..	..	..	..	..	7 11	..	..	..	..	..	..	..	..	..	..	..	..	..	..	..	..	..	..	..	..	..	..	8 11	..
Page 359 Newport "	..	..	..	..	..	7 6	..	..	..	..	..	..	..	..	..	..	..	..	..	..	..	..	..	..	..	..	..	..	8 6	..
Page 359 Cowes "	..	..	..	..	..	7 50	..	..	..	..	..	..	..	..	..	..	..	..	..	..	..	..	..	..	..	..	..	..	8 20	..
Page 359 Yarmouth "	..	..	..	..	..	7 40	..	..	..	..	..	..	..	..	..	..	..	..	..	..	..	..	..	..	..	..	..	..	..	..

3 Third class only. * Change at East Croydon. *a* Dep. 5 mins. later. *c* Arr. 3 mins. *earlier*. *d* Departure time. P Pullman Car facilities available.
R Refreshment Car facilities available. RB Refreshment Car facilities available between London and Bognor Regis. SO Sats only. SX Sats excepted.
U Calls to take up only. *y* Arr. 2 mins. *earlier*

For Other Notes, see page 195

For SERVICES from LONDON (Waterloo) to PORTSMOUTH and ISLE OF WIGHT, see pages 359 to 365

From LONDON to THE SOUTH COAST—Week Days—*continued*

Station	1	2	3	4	5	6	7	8	9	10
	p.m	p.m	p.m	p.m	p.m	p.m	p.m	p.m	p.m	p.m
			P				P	P		
VICTORIA dep.	..	4 16	4 25	4 28	4 28	..	4A45	4 45	..	..
Clapham Junction "	..	4U21	..	..	4 34	..	..	..	..	..
LONDON BRIDGE dep.	4 16	4S16	4*20	4*20	4*18	..	4*40	4S31	..	..
New Cross Gate "	..	..	..	..	..	..	..	..	..	..
Norwood Junction **B** "	4 29	4S28	4S28		..		4S47	4S43	..	..
East Croydon dep	4 34	4 34	4 40	4 46	4 46	..	5 0	5 1	..	..
Purley	4 40	4 40	Saturdays excepted	..	..	..	Saturdays excepted	Saturdays only	..	..
Coulsdon South	4 43	4 44		..	..	..			..	..
Merstham	4 49	4 50		..	..	..			..	..
Redhill 246	4 57	4 56		5 1	5 2	..			..	..
Earlswood	4 59	4 58		..	..	..			..	..
Salfords	5 3	5 2		..	..	..			..	..
Horley	5 7	5 6		..	..	..			..	..
Gatwick Airport	5 10	5 9		5 10	5 10	..			..	..
Three Bridges (*below*) 234	5 15	5 14	5 3	..	..	..			..	..
Balcombe	5 21	5 21	..	..	..	..			..	..
Horsted Keynes dep.	..	..	..	..	..	..	..	..	..	..
Ardingly	..	..	..	..	..	..	..	..	..	..
Haywards Heath C 239	5 28	5C33	5 14	5 23	5 23	..	5 29	5 32	..	..
Wivelsfield (*below*)	5 32	5 37	..	..	..	..	..	..	..	..
Burgess Hill	5 35	5 40	..	..	..	..	..	..	..	..
Hassocks **D**	5 39	5 43	..	..	..	..	..	..	..	..
Preston Park	5 47	5 51	..	5 37	5 38	..	..	..	..	..
Brighton (*below*) arr.	5 50	5 55	..	5 41	5 41	..	..	..	..	..
Haywards Heath dep			..		Saturdays only	..	5 29	5 33	5 36	..
Wivelsfield (*above*)			..			..	..	..	5 40	..
Plumpton			..			..	..	..	5 46	..
Cooksbridge			..			..	..	..	5 51	..
Lewes 239 arr.			..			..	5 46	5 49	5 56	..
Brighton dep.	Saturdays only	Saturdays excepted	Through Train Victoria to Littlehampton.	Saturdays excepted		5 30	..	..	Stop	..
London Road (Brighton)						5 32	..	..		..
Falmer						5 36	..	..	..	..
Lewes arr.						5 44	..	..	..	..
Lewes dep.					..	5 44	5 56	..	..	..
Southease and Rodmell					..	5 50	..	..	..	..
Newhaven Town [Halt					..	5 55	6 5	..	..	..
" Harbour					..	5 56	6 7	..	..	..
Bishopstone		Stop		Stop	..	6 1	..	..	..	..
Seaford arr.	Stop	..		..	..	6 4	6 12	..	..	..
Lewes dep.	..	..		..	..	Stop	5 47	5 50	..	..
Glynde	..	..		..	..		..	..	..	..
Berwick	..	..		..	..	..	..	..	p.m	..
Polegate 239	..	..		..	..	..	..	..	6 5	..
Hampden Park **F**	..	..		..	..	..	..	..	6 11	6 15
Eastbourne arr.	..	..		..	..	..	6 6	6 9	6 16	6 19
Eastbourne dep.	..	..		..	..	..	6 10	6 13	Stop	Stop
Hampden Park **F**	..	..		..	..	..	..	..		
Pevensey and Westham	..	..		..	..	..	6 19	..	..	..
Pevensey Bay Halt	..	..		..	..	..	..	..	..	..
Norman's Bay Halt	..	..		..	..	..	..	..	..	..
Cooden Beach	..	..		..	..	..	6 25	6 26	..	..
Collington Halt	..	..		..	..	..	..	..	..	..
Bexhill (Central) **G**	..	..		..	..	..	6 30	6 31	..	..
St. Leonards (W.M.)	..	..		..	..	..	..	..	..	..
" (W.S.)	..	..		..	..	..	6 38	6 38	..	..
Hastings 56, 59	..	..		..	..	..	6 40	6 40	..	..
Ore arr	..	..		..	..	..	6 44	6 44	..	p.m

Station	11	12	13	14	15	16	17	18	19	20
	p.m	p.m	p.m	p.m	p.m	p.m	p.m	p.m	p.m	p.m
			P	P						R
VICTORIA dep.		4A*45	..	5 0	4 48	..	..	..	..	..
Clapham Junction "	..	..	..	..	4 53	..	..	..	..	..
LONDON BRIDGE dep.	..	4 47	5 0		4S31	..	..	..	..	5 3
New Cross Gate "	..	..	..	..	..	..	..	..	..	..
Norwood Junction **B** "	..	..	..		4S43	..	..	..	..	..
East Croydon dep	..	5 2	Saturdays excepted	Saturdays only	5 5	..	..	..	..	Saturdays excepted
Purley	..	5 7			5 11	..	..	..	..	
Coulsdon South	..	5 11			5 14	..	..	..	..	
Merstham	..	5 17			5 20	..	..	..	..	
Redhill 246	..	5 23			5 27	..	..	..	..	
Earlswood	..	5 25			5 29	..	..	..	..	
Salfords	..	5 29			5 33	..	..	..	..	
Horley	..	5 33			5 37	..	..	..	..	
Gatwick Airport	..	5 36		..	5 40	..	..	..	..	
Three Bridges (*below*) 234	..	5 41		..	5y46	..	..	..	..	
Balcombe	..	5 48		..	5 53	..	..	..	..	
Horsted Keynes dep.	Saturdays only	..	..	..	..	..	..	..	..	..
Ardingly		..	..	..	..	..	..	..	..	..
Haywards Heath C 239		5 56	..	..	6 0	..	Saturdays only	Saturdays only	Saturdays excepted	5 45
Wivelsfield (*below*)		6 0	..	..	6 4	Saturdays excepted				..
Burgess Hill		6 3	..	..	6 7					..
Hassocks **D**		6 7	..	..	6 11					..
Preston Park		6 15	..	..	6 19					..
Brighton (*below*) arr.		6 18	6 0	6 0	6 22					..
Haywards Heath dep			Stop	Stop						5 46
Wivelsfield (*above*)			..	..						..
Plumpton			..	..			..			5 55
Cooksbridge			..	..						6 0
Lewes 239 arr.			..	..			..			6 5
Brighton dep.	5 36	Saturdays excepted	..	..	Saturdays only	5 36	5 45		5 44	..
London Road (Brighton)	..		..	..		5 38	5 47		5 47	..
Falmer	..		..	..		5 42	5 52		..	..
Lewes arr.	5 52		..	..		5 50	5 59		6 2	..
Lewes dep.	Stop		..	..		..	..	6 4	..	6 9
Southease and Rodmell	..		..	..		..	..	6 9	..	6 14
Newhaven Town [Halt	..		..	..		..	..	6 14	..	6 19
" Harbour	..		..	..		..	..	6 15	..	6 21
Bishopstone	..	Stop	..	..		..	..	6 20	..	6 26
Seaford arr.	..	..	..	..	Stop	..	..	6 22	..	6 29
Lewes dep.	..	..	..	..	..	5 51	6 0	Stop	..	6 7
Glynde	..	..	..	..	..	5 56	6 5	..	..	6 12
Berwick	..	..	..	..	..	6 2	6 11	..	..	6 18
Polegate 239	..	..	..	..	..	6 9	6 18	..	..	6 24
Hampden Park **F**	..	..	..	..	..	6 12	6 21	..	..	6 28
Eastbourne arr.	..	..	..	..	..	6 16	6 25	..	..	6 31
Eastbourne dep.	..	..	..	..	..	6 27	6 28	..	..	Stop
Hampden Park **F**	..	..	..	..	..	6 30	6 31	..	..	
Pevensey and Westham	..	..	..	..	..	6 37	6 38	..	..	..
Pevensey Bay Halt	..	..	..	..	..	6 39	6 40	..	..	..
Norman's Bay Halt	..	..	..	..	..	6 42	6 43	..	..	..
Cooden Beach	..	..	..	..	..	6 46	6 47	..	..	..
Collington Halt	..	..	..	..	..	6 49	6 50	..	..	..
Bexhill (Central) **G**	..	..	..	..	..	6 52	6 52	..	..	..
St. Leonards (W.M.)	..	..	..	..	..	6 57	6 57	..	..	..
" (W.S.)	..	..	..	..	..	7 0	7 0	..	..	..
Hastings 56, 59	..	..	..	..	..	7 2	7 2	..	..	..
Ore arr	..	..	p.m	..	..	7 5	7 5	p.m	..	..

Station	21	22	23	24	25	26	27	28	29	30	31
	p.m	p.m	p.m	p.m	p.m	p.m	p.m	p.m	p.m	p.m	p.m
	R		RB	R			R		R	P	R
VICTORIA dep.	..	..	..	5 4	..	..	5 18	..	5 30	5 20	5 20
Clapham Junction "	..	..	..	..	..	..	..	..	..	..	..
LONDON BRIDGE dep.	5 6	..	5 15	..	..	..	..	..	..	..	..
New Cross Gate "	..	..	..	..	..	..	..	..	..	..	..
Norwood Junction **B** "	..	..	..	..	..	..	..	..	..	..	..
East Croydon dep	Saturdays excepted	..	Saturdays excepted	Saturdays excepted	..	..	Saturdays only	..	Saturdays excepted	Saturdays excepted	Saturdays excepted
Purley		..			..	..		..			
Coulsdon South		..			..	..		..			
Merstham		..			..	..		..			
Redhill 246		..			..	..		..			
Earlswood		..			..	..		..			
Salfords		..			..	..		..			
Horley		..	5 49		..	..		..			
Gatwick Airport		..	..		..	..		..			
Three Bridges (*below*) 234		..	5 55		..	..		..			
Balcombe		..	..		..	..		..			
Horsted Keynes dep.	..	..	..	..	..	..	..	..	..	..	..
Ardingly	..	..	..	..	..	..	..	..	..	..	..
Haywards Heath C 239	5 50	..	..	..	..	..	..	..	..	6 4	6 4
Wivelsfield (*below*)	..	..	..	..	..	..	..	..	..	..	..
Burgess Hill	..	..	..	..	..	..	..	..	..	..	..
Hassocks **D**	6 4	..	..	..	..	..	..	..	..	..	..
Preston Park	..	..	..	..	..	..	..	..	..	..	..
Brighton (*below*) arr.	..	..	..	..	..	..	..	..	..	..	..
Haywards Heath dep	..	..	..	..	..	..	..	..	..	6 5	6 5
Wivelsfield (*above*)	..	..	..	..	..	..	..	..	..	..	..
Plumpton	..	..	..	..	..	..	..	..	..	..	..
Cooksbridge	..	..	..	..	..	..	..	..	..	..	..
Lewes 239 arr.	..	..	..	..	..	..	..	..	..	6 21	6 21
Brighton dep.	Through Train London Bridge to Littlehampton	..	Through Train London Bridge to Bognor Regis.	Through Train Victoria to Littlehampton.	..	..	..	..	..	..	..
London Road (Brighton)		..			..	..	..	..	..	..	..
Falmer		..			..	..	..	..	..	..	..
Lewes arr.		..			..	..	..	..	..	..	..
Lewes dep.		..			..	..	..	..	..	..	6 25
Southease and Rodmell		..			..	..	..	..	..	..	..
Newhaven Town [Halt		..			..	..	..	..	..	..	6 34
" Harbour		..			..	..	..	..	..	..	6 36
Bishopstone		..			..	..	..	..	..	..	6 39
Seaford arr.		..			..	..	..	..	..	..	6 42
Lewes dep.		..			..	..	..	..	..	6 23	..
Glynde		..			..	..	..	..	..	..	..
Berwick		..			..	..	..	..	..	..	..
Polegate 239		..			..	..	..	..	..	6 36	..
Hampden Park **F**		..			..	..	..	..	..	..	..
Eastbourne arr.		..			..	..	..	..	..	6 43	..
Eastbourne dep.		..	..	..	..	..	Through Train, Victoria to Bognor Regis	..	Through Train, Victoria to Bognor Regis	6 47	..
Hampden Park **F**		..	..	..	..	..		..		..	..
Pevensey and Westham	..	..	..	..	..	..		..		6 56	..
Pevensey Bay Halt	..	..	..	..	..	..		..		..	..
Norman's Bay Halt	..	..	..	..	..	..		..		..	..
Cooden Beach	..	..	..	..	..	..		..		7 2	..
Collington Halt	..	..	..	..	..	..		..		..	..
Bexhill (Central) **G**	..	..	..	..	..	..		..		7 6	..
St. Leonards (W.M.)	..	..	..	..	..	..		..		..	..
" (W.S.)	..	..	..	..	..	..		..		7 13	..
Hastings 56, 59	..	..	..	..	..	..		..		7 16	..
Ore arr	..	..	..	..	..	..		..		7 21	..

Station	1	2	3	4	5	6	7	8
Three Bridges (above) dep.	..	..	..	..	..	Saturdays excepted	..	Stop
Crawley	..	..	..	..	..		..	..
Ifield	..	..	..	..	..		..	..
Fay Gate	..	..	..	..	..		..	..
Littlehaven Halt	..	..	..	..	..		..	..
Horsham 244, 245 arr.	..	..	..	..	..		..	..
Sutton dep.	..	..	Saturdays excepted	..	..		..	..
Dorking North H	..	..		..	..		..	..
Horsham 244, 245 arr.	..	..		..	..		..	..
Horsham dep.	..	..		..	..		..	..
Christ's Hospital, West Horsham	..	..		..	..		..	..
Billingshurst	..	..		..	..		..	..
Pulborough J 374	..	..		..	..		..	..
Amberley	..	..		..	..		..	..
Arundel	p.m	..		p.m	..	p.m	..	..
Brighton dep.	5 20	..	P	5 33	..	5 45	..	..
Holland Road Halt	5SX22	..	..	5 35	..	..	..	..
Hove	5 23	..	5 34	5 37	..	5 48	..	..
Aldrington Halt	5 25	..	..	5 39	..	..	..	..
Portslade and West Hove	5 28	..	..	5 42	..	5 51	..	..
Fishersgate Halt	..	..	..	5 44	..	..	..	..
Southwick	5 31	..	..	5 47	..	5 54	..	..
Shoreham-by-Sea K	5 34	..	5 41	5 50	..	5 58	..	..
Lancing	5 38	..	..	5 55	..	6 2	..	..
Ham Bridge Halt N	..	..	..	5 58	..	..	..	..
Worthing Central	5 42	..	5 49	6 1	..	6 9	..	..
West Worthing U	5 46	..	5 52	6 3	..	6 11	..	..
Durrington-on-Sea	..	..	5 54	..	..	6 13	..	..
Goring-by-Sea	..	..	5 57	..	..	6 16	..	..
Angmering I	..	p.m	6 1	..	..	6 20	..	..
Ford (Sussex) dep.	..	6 2	..	..	..	..	..	..
Littlehampton arr.	..	6 7	6 10	..	..	6 30	..	p.m
Littlehampton dep.	..	..	..	..	..	..	..	6SX22
Ford (Sussex)	..	..	..	..	..	..	..	6SX26
Barnham arr.	..	..	..	..	..	..	..	6SX30
Bognor Regis arr.	..	..	..	..	..	..	..	6SX42
Bognor Regis dep.	..	..	..	..	..	..	..	6SX5
Barnham dep.	..	..	..	..	..	..	..	6SX30
Chichester Z	..	..	..	..	..	..	..	6‡39
Fishbourne Halt	..	..	..	..	..	..	..	6‡42
Bosham	..	..	..	..	..	..	..	6‡45
Nutbourne Halt	..	..	..	..	..	..	..	6‡48
Southbourne Halt	..	..	..	..	..	..	..	6‡51
Emsworth	..	..	..	..	..	..	..	6‡54
Warblington Halt	..	..	..	..	..	..	..	6‡57
Havant 244, 366	..	..	..	..	..	..	..	6‡59
244 Hayling Island arr.	..	..	..	..	..	..	..	..
Bedhampton Halt	..	..	..	..	..	..	..	7‡1
Hilsea Halt	..	..	..	..	..	..	..	..
Fratton 380	..	..	..	..	..	..	..	7‡9
Portsmouth & Southsea arr	..	..	..	..	..	..	..	7‡12
Portsmouth Harbour "	..	..	..	..	..	..	..	..
500 Ryde Pier (Boat) arr	..	..	..	..	..	..	..	..
Page 359 Sandown "	..	..	..	..	..	..	..	..
Shanklin "	..	..	..	..	..	..	..	..
Ventnor "	..	..	..	..	..	..	..	..
Newport "	..	..	..	..	..	..	..	..
Cowes "	..	..	..	..	..	..	..	..
Yarmouth "	..	..	..	..	..	..	..	..

Station	9	10	11	12	13	14	15	16
Three Bridges (above) dep.	Saturdays excepted	5 15	..	..	5 42	Saturdays only	Saturdays only	Stop
Crawley		5 18	..	..	5 45			..
Ifield		5 21	..	..	5 48			..
Fay Gate		5 25	..	..	..			..
Littlehaven Halt		5 29	..	..	5 55			..
Horsham 244, 245 arr.		5 32	..	..	5 58			..
Sutton dep.		Stop	..	..				..
Dorking North H		..	..	..				..
Horsham 244, 245 arr.		..	..	..				..
Horsham dep.		..	..	..				..
Christ's Hospital, West Horsham		..	..	..				..
Billingshurst		..	..	..				..
Pulborough J 374		..	..	..	Saturdays excepted			..
Amberley		..	..	..				..
Arundel	p.m	..	p.m	..		p.m	p.m	..
Brighton dep.	5 48	..	5 48	..		5 55	6 3	..
Holland Road Halt	5 50	..	..	..		..	6 5	..
Hove	5 52	..	5 51	..		5 59	6 7	..
Aldrington Halt	5 54	..	5 53	..		..	6 9	..
Portslade and West Hove	5 57	..	5 56	..	..	..	6 12	..
Fishersgate Halt	5 59	..	..	..	..	..	6 14	..
Southwick	6 1	..	5 59	..	..	..	6 17	..
Shoreham-by-Sea K	6 5	..	6 3	..	..	6 8	6 20	..
Lancing	6 10	..	6 8	..	..	..	6 25	..
Ham Bridge Halt N	..	..	..	..	..	..	6 28	..
Worthing Central	6 15	..	6 12	..	..	..	6 31	..
West Worthing U	6 18	..	6 14	..	..	..	6 33	..
Durrington-on-Sea	..	..	6 16	..	..	..	..	..
Goring-by-Sea	..	..	6 19	..	..	..	..	..
Angmering I	..	..	6 23	p.m	..	..	..	..
Ford (Sussex) dep.	..	..	..	6 29	..	..	..	..
Littlehampton arr.	..	p.m	6 33	6 34	..	..	..	..
Littlehampton dep.	..	6 25			..	..	..	..
Ford (Sussex)	..	6 29			..	..	..	p.m
Barnham arr.	..				..	..	..	6 36
Bognor Regis arr.	..				..	..	..	6 42
Bognor Regis dep.	..				..	..	..	..
Barnham dep.	..		Saturdays only	Saturdays excepted	..	..	..	..
Chichester Z	..	Saturdays only			..	..	..	..
Fishbourne Halt	..				..	..	..	..
Bosham	..				..	..	..	..
Nutbourne Halt	..				..	..	..	..
Southbourne Halt	..			..	..	..	..	..
Emsworth	..			..	..	..	..	..
Warblington Halt	..			..	..	..	..	..
Havant 244, 366	..			..	..	..	..	..
244 Hayling Island arr.	..		..	..	..	..	..	..
Bedhampton Halt	..	..	..	..	..	..	..	..
Hilsea Halt	..	..	..	..	..	..	..	..
Fratton 380	..	..	..	..	..	..	..	..
Portsmouth & Southsea arr	..	..	..	..	..	..	..	..
Portsmouth Harbour "	..	..	..	..	..	..	..	..
500 Ryde Pier (Boat) arr	..	..	..	..	..	..	..	..
Page 359 Sandown "	..	..	..	..	..	..	..	..
Shanklin "	..	..	..	..	..	..	..	..
Ventnor "	..	..	..	..	..	..	..	..
Newport "	..	..	..	..	..	..	..	..
Cowes "	..	..	..	..	..	..	..	..
Yarmouth "	..	..	..	..	..	..	..	..

Station	17	18	19	20	21	22	23	24
Three Bridges (above) dep.	..	5 47	..	..	..	..	5 55	..
Crawley	..	5 51	..	..	..	..	5 59	..
Ifield	..	5 53	..	..	..	..	..	..
Fay Gate	..	5 58	..	..	..	..	..	..
Littlehaven Halt	..	6 2	..	..	..	..	..	..
Horsham 244, 245 arr.	..	6 5	..	..	..	..	6 8	..
Sutton dep.	..	..	..	..	Saturdays excepted	Saturdays excepted	..	5 27
Dorking North H	..	..	..	..			..	5 46
Horsham 244, 245 arr.	..	..	..	..			..	6 10
Horsham dep.	..	6 5	..	..			6 9	6 12
Christ's Hospital, West Horsham	..	6 9	..	..			..	6 16
Billingshurst	..	6 16	..	..			..	6 23
Pulborough J 374	..	6 23	..	..			6 23	6 30
Amberley	..	6 31	..	..			..	6 38
Arundel	..	6 36	..	..			6 34	6 44
Brighton dep.	..	..	..	Saturdays only	R	6 9	RB	R
Holland Road Halt	..		..		..	6 11		..
Hove	..		..		6 8	6 14		..
Aldrington Halt	..		..		..	6 16	Saturdays excepted	
Portslade and West Hove	..	Saturdays only	..		..	6 19		Saturdays excepted
Fishersgate Halt	..		..		..	6 21		
Southwick	..		..		..	6 23		
Shoreham-by-Sea K	..		..		6 15	6 27		
Lancing	..		..		6 20	6 32		
Ham Bridge Halt N	..		..		..	6 35		
Worthing Central	..		..		6 26	6 37		
West Worthing U	..		..		6 28	6 40		
Durrington-on-Sea	..		..		6 30	..	..	
Goring-by-Sea	..	..	..		6 33	..	..	..
Angmering I	..	..	..	p.m	6 37	..	..	..
Ford (Sussex) dep.	..	..	..	6 42	..	..	..	..
Littlehampton arr.	..	6 44	..	6 46	6 47	..	..	6 52
Littlehampton dep.	..	6 47	..	..	..	..	..	..
Ford (Sussex)	..	6a51	..	..	..	..	..	..
Barnham arr.	..	7 2	..	..	..	..	6 42	..
Bognor Regis arr.	..	7 9	..	..	..	..	6 50	..
Bognor Regis dep.	..	..	..	..	..	..	..	..
Barnham dep.	..	..	..	..	..	..	6 46	..
Chichester Z	..	..	..	..	..	..	6 56	..
Fishbourne Halt	..	..	..	..	..	..	..	..
Bosham	..	..	..	..	..	..	7 2	..
Nutbourne Halt	..	..	..	..	..	..	..	..
Southbourne Halt	..	..	..	..	..	..	..	..
Emsworth	..	..	..	..	..	..	7 10	..
Warblington Halt	..	..	..	..	..	..	..	..
Havant 244, 366	..	..	..	..	..	..	7 15	..
244 Hayling Island arr.	..	..	..	..	..	..	7 33	..
Bedhampton Halt	..	..	..	..	..	..	..	..
Hilsea Halt	..	..	..	..	..	..	..	..
Fratton 380	..	..	..	..	..	..	7 23	..
Portsmouth & Southsea arr	..	..	..	..	..	..	7 27	..
Portsmouth Harbour "	..	..	..	..	..	..	7 31	..
500 Ryde Pier (Boat) arr	..	..	..	..	..	..	..	..
Page 359 Sandown "	..	..	..	..	..	..	..	..
Shanklin "	..	..	..	..	..	..	..	..
Ventnor "	..	..	..	..	..	..	..	..
Newport "	..	..	..	..	..	..	..	..
Cowes "	..	..	..	..	..	..	..	..
Yarmouth "	..	..	..	..	..	..	..	..

Station	25	26	27	28	29	30	31
Three Bridges (above) dep.	..	..	..	..	..	..	..
Crawley	..	..	..	..	..	..	..
Ifield	..	..	..	..	..	..	..
Fay Gate	..	..	..	..	..	..	..
Littlehaven Halt	..	..	..	..	..	..	..
Horsham 244, 245 arr.	..	..	..	..	..	..	..
Sutton dep.	Saturdays excepted	..	5 39	Saturdays only	..	..	..
Dorking North H		..	5 56		6 4	..	..
Horsham 244, 245 arr.		..	6 13		6 21	..	..
Horsham dep.		..	6 14		6 22	..	..
Christ's Hospital, West Horsham		..	..		..	..	..
Billingshurst		..	6 24		..	..	..
Pulborough J 374		..	6 31		6 37	..	..
Amberley		..	6 39		..	..	..
Arundel		..	6 45		6 48	..	..
Brighton dep.	6 15	..	R	6 17	R	..	..
Holland Road Halt	..	..	..	..		..	..
Hove	6 20	..	..	6 20	Saturdays excepted	..	..
Aldrington Halt	..	..	..	..		..	..
Portslade and West Hove	6 24	..	..	..		..	..
Fishersgate Halt	..	..		..		..	..
Southwick	6 27	..	Saturdays only	..		..	..
Shoreham-by-Sea K	6 31	..		6 26		..	..
Lancing	..	..		..		..	..
Ham Bridge Halt N	..	..		..		..	..
Worthing Central	..	..		6 35		..	..
West Worthing U	..	..		6 37	..	..	..
Durrington-on-Sea	..	..		..	..	..	..
Goring-by-Sea	..	..		6 41	..	..	..
Angmering I	..	..		6 45	..	..	..
Ford (Sussex) dep.	..	6 53	..	..	..	..	..
Littlehampton arr.	..	6 57	..	..	..	..	..
Littlehampton dep.	..	Stop	..	6 47	..	..	..
Ford (Sussex)	..		..	6 52	6 53	..	..
Barnham arr.	..	..	6 53	6 57	6 58	..	..
Bognor Regis arr.	..	..	7 0	7 9	7 5	..	..
Bognor Regis dep.	..	..	..	6 40	..	..	..
Barnham dep.	..	..	..	6 57	..	..	..
Chichester Z	..	..	..	7 7	..	..	..
Fishbourne Halt	..	..	..	7 10	..	..	..
Bosham	..	..	..	7 13	..	..	..
Nutbourne Halt	..	..	..	7 16	..	..	..
Southbourne Halt	..	..	..	7 19	..	..	..
Emsworth	..	..	..	7 22	..	..	..
Warblington Halt	..	..	..	7 25	..	..	..
Havant 244, 366	..	..	..	7 27	..	..	..
244 Hayling Island arr.	..	..	..	7 47	..	..	..
Bedhampton Halt	..	..	..	..	..	..	..
Hilsea Halt	..	..	..	..	..	..	..
Fratton 380	..	..	..	7 36	..	..	..
Portsmouth & Southsea arr	..	p.m	..	7 38	..	..	..
Portsmouth Harbour "	..	7d35	..	7 42	..	..	..
500 Ryde Pier (Boat) arr	..	8 5	..	..	..	..	..
Page 359 Sandown "	..	8 48	..	..	..	..	..
Shanklin "	..	8 55	..	..	..	..	..
Ventnor "	..	9 11	..	..	..	..	..
Newport "	..	9 6	..	..	..	..	..
Cowes "	..	9 20	..	..	..	..	..
Yarmouth "	..	..	..	..	..	..	..

3 Third class only. * Change at East Croydon. ‡ 2 mins *earlier* on Sats. ǂ Local Passengers between Victoria and East Croydon not conveyed from Mons. to Fris. *a* Dep. 5 mins. later. *d* Arr. 7 mins. *earlier*. **P** Pullman Car facilities available. **R** Refreshment Car facilities available. **RB** Refreshment Car facilities available between London and Bognor Regis. **SO** Sats. only. **SX** Sats. excepted. § Calls to take up only. *y* Arr. 2 mins. *earlier*.

For Other Notes, see page 195

For SERVICES from LONDON (Waterloo) to PORTSMOUTH and ISLE OF WIGHT, see pages 359 to 365

From LONDON to THE SOUTH COAST—Week Days—*continued*

Station	1 p.m P	2 p.m	3 p.m	4 p.m	5 p.m	6 p.m	7 p.m	8 p.m P
VICTORIA dep.	5 25	..	5*9		5*9	..	5 28	5 35
Clapham Junction "	..	..	..		..	..	5 34	..
LONDON BRIDGE dep.	..	..	5 12	Saturdays excepted.	5 16	5 30	5*16	..
New Cross Gate "	..	..	..		..	..	..	..
Norwood Junction B "	..	..	..		5 28	..	5*28	..
East Croydon dep.	Saturdays excepted	..	5 28		5 34	..	5 46	..
Purley		..	5 34		5 40	..	..	Saturdays excepted
Coulsdon South		..	..		5 43	..	..	
Merstham		..	5 42		5 49	..	..	
Redhill 246		..	5 47	5 49	5 57	..	6 1	
Earlswood		..	..	5 52	5 59	Saturdays excepted	..	
Salfords		..	..	5 56	6 3		..	
Horley		..	..	6 0	6 7		..	6 9
Gatwick Airport		..	..	6 4	6 10		6 10	..
Three Bridges (below) 234		..	6 0	6 8	6 15		..	..
Balcombe		..	6 6	..	6 21		..	..
Horsted Keynes dep.	..	6 0	..	..	6 16		..	..
Ardingly	..	6 4		..	6 20		..	..
Haywards Heath C 239	..	6 8	6 13	..	6 28	6 17	6 23	6 24
Wivelsfield (below)	..	Stop	..	..	6 32	..	..	..
Burgess Hill	..		..	..	6 35	6 23	..	..
Hassocks D	..	..	..	..	6 39	6 27	..	..
Preston Park	..	..	..	..	6 47	6 35	6 37	6 39
Brighton (below) arr.	6 25	..	6 29	..	6 50	6 39	6 41	..
Haywards Heath dep.	Stop	..	☞	..	Saturdays only	Stop	☞	..
Wivelsfield (above)		..		..		..		..
Plumpton	..	..		..		..		..
Cooksbridge	..	..		..		..		..
Lewes 239 arr.	..	p.m		..		..		..
Brighton (below) dep.	..	6 15	Saturdays excepted	..		..	Saturdays only	..
London Road (Brighton)	..	6 17		..		..		..
Falmer	..	6 21		..		..		..
Lewes arr.	..	6 29		..		..		..
Lewes dep.	..	..		..	..	..		..
Southease and Rodmell	..	..		..	..	..		..
Newhaven Town [Halt	..	..		..	..	..		..
" Harbour	..	..		..	..	..		..
Bishopstone	..	..		..	..	..		..
Seaford arr.	..	..	Stop	..	..	..	Stop	..
Lewes dep.	..	6 29	..	..	..	..	..	Through Train, Victoria to Littlehampton.
Glynde	..	6 34	..	..	..	..	..	
Berwick	..	6 40	..	..	..	p.m	..	
Polegate 239	p.m	6 46	..	..	..	6 57	..	
Hampden Park F	6 45	6 50	..	..	..	7 2	..	
Eastbourne arr.	6 49	6 54	..	..	..	7 7	..	
Eastbourne dep.	Stop	6 57	..	..	..	Stop	..	
Hampden Park F		7 0	..	..	..		..	
Pevensey and Westham	..	7 7	..	..	..	..	..	
Pevensey Bay Halt	..	7 9	..	..	..	..	..	
Norman's Bay Halt	..	7 12	..	..	..	..	..	
Cooden Beach	..	7 16	..	..	..	..	..	
Collington Halt	..	7 19	..	..	..	..	..	
Bexhill (Central) G	..	7 22	..	..	..	..	..	
St. Leonards (W.M.)	..	7 26	..	..	..	..	..	
" (W.S.)	..	7 29	..	..	..	..	..	
Hastings 56, 59	..	7 31	..	..	..	..	..	
Ore arr.	..	7 34	..	..	..	..	..	

Station	9 p.m	10 pm	11 p.m P	12 p.m R	13 p.m	14 p.m	15 p.m	16 p.m
VICTORIA dep.	5 38	..	..	..	..	..	..	..
Clapham Junction "	..	..	..	..	..	..		..
LONDON BRIDGE dep.	Sats. excepted	..	5 45	5 45	..	..	Saturdays only ☞	..
New Cross Gate "		..	..	..	..	..		..
Norwood Junction B "		..	..	..	..	..		..
East Croydon dep.		..	Saturdays excepted	Saturdays excepted	..	..		..
Purley	5 58	..			..	..		..
Coulsdon South	..	..			..	..		..
Merstham	..	..			..	..		..
Redhill 246	..	..			..	..		..
Earlswood	6 9	..			..	..		..
Salfords	..	..			..	..		..
Horley	..	..			..	..		..
Gatwick Airport	..	..			..	..		..
Three Bridges (below) 234	6 21	..			..	..		..
Balcombe	6 27	..			..	..		..
Horsted Keynes dep.	6 16	..	6 16	6 16	..	..	6 16	..
Ardingly	6 20	..	6 20	6 20	..	..	6 20	..
Haywards Heath C 239	6 33	..	6 28	6 29	..	..	6 24	..
Wivelsfield (below)	6 38	..	..	..	..	..	..	..
Burgess Hill	6 40	..	..	6 34	..	..	..	..
Hassocks D	6 44	..	..	..	..	..	..	..
Preston Park	..	..	..	..	..	..	..	..
Brighton (below) arr.	6 55	..	..	..	..	..	..	..
Haywards Heath dep.	..	..	6 31	Through Train, London Bridge to Littlehampton	Saturdays excepted	..	6 35	..
Wivelsfield (above)	..	..	..			..	6 39	..
Plumpton	..	..	6 40			..	6 45	..
Cooksbridge	..	..	6 45			..	6 50	..
Lewes 239 arr.	..	..	6 50			..	6 55	..
Brighton (below) dep.	..	631	..			..	Stop	..
London Road (Brighton)	..	633	..			..		..
Falmer	..	637	..			..	..	..
Lewes arr.	..	645	..			..	..	..
Lewes dep.	..	646	..		6 56	..	..	..
Southease and Rodmell	..	651	..		..	..	..	..
Newhaven Town [Halt	..	656	..		7 5	..	..	..
" Harbour	..	657	..		7 6	..	..	..
Bishopstone	..	7 2	..		..	..	..	..
Seaford arr.	..	7 5	..		7 11	..	..	..
Lewes dep.	..	..	6 51		Stop	..	..	..
Glynde	..	..	..			..	..	..
Berwick	..	..	7 1		..	..	..	..
Polegate 239	..	..	7 8		..	7 10	..	..
Hampden Park F	..	..	..		..	..	..	7 17
Eastbourne arr.	..	..	7 14		..	7 18	..	7 21
Eastbourne dep.	..	..	7 18	..	..	Stop	..	Stop
Hampden Park F	..	..	..	..	..		..	
Pevensey and Westham	..	..	7 26	..	..	..	..	..
Pevensey Bay Halt	..	..	..	..	..	..	..	..
Norman's Bay Halt	..	..	..	..	..	..	..	..
Cooden Beach	..	..	7 32	..	..	..	..	..
Collington Halt	..	..	..	..	..	..	..	..
Bexhill (Central) G	..	..	7 37	..	..	..	..	..
St. Leonards (W.M.)	..	..	..	..	..	..	..	..
" (W.S.)	..	..	7 45	..	..	..	..	..
Hastings 56, 59	..	..	7 48	..	..	..	..	..
Ore arr.	..	..	7 53	..	..	..	..	..

Station	17 p.m	18 p.m	19 p.m	20 p.m	21 p.m	22 p.m	23 p.m P	24 p.m RB
VICTORIA dep.	..	..	..	..	..	5 48	6 0	6 18
Clapham Junction "	..	..	..	..	..	5 53	..	
LONDON BRIDGE dep.	..	..	5 48	..	5 50	5Ⓑ31	..	..
New Cross Gate "	..	..	..	..	..	..	..	..
Norwood Junction B "	..	..	..	..	..	5Ⓑ43	..	..
East Croydon dep.	..	..	Saturdays excepted	..	6 5	6 5	..	Saturdays excepted
Purley	..	..		..	6 11	6 11	..	
Coulsdon South	..	..		..	6 14	6 14	..	
Merstham	..	..		..	6 20	6 20	..	
Redhill 246	..	..		..	6 26	6 27	..	
Earlswood	..	..		..	6 29	6 29	..	
Salfords	..	..		..	6 32	6 33	..	
Horley	..	..	6 21	..	6 37	6 37	..	
Gatwick Airport	..	..	..	..	6 40	6 40	..	
Three Bridges (below) 234	..	..	6 26	..	6 44	6y46	..	
Balcombe	..	..	..	..	6 50	6 53	..	
Horsted Keynes dep.	..	..	..	6 40	..	..	..	..
Ardingly	..	..	..	6 44		..	..	..
Haywards Heath C 239	..	..	..	6 49	6 56	7 0	..	Through Train Victoria to Bognor Regis.
Wivelsfield (below)	..	..	..	Stop	..	7 4	..	
Burgess Hill	..	..	..		7 2	7 7	..	
Hassocks D	..	..	..	..	7 6	7 11	..	
Preston Park	..	..	..	..	7 14	7 19	..	
Brighton (below) arr.	..	..	..	..	7 17	7 22	7 0	
Haywards Heath dep.	..	Saturdays only	..	..	Saturdays excepted	☞	Stop	
Wivelsfield (above)	..		..	..				
Plumpton	..		..	..			..	
Cooksbridge	..		..	..			..	
Lewes 239 arr.	..		..	..			..	
Brighton (below) dep.	6 45		..	..		Saturdays only	..	
London Road (Brighton)	6 47		..	..			..	
Falmer	6 52		..	..			..	
Lewes arr.	6 59		..	..			..	
Lewes dep.	..	7 4	..	..	..		..	
Southease and Rodmell	..	7 9	..	..	..		..	
Newhaven Town [Halt	..	7 14	..	..	..		..	
" Harbour	..	7 15	..	..	..		..	
Bishopstone	..	7 20	..	..	..		..	
Seaford arr.	..	7 22	..	..	..		..	
Lewes dep.	7 1	..	Through Train, London Bridge to Bognor Regis.	..	..	Stop	..	
Glynde	7 6	..		..	..	..	..	
Berwick	7 12	..		..	..	..	..	
Polegate 239	7 20	..		..	..	..	..	
Hampden Park F	7 23	..		..	..	..	..	
Eastbourne arr.	7 27	..		..	..	..	..	
Eastbourne dep.	7 33	..		..	..	..	..	..
Hampden Park F	7 36	..		..	..	..	..	..
Pevensey and Westham	7 43	..		..	..	..	..	..
Pevensey Bay Halt	7 45	..		..	..	..	..	..
Norman's Bay Halt	7 49	..		..	..	..	..	..
Cooden Beach	7 52	..		..	..	..	..	..
Collington Halt	7 55	..		..	..	..	..	..
Bexhill (Central) G	7 58	..		..	..	..	..	..
St. Leonards (W.M.)	8 3	..		..	..	..	..	..
" (W.S.)	8 6	..		..	..	..	..	..
Hastings 56, 59	8 8	..		..	..	..	..	..
Ore arr.	8 11	..		p.m	..	..	..	..

Station	25 p.m	26 p.m P	27 p.m R	28 p.m	29 p.m	30 p.m	31 p.m	32 p.m
VICTORIA dep.	..	..	..	..	..	..	..	6 4
Clapham Junction "	..	..	..	..	..	..	..	6U9
LONDON BRIDGE dep.	..	6 5	6 5	..	..	..	..	5Ⓑ55
New Cross Gate "	..	..	..	..	..	..	..	..
Norwood Junction B "	..	..	..	..	..	..	..	..
East Croydon dep.	..	..	..	..	..	..	..	6 21
Purley	..	..	..	Saturdays excepted	..	..	..	..
Coulsdon South	..	..	..		..	..	..	..
Merstham	..	Saturdays excepted	Saturdays excepted		..	..	..	..
Redhill 246	..				..	..	..	6 36
Earlswood	..				..	..	..	..
Salfords	..				..	..	..	..
Horley	..				..	..	..	6 44
Gatwick Airport	..				..	..	..	6 47
Three Bridges (below) 234	..				..	..	..	6 51
Balcombe	..			..	..	..	..	6 58
Horsted Keynes dep.	..			..	..	..	..	..
Ardingly	..			..	..	..	..	..
Haywards Heath C 239	..	6 48	6 48		..	..	..	7 4
Wivelsfield (below)	..	..	..		..	..	..	..
Burgess Hill	..	..	..		Saturdays excepted ☞	..	..	..
Hassocks D	..	..	..			..	..	..
Preston Park	..	7 4	7 5			..	..	..
Brighton (below) arr.	..	7 7	..			..	..	7 20
Haywards Heath dep.	..	..	Through Train, London Bridge to Littlehampton.	6 50		..	..	Saturdays excepted
Wivelsfield (above)	..	..		6 54		..	..	
Plumpton	..	..		7 0		..	..	
Cooksbridge	..	..		7 5		..	..	
Lewes 239 arr.	..	..		7 10		..	..	
Brighton (below) dep.	..	..		..		7 14	..	
London Road (Brighton)	..	..		..		7 16	..	
Falmer	..	..		..		7 21	..	
Lewes arr.	..	..		..		7 28	..	
Lewes dep.	..	..		..	7 14	..	..	..
Southease and Rodmell	..	..		..	7 19	..	..	..
Newhaven Town [Halt	..	..		..	7 24	..	..	..
" Harbour	..	..		..	7 25	..	..	..
Bishopstone	..	..		..	7 30	..	..	..
Seaford arr.	..	..		..	7 33	..	..	..
Lewes dep.	..	..		7 12	Stop	7 29	..	..
Glynde	..	..		7 17		7 34	..	..
Berwick	..	..		7 23	..	7 40	..	..
Polegate 239	..	..		7 29	..	7 47	..	..
Hampden Park F	..	..		7 33	..	7 50	..	..
Eastbourne arr.	..	..		7 37	..	7 54	..	..
Eastbourne dep.	..	..	..	Stop	..	7 57	..	..
Hampden Park F	..	..	..		..	8 0	..	..
Pevensey and Westham	..	..	..	..	..	8 7	..	..
Pevensey Bay Halt	..	..	..	..	..	8 9	..	..
Norman's Bay Halt	..	..	..	..	..	8 12	..	..
Cooden Beach	..	..	..	..	..	8 16	..	..
Collington Halt	..	..	..	..	..	8 19	..	..
Bexhill (Central) G	..	..	..	..	..	8 22	..	..
St. Leonards (W.M.)	..	..	..	..	..	8 26	..	..
" (W.S.)	..	..	..	..	..	8 29	..	..
Hastings 56, 59	..	..	..	..	..	8 31	..	..
Ore arr.	..	..	..	..	..	8 34	..	..

Station	1	2	3	4	5	6	7	8	9	10	11	12	13	14	15	16	17	18	19	20	21	22	23	24	25	26	27	28	29	30	31	32
Three Bridges (*above*) dep	..		..	6 8	..	Saturdays excepted	Saturdays only	..	..	..	..	..	Saturdays excepted	Saturdays only	Saturdays only	..	..	..	6 27	6 38	..	..	Saturdays excepted	..	..	..	..	Saturdays excepted	..	..	6 47	..
Crawley	..	Stop	..	6 12	..			..	..	..	..	..				..	..	..	6 30	6 41	..	..		..	..	..	..		..	..	6 51	..
Ifield	..	..	..	6 15	..			..	..	..	..	..				..	..	..	6 33	6 44	..	..		..	..	..	..		..	..	6 53	..
Fay Gate	..	..	..	6 21	..			..	..	..	..	..				..	..	..	6 38	6 49	..	..		..	..	..	..		..	..	6 58	..
Littlehaven Halt	..	..	..	6 26	..			..	..	..	..	..				..	..	..	..	6 53	..	..		..	..	..	..		..	..	7 2	..
Horsham 244, 245 arr.	..	..	..	6 29	..			..	..	..	..	..				..	..	..	6 44	6 56	..	..		7 5	..	..	..		..	..	7 5	..
Sutton dep.	..	..	..	..	..			Saturdays excepted	..	..	..	Saturdays excepted				..	..	..	..	Saturdays excepted	..	..		..	Saturdays only	..	Saturdays excepted		..	..	..	..
Dorking North **H**	..	..	..	..	..				..	..	..					..	..	..	..		..	..		..		..			..	..	..	..
Horsham 244, 245 arr.	..	..	..	..	..				..	..	..					..	..	..	..		..	..		..		..			..	..	..	..
Horsham 244, 245 dep	..	..	..	6 30	..				..	..	..					..	..	..	6 45		..	..		7 5		..			..	..	7 5	..
Christ's Hospital, West Horsham	..	..	..	6 34	..				..	..	..					..	..	..	..		..	..		..		..			..	..	7 9	..
Billingshurst	..	..	..	6 41	..				..	..	..					..	..	..	6 56		..	..		..		..			..	..	7 16	..
Pulborough **J** 374	..	..	..	6 48	..				..	..	..					..	..	..	7 4		..	..		7 20		..			..	..	7 23	..
Amberley	..	..	..	6 55	..				..	..	..					..	..	..	..		..	..		..		..			..	..	7 30	..
Arundel	..	..	p.m	7 2	..	p.m	p.m		..	..	..		p.m	p.m	p.m	..	..	..	7 16		..	..	p.m	7 31		..		p.m	..	..	7 36	..
Brighton dep	..	..	6 21	Saturdays excepted	..	6 30	6 33	P	..	..	..	R	6 46	6 47	6 50	..	..	..	..		..	..	6 58	RB	7 3	..	R	7 8	..	..	Saturdays only	..
Holland Road Halt	..	..	..		..	..	6 35	..	..	..	..	..	6 48	..	..	..	..	..	..		..	..	..	..	7 5	..	..	7 10	..	..		..
Hove	Saturdays excepted	..	6 25		..	6 33	6 37	6 43	..	..	..	6 48	6 51	6 50	6 53	..	..	..	..		..	..	7 2	..	7 7	..	7 9	7 12	..	..		..
Aldrington Halt		..	..		..	6 35	6 39	..	..	..	..	..	6 53	..	..	..	..	..	..		..	Saturdays only	..	Saturdays excepted	7 9	..	..	7 14	..	..		..
Portslade and West Hove		..	6 28		..	6 38	6 42	..	..	..	..	6 51	6 55	..	6 56	..	..	..	..	..	..		7 5		7 12	..	..	7 17	..	..		..
Fishersgate Halt		..	..		..	..	6 44	..	..	..	..	..	6 57	..	..	..	..	..	..	..	..		..		7 14	..	..	7 19	..	..		..
Southwick		..	6 31		..	6 41	6 47	..	..	..	..	..	7 0	..	6 59	..	..	..	Saturdays excepted	..	..		7 8		7 17	..	..	7 22	..	..		..
Shoreham-by-Sea **K**		..	6 35		..	6 44	6 50	6 51	..	..	..	6 57	7 3	6 57	7 3	..	..	..		..	..		7 11		7 20	..	7 16	7 25	..	..		..
Lancing		..	6 39		..	6 48	6 55	..	..	..	..	7 1	7 8	..	7 7	..	..	..		..	..		7 15		7 25	..	..	7 30	..	..		..
Ham Bridge Halt **N**		..	..		..	..	6 58	..	..	..	..	..	7 11	..	..	..	..	..		..	..		..		7 28	..	..	7 33	..	..		..
Worthing Central		..	6 43	..	..	6 52	7 1	6 59	..	..	..	7 6	7 14	7 6	7 12	..	..	..		..	..		7 20		7 31	..	7 24	7 36	..	..		..
West Worthing **U**		..	6 45	..	..	6 55	7 3	7 1	..	..	..	7 8	7 16	..	7 14	Saturdays only	..	..		..	..		7 22		7 33	..	7 26	7 38	..	..		..
Durrington-on-Sea		..	6SX47		..	..	..	7 3	..	..	..	7 10	..	..	7 16		..	..		..	..		..		..	..	7 28	Stop	..	..	..	..
Goring-by-Sea		..	6SX49		..	..	..	7 6	..	..	..	7 13	..	..	7 18		..	..		..	..		7 25	..	..	..	7 31	..	..	..	..	..
Angmering **L**		..	6SX55		..	..	..	7 10	..	..	..	7 18	7 23	..	7 23		..	..		..	..		7 30	..	..	..	7 36	..	..	..	..	..
Ford (Sussex) dep.		..	..	..	..	..	..	..	..	..	..	..	..	..	..		..	..		..	..		..	..	..	..	..	..	..	..	..	..
Littlehampton arr.	p.m	..	7SX4	7 9	..	..	..	7 20	..	..	..	7 27	7 32	..	7 32		..	..		..	..		..	7 48	..	..	7 45	..	..	..	7 43	..
Littlehampton dep.	6 54	..	Stop	7 12	..	..	..	..	..	..	..	..	..	..	..		..	..	7 12	..	..		..	..	..	..	..	..	..	..	7 46	..
Ford (Sussex)	6 58	p.m		..	..	..	..	..	..	..	..	..	..	..	..		..	..	..	..	..	p.m	..	..	..	..	..	p.m	..	..	7a50	..
Barnham arr.	7 3	7d8	..	7 20	..	..	..	..	..	..	..	..	..	7 22	..		..	..	7 24	..	..	7d36	7 44	7 39	..	..	..	7d50	..	..	8 1	..
Bognor Regis arr.	7 14	7 14	..	7 26	..	..	..	..	..	..	..	..	..	7 42	..		..	..	7 33	..	..	7 42	7 56	7 48	..	..	..	7 56	..	..	8 7	..
Bognor Regis dep.	6 40		..	..	..	..	..	..	..	..	..	..	..	7 10	..		..	..	..	..	..	..	7 20	7 20	..	..	..		..	..	..	..
Barnham dep.	7 3	Saturdays excepted	p.m	..	..	..	..	..	..	..	..	..	..	7 22	..	p.m	..	..	7 25	..	..	..	7 45	7 40	..	..	..	Saturdays excepted	..	..	..	..
Chichester **Z**	7 12		7 19	..	..	..	..	..	..	..	..	..	..	7 32	..	7 37	..	..	7 34	..	..	..	7 55	7 49	..	..	..		..	..	..	..
Fishbourne Halt	..		7 22	..	..	..	..	..	..	..	..	..	..	..	..	7 40	..	..	..	..	..	..	..	..	..	..	..		..	..	..	..
Bosham	7 17		7 25	..	..	..	..	..	..	..	..	..	..	..	..	7 43	..	..	..	..	..	..	8 1	..	..	..	..		..	..	..	..
Nutbourne Halt	..		7 29	..	..	..	..	..	..	..	..	..	..	..	..	7 46	..	..	..	..	..	..	8 4	..	..	..	..		..	..	..	..
Southbourne Halt	..		7 31	..	..	..	..	..	..	..	..	..	..	..	..	7 49	..	..	..	..	..	..	8 6	..	..	..	..		..	..	..	..
Emsworth	7 23		7 34	..	..	..	..	..	..	..	..	..	..	..	..	7 52	..	..	..	..	..	..	8 10	7 59	..	..	..		..	..	..	..
Warblington Halt	..		7 37	..	..	..	..	..	..	..	..	..	..	..	..	7 55	..	..	..	..	..	..	..	..	..	..	..		..	..	..	..
Havant 244, 366	7 27		7 39	..	..	..	..	..	..	..	..	..	..	7 45	..	7 57	..	..	7 45	..	..	..	8 14	8 5	..	..	..		..	..	..	..
244 Hayling Island arr.	..		..	..	..	..	..	..	..	..	..	..	..	..	..	..	..	..	..	..	..	..	8 33	8 33	..	..	..		..	..	..	..
Bedhampton Halt	..		7 41	..	..	..	..	..	..	..	..	..	..	..	..	7 59	..	..	..	..	..	..	..	..	..	..	..		..	..	..	..
Hilsea Halt	..	..	..	..	..	..	..	..	..	..	..	..	..	..	..	..	..	..	..	..	..	..	..	..	..	..	..		..	..	..	..
Fratton 380	7 36	..	7 49	..	..	..	..	..	..	..	..	..	..	7 54	..	8 7	..	..	7 53	..	..	..	8 24	8 14	..	..	..		..	..	..	..
Portsmouth & Southsea arr	7 38	..	7 52	..	..	..	..	..	..	..	..	..	..	7 56	..	8 10	..	..	7 56	..	..	..	8 26	8 17	..	..	..		..	..	..	..
Portsmouth Harbour "	7 42	..		..	..	..	..	..	..	..	..	..	..	8 0	..	..	..	..	..	..	..	..	8 30	8 21	..	..	..		p.m 8d40	..	..	..
500 Ryde Pier (Boat) arr	..	..	③ Saturdays excepted	..	..	..	..	..	..	..	..	..	..	..	..	..	..	..	..	..	..	..	..	..	..	..	..	..	9 10	..	..	..
Sandown " (Page 359)	..	..		..	..	..	..	..	..	..	..	..	..	..	..	..	..	..	..	..	..	..	..	..	..	..	..	..	9 48	..	..	..
Shanklin "	..	..		..	..	..	..	..	..	..	..	..	..	..	..	..	..	..	..	..	..	..	..	..	..	..	..	..	9 55	..	..	..
Ventnor "	..	..		..	..	..	..	..	..	..	..	..	..	..	..	..	..	..	..	..	..	..	..	..	..	..	..	..	1011	..	..	..
Newport "	..	..		..	..	..	..	..	..	..	..	..	..	..	..	..	..	..	..	..	..	..	..	..	..	..	..	..	10 6	..	..	..
Cowes "	..	..		..	..	..	..	..	..	..	..	..	..	..	..	..	..	..	..	..	..	..	..	..	..	..	..	..	1020	..	..	..
Yarmouth "	..	..		..	..	..	..	..	..	..	..	..	..	..	..	..	..	..	..	..	..	..	..	..	..	..	..	..	..	..	..	..

③ Third class only. * Change at East Croydon. *a* Dep. 5 mins. later. *d* Departure time. **P** Pullman Car facilities available.
R Refreshment Car facilities available. **RB** Refreshment Car facilities available between London and Bognor Regis. **SX** Saturdays excepted.

‖ Calls to take up only. *y* Arr. 2 mins. earlier

For Other Notes, see page 195

For SERVICES from LONDON (Waterloo to PORTSMOUTH and ISLE OF WIGHT, see pages 359 to 365

From LONDON to THE SOUTH COAST—Week Days—*continued*

Station	p.m	p.m	p.m	p.m	p.m	p.m	p.m P	p.m	p.m	p.m		p.m P	p.m	p.m P	p.m	p.m
VICTORIA .... dep.	6 *4	..	6*10	..	6*10	..	6 30	..	..	6 28	..	6 35	6 38	6 45	..	..
Clapham Junction .... "	6*U9	..	6*16	..	..	..	..	..	..	6U34	..	..	6U43	..	..	..
LONDON BRIDGE .. dep.	6 9	..	6 16	..	6 20	..	Saturdays excepted	..	..	6*16	..	..	6Ⓑ35	6Ⓑ35	..	..
New Cross Gate .... "	..	..	..	..	..	..		..	..	..	..	..	..	..	..	..
Norwood Junction B "	..	..	6 28	..	..	..		..	..	6*28	..	..	..	..	..	..
East Croydon .... dep.	6 24	..	6 34	Saturdays excepted	6 35	..		..	..	6 46	..	..	6 55	7 1	Saturdays excepted	..
Purley	..	..	6 40		6 40	..		..	..	..	..	..	7 0	Saturdays excepted		..
Coulsdon South	6 32	..	6 43		6 45	..		..	..	..	..	..	7 4			..
Merstham	6 38	..	6 49		6 51	..	..	..	..	..	..	..	7 10			..
Redhill 246	6 46	..	6 57		6 58	..	..	..	..	7 2	..	..	7 17			..
Earlswood	6 48	..	6 59		7 0	..	..	..	..	..	..	..	7 19			..
Salfords	6 52	..	7 3		7 4	..	..	..	..	..	..	..	7 23			..
Horley	6 56	..	7 7		7 8	..	..	..	..	..	..	7 7	7 27			..
Gatwick Airport	6 59	..	7 10		7 11	..	..	..	..	7 10	..	..	7·30			..
Three Bridges *(below)* 234.	7 3	..	7 15		7 15	..	..	..	..	..	..	..	7c37			..
Balcombe		..	7 22		7 22	..	..	..	..	..	..	..	7 43	..		..
Horsted Keynes ...... dep.	Saturdays excepted	..	..	7 16	..	..	..	..	..	..	..	..	..	..	7 16	..
Ardingly		..	..	7 20	..	..	..	..	..	..	..	..	..	..	7 20	..
Haywards Heath C 239 ...		..	7 28	7 24	7 28	..	..	..	..	7 23	..	7 22	7 50	7 32	7 24	..
Wivelsfield *(below)*		..	7 33	Stop	7 33	..	..	..	..	..	..	..	7 55	..	..	..
Burgess Hill		..	7 35	..	7 35	..	..	..	..	..	..	..	7 57	..	..	..
Hassocks D		..	7 39	..	7 39	..	..	..	..	..	..	..	8 1	..	..	..
Preston Park		..	7 47	..	7 47	..	..	..	..	7 37	..	7 37	8 9	..	..	..
Brighton *(below)* ...... arr.		..	7 51	..	7 51	..	7 30	..	..	7 41	..	..	8 13	..	..	..
Haywards Heath ... dep.	..	..	..	..		..	Stop	..	..		..	..	Saturdays excepted	7 32	7 35	..
Wivelsfield *(above)*	..	..	..	..		..	..	..	..		..	..		..	7 39	..
Plumpton	..	..	..	..		..	..	..	..		..	..		..	7 45	..
Cooksbridge	..	..	Saturdays only	..		..	..	..	..		..	Saturdays excepted		..	7 50	..
Lewes 239 .... arr.	..	..		..		..	..	..	..		..			7 48	7 55	..
Brighton .... dep.	..	..		..	Saturdays excepted	..	..	7 30	7 34	Saturdays only	..			..	..	7 46
London Road (Brighton) ..	..	..		..		..	..	7 32	7 37		..			..	..	7 48
Falmer	..	..		..		..	..	7 37	..		..			..	..	7 52
Lewes .... arr.	..	..		..		..	..	7 45	7 52		..			..	..	8 0
Lewes .... dep.	..	..		..		..	..	7 46	Stop		..	..	..	..	..	..
Southease and Rodmell	..	..		..		..	..	7 51	..		..	..	..	..	..	..
Newhaven Town ... [Halt	..	..	..	..		..	..	7 56	..		..	..	..	..	..	..
" Harbour	..	..	..	..		..	..	7 57	..		..	..	..	..	..	..
Bishopstone	..	..	..	..	Stop	..	..	8 2	..		..	..	..	..	..	..
Seaford .... arr.	..	..	..	..	..	..	..	8 5	..	Stop	..	..	..	..	..	..
Lewes .... dep.	..	..	..	..	..	..	..	Stop	..	..	..	Through Train, Victoria to Littlehampton	..	7 49	7 56	8 1
Glynde	..	..	..	..	..	..	..		..	..	..		..	..	8 1	8 6
Berwick	..	..	..	..	..	..	..	..	..	..	..		..	..	8 7	8 12
Polegate 239	..	..	..	..	..	..	p.m	..	..	..	..		..	..	8 14	8 19
Hampden Park F	..	..	..	..	..	..	8 15	..	..	..	..		..	..	8 18	8 22
Eastbourne .... arr.	..	..	..	..	..	..	8 19	..	..	..	..		..	8 8	8 22	8 26
Eastbourne .... dep.	..	..	..	..	..	..	Stop	..	..	..	..		..	8 12	Stop	8 29
Hampden Park F	..	..	..	..	..	..	..	..	..	..	..		..	..	..	8 32
Pevensey and Westham ...	..	..	..	..	..	..	..	..	..	..	..		..	8 20	..	8 39
Pevensey Bay Halt	..	..	..	..	..	..	..	..	..	..	..		..	..	..	8 41
Norman's Bay Halt	..	..	..	..	..	..	..	..	..	..	..		..	..	..	8 44
Cooden Beach	..	..	..	..	..	..	..	..	..	..	..		..	8 26	..	8 48
Collington Halt	..	..	..	..	..	..	..	..	..	..	..		..	..	..	8 51
Bexhill (Central) G	..	..	..	..	..	..	..	..	..	..	..		..	8 30	..	8 54
St. Leonards (W.M.)	..	..	..	..	..	..	..	..	..	..	..		..	..	..	8 58
" (W.S.)	..	..	..	..	..	..	..	..	..	..	..		..	8 37	..	9 1
Hastings 56, 59	..	..	..	..	..	..	..	..	..	..	..		..	8 39	..	9 3
Ore .... arr.	..	..	..	..	p.m	..	..	..	..	..	..		..	8 47	..	9 6
	1	2	3	4	5	6	7	8	9	10	11	12	13	14	15	16

Station	p.m	p.m	p.m	p.m	p.m	p.m	p.m	p.m	p.m	p.m	p.m R	p.m	p.m	p.m P	p.m
VICTORIA .... dep.	..	..	..	..	6 48	..	..	6*45	7 0	7 5	7 18	..	..	7 25	..
Clapham Junction .... "	..	..	..	..	6U53	..	..	..	..	7U10	..	..	..	..	..
LONDON BRIDGE .. dep.	..	..	..	..	6Ⓑ31	..	..	6 48	..	6Ⓑ55	..	..	..	7*18	7 18
New Cross Gate .... "	..	..	..	..	..	..	..	..	Brighton Belle 1st and 3rd class Pullman Cars only	..	..	..	..	..	..
Norwood Junction B "	..	..	..	..	6Ⓑ43	..	..	7 0		..	..	..	..	7*30	7 30
East Croydon .... dep.	..	..	..	..	7 5	..	..	7 5		7 22	Through Train Victoria to Bognor Regis	..	..	7 41	7 35
Purley	..	..	..	..	7 11	..	..	7 11		..		..	..	..	7 40
Coulsdon South	..	..	..	..	7 14	..	..	7 14		..		..	..	..	7 44
Merstham	..	..	..	..	7 20	..	..	7 20		..		..	..	..	7 50
Redhill 246	..	..	..	..	7 27	..	..	7 28		7 37		..	..	..	7 57
Earlswood	..	..	..	..	7 29	..	..	7 30		..		..	..	..	7 59
Salfords	..	..	..	..	7 33	..	..	7 34		..		..	..	..	8 3
Horley	..	..	..	..	7 37	..	..	7 38		7 44		..	..	..	8 7
Gatwick Airport	..	..	..	..	7 40	..	..	7 41		..		..	..	..	8 10
Three Bridges *(below)* 234.	..	..	..	..	7y46	..	..	7 45		7 50		..	..	..	8 15
Balcombe	..	..	..	..	7 53	..	..	7 52		..		..	..	..	8 21
Horsted Keynes ...... dep.	..	..	..	..	..	..	..	..		..		..	..	..	..
Ardingly	..	..	..	..	..	..	..	..		..		..	..	..	..
Haywards Heath C 239 ...	..	Saturdays only	..	..	8y1	..	..	8‖4		8 1		Saturdays only	..	8 14	8 28
Wivelsfield *(below)*	..		..	..	8 5	..	..	8 9		..			..	Through Train Victoria to Littlehampton	8 32
Burgess Hill	..		..	..	8 8	..	..	8 11		..			..		8 35
Hassocks D	..		..	..	8 12	..	..	8 15		..			..		8 39
Preston Park	..		..	..	8 20	..	..	8 23		8 15			..		8 47
Brighton *(below)* ...... arr.	..		..	..	8 23	..	..	8 27	8 0	8 18			..		8 50
Haywards Heath ... dep.	Saturdays excepted	7 35	..	..	Saturdays only	..	..	Saturdays excepted	..	Saturdays excepted			..		Stop
Wivelsfield *(above)*		7 39	..	..		..	..		..				..		..
Plumpton		7 45	..	..		..	..		..				..		..
Cooksbridge		7 50	..	..		..	..		..				..		..
Lewes 239 .... arr.		7 55	..	..		..	..		..				..		..
Brighton .... dep.		..	..	..		..	8 14		..			8 31	..		..
London Road (Brighton) ..		..	..	..		..	8 16		..			8 33	..		..
Falmer		..	..	..		..	8 20		..			8 37	..		..
Lewes .... arr.		..	..	..		..	8 28		..			8 45	..		..
Lewes .... dep.	8 4	8 4	..	..	..	..	..	..	..	..	..	8 52	..	..	..
Southease and Rodmell	8 9	8 9	..	..	..	..	..	..	..	..	..	8 57	..	..	..
Newhaven Town ... [Halt	8 14	8 14	..	..	..	..	..	..	..	..	..	9 2	..	..	..
" Harbour	8 15	8 15	..	..	..	..	..	..	..	..	..	9 3	..	..	..
Bishopstone	8 20	8 20	..	..	..	..	..	..	..	..	..	9 8	..	..	..
Seaford .... arr.	8 23	8 23	..	..	..	..	..	..	..	..	..	9 11	..	..	..
Lewes .... dep.	..	..	..	..	..	..	8 29	..	..	..	..	Stop	..	..	..
Glynde	..	..	..	..	..	..	8 34	..	..	..	..	..	..	..	..
Berwick	..	..	..	..	..	..	8 40	..	..	..	..	..	..	..	..
Polegate 239	..	..	..	..	..	..	8 47	..	..	..	..	..	..	..	p.m
Hampden Park F	..	..	8 45	..	..	..	8 50	..	..	..	..	..	..	..	9 15
Eastbourne .... arr.	..	..	8 49	..	..	..	8 54	..	..	..	..	..	..	..	9 19
Eastbourne .... dep.	..	..	Stop	..	..	..	8 57	..	..	..	..	..	..	..	Stop
Hampden Park F	..	..	..	..	..	..	9 0	..	..	..	..	..	..	..	..
Pevensey and Westham ...	..	..	..	..	..	..	9 7	..	..	..	..	..	..	..	..
Pevensey Bay Halt	..	..	..	..	..	..	9 9	..	..	..	..	..	..	..	..
Norman's Bay Halt	..	..	..	..	..	..	9 12	..	..	..	..	..	..	..	..
Cooden Beach	..	..	..	..	..	..	9 16	..	..	..	..	..	..	..	..
Collington Halt	..	..	..	..	..	..	9 19	..	..	..	..	..	..	..	..
Bexhill (Central) G	..	..	..	..	..	..	9 22	..	..	..	..	..	..	..	..
St. Leonards (W.M.)	..	..	..	..	..	..	9 26	..	..	..	..	..	..	..	..
" (W.S.)	..	..	..	..	..	..	9 29	..	..	..	..	..	..	..	..
Hastings 56, 59	..	..	..	..	..	..	9 32	..	..	..	..	..	..	..	..
Ore .... arr.	..	..	..	..	..	..	9 37	..	..	..	..	..	..	..	..
	17	18	19	20	21	22	23	24	25	26	27	28	29	30	31

Station	1	2	3	4	5	6	7	8	9	10	11	12	13	14	15	16	17	18	19	20	21	22	23	24	25	26	27	28	29	30	31
Three Bridges (*above*)..dep.	7 3	..	..	..	7 17	..	..	..	Saturdays excepted	Saturdays only	..	..	..		..		..	..	..	7 37	..	7 47		..	..	..	..	..	7 52	..	..
Crawley	7 7	..	..	..	7 21	..	..	..			..	..	..	Stop	..	Stop	..	..	..	7 41	..	7 51	Stop	..	..	..	..	..	7 55	..	..
Ifield	7 9	..	..	..	7 23	..	..	..			..	..	..	..	..	..	..	..	..	7 43	..	7 53	..	..	..	..	..	..	7 58	..	..
Fay Gate	7 14	..	..	..	7 28	..	..	Saturdays excepted			..	..	..	..	..	..	..	..	..	7 48	..	7 58	..	..	..	..	..	..	8 2	..	..
Littlehaven Halt	7 19	..	..	..	7 32	..	..				..	..	..	..	..	..	..	..	..	7 52	..	8 2	..	..	..	..	..	..	8 6	..	..
Horsham 244, 245 ..... arr.	7 23	..	..	..	7 34	..	..				..	..	..	..	..	..	..	..	..	7 55	..	8 5	..	..	..	..	..	..	8 9	..	..
Sutton .... dep.	Saturdays excepted	..	..	..	Saturdays excepted	Saturdays only	..				..	Saturdays excepted	..	..	..	..	..	..	..	..	..	..	..	..	..	..	7 39	..	Saturdays excepted.	..	..
Dorking North **H**		..	..	..			..				..		..	..	..	..	..	..	..	..	..	..	..	..	..	..	7 56	..		..	..
Horsham 244, 245 .... arr.		..	..	..			..				..		..	..	..	..	..	..	..	..	..	..	..	..	..	..	8 13	..		..	..
Horsham 244, 245 .... dep.		7 9	..	..			..				..		..	..	..	..	..	..	..	8 3	..	8 5	..	..	..	..	8 15	..		..	..
Christ's Hospital, West [Horsham		7 13	..	..			..				..		..	..	..	..	..	..	..	8 7	..	8 9	..	..	..	..	..	..		..	..
Billingshurst		7 20	..	..			..				..		..	..	..	..	..	..	..	8 15	..	8 16	..	..	..	..	8 25	..		..	..
Pulborough **J** 374		7 27	..	..			..				..		..	..	..	..	..	..	..	8 23	..	8 23	..	..	..	..	8 32	..		..	..
Amberley		7 34	..	..			..				..		..	..	..	..	..	..	..	8 30	..	8 30	..	..	..	..	..	..		..	..
Arundel		7 41	..	..			p.m	p.m	p.m	p.m	..		..	p.m.	p.m	p.m	..	..	p.m	8 36	..	8 36	p.m	..	..	..	8 43	p.m		..	p.m
Brighton .... dep.	..	Saturdays excepted	..	..		7 13	7 15	7 22	7 26	7 33	..	**P**	..	7 40	7 47	7 50	..	..	8 3	Saturdays excepted	..	Saturdays only	8 12	..	..	..	**R**	8 17		..	8 33
Holland Road Halt	..		..	..		..	..	..	7 28	7 35	..	..	..	7 42	..	..	..	..	8 5		..		..	..	..	..	..	..		**P**	8 35
Hove	..		..	..		7 16	7 19	7 25	7 30	7 37	..	7 42	..	7 44	7 50	7 53	..	..	8 7		..		8 16	..	..	..	..	8 20		8 33	8 37
Aldrington Halt	..		..	..		..	..	..	7 32	7 39	..	..	..	7 46	..	..	..	..	8 9		..		..	..	..	..	..	..		..	8 39
Portslade and West Hove	..		..	..		7 19	7 22	..	7 35	7 42	..	..	..	7 49	..	7 56	..	..	8 12		..		..	..	..	..	..	..		..	8 42
Fishersgate Halt	..		..	..		..	..	..	7 37	7 44	..	..	..	..	..	..	..	..	8 14		..		..	..	..	..	..	..	Stop	..	8 44
Southwick	..		..	..	..	..	..	..	7 40	7 47	..	..	..	7 51	..	7 59	..	..	8 17		..		..	..	..	..	..	..	..	..	8 47
Shoreham-by-Sea **K**	..		..	..	..	7 25	7 28	7 32	7 43	7 50	..	7 50	..	7 56	7 59	8 3	..	..	8 20		..		8 24	..	..	..	..	8 28	..	8 40	8 50
Lancing	..		..	..	..	..	..	..	7 47	7 55	..	..	..	8 0	..	8 8	..	..	8 23		..		..	..	..	..	..	..	..	..	8 54
Ham Bridge Halt **N**	..		..	..	..	..	..	..	7 50	7 58	..	..	..	..	..	..	..	..	8 28		..		..	..	..	..	..	..	..	..	8 57
Worthing Central	..		..	..	..	7 35	..	7 40	7 53	8 1	..	7 57	..	8 4	8 9	8 12	..	..	8 31		..		..	..	..	..	..	8 35	..	8 48	9 0
West Worthing **U**	..	..	..	..	..	7 37	..	..	7 53	8 3	..	8 0	..	8 6		8 14	..	..	8 33		..		..	..	..	..	..	8 37	..	8 51	9 2
Durrington-on-Sea	..	..	..	..	..	..	..	..	..	..	..	8 2	..		Saturdays excepted	8 16	..	..		..	..	..	..	..	..	..	..	..	..	8 53	..
Goring-by-Sea	..	..	..	..	..	7 41	..	..	..	..	..	8 5	..			8 19	..	..	Stop	..	..	..	..	..	..	..	..	8 41	..	8 56	..
Angmering **L**	..	..	..	p.m	..	7 45	..	..	..	..	..	8 9	..			8 23	..	..	..	..	..	..	..	..	..	..	..	8 45	p.m	9 0	..
Ford (Sussex) ...... dep.	..	..	..	7 53	..	..	..	..	..	..	..	..	..			..	..	..	..	..	..	..	..	..	..	..	..	..	9 2	..	..
Littlehampton .... arr.	..	7 48	..	7 57	..	..	..	..	..	..	..	8 19	..			8 33	..	..	..	8 43	..	8 43	..	..	..	..	..	..	9 7	9 10	..
Littlehampton .... dep.	..	7 54	..	..	..	7 46	..	..	..	..	..	..	..			Stop	..	..	..	8 46	..	8 46	..	..	..	..	..	8 46	..	..	..
Ford (Sussex)	..	7 58	..	..	..	7 52	..	7 52	..	..	..	..	..	Saturdays excepted		..	..	..	p.m	8a50	..	8a50	..	..	..	..	..	8 52	..	..	..
Barnham .... arr.	..	8 5	..	..	..	7 57	..	7 57	..	..	..	..	..		8 26	..	..	..	8d31	9 1	..	9 1	..	..	..	..	8 51	8 57	..	..	..
Bognor Regis ...... arr.	..	8 11	..	..	..	8 7	..	8 11	..	..	..	..	..		8 37	..	..	..	8 37	9 7	..	9 7	..	..	..	..	8 58	9 7	..	..	..
Bognor Regis ...... dep.	..	..	..	..	..	7 40	..	7 40	..	..	..	..	..		8 10	..	..	..	Saturdays excepted	..	..	..	..	..	..	..	..	8 45	..	..	..
Barnham .... dep.	..	..	..	..	..	7 57	..	7 57	..	..	..	..	..		8 26	p.m	..	..		..	..	..	..	..	..	..	..	8 57	..	..	..
Chichester **Z**	..	..	..	..	..	8 7	..	8 7	..	..	..	..	..		8 35	8 37	..	..		..	..	..	..	..	..	..	..	9 7	..	..	..
Fishbourne Halt	..	..	..	..	..	8 10	..	8 10	..	..	..	..	..	..	..	8 40	..	..		..	..	..	..	..	..	..	..	9 10	..	..	..
Bosham	..	..	..	..	..	8 13	..	8 13	..	..	..	..	..	..	..	8 43	..	..		..	..	..	..	..	..	..	..	9 13	..	..	..
Nutbourne Halt	..	..	..	..	..	8 16	..	8 16	..	..	..	..	..	..	..	8 46	..	..		..	..	..	..	..	..	..	..	9 16	..	..	..
Southbourne Halt	..	..	..	..	..	8 19	..	8 19	..	..	..	..	..	..	..	8 49	..	..		..	..	..	..	..	..	..	..	9 19	..	..	..
Emsworth	..	..	..	..	..	8 22	..	8 22	..	..	..	..	..	..	..	8 52	..	..		..	..	..	..	..	..	..	..	9 22	..	..	..
Warblington Halt	..	..	..	..	..	8 25	..	8 25	..	..	..	..	..	..	..	8 55	..	..		..	..	..	..	..	..	..	..	9 25	..	..	..
Havant **244, 366**	..	..	..	..	..	8 27	..	8 27	..	..	..	..	..	..	8 49	8 57	..	..		..	..	..	..	..	..	..	..	9 27	..	..	..
244 **Hayling Island** ....arr.	..	..	..	..	..	8 47	..	..	..	..	..	..	..	..	..	..	..	..		..	..	..	..	..	..	..	..	..	..	..	..
Bedhampton Halt	..	..	..	..	..	..	..	..	..	..	..	..	..	..	..	8 59	..	..		..	..	..	..	..	..	..	..	..	..	..	..
Hilsea Halt	..	..	..	..	..	..	..	..	..	..	..	..	..	..	..	..	..	..		..	..	..	..	..	..	..	..	..	..	..	..
Fratton 380	..	..	..	..	..	8 36	..	8 36	..	..	..	..	..	..	8 57	9 7	..	..		..	..	..	..	..	..	..	..	9 36	..	..	..
Portsmouth & Southsea arr	..	..	..	..	..	8 38	..	8 38	..	..	..	..	..	..	8 59	9 10	..	..		..	..	..	..	..	..	..	..	9 38	..	..	..
Portsmouth Harbour .. "	..	..	..	..	..	8 42	..	8 42	..	..	..	..	..	..	9 3	..	..	..		..	..	..	..	..	..	..	..	9 42	..	..	..
500 RYDE PIER (Boat) .. arr.	..	..	..	..	..	..	..	..	..	..	..	..	..	..	..	..	..	..	..	..	..	..	..	..	..	..	..	..	..	..	..
Page 359 SANDOWN .. "	..	..	..	..	..	..	..	..	..	..	..	..	..	..	..	..	..	..	..	..	..	..	..	..	..	..	..	..	..	..	..
Page 359 SHANKLIN .. "	..	..	..	..	..	..	..	..	..	..	..	..	..	..	..	..	..	..	..	..	..	..	..	..	..	..	..	..	..	..	..
Page 359 VENTNOR .. "	..	..	..	..	..	..	..	..	..	..	..	..	..	..	..	..	..	..	..	..	..	..	..	..	..	..	..	..	..	..	..
Page 359 NEWPORT .. "	..	..	..	..	..	..	..	..	..	..	..	..	..	..	..	..	..	..	..	..	..	..	..	..	..	..	..	..	..	..	..
Page 359 COWES .. "	..	..	..	..	..	..	..	..	..	..	..	..	..	..	..	..	..	..	..	..	..	..	..	..	..	..	..	..	..	..	..
Page 359 YARMOUTH .. "	..	..	..	..	..	..	..	..	..	..	..	..	..	..	..	..	..	..	..	..	..	..	..	..	..	..	..	..	..	..	..

3 Third class only. * Change at East Croydon. ‖ Arr. 6 mins. *earlier*. *a* Dep. 5 mins. later. *c* Arr. 3 mins. *earlier*. *d* Departure time.
P Pullman Car facilities available **R** Refreshment Car facilities available. Ụ Calls to take up only. *y* Arr. 2 mins. *earlier*.

For Other Notes, see page 195

For SERVICES from LONDON (Waterloo) to PORTSMOUTH and ISLE OF WIGHT, see pages 359 to 365

From LONDON to THE SOUTH COAST—Week Days—*continued*

Station	1	2	3	4	5	6	7	8	9	10	11	12	13	14	15
	p.m	p.m P	p.m	p.m	p.m P	p.m	p.m	p.m	p.m	p.m	p.m		p.m	p.m	p.m
VICTORIA .... dep	7 28	7 45	7 48	..	8 0	..	..	8*2	..	..	8 28	..	..	..	..
Clapham Junction .... "	7 34	..	7U53	..	..	..	..	..	..	..	8 34	..	..	..	..
LONDON BRIDGE .. dep	7*18	7V31	7V31	..	..	..	..	8 16	..	..	8*16	..	..	Saturdays only	Saturdays excepted
New Cross Gate .... "	..	..	..	..	..	..	..	..	..	..	..	..	..		
Norwood Junction B "	7*30	7B44	7B44	..	..	..	..	8 28	..	..	8*28	..	..		
East Croydon ...... dep	7 46	8 1	8 5	..	Saturdays excepted	..	..	8 34	..	..	8 46	..	..		
Purley	..	..	8 11	..		..	..	8 40	..	..	..	..	..		
Coulsdon South	..	..	8 14	..		..	..	8 43	..	..	..	..	..		
Merstham	..	..	8 20	..		..	..	8 49	..	..	..	..	..		
Redhill 246	8 1	..	8 27	..		..	..	8 57	..	..	9 1	..	..		
Earlswood	..	..	8 30	..		..	..	8 59	..	..	..	..	..		
Salfords	..	..	8 33	..		..	..	9 3	..	..	..	..	..		
Horley	..	..	8 37	..		..	..	9 7	..	..	..	..	..		
Gatwick Airport	8 10	..	8 40	..		..	..	9 10	..	..	9 9	..	..		
Three Bridges *(below)* 234	..	..	8y46	..		..	..	9 15	..	..	..	..	..		
Balcombe	..	..	8 52	..		..	..	9 22	..	..	..	..	..		
Horsted Keynes ..... dep	..	..	..	..	..	..	..	9 16	..	Saturdays only	..	..	9 16	9 32	9 45
Ardingly	..	..	..	..	..	..	..	9 20	..		..	..	9 20	9 38	9 51
Haywards Heath C 239	8y24	8 32	8 59	..	..	..	..	9 28	..		9 23	..	9 24	9 44	9 57
Wivelsfield *(below)*	..	..	9 3	..	..	..	..	9 33	..		..	..	..	Stop	Stop
Burgess Hill	..	..	9 6	..	..	..	..	9 35	..		..	..	..	..	..
Hassocks D	..	..	9 10	..	..	..	..	9 39	..		..	..	..	..	..
Preston Park	8 39	..	9 18	..	..	..	..	9 47	..		9 37	..	..	..	..
Brighton *(below)* ...... arr	8 42	..	9 21	..	9 0	..	..	9 51	..		9 41	..	..	..	..
Haywards Heath ... dep	Stop	8 33	..	..	..	..	..	Stop	..		Stop	..	9 35	..	..
Wivelsfield *(above)*	..	..	..	..	..	..	..	..	..		..	..	9 39	..	..
Plumpton	..	8 42	..	..	..	..	..	..	..		..	..	9 45	..	..
Cooksbridge	..	8 47	..	..	..	..	..	..	..		..	..	9 50	..	..
Lewes 239 .... arr	..	8 53	..	..	..	..	..	..	..		p.m	..	9 55	p.m	..
Brighton .... dep	..	..	..	..	..	8 46	..	..	9 14	9 26	9 30	..	..	9 46	..
London Road (Brighton)	..	..	..	..	..	8 48	..	..	9 16	9 28	..	..	..	9 48	..
Falmer	..	..	..	..	..	8 52	..	..	9 21	9 32	..	..	..	9 53	..
Lewes .... arr	..	..	..	..	..	9 0	..	..	9 28	9 40	9 46	..	..	10 0	p.m
Lewes .... dep	..	..	..	..	..	..	9 4	..	..	9 41	Stop	..	9 56	..	1018
Southease and Rodmell	..	..	..	..	..	..	9 9	..	..	9 46		..	10 1	..	1023
Newhaven Town ...[Halt	..	..	..	..	..	..	9 14	..	..	9 51	..	..	10 6	..	1028
" Harbour	..	..	..	..	..	..	9 15	..	..	9 52	..	..	10 7	..	1029
Bishopstone	..	..	..	..	..	..	9 19	..	..	9 57	..	..	1012	..	1034
Seaford .... arr	..	..	..	..	..	..	9 22	..	..	10 0	..	..	1015	..	1037
Lewes .... dep	..	8 54	..	..	..	9 1	Stop	..	9 29	Stop	..	..	Stop	10 1	Stop
Glynde	..	..	..	..	..	9 6		..	9 34		..	..		10 6	
Berwick	..	..	..	..	..	9 12	p.m	..	9 40	..	p.m	—	..	1012	..
Polegate 239	..	..	..	..	..	9 19	9 22	p.m	9 47	..	9 53	..	p.m	1019	p.m
Hampden Park F	..	..	..	..	..	9 22	9 26	9 45	9 50	..	9 58	..	1015	1022	1045
Eastbourne .... arr	..	9 13	..	..	..	9 26	9 31	9 49	9 54	..	10 3	..	1019	1026	1049
Eastbourne .... dep	..	9 17	..	..	..	9 29	Stop	Stop	9 57	..	Stop	..	..	Stop	..
Hampden Park F	..	..	..	..	..	9 32			10 0	..		..	..		..
Pevensey and Westham	..	..	..	..	..	9 39	..	..	10 7	..	..	..	..	..	..
Pevensey Bay Halt	..	..	..	..	..	9 41	..	..	10 9	..	..	..	..	..	..
Norman's Bay Halt	..	..	..	..	..	9 44	..	..	1012	..	..	..	..	..	..
Cooden Beach	..	9 30	..	..	..	9 48	..	..	1016	..	..	..	..	..	..
Collington Halt	..	..	..	..	..	9 51	..	..	1019	..	..	..	..	..	..
Bexhill (Central) G	..	9 34	..	..	..	9 54	..	..	1022	..	..	..	..	..	..
St. Leonards (W.M.)	..	..	..	..	..	9 58	..	..	1026	..	..	..	..	..	..
" (W.S.)	..	9 41	..	..	..	10 1	..	..	1029	..	..	..	..	..	..
Hastings 56, 59	..	9 44	..	..	..	10 3	..	..	1031	..	..	..	..	..	..
Ore .... arr	..	9 49	..	..	..	10 6	..	..	1034	..	..	..	..	..	..

Station	16	17	18	19	20	21	22	23	24	25	26	27	28	29	30
	p.m	p.m	p.m RB	p.m	p.m PX	p.m	p.m	p.m	p.m	p.m P	p.m P	p.m	p.m	p.m PR	p.m.
VICTORIA .... dep	8 48	..	9 18	..	9 28	..	9 48	..	..	10 25	10 25	10 28	1048	11 0	11 15
Clapham Junction .... "	8 53	..	..	..	9 34	..	9 53	..	..	..	..	10 34	1053	..	11 21
LONDON BRIDGE .. dep	8B31		8B53	9 16	9*16		9B31	..	1016	10*16	10*16	10*16	10B31		11B11
New Cross Gate .... "	..	..	..	..	..	..	..	..	..	..	..	..	..		..
Norwood Junction B "	8B44	..	..	9 28	9*28		9B44	..	1028	10*28	10*28	10*28	10B44		11B23
East Croydon ...... dep	9 5	..	Through Train Victoria to Bognor Regis	9 34	9 46	..	10 5	..	1034	10 42	10 42	10 46	11 5	..	11 33
Purley	9 11	..		9 40	..	—	1011	..	1040	..	..	..	1110	..	11 39
Coulsdon South	9 14	..		9 43	..	..	1014	..	1043	..	..	..	1114	..	11 42
Merstham	9 20	..		9 49	..	—	1020	..	1049	..	..	..	1120	..	11 48
Redhill 246	9 28	..		9 57	10 1	..	1027	..	1057	..	..	11 1	1129	..	11 56
Earlswood	9 31	..		9 59	..	..	1029	..	1059	..	..	..	1132	..	11 58
Salfords	9 34	..		10 3	..	..	1033	..	11 3	..	..	..	1135	..	12 2
Horley	9 38	..		10 7	..	..	1037	..	11 7	..	..	..	1139	..	12 6
Gatwick Airport	9 41	..		1010	..	..	1040	..	1110	..	..	..	1142	..	12 9
Three Bridges *(below)* 234	9y47	..		1014	1012		10y46	..	1115	..	..	11 12	1147	..	12 13
Balcombe	9 54	..		1021	..	..	1052	..	1121	..	..	..	1153	..	..
Horsted Keynes ..... dep	..	..		..	..	..	..	..	..	..	..	..	..	..	..
Ardingly	..	..		..	..	..	..	..	..	..	..	..	..	..	..
Haywards Heath C 239	10 9	..		1027	1023	..	11 0	..	1128	11 14	11 13	11y25	12 0	1146	..
Wivelsfield *(below)*	10 5	..		1032	..	..	11 4	..	1132	..	..	..	12 4	—	..
Burgess Hill	10 7	..		1034	..	..	11 7	..	1135	..	..	..	12 7	..	..
Hassocks D	10 11	..		1038	..	..	1111	..	1139	..	..	..	1211	..	..
Preston Park	10 19	..		1046	1038	..	1119	..	1147	..	..	11 39	1220	..	..
Brighton *(below)* ...... arr	10 23	..		1050	1041	..	1122	..	1150	..	..	11 42	1223	12 2	..
Haywards Heath ... dep	Stop	..	..	Stop	Stop	..	..	..	..	Through Train Victoria to Littlehampton	11 17	Stop	Stop	..	..
Wivelsfield *(above)*	..	..	..	..	..	..	..	..	..		..	..	..	..	..
Plumpton	..	..	..	..	..	..	..	..	..		..	..	..	..	..
Cooksbridge	..	..	..	..	..	..	..	..	..		..	..	..	..	..
Lewes 239 .... arr	p.m	..	..	..	..	..	..	..	..		11 33	..	p.m	..	..
Brighton .... dep	10 16	10 46	..	..	..	..	..	..	..		..	..	1117	..	..
London Road (Brighton)	10 18	10 48	..	..	..	..	..	..	..		..	..	1119	..	..
Falmer	10 23	10 52	..	..	..	..	..	..	..		..	..	1123	..	..
Lewes .... arr	10 30	11 1	..	..	..	..	..	..	..		..	..	1131	..	..
Lewes .... dep	..	11 1	..	..	..	..	..	..	..		..	..	1136	..	..
Southease and Rodmell	..	11 6	—	..	..	..	..	..	..		..	..	1141	..	..
Newhaven Town ...[Halt	..	11 11	..	..	..	..	..	..	..		..	..	1146	..	..
" Harbour	..	11 12	..	..	..	..	..	..	..		..	..	1147	..	..
Bishopstone	..	11 17	..	..	..	..	..	..	..		..	..	1152	..	..
Seaford .... arr	..	11 20	..	..	..	..	..	..	..		..	..	1155	..	..
Lewes .... dep	10 31	Stop	..	..	..	..	..	—	..		11 34	..	Stop	..	—
Glynde	10 36		..	..	..	..	..	..	..		..	..		..	..
Berwick	10 42	..	..	..	..	..	..	..	—		..	..	..	..	..
Polegate 239	10 49	..	..	..	..	..	..	..	..		11 49	..	..	..	..
Hampden Park F	10 52	..	..	..	..	..	..	..	..		11 52	..	..	..	..
Eastbourne .... arr	10 56	..	..	..	..	..	..	..	..		11 56	..	..	..	..
Eastbourne .... dep	10 59	..	..	..	..	..	..	..	..	..	12 0	..	..	..	..
Hampden Park F	11 2	..	..	..	..	..	..	..	..	..	12N3	..	..	..	..
Pevensey and Westham	11 9	..	..	..	..	..	..	..	..	..	..	..	..	..	..
Pevensey Bay Halt	11 11	..	..	..	..	..	..	..	..	..	..	..	..	..	..
Norman's Bay Halt	11 14	..	..	..	..	..	..	..	..	..	..	..	..	..	..
Cooden Beach	11 18	..	..	..	..	..	..	..	..	..	12 14	..	..	..	..
Collington Halt	11 21	..	..	..	..	..	..	..	..	..	..	..	..	..	..
Bexhill (Central) G	11 24	..	..	..	..	..	..	..	..	..	12 18	..	..	..	..
St. Leonards (W.M.)	11 28	..	..	..	..	..	..	..	..	..	..	..	..	..	..
" (W.S.)	11 31	..	..	..	..	..	..	..	..	..	12 25	..	..	..	..
Hastings 56, 59	11 33	..	..	..	..	..	..	..	..	..	12 27	..	..	..	..
Ore .... arr	11 36	p.m	..	..	..	..	..	..	..	..	12 32	..	..	..	..

Station	1	2	3	4	5	6	7	8	9	10	11	12	13	14	15	16	17	18	19	20	21	22	23	24	25	26	27	28	29	30
Three Bridges (*above*)..dep				8 47													9 50						1017							
Crawley		Stop		8 51												Stop	9 54						1021							
Ifield				8 53													9 56						1023							
Fay Gate				8 58													10 1						1028							
Littlehaven Halt				9 2													10 5						1032							
Horsham 244, 245.....arr.				9 5													10 8						1035							
Sutton.....dep.																		9 39												
Dorking North H																	Stop	9 56												
Horsham 244, 245... arr.																		1013												
Horsham 244, 245... dep.				9 5														1015												
Christ's Hospital, West Horsham				9 9																										
Billingshurst				9 16																										
Pulborough J 374				9 23														1032												
Amberley				9 31																										
Arundel	p.m	p.m		9 36			p.m	p.m						p.m		p.m	p.m	1043	p.m								p.m	a.m		
Brighton.....dep.	8 50	9 4					9 17	9 33						9 50		9 57	10 15	RB	1033		1050				P		11 34	12 5		
Holland Road Halt		9 6						9 35																						
Hove	8 53	9 8					9 20	9 37						9 53		10 1	10 18		1036		1053				11 32		11 37	12 8		
Aldrington Halt	8 55	9 10						9 39						9 55			10 20		1038		1055						11 39			
Portslade and West Hove	8 58	9 13						9 42						9 58		10 5	10 23		1041		1058						11 42	1211		
Fishersgate Halt		9 15						9 44									10 25										11 44			
Southwick	9 1	9 18						9 47						10 1		10 8	10 27		1045		11 2						11 47	1214		
Shoreham-by-Sea K	9 4	9 21					9 27	9 50						10 4		10 12	10 31		1049		11 6				11 39		11 50	1218		
Lancing	9 8	9 25						9 54						10 8		Stop	10 35		1053		1110						11 54	1222		
Ham Bridge Halt N		9 28						9 57									10 38		1056		1113						11 57			
Worthing Central	9 12	9 31					9 35	10 0						1012			10 40		1058		1115				11 47		12 0	1226		
West Worthing U	9 14	9 33					9 37	10 2						1014			10 43		11 1		1117				11 50		12 2	1228		
Durrington-on-Sea	9 16													1016							1119				11 52		12 4			
Goring-by-Sea	9 19						9 41							1019							1122				11 55		12 6			
Angmering L	9 23						9 45			p.m	p.m			1023						p.m	1126				11 59		12 11			
Ford (Sussex).....dep.										10 2	1012									1053										
Littlehampton ... arr.	9 33			9 43			10 7			10 7	1017			1033				1057		1057	1136				12 9		12 20			
Littlehampton ... dep.	Stop			9 46			9 46							1037				1037									12 23			
Ford (Sussex)				9a51			9 52							1041		p.m		1048									12 27			
Barnham.....arr.				10 1			9 57							1046		10d48		1053									12 32			
Bognor Regis..... arr.				10 7			10 7							1054		10 54		11 7									12 39			
Bognor Regis..... dep.							9 45							1030				1030												
Barnham.....dep.	p.m						9 57							11 0				1053												
Chichester Z	9 37						10 7							1110				11 5												
Fishbourne Halt	9 40						1010							1113																
Bosham	9 43						1013							1117																
Nutbourne Halt	9 46						1016							1120																
Southbourne Halt	9 49						1019							1123																
Emsworth	9 52						1022							1127																
Warblington Halt	9 55						1025							1130																
Havant 244, 366	9 57						1027							1134				1118												
244 Hayling Island.....arr.																														
Bedhampton Halt	9 59						1029							1136																
Hilsea Halt																														
Fratton 380	10 7						1038							1145				1126												
Portsmouth & Southsea arr	1010						1040							1148				1132												
Portsmouth Harbour ... "																														
500 Ryde Pier (Boat)..arr.																														
Sandown (Page 359) "																														
Shanklin "																														
Ventnor "																														
Newport "																														
Cowes "																														
Yarmouth "																														

3 Third class only. * Change at East Croydon. *a* Dep 5 mins. later. *d* Departure time. **N** Calls only to set down passengers. **P** Pullman Car facilities available. **PR** Pullman Car facilities available on Saturdays and Refreshment Car Mons. to Fris.. **PX** Pullman Car facilities available Mons. to Fris.,

RB Refreshment Car facilities available between London and Bognor Regis. **U** Calls to take up only. **V** Third class only. Dep. 7 42 p.m on Saturdays
y Arr 2 mins. *earlier*.

For Other Notes, see page 195

For SERVICES from LONDON (Waterloo) to PORTSMOUTH and ISLE OF WIGHT, see pages 359 to 365

From LONDON to THE SOUTH COAST—Sundays

Station	a.m	a.m	a.m	a.m	a.m	a.m	a.m	a.m	a.m	a.m	a.m	a.m	a.m	a.m	a.m	a.m	a.m	a.m	a.m	a.m	a.m	a.m	a.m	a.m	a.m	a.m	a.m		a.m	a.m	a.m	a.m
																										P			RB			
VICTORIA ... dep.	..	4 45	..	..	..	..	..	..	..	6 40	..	..	..	..	..	7 46	..	..	..	..	..	8 28	..	..	..	9 0	..	..	9 18	..	..	..
Clapham Junction ... "	..	..	..	..	..	..	..	..	..	6 46	..	..	..	..	..	7 51	..	..	..	..	..	8 33	..	..	..	..	..	..	..	..	..	..
LONDON BRIDGE .. dep.	..	(3)	..	..	..	..	..	..	..	..	..	..	..	7 16	7 40	7*40	..	..	..	..	8 16	8*16	..	..	8 49	..	..	..	8 55 (3)	..	..	..
New Cross Gate ... "	..		..	..	..	..	..	..	..	..	..	..	..	7 21	7 45	7*45	..	..	..	..	8 21	8*21	..	..	..	..	..	..	..	..	..	..
Norwood Junction B "	..		..	..	..	..	..	..	..	..	..	..	..	7 30	7 54	7*54	..	..	..	..	8 30	8*30	..	..	9 1	..	..	..	..	..	..	..
East Croydon ... dep.	..	5 5	..	..	..	..	..	..	..	7 3	..	..	..	7 35	8 6	8 5	..	..	..	..	8 35	8 46	..	..	9 6	..	..	..	Through Train, Victoria to Bognor Regis	..	..	..
Purley	..	..	..	..	..	..	..	..	..	7 9	..	..	..	7 40	..	8 10	..	..	..	..	8 40	..	..	..	9 11	..	..	..		..	..	..
Coulsdon South	..	..	..	..	..	..	..	..	..	7 12	..	..	..	7 44	..	8 14	..	..	..	..	8 44	..	..	..	9 15	..	..	..		..	..	..
Merstham	..	..	..	..	..	..	..	..	..	7 18	..	..	..	7 50	..	8 20	..	..	..	..	8 50	..	..	..	9 21	..	..	..		..	..	..
Redhill 246	..	5N25	..	..	..	..	..	..	..	7 24	..	..	..	7 55	8 15	8 25	..	..	..	..	8 57	9 1	..	..	9 27	..	..	..		..	..	..
Earlswood	..	..	..	..	..	..	..	..	..	7 26	..	..	..	7 58	..	8 28	..	..	..	..	8 59	..	..	..	9 29	..	..	..		..	..	..
Salfords	..	..	..	..	..	..	..	..	..	7 30	..	..	..	8 1	..	8 31	..	..	..	..	9 3	..	..	..	9 33	..	..	..		..	..	..
Horley	..	5N35	..	..	..	..	..	..	..	7 34	..	..	..	8 5	8 23	8 35	..	..	..	..	9 7	..	..	..	9 37	..	..	..		..	..	..
Gatwick Airport	..	..	..	..	..	..	..	..	..	7 37	..	..	..	8 9	..	8 39	..	..	..	..	9 10	9 10	..	..	9 40	..	..	..		..	..	..
Three Bridges (below) 234	..	5N46	..	..	..	..	..	..	..	7 41	..	..	..	8 14	8 30	8 44	..	..	..	..	9 15	9 13	..	..	9y46	..	..	..		..	..	..
Balcombe	..	..	..	..	..	..	..	..	..	7 48	..	..	..	8 20	..	8 50	..	..	..	..	9 22	..	..	..	9 53	..	..	..		..	..	..
Horsted Keynes ... dep.	..	..	..	..	..	..	..	..	..	..	..	..	..	..	..	..	..	..	..	..	..	..	..	..	..	..	..	..		..	..	..
Ardingly	..	..	..	..	..	..	..	..	..	..	..	..	..	..	..	..	..	..	..	..	..	..	..	..	..	..	..	..		..	..	..
Haywards Heath C 239	..	6N0	..	..	..	..	..	..	..	7 55	..	..	..	8 27	8 41	8 57	..	..	..	..	9 28	9 25	..	..	9 59	..	..	..		..	..	..
Wivelsfield (below)	..	..	..	..	..	..	..	..	..	8 0	..	..	..	8 32	..	9 2	..	..	..	..	9 33	..	..	..	10 3	..	..	..		..	..	..
Burgess Hill	..	..	..	..	..	..	..	..	..	8 2	..	..	..	8 34	..	9 4	..	..	..	..	9 36	..	..	..	10 6	..	..	..		..	..	..
Hassocks D	..	..	..	..	..	..	..	..	..	8 6	..	..	..	8 38	..	9 8	..	..	..	..	9 40	..	..	..	1010	..	..	..		..	..	..
Preston Park	..	6N25	..	..	..	..	..	..	..	8 15	..	..	..	8 47	..	9 17	..	..	..	..	9 48	9 39	..	..	1018	..	..	..	..	..	..	..
Brighton (below) ... arr	..	6 29	..	..	..	..	..	..	..	8 18	..	..	..	8 50	..	9 20	..	..	..	..	9 52	9 42	..	..	1021	10 0	..	..	..	..	..	..
Haywards Heath .. dep.	..	..	..	..	..	..	..	..	..	Stop	..	..	..	Stop	8 42	Stop	..	..	..	..	Stop	Stop	..	..	Stop	Stop	..	..	..	..	..	..
Wivelsfield (above)	..	..	..	..	..	..	..	..	..	..	..	..	..	..	..	..	..	..	..	..	..	..	..	..	..	..	..	..	..	..	..	..
Plumpton	..	..	..	..	..	..	..	..	..	..	..	..	..	..	8 51	..	..	..	..	..	..	..	..	..	..	..	..	..	..	..	..	..
Cooksbridge	..	..	..	..	..	..	..	..	..	..	..	..	..	..	8 56	..	..	..	..	..	..	..	..	..	..	..	..	..	..	..	..	..
Lewes 239 ... arr.	..	..	..	..	..	..	..	..	..	..	..	..	..	a.m	9 2	..	..	..	..	..	..	..	..	..	a.m	a.m	..	..	..	..	..	..
Brighton ... dep.	..	6 37	..	..	..	..	..	7 14	..	..	..	8 14	8 32	8 44	..	..	..	..	..	9 14	..	..	..	..	9 46	9 50	..	..	..	..	1014	..
London Road (Brighton)	..	..	..	..	..	..	..	7 16	..	..	..	8 16	8 35	8 46	..	..	..	..	..	9 16	..	..	..	..	9 48	..	..	..	..	..	1016	..
Falmer	..	..	..	..	..	..	..	7 20	..	..	..	8 20	..	8 50	..	..	..	..	..	9 20	..	..	..	..	9 53	..	..	..	..	..	1020	..
Lewes ... arr.	..	6 53	..	..	..	..	..	7 28	..	..	..	8 28	8 50	8 53	..	..	..	..	..	9 28	..	..	..	..	10 0	10 6	..	..	..	..	1028	..
Lewes ... dep.	..	7 0	..	..	..	..	..	..	..	..	..	..	Stop	9 5	9 5	..	..	..	..	..	..	..	..	..	10 4	Stop	..	..	..	..	..	..
Southease and Rodmell	..	..	..	..	..	..	..	..	..	..	..	..	..	9 10	9 10	..	..	..	..	..	..	..	..	..	10 9	..	..	..	..	..	..	..
Newhaven Town ... [Halt	..	7 10	..	..	..	..	..	..	..	..	..	..	..	9 15	9 15	..	..	..	..	..	..	..	..	..	1014	..	..	..	..	..	..	..
" Harbour	..	..	..	..	..	..	..	..	..	..	..	..	..	9 16	9 16	..	..	..	..	..	..	..	..	..	1015	..	..	..	..	..	..	..
Bishopstone	..	..	..	..	..	..	..	..	..	..	..	..	..	9 21	9 21	..	..	..	..	..	..	..	..	..	1020	..	..	..	..	..	..	..
Seaford ... arr.	..	7 18	..	..	..	..	..	..	..	..	..	..	..	9 23	9 23	..	..	..	..	..	..	..	..	..	1022	..	..	..	..	..	..	..
Lewes ... dep.	..	6 56	..	..	..	..	..	7 29	..	..	..	8 29	..	Stop	9 3	..	..	..	..	9 29	..	..	..	..	10 1	..	..	..	..	..	1029	..
Glynde	..	..	..	..	..	..	..	7 34	..	..	..	8 34	..	..	..	..	..	..	..	9 34	..	..	..	..	10 6	..	..	..	..	..	1034	..
Berwick	..	..	..	..	..	..	..	7 40	..	..	..	8 40	..	a.m	..	..	..	..	..	9 40	..	..	..	..	1012	a.m	..	..	..	..	1040	..
Polegate 239	..	7 14	..	..	..	..	..	7 47	..	..	..	8 47	a.m	9 14	9 18	..	..	..	..	9 47	..	..	..	..	1019	1021	..	..	..	..	1047	..
Hampden Park F	7 15	7 19	..	..	..	..	7 47	7 50	..	..	8 45	8 50	9 15	9 18	9 23	..	..	..	..	9 50	..	..	..	1015	1022	1026	..	..	..	1045	1050	..
Eastbourne ... arr.	7 19	7 24	..	..	..	..	7 51	7 54	..	..	8 49	8 54	9 19	9 23	9 26	..	..	..	..	9 54	..	..	..	1019	1026	1031	..	..	..	1049	1054	..
Eastbourne ... dep.	Stop	Stop	..	..	..	..	Stop	7 59	..	..	Stop	8 57	Stop	Stop	9 29	..	..	..	..	9 57	..	..	..	Stop	1029	Stop	..	..	..	..	1057	..
Hampden Park F	..	..	..	..	..	..	..	8 2	..	..	..	9 0	..	..	9 32	..	..	..	..	10 0	..	..	..	..	1032	..	..	..	..	..	11 0	..
Pevensey and Westham	..	..	..	..	..	..	..	8 9	..	..	..	9 7	..	..	9 38	..	..	..	..	10 7	..	..	..	..	1039	..	..	..	..	..	11 7	..
Pevensey Bay Halt	..	..	..	..	..	..	..	8 11	..	..	..	9 9	..	..	..	..	..	..	..	10 9	..	..	..	..	1041	..	..	..	..	..	11 9	..
Norman's Bay Halt	..	..	..	..	..	..	..	8 14	..	..	..	9 12	..	..	..	..	..	..	..	1012	..	..	..	..	1044	..	..	..	..	..	1112	..
Cooden Beach	..	..	..	..	..	..	..	8 18	..	..	..	9 16	..	..	9 44	..	..	..	..	1016	..	..	..	..	1048	..	..	..	..	..	1116	..
Collington Halt	..	..	..	..	..	..	..	8 21	..	..	..	9 19	..	..	..	..	..	..	..	1019	..	..	..	..	1051	..	..	..	..	..	1119	..
Bexhill (Central) G	..	..	..	..	..	..	..	8 24	..	..	..	9 22	..	..	9 49	..	..	..	..	1022	..	..	..	..	1054	..	..	..	..	..	1122	..
St. Leonards (W.M.)	..	..	..	..	..	..	..	8 28	..	..	..	9 26	..	..	9 53	..	..	..	..	1026	..	..	..	..	1058	..	..	..	..	..	1126	..
" (W.S.)	..	..	..	..	..	..	..	8 31	..	..	..	9 29	..	..	9 56	..	..	..	..	1029	..	..	..	..	11 1	..	..	..	..	..	1129	..
Hastings 58, 59	..	..	..	..	..	..	..	8 33	..	..	..	9 31	..	..	10 0	..	..	..	..	1031	..	..	..	..	11 3	..	..	..	..	..	1131	..
Ore ... arr.	..	..	..	..	..	..	..	8 37	..	..	a.m	9 34	..	..	10 4	..	..	..	..	1035	..	..	..	..	11 6	..	..	..	..	..	1134	..
	1	2	3	4	5	6	7	8	9	10	11	12	13	14	15	16	17	18	19	20	21	22	23	24	25	26	27	28	29	30	31	32

	1	2	3	4	5	6	7	8	9	10	11	12	13	14	15	16	17	18	19	20	21	22	23	24	25	26	27	28	29	30	31	32
Three Bridges (*above*)..dep.	..	..	..	..	..	..	..	..	..	..	7 47	..	..	..	..	..	8 47	..	..	..	..	..	..	..	..	..	9 47	..	..	..	..	..
Crawley	..	..	..	..	..	..	..	Stop	..	..	7 51	Stop	..	..	Stop	..	8 51	..	..	..	..	..	..	..	Stop	..	9 51	..	..	..	Stop	..
Ifield	..	..	..	..	..	..	..	..	..	..	7 53	..	..	..	..	..	8 53	..	..	..	..	..	..	..	..	..	9 53	..	..	..	..	..
Fay Gate	..	..	..	..	..	..	..	..	..	..	7 58	..	..	..	..	..	8 58	..	..	..	..	..	..	..	..	..	9 58	..	..	..	..	..
Littlehaven Halt	..	..	..	..	..	..	..	..	..	..	8 2	..	..	..	..	..	9 2	..	..	..	..	..	..	..	..	..	10 2	..	..	..	..	..
Horsham 244, 245 ....arr.	..	..	..	..	..	..	..	..	..	..	8 5	..	..	..	..	..	9 5	..	..	..	..	..	..	..	..	..	10 5	..	..	..	..	..
Sutton ....dep.	..	..	..	..	..	..	..	..	..	..	..	..	..	..	..	..	..	..	..	..	..	..	..	..	..	..	..	..	9 39	..	..	..
Dorking North **H**	..	..	..	..	..	..	..	..	..	..	..	..	..	..	..	..	..	..	..	..	..	..	..	..	..	..	..	..	9 56	..	..	..
Horsham 244, 245 .. arr.	..	..	..	..	..	..	..	..	..	..	..	..	..	..	..	..	..	..	..	..	..	..	..	..	..	..	..	..	1013	..	..	..
Horsham 244, 245 .. dep.	..	..	..	..	..	..	..	..	..	..	8 5	..	..	..	..	..	9 5	..	..	..	..	..	..	..	..	..	10 5	..	1015	..	..	..
Christ's Hospital, West Horsham	..	..	..	..	..	..	..	..	..	..	8 9	..	..	..	..	..	9 9	..	..	..	..	..	..	..	..	..	10 9	..	..	..	..	..
Billingshurst	..	..	..	..	..	..	..	..	..	..	8 16	..	..	..	..	..	9 16	..	..	..	..	..	..	..	..	..	1016	..	..	..	..	..
Pulborough **J** 374	..	..	..	..	..	..	..	..	..	..	8 23	..	..	..	..	..	9 23	..	..	..	..	..	..	..	..	..	1023	..	1030	..	..	..
Amberley	..	..	..	..	..	..	..	..	..	..	8 30	..	..	..	..	..	9 30	..	..	..	..	..	..	..	..	..	1030	..	..	..	..	..
Arundel	..	..	..	..	..	..	a.m	a.m	..	a.m	8 36	a.m	a.m	a.m	a.m	a.m	9 36	..	..	..	a.m	a.m	..	a.m	..	a.m	1036	..	1041	..	a.m	..
Brighton ....dep.	..	..	6 40	6 50	7 3	7 17	7 20	7 23	7 35	7 50	..	8 3	8 17	8 20	8 33	8 50	..	9 3	9 17	..	9 20	9 33	9 47	9 50	..	10 3	..	..	RB	..	10 7	1017
Holland Road Halt	..	..	..	..	..	..	..	..	..	..	..	8 5	..	..	8 35	..	..	9 5	..	..	..	9 35	..	..	..	10 5	..	..	..	..	..	..
Hove	..	..	6 44	6 53	7 6	7 20	7 23	7 28	7 38	7 53	..	8 7	8 20	8 23	8 37	8 53	..	9 7	9 20	..	9 23	9 37	9 50	9 53	..	10 7	..	..	..	..	1012	1020
Aldrington Halt	..	..	..	6 55	7 8	..	7 25	..	7 40	7 55	..	8 9	..	..	8 39	8 55	..	9 9	..	..	..	9 39	..	9 55	..	10 9	..	..	..	..	..	..
Portslade and West Hove	..	..	6 48	6 58	7 11	..	7 28	7 32	7 43	7 58	..	8 12	..	8 27	8 42	8 58	..	9 12	..	..	9 27	9 42	..	9 58	..	1012	..	..	..	..	1016	..
Fishersgate Halt	..	..	..	..	7 13	..	..	..	7 45	..	..	8 14	..	..	8 44	..	..	9 14	..	..	..	9 44	..	..	..	1014	..	..	..	..	..	..
Southwick	..	..	6 52	7 1	7 15	..	7 31	7 36	7 47	8 1	..	8 17	..	8 30	8 47	9 1	..	9 17	..	..	9 30	9 47	..	10 1	..	1017	..	..	..	..	1020	..
Shoreham-by-Sea **K**	..	..	6 57	7 4	7 19	7 27	7 35	7 40	7 51	8 4	..	8 20	8 27	8 33	8 50	9 4	..	9 20	9 27	..	9 33	9 50	9 57	10 4	..	1020	..	..	..	..	1024	1028
Lancing	..	..	7 2	7 8	7 23	..	7 39	..	7 55	8 8	..	8 24	..	8 37	8 55	9 8	..	9 25	..	..	9 37	9 55	..	10 8	..	1025	..	..	..	..	..	..
Ham Bridge Halt **N**	..	..	..	..	7 26	..	..	Stop	7 58	..	..	8 27	..	..	8 58	..	..	9 28	..	..	..	9 58	..	..	..	1028	..	..	..	..	..	..
Worthing Central	..	..	7 7	7 12	7 28	7 35	7 43	..	8 0	8 12	..	8 30	8 35	8 41	9 1	9 12	..	9 31	9 35	..	9 41	10 1	10 6	1012	..	1031	..	..	..	..	..	1035
West Worthing **U**	..	..	7 9	7 14	7 31	7 37	7 45	..	8 3	8 14	..	8 32	8 37	8 44	9 3	9 14	..	9 33	9 37	..	9 44	10 3	..	1014	..	1033	..	..	..	..	..	1037
Durrington-on-Sea	..	..	..	7 16	..	..	..	..	..	8 16	..	..	..	..	..	9 16	..	..	..	..	..	..	..	1016	..	..	..	..	..	..	..	..
Goring-by-Sea	..	..	Stop	7 19	Stop	7 41	Stop	..	..	8 19	..	Stop	8 41	Stop	Stop	9 19	..	Stop	9 41	..	..	..	..	1019	..	..	..	..	..	..	..	1041
Angmering **L**	a.m	a.m	..	7 23	a.m	7 45	..	a.m	..	8 23	..	a.m	8 45	..	a.m	9 23	..	a.m	9 45	..	..	..	..	1023	..	..	..	..	..	..	..	1045
Ford (Sussex)....dep.	6 56	7 0	..	..	7 41	..	..	7 52	..	..	..	8 41	..	..	9 2	..	..	9 52	..	..	..	..	..	..	..	..	..	..	..	..	..	..
Littlehampton .... arr.	7 0	7 4	..	7 33	7 45	..	a.m	7 57	..	8 33	8 43	8 46	9 7	..	9 7	9 33	9 43	9 57	..	..	..	..	..	1033	..	..	1043	..	11 7	..	..	11 7
Littlehampton .... dep.	..	..	..	7 36	..	7 36	7 54	..	..	..	8 46	..	8 46	..	..	..	9 46	..	9 46	..	..	..	..	..	..	..	1046	..	..	..	..	1046
Ford (Sussex)	..	..	a.m	7 40	..	7 52	7 59	..	..	..	8a50	..	8 52	..	..	..	9a50	..	9 52	..	..	..	..	..	a.m	..	10a50	..	1047	..	..	1053
Barnham ....arr.	..	..	7d6	7 47	..	7 57	8 6	..	..	..	9 1	..	8 57	..	..	..	10 1	..	9 57	..	..	..	1022	..	10d36	..	11 2	..	1052	..	..	1058
Bognor Regis .... arr.	..	..	7 12	7 53	..	8 12	8 12	..	..	..	9 7	..	9 7	..	..	..	10 7	..	10 7	..	..	..	1042	..	1042	..	11 8	..	11 2	..	..	11 8
Bognor Regis .... dep.	..	..	..	..	..	7 40	..	..	..	..	..	..	8 45	..	..	..	..	..	9 40	..	..	..	1010	..	..	..	..	..	1045	..	..	1045
Barnham ....dep.	..	..	..	..	..	7 57	..	..	..	..	..	..	8 57	..	..	..	..	..	9 57	..	..	..	1022	..	..	..	..	..	1054	..	..	1059
Chichester **Z**	..	..	..	..	..	8 7	..	..	..	..	..	..	9 7	..	..	..	..	..	10 7	..	..	..	1032	..	..	..	..	..	11 4	..	..	11 8
Fishbourne Halt	..	..	..	..	..	8 10	..	..	..	..	..	..	9 10	..	..	..	..	..	1010	..	..	..	..	..	..	..	..	..	..	..	..	1111
Bosham	..	..	..	..	..	8 13	..	..	..	..	..	..	9 13	..	..	..	..	..	1013	..	..	..	..	..	..	..	..	..	..	..	..	1114
Nutbourne Halt	..	..	..	..	..	8 16	..	..	..	..	..	..	9 16	..	..	..	..	..	1016	..	..	..	..	..	..	..	..	..	..	..	..	1117
Southbourne Halt	..	..	..	..	..	8 19	..	..	..	..	..	..	9 19	..	..	..	..	..	1019	..	..	..	..	..	..	..	..	..	..	..	..	1120
Emsworth	..	..	..	..	..	8 22	..	..	..	..	..	..	9 22	..	..	..	..	..	1022	..	..	..	..	..	..	..	..	..	1113	..	..	1123
Warblington Halt	..	..	..	..	..	8 25	..	..	..	..	..	..	9 25	..	..	..	..	..	1025	..	..	..	..	..	..	..	..	..	..	..	..	1126
Havant 244, 366	..	..	..	..	..	8 27	..	..	..	..	..	..	9 27	..	..	..	..	..	1027	..	..	..	1045	..	..	..	..	..	1119	..	..	1128
244 **Hayling Island** ....arr.	..	..	..	..	..	..	..	..	..	..	..	..	..	..	..	..	..	..	..	..	..	..	..	..	..	..	..	..	..	..	..	..
Bedhampton Halt	..	..	..	..	..	..	..	..	..	..	..	..	..	..	..	..	..	..	..	..	..	..	..	..	..	..	..	..	..	..	..	..
Hilsea Halt	..	..	..	..	..	..	..	..	..	..	..	..	..	..	..	..	..	..	..	..	..	..	..	..	..	..	..	..	..	..	..	..
Fratton 380	..	..	..	..	..	8 37	..	..	..	..	..	..	9 36	..	..	..	..	..	1036	..	..	..	1054	..	..	..	..	..	1127	..	..	1137
Portsmouth & Southsea arr	..	..	..	..	..	8 40	..	..	..	..	..	..	9 38	a.m	..	..	..	..	1038	..	..	..	1056	..	..	..	..	..	1132	..	..	1139
Portsmouth Harbour .. "	..	..	..	..	..	8 44	..	..	..	..	..	..	9 42	10d35	..	..	..	..	1042	..	..	..	11 0	..	..	..	..	..	1136	..	..	1143
500 Ryde Pier (Boat)..arr.	..	..	..	..	..	..	..	..	..	..	..	..	..	11 5	..	..	..	..	..	..	..	..	..	..	..	..	..	..	..	..	..	..
Page 359 Sandown "	..	..	..	..	..	..	..	..	..	..	..	..	..	1148	..	..	..	..	..	..	..	..	..	..	..	..	..	..	..	..	..	..
Page 359 Shanklin "	..	..	..	..	..	..	..	..	..	..	..	..	..	1155	..	..	..	..	..	..	..	..	..	..	..	..	..	..	..	..	..	..
Page 359 Ventnor "	..	..	..	..	..	..	..	..	..	..	..	..	..	1211	..	..	..	..	..	..	..	..	..	..	..	..	..	..	..	..	..	..
Page 359 Newport "	..	..	..	..	..	..	..	..	..	..	..	..	..	12 6	..	..	..	..	..	..	..	..	..	..	..	..	..	..	..	..	..	..
Page 359 Cowes "	..	..	..	..	..	..	..	..	..	..	..	..	..	1220	..	..	..	..	..	..	..	..	..	..	..	..	..	..	..	..	..	..
Page 359 Yarmouth "	..	..	..	..	..	..	..	..	..	..	..	..	..	1246	..	..	..	..	..	..	..	..	..	..	..	..	..	..	..	..	..	..

B Third class only * Change at East Croydon *a* Dep. 5 mins. later *d* Departure time **N** Calls only to set down passengers
P Pullman Car facilities available **RB** Refreshment Car facilities available between London and Bognor Regis *y* Arr. 2 mins. earlier

For Other Notes, see page 195

For SERVICES from LONDON (Waterloo) to PORTSMOUTH and ISLE OF WIGHT, see pages 359 to 365

From LONDON to THE SOUTH COAST—Sundays—*continued*

	1	2	3	4	5	6	7	8	9	10	11	12	13	14
	a.m	a.m	a.m P	a.m	a.m P	a.m	a.m	a.m	a.m P		a.m RB	a.m	a.m	a.m P
VICTORIA ......dep.	..	..	9 25	9 28	9 45	..	..	9 48	10 0	..	10 18	..	10*18	10 25
Clapham Junction ..... "	..	..	..	9 33	..	..	..	9 53	..	..	..	..	..	..
LONDON BRIDGE...dep.	..	9 16	9*16	9*16	9Ⓑ30	..	..	9Ⓑ30		..	10Ⓑ 0		10 16	10*16
New Cross Gate..... "	..	9 21	9*21	9*21	9Ⓑ35	..	..	9Ⓑ35		..	10Ⓑ 5		10 21	10*21
Norwood Junction B "	..	9 30	9*30	9*30	9Ⓑ44	..	..	9Ⓑ44		..	10Ⓑ14		10 30	10*30
East Croydon ......dep.	..	9 35	9 42	9 46	10 1	..	..	10 5		..	10 34	..	10 36	10 42
Purley	..	9 40	..	..	..	..	..	1011	..	..	..	..	10 41	..
Coulsdon South	..	9 44	..	..	..	..	..	1014	..	..	..	..	10 45	..
Merstham	..	9 50	..	..	..	..	..	1020	..	..	..	..	10 51	..
Redhill 246	..	9 57	..	10 1	..	..	..	1027	..	..	10 50	..	10 57	..
Earlswood	..	9 59	..	..	..	..	..	1029	..	..	..	..	10 59	..
Salfords	..	10 3	..	..	..	..	..	1033	..	..	..	..	11 3	..
Horley	..	10 7	..	..	..	..	..	1037	..	..	..	..	11 7	..
Gatwick Airport	..	1010	..	10 9	..	..	..	1040	..	..	..	..	11 10	..
Three Bridges (*below*) 234	..	1015	..	..	..	..	..	1043	..	..	11 1	..	11 14	..
Balcombe	..	1022	..	..	..	..	..	1050	..	..	..	..	11 21	..
Horsted Keynes ......dep.	1016	..	..	..	..	1010	..	..	..	..	..	..	..	..
Ardingly	1020	..	..	..	..	1020	..	..	..	..	..	..	..	..
Haywards Heath C 239	1024	1029	1014	1022	10 35	1024	..	1056	..	..	Through Train, Victoria to Bognor Regis	..	11 28	11 14
Wivelsfield (*below*)	..	1033	..	..	..	..	..	11 0	..	..		..	11 32	..
Burgess Hill	..	1036	..	..	..	..	..	11 3	..	..		..	11 35	..
Hassocks D	..	1040	..	..	..	..	..	11 7	..	..		..	11 39	..
Preston Park	..	1048	..	1037	..	..	..	1115	..	..		..	11 47	..
Brighton (*below*) ......arr.	..	1051	..	1040	..	..	..	1118	11 0	..		..	11 50	..
Haywards Heath ...dep.	..	Stop	..	Stop	10 36	1039	..	Stop	Stop	..		..	Stop	..
Wivelsfield (*above*)	..	..	..	..	..	1043	..	..	..	..		..	..	..
Plumpton	..	..	..	..	..	1049	..	..	..	..		..	..	..
Cooksbridge	..	..	..	..	..	1054	..	..	..	..		..	..	..
Lewes 239 ......arr.	..	..	..	..	10 53	1059	..	..	..	..		..	a.m	..
Brighton ......dep.	..	..	Through Train Victoria to Littlehampton	..	..	..	1046	..	..	..		..	11 14	Through Train Victoria to Littlehampton
London Road (Brighton)	..	..		..	..	..	1048	..	..	..		..	11 16	
Falmer	..	..		..	..	..	1053	..	..	..		..	11 20	
Lewes ......arr.	..	..		..	..	..	11 0	..	..	..		..	11 28	
Lewes ......dep.	..	..		..	..	11 4	11 4	..	..	..	..	..	..	
Southease and Rodmell	..	..		..	..	11 9	11 9	..	..	..	..	..	..	
Newhaven Town ...[Halt	..	..		..	..	1114	1114	..	..	..	..	..	..	
" Harbour	..	..		..	..	1115	1115	..	..	..	..	..	..	
Bishopstone	..	..		..	..	1120	1120	..	..	..	..	..	..	
Seaford ......arr.	..	..		..	..	1122	1122	..	..	..	..	..	..	
Lewes ......dep.	..	..		..	10 54	Stop	11 1	..	..	..	..	..	11 29	
Glynde	..	..		..	..		11 6	..	..	..	..	..	11 34	
Berwick	..	..		..	..	..	1112	a.m	..	..	..	..	11 40	
Polegate 239	..	..		..	..	a.m	1119	1138	..	..	..	..	11 47	
Hampden Park F	..	..		..	..	1115	1122	..	..	..	..	1145	11 50	
Eastbourne ......arr.	..	..		..	11 13	1119	1126	1146	..	..	..	1149	11 54	
Eastbourne ......dep.	..	..		..	11 17	Stop	1129	Stop	..	..	..	Stop	11 57	
Hampden Park F	..	..		..	..		1132		..	..	..		12 0	
Pevensey and Westham	..	..		..	..	..	1139	..	..	..	..	..	12 7	
Pevensey Bay Halt	..	..		..	..	..	1141	..	..	..	..	..	12 9	
Norman's Bay Halt	..	..		..	..	..	1144	..	..	..	..	..	12 12	
Cooden Beach	..	..		..	11 30	..	1148	..	..	..	..	..	12 16	
Collington Halt	..	..		..	..	..	1151	..	..	..	..	..	12 19	
Bexhill (Central) G	..	..		..	11 35	..	1154	..	..	..	..	..	12 22	
St. Leonards (W.M.)	..	..		..	..	..	1158	..	..	..	..	..	12 26	
" (W.S.)	..	..		..	11 42	..	12 1	..	..	..	..	..	12 29	
Hastings 56, 59	..	..		..	11 44	..	12 3	..	..	..	..	..	12 31	
Ore ......arr.	..	..		..	11 48	..	12 6	..	a.m	..	..	..	12 34	

	15	16	17	18	19	20	21	22	23	24	25	26	27	28
	a.m	a.m P	a.m	a.m	p.m	p.m	p.m	a.m P	a.m	p.m	p.m	a.m	p.m	noon P
VICTORIA ......dep.	10 28	10 45	10 48	11 0	..	..	..	11 25	11 28	..	..	11 48	..	12 0
Clapham Junction ..... "	10 33	..	10 53	..	..	..	..	..	11 33	..	..	11 53	..	..
LONDON BRIDGE...dep.	10*16	10Ⓑ30	10Ⓑ30	Brighton Belle 1st and 3rd class Pullman Cars only	..	..	..	11Ⓑ 0	11Ⓑ 0	..	..	11Ⓑ30	..	..
New Cross Gate..... "	10*21	10Ⓑ35	10Ⓑ35		..	..	..	11Ⓑ 5	11Ⓑ 5	..	..	11Ⓑ35	..	..
Norwood Junction B "	10*30	10Ⓑ44	10Ⓑ44		..	..	..	11Ⓑ14	11Ⓑ14	..	..	11Ⓑ44	..	..
East Croydon ......dep.	10 46	11 1	11 5		..	..	..	11 42	11 46	..	..	12 5	..	..
Purley	..	..	11 11		..	..	..	..	..	..	..	12 11	..	..
Coulsdon South	..	..	11 14		..	..	..	..	..	..	..	12 14	..	..
Merstham	..	..	11 20		..	..	..	..	..	..	..	12 20	..	..
Redhill 246	11 1	..	11 27		..	..	..	..	12 1	..	..	12 27	..	..
Earlswood	..	..	11 29		..	..	..	..	..	..	..	12 29	..	..
Salfords	..	..	11 33		..	..	..	..	..	..	..	12 33	..	..
Horley	..	..	11 37		..	..	..	..	..	..	..	12 37	..	..
Gatwick Airport	11 9	..	11 40		..	..	..	..	12 9	..	..	12 40	..	..
Three Bridges (*below*) 234	..	..	11 45		..	..	..	..	..	..	..	12 45	..	..
Balcombe	..	..	11 51		..	..	..	..	..	..	..	12 51	..	..
Horsted Keynes ......dep.	..	..	..		..	..	..	..	..	1216	..	..	..	..
Ardingly	..	..	..		..	..	..	..	..	1220	..	..	..	..
Haywards Heath C 239	11 22	11 32	11 58		..	..	..	12 14	12 22	1224	..	12 58	..	..
Wivelsfield (*below*)	..	..	12 3		..	..	..	..	..	..	..	1 3	..	..
Burgess Hill	..	..	12 5		..	..	..	..	..	..	..	1 5	..	..
Hassocks D	..	..	12 9		..	..	..	..	..	..	..	1 9	..	..
Preston Park	11 37	..	12 18		..	..	..	..	12 37	..	..	1 18	..	..
Brighton (*below*) ......arr.	11 40	..	12 21	12 0	..	..	..	..	12 40	..	..	1 21	..	1 0
Haywards Heath ...dep.	Stop	11 33	Stop	Stop	..	..	..	Through Train, Victoria to Littlehampton.	Stop	1235	..	Stop	..	Stop
Wivelsfield (*above*)	..	..	..	..	..	..	..		..	1239	..	..	..	..
Plumpton	..	11 42	..	..	..	..	..		..	1245	..	..	..	..
Cooksbridge	..	11 47	..	..	..	..	..		..	1250	..	..	..	..
Lewes 239 ......arr.	..	11 53	..	..	..	..	..		..	1255	..	..	..	..
Brighton ......dep.	..	..	..	..	..	1214	..		..	Stop	1246	..	..	..
London Road (Brighton)	..	..	..	..	..	1216	..		..		1248	..	..	..
Falmer	..	..	..	..	..	1220	..		..	..	1253	..	..	..
Lewes ......arr.	..	..	..	..	..	1228	..		..	..	1 0	..	..	p.m
Lewes ......dep.	..	12 4	..	..	..	..	..		..	..	..	..	..	1 4
Southease and Rodmell	..	12 9	..	..	..	..	..		..	..	..	..	..	1 9
Newhaven Town ...[Halt	..	12 14	..	..	..	..	..		..	..	..	..	..	1 14
" Harbour	..	12 15	..	..	..	..	..		..	..	..	..	..	1 15
Bishopstone	..	12 20	..	..	..	..	..		..	..	..	..	..	1 20
Seaford ......arr.	..	12 22	..	..	..	..	..		..	..	..	..	..	1 22
Lewes ......dep.	..	11 54	..	..	..	1229	..	..	..	..	1 0	..	..	Stop
Glynde	..	..	..	..	..	1234	..	..	..	..	1 6	..	..	
Berwick	..	..	..	..	..	1240	..	..	..	..	1 12	..	..	..
Polegate 239	..	..	p.m	..	..	1247	..	..	p.m	..	1 19	..	..	p.m
Hampden Park F	..	..	12 15	..	1245	1250	..	..	1 15	..	1 22	..	..	1 45
Eastbourne ......arr.	..	12 13	12 19	..	1249	1254	..	..	1 19	..	1 26	..	..	1 49
Eastbourne ......dep.	..	12 17	Stop	..	Stop	1257	..	..	Stop	..	1 29	..	..	Stop
Hampden Park F	..	..		..		1 0	..	..		..	1 32	..	..	
Pevensey and Westham	..	..	..	..	..	1 7	..	..	..	..	1 39	..	..	..
Pevensey Bay Halt	..	..	..	..	..	1 9	..	..	..	..	1 41	..	..	..
Norman's Bay Halt	..	..	..	..	..	1 12	..	..	..	..	1 44	..	..	..
Cooden Beach	..	12 30	..	..	..	1 16	..	..	..	..	1 48	..	..	..
Collington Halt	..	..	..	..	..	1 19	..	..	..	..	1 51	..	..	..
Bexhill (Central) G	..	12 35	..	..	..	1 23	..	..	..	..	1 54	..	..	..
St. Leonards (W.M.)	..	..	..	..	..	1 28	..	..	..	..	1 58	..	..	..
" (W.S.)	..	12 42	..	..	..	1 31	..	..	..	..	2 1	..	..	..
Hastings 56, 59	..	12 44	..	..	..	1 33	..	..	..	..	2 3	..	..	..
Ore ......arr.	..	12 48	..	a.m	..	1 36	..	..	..	..	2 6	..	..	..

Station	1	2	3	4	5	6	7	8	9	10	11	12	13	14	15	16	17	18	19	20	21	22	23	24	25	26	27	28
Three Bridges *(above)*..dep.	..	..	..	..	—	..	—	..	10 47	..	11 1	..	—	..	..	..	..	11 47	..	—	..	..	..	..	..	..	1247	..
Crawley	..	..	..	..	Stop	..	Stop	..	10 51	..	..	..	Stop	..	..	..	..	11 51	..	Stop	..	..	..	..	..	..	1251	..
Ifield	..	..	..	..	..	..	..	..	10 53	..	..	..	..	..	..	..	..	11 53	..	..	..	..	..	..	..	..	1253	..
Fay Gate	..	..	..	..	..	..	..	..	10 58	..	..	..	..	..	..	..	..	11 58	..	..	..	..	..	..	..	..	1258	..
Littlehaven Halt	..	..	..	..	..	..	..	..	11 2	..	..	..	..	..	..	..	..	12 2	..	..	..	..	..	..	..	..	1 2	..
Horsham 244, 245 ......arr.	..	..	..	..	..	..	..	..	11 5	..	11 13	..	..	..	..	..	..	12 5	..	..	..	..	..	..	..	..	1 5	..
Sutton ....dep.	..	..	..	..	..	..	..	..	..	..	..	..	..	..	..	..	..	..	..	..	..	..	..	..	..	..	..	..
Dorking North **H**	..	..	..	..	..	..	..	..	..	..	..	..	..	..	..	..	..	..	..	..	..	..	..	..	..	..	..	..
Horsham 244, 245 arr.	..	..	..	..	..	..	..	..	..	..	..	..	..	..	..	..	..	..	..	..	..	..	..	..	..	..	..	..
Horsham 244, 245 dep.	..	..	..	..	..	..	..	..	11 5	..	11 15	..	..	..	..	..	..	12 5	..	..	..	..	..	..	..	..	1 5	..
Christ's Hospital, West Horsham	..	..	..	..	..	..	..	..	11 9	..	..	..	..	..	..	..	..	12 9	..	..	..	..	..	..	..	..	1 9	..
Billingshurst	..	..	..	..	..	..	..	..	11 16	..	..	..	..	..	..	..	..	12 16	..	..	..	..	..	..	..	..	1 16	..
Pulborough **J** 374	..	..	..	..	..	..	..	..	11 23	..	11 30	..	..	..	..	..	..	12 23	..	..	..	..	..	..	..	..	1 23	..
Amberley	..	..	..	..	..	..	..	..	11 31	..	..	..	..	..	..	..	..	12 31	..	..	..	..	..	..	..	..	1 31	..
Arundel	..	a.m	..	a.m	a.m	..	a.m	a.m	11 36	..	11 41	a.m	a.m	..	a.m	..	a.m	12 36	p.m	p.m	..	..	p.m	p.m	..	p.m	1 36	p.m
Brighton ....dep.	..	1020	**P**	1033	10 47	..	1056	11 3	..	..	**RB**	1117	11 20	**P**	11 33	..	11 50	..	12 3	1215	1221	**P**	12 33	1250	..	1 3	..	1 15
Holland Road Halt	..	..	..	1035	..	..	..	11 5	..	..	..	..	..	..	11 35	..	..	..	12 5	..	..	..	12 35	..	..	1 5	..	..
Hove	..	1023	1033	1037	10 50	..	1053	11 7	..	..	..	1120	11 23	11 33	11 37	..	11 53	..	12 7	1218	1224	12 33	12 37	1253	..	1 7	..	1 18
Aldrington Halt	..	..	..	1039	..	..	1055	11 9	..	..	..	..	..	..	11 39	..	..	..	12 9	..	..	..	12 39	1255	..	1 9	..	..
Portslade and West Hove	..	1026	..	1042	..	..	1058	1112	..	..	..	..	11 26	..	11 42	..	11 56	..	1212	..	1227	..	12 42	1258	..	1 12	..	..
Fishersgate Halt	..	..	..	1044	..	..	..	1114	..	..	..	..	..	..	11 44	..	..	..	1214	..	..	..	12 44	..	..	1 14	..	..
Southwick	..	1029	..	1047	..	..	11 1	1117	..	..	..	..	11 29	..	11 47	..	11 59	..	1217	..	1230	..	12 47	1 1	..	1 17	..	..
Shoreham-by-Sea **K**	..	1033	1040	1050	10 57	..	11 4	1120	..	..	..	1127	11 33	11 40	11 50	..	12 3	..	1220	1226	1234	12 46	12 50	1 4	..	1 20	..	1 27
Lancing	..	1037	..	1055	..	..	11 8	1125	..	..	..	..	11 38	..	11 55	..	12 7	..	1225	..	1238	..	12 55	1 8	..	1 25	..	..
Ham Bridge Halt **N**	..	..	..	1058	..	..	..	1128	..	..	..	..	..	..	11 58	..	..	..	1228	..	..	..	12 58	..	..	1 28	..	..
Worthing Central	..	1041	1049	11 1	11 6	..	1112	1131	..	..	..	1135	11 42	11 49	12 1	..	12 11	..	1231	1234	1242	12 49	1 1	1 12	..	1 31	..	1 35
West Worthing **U**	..	1043	1051	11 3	..	..	1114	1133	..	..	..	1137	11 44	11 51	12 3	..	12 13	..	1233	1236	1244	12 52	1 3	1 14	..	1 33	..	1 37
Durrington-on-Sea	..	..	1053	—	..	..	1116	..	..	..	..	..	—	11 53	..	..	12 15	..	..	..	—	12 54	—	1 16	..	..	..	..
Goring-by-Sea	..	..	1056	Stop	..	..	1119	..	..	..	..	1140	Stop	11 56	..	..	12 17	..	..	1240	Stop	12 58	Stop	1 19	..	..	..	1 41
Angmering **L**	..	..	11 0	a.m	..	..	1123	..	..	..	..	1145	p.m	12 0	..	..	12 22	..	..	1244	p.m	1 3	..	1 23	..	..	..	1 45
Ford (Sussex) ......dep.	..	..	..	11 2	..	..	..	..	..	..	..	..	12 2	..	..	..	..	..	..	..	1 2	..	..	..	..	..	..	..
Littlehampton arr.	..	..	1110	11 7	..	..	1133	..	11 43	..	12 7	12 7	12 7	12 10	..	..	12 32	12 43	..	1 7	1 7	1 12	..	1 33	..	..	1 43	2 7
Littlehampton dep.	..	..	..	..	..	..	—	..	11 46	..	..	1146	..	..	..	..	..	12 46	..	1246	..	..	..	..	..	..	1 46	1 46
Ford (Sussex)	..	..	..	..	..	a.m	Stop	..	11a50	..	11 47	1153	..	..	..	..	..	12a50	..	1252	..	..	..	..	..	..	1a50	1 52
Barnham ....arr.	..	..	..	..	11 22	11d36	..	..	12 2	..	11 52	1157	..	..	..	..	..	1 2	..	1257	..	..	..	..	..	..	2 1	1 57
Bognor Regis arr.	..	..	..	..	11 42	1142	..	..	12 8	..	12 2	12 8	..	..	..	..	..	1 8	..	1 8	..	..	..	..	..	..	2 7	2 7
Bognor Regis dep.	..	..	..	..	11 10	..	..	..	..	..	11 45	1145	..	..	..	..	..	..	..	1245	..	..	..	..	..	..	..	1 45
Barnham ....dep.	..	..	..	..	11 22	..	..	..	..	..	11 54	1159	..	..	..	..	..	..	..	1259	..	..	..	..	..	..	..	1 57
Chichester **Z**	..	..	..	..	11 32	..	..	..	..	..	12 4	12 8	..	..	..	..	..	..	..	1 8	..	..	..	..	..	..	..	2 7
Fishbourne Halt	..	..	..	..	..	..	..	..	..	..	..	1211	..	..	..	..	..	..	..	1 11	..	..	..	..	..	..	..	2 10
Bosham	..	..	..	..	..	..	..	..	..	..	..	1214	..	..	..	..	..	..	..	1 14	..	..	..	..	..	..	..	2 13
Nutbourne Halt	..	..	..	..	..	..	..	..	..	..	..	1217	..	..	..	..	..	..	..	1 17	..	..	..	..	..	..	..	2 16
Southbourne Halt	..	..	..	..	..	..	..	..	..	..	..	1220	..	..	..	..	..	..	..	1 20	..	..	..	..	..	..	..	2 19
Emsworth	..	..	..	..	..	..	..	..	..	..	..	1223	..	..	..	..	..	..	..	1 23	..	..	..	..	..	..	..	2 22
Warblington Halt	..	..	..	..	..	..	..	..	..	..	..	1226	..	..	..	..	..	..	..	1 26	..	..	..	..	..	..	..	2 25
Havant 244, 366	..	..	..	..	11 45	..	..	..	..	..	12 19	1228	..	..	..	..	..	..	..	1 28	..	..	..	..	..	..	..	2 27
244 Hayling Island .....arr.	..	..	..	..	..	..	..	..	..	..	..	..	..	..	..	..	..	..	..	..	..	..	..	..	..	..	..	..
Bedhampton Halt	..	..	..	..	..	..	..	..	..	..	..	..	..	..	..	..	..	..	..	..	..	..	..	..	..	..	..	..
Hilsea Halt	..	..	..	..	..	..	..	..	..	..	..	..	..	..	..	..	..	..	..	..	..	..	..	..	..	..	..	..
Fratten 380	..	..	..	..	11 54	..	..	..	..	..	12 30	1237	..	..	..	..	..	..	..	1 37	..	..	..	..	..	..	..	2 36
Portsmouth & Southsea arr	..	..	..	..	11 56	..	p.m	..	..	..	12 32	1239	..	..	..	..	..	..	..	1 39	..	..	p.m	..	..	..	..	2 38
Portsmouth Harbour "	..	..	..	..	12 0	..	12d35	..	..	..	12 36	1243	..	..	..	..	..	..	..	1 43	..	..	2d35	..	..	..	..	2 42
500 Ryde Pier (Boat)..arr.	..	..	..	..	..	..	1 5	..	..	..	..	..	..	..	..	..	..	..	..	..	..	..	3 5	..	..	..	..	..
Page 359 Sandown "	..	..	..	..	..	..	1 48	..	..	..	..	..	..	..	..	..	..	..	..	..	..	..	3 48	..	..	..	..	..
Page 359 Shanklin "	..	..	..	..	..	..	1 55	..	..	..	..	..	..	..	..	..	..	..	..	..	..	..	3 55	..	..	..	..	..
Page 359 Ventnor "	..	..	..	..	..	..	2 11	..	..	..	..	..	..	..	..	..	..	..	..	..	..	..	4 11	..	..	..	..	..
Page 359 Newport "	..	..	..	..	..	..	2 6	..	..	..	..	..	..	..	..	..	..	..	..	..	..	..	4 6	..	..	..	..	..
Page 359 Cowes "	..	..	..	..	..	..	2 30	..	..	..	..	..	..	..	..	..	..	..	..	..	..	..	4 20	..	..	..	..	..
Page 359 Yarmouth "	..	..	..	..	..	..	2 50	..	..	..	..	..	..	..	..	..	..	..	..	..	..	..	4 41	..	..	..	..	..

3 Third class only. * Change at East Croydon. *a* Dep. 5 mins. later. *d* Departure time. **P** Pullman Car facilities available.

RB Refreshment Car facilities available between London and Bognor Regis

For Other Notes, see page 195

For SERVICES from LONDON (Waterloo) to PORTSMOUTH and ISLE OF WIGHT, see pages 359 to 365

From LONDON to THE SOUTH COAST—Sundays—*continued*

Station	1	2	3	4	5	6	7	8	9	10	11	12	13	14	15
	p.m	p.m	p.m	p.m	p.m	p.m	p.m	p.m	p.m	p.m	p.m	p.m	p.m	p.m	p.m
VICTORIA ... dep.	..	..	12 28	12 48	..	..	..	..	..	1 28	..	..	1 48	..	..
Clapham Junction ... "	..	..	12 33	12 53	..	..	..	..	..	1 33	..	..	1 53	..	..
LONDON BRIDGE ... dep.	..		12B 0	12B30	..	..	..	..	..	1B 0	..	..	1B30	..	..
New Cross Gate ... "	..		12B 5	12B35	..	..	..	..	..	1B 5	..	..	1B35	..	..
Norwood Junction **B** "	..		12B14	12B44	..	..	..	..	..	1B14	..	..	1B44	..	..
East Croydon ... dep.	..	..	12 46	1 5	..	..	..	..	..	1 46	..	..	2 5	..	..
Purley ...	..	..	..	1 11	..	..	..	..	..	..	..	..	2 11	..	..
Coulsdon South ...	..	..	..	1 14	..	..	..	..	..	..	..	..	2 14	..	..
Merstham ...	..	..	..	1 20	..	..	..	..	..	..	..	..	2 20	..	..
Redhill 246 ...	..	..	1 1	1 27	..	..	..	..	..	2 1	..	..	2 27	..	..
Earlswood ...	..	..	..	1 29	..	..	..	..	..	..	..	..	2 29	..	..
Salfords ...	..	..	..	1 33	..	..	..	..	..	..	..	..	2 33	..	..
Horley ...	..	..	..	1 37	..	..	..	..	..	..	..	..	2 37	..	..
Gatwick Airport ...	..	..	1 9	1 40	..	..	..	..	..	..	..	..	2 40	..	..
Three Bridges *(below)* 234	..	..	..	1 45	..	..	..	..	..	..	..	..	2 45	..	..
Balcombe ...	..	..	..	1 51	..	..	..	..	..	..	..	..	2 51	..	..
Horsted Keynes ... dep.	..	..	..	..	..	..	..	..	..	..	..	2 16	..	..	..
Ardingly ...	..	..	..	..	..	..	..	..	..	..	..	2 20	..	..	..
Haywards Heath **C** 239 ...	..	..	1 22	1 58	..	..	..	..	..	2 22	..	2 24	2 58	..	..
Wivelsfield *(below)* ...	..	..	..	2 3	..	..	..	..	..	..	..	..	3 3	..	..
Burgess Hill ...	..	..	..	2 5	..	..	..	..	..	..	..	..	3 5	..	..
Hassocks **D** ...	..	..	..	2 9	..	..	..	..	..	..	..	..	3 9	..	..
Preston Park ...	..	..	1 37	2 18	..	..	..	..	..	2 37	..	..	3 18	..	..
Brighton *(below)* ... arr.	..	..	1 40	2 21	..	..	..	..	..	2 40	..	..	3 21	..	..
Haywards Heath ... dep.	..	..	Stop	Stop	..	..	..	..	..	Stop	..	2 35	Stop	..	..
Wivelsfield *(above)* ...	..	..			..	..	..	..	..		..	2 39		..	..
Plumpton ...	..	..	..	..	..	..	..	..	..	..	..	2 45	..	..	..
Cooksbridge ...	..	..	..	..	..	..	..	..	..	..	..	2 50	..	..	..
Lewes 239 ... arr.	..	..	..	..	..	..	..	..	..	p.m	..	2 55	p.m	..	..
Brighton ... dep.	..	1 14	..	..	..	..	1 46	..	..	2 14	..	Stop	2 46	..	..
London Road (Brighton) ...	..	1 16	..	..	..	..	1 48	..	..	2 16	..		2 48	..	..
Falmer ...	..	1 20	..	..	..	..	1 53	..	..	2 20	..	..	2 52	..	..
Lewes ... arr.	..	1 28	..	..	..	..	2 0	..	..	2 28	..	..	3 0	..	..
Lewes ... dep.	..	..	..	..	..	..	..	2 4	..	..	..	..	..	..	3 4
Southease and Rodmell	..	..	..	..	..	..	..	2 9	..	..	..	..	..	..	3 9
Newhaven Town ... [Halt	..	..	..	..	..	..	..	2 14	..	..	..	..	..	..	3 14
" Harbour ...	..	..	..	..	..	..	..	2 15	..	..	..	..	..	..	3 15
Bishopstone ...	..	..	..	..	..	..	..	2 20	..	..	..	..	..	..	3 20
Seaford ... arr.	..	..	..	..	..	..	..	2 22	..	..	..	..	..	..	3 22
Lewes ... dep.	..	1 29	..	..	..	..	2 1	Stop	..	2 29	..	..	3 1	..	Stop
Glynde ...	..	1 34	..	..	..	..	2 6		..	2 34	..	..	3 6	..	
Berwick ...	..	1 40	p.m	..	..	..	2 12	..	..	2 40	..	..	3 12	..	..
Polegate 239 ...	..	1 47	2 5	p.m	..	..	2 19	..	..	2 47	..	..	3 19	..	p.m
Hampden Park **F** ...	..	1 50	2 10	2 15	..	..	2 22	..	2 45	2 50	3 15	..	3 22	..	3 45
Eastbourne ... arr.	..	1 54	2 15	2 19	..	..	2 26	..	2 49	2 54	3 19	..	3 26	..	3 49
Eastbourne ... dep.	..	1 57	Stop	Stop	..	..	2 29	..	Stop	2 57	Stop	..	3 29	..	Stop
Hampden Park **F** ...	..	2 0			..	..	2 32	..		3 0		..	3 32	..	
Pevensey and Westham ...	..	2 7	..	..	..	..	2 39	..	..	3 7	..	..	3 39	..	..
Pevensey Bay Halt ...	..	2 9	..	..	..	..	2 41	..	..	3 9	..	..	3 41	..	..
Norman's Bay Halt ...	..	2 12	..	..	..	..	2 44	..	..	3 12	..	..	3 44	..	..
Cooden Beach ...	..	2 16	..	..	..	..	2 48	..	..	3 16	..	..	3 48	..	..
Collington Halt ...	..	2 19	..	..	..	..	2 51	..	..	3 19	..	..	3 51	..	..
Bexhill (Central) **G** ...	..	2 22	..	..	..	..	2 54	..	..	3 22	..	..	3 54	..	..
St. Leonards (W.M.) ...	..	2 26	..	..	..	..	2 58	..	..	3 26	..	..	3 58	..	..
" (W.S.) ...	..	2 29	..	..	..	..	3 1	..	..	3 29	..	..	4 1	..	..
Hastings 56, 59 ...	..	2 31	..	..	..	..	3 3	..	..	3 31	..	..	4 3	..	..
Ore ... arr.	..	2 34	..	..	..	..	3 6	..	..	3 34	..	..	4 6	..	..

Station	16	17	18	19	20	21	22	23	24	25	26	27	28	29
	p.m	p.m	p.m	p.m	p.m	p.m	p.m RB	p.m	p.m	p.m	p.m P	p.m	p.m	p.m
VICTORIA ... dep.	..	..	2 28	2 48	..	..	3 18	..	3 28	..	3 45	..	3 48	..
Clapham Junction ... "	..	..	2 33	2 53	..	..	..	..	3 33	..	..	..	3 53	..
LONDON BRIDGE ... dep.	..	..	2B 0	2B30	..	..	2B55	..	3B 0	..	3B30	..	3B30	..
New Cross Gate ... "	..	..	2B 5	2B35	..	..	..	..	3B 5	..	3B35	..	3B35	..
Norwood Junction **B** "	..	..	2B14	2B44	..	..	..	..	3B14	..	3B44	..	3B44	..
East Croydon ... dep.	..	..	2 46	3 5	..	..	Through Train, Victoria to Bognor Regis	..	3 46	..	4 1	..	4 5	..
Purley ...	..	..	..	3 11	..	..		..	..	..	..	..	4 11	..
Coulsdon South ...	..	..	..	3 14	..	..		..	..	..	..	..	4 14	..
Merstham ...	..	..	..	3 20	..	..		..	..	..	..	..	4 20	..
Redhill 246 ...	..	..	3 1	3 27	..	..		..	4 1	..	..	..	4 27	..
Earlswood ...	..	..	..	3 29	..	..		..	..	..	..	..	4 29	..
Salfords ...	..	..	..	3 33	..	..		..	..	..	..	..	4 33	..
Horley ...	..	..	..	3 37	..	..		..	..	..	..	..	4 37	..
Gatwick Airport ...	..	..	3 9	3 40	..	..		..	4 9	..	..	..	4 40	..
Three Bridges *(below)* 234	..	..	..	3 45	..	..		..	..	..	..	..	4 45	..
Balcombe ...	..	..	..	3 51	..	..		..	..	..	..	..	4 51	..
Horsted Keynes ... dep.	..	..	..	..	..	..		..	..	4 16	..	4 16	..	..
Ardingly ...	..	..	..	..	..	..		..	..	4 20	..	4 20	..	..
Haywards Heath **C** 239 ...	..	..	3 22	3 58	..	..		..	4 22	4 24	4 32	4 24	4 58	..
Wivelsfield *(below)* ...	..	..	..	4 3	..	..		..	..	Stop	..	..	5 3	..
Burgess Hill ...	..	..	..	4 5	..	..		..	..		..	..	5 5	..
Hassocks **D** ...	..	..	..	4 9	..	..		..	..	..	..	..	5 9	..
Preston Park ...	..	..	3 37	4 18	..	..		..	4 37	..	..	..	5 18	..
Brighton *(below)* ... arr.	..	..	3 40	4 21	..	..		..	4 40	..	..	..	5 21	..
Haywards Heath ... dep.	..	..	Stop	Stop	..	..	..	..	Stop	..	4 33	4 35	Stop	..
Wivelsfield *(above)* ...	..	..			..	..	..	..		..	..	4 39		..
Plumpton ...	..	..	..	..	..	..	..	..	..	..	..	4 45	..	..
Cooksbridge ...	..	..	..	..	..	..	..	..	..	..	..	4 50	..	..
Lewes 239 ... arr.	..	..	..	p.m	..	..	..	..	p.m	..	4 48	4 55	p.m	..
Brighton ... dep.	3 14	3 31	..	3 45	..	..	..	4 14	4 31	..	..	Stop	4 46	..
London Road (Brighton) ...	3 16	3 33	..	3 47	..	..	..	4 16	4 33	..	..		4 48	..
Falmer ...	3 20	3 37	..	3 52	..	..	..	4 20	4 37	..	..	..	4 53	..
Lewes ... arr.	3 28	3 45	..	3 59	..	..	..	4 28	4 45	..	..	..	5 0	..
Lewes ... dep.	..	3 46	..	..	4 4	..	..	..	4 46	..	..	..	..	..
Southease and Rodmell	..	3 51	..	..	4 9	..	..	..	4 51	..	..	..	..	..
Newhaven Town ... [Halt	..	3 56	..	..	4 14	..	..	..	4 56	..	..	..	..	..
" Harbour ...	..	3 57	..	..	4 15	..	..	..	4 57	..	..	..	..	..
Bishopstone ...	..	4 2	..	..	4 20	..	..	..	5 2	..	..	..	..	..
Seaford ... arr.	..	4 5	..	..	4 22	..	..	..	5 5	..	..	..	..	..
Lewes ... dep.	3 29	Stop	..	3 59	Stop	..	..	4 29	..	..	4 50	..	5 1	..
Glynde ...	3 34		..	4 4		..	..	4 34	..	..	..	..	5 6	..
Berwick ...	3 40	..	..	4 11	..	..	..	4 40	..	..	..	..	5 12	..
Polegate 239 ...	3 47	p.m	..	4 17	p.m	..	..	4 47	..	..	..	p.m	5 19	..
Hampden Park **F** ...	3 50	4 15	..	4 20	4 45	..	..	4 50	..	..	..	5 15	5 22	..
Eastbourne ... arr.	3 54	4 19	..	4 24	4 49	..	..	4 54	..	..	5 9	5 19	5 26	..
Eastbourne ... dep.	3 57	Stop	..	4 29	Stop	..	..	4 57	..	..	5 13	Stop	5 29	..
Hampden Park **F** ...	4 0		..	4 32		..	..	5 0	..	..	..		5 32	..
Pevensey and Westham ...	4 7	..	..	4 39	..	..	..	5 7	..	..	..	..	5 39	..
Pevensey Bay Halt ...	4 9	..	..	4 41	..	..	..	5 9	..	..	..	..	5 41	..
Norman's Bay Halt ...	4 12	..	..	4 44	..	..	..	5 12	..	..	..	..	5 44	..
Cooden Beach ...	4 16	..	..	4 48	..	..	..	5 16	..	..	5 26	..	5 48	..
Collington Halt ...	4 19	..	..	4 51	..	..	..	5 19	..	..	..	..	5 51	..
Bexhill (Central) **G** ...	4 22	..	..	4 54	..	..	..	5 22	..	..	5 31	..	5 54	..
St. Leonards (W.M.) ...	4 27	..	..	4 58	..	..	..	5 26	..	..	..	..	5 58	..
" (W.S.) ...	4 30	..	..	5 1	..	..	..	5 29	..	..	5 38	..	6 1	..
Hastings 56, 59 ...	4 32	..	..	5 3	..	..	..	5 31	..	..	5 40	..	6 3	..
Ore ... arr.	4 35	..	..	5 6	..	..	..	5 35	..	..	5 44	..	6 6	..

Station	1	2	3	4	5	6	7	8	9	10	11	12	13	14	15	16	17	18	19	20	21	22	23	24	25	26	27	28	29
Three Bridges (*above*)..dep.	..	..	..	..	1 47	..	..	..	..	Stop	..	..	Stop	2 47	..	Stop	..	..	..	..	3 47	..	..	..	..	Stop	..	Stop	4 47
Crawley	..	..	..	..	1 51	..	..	..	..	..	..	..	..	2 51	..	..	..	..	..	..	3 51	..	..	..	..	..	..	..	4 51
Ifield	..	..	..	..	1 53	..	..	..	..	..	..	..	..	2 53	..	..	..	..	..	..	3 53	..	..	..	..	..	..	..	4 53
Fay Gate	..	..	..	..	1 58	..	..	..	..	..	..	..	..	2 58	..	..	..	..	..	..	3 58	..	..	..	..	..	..	..	4 58
Littlehaven Halt	..	..	..	..	2 2	..	..	..	..	..	..	..	..	3 2	..	..	..	..	..	..	4 2	..	..	..	..	..	..	..	5 2
Horsham 244, 245 ......arr.	..	..	..	..	2 5	..	..	..	..	..	..	..	..	3 5	..	..	..	..	..	..	4 5	..	..	..	..	..	..	..	5 5
Sutton ......dep.	..	..	..	..	..	..	..	..	..	..	..	..	..	..	..	..	..	..	..	..	..	3 39	..	..	..	..	..	..	..
Dorking North **H**	..	..	..	..	..	..	..	..	..	..	..	..	..	..	..	..	..	..	..	..	..	3 56	..	..	..	..	..	..	..
Horsham 244, 245 ....arr.	..	..	..	..	..	..	..	..	..	..	..	..	..	..	..	..	..	..	..	..	..	4 13	..	..	..	..	..	..	..
Horsham 244, 245 ....dep.	..	..	..	..	2 5	..	..	..	..	..	..	..	..	3 5	..	..	..	..	..	..	4 5	4 15	..	..	..	..	..	..	5 5
Christ's Hospital, West Horsham	..	..	..	..	2 9	..	..	..	..	..	..	..	..	3 9	..	..	..	..	..	..	4 9	..	..	..	..	..	..	..	5 9
Billingshurst	..	..	..	..	2 16	..	..	..	..	..	..	..	..	3 16	..	..	..	..	..	..	4 16	..	..	..	..	..	..	..	5 16
Pulborough **J** 374	..	..	..	..	2 23	..	..	..	..	..	..	..	..	3 23	..	..	..	..	..	..	4 23	4 30	..	..	..	..	..	..	5 23
Amberley	..	..	..	..	2 31	..	..	..	..	..	..	..	..	3 31	..	..	..	..	..	..	4 31	..	..	..	..	..	..	..	5 31
Arundel	..	..	p.m	p.m	2 36	..	..	p.m	p.m	p.m	p.m	p.m	..	3 36	p.m	..	p.m	p.m	..	p.m	4 36	4 41	..	..	p.m	p.m	p.m	p.m	5 36
Brighton ......dep.	1 33	..	1 50	2 3	..	2 17	..	2 25	2 33	2 47	2 50	3 3	..	..	3 17	..	3 33	3 50	..	4 3	..	**RB**	..	..	4 17	4 20	4 33	4 50	..
Holland Road Halt	1 35	..	..	2 5	..	..	..	..	2 35	..	..	3 5	..	..	..	..	3 35	..	..	4 5	..	..	..	..	..	..	4 35	..	..
Hove	1 37	..	1 53	2 7	..	2 20	..	2 29	2 37	2 50	2 53	3 7	..	..	3 20	..	3 37	3 53	..	4 7	..	..	..	..	4 20	4 23	4 37	4 53	..
Aldrington Halt	1 39	..	1 55	2 9	..	..	..	..	2 39	..	2 55	3 9	..	..	..	..	3 39	3 55	..	4 9	..	..	..	..	..	4 25	4 39	4 55	..
Portslade and West Hove	1 42	..	1 58	2 12	..	..	..	2 33	2 42	..	2 58	3 12	..	..	..	..	3 42	3 58	..	4 12	..	..	..	..	..	4 28	4 42	4 58	..
Fishersgate Halt	1 44	..	..	2 14	..	..	..	..	2 44	..	..	3 14	..	..	..	..	3 44	..	..	4 14	..	..	..	..	..	..	4 44	..	..
Southwick	1 47	..	2 1	2 17	..	..	..	2 37	2 47	..	3 1	3 17	..	..	..	..	3 47	4 1	..	4 17	..	..	..	..	..	4 31	4 47	5 1	..
Shoreham-by-Sea **K**	1 50	..	2 4	2 20	..	2 27	..	2 41	2 50	2 57	3 4	3 20	..	..	3 27	..	3 50	4 4	..	4 20	..	..	..	..	4 27	4 34	4 50	5 4	..
Lancing	1 55	..	2 8	2 25	..	..	..	Stop	2 55	..	3 8	3 25	..	..	..	..	3 55	4 8	..	4 25	..	..	..	..	..	4 39	4 55	5 8	..
Ham Bridge Halt **N**	1 58	..	..	2 28	..	..	..	..	2 58	..	..	3 28	..	..	..	..	3 58	..	..	4 28	..	..	..	..	..	..	4 58	..	..
Worthing Central	2 1	..	2 12	2 31	..	2 35	..	..	3 1	3 6	3 12	3 31	..	..	3 35	..	4 1	4 12	..	4 31	..	..	..	..	4 35	4 43	5 1	5 12	..
West Worthing **U**	2 3	..	2 14	2 33	..	2 37	..	..	3 3	..	3 14	3 33	..	..	3 37	..	4 3	4 14	..	4 33	..	..	..	..	4 37	4 46	5 3	5 14	..
Durrington-on-Sea	Stop	..	2 16	..	..	..	..	..	..	..	3 16	Stop	..	..	..	..	..	4 16	..	..	..	..	..	..	..	Stop	..	5 16	..
Goring-by-Sea	..	..	2 19	..	..	2 41	..	..	..	..	3 19	..	..	..	3 41	..	..	4 19	..	..	..	..	..	..	4 41	..	..	5 19	..
Angmering **L**	p.m	..	2 23	..	..	2 45	..	p.m	..	..	3 23	..	..	..	3 45	p.m	..	4 23	..	..	..	..	..	..	4 45	p.m	..	5 23	..
Ford (Sussex) ......dep.	2 2	..	..	..	..	..	..	3 2	..	..	..	..	..	..	..	3 52	..	..	..	..	..	..	..	..	..	5 2	..	..	..
Littlehampton ....arr.	2 7	..	2 33	..	2 43	3 7	..	3 7	..	..	3 33	..	..	3 43	..	3 57	..	4 33	..	..	4 43	..	..	..	5 7	5 7	..	5 33	5 43
Littlehampton ....dep.	..	..	..	..	2 46	2 46	..	..	..	..	..	..	..	3 46	3 46	..	..	..	..	..	4 46	..	..	..	4 46	Stop	..	..	5 46
Ford (Sussex)	..	..	..	..	2a50	2 52	..	..	..	..	..	..	p.m	3a50	3 52	..	..	..	..	..	4a50	..	..	..	4 52	..	..	..	5a50
Barnham ......arr.	..	..	..	..	3 1	2 57	..	..	..	3 22	..	..	3d36	4 1	3 57	..	..	..	..	..	5 1	4 49	..	..	4 57	..	..	..	6 1
Bognor Regis .....arr.	..	..	..	..	3 7	3 7	..	..	..	3 42	..	..	3 42	4 7	4 7	..	..	..	..	..	5 7	5 0	..	..	5 7	..	..	..	6 7
Bognor Regis .....dep.	..	..	..	..	..	2 45	..	..	..	3 10	..	..	..	..	3 40	..	..	..	..	..	..	4 44	..	..	4 44	..	..	..	..
Barnham ......dep.	..	..	..	..	..	2 57	..	..	..	3 22	..	..	..	..	3 57	..	..	..	..	..	..	4 52	..	..	4 57	..	..	..	..
Chichester **Z**	..	..	..	..	..	3 7	..	..	..	3 32	..	..	..	..	4 7	..	..	..	..	..	..	5 2	..	..	5 7	..	..	..	..
Fishbourne Halt	..	..	..	..	..	3 10	..	..	..	..	..	..	..	..	4 10	..	..	..	..	..	..	..	..	..	5 10	..	..	..	..
Bosham	..	..	..	..	..	3 13	..	..	..	..	..	..	..	..	4 13	..	..	..	..	..	..	..	..	..	5 13	..	..	..	..
Nutbourne Halt	..	..	..	..	..	3 16	..	..	..	..	..	..	..	..	4 16	..	..	..	..	..	..	..	..	..	5 16	..	..	..	..
Southbourne Halt	..	..	..	..	..	3 19	..	..	..	..	..	..	..	..	4 19	..	..	..	..	..	..	..	..	..	5 19	..	..	..	..
Emsworth	..	..	..	..	..	3 22	..	..	..	..	..	..	..	..	4 22	..	..	..	..	..	..	..	..	..	5 22	..	..	..	..
Warblington Halt	..	..	..	..	..	3 25	..	..	..	..	..	..	..	..	4 25	..	..	..	..	..	..	..	..	..	5 25	..	..	..	..
Havant 244, 366	..	..	..	..	..	3 27	..	..	..	3 45	..	..	..	..	4 27	..	..	..	..	..	..	5 15	..	..	5 27	..	..	..	..
244 Hayling Island ....arr.	..	..	..	..	..	..	..	..	..	..	..	..	..	..	..	..	..	..	..	..	..	..	..	..	..	..	..	..	..
Bedhampton Halt	..	..	..	..	..	..	..	..	..	..	..	..	..	..	..	..	..	..	..	..	..	..	..	..	..	..	..	..	..
Hilsea Halt	..	..	..	..	..	..	..	..	..	..	..	..	..	..	..	..	..	..	..	..	..	..	..	..	..	..	..	..	..
Fratton 380	..	..	..	..	..	3 36	..	..	..	3 54	..	..	..	..	4 36	..	..	..	..	..	..	5 23	..	..	5 36	..	..	..	..
Portsmouth & Southsea arr	..	..	..	..	..	3 38	..	..	..	3 56	..	p.m	..	..	4 38	..	..	..	..	..	..	5 26	..	..	5 38	p.m	..	..	..
Portsmouth Harbour ... "	..	..	..	..	..	3 42	..	..	..	4 0	..	4d35	..	..	4 42	..	..	..	..	..	..	5 30	..	..	5 42	6d35	..	..	..
500 Ryde Pier (Boat)...arr.	..	..	..	..	..	..	..	..	..	..	..	5 5	..	..	..	..	..	..	..	..	..	..	..	..	..	7 5	..	..	..
Sandown (Page 359) "	..	..	..	..	..	..	..	..	..	..	..	5 48	..	..	..	..	..	..	..	..	..	..	..	..	..	7 48	..	..	..
Shanklin "	..	..	..	..	..	..	..	..	..	..	..	5 55	..	..	..	..	..	..	..	..	..	..	..	..	..	7 55	..	..	..
Ventnor "	..	..	..	..	..	..	..	..	..	..	..	6 11	..	..	..	..	..	..	..	..	..	..	..	..	..	8 11	..	..	..
Newport "	..	..	..	..	..	..	..	..	..	..	..	6 6	..	..	..	..	..	..	..	..	..	..	..	..	..	8 6	..	..	..
Cowes "	..	..	..	..	..	..	..	..	..	..	..	6 20	..	..	..	..	..	..	..	..	..	..	..	..	..	8 30	..	..	..
Yarmouth "	..	..	..	..	..	..	..	..	..	..	..	7 51	..	..	..	..	..	..	..	..	..	..	..	..	..	..	..	..	..

3 Third class only. *a* Dep. 5 mins. later. *d* Departure time. **P** Pullman Car facilities available.
RB Refreshment Car facilities available between London and Bognor Regis

For Other Notes, see page 195

For SERVICES from LONDON (Waterloo) to PORTSMOUTH and ISLE OF WIGHT, see pages 359 to 365

From LONDON to THE SOUTH COAST—Sundays—*continued*

	1	2	3	4	5	6	7	8	9	10	11	12	13	14	15	16	17	18	19	20	21	22	23	24	25	26	27	28	29	30	31
	p.m	p.m	p.m	p.m	p.m	p.m	p.m	p.m	p.m	p.m	p.m	p.m	p.m	p.m	p.m	p.m	p.m	p.m	p.m P	p.m	p.m	p.m	p.m	p.m P	p.m	p.m	p.m P	p.m	p.m RB	p.m	p.m
VICTORIA ....dep.	..	..	..	..	..	..	4 28	..	4 48	..	..	..	..	..	5 28	..	..	5 48	6 0	..	..	..	6 28	6 45	..	6 48	7 0	..	7 18	..	..
Clapham Junction .... "	..	..	..	..	..	..	4 33	..	4 53	..	..	..	..	..	5 33	..	..	5 53	..	..	..	..	6 33	..	..	6 53	..	..	..	..	..
LONDON BRIDGE ..dep.	..	..	..	..	..	..	4S0	..	4S30	..	..	..	..	..	5S0	..	..	5S30	..	..	..	..	6S0	6S30	..	6*40	..	..	6S55	..	..
New Cross Gate .... "	..	..	..	..	..	..	4S5	..	4S35	..	..	..	..	..	5S5	..	..	5S35	..	..	..	..	6S5	6S35	..	6*47	..	..		..	..
Norwood Junction B "	..	..	..	..	..	..	4S14	..	4S44	..	..	..	..	..	5S14	..	..	5S44	..	..	..	..	6S14	6S44	..	6*59	..	..		..	..
East Croydon ....dep.	..	..	..	..	..	..	4 46	..	5 5	..	..	..	..	..	5 46	..	..	6 5	..	..	..	..	6 46	7 2	..	7 5	..	..	Through Train Victoria to Bognor Regis.	..	..
Purley	..	..	..	..	..	..	..	..	5 11	..	..	..	..	..	..	..	..	6 11	..	..	..	..	..	..	..	7 11	..	..		..	..
Coulsdon South	..	..	..	..	..	..	..	..	5 14	..	..	..	..	..	..	..	..	6 14	..	..	..	..	..	..	..	7 14	..	..		..	..
Merstham	..	..	..	..	..	..	..	..	5 20	..	..	..	..	..	..	..	..	6 20	..	..	..	..	..	..	..	7 20	..	..		..	..
Redhill 246	..	..	..	..	..	..	5 1	..	5 27	..	..	..	..	..	6 1	..	..	6 27	..	..	..	..	7 2	..	..	7 27	..	..		..	..
Earlswood	..	..	..	..	..	..	..	..	5 29	..	..	..	..	..	..	..	..	6 29	..	..	..	..	..	..	..	7 29	..	..		..	..
Salfords	..	..	..	..	..	..	..	..	5 33	..	..	..	..	..	..	..	..	6 33	..	..	..	..	..	..	..	7 33	..	..		..	..
Horley	..	..	..	..	..	..	..	..	5 37	..	..	..	..	..	..	..	..	6 37	..	..	..	..	7 9	..	..	7 37	..	..		..	..
Gatwick Airport	..	..	..	..	..	..	5 9	..	5 40	..	..	..	..	..	6 9	..	..	6 40	..	..	..	..	7 12	..	..	7 40	..	..		..	..
Three Bridges (*below*) 234.	..	..	..	..	..	..	5 13	..	5 45	..	..	..	..	..	..	..	..	6 45	..	..	..	..	7 16	..	..	7 44	..	..		..	..
Balcombe	..	..	..	..	..	..	..	..	5 51	..	..	..	..	..	..	..	..	6 51	..	..	..	..	..	..	..	7 51	..	..		..	..
Horsted Keynes ....dep.	..	..	..	..	..	..	..	..	..	..	..	..	..	..	..	..	6 16	..	..	..	..	..	..	..	..	..	..	..		..	..
Ardingly	..	..	..	..	..	..	..	..	..	..	..	..	..	..	..	..	6 20	..	..	..	..	..	..	..	..	..	..	..		..	..
Haywards Heath C 239...	..	..	..	..	..	..	5 24	..	5 58	..	..	..	..	..	6 22	..	6 24	6 58	..	..	..	..	7 28	7 34	..	7 58	..	..	..	..	..
Wivelsfield (*below*)........	..	..	..	..	..	..	..	..	6 3	..	..	..	..	..	..	..	..	7 3	..	..	..	..	..	..	..	8 3	..	..	..	..	..
Burgess Hill........	..	..	..	..	..	..	..	..	6 5	..	..	..	..	..	..	..	..	7 5	..	..	..	..	7 33	..	..	8 5	..	..	..	..	..
Hassocks D........	..	..	..	..	..	..	..	..	6 9	..	..	..	..	..	..	..	..	7 9	..	..	..	..	7 37	..	..	8 9	..	..	..	..	..
Preston Park........	..	..	..	..	..	..	5 39	..	6 18	..	..	..	..	..	6 37	..	..	7 18	..	..	..	..	7 45	..	..	8 18	..	..	..	..	..
Brighton (*below*) ....arr.	..	..	..	..	..	..	5 42	..	6 21	..	..	..	..	..	6 40	..	..	7 21	7 0	..	..	..	7 49	..	..	8 21	8 0	..	..	..	..
Haywards Heath ...dep.	..	..	..	..	..	..	Stop	..	Stop	..	..	..	..	..	Stop	..	6 35	Stop	Stop	..	..	..	Stop	7 35	..	Stop	Stop	..	..	..	..
Wivelsfield (*above*)........	..	..	..	..	..	..	..	..	..	..	..	..	..	..	..	..	6 39	..	..	..	..	..	..	..	..	..	..	..	..	..	..
Plumpton	..	..	..	..	..	..	..	..	..	..	..	..	..	..	..	..	6 45	..	..	..	..	..	..	..	..	..	..	..	..	..	..
Cooksbridge	..	..	..	..	..	..	..	..	..	..	..	..	..	..	..	..	6 50	..	..	..	..	..	..	..	..	..	..	..	..	..	..
Lewes 239 ....arr.	..	..	..	..	..	..	..	..	..	..	..	..	..	..	p.m	..	6 55	p.m	..	..	..	..	..	7 50	..	p.m	..	..	..	..	..
Brighton ....dep.	..	..	..	5 14	5 31	..	..	..	..	..	5 45	..	6 14	..	6 18	6 31	Stop	6 46	..	6 50	7 31	..	..	..	..	7 46	..	..	..	..	..
London Road (Brighton)...	..	..	..	5 16	5 33	..	..	..	..	..	5 47	..	6 16	..	6 21	6 33	..	6 48	..	..	7 33	..	..	..	..	7 48	..	..	..	..	..
Falmer	..	..	..	5 21	5 37	..	..	..	..	..	5 51	..	6 20	..	..	6 37	..	6 53	..	..	7 37	..	..	..	..	7 53	..	..	..	..	..
Lewes ....arr.	..	..	..	5 28	5 45	..	..	..	..	..	5 59	..	6 28	..	6 36	6 45	..	7 0	p.m	7 6	7 45	..	..	..	..	8 0	p.m	..	..	..	..
Lewes ....dep.	5 4	..	..	..	5 46	..	..	..	..	..	..	6 4	..	..	Stop	6 46	..	..	7 3	Stop	7 46	..	..	..	..	..	8 4	..	..	..	..
Southease and Rodmell	5 9	..	..	..	5 51	..	..	..	..	..	..	6 9	..	..	..	6 51	..	..	7 8	..	7 51	..	..	..	..	..	8 9	..	..	..	..
Newhaven Town ...[Halt	5 14	..	..	..	5 56	..	..	..	..	..	..	6 14	..	..	..	6 56	..	..	7 13	..	7 56	..	..	..	..	..	8 14	..	..	..	..
" Harbour......	5 15	..	..	..	5 57	..	..	..	..	..	..	6 15	..	..	..	6 57	..	..	7 14	..	7 57	..	..	..	..	..	8 15	..	..	..	..
Bishopstone	5 20	..	..	..	6 2	..	..	..	..	..	..	6 20	..	..	..	7 2	..	..	7 19	..	8 2	..	..	..	..	..	8 20	..	..	..	..
Seaford ....arr.	5 22	..	..	..	6 5	..	..	..	..	..	..	6 22	..	..	..	7 5	..	..	7 22	..	8 5	..	..	..	..	..	8 22	..	..	..	..
Lewes ....dep.	..	..	..	5 29	Stop	..	..	..	..	..	5 59	Stop	6 29	..	..	Stop	..	7 1	Stop	..	Stop	..	..	7 52	..	8 1	..	..	..	..	..
Glynde	..	..	..	5 34	..	..	..	..	..	..	6 4	..	6 34	..	..	..	..	7 6	..	..	..	..	..	..	..	8 6	..	..	..	..	..
Berwick	..	..	..	5 40	..	..	..	..	..	..	6 10	..	6 40	..	..	..	..	7 12	..	..	..	..	..	..	..	8 12	..	..	..	..	..
Polegate 239	..	..	..	5 47	..	..	..	..	p.m	..	6 17	p.m	6 47	..	p.m	..	..	7 19	..	..	..	..	..	..	..	8 19	..	..	..	..	..
Hampden Park F........	..	..	5 45	5 50	..	..	..	..	6 15	..	6 20	6 45	6 50	..	7 15	..	..	7 22	..	..	..	..	..	..	8 15	8 22	..	..	..	..	..
Eastbourne ....arr.	..	..	5 49	5 54	..	..	..	..	6 19	..	6 24	6 49	6 54	..	7 19	..	..	7 26	..	..	..	..	..	8 12	8 19	8 26	..	..	..	..	..
Eastbourne ....dep.	..	..	Stop	5 57	..	..	..	..	Stop	..	6 29	Stop	6 57	..	..	..	..	7 29	..	..	..	..	..	8 16	Stop	8 29	..	..	..	..	..
Hampden Park F........	..	..	..	6 0	..	..	..	..	..	..	6 32	..	7 0	..	..	..	..	7 32	..	..	..	..	..	..	..	8 32	..	..	..	..	..
Pevensey and Westham....	..	..	..	6 7	..	..	..	..	..	..	6 39	..	7 7	..	..	..	..	7 39	..	..	..	..	..	..	..	8 39	..	..	..	..	..
Pevensey Bay Halt........	..	..	..	6 9	..	..	..	..	..	..	6 41	..	7 9	..	..	..	..	7 41	..	..	..	..	..	..	..	8 41	..	..	..	..	..
Norman's Bay Halt........	..	..	..	6 12	..	..	..	..	..	..	6 44	..	7 12	..	..	..	..	7 44	..	..	..	..	..	..	..	8 44	..	..	..	..	..
Cooden Beach	..	..	..	6 16	..	..	..	..	..	..	6 48	..	7 16	..	..	..	..	7 48	..	..	..	..	..	8 31	..	8 48	..	..	..	..	..
Collington Halt	..	..	..	6 19	..	..	..	..	..	..	6 51	..	7 19	..	..	..	..	7 51	..	..	..	..	..	..	..	8 51	..	..	..	..	..
Bexhill (Central) G........	..	..	..	6 22	..	..	..	..	..	..	6 54	..	7 22	..	..	..	..	7 54	..	..	..	..	..	8 36	..	8 54	..	..	..	..	..
St. Leonards (W.M.).......	..	..	..	6 27	..	..	..	..	..	..	6 58	..	7 26	..	..	..	..	7 58	..	..	..	..	..	..	..	8 58	..	..	..	..	..
" (W.S.)	..	..	..	6 29	..	..	..	..	..	..	7 1	..	7 29	..	..	..	..	8 1	..	..	..	..	..	8 43	..	9 1	..	..	..	..	..
Hastings 56, 59........	..	..	..	6 31	..	..	..	..	..	..	7 3	..	7 31	..	..	..	..	8 3	..	..	..	..	..	8 46	..	9 3	..	..	..	..	..
Ore........arr.	..	..	..	6 35	..	..	..	..	..	..	7 6	..	7 35	..	..	..	..	8 6	p.m	..	..	..	..	8 50	..	9 6	..	..	..	..	..

	1	2	3	4	5	6	7	8	9	10	11	12	13	14	15	16	17	18	19	20	21	22	23	24	25	26	27	28	29	30	31
Three Bridges (above). dep										5 47									6 47									7 47			
Crawley										5 51	Stop		Stop					Stop	6 51					Stop		Stop		7 51			
Ifield										5 53									6 53									7 53			
Fay Gate										5 58									6 58									7 58			
Littlehaven Halt										6 2									7 2									8 2			
Horsham 244, 245 arr.										6 5									7 5									8 5			
Sutton dep.																													7 39		
Dorking North H																													7 56		
Horsham 244, 245 arr.																													8 13		
Horsham 244, 245 dep.										6 5									7 5									8 5	8 15		
Christ's Hospital, West Horsham										6 9									7 9									8 9			
Billingshurst										6 16									7 16									8 16	8 25		
Pulborough J 374										6 23									7 23									8 23	8 32		
Amberley										6 31									7 31									8 31			
Arundel			p.m		p.m		p.m			6 36	p.m	p.m	p.m			p.m	p.m	p.m	7 36	p.m			p.m	p.m		p.m		8 36	8 43		
Brighton dep.		5 3	5 17		5 20	5 30	5 47	5 50			6 3	6 17	6 20	6 25		6 35	6 50	7 3		7 17		7 33	7 46	7 48		8 3			RB	8 17	
Holland Road Halt		5 5				5 32					6 5					6 37		7 5				7 35				8 5					
Hove		5 7	5 20		5 23	5 37	5 50	5 53			6 7	6 20	6 23	6 29		6 39	6 53	7 7		7 20		7 37	7 49	7 51		8 7				8 20	
Aldrington Halt		5 9			5 25	5 39		5 55			6 9					6 41	6 55	7 9				7 39		7 53		8 9					
Portslade and West Hove		5 12			5 28	5 42		5 58			6 12		6 26	6 33		6 44	6 58	7 12				7 42		7 56		8 12					
Fishersgate Halt		5 14				5 44					6 14					6 46		7 14				7 44				8 14					
Southwick		5 17			5 31	5 46		6 1			6 17		6 29	6 37		6 49	7 1	7 17				7 47		7 59		8 17					
Shoreham-by-Sea K		5 20	5 27		5 34	5 50	5 57	6 4			6 20	6 27	6 33	6 41		6 52	7 4	7 20		7 27		7 50	7 56	8 3		8 20				8 27	
Lancing		5 25			5 38	5 55		6 8			6 25		6 37	Stop		6 57	7 8	7 25				7 55		8 7		8 25					
Ham Bridge Halt N		5 28				5 58					6 28					7 0		7 28				7 58				8 28					
Worthing Central		5 31	5 35		5 42	6 1	6 6	6 12			6 31	6 35	6 41			7 3	7 12	7 31		7 35		8 1	8 5	8 12		8 31				8 35	
West Worthing U		5 33	5 37		5 45	6 3		6 14			6 33	6 37	6 43			7 5	7 14	7 33		7 37		8 3		8 14		8 33				8 37	
Durrington-on-Sea					Stop			6 16									7 16							8 16							
Goring-by-Sea			5 41					6 19				6 41					7 19			7 40				8 18						8 41	
Angmering L			5 45		p.m			6 23				6 45		p.m			7 23			7 45	p.m			8 23						8 46	
Ford (Sussex) dep.					5 52									6 52							7 52										9 2
Littlehampton arr.					5 57			6 33		6 43				6 57			7 33		7 43		7 57			8 32				8 43	9 7	9 7	9 7
Littlehampton dep.			5 46						p.m	6 46		6 46		Stop					7 46	7 46								8 43		8 48	
Ford (Sussex)			5 52							6a50		6 52							7a50	7 52					p.m			8c52	8 49	8 56	
Barnham arr.			5 57				6 22		6d36	7 1		6 57							8 1	7 56			8 21		8d36			9 5	8 54	9 1	
Bognor Regis arr.			6 7				6 42		6 42	7 7		7 7							8 7	8 7			8 42		8 42			9 11	9 4	9 11	
Bognor Regis dep.			5 40				6 10					6 40								7 40			8 10						8 45	8 45	
Barnham dep.			5 57				6 22					6 57								7 57			8 22						8 55	9 1	
Chichester Z			6 7				6 32					7 7								8 7			8 32						9 5	9 11	
Fishbourne Halt			6 10									7 10								8 10										9 14	
Bosham			6 13									7 13								8 13									9 12	9 17	
Nutbourne Halt			6 16									7 16								8 16										9 20	
Southbourne Halt			6 19									7 19								8 19										9 23	
Emsworth			6 22									7 22								8 22									9 19	9 26	
Warblington Halt			6 25									7 25								8 25										9 29	
Havant 244, 366			6 27				6 45					7 27								8 27			8 45						9 23	9 31	
244 Hayling Island arr.																															
Bedhampton Halt																															
Hilsea Halt																															
Fratton 380			6 36				6 54					7 36								8 36			8 54						9 31	9 40	
Portsmouth & Southsea arr			6 38				6 56					7 38		p.m						8 38			8 56						9 35	9 42	
Portsmouth Harbour "			6 42				7 0					7 42		8d40						8 42			9 0						9 39	9 46	
500 Ryde Pier (Boat) arr.														9 10																	
Page 359 Sandown "														9 48																	
Shanklin "														9 55																	
Ventnor "														10 11																	
Newport "														10 6																	
Cowes "														10 20																	
Yarmouth "																															

3 Third class only. * Change at East Croydon. *a* Dep. 5 mins. later. *c* Dep. 8 mins. later. *d* Departure time. **P** Pullman Car facilities available.
RB Refreshment Car facilities available between London and Bognor Regis.

For Other Notes, see page 195

For SERVICES from LONDON (Waterloo) to PORTSMOUTH and ISLE OF WIGHT, see pages 359 to 365

From LONDON to THE SOUTH COAST—Sundays—*continued*

	p.m P	p.m	p.m	p.m	p.m	p.m	p.m	p.m	p.m P	p.m	p.m	p.m	p.m P	p.m	p.m	p.m	p.m	p.m RB	p.m	p.m P	p.m	p.m	p.m	p.m P	p.m	p.m P		p.m P	p.m P	p.m
VICTORIA......dep.	7 25	7 28	..	..	..	7 48	..	..	8 0	..	8 28	..	8 45	8 48	..	..	..	9 18	..	9 25	..	..	9 28	9 45	9 48	10 0	..	1028	11 0	1116
Clapham Junction.... "	..	7 33	..	..	..	7 53	..	..	..	..	8 35	..	..	8 53	..	..	..	..	..	..	..	..	9 34	..	9 53	..	..	1033	..	1122
LONDON BRIDGE...dep.	7Ⓢ0	7Ⓢ0	..	..	..	7Ⓢ30	..	..	..	8 16	8*16	..	8Ⓢ30	8Ⓢ30	..	..	..	8Ⓢ55	9 16	9*16	..	..	9*16	9Ⓢ30	9Ⓢ30	..	..	10Ⓢ0	..	11Ⓢ0
New Cross Gate..... "	7Ⓢ5	7Ⓢ5	..	..	..	7Ⓢ35	..	..	..	8 21	8*21	..	8Ⓢ35	8Ⓢ35	..	..	..	--	9 21	9*21	..	..	9*21	9Ⓢ35	9Ⓢ35	..	..	10Ⓢ5	..	11Ⓢ5
Norwood Junction B "	7Ⓢ14	7Ⓢ14	..	..	..	7Ⓢ44	..	..	..	8 30	8*30	..	8Ⓢ44	8Ⓢ44	..	..	..	--	9 30	9*30	..	..	9*30	9Ⓢ44	9Ⓢ44	..	..	10Ⓢ14	..	11Ⓢ14
East Croydon......dep.	7 42	7 46	..	..	..	8 5	..	..	..	8 35	8 48	..	9 1	9 5	..	..	..	--	9 35	9 44	..	..	9 47	10 1	10 5	..	..	1046	..	1135
Purley..........	..	7 51	..	..	..	8 11	..	..	..	8 40	..	..	..	9 11	..	..	..	..	9 40	..	..	..	..	..	10 11	..	..	..	..	1140
Coulsdon South..........	..	..	..	..	..	8 14	..	..	..	8 44	..	..	..	9 14	..	..	..	..	9 44	..	..	..	..	..	10 14	..	..	..	..	1144
Merstham..........	..	..	..	..	..	8 20	..	..	..	8 50	..	..	..	9 20	..	..	..	..	9 50	..	..	..	..	..	10 20	..	..	..	..	1150
Redhill 246..........	..	8 2	..	..	..	8 27	..	..	..	8 57	9 4	..	..	9 27	..	..	..	..	9 57	..	..	..	10 2	..	10 27	..	..	11 1	..	1155
Earlswood..........	..	..	..	..	..	8 29	..	..	..	8 59	..	..	..	9 29	..	..	..	..	9 59	..	..	..	..	..	10 29	..	..	..	..	1158
Salfords..........	..	..	..	..	..	8 33	..	..	..	9 3	..	..	..	9 33	..	..	..	..	10 3	..	..	..	..	..	10 33	..	..	..	..	12 1
Horley..........	..	..	..	..	..	8 37	..	..	..	9 7	..	..	..	9 37	..	..	..	..	10 7	..	..	..	..	..	10 37	..	..	..	..	12 5
Gatwick Airport..........	..	8 11	..	..	..	8 40	..	..	..	9 10	9 12	..	..	9 40	..	..	..	..	10 10	..	..	..	..	..	10 40	..	..	..	..	..
Three Bridges (*below*) 234..	..	..	..	..	..	8 45	..	..	..	9 14	9 17	..	..	9 45	..	..	..	..	10 15	..	..	..	1014	..	10 45	..	..	1113	..	1218
Balcombe..........	..	..	..	..	..	8 51	..	..	..	Stop	..	..	..	9 51	..	..	..	..	10 23	..	..	..	..	..	10 51	..	..	..	..	Stop
Horsted Keynes......dep.	..	..	8 16	..	..	..	..	..	..	..	..	..	..	..	..	..	..	..	..	..	..	..	..	..	..	..	..	..	..	..
Ardingly..........	..	..	8 20	..	..	..	..	..	..	..	..	..	..	..	..	..	..	..	..	..	..	..	..	..	..	..	..	..	..	..
Haywards Heath C 239...	8 14	8 24	8 24	..	..	8 58	..	..	..	..	9 28	..	9 32	9 58	..	..	..	Through Train, Victoria to Bognor Regis.	10 29	1015	..	..	1025	10 32	10 58	..	..	1124	..	..
Wivelsfield (*below*)..........	..	..	..	..	..	9 2	..	..	..	..	9 32	..	..	10 3	..	..	..		10 34	Through Train Victoria to Littlehampton.	..	..	..	..	11 3	..	..	..	..	..
Burgess Hill..........	..	..	..	..	..	9 5	..	..	..	..	9 34	..	..	10 5	..	..	..		10 37		..	..	..	..	11 5	..	..	..	..	..
Hassocks D..........	..	..	..	..	..	9 10	..	..	..	..	9 38	..	..	10 9	..	..	..		10 41		..	..	..	..	11 9	..	..	..	..	..
Preston Park..........	..	8 38	..	..	..	9 18	..	..	..	..	9 46	..	..	1018	..	..	..		10 49		..	..	1039	..	11 18	..	..	1139	..	..
Brighton (*below*)......arr.	..	8 41	..	..	..	9 21	..	..	9 0	..	9 50	..	..	1021	..	..	..		10 53		..	..	1042	..	11 21	11 0	..	1142	12 0	..
Haywards Heath....dep	Through Train Victoria to Littlehampton	Stop	8 35	..	..	Stop	..	..	..	..	Stop	..	9 33	Stop	..	..	..		Stop		..	..	Stop	10 33	Stop	Stop	..	Stop	Stop	..
Wivelsfield (*above*)..........		..	8 39	..	..	..	..	..	..	..	..	..	..	..	..	..	..		..		..	..	..	..	..	..	..	..	..	..
Plumpton..........		..	8 45	..	..	..	..	..	..	..	..	..	..	..	..	..	..		..		..	..	..	..	..	..	..	..	..	..
Cooksbridge..........		..	8 50	..	..	..	..	..	..	..	..	..	..	..	..	..	..		..		..	..	..	..	..	..	..	..	..	..
Lewes 239......arr.		..	8 55	..	..	..	..	..	..	..	..	..	9 48	..	..	..	..		p.m		..	..	..	10 48	..	..	..	..	..	..
Brighton......dep.		..	Stop	8 46	..	..	..	9 2	..	..	..	..	..	..	9 36	10 6	1012		10 31		..	..	..	..	..	..	..	..	..	..
London Road (Brighton)...		..	..	8 48	..	..	..	9 4	..	..	..	..	..	..	9 39	10 8	1014		10 33		..	..	..	..	..	..	..	..	..	..
Falmer..........		..	..	8 53	..	..	..	9 8	..	..	..	..	..	..	..	1013	1018		10 37		..	..	..	..	..	..	..	..	..	..
Lewes......arr.		..	..	9 0	..	..	..	9 16	..	..	..	..	..	..	9 54	1020	1026		10 45		..	..	..	..	..	..	..	..	..	..
Lewes......dep.		..	..	..	9 4	..	..	9 18	..	..	..	..	..	..	Stop	..	1026		10 52		..	..	..	..	..	..	..	..	..	..
Southease and Rodmell		..	..	..	9 9	..	..	9 23	..	..	..	..	..	..	..	..	1031		10 57		..	..	..	..	..	..	..	..	..	..
Newhaven Town...[Halt		..	..	..	9 14	..	..	9 28	..	..	..	..	..	..	..	..	1036		11 2		..	..	..	..	..	..	..	..	..	..
" Harbour.....		..	..	..	9 15	..	..	9 31	..	..	..	..	..	..	..	..	1037		11 3		..	..	..	..	..	..	..	..	..	..
Bishopstone..........		..	..	..	9 18	..	..	9 36	..	..	..	..	..	..	..	..	1040		11 8		..	..	..	..	..	..	..	..	..	..
Seaford......arr.		..	..	..	9 21	..	..	9 39	..	..	..	..	..	..	..	..	1042		11 11		..	..	..	..	..	..	..	..	..	..
Lewes......dep.	..	..	..	9 1	Stop	..	..	Stop	..	..	..	..	9 50	..	..	1021	..	..	Stop	..	..	..	..	10 50	..	..	..	..	..	..
Glynde..........	..	..	..	9 6	..	..	..	..	..	..	..	..	..	..	..	1026	..	..	..	..	..	..	..	..	..	..	..	..	..	..
Berwick..........	..	p.m	..	9 12	..	..	..	..	..	..	p.m	..	..	..	..	1032	..	..	..	..	..	..	..	..	..	..	..	..	..	..
Polegate 239..........	..	8 53	p.m	9 19	..	..	..	..	..	..	9 56	..	10 4	..	p.m	1039	..	..	..	..	..	..	..	..	..	..	..	..	..	..
Hampden Park F..........	..	8 58	9 15	9 22	..	..	..	..	..	..	10 2	..	..	..	1015	1042	..	..	..	..	..	..	..	..	..	..	..	..	..	..
Eastbourne......arr.	..	9 3	9 19	9 26	..	..	..	..	..	..	10 7	..	10 11	..	1019	1046	..	..	..	..	..	..	..	11 9	..	..	..	..	..	..
Eastbourne......dep	..	Stop	Stop	9 29	..	..	..	..	..	..	..	..	10 15	..	Stop	1049	..	..	..	..	..	..	..	11 13	..	..	..	..	..	..
Hampden Park F..........	..	..	..	9 32	..	..	..	..	..	..	..	..	..	..	..	1052	..	..	..	..	..	..	..	..	..	..	..	..	..	..
Pevensey and Westham....	..	..	..	9 39	..	..	..	..	..	..	..	..	..	..	..	1059	..	..	..	..	..	..	..	..	..	..	..	..	..	..
Pevensey Bay Halt..........	..	..	..	9 41	..	..	..	..	..	..	..	..	..	..	..	11 1	..	..	..	..	..	..	..	..	..	..	..	..	..	..
Norman's Bay Halt..........	..	..	..	9 44	..	..	..	..	..	..	..	..	..	..	..	11 4	..	..	..	..	..	..	..	..	..	..	..	..	..	..
Cooden Beach..........	..	..	..	9 48	..	..	..	..	..	..	..	..	10 28	..	..	11 8	..	..	..	..	..	..	..	11 26	..	..	..	..	..	..
Collington Halt..........	..	..	..	9 51	..	..	..	..	..	..	..	..	..	..	..	1111	..	..	..	..	..	..	..	..	..	..	..	..	..	..
Bexhill (Central) G..........	..	..	..	9 54	..	..	..	..	..	..	..	..	10 33	..	..	1114	..	..	..	..	..	..	..	11 31	..	..	..	..	..	..
St. Leonards (W.M.)..........	..	..	..	9 58	..	..	..	..	..	..	..	..	..	..	..	1118	..	..	..	..	..	..	..	..	..	..	..	..	..	..
" (W.S.)..........	..	..	..	10 1	..	..	..	..	..	..	..	..	10 40	..	..	1121	..	..	..	..	..	..	..	11 38	..	..	..	..	..	..
Hastings 56, 59..........	..	..	..	10 3	..	..	..	..	..	..	..	..	10 42	..	..	1123	..	..	..	..	..	..	..	11 40	..	..	..	..	..	..
Ore......arr.	..	..	..	10 6	..	..	..	..	..	..	..	..	10 47	..	..	1126	..	..	..	..	..	..	..	11 45	..	..	..	..	..	..
	1	2	3	4	5	6	7	8	9	10	11	12	13	14	15	16	17	18	19	20	21	22	23	24	25	26	27	28	29	30

	1	2	3	4	5	6	7	8	9	10	11	12	13	14	15	16	17	18	19	20	21	22	23
Three Bridges (*above*)., dep.	..	..	..		..	..	8 47	..	..	..	..	9 22	..	..	..	..	..	..	..	..	..	..	..
Crawley	..	..	..	Stop	..	..	8 51	..	..	..	..	9 26	..	..	..	..	..	..	..	..	..	..	..
Ifield	..	..	..	..	..	..	8 53	..	..	..	..	9 28	..	..	..	..	..	..	..	..	..	..	..
Fay Gate	..	..	..	..	..	..	8 58	..	..	..	..	9 33	..	..	..	..	..	..	..	..	..	..	..
Littlehaven Halt	..	..	..	..	..	..	9 2	..	..	..	..	9 37	..	..	..	..	..	..	..	..	..	..	..
Horsham 244, 245 ..... arr.	..	..	..	..	..	..	9 5	..	..	..	..	9 40	..	..	..	..	..	..	..	..	..	..	..
Sutton ..... dep.	..	..	..	..	..	..	..	..	..	..	..	..	..	..	..	..	..	9 39	..	..	..	..	..
Dorking North H	..	..	..	..	..	..	..	..	..	..	..	..	..	..	..	..	..	9 56	..	..	..	..	..
Horsham 244, 245 ... arr.	..	..	..	..	..	..	..	..	..	..	..	..	..	..	..	..	..	1013	..	..	..	..	..
Horsham 244, 245 ... dep.	..	..	..	..	..	..	9 5	..	..	..	..	..	..	..	..	..	..	1014	..	..	..	..	..
Christ's Hospital, West Horsham	..	..	..	..	..	..	9 9	..	..	..	..	..	..	..	..	..	..	..	..	..	..	..	..
Billingshurst	..	..	..	..	..	..	9 16	..	..	..	..	..	..	..	..	..	..	..	..	..	..	..	..
Pulborough J 374	..	..	..	..	..	..	9 23	..	..	..	..	..	..	..	..	..	..	1032	..	..	..	..	..
Amberley	..	..	..	..	..	..	9 31	..	..	..	..	..	..	..	..	..	..	..	..	..	..	..	..
Arundel	..	p.m	p.m	p.m	p.m	p.m	9 36	p.m	..	p.m	..	..	..	p.m	p.m	..	..	1043	..	..	..	..	p.m
Brighton ..... dep.	P	8 33	8 47	8 50	8 55	9 3	..	9 17	..	9 36	..	..	..	9 50	10 3	..	..	RB	..	P	1033	1047	11 5
Holland Road Halt	..	8 35	..	..	..	9 5	..	..	..	9 38	..	..	..	..	..	..	..	..	..	..	..	..	..
Hove	8 33	8 37	8 50	8 53	8 59	9 7	..	9 20	..	9 40	..	..	..	9 53	10 6	..	..	..	..	1033	1036	1050	11 8
Aldrington Halt	..	8 39	..	8 55	..	9 9	..	..	..	9 42	..	..	..	9 55	10 8	..	..	..	..	..	1038	..	1110
Portslade and West Hove	..	8 42	..	8 58	9 [illegible]	9 12	..	..	..	9 45	..	..	..	9 58	1011	..	..	..	..	..	1041	..	1113
Fishersgate Halt	..	8 44	..	..	..	..	..	..	..	..	..	..	..	..	..	..	..	..	..	..	..	..	..
Southwick	..	8 47	..	9 1	9 7	9 17	..	..	..	9 50	..	..	..	10 1	1015	..	..	..	..	..	1045	..	1117
Shoreham-by-Sea K	8 42	8 50	8 57	9 4	9 11	9 20	..	9 28	..	9 53	..	..	..	10 4	1019	..	..	..	..	1040	1049	1057	1121
Lancing	..	8 54	..	9 8		9 24	..	..	..	9 57	..	..	..	10 8	1023	..	..	..	..	..	1053	..	1125
Ham Bridge Halt N	..	8 57	..	..	Stop	9 27	..	..	..	10 0	..	..	..	..	1026	..	..	..	..	..	1056	..	1128
Worthing Central	8 51	9 0	9 6	9 12	..	9 30	..	9 35	..	10 3	..	..	..	1012	1028	..	..	..	..	1048	1058	11 5	1130
West Worthing U	8 53	9 2	..	9 14	..	9 32	..	9 37	..	10 5	..	..	..	1014	1031	..	..	..	..	1051	11 1	11 7	1132
Durrington-on-Sea	8 55	..	..	9 16	..	..	..	..	..		..	..	..	1016	..	..	..	..	..	1053	..	..	..
Goring-by-Sea	8 58	..	..	9 19	..	..	..	9 41	..	Stop	..	..	..	1019	..	..	..	..	..	1056	..	1111	..
Angmering L	9 3	..	..	9 23	..	..	..	9 45	..	p.m	..	..	..	1023	..	..	..	..	p.m	11 0	..	1115	..
Ford (Sussex) ..... dep.	..	..	..	..	..	..	..	..	..	10 2	..	..	..	..	..	..	..	..	10 50	..	..	..	..
Littlehampton ... arr.	9 12	..	..	9 33	..	..	9 43	10 7	..	10 7	..	..	..	1033	..	..	..	1054	10 54	1110	..	..	..
Littlehampton ... dep.	..	..	..	..	..	..	9 46	9 46	..	..	..	..	..	..	..	..	..	1040	..	..	..	..	..
Ford (Sussex)	..	..	..	..	p.m	..	9a50	9 52	..	..	..	..	..	..	..	..	..	1048	..	..	..	1122	..
Barnham ..... arr.	..	..	9 22	..	9d36	..	10 1	9 57	..	..	..	..	..	..	..	..	..	1053	..	..	..	1127	..
Bognor Regis ..... arr.	..	..	9 42	..	9 42	..	10 7	10 7	..	..	..	..	..	..	..	..	..	11 4	..	..	..	..	..
Bognor Regis ..... dep.	..	..	9 10	..	..	..	..	9 45	..	..	..	..	..	..	..	..	..	..	..	..	..	..	..
Barnham ..... dep.	..	..	9 22	..	..	..	..	9 57	..	..	..	..	..	..	..	..	..	1056	..	..	..	1127	..
Chichester Z	..	..	9 32	..	..	..	..	10 7	..	..	..	..	..	..	..	..	..	11 5	..	..	..	1137	..
Fishbourne Halt	..	..	..	..	..	..	..	1010	..	..	..	..	..	..	..	..	..	..	..	..	..	1140	..
Bosham	..	..	..	..	..	..	..	1013	..	..	..	..	..	..	..	..	..	1111	..	..	..	1143	..
Nutbourne Halt	..	..	..	..	..	..	..	1016	..	..	..	..	..	..	..	..	..	..	..	..	..	1146	..
Southbourne Halt	..	..	..	..	..	..	..	1019	..	..	..	..	..	..	..	..	..	..	..	..	..	1149	..
Emsworth	..	..	..	..	..	..	..	1022	..	..	..	..	..	..	..	..	..	1118	..	..	..	1152	..
Warblington Halt	..	..	..	..	..	..	..	1025	..	..	..	..	..	..	..	..	..	..	..	..	..	1155	..
Havant 244, 366	..	..	9 45	..	..	..	..	1027	..	..	..	..	..	..	..	..	..	1122	..	..	..	1157	..
244 Hayling Island ..... arr.	..	..	..	..	..	..	..	..	..	..	..	..	..	..	..	..	..	..	..	..	..	..	..
Bedhampton Halt	..	..	..	..	..	..	..	..	..	..	..	..	..	..	..	..	..	..	..	..	..	..	..
Hilsea Halt	..	..	..	..	..	..	..	..	..	..	..	..	..	..	..	..	..	..	..	..	..	..	..
Fratton 380	..	..	9 54	..	..	..	..	1036	..	..	..	..	..	..	..	..	..	1130	..	..	..	12 6	..
Portsmouth & Southsea arr	..	..	9 56	..	..	..	..	1038	..	..	..	..	..	..	..	..	..	1133	..	..	..	12 9	..
Portsmouth Harbour .. "	..	..	10 0	..	..	..	..	1042	..	..	..	..	..	..	..	..	..	..	..	..	..	..	..
500 Ryde Pier (Boat) arr.	..	..	..	..	..	..	..	..	..	..	..	..	..	..	..	..	..	..	..	..	..	..	..
Page 359 Sandown "	..	..	..	..	..	..	..	..	..	..	..	..	..	..	..	..	..	..	..	..	..	..	..
Page 359 Shanklin "	..	..	..	..	..	..	..	..	..	..	..	..	..	..	..	..	..	..	..	..	..	..	..
Page 359 Ventnor "	..	..	..	..	..	..	..	..	..	..	..	..	..	..	..	..	..	..	..	..	..	..	..
Page 359 Newport "	..	..	..	..	..	..	..	..	..	..	..	..	..	..	..	..	..	..	..	..	..	..	..
Page 359 Cowes "	..	..	..	..	..	..	..	..	..	..	..	..	..	..	..	..	..	..	..	..	..	..	..
Page 359 Yarmouth "	..	..	..	..	..	..	..	..	..	..	..	..	..	..	..	..	..	..	..	..	..	..	..

For Return Journey, see pages 196 to 233

NOTES

- § Third class only.
- * Change at East Croydon.
- *a* Dep. 5 mins. later.
- **B** Norwood Junc. and South Norwood for Woodside.
- **C** Station for Cuckfield (2 mls.)
- **D** Station for Hurstpierpoint (1½ miles)
- *d* Departure time
- **F** Station for Willingdon (1½ miles).
- **G** Over ½ mile to Bexhill West Station.
- **H** Nearly 1¼ miles to Dorking Town and under ½ mile to Deepdene Station.
- **J** Sta. for Storrington (5 miles)
- **K** Station for Lancing College (2 miles).
- **L** Angmering & Angmering-on-Sea.
- **N** Ham Bridge Halt for East Worthing.
- **P** Pullman Car facilities available.
- **RB** Refreshment Car facilities available between London and Bognor Regis.
- **U** Station for West Tarring (1 mile).
- **Z** Station for Bracklesham Bay, East & West Wittering and Selsey. Frequent service by Southdown Omnibuses.

LOCAL TRAINS and intermediate Stations

Other Trains

For SERVICES from ISLE OF WIGHT and PORTSMOUTH to LONDON (Waterloo), see pages 366 to 372

From THE SOUTH COAST to LONDON—Week Days

Miles from Portsmouth Harbour	Miles from Portsmouth Harbour	Miles from Ore	Station	1	2	3	4	5	6	7	8	9	10	11	12	13	14	15	16	17	18	19	20	21	22	23	24	25	26	27	28	29
				a.m	a.m	a.m	a.m	a.m	a.m	a.m	a.m	a.m	a.m	a.m	a.m	a.m	a.m	a.m	a.m	a.m	a.m	a.m	a.m	a.m	a.m	a.m	a.m	a.m.	a.m	a.m	a.m	a.m.
			Page 366 Yarmouth ....dep.	..	..	..	..	..	..	..	..	..	..	..	..	..	..	..	..	..	..	..	..	..	..	..	..	..	..	..	..	..
			Cowes .... "	..	..	..	..	..	..	..	..	..	..	..	..	..	..	..	..	..	..	..	..	..	..	..	..	..	..	..	..	..
			Newport .... "	..	..	..	..	..	..	..	..	..	..	..	..	..	..	..	..	..	..	..	..	..	..	..	..	..	..	..	..	..
			Ventnor .... "	..	..	..	..	..	..	..	..	..	..	..	..	..	..	..	..	..	..	..	..	..	..	..	..	..	..	..	..	..
			Shanklin .... "	..	..	..	..	..	..	..	..	..	..	..	..	..	..	..	..	..	..	..	..	..	..	..	..	..	..	..	..	..
			Sandown .... "	..	..	..	..	..	..	..	..	..	..	..	..	..	..	..	..	..	..	..	..	..	..	..	..	..	..	..	..	..
			500 Ryde Pier (Boat). "	..	..	..	..	..	..	..	..	..	..	..	..	..	..	..	..	..	..	..	..	..	..	..	..	..	..	..	..	..
		—	Portsmouth Harbour..dep.	..	..	..	..	..	..	..	..	..	..	..	..	..	..	..	..	..	..	Through Train Littlehampton to London Bridge	..	..	..	..	..	..	..	..	..	..
¾	¾	—	Portsmouth & Southsea "	..	..	..	..	..	..	..	..	..	..	..	..	..	5 30	..	..	..	..		5 55	6 13	..	..	..	..	..	..	..	6 30
1½	1½	—	Fratton	..	..	..	..	..	..	..	..	..	..	..	..	..	5 43	..	..	..	..		5 58	6 19	..	..	..	..	..	..	..	6 32
3¾	3¾	—	Hilsea Halt	..	..	..	..	..	..	..	..	..	..	..	..	..	..	..	..	..	..		..	6 23	..	..	..	..	..	..	..	..
7¼	7¼	—	Bedhampton Halt........	..	..	..	..	..	..	..	..	..	..	..	..	..	5 52	..	..	..	..		..	..	..	..	..	..	..	..	..	6 40
—	—	—	245 Hayling Island ....dep.	..	..	..	..	..	..	..	..	..	..	..	..	..	..	..	..	..	..		..	..	..	..	..	..	..	..	..	..
8	8	—	Havant 244	..	..	..	..	..	..	..	..	..	..	..	..	..	5 55	..	Saturdays excepted	..	..		6 8	6 30	..	..	..	..	..	..	..	6 42
8½	8½	—	Warblington Halt........	..	..	..	..	..	..	..	..	..	..	..	..	..	..	..		..	..		6 10	6 32	..	..	..	..	..	..	..	6 44
9¾	9¾	—	Emsworth........	..	..	..	..	..	..	..	..	..	..	..	..	..	6 0	..		..	..		6 14	6 36	..	..	..	..	..	..	..	6 50
11½	11½	—	Southbourne Halt........	..	..	..	..	..	..	..	..	..	..	..	..	..	6 3	..		..	..		6 18	6 39	..	..	..	..	..	..	..	6 53
12¾	12¾	—	Nutbourne Halt........	..	..	..	..	..	..	..	..	..	..	..	..	..	6 6	..		..	..		6 21	6 42	..	..	..	..	..	..	..	6 56
14	14	—	Bosham	..	..	..	..	..	..	..	..	..	..	..	..	..	6 10	..		..	..		6 25	6 46	..	..	..	..	..	..	..	7 0
15½	15½	—	Fishbourne Halt........	..	..	..	..	..	..	..	..	..	..	..	..	..	6 13	..		..	..		6 28	6 49	..	..	..	..	..	..	..	7 3
16¾	16¾	—	Chichester Z	..	..	..	..	..	..	..	..	..	..	..	..	..	6 18	..		..	..		6 34	6 53	..	7 0	..	..	..	..	..	7 10
23	23	—	Barnham ....arr.	..	..	..	..	..	..	..	..	..	..	..	..	..	6 27	..		..	..		6 43	Stop	..	7 9	..	..	..	..	..	7 19
26½	26½	—	Bognor Regis ......arr.	..	..	..	..	..	..	..	..	..	..	..	..	..	6 51	..	..	..	..		7 14		..	RB	..	..	..	..	..	7 37
			Bognor Regis ......dep.	5 25	..	..	..	..	..	5 38	..	..	..	..	..	..	Stop	6 22	..	..	..		..	..	6 42	7 5	..	..	..	..	..	7 11
—	—	—	Barnham ....dep.	5a30	..	..	..	..	..	5 46	..	..	..	..	..	..		6 28	..	..	..		6 43	..	6 50	7 11	..	..	..	..	..	7 19
25¾	25¾	—	Ford (Sussex)........	Stop	..	..	..	5 43	..	5 50	6 2	..	..	..	..	..	..	6 32	..	..	..		6 49	..	6 55	..	..	..	..	..	..	7 24
27¾	27¾	—	Littlehampton ....arr.		..	..	..	5 47	..	5 55	6 6	..	..	..	..	..	..	6 37	..	..	..	R	6 59	a.m	6 59	..	..	..	..	..	..	7 28
			Littlehampton ....dep.	..	..	..	5 30	Stop	5 53	5 57	Stop	6 36	..	..	..	..	..	Stop	..	..	6 49	6 39	..	6 58	7 7	7 7	..	..	..	..	..	Stop
—	—	—	Ford (Sussex) ....arr.	..	..	..	5 34		5 57	..		6 40	..	..	..	..	..		..	..	..	..	..	7 2	..		..	..	..	..	..	
30	—	—	Angmering L........	..	..	..	Stop	..	Stop	6 7	..	Stop	..	..	..	..	..	..	..	..	..	6 49	6 57	..	..	Through Train Bognor Regis to Victoria	..	..	..	..	..	..
32½	—	—	Goring-by-Sea	..	..	..		..		6 11	..		..	..	..	..	..	..	..	..	..	6 54	7 2	..	..		..	..	..	..	..	..
33½	—	—	Durrington-on-Sea........	a.m	..	..	..	..	..	6 14	a.m	..	..	..	..	..	..	..	..	..	..	6 57	7 5	..	..		..	..	..	..	..	a.m
34	—	—	West Worthing U........	5 16	..	5 40	..	..	..	6 16	6 35	..	..	..	..	..	..	..	6 50	6 54	..	7 0	7 7	..	..		..	..	..	..	..	7 24
35	—	—	Worthing Central........	5 18	..	5 42	..	..	..	6 18	6 37	..	..	..	..	..	..	..	6 53	6 56	..	7 4	7 10	..	..		..	..	..	..	..	7 26
35¾	—	—	Ham Bridge Halt N........	5 20	..	5 44	..	..	..	6 20	..	..	..	..	..	..	..	..	..	6 58	..	..	..	..	..		..	..	..	..	..	7 28
37½	—	—	Lancing........	5 23	..	5 47	..	..	..	6 23	6 41	..	..	..	..	..	..	..	6 57	7 1	..	7 9	7 14	..	..		..	..	..	..	..	7 31
39½	—	—	Shoreham-by-Sea K 244....	5 27	..	5 51	..	..	..	6 27	6 45	..	..	..	..	..	..	..	7 2	7 5	..	7 14	7 18	..	..		..	..	..	..	..	7 36
41	—	—	Southwick	5 31	..	5 55	..	..	..	6 31	6 48	..	..	..	..	..	..	..	..	7 9	..	..	7 21	..	..		..	..	..	..	..	7 40
42	—	—	Fishersgate Halt........	5 33	..	5 57	..	..	..	6 33	6 51	..	..	..	..	..	..	..	..	7 11	..	..	..	..	..		..	..	..	..	..	7 42
42½	—	—	Portslade and West Hove..	5 35	..	5 59	..	..	..	6 35	6 53	..	..	..	..	..	..	..	7 7	7 13	..	7 20	7 25	..	..		..	..	..	..	..	7 44
43½	—	—	Aldrington Halt	5 38	..	6 2	..	..	..	6 38	6 55	..	..	..	..	..	..	..	..	7 16	..	..	7 28	..	..		..	..	..	..	..	7 47
44	—	—	Hove........	5 40	..	6 4	..	..	..	6 40	6 57	..	..	..	..	..	..	..	7 13	7 18	..	7 25	7 30	..	..		..	..	..	..	..	7 49
44½	—	—	Holland Road Halt	..	..	6 6	..	..	..	6 42	6 59	..	..	..	..	..	..	..	Through Train West Worthing to London Bridge	7 20	..	..	7 32	..	..		..	..	..	..	..	7 51
45½	—	—	Brighton (below) ....arr.	5 44	..	6 9	..	..	..	6 45	7 2	..	..	..	..	..	..	..		7 23	..	..	7 35	..	..		..	..	..	..	..	7 54
—	28½	—	Arundel	Stop	..	Stop	..	..	..	Stop	Stop	..	..	..	..	..	..	..		..	6 55	..	..	..	7 14	7 19	..	..	..	..	7 26	Stop
—	31¾	—	Amberley		..		..	..	..			..	..	..	..	..	..	..		..	7 1	..	..	..	..	..	..	..	..	..	7 30	
—	36½	—	Pulborough J 374........	..	..	..	..	..	..	..	..	..	..	..	..	..	..	..		..	7 8	..	..	..	..	7 30	..	..	..	..	7 39	..
—	41½	—	Billingshurst.....[Horsham	..	..	..	..	..	..	..	..	..	..	..	..	..	..	..		..	7 15	..	..	..	..	..	..	..	..	..	7 46	..
—	46¼	—	Christ's Hospital, West	..	..	..	..	..	..	..	..	..	..	..	..	..	..	..		..	7 22	..	..	..	..	..	..	..	..	..	7 53	..
—	48¾	—	Horsham 244, 245, 285, 427 arr.	..	..	..	..	..	..	..	..	..	..	..	..	..	..	..		..	7 26	..	..	..	..	7 45	..	..	..	..	7 57	..
			Horsham 244, 245, 285, 427 dep.	..	..	..	..	..	..	..	..	..	..	..	..	..	..	..		..	..	..	..	..	..	..	..	..	..	..	..	..
—	62¼	—	Dorking North H 285, 427..	..	..	..	..	..	..	..	..	..	..	..	..	..	..	..		..	..	..	..	..	..	..	..	..	..	..	..	..
—	74	—	Sutton 285, 322........arr.	..	..	..	..	..	a.m	..	..	a.m	..	..	..	..	..	..		..	..	..	..	..	..	..	..	..	..	..	..	..
—	—	—	Horsham ....dep.	..	6 17	..	..	..	6 45	..	..	7 7	..	..	..	..	..	..		..	7 27	..	..	..	..	7 46	..	..	..	..	7 59	..
—	49¾	—	Littlehaven Halt	..	6 19	..	..	..	6 47	..	..	7 9	..	..	..	..	..	..		..	7 29	..	..	..	..	..	..	..	..	..	8 1	..
—	52	—	Fay Gate........	..	6 23	..	..	..	6 51	..	..	7 13	..	..	..	..	..	..		..	7 33	..	..	..	..	..	..	..	..	..	8 5	..
—	54½	—	Ifield........	..	6 28	..	..	..	6 56	..	..	7 18	..	..	..	..	..	..		..	7 38	..	..	..	..	..	..	..	..	..	8 10	..
—	55¾	—	Crawley........[234	..	6 31	..	..	..	6 59	..	..	7 21	..	..	..	..	..	..		..	7 41	..	..	..	..	7 55	..	..	..	..	8 13	a.m
—	57¼	—	Three Bridges (below)..arr.	..	6 34	..	..	..	7 2	..	..	7 24	..	..	..	..	..	..		..	7 44	..	..	..	..	7 59	..	..	..	..	8 16	P
				1	2	3	4	5	6	7	8	9	10	11	12	13	14	15	16	17	18	19	20	21	22	23	24	25	26	27	28	29

				1	2	3	4	5	6	7	8	9	10	11	12	13	14	15	16	17	18	19	20	21	22	23	24	25	26	27	28	29
—	—	—	Ore .... dep.	..	Stop	..	..	..	..	..	..	Stop	..	..	6 5	..	..	..	..	..	Stop	..	..	..	..	..	..	..	6 33	..	..	6 49
—	—	1	Hastings	..		..	..	..	..	..	..		..	..	6 8	..	..	..	..	..		..	..	..	..	..	..	..	6 37	..	..	6 53
—	—	1¾	St. Leonards (W.S.)	..	..	..	..	..	..	..	..	..	..	..	6 10	..	..	..	..	..	..	..	..	..	..	..	..	..	6 40	..	..	6 56
—	—	2¾	" (W.M.)	..	..	..	..	..	..	..	..	..	..	..	6 12	..	..	..	..	..	..	..	..	..	..	..	..	..	6 43	..	..	..
—	—	5½	Bexhill (Central) G	..	..	..	..	..	..	..	..	..	..	..	6 17	..	..	..	..	..	..	..	..	..	..	..	..	..	6 49	..	..	7 3
—	—	6½	Collington Halt	..	..	..	..	..	..	..	..	..	..	..	6 20	..	..	..	..	..	..	..	..	..	..	..	..	..	..	..	..	..
—	—	7¾	Cooden Beach	..	..	..	..	..	..	..	..	..	..	..	6 23	..	..	..	..	..	..	..	..	..	..	..	..	..	6 53	..	..	7 7
—	—	9½	Norman's Bay Halt	..	..	..	..	..	..	..	..	..	..	..	6 26	..	..	..	..	..	..	..	..	..	..	..	..	..	..	..	..	..
—	—	11½	Pevensey Bay Halt	..	..	..	..	..	..	..	..	..	..	..	6 30	..	..	..	..	..	..	..	..	..	..	..	..	..	..	..	..	..
—	—	12¼	Pevensey and Westham	..	..	..	..	..	..	..	..	..	..	..	6 32	..	..	..	..	..	..	..	..	..	..	..	..	..	6 59	..	..	7 13
—	—	15½	Hampden Park F	..	..	..	..	..	..	..	..	..	..	..	6 37	..	..	..	..	..	..	..	..	..	..	..	..	..	7 5	..	..	7 19
—	—	17½	Eastbourne .... arr.	..	..	..	..	..	..	..	a.m	..	..	..	6 41	..	..	..	..	..	..	..	..	..	..	..	..	..	7 9	..	..	7 23
			Eastbourne .... dep.	..	..	..	..	..	..	..	6 20	..	6 25	6 37	6 45	6 53	..	..	..	..	..	..	..	..	..	..	..	..	7 12	7 29	..	7 27
—	—	—	Hampden Park F	..	..	..	..	..	..	..	6 23	..	6 28	6 41	6 48	..	..	..	..	..	..	..	..	..	..	..	..	..	7 16	7 32	..	..
—	—	15¾	Polegate 239	..	..	..	..	..	..	..	6 27	..	Stop	6 46	6 52	6 59	..	..	..	..	..	..	..	..	..	..	..	..	7 21	Stop	..	..
—	—	19¾	Berwick	..	..	..	..	..	..	..	Stop	..		Stop	6 58	..	..	..	..	..	..	..	..	..	..	..	..	..	7 27		..	..
—	—	24¼	Glynde	..	..	..	..	..	..	..		..	..		7 4	..	..	..	..	..	..	..	..	..	..	..	..	..	..	..	..	..
—	—	27¼	Lewes 239 .... arr.	..	..	..	..	..	..	..	a.m	..	..	..	7 9	7 14	..	..	..	..	..	..	..	..	..	..	..	..	7 37	..	..	7 46
—	—	—	Mls Seaford .... dep.	..	..	..	..	..	..	..	6 27	..	..	..	6 53	..	..	..	Saturdays excepted	..	..	..	..	..	..	..	..	..	..	..	..	7 25
—	—	—	1 Bishopstone	..	..	..	..	..	..	..	6 29	..	..	..	6 55	..	..	..		..	..	..	..	..	..	..	..	..	..	..	..	7 27
—	—	—	2½ Newhaven Harbour	..	..	..	..	..	..	..	6 34	..	..	..	7 0	..	..	..		..	..	..	..	..	..	..	..	..	..	..	..	7 32
—	—	—	2¾ " Town..[Halt	..	..	..	..	..	..	..	6 35	..	..	..	7 1	..	..	..		..	..	..	..	..	..	..	..	..	..	..	..	7 33
—	—	—	5½ Southease and Rodmell	..	..	..	..	..	..	..	6 40	..	..	..	7 6	..	..	..		..	..	..	..	..	..	..	..	..	..	..	..	7 38
—	—	—	9 Lewes 239 .... arr.	..	..	..	..	..	..	..	6 46	..	..	..	7 12	..	..	..		..	..	..	..	..	..	..	..	..	..	..	..	7 44
—	—	—	Lewes .... dep.	..	..	..	..	..	..	..	6 49	..	..	..	7 20	..	..	..		..	..	..	..	..	..	..	..	..	..	..	..	..
—	—	31¾	Falmer	..	..	..	..	..	..	..	6 56	..	..	..	7 27	..	..	..		..	..	..	..	..	..	..	..	..	..	..	..	..
—	—	34½	London Road (Brighton)	..	..	..	..	..	..	..	7 0	..	..	..	7 31	..	..	..		..	..	..	..	..	..	..	..	..	..	..	..	..
—	—	35¼	Brighton .... arr.	..	..	..	..	..	..	..	7 3	..	..	..	7 34	..	..	..		..	..	..	..	..	..	..	..	..	..	..	..	..
—	—	—	Lewes .... dep.	..	..	..	..	..	..	..	Stop	..	..	..	..	7 14	..	..	..	..	..	..	..	..	..	..	..	..	7 38	..	..	7 47
—	—	30	Cooksbridge	..	..	..	..	..	..	..		..	..	..	..	7 20	..	..	..	..	..	..	..	..	..	..	..	..	7 44	..	..	7 53
—	—	32¾	Plumpton	..	..	..	..	..	..	..	..	..	..	..	..	7 25	..	..	..	..	..	..	..	..	..	..	..	..	7 49	..	..	7 58
—	—	36¾	Wivelsfield (below)	..	..	..	..	..	..	..	..	..	..	..	..	7 31	..	..	..	..	..	..	..	..	..	..	..	..	..	..	..	..
—	—	39½	Haywards Heath .... arr.	..	a.m	a.m	..	a.m	..	a.m	..	a.m	a.m	a.m	..	7 36	..	..	..	..	a.m	..	..	..	..	..	..	..	7 59	a.m	..	8 7
—	—	—	Brighton .... dep.	..	5 58	6 15	..	6 25	..	6 28	..	6 51	7 6	7 8	..	..	..	..	..	..	7 19	..	..	..	..	..	7 28	7 40	..	7 45	..	..
46¾	—	—	Preston Park	..	6 1	6 18	..	6 28	..	6 31	..	6 54	..	7 11	..	..	..	..	..	..	7 22	..	..	..	..	..	7 31	..	..	7 48	..	..
52½	—	—	Hassocks D	..	6 10	6 26	..	..	..	6 39	..	7 2	7 10	..	..	..	..	..	..	..	7 31	..	..	..	..	..	7 39	..	..	7 56	..	..
54½	—	—	Burgess Hill	..	6 15	6 30	..	..	..	6 43	..	7 6	7 14	..	..	..	..	..	..	..	7 35	..	..	..	..	..	7 43	..	..	..	..	..
55½	—	—	Wivelsfield (above)	..	6 17	6 32	..	..	..	6 45	a.m	7 8	7 16	..	..	..	..	a.m	..	..	..	..	..	..	..	..	7 46	..	..	..	..	..
58¼	—	—	Haywards Heath C	..	6 23	6 37	..	6 44	..	6 51	7 6	7 14	7 21	7 25	..	7 37	..	7 33	7 39	..	7 40	7 45	..	..	..	..	7 51	7 56	7 59	8 5	..	8 9
60¾	—	42	Ardingly	..	..	..	..	..	..	..	7 10	..	..	..	..	7 43	..	..	..	..	..	R	..	..	..	RB	..	P	..	..	..	P
63	—	44¼	Horsted Keynes 239 . arr.	..	..	..	..	..	..	..	7 14	..	..	..	..	7 47	..	..	..	..	..	..	..	..	..	..	..	..	..	..	..	..
62¼	—	43½	Balcombe	a.m	6 29	..	a.m	..	..	6 57	..	7 20	..	..	..	..	a.m	7 39	..	..	..	..	..	..	..	..	7 57	..	..	8 11	..	..
66¾	—	48	Three Bridges (above)	6 7	6 37	..	6 46	6 55	..	7 4	..	7 28	..	..	..	..	7 38	7 47	..	..	..	..	..	..	..	7 59	8 6	..	8 10	..	..	8 21
69	59½	50½	Gatwick Airport	6 10	6 41	..	6 50	..	..	7 8	..	7 32	..	..	..	..	7 41	7 51	..	..	..	..	..	..	..	..	8 10	..	..	..	..	..
70¼	60¾	51½	Horley	6 14	6 44	..	6 53	..	..	7 11	..	7 35	..	..	..	..	7 44	7 54	..	..	..	..	..	..	..	..	8 13	..	8 16	..	..	8 27
72½	63	53¾	Salfords	6 18	6 48	..	6 57	..	..	7 15	..	7 39	..	..	..	..	7 48	7 58	..	..	..	..	..	..	..	..	8 17	..	..	..	..	..
74½	65	55¾	Earlswood	6 22	6 52	..	7 1	..	..	7 19	..	7 43	..	..	..	..	7 52	8 2	..	..	..	..	..	..	..	..	8 21	..	..	..	..	..
75¼	65¾	56½	Redhill 246	6 29	6 59	..	7 3	7 7	..	7 26	..	7 50	..	..	..	..	..	8 9	..	..	..	..	..	..	..	..	8 28	..	..	..	..	..
77¼	67¾	58½	Merstham	6 33	7 3	..	..	..	..	7 30	..	7 54	..	..	..	..	..	8 13	..	..	..	..	..	..	..	..	8 32	..	..	..	..	..
81	71½	62¼	Coulsdon South	6 39	7 9	..	..	..	..	7 36	..	8 0	..	..	..	..	..	8 19	..	..	..	..	..	..	..	..	8 38	..	..	..	..	..
82¾	73¼	64	Purley	6 43	7 13	..	..	..	..	7 39	..	8 4	..	..	..	..	8 6	..	..	..	..	..	..	..	..	..	..	..	8 31	8 35	..	8 44
85¾	76¼	67	East Croydon 285 ..... arr.	6 48	7 18	..	..	7 21	..	7 45	..	8 9	..	7 57	..	..	8 11	8 26	8 12	..	..	8 18	..	..	..	8 20	8 47	8 30	8 36	8 40	..	8 50
87½	78	68¾	Norwood Junction B arr.	..	..	..	..	..	..	..	..	..	..	..	..	..	..	..	..	..	..	..	..	..	..	..	..	..	..	..	..	..
93¾	83¾	74½	New Cross Gate ..... "	7 1	..	..	..	..	..	..	..	..	..	..	..	..	..	8 38	..	..	..	..	..	..	..	8*38	..	..	..	..	..	..
96	86½‡	77¼	LONDON BRIDGE... "	7 7	7*39	..	..	7 39	..	8 0	..	8 26	..	8 13	..	..	8 ③31	8 43	8 29	..	..	8 33	..	..	..	8*43	9 3	8③50	8*55	8 55	..	9 6
93½	84¶	74¾	Clapham Junction A .. arr.	..	7 30	..	..	..	..	8*0	..	8*23	..	..	..	..	8 23	8*48	8*31	..	..	8*31	..	..	..	8 31	..	..	8 48	..	..	9③10
96¼	86¾¶	77½	VICTORIA .... "	..	7 36	..	..	..	..	8*7	..	8*28	..	8 15	..	..	8 28	8*46	8*37	..	..	8*37	..	..	..	8 37	9 *8	8 46	8 53	9 *8	..	9*8

③ Third class only. * Change at East Croydon. ‡ Add 1¼ miles via Sutton. ¶ Subtract ¾ mile via Sutton. *a* Arrival time.
P Pullman Car facilities available. R Refreshment Car facilities available.
RB Refreshment Car facilities available between Bognor Regis and London.

For Other Notes, see page 233

For SERVICES from ISLE OF WIGHT and PORTSMOUTH to LONDON (Waterloo), see pages 366 to 372

From THE SOUTH COAST to LONDON—Week Days—*continued*

Station	a.m	a.m	a.m	a.m	a.m	a.m	a.m	a.m	a.m	a.m	a.m	a.m	a.m	a.m	a.m	am	a.m	a.m	a.m	a.m	a.m	a.m	a.m	a.m	a.m	a.m	a.m	a.m	a.m	a.m
(Page 366) Yarmouth ....dep	..	..	..	..	..	..	..	..	..	..	..	..	..	..	..	..	..	..	..	..	..	..	..	..	..	..	..	..	..	..
Cowes .... "	..	..	..	..	..	..	..	..	..	..	..	..	..	..	..	..	..	..	..	..	..	..	..	..	..	..	..	..	..	..
Newport .... "	..	..	..	..	..	..	..	..	..	..	..	..	..	..	..	..	..	..	..	..	..	..	..	..	..	..	..	..	..	..
Ventnor .... "	..	..	..	..	..	..	..	..	..	..	..	..	..	..	..	..	..	..	..	..	..	..	..	..	..	..	..	..	..	..
Shanklin .... "	..	..	..	..	..	..	..	..	..	..	..	..	..	..	..	..	..	..	..	..	..	..	..	..	..	..	..	..	..	..
Sandown .... "	..	..	..	..	..	..	..	..	..	..	..	..	..	..	..	..	..	..	..	..	..	..	..	..	..	..	..	..	..	..
500 Ryde Pier (Boat) . "	..	..	..	..	..	..	..	..	..	..	..	..	..	..	..	..	..	..	..	..	..	..	..	..	..	..	..	..	..	..
Portsmouth Harbour..dep.	..	..	..	..	..	..	..	..	..	6 57	..	..	..	7 18	..	..	..	..	..	..	..	Saturdays excepted ☞	..	..	..	..	..	..	..	..
Portsmouth & Southsea "	..	..	..	..	..	..	..	..	..	7 0	7 11	..	..	7 22	..	..	..	..	..	..	..		7 42	..	..	..	..	..	..	..
Fratton........	..	..	..	..	..	..	..	..	..	7 3	7 14	..	..	7 25	..	..	..	..	..	..	..		7 44	..	..	..	..	..	..	..
Hilsea Halt........	..	..	..	..	..	..	..	..	..	7 7	..	..	..	..	..	..	..	..	..	..	..		7 48	..	..	..	..	..	..	..
Bedhampton Halt........	..	..	..	..	..	..	..	..	..	..	..	..	..	..	..	..	..	..	..	..	..		7 53	..	..	..	..	..	..	..
245 Hayling Island....dep.	..	..	..	..	..	..	..	..	..	..	6 58	..	..	..	..	..	..	..	..	..	..		..	..	..	..	..	..	..	..
Havant 244	..	..	..	..	..	..	..	..	..	7 13	7 23	..	..	7 34	..	..	..	..	..	..	..		7 55	..	..	..	Saturdays excepted	..	..	..
Warblington Halt........	..	..	..	..	..	..	..	..	..	..	7 25	..	..	..	..	..	..	..	..	..	..		7 57	..	..	..		..	..	..
Emsworth	..	..	..	..	..	..	..	..	..	7 17	7 28	..	..	7 38	..	..	..	..	..	..	..		8 0	..	..	..		..	..	..
Southbourne Halt........	..	..	..	..	..	..	..	..	..	..	7 31	..	..	..	..	..	..	..	..	..	..		8 3	..	..	..		..	..	..
Nutbourne Halt	..	..	..	..	..	..	..	..	..	..	7 33	..	..	..	..	..	..	..	..	..	..		8 6	..	..	..		..	..	..
Bosham........	..	..	..	..	..	..	..	..	..	7 23	7 37	..	..	7 44	..	..	..	..	..	..	..		8 9	..	..	..		..	..	..
Fishbourne Halt........	..	..	..	..	..	..	..	..	..	..	7 40	..	..	..	..	..	..	..	..	..	..		8 12	..	..	..		..	..	..
Chichester Z	..	..	..	..	..	..	..	..	..	7 29	7 44	..	..	7 50	..	..	..	..	..	..	..		8 15	..	..	..		..	..	..
Barnham........arr.	..	..	..	..	..	..	..	..	..	7 38	7 53	..	..	7 59	..	..	..	..	..	..	..		8 24	..	..	..		..	..	..
Bognor Regis .... arr.	..	..	..	..	..	..	..	..	..	7 49	8 12	..	..	8 12	..	..	..	..	..	..	..		8 39	..	..	..	R	..	..	..
Bognor Regis .... dep.	..	..	..	..	..	7 20	..	..	..	7 35	7 35	..	..	7 55	..	..	..	..	..	..	8 4	8 14	Stop	..	..	..	8 28	8 40	..	..
Barnham........dep.	..	..	..	..	..	7 26	..	..	..	7 43	7 53	..	..	8 4	..	..	..	..	..	..	8 10	8a20		..	..	..	8 34	8a46	..	..
Ford (Sussex)........	..	..	..	..	..	7 30	..	..	7 44	7 49	7 57	..	..	RB	..	..	..	..	..	..	8 14	Stop	..	..	8 30	..	..	Stop	..	..
Littlehampton .... arr.	..	..	..	..	..	7 35	P	..	7 50	..	..	..	..	8 19	..	..	..	..	P	..	8 19	..	..	..	8 35	..	..	..	..	..
Littlehampton .... dep.	7 17	..	7 20	..	7 34	Stop	7 37	7 43	Stop	7 37	..	7 56	8 0	8 0	..	..	..	..	8 9	8 18	8 22	..	..	8 33	Stop	8 43	8 22	..	..	8 46
Ford (Sussex)........arr.	..	..	7 24	..	7 38		..	..		..	..	8 0	..	..	..	..	..	..	..	8 23	..	..	..	8 37		..		..	..	8 50
Angmering L	7 26	..	Stop	..	Stop	..	7 46	..	..	..	8 5	Stop	..	Through Train, Bognor Regis to Victoria.	..	..	..	..	8 19	Stop	..	..	..	Stop	..	8 53	Through Train Bognor Regis to London Bridge	..	..	Stop
Goring-by-Sea	7 31	..		..		..	7 50	..	..	..	8 9		..		..	..	..	..	8 24		..	..	..		..	8 57		..	..	
Durrington-on-Sea	7 33	..	..	..	a.m	..	7 53	..	..	..	8 12	a.m	..		..	..	..	..	8 27	a.m	..	..	..	a.m	..	9 0		..	..	..
West Worthing U	7 36	..	..	..	7 45	..	7 55	..	..	8 1	8 14	8 20	..		..	..	..	..	8 30	8 38	..	..	..	8 49	..	9 2		..	..	..
Worthing Central........	7 38	..	..	..	7 47	..	8 0	..	..	8 5	8 16	8 22	..		..	..	..	..	8 35	8 40	..	..	..	8 51	..	9 6		..	..	..
Ham Bridge Halt N........	..	..	..	..	7 49	..	..	..	..	..	..	8 24	..		..	..	..	..	..	..	..	..	..	8 53	..	..		..	..	..
Lancing	7 42	..	a.m	..	7 52	..	..	..	a.m	8 10	8 20	8 27	..		..	..	..	..	..	8 44	..	..	..	8 56	a.m	9 10		..	..	..
Shoreham-by-Sea K 244...	7 46	..	7 51	..	7 56	..	8 7	..	8 10	8 14	8 24	8 31	..		..	..	..	..	8 42	8 48	..	..	..	9 1	9 5	9 14		..	..	..
Southwick........	7 49	..	7 55	..	8 0	..	..	..	..	8 17	8 28	8 35	..		..	..	..	..	..	8 51	..	..	..	9 5	9 9	9 17		..	..	..
Fishersgate Halt........	..	..	..	..	8 2	..	..	..	..	..	..	8 37	..		..	..	..	..	..	..	..	..	..	9 7	..	..		..	..	..
Portslade and West Hove..	7 52	..	7 58	..	8 4	a.m	..	..	8 16	8 20	8 31	8 39	..		..	..	..	..	..	8 54	..	..	..	9 9	9 13	9 20		..	..	..
Aldrington Halt	7 55	..	..	..	8 7	P	..	..	..	8 23	8 33	8 42	..		..	..	..	..	..	8 57	..	..	..	9 12	..	9 23		..	..	..
Hove........	7 57	..	8 2	..	8 9	8 7	8 15	..	8 19	8 25	8 36	8 44	..		..	..	..	..	8 50	8 59	..	..	..	9 14	9 17	9 25		..	..	..
Holland Road Halt	..	..	8 4	..	8 11	..		..	..	..	..	8 46	..		..	..	..	..		..	..	..	..	9 16	..	..		..	..	..
Brighton (*below*)........arr.	8 2	..	8 7	..	8 14	..		..	8 24	8 29	8 39	8 50	..		..	..	..	..		9 2	..	..	..	9 18	9 22	9 28		..	..	..
Arundel	Stop	..	Stop	..	Stop	..	Through Train Littlehampton to Victoria.	7 51	..	Stop	..	..	8 7	8 12	..	..	..	..	Through Train Littlehampton to London Bridge.	Stop	8 29	..	..	Stop	Stop	Stop	8 42	..	..	..
Amberley........		..		..		..		7 56	..		..	..	..	..	..	..	..	..			8 34	..	..				..	..	..	..
Pulborough J 374	..	..	..	..	..	Saturdays excepted.		8 5	..	..	..	..	..	8 23	..	..	..	..		..	8 42	..	..	..	..	..	8 53	..	..	..
Billingshurst.....[Horsham	..	..	..	..	..			8 12	..	..	..	..	..	..	..	..	..	..		..	8 49	..	..	..	..	..	..	..	..	..
Christ's Hospital, West	..	..	..	..	..			8 20	..	..	..	..	..	..	..	..	..	..		..	8 56	..	..	..	..	..	..	..	..	..
Horsham 244, 245, 285, 427 arr.	..	..	..	..	..			8 25	..	..	..	..	..	8 38	..	..	..	..		..	9 0	..	..	..	..	..	9 8	..	..	..
Horsham 244, 245, 285, 427 dep.	..	..	..	..	..			..	..	..	..	..	..	..	..	..	..	..		..	9 1	..	..	..	..	..	..	..	..	..
Dorking North H 285, 427..	..	..	..	..	..			..	..	..	..	..	..	..	..	..	..	..		..	9 26	..	..	..	..	..	..	..	..	..
Sutton 285, 322 ....arr.	..	..	..	..	..			..	..	..	..	..	..	..	..	..	..	..		..	9 43	..	..	..	..	..	..	..	..	..
Horsham........dep.	..	..	..	..	..			8 26	..	..	..	..	..	8 39	..	..	..	8 46		..	..	..	..	..	..	..	9 9	..	..	..
Littlehaven Halt	..	..	..	..	..			8 28	..	..	..	..	..	..	..	..	..	8 48		..	..	..	..	..	..	..	..	..	..	..
Fay Gate........	..	..	..	..	..			8 32	..	..	..	..	..	..	..	..	..	8 52		..	..	..	..	..	..	..	..	..	..	..
Ifield........	..	..	..	..	..			8 37	..	..	..	..	..	..	..	..	..	8 57		..	..	..	..	..	..	..	..	..	..	..
Crawley........ [234	..	..	..	..	..	..		8 40	..	..	..	..	..	..	..	..	..	8 59		..	..	..	..	..	..	..	..	..	..	..
Three Bridges (*below*)..arr.	..	..	..	..	..	..		8 43	..	..	..	..	..	8 50	..	..	P	9 2		..	..	..	..	a.m	..	..	..	..	P	..
	1	2	3	4	5	6	7	8	9	10	11	12	13	14	15	16	17	18	19	20	21	22	23	24	25	26	27	28	29	30

Station	1	2	3	4	5	6	7	8	9	10	11	12	13	14	15	16	17	18	19	20	21	22	23	24	25	26	27	28	29	30
Ore .... dep.	..	..	..	7 9	..	..	..	..	..	..	..	..	..	..	..	..	7 30	..	..	..	..	..	..	7 43	..	..	..	..	8 0	..
Hastings	..	..	..	7 12	..	..	..	..	..	..	..	..	..	..	..	..	7 35	..	..	..	..	..	..	7 46	..	..	..	..	8 4	..
St. Leonards (W.S.)	..	..	..	7 14	..	..	..	..	..	..	..	..	..	..	..	..	7 38	..	..	..	..	..	..	7 48	..	..	..	..	8 7	..
" (W.M.)	..	..	..	7 16	..	..	..	..	..	..	..	..	..	..	..	..	..	..	..	..	..	..	..	7 51	..	..	..	..	..	..
Bexhill (Central) **G**	..	..	..	7 21	..	..	..	..	..	..	..	..	..	..	..	..	7 44	..	..	..	..	..	..	7 56	..	..	..	..	8 14	..
Collington Halt	..	..	..	7 24	..	..	..	..	..	..	..	..	..	..	..	..	..	..	..	..	..	..	..	7 58	..	..	..	..	..	..
Cooden Beach	..	..	..	7 27	..	..	..	..	..	..	..	..	..	..	..	..	7 48	..	..	..	..	..	..	8 1	..	..	..	..	8 18	..
Norman's Bay Halt	..	..	..	7 30	..	..	..	..	..	..	..	..	..	..	..	..	..	..	..	..	..	..	..	8 4	..	..	..	..	..	..
Pevensey Bay Halt	..	..	..	7 34	..	..	..	..	..	..	..	..	..	..	..	..	..	..	..	..	..	..	..	8 8	..	..	..	..	..	..
Pevensey and Westham	..	..	..	7 36	..	..	..	..	..	..	..	..	..	..	..	..	7 54	..	..	..	..	..	..	8 10	..	..	..	..	..	..
Hampden Park **F**	..	..	..	7 42	..	..	..	..	..	..	..	..	..	..	..	..	..	..	..	..	..	..	..	8 15	..	..	..	..	..	..
Eastbourne .... arr.	a.m	..	..	7 46	a.m	..	..	..	..	a.m	..	..	..	..	..	..	8 2	..	..	a.m	..	..	..	8 19	a.m	..	..	..	8 31	a.m
Eastbourne .... dep.	7 42	..	..	7 49	7 52	..	..	..	..	7 57	..	..	..	..	..	..	8 6	..	..	8 16	..	..	..	8 22	8 27	..	..	..	8 36	8 42
Hampden Park **F**	7 45	..	..	7 52	7 56	..	..	..	..	8 0	..	..	..	..	..	..	..	..	..	8 20	..	..	..	8 25	8 30	..	..	..	..	8 45
Polegate 239	7 49	..	..	7 57	8 1	..	..	..	..	Stop	..	..	..	..	..	..	..	..	..	8 25	..	..	..	8 29	..	..	..	..	..	Stop
Berwick	Stop	..	..	8 3	..	..	..	..	..	..	..	..	..	..	..	..	..	..	..	Stop	..	..	..	8 35	..	..	..	..	..	..
Glynde	..	..	..	8 9	..	..	..	..	..	..	..	..	..	..	..	..	..	..	..	..	..	..	..	8 41	..	..	..	..	..	..
Lewes 239 .... arr.	..	..	..	8 14	..	..	..	..	..	..	..	..	..	..	**R**	..	8 25	..	..	..	..	..	a.m	8 46	..	a.m	..	..	8 55	..
Seaford .... dep	..	7 25	..	..	..	Saturdays excepted	..	..	..	..	..	..	..	..	8 5	..	..	..	..	..	..	..	8 14	..	..	8 25	..	..	8 38	..
Bishopstone	..	7 27	..	..	..		..	..	..	..	..	..	..	..	..	..	..	..	..	..	..	..	8 16	..	..	8 27	..	..	**RL**	..
Newhaven Harbour	..	7 32	..	..	..		..	..	..	..	..	..	..	..	8 9	..	..	..	..	..	..	..	8 21	..	..	8 32	..	..	8 42	..
" Town	..	7 33	..	..	..		..	..	..	..	..	..	..	..	8 11	—	..	..	..	..	..	..	8 22	..	..	8 33	..	..	8 44	..
Southease & Rodmell Halt	..	7 38	..	..	..		..	..	..	..	..	..	..	..	..	..	..	..	..	..	..	..	8 27	..	..	8 38	..	..	..	..
Lewes 239 .... arr.	..	7 44	a.m	..	..		..	..	..	..	..	..	..	..	8 20	..	..	..	..	..	..	..	8 33	..	..	8 44	..	a.m	8 53	..
Lewes .... dep.	..	7 45	8 5	8 15	..		..	..	..	..	..	..	..	..	..	821	..	..	..	..	..	..	Stop	8 47	..	..	..	8 51	..	..
Falmer	a.m	..	..	8 22	..		..	..	..	..	..	..	..	..	..	..	..	..	..	..	..	..	..	8 55	..	..	..	..	..	..
London Road (Brighton)	7 49	7 59	8 20	8 26	..		..	..	..	..	..	..	..	..	..	836	..	..	..	..	..	..	..	8 59	..	..	..	9 6	..	..
Brighton .... arr.	7 51	8 4	8 24	8 29	..		..	..	..	..	..	..	..	..	..	839	..	..	..	..	..	..	..	9 2	..	..	..	9 10	..	..
Lewes .... dep.	Stop	..	Stop	Stop	..	..	..	..	..	..	..	..	..	..	8 20	..	8 26	..	..	..	..	..	..	..	..	8 49	Saturdays excepted	..	8 58	..
Cooksbridge	..	..	..	..	..	..	..	..	..	..	..	..	..	..	..	..	8 30	..	..	..	..	..	..	..	..	8 54		..	..	..
Plumpton	..	..	..	..	..	..	..	..	..	..	..	..	..	..	8 29	..	..	..	..	..	..	..	..	..	..	8 59		..	..	..
Wivelsfield (*below*)	..	..	..	..	..	..	..	..	..	..	..	..	..	..	..	..	..	..	..	..	..	..	..	..	..	9 6		..	..	..
Haywards Heath .... arr.	a.m	..	a.m	..	..	..	..	..	..	a.m	..	..	..	..	8 38	..	8 44	..	..	a.m	..	a.m	a.m	..	..	9 11		..	9 15	a.m
Brighton .... dep.	7 50	..	8 0	..	..	..	..	..	..	8 20	..	..	..	..	..	..	..	..	..	8 25	..	8 35	8 43	..	..	..		..	..	8 56
Preston Park	7 53	..	8 3	..	..	8 10	..	..	..	..	..	..	..	..	..	..	..	..	..	8 28	..	8 38	..	..	..	..		..	..	8 59
Hassocks **D**	8 1	..	..	..	..	8 18	..	..	..	..	..	..	..	..	..	..	..	..	..	8 36	..	..	..	..	..	..		..	..	9 7
Burgess Hill	8 5	..	..	..	..	8 22	..	..	..	..	..	..	..	..	..	..	..	..	..	8 40	..	..	..	..	..	..		..	..	9 11
Wivelsfield (*above*)	8 7	..	..	a.m	..	..	..	..	..	..	..	..	..	..	..	..	..	..	..	8 43	..	..	..	..	..	..		..	..	9 13
Haywards Heath C	8 12	..	..	8 15	..	8 28	8 32	..	..	8 36	..	..	..	..	8 45	..	8 45	..	..	8 48	..	8 53	8 59	..	..	9 11		..	9 15	9 18
Ardingly	..	..	**P**	8 19	..	**P**	**P**	..	..	**PR**	..	..	..	**RB**	**R**	..	**P**	..	**P**	..	..	**P**	**P**	..	..	9 15	**R**	..	**P**	..
Horsted Keynes 239 .. arr.	..	..	..	8 23	..	..	..	..	..	..	..	..	..	..	..	..	..	..	..	..	..	..	..	..	..	9 19	..	..	..	..
Balcombe	8 18	..	..	..	..	..	..	..	..	..	..	..	..	..	..	..	..	..	..	8 54	..	..	..	..	..	..	..	..	..	9 24
Three Bridges (*above*)	8 25	..	..	..	..	..	..	8 43	..	..	..	..	..	8 50	..	..	..	..	..	9 4	..	..	..	..	..	..	..	..	..	..
Gatwick Airport	8 29	..	..	..	..	..	..	8 47	..	..	..	..	..	..	..	..	..	..	..	..	..	9 5	..	..	..	..	..	..	..	9 33
Horley	8 32	..	..	..	..	..	..	8 50	..	..	..	..	..	8 56	..	..	..	..	..	9 11	..	9 8	..	..	..	..	9 25	..	..	..
Salfords	8 36	..	..	..	..	..	..	8 54	..	..	..	..	..	..	..	..	..	..	..	9 15	..	..	..	..	..	..	..	..	..	..
Earlswood	8 40	..	..	..	..	..	..	8 58	..	..	..	..	..	..	..	..	..	..	..	9 19	..	..	..	..	..	..	..	..	..	..
Redhill 246	8 47	..	..	..	..	..	..	9 4	..	..	..	..	..	..	..	..	..	..	..	..	..	..	..	..	..	..	..	..	..	..
Merstham	8 51	..	..	..	..	..	..	9 8	..	..	..	..	..	..	..	..	..	..	..	..	..	..	..	..	..	..	..	..	..	..
Coulsdon South	8 58	..	..	..	..	..	..	9 14	..	..	..	..	..	..	..	..	..	..	..	..	..	..	..	..	..	..	..	..	..	..
Purley	..	..	..	..	..	..	..	9 17	..	..	..	..	..	..	..	..	..	..	..	9 31	..	..	..	..	..	..	..	..	..	..
East Croydon 285 .... arr.	9 5	..	..	..	..	9 0	..	9 23	..	9 8	..	..	..	9 16	9 17	..	9 17	..	..	9 37	..	9 26	..	..	..	..	..	..	9 47	9 54
Norwood Junction **B** arr.	..	..	..	..	..	..	..	..	..	..	..	..	..	..	..	..	..	..	..	..	..	..	..	..	..	..	..	..	..	..
New Cross Gate ..... "	..	..	..	..	..	..	..	..	..	..	..	..	..	..	..	..	..	..	..	..	..	..	..	..	..	..	..	..	..	..
LONDON BRIDGE ... "	9 20	..	..	..	..	..	9‡23	9 38	..	9 23	..	..	..	9*38	9 33	..	9 33	..	9 51	9③55	10 4	9③55	9 45	..	..	..	9 57	..	10SX2	..
Clapham Junction **A** ... arr.	9③u22	..	..	..	..	..	..	..	..	9*28	..	..	..	9 28	..	..	..	..	..	9 49	10③8	..	..	..	..	..	..	..	..	10 5
VICTORIA .... "	9③u27	..	9 4	..	..	9 18	9 21	9*42	..	9*34	..	..	..	9 34	9*37	..	9*37	..	..	9 55	10③13	9 42	..	..	..	..	..	..	10SO3	1010

③ Third class only. * Change at East Croydon. ‡ Change at Haywards Heath. *a* Arrival time. **P** Pullman Car facilities available. **PR** Pullman Car facilities available on Saturdays. Refreshment Car, Mondays to Fridays. **R** Refreshment Car facilities available. **RB** Refreshment Car facilities available between Bognor Regis and London. **RL** Refreshment Car facilities available between Seaford and London.

SO Saturdays only. **SX** Saturdays excepted. *u* 6 mins. later on Saturdays

For Other Notes, see page 233

For SERVICES from ISLE OF WIGHT and PORTSMOUTH to LONDON (Waterloo), see pages 366 to 372

From THE SOUTH COAST to LONDON—Week Days—continued

Station	a.m	a.m	a.m		a.m		a.m	a.m	a.m	a.m	a.m	a.m	a.m	a.m	a.m	a.m	a.m	a.m	a.m	a.m	a.m	a.m	a.m	a.m	a.m	a.m	a.m	a.m	a.m	a.m
Page 366 Yarmouth dep.	..	..	..	..	..	..	..	..	..	..	..	..	..	..	..	..	..	..	..	..	..	..	..	..	..	..	..	..	..	..
Cowes "	..	..	..	..	..	..	6 20	..	..	..	..	..	..	..	..	..	..	..	..	..	..	..	..	..	..	..	6 56	..	..	..
Newport "	..	..	..	..	..	..	6 35	..	..	..	..	..	..	..	..	..	..	..	..	..	..	..	..	..	..	..	7 38	..	..	..
Ventnor "	..	..	..	..	..	..	6 30	..	..	..	..	..	..	..	..	..	..	..	..	..	..	..	..	..	..	..	7 40	..	..	..
Shanklin "	..	..	..	..	..	..	6 42	..	..	..	..	..	..	..	..	..	..	..	..	..	..	..	..	..	..	..	7 52	..	..	..
Sandown "	..	..	..	..	..	..	6 50	..	..	..	..	..	..	..	..	..	..	..	..	..	..	..	..	..	..	..	7 58	..	..	..
500 Ryde Pier (Boat) "	..	..	..	..	..	..	7 30	..	..	..	..	..	..	..	..	..	..	..	..	..	..	..	..	..	..	..	8 35	..	..	..
Portsmouth Harbour dep.	..	..	..	..	8 8	..	8 23	..	..	..	..	..	..	..	Saturdays excepted. (see below)	..	..	..	..	8 48	..	..	..	..	..	9 8	9 23	..	..	..
Portsmouth & Southsea "	..	..	..	..	8 12	..	8 27	..	..	..	8 39	..	..	..		..	..	..	..	8 52	..	..	..	..	..	9 12	9 27	..	..	9 42
Fratton	..	..	..	..	8 14	..	8 30	..	..	..	8 42	..	..	..		..	..	..	..	8 54	..	..	..	..	..	9 14	9 30	..	..	9 45
Hilsea Halt	..	..	..	..	..	..	..	..	..	..	8 46	..	..	..		..	..	..	..	..	..	..	..	..	..	..	..	..	..	..
Bedhampton Halt	..	..	..	..	..	..	..	..	..	..	8 51	..	..	..		..	..	..	..	..	..	..	..	..	..	..	..	..	..	9 53
245 Hayling Island dep.	..	..	..	..	7 46	..	..	..	..	..	..	..	..	..		..	..	..	..	8 40	..	..	..	..	..	8 40	..	..	..	..
Havant 244	..	..	..	..	8 23	..	8 39	..	..	..	8 53	..	..	..		..	..	..	..	9 5	..	..	..	..	..	9 23	9 39	..	..	9 55
Warblington Halt	..	..	..	..	8 25	..	..	..	..	..	8 55	..	..	..		..	..	..	..	..	..	..	..	..	..	9 25	..	..	..	9 57
Emsworth	..	..	..	..	8 28	..	8 42	..	..	..	9 1	..	..	..		..	..	..	..	..	..	..	..	..	..	9 28	..	..	..	10 0
Southbourne Halt	..	..	..	..	8 31	..	..	..	..	..	9 4	..	..	..		..	..	..	..	..	..	..	..	..	..	9 31	..	..	..	10 3
Nutbourne Halt	..	..	..	..	8 34	..	..	..	..	..	9 6	..	..	..		..	..	..	..	..	..	..	..	..	..	9 34	..	..	..	10 5
Bosham	..	..	..	..	8 37	..	8 48	..	..	..	9 10	..	..	..		..	..	..	..	..	..	..	..	..	..	9 37	..	..	..	10 9
Fishbourne Halt	..	..	..	..	8 40	..	..	..	..	..	9 13	..	..	..		..	..	..	..	..	..	..	..	..	..	9 40	..	..	..	1012
Chichester Z	..	..	..	..	8 44	..	8 54	..	..	..	9 16	..	..	..		..	..	..	..	9 22	..	..	..	..	..	9 44	9 54	..	..	1015
Barnham arr.	..	..	..	..	8 53	..	9 3	..	..	..	Stop	..	..	..		..	..	..	..	9 31	..	..	..	..	..	9 53	10 3	..	..	Stop
Bognor Regis arr.	..	..	..	..	9 7	..	RB	..	..	..	..	..	..	..	..	..	..	..	..	9 42	..	..	..	..	..	10 8	RB	..	..	..
Bognor Regis dep.	..	..	..	..	8 40	..	8 55	..	..	..	..	..	..	..	9 10	..	..	..	..	9 10	..	..	..	..	9 40	9 40	9 55	..	..	..
Barnham dep.	..	..	..	..	8 54	..	9 5	..	..	..	..	..	..	..	9a16	..	..	..	..	9 31	..	..	..	..	9 47	9 54	10 5	..	..	..
Ford (Sussex)	..	..	..	..	8 59	..	..	..	..	..	..	..	..	..	Stop	..	..	..	..	..	..	..	..	..	9 52	9 59	..	..	..	..
Littlehampton arr.	..	R	..	..	..	..	..	..	..	..	..	P	..	..	..	..	..	..	..	Saturdays excepted.	..	..	..	..	9 57	..	..	..	..	..
Littlehampton dep.	..	8 59	..	..	..	..	8 59	..	..	..	..	9 9	..	..	..	..	..	9 35	9 46		..	..	9 49	..	9 59	..	9 59	..	..	..
Ford (Sussex)	..	..	..	..	..	..	..	..	..	..	..	..	..	..	..	..	..	..	9 50		..	..	..	..	..	..	..	..	..	..
Angmering L	..	..	..	..	9 6	..	Through Train Bognor Regis to Victoria.	..	..	..	..	9 19	..	..	..	..	..	..	Stop		..	..	9 58	..	..	10 6	Through Train, Bognor Regis to Victoria	..	..	..
Goring-by-Sea	..	..	..	..	9 11	..		..	..	..	..	9 24	..	..	..	..	..	..	..	..	..	..	10 3	..	..	1011		..	..	..
Durrington-on-Sea	..	..	..	..	..	..		..	..	..	a.m	9 27	..	..	..	..	..	..	..	..	..	..	10 5	..	..	..		..	..	a.m
West Worthing U	..	..	..	..	9 14	..		..	..	..	9 20	9 30	..	..	..	..	9 39	..	..	..	9 50	..	10 7	..	..	1014		..	..	1020
Worthing Central	..	..	..	..	9 17	..		..	..	..	9 22	9 35	..	..	..	..	9 41	..	..	9 48	9 52	..	10 9	..	..	1017		..	..	1022
Ham Bridge Halt N	..	..	..	..	..	..		..	..	..	9 24	..	..	..	..	..	..	..	..	..	9 55	..	..	..	..	..		..	..	1024
Lancing	..	..	..	..	..	..		..	..	..	9 27	..	..	..	..	..	9 45	..	..	..	9 58	..	1013	..	..	..		..	..	1027
Shoreham-by-Sea K 244	..	..	..	..	9 25	..		..	..	..	9 32	9 42	..	..	..	..	9 49	..	..	9 56	10 3	..	1017	..	..	1025		..	..	1032
Southwick	..	..	..	..	..	..		..	..	..	9 36	..	..	..	..	..	9 52	..	..	..	10 6	..	1021	..	..	..		..	..	1036
Fishersgate Halt	..	..	..	..	..	..		..	..	..	9 38	..	..	..	..	..	..	..	..	..	10 9	..	..	..	..	..		..	..	1038
Portslade and West Hove	..	..	..	..	..	..		..	..	..	9 40	..	..	..	..	..	9 55	..	..	..	1011	..	1024	..	..	..		..	..	1040
Aldrington Halt	..	..	..	..	..	..		..	..	..	9 43	..	..	..	..	..	9 58	..	..	..	1014	..	1027	..	..	..		..	..	1043
Hove	..	..	..	..	9 33	..		..	..	..	9 45	9 51	..	..	..	..	10 0	..	..	10 3	1016	..	1029	..	..	1033		..	..	1045
Holland Road Halt	..	..	..	..	..	..		..	..	..	9 47	..	..	..	..	..	..	..	..	..	1018	..	..	..	..	..		..	..	1047
Brighton (below) arr.	..	..	..	..	9 36	..		..	..	..	9 51	..	..	..	..	..	10 3	..	..	10 6	1020	..	1034	..	..	1036		..	..	1050
Arundel	..	9 5	..	..	..	..	9 14	..	..	..	..	Through Train Littlehampton to Victoria	..	..	..	..	..	9 41	..	..	..	..	Stop	..	10 5	..	1014	..	..	..
Amberley	..	9 11	..	..	..	..	..	..	..	..	..		..	..	..	..	..	9 46	..	..	..	..	..	..	1011	..	..	..	..	..
Pulborough J 374	..	9 18	..	..	..	..	9 26	..	..	..	..		..	..	..	..	..	9 54	..	..	..	..	..	..	1018	..	1026	..	..	..
Billingshurst	..	9 25	..	..	..	..	..	..	..	..	..		..	..	..	..	..	10 1	..	..	..	..	..	..	1025	..	..	..	..	..
Christ's Hospital, West Horsham	..	9 32	..	..	..	..	..	..	..	..	..		..	..	..	..	..	10 8	..	..	..	..	..	..	1032	..	..	..	..	..
Horsham 244, 245, 285, 427 arr.	..	9 37	..	..	..	..	9 41	..	..	..	..		..	..	..	..	..	1012	..	..	..	..	..	..	1037	..	1041	..	..	..
Horsham dep.	..	9 37	..	..	..	..	..	..	..	..	..		..	..	..	..	..	..	..	..	..	..	..	..	..	..	..	..	..	..
Dorking North H 285, 427	..	10 3	..	..	..	..	..	..	..	..	..		..	..	..	..	..	..	..	..	..	..	..	..	..	..	..	..	..	..
Sutton 285, 322 arr.	..	1022	..	..	..	..	..	..	..	..	..		..	..	..	..	..	..	..	..	..	..	..	..	..	..	..	..	..	..
Horsham dep.	9 16	..	..	..	..	..	9 42	..	..	9 48	..		..	..	..	..	..	1015	..	..	..	..	..	..	1048	..	1043	..	..	..
Littlehaven Halt	..	..	..	..	..	..	..	..	..	9 50	..		..	..	..	..	..	1017	..	..	..	..	..	..	1050	..	..	..	..	..
Fay Gate	9 21	..	..	..	..	..	..	..	..	9 54	..		..	..	..	..	..	1021	..	..	..	..	..	..	1054	..	..	..	..	..
Ifield	9 26	..	..	..	..	..	..	..	..	9 59	..		..	..	..	..	..	1025	..	..	..	..	..	..	1059	..	..	..	..	..
Crawley [234	9 28	..	..	..	..	..	..	..	..	10 1	..		..	..	..	P	..	1029	..	..	..	..	..	..	11 2	..	..	..	..	..
Three Bridges (below) arr.	9 32	..	..	..	..	..	..	..	..	10 5	..		..	..	..	..	..	1032	..	..	..	..	..	..	11 5	..	..	..	..	..
	1	2	3	4	5	6	7	8	9	10	11	12	13	14	15	16	17	18	19	20	21	22	23	24	25	26	27	28	29	30

	1	2	3	4	5	6	7	8	9	10	11	12	13	14	15	16	17	18	19	20	21	22	23	24	25	26	27	28	29	30
Ore......dep.	..	..	..	..	..	..	..	8 13	..	Stop	..	..	..	8 42	..	9 0	..	..	..	..	..	..	..	9 12	..	..	..	..	..	..
Hastings......	..	..	..	..	..	..	..	8 16	..	..	..	..	..	8 45	..	9 5	..	..	..	..	..	..	..	9 15	..	..	..	..	..	..
St. Leonards (W.S.)......	..	..	..	..	..	..	..	8 18	..	..	..	..	..	8 47	..	9 8	..	..	..	..	..	..	..	9 17	..	..	..	..	..	..
" (W.M.)......	..	..	..	..	..	..	..	8 21	..	..	..	..	..	8 49	..	..	..	..	..	..	..	..	..	9 20	..	..	..	..	..	..
Bexhill (Central) **G**......	..	..	..	..	..	..	..	8 26	..	..	..	..	..	8 54	..	9 15	..	..	..	..	..	..	..	9 25	..	..	..	..	..	..
Collington Halt......	..	..	..	..	..	..	..	8 28	..	..	..	..	..	8 57	..	..	..	..	..	..	..	..	..	9 27	..	..	..	..	..	..
Cooden Beach......	..	..	..	..	..	..	..	8 31	..	..	..	..	..	9 0	..	9 19	..	..	..	..	..	..	..	9 30	..	..	..	..	..	..
Norman's Bay Halt......	..	..	..	..	..	..	..	8 34	..	..	..	..	..	9 3	..	..	..	..	..	..	..	..	..	9 34	..	..	..	..	..	..
Pevensey Bay Halt......	..	..	..	..	..	..	..	8 38	..	..	..	..	..	9 7	..	..	..	..	..	..	..	..	..	9 38	..	..	..	..	..	..
Pevensey and Westham......	..	..	..	..	..	..	..	8 40	..	..	..	..	..	9 9	..	..	..	..	..	..	..	..	..	9 40	..	..	..	..	..	..
Hampden Park **F**......	..	..	..	..	..	..	..	8 45	..	..	..	..	..	9 15	..	..	..	..	..	..	..	..	..	9 45	..	..	..	..	..	..
Eastbourne...... arr.	..	..	..	..	..	..	..	8 49	..	..	..	..	..	9 19	a.m	9 32	..	..	..	..	..	..	..	9 49	..	..	..	..	..	..
Eastbourne...... dep.	..	..	8 45	..	..	..	..	8 52	8 57	..	..	..	..	9 22	9 27	9 36	..	..	..	..	..	..	..	9 52	..	..	..	9 55	9 57	..
Hampden Park **F**......	..	..	8 49	..	..	..	..	8 55	9 0	..	..	..	..	9 25	9 30	..	..	..	..	..	..	..	..	9 55	..	..	..	..	10 0	..
Polegate 239......	..	..	8 54	..	..	..	..	8 59		..	..	..	..	9 29		..	..	..	..	..	..	..	..	9 59	..	..	..	10 4		..
Berwick......	..	..	..	..	..	..	..	9 5	Stop	..	..	..	..	9 35	Stop	..	..	..	..	..	..	..	..	10 5	..	..	..		Stop	..
Glynde......	..	..	..	..	..	..	..	9 11	..	..	..	..	..	9 41	..	..	..	..	..	..	..	..	..	1011	..	..	..	Stop	..	..
Lewes 239...... arr.	..	..	..	..	..	..	..	9 16	a.m	..	..	..	..	9 46	a.m	9 56	..	..	..	..	..	..	..	1017	..	..	..	..	..	..
Seaford...... dep.	..	..	..	..	..	..	..	..	9 11	..	..	..	..	..	9 35	9 35	..	..	..	..	..	..	..	..	..	..	..	..	..	..
Bishopstone......	..	..	..	..	..	..	..	..	9 13	..	..	..	..	..	9 37	9 37	..	..	..	..	..	..	..	..	..	..	..	..	..	..
Newhaven Harbour......	..	..	..	..	..	..	..	..	9 18	..	..	..	..	..	9 42	9 42	..	..	..	..	..	..	..	..	..	..	..	..	..	..
" Town......	..	..	..	..	..	..	..	..	9 19	..	..	..	..	..	9 43	9 43	..	..	..	..	..	..	..	..	..	..	..	..	..	..
Southease & Rodmell Halt	..	..	..	..	..	..	..	..	..	..	..	..	..	..	9 48	9 48	..	..	..	..	..	..	..	..	..	..	..	..	..	..
Lewes 239...... arr.	..	..	..	..	..	..	..	..	9 28	..	..	..	..	..	9 54	9 54	..	..	..	..	..	..	..	..	..	..	..	..	a.m	..
Lewes...... dep.	..	..	..	Saturdays excepted.	..	..	..	9 17	9 32	..	..	..	..	9 47	10 2	..	..	..	..	..	..	..	..	1019	..	..	..	..	1034	..
Falmer......	..	..	..		..	..	..	9 24	9 39	..	..	..	..	9 54	10 9	..	..	..	..	..	..	..	..	1026	..	..	..	..	..	..
London Road (Brighton)...	..	..	..		..	..	..	9 28	9 43	..	..	..	..	9 58	1014	..	..	..	..	..	..	..	..	1030	..	..	..	..	1051	..
Brighton...... arr.	..	..	..		..	..	..	9 31	9 46	..	..	..	..	10 1	1016	..	..	..	..	..	..	..	..	1033	..	..	..	..	1055	..
Lewes...... dep.	..	..	..		..	..	..	..		..	..	..	..	..	..	9 58	..	..	..	..	..	..	..	..	..	..	..	..	..	..
Cooksbridge......	..	..	..		..	..	..	..	Stop	..	..	..	..	..	..	..	..	..	..	..	..	..	..	..	..	..	..	..	..	..
Plumpton......	..	..	..		..	..	..	..	..	..	..	..	..	..	..	..	..	..	..	..	..	..	..	..	..	..	..	..	..	..
Wivelsfield *(below)*......	..	..	..		..	..	..	..	..	..	..	..	..	..	..	..	..	..	..	..	..	..	..	..	..	..	..	..	..	..
Haywards Heath... arr.	..	..	..	..	..	..	..	..	a.m	a.m	..	..	..	..	..	1014	..	..	a.m	..	..	..	a.m	..	..	..	..	a.m	..	..
Brighton...... dep.	..	..	..	9 15	..	..	..	..	9 19	9 35	..	..	9 38	..	..	..	..	..	9 56	..	..	10 8	1025	..	..	..	..	10 28	..	..
Preston Park......	..	..	..	..	..	..	..	..	9 22	..	..	..	9 41	..	..	..	..	..	9 59	..	..	10 11	..	..	..	..	..	10 31	..	..
Hassocks **D**......	..	..	..	..	..	..	..	..	9 30	..	..	..	9 49	..	..	..	..	..	10 7	..	..	..	..	..	..	..	..	10 39	..	..
Burgess Hill......	..	..	..	..	..	..	..	..	9 34	..	..	..	9 53	..	..	..	..	..	1011	..	..	..	..	..	..	..	..	10 43	..	..
Wivelsfield *(above)*......	..	..	..	..	..	..	..	..	9 36	..	..	..	9 55	..	..	..	..	..	1013	..	..	..	..	..	..	..	..	10 45	..	..
Haywards Heath C......	..	..	..	9 32	..	..	..	..	9 43	..	..	10 8	10 1	..	..	1015	..	..	1019	..	..	10 27	..	..	..	..	..	10 52	..	..
Ardingly......	..	**R**	..	..	..	..	**RB**	..	..	**P**	..	**P**	..	..	..	**P**	..	..	..	..	..	..	**P**	..	..	..	**RB**	..	..	..
Horsted Keynes 239.. arr.	..	..	..	..	..	..	..	..	..	..	..	..	..	..	..	..	..	..	..	..	..	..	..	..	..	..	..	..	..	..
Balcombe......	..	..	..	..	..	..	..	..	9 49	Saturdays excepted.	..	..	10 7	..	..	..	..	..	1025	..	..	..	Saturdays only	..	..	..	..	10 58	..	..
Three Bridges *(above)*......	9 32	..	..	9 43	..	..	..	..	9 57		..	..	1017	..	..	..	..	..	1037	..	..	..		..	..	..	..	11 8	..	..
Gatwick Airport......	9 36	..	..	..	..	..	..	..	10 1		..	..	1021	..	..	..	..	..	1041	..	..	..		..	..	..	..	11 11	..	..
Horley......	9 40	..	..	..	..	..	..	..	10 4		..	..	1024	..	..	..	..	..	1044	..	..	..		..	..	..	..	11 14	..	..
Salfords......	9 44	..	..	..	..	..	..	..	10 8		..	..	1028	..	..	..	..	..	1048	..	..	..		..	..	..	..	11 18	..	..
Earlswood......	9 48	..	..	..	..	..	..	..	1012		..	..	1032	..	..	..	..	..	1052	..	..	..		..	..	..	..	11 22	..	..
Redhill 246......	9 50	..	..	..	..	..	..	..	1019		..	..	1038	..	..	..	..	..	1059	..	..	10 50		..	..	..	..	11 28	..	..
Merstham......	9 54	..	..	..	..	..	..	..	1023		..	..	1042	..	..	..	..	..	11 3	..	..	..		..	..	..	..	11 32	..	..
Coulsdon South......	10 0	..	..	..	..	..	..	..	1029	..	..	..	1048	..	..	..	..	..	11 9	..	..	..		..	..	..	..	11 38	..	..
Purley......	10 4	..	..	..	..	..	..	..	1032	..	..	..	1052	..	..	..	..	..	1112	..	..	..		..	..	..	..	11 42	..	..
East Croydon 285...... arr.	10 9	..	..	10 6	..	..	10 15	..	1038	..	..	10 41	1057	..	..	1045	..	..	1118	..	..	11 4		..	..	..	1115	11 47	..	..
Norwood Junction B arr.	..	..	..	..	..	..	..	..	1042	..	..	10 [3] 58	..	..	..	10 [3] 58	..	..	..	..	..	11 [3] 18	..	..	..	..	..	11SO53	..	..
New Cross Gate...... "	..	..	..	..	..	..	..	..	..	..	..	..	..	..	..	..	..	..	..	..	..	..	..	..	..	..	..	..	..	..
LONDON BRIDGE... "	10*40	11 [3] 5	..	10 21	..	..	10*40	..	1056	..	..	11 [3] 11	..	..	..	11 [3] 11	..	..	..	..	..	11 [3] 31	..	..	..	..	..	12SO5	..	..
Clapham Junction A... arr.	10 20	..	..	10*20	..	..	..	..	..	..	..	..	1111	..	..	..	..	..	1130	..	..	11 16	..	..	..	..	..	12SX1	..	..
VICTORIA...... "	10 26	10 42	..	10*26	..	..	10 31	..	..	1035	..	10 57	1117	..	..	11 3	..	..	1137	..	..	11 21	1125	..	..	..	1132	12SX6	..	..

[3] Third class only. * Change at East Croydon. *a* Arrival time. **P** Pullman Car facilities available. **R** Refreshment Car facilities available.
RB Refreshment Car facilities available between Bognor Regis and London. **SO** Saturdays only. **SX** Saturdays excepted.

For Other Notes, see page 233

For SERVICES from ISLE OF WIGHT and PORTSMOUTH to LONDON (Waterloo), see pages 366 to 372

From THE SOUTH COAST to LONDON—Week Days—*continued*

Station	1	2	3	4	5	6	7	8	9	10	11	12	13	14	15	16	17	18	19	20	21	22	23	24	25	26	27
	a.m		a.m	a.m	a.m	a.m	a.m	a.m	a.m	a.m	a.m	a.m	a.m	a.m	a.m	a.m		a.m	a.m		a.m	a.m	a.m	a.m	a.m	a.m	a.m
(Page 366) Yarmouth dep.	..	..	..	..	..	..	..	..	..	..	..	..	..	..	..	..	..	..	..	..	..	7 55	..	..	..	..	..
Cowes "	..	..	..	..	..	..	..	..	..	..	..	..	..	..	..	..	..	..	..	..	..	8 29	..	..	..	..	..
Newport "	..	..	..	..	..	..	..	..	..	..	..	..	..	..	..	..	..	..	..	..	..	8 42	..	..	..	..	..
Ventnor "	..	..	..	..	..	..	..	..	..	..	..	..	..	..	..	..	..	..	..	..	..	8 40	..	..	..	..	..
Shanklin "	..	..	..	..	..	..	..	..	..	..	..	..	..	..	..	..	..	..	..	..	..	8 52	..	..	..	..	..
Sandown "	..	..	..	..	..	..	..	..	..	..	..	..	..	..	..	..	..	..	..	..	..	8 58	..	..	..	..	..
500 Ryde Pier (Boat) "	..	..	..	..	..	..	..	..	..	..	..	..	..	..	..	..	..	..	..	..	..	9 35	..	..	..	..	..
Portsmouth Harbour dep.	..	..	..	9 53	..	..	..	..	..	..	..	..	..	..	..	..	..	..	10 8	..	..	10 23	..	..	..	..	..
Portsmouth & Southsea "	..	..	..	9 57	..	..	..	..	..	..	..	..	..	..	..	..	..	..	10 12	..	..	10 27	..	..	..	1042	..
Fratton	..	..	..	9 59	..	..	..	..	..	..	..	..	..	..	..	..	..	..	10 14	..	..	10 30	..	..	..	1045	..
Hilsea Halt	..	..	..	..	..	..	..	..	..	..	..	..	..	..	..	..	..	..	..	..	..	..	..	..	..	..	..
Bedhampton Halt	..	..	..	..	..	..	..	..	..	..	..	..	..	..	..	..	..	..	..	..	..	..	..	..	..	1053	..
245 Hayling Island dep.	..	..	..	9 45	..	..	..	..	..	..	..	..	..	..	..	..	..	..	..	..	..	..	..	..	..	..	..
Havant 244	..	..	..	10 8	..	..	..	..	..	..	..	..	..	..	..	..	..	..	10 23	..	..	10 39	..	..	..	1055	..
Warblington Halt	..	..	..	..	..	..	..	..	..	..	..	..	..	..	..	..	..	..	10 25	..	..	..	..	..	..	1057	..
Emsworth	..	..	..	..	..	..	..	..	..	..	..	..	..	..	..	..	..	..	10 28	..	..	..	..	..	..	11 0	..
Southbourne Halt	..	..	..	..	..	..	..	..	..	..	..	..	..	..	..	..	..	..	10 31	..	..	..	..	..	..	11 3	..
Nutbourne Halt	..	..	..	..	..	..	..	..	..	..	..	..	..	..	..	..	..	..	10 34	..	..	..	..	..	..	11 5	..
Bosham	..	..	..	..	..	..	..	..	..	..	..	..	..	..	..	..	..	..	10 37	..	..	..	..	..	..	11 9	..
Fishbourne Halt	..	..	..	..	..	..	..	..	..	..	..	..	..	..	..	..	..	..	10 40	..	..	..	..	..	..	1112	..
Chichester Z	..	..	..	10 22	..	..	..	..	..	..	..	..	..	..	..	..	..	..	10 44	..	..	10 54	..	..	..	1115	..
Barnham arr.	..	..	..	10 31	..	..	..	..	..	..	..	..	..	..	..	..	..	..	10 53	..	..	11 3	..	..	..	..	..
Bognor Regis arr.	..	..	..	10 42	..	..	..	..	..	..	..	..	..	..	..	..	..	..	11 7	..	..	RB	..	..	..	..	..
Bognor Regis dep.	..	..	10 10	10 10	..	..	..	..	..	..	..	..	..	..	10 40	..	..	..	10 40	..	..	10 55	..	11 10	..	..	..
Barnham dep.	..	..	10a16	10 31	..	..	..	..	..	..	..	..	..	..	10 47	..	..	..	10 54	..	..	11 5	..	11a16	Saturdays only	..	..
Ford (Sussex)	..	..	Stop	..	..	..	..	..	..	..	..	..	..	..	10 52	..	..	..	10 59	..	..	..	..	Stop		..	..
Littlehampton arr.	P	..		..	..	..	..	..	..	..	..	..	..	..	10 57	..	..	..	..	..	..	..	..	..		..	..
Littlehampton dep.	10 9	..	..	..	..	..	..	..	10 35	10 46	..	1049	..	..	10 59	..	..	..	..	..	..	10 59	..	..		..	..
Ford (Sussex) arr.	..	..	..	..	..	..	..	..	..	10 50	..	..	..	..	..	..	..	..	..	..	..	..	..	..		..	..
Angmering L	10 19	..	..	..	..	..	..	..	..	Stop	..	1058	..	..	..	..	..	..	11 6	..	..	Through Train Bognor Regis to Victoria	..	..	..	..	..
Goring-by-Sea	10 24	..	..	..	..	..	..	..	..	..	..	11 3	..	..	..	..	..	..	11 11	..	..		..	..	..	..	..
Durrington-on-Sea	10 27	..	a.m	..	..	..	..	..	..	a.m	..	11 5	..	..	..	..	..	..	..	..	..		..	a.m	..	..	..
West Worthing **U**	10 30	..	10 39	..	..	..	..	..	..	10 50	..	11 7	..	..	..	..	..	..	11 14	..	..		..	11 20	1139	..	..
Worthing Central	10 35	..	10 41	10 48	..	..	..	..	..	10 52	..	11 9	..	..	..	..	..	..	11 17	..	..		..	11 22	1141	..	..
Ham Bridge Halt **N**	..	..	..	..	..	..	..	..	..	10 55	..	..	..	..	..	..	..	..	..	..	..		..	11 24	..	..	..
Lancing	..	..	10 45	..	..	..	..	..	..	10 58	..	1113	..	..	..	..	..	..	..	..	..		..	11 27	1145	..	..
Shoreham-by-Sea K 244	10 42	..	10 50	10 56	..	..	..	..	..	11 3	1112	1117	..	..	..	..	..	..	11 25	..	..		..	11 32	1150	..	..
Southwick	..	..	10 54	..	..	..	..	..	..	11 6	..	1121	..	..	..	..	..	..	..	..	..		..	11 36	1153	..	..
Fishersgate Halt	..	..	..	..	..	..	..	..	..	11 9	..	..	..	..	..	..	..	..	..	..	..		..	11 38	..	..	..
Portslade and West Hove	..	..	10 57	..	..	..	..	..	..	11 11	1117	1124	..	..	..	..	..	..	..	..	..		..	11 40	1156	..	..
Aldrington Halt	..	..	..	..	..	..	..	..	..	11 14	..	1127	..	..	..	..	..	..	..	..	..		..	11 43	..	..	..
Hove	10 51	..	11 0	11 3	..	..	..	..	..	11 16	1121	1129	..	..	..	..	..	..	11 33	..	..		..	11 45	12 0	..	..
Holland Road Halt	..	..	..	..	..	..	..	..	..	11 18	..	..	..	..	..	..	..	..	..	..	..		..	11 47	..	..	..
Brighton (*below*) arr.	..	..	11 5	11 7	..	..	..	..	..	11 20	1126	1132	..	..	..	..	..	..	11 36	..	..		..	11 50	12 3	..	..
Arundel	Through Train, Littlehampton to Victoria	..	Stop	..	..	..	..	..	10 41	..	Stop	Stop	..	..	11 5	..	..	..	..	..	..	11 14	..	Stop	..	..	..
Amberley		..	..	..	..	..	..	..	10 46	..	..	..	..	..	11 11	..	..	..	..	..	..	..	..	..	..	..	..
Pulborough **J** 374		..	..	..	..	..	..	..	10 54	..	..	..	..	..	11 18	..	..	..	..	..	..	11 26	..	..	..	..	..
Billingshurst		..	..	..	..	..	..	..	11 1	..	..	..	..	..	11 25	..	..	..	..	..	..	..	..	..	..	..	..
Christ's Hospital, West Horsham		..	..	..	..	..	..	..	11 8	..	..	..	..	..	11 32	..	..	..	..	..	..	..	..	..	..	..	..
Horsham 244, 245, 285, 427 arr.		..	..	..	..	..	..	..	11 12	..	..	..	..	..	11 37	..	..	..	..	..	..	11 42	..	..	..	..	..
Horsham 244, 245, 285, 427 dep.		..	..	..	..	..	..	..	..	..	..	..	..	..	..	..	..	..	..	..	..	11 43	..	..	..	..	..
Dorking North **H** 285, 427		..	..	..	..	..	..	..	..	..	..	..	..	..	..	..	..	..	..	..	..	12 2	..	..	..	..	..
Sutton 285, 322 arr.		..	..	..	..	..	..	..	..	..	..	..	..	..	..	..	..	..	..	..	..	12 19	..	..	..	..	..
Horsham dep.		..	..	..	..	..	..	..	11 15	..	..	..	..	..	11 48	..	..	..	..	..	..	..	..	..	..	..	..
Littlehaven Halt		..	..	..	..	..	..	..	11 17	..	..	..	..	..	11 50	..	..	..	..	..	..	..	..	..	..	..	..
Fay Gate		..	..	..	..	..	..	..	11 21	..	..	..	..	..	11 54	..	..	..	..	..	..	..	..	..	..	..	..
Ifield		..	..	..	..	..	..	..	11 26	..	..	..	..	..	11 59	..	..	..	..	..	..	..	..	..	..	..	..
Crawley [234		..	..	..	..	..	..	..	11 29	..	..	..	..	..	12 2	..	..	..	..	..	..	..	..	..	..	..	..
Three Bridges (*below*) arr.		..	..	..	..	..	..	P	11 32	..	..	..	..	..	12 5	..	..	..	..	..	..	..	..	..	..	..	P

	1	2	3	4	5	6	7	8	9	10	11	12	13	14	15	16	17	18	19	20	21	22	23	24	25	26	27
Ore ......dep.	..	..	..	..	9 42	..	..	10 0	..	..	..	..	..	1013	..	..	..	..	..	..	..	..	10 43	..	..	..	11 0
Hastings	..	..	..	..	9 45	..	..	10 5	..	..	..	..	..	1016	Stop	..	..	..	..	..	..	..	10 46	..	..	..	11 5
St. Leonards (W.S.)	..	..	..	..	9 47	..	..	10 8	..	..	..	..	..	1018	..	..	..	..	..	..	..	..	10 48	..	..	..	11 8
" (W.M.)	..	..	..	..	9.49	..	..	..	..	..	..	..	..	1021	..	..	..	..	..	..	..	..	10 50	..	..	..	..
Bexhill (Central) **G**	..	..	..	..	9 54	..	..	10 15	..	..	..	..	..	1026	..	..	..	..	..	..	..	..	10 55	..	..	..	11 15
Collington Halt	..	..	..	..	9 57	..	..	..	..	..	..	..	..	1028	..	..	..	..	..	..	..	..	10 58	..	..	..	..
Cooden Beach	..	..	..	..	10 0	..	..	10 19	..	..	..	..	..	1031	..	..	..	..	..	..	..	..	11 1	..	..	..	11 19
Norman's Bay Halt	..	..	..	..	10 3	..	..	..	..	..	..	..	..	1034	..	..	..	..	..	..	..	..	11 4	..	..	..	..
Pevensey Bay Halt	..	..	..	..	10 7	..	..	..	..	..	..	..	..	1038	..	..	..	..	..	..	..	..	11 8	..	..	..	..
Pevensey and Westham	..	..	..	..	10 9	..	..	..	..	..	..	..	..	1040	..	..	..	..	..	..	..	..	11 10	..	..	..	..
Hampden Park **F**	..	..	..	..	10 15	..	..	..	..	..	..	..	..	1045	..	..	..	..	..	..	..	..	11 15	..	..	..	..
Eastbourne arr.	..	..	..	..	10 19	..	..	10 32	..	..	a.m	..	..	1049	..	..	..	..	..	..	..	..	11 19	a.m	..	..	11 32
Eastbourne dep.	..	..	..	..	10 22	1029	**Saturdays only**	10 36	..	..	1040	..	..	1052	..	1057	..	..	..	..	..	..	11 22	11 29	..	..	11 36
Hampden Park **F**	..	..	..	..	10 25	1032		..	..	..	1045	..	..	1055	..	11 0	..	..	..	..	..	..	11 25	11 32	..	..	..
Polegate 239	..	..	..	..	10 29	..		..	..	..	1050	..	..	1059	..	Stop	..	..	..	..	..	..	11 29	..	..	..	..
Berwick	..	..	..	..	10 35	..		..	..	..	..	..	..	11 5	..	..	..	..	..	..	..	..	11 35	..	..	..	..
Glynde	..	..	..	..	10 41	..		..	..	..	..	..	..	1111	..	..	..	..	..	..	..	..	11 41	..	..	..	..
Lewes 239 ......arr.	..	..	a.m	..	10 46	..		10 56	..	..	..	..	..	1116	..	..	..	..	..	..	..	..	11 46	..	..	..	11 56
Seaford ......dep.	..	..	10 25	..	..	..	1043	..	..	..	..	..	..	..	..	..	..	..	..	..	11 25	..	..	..	..	..	**Saturdays only**
Bishopstone	..	..	10 27	..	..	..	1045	..	..	..	..	..	..	..	..	..	..	..	..	..	11 27	..	..	..	..	..	
Newhaven Harbour	..	..	10 32	..	..	..	1050	..	..	..	..	..	..	..	..	..	..	..	..	..	11 32	..	..	..	..	..	
" Town	..	..	10 33	..	..	..	1051	..	..	..	..	..	..	..	..	..	..	..	..	..	11 33	..	..	..	..	..	
Southease & Rodmell Halt	..	..	10 38	..	..	..	1056	..	..	..	..	..	..	..	..	..	..	..	..	..	11 38	..	..	..	..	..	
Lewes 239 ......arr.	..	..	10 44	..	..	..	11 2	..	..	..	..	..	..	..	..	a.m	..	..	..	..	11 44	..	..	..	..	..	
Lewes ......dep.	..	..	..	..	10 47	..	11 3	..	..	..	..	..	..	1118	..	1126	..	..	..	..	..	..	11 47	..	..	..	
Falmer	..	..	..	..	10 54	..	1110	..	..	..	..	..	..	1125	..	..	..	..	..	..	..	..	11 54	..	..	..	
London Road (Brighton)	..	..	..	..	10 58	..	1114	..	..	..	..	..	..	1129	..	..	..	..	..	..	..	..	11 58	..	..	..	
Brighton ......arr.	..	..	..	..	11 1	..	1117	..	..	..	..	..	..	1132	..	1143	..	..	..	..	..	..	12 1	..	..	..	
Lewes ......dep.	..	..	10 44	..	..	..	..	10 58	..	..	..	..	..	..	..	..	..	..	..	..	11 44	..	..	..	..	..	11 58
Cooksbridge	..	..	10 49	..	..	..	..	..	..	..	..	..	..	..	..	..	..	..	..	..	11 49	..	..	..	..	..	..
Plumpton	..	..	10 54	..	..	..	..	..	..	..	..	..	..	..	..	..	..	..	..	..	11 54	..	..	..	..	..	..
Wivelsfield (*below*)	..	..	11 0	..	..	..	..	..	..	..	..	..	..	..	..	..	..	..	..	..	12 0	..	..	..	..	..	..
Haywards Heath ....arr.	..	..	11 5	..	..	..	..	11 14	..	..	..	a.m	..	..	a.m	..	..	..	..	..	12 5	..	..	..	..	..	12 14
Brighton ......dep.	..	..	..	..	..	..	..	..	..	..	..	1058	11 8	..	11 25	..	..	11 28	..	..	..	..	..	..	..	..	..
Preston Park	..	..	..	..	..	..	..	..	..	..	..	11 1	11 11	..	..	..	..	11 31	..	..	..	..	..	..	..	..	..
Hassocks **D**	..	..	..	..	..	..	..	..	..	..	..	11 9	..	..	..	..	..	11 39	..	..	..	..	..	..	..	..	..
Burgess Hill	..	..	..	..	..	..	..	..	..	..	..	1113	..	..	..	..	..	11 43	..	..	..	..	..	..	..	..	..
Wivelsfield (*above*)	..	..	..	..	..	..	..	..	..	..	..	1115	..	..	..	..	..	11 45	..	..	..	..	..	..	..	..	..
Haywards Heath C	11 9	..	..	..	..	..	..	11 15	..	..	..	1122	11 27	..	..	..	..	11 52	..	..	12 6	..	..	..	..	..	12 15
Ardingly	P	..	..	..	..	..	..	P	..	..	..	..	..	..	P	..	..	..	..	..	12 10	RB	..	..	..	..	P
Horsted Keynes 239 ..arr.	..	..	..	..	..	..	..	..	..	..	..	..	..	..	..	..	..	..	..	..	12 14	..	..	..	..	..	..
Balcombe	..	..	..	..	..	..	..	..	..	..	..	1128	..	..	..	..	..	11 58	..	..	..	..	..	..	..	..	..
Three Bridges (*above*)	..	..	..	..	..	..	..	..	..	..	..	1137	..	..	..	..	..	12 8	..	..	..	..	..	..	..	..	..
Gatwick Airport	..	..	..	..	..	..	..	..	..	..	..	1141	11 40	..	..	..	..	12 12	..	..	..	..	..	..	..	..	..
Horley	..	..	..	..	..	..	..	..	..	..	..	1144	..	..	..	..	..	12 15	..	..	..	..	..	..	..	..	..
Salfords	..	..	..	..	..	..	..	..	..	..	..	1148	..	..	..	..	..	12 19	..	..	..	..	..	..	..	..	..
Earlswood	..	..	..	..	..	..	..	..	..	..	..	1152	..	..	..	..	..	12 23	..	..	..	..	..	..	..	..	..
Redhill 246	..	..	..	..	..	..	..	..	..	..	..	1159	11 50	..	..	..	..	12 30	..	..	..	..	..	..	..	..	..
Merstham	..	..	..	..	..	..	..	..	..	..	..	12 3	..	..	..	..	..	12 34	..	..	..	..	..	..	..	..	..
Coulsdon South	..	..	..	..	..	..	..	..	..	..	..	12 9	..	..	..	..	..	12 40	..	..	..	..	..	..	..	..	..
Purley	..	..	..	..	..	..	..	..	..	..	..	1213	..	..	..	..	..	12 44	..	..	..	..	..	..	..	..	..
East Croydon 285 ....arr.	11 41	..	..	..	..	..	..	11 46	..	..	..	1218	12 4	..	..	..	..	12 49	..	..	..	..	..	..	..	..	12 45
Norwood Junction **B** arr.	11£58	..	..	..	..	..	..	11£58	..	..	..	1224	12£18	..	..	..	..	12£58	..	..	..	..	..	..	..	..	12£58
New Cross Gate ... "	..	..	..	..	..	..	..	..	..	..	..	..	..	..	..	..	..	..	..	..	..	..	..	..	..	..	..
LONDON BRIDGE ... "	12£11	..	..	..	..	..	..	12£11	..	..	..	1238	12£31	..	..	..	..	1£11	..	..	..	..	..	..	..	..	1£11
Clapham Junction **A** ..arr.	..	..	..	..	..	..	..	..	..	..	..	..	12 16	..	..	..	..	1 2	..	..	..	..	..	..	..	..	..
VICTORIA ......"	11 57	..	..	..	..	..	..	12 3	..	..	..	..	12 21	..	12 25	..	..	1 8	..	..	..	12 40	..	..	..	..	1 3

£ Third class only. * Change at East Croydon. *a* Arrival time. **P** Pullman Car facilities available.
RB Refreshment Car facilities available between Bognor Regis and London.

For Other Notes, see page 233

For SERVICES from ISLE OF WIGHT and PORTSMOUTH to LONDON (Waterloo), see pages 366 to 372

From THE SOUTH COAST to LONDON—Week Days—continued

Station	a.m		a.m	a.m	a.m	a.m	p.m	a.m	p.m	a.m	a.m	a.m	p.m	p.m	a.m	p.m	p.m	p.m	a.m	a.m	p.m	a.m	p.m	p.m	p.m	p.m	p.m	p.m	p.m
Page 366 Yarmouth ....dep.	..	..	..	..	..	..	..	..	..	..	..	..	..	..	..	..	..	..	..	..	..	..	..	..	..	..	..	..	..
Cowes .... "	..	..	..	..	..	..	..	..	..	..	..	..	..	..	..	..	..	..	..	9 26	..	..	..	..	..	..	..	..	..
Newport .... "	..	..	..	..	..	..	..	..	..	..	..	..	..	..	..	..	..	..	..	9 38	..	..	..	..	..	..	..	..	..
Ventnor .... "	..	..	..	..	..	..	..	..	..	..	..	..	..	..	..	..	..	..	..	9 42	..	..	..	..	..	..	..	..	..
Shanklin .... "	..	..	..	..	..	..	..	..	..	..	..	..	..	..	..	..	..	..	..	9 54	..	..	..	..	..	..	..	..	..
Sandown .... "	..	..	..	..	..	..	..	..	..	..	..	..	..	..	..	..	..	..	..	10 1	..	..	..	..	..	..	..	..	..
500 Ryde Pier (Boat) . "	..	..	..	..	..	..	..	..	..	..	..	..	..	..	..	..	..	..	..	10 35	..	..	..	..	..	..	..	..	..
Portsmouth Harbour ..dep.	..	..	10 53	..	..	..	..	..	..	11 8	..	..	..	..	..	..	..	..	..	11a 5		1153	..	..	..	..	..	..	12 8
Portsmouth & Southsea "	..	..	10 57	..	..	..	..	..	..	11 12	..	..	..	..	..	..	..	..	11 42	Stop		1157	..	..	..	..	..	..	12 12
Fratton	..	..	10 59	..	..	..	..	..	..	11 14	..	..	..	..	..	..	..	..	11 45			1159	..	..	..	..	..	..	12 14
Hilsea Halt	..	..	..	..	..	..	..	..	..	..	..	..	..	..	..	..	..	..	..	..		..	..	..	..	..	..	..	..
Bedhampton Halt	..	..	..	..	..	..	..	..	..	..	..	..	..	..	..	..	..	..	11 53	..		..	..	..	..	..	..	..	..
245 **Hayling Island** ....dep.	..	..	..	..	..	..	..	..	..	..	..	..	..	..	..	..	..	..	..	..		..	..	..	..	..	..	..	..
Havant 244	..	..	11 8	..	..	..	..	..	..	11 23	..	..	..	..	..	..	..	..	11 55	..	Saturdays only ☞	12 8	..	..	..	..	..	..	12 23
Warblington Halt	..	..	..	..	..	..	..	..	..	11 25	..	Saturdays only	..	..	..	..	..	..	11 57	..		..	..	..	..	..	..	..	12 25
Emsworth	..	..	..	..	..	..	..	..	..	11 28	..		..	..	..	..	..	..	12 0	..		..	..	..	..	..	..	..	12 28
Southbourne Halt	..	..	..	..	..	..	..	..	..	11 31	..		..	..	..	..	..	..	12 3	..		..	..	..	..	..	..	..	12 31
Nutbourne Halt	..	..	..	..	..	..	..	..	..	11 34	..		..	..	..	..	..	..	12 5	..		..	..	..	..	..	..	..	12 34
Bosham	..	..	..	..	..	..	..	..	..	11 37	..		..	..	..	..	..	..	12 9	..		..	..	..	..	..	..	..	12 37
Fishbourne Halt	..	..	..	..	..	..	..	..	..	11 40	..		..	..	..	..	..	..	12 12	..		..	..	..	..	..	..	..	12 40
Chichester Z	..	..	11 22	..	..	..	..	..	..	11 44	..		..	..	..	..	..	..	12 15	..		1222	..	..	..	..	..	..	12 44
Barnham ....arr.	..	..	11 31	..	..	..	..	..	..	11 53	..		..	..	..	..	..	..	Stop	..		1231	..	..	..	..	..	..	12 53
Bognor Regis ....arr.	..	..	11 42	..	..	..	..	..	..	12 7	..	R	..	..	..	..	..	..		..		..	..	..	..	..	..	..	1 7
Bognor Regis ....dep.	..	..	11 10	..	..	..	..	..	..	11 45	11 45	1155	..	..	..	..	..	..	..	..	12 10	1210	..	..	..	..	..	..	12 45
Barnham ....dep.	..	..	11 31	..	..	..	..	..	..	11 54	11b58	12 2	..	..	..	..	..	..	..	..	12a16	1231	..	..	..	..	..	..	12 54
Ford (Sussex)	..	..		..	..	..	..	..	..	11 59	12 2	..	..	..	..	..	..	..	..	..		..	..	..	..	..	..	..	12 59
Littlehampton ....arr.	..	..	Saturdays only	..	..	..	..	..	..	12 7	12 7	..	..	..	..	..	..	P	..	p.m	Stop	Saturdays only	..	..	..	..	..	..	1 7
Littlehampton ....dep.	1135	..		..	1146	..	..	11 49	..	..	12 9	..	Wednesdays only	..	..	..	..	12 5	..	12 35	..		1246	..	1249	..	..	..	..
Ford (Sussex) ....arr.	..	..		..	1150	..	..	..	..	..	..	..		..	..	..	..	..	..	..	..		1250	..	..	..	..	..	..
Angmering L	..	..		..	Stop	..	Saturdays only	11 58	..	12 6	..	Through Train, Bognor Regis to Victoria		..	..	..	..	1216	..	..	..		Stop	..	1258	..	..	..	1 6
Goring-by-Sea	..	..		..		..		12 3	..	12 11	..			..	..	..	..	1222	..	..	..			..	1 3	..	..	..	1 11
Durrington-on-Sea	..	..		..	..	..		12 5	..	..	..			..	..	..	..	1225	p.m	..	..		..	..	1 5	..	..	..	..
West Worthing U	..	..		..	..	1149		12 7	..	12 14	..			12 18	..	..	..	1230	12f37	..	..		..	1250	1 7	..	..	..	1 14
Worthing Central	..	..	11 48	..	..	1151		12 9	..	12 17	..			12 20	..	..	..	1235	12f39	..	..	1249	..	1252	1 9	..	..	..	1 17
Ham Bridge Halt N	..	..	..	..	..	1153		..	..	..	..			12 22	..	..	..	..	..	..	..	..	..	1255	..	..	..	..	..
Lancing	..	..	..	..	..	1156		12 13	..	..	..			12 25	..	..	..	..	12f43	..	..	..	..	1258	1 13	..	..	..	..
Shoreham-by-Sea K 244	..	..	11 56	..	..	12 1	1213	12 17	..	12 24	..		1227	12 31	..	..	..	1242	12f47	..	..	1258	..	1 3	1 17	..	..	..	1 25
Southwick	..	..	..	..	..	12 5	..	12 21	..	..	..		..	12 34	..	..	..	..	12f50	..	..	..	..	1 6	1 21	..	..	..	..
Fishersgate Halt	..	..	..	..	..	12 7	..	..	..	..	..		..	12 37	..	..	..	..	..	..	..	..	..	1 9	..	..	..	..	..
Portslade and West Hove ..	..	..	..	..	..	12 9	1219	12 24	..	..	..		..	12 39	..	..	..	..	12f53	..	..	..	..	1 11	1 24	..	..	..	..
Aldrington Halt	..	..	..	..	..	1212	..	12 26	..	..	..		..	12 42	..	..	..	..	12f56	..	..	..	..	1 14	..	..	..	..	..
Hove	..	..	12 3	..	..	1214	1223	12 28	..	12 31	..		1235	12 44	..	..	..	1250	12f58	..	..	1 6	..	1 16	1 28	..	..	..	1 32
Holland Road Halt	..	..	..	..	..	1216	..	..	..	..	..		..	12 46	..	..	..	..	..	..	..	..	..	1 18	..	..	..	..	..
Brighton (*below*) ....arr.	..	..	12 6	..	..	1219	1228	12 32	..	12 36	..		1240	12 48	..	..	..	..	1 f2	..	..	1 10	..	1 20	1 31	..	..	..	1 36
Arundel	1141	..	..	..	..	..	..	Stop	..	..	12 16	1211	..	Stop	..	..	..	Through Train, Littlehampton to Victoria	Stop	12 41	Saturdays only ☞	Stop	..	Stop	..	..	..	..	..
Amberley	1146	..	..	..	..	..	..		..	..	12 21	..	..		..	..	..			12 46			..		..	..	..	..	..
Pulborough J 374	1154	..	..	..	..	..	..	..	..	..	12 29	1224	..	..	..	..	..		..	12 54		..	..	..	..	..	..	..	..
Billingshurst	12 1	..	..	..	..	..	..	..	..	..	12 36	..	..	..	..	..	..		..	1 1		..	..	..	..	..	..	..	..
Christ's Hospital, West Horsham	12 8	..	..	..	..	..	..	..	..	..	12 43	..	..	..	..	..	..		..	1 8		..	..	..	..	..	..	..	..
Horsham 244, 245, 285, 427 arr.	1212	..	..	..	..	..	..	..	..	..	12 47	1239	..	..	..	..	..		..	1 12		..	..	..	..	..	..	..	..
Horsham 244, 245, 285, 427 dep.	..	..	..	..	..	..	..	..	..	..	..	..	..	..	..	..	..		..	..		..	..	..	..	..	..	..	..
Dorking North H 285, 427 ..	..	..	..	..	..	..	..	..	..	..	..	..	..	..	..	..	..		..	..		..	..	..	..	..	..	..	..
Sutton 285, 322 ....arr.	..	..	..	..	..	..	..	..	..	..	..	..	..	..	..	..	..		..	..		..	..	..	..	..	..	..	..
Horsham ....dep.	1215	..	..	..	..	..	..	..	..	..	12 48	1243	..	..	..	..	..		..	1 15		..	..	..	..	..	..	..	..
Littlehaven Halt	1217	..	..	..	..	..	..	..	..	..	12 50	..	..	..	..	..	..		..	1 17		..	..	..	..	..	..	..	..
Fay Gate	1221	..	..	..	..	..	..	..	..	..	12 54	..	..	..	..	..	..		..	1 21		..	..	..	..	..	..	..	..
Ifield	1226	..	..	..	..	..	..	..	..	..	12 59	..	..	..	..	..	..		..	1 28		..	..	..	..	..	..	..	..
Crawley ....[234	1229	..	..	..	..	..	..	..	..	..	1 2	..	..	..	..	..	..		..	1 29	non	..	..	..	..	..	..	..	..
Three Bridges (*below*)..arr.	1232	..	..	..	..	..	..	..	..	..	1 5	1255	..	..	..	..	..		a.m	1 32	P	..	..	..	..	..	..	..	..
	1	2	3	4	5	6	7	8	9	10	11	12	13	14	15	16	17	18	19	20	21	22	23	24	25	26	27	28	29

	1	2	3	4	5	6	7	8	9	10	11	12	13	14	15	16	17	18	19	20	21	22	23	24	25	26	27	28	29
Ore dep.	..	..	..	..	..	..	..	..	..	..	..	..	..	..	1120	..	..	..	11 43	—	12 0	..	..	..	..	..	..	..	..
Hastings	..	..	..	..	..	..	..	..	..	..	..	..	..	..	1123	..	..	..	11 46	Stop	12 5	..	..	..	..	..	..	..	..
St. Leonards (W.S.)	..	..	..	..	..	..	..	..	..	..	..	..	..	..	1125	..	..	..	11 48	..	12 8	Saturdays only	..	..	..	..	..	..	..
" (W.M.)	..	..	..	..	..	..	..	..	..	..	..	..	..	..	1127	..	..	..	11 50	..	..		..	..	..	..	..	..	..
Bexhill (Central) **G**	..	..	..	..	..	..	..	..	..	..	..	..	..	..	1132	..	..	..	11 55	..	12 15		..	..	..	..	..	..	..
Collington Halt	..	..	..	..	..	..	..	..	..	..	..	..	..	..	1135	..	..	..	11 58	..	..		..	..	..	..	..	..	..
Cooden Beach	..	..	..	..	..	..	..	..	..	..	..	..	..	..	1138	..	..	..	12 1	..	12 19		..	..	..	..	..	..	..
Norman's Bay Halt	..	..	..	Saturdays only	..	..	..	..	..	..	..	..	..	..	1141	..	..	..	12 4	..	..		..	..	..	..	..	..	..
Pevensey Bay Halt	..	..	..		..	..	..	..	..	..	..	..	..	..	1145	..	..	..	12 8	..	..		..	..	..	..	..	..	..
Pevensey and Westham	..	..	..		..	..	..	..	..	..	..	..	..	..	1147	..	..	..	12 10	..	..		..	..	..	..	..	..	..
Hampden Park **F**	..	..	..		..	..	..	..	..	..	..	..	..	..	1153	..	..	..	12 15	..	..		..	..	..	..	..	..	..
Eastbourne arr.	..	..	..		..	..	..	..	..	..	..	..	..	a.m	1157	..	..	..	12 19	p.m	12 32		p.m	..	..	..	..	..	..
Eastbourne dep.	..	..	..		..	..	..	..	..	..	..	..	..	11 57	12 0	..	1217	..	12 22	12 29	12 36		1245	..	..	..	..	..	..
Hampden Park **F**	..	..	..		..	..	..	..	..	..	..	..	..	12 0	12 3	..	1221	..	12 25	12 32	..		1249	..	..	..	..	..	..
Polegate 239	..	..	..		..	..	..	..	..	..	..	..	..	—	12 7	..	1225	..	12 29	..	..		1254	..	..	..	..	..	..
Berwick	..	..	..		..	..	..	..	..	..	..	..	..	Stop	1213	..	..	..	12 35	..	..		..	..	..	..	..	..	..
Glynde	..	..	..		..	..	..	..	..	..	..	..	..	..	1219	..	..	..	12 41	..	..		..	..	..	..	..	..	..
Lewes 239 arr.	..	..	..		..	..	..	..	..	..	..	..	..	..	1224	..	..	..	12 46	..	12 56	p.m	..	..	..	..	..	..	..
Seaford dep.	..	..	..	1143	..	..	..	..	..	..	..	..	..	..	..	1225	..	..	..	..	..	1246	..	..	..	..	..	..	..
Bishopstone	..	..	..	1145	..	..	..	..	..	..	..	..	..	..	..	1227	..	..	..	..	..	1248	..	..	..	..	..	..	..
Newhaven Harbour	..	..	..	1150	..	..	..	..	..	..	..	..	..	..	..	1232	..	..	..	..	Saturdays only	1253	..	..	..	..	..	..	..
" Town	..	..	..	1151	..	..	..	..	..	..	..	..	..	..	..	1233	..	..	..	..		1254	..	..	..	..	..	..	..
Southease & Rodmell Halt	..	..	..	1156	..	..	..	..	..	..	..	..	..	..	..	1238	..	..	..	..		1259	..	..	..	..	..	..	..
Lewes 239 arr.	..	..	..	12 2	..	..	..	..	..	..	..	..	..	..	..	1244	..	..	..	..		1 5	..	..	..	..	..	..	..
Lewes dep.	..	..	..	12 2	..	..	..	..	..	..	..	..	..	..	1225	..	..	..	12 47	..		1 5	..	..	..	..	..	..	..
Falmer	..	..	..	12 9	..	..	..	..	..	..	..	..	..	..	1232	..	..	..	12 54	..		1 12	..	..	..	..	..	..	..
London Road (Brighton)	..	..	..	1213	..	..	..	..	..	..	..	..	..	..	1236	..	..	..	12 58	..		1 17	..	..	..	..	..	..	..
Brighton arr.	..	..	..	1216	..	..	..	..	..	..	..	..	..	..	1239	..	..	..	1 1	..		1 19	..	..	..	..	..	..	..
Lewes dep.	..	..	..	..	..	..	..	..	..	..	..	..	..	..	..	1244	..	..	..	..	12 58	..	..	..	..	..	..	..	..
Cooksbridge	..	..	..	..	..	..	..	..	..	..	..	..	..	..	..	1249	..	..	..	..	..	..	..	..	..	..	..	..	..
Plumpton	..	..	..	..	..	..	..	..	..	..	..	Saturdays only	..	..	..	1254	..	..	..	..	..	..	..	..	..	..	..	..	..
Wivelsfield *(below)*	..	..	..	..	..	..	..	..	..	..	..		..	..	..	..	..	..	..	..	..	..	..	..	..	..	..	..	..
Haywards Heath arr.	..	..	..	..	a.m	..	..	p.m	..	..	..		..	p.m	..	1 4	..	..	..	..	1 14	..	..	p.m	..	..	..	..	..
Brighton dep.	..	..	..	..	1158	..	..	12 8	12 25	..	..		..	12 28	..	..	..	..	..	..	..	..	..	1258	..	1 8	1 25	..	..
Preston Park	..	..	..	..	12 1	..	..	12 11	..	..	..		..	12 31	..	..	..	..	..	..	..	..	..	1 1	..	1 11	Brighton Belle 1st and 3rd class Pullman Cars only	..	..
Hassocks **D**	..	..	..	..	12 9	..	..	..	..	..	..		..	12 39	..	..	..	..	..	..	..	..	..	1 9	..	..		..	..
Burgess Hill	..	..	..	..	1213	..	..	..	..	..	..		..	12 42	..	..	..	..	..	..	..	..	..	1 13	..	..		..	..
Wivelsfield *(above)*	..	..	..	..	1215	..	..	..	..	..	..		..	12 45	..	..	..	..	..	..	..	..	..	1 15	..	..		..	..
Haywards Heath C	..	..	..	..	1222	..	..	12 26	..	..	..	..	..	12 55	..	1 4	..	1 8	..	..	1 15	..	..	1 21	..	1 27		1 45	..
Ardingly	..	..	..	..	..	..	..	..	**P**	..	..	**R**	..	..	..	1 8	..	**P**	..	..	**P**	..	..	..	..	..		1 50	..
Horsted Keynes 239 arr.	..	..	..	..	..	..	..	..	..	..	..	..	..	..	..	1 12	..	..	..	..	..	..	..	..	..	..		1 56	..
Balcombe	..	..	..	..	1228	..	..	..	Saturdays only	..	..	..	..	1 1	..	..	..	..	..	..	..	..	..	1 28	..	..		..	..
Three Bridges *(above)*	..	..	..	..	1237	..	..	12 37		..	..	1256	..	1 8	..	..	..	..	..	..	..	..	..	1 37	..	..		..	..
Gatwick Airport	..	..	..	..	1241	..	..	12 40		..	..	..	..	1 12	..	..	..	..	..	..	..	..	..	1 41	..	1 40		..	..
Horley	..	..	..	..	1244	..	..	..		..	..	..	..	1 15	..	..	..	..	..	..	..	..	..	1 44	..	..		..	..
Salfords	..	..	..	..	1248	..	..	..		..	..	..	..	1 19	..	..	..	..	..	..	..	..	..	1 48	..	..		..	..
Earlswood	..	..	..	..	1252	..	..	..		..	..	..	..	1 23	..	..	..	..	..	..	..	..	..	1 52	..	..		..	..
Redhill 246	..	..	..	..	1259	..	..	12 50		..	..	1 9	..	1 30	..	..	..	..	..	..	..	..	..	1 59	..	1 50		..	..
Merstham	..	..	..	..	1 3	..	..	..		..	..	..	..	1 34	..	..	..	..	..	..	..	..	..	2 3	..	..		..	..
Coulsdon South	..	..	..	..	1 9	..	..	..		..	..	..	..	1 40	..	..	..	..	..	..	..	..	..	2 9	..	..		..	..
Purley	..	..	..	..	1 13	..	..	..		..	..	..	..	1 43	..	..	..	..	..	..	..	..	..	2 13	..	..		..	..
East Croydon 285 arr.	..	..	..	..	1 18	..	..	1 4		..	..	1 23	..	1 49	..	..	..	1 41	..	..	1 45	..	..	2 18	..	2 4		..	..
Norwood Junction B arr.	..	..	..	..	1 24	..	..	1③18	..	..	..	..	..	1③58	..	..	..	1③58	..	..	1③58	..	..	2 24	..	2*24		..	..
New Cross Gate "	..	..	..	..	..	..	..	..	..	..	..	..	..	..	..	..	..	..	..	..	..	..	..	..	..	..		..	..
LONDON BRIDGE "	..	..	..	..	1 36	..	..	1③31	..	..	..	..	..	2③11	..	..	..	2③11	..	..	2③11	..	..	2 36	..	2*36		..	..
Clapham Junction **A** arr.	..	..	..	..	..	..	..	1 16	..	..	..	..	..	2 1	..	..	..	..	..	..	..	..	..	..	..	2 16		..	..
VICTORIA "	..	..	..	..	—	..	..	1 21	1 25	..	..	1 40	..	2 7	—	..	..	1 57	..	..	2 2	..	..	..	..	2 21	2 25	..	..

③ Third class only. * Change at East Croydon. *a* Arrival time. *b* Arr 7 minutes *earlier* *f* 4 minutes later on Saturdays

P Pullman Car facilities available **R** Refreshment Car facilities available

For Other Notes, see page 233

For SERVICES from ISLE OF WIGHT and PORTSMOUTH to LONDON (Waterloo), see pages 366 to 372

From THE SOUTH COAST to LONDON—Week Days—*continued*

Station	p.m	p.m	p.m	p.m	p.m	p.m	a.m	p.m	p.m	p.m	p.m	p.m	p.m	p.m	p.m	p.m	p.m	p.m	p.m	p.m	p.m	p.m	p.m	p.m	p.m	a.m	pm	p.m	p.m	p.m
Page 366 Yarmouth dep.	..	..	..	..	..	..	10 0	..	..	..	..	..	..	..	..	..	..	..	..	..	..	..	..	..	..	..	..	..	..	..
Cowes "	..	..	..	..	..	..	10 3	..	..	..	..	..	..	..	..	..	..	..	..	..	..	..	..	..	..	11 26	..	..	..	..
Newport "	..	..	..	..	..	..	10 38	..	..	..	..	..	..	..	..	..	..	..	..	..	..	..	..	..	..	11 38	..	..	..	..
Ventnor "	..	..	..	..	..	..	10 42	..	..	..	..	..	..	..	..	..	..	..	..	..	..	..	..	..	..	11 42	..	..	..	..
Shanklin "	..	..	..	..	..	..	10 54	..	..	..	..	..	..	..	..	..	..	..	..	..	..	..	..	..	..	11 54	..	..	..	..
Sandown "	..	..	..	..	..	..	11 1	..	..	..	..	..	..	..	..	..	..	..	..	..	..	..	..	..	..	12 1	..	..	..	..
500 Ryde Pier (Boat) "	..	..	..	..	..	..	11 35	..	..	..	..	..	..	..	..	..	..	..	..	..	..	..	..	..	..	12 35	..	..	..	..
Portsmouth Harbour dep.	..	Saturdays only	..	..	..	..	12a5	..	..	..	..	..	..	..	..	..	..	..	..	..	..	..	..	..	1 8	1 23	..	..	..	..
Portsmouth & Southsea "	..		..	..	..	..	Stop	..	..	12 42	..	..	..	..	..	..	..	..	..	..	..	..	..	..	1 12	1 27	..	..	..	..
Fratton	..		..	..	..	..	..	..	..	12 45	..	..	..	..	..	..	..	..	..	..	..	..	..	..	1 14	1 30	..	..	..	..
Hilsea Halt	..		..	..	..	..	..	..	..	12S49	..	..	..	..	..	..	..	..	..	..	..	..	..	..	..	..	..	..	..	..
Bedhampton Halt	..		..	..	..	..	..	..	..	12 53	..	..	..	..	..	..	..	..	..	..	..	..	..	..	..	..	..	..	..	..
245 Hayling Island dep.	..		..	..	..	..	..	..	..	12 27	..	..	..	..	..	..	..	..	..	..	..	..	..	..	..	1 12	..	..	..	..
Havant 244	..		..	..	Saturdays excepted	..	..	Saturdays only	..	12 55	..	..	..	..	..	..	..	..	..	..	..	..	..	..	1 23	1 39	..	..	..	..
Warblington Halt	..		..	..		..	..		..	12 57	..	..	..	..	..	..	..	..	..	..	..	..	..	..	1 25	..	..	..	..	..
Emsworth	..		..	..		..	..		..	1 0	..	..	..	..	..	..	..	..	..	..	..	..	..	..	1 28	..	..	..	..	..
Southbourne Halt	..		..	..		..	..		..	1 3	..	..	..	..	..	..	..	..	..	..	..	..	..	..	1 31	..	..	..	..	..
Nutbourne Halt	..		..	..		..	..		..	1 5	..	..	..	..	..	..	..	..	..	..	..	..	..	..	1 34	..	..	..	..	..
Bosham	..		..	..		..	..		..	1 9	..	..	..	..	..	..	..	..	..	..	..	..	..	..	1 37	..	..	..	..	..
Fishbourne Halt	..		..	..		..	..		..	1 12	..	..	..	..	..	..	..	..	..	..	..	..	..	..	1 40	..	..	..	..	..
Chichester Z	..		..	..		..	..		..	1 15	..	..	..	..	..	..	..	..	..	..	..	..	..	..	1 44	1 54	..	..	..	..
Barnham arr.	..		..	..		..	..		..	Stop	..	..	..	..	..	..	..	..	..	..	..	..	..	..	1 53	2 3	..	..	..	..
Bognor Regis arr.	..	R	..	..		..	..	..	..	..	..	..	..	..	..	..	..	..	..	..	..	..	..	..	2 7	RB	..	..	..	..
Bognor Regis dep.	12 45	1255	..	..		..	..	1 10	..	..	..	..	..	..	..	..	..	..	..	..	..	1 46	..	..	1 40	1 55	..	..	..	..
Barnham dep.	12b58	1 4	..	..		..	..	1 16	..	..	..	..	..	..	..	..	..	..	..	..	..	1 47	..	..	1 54	2 5	..	..	..	..
Ford (Sussex)	1 2	..	..	..		..	..	..	..	..	..	..	..	..	..	..	..	..	..	..	..	1 52	..	..	1 59	..	..	..	..	..
Littlehampton arr.	1 7	..	..	..	P	..	..	..	..	..	..	..	..	..	..	..	..	..	..	..	..	1 57	..	..	..	..	..	..	..	..
Littlehampton dep.	1 9	..	..	..	1 5	..	..	..	..	..	..	..	..	1 46	..	1 35	..	..	..	..	1 49	1 59	..	..	..	1 59	..	..	..	..
Ford (Sussex) arr.	..	Through Train Bognor Regis to Victoria	..	..	..	..	..	..	..	..	..	..	..	1 50	..	..	..	..	..	..	..	..	..	..	..	..	..	..	..	..
Angmering L	..		..	..	1 16	..	..	..	..	..	..	..	..	Stop	..	..	..	..	..	..	1 58	..	..	..	2 6	Through Train Bognor Regis to Victoria	..	..	..	..
Goring-by-Sea	..		..	..	1 22	..	..	..	..	..	..	..	..	..	..	..	..	..	..	..	2 3	..	..	..	2 11		..	..	..	..
Durrington-on-Sea	..		..	..	1 25	..	..	..	..	..	..	..	..	..	..	..	..	..	..	..	2 5	..	..	..	..		..	..	..	..
West Worthing U	..		1 20	..	1 30	..	..	..	1 36	..	..	1 50	..	..	..	..	..	..	..	..	2 7	..	..	..	2 14		..	..	..	2 20
Worthing Central	..		1 22	..	1 35	..	..	..	1 38	..	..	1 52	..	..	..	..	..	..	..	..	2 9	..	..	..	2 17		..	..	..	2 22
Ham Bridge Halt N	..		1 24	..	..	..	..	..	..	..	..	1 54	..	..	..	..	..	..	..	..	..	..	..	..	..		..	..	..	2 24
Lancing	..		1 27	..	..	..	..	..	1 42	..	..	1 57	..	..	..	..	..	..	..	..	2 13	..	..	..	..		..	..	..	2 27
Shoreham-by-Sea K 244	..		1 32	..	1 42	..	..	..	1 46	..	..	2 2	..	..	..	..	..	..	..	..	2 17	..	..	..	2 25		..	2 28	..	2 32
Southwick	..		1 36	..	..	..	..	..	1 49	..	..	2 6	..	..	..	..	..	..	..	..	2 21	..	..	..	..		..	2 32	..	2 36
Fishersgate Halt	..		1 38	..	..	..	..	..	1 52	..	..	2 8	..	..	..	..	..	..	..	..	..	..	..	..	..		..	..	..	2 38
Portslade and West Hove	..		1 40	..	..	..	..	..	1 54	..	..	2 10	..	..	..	..	..	..	..	..	2 24	..	..	..	..		..	..	..	2 40
Aldrington Halt	..		1 43	..	..	..	..	..	1 57	..	..	2 13	..	..	..	..	..	..	..	..	2 27	..	..	..	..		..	..	..	2 43
Hove	..		1 45	..	1 50	..	..	..	1 59	..	..	2 15	..	..	..	..	..	..	..	..	2 29	..	..	..	2 33		..	2 38	..	2 45
Holland Road Halt	..		1 47	..	..	..	..	..	2 1	..	..	2 17	..	..	..	..	..	..	..	..	..	..	..	..	..		..	..	..	2 47
Brighton (*below*) arr.	..		1 49	..	..	..	..	..	2y 3	..	..	2 21	..	..	..	..	..	..	..	..	2 32	..	..	..	2 36		..	2 43	..	2 50
Arundel	1 16	1 12	..	..	Through Train Littlehampton to Victoria	..	..	..	..	..	..	Stop	..	..	..	1 41	..	..	..	..	..	2 5	..	..	..	2 15	..	Stop	..	Stop
Amberley	1 21	..	..	..		..	..	..	..	..	..	..	..	..	..	1 46	..	..	..	..	..	2 11	..	..	..	..	..	..	..	..
Pulborough J 374	1 29	1 24	..	..		..	..	..	..	..	..	..	..	..	..	1 54	..	..	..	..	..	2 18	..	..	..	2 26	..	..	..	..
Billingshurst	1 36	..	..	..		..	..	..	..	..	..	..	..	..	..	2 1	..	..	..	..	..	2 25	..	..	..	..	..	..	..	..
Christ's Hospital, West Horsham	1 43	..	..	..		..	..	..	..	..	..	..	..	..	..	2 8	..	..	..	..	..	2 32	..	..	..	..	..	..	..	..
Horsham 244, 245, 285, 427 arr.	1 47	1 39	..	..		..	..	..	..	..	..	..	..	..	..	2 12	..	..	..	..	..	2 37	..	..	..	2 42	..	..	..	..
Horsham dep.	..	1 43	..	..		..	..	..	..	..	..	..	..	..	..	..	..	..	..	..	..	..	..	..	..	2 43	..	..	..	..
Dorking North H 285, 427	..	2 2	..	..		..	..	..	..	..	..	..	..	..	..	..	..	..	..	..	..	..	..	..	..	3 2	..	..	..	..
Sutton 285, 322 arr.	..	2 19	..	..		..	..	..	..	..	..	..	..	..	..	..	..	..	..	..	..	..	..	..	..	3 19	..	..	..	..
Horsham dep.	1 48	..	..	..		..	..	..	..	..	..	..	..	..	..	2 15	..	..	..	..	..	2 48	..	..	..	..	..	..	..	..
Littlehaven Halt	1 50	..	..	..		..	..	..	..	..	..	..	..	..	..	2 17	..	..	..	..	..	2 50	..	..	..	..	..	..	..	..
Fay Gate	1 54	..	..	..		..	..	..	..	..	..	..	..	..	..	2 21	..	..	..	..	..	2 54	..	..	..	..	..	..	..	..
Ifield	1 59	..	..	..		..	..	..	..	..	..	..	..	..	..	2 26	..	..	..	..	..	2 59	..	..	..	..	..	..	..	..
Crawley [234	2 2	..	..	..		..	..	..	..	..	..	..	..	..	..	2 29	..	..	..	..	..	3 2	..	..	..	..	..	..	..	..
Three Bridges (*below*) arr.	2 5	..	..	..		..	..	..	..	..	..	..	..	..	P	2 32	..	..	..	..	..	3 5	..	..	..	..	..	..	..	p.m
	1	2	3	4	5	6	7	8	9	10	11	12	13	14	15	16	17	18	19	20	21	22	23	24	25	26	27	28	29	30

	1	2	3	4	5	6	7	8	9	10	11	12	13	14	15	16	17	18	19	20	21	22	23	24	25	26	27	28	29	30
Ore .... dep	..	..	..	..	..	1212	..	..	..	..	..	..	1242	..	1 0	..	..	..	1 12	..	..	..	..	..	..	..	..	..	..	1 42
Hastings	..	..	..	..	..	1215	..	..	..	..	..	..	1245	..	1 5	..	..	..	1 15	..	..	..	..	..	..	..	..	..	..	1 45
St. Leonards (W.S.)	..	..	..	..	..	1217	..	..	..	..	..	..	1247	..	1 8	..	..	..	1 17	..	..	..	..	..	..	..	..	..	..	1 47
" (W.M.)	..	..	..	..	..	1219	..	..	..	..	..	..	1249	..	..	..	..	..	1 19	..	..	..	..	..	..	..	..	..	..	1 49
Bexhill (Central) **G**	..	..	..	..	..	1224	..	..	..	..	..	..	1254	..	1 15	..	..	..	1 24	..	..	..	..	..	..	..	..	..	..	1 54
Collington Halt	..	..	..	..	..	1227	..	..	..	..	..	..	1257	..	..	..	..	..	1 27	..	..	..	..	..	..	..	..	..	..	1 57
Cooden Beach	..	..	..	..	..	1230	..	..	..	..	..	..	1 0	..	1 19	..	..	..	1 30	..	..	..	..	..	..	..	..	..	..	2 0
Norman's Bay Halt	..	..	..	..	..	1233	..	..	..	..	..	..	1 3	..	..	..	..	..	1 33	..	..	..	..	..	..	..	..	..	..	2 3
Pevensey Bay Halt	..	..	..	..	..	1237	..	..	..	..	..	..	1 7	..	..	..	..	..	1 37	..	..	..	..	..	..	..	..	..	..	2 7
Pevensey & Westham	..	..	..	..	..	1239	..	..	..	..	..	..	1 9	..	..	..	..	..	1 39	..	..	..	..	..	..	..	..	..	..	2 9
Hampden Park **F**	..	..	..	..	..	1245	..	..	..	..	..	..	1 15	..	..	..	..	..	1 45	..	..	..	..	..	..	..	..	..	..	2 15
Eastbourne .... arr.	..	..	..	..	..	1249	p.m	..	..	..	..	..	1 19	p.m	1 32	..	..	..	1 49	..	..	..	..	..	..	..	..	..	..	2 19
Eastbourne .... dep.	..	..	..	..	..	1252	12 59	..	..	..	1 17	..	1 22	1 27	1 36	..	..	..	1 52	..	..	..	..	1 57	..	..	2 9	..	..	2 22
Hampden Park **F**	..	..	..	..	..	1255	1 2	..	..	..	1 21	..	1 25	1 30	..	..	..	..	1 55	..	..	..	..	2 0	..	..	213	..	..	2 25
Polegate 239	..	..	..	..	..	1259	..	..	..	..	1 25	..	1 29	..	..	..	..	..	1 59	..	..	..	..	..	..	..	218	..	..	2 29
Berwick	..	..	..	..	..	1 5	..	..	..	..	..	..	1 35	..	..	..	..	..	2 5	..	..	..	..	..	..	..	..	..	..	2 35
Glynde	..	..	..	..	..	1 11	..	..	..	..	..	..	1 41	..	..	..	..	..	2 11	..	..	..	..	..	..	..	..	..	..	2 41
Lewes 239 .... arr.	..	..	..	..	..	1 16	..	..	..	..	..	p.m	1 46	..	1 56	..	..	..	2 16	..	..	..	..	..	..	..	..	..	..	2 46
Seaford .... dep.	..	..	..	..	Saturdays excepted	..	..	..	..	..	..	1 25	..	..	..	..	..	..	..	..	..	..	..	..	..	..	..	..	2 26	..
Bishopstone	..	..	..	..		..	..	..	..	..	..	1 27	..	..	..	..	..	..	..	..	..	..	..	..	..	..	..	..	2 28	..
Newhaven Harbour	..	..	..	..		..	..	..	..	..	..	1 32	..	..	..	..	..	..	..	..	..	..	..	..	..	..	..	..	2 33	..
" Town	..	..	..	..		..	..	..	..	..	..	1 33	..	..	..	..	..	..	..	..	..	..	..	..	..	..	..	..	2 34	..
Southease & Rodmell Halt	..	..	..	..		..	..	..	..	..	..	1 38	..	..	..	..	..	..	..	..	..	..	..	..	..	..	..	..	2 39	..
Lewes 239 .... arr.	..	..	..	..		..	..	..	..	p.m	..	1 44	..	..	..	..	..	..	..	..	..	..	..	..	..	..	..	p.m	2 45	..
Lewes .... dep.	..	..	..	..		1 17	..	..	..	1 36	..	..	1 47	..	..	..	..	..	2 17	..	..	..	..	..	..	..	..	2 34	..	2 47
Falmer	..	..	..	..		1 24	..	..	..	..	..	..	1 54	..	..	..	..	..	2 24	..	..	..	..	..	..	..	..	..	..	2 54
London Road (Brighton)	..	..	..	..		1 28	..	..	..	1 51	..	..	1 58	..	..	..	..	..	2 28	..	..	..	..	..	..	..	..	2 50	..	2 58
Brighton .... arr.	..	..	..	..		1 31	..	..	..	1 55	..	..	2 1	..	..	..	..	..	2 31	..	..	..	..	..	..	..	..	2 54	..	3 1
Lewes .... dep.	..	..	..	..	..	..	..	..	..	..	..	1 44	..	..	1 58	..	..	..	..	..	..	..	..	..	..	..	..	..	2 45	..
Cooksbridge	..	..	..	..	..	..	..	..	..	..	..	1 49	..	..	..	..	..	..	..	..	..	..	..	..	..	..	..	..	2 50	..
Plumpton	..	..	..	..	..	..	..	..	..	..	..	1 54	..	..	..	..	..	..	..	..	..	..	..	..	..	..	..	..	2 55	..
Wivelsfield (*below*)	..	..	..	..	..	..	..	..	..	..	..	..	..	..	..	..	..	..	..	..	..	..	..	..	..	..	..	..	..	..
Haywards Heath .... arr.	..	..	..	..	..	..	..	..	..	..	..	2 4	..	..	2 14	..	..	..	..	..	..	..	..	..	..	..	..	..	3 5	..
Brighton .... dep.	..	..	..	1 28	..	..	..	..	..	..	..	..	..	..	..	..	1 58	2 8	..	2 25	..	..	2 28	..	..	..	..	..	..	..
Preston Park	..	..	..	1 31	..	..	..	..	..	..	..	..	..	..	..	..	2 1	2 11	..	..	..	..	2 31	..	..	..	..	..	..	..
Hassocks D	..	..	..	1 39	..	..	..	..	..	..	..	..	..	..	..	..	2 9	..	..	..	..	..	2 39	..	..	..	..	..	..	..
Burgess Hill	..	..	..	1 43	..	..	..	..	..	..	..	..	..	..	..	..	2 13	..	..	..	..	..	2 43	..	..	..	..	..	..	..
Wivelsfield (*above*)	..	..	..	1 45	..	..	..	..	..	..	..	..	..	..	..	..	2 15	..	..	..	..	..	2 45	..	..	..	..	..	..	..
Haywards Heath C	..	..	..	1 54	2 8	..	..	..	..	..	..	2 4	..	..	2 15	..	2 22	2 27	..	..	..	..	2 52	..	..	..	..	..	3 5	..
Ardingly	..	R	..	..	P	..	..	..	..	..	..	2 8	..	..	P	..	..	..	..	P	..	..	..	..	..	RB	..	..	3 9	..
Horsted Keynes 239 .. arr.	..	..	..	..	..	..	..	..	..	..	..	2 12	..	..	..	..	..	..	..	..	..	..	..	..	..	..	..	..	3 13	..
Balcombe	..	Saturdays only	..	2 0	..	..	..	..	..	..	..	..	..	..	..	..	2 28	..	..	..	..	..	2 58	..	..	..	..	..	..	..
Three Bridges (*above*)	..		..	2 8	..	..	..	..	..	..	..	..	..	..	..	..	2 38	..	..	..	..	..	3 8	..	..	..	..	..	..	..
Gatwick Airport	..		..	2 12	..	..	..	..	..	..	..	..	..	..	..	..	2 41	2 40	..	..	..	..	3 12	..	..	..	..	..	..	..
Horley	..		..	2 15	..	..	..	..	..	..	..	..	..	..	..	..	2 44	..	..	..	..	..	3 15	..	..	..	..	..	..	..
Salfords	..		..	2 19	..	..	..	..	..	..	..	..	..	..	..	..	2 48	..	..	..	..	..	3 19	..	..	..	..	..	..	..
Earlswood	..		..	2 23	..	..	..	..	..	..	..	..	..	..	..	..	2 52	..	..	..	..	..	3 23	..	..	..	..	..	..	..
Redhill 246	..		..	2 31	..	..	..	..	..	..	..	..	..	..	..	..	2 59	2 50	..	..	..	..	3 30	..	..	..	..	..	..	..
Merstham	..		..	2 35	..	..	..	..	..	..	..	..	..	..	..	..	3 3	..	..	..	..	..	3 34	..	..	..	..	..	..	..
Coulsdon South	..		..	2 41	..	..	..	..	..	..	..	..	..	..	..	..	3 9	..	..	..	..	..	3 41	..	..	..	..	..	..	..
Purley	..		..	2 45	..	..	..	..	..	..	..	..	..	..	..	..	3 13	..	..	..	..	..	3 44	..	..	..	..	..	..	..
East Croydon 285 .... arr.	..	..	..	2 50	2 41	..	..	..	..	..	..	..	..	..	2 46	..	3 18	3 4	..	..	..	..	3 50	..	..	..	..	..	..	..
Norwood Junction **B** arr.	..	..	..	2 (3) 58	2*50	..	..	..	..	..	..	..	..	..	2 (3) 58	..	3 23	3*23	..	..	..	..	..	..	..	..	..	..	..	..
New Cross Gate ...... "	..	..	..	..	..	..	..	..	..	..	..	..	..	..	..	..	..	..	..	..	..	..	..	..	..	..	..	..	..	..
LONDON BRIDGE ... "	..	..	..	3 (3) 11	3 *5	..	..	..	..	..	..	..	..	..	3 (3) 11	..	3 35	3*35	..	..	..	..	4 (3) y8	..	..	..	..	..	..	..
Clapham Junction **A** .. arr.	..	..	..	3 2	..	..	..	..	..	..	..	..	..	..	..	..	3*35	3 16	..	..	..	..	4 2	..	..	..	..	..	..	..
VICTORIA .... "	..	2 40	..	3 8	2 57	..	..	..	..	..	..	..	..	..	3 3	..	3*42	3 22	..	3 25	..	..	4 7	..	..	3 40	..	..	..	..

(3) Third class only. * Change at East Croydon *a* Arrival time. *b* Arr. 7 minutes *earlier* **P** Pullman Car facilities available

R Refreshment Car facilities available. **RB** Refreshment Car facilities available between Bognor Regis and London. *y* 3 minutes later on Saturdays.

For Other Notes, see page 233

For SERVICES from ISLE OF WIGHT and PORTSMOUTH to LONDON (Waterloo), see pages 366 to 372

From THE SOUTH COAST to LONDON—Week Days—*continued*

Station	p.m	p.m	p.m	p.m	p.m	p.m	p.m	p.m	p.m	p.m.
Page 366 Yarmouth ....dep.										
Cowes .... "										
Newport .... "										
Ventnor .... "										
Shanklin .... "										
Sandown .... "										
500 Ryde Pier (Boat).. "										
Portsmouth Harbour..dep.							1 53			
Portsmouth & Southsea "			1 42				1 57			
Fratton........			1 45				1 59			
Hilsea Halt........										
Bedhampton Halt........			1 53							
245 Hayling Island....dep.										
Havant 244........			1 55				2 8			
Warblington Halt........			1 57							
Emsworth........			2 0							
Southbourne Halt........			2 3							
Nutbourne Halt........			2 5							
Bosham........			2 9							
Fishbourne Halt........			2 12							
Chichester Z........			2 15				2 22			
Barnham........arr.			Stop				2 31			
Bognor Regis .... arr.										
Bognor Regis .... dep.										
Barnham........dep.							2 31			
Ford (Sussex)........							Saturdays only			
Littlehampton........ arr.	P									
Littlehampton........ dep.	2 9			2 35	2 46				2 49	
Ford (Sussex)........arr.					2 50					
Angmering L........	2 19				Stop				2 58	
Goring-by-Sea........	2 24								3 3	
Durrington-on-Sea........	2 27								3 5	
West Worthing U........	2 30					2 39		2 50	3 7	
Worthing Central........	2 35					2 41	2 48	2 52	3 9	
Ham Bridge Halt N........								2 55		
Lancing........						2 45		2 58	3 13	
Shoreham-by-Sea K 244........	2 42					2 49	2 56	3 3	3 17	
Southwick........						2 52		3 6	3 21	
Fishersgate Halt........								3 9		
Portslade and West Hove........						2 55		3 11	3 24	
Aldrington Halt........								3 14	3 27	
Hove........	2 51					2 59	3 3	3 16	3 29	
Holland Road Halt........								3 18		
Brighton (below)........arr.						3 2	3 6	3 20	3 32	
Arundel........	Through Train Littlehampton to Victoria			2 41				Stop	Stop	
Amberley........				2 46						
Pulborough J 374........				2 54						
Billingshurst........[Horsham				3 1						
Christ's Hospital, West				3 8						
Horsham 244, 245, 285, 427........ arr.				3 12						
Horsham 244, 245, 285, 427........ dep.										
Dorking North H 385, 427..										
Sutton 285, 322........arr.										
Horsham........dep.				3 15						
Littlehaven Halt........				3 17						
Fay Gate........				3 21						
Ifield........				3 26						
Crawley........ [234			p.m	3 29						
Three Bridges (below) arr.			P	3 32					p.m	
	1	2	3	4	5	6	7	8	9	10

Station	p.m	p.m	p.m	p.m	p.m		p.m	p.m	p.m	p.m
Page 366 Yarmouth ....dep.										
Cowes .... "										
Newport .... "										
Ventnor .... "										
Shanklin .... "										
Sandown .... "										
500 Ryde Pier (Boat).. "										
Portsmouth Harbour..dep.	2 8									
Portsmouth & Southsea "	2 12									
Fratton........	2 14									
Hilsea Halt........										
Bedhampton Halt........										
245 Hayling Island....dep.	1S57									
Havant 244........	2 23									
Warblington Halt........	2 25			Saturdays only						
Emsworth........	2 28									
Southbourne Halt........	2 31									
Nutbourne Halt........	2 34									
Bosham........	2 37									
Fishbourne Halt........	2 40									
Chichester Z........	2 44									
Barnham........arr.	2 53									
Bognor Regis .... arr.	3 7									
Bognor Regis .... dep.	2 45				2 45					3 10
Barnham........dep.	2 54				2b58					3a16
Ford (Sussex)........	2 59				3 2					Stop
Littlehampton........ arr.	3 7			P	3 7					
Littlehampton........ dep.				3 5	3 9				3 35	
Ford (Sussex)........arr.										
Angmering L........	3 6			3 16						
Goring-by-Sea........	3 11			3 22						
Durrington-on-Sea........				3 25						p.m
West Worthing U........	3 14		3 20	3 30						3 38
Worthing Central........	3 17		3 22	3 35						3 40
Ham Bridge Halt N........			3 24							
Lancing........			3 27							3 44
Shoreham-by-Sea K 244........	3 25		3 32	3 42						3 48
Southwick........			3 36							3 51
Fishersgate Halt........			3 38							
Portslade and West Hove........			3 40							3 54
Aldrington Halt........			3 43							3 57
Hove........	3 33		3 45	3 51						3 59
Holland Road Halt........			3 47							
Brighton (below)........arr.	3 36		3 50							4 2
Arundel........	Stop		Stop	Through Train, Littlehampton to Victoria	3 16				3 41	Stop
Amberley........					3 21				3 46	
Pulborough J 374........					3 29				3 54	
Billingshurst........[Horsham					3 36				4 1	
Christ's Hospital, West					3 43				4 8	
Horsham 244, 245, 285, 427........ arr.					3 47				4 12	
Horsham 244, 245, 285, 427........ dep.										
Dorking North H 385, 427..										
Sutton 285, 322........arr.										
Horsham........dep.					3 48				4 15	
Littlehaven Halt........					3 50				4 17	
Fay Gate........					3 54				4 21	
Ifield........					3 59				4 26	
Crawley........ [234					4 2				4 29	
Three Bridges (below) arr.					4 5				4 32	
	11	12	13	14	15	16	17	18	19	20

Station	p.m	noon	p.m	p.m		p.m	p.m	p.m	p.m	p.m
Page 366 Yarmouth ....dep.		12 0								
Cowes .... "		1226								
Newport .... "		1238								
Ventnor .... "		1242								
Shanklin .... "		1254								
Sandown .... "		1 1								
500 Ryde Pier (Boat).. "		1 35								
Portsmouth Harbour..dep.		2a 5				2 53				
Portsmouth & Southsea "				2 42		2 57				
Fratton........				2 45		2 59				
Hilsea Halt........										
Bedhampton Halt........				2 53						
245 Hayling Island....dep.										
Havant 244........		Saturdays only		2 55		3 8				
Warblington Halt........				2 57						
Emsworth........				3 0						
Southbourne Halt........				3 3						
Nutbourne Halt........				3 5						
Bosham........				3 9						
Fishbourne Halt........				3 12						
Chichester Z........				2 15		3 22				
Barnham........arr.		Stop		Stop		3 31				
Bognor Regis .... arr.						3 42				
Bognor Regis .... dep.						3 10				
Barnham........dep.						3 31				
Ford (Sussex)........						Saturdays only				
Littlehampton........ arr.										
Littlehampton........ dep.										3 46
Ford (Sussex)........arr.										3 50
Angmering L........										Stop
Goring-by-Sea........										
Durrington-on-Sea........										
West Worthing U........										
Worthing Central........						3 48				
Ham Bridge Halt N........										
Lancing........										
Shoreham-by-Sea K 244........						3 56				
Southwick........										
Fishersgate Halt........										
Portslade and West Hove........										
Aldrington Halt........										
Hove........						4 3				
Holland Road Halt........										
Brighton (below)........arr.						4 6				
Arundel........										
Amberley........										
Pulborough J 374........										
Billingshurst........[Horsham										
Christ's Hospital, West										
Horsham 244, 245, 285, 427........ arr.										
Horsham 244, 245, 285, 427........ dep.										
Dorking North H 385, 427..										
Sutton 285, 322........arr.										
Horsham........dep.										
Littlehaven Halt........										
Fay Gate........										
Ifield........										
Crawley........ [234										
Three Bridges (below) arr.	P									
	21	22	23	24	25	26	27	28	29	30

Printed and Published by—
Henry Blacklock & Co. Ltd.,
London, and
Albert Square, Manchester, 2.

	1	2	3	4	5	6	7	8	9	10	11	12	13	14	15	16	17	18	19	20	21	22	23	24	25	26	27	28	29	30
Ore dep	..	..	2 0	..	..	..	..	..	2 13	..	..	..	..	..	..	..	..	2 42	..	..	3 0	..	..	..	..	..	3 13	..	..	..
Hastings	..	..	2 5	..	..	..	..	..	2 16	..	..	..	..	..	..	..	..	2 45	..	..	3 5	..	..	..	..	..	3 16	..	..	..
St. Leonards (W.S.)	..	..	2 8	..	..	..	..	..	2 18	..	..	..	..	..	..	..	..	2 47	..	..	3 8	..	..	..	..	..	3 18	..	..	..
" (W.M.)	..	..	..	..	..	..	..	..	2 20	..	..	..	..	..	..	..	..	2 49	..	..	..	..	..	..	..	..	3 20	..	..	..
Bexhill (Central) **G**	..	..	2 15	..	..	..	..	..	2 25	..	..	..	..	..	..	..	..	2 54	..	..	3 15	**Saturdays only.**	..	..	..	..	3 25	..	..	..
Collington Halt	..	..	..	..	..	..	..	..	2 28	..	..	..	..	..	..	..	..	2 57	..	..	..		..	..	..	..	3 28	..	..	..
Cooden Beach	..	..	2 19	..	..	..	..	..	2 31	..	..	..	..	..	..	..	..	3 0	..	..	3 19		..	..	..	..	3 31	..	..	..
Norman's Bay Halt	..	..	..	..	..	..	..	..	2 34	..	..	..	..	..	..	..	..	3 3	..	..	..		..	..	..	..	3 34	..	..	..
Pevensey Bay Halt	..	..	..	..	..	..	..	..	2 38	..	..	..	..	..	..	..	..	3 7	..	..	..		..	..	..	..	3 38	..	..	..
Pevensey and Westham	..	..	..	..	..	..	..	..	2 40	..	..	..	..	..	..	..	..	3 9	..	..	..		..	..	..	..	3 40	..	..	..
Hampden Park **F**	..	..	..	..	..	..	..	..	2 45	..	..	..	..	..	..	..	..	3 15	..	..	..		..	..	..	..	3 45	..	..	..
Eastbourne arr.	..	..	2 32	..	..	..	..	..	2 49	..	p.m	..	..	..	..	..	..	3 19	..	p.m	3 32		**Saturdays excepted.**	p.m	..	..	3 49	..	..	p.m
Eastbourne dep.	..	2 29	2 36	..	..	..	..	..	2 52	..	2 57	..	..	..	..	..	..	3 22	..	3 29	3 36			3 39	..	..	3 52	..	..	3 57
Hampden Park **F**	..	2 32	..	..	..	..	..	..	2 55	..	3 0	..	..	..	..	..	..	3 25	..	3 32	..			3 43	..	..	3 55	..	..	4 0
Polegate 239	..	..	..	..	..	..	..	..	2 59	..	..	..	..	..	..	..	..	3 29	..	..	..			3 48	..	..	3 59	..	..	..
Berwick	..	..	..	..	..	..	..	..	3 5	..	..	..	..	..	..	..	..	3 35	..	..	..			..	..	..	4 5	..	..	..
Glynde	..	..	..	..	..	..	..	..	3 11	..	..	..	..	..	..	..	..	3 41	..	..	..			..	..	..	4 11	..	..	..
Lewes 239 arr.	..	..	2 56	..	..	..	..	..	3 16	..	..	..	..	..	..	..	..	3 46	..	..	3 56	p.m		..	..	..	4 16	..	..	..
Seaford dep.	..	..	..	..	..	..	..	..	..	..	..	..	..	..	..	..	3 25	..	..	..	..	3 41	3 45	..	..	..	..	..	..	..
Bishopstone	..	..	..	..	..	..	..	..	..	..	..	..	..	..	..	..	3 27	..	..	..	..	3 43	3 47	..	..	..	..	..	..	..
Newhaven Harbour	..	..	..	..	..	..	..	..	..	..	..	..	..	..	..	..	3 32	..	..	..	..	3 48	3 52	..	..	..	..	..	..	..
" Town	..	..	..	..	..	..	..	..	..	..	..	..	..	..	..	..	3 33	..	..	..	..	3 49	3 53	..	..	..	..	..	..	..
Southease & Rodmell Halt	..	..	..	..	..	..	..	..	..	..	..	..	..	..	..	..	3 38	..	..	..	..	3 54	3 58	..	..	..	..	..	..	..
Lewes 239 arr.	..	..	..	..	..	..	..	..	..	..	..	..	..	..	..	..	3 44	..	..	..	..	4 0	4 4	..	..	..	..	..	..	..
Lewes dep.	..	..	..	..	..	..	..	..	3 17	..	..	..	..	..	..	..	..	3 47	..	..	..	4 0	4 4	..	..	..	4 17	..	..	..
Falmer	..	..	..	..	..	..	..	..	3 24	..	..	..	..	..	..	..	..	3 54	..	..	..	4 7	4 11	..	..	..	4 24	..	..	..
London Road (Brighton)	..	..	..	..	..	..	..	..	3 29	..	..	..	..	..	..	..	..	3 58	..	..	..	4 12	4 16	..	..	..	4 28	..	..	..
Brighton arr.	..	..	..	..	..	..	..	..	3 31	..	..	..	..	..	..	..	..	4 1	..	..	..	4 14	4 18	..	..	..	4 31	..	..	..
Lewes dep.	..	..	2 58	..	..	..	..	..	..	..	..	..	..	..	..	..	3 44	..	..	..	3 57	..	..	..	..	..	..	..	..	..
Cooksbridge	..	..	..	..	..	..	..	..	..	..	..	..	..	**Saturdays only**	..	..	3 49	..	..	..	..	..	..	..	..	..	..	..	..	..
Plumpton	..	..	..	..	..	..	..	..	..	..	..	..	..		..	..	3 54	..	..	..	..	..	..	..	..	..	..	..	..	..
Wivelsfield (*below*)	..	..	..	..	..	..	..	..	..	..	..	..	..		..	..	4 0	..	..	..	..	..	..	..	..	..	..	..	..	..
Haywards Heath arr.	..	..	3 14	..	p.m	..	..	p.m	..	..	..	p.m	p.m		..	..	4 5	..	..	..	4 14	..	..	..	..	..	..	..	..	..
Brighton dep.	..	..	..	..	2 58	..	..	3 8	..	..	..	3 25	3 28		..	..	..	..	..	..	..	..	..	..	..	..	..	3 58	4 8	..
Preston Park	..	..	..	..	3 1	..	..	3 11	..	..	..	..	3 31		..	..	..	..	..	..	..	..	..	..	..	..	..	4 1	4 11	..
Hassocks **D**	..	..	..	..	3 9	..	..	..	..	..	..	..	3 39		..	..	..	..	..	..	..	..	..	..	..	..	..	4 9	..	..
Burgess Hill	..	..	..	..	3 13	..	..	..	..	..	..	..	3 43		..	..	..	..	..	..	..	..	..	..	..	..	..	4 13	..	..
Wivelsfield (*above*)	..	..	..	..	3 15	..	..	..	..	..	..	..	3 45	..	..	..	..	..	..	..	..	..	..	..	..	..	..	4 15	..	..
Haywards Heath C	3 8	..	3 15	..	3 21	..	..	3 26	..	3 28	..	..	3 52	4 8	..	..	4 6	..	..	..	4 14	..	..	..	..	..	..	4 22	4 27	..
Ardingly	P	..	P	..	..	..	..	..	..	3 34	..	P	..	P	..	..	4 10	..	..	..	P	..	..	..	..	..	..	..	..	..
Horsted Keynes 239 arr.	..	..	..	..	..	..	..	..	..	3 39	..	..	..	..	..	..	4 14	..	..	..	..	..	..	..	..	..	..	..	..	..
Balcombe	..	..	..	..	3 27	..	..	..	..	..	..	..	3 58	..	..	..	..	..	..	..	..	..	..	..	..	..	..	4 28	..	..
Three Bridges (*above*)	..	..	..	..	3 37	..	..	..	..	..	..	..	4 8	..	..	..	..	..	..	..	..	..	..	..	..	..	..	4 38	..	..
Gatwick Airport	..	..	..	..	3 41	..	..	3 40	..	..	..	..	4 11	..	..	..	..	..	..	..	..	..	..	..	..	..	..	4 42	4 40	..
Horley	..	..	..	..	3 44	..	..	..	..	..	..	..	4 15	..	..	..	..	..	..	..	..	..	..	..	..	..	..	4 45	..	..
Salfords	..	..	..	..	3 48	..	..	..	..	..	..	..	4 19	..	..	..	..	..	..	..	..	..	..	..	..	..	..	4 49	..	..
Earlswood	..	..	..	..	3 52	..	..	..	..	..	..	..	4 23	..	..	..	..	..	..	..	..	..	..	..	..	..	..	4 53	..	..
Redhill 246	..	..	..	..	3 58	..	..	3 50	..	..	..	..	4 29	..	..	..	..	..	..	..	..	..	..	..	..	..	..	4 59	4 50	..
Merstham	..	..	..	..	4 2	..	..	..	..	..	..	..	4 33	..	..	..	..	..	..	..	..	..	..	..	..	..	..	5 3	..	..
Coulsdon South	..	..	..	..	4 8	..	..	..	..	..	..	..	4 39	..	..	..	..	..	..	..	..	..	..	..	..	..	..	5 9	..	..
Purley	..	..	..	..	4 12	..	..	..	..	..	..	..	4 43	..	..	..	..	..	..	..	..	..	..	..	..	..	..	5 13	..	..
East Croydon 285 arr.	3 41	..	3 45	..	4 17	..	..	4 4	..	..	..	..	4 48	4 41	..	..	..	..	..	..	4 45	..	..	..	..	..	..	5 18	5 5	..
Norwood Junction B arr.	..	..	..	..	4 22	..	..	4*22	..	..	..	..	..	4③58	..	..	..	..	..	..	..	..	..	..	..	..	..	5 24	..	..
New Cross Gate "	..	..	..	..	..	..	..	..	..	..	..	..	..	..	..	..	..	..	..	..	..	..	..	..	..	..	..	..	..	..
LONDON BRIDGE "	4③y8	..	4③y8	..	4 36	..	..	4*36	..	..	..	..	5 H3	5③11	..	..	..	..	..	..	5*H3	..	..	..	..	..	..	5 38	5K*30	..
Clapham Junction A arr	..	..	..	..	..	..	..	4 16	..	..	..	..	5SO2	..	..	..	..	..	..	..	..	..	..	..	..	..	..	..	5 16	..
VICTORIA "	3 58	..	4 3	..	..	..	..	4 22	..	..	..	4 25	5SO7	4 58	..	..	..	..	..	..	5 2	..	..	..	..	..	..	..	5 22	..

③ Third class only. * Change at East Croydon. *a* Arrival time. *b* Arr. 7 minutes *earlier*. H Arr. 5③11 p.m on Saturdays.
K Third class only Mons. to Fris. and arrives London Bridge 5 38 p.m on Sats. **P** Pullman Car facilities available SO Sats. only.
SX Sats. excepted. *y* 3 mins. later on Sats.

For Other Notes, see page 233

For SERVICES from ISLE OF WIGHT and PORTSMOUTH to LONDON (Waterloo), see pages 366 to 372

From THE SOUTH COAST to LONDON—Week Days—continued

Station	1 p.m	2 p.m	3 p.m	4	5 p.m	6 p.m	7 p.m	8 p.m	9 p.m	10 noon	11 p.m	12 p.m	13 p.m	14 p.m	15 p.m	16 p.m
Yarmouth (Page 366) dep.										12SX0	Saturdays only				Saturdays excepted	
Cowes "										1 26						
Newport "										1 38						
Ventnor "										1 42						
Shanklin "										1 54						
Sandown "										2 1						
500 Ryde Pier (Boat) "										2 35						
Portsmouth Harbour dep.								3 8		3 23						
Portsmouth & Southsea "								3 12		3 27						
Fratton								3 14		3 30						
Hilsea Halt																
Bedhampton Halt																
245 Hayling Island dep.										3u18						
Havant 244								3 23		3 39						
Warblington Halt								3 25								
Emsworth								3 28								
Southbourne Halt								3 31								
Nutbourne Halt								3 34								
Bosham								3 37								
Fishbourne Halt								3 40								
Chichester Z								3 44		3 54					4 10	
Barnham arr.								3 53		4 3					4 19	
Bognor Regis arr.								4 7		RB					4 28	
Bognor Regis dep.						3 40		3 40		3 55	4 10					
Barnham dep						3 47		3 54		4 5	4a16					
Ford (Sussex)						3 52		3 59								
Littlehampton arr.						3 57										
Littlehampton dep.					3 49	3 59				3 59				4 35		
Ford (Sussex) arr.																
Angmering L					3 58			4 6		Through Train Bognor Regis to Victoria						
Goring-by-Sea					4 3			4 11								
Durrington-on-Sea					4 5											
West Worthing U	3 50				4 7			4 14	4 20							
Worthing Central	3 52				4 9			4 17	4 22							
Ham Bridge Halt N	3 55								4 24							
Lancing	3 58				4 13				4 27							
Shoreham-by-Sea K 244	4 3	4 9			4 17			4 25	4 32							
Southwick	4 6	4 13			4 21				4 36							
Fishersgate Halt	4 9								4 38							
Portslade and West Hove	4 11	4 17			4 24				4 40							
Aldrington Halt	4 14				4 27				4 43							
Hove	4 16	4 21			4 29			4 33	4 45							
Holland Road Halt	4 18								4 47							
Brighton (below) arr.	4 20	4 26			4 32			4 36	4 51							
Arundel	Stop	Stop				4 5		Stop	Stop	4 14				4 41		
Amberley						4 11								4 46		
Pulborough J 374						4 18				4 26				4 54		
Billingshurst						4 25								5 1		
Christ's Hospital, West Horsham						4 32								5 8		
Horsham 244, 245 arr.						4 37				4 42				5 12		
Horsham 285, 427 dep.										4 43						
Dorking North H 285, 427										5 2						
Sutton 285, 322 arr.										5 19						
Horsham dep.						4 47								5 15		
Littlehaven Halt						4 49								5 17		
Fay Gate						4 53								5 21		
Ifield						4 58								5 26		
Crawley 234						5 1								5 29		
Three Bridges (below) arr.						5 4			p.m					5 32		

Station	17 p.m	18 p.m	19 p.m	20 p.m	21 p.m	22 p.m R	23 p.m	24	25 p.m	26 p.m	27 p.m	28 p.m	29 p.m	30 p.m	31 p.m
Yarmouth (Page 366) dep.						Thro Train Plymouth (dep 10 0 a.m.) to Brighton, pages 348 and 377			Saturdays excepted	Saturdays only					Saturdays only P
Cowes "															
Newport "															
Ventnor "															
Shanklin "															
Sandown "															
500 Ryde Pier (Boat) "															
Portsmouth Harbour dep.												4 8			
Portsmouth & Southsea "	3 42											4 12			
Fratton	3 45											4 14			
Hilsea Halt															
Bedhampton Halt	3 53														
245 Hayling Island dep.															
Havant 244	3 55											4 23			
Warblington Halt	3 57											4 25			
Emsworth	4 0											4 28			
Southbourne Halt	4 3											4 31			
Nutbourne Halt	4 5											4 34			
Bosham	4 9											4 37			
Fishbourne Halt	4 12											4 40			
Chichester Z	4 16					4 30						4 44			
Barnham arr.	Stop					4 41						4 53			
Bognor Regis arr.						5 2						5 9			
Bognor Regis dep.												4 40			
Barnham dep						4 41						4 54			
Ford (Sussex)												4 58			
Littlehampton arr.															
Littlehampton dep.				4 46					4 49	4 52					5 9
Ford (Sussex) arr.				4 50											
Angmering L				Stop					4 58	5 1		5 6			5 19
Goring-by-Sea									5 3	5 6		5 10			5 24
Durrington-on-Sea									5 5	5 8					5 27
West Worthing U		4 40			4 49				5 7	5 10		5 14		5 17	5 30
Worthing Central		4 42			4 51	5 0			5 9	5 12		5 17		5 19	5 35
Ham Bridge Halt N					4 53									5 22	
Lancing		4 46			4 56				5 13	5 16				5 25	
Shoreham-by-Sea K 244		4 50			5 1		5 11		5 17	5 20		5 25		5 30	5 42
Southwick		4 53			5 5				5 21	5 24				5 33	
Fishersgate Halt					5 7									5 36	
Portslade and West Hove		4 56			5 9		5 16		5 24	5 27				5 38	
Aldrington Halt		4 59			5 12				5 27	5 30				5 40	
Hove		5 1			5 14		5 20		5 29	5 32		5 33		5 42	5 52
Holland Road Halt					5 16									5 44	
Brighton (below) arr.		5 5			5 18	5 22	5 25		5 34	5 36		5 38		5 50	Through Train Littlehampton to Victoria
Arundel		Stop			Stop		Stop								
Amberley															
Pulborough J 374															
Billingshurst															
Christ's Hospital, West Horsham															
Horsham 244, 245 arr.															
Horsham 285, 427 dep.															
Dorking North H 285, 427															
Sutton 285, 322 arr.															
Horsham dep.															
Littlehaven Halt															
Fay Gate															
Ifield															
Crawley 234															
Three Bridges (below) arr.		p.m													

	1	2	3	4	5	6	7	8	9	10	11	12	13	14	15	16	17	18	19	20	21	22	23	24	25	26	27	28	29	30	31
Ore .... dep	..	..	Saturdays excepted	..	..	Stop	..	..	3 42	..	..	..	..	..	..	..	..	4 12	..	..	..	..	..	..	..	..	..	..	4 43	..	..
Hastings	..	..		..	..		..	..	3 45	..	..	..	..	Stop	..	..	..	4 15	..	..	..	..	..	..	..	..	..	..	4 46	..	..
St. Leonards (W.S.)	..	..		..	..	..	..	..	3 47	..	..	..	..	..	..	..	..	4 17	..	..	..	..	..	..	..	..	..	..	4 48	..	..
" (W.M.)	..	..		..	..	..	..	..	3 49	..	..	..	..	..	..	..	..	4 19	..	..	..	..	..	..	..	..	..	..	4 50	..	..
Bexhill (Central) **G**	..	..		..	..	..	..	..	3 54	..	..	..	..	..	..	..	..	4 24	..	..	..	..	..	..	..	..	..	..	4 55	..	..
Collington Halt	..	..		..	..	..	..	..	3 57	..	..	..	..	..	..	..	..	4 27	..	..	..	..	..	..	..	..	..	..	4 58	..	..
Cooden Beach	..	..		..	..	..	..	..	4 0	..	..	..	..	..	..	..	..	4 30	..	..	..	..	..	..	..	..	..	..	5 1	..	..
Norman's Bay Halt	..	..		..	..	..	..	..	4 3	..	..	..	..	..	..	..	..	4 33	..	..	..	..	..	..	..	..	..	..	5 4	..	..
Pevensey Bay Halt	..	..		..	..	..	..	..	4 7	..	..	..	..	..	..	..	..	4 37	..	..	..	..	..	..	..	..	..	..	5 8	..	..
Pevensey and Westham	..	..		..	..	..	..	..	4 9	..	..	..	..	..	..	..	..	4 39	..	..	..	..	..	..	..	..	..	..	5 10	..	..
Hampden Park **F**	..	..		..	..	..	..	..	4 15	..	..	..	..	..	..	..	..	4 45	..	..	..	..	..	..	..	..	..	..	5 15	..	..
Eastbourne arr.	..	p.m		..	..	..	..	..	4 19	..	..	..	..	p.m	..	..	..	4 49	..	p.m	..	..	..	..	..	..	..	..	5 19	..	..
Eastbourne dep.	..	4 0	4 6	..	..	..	..	..	4 22	..	..	..	4 29	4 39	..	..	..	4 52	..	4 57	..	..	..	..	..	..	..	..	5 22	..	..
Hampden Park **F**	..	4 4	..	..	..	..	..	..	4 25	..	..	..	4 32	4 43	..	..	..	4 55	..	5 0	..	..	..	..	..	..	..	..	5 25	..	..
Polegate 239	..	4 9	..	..	..	..	..	..	4 29	..	..	..	Stop	4 48	..	..	..	4 59	..	Stop	..	..	..	..	..	..	..	..	5 30	..	..
Berwick	..	..	..	..	..	..	..	..	4 35	..	..	..	..	..	..	..	..	5 5	..	..	..	..	..	..	..	..	..	..	5 36	..	..
Glynde	..	..	..	..	..	..	..	..	4 41	..	..	..	..	..	..	..	..	5 11	..	..	..	..	..	..	..	..	..	..	5 42	..	..
Lewes 239 .... arr.	..	..	4 26	..	..	p.m	..	..	4 46	..	..	..	..	..	..	..	p.m	5 16	..	..	..	..	..	..	..	..	..	..	5 47	..	..
Seaford .... dep.	..	..	..	..	..	4 25	..	Saturdays excepted	..	..	..	..	..	..	..	..	4 48	..	..	..	..	..	..	..	..	..	5 25	..	..	..	..
Bishopstone	..	..	..	..	..	4 27	..		..	..	..	..	..	..	..	..	4 50	..	..	..	..	..	..	..	..	..	5 27	..	..	..	..
Newhaven Harbour	..	..	..	..	..	4 32	..		..	..	..	..	..	..	..	..	4 55	..	..	..	..	..	..	..	..	..	5 30	..	..	..	..
" Town	..	..	..	..	..	4 33	..		..	..	..	..	..	..	..	..	4 57	..	..	..	..	..	..	..	..	..	5 32	..	..	..	..
Southease & Rodmell Halt	..	..	..	..	..	4 37	..		..	..	..	..	..	..	..	..	5 2	..	..	..	..	..	..	..	..	..	5 37	..	..	..	..
Lewes 239 .... arr.	..	..	..	..	..	4 44	..		..	..	..	..	..	..	..	..	5 8	..	..	..	p.m	..	..	..	..	..	5 42	..	..	..	..
Lewes .... dep.	..	..	..	..	..	..	Saturdays only.		4 47	..	..	4 53	..	..	..	..	5 10	5 17	..	..	5 37	..	..	..	..	..	..	..	5 49	..	..
Falmer	..	..	..	..	..	..			4 54	..	..	..	..	..	..	..	5 17	5 24	..	..	..	..	..	..	..	..	..	..	5 56	..	..
London Road (Brighton)	..	..	..	..	..	..			4 58	..	..	5 9	..	..	..	..	5 21	5 28	..	..	5 52	..	..	..	..	..	..	..	6 0	..	..
Brighton .... arr.	..	..	..	..	..	..		☞	5 1	..	..	5 13	p.m	..	..	..	5 24	5 31	..	..	5 56	..	..	..	..	..	..	..	6 3	..	..
Lewes .... dep.	..	..	4 27	..	..	..			..	..	..	..	4 54	..	..	..	Stop	..	Saturdays excepted	..	..	..	..	..	..	..	5 44	..	..	..	..
Cooksbridge	..	..	4 32	..	..	..			..	..	..	..	4 59	..	..	..	..	..		..	..	..	..	..	..	..	5 49	..	..	..	..
Plumpton	..	..	4 37	..	..	..			..	..	..	..	5 4	..	..	..	..	..		..	..	..	..	..	..	..	5 54	..	..	..	..
Wivelsfield (*below*)	..	..	4 43	..	..	..			..	..	..	..	5 12	..	..	..	..	..		..	..	..	..	..	..	..	6 0	..	..	..	..
Haywards Heath .... arr.	p.m	..	4 48	..	..	..		p.m	..	..	..	..	5 17	..	..	..	p.m	..		..	..	..	p.m	..	..	..	6 5	..	..	..	Saturdays only.
Brighton .... dep.	4 25	..	..	..	..	..	4 28	4 28	..	..	..	..	..	..	..	4 58	5 3	..	5 12	..	..	..	5 25	..	..	..	..	..	..	..	
Preston Park	..	..	..	..	..	..	4 31	4 31	..	..	..	..	..	..	..	5 1	5 11	..	5 15	..	..	..		..	..	..	..	..	..	..	
Hassocks **D**	..	..	..	..	..	..	4 39	4 39	..	..	..	..	..	..	..	5 9	..	..	5 23	..	..	..		..	..	..	..	..	..	..	
Burgess Hill	..	..	..	..	..	..	4 43	4 43	..	..	..	..	..	..	..	5 13	..	..	5 27	..	..	..		..	..	..	..	..	..	..	
Wivelsfield (*above*)	..	..	..	..	..	..	4 45	4 45	..	..	..	..	..	..	..	5 15	..	..	5 29	p.m	..	..		..	..	..	..	..	..	..	
Haywards Heath C	..	..	..	..	..	..	4 52	4 52	..	..	..	..	..	..	..	5 23	5 27	..	5 34	5 36	..	..		..	..	..	6 6	..	..	..	6 9
Ardingly	P	..	..	..	..	..	..	..	..	RB	..	..	..	..	..	..	..	..	..	5 40	..	..		..	..	..	6 10	..	..	..	P
Horsted Keynes 239 .. arr.	..	..	..	..	..	..	..	..	..	..	..	..	..	..	..	..	..	..	..	5 44	..	..		..	..	..	6 14	..	..	..	..
Balcombe	Saturdays excepted	..	..	..	..	..	4 58	4 58	..	..	..	..	..	..	..	5 27	..	..	..	..	..	..	Brighton Belle 1st and 3rd class Pullman Cars only	..	..	..	..	..	..	..	..
Three Bridges (*above*)		..	..	..	..	..	5 8	5 10	..	..	..	..	..	..	..	5 37	..	..	..	..	..	..		..	..	..	..	..	..	..	..
Gatwick Airport		..	..	..	..	..	5 12	5 14	..	..	..	..	..	..	..	5 41	5 40	..	..	..	..	..		..	..	..	..	..	..	..	..
Horley		..	..	..	..	..	5 15	5 17	..	..	..	..	..	..	..	5 44	..	..	..	..	..	..		..	..	..	..	..	..	..	..
Salfords		..	..	..	..	..	5 19	5 21	..	..	..	..	..	..	..	5 48	..	..	..	..	..	..		..	..	..	..	..	..	..	..
Earlswood		..	..	..	..	..	5 23	5 25	..	..	..	..	..	..	..	5 52	..	..	..	..	..	..		..	..	..	..	..	..	..	..
Redhill 246		..	..	..	..	..	5 30	5 31	..	..	..	..	..	..	..	5 59	5 50	..	..	..	..	..		..	..	..	..	..	..	..	..
Merstham		..	..	..	..	..	5 34	5 35	..	..	..	..	..	..	..	6 2	..	..	..	..	..	..		..	..	..	..	..	..	..	..
Coulsdon South	..	..	..	..	..	..	5 40	5 41	..	..	..	..	..	..	..	6 8	..	..	..	..	..	..		..	..	..	..	..	..	..	..
Purley	..	..	..	..	..	..	5 44	5 44	..	..	..	..	..	..	..	6 12	..	..	..	..	..	..		..	..	..	..	..	..	..	..
East Croydon 285 .... arr.	..	..	..	..	..	..	5 50	5 50	..	..	..	..	..	..	..	6 18	6 5	..	..	..	..	..		..	..	..	..	..	..	..	6 41
Norwood Junction **B** arr.	..	..	..	..	..	..	5 Ⓣ55	..	..	..	..	..	..	..	..	6 23	6 SO Ⓣ18		..	..	..	..		..	..	..	..	..	..	..	..
New Cross Gate ..... "	..	..	..	..	..	..	..	..	..	..	..	..	..	..	..	..	..	..	..	..	..	..		..	..	..	..	..	..	..	..
LONDON BRIDGE ... "	..	..	..	..	..	..	6 Ⓣ11	6 Ⓣ11		6 Ⓣ I2	..	..	..	..	..	6 36	6 Ⓣ30		..	..	..	..		..	..	..	..	..	..	..	..
Clapham Junction **A** .. arr.	..	..	..	..	..	..	6 2	..	..	5 37	..	..	..	..	..	..	6 16	..	..	..	..	..		..	..	..	..	..	..	..	..
VICTORIA .... "	5 25	..	..	..	..	..	6 8	6 6	..	5 43	..	..	..	..	..	..	6 22	..	..	..	..	..	6 25	..	..	..	..	..	..	..	6 58

Ⓣ Third class only * Change at East Croydon *a* Arrival time **P** Pullman Car facilities available **R** Refreshment Car facilities available
RB Refreshment Car facilities available between Bognor Regis and London **SO** Saturdays only **SX** Saturdays excepted
I 5 mins. later on Saturdays *u* Dep. 3 22 p.m. on Saturdays

For Other Notes, see page 233

For SERVICES from ISLE OF WIGHT and PORTSMOUTH to LONDON (Waterloo), see pages 366 to 372

From THE SOUTH COAST to LONDON—Week Days—*continued*

Station	p.m	p.m.		p.m	p.m	p.m	p.m	p.m	p.m	p.m	p.m	p.m	p.m	p.m	p.m
Page 366 Yarmouth dep.	..	..		..	..	..	2 0	..	..	..	..	..	..	..	..
Cowes "	..	..		..	..	..	2 26	..	..	..	..	..	..	..	..
Newport "	..	..		..	..	..	2 38	..	..	..	..	..	..	..	..
Ventnor "	..	..		..	..	..	2 42	..	..	..	..	..	..	..	..
Shanklin "	..	..		..	..	..	2 54	..	..	..	..	..	..	..	..
Sandown "	..	..		..	..	..	3 1	..	..	..	..	..	..	..	..
500 Ryde Pier (Boat) "	..	..		..	..	..	3 35	..	..	..	..	..	..	..	..
Portsmouth Harbour dep.	..	..		..	..	..	4 23	..	..	4 53	..	..	..	..	..
Portsmouth & Southsea "	..	..		..	..	..	4 27	..	4 42	4 57	..	..	..	..	..
Fratton	..	..		..	..	..	4 30	..	4 45	4 59	..	..	..	..	..
Hilsea Halt	..	..		..	..	..	..	..	..	..	..	..	..	..	..
Bedhampton Halt	..	..		..	..	..	..	..	4 53	..	..	..	..	..	..
245 **Hayling Island** dep.	..	..		..	..	..	..	..	..	..	..	..	..	..	..
Havant 244	..	..		..	..	..	4 39	Saturdays only	4 55	5 8	..	..	..	..	..
Warblington Halt	..	..		..	..	..	..		4 57	..	..	..	..	..	..
Emsworth	..	..		..	..	..	..		5 0	..	..	..	..	..	..
Southbourne Halt	..	..		..	..	..	..		5 3	..	..	..	..	..	..
Nutbourne Halt	..	..		..	..	..	..		5 5	..	..	..	..	..	..
Bosham	..	..		..	..	..	..		5 9	..	..	..	..	..	..
Fishbourne Halt	..	..		..	..	..	..		5 12	..	..	..	..	..	..
Chichester **Z**	..	..		..	..	..	4 54		5 15	5 22	..	..	..	..	..
Barnham arr.	..	..		..	..	..	5 3		Stop	5 31	..	..	..	..	..
Bognor Regis arr.	..	..		..	..	..	RB	..		5k52	..	Saturdays excepted	..	..	..
Bognor Regis dep.	..	4 40		..	..	..	4 55	5 10	..	5SO10	..		..	..	..
Barnham dep.	..	4 47		..	..	..	5 5	5a16	..	5 31	..		..	..	..
Ford (Sussex)	..	4 52		..	..	..	..	..	..	..	..		..	..	..
Littlehampton arr.	..	4 57		..	..	..	..	..	..	5SX46	..		..	..	..
Littlehampton dep.	..	4 59		..	..	..	4 59	..	..	..	..	5 36	..	5 46	..
Ford (Sussex) arr.	..	..		..	..	..	..	..	..	..	..	5 40	..	5 50	..
Angmering L	..	..		..	..	..	..	..	..	..	..	..	..	Stop	..
Goring-by-Sea	..	..		..	..	..	..	..	..	..	..	..	..	..	..
Durrington-on Sea	..	..		..	..	..	..	..	p.m	..	..	..	..	..	..
West Worthing **U**	..	..		..	..	..	..	..	5 36	5 46	..	..	5 50	..	..
Worthing Central	..	..		..	..	..	..	..	5 38	5 49	..	..	5 52	..	..
Ham Bridge Halt **N**	..	..		..	..	..	..	..	..	..	..	..	5 55	..	..
Lancing	..	..		..	..	..	..	..	5 42	..	..	..	5 58	..	..
Shoreham-by-Sea **K** 244	..	..		..	..	..	..	..	5 46	5 57	..	..	6 3	..	6 11
Southwick	..	..		..	..	..	..	..	5 49	..	..	..	6 6	..	6 16
Fishersgate Halt	..	..		..	..	..	..	..	..	..	..	..	6 9	..	..
Portslade and West Hove	..	..		..	..	..	..	..	5 52	..	..	..	6 11	..	6 19
Aldrington Halt	..	..		..	..	..	..	..	5 55	..	..	..	6 13		..
Hove	..	..		..	..	..	..	..	5 57	6 4	..	..	6 15		6 23
Holland Road Halt	..	..		..	..	..	..	..	..	..	..	..	6 17		..
Brighton (*below*) arr.	..	..		..	..	..	..	..	6 1	6 7	..	..	6 20	Saturdays excepted	6 28
Arundel	..	5 5	Saturdays only	..	..	..	5 14	..	Stop	Stop	..	..	Stop		Stop
Amberley	..	5 11		..	..	..	..	..	..	..	..	..	..		..
Pulborough **J** 374	..	5 18		..	..	..	5 26	..	..	..	..	..	..		..
Billingshurst	..	5 25		..	..	..	..	..	..	..	..	..	..		..
Christ's Hospital, West Horsham	..	5 32		..	..	..	..	..	..	..	..	..	..		..
Horsham 244, 245, 285, 427 arr.	..	5 37		..	..	..	5 42	..	..	..	..	..	..		..
Horsham dep.	..	.. Saturdays excepted		..	..	..	5 43	..	..	..	..	..	..		..
Dorking North **H** 285, 427	..	..		..	..	..	6 2	..	..	..	..	..	..		..
Sutton 285, 322 arr.	..	..		..	..	..	6 19	..	..	..	..	..	..	p.m	..
Horsham dep.	..	5 37	5 48	..	..	..	..	..	..	..	..	..	..	6 0	..
Littlehaven Halt	..	5 39	5 50	..	..	..	..	..	..	..	..	..	..	6 2	..
Fay Gate	..	5 43	5 54	..	..	..	..	..	..	..	..	..	..	6 6	..
Ifield	..	5 48	5 59	..	..	..	..	..	..	..	..	..	..	6 11	..
Crawley [234	..	5 51	6 2	..	..	..	..	..	..	..	..	..	..	6 14	..
Three Bridges (*below*) arr.	..	5 54	6 5	..	..	P	..	..	..	..	..	..	..	6 17	..
	1	2	3	4	5	6	7	8	9	10	11	12	13	14	15

Station	p.m	p.m	p.m	p.m	p.m	p.m	p.m	p.m	p.m	p.m	p.m	p.m	p.m	p.m	p.m
Page 366 Yarmouth dep.	..	..	..	..	..	Through Train Cardiff (dep 10 p.m) to Brighton, see pages 494 and 377	..	..	..	..	..	..	..	..	..
Cowes "	..	..	..	..	..		..	3 26	..	..	..	..	..	..	..
Newport "	..	..	..	..	..		..	3 38	..	..	..	..	..	..	..
Ventnor "	..	..	..	..	..		..	3 42	..	..	..	..	..	..	..
Shanklin "	..	..	..	..	..		..	3 54	..	..	..	..	..	..	..
Sandown "	..	..	..	..	..		..	4 1	..	..	..	..	..	..	..
500 Ryde Pier (Boat) "	..	..	..	..	..		..	4 35	..	..	..	..	..	..	..
Portsmouth Harbour dep.	..	5 8	..	..	..		..	5a5	..	..	5 53	5 53	..	..	..
Portsmouth & Southsea "	..	5 12	..	..	..		..	Stop	5 42	..	5 57	5 57	..	..	..
Fratton	..	5 14	..	..	..		..		5 45	..	5 59	5 59	..	..	..
Hilsea Halt	..	..	..	..	..		..	..	5SX49	..	..	..	..	..	..
Bedhampton Halt	..	..	..	..	..		..	..	5 53	..	..	..	..	..	..
245 **Hayling Island** dep.	..	5 6	..	..	..		..	..	..	..	..	..	..	..	..
Havant 244	..	5 23	..	Saturdays excepted	..		Saturdays only	..	5 55	..	6 8	6 8	..	..	..
Warblington Halt	..	5 25	..		..			..	5 57	..	..	..	..	..	..
Emsworth	..	5 28	..		..			..	6 0	..	6 12	6 13	..	..	..
Southbourne Halt	..	5 31	..		..			..	6 3	..	..	..	..	..	Saturdays only
Nutbourne Halt	..	5 34	..		..			..	6 5	..	..	..	..	..	
Bosham	..	5 37	..		..			..	6 9	..	..	6 19	..	..	
Fishbourne Halt	..	5 40	..		..			..	6 12	..	..	..	..	..	
Chichester **Z**	..	5 44	..		..	5 51		..	6 15	..	6 22	6 24	..	..	
Barnham arr.	..	5 54	..		..	6 2		..	6SX25	..	6 30	6 33	..	..	
Bognor Regis arr.	..	6 9	..	..	..	..	..	..	..	..	6 42	6 42	..	..	..
Bognor Regis dep.	5SX24	5 45	5 45	6 5	..	..	6 20	..	6SX5	..	6 20	..	3 mins. *earlier* on Saturdays	..	..
Barnham dep.	5SX36	5 54	5b58	6a11	..	6 3	6a26	..	6SX25	..	6 31	6 33		..	6 42
Ford (Sussex)	5SX41	5 59	6 2	Stop	..	..	Stop	..	6SX29	..	6 36	6 38		..	6 46
Littlehampton arr.	5SX46	6 7	6 7	..	..	..	..	p.m	6SX34	..	6 46	6 57		..	..
Littlehampton dep.	5 49	..	6 9	..	..	..	..	6y22		..	6 25	6 22		..	..
Ford (Sussex) arr.	..	..	..	..	..	..	..	6y26	Stop	..	..	..		..	..
Angmering L	5 58	6 6	..	..	..	..	..	Stop	..	..	..	6 45		..	..
Goring-by-Sea	6 3	6 11	..	..	..	..	..	..	..	..	..	..		..	..
Durrington-on Sea	6 5	..	..	..	..	..	p.m	..	p.m	..	..	..	..	..	..
West Worthing **U**	6 7	6 14	..	..	6 18	..	6 37	..	6 40	..	6 49	6 52	6 55	..	..
Worthing Central	6 9	6 17	..	..	6 20	6 26	6 39	..	6 42	..	6 52	6 54	6 57	..	..
Ham Bridge Halt **N**	..	..	..	..	6 22		..	..	6 44	..	..	..	7 0	..	..
Lancing	6 13	..	..	..	6 25	Saturdays only	6 43	..	6 47	..	..	6 58	7 3	..	..
Shoreham-by-Sea **K** 244	6 19	6 25	..	..	6 30		6 48	..	6 52	..	6 59	7 3	7 8	..	..
Southwick	6 23	..	..	..	6 34		6 51	..	6 56	..	..	..	7 11	..	..
Fishersgate Halt	..	..	..	..	6 36		..	..	6 58	..	..	..	7 14	..	..
Portslade and West Hove	6 26	..	..	..	6 38		6 54	..	7 0	..	..	..	7 16	..	..
Aldrington Halt	6 28	..	..	..	6 41		6 57	..	7 3	..	..	..	7 19	..	..
Hove	6 30	6 34	..	..	6 44		6 59	..	7 5	..	7 7	7 11	7 21	..	..
Holland Road Halt	..	..	..	..	6 47		..	..	..	..	..	..	7 23	..	..
Brighton (*below*) arr.	6 35	6 38	..	..	6 50	6 54	7 4	..	7 8	..	7 10	7 17	7 25	..	..
Arundel	Stop	Stop	6 16	..	Stop	Stop		..		..	..	..	Stop	..	..
Amberley	..	..	6 21	..	..	..		..		..	..	..	..	..	..
Pulborough **J** 374	..	..	6 29	..	..	..		..		..	..	..	..	..	..
Billingshurst	..	..	6 36	..	..	..		..		..	..	..	..	..	..
Christ's Hospital, West Horsham	..	..	6 43	..	..	..		..		..	..	..	..	..	..
Horsham 244, 245, 285, 427 arr.	..	..	6 47	..	..	..		..		..	..	..	..	..	..
Horsham dep.	..	..	..	..	..	..	Saturdays only	..	Saturdays excepted	..	Saturdays only	Saturdays excepted	..	..	..
Dorking North **H** 285, 427	..	..	..	..	..	..		..		..			..	..	..
Sutton 285, 322 arr.	..	..	..	..	..	..		..		..			..	..	..
Horsham dep.	..	..	6 48	..	..	..		..		..			..	..	..
Littlehaven Halt	..	..	6 50	..	..	..		..		..			..	..	..
Fay Gate	..	..	6 54	..	..	..		..		..			..	..	..
Ifield	..	..	6 59	..	..	..		..		..			..	..	..
Crawley [234	..	..	7 2	..	..	..		..		..	..	..	..	..	..
Three Bridges (*below*) arr.	..	..	7 5	..	..	..	Stop	p.m	Stop	..	..	..	..	..	..
	16	17	18	19	20	21	22	23	24	25	26	27	28	29	30

	1	2	3	4	5	6	7	8	9	10	11	12	13	14	15	16	17	18	19	20	21	22	23	24	25	26	27	28	29	30
Ore ......dep.	..	..	..	..	..	5 0	..	..		..	5 13	..	..	..	..	..	..	Stop	..	..	..	..	5 42	..	..	..	..	..	6 12	..
Hastings	..	..	..	..	..	5 5	..	..		..	5 16	..	..	..	..	..	..		..	..	..	..	5 45	..	..	..	..	..	6 15	..
St. Leonards (W.S.)	..	..	..	..	..	5 8	..	..		..	5 18	..	..	..	..	..	..	..	..	..	..	..	5 47	..	..	..	..	..	6 17	..
" (W.M.)	..	..	..	..	..	..	..	..			5 20	..	..	..	..	..	..	..	..	..	..	..	5 49	..	..	..	..	..	6 19	..
Bexhill (Central) G	..	..	..	..	..	5 15	..	..	Saturdays only ☞ p.m	Saturdays excepted ☞ p.m	5 25	..	..	..	..	..	..	..	Saturdays excepted ☞ p.m	..	..	..	5 54	..	..	..	..	..	6 24	..
Collington Halt	..	..	..	..	..	..	..	..			5 28	..	..	..	..	..	..	..		..	..	..	5 57	..	..	..	..	..	6 27	..
Cooden Beach	..	..	..	..	..	5 19	..	..			5 31	..	..	..	..	..	..	..		..	..	..	6 0	..	..	..	..	..	6 30	..
Norman's Bay Halt	..	..	..	..	..	..	..	..			5 34	..	..	..	..	..	..	..		..	..	..	6 3	..	..	..	..	..	6 33	..
Pevensey Bay Halt	..	..	..	..	..	..	..	..			5 38	..	..	..	..	..	..	..		..	..	..	6 7	..	..	..	..	..	6 37	..
Pevensey and Westham	..	..	..	..	..	..	..	..			5 40	..	..	..	..	..	..	..		..	..	..	6 9	..	..	..	..	..	6 39	..
Hampden Park F	..	..	..	..	..	..	..	..			5 45	..	..	..	..	..	..	..		..	..	..	6 15	..	..	..	..	..	6 45	..
Eastbourne ......arr.	..	..	..	..	..	5 32	..	..			5 49	..	..	..	p.m	..	..	..		..	..	..	6 19	p.m	..	..	..	..	6 49	..
Eastbourne ......dep.	Saturdays excepted	..	..	..	5 29	5 36	..	..			5 52	..	..	..	5 59	..	..	..		..	..	..	6 23	6 27	6 32	..	..	..	6 52	..
Hampden Park F		..	..	..	5 32	..	..	..			5 55	..	..	..	6 2	..	..	..		..	..	..	6 26	6 30	..	..	..	..	6 55	..
Polegate 239		..	..	..	Stop	..	..	..			5 59	..	..	..	Stop	..	..	..		..	..	..	6 30	Stop	6 39	..	..	..	6 59	..
Berwick		..	..	..		..	..	..			6 5	..	..	..		..	..	..		..	..	..	6 36		Stop	..	..	..	7 5	..
Glynde		..	..	..	..	..	..	..			6 11	..	..	..	..	..	..	..		..	..	..	6 42	..		..	..	..	7 11	..
Lewes 239 ......arr.		..	..	..	..	5 56	..	..	p.m	p.m	6 16	..	..	..	..	..	..	..	p.m	..	..	p.m	6 47	..	..	..	..	p.m	7 16	..
Seaford ......dep.	5 35	..	..	..	..	..	..	..	5 43	5 49	..	..	..	..	..	..	..	..	6 13	..	..	6 25	..	..	..	..	..	6 49	..	..
Bishopstone	5 37	..	..	..	..	..	..	..	5 45	..	..	..	..	..	..	..	..	..	6 15	..	..	6 27	..	..	..	..	..	6 51	..	..
Newhaven Harbour	5 40	..	..	..	..	..	..	..	5 50	..	..	..	..	..	..	..	..	..	6 20	..	..	6 32	..	..	..	..	..	6 56	..	..
" Town	5 42	..	..	..	..	..	..	..	5 51	5 54	..	..	..	..	..	..	..	..	6 21	..	..	6 33	..	..	..	..	..	6 57	..	..
Southease & Rodmell Halt	5 47	..	..	..	..	..	..	..	5 56	..	..	..	..	..	..	..	..	..	6 26	..	..	6 38	..	..	..	..	..	7 2	..	..
Lewes 239 ......arr.	5 52	..	..	..	..	..	..	..	6 2	6 6	..	..	..	..	..	..	..	..	6 32	p.m	..	6 44	..	..	p.m	..	..	7 8	..	..
Lewes ......dep.	5 59	..	..	..	..	..	..	..	6 2	..	6 17	..	..	..	..	..	..	..	6 32	6 37		..	6 48	..	7 0	..	..	7 9	7 23	..
Falmer	6 6	..	..	..	..	..	..	..	6 9	..	6 24	..	..	..	..	..	..	..	6 39	..		..	6 55	..	..	..	..	7 16	7 30	..
London Road (Brighton)	6 10	..	..	..	..	..	..	..	6 14	..	6 28	..	..	..	..	..	..	..	6 44	6 52		..	6 59	..	7 15	..	..	7 21	7 34	..
Brighton ......arr.	6 13	..	..	..	..	..	..	..	6 16	..	6 32	..	..	..	..	..	..	..	6 46	6 56		..	7 2	..	7 19	..	..	7 23	7 36	..
Lewes ......dep.	..	..	..	..	..	5 57	..	..	..	6 9	..	..	..	..	..	..	..	..	..	..	Saturdays excepted ☞	..	..	..	..	..	..	..	..	..
Cooksbridge	..	..	..	..	..	..	..	..	..	6 15	..	..	..	..	..	..	..	..	..	..		..	..	..	..	..	..	..	..	..
Plumpton	..	..	..	..	..	..	..	..	..	6 20	..	..	..	..	..	..	..	..	..	..		..	..	..	..	..	..	..	..	..
Wivelsfield (below)	..	..	..	..	..	..	..	..	..	6 26	..	..	..	..	..	..	..	..	..	..		..	..	..	..	..	..	..	..	..
Haywards Heath ......arr.	..	..	..	..	..	6 13	..	..	..	6 31	..	..	p.m	..	..	p.m	p.m	p.m	..	..		..	..	p.m	..	..	..	..	..	..
Brighton ......dep.	..	..	..	5 28	..	..	..	..	..	..	..	..	5 58	..	..	6 8	6 25	6 28	..	..		..	..	6 58	..	..	..	..	..	..
Preston Park	..	..	..	5 31	..	..	..	..	..	..	..	..	6 1	..	..	6 11	..	6 31	..	..		..	..	7 1	..	..	..	..	..	..
Hassocks D	..	..	..	5 39	..	..	..	..	..	..	..	..	6 9	..	..	..	..	6 39	..	..		..	..	7 9	..	..	..	..	..	..
Burgess Hill	..	..	..	5 44	..	..	..	..	..	..	..	..	6 14	..	..	..	..	6 43	..	..		..	..	7 13	..	..	..	..	..	..
Wivelsfield (above)	..	..	..	5 46	p.m	..	..	..	..	..	..	..	6 17	..	p.m	..	..	6 45	..	..	p.m	..	..	7 15	..	..	..	..	..	..
Haywards Heath C	..	..	..	5 52	6 6	6 14	..	..	..	..	..	..	6 22	..	6 25	6 26	..	6 52	..	..	6 53	..	..	7 22	..	..	..	..	..	..
Ardingly	..	..	..	..	6 10	P	RB	..	..	..	..	..	..	..	6 29	..	P	..	..	..	6 58	..	..	..	..	..	..	..	..	..
Horsted Keynes 239 ......arr.	..	..	..	..	6 14	..	..	..	..	..	..	..	..	..	6 33	..	..	..	..	..	7 2	..	..	..	..	..	..	..	..	..
Balcombe	..	..	..	5 58	..	..	..	..	..	..	..	..	6 28	..	..	..	..	6 58	..	..	..	..	..	7 28	..	..	..	..	..	..
Three Bridges (above)	..	..	..	6 8	..	..	..	..	..	..	..	..	6 37	..	..	6 37	..	7 8	..	..	..	..	..	7 37	..	..	..	..	..	..
Gatwick Airport	..	..	..	6 12	..	..	..	..	..	..	..	..	6 41	..	..	6 41	..	7 12	..	..	..	..	..	7 41	..	..	..	..	..	..
Horley	..	..	..	6 15	..	..	..	..	..	..	..	..	6 44	..	..	..	..	7 15	..	..	..	..	..	7 44	..	..	..	..	..	..
Salfords	..	..	..	6 19	..	..	..	..	..	..	..	..	6 48	..	..	..	..	7 19	..	..	..	..	..	7 48	..	..	..	..	..	..
Earlswood	..	..	..	6 23	..	..	..	..	..	..	..	..	6 52	..	..	..	..	7 23	..	..	..	..	..	7 52	..	..	..	..	..	..
Redhill 246	..	..	..	6 30	..	..	..	..	..	..	..	..	6 59	..	..	6 50	..	7 30	..	..	..	..	..	7 59	..	..	..	..	..	..
Merstham	..	..	..	6 34	..	..	..	..	..	..	..	..	7 3	..	..	..	..	7 34	..	..	..	..	..	8 3	..	..	..	..	..	..
Coulsdon South	..	..	..	6 41	..	..	..	..	..	..	..	..	7 9	..	..	..	..	7 41	..	..	..	..	..	8 9	..	..	..	..	..	..
Purley	..	..	..	6 45	..	..	..	..	..	..	..	..	7 13	..	..	..	..	7 44	..	..	..	..	..	8 13	..	..	..	..	..	..
East Croydon 285 ......arr.	..	..	..	6 50	..	6 46	..	..	..	..	..	..	7 19	..	..	7 4	..	7 50	..	..	..	..	..	8 18	..	..	..	..	..	..
Norwood Junction B arr.	..	..	..	6 (3) 58	..	6 (3) 58	..	..	..	..	..	..	7 24	..	..	7 (3) 16	..	7 (3) 58	..	..	..	..	..	8 24	..	..	..	..	..	..
New Cross Gate ...... "	..	..	..	..	..	..	..	..	..	..	..	..	7 33	..	..	..	..	..	..	..	..	..	..	..	..	..	..	..	..	..
LONDON BRIDGE ...... "	..	..	..	7 (3) 11	..	7 (3) 11	..	..	..	..	..	..	7 38	..	..	7 (3) 31	..	8 (3) 11	..	..	..	..	..	8 36	..	..	..	..	..	..
Clapham Junction A ......arr.	..	..	..	7 2	..	..	..	..	..	..	..	..	..	..	..	7 16	..	8 2	..	..	..	..	..	..	..	..	..	..	..	..
VICTORIA ...... "	..	..	..	7 8	..	7 2	6 40	..	..	..	..	..	..	..	..	7 22	7 25	8 8	..	..	..	..	..	..	..	..	..	..	..	..

(3) Third class only. *a* Arrival time. *b* Arr 7 mins. *earlier*. *k* 10 mins. *earlier* on Saturdays. **P** Pullman Car facilities available.
RB Refreshment Car facilities available between Bognor Regis and London. **SO** Saturdays only. **SX** Saturdays excepted. *y* 3 mins. later on Saturdays.

For Other Notes, see page 233

For SERVICES from ISLE OF WIGHT and PORTSMOUTH to LONDON (Waterloo), see pages 366 to 372

From THE SOUTH COAST to LONDON—Week Days—continued

Station	1	2	3	4	5	6	7	8	9	10	11	12	13	14	15	16	17	18	19	20	21	22	23	24	25	26	27	28	29	30
	p.m	p.m	p.m	p.m	p.m	p.m	p.m	p.m	p.m	p.m	p.m	p.m	p.m	p.m	p.m	p.m	p.m	p.m	p.m	p.m	p.m	p.m	p.m	p.m	p.m	p.m	p.m	p.m	p.m	p.m
(Page 366) Yarmouth dep.	..	..	..	..	..	..	..	..	..	3 30	..	..	..	..	..	..	..	..	..	..	..	..	..	..	..	..	..	..	..	..
Cowes "	..	..	..	..	..	..	..	..	..	4 26	..	..	..	..	..	..	..	..	..	..	..	..	5 26	..	..	..	..	..	..	..
Newport "	..	..	..	..	..	..	..	..	..	4 38	..	..	..	..	..	..	..	..	..	..	..	..	5 38	..	..	..	..	..	..	..
Ventnor "	..	..	..	..	..	..	..	..	..	4 42	..	..	..	..	..	..	..	..	..	..	..	..	5 42	..	..	..	..	..	..	..
Shanklin "	..	..	..	..	..	..	..	..	..	4 54	..	..	..	..	..	..	..	..	..	..	..	..	5 54	..	..	..	..	..	..	..
Sandown "	..	..	..	..	..	..	..	..	..	5 1	..	..	..	..	..	..	..	..	..	..	..	..	6 1	..	..	..	..	..	..	..
509 Ryde Pier (Boat) "	..	..	..	..	..	..	..	..	..	5 35	..	..	..	..	..	..	..	..	..	..	..	..	6 35	..	..	..	..	..	..	..
Portsmouth Harbour dep.	..	..	..	..	..	..	..	6 8	..	6 23	6 39	..	..		..	6 53	..	..	..	..	..	7 8	7a 5	7 23	..	..	..	..	..	..
Portsmouth & Southsea "	..	..	..	..	..	..	..	6 12	..	6 27	6 42	..	..		..	6 57	..	..	..	..	..	7 12	Stop	7 27	..	..	..	..	..	7 42
Fratton	..	..	..	..	..	..	..	6 14	..	6 30	6 45	..	..		..	6 59	..	..	..	..	..	7 14	..	7 30	..	..	..	..	..	7 45
Hilsea Halt	..	..	..	..	..	..	..	..	..	..	..	..	..		..	..	..	..	..	..	..	..	..	..	..	..	..	..	..	7 53
Bedhampton Halt	..	..	..	..	..	..	..	..	..	..	6 53	..	..		..	..	..	..	..	..	..	..	..	..	..	..	..	..	..	..
245 Hayling Island dep.	..	..	..	..	..	..	..	5 57	..	..	..	..	..		..	6 52	..	..	..	..	..	6 52	..	..	..	..	..	..	..	..
Havant 244		..	..	..		..	..	6 23	..	6 39	6 55	..			..	7 8	..	..	..	..	..	7 23	..	7 39	..		..	..	..	7 55
Warblington Halt		..	..	..		..	..	6 25	..	..	6 57	..			..	..	..	..	..	..	..	7 25	..	..	..		..	..	..	7 57
Emsworth		..	..	..		..	..	6 28	..	..	7 0	..			..	..	..	..	..	..	..	7 28	..	..	..		..	..	..	8 0
Southbourne Halt	Saturdays only ☞	..	..	..	Saturdays excepted ☞	..	..	6 31	..	..	7 3	..	Saturdays only ☞	Runs 10 minutes *earlier* on Saturdays ☞	..	..	..	..	..	..	..	7 31	..	..	..		..	..	..	8 3
Nutbourne Halt		..	..	..		..	..	6 34	..	..	7 5	..			..	..	..	..	..	..	..	7 34	..	..	..	Saturdays excepted ☞	..	..	..	8 5
Bosham		..	..	..		..	..	6 37	..	..	7 9	..			..	..	..	..	..	..	..	7 37	..	..	..		..	..	..	8 9
Fishbourne Halt		..	..	..		..	..	6 40	..	..	7 12	..			..	..	..	..	..	..	..	7 40	..	..	..		..	..	..	8 12
Chichester Z		..	..	..		..	..	6 44	..	6 54	7 15	..			..	7 22	..	..	..	..	..	7 44	..	7 54	..		..	..	..	8 15
Barnham arr.		..	..	..		..	..	6 53	..	7 3	Stop	..			..	7 31	..	..	..	Saturdays excepted ☞	..	7 53	..	8 3	..		..	..	..	Stop
Bognor Regis arr.		..	..	..		..	..	7z 5		7SX14	..	..			..	7r48		..	..		..	8z11	..	RB	..		..	..	..	..
Bognor Regis dep.		..	..	..		6 40	..	6 40	..	6 55	..	..		7 20	..	7u20		..	..		7 40	7 40	..	7 55	..	8 10	..	..	..	..
Barnham dep.		..	..	..		6 47	..	6 54	..	7 5	..	..		7a26	..	7 31		..	..		7 47	7 54	..	8 5	..	8a16	..	..	..	..
Ford (Sussex)		..	..	..		6 53	..	6 59	..	..	..	..		Stop	..	..		..	..		7 53	7 59	..	..	..	Stop	..	..	..	..
Littlehampton arr.		..	..	..		6 57	..	..	..	RB	..	P		..	..	..		..	..		7 57	..	..	..	PR	..	..	..	..	..
Littlehampton dep.	6 47			6 48	6 54	7 0	..	..	..	7 0	..	7 9	7 46	..	..	..		..	7 49	7 54	8 0	..	..	8 0	8 9	..	..	..	8 46	..
Ford (Sussex) arr.	6 51			..	6 58	..	..	..	..	..	..	..	7 50	..	..	..		..	..	7 58	..	..	..	..	..	..	..	..	8 50	..
Angmering L	Stop			6 58	Stop	..	..	7 6	..		..	7 19	Stop	..	..	..		..	7 58	Stop	..	8 6	..		8 19	..	..	..	Stop	..
Goring-by-Sea	..	Saturdays only	Saturdays excepted	7 2	..	..	..	7 11	..		..	7 24	..	..	..	..		..	8 3	..	..	8 11	..		8 24	..	..	..	..	..
Durrington-on-Sea	..			7 5	..	..	..	..	..		..	7 27	..	p.m	..	..		..	8 5	..	..	..	p.m		8 27	..	..	..	..	p.m
West Worthing U	..			7 7	..	..	..	7 14	..		..	7 30	..	7 37	..	..	7 50	..	8 7	..	..	8 14	8 18		8 30	..	..	..	..	8 39
Worthing Central	..			7 9	..	..	..	7 17	..		..	7 35	..	7 39	..	7 48	7 52	..	8 9	..	..	8 17	8 20		8 35	..	..	..	..	8 41
Ham Bridge Halt N	..	..	..	..	..	..	..	..	..		..	..	..	7 41	..	..	7 55	..	..	..	..	..	8 23		..	..	..	..	..	..
Lancing	..	..	..	7 13	..	..	..	..	..		..	..	..	7 44	..	..	7 58	..	8 13	..	..	..	8 26		..	..	..	..	..	8 45
Shoreham-by-Sea K 244	..	7 8	7 13	7 17	..	..	..	7 25	..	Through Train, Bognor Regis to Victoria	..	7 42	..	7 49	..	7 56	8 3	8 9	8 17	..	..	8 25	8 30	Saturdays only	8 42	..	..	..	..	8 49
Southwick	..	7 12	..	7 20	..	..	..	..	..		..	..	..	7 53	..	..	8 6	8 12	8 21	..	..	..	8 33		..	..	..	..	..	8 52
Fishersgate Halt	..	..	..	..	..	..	..	..	..		..	..	..	7 55	..	..	8 9	..	..	..	..	..	8 36		..	..	..	..	..	..
Portslade and West Hove	..	7 17	7 19	7 23	..	..	..	..	..		..	..	..	7 57	..	..	8 11	8 16	8 24	..	..	..	8 38		..	..	..	..	..	8 55
Aldrington Halt	..	..	..	7 26	..	..	..	..	..		..	..	..	8 0	..	..	8 14	..	8 27	..	..	..	8 41		..	..	..	..	..	..
Hove	..	7 21	7 24	7 28	..	..	..	7 33	..		..	7 50	..	8 2	..	8 5	8 16	8 20	8 29	..	..	8 33	8 43	..	8 50	..	..	..	..	8 59
Holland Road Halt	..	..	..	..	..	..	..	..	..		..	..	..	..	..	..	8 18	..	..	..	..	..	8 45	..	..	..	..	..	..	..
Brighton *below* arr.	..	7 26	7 29	7 32	..	..	..	7 36	..		..	..	..	8 5	..	8 8	8 20	8 25	8 32	..	..	8 36	8 48	..	..	..	..	..	..	9 2
Arundel	..	..	..	Stop	..	7 6	..	..	..	7 13	..		..	Stop	..	Stop	..	Stop	Stop	..	8 6	Stop	..	8 14		..	..	..	..	Stop
Amberley	..	..	..	..	..	7 11	..	..	..	..	..		..	..	..	..	..	..	..	..	8 11	..	..	..		..	..	..	..	..
Pulborough J 374	..	..	..	..	..	7 19	..	..	..	7 26	..		..	..	..	..	..	..	..	..	8 19	..	..	8 26		..	..	..	..	..
Billingshurst [Horsham	..	..	..	..	..	7 26	..	..	..	..	..		..	..	..	..	..	..	..	..	8 26	..	..	..		..	..	..	..	..
Christ's Hospital, West	..	..	..	..	..	7 33	..	..	..	..	..		..	..	..	..	..	..	..	..	8 33	..	..	..		..	..	..	..	..
Horsham 244, 245, 285, 427 arr.	..	..	..	..	..	7 37	..	..	..	7 42	..		..	..	..	..	..	..	..	..	8 37	..	..	8 42		..	..	..	..	..
Horsham dep.	..	..	..	..	..	..	..	..	..	7 43	..	Through Train, Littlehampton to Victoria	..	..	..	..	..	..	..	..	..	..	..	8 43		..	..	..	..	..
Dorking North H 285, 427	..	..	..	..	..	..	..	..	..	8 2	..		..	..	..	..	..	..	..	..	..	..	..	9 2	Through Train Littlehampton to Victoria	..	..	..	..	..
Sutton 285, 322 arr.	..	..	..	..	..	..	..	..	..	8 19	..		..	..	..	..	..	..	..	..	..	..	..	9 19		..	..	..	..	..
Horsham dep.	..	..	..	..	..	7 46	..	..	..	..	..		..	..	..	..	..	..	..	..	8 48	..	..	..		..	..	9 17	..	..
Littlehaven Halt	..	..	..	..	..	7 49	..	..	..	..	..		..	..	..	..	..	..	..	..	8 50	..	..	..		..	..	9 19	..	..
Fay Gate	..	..	..	..	..	7 53	..	..	..	..	..		..	..	..	..	..	..	..	..	8 54	..	..	..		..	..	9 23	..	..
Ifield	..	..	..	..	..	7 58	..	..	..	..	..	..	..	..	..	..	..	..	..	..	8 59	..	..	..		..	..	9 28	..	..
Crawley [234	..	..	..	..	..	8 1	..	..	..	..	..	..	..	p.m	..	..	..	..	..	..	9 2	..	..	..		..	..	9 31	..	..
Three Bridges (*below*) arr.	..	..	..	..	..	8 4	..	..	..	..	..	..	..	P	..	..	..	..	..	..	9 5	..	..	..		..	..	9 34	..	..

	1	2	3	4	5	6	7	8	9	10	11	12	13	14	15	16	17	18	19	20	21	22	23	24	25	26	27	28	29	30
Ore ..... dep.	..	..	..	..	..	..	..	..	6 44	..	..	..	..	7 0	..	..	..	..	Saturdays excepted	..	Stop	..	..	..	..	..	7 43	Stop	Saturdays only	..
Hastings	..	..	..	..	..	..	..	..	6 47	..	..	..	..	7 5	..	..	..	..		..		..	..	..	..	..	7 46			..
St. Leonards (W.S.)	..	..	..	..	..	..	..	..	6 49	..	..	..	..	7 8	..	..	..	..		..	..	..	..	..	..	..	7 48	..		..
" (W.M.)	..	..	..	..	..	..	..	..	6 51	..	..	..	..	..	..	..	..	..		..	..	..	..	..	..	..	7 51	..		..
Bexhill (Central) **G**	..	..	..	..	..	..	..	..	6 56	..	..	..	..	7 15	..	..	..	..		..	..	..	..	..	..	..	7 56	..		..
Collington Halt	..	..	..	..	..	..	..	..	6 59	..	..	..	..	..	..	..	..	..		..	..	..	..	..	..	..	7 58	..		..
Cooden Beach	..	..	..	..	..	..	..	..	7 2	..	..	..	..	7 19	..	..	..	..		..	..	..	..	..	..	..	8 1	..		..
Norman's Bay Halt	..	..	..	..	..	..	..	..	7 5	..	..	..	..	..	..	..	..	..		..	..	..	..	..	..	..	8 4	..		..
Pevensey Bay Halt	..	..	..	..	..	..	..	..	7 9	..	..	..	..	..	..	..	..	..		..	..	..	..	..	..	..	8 8	..		..
Pevensey and Westham	..	..	..	..	..	..	..	..	7 11	..	..	..	..	..	..	..	..	..		..	..	..	..	..	..	..	8 10	..		..
Hampden Park **F**	..	..	..	..	..	..	..	..	7 17	..	..	..	..	..	..	..	..	..		..	..	..	..	..	..	..	8 15	..		..
Eastbourne arr.	p.m	..	..	..	..	..	..	..	7 21	..	p.m	..	p.m	7 32	..	..	..	..	p.m	..	..	p.m	..	..	..	..	8 19	p.m		..
Eastbourne dep.	6 58	..	..	..	..	..	..	..	7 24	..	7 29	..	7 33	7 36	..	..	..	..	7 52	Saturdays excepted	..	7 57	..	..	..	..	8 22	8 29		..
Hampden Park **F**	7 1	..	..	..	..	..	..	..	7 27	..	..	..	7 36	..	..	..	..	..	7 55		..	8 0	..	..	..	..	8 25	8 32		..
Polegate 239	Stop	..	..	..	..	..	..	..	7 31	..	7 36	..	..	..	..	..	..	..	7 59		..	Stop	..	..	..	..	8 30	Stop		..
Berwick		..	..	..	..	..	..	..	7 37	..	..	..	..	..	..	..	..	..	8 5		..		..	..	..	..	8 36			..
Glynde	..	..	..	..	..	..	..	..	7 43	..	..	..	..	..	..	..	..	..	8 11		..	..	..	..	..	..	8 42	..		..
Lewes 239 arr.	..	..	..	..	..	..	..	..	7 48	..	..	..	..	7 56	..	..	..	p.m	8 16		..	..	..	..	..	p.m	8 47	..	p.m	..
Seaford dep.	..	..	..	..	..	..	7 20	..	..	..	..	..	..	..	..	..	..	7 43	..		..	..	..	..	..	8 25	..	..	8 43	..
Bishopstone	..	..	..	..	..	..	7 22	..	..	..	..	..	..	..	..	..	..	7 45	..		..	..	..	..	..	8 27	..	..	8 45	..
Newhaven Harbour	..	..	..	..	..	..	7 27	..	..	..	..	..	..	..	..	..	..	7 50	..		..	..	..	..	..	8 32	..	..	8 50	..
" Town	..	..	..	..	..	..	7 28	..	..	..	..	..	..	..	..	..	..	7 51	..		..	..	..	..	..	8 33	..	..	8 51	..
Southease & Rodmell Halt	..	..	..	..	..	..	7 33	..	..	..	..	..	..	..	..	..	..	7 56	..		..	..	..	..	..	8 38	..	..	8 56	..
Lewes 239 arr.	..	..	..	..	..	..	7 39	..	..	..	..	..	..	..	..	..	..	8 2	..	p.m	..	..	..	..	..	8 44	..	..	9 2	..
Lewes dep.	..	..	..	..	..	..	..	..	7 50	..	..	..	..	..	..	..	..	8 2	8 17	8 35	..	..	..	..	..	..	8 48	..	9 2	..
Falmer	..	..	..	..	..	..	..	..	7 57	..	..	..	..	..	..	..	..	8 9	8 24	..	..	..	..	..	..	..	8 55	..	9 9	..
London Road (Brighton)	..	..	..	..	..	..	..	..	8 2	..	..	..	..	..	..	..	..	8 14	8 28	8 50	..	..	..	..	..	..	8 59	..	9 14	..
Brighton arr.	..	..	..	..	..	..	..	..	8 5	..	..	..	..	..	..	..	..	8 16	8 31	8 55	..	..	..	..	..	..	9 2	..	9 16	..
Lewes dep.	..	..	..	..	..	..	7 39	..	..	..	..	..	..	7 57	..	..	..	Stop	..	..	..	..	..	..	..	8 44	..	..	..	..
Cooksbridge	..	..	..	..	..	..	7 44	..	..	..	..	..	..	..	..	..	..		..	..	..	..	..	..	..	8 49	..	..	..	..
Plumpton	..	..	..	..	..	..	7 49	..	..	..	..	..	..	..	..	..	..	..	..	..	..	..	..	..	..	8 54	..	..	..	..
Wivelsfield *(below)*	..	..	..	..	..	..	..	..	..	..	..	..	..	..	..	..	..	..	..	..	..	..	..	..	..	9 0	..	..	..	..
Haywards Heath arr.	p.m	..	..	p.m	p.m	..	7 59	..	..	..	..	..	..	8 13	..	p.m	..	..	..	..	p.m	p.m	..	..	..	9 5	..	p.m	..	p.m
Brighton dep.	7 8	..	..	7 25	7 28	..	..	..	..	..	..	..	..	..	7 58	8 8	..	..	..	..	8 25	8 28	..	..	..	..	..	8 58	..	9 8
Preston Park	7 11	..	..	..	7 31	..	..	..	..	..	..	..	..	..	8 1	8 11	..	..	..	..	..	8 31	..	..	..	..	..	9 1	..	9 11
Hassocks **D**	..	..	..	..	7 39	..	..	..	..	..	..	..	..	..	8 9	..	..	..	..	..	..	8 39	..	..	..	..	..	9 9	..	..
Burgess Hill	..	..	..	..	7 43	..	..	..	..	..	..	..	..	..	8 13	..	..	..	..	..	..	8 43	..	..	..	..	..	9 13	..	..
Wivelsfield *(above)*	..	..	..	..	7 45	..	..	..	..	..	..	..	..	..	8 15	..	..	p.m	..	..	..	8 45	..	..	..	..	..	9 15	..	..
Haywards Heath C	7 27	..	..	..	7 52	..	..	..	..	..	..	8 8	..	8 14	8 22	8 27	..	8 35	..	..	..	8 52	..	..	9 8	9 6	..	9 22	..	9 27
Ardingly	..	..	..	P	..	..	..	..	..	RB	..	P	..	P	..	..	..	8 40	..	..	P	..	..	RB	PR	9 10	..	..	..	..
Horsted Keynes 239 arr.	..	..	..	..	..	..	..	..	..	..	..	..	..	..	..	..	..	8 46	..	..	..	..	..	..	..	9 14	..	..	..	..
Balcombe	..	..	..	..	7 59	..	..	..	..	..	..	..	..	..	8 28	..	..	..	..	..	Saturdays only	8 58	..	Saturdays only	..	..	..	9 28	..	..
Three Bridges *(above)*	..	..	..	..	8 7	..	..	..	..	..	..	..	..	..	8 37	..	..	..	..	..		9 7	..		..	..	..	9 37	..	..
Gatwick Airport	7 40	..	..	..	8 10	..	..	..	..	..	..	..	..	..	8 41	8 40	..	..	..	..		9 11	..		..	..	..	9 41	..	..
Horley	..	..	..	..	8 13	..	..	..	..	..	..	..	..	..	8 44	..	..	..	..	..		9 14	..		..	..	..	9 44	..	..
Salfords	..	..	..	..	8 17	..	..	..	..	..	..	..	..	..	8 48	..	..	..	..	..		9 18	..		..	..	..	9 48	..	..
Earlswood	..	..	..	..	8 21	..	..	..	..	..	..	..	..	..	8 52	..	..	..	..	..		9 22	..		..	..	..	9 52	..	..
Redhill 246	7 50	..	..	..	8 29	..	..	..	..	..	..	..	..	..	8 59	3 50	..	..	..	..		9 29	..		..	..	..	9 59	..	9 50
Merstham	..	..	..	..	8 33	..	..	..	..	..	..	..	..	..	9 3	..	..	..	..	..		9 33	..		..	..	..	10 3	..	..
Coulsdon South	..	..	..	..	8 39	..	..	..	..	..	..	..	..	..	9 9	..	..	..	..	..		9 39	..		..	..	..	10 9	..	..
Purley	..	..	..	..	8 43	..	..	..	..	..	..	..	..	..	9 13	..	..	..	..	..		9 43	..		..	..	..	1013	..	..
East Croydon 285 arr.	8 4	..	..	..	8 48	..	..	..	..	..	..	8 41	..	8 46	9 18	9 4	..	..	..	..		9 48	..	..	9 41	..	..	1018	..	10 4
Norwood Junction B arr.	8 18	..	..	..	8 58	..	..	..	..	..	..	..	..	8 58	9 24	9 18	..	..	..	..	..	9 58	..		9 58	..	..	1024	..	..
New Cross Gate "	..	..	..	..	..	..	..	..	..	..	..	..	..	..	..	..	..	..	..	..	..	..	..		..	..	..	1033	..	..
LONDON BRIDGE "	8 31	..	..	..	9 11	..	..	..	..	..	..	..	..	9 11	9 36	9 31	..	..	..	..	..	10 11	..		10 11	..	..	1039	..	..
Clapham Junction A arr.	8 16	..	..	..	9 1	..	..	..	..	..	..	..	..	..	..	9 16	..	..	..	..	..	10 1	..	..	..	..	..	..	..	1016
VICTORIA "	8 22	..	..	8 25	9 7	..	..	..	..	8 40	..	8 57	..	9 3	..	9 22	..	..	..	..	9 25	10 7	..	9 40	9 57	..	..	..	..	1022

l Third class only. Mondays to Fridays. *a* Arrival time. **P** Pullman Car facilities available. **PR** Pullman car facilities available on Saturdays and Refreshment Car on Mondays to Fridays. **RB** Refreshment Car facilities available between Bognor Regis and London. *r* 5 mins. *earlier* on Saturdays. **SX** Sats. excepted. *u* 10 mins. *earlier* on Saturdays *x* 4 minutes later on Saturdays. *z* 4 minutes *earlier* on Saturdays.

For Other Notes, see page 233

For SERVICES from ISLE OF WIGHT and PORTSMOUTH to LONDON (Waterloo), see pages 366 to 372

From THE SOUTH COAST to LONDON—Week Days—*continued*

	p.m	p.m	p.m	p.m	p.m	p.m	p.m	p.m	p.m	p.m		p.m	p.m	p.m	p.m	p.m	p.m	p.m	p.m	p.m	p.m	p.m	p.m	p.m	p.m	p.m	p.m	p.m	p.m	ngt.
(Page 366) Yarmouth dep.							5 27																							
Cowes "							6 26																7 26							
Newport "							6 38																7 38							
Ventnor "							6 42																7 42							
Shanklin "							6 54																7 54							
Sandown "							7 1																8 1							
500 Ryde Pier (Boat) "							7 35																8 35							
Portsmouth Harbour dep.				8 8			8a5											9 8					9a5				10 5			
Portsmouth & Southsea "				8 12			Stop						8 42					9 12					Stop				10 8			
Fratton				8 14									8 45					9 14												
Hilsea Halt																											1016			
Bedhampton Halt													8 53																	
245 Hayling Island dep.				7 52														8 52												
Havant 244				8 23									8 55					9 23									1018			
Warblington Halt				8 25									8 57					9 25									1020			
Emsworth				8 28									9 0					9 28									1023			
Southbourne Halt				8 31									9 3					9 31									1026			
Nutbourne Halt				8 34									9 5					9 34									1028			
Bosham				8 37									9 9					9 37									1032			
Fishbourne Halt				8 40									9 12					9 40									1035			
Chichester Z				8 44									9 15					9 44									1038			
Barnham arr.				8 53														9 53									1048			
Bognor Regis arr.				9 7														10 7					p.m				11 7			
Bognor Regis dep.				8 45	8 45													9 45	9 45			10 2	10 30							
Barnham dep.				8 54	8b58													9 54	9b58			10 8	10a36				1048			
Ford (Sussex)				8 59	9 2													9 59	10 2			1012					1053			
Littlehampton arr.				9 7	9 7													10 7	10 7			1017					1057			
Littlehampton dep.		8 49			9 9											9 46	9 49					1019				1037				1223
Ford (Sussex) arr.																9 50										1041				1227
Angmering L		8 58		9 6												Stop	9 58	10 6				1029				Stop				Stop
Goring-by-Sea		9 3		9 11													10 3	10 11				1033								
Durrington-on-Sea		9 5															10 5					1036								
West Worthing U		9 7		9 14						9 19				9 50			10 7	10 14			1020	1038						11 0	11 21	
Worthing Central		9 9		9 17						9 21				9 52			10 9	10 17			1022	1040						11 2	11 24	
Ham Bridge Halt N										9 23				9 54							1024									
Lancing		9 13								9 26				9 57			1013				1027	1044						11 6	11 28	
Shoreham-by-Sea K 244	9 8	9 17		9 25						9 30				10 1			1017	10 25			1031	1048						1110	11 32	
Southwick	9 12	9 21								9 34				10 5			1021				1035	1051						1113	11 35	
Fishersgate Halt										9 36				10 7							1037									
Portslade and West Hove	9 16	9 24								9 38				10 9			1024				1039	1054						1116	11 38	
Aldrington Halt		9 27								9 41				1012			1027				1042								11 41	
Hove	9 21	9 29		9 34						9 43				1014			1029	10 33			1044	1058						1121	11 43	
Holland Road Halt										9 45																				
Brighton (below) arr.	9 26	9 34		9 37						9 48				1018			1032	10 36			1048	11 1						1125	11 47	
Arundel	Stop	Stop		Stop	9 16									Stop			Stop											Stop	Stop	
Amberley					9 21																									
Pulborough J 374					9 29																									
Billingshurst					9 36																									
Christ's Hospital, West Horsham					9 43																									
Horsham 244, 245, 285, 427 arr.					9 47																									
Horsham dep.																														
Dorking North H 285, 427																														
Sutton 285, 322 arr.																														
Horsham dep.					9 48																									
Littlehaven Halt					9 50																									
Fay Gate					9 54																									
Ifield					9 59																									
Crawley [234					10 2																									
Three Bridges (below) arr.	p.m				10 5		p.m																					p.m		
	1	2	3	4	5	6	7	8	9	10	11	12	13	14	15	16	17	18	19	20	21	22	23	24	25	26	27	28	29	30

	1	2	3	4	5	6	7	8	9	10	11	12	13	14	15	16	17	18	19	20	21	22	23	24	25	26	27	28	29	30
Ore .... dep.	8 12						8 42					Saturdays only			9 12									9 42				1012		
Hastings	8 15						8 45								9 15									9 45				1015		
St. Leonards (W.S.)	8 17						8 47								9 17									9 47				1017		
" (W.M.)	8 19						8 49								9 19									9 49				1019		
Bexhill (Central) **G**	8 24						8 54								9 24									9 54				1024		
Collington Halt	8 27						8 57								9 27									9 57				1027		
Cooden Beach	8 30						9 0								9 30									10 0				1030		
Norman's Bay Halt	8 33						9 3								9 33									10 3				1033		
Pevensey Bay Halt	8 37						9 7								9 37									10 7				1037		
Pevensey and Westham	8 39						9 9								9 39									10 9				1039		
Hampden Park **F**	8 45						9 15								9 45									1015				1045		
Eastbourne .... arr.	8 49	p.m					9 19								9 49		p.m							1019				1049	p.m	ngt.
dep.	8 52	8 57	9 16				9 22	9 29							9 52		9 57							1022	1044			1052	10 59	12 0
Hampden Park **F**	8 55	9 0	9 20				9 25	9 32							9 55		10 0							1025	1048			1055	11 2	12 3
Polegate 239	9 0	—	9 25				9 30	—							9 59									1029	1053			1059		
Berwick	9 6	Stop					9 36	Stop							10 5									1035				11 5		
Glynde	9 12						9 42								1011									1041				1111		
Lewes 239 .... arr.	9 17						9 47								1016	p.m								1046				1116		
Seaford .... dep						9 26						9 43				1013														
Bishopstone						9 28						9 45				1015														
Newhaven Harbour						9 33						9 50				1020														
" Town						9 34						9 51				1021														
Southease & Rodmell Halt						9 39						9 56				1026														
Lewes 239 .... arr.				p.m		9 45						10 2				1032														
Lewes .... dep.	9 18			9 25			9 48					10 2			1017	1032				1035				1047				1117		
Falmer	9 25						9 55					10 9			1024	1039								1054				1124		
London Road (Brighton)	9 29						9 59					1013			1028	1044				1050				1058				1128		
Brighton .... arr.	9 32			9 42			10 2					1016			1031	1046				1055				11 1				1131		
Lewes .... dep.																														
Cooksbridge																														
Plumpton																														
Wivelsfield (*below*)																														
Haywards Heath .. arr.		p.m						p.m						p.m												p.m				
Brighton .... dep		9 25						9 28	10 8					1028												1110				
Preston Park		Brighton Belle 1st and 3rd class Pullman Cars only						9 31	10 11					1031												1113				
Hassocks **D**								9 39						1039												1121				
Burgess Hill								9 43						1043												1125				
Wivelsfield (*above*)								9 45						1045												1127				
Haywards Heath C								9 52	10 28					1052												1132				
Ardingly																														
Horsted Keynes 239 .. arr.																														
Balcombe								9 58						1058																
Three Bridges (*above*)								10 8						11 7																
Gatwick Airport								10 11						1111																
Horley								10 14						1114																
Salfords								10 18						1118																
Earlswood								10 22						1122																
Redhill 246								10 30	10 50					1129																
Merstham								10 34						1133																
Coulsdon South								10 40						1139																
Purley								10 44						1143																
East Croydon 285 .... arr.								10 50	11 4					1149																
Norwood Junction B arr.								10 ③ 58																						
New Cross Gate .... "																														
LONDON BRIDGE ... "								11 ③ 11																						
Clapham Junction **A** .. arr.								11 2	11 16					12 1																
VICTORIA .... "		10 25						11 7	11 21					12 7																

③ Third class only. *a* Arrival time. *b* Arr. 7 mins. *earlier* **P** Pullman Car facilities available.

For Other Notes, see page 233

For SERVICES from ISLE OF WIGHT and PORTSMOUTH to LONDON (Waterloo), see pages 366 to 372

From THE SOUTH COAST to LONDON—Sundays

Station	a.m	a.m	a.m	a.m	a.m	a.m	a.m	a.m	a.m	a.m	a.m	a.m	a.m		a.m	a.m	a.m	a.m	a.m	a.m	a.m	a.m	a.m	a.m	a.m	a.m	a.m	a.m	a.m	a.m	a.m
Page 366 Yarmouth dep.	..	..	..	..	..	..	..	..	..	..	..	..	..	..	..	..	..	..	..	..	..	..	..	..	..	..	..	..	..	..	..
Cowes "	..	..	..	..	..	..	..	..	..	..	..	..	..	..	..	..	..	..	..	..	..	..	..	..	..	..	..	..	..	..	..
Newport "	..	..	..	..	..	..	..	..	..	..	..	..	..	..	..	..	..	..	6 20	..	..	..	..	..	..	..	..	..	..	..	..
Ventnor "	..	..	..	..	..	..	..	..	..	..	..	..	..	..	..	..	..	..	..	..	..	..	..	..	..	..	..	..	..	..	..
Shanklin "	..	..	..	..	..	..	..	..	..	..	..	..	..	..	..	..	..	..	..	..	..	..	..	..	..	..	..	..	..	..	..
Sandown "	..	..	..	..	..	..	..	..	..	..	..	..	..	..	..	..	..	..	..	..	..	..	..	..	..	..	..	..	..	..	..
500 Ryde Pier (Boat) "	..	..	..	..	..	..	..	..	..	..	..	..	..	..	..	..	..	..	7 30	..	..	..	..	..	..	..	..	..	..	..	..
Portsmouth Harbour dep.	..	..	..	..	..	..	..	..	..	7 8	..	..	..	..	..	..	..	..	8 8	..	..	..	..	..	..	..	..	..	..	..	9 8
Portsmouth & Southsea "	..	..	..	..	..	6 5	..	..	..	7 12	..	7 27	..	..	..	..	..	..	8 12	..	..	..	..	..	..	..	..	..	..	..	9 12
Fratton	..	..	..	..	..	6 8	..	..	..	7 14	..	7 30	..	..	..	..	..	..	8 14	..	..	..	..	..	..	..	..	..	..	..	9 14
Hilsea Halt	..	..	..	..	..	..	..	..	..	..	..	..	..	..	..	..	..	..	..	..	..	..	..	..	..	..	..	..	..	..	..
Bedhampton Halt	..	..	..	..	..	..	..	..	..	..	..	..	..	..	..	..	..	..	..	..	..	..	..	..	..	..	..	..	..	..	..
245 Hayling Island dep.	..	..	..	..	..	..	..	..	..	..	..	..	..	..	..	..	..	..	..	..	..	..	..	..	..	..	..	..	..	..	..
Havant 244	..	..	..	..	..	6 25	..	..	..	7 23	..	7 39	..	..	..	..	..	..	8 23	..	..	..	..	..	..	..	..	..	..	..	9 23
Warblington Halt	..	..	..	..	..	..	..	..	..	7 25	..	..	..	..	..	..	..	..	8 25	..	..	..	..	..	..	..	..	..	..	..	9 25
Emsworth	..	..	..	..	..	6 29	..	..	..	7 28	..	..	..	..	..	..	..	..	8 28	..	..	..	..	..	..	..	..	..	..	..	9 28
Southbourne Halt	..	..	..	..	..	..	..	..	..	7 31	..	..	..	..	..	..	..	..	8 31	..	..	..	..	..	..	..	..	..	..	..	9 31
Nutbourne Halt	..	..	..	..	..	..	..	..	..	7 34	..	..	..	..	..	..	..	..	8 34	..	..	..	..	..	..	..	..	..	..	..	9 34
Bosham	..	..	..	..	..	6 36	..	..	..	7 37	..	..	..	..	..	..	..	..	8 37	..	..	..	..	..	..	..	..	..	..	..	9 37
Fishbourne Halt	..	..	..	..	..	..	..	..	..	7 40	..	..	..	..	..	..	..	..	8 40	..	..	..	..	..	..	..	..	..	..	..	9 40
Chichester **Z**	..	..	..	..	..	6 45	..	..	..	7 44	..	7 54	..	..	..	..	..	..	8 44	..	..	..	..	..	..	..	..	..	..	..	9 44
Barnham arr.	..	..	..	..	..	6 54	..	..	..	7 53	..	8 2	..	..	..	..	..	..	8 53	..	..	..	..	..	..	..	..	..	..	..	9 53
Bognor Regis arr.	..	..	..	..	..	7 12	..	..	..	8 12	..	RB	..	..	..	..	..	..	9 7	..	..	..	..	..	..	..	..	..	..	..	10 7
Bognor Regis dep.	..	..	..	6 44	..	6 44	6 55	..	7 30	7 40	7 40	7 55	..	..	..	..	..	8 30	8 45	8 45	..	..	..	..	..	..	..	..	..	..	9 40
Barnham dep	..	..	..	6 51	..	6 55	7 a 1	..	7 36	7 54	7 47	8 5	..	..	..	..	..	8 36	8 54	8 58	..	..	..	..	..	..	..	..	..	..	9 54
Ford (Sussex)	..	..	..	6 56	..	7 0	Stop	..	7 41	7 59	7 52	..	..	..	..	..	..	8 41	8 59	9 2	..	..	..	..	..	..	..	..	..	..	9 59
Littlehampton arr.	..	..	..	7 0	..	7 4		..	7 45	..	7 57	..	..	..	..	..	..	8 46	..	9 7	..	..	..	..	..	..	..	..	..	..	..
Littlehampton dep.	..	..	..	7 6	..	7 10	..	7 36	7 49	..	7 59	7 59	7 54	..	..	..	8 46	8 49	..	9 9	..	..	..	..	..	..	9 46	..	..	9 49	..
Ford (Sussex) arr.	..	..	..	..	..	..	..	7 40	..	..	..	..	7 59	..	..	..	8 50	..	..	..	..	..	..	..	..	..	9 50	..	..	..	..
Angmering L	..	..	..	..	..	7 19	..	Stop	7 58	8 6	..	Through Train Bognor Regis to Victoria	Stop	..	..	..	Stop	8 58	9 6	..	..	..	..	..	..	..	Stop	..	..	9 58	10 6
Goring-by-Sea	..	..	..	..	..	7 24	..		8 3	8 11	..		..	..	..	..		9 3	9 11	..	..	..	..	..	..	..		..	..	10 3	1011
Durrington-on-Sea	..	..	..	..	..	7 26	a.m	a.m	8 5	..	..		a.m	..	..	..	..	9 5	..	..	..	..	..	..	..	..	a.m	..	..	10 5	..
West Worthing **U**	..	..	6 50	..	7 20	7 28	7 43	7 50	8 7	8 14	..		8 20	..	8 39	8 50	..	9 7	9 14	..	9 20	..	..	9 39	..	..	9 50	..	..	10 7	1014
Worthing Central	..	..	6 52	..	7 22	7 31	7 45	7 52	8 9	8 17	..		8 22	..	8 41	8 52	..	9 9	9 17	..	9 22	..	..	9 41	..	..	9 52	..	..	10 9	1017
Ham Bridge Halt **N**	..	..	6 54	..	..	..	..	7 54	..	..	..		8 24	..	..	8 54	..	..	..	..	9 24	..	..	..	..	..	9 54	..	..	..	..
Lancing	..	..	6 57	..	7 26	..	7 49	7 57	8 13	..	..		8 27	..	8 45	8 57	a.m	9 13	..	..	9 27	..	..	9 45	..	..	9 57	..	..	1013	..
Shoreham-by-Sea **K** 244	..	..	7 1	..	7 30	7 38	7 53	8 1	8 17	8 25	..		8 32	..	8 49	9 2	9 9	9 17	9 25	..	9 32	..	..	9 49	..	..	10 2	..	10 9	1017	1025
Southwick	..	..	7 5	..	7 33	..	7 56	8 5	8 21	..	..		8 36	..	8 52	9 6	9 13	9 21	..	..	9 36	..	..	9 52	..	..	10 6	..	1013	1021	..
Fishersgate Halt	..	..	7 7	..	..	..	..	8 7	..	..	..		8 38	..	..	9 8	..	..	..	..	9 28	..	..	..	..	..	10 8	..	..	..	..
Portslade and West Hove	..	..	7 9	..	7 36	7 43	7 59	8 9	8 24	..	..		8 40	..	8 55	9 10	9 16	9 24	..	..	9 40	..	..	9 55	..	..	1010	..	1018	1024	..
Aldrington Halt	..	..	7 12	..	..	..	..	8 12	8 27	..	..		8 43	..	..	9 13	..	9 27	..	..	9 43	..	..	..	..	..	1013	..	..	1027	..
Hove	..	..	7 14	..	7 40	7 47	8 3	8 14	8 29	8 33	..		8 45	..	8 59	9 15	9 20	9 29	9 33	..	9 45	..	..	9 59	..	..	1015	..	1022	1029	1033
Holland Road Halt	..	..	..	..	..	..	..	8 16	..	..	..		8 47	..	..	9 17	..	..	..	..	9 47	..	..	..	..	..	1017	..	..	..	..
Brighton (*below*) arr.	..	..	7 18	..	7 43	7 50	8 6	8 19	8 32	8 36	..		8 50	..	9 2	9 20	9 25	9 32	9 36	..	9 50	..	..	10 2	..	..	1020	..	1027	1032	1036
Arundel	..	..	Stop	7 12	Stop	Stop	Stop	Stop	Stop	Stop	8 5	8 14	Stop	..	..	..	Stop	Stop	Stop	9 16	Stop	..	..	Stop	..	..	Stop	..	Stop	Stop	..
Amberley	..	..		7 18							8 11	..		..	..	..				9 21		..	..		..	..		..			..
Pulborough **J** 374	..	..	..	7 25	..	..	..	..	..	..	8 18	8 26	..	..	..	..	..	..	..	9 29	..	..	..	..	..	..	..	..	..	..	..
Billingshurst	..	..	..	7 32	..	..	..	..	..	..	8 25	..	..	..	..	..	..	..	..	9 36	..	..	..	..	..	..	..	..	..	..	..
Christ's Hospital, West Horsham	..	..	..	7 39	..	..	..	..	..	..	8 32	..	..	..	..	..	..	..	..	9 43	..	..	..	..	..	..	..	..	..	..	..
Horsham 244, 245, 285, 427 arr.	..	..	..	7 44	..	..	..	..	..	..	8 37	8 41	..	..	..	..	..	..	..	9 47	..	..	..	..	..	..	..	..	..	..	..
Horsham 244, 245, 285, 427 dep.	..	..	..	..	..	..	..	..	..	..	..	..	..	..	..	..	..	..	..	..	..	..	..	..	..	..	..	..	..	..	..
Dorking North **H** 285, 427	..	..	..	..	..	..	..	..	..	..	..	..	..	..	..	..	..	..	..	..	..	..	..	..	..	..	..	..	..	..	..
Sutton 285, 322 arr.	..	..	..	..	..	..	..	..	..	..	..	..	..	..	..	..	..	..	..	..	..	..	..	..	..	..	..	..	..	..	..
Horsham dep.	..	..	..	7 46	..	..	..	..	..	..	8 48	8 43	..	..	..	..	..	..	..	9 48	..	..	..	..	..	..	..	..	..	..	..
Littlehaven Halt	..	..	..	7 48	..	..	..	..	..	..	8 50	..	..	..	..	..	..	..	..	9 50	..	..	..	..	..	..	..	..	..	..	..
Fay Gate	..	..	..	7 52	..	..	..	..	..	..	8 54	..	..	..	..	..	..	..	..	9 54	..	..	..	..	..	..	..	..	..	..	..
Ifield	..	..	..	7 57	..	..	..	..	..	..	8 59	..	..	..	..	..	..	..	..	9 59	..	..	..	..	..	..	..	..	..	..	..
Crawley [234	..	..	..	8 0	..	..	..	..	..	..	9 2	..	..	..	..	..	..	..	..	10 2	..	..	..	..	..	..	..	..	..	..	..
Three Bridges (*below*) arr.	..	..	..	8 3	..	a.m	..	..	a.m	..	9 5	..	..	..	..	..	a.m	..	..	10 5	..	..	..	..	P	..	..	..	..	a.m	..
	1	2	3	4	5	6	7	8	9	10	11	12	13	14	15	16	17	18	19	20	21	22	23	24	25	26	27	28	29	30	31

	1	2	3	4	5	6	7	8	9	10	11	12	13	14	15	16	17	18	19	20	21	22	23	24	25	26	27	28	29	30	31
Ore .... dep.	..	..	..	..	..	6 42	..	..	7 15	..	..	..	..	..	..	..	8 12	..	..	..	..	..	8 42	..	9 0	..	..	..	..	9 42	..
Hastings	..	..	..	..	..	6 45	..	..	7 19	..	..	..	..	..	..	..	8 15	..	..	..	..	..	8 45	..	9 5	..	..	..	..	9 45	..
St. Leonards (W.S.)	..	..	..	..	..	6 47	..	..	7 21	..	..	..	..	..	..	..	8 17	..	..	..	..	..	8 47	..	9 8	..	..	..	..	9 47	..
" (W.M.)	..	..	..	..	..	6 49	..	..	7 24	..	..	..	..	..	..	..	8 19	..	..	..	..	..	8 49	..	..	..	..	..	..	9 49	..
Bexhill (Central) G	..	..	..	..	..	6 54	..	..	7 30	..	..	..	..	..	..	..	8 24	..	..	..	..	..	8 54	..	9 15	..	..	..	..	9 54	..
Collington Halt	..	..	..	..	..	6 57	..	..	..	..	..	..	..	..	..	..	8 27	..	..	..	..	..	8 57	..	..	..	..	..	..	9 57	..
Cooden Beach	..	..	..	..	..	7 0	..	..	7 34	..	..	..	..	..	..	..	8 30	..	..	..	..	..	9 0	..	9 19	..	..	..	..	10 0	..
Norman's Bay Halt	..	..	..	..	..	7 3	..	..	..	..	..	..	..	..	..	..	8 33	..	..	..	..	..	9 3	..	..	..	..	..	..	10 3	..
Pevensey Bay Halt	..	..	..	..	..	7 7	..	..	..	..	..	..	..	..	..	..	8 37	..	..	..	..	..	9 7	..	..	..	..	..	..	10 7	..
Pevensey and Westham	..	..	..	..	..	7 9	..	..	7 41	..	..	..	..	..	..	..	8 39	..	..	..	..	..	9 9	..	..	..	..	..	..	10 9	..
Hampden Park F	..	..	..	..	..	7 15	..	..	7 47	..	..	..	..	..	..	..	8 45	..	..	..	..	..	9 15	..	..	..	..	..	..	1015	..
Eastbourne .... arr.	..	..	..	..	..	7 19	..	..	7 51	a.m	..	..	..	..	..	..	8 49	..	a.m	..	..	..	9 19	a.m	9 32		a.m	..	a.m	1019	..
Eastbourne .... dep.	..	..	..	..	..	7 22	..	..	7 54	7 59	..	..	..	..	..	..	8 52	..	8 57	..	..	..	9 22	9 29	9 36	..	9 46	9 57	1016	1022	..
Hampden Park F	..	..	..	..	..	7 25	..	..	7 57	8 2	..	..	..	..	..	..	8 55	..	9 0	..	..	..	9 25	9 32	..	..	9 50	10 0	1020	1025	..
Polegate 239	..	..	..	..	..	7 29	..	..	8 3	..	..	..	..	..	..	..	8 59	..	..	..	..	..	9 29	..	..	..	9 55	Stop	1025	1029	..
Berwick	..	..	..	..	..	7 35	..	..	8 9	..	..	..	..	..	..	..	9 5	..	..	..	..	..	9 35	..	..	..	..	..	..	1035	..
Glynde	..	..	..	..	..	7 41	..	..	8 16	..	..	..	..	..	..	..	9 11	..	..	..	..	..	9 41	..	..	..	..	..	..	1041	..
Lewes 239 .... arr.	..	..	..	..	..	7 46	..	a.m	8 21	..	..	..	..	..	..	..	9 16	..	..	..	..	..	9 46	..	9 56	..	..	a.m	..	1046	..
Seaford .... dep.	..	..	..	..	..	..	..	8 0	..	..	..	..	..	..	..	..	..	..	..	..	..	9 25	..	..	..	9 43	..	1025	..	..	..
Bishopstone	..	..	..	..	..	..	..	8 2	..	..	..	..	..	..	..	..	..	..	..	..	..	9 27	..	..	..	9 45	..	1027	..	..	..
Newhaven Harbour	..	..	..	..	..	..	..	8 7	..	..	..	..	..	..	..	..	..	..	..	..	..	9 32	..	..	..	9 50	..	1032	..	..	..
" Town	..	..	..	..	..	..	..	8 8	..	..	..	..	..	..	..	..	..	..	..	..	..	9 33	..	..	..	9 51	..	1033	..	..	..
Southease & Rodmell Halt	..	..	..	..	..	..	..	8 13	..	..	..	..	..	..	..	..	..	..	..	..	..	9 38	..	..	..	9 56	..	1039	..	..	..
Lewes 239 .... arr.	..	..	..	..	..	..	..	8 19	..	..	..	..	..	..	..	..	..	..	..	..	..	9 44	..	..	..	10 2	..	1044	..	..	..
Lewes .... dep.	..	..	..	..	..	7 47	..	8 25	..	..	..	..	..	..	..	..	9 17	..	..	..	..	..	9 47	..	..	10 2	..	Stop	..	1047	..
Falmer	..	..	..	..	..	7 54	..	8 32	..	..	..	..	..	..	..	..	9 24	..	..	..	..	..	9 54	..	..	10 9	..	..	..	1054	..
London Road (Brighton)	..	..	..	..	..	7 58	..	8 36	..	..	..	..	..	..	..	..	9 28	..	..	..	..	..	9 58	..	..	1014	..	..	..	1058	..
Brighton .... arr.	..	..	..	..	..	8 1	..	8 39	..	..	..	..	..	..	..	..	9 31	..	..	..	..	..	10 1	..	..	1016	..	..	..	11 1	..
Lewes .... dep.	..	..	..	..	..	Stop	..	..	8 24	..	..	..	..	..	..	..	..	..	..	..	..	9 45	..	..	9 57	..	..	..	..	..	..
Cooksbridge	..	..	..	..	..		..	..	8 30	..	..	..	..	..	..	..	..	..	..	..	..	9 50	..	..	..	..	..	..	..	..	..
Plumpton	..	..	..	..	..	..	..	..	8 35	..	..	..	..	..	..	..	..	..	..	..	..	9 55	..	..	..	..	..	..	..	..	..
Wivelsfield (*below*)	..	..	..	..	..	..	..	..	..	..	..	..	..	..	..	..	..	..	..	..	..	..	..	..	..	..	..	..	..	..	..
Haywards Heath .... arr.	..	..	a.m	..	a.m	a.m	a.m	..	8 45	..	..	..	a.m	..	..	..	..	a.m	..	..	a.m	10 5	..	..	10 14	..	..	a.m	..	..	..
Brighton .... dep.	..	6 58	7 25	..	7 28	7 55	7 58	..	..	..	..	..	8 28	..	..	..	..	9 8	..	..	9 28	..	..	..	..	..	..	10 8	..	..	..
Preston Park	..	7 1	..	..	7 31	7 58	8 1	..	..	..	..	..	8 31	..	..	..	..	9 11	..	..	9 31	..	..	..	..	..	..	1011	..	..	..
Hassocks D	..	7 9	..	..	7 39	..	8 9	..	..	..	..	..	8 39	..	..	..	..	..	..	..	9 39	..	..	..	..	..	..	..	..	..	..
Burgess Hill	..	7 13	..	..	7 43	..	8 13	..	..	..	..	..	8 43	..	..	..	..	..	..	..	9 43	..	..	..	..	..	..	..	..	..	..
Wivelsfield (*above*)	..	7 15	..	..	7 45	..	8 15	..	..	..	..	..	8 45	..	..	..	..	..	..	..	9 45	..	..	..	..	..	..	..	..	..	..
Haywards Heath C	..	7 22	..	..	7 52	8 15	8 22	..	8 46	..	..	..	8 52	..	..	..	..	9 26	..	..	9 52	10 5	..	..	10 15	..	..	1026	..	..	..
Ardingly	..	..	P	..	..	..	..	..	..	..	..	RB	..	..	..	..	..	..	..	..	..	10 9	..	..	P	..	..	P	..	..	..
Horsted Keynes 239 .. arr.	..	..	..	..	..	..	..	..	..	..	..	..	..	..	..	..	..	..	..	..	..	1013	..	..	..	..	..	..	..	..	..
Balcombe	..	7 28	..	..	7 58	..	8 28	..	..	..	..	..	8 58	..	..	..	..	..	..	..	9 58	..	..	..	..	..	..	..	..	..	..
Three Bridges (*above*)	7 5	7 37	..	..	8 5	8 27	8 35	..	8 58	..	..	..	9 8	..	..	..	..	..	..	..	10 8	..	..	..	..	..	..	..	..	..	..
Gatwick Airport	7 9	7 41	..	..	8 9	8 31	8 39	..	..	..	..	..	9 11	..	..	..	..	..	..	..	10 11	..	..	..	..	..	..	..	..	..	..
Horley	7 12	7 44	..	..	8 12	..	8 42	..	9 3	..	..	..	9 14	..	..	..	..	9 40	..	..	10 14	..	..	..	..	..	..	1040	..	..	..
Salfords	7 16	7 48	..	..	8 16	..	8 46	..	..	..	..	..	9 18	..	..	..	..	..	..	..	10 18	..	..	..	..	..	..	..	..	..	..
Earlswood	7 20	7 52	..	..	8 20	..	8 50	..	..	..	..	..	9 22	..	..	..	..	..	..	..	10 22	..	..	..	..	..	..	..	..	..	..
Redhill 246	7 27	7 57	..	..	8 27	..	8 57	..	..	..	..	..	9 29	..	..	..	..	..	..	..	10 29	..	..	..	..	..	..	..	..	..	..
Merstham	7 31	8 1	..	..	8 31	..	9 1	..	..	..	..	..	9 33	..	..	..	..	9 49	..	..	10 33	..	..	..	..	..	..	1049	..	..	..
Coulsdon South	7 37	8 7	..	..	8 37	..	9 7	..	..	..	..	..	9 39	..	..	..	..	..	..	..	10 39	..	..	..	..	..	..	..	..	..	..
Purley	7 41	8 11	..	..	8 41	..	9 11	..	..	..	..	..	9 43	..	..	..	..	..	..	..	10 43	..	..	..	..	..	..	..	..	..	..
East Croydon 285 .... arr.	7 46	8 16	8 10	..	8 46	8 53	9 16	..	9 23	..	..	9 16	9 48	..	..	..	..	10 3	..	..	10 49	..	..	..	10 46	..	..	11 3	..	..	..
Norwood Junction B arr.	7 51	8 21	8*21	..	8③55		9 21	..	..	..		9③25	9③55	..	..	..		10③25		..	10③55	..	..	..	10③55			11③25		..	..
New Cross Gate .... "	8 0	..	..	..	9③4		9 30	..	..	..		9③34	10③4	..	..	..		10③34		..	11③4	..	..	..	11③4			11③34		..	..
LONDON BRIDGE .... "	8 5	8 34	8*34	..	9③10		9 35	..	..	..		9③40	10③10	..	..	..		10③40		..	11③10	..	..	..	11③10			11③40		..	..
Clapham Junction A .. arr.	..	..	8 22	..	8 59	9 6	9*36	..	9 36	..	..	..	10 0	..	..	..	..	1015	..	..	11 1	..	..	..	..	..	..	1115	..	..	..
VICTORIA .... "	..	..	8 27	..	9 5	9 12	9*42	..	9 42	..	..	9 31	10 6	..	..	..	..	1020	..	..	11 6	..	..	..	11 3	..	..	1120	..	..	..

③ Third class only. * Change at East Croydon. *a* Arrival time. **P** Pullman Car facilities available.
RB Refreshment Car facilities available between Bognor Regis and London.

For Other Notes, see page 233

For SERVICES from ISLE OF WIGHT and PORTSMOUTH to LONDON (Waterloo), see pages 366 to 372

From THE SOUTH COAST to LONDON—Sundays—*continued*

	a.m	a.m	a.m	a.m	a.m	a.m	a.m	a.m	a.m	a.m	a.m	a.m	a.m	a.m	a.m	a.m	a.m	a.m	a.m	p.m	p.m	p.m.	p.m	p.m	p.m	p.m	p.m	p.m	p.m	p.m	p.m
(Page 366) Yarmouth dep.															7 35																
Cowes "															8 8																
Newport "															8 23																
Ventnor "															8 30																
Shanklin "															8 42																
Sandown "															8 48																
500 Ryde Pier (Boat) "															9 35																
Portsmouth Harbour dep.		9 23			9 53				10 8						10a5			11 8							12 8						
Portsmouth & Southsea "		9 27			9 57				1012						Stop			1112							1212						
Fratton		9 30			9 59				1014									1114							1214						
Hilsea Halt																															
Bedhampton Halt																															
245 Hayling Island dep.																															
Havant 244		9 39			10 8				1023									1123							1223						
Warblington Halt									1025									1125							1225						
Emsworth									1028									1128							1228						
Southbourne Halt									1031									1131							1231						
Nutbourne Halt									1034									1134							1234						
Bosham									1037									1137							1237						
Fishbourne Halt									1040									1140							1240						
Chichester Z		9 54			10 22				1044									1144							1244						
Barnham arr.		10 3			10 31				1053									1153							1253						
Bognor Regis arr.		RB			10 42				11 8									12 8							1 8						
Bognor Regis dep.	9 40	9 55	10 10		10 10				1045	1045			11 10					1145	1145						1245	1245					
Barnham dep.	9 47	10 5	10a16		10 31				1054	1058			11a16					1154	1158						1254	1258					
Ford (Sussex)	9 52		Stop						1059	11 2			Stop					1159	12 2						1259	1 2					
Littlehampton arr.	9 57								11 7	11 7								12 7	12 7						1 7	1 7					
Littlehampton dep.	9 59	9 59					1046	1049		11 9						1146	1149		12 9				1246	1249		1 9				1 46	
Ford (Sussex) arr.							1050									1150							1250							1 50	
Angmering L		Through Train Bognor Regis to Victoria.					Stop	1058	11 6							Stop	1158	12 6					Stop	1258	1 6					Stop	
Goring-by-Sea								11 3	1111								12 3	1211						1 3	1 11						
Durrington-on-Sea			a.m				a.m	11 5							a.m	a.m	12 5						p.m	1 5							
West Worthing U			10 19	1039			1050	11 7	1114					1120	1139	1149	12 7	1214			1219	12 37	1250	1 7	1 14		1 20				1 50
Worthing Central			10 21	1041	10 48		1052	11 9	1117					1122	1141	1151	12 9	1217			1221	12 39	1252	1 9	1 17		1 22				1 52
Ham Bridge Halt N			10 23				1054							1124		1154					1223		1254				1 24				1 55
Lancing			10 26	1045			1057	1113						1127	1145	1157	1213				1226	12 43	1257	1 13			1 27				1 58
Shoreham-by-Sea K 244			10 31	1049	10 56		11 2	1117	1125					1132	1149	12 2	1217	1225			1231	12 48	1 2	1 17	1 25		1 32				2 3
Southwick			10 35	1052			11 6	1121						1136	1152	12 5	1221				1235	12 51	1 6	1 21			1 36				2 6
Fishersgate Halt			10 37				11 8							1138		12 8					1237		1 8				1 38				2 9
Portslade and West Hove			10 39	1055			1110	1124						1140	1155	1210	1224				1239	12 54	1 10	1 24			1 40				2 11
Aldrington Halt			10 42				1113	1127						1143		1212	1227				1242		1 13	1 27			1 43				2 14
Hove			10 44	1059	11 3		1115	1129	1133					1145	1159	1214	1229	1233			1244	12 58	1 15	1 29	1 33		1 45				2 16
Holland Road Halt			10 46				1117							1147		1216					1246		1 17				1 47				2 18
Brighton (below) arr.			10 49	11 2	11 6		1120	1132	1136					1150	12 2	1219	1232	1236			1249	1 1	1 20	1 32	1 36		1 50				2 20
Arundel	10 5	1014	Stop		Stop			Stop		1116				Stop		Stop	Stop		1216		Stop	Stop		Stop	Stop	1 16	Stop				Stop
Amberley	1011									1121									1221							1 21					
Pulborough J 374	1018	1026								1129									1229							1 29					
Billingshurst	1025									1136									1236							1 36					
Christ's Hospital, West Horsham	1032									1143									1243							1 43					
Horsham 244, 245, 285, 427 arr.	1037	1042								1147									1247							1 47					
Horsham dep.		1043																													
Dorking North H 285, 427		11 2																													
Sutton 285, 322 arr.		1120																													
Horsham dep.	1048									1148									1248							1 48					
Littlehaven Halt	1050									1150									1250							1 50					
Fay Gate	1054									1154									1254							1 54					
Ifield	1059									1159									1259							1 59					
Crawley [234	11 2									12 2									1 2							2 2					
Three Bridges (below) arr.	11 5									12 5									1 5							2 5					
								a.m					a.m			a.m					a.m			p.m							p.m
	1	2	3	4	5	6	7	8	9	10	11	12	13	14	15	16	17	18	19	20	21	22	23	24	25	26	27	28	29	30	31

Station	1	2	3	4	5	6	7	8	9	10	11	12	13	14	15	16	17	18	19	20	21	22	23	24	25	26	27	28	29	30	31
Ore .... dep.	Stop	..	..	..	..	..	..	1012	..	Stop	..	..	10 42	..	..	1112	..	..	..	..	1142	..	..	1212	..	..	..	..	1242	..	1 12
Hastings	..	..	..	..	..	..	..	1015	..	..	..	..	10 45	..	..	1115	..	..	..	..	1145	..	..	1215	..	..	..	..	1245	..	1 15
St. Leonards (W.S.)	..	..	..	..	..	..	..	1017	..	..	..	..	10 47	..	..	1117	..	..	..	..	1147	..	..	1217	..	..	..	..	1247	..	1 17
" (W.M.)	..	..	..	..	..	..	..	1019	..	..	..	..	10 49	..	..	1119	..	..	..	..	1149	..	..	1219	..	..	..	..	1249	..	1 19
Bexhill (Central) **G**	..	..	..	..	..	..	..	1024	..	..	..	..	10 54	..	..	1124	..	..	..	..	1154	..	..	1224	..	..	..	..	1254	..	1 24
Collington Halt	..	..	..	..	..	..	..	1027	..	..	..	..	10 57	..	..	1127	..	..	..	..	1157	..	..	1227	..	..	..	..	1257	..	1 27
Cooden Beach	..	..	..	..	..	..	..	1030	..	..	..	..	11 0	..	..	1130	..	..	..	..	12 0	..	..	1230	..	..	..	..	1 0	..	1 30
Norman's Bay Halt	..	..	..	..	..	..	..	1033	..	..	..	..	11 3	..	..	1133	..	..	..	..	12 3	..	..	1233	..	..	..	..	1 3	..	1 33
Pevensey Bay Halt	..	..	..	..	..	..	..	1037	..	..	..	..	11 7	..	..	1137	..	..	..	..	12 7	..	..	1237	..	..	..	..	1 7	..	1 37
Pevensey and Westham	..	..	..	..	..	..	..	1039	..	..	..	..	11 9	..	..	1139	..	..	..	..	12 9	..	..	1239	..	..	..	..	1 9	..	1 39
Hampden Park **F**	..	..	..	..	..	..	..	1045	..	..	..	..	11 15	..	..	1145	..	..	..	..	1215	..	..	1245	..	..	..	..	1 15	..	1 45
Eastbourne arr.	a.m	..	..	..	..	..	..	1049	..	a.m	..	..	11 19	a.m	..	1149	a.m	..	..	..	1219	p.m	..	1249	p.m	..	..	..	1 19	p.m	1 49
Eastbourne dep.	1029	..	..	..	..	..	..	1052	..	1057	..	..	11 22	1129	..	1152	1157	..	..	..	1222	12 43	..	1252	1257	..	..	..	1 22	1 29	..
Hampden Park **F**	1032	..	..	..	..	..	..	1055	..	11 0	..	..	11 25	1132	..	1155	12 0	..	..	..	1225	12 47	..	1255	1 0	..	..	..	1 25	1 32	..
Polegate 239	..	..	..	..	..	..	..	1059	..	..	..	..	11 29	..	..	1159	..	..	..	..	1229	12 52	..	1259	Stop	..	..	..	1 29	Stop	..
Berwick	..	..	..	..	..	..	..	11 5	..	..	..	..	11 35	..	..	12 5	..	..	..	..	1235	Stop	..	1 5	..	..	..	..	1 35	..	..
Glynde	..	..	..	..	..	..	..	1111	..	..	..	..	11 41	..	..	1211	..	..	..	..	1241	..	..	1 11	..	..	..	..	1 41	..	..
Lewes 239 arr.	..	..	..	..	..	..	..	1116	..	..	..	..	11 46	..	..	1216	..	..	..	..	1246	..	..	1 16	..	..	..	..	1 46	..	..
Seaford dep.	..	..	..	..	..	..	..	..	..	..	..	1125	..	..	..	..	..	..	..	1225	..	..	..	..	..	..	..	1 25	..	..	..
Bishopstone	..	..	..	..	..	..	..	..	..	..	..	1127	..	..	..	..	..	..	..	1227	..	..	..	..	..	..	..	1 27	..	..	..
Newhaven Harbour	..	..	..	..	..	..	..	..	..	..	..	1132	..	..	..	..	..	..	..	1232	..	..	..	..	..	..	..	1 32	..	..	..
" Town	..	..	..	..	..	..	..	..	..	..	..	1133	..	..	..	..	..	..	..	1233	..	..	..	..	..	..	..	1 33	..	..	..
Southease & Rodmell Halt	..	..	..	..	..	..	..	..	..	..	..	1138	..	..	..	..	..	..	..	1238	..	..	..	..	..	..	..	1 38	..	..	..
Lewes 239 arr.	..	..	..	..	a.m	..	..	..	..	..	..	1144	..	..	..	..	..	..	..	1244	..	..	..	..	..	..	..	1 44	..	..	..
Lewes dep.	..	..	..	..	10 51	11 7	..	1119	..	..	..	..	11 47	..	..	1217	..	..	..	Stop	1247	..	..	1 17	..	..	..	..	1 47	..	..
Falmer	..	..	..	..	..	..	..	1126	..	..	..	..	11 54	..	..	1224	..	..	..	..	1254	..	..	1 24	..	..	..	..	1 54	..	..
London Road (Brighton)	..	..	..	..	11 6	1122	..	1132	..	..	..	..	11 58	..	..	1228	..	..	..	..	1259	..	..	1 28	..	..	..	..	1 58	..	..
Brighton arr.	..	..	..	..	11 10	1126	..	1134	..	..	..	..	12 1	..	..	1231	..	..	..	..	1 1	..	..	1 31	..	..	..	..	2 1	..	..
Lewes dep.	..	..	..	..	Stop	..	..	..	..	..	..	1144	Stop	..	..	..	..	..	..	..	..	..	..	..	..	..	..	1 44	..	..	..
Cooksbridge	..	..	..	..	..	..	..	..	..	..	..	1149	..	..	..	..	..	..	..	..	..	..	..	..	..	..	..	1 49	..	..	..
Plumpton	..	..	..	..	..	..	..	..	..	..	..	1154	..	..	..	..	..	..	..	..	..	..	..	..	..	..	..	1 54	..	..	..
Wivelsfield *(below)*	..	..	..	..	..	..	..	..	..	..	..	12 0	..	..	..	..	..	..	..	..	..	..	..	..	..	..	..	2 0	..	..	..
Haywards Heath arr.	..	..	a.m	..	a.m	..	..	..	..	..	..	12 5	p.m	..	..	..	..	..	..	p.m	..	p.m	..	..	p.m	..	p.m	2 5	..	p.m	..
Brighton dep.	..	..	10 28	..	11 8	..	..	..	..	..	1128	..	12 8	..	..	..	..	..	..	1228	..	1 8	..	..	1 25	..	1 28	..	..	2 8	..
Preston Park	..	..	10 31	..	11 11	..	..	..	..	..	1131	..	12 11	..	..	..	..	..	..	1231	..	1 11	..	..	..	..	1 31	..	..	2 11	..
Hassocks **D**	..	..	10 39	..	..	..	..	..	..	..	1139	..	..	..	..	..	..	..	..	1239	..	..	..	..	..	..	1 39	..	..	..	..
Burgess Hill	..	..	10 43	..	..	..	..	..	..	..	1143	..	..	..	..	..	..	..	..	1243	..	..	..	..	..	..	1 43	..	..	..	..
Wivelsfield *(above)*	..	..	10 45	..	..	..	..	..	..	..	1145	..	..	..	..	..	..	..	..	1245	..	..	..	..	..	..	1 45	..	..	..	..
Haywards Heath C	..	..	10 52	..	11 26	..	..	..	..	..	1152	12 6	12 26	..	..	..	..	..	..	1252	..	1 26	..	..	..	..	1 52	2 6	..	2 26	..
Ardingly	..	**RB**	..	..	..	..	..	..	..	..	..	1210	..	..	..	..	..	..	..	..	..	..	..	..	**P**	..	..	2 10	..	..	..
Horsted Keynes 239 arr.	..	..	..	..	..	..	..	..	..	..	..	1214	..	..	..	..	..	..	..	..	..	..	..	..	..	..	..	2 14	..	..	..
Balcombe	..	..	10 58	..	..	..	..	..	..	..	1158	..	..	..	..	..	..	..	..	1258	..	..	..	..	..	..	1 58	..	..	..	..
Three Bridges *(above)*	..	..	11 8	..	..	..	..	..	..	..	12 8	..	..	..	..	..	..	..	..	1 8	..	..	..	..	..	..	2 8	..	..	..	..
Gatwick Airport	..	..	11 11	..	11 40	..	..	..	..	..	1211	..	12 40	..	..	..	..	..	..	1 11	..	1 40	..	..	..	..	2 11	..	..	2 40	..
Horley	..	..	11 14	..	..	..	..	..	..	..	1214	..	..	..	..	..	..	..	..	1 14	..	..	..	..	..	..	2 14	..	..	..	..
Salfords	..	..	11 18	..	..	..	..	..	..	..	1218	..	..	..	..	..	..	..	..	1 18	..	..	..	..	..	..	2 18	..	..	..	..
Earlswood	..	..	11 22	..	..	..	..	..	..	..	1222	..	..	..	..	..	..	..	..	1 22	..	..	..	..	..	..	2 22	..	..	..	..
Redhill 246	..	..	11 29	..	11 49	..	..	..	..	..	1229	..	12 49	..	..	..	..	..	..	1 29	..	1 49	..	..	..	..	2 29	..	..	2 49	..
Merstham	..	..	11 33	..	..	..	..	..	..	..	1233	..	..	..	..	..	..	..	..	1 33	..	..	..	..	..	..	2 33	..	..	..	..
Coulsdon South	..	..	11 39	..	..	..	..	..	..	..	1239	..	..	..	..	..	..	..	..	1 39	..	..	..	..	..	..	2 39	..	..	..	..
Purley	..	..	11 43	..	..	..	..	..	..	..	1243	..	..	..	..	..	..	..	..	1 43	..	..	..	..	..	..	2 43	..	..	..	..
East Croydon 285 arr.	..	..	11 49	..	12 3	..	..	..	..	..	1249	..	1 3	..	..	..	..	..	..	1 49	..	2 3	..	..	..	..	2 49	..	..	3 3	..
Norwood Junction **B** arr.	..		11③55		12③25	..	..	..	..		12③55	..	1③25	..	..	..	..	..		1③55	..	2③25	..	..	..		2③55	..	..	3③25	..
New Cross Gate "	..		12③4		12③34	..	..	..	..		1③4	..	1③34	..	..	..	..	..		2③4	..	2③34	..	..	..		3③4	..	..	3③34	..
LONDON BRIDGE "	..		12③10		12③40	..	..	..	..		1③10	..	1③40	..	..	..	..	..		2③10	..	2③40	..	..	..		3③10	..	..	3③40	..
Clapham Junction A arr.	..	..	12 1	..	12 15	..	..	..	..	..	1 0	..	1 15	..	..	..	..	..	..	2 1	..	2 15	..	..	..	..	3 0	..	..	3 15	..
VICTORIA "	..	1143	12 7	..	12 20	..	..	..	..	..	1 6	..	1 20	..	..	..	..	..	..	2 7	..	2 20	..	..	2 25	..	3 6	..	..	3 20	..

③ Third class only. *a* Arrival time. **P** Pullman Car facilities available.

RB Refreshment Car facilities available between Bognor Regis and London.

For Other Notes, see page 233

For SERVICES from ISLE OF WIGHT and PORTSMOUTH to LONDON (Waterloo), see pages 366 to 372

From THE SOUTH COAST to LONDON—Sundays—continued

	a.m	p.m	p.m	p.m	p.m	p.m	p.m	p.m	p.m	p.m
Page 366 Yarmouth ....dep.	..	..	..	..	..	..	..	..	..	..
Cowes .... "	1026	..	..	..	..	..	..	..	..	..
Newport .... "	1038	..	..	..	..	..	..	..	..	..
Ventnor .... "	1030	..	..	..	..	..	..	..	..	..
Shanklin .... "	1042	..	..	..	..	..	..	..	..	..
Sandown .... "	1048	..	..	..	..	..	..	..	..	..
500 Ryde Pier (Boat).. "	1135	..	..	..	..	..	..	..	..	..
Portsmouth Harbour..dep.	12a5	1 8	..	..	..	1 53	..	..	2 8	..
Portsmouth & Southsea "	—	1 12	..	..	..	1 57	..	..	2 12	..
Fratton	Stop	1 14	..	..	..	1 59	..	..	2 14	..
Hilsea Halt	..	..	..	..	..	..	..	..	..	..
Bedhampton Halt	..	..	..	..	..	..	..	..	..	..
245 Hayling Island....dep.	..	..	..	..	..	..	..	..	..	..
Havant 244	..	1 23	..	..	..	2 8	..	..	2 23	..
Warblington Halt	..	1 25	..	..	..	..	..	..	2 25	..
Emsworth	..	1 28	..	..	..	..	..	..	2 28	..
Southbourne Halt	..	1 31	..	..	..	..	..	..	2 31	..
Nutbourne Halt	..	1 34	..	..	..	..	..	..	2 34	..
Bosham	..	1 37	..	..	..	..	..	..	2 37	..
Fishbourne Halt	..	1 40	..	..	..	..	..	..	2 40	..
Chichester Z	..	1 44	..	..	..	2 22	..	..	2 44	..
Barnham ....arr.	..	1 53	..	..	..	2 31	..	..	2 53	..
Bognor Regis ......arr	..	2 7	..	..	..	..	..	..	3 7	..
Bognor Regis ......dep.	..	1 45	1 45	..	..	..	..	..	2 45	2 45
Barnham ....dep.	..	1 54	1 58	..	..	2 31	..	..	2 54	2 58
Ford (Sussex)	..	1 59	2 2	..	..	..	..	..	2 59	3 2
Littlehampton ....arr.	p.m	2 7	2 7	..	..	..	..	..	3 7	3 7
Littlehampton ....dep.	1 49	..	2 9	..	..	..	2 46	2 49	..	3 9
Ford (Sussex) ......arr.	..	..	..	..	..	..	2 50	..	..	..
Angmering L	1 58	2 6	..	..	..	..	Stop	2 58	3 6	..
Goring-by-Sea	2 3	2 11	..	..	..	..		3 3	3 11	..
Durrington-on-Sea	2 5	..	..	..	..	..	p.m	3 5	..	..
West Worthing U	2 7	2 14	..	2 20	..	..	2 50	3 7	3 14	..
Worthing Central	2 9	2 17	..	2 22	..	2 48	2 52	3 9	3 17	..
Ham Bridge Halt N	..	..	..	2 24	..	..	2 55	..	..	..
Lancing	2 13	..	..	2 27	..	..	2 58	3 13	..	..
Shoreham-by-Sea K 244	2 17	2 25	..	2 32	..	2 56	3 3	3 18	3 25	..
Southwick	2 21	..	..	2 36	..	..	3 6	3 22	..	..
Fishersgate Halt	..	..	..	2 38	..	..	3 9	..	..	..
Portslade and West Hove	2 24	..	..	2 40	..	..	3 11	3 25	..	..
Aldrington Halt	2 27	..	..	2 43	..	..	3 14	3 27	..	..
Hove	2 29	2 33	..	2 45	..	3 3	3 16	3 29	3 33	..
Holland Road Halt	..	..	..	2 47	..	..	3 18	..	..	..
Brighton (below) ......arr.	2 32	2 36	..	2 50	..	3 6	3 20	3 33	3 36	..
Arundel	Stop	Stop	2 16	Stop	..	Stop	Stop	Stop	Stop	3 16
Amberley			2 21		..					3 21
Pulborough J 374	..	..	2 29	..	..	..	..	..	..	3 29
Billingshurst	..	..	2 36	..	..	..	..	..	..	3 36
Christ's Hospital, West Horsham	..	..	2 43	..	..	..	..	..	..	3 43
Horsham 244, 245, 285, 427 ..arr.	..	..	2 47	..	..	..	..	..	..	3 47
Horsham 244, 245, 285, 427 ..dep.	..	..	..	..	..	..	..	..	..	..
Dorking North H 285, 427	..	..	..	..	..	..	..	..	..	..
Sutton 285, 322 ......arr.	..	..	..	..	..	..	..	..	..	..
Horsham ....dep.	..	..	2 48	..	..	..	..	..	..	3 48
Littlehaven Halt	..	..	2 50	..	..	..	..	..	..	3 50
Fay Gate	..	..	2 54	..	..	..	..	..	..	3 54
Ifield	..	..	2 59	..	..	..	..	..	..	3 59
Crawley .... [234	..	..	3 2	..	..	..	..	..	..	4 2
Three Bridges (below)..arr.	..	p.m	3 5	..	..	..	p.m	..	..	4 5
	1	2	3	4	5	6	7	8	9	10

	a.m	p.m	p.m	p.m	p.m	p.m	p.m	p.m	p.m	p.m
Yarmouth ....dep.	1140	..	..	..	..	..	..	..	..	..
Cowes	1226	..	..	..	..	..	..	..	..	..
Newport	1238	..	..	..	..	..	..	..	..	..
Ventnor	1230	..	..	..	..	..	..	..	..	..
Shanklin	1242	..	..	..	..	..	..	..	..	..
Sandown	1248	..	..	..	..	..	..	..	..	..
500 Ryde Pier (Boat)	1 35	..	..	..	..	..	..	..	..	..
Portsmouth Harbour..dep.	2a5	..	..	2 53	..	..	..	3 8	..	3 23
Portsmouth & Southsea	—	..	..	2 57	..	..	..	3 12	..	3 27
Fratton	Stop	..	..	2 59	..	..	..	3 14	..	3 30
Hilsea Halt	..	..	..	..	..	..	..	..	..	..
Bedhampton Halt	..	..	..	..	..	..	..	..	..	..
245 Hayling Island....dep.	..	..	..	..	..	..	..	..	..	..
Havant 244	..	..	..	3 8	..	..	..	3 23	..	3 39
Warblington Halt	..	..	..	..	..	..	..	3 25	..	..
Emsworth	..	..	..	..	..	..	..	3 28	..	..
Southbourne Halt	..	..	..	..	..	..	..	3 31	..	..
Nutbourne Halt	..	..	..	..	..	..	..	3 34	..	..
Bosham	..	..	..	..	..	..	..	3 37	..	..
Fishbourne Halt	..	..	..	..	..	..	..	3 40	..	..
Chichester Z	..	..	..	3 22	..	..	..	3 44	..	3 54
Barnham ....arr.	..	..	..	3 31	..	..	..	3 53	..	4 3
Bognor Regis ......arr	..	..	..	3 42	..	..	..	4 7	..	RB
Bognor Regis ......dep.	..	3 10	..	3 10	..	..	3 40	3 40	..	3 55
Barnham ....dep.	..	3a16	..	3 31	..	..	3 47	3 54	..	4 5
Ford (Sussex)	..	Stop	..	..	..	..	3 52	3 59	..	..
Littlehampton ....arr.	..		P	..	..	..	3 57	..	..	4 43
Littlehampton ....dep.	..	..	3 5	..	3 46	3 49	3 59	..	..	3 59
Ford (Sussex) ......arr.	..	..	..	..	3 50	..	..	..	..	..
Angmering L	..	..	3 16	..	Stop	3 58	..	4 6	..	Through Train. Bognor Regis to Victoria.
Goring-by-Sea	..	..	3 22	..		4 3	..	4 11	..	
Durrington-on-Sea	..	p.m	3 25	..	p.m	4 5	..	..	..	
West Worthing U	..	3 20	3 30	..	3 50	4 7	..	4 14	4 20	
Worthing Central	..	3 22	3 35	3 48	3 52	4 9	..	4 17	4 22	
Ham Bridge Halt N	..	3 24	..	..	3 55	..	..	..	4 24	
Lancing	p.m	3 27	..	..	3 58	4 13	..	..	4 27	
Shoreham-by-Sea K 244	3 28	3 32	3 42	3 56	4 3	4 17	..	4 25	4 32	
Southwick	..	3 36	..	..	4 6	4 21	..	..	4 36	
Fishersgate Halt	..	3 38	..	..	4 9	..	..	..	4 38	
Portslade and West Hove	..	3 40	..	..	4 11	4 24	..	..	4 40	
Aldrington Halt	..	3 43	..	..	4 14	4 27	..	..	4 43	
Hove	3 36	3 45	3 50	4 3	4 16	4 29	..	4 33	4 45	
Holland Road Halt	..	3 47		..	4 18	..	..	..	4 47	
Brighton (below) ......arr.	3 41	3 50		4 6	4 20	4 32	.	4 36	4 50	
Arundel	Stop	Stop	Through Train, Littlehampton to Victoria.	Stop	Stop	Stop	4 5	Stop	Stop	4 14
Amberley							4 11			..
Pulborough J 374	..	..		..	..	..	4 18	..	..	4 26
Billingshurst	..	..		..	..	..	4 25	..	..	..
Christ's Hospital, West Horsham	..	..		..	..	..	4 32	..	..	..
Horsham 244, 245, 285, 427 ..arr.	..	..		..	..	..	4 37	..	..	4 42
Horsham 244, 245, 285, 427 ..dep.	..	..		..	..	..	..	..	..	4 43
Dorking North H 285, 427	..	..		..	..	..	..	..	..	5 2
Sutton 285, 322 ......arr.	..	..		..	..	..	..	..	..	5 20
Horsham ....dep.	..	..		..	..	..	4 48	..	..	..
Littlehaven Halt	..	..		..	..	..	4 50	..	..	..
Fay Gate	..	..		..	..	..	4 54	..	..	..
Ifield	..	..		..	..	..	4 59	..	..	..
Crawley .... [234	..	..		..	..	..	5 2	..	..	..
Three Bridges (below)..arr.	..	p.m		..	p.m	..	5 5	..	p.m	..
	11	12	13	14	15	16	17	18	19	20

	p.m	p.m	p.m	p.m	p.m	p.m	p.m	p.m	p.m	p.m
Yarmouth ....dep.	..	..	..	..	..	..	..	..	..	..
Cowes	..	..	..	..	..	..	..	..	..	..
Newport	..	..	..	..	..	..	..	..	..	..
Ventnor	..	..	..	..	..	..	..	..	..	..
Shanklin	..	..	..	..	..	..	..	..	..	..
Sandown	..	..	..	..	..	..	..	..	..	..
500 Ryde Pier (Boat)	..	..	..	..	..	..	..	..	..	..
Portsmouth Harbour..dep.	..	..	..	..	..	4 8	..	..	..	..
Portsmouth & Southsea	..	..	..	..	..	4 12	..	..	..	..
Fratton	..	..	..	..	..	4 14	..	..	..	..
Hilsea Halt	..	..	..	..	..	..	..	..	..	..
Bedhampton Halt	..	..	..	..	..	..	..	..	..	..
245 Hayling Island....dep.	..	..	..	..	..	..	..	..	..	..
Havant 244	..	..	..	..	..	4 23	..	..	..	..
Warblington Halt	..	..	..	..	..	4 25	..	..	..	..
Emsworth	..	..	..	..	..	4 28	..	..	..	..
Southbourne Halt	..	..	..	..	..	4 31	..	..	..	..
Nutbourne Halt	..	..	..	..	..	4 34	..	..	..	..
Bosham	..	..	..	..	..	4 37	..	..	..	..
Fishbourne Halt	..	..	..	..	..	4 40	..	..	..	..
Chichester Z	..	..	..	..	..	4 44	..	..	..	..
Barnham ....arr.	..	..	..	..	..	4 53	..	..	..	..
Bognor Regis ......arr	..	..	..	..	..	5 7	..	..	..	..
Bognor Regis ......dep.	..	..	..	..	..	4 44	4 44	..	..	..
Barnham ....dep.	..	..	..	..	..	4 54	4 58	..	..	..
Ford (Sussex)	..	..	..	..	..	4 59	5 2	..	..	..
Littlehampton ....arr.	..	..	..	..	..	5 7	5 7	..	..	..
Littlehampton ....dep.	..	..	4 46	..	4 50	..	5 9	..	..	..
Ford (Sussex) ......arr.	..	..	4 50	..	..	..	..	..	..	..
Angmering L	..	..	Stop	..	4 59	5 6	..	..	..	..
Goring-by-Sea	..	..		..	5 4	5 11	..	..	..	..
Durrington-on-Sea	..	..	p.m	..	5 6	..	..	..	..	..
West Worthing U	..	4 39	4 50	..	5 8	5 14	..	..	..	5 20
Worthing Central	..	4 41	4 52	..	5 10	5 17	..	..	..	5 22
Ham Bridge Halt N	..	..	4 55	..	..	..	..	..	..	5 24
Lancing	..	4 45	4 58	..	5 14	..	..	..	..	5 27
Shoreham-by-Sea K 244	..	4 49	5 3	5 13	5 18	5 25	..	..	..	5 32
Southwick	..	4 52	5 6	..	5 22	..	..	..	..	5 36
Fishersgate Halt	..	..	5 9	..	..	..	..	..	..	5 38
Portslade and West Hove	..	4 55	5 11	5 19	5 25	..	..	..	..	5 40
Aldrington Halt	..	..	5 13	..	5 28	..	..	..	..	5 43
Hove	..	4 59	5 15	5 23	5 30	5 33	..	..	..	5 45
Holland Road Halt	..	..	5 17	..	..	..	..	..	..	5 47
Brighton (below) ......arr.	..	5 2	5 20	5 28	5 33	5 36	..	..	..	5 50
Arundel	..	Stop	Stop	Stop	Stop	Stop	5 16	..	..	Stop
Amberley	..						5 21	..	..	
Pulborough J 374	..	..	..	..	..	..	5 29	..	..	..
Billingshurst	..	..	..	..	..	..	5 36	..	..	..
Christ's Hospital, West Horsham	..	..	..	..	..	..	5 43	..	..	..
Horsham 244, 245, 285, 427 ..arr.	..	..	..	..	..	..	5 47	..	..	..
Horsham 244, 245, 285, 427 ..dep.	..	..	..	..	..	..	..	..	..	..
Dorking North H 285, 427	..	..	..	..	..	..	..	..	..	..
Sutton 285, 322 ......arr.	..	..	..	..	..	..	..	..	..	..
Horsham ....dep.	..	..	..	..	..	..	5 48	..	..	..
Littlehaven Halt	..	..	..	..	..	..	5 50	..	..	..
Fay Gate	..	..	..	..	..	..	5 54	..	..	..
Ifield	..	..	..	..	..	..	5 59	..	..	..
Crawley .... [234	..	p.m	..	..	..	..	6 2	..	..	..
Three Bridges (below)..arr.	..	P	..	p.m	..	..	6 5	..	..	p.m
	21	22	23	24	25	26	27	28	29	30

Station	1	2	3	4	5	6	7	8	9	10	11	12	13	14	15	16	17	18	19	20	21	22	23	24	25	26	27	28	29	30
Ore dep	..	1 42	..	..	..	..	2 12	..	..	..	..	2 42	..	..	3 12	..	..	..	3 42	..	..	3 55	..	4 12	..	..	..	..	..	4 42
Hastings	..	1 45	..	..	..	..	2 15	..	..	..	..	2 45	..	..	3 15	..	..	..	3 45	..	..	4 0	..	4 15	..	..	..	..	..	4 45
St. Leonards (W.S.)	..	1 47	..	..	..	..	2 17	..	..	..	..	2 47	..	..	3 17	..	..	..	3 47	..	..	4 3	..	4 17	..	..	..	..	..	4 47
" (W.M.)	..	1 49	..	..	..	..	2 19	..	..	..	..	2 49	..	..	3 19	..	..	..	3 49	..	..	..	..	4 19	..	..	..	..	..	4 49
Bexhill (Central) **G**	..	1 54	..	..	..	..	2 24	..	..	..	..	2 54	..	..	3 24	..	..	..	3 54	..	..	4 10	..	4 24	..	..	..	..	..	4 54
Collington Halt	..	1 57	..	..	..	..	2 27	..	..	..	..	2 57	..	..	3 27	..	..	..	3 57	..	..	..	..	4 27	..	..	..	..	..	4 57
Cooden Beach	..	2 0	..	..	..	..	2 30	..	..	..	..	3 0	..	..	3 30	..	..	..	4 0	..	..	4 14	..	4 30	..	..	..	..	..	5 0
Norman's Bay Halt	..	2 3	..	..	..	..	2 33	..	..	..	..	3 3	..	..	3 33	..	..	..	4 3	..	..	..	..	4 33	..	..	..	..	..	5 3
Pevensey Bay Halt	..	2 7	..	..	..	..	2 37	..	..	..	..	3 7	..	..	3 37	..	..	..	4 7	..	..	..	..	4 37	..	..	..	..	..	5 7
Pevensey and Westham	..	2 9	..	..	..	..	2 39	..	..	..	..	3 9	..	..	3 39	..	..	..	4 9	..	..	..	..	4 39	..	..	..	..	..	5 9
Hampden Park **F**	..	2 15	..	..	..	..	2 45	..	..	..	..	3 15	..	..	3 45	..	..	..	4 15	..	..	..	..	4 45	..	..	..	..	..	5 15
Eastbourne arr.	p.m	2 19	..	p.m	..	..	2 49	p.m	..	..	..	3 19	..	p.m	3 49	p.m	..	..	4 19	..	..	4 27	..	4 49	p.m	..	..	..	..	5 19
Eastbourne dep.	1 57	2 22	..	2 29	..	..	2 52	2 57	..	..	..	3 22	..	3 29	3 52	3 57	..	..	4 22	..	4 29	4 32	..	4 52	4 57	..	..	..	..	5 22
Hampden Park **F**	2 0	2 25	..	2 32	..	..	2 55	3 0	..	..	..	3 25	..	3 32	3 55	4 0	..	..	4 25	..	4 32	..	..	4 55	5 0	..	..	..	..	5 25
Polegate 239		2 29	..		..	..	2 59	..	..	..	..	3 29	..		3 59		..	..	4 29	..		..	..	4 59	..	..	..	..	..	5 30
Berwick	Stop	2 35	..	Stop	..	..	3 5	..	..	..	..	3 35	..	Stop	4 5	Stop	..	..	4 35	..	Stop	..	..	5 5	..	..	..	..	..	5 36
Glynde	..	2 41	..	..	..	..	3 11	..	..	..	..	3 41	..	..	4 11	..	..	..	4 41	..	..	..	..	5 12	..	..	..	..	..	5 42
Lewes 239 arr.	p.m	2 46	..	..	..	..	3 16	..	..	..	p.m	3 46	..	p.m	4 16	..	..	p.m	4 46	..	..	4 52	p.m	5 17	..	..	..	..	..	5 47
Seaford dep.	2 25	..	..	..	..	..	..	..	..	..	3 25	..	..	3 43	..	..	..	4 25	..	..	..	..	4 47	..	..	..	..	..	5 25	..
Bishopstone	2 27	..	..	..	..	..	..	..	..	..	3 27	..	..	3 45	..	..	..	4 27	..	..	..	..	4 49	..	..	..	..	..	5 27	..
Newhaven Harbour	2 32	..	..	..	..	..	..	..	..	..	3 32	..	..	3 50	..	..	..	4 32	..	..	..	..	4 56	..	..	..	..	..	5 32	..
" Town	2 33	..	..	..	..	..	..	..	..	..	3 33	..	..	3 51	..	..	..	4 33	..	..	..	..	4 57	..	..	..	..	..	5 33	..
Southease & Rodmell Halt	2 38	..	..	..	..	..	..	..	..	..	3 38	..	..	3 56	..	..	..	4 38	..	..	..	..	5 2	..	..	..	..	..	5 38	..
Lewes 239 arr.	2 44	..	..	..	..	..	..	..	..	..	3 44	..	..	4 2	..	..	..	4 44	..	..	..	..	5 8	..	..	..	..	..	5 44	..
Lewes dep.	..	2 47	..	..	2 51	..	3 17	..	..	..	..	3 47	..	4 2	4 17	..	..	..	4 47	..	..	..	5 8	5 18	..	..	..	5 36	..	5 48
Falmer	..	2 54	..	..	..	..	3 24	..	..	..	..	3 54	..	4 9	4 24	..	..	..	4 54	..	..	..	5 15	5 25	..	..	..	..	..	5 55
London Road (Brighton)	..	2 58	..	..	3 5	..	3 28	..	..	..	..	3 58	..	4 14	4 28	..	..	..	4 58	..	..	..	5 20	5 29	..	..	..	5 51	..	5 59
Brighton arr.	..	3 1	..	..	3 9	..	3 31	..	..	..	..	4 1	..	4 16	4 31	..	..	..	5 1	..	..	..	5 22	5 32	..	..	..	5 55	..	6 2
Lewes dep.	..	..	..	..	..	..	..	..	..	..	3 44	..	..	..		..	..	..	..	..	..	4 54		..	..	..	..		5 44	..
Cooksbridge	..	..	..	..	..	..	..	..	..	..	3 49	..	..	..	Stop	..	..	..	..	..	..	5 0	Stop	..	..	..	..	Stop	5 49	..
Plumpton	..	..	..	..	..	..	..	..	..	..	3 54	..	..	..	..	..	..	..	..	..	..	5 5	..	..	..	..	..	..	5 54	..
Wivelsfield *(below)*	..	..	..	..	..	..	..	..	..	..	..	..	..	..	..	..	..	..	..	..	..	..	..	..	..	..	..	..	..	..
Haywards Heath arr.	..	..	..	p.m	..	p.m	..	..	p.m	..	4 4	..	..	..	p.m	p.m	..	..	..	..	p.m	5 15	p.m	..	..	p.m	..	p.m	6 4	..
Brighton dep.	..	..	..	2 28	..	3 8	..	..	3 28	..	..	..	..	..	4 8	4 25	..	..	..	..	4 28	..	5 8	..	..	5 25	..	5 28	..	..
Preston Park	..	..	..	2 31	..	3 11	..	..	3 31	..	..	..	..	..	4 11	..	..	..	..	..	4 31	..	5 11	..	..	..	..	5 31	..	..
Hassocks **D**	..	..	..	2 39	..	..	..	..	3 39	..	..	..	..	..	..	..	..	..	..	..	4 39	..	..	..	..	..	..	5 39	..	..
Burgess Hill	..	..	..	2 43	..	..	..	..	3 43	..	..	..	..	..	..	..	..	..	..	..	4 43	..	..	..	..	..	..	5 43	..	..
Wivelsfield *(above)*	..	..	..	2 45	..	..	..	..	3 45	..	..	..	..	..	..	..	..	..	..	..	4 45	..	..	..	..	..	..	5 45	..	..
Haywards Heath C	..	..	..	2 52	..	3 26	..	..	3 52	..	4 4	..	4 8	..	4 26	..	..	..	..	..	4 52	5 15	5 26	..	..	Brighton Belle 1st and 3rd class Pullman Cars only	..	5 51	6 4	..
Ardingly	..	..	..	..	..	..	..	..	..	..	4 8	..	P	..	..	P	..	..	..	RB	..	P	..	..	..		..	..	6 8	..
Horsted Keynes 239 arr.	..	..	..	..	..	..	..	..	..	..	4 12	..	..	..	..	..	..	..	..	..	..	..	..	..	..		..	..	6 12	..
Balcombe	..	..	..	2 58	..	..	..	..	3 58	..	..	..	..	..	..	..	..	..	..	..	4 58	..	..	..	..		..	5 57	..	..
Three Bridges *(above)*	..	..	..	3 8	..	..	..	..	4 8	..	..	..	..	..	..	..	..	..	..	..	5 8	..	..	..	..		..	6 8	..	..
Gatwick Airport	..	..	..	3 11	..	3 40	..	..	4 11	..	..	..	..	..	4 40	..	..	..	..	..	5 11	..	5 41	..	..		..	6 11	..	..
Horley	..	..	..	3 14	..	..	..	..	4 14	..	..	..	..	..	..	..	..	..	..	..	5 14	..	..	..	..		..	6 14	..	..
Salfords	..	..	..	3 18	..	..	..	..	4 18	..	..	..	..	..	..	..	..	..	..	..	5 18	..	..	..	..		..	6 18	..	..
Earlswood	..	..	..	3 22	..	..	..	..	4 22	..	..	..	..	..	..	..	..	..	..	..	5 22	..	..	..	..		..	6 22	..	..
Redhill 246	..	..	..	3 29	..	3 49	..	..	4 29	..	..	..	..	..	4 49	..	..	..	..	..	5 29	..	5 49	..	..		..	6 29	..	..
Merstham	..	..	..	3 33	..	..	..	..	4 33	..	..	..	..	..	..	..	..	..	..	..	5 33	..	..	..	..		..	6 33	..	..
Coulsdon South	..	..	..	3 39	..	..	..	..	4 39	..	..	..	..	..	..	..	..	..	..	..	5 39	..	..	..	..		..	6 39	..	..
Purley	..	..	..	3 43	..	..	..	..	4 43	..	..	..	..	..	..	..	..	..	..	..	5 43	..	..	..	..		..	6 43	..	..
East Croydon 285 arr.	..	..	..	3 49	..	4 3	..	..	4 49	..	..	..	4 41	..	5 3	..	..	..	..	..	5 49	5 46	6 4	..	..		..	6 49	..	..
Norwood Junction **B** arr.	..	..	..	3③55	..	4③25	..	..	4③55	..	..	..	4③55	..	5③25	..	..	..	..	..	5③55	5③55	6③25	..	..		..	6③55	..	..
New Cross Gate "	..	..	..	4③ 4	..	4③34	..	..	5③ 4	..	..	..	5③ 4	..	5③34	..	..	..	..	..	6③ 4	6③ 4	6③34	..	..		..	7③ 4	..	..
LONDON BRIDGE "	..	..	..	4③10	..	4③40	..	..	5③10	..	..	..	5③10	..	5③40	..	..	..	..	6③3	6③10	6③10	6③40	..	..		..	7③10	..	..
Clapham Junction A arr.	..	..	..	4 1	..	4 15	..	..	5 1	..	..	..	..	..	5 15	..	..	..	..	..	6 1	..	6 16	..	..	..	..	7 1	..	..
VICTORIA "	..	..	..	4 7	..	4 20	..	..	5 7	..	..	..	4 57	..	5 20	5 25	..	..	..	5 44	6 7	6 2	6 21	..	..	6 25	..	7 7	..	..

③ Third class only. * Change at East Croydon. *a* Arrival time.

P Pullman Car facilities available. **RB** Refreshment Car facilities available between Bognor Regis and London.

For Other Notes, see page 233

For SERVICES from ISLE OF WIGHT and PORTSMOUTH to LONDON (Waterloo), see pages 366 to 372

From THE SOUTH COAST to LONDON—Sundays—*continued*

Station	1	2	3	4	5	6	7	8	9	10
	p.m	p.m	p.m	p.m	p.m	p.m	p.m	p.m	p.m	p.m
Page 368 Yarmouth ....dep.	..	..	..	..	..	..	..	..	1 40	..
Cowes .... "	..	..	..	..	..	..	..	..	2 6	..
Newport .... "	..	..	..	..	..	..	..	..	2 42	..
Ventnor .... "	..	..	..	..	..	..	..	..	2 30	..
Shanklin .... "	..	..	..	..	..	..	..	..	2 42	..
Sandown .... "	..	..	..	..	..	..	..	..	2 48	..
500 Ryde Pier (Boat) .. "	..	..	..	..	..	..	..	..	3 35	..
Portsmouth Harbour dep.	..	..	..	..	..	..	..	..	4a5	5 8
Portsmouth & Southsea "	..	..	..	..	..	..	..	..	Stop	5 12
Fratton	..	..	..	..	..	..	..	..	..	5 14
Hilsea Halt	..	..	..	..	..	..	..	..	..	..
Bedhampton Halt	..	..	..	..	..	..	..	..	..	..
245 Hayling Island ....dep.	..	..	..	..	..	..	..	..	..	..
Havant 244	..	..	..	..	..	..	..	..	..	5 24
Warblington Halt	..	..	..	..	..	..	..	..	..	5 26
Emsworth	..	..	..	..	..	..	..	..	..	5 29
Southbourne Halt	..	..	..	..	..	..	..	..	..	5 32
Nutbourne Halt	..	..	..	..	..	..	..	..	..	5 34
Bosham	..	..	..	..	..	..	..	..	..	5 38
Fishbourne Halt	..	..	..	..	..	..	..	..	..	5 41
Chichester. Z	..	..	..	..	..	..	..	..	..	5 45
Barnham ....arr.	..	..	..	..	..	..	..	..	..	5 54
Bognor Regis ..... arr.	..	..	..	..	..	..	..	..	p.m	6 7
Bognor Regis ..... dep.	..	..	..	..	..	..	..	..	5 40	5 40
Barnham ....dep.	..	..	..	..	..	..	..	..	5 47	5 54
Ford (Sussex)	..	..	..	..	..	..	..	..	5 52	5 59
Littlehampton ... arr.	..	P	..	..	..	..	..	..	5 57	..
Littlehampton ... dep.	..	5 5	5 46	..	..	..	..	5 49	5 59	..
Ford (Sussex)........arr.	..	..	5 50	..	..	..	..	..	..	..
Angmering L	..	5 16	Stop	..	..	..	..	5 58	..	6 6
Goring-by-Sea	..	5 22	..	..	..	..	..	6 3	..	6 11
Durrington-on-Sea	..	5 25	..	..	..	..	..	6 5	..	..
West Worthing U	..	5 30	..	..	5 39	5 49	..	6 7	..	6 14
Worthing Central	..	5 35	..	..	5 41	5 51	..	6 9	..	6 17
Ham Bridge Halt N	..	..	..	..	..	5 54	..	..	..	..
Lancing	..	..	..	..	5 45	5 57	..	6 13	..	..
Shoreham-by Sea K 244	..	5 42	..	..	5 49	6 2	..	6 17	..	6 25
Southwick	..	..	..	..	5 52	6 5	..	6 21	..	..
Fishersgate Halt	..	..	..	..	..	6 8	..	..	..	..
Portslade and West Hove	..	..	..	..	5 55	6 10	..	6 24	..	..
Aldrington Halt	..	..	..	..	..	6 13	..	6 27	..	..
Hove	..	5 50	..	..	5 59	6 15	..	6 29	..	6 33
Holland Road Halt	..	..	..	..	..	6 17	..	..	..	..
Brighton (below) ....arr.	..	..	..	..	6 2	6 19	..	6 32	..	6 36
Arundel	..	Through Train Littlehampton to Victoria	..	..	Stop	Stop	..	Stop	6 5	Stop
Amberley	..		..	..	..	..	..	..	6 10	..
Pulborough J 374	..		..	..	..	..	..	..	6 18	..
Billingshurst .... [Horsham	..		..	..	..	..	..	..	6 25	..
Christ's Hospital, West	..		..	..	..	..	..	..	6 32	..
Horsham 244, 245, 285, 427 arr.	..		..	..	..	..	..	..	6 37	..
Horsham 244, 245, 285, 427 dep.	..		..	..	..	..	..	..	..	..
Dorking North H 285, 427	..		..	..	..	..	..	..	..	..
Sutton 285, 322 ....arr.	..		..	..	..	..	..	..	..	..
Horsham..........dep.	..		..	..	..	..	..	..	6 46	..
Littlehaven Halt	..		..	..	..	..	..	..	6 48	..
Fay Gate	..		..	..	..	..	..	..	6 52	..
Ifield	..		..	..	..	..	..	..	6 57	..
Crawley .... [234	..		p.m.	..	..	..	..	..	7 0	..
Three Bridges (below) .. arr.	..		P	..	..	..	..	..	7 3	..

Station	11	12	13	14	15	16	17	18	19	20
	p.m	p.m	p.m		p.m	p.m	p.m	p.m	p.m	p.m
Page 368 Yarmouth ....dep.	..	..	..	..	..	..	..	..	..	..
Cowes .... "	..	..	..	..	..	..	..	..	..	..
Newport .... "	..	..	..	..	..	..	..	..	..	..
Ventnor .... "	..	..	..	..	..	..	..	..	..	..
Shanklin .... "	..	..	..	..	..	..	..	..	..	..
Sandown .... "	..	..	..	..	..	..	..	..	..	..
500 Ryde Pier (Boat) .. "	..	..	..	..	..	..	..	..	..	..
Portsmouth Harbour dep.	..	5 23	..	..	..	..	5 53	..	..	..
Portsmouth & Southsea "	..	5 27	..	..	..	..	5 57	..	..	..
Fratton	..	5 30	..	..	..	..	5 59	..	..	..
Hilsea Halt	..	..	..	..	..	..	..	..	..	..
Bedhampton Halt	..	..	..	..	..	..	..	..	..	..
245 Hayling Island ....dep.	..	..	..	..	..	..	..	..	..	..
Havant 244	..	5 39	..	..	..	..	6 8	..	..	..
Warblington Halt	..	..	..	..	..	..	..	..	..	..
Emsworth	..	5 42	..	..	..	..	..	..	..	..
Southbourne Halt	..	..	..	..	..	..	..	..	..	..
Nutbourne Halt	..	..	..	..	..	..	..	..	..	..
Bosham	..	..	..	..	..	..	..	..	..	..
Fishbourne Halt	..	..	..	..	..	..	..	..	..	..
Chichester. Z	..	5 54	..	..	..	..	6 22	..	..	..
Barnham ....arr.	..	6 3	..	..	..	..	6 31	..	..	..
Bognor Regis ..... arr.	..	RB	..	..	..	..	6 42	..	..	..
Bognor Regis ..... dep.	..	5 55	..	..	..	6 10	6 10	..	..	..
Barnham ....dep.	..	6 5	..	..	..	6a16	6 31	..	..	..
Ford (Sussex)	..	..	..	..	..	Stop	..	..	..	..
Littlehampton ... arr.	..	..	..	..	P	..	..	..	..	..
Littlehampton ... dep.	..	5 59	..	..	6 9	..	..	6 46	..	6 48
Ford (Sussex)........arr.	..	..	..	..	..	..	..	6 50	..	..
Angmering L	..	Through Train, Bognor Regis to Victoria.	..	..	6 19	..	..	Stop	..	6 58
Goring-by-Sea	..		..	..	6 24	..	..	..	..	7 2
Durrington-on-Sea	..		..	..	6 27	..	..	p.m	..	7 5
West Worthing U	6 20		..	..	6 30	..	..	6 50	..	7 7
Worthing Central	6 22		..	..	6 35	..	6 48	6 52	..	7 9
Ham Bridge Halt N	6 24		..	..	..	..	..	6 55	..	..
Lancing	6 27		..	..	..	..	..	6 58	..	7 13
Shoreham-by Sea K 244	6 32		..	..	6 42	..	6 56	7 3	..	7 17
Southwick	6 36		..	..	..	..	..	7 6	..	7 20
Fishersgate Halt	6 38		..	..	..	..	..	7 9	..	..
Portslade and West Hove	6 40		..	..	..	..	..	7 11	..	7 23
Aldrington Halt	6 43		..	..	..	..	..	7 14	..	..
Hove	6 45		..	..	6 50	..	7 3	7 16	..	7 27
Holland Road Halt	6 47		..	..	..	..	..	7 18	..	..
Brighton (below) ....arr.	6 50		..	..	..	..	7 6	7 20	..	7 30
Arundel	Stop	6 14	..	..	Through Train, Littlehampton to Victoria.	..	Stop	Stop	..	Stop
Amberley	..	..	..	..		..	..	..	..	..
Pulborough J 374	..	6 25	..	..		..	..	..	..	..
Billingshurst .... [Horsham	..	..	..	..		..	..	..	..	..
Christ's Hospital, West	..	..	..	..		..	..	..	..	..
Horsham 244, 245, 285, 427 arr.	..	6 42	..	..		..	..	..	..	..
Horsham 244, 245, 285, 427 dep.	..	6 43	..	..		..	..	..	..	..
Dorking North H 285, 427	..	7 2	..	..		..	..	..	..	..
Sutton 285, 322 ....arr.	..	7 20	..	..		..	..	..	..	..
Horsham..........dep.	..	..	..	..		..	..	..	..	..
Littlehaven Halt	..	..	..	..		..	..	..	..	..
Fay Gate	..	..	..	..		..	..	..	..	..
Ifield	..	..	..	..		..	..	..	..	..
Crawley .... [234	..	..	..	..	..	..	p.m	..	..	..
Three Bridges (below) .. arr.	..	..	..	..	..	..	P	..	..	p.m

Station	21	22	23	24	25	26	27	28	29	30
		p.m	p.m	p.m	p.m	p.m	p.m	p.m	p.m	p.m
Page 368 Yarmouth ....dep.	..	..	..	..	..	..	..	..	3 30	..
Cowes .... "	..	..	..	..	..	..	..	..	4 26	..
Newport .... "	..	..	..	..	..	..	..	..	4 38	..
Ventnor .... "	..	..	..	..	..	..	..	..	4 30	..
Shanklin .... "	..	..	..	..	..	..	..	..	4 42	..
Sandown .... "	..	..	..	..	..	..	..	..	4 48	..
500 Ryde Pier (Boat) .. "	..	..	..	..	..	..	..	..	5 35	..
Portsmouth Harbour dep.	..	..	..	..	..	6 8	..	..	6 23	..
Portsmouth & Southsea "	..	..	..	..	..	6 12	..	..	6 27	..
Fratton	..	..	..	..	..	6 14	..	..	6 30	..
Hilsea Halt	..	..	..	..	..	..	..	..	..	..
Bedhampton Halt	..	..	..	..	..	..	..	..	..	..
245 Hayling Island ....dep.	..	..	..	..	..	..	..	..	..	..
Havant 244	..	..	..	..	..	6 23	..	..	6 39	..
Warblington Halt	..	..	..	..	..	6 25	..	..	..	..
Emsworth	..	..	..	..	..	6 28	..	..	..	..
Southbourne Halt	..	..	..	..	..	6 31	..	..	..	..
Nutbourne Halt	..	..	..	..	..	6 34	..	..	..	..
Bosham	..	..	..	..	..	6 37	..	..	..	..
Fishbourne Halt	..	..	..	..	..	6 40	..	..	..	..
Chichester. Z	..	..	..	..	..	6 44	..	..	6 54	..
Barnham ....arr.	..	..	..	..	..	6 53	..	..	7 3	..
Bognor Regis ..... arr.	..	..	..	..	..	7 7	..	..	RB	..
Bognor Regis ..... dep.	..	..	6 40	..	..	6 40	..	..	6 55	..
Barnham ....dep.	..	..	6 47	..	..	6 54	..	..	7 5	..
Ford (Sussex)	..	..	6 52	..	..	6 59	..	..	..	..
Littlehampton ... arr.	..	..	6 57	..	..	..	..	..	..	..
Littlehampton ... dep.	..	..	6 59	..	..	..	..	..	6 59	..
Ford (Sussex)........arr.	..	..	..	..	..	..	..	..	..	..
Angmering L	..	..	..	..	..	7 6	..	..	Through Train, Bognor Regis to Victoria	..
Goring-by-Sea	..	..	..	..	..	7 11	..	..		..
Durrington-on-Sea	..	..	..	..	..	..	..	..		..
West Worthing U	..	..	..	..	..	7 14	..	7 20		..
Worthing Central	..	..	..	..	..	7 18	..	7 22		..
Ham Bridge Halt N	..	..	..	..	..	..	..	7 24		..
Lancing	..	..	..	..	..	..	..	7 27		..
Shoreham-by Sea K 244	..	..	..	..	..	7 25	..	7 32		..
Southwick	..	..	..	..	..	..	..	7 36		..
Fishersgate Halt	..	..	..	..	..	..	..	7 38		..
Portslade and West Hove	..	..	..	..	..	..	..	7 40		..
Aldrington Halt	..	..	..	..	..	..	..	7 43		..
Hove	..	..	..	..	..	7 34	..	7 45		..
Holland Road Halt	..	..	..	..	..	..	..	7 47		..
Brighton (below) ....arr.	..	..	..	..	..	7 37	..	7 50		..
Arundel	..	..	7 5	..	..	..	..	..	7 14	..
Amberley	..	..	7 11	..	..	..	..	..	..	..
Pulborough J 374	..	..	7 18	..	..	..	..	..	7 26	..
Billingshurst .... [Horsham	..	..	7 25	..	..	..	..	..	..	..
Christ's Hospital, West	..	..	7 32	..	..	..	..	..	..	..
Horsham 244, 245, 285, 427 arr.	..	..	7 37	..	..	..	..	..	7 41	..
Horsham 244, 245, 285, 427 dep.	..	..	..	..	..	..	..	..	7 43	..
Dorking North H 285, 427	..	..	..	..	..	..	..	..	8 2	..
Sutton 285, 322 ....arr.	..	..	..	..	..	..	..	..	8 20	..
Horsham..........dep.	..	..	7 48	..	..	..	..	..	..	..
Littlehaven Halt	..	..	7 50	..	..	..	..	..	..	..
Fay Gate	..	..	7 54	..	..	..	..	..	..	..
Ifield	..	..	7 59	..	..	..	..	..	..	..
Crawley .... [234	..	..	8 2	..	..	..	..	..	..	..
Three Bridges (below) .. arr.	..	..	8 5	..	..	..	..	..	..	P

Station	1	2	3	4	5	6	7	8	9	10	11	12	13	14	15	16	17	18	19	20	21	22	23	24	25	26	27	28	29	30
Ore dep.			5 0				5 12		Stop				5 42				6 0			6 12					6 42					7 0
Hastings			5 5				5 15						5 45				6 5			6 15					6 45					7 5
St. Leonards (W.S.)			5 8				5 17						5 47				6 8			6 17					6 47					7 8
" (W.M.)							5 19						5 49							6 19					6 49					
Bexhill (Central) C			5 15				5 24						5 54				6 15			6 24					6 54					7 15
Collington Halt							5 27						5 57							6 27					6 57					
Cooden Beach			5 19				5 30						6 0				6 19			6 30					7 0					7 19
Norman's Bay Halt							5 33						6 3							6 33					7 3					
Pevensey Bay Halt							5 37						6 7							6 37					7 7					
Pevensey and Westham							5 39						6 9							6 39					7 9					
Hampden Park F							5 45						6 15							6 45					7 15					
Eastbourne arr.			5 32				5 49	p.m	p.m				6 19			p.m	6 32			6 49					7 19					7 32
Eastbourne dep.	5 29		5 36				5 52	5 57	6 16				6 23			6 29	6 36		6 45	6 52		6 57			7 22		7 29			7 36
Hampden Park F	5 32						5 55	6 0	6 20				6 26			6 32			6 48	6 55		7 0			7 25		7 32			
Polegate 239							5 59		6 25				6 30						6 53	6 59		Stop			7 29					
Berwick							6 5						6 36							7 5					7 35					
Glynde							6 11						6 42							7 11					7 41					
Lewes 239 arr.			5 56				6 16				p.m		6 47				6 56	p.m	7 8	7 16					7 46					7 56
Seaford dep.				5 47							6 25							6 43						7 23						
Bishopstone				5 49							6 27							6 45						7 25						
Newhaven Harbour				5 54							6 32							6 50						7 30						
" Town				5 55							6 33							6 51						7 32						
Southease & Rodmell Halt				6 0							6 38							6 56						7 37						
Lewes 239 arr.				6 6							6 44							7 2						7 43						
Lewes dep.				6 6			6 17				Stop		6 49					7 2		7 17					7 47					
Falmer				6 13			6 24						6 56					7 9		7 24					7 54					
London Road (Brighton)				6 18			6 28						7 1					7 14		7 28					7 58					
Brighton arr.				6 20			6 31						7 4					7 16		7 31					8 1					
Lewes dep.			5 58														6 58	Stop	7 10	Stop				7 44						7 57
Cooksbridge																			7 16					7 49						
Plumpton																			7 21					7 54						
Wivelsfield (*below*)																														
Haywards Heath arr.			6 14		p.m	p.m				p.m	p.m						7 15	p.m	7 31	p.m		p.m		8 4						8 13
Brighton dep.					5 58	6 8				6 25	6 28							7 8		7 25		7 28								
Preston Park					6 1	6 11					6 31							7 11				7 31								
Hassocks D					6 9						6 39											7 40								
Burgess Hill					6 13						6 43											7 45								
Wivelsfield (*above*)					6 15						6 45											7 47								
Haywards Heath C		6 8	6 15		6 21	6 26					6 51				7 8		7 16	7 27	7 31			7 54		8 4						8 14
Ardingly		P	P							P		RB			P		P			P				8 8					RB	P
Horsted Keynes 239 arr.																								8 12						
Balcombe					6 27						6 57											8 0								
Three Bridges (*above*)					6 35						7 8								7 43			8 8								
Gatwick Airport					6 39	6 40					7 11							7 40				8 12								
Horley					6 42						7 14								7 48			8 16								
Salfords					6 46						7 18								7 52			8 20								
Earlswood					6 50						7 22								7 56			8 24								
Redhill 246					6 57	6 49					7 29							7 50	8 4			8 31								
Merstham					7 1						7 33								8 8			8 36								
Coulsdon South					7 7						7 39								8 14			8 42								
Purley					7 11						7 43								8 18			8 47								
East Croydon 285 arr.		6 41	6 46		7 16	7 4					7 49				7 38		7 47	8 4	8 24			8 52								8 46
Norwood Junction B arr.		6£55	6£55		7 21	7*21					7£55						7£55	8£25	8 30			9*11								8£55
New Cross Gate "		7£4	7£4		7 30	7*30					8£4						8£4	8£35	8 39			9*22								9£4
LONDON BRIDGE "		7£10	7£10		7 35	7*35					8£10	8£3					8£10	8£40	8 44			9*28							9£4	9£10
Clapham Junction A arr.						7 16					8 1							8 16				9 7								
VICTORIA "		6 57	7 3			7 21				7 25	8 7	7 44			7 55		8 3	8 22		8 25		9 13							8 43	9 4

£ Third class only. ⁴ Change at East Croydon. *a* Arrival time. **P** Pullman Car facilities available. **R** Refreshment Car facilities available.
RB Refreshment Car facilities available between Bognor Regis and London

For Other Notes, see page 233

For SERVICES from ISLE OF WIGHT and PORTSMOUTH to LONDON (Waterloo), see pages 366 to 372

From THE SOUTH COAST to LONDON— Sundays—*continued*

Station	1 p.m	2 p.m	3 p.m	4 p.m	5 p.m	6 p.m	7 p.m	8 p.m	9 p.m	10 p.m
Page 366 Yarmouth dep	..	..	..	..	..	..	..	..	..	..
Cowes "	..	..	..	..	..	..	..	..	..	..
Newport "	..	..	..	..	..	..	..	..	..	..
Ventnor "	..	..	..	..	..	..	..	..	..	..
Shanklin "	..	..	..	..	..	..	..	..	..	..
Sandown "	..	..	..	..	..	..	..	..	..	..
500 Ryde Pier (Boat) "	..	..	..	..	..	..	..	..	..	..
Portsmouth Harbour dep	..	..	..	..	7 8	..	..	..	..	..
Portsmouth & Southsea "	..	..	..	..	7 12	..	..	..	..	..
Fratton	..	..	..	..	7 14	..	..	..	..	..
Hilsea Halt	..	..	..	..	..	..	..	..	..	..
Bedhampton Halt	..	..	..	..	..	..	..	..	..	..
45 Hayling Island dep.	..	..	..	..	..	..	..	..	..	..
Havant 244	..	..	..	..	7 23	..	..	..	..	..
Warblington Halt	..	..	..	..	7 25	..	..	..	..	..
Emsworth	..	..	..	..	7 28	..	..	..	..	..
Southbourne Halt	..	..	..	..	7 31	..	..	..	..	..
Nutbourne Halt	..	..	..	..	7 34	..	..	..	..	..
Bosham	..	..	..	..	7 37	..	..	..	..	..
Fishbourne Halt	..	..	..	..	7 40	..	..	..	..	..
Chichester Z	..	..	..	..	7 44	..	..	..	..	..
Barnham arr	..	..	..	..	7 53	..	..	..	..	..
Bognor Regis arr.	..	..	..	..	8 7	..	R	..	..	..
Bognor Regis dep.	..	..	..	7 40	7 40	..	7 55	..	8 10	..
Barnham dep.	..	..	..	7 47	7 54	..	8 5	..	8 16	..
Ford (Sussex)	..	..	..	7 52	7 58	..	..	..		..
Littlehampton arr.	..	..	..	7 57	..	..	..	..	Stop	P
Littlehampton dep.	7 46	..	7 48	7 59	..	..	7 59	..	..	8 9
Ford (Sussex) arr.	7 50	..	..	..	..	..	..	..	..	..
Angmering L	Stop	..	7 57	..	8 6	..	..	..	..	8 19
Goring-by-Sea		..	8 2	..	8 11	..	Through Train, Bognor Regis to Victoria	..	..	8 24
Durrington-on-Sea	..	..	8 4	..	..	..		..	..	8 27
West Worthing U	..	7 47	8 6	..	8 14	8 20		..	..	8 30
Worthing Central	..	7 49	8 8	..	8 17	8 22		..	..	8 35
Ham Bridge Halt N	..	7 51	..	..	..	8 24		..	..	..
Lancing	..	7 54	8 12	..	..	8 27		..	..	..
Shoreham-by-Sea K 244	..	7 59	8 16	..	8 25	8 32		..	..	8 42
Southwick	..	8 3	8 20	..	..	8 36		..	..	..
Fishersgate Halt	..	8 5	..	..	..	8 38		..	..	..
Portslade and West Hove	..	8 7	8 23	..	..	8 40		..	..	..
Aldrington Halt	..	8 10	..	..	..	8 43		..	..	..
Hove	..	8 12	8 27	..	8 33	8 45		..	..	8 50
Holland Road Halt	..	8 14	..	..	..	8 47		..	..	..
Brighton (below) arr.	..	8 16	8 30	..	8 36	8 50		..	..	..
Arundel	..	Stop	..	8 5	Stop	Stop	8 14	..	..	Through Train Littlehampton to Victoria
Amberley	..		..	8 11			..	..	..	
Pulborough J 374	..	..	..	8 18	..	..	8 26	..	..	
Billingshurst	..	..	..	8 25	..	..	..	..	..	
Christ's Hospital, West Horsham	..	..	..	8 32	..	..	..	..	..	
Horsham 244, 245, 285, 427 arr.	..	..	..	8 37	..	..	8 42	..	..	
Horsham 244, 245, 285, 427 dep	..	..	..	..	..	..	..	..	..	
Dorking North H 285, 427	..	..	..	..	..	..	..	..	..	
Sutton 285, 322 arr.	..	..	..	..	..	..	..	..	..	
Horsham dep.	..	..	..	8 48	..	..	8 43	..	..	
Littlehaven Halt	..	..	..	8 50	..	..	..	..	..	
Fay Gate	..	..	..	8 54	..	..	..	..	..	
Ifield	..	..	..	8 59	..	..	..	..	..	
Crawley [234	..	..	..	9 2	..	..	..	..	..	
Three Bridges (below) arr.	..	..	..	9 5	..	..	8 55	..	..	

Station	11 p.m	12 p.m	13 p.m	14 p.m	15 p.m	16 p.m	17 p.m	18 p.m	19 p.m	20 p.m
Page 366 Yarmouth dep	..	..	..	..	..	..	..	5 0	..	..
Cowes "	..	..	..	..	..	..	..	6 26	..	..
Newport "	..	..	..	..	..	..	..	6 38	..	..
Ventnor "	..	..	..	..	..	..	..	6 30	..	..
Shanklin "	..	..	..	..	..	..	..	6 42	..	..
Sandown "	..	..	..	..	..	..	..	6 48	..	..
500 Ryde Pier (Boat) "	..	..	..	..	..	..	..	7 35	..	..
Portsmouth Harbour dep	7 53	..	..	..	..	8 8	..	8a5	..	..
Portsmouth & Southsea "	7 57	..	..	..	..	8 12	..		..	..
Fratton	7 59	..	..	..	..	8 14	..	Stop	..	..
Hilsea Halt	..	..	..	..	..	..	..	..	..	..
Bedhampton Halt	..	..	..	..	..	..	..	..	..	..
45 Hayling Island dep.	..	..	..	..	..	..	..	..	..	..
Havant 244	8 8	..	..	..	..	8 23	..	..	..	..
Warblington Halt	..	..	..	..	..	8 25	..	..	..	..
Emsworth	..	..	..	..	..	8 28	..	..	..	..
Southbourne Halt	..	..	..	..	..	8 31	..	..	..	..
Nutbourne Halt	..	..	..	..	..	8 34	..	..	..	..
Bosham	..	..	..	..	..	8 37	..	..	..	..
Fishbourne Halt	..	..	..	..	..	8 40	..	..	..	..
Chichester Z	8 22	..	..	..	..	8 44	..	..	..	..
Barnham arr	8 31	..	..	..	..	8 53	..	..	..	..
Bognor Regis arr.	8 42	..	..	..	..	9 11	..	..	..	..
Bognor Regis dep.	8 10	..	..	..	..	8 45	8 45	..	..	9 10
Barnham dep.	8 31	..	..	..	..	8 54	8 58	..	..	9a16
Ford (Sussex)	..	..	..	..	..	8 59	9 2	..	..	
Littlehampton arr.	..	..	..	..	..	9 6	9 6	..	..	Stop
Littlehampton dep.	..	..	8 48	8 50	..	..	9 9	..	..	..
Ford (Sussex) arr.	..	..	8 52	..	..	..	..	..	..	..
Angmering L	..	..	Stop	9 0	..	9 6	..	..	..	..
Goring-by-Sea	..	..		9 4	..	9 11	..	..	..	..
Durrington-on-Sea	..	..	..	9 7	..	..	..	..	..	..
West Worthing U	..	8 50	..	9 9	..	9 14	..	..	9 19	..
Worthing Central	8 48	8 52	..	9 11	..	9 17	..	..	9 21	..
Ham Bridge Halt N	..	8 55	..	..	..	..	..	..	9 23	..
Lancing	..	8 58	p.m	9 15	..	..	..	..	9 26	..
Shoreham-by-Sea K 244	8 56	9 2	9 9	9 19	..	9 25	..	..	9 30	..
Southwick	..	9 5	..	9 22	..	..	..	..	9 34	..
Fishersgate Halt	..	..	..	..	..	..	..	..	..	..
Portslade and West Hove	..	9 10	..	9 25	..	..	..	..	9 38	..
Aldrington Halt	..	9 13	..	..	..	..	..	..	9 41	..
Hove	9 3	9 15	9 18	9 29	..	9 32	..	..	9 43	..
Holland Road Halt	..	9 17	..	..	..	..	..	..	9 45	..
Brighton (below) arr.	9 6	9 19	9 23	9 32	..	9 35	..	..	9 48	..
Arundel	..	Stop	Stop	Stop	..	Stop	9 16	..	Stop	..
Amberley	..				..		9 21	..		..
Pulborough J 374	..	..	..	..	..	..	9 29	..	..	..
Billingshurst	..	..	..	..	..	..	9 36	..	..	..
Christ's Hospital, West Horsham	..	..	..	..	..	..	9 43	..	..	..
Horsham 244, 245, 285, 427 arr.	..	..	..	..	..	..	9 47	..	..	..
Horsham 244, 245, 285, 427 dep	..	..	..	..	..	..	..	..	..	..
Dorking North H 285, 427	..	..	..	..	..	..	..	..	..	..
Sutton 285, 322 arr.	..	..	..	..	..	..	..	..	..	..
Horsham dep.	..	..	..	..	..	..	9 48	..	..	..
Littlehaven Halt	..	..	..	..	..	..	9 50	..	..	..
Fay Gate	..	..	..	..	..	..	9 54	..	..	..
Ifield	..	..	..	..	..	..	9 59	..	..	..
Crawley [234	..	..	..	..	..	..	10 2	..	..	..
Three Bridges (below) arr.	..	..	..	..	..	..	10 5	..	..	..

Station	21 p.m	22 p.m	23 p.m	24 p.m	25 p.m	26 p.m	27 p.m	28 p.m	29 p.m	30 p.m
Page 366 Yarmouth dep	..	..	..	..	..	..	..	..	..	..
Cowes "	..	..	..	..	..	..	..	..	..	..
Newport "	..	..	..	..	..	..	..	..	..	..
Ventnor "	..	..	..	..	..	..	..	..	..	..
Shanklin "	..	..	..	..	..	..	..	..	..	..
Sandown "	..	..	..	..	..	..	..	..	..	..
500 Ryde Pier (Boat) "	..	..	..	..	..	..	..	..	..	..
Portsmouth Harbour dep	8 53	..	..	..	9 8	..	..	9 53	..	..
Portsmouth & Southsea "	8 57	..	..	..	9 12	..	..	9 57	..	..
Fratton	8 59	..	..	..	9 14	..	..	9 59	..	..
Hilsea Halt	..	..	..	..	..	..	..	..	..	..
Bedhampton Halt	..	..	..	..	..	..	..	..	..	..
45 Hayling Island dep.	..	..	..	..	..	..	..	..	..	..
Havant 244	9 8	..	..	..	9 23	..	..	10 8	..	..
Warblington Halt	..	..	..	..	9 25	..	..	..	..	..
Emsworth	..	..	..	..	9 28	..	..	..	..	..
Southbourne Halt	..	..	..	..	9 31	..	..	..	..	..
Nutbourne Halt	..	..	..	..	9 34	..	..	..	..	..
Bosham	..	..	..	..	9 37	..	..	..	..	..
Fishbourne Halt	..	..	..	..	9 40	..	..	..	..	..
Chichester Z	9 22	..	..	..	9 44	..	..	1022	..	..
Barnham arr	9 31	..	..	..	9 53	..	..	1031	..	..
Bognor Regis arr.	9 42	..	..	..	10 7	..	..	11 4	..	..
Bognor Regis dep.	9 10	..	..	..	9 45	9 45	..	..	..	..
Barnham dep.	9 32	..	..	..	9 54	9 58	..	1031	..	..
Ford (Sussex)	..	..	..	..	9 59	10 2	..	1036	..	1050
Littlehampton arr.	..	..	..	..	10 7	10 7	..	1054	..	1054
Littlehampton dep.	..	9 46	..	9 49	..	..	..	..	1040	
Ford (Sussex) arr.	..	9 50	..	..	..	..	..	..	1044	Stop
Angmering L	..	Stop	..	9 58	10 6	..	..	..	..	..
Goring-by-Sea	..		..	10 3	10 11	..	..	..	..	..
Durrington-on-Sea	..	..	..	10 5	..	..	..	..	..	p.m
West Worthing U	..	..	9 50	10 7	10 14	..	1020	..	..	11 7
Worthing Central	9 49	..	9 52	10 9	10 17	..	1022	1050	..	11 9
Ham Bridge Halt N	..	..	9 55	..	..	..	1024	..	..	..
Lancing	..	..	9 58	1013	..	..	1027	..	..	1113
Shoreham-by-Sea K 244	9 56	..	10 2	1017	10 25	..	1031	1057	..	1117
Southwick	..	..	10 5	1021	..	..	1035	..	..	1121
Fishersgate Halt	..	..	..	..	..	..	..	..	..	..
Portslade and West Hove	..	..	1010	1024	..	..	1039	..	..	1124
Aldrington Halt	..	..	1013	1027	..	..	1042	..	..	..
Hove	10 4	..	1015	1029	10 32	..	1044	11 4	..	1129
Holland Road Halt	..	..	..	..	..	..	..	..	..	..
Brighton (below) arr.	10 7	..	1018	1032	10 37	..	1050	11 8	..	1132
Arundel	Stop	..	..	..	..	..	..	..	..	..
Amberley		..	..	..	..	..	..	..	..	..
Pulborough J 374	..	..	..	..	..	..	..	..	..	..
Billingshurst	..	..	..	..	..	..	..	..	..	..
Christ's Hospital, West Horsham	..	..	..	..	..	..	..	..	..	..
Horsham 244, 245, 285, 427 arr.	..	..	..	..	..	..	..	..	..	..
Horsham 244, 245, 285, 427 dep	..	..	..	..	..	..	..	..	..	..
Dorking North H 285, 427	..	..	..	..	..	..	..	..	..	..
Sutton 285, 322 arr.	..	..	..	..	..	..	..	..	..	..
Horsham dep.	..	..	..	..	..	..	..	..	..	..
Littlehaven Halt	..	..	..	..	..	..	..	..	..	..
Fay Gate	..	..	..	..	..	..	..	..	..	..
Ifield	..	..	..	..	..	..	..	..	..	..
Crawley [234	..	..	..	..	..	..	..	..	..	..
Three Bridges (below) arr.	p.m	..	..	..	..	..	..	..	..	..

	1	2	3	4	5	6	7	8	9	10	11	12	13	14	15	16	17	18	19	20	21	22	23	24	25	26	27	28	29	30
Ore ....dep	..	..	..	Stop	..	..	..	7 42	..	..	..	..	..	..	8 42	..	Stop	..	..	..	9 42	..	..	..	..	..	..	..	..	..
Hastings	..	..	..		..	..	..	7 45	..	..	..	..	..	..	8 45	..		..	..	..	9 45	..	..	..	..	..	..	..	..	..
St. Leonards (W.S.)	..	..	..	..	..	..	..	7 47	..	..	..	..	..	..	8 47	..	..	..	..	..	9 47	..	..	..	..	..	..	..	..	..
" (W.M.)	..	..	..	..	..	..	..	7 49	..	..	..	..	..	..	8 49	..	..	..	..	..	9 49	..								
Bexhill (Central) G	..	..	..	..	..	..	..	7 54	..	..	..	..	..	..	8 54	..	..	..	..	..	9 54	..								
Collington Halt	..	..	..	..	..	..	..	7 57	..	..	..	..	..	..	8 57	..	..	..	..	..	9 57	..								
Cooden Beach	..	..	..	..	..	..	..	8 0	..	..	..	..	..	..	9 0	..	..	..	..	..	10 0	..								
Norman's Bay Halt	..	..	..	..	..	..	..	8 3	..	..	..	..	..	..	9 3	..	..	..	..	..	10 3	..								
Pevensey Bay Halt	..	..	..	..	..	..	..	8 7	..	..	..	..	..	..	9 7	..	..	..	..	..	10 7	..								
Pevensey and Westham	..	..	..	..	..	..	..	8 9	..	..	..	..	..	..	9 9	..	..	..	..	..	10 9	..								
Hampden Park F	..	..	..	..	..	..	..	8 15	..	..	..	..	..	..	9 15	..	..	..	..	..	10 15	..								
Eastbourne arr.	..	..	..	p.m	..	..	..	8 19	p.m	..	..	..	..	..	9 19	..	..	..	..	p.m	10 19	p.m								
Eastbourne dep.	..	..	..	8 18	..	..	..	8 22	8 29	..	..	..	..	..	9 22	..	..	..	..	9 29	10 22	1049								
Hampden Park F	..	..	..	8 22	..	..	..	8 25	8 32	..	..	..	..	..	9 25	..	..	..	..	9 32	10 25	1052								
Polegate 239	..	..	..	8 27	..	..	..	8 32	Stop	..	..	..	..	..	9 29	..	..	..	..	..	10 29	..								
Berwick	..	..	..	..	..	..	..	8 38		..	..	..	..	..	9 35	..	..	..	..	..	10 35	..								
Glynde	..	..	..	..	..	..	..	8 44	..	..	..	..	..	..	9 41	..	..	..	..	..	10 41	..								
Lewes 239 ....arr.	..	p.m	..	..	..	p.m	..	8 49	..	..	..	..	..	p.m	9 46	..	p.m	..	..	..	10 46	..								
Seaford ....dep.	..	8 13	..	..	..	8 25	..	..	..	..	..	..	..	9 25	..	..	9 43	..	..	..	..	..								
Bishopstone	..	8 15	..	..	..	8 27	..	..	..	..	..	..	..	9 27	..	..	9 45	..	..	..	..	..								
Newhaven Harbour	..	8 20	..	..	..	8 32	..	..	..	..	..	..	..	9 30	..	..	9 50	..	..	..	..	..								
" Town	..	8 21	..	..	..	8 33	..	..	..	..	..	..	..	9 32	..	..	9 51	..	..	..	..	..								
Southease & Rodmell Halt	..	8 26	..	..	..	8 38	..	..	..	..	..	..	..	..	..	..	9 56	..	..	..	..	..								
Lewes 239 ....arr.	..	8 32	..	..	..	8 44	..	..	p.m	..	..	..	..	9 42	..	p.m	10 2	..	..	..	..	..								
Lewes ....dep.	..	8 32	..	..	..	..	..	8 50	9 6	..	..	..	..	9 44	9 47	9 54	10 3	..	..	..	10 47	..								
Falmer	..	8 39	..	..	..	..	..	8 57	..	..	..	..	..	..	9 54	..	1010	..	..	..	10 54	..								
London Road (Brighton)	..	8 44	..	..	..	..	..	9 1	9 21	..	..	..	..	..	9 58	10 9	1014	..	..	..	10 58	..								
Brighton ....arr.	..	8 46	..	..	..	..	..	9 4	9 25	..	..	..	..	9 56	10 1	1013	1017	..	..	..	11 1	..								
Lewes ....dep.	..	..	..	..	..	..	..	Stop	..	..	..	..	..	Stop	..	..	..	..	..	..	..	..								
Cooksbridge	..	..	..	..	..	..	..		..	..	..	..	..		..	..	..	..	..	..	..	..								
Plumpton	..	..	..	..	..	..	..	..	..	..	..	..	..	..	..	..	..	..	..	..	..	..								
Wivelsfield (*below*)	..	..	..	..	..	..	..	..	..	..	..	..	..	..	..	..	..	..	..	..	..	..								
Haywards Heath ....arr.	p.m	..	..	..	p.m	..	..	p.m	..	..	..	p.m	p.m	p.m	..	..	..	p.m	p.m	..	..	..								
Brighton ....dep.	8 8	..	..	..	8 25	..	..	8 28	..	..	..	8 58	9 8	9 25	..	..	..	9 28	10 8	..	..	..								
Preston Park	8 11	..	..	..	..	..	..	8 31	..	..	..	9 1	..	..	..	..	..	9 31	1011	..	..	..								
Hassocks D	..	..	..	..	..	..	..	8 38	..	..	..	9 9	..	..	..	..	..	9 39	..	..	..	..								
Burgess Hill	..	..	..	..	..	..	..	8 43	..	..	..	9 13	..	..	..	..	..	9 43	..	..	..	..								
Wivelsfield (*above*)	..	..	..	..	..	..	..	8 45	..	..	..	9 15	..	..	..	..	..	9 45	..	..	..	..								
Haywards Heath C	8 27	..	..	..	..	..	..	8 50	..	9 9	..	9 21	9 27	..	..	..	..	9 52	1027	..	..	..								
Ardingly	..	..	..	..	P	..	R	..	..	P	..	..	..	P	..	..	..	..	..	..	..	..								
Horsted Keynes 239 ..arr.	..	..	..	..	..	..	..	..	..	..	..	..	..	..	..	..	..	..	..	..	..	..								
Balcombe	..	..	..	..	..	..	..	8 56	..	..	..	9 27	..	..	..	..	..	9 58	..	..	..	..								
Three Bridges (*above*)	..	..	..	..	..	..	8 56	9 8	..	..	..	9 36	..	..	..	..	..	10 7	..	..	..	..								
Gatwick Airport	8 40	..	..	..	..	..	..	9 11	..	..	..	9 39	..	..	..	..	..	10 10	..	..	..	..								
Horley	..	..	..	..	..	..	..	9 14	..	..	..	9 42	..	..	..	..	..	10 13	..	..	..	..								
Salfords	..	..	..	..	..	..	..	9 18	..	..	..	9 46	..	..	..	..	..	10 17	..	..	..	..								
Earlswood	..	..	..	..	..	..	..	9 22	..	..	..	9 50	..	..	..	..	..	10 21	..	..	..	..								
Redhill 246	8 49	..	..	..	..	..	..	9 29	..	..	..	9 57	9 50	..	..	..	..	10 27	1049	..	..	..								
Merstham	..	..	..	..	..	..	..	9 33	..	..	..	10 1	..	..	..	..	..	10 31	..	..	..	..								
Coulsdon South	..	..	..	..	..	..	..	9 39	..	..	..	10 7	..	..	..	..	..	10 37	..	..	..	..								
Purley	..	..	..	..	..	..	..	9 42	..	..	..	1011	..	..	..	..	..	10 41	..	..	..	..								
East Croydon 285 ....arr.	9 3	..	..	..	..	..	9 20	9 48	..	9 42	..	1016	10 4	..	..	..	..	10 47	11 3	..	..	..								
Norwood Junction B arr.	9*11	..	..	..	..	..	..	9 52	..	9*52	..	1021	10*21	..	..	..	..	10§55	..	..	..	..								
New Cross Gate ...."	9*22	..	..	..	..	..	..	10 1	..	10*1	..	1030	10*30	..	..	..	..	11§4	..	..	..	..								
LONDON BRIDGE ..."	9*28	..	..	..	..	..	..	10 7	..	10*7	..	1035	10*35	..	..	..	..	11§10	..	..	..	..								
Clapham Junction A ..arr.	9 15	..	..	..	..	..	..	10*15	..	..	..	..	10 15	..	..	..	..	10 59	1115	..	..	..								
VICTORIA ...."	9 22	..	..	..	9 25	..	9 40	10*20	..	9 59	..	..	10 20	10 25	..	..	..	11 4	1120	..	..	..								

§ Third class only
* Change at East Croydon.
A Mid Battersea, 1¼ mls. to Clapham
a Arrival time
B Norwood Junc. & South Norwood, for Woodside
C Station for Cuckfield (2 miles)
D Station for Hurstpierpoint (1½ miles)
F Station for Willingdon (1½ miles)
G Over ½ mile to Bexhill West Station
H Nearly 1½ miles to Dorking Town & under ¼ mile to Deepdene Stas.
J Station for Storrington (5 miles)
K Station for Lancing College (2 miles).
L Angmering & Angmering-on-Sea
N Ham Bridge Halt for East Worthing.

Local Trains and intermediate Stations

BETWEEN	PAGE
Sutton & London	285, 322
Redhill & East Croydon	285
East Croydon & London	285

Other Trains

Portsmouth & Fratton	380
Portsmouth, Havant and London	366
Christ's Hospital & Horsham	244, 245
Horsham & London	285, 427
Dorking Town & London	249
Ore & Hastings	58
Hastings, Bexhill West and London	56
Eastbourne, Polegate and London	239
Haywards Heath & Horsted Keynes	239

P Pullman Car facilities available **R** Refreshment Car facilities available. **U** Station for West Tarring (1 mile).
Z Station for Bracklesham Bay, East and West Wittering and Selsey. Frequent service by Southdown Bus.

For Return Journey, see pages 158 to 195

LONDON, TUNBRIDGE WELLS WEST, EAST GRINSTEAD, BRIGHTON, and EASTBOURNE

Miles from London Bg	Down	Week Days																				
		a.m	am	a.m	a.m	a.m	a.m	a.m	a.m	a.m	a.m	a.m	a.m	a.m	a.m	a.m	a.m	a.m	am	a.m	a.m	a.m
	Victoria ... dep						5 20	5 B51	6 30						7 47			8*0		9 8		
	Clapham Junction ... "						5 28	5 B56	6 37						7 52			8*5				
	London Bridge ... "						5*25	6 16	6 B35			7 20			7 B35			8 3		9*0		
	New Cross Gate ... "						5*31	6 21												9*5		
—	East Croydon ... dep						5 49	6 35	6 54			7 39			8 5			8 25		9 28		
11¼	South Croydon ...						5 54											8 30		9 32		
11¾	Selsdon ...																	8 32				
12¾	Sanderstead ...								7 2									8 35		9 36		
13¾	Riddlesdown ...																	8 40		9 41		
15½	Upper Warlingham ...						6 3		7 10									8 46		9 47		
17	Woldingham ...						6 8		7 16									8 51		9 53		
20¼	Oxted B ... arr						6 15		7 23									8 58		10 0		
—	Oxted ... dep						6 17			7 36									9 9	10 2		1055
21½	Hurst Green Halt ...									7 38									911			1057
23¼	Monks Lane Halt ¶ ...																					
25¼	Edenbridge Town C ...						6 29			7 47									919	1012		11 6
27¼	Hever ...						6 33			7 51									923	1016		1110
29¼	Cowden ...						6 38			7 56									928	1021		1115
32	Ashurst ...						6 45			8 3									934	1027		1121
34¼	Groombridge 239 *& below* ...						6 50			8 6									938	1034		1125
36¼	High Rocks Halt ...									8 11									943			1130
37¼	Tunbridge Wells West arr						7 1			8 14									946	1041		1133
—	Ashurst ... dep																					
—	Eridge *(below)* ... arr						Stop			Stop										Stop		Stop
—	Oxted ... dep								7 25									8 59			10 7	
21½	Hurst Green Halt ...								7 29									9 2			10 9	
26½	Lingfield ...								7 40									9 11			1018	
27¾	Dormans ...								7 45									9 16			1023	
29¾	East Grinstead 239 ... arr								7 52									9 23			1030	
29½	Three Bridges ... dep					7 8		7 32				8 32			9 6							
31¼	Rowfant ...					7 14		7 38				8 38			9 12							
33½	Grange Road D ...					7 18		7 42				8 43			9 16							
36	East Grinstead 239 ... arr					7 24		7 48				8 48			9 23					a.m		
—	East Grinstead ... dep					7 25		Stop	8 11											9 33	1042	
33	Forest Row F ...					7 33			8 20			Stop	Saturdays only		Stop					9 42	1049	
36½	Hartfield ...								8 28											9 50	1057	
37¾	Withyham ...					Stop			8 32											9 53	11 0	
40½	Groombridge 239 *& below* ...								8 40											10 1	11 6	
42½	High Rocks Halt ...																					
43¼	Tunbridge Wells West arr								8 48			a.m								10 9	1113	
—	East Grinstead ... dep	6 38					Dep Sevenoaks 6 9 a.m., see pages 54 and 54a		Stop	Dep. Tonbridge 7 25 a.m., see pages 51 and 54a	8 13	8 13	8 13					9 37				
31½	Kingscote ...	6 43									8 18	8 18	8 18					9 42				
33½	West Hoathly ...	6 48									8 23	8 23	8 23	8 52				9 47				
36	Horsted Keynes ...	6 54						a.m			8 28	8 28	8 28	8 57				9 53				
—	Horsted Keynes ... dep		Saturdays excepted	7 20	7 20			7 58			8 30	8 30	8 30	8 57		9 21						
38½	Ardingly ...			7 24	7 24			8 2			8 34	8 34	8 34	9 3		9 25						
40½	Haywards Heath G 197 arr			7 28	7 28			8 6			8 38	8 38	8 38	9 8	a.m	9 30						
	dep			7 30	7 34			8 18			8 40	8 44	8 58	9 12	9 23	9 30	9 33					
43½	Wivelsfield ...			7 34	7 38			8 22			8 45	8 48		9 16		9 34						
44½	Burgess Hill ...			7 37	Arr. Lewes 7 55 a.m			8 25				8 51				9 37						
46½	Hassocks H ...			7 41				8 29				8 55				9 41						
52½	Preston Park ...			7 49				8 38				9 3	9 15		9 37	9 49						
53½	Brighton 159 ... arr			7 52				8 41	a.m			9 6	9 19		9 41	9 52						
40½	Sheffield Park ...	7 7							8 0									10 2				
42½	Newick and Chailey ...	7 13		Stop				Stop	8 5							Stop		10 8				
45½	Barcombe W ...	7 20				a.m	a.m		8 11	a.m						a.m		1014				a.m
—	Tunbridge Wells West dep	Arr. Lewes 7 34 a.m	630			6 54	6 54			7 53		Saturdays excepted				9 0	Saturdays only	Arr. Lewes 10 24 a.m				1030
—	High Rocks Halt ...																					
—	Groombridge *(above)* ...		635			7 2	7 7			8 1						9 12						1038
36½	Eridge *(above)* ...		641			7 8	7 15			8 6						9 17						1044
40	Crowboro' & Jarvis Brook					Arr. Mayfield at 7 28 a.m	7 23			8 14												1051
44½	Buxted ...						7 34			8 24												11 1
47	Uckfield ...						7 41			8 30						Arr. Polegate 10 23 a.m						11 6
49¾	Isfield ...						7 48			8 36												1111
51¾	Barcombe Mills Q ...						7 55			8 42												1117
55½	Lewes 158, 197 ...	7 45			7 59		8 5		8 21	8 51	9 2			9 33			9 50	1034				1126
60	Falmer ...																					
62¾	London Road (Brighton) ...	7 59					8 20		8 35	9 6								1051				
63½	Brighton 159 ... arr	8 4					8 24		8 39	9 10								1055				1143
39½	Rotherfield and Mark Cross	Stop	649			7 16										9 25						
42½	Mayfield ...		658			7 33			Stop							9 34						Stop
46½	Heathfield ...	a.m	710			7 46										9 46						
48¾	Waldron and Horam ...	6 40				7 55										10 1						
52½	Hellingly ...	6 47		a.m		8 5		a.m	a.m							1010						a.m
54	Hailsham ...	7 0		7 33		8 11		8 45	9 38							1015						1119
57	Polegate 158, 197 ...	7 8		7 40		8 24		8 52	9 47							1028						1127
59½	Hampden Park L ...	7 13		7 45	8 20	8 30		8 56	9 50							1033						1132
61½	Eastbourne ... arr	7 18		7 50	8 24	8 35		9 1	9 54							1038	10 9					1137

For Notes, see page 243

LONDON, TUNBRIDGE WELLS WEST, EAST GRINSTEAD, BRIGHTON, and EASTBOURNE

Down	Week Days—*continued*																				
	a.m	p.m	p.m	a.m	p.m	p.m	p.m	p.m	p.m	p.m	p.m	p.m	p.m	p.m	p.m	p.m	p.m	p.m	p.m	p.m	p.m
Victoria ....dep	9 48	..	..	11 8	..	12 3	..	12*3	12*18	12*25	..	12*48	..	..	1 25	1*28	1*45	1*28	..	..	..
Clapham Junction ,,	9 53	..	..	..	..	..	..	..	..	..	..	12*U53	..	..	..	1*U34	1*34	1*34	..	..	..
London Bridge ,,	1016	..	..	..	..	..	..	1218	12 20	12 30	..	12 47	..	1 18	1*16	1 40	1 42	1 31	..	..	..
New Cross Gate ,,	..	..	..	..	..	..	..	..	..	..	..	..	..	..	..	..	..	..	..	..	..
East Croydon ....dep	1032	..	..	1127	..	1221	..	1236	12 38	12 47	..	1 5	..	1 35	1 42	1 55	2 0	2 1	..	..	..
South Croydon	..	..	..	..	..	1225	..	..	12 42	..	..	..	..	..	..	..	2 3	2 3	..	..	..
Selsdon	..	..	..	..	..	..	..	..	12 45	..	..	..	..	..	..	..	..	..	..	..	..
Sanderstead	..	..	..	1133	..	1229	..	..	12 48	..	..	1 11	..	Saturdays excepted	1 48	Saturdays only	2 7	2 7	..	..	..
Riddlesdown	..	..	..	1138	..	1234	..	..	12 53	..	..	1 16	..		1 53		2 12	2 12	..	..	..
Upper Warlingham	..	..	..	1144	..	1240	..	..	12 59	..	..	1 22	..		1 58		2 18	2 18	..	..	..
Woldingham	..	..	..	1149	..	1245	..	..	1 4	..	..	1 27	..		2 3		2 22	2 22	..	..	..
Oxted B ....arr	..	..	..	1156	..	1252	..	..	1 11	..	..	1 34	..		2 10		2 29	2 29	..	..	..
Oxted ....dep	..	..	..	1158	..	..	1258	..	1 12		..		..	..		..	2 30	2 30	..	..	
Hurst Green Halt	..	..	..	12 1	..	..	1 0	..	1 15		..		..	..		..	..	2 33	..	..	
Monks Lane Halt ¶	..	..	..	..	..	..	..	Saturdays excepted	..		..	Saturdays only	..	..	Saturdays only	..	..	..	..	..	Saturdays only
Edenbridge Town C	..	..	..	1210	..	..	1 9		1 24		..		..	..		..	2 40	2 42	..	..	
Hever	..	..	..	1214	..	..	1 13		1 2[illegible]		..		..	..		..	2 44	2 46	..	..	
Cowden	..	..	..	1219	..	..	1 18		1 33	Saturdays only	..		..	..		..	2 49	2 51	..	..	
Ashurst	..	..	..	1225	..	..	1 24		1 39		..		..	..		..	2 55	2 57	..	..	
Groombridge 239 & *below*	..	..	..	1231	..	..	1 28		1 45		..		..	..		..	3 1	3 3	..	..	
High Rocks Halt	..	..	..	..	..	..	1 33	..	..		..		..	..		..	..	..	..	..	
Tunbridge Wells West arr	..	..	..	1239	..	..	1 36	..	1 52		..		..	..		..	3 8	3 10	..	..	
Ashurst ....dep	..	..	..	Stop	..	..	..	..			..		..	..		..			..	..	
Eridge (*below*) ....arr	..	..	..		..	..	..	..			..		..	..		..			..	..	
Oxted ....dep	..	..	..	..	..	1253	..	..			..	1 36	..	..	2 11	..			..	..	2 34
Hurst Green Halt	..	..	..	..	..	1256	..	..			..	..	..	..	2 13	..			..	..	2 36
Lingfield	..	..	..	..	..	1 5	..	..			..	1 45	..	..	2 22	..			..	..	2 46
Dormans	..	..	..	..	..	1 10	..	..			..	1 50	..	..	2 27	..	Saturdays only	Saturdays excepted	..	..	2 50
East Grinstead 239 ....arr	..	..	..	..	..	1 17	..	..			..	1 57	..	..	2 34	..			..	..	2 56
Three Bridges ....dep	1121	..	..	..	..	..	..	1 20	Saturdays only	1 20		..	..	2 39	..	2 39			..	..	..
Rowfant	1127	..	..	..	..	..	..	1 26		1 26		..	..	2 45	..	2 45			..	..	..
Grange Road D	1132	..	..	..	..	..	..	1 31		1 31		..	..	2 49	..	2 49			..	..	..
East Grinstead 239 arr	1138	..	..	..	..	..	..	1 37		1 37		..	..	2 55	..	2 55			..	..	..
East Grinstead ....dep	Stop	..	..	..	..	..	..	..		..	Saturdays excepted	1 58	..	2 57	2 35	2 57			..	..	3 15
Forest Row F	..	..	..	..	..	..	..	..		..		2 6	..	3 5	2h48	3 5		Stop	..	..	3 22
Hartfield	..	..	..	..	..	..	..	..	Stop	..		2 14	..	3 13	2 57	3 13		..	..	..	3 30
Withyham	..	..	..	..	..	..	..	..	..	..		2 18	..	3 16	3 1	3 16	Stop	..	..	..	3 34
Groombridge 239 & *below*	..	..	..	..	..	..	..	..	..	..		2 26	..	3 23	3 9	3 23		..	..	..	3 41
High Rocks Halt	..	..	..	..	..	..	..	..	..	..		..	..	..	..	..	..	..	..	..	..
Tunbridge Wells West arr	..	..	..	..	..	..	..	..	..	..		2 33	..	3 31	3 17	3 31	p.m	..	..	..	3 48
East Grinstead ....dep	..	..	..	..	..	1 30	..	..	..	..		Stop	..	Stop	..	Stop	3 0	..	..	..	..
Kingscote	..	..	..	..	..	1 35	..	..	..	..		..	..	..	..		3 5	..	..	..	..
West Hoathly	..	..	..	..	..	1 40	..	..	..	..		..	..	..	..		3 9	..	..	..	..
Horsted Keynes	p.m	..	..	p.m	..	1 47	..	..	p.m	..		..	..	..	..		3 14	p.m	..	..	..
Horsted Keynes ....dep	1216	..	..	1 16	..	..	..	..	2 16	..	2 16	..	..	..	..	Arr. Lewes 2 57 p.m	..	3 16	..	..	..
Ardingly	1220	..	..	1 20	..	..	..	..	2 20	..	2 20	..	..	..	..		..	3 20	..	..	..
Haywards Heath G 197 arr	1224	..	..	1 24	..	..	..	..	2 24	..	2 24	p.m	..	p.m	..		..	3 24	..	..	..
Haywards Heath G 197 dep	1228	1233	..	1 28	1 33	..	..	..	2 27	..	2 28	2 33	..	2 35	..		..	3 28	3 33	3 35	..
Wivelsfield	1232	..	..	1 32	..	..	..	..	..	..	2 32	..	..	2 39	..		..	3 32	..	..	..
Burgess Hill	1235	..	..	1 35	..	..	..	..	..	..	2 35	..	..	..	..		..	3 35	..	..	..
Hassocks H	1239	..	..	1 39	..	..	..	..	..	..	2 39	Saturdays only	..	..	..		..	3 39	..	..	..
Preston Park	1247	..	..	1 47	..	..	..	..	2 42	..	2 47		..	..	..		..	3 47	..	..	..
Brighton 159 ....arr	1250	..	..	1 50	..	..	..	..	2 45	..	2 5[illegible]		..	..	..	..	..	3 50	..	..	..
Sheffield Park		..	..		..	2 1	..	..		..	Stop		..	..	..		3 22	..	..	..	..
Newick and Chailey	Stop	..	..	Stop	..	2 8	..	..		..			..	..	..		3 28	..	..	..	..
Barcombe W	..	..	..	p.m	..	2 15	..	..		..	..		..	..	..	p.m	3 34	..	..	..	..
Tunbridge Wells West dp	..	..	1228	1236	..	..	..	..	Saturdays only	..	..		1 54	Saturdays excepted	..	2 2	..	..	Saturdays only	Saturdays excepted	..
High Rocks Halt	..	..	..	..	..	..	..	..		..	..	..	..		..	2 5	..	..			..
Groombridge (*above*)	..	..	1235	1242	..	Arr. Lewes 2 26 p.m	..	..		..	..	..	2 0		..	2 9	Arr Lewes 3 45 p.m	..			..
Eridge (*above*)	..	..	1240	1247	..		..	..		..	..	..	2 7		..	2 14		..			..
Crowboro' & Jarvis Brook	..	..	..	1254	..		..	..		..	..	..	..		..	2 21		..			..
Buxted	..	..	..	1 4	..		..	..		..	..	..	..		..	2 31		..			..
Uckfield	..	..	..	1 12	..		..	..		..	..	..	..	..	..	2 36		..			..
Isfield	..	..	..	1 18	..		..	..		..	..	..	..	..	..	2 42		..			..
Barcombe Mills Q	..	..	..	1 25	..		..	..		..	..	..	..	..	..	2 48		..			..
Lewes 158, 197	..	1250	..	1 36	1 49	2 34	..	..		..	..	2 54	..	3 1	..	3 17	3 47	..	3 50	4 1	..
Falmer	..	..	..	..	..	..	..	..	..	..	..	..	..	..	..	3 24	3 54	..	..	..	..
London Road (Brighton)	..	..	..	1 51	..	2 50	..	..	..	..	..	..	..	..	..	3 29	3 58	..	..	..	..
Brighton 159 ....arr	..	..	..	1 55	..	2 54	..	..	..	..	..	..	..	..	..	3 31	4 1	..	..	..	..
Rotherfield and Mark Cross	..	..	1248	..	..	Stop	..	..	..	..	..	..	2 15	Arr. Lewes 2 55 p.m	..	Stop	..	..	..	Arr. Lewes 3 55 p.m	..
Mayfield	..	..	1257	..	..		..	..	..	..	..	..	2 24		..		..	..	..		..
Heathfield	..	..	1 10	..	..	..	..	..	..	..	..	..	2 36		..	..	..	..	..		..
Waldron and Horam	..	..	1 20	..	..	..	..	..	..	..	..	..	2 45		..	..	..	..	..		..
Hellingly	p.m	..	1 30	..	..	p.m	..	..	..	..	p.m	..	2 53		..	p.m	..	..	..		..
Hailsham	1 14	..	1 35	..	..	2 0	..	..	..	..	2 37	..	2 58		..	3 30	..	..	..		..
Polegate 158, 197	1 24	..	1 47	..	..	2p 7	..	..	..	..	2 47	..	3p 6		..	3 37	..	..	..		..
Hampden Park L	1 30	..	1 50	..	..	2p11	..	..	..	..	2 50	..	3p11		..	3 41	..	..	..	..	..
Eastbourne ....arr	1 35	1 9	1 54	..	2 11	2p16	..	..	..	..	2 54	3 13	3p16	3 26	..	3 46	..	..	4 9	4 26	..

For Notes, see page 243; for Continuation of Trains, see pages 236 to 238

LONDON, TUNBRIDGE WELLS WEST, EAST GRINSTEAD, BRIGHTON, and EASTBOURNE

Week Days—*continued*

Down	p.m	p.m	p.m	p.m	p.m	p.m	p.m	p.m	p.m	p.m	p.m	p.m	p.m	p.m	p.m	p.m	p.m	p.m	p.m	p.m	p.m
Victoria dep	2 30						2 48		3 55	3 55	3 48		4*16			4 25					4*16
Clapham Junction "	2‖37						2‖53				3 53		4‖*22								4‖*22
London Bridge "	2Ⓢd31						2ⓈSX31		3Ⓢ51	3Ⓢ51	3Ⓢ31	4 18	4 20			4*20					4 20
New Cross Gate "																					
East Croydon dep	2 52						3 5		4‖12	4‖12	4 5	4 35	4 39			4 40					4 42
South Croydon	2 56											4 38									4 46
Selsdon																					
Sanderstead	3 0											4 42									4 50
Riddlesdown	3 5											4 46									4 54
Upper Warlingham	3 11											4 52									5 0
Woldingham	3 16											4 57									5 5
Oxted R arr	3 23								4 28	4 28		5 4	4 56								5 12
Oxted dep	3 25								4 28	4 28											5 13
Hurst Green Halt																					5 16
Monks Lane Halt ¶																					
Edenbridge Town C	3 36							Saturdays excepted	4 38	4 38	Saturdays only	Saturdays only	Saturdays excepted			Saturdays excepted					5 25
Hever	3 40																				5 28
Cowden	3 45																				5 33
Ashurst	3 51																				5 38
Groombridge 239 & *below*	3 57								5‖4	5‖4											5 45
High Rocks Halt																					
Tunbridge Wells West arr	4 5								5‖11	5‖11											5 52
Ashurst dep	Stop																				
Eridge (*below*) arr									4 53	4 53											
Oxted dep		3 35						4 10				5 5	4 56								Saturdays excepted
Hurst Green Halt		3 37						4 12				5 8	4 59								
Lingfield		3 46						4 21				5 17	5 8								
Dormans		3 51						4 26				5 21	5 13								
East Grinstead 239 arr		3 58						4 33				5 28	5 20								
Three Bridges dep							3 48				5 9					5 9					Stop
Rowfant							3 54				5 15					5 15					
Grange Road D							3 58				5 19					5 19					
East Grinstead 239 arr							4 4				5 26					5 26					
East Grinstead dep							Stop	4 33			5 32					5 32					
Forest Row F								4h46			5 39					5 39					
Hartfield								4 54			5 47					5 47					
Withyham					Saturdays excepted	Saturdays only	Sats. excepted	4 58			5 50			Saturdays excepted	Saturdays only	5 50	Saturdays only	Saturdays excepted	Saturdays excepted	Saturdays only	Saturdays excepted
Groombridge 239 & *below*								5 7			5 58					5 58					
High Rocks Halt								5 14													
Tunbridge Wells West arr								5 18			6 6					6 6					
East Grinstead dep		3 59						Stop				5 30	5 30			Stop					
Kingscote		4 5										5 37	5 37								
West Hoathly		4 10										5 43	5 43								
Horsted Keynes		4 16										5 49	5 49								p.m
Horsted Keynes dep			4 17		4 45	4 45								6 0	6 0		6 16	6 16			6 40
Ardingly			4 21		4 50	4 50								6 4	6 4		6 20	6 20			6 44
Haywards Heath G 197 arr			4 25		4 56	4 56	p.m					Arr. Sheffield Park 5 59 p.m	Arr. Sheffield Park 5 59 p.m	6 8	6 8	p.m	6 24	6 24			6 49
Haywards Heath G 197 dep			4 28	4 33	4 59	5 1	5 5							6 13	6 23	6 17	6 28	6 33	6 31	6 35	6 56
Wivelsfield			4 32			5 5	5 9										6 32	6 38			
Burgess Hill			4 35			5 8	5 12									6 23	6 35	6 40			7 2
Hassocks H			4 39			5 12	5 16									6 27	6 39	6 44			7 6
Preston Park			4 47			5 20	5 24								6 37	6 35	6 47				7 14
Brighton 159 arr			4 50			5 23	5 27							6 29	6 41	6 39	6 50	6 55			7 17
Sheffield Park		4 29				Stop	Stop					6 4	6 4								
Newick and Chailey		4 34										6 12	6 12								
Barcombe W	p.m	4 42						p.m				6 21	6 21								
Tunbridge Wells West dep	3 11							4 37													
High Rocks Halt																					
Groombridge (*above*)	3 17							4 45													
Eridge (*above*)	3 22							4 49	4 54	4 58											
Crowboro' & Jarvis Brook	3 29								5 2												
Buxted	3 38								5 12												
Uckfield	3 43						Saturdays excepted		5 17	Arr. Polegate 5 59 p.m						Saturdays excepted				Arr. Lewes 6 55 p.m	
Isfield	3 49								5 23												
Barcombe Mills Q	3 54								5 28												
Lewes 158, 197	4 17	4 53		4 50	5 16				5 37			6 37	6 37						6 51	7 1	
Falmer	4 24																				
London Road (Brighton)	4 28	5 9							5 52			6 52	6 52								
Brighton 159 arr	4 31	5 13							5 56			6 56	6 56								
Rotherfield and Mark Cross		Stop							Stop	5 6		Stop									
Mayfield										5 15											
Heathfield	Arr. Lewes 4 3 p.m									5 28											
Waldron and Horam		p.m								5 33											
Hellingly		4z31				p.m			p.m	5 44		p.m									
Hailsham		4 36				5 21	p.m		5 44	5 49		6 50									
Polegate 158, 197		4l46				5 28	5 33		5 51	6 5		6 57									
Hampden Park L		4 50					5 37		5 56	6 11		7 2									
Eastbourne arr		4 54		5 11	5 41		5 41		6 1	6 16		7 7							7 14	7 27	

For Notes, see page 243

LONDON, TUNBRIDGE WELLS WEST, EAST GRINSTEAD, BRIGHTON, and EASTBOURNE

Down	Week Days—continued																			
	p.m	p.m	p.m	p.m	p.m	p.m	p.m	p.m	p.m	p.m	p.m	p.m	p.m	p.m	p.m	p.m	p.m	p.m	p.m	p.m
Victoria ... dep	4[R]35	4 48	4 50	....	....	5 9	....	5[R]32	5 50	6 10	6 10	6 10	6 10	....	6 48	6 53	7* 5	....	....	7*45
Clapham Junction ... "	4[R]40	4 53	..	..	..	..	..	..	..	....	..	....	6 16	..	6U53	..	7*U10	..	..	..
London Bridge ... "	4 40	4[R]31	4[R]a54		5 15	5r12	5 20	5 40	5A50	6* 9	6* 9	6 * 9	..	6 30	6*48	6[R]51	6[R]55	....	....	7 42
New Cross Gate ... "	....	....	..	..	..	..	..	..	..	....	..	..	..	..	..	..	..	..	..	..
East Croydon ... dep	4 57	5 5	5 10	....		5 28	5 38	5 57	6 8	6 29	6 29	6 33	6 31	6 47	7 10	7 11	7 24		....	8 0
South Croydon ...	....	....	..	..		5 32	5 42	..	..	....	..	....	..	..	7 15	7 15	..		..	8 3
Selsdon ...	..	..	....	....	....	..	....	..	....	..	....	..	..	....	..	..	....		....	..
Sanderstead ...	5 3	....	5 16	..	Saturdays excepted	5 35	5 46	6 3	6 14	....	..	6 40	6 38	6 55	7 19	7 19	7 30	Saturdays only	..	8 7
Riddlesdown ...	5 8	..	5 21	....		5 39	5 51	6 8	6 19	..	....	6 45	6 43	7 0	7 24	7 24	7 35		....	8 12
Upper Warlingham ...	5 14	....	5 27	..		5 45	5 57	6 14	6 25	....	..	6 51	6 49	7 6	7 30	7 30	7 40		.	8 18
Woldingham ...	5 18	..	5 31	....		5 50	6 2	6 18	6 30	..	....	6 56	6 54	7 11	7 35	7 35	7 45		....	8 23
Oxted B ... arr	5 25	....	5 38	..		5 57	6 9	6 25	6 37	6 48	6 48	7 3	7 1	7 18	7 42	7 42	7 52		..	8 30
Oxted ... dep	5 26		5 38	....		..	6 10		....	6 49	6 49	7 4	7 2				7 53	7 53	....	....
Hurst Green Halt ...	5 29		..	..		..	..		..	....	....	7 7	7 5				7 56	7 56	..	..
Monks Lane Halt ¶ ...	..		....	....	....	..	....		....	..	..	..	..				....	....	....	....
Edenbridge Town C ...	5 38	Saturdays only	5 48	..	..	..	6 22	Saturdays excepted	..	6 59	6 59	7 16	7 14	Saturdays excepted	Saturdays excepted	Saturdays only	8 6	8 6	..	Saturdays only
Hever ...	..		5 52	....	....	..	6 26		....	..	..	7 20	7 18				8 10	8 10	....	
Cowden ...	....		5 56	╯	..	..	6 30		..	....	....	7 25	7 23				8 15	8 15	.	
Ashurst ...	..		6 2	6 7	....	..	6 36		....	..	..	7T22	7L32				8 21	8 21	....	
Groombridge 239 *& below* ...	....		..	6 14	..	..	6 42		..	7‖22	7‖22	7 39	7 39				8 27	8 27	..	
High Rocks Halt ...	..		....	....	....	..	....		....	....	....	7 47	7 47					Stop	....	
Tunbridge Wells West arr	....		..	6 21	..	..	6 50		..	7‖29	7‖29	7 51	7 51						..	
Ashurst ... dep	..	..	6 3	Stop	....	..			....	..	..	..		..	....	..		....	....	
Eridge (*below*) ... arr	5 53	....	6 9		..	..			..	7 14	7 14	....		..	..	..		..	..	
Oxted ... dep		..	....	..	....	5 59		6 26	6 38					7 19	7 43	7 43		....	....	8 31
Hurst Green Halt ...		....	..	..	..	6 2		..	6 41					7K22	7 46	..		..	..	8 34
Lingfield ...	Saturdays excepted	..	....	..	....	6 10	Saturdays excepted	6 35	6 49	Saturdays excepted	Saturdays excepted	Saturdays excepted	Saturdays only	7 30	7 54	7 53	Saturdays excepted	....	....	8 44
Dormans ...		....	..	..	..	6 14		6 40	6 55					7 36	8 0	7 59		..	..	8 49
East Grinstead 239 ... arr		..	....	..	....	6 21		6 47	7 2					7 44	8 8	8 7		....	....	8 56
Three Bridges ... dep		5 56	..	..	6 3	..		Stop	..					..	Stop	..		..	..	..
Rowfant ...		6 2	....	..	6 9	..			....					....		..		....	....	....
Grange Road D ...		6 6	..	..	6 14	..	Stop	..	..					..	..	..		..	..	..
East Grinstead 239 .. arr		6 12	....	..	6 23	..		..	....				Stop	....	....	..		....	....	....
East Grinstead ... dep	....	6 12	..	..	6 24	6SX24		..	7 3	..	..	..		7 45	..	8 10	Stop	..	..	..
Forest Row F ...	..	6 20	....	....	6 32	6SX32		..	7 11	....	....	....	..	7 53	....	8 20		....	....	....
Hartfield ...	....	Stop	..	..	Stop	Stop	..	..	7 19	..	..	..	..	8 1	..	8 25	..	..	..	..
Withyham ...	..		....	....			..	..	7 23	....	....	....	..	8 5	....	8 31	....	....	....	....
Groombridge 239 *& below* ..	....	....	..	..	..	..	..	..	7 31	..	..	..	..	8 13	..	8 39	..	..	..	..
High Rocks Halt ...	..	..	....	....	....	..	....	..	....	....	....	....	..	....	....	..	....	....	....	....
Tunbridge Wells West arr	....	....	..	..	..	..	..	..	7 38	..	..	..	..	8 20	..	8 46	..	..	..	..
East Grinstead ... dep	..	..	....	....	....	....	....	..	7 7	..	..	..	....	Stop	....	..	....	....	....	9 15
Kingscote ...	....	....	..	..	..	..	..	..	7 12	....	....	....	..	..	..	..	..	..	..	9 20
West Hoathly ...	..	..	....	....	....	....	....	..	7 18	..	..	..	....	....	....	..	....	....	....	9 26
Horsted Keynes ...	....	p.m	..	..	p.m	..	p.m	p.m	7 26	....	....	....	..	..	..	..	p.m	p.m	..	9 32
Horsted Keynes ... dep	..	6 40	....	....	6 40	..	7 16	7 16	....	..	..	..			....	..	8 55	9 16	....	9 32
Ardingly ...	....	6 44	..	..	6 44	..	7 20	7 20	..	....	....	....			..	..	..	9 20	..	9 38
Haywards Heath G 197 arr	..	6 49	....	....	6 49	..	7 24	7 24	....	..	..	..	Saturdays excepted	Saturdays only	....	..	....	9 24	....	9 44
Haywards Heath G 197 dep	....	7 0	..	..	6 50	..	7 28	7 32	..	....	....	....			..	..	..	9 28	9 35	10 0
Wivelsfield ...	..	7 4	....	....	6 54	..	7 33	..	....	..	..	..			....	..	....	9 33	....	10 5
Burgess Hill ...	....	7 7	..	..	..	..	7 35	..	..	....	....	....			..	..	..	9 35	..	10 7
Hassocks H ...	..	7 11	....	....	....	..	7 39	..	....	..	..	..			....	..	....	9 39	....	1011
Preston Park ...	....	7 19	..	..	..	..	7 47	..	..	....	....	....			..	..	..	9 47	..	1019
Brighton 159 ... arr	..	7 22	....	....	....	..	7 51	..	....	..	..	..			....	..	....	9 51	....	1023
Sheffield Park ...	....		..	..	..	p.m			7 38	....	....	....			..	..	9 3	..	..	..
Newick and Chailey ...	..		....	....	....	7 21			7 44	..	..	..			....	..	9 8	....	....	..
Barcombe W ...	....		..	p.m	..	7 27			7 49	....	....	....	p.m	p.m	p.m	..	9 15	..	..	..
Tunbridge Wells West dep	..		....	5 55		....			....	..	7 8	..	7 37	7 37	7 50	..	....	....	....	..
High Rocks Halt ...	....		..	..		..			..	....	..	....	..	..	..	..	..	..	..	..
Groombridge (*above*) ...	..		....	6 1					....	..	7 14	..	7 44	7 44	7 57	..	....	....	....	..
Eridge (*above*) ...	5 54		6 11	6 12					..	7 15	7 20	....	7 49	7 49	8 2	..	..	..	..	..
Crowboro' & Jarvis Brook	6 2	Saturdays only	6 20	╯	Saturdays excepted	Arr. Lewes 7 37 p.m	Saturdays excepted	Saturdays excepted	....	7 23	..	..	7 57	7 57	..	..	....	....	....	..
Buxted ...	6 12		6 30						..	7 33	....	....	8 7	8 7	..	..	..	..	..	..
Uckfield ...	6 17		6 38	Arr. Eridge 6 6 p.m				..	....	7 38	..	..	8 14	8 14	..	..	....	....	....	..
Isfield ...	....		6 44					..	..	....	....	....	8 20	8 20	..	..	..	..	..	..
Barcombe Mills Q ...	..		6 50					..	....	..	..	..	8 26	8 26	..	..	....	....	....	..
Lewes 158, 197 ...	....		7 0		7 12	7 50		7 49	7 58	....	....	....	8 35	8 48	..	..	9 25	..	10 1	..
Falmer ...	..		....		....	7 57	....	..	....	..	..	..	....	8 55	..	..	....	....	....	..
London Road (Brighton) ..	....		7 15		..	8 2	..	..	..	....	....	....	8 50	8 59	..	..	..	..	..	..
Brighton 159 ... arr	..		7 19		....	8 5	....	..	....	.	..	..	8 55	9 2	..	..	9 42	....	....	..
Rotherfield and Mark Cross	....	....	....	6 20	..	..	..	..	..	....	7 28	....	..		8 10	..	Stop	..		..
Mayfield ...	..	..	..	6 29	....	....	....	..	....	..	7 37	..	....		8h25	..		....		..
Heathfield ...	....	....	....	6 42	..	..	..	..	..	....	7 50	....	..		8 37	..	....	..		..
Waldron and Horam ...	..	..	..	6 50	....	....	....	..	....	..	..	..	....	Arrive Lewes 8 35 p.m	8h53	..	..	....	Arr Lewes 9 55 p.m	..
Hellingly ...	....	....	....	6 57	..	..	..	..	..	....	....	....	..		9 4	..	p.m	..		..
Hailsham ...	..	..	..	7 2	....	....	....	..	....	..	..	..	....		9 9	..	9 45	....		..
Polegate 158, 197 ...	....	....	....	7 10	..	..	..	..	..	....	....	....	..		9 19	..	9 53	..		..
Hampden Park L ...	..	..	..	....	....	....	....	..	....	..	..	..	....		9 22	..	9 58	....		..
Eastbourne ... arr	....	....	....	7 18	7 37	..	..	8 8	..	....	....	....	..		9 26	..	10 3	..	1026	..

For Notes, see page 243; for Continuation of Trains, see page 238.

LONDON, TUNBRIDGE WELLS WEST, EAST GRINSTEAD, BRIGHTON, and EASTBOURNE

Down	Week Days—*contd.*						Sundays															
	p.m	p.m	p.m	p.m	p.m	p.m	a.m	a.m	a.m	a.m	a.m	a.m	p.m	pm	pm	pm	p.m	pm	p.m	p.m	p.m	p.m
Victoria .... dep	7 48	8 2	..	9 20	1030	1030	8 28	8*28	8 50	..	..	1030	..	..	..	..	2 30	..	6 48	6*48	7 8	9 20
Clapham Junction .... "	7U53	..	..	9 26	1037	1037	8 33	8*33	8 57	..	..	1037	..	..	..	..	2 37	..	6 53	6*53	7 15	9 26
London Bridge .... "	7y31	7Ⓑ51		9*16	10Ⓑ31	10Ⓑ31	8 16	8 36	8*49	..	..	10Ⓑ30		..	..	..	2Ⓑ30		6*40	6 40	7Ⓑ0	9*16
New Cross Gate	7Y36	..	..	..	..	..	8 21	..	..	..	..	10Ⓑ35		..	..	..	2Ⓑ35		6*47	6 47	7Ⓑ5	9*21
East Croydon .... dep	8 5	8 23	..	9 41	1052	1052	8 46	8 58	9 14	..	..	1053	..	..	..	..	3 0	..	7 5	7 6	7 31	9 42
South Croydon	..	8 27	..	..	1056	1056	..	9 2	..	..	..	1057	..	..	..	..	3 4	..	..	7 9	7 34	..
Selsdon	..	..	..	..	..	..	..	..	..	..	..	..	..	..	..	..	..	..	..	..	..	..
Sanderstead	..	8 32	..	9 47	11 0	11 0	..	9 5	..	..	..	11 1	..	..	..	..	3 8	..	..	7 13	..	..
Riddlesdown	..	8 37	..	9 52	11 5	11 5	..	9 10	..	..	..	11 6	..	..	..	..	3 12	..	..	7 18	..	9 50
Upper Warlingham	..	8 43	..	9 58	1111	1111	..	9 15	9 28	..	..	1112	..	..	..	..	3 18	..	..	7 24	7 44	..
Woldingham	..	8 47	..	10 2	1116	1116	..	9 20	..	..	..	1117	..	..	..	..	3 23	..	..	7 29	7 48	9 58
Oxted ¶ .... arr	..	8 54	..	1010	1123	1123	..	9 27	9 37	..	..	1124	..	..	..	..	3 30	..	..	7 36	7 55	10 5
Oxted .... dep	..	8 54	..	..	..		..	..	9 38	..	..	..	..	..	..	..	3 32	..	..	..	7 56	..
Hurst Green Halt	..	8K57	..	..	..		..	..	9 41	..	..	..	..	..	..	..	3 34	..	..	..	7 59	..
Monks Lane Halt ¶	..	..		..	..		..	..	..	..	..	..	..	..	..	..	..	..	..	..	..	..
Edenbridge Town C	..	9 6	Saturdays Excepted	..	..	Wednesdays only	..	..	9 50	..	..	..	..	..	..	..	3 43	..	..	..	8 8	..
Hever	..	9 10		..	..		..	..	9 54	..	..	..	..	..	..	..	3 47	..	..	..	8 12	..
Cowden	..	9 14		..	..		..	..	9 59	..	..	..	..	..	..	..	3 52	..	..	..	8 17	..
Ashurst	..	9 20		..	..		..	..	10 5	..	..	..	..	..	..	..	3 58	..	..	..	8 23	..
Groombridge 239 *& below* ..	..	9 26		..	..		..	..	1012	..	..	..	..	..	..	..	4 4	..	..	..	8 30	..
High Rocks Halt	..	9 30		..	..		..	..	..	..	..	..	..	..	..	..	4 8	..	..	..	..	..
Tunbridge Wells West arr	..	9 34	..	..	..		..	..	1019	..	..	..	..	..	..	..	4 12	..	..	..	8 37	..
Ashurst .... dep	..	Stop	..	..	..		..	..	Stop	..	..	..	..	..	..	..	Stop	..	..	..	Stop	..
Eridge *(below)* ...... arr	..		..	..	..		..	..		..	..	..	..	..	..	..		..	..	..		..
Oxted .... dep	..	..	9 0	1010	..	1124	..	9 28	..	..	..	1125	..	..	..	..	..	..	..	7 38	..	10 6
Hurst Green Halt	..	..	9 2	1013	..	11K27	..	9 31	..	..	..	1128	..	..	..	..	..	..	..	7 41	..	10 9
Lingfield	..	..	9 11	1022	..	11K36	..	9 40	..	..	..	1137	..	..	..	..	..	..	..	7 50	..	1018
Dormans	..	..	9 16	1026	..	11K41	..	9 45	..	..	..	1142	..	..	..	..	..	..	..	7 55	..	1023
East Grinstead 239 .... arr	..	..	9 23	1033	..	1148	..	9 52	..	..	..	1149	..	..	..	..	..	..	..	8 2	..	1030
Three Bridges ...... dep	8 50	..	..	..	..	..	9 20	..	..	..	..	..	..	..	..	..	..	..	7 47	..	..	..
Rowfant	8 56	..	..	..	..	..	9 26	..	..	..	..	..	..	..	..	..	..	..	7 53	..	..	..
Grange Road D	9 1	..	..	..	..	..	9 31	..	..	..	..	..	..	..	..	..	..	..	7 58	..	..	..
East Grinstead 239 .. arr	9 7	..	..	..	..	..	9 37	..	..	..	..	..	..	..	..	..	..	..	8 4	..	..	..
East Grinstead ...... dep	9 10	..	9 25	1035	..	..	9 55	9 55	..	..	..	1150	..	..	..	..	..	..	8 6	..	..	1032
Forest Row F	9 19	..	9 36	1043	..	..	10 2	10 2	..	..	..	1157	..	..	..	..	..	..	8 14	..	..	1040
Hartfield	9 27	..	9 45	1053	..	..	1010	1010	..	..	..	12 5	..	..	..	..	..	..	8 22	..	..	1050
Withyham	9 31	..	9 49	1057	..	..	1014	1014	..	..	..	12 9	..	..	..	..	..	..	8 26	..	..	1054
Groombridge 239 & *below*	9 39	Dep. Tonbridge 9 20 p.m. see pages 54 and 54a	9 57	11 5	..	..	1022	1022	..	..	..	1216	..	..	..	..	..	..	8 37	..	..	11 2
High Rocks Halt	..		..	..	..	..	1027	1027	..	..	..	..	..	..	..	..	..	..	8 41	..	..	..
Tunbridge Wells West arr	9 46		10 3	1112	..	..	1031	1031	..	..	..	1224	..	..	..	..	..	..	8 45	..	..	11 9
East Grinstead .... dep	..		9 26	..	..	..	Stop	9 56	..	..	..	Stop	..	..	..	..	..	..	Stop	8 8	..	Stop
Kingscote	..		9 33	..	..	..		10 3	..	..	..		..	..	..	..	..	..		8 15	..	
West Hoathly	..		9 39	..	..	..	..	10 8	..	..	..	..	..	..	..	..	..	..	..	8 22	..	..
Horsted Keynes	..		9 45	..	..	..	..	1015	a.m	..	..	p.m	..	..	..	..	..	..	p.m	8 29	..	..
Horsted Keynes ...... dep	..		9 45	..	..	..	..	..	1016	..	..	1216	..	..	216	416	..	616	8 16	..	..	Dep. Tonbridge at 8 33 p.m. see page 55
Ardingly	..		9 51	..	..	..	..	..	1020	..	..	1220	..	..	220	420	..	620	8 20	..	..	
Haywards Heath G 197 arr	..		9 57	..	..	..	..	..	1024	..	..	1224	..	..	224	424	..	624	8 24	..	..	
Haywards Heath G 197 dep	..		10 0	..	..	..	..	..	1029	1036	..	1235	..	..	235	433	..	635	8 35	..	..	
Wivelsfield	..		10 5	..	..	..	..	..	1035	..	..	1239	..	..	239	..	..	639	8 39	..	..	
Burgess Hill	..		10 7	..	..	..	..	..	1036	..	..	..	..	..	..	..	..	..	..	..	..	
Hassocks H	..	☞	1011	..	..	..	..	..	1040	..	..	..	..	..	..	..	..	..	..	..	..	
Preston Park	..		1019	..	..	..	..	..	1048	..	..	..	..	..	..	..	..	..	..	..	..	
Brighton 159 .... arr	..		1023	..	..	..	..	..	1051	..	..	..	..	..	..	..	..	..	..	..	..	
Sheffield Park	..		..	..	..	..	..	1024	..	..	..	..	..	..	..	..	..	..	..	8 39	..	
Newick and Chailey	..		..	..	..	..	..	1031	Stop	..	..	..	..	..	..	..	..	..	..	8 46	..	
Barcombe W	..	p.m	..	..	..	..	..	1038	a.m	..	..	..	..	..	..	..	p.m	..	..	8 54	p.m	p.m
Tunbridge Wells West dep	..	9 40	..	..	..	..	..	..	1010	..	1020	Arr Lewes 12 55 p.m	..	155	Arr Lewes 2 55 p.m	..	4 40	Arr Lewes 6 55 p.m	..	..	8 27	8 58
High Rocks Halt	..	..	..	..	..	..	..	..	..	..	1023		..	..		..	..		..	..	8 30	..
Groombridge *above*	..	9 46	..	..	..	..	..	..	1017	..	1029		..	2 1		..	4 46		..	..	8 35	9 4
Eridge *(above)*	..	9 51	..	..	..	..	..	..	1022	..	1034		..	2 6		..	4 52		..	..	8 40	9 9
Crowboro' & Jarvis Brook	..	9 59	..	..	..	..	..	..	1030	..	..	..	..	214		..	5 0		Arr Lewes 8 55 p.m	..	..	9 17
Buxted	..	10 9	..	..	..	..	..	..	1040	..	..	..	..	224		..	5 10			..	..	9 27
Uckfield	..	1014	..	..	..	..	..	..	1045	..	..	..	..	230		..	5 16			..	..	9 34
Isfield	..	1020	..	..	..	..	..	..	1051	..	..	..	..	236		..	5 21			..	..	9 40
Barcombe Mills Q	..	1026	..	..	..	..	..	..	1057	..	..	..	..	242		..	5 27			..	..	9 46
Lewes 158, 197	..	1035	..	..	..	..	..	1051	11 7	1054	..	1 1	..	251	3 1	450	5 36	7 1	9 1	9 6	..	9 54
Falmer	..	..	..	..	..	..	..	..	..	..	..	..	..	..	..	..	..	..	..	..	..	..
London Road (Brighton) ..	..	1050	..	..	..	..	..	11 6	1122	..	..	..	..	3 5	..	..	5 51	..	..	9 21	..	10 9
Brighton 159 .... arr	..	1055	..	..	..	..	..	1110	1126	..	..	..	..	3 9	..	..	5 55	..	..	9 25	..	1018
Rotherfield and Mark Cross	..	..	..	..	..	..	..	Stop	..	..	1042	..	..	..	..	..	..	..	..	Stop	8 48	..
Mayfield	..	..	..	..	..	..	a.m		..	..	1051	..	..	..	..	..	..	..	..		8 57	..
Heathfield	..	..	..	..	..	..	8 45	..	..	..	11 3	..	1 35	..	..	..	..	..	..	..	9 9	..
Waldron and Horeham	..	..	..	..	..	..	8 53	..	..	..	11 17	..	1 43	..	..	..	..	..	..	..	9 24	..
Hellingly	..	..	..	..	..	..	9 1	a.m	..	..	1125	..	1 52	..	..	..	..	..	..	p.m	9 34	..
Hailsham	..	..	..	..	..	..	9 5	1012	..	..	1130	..	1 57	..	..	..	..	..	..	8 45	9 40	..
Polegate 158, 197	..	..	..	..	..	..	9 14	1021	..	..	1138	..	2 5	..	..	..	..	..	..	8 53	9 56	..
Hampden Park L	..	..	..	..	..	..	9 18	1026	..	..	..	..	2 10	..	..	..	..	..	..	8 58	10 2	..
Eastbourne .... arr	..	..	..	..	..	..	9 23	1031	..	1113	1146	1 26	2 15	..	326	5 9	..	726	9 26	9 3	10 7	..

For Notes, see page 243

EASTBOURNE, BRIGHTON, EAST GRINSTEAD, TUNBRIDGE WELLS WEST, and LONDON

Miles	Miles from Brighton	Mls	Up	Week Days a.m	a.m	a.m	a.m	a.m	a.m	a.m	a.m	a.m	a.m	a.m	a.m	a.m	a.m	a.m	a.m	a.m	a.m	a.m	a.m
			Eastbourne dep											6 53		6 37		7 27					
2			Hampden Park I													6 41							
4½			Polegate													6 47							
7¾			Hailsham													6 55							
9			Hellingly													7 1							
12¼			Waldron and Horam													7 10							
15			Heathfield													7 20				8 10			
18¾			Mayfield													7 39				8 21			
21½			Rotherfield and Mark Cross													7 51				8 29			
—	—	Mls	Brighton dep							6 15					6 58	Arr Mayfield 7 34 a.m.	7 7			Arr. Eridge 8 36 a.m.			
—	¾	¾	London Road (Brighton)							6 18					7 1		7 10						
—	3½	3½	Falmer																				
—	8	8	Lewes							6 37				7 14	7 19		7 26						
—	—	11¼	Barcombe Mills Q												7 28								
—	—	13¼	Isfield												7 34								
—	—	16½	Uckfield												7 40				8 18				
—	—	18¾	Buxted												7 46				8 23				
—	—	23½	Crowboro' & Jarvis Brook												7 57				8 34				
24¾	—	27	Eridge (below)												8 5	8 F9			8 42	8 45			
—	—	29	Groombridge (below)													8 15				8 51			
—	—	31½	High Rocks Halt																				
—	—	32	Tunbridge Wells W. arr													8 23				8 58			
—	12¼		Barcombe W							6 47							7 36						
—	15¼		Newick and Chailey							6 55							7 43						
—	17½		Sheffield Park							7 4							7 49						
—	—	Mls	Brighton dep						6 28				7 8			Arr. Tonbridge 8 41 a.m. see pages 55 and 56	Stop					7 50	
—	—	1½	Preston Park						6 31				7 11									7 53	
—	—	7	Hassocks H						6 39													8 1	
—	—	9	Burgess Hill						6 43													8 5	
—	—	10	Wivelsfield						6 45					7 31								8 7	
—	—	12¾	Haywards Heath G 158 arr						6 50				7 25	7 36				8 7	Saturdays excepted	Saturdays excepted		8 12	
—	—		Haywards Heath dep						7 6				Stop	7 37				8 15				8 15	
—	—	15½	Ardingly						7 10					7 43				8 19				8 19	
—	—	17¾	Horsted Keynes 234 arr						7 14					7 47				8 23				8 23	
—	22		Horsted Keynes						Stop	7 16				Stop				8 37				8 37	
—	24¼		West Hoathly							7 23								8 42				8 42	
—	26½		Kingscote							7 29													
—	28¾		East Grinstead 234 arr							7 34				a.m				Stop					
—	—	Mls	Tunbridge Wells W. dep								7 6			7 36									8 30
—	—	¾	High Rocks Halt																				
—	—	3	Groombridge (below)								7 12			7 42									8 37
—	—	5½	Withyham								7 20			7 49									8 44
—	—	6¾	Hartfield								7 25			7 53			a.m						8 49
—	—	10½	Forest Row F	6 23							7 39			8 1			8 21	Saturdays excepted					8 56
—	—	13¾	East Grinstead 234 arr	6 31							7 52			8 10			8 31						9 5
—	—	—	East Grinstead dep	6 37								8 0											
—	—	16½	Grange Road D	6 42								8 5											
—	—	17¾	Rowfant	6 45				Saturdays excepted				8 9											
—	—	20¼	Three Bridges 197 arr	6 51								8 15											
—	—		East Grinstead dep			6 33				7 41	7 54			8 12			8 32				Saturdays only		9 6
—	30¼		Dormans			6 37				7 45	8 0			8 18			8 37						9 12
—	31¾		Lingfield			6 41				7 49	8 4			8 21			8 41						9 15
—	36¼		Hurst Green Halt			6 50				7 58				8 30									
—	37½		Oxted B 234 arr			6 54				8 2	8 15			8 34			8 52						9 25
—	—		Eridge (above) dep												8 7				8 43	8 45			
29½	—		Ashurst arr						a.m				a.m		8 14			a.m					
—	—	Mls	Tunbridge Wells W dep		6 6		6 40	Dep. Edenbridge 7 26 a.m.	7 12				7 47					8 23			8 40		
—	—	¾	High Rocks Halt																				
—	—	3	Groombridge (above)		6 13		6 46		7 18				7 53					8 30			8 46		
—	—	5½	Ashurst		6 17		6 52		7 23				7 59		8 15			8 37			8 52		
32	—	8¾	Cowden		6 22		6 58		7 29				8 4		8 20			8 41			8 57		
34	—	10¾	Hever				7 3		7 34				8 9		8 25			8 46			9 3		
35¾	—	12	Edenbridge Town C		6 29		7 7		7 38				8 13		8 30			8 50	8 59	8 59	9 7		
37¾	—	14	Monks Lane Halt ¶																				
40	—	16½	Hurst Green Halt				7 16		7 47				8 22					8 59			9 16		
41	—	17¾	Oxted B 234 arr		6 39		7 20	7 36	7 51				8 26		8 41			9 3	9 10	9 10	9 20		
—	—		Oxted dep			6 55	7 22	7 37	7 52	8 3	8 16		8 27		8 43		8 53		9 11	9 11			9 26
44½	41		Woldingham			7 3	7 29	7 44	8 0	8 11	8 24		8 35		8 51		9 1						9 34
46	42¾		Upper Warlingham			7 8	7 33	7 49	8 5	8 16	8 29		8 40		8 56		9 6						9 38
47¾	44½		Riddlesdown			7 13	7 37	7 53	8 10	8 20	8 34		8 45		9 1		9 11						
49	45¾		Sanderstead 119			7 17	7 41	7 57	8 14	8 24	8 38		8 49		9 5		9 14						
49¾	46¼		Selsdon						8 18	8 27			8 52										
50	46¾		South Croydon			7 21	7 45		8 20				8 54										
51	47¾		East Croydon 285 arr	7 21		7 25	7 48	8 4	8 23	8 31	8 44	8 50	8 57		9 11		9 20		9 28	9 28			9 50
59	55¾		New Cross Gate arr			7 37			8*38														
61½	58		London Bridge "	7 39		7 43	8 Ⓢ10	8 20	8*43	8 47	9 0	9 6	9 14		9 28		9*38						10 8
58¾	55½		Clapham Junction M "	—			8 0	8*23	8 36	8*48		9Ⓢ10	9Ⓢ10										10*5
61¾	58¾		Victoria "				8 7	8*28	8 43	8*53	9* 8	9* 8	9Ⓢ15		9*34		9 37		9 46	9 46			10*10

For Notes, see page 243; for Continuation of Trains, see pages 240 to 243

EASTBOURNE, BRIGHTON, EAST GRINSTEAD, TUNBRIDGE WELLS WEST, and LONDON

Up	Week Days—continued																				
	a.m	a.m	a.m	a.m	a.m	am	a.m	a.m	a.m	a.m	a.m	a.m	a.m	a.m	a.m	a.m	p.m	p.m	p.m	p.m	p.m
Eastbourne.........dep	7 52	Arr. Lewes 8 16 a.m.	Arr. Lewes 8 28 a.m.	8 16		822	8 45			9 55		1052							1217		1245
Hampden Park L........	7 56			8 20			8 49					1055							1221		1249
Polegate................	8 2			8 30			8 54			10 4		11J3							1225		1254
Hailsham................	8 14			8 39			9 2			10 17		1111							1233		1 2
Hellingly................	8 21						Stop			10 22		Stop							Stop		1 8
Waldron and Horam ..	8 32									10 33											1h23
Heathfield................	8 43									10 43											1 32
Mayfield..........[Cross	8 53									10 56											1 45
Rotherfield and Mark	9 4						a.m			11 4											1 53
Brighton.........dep	Arr. Hailsham 8 9 a.m.	8 0	8 14	Arr. Polegate 8 25 a.m ☞	8 43		8 48			Arr. Hailsham 10 12 a.m	10 18			1050			12 5				
London Rd. (Brighton)			8 16				8 51				10 21						12 8				
Falmer................			8 20																		
Lewes................		8 20	8 32			849	9 6				10 37			11 8		1144	1224	1244			
Barcombe Mills Q...			8 39	Stop			9 14				10 45						1232				
Isfield................			8 45				9 20				10 51						1238				
Uckfield................			8 52				9 26				10 58						1244				
Buxted.........[Brook			8 58				9 32				11 3						1250				
Crowborough & Jarvis			9 8	a.m		Arr. Lewes 8 46 a.m.	9 42				11 13	a.m					1 1				
Eridge (below)	9 11		9 15	9 23			9 49			11 12	11 20	1127					1 9				2 0
Groombridge (below)..				9 29			9 54					1132					1 13				2 6
High Rocks Halt																					
Tunbridge Wells W. arr				9 36			10 1					1139					1 20				2 13
Barcombe W..........		8 31		☞			Stop					Stop		1120			☞				Stop
Newick and Chailey.....		8 39												1127							
Sheffield Park..........		8 46												1133					p.m		p.m
Brighton.........dep				Arr. Tonbridge 9 55 a.m. see pages 55 and 56											11 28				1228	1 8	1 28
Preston Park..........															11 31				1231	1 11	1 31
Hassocks H..........															11 39		Arr. Tonbridge 1SX49, 1SO42 p.m see pages 55 and 56		1239		1 39
Burgess Hill..........															11 43				1243		1 43
Wivelsfield..........						9 6									11 45	12 0			1245		1 45
Haywards Heath G 158 arr					8 59	911									11 50	12 5		1 4	1250	1 26	1 50
Haywards Heath G 158 dep					9 11	911									12 6	12 6		1 4	1 4	1 45	2 4
Ardingly..........					9 15	915									12 10	1210		1 8	1 8	1 50	2 8
Horsted Keynes 234 arr					9 19	919									12 14	1214		1 12	1 12	1 56	2 12
Horsted Keynes........		8L58			Stop									1145		Stop		Stop	Stop	1 57	Stop
West Hoathly..........		9 7												1151						2 3	
Kingscote..........		9 14												1157						2 9	
East Grinstead 234 arr		9 20			a.m									12 4		p.m		p.m		2 15	p.m
Tunbridge Wells W. dp					8 50			10 6								1 8		1 8			2 19
High Rocks Halt																					
Groombridge (below)..					8 56			1012								1 15		1 15			2 26
Withyham..........				Stop	9 3			1020								1 23		1 23			2 33
Hartfield..........					9 7			1025								1 28		1 28			2 38
Forest Row F..........					9 14			1032								1 38		1 38			2 45
East Grinstead 234 arr					9 23			1040								1 47	Stop	1 47			2 54
East Grinstead..dep					9 24								11 45			1 49					2 56
Grange Road D.....					9 31								11 50			1 53					3 3
Rowfant..........					9 34								11 54			1 57					3 6
Three Bridges 197 arr					9 40								12 0			2 3					3 12
East Grinstead.....dep		9 30						1042						1218				1 53			
Dormans..........		9 36						1047						1225				1 58			
Lingfield..........		9 40						1051						1229				2 1			
Hurst Green Halt......		9 49												1238							
Oxted B 234......arr		9 53						11 1						1242				2 11			
Eridge (above) dep	9 20		9 20							11 22	11 22										
Ashurst ...arr				a.m			a.m					a.m					p.m		p.m		
Tunbridge Wells W dp				9 28			9 55		10 52			1147					1 20		2 10		
High Rocks Halt							9 58					1149									
Groombridge (above)..				9 34			10 6		10 58			1153					1 26		2 19		
Ashurst..........				9 40			1013		11 4			1159					1 31		2 25		
Cowden..........				9 45			1017		11 9			12 4					1 37		2 31		
Hever..........				9 50			1021		11 14			12 8					1 42		2 36		
Edenbridge Town C..	9 36		9 36	9 55			1025		11 18	11 40	11 40	1212					1 46		2 40		
Monks Lane Halt ¶..																					
Hurst Green Halt....							1035		11 27			1222					1 55		2 49		
Oxted B 234..... arr	9 46		9 46	10 6			1039		11 31	11 50	11 50	1226					1 59		2 53		
Oxted..........dep	9 46	9 54	9 46	10 8				11 1	11 32	11 52	11 52			1243				2 14	2 55		
Woldingham..........		10 2						11 8	11 38					1251				2 22	3 3		
Upper Warlingham		10 7						1113	11 43					1256				2 27	3 8		
Riddlesdown..........		10 12						1118	11 48					1 1				2 32	3 13		
Sanderstead 119.......		10 16		10 22				1122	11 52					1 5				2 37	3 17		
Selsdon..........																					
South Croydon..........									11 57									2 41			
East Croydon 285 arr	10 4	10 22	10 4	10 27	10SX6			1127	12 0	12 11	12 11		12 49	1 12		2 50		2 44	3 22		4 17
New Cross Gate.... arr									12 18												
London Bridge..... "	10r21	10 40	10r21	10*56	10SX21				12 25	12S31	12S31		1S11	1S31		3S11		3 5			4 36
Clapham Junction M "		10*40		10 40	10r20			1140	12*16	12S25	12S25		1 2	1 29		3 2		3*2	[illegible] 35		
Victoria.......... "	10 21	10*50	10 21	10 50	10r26			1147	12*21	12S33	12S33		1 8	1 36		3 8		3*8	3 42		

For Notes, see page 243

EASTBOURNE, BRIGHTON, EAST GRINSTEAD, TUNBRIDGE WELLS WEST, and LONDON

Week Days—*continued*

Up	p.m	p.m	p.m	p.m	p.m	p.m	p.m	p.m	p.m	p.m	p.m	p.m	p.m	p.m	p.m	p.m	p.m	p.m	p.m	p.m	p.m	p.m
Eastbourne..........dep				1 17	2 9					3 39	4 0			4 39		4 52		5 22	Saturdays only	5 36	Saturdays excepted	Saturdays excepted
Hampden Park L........				1 21	2 13					3 43	4 4			4 43		4 55		5 25				
Polegate..................				1 25	2L21			3 19		3 49	4 10			4 50		5 10		5h34				
Hailsham..................				1 33	2 28			3 26		3 57	4 17			4 58		5 17		5 41				
Hellingly..................				Stop	Stop			Stop		4 2	4l22			5 4				Stop				
Waldron and Horam....										4 11	Stop			5 14								
Heathfield										4 20				5h30								
Mayfield..........[Cross										4 33				5 43								
Rotherfield and Mark										4 41				5 51				p.m				
Brighton .... dep		1 20				3 5			3 46				4 36					5 18	5 36		5 44	
London Rd (Brighton).		1 23				3 8			3 48	Arr Eridge 4 48 p.m								5 21			5 47	☞
Falmer					p.m			p.m	3 52		p.m											
Lewes	1 44	1 39			2 45	3 25		3 44	4 5		4 11		4 52				5 44	5 37	5L55	5 57	6 2	
Barcombe Mills Q........						3 33			Arr. Lewes 4 0 p.m		4 18		5 0		Saturdays excepted	Arr Polegate 4 59 p.m			6 2		6 9	
Isfield						3 38					4 24		5 5						6 8		6 15	
Uckfield						3 44					4 32		5 11						6 15		6 22	6 54
Buxted ....[Brook						3 50					4 37		5 17						6 21		6 28	6 59
Crowborough & Jarvis						4 0					4 48		5 27						6 33		6 38	7 9
Eridge (*below*)						4 7				4 58	4 55		5 34	5 58					6 42		6 46	7 16
Groombridge (*below*)..						4 12				5 4			5 38	6 5		Stop			6 47		6 51	7 22
High Rocks Halt.......						4 16																
Tunbridge Wells W.ar						4 20				5 11			5 46	6 12					6 54		6 58	7 29
Barcombe W............		1 47				Stop			4 14					Stop				5 47				Stop
Newick and Chailey....		1 54							4 21									5 55				
Sheffield Park		2h3		p.m		p.m			4 26					p.m		p.m		6 4				p.m
Brighton .... dep		Arr. Horsted Keynes 2 14 p.m		2 28		3 8	3 28							5SO8	5 12	5 28						5 58
Preston Park..........				2 31		3 11	3 31							5SO11	5 15	5 31						6 1
Hassocks H				2 39			3 39								5 23	5 39						6 9
Burgess Hill............				2 43			3 43								5 27	5 44						6 14
Wivelsfield				2 45			3 45	4 0							5 29	5 46	6 0					6 17
Haywards Heath G 158 arr	2 4			2 50	3 5	3 25	3 50	4 5						5SO26	5 34	5 51	6 5		Arr. Tonbridge 7 12 p.m see page 56	6 13	Arr. Tonbridge 7 17 p.m see page 56	6 22
Haywards Heath G 158 dep	2 4			3 5	3 5	3 28	4 6	4 6						5SO36	5 36	6 6	6 6			6 25		6 25
Ardingley	2 8			3 9	3 9	3 34	4 10	4 10						5SO40	5 40	6 10	6 10			6 29		6 29
Horsted Keynes 234 ar	2 12			3 13	3 13	3 39	4 14	4 14						5SO44	5 44	6 14	6 14			6 33		6 33
Horsted Keynes		2 25		Stop		3 40	Stop		4 38					Stop		Stop		6 17				
West Hoathly...........		2 31				3 45												6 23				
Kingscote................		2 37				3 50												6 29				
East Grinstead 234..arr		2 43				3 56								p.m				6 35				
Tunbridge Wells W.dp												4 55		5 14								
High Rocks Halt........												4 58										
Groombridge (*below*)..												5 2		5 20								
Withyham...............												5 10		5 27								
Hartfield												5 14		5 31								
Forest Row F...........												5 21		5h43								
East Grinstead 234 arr							p.m					5 29		5 51								
East Grinstead dep							4 15					5 30										
Grange Road D....			Saturdays only				4 20					5 37										
Rowfant............							4 23					5 40										
Three Bridges 197 ar							4 29					5 46										
East Grinstead..... dep		2 59				4 6								6k11				7 4				
Dormans................		3 5				4 12								6l16				7 9				
Lingfield................		3 9				4 16								6 21				7 14				
Hurst Green Halt......		3 19				4 25								6 30				7 23				
Oxted B 234 .... arr		3 23				4 29								6 34				7 27				
Eridge (*above*)... dep				Saturdays excepted							4 56											
Ashurst .... arr											5 2					p.m						
Tunbridge Wells W.dp			3 20								4 45					6 30						
High Rocks Halt.......																6 33						
Groombridge (*above*) ..			3 28								4 51					6 37						
Ashurst..................			3 33								5R4					6 43						
Cowden			3 39	☞							5 11					6 49						
Hever....................			3 44								5 16					6 54						
Edenbridge Town C..			3 48								5 20					6 59						
Monks Lane Halt ¶..																						
Hurst Green Halt.....											5 29					7 9						
Oxted B 234...... arr			3 58	p.m							5 33					7 13						
Oxted .... dep			3 59	4 0		4 31					5 34			6 34				7 28				
Woldingham			4 6	4 7		4 39					5 42			6 42				7 36				
Upper Warlingham.....			4 11	4 12		4 44					5 47			6 47				7 41				
Riddlesdown............			4 16	4 16		4 49					5 51			6 51				7 46				
Sanderstead 119........			4 20	4 20		4 53					5 55			6 55				7 50				
Selsdon..................																						
South Croydon.........			4 23	4 24		4 57												7 54				
East Croydon 285... arr			4 27	4 27		5 0	5 18				6 0	6 50		7 0				7 57				
New Cross Gate.... arr																						
London Bridge..... "				4Ⓑ49		5 20	5 38				6Ⓑ30	7£11		7Ⓑ31								
Clapham Junction M "			4 41			5*16						7 2		7*N16								
Victoria................ "			4 48			5*22					6 18	7 8		7*N22				8 15				

For Notes, see page 243 ; for Continuation of Trains, see pages 242 and 243

EASTBOURNE, BRIGHTON, EAST GRINSTEAD, TUNBRIDGE WELLS WEST, and LONDON

Up	Week Days—continued																	Sundays				
	p.m	p.m	p.m	p.m	p.m	p.m	p.m	p.m	p.m	p.m	p.m	p.m	p.m	p.m	p.m	p.m	p.m	a.m	a.m	a.m	a.m	a.m
Eastbourne..........dep	6 32			Arr. Lewes 7 52 p.m	7 29	7 36				Saturdays excepted			Saturdays only		9 22	Arr. Lewes 9 46 p.m	10 44	7 22				
Hampden Park L															9 25		10 48	7 25				
Polegate	6 39				7h39										9 32		10 54	7h40				
Hailsham	6 47				7 48										9 39		11 1	7 47				
Hellingly					7 53													7 52				
Waldron and Horam	Stop				8 3													8C23				
Heathfield					8 12					8 43					Arr. Polegate 9 29 p.m			8 33				
Mayfield [Cross					8h28					8 54												
Rotherfield and Mark					8 37					9 2								Stop				
Brighton..........dep		6 31		7 34			7 46						8 46			9 30				8 32		
London Rd. (Brighton)		6 33		7 37			7 48						8 48							8 35		
Falmer		6 37					7 52						8 52									
Lewes		6 58		7 55		7 57	8 5					8 44	9 2			9 51				8 52		9 45
Barcombe Mills Q				8 3									9 9			9 59						
Isfield		Arr. Lewes 6 45 p.m		8 8			Arr. Lewes 8 0 p.m						9 15			10 4						
Uckfield				8 14									9 20			1010						
Buxted [Brook				8 20									9 25			1016						
Crowborough & Jarvis				8 30									9 35			1026						
Eridge (below)				8 37	8 45					9 12			9 42									
Groombridge (below)				8 43	8 52					9 17			9 47			1036						
High Rocks Halt																						
Tunbridge Wells W. arr.				8 50	9 0					9 24			9 53			1043						
Barcombe W		7 6					8 13						Stop							9 4		
Newick and Chailey		7 13					8 20													9 12		
Sheffield Park	p.m				Arr. Tonbridge 9 21 p.m see page 56		8 25									Arr. Tonbridge 10 59 p.m see page 56				9 18		
Brighton..........dep	6 28							7 58	8 8		8 28										9 28	
Preston Park	6 31							8 1	8 11		8 31										9 31	
Hassocks H	6 39							8 9			8 39			Saturdays excepted							9 39	
Burgess Hill	6 43							8 13			8 43										9 43	
Wivelsfield	6 45							8 15			8 45	9 0									9 45	
Haywards Heath G 158 arr	6 50					8 13		8 20	8 26		8 50	9 5									9 50	10 5
Haywards Heath G 158 dep	6 53								8 35		9 6	9 6									10 5	10 5
Ardingly	6 58								8 40		9 10	9 10									10 9	10 9
Horsted Keynes 234 ar	7 2						8 34		8 46		9 14	9 14									1013	1013
Horsted Keynes									8 48											9 29		
West Hoathly									8 55		Stop									9 37		
Kingscote									9 1											9 44		
East Grinstead 234 arr									9 7				p.m					a.m		9 50		
Tunbridge Wells W. dp	Saturdays excepted												8 37	8 37				7 50				
High Rocks Halt																						
Groombridge (below)													8 43	8 43				7 56				
Withyham			Saturdays excepted										8 50	8 50				8 3				
Hartfield													8 54	8 54				8 7				
Forest Row F													9 1	9 1				8 14				
East Grinstead 234 ar													9 10	9 10				8 23				
East Grinstead..dep													9 12	9 25				8 24				
Grange Road D													9 18	9 30				8 2[illegible]				
Rowfant													9 21	9 34				8 33				
Three Bridges 197 ar													9 27	9 39				8 40				
East Grinstead.....dep			8 9						9 13											9 55		
Dormans			8 13						9 20											10 2		
Lingfield			8 17						9 24											10 7		
Hurst Green Halt			8 26																	1016		
Oxted B 234.......arr			8 30						9 34											1020		
Eridge (above)..dep																						
Ashurst........arr											p.m											
Tunbridge Wells W. dp											9 0								8 37			
High Rocks Halt											9 3											
Groombridge (above)											9 10								8 45			
Ashurst											9 16								8 50			
Cowden											9 22								8 56			
Hever											9 27								9 2			
Edenbridge Town C											9 31								9 7			
Monks Lane Halt ¶																						
Hurst Green Halt											9 39								9 15			
Oxted B 234......arr											9 43								9 19			
Oxted..............dep			8 30						9 35		9 44		Saturdays only						9 20	1022		
Woldingham			8 38								9 52								9 28	1029		
Upper Warlingham			8 42						9 45		9 57								9 33	1034		
Riddlesdown			8 47								10 2								9 38	1039		
Sanderstead 119			8 51								10 6								9 43	1043		
Selsdon																						
South Croydon			8 54								10 9								9 47	1047		
East Croydon 285 .arr			8 57						9 58		10 12		1018	10 50				9 23	9 51	1051		
New Cross Gate ...arr											10*33		1033									
London Bridge .... "			9 18						10 20		10*39		1039	11B11								
Clapham Junction M "			9*16						10*16		10 29			11 2				9 36	10 4	11 5		
Victoria .... "			9*22						10*22		10 36			11 7				9 42	1011	1112		

For Notes, see page 243

EASTBOURNE, BRIGHTON, EAST GRINSTEAD, TUNBRIDGE WELLS WEST, and LONDON.

Sundays—*continued*

Up.	a.m	a.m	a.m	p.m	p.m	p.m	p.m	p.m	p.m	p.m	p.m	p.m	p.m	p.m	p.m
Eastbourne dep	9 46	1022		1243									6 16		8 18
Hampden Park **L**	9 50	1025		1247									6 20		8 22
Polegate	9 55	1030		1254									6 25		8L30
Hailsham	10 3	1038		1 2									6 33		8 38
Hellingly		1043		1 7									6 38		
Waldron and Horam	Stop	1052		1 16									6 49		Stop
Heathfield		11h7		1 24									7 0		
Mayfield		1122											7 11		
Rotherfield and Mark Cross	a.m	1132		Stop									7 20		p.m
Brighton dep	9 50									6 18		6 50			9 33
London Rd (Brighton)										6 21					9 39
Falmer															
Lewes	10 7		1144		1 44		3 44		5 44	6 36		7 8		7 44	9 54
Barcombe Mills **Q**	1014									6 43					10 2
Isfield	1020									6 49					10 8
Uckfield	1026									6 55					1014
Buxted	1032									7 2					1019
Crowborough & Jarvis Brook	1043									7 13					1030
Eridge (*below*)	1051	1141								7 21			7 29		1037
Groombridge (*below*)	1057	1146								7 25			7 36		1042
High Rocks Halt		1150											7 40		
Tunbridge Wells W. arr	11 4	1154								7 32			7 44		1049
Barcombe **W**	Stop	Stop										7 18			
Newick and Chailey												7 26			
Sheffield Park		a.m		p.m								7 32			
Brighton dep		1128		1 28		3 28		5 28		Arr. Tonbridge 7 48 p.m see page 57	7 28		Arr. Tonbridge 8 7 p.m see page 57		
Preston Park		1131		1 31		3 31		5 31			7 31				
Hassocks **H**		1139		1 39		3 39		5 39			7 40				
Burgess Hill		1143		1 43		3 43		5 43			7 45				
Wivelsfield		1145	12 0	1 45	2 0	3 45		5 45			7 47				
Haywards Heath G 158 arr		1150	12 5	1 50	2 5	3 50	4 4	5 50	6 4		7 52			8 4	
Haywards Heath G 158 dep		12 6	12 6	2 6	2 6	4 4	4 4	6 4	6 4		8 4			8 4	
Ardingley		1210	1210	2 10	2 10	4 8	4 8	6 8	6 8		8 8			8 8	
Horsted Keynes 234 ar		1214	1214	2 14	2 14	4 12	4 12	6 12	6 12		8 12			8 12	
Horsted Keynes					Stop				Stop	Stop	Stop	7 43			
West Hoathly												7 51			
Kingscote												7 57			
East Grinstead 234 arr					p.m					p.m		8 3			
Tunbridge Wells W. dp					3 47					6 30					
High Rocks Halt					3 50					6 33					
Groombridge (*below*)					3 55					6 37					
Withyham					4 2					6 44					
Hartfield					4 6					6 48					
Forest Row **F**					4 14					6 55					
East Grinstead 234 arr					4 24					7 4					
East Grinstead dep										7 5					
Grange Road **D**										7 10					
Rowfant										7 14					
Three Bridges 197 arr										7 21					
East Grinstead dep					4 24							8 10			
Dormans					4 30							8 16			
Lingfield					4 34							8 23			
Hurst Green Halt					4 43							8 33			
Oxted B 234 arr					4 47							8 37			
Eridge (*above*) dep															
Ashurst arr	a.m								p.m		p.m				
Tunbridge Wells W dp	1154								6 50		7 45				
High Rocks Halt	1157														
Groombridge (*above*)	12 2								6 56		7 52				
Ashurst	12 7								7 2		8 0				
Cowden	1213								7 8		8 7				
Hever	1218								7 13		8 12				
Edenbridge Town **C**	1222								7 17		8 16				
Monks Lane Halt ¶															
Hurst Green Halt	1230								7 25						
Oxted B 234 arr	1234								7 28		8 26				
Oxted dep	1234				4 47				7 29		8 27	8 37			
Woldingham					4 55				7 37			8 45			
Upper Warlingham					5 0				7 42			8 50			
Riddlesdown					5 5				7 47			8 55			
Sanderstead 119	1250				5 9				7 51			8 59			
Selsdon															
South Croydon	1254				5 13										
East Croydon 235 arr	1257				5 16				8 0	8 24	8 46	9 6			
New Cross Gate arr					5ℚ34					8 39	9ℚ4	9 21			
London Bridge "					5ℚ40					8 44	9ℚ10	9 28			
Clapham Junction M "	1 10				5 31				8 13		9 1				
Victoria "	1 17				5 38				8 19		9 8	9*40			

ℚ Third class only
* Change at East Croydon
‖ Via Eridge
¶ Closed
A Change at East Croydon except Sats. Dep. 5ℚ51 p.m on Sats.
a Dep. 3 mins. *earlier* on Sats.
B Station for Limpsfield (1 mile)
B 5 mins. later on Saturdays
C 1 mile to Edenbridge Station
C Arr. 8 1 a.m
D Station for Crawley Down (1 ml) and Turner's Hill (1 ml)
d Dep 2 18 p.m on Saturdays, changing at East Croydon
F Station for Ashdown Forest and Ashdown Park (3 miles)
F Arr. 7 59 a.m
G Station for Cuckfield (2 miles)
H Station for Hurstpierpoint (1½ miles)
H Arr. 7 59 a.m
h Arr. 5 mins. *earlier*.
J Arr. 10 59 a.m
K Calls to set down only
k 3 mins. later on Sats.
L Sta. for Willingdon (1½ mls)
L Arr. 3 minutes *earlier*
l 2 mins. later on Sats.
M Mid Battersea (1½ miles to Clapham)
N Arr. Clapham Junction 7 12 and Victoria 7 19 p.m on Sats.
P 6 mins. later on Saturdays
p 7 mins. later on Saturdays
Q Nearly 1½ miles to Barcombe Station
R Arr. 4 57 p.m
r Saturdays excepted. Change at East Croydon
S O or SO Saturdays only
SX or SX Saturdays excepted
T Arr. 2 minutes *earlier*
U Calls to take up only
V Dep. 3 12 p.m on Saturdays
W Nearly 1½ miles to Barcombe Mills Station
Y Saturdays only. Change at East Croydon
y Except Sats. Third class only. Dep. 7 42 p.m on Sats changing at East Croydon
Z On Tuesdays and Saturdays, also on alternate Wednesdays (Asylum Visiting days only)
z Arr. 9 48 p.m

LOCAL TRAINS

LOCAL TRAINS and Intermediate Stations

OTHER TRAINS

HORSHAM, SHOREHAM-BY-SEA, and BRIGHTON

Miles	Down	Week Days a.m	a.m	a.m	a.m	a.m SO	p.m WO	p.m SX	p.m SO	p.m SX	p.m SO	p.m	p.m SO	p.m SX	p.m SO	p.m SX	p.m SO	p.m SX	p.m		Sundays a.m	a.m		p.m	p.m	p.m
	394 Victoria........ dep	..	5*20	6 40	9 18	10 18	..	12 * 3	12 18	1 48	2 18	3 18	4 18	4 18	5 18	5 30	5 48	6 18	7 18	..	3 40	7 46	..	12 48	3 18	7 18
	394 London Bridge. "	..	5 25	6③35	9③15	10③8	..	12 18	12 * 15	1③31	2③8	..	..	4③7	..	5 15	5③31	5 48	..	..	..	7③55	..	..	2③35	6③55
	394 Waterloo...... "	..	..	6③27	9③ 7	9③47	..	12③ 7	12③ 7	..	2③7	2③SO27	4③ 7	4③7	5③ 7	5③7	..	6③7	..	..	..	8③ 2	..	12③42	2③42	7 ③2
—	Horsham............ dep	..	7 14	8 12	10 23	11 25	..	1 39		3 19		4 19	5 19		6 19	6 25	7 19		8 19	..	8 19	9 19	..	2 40	4 19	8 19
2¼	Christ's Hospital K....	..	7 21	8 16	10 27	11 29	..	1 43		3 23		4 23	5 23		6 23	6 29	7 23		8 23	..	8 23	9 23	..	2 44	4 23	8 23
4½	Southwater	..	7 27	8 22	10 32	11 35	..	1 48		3 29		4 29	5 29		6 29	6 35	7 29		8 29	..	8 29	9 29	..	2 49	4 29	8 29
7	West Grinstead	..	7 35	8 29	10 39	11 42	..	1 55		3 36		4 36	5 36		6 36	6 42	7 36		8 36	..	8 36	9 36	..	2 56	4 36	8 36
9¼	Partridge Green	..	7 41	8 36	10 45	11 48	..	2 1		3 43		4 43	5 43		6 43	6 48	7 43		8 43	..	8 43	9 43	..	3 2	4 43	8 42
11¾	Henfield	..	7 46	8 41	10 50	11 53	..	2 6		3 48		4 48	5 48		6 48	6 53	7 48		8 48	..	8 48	9 48	..	3 7	4 48	8 47
15½	Steyning	7 40	7 56	8 50	10 59	12 1	12 16	2 14		3 56		4 57	5 58		6 56	7 1	7 56		8 56	..	8 57	9 57	..	3 16	4 57	8 56
16	Bramber	7 42	7 59	8 54	11 2	12 4	12 18	2 18		4 0		5 1	6 1		6 59	7 4	7 59		8 59	..	9 0	10 0	..	3 19	5 2	8 59
20	Shoreham-by-Sea J 159	7 51	8 10	9 5	11 12	12 13	12 27	2 28		4 9		5 11	6 11		7 9	7 13	8 9		9 8	..	9 9	10 9	..	3 28	5 13	9 9
21½	Southwick	7 55	..	9 9	..	..	..	2 32		4 13		..	6 16		7 12	..	8 12		9 12	..	9 13	10 13	..	..	..	..
23	Portslade and West Hove	7 58	8 16	9 13	11 17	12 19	..	..		4 17		5 16	6 19		7 17	7 19	8 16		9 16	..	9 16	10 18	..	..	5 19	..
24½	Hove	8 2	8 19	9 17	11 21	12 23	12 35	2 38		4 21		5 20	6 23		7 21	7 24	8 20		9 21	..	9 20	10 22	..	3 36	5 23	9 18
26	Brighton 158, 197, 239. arr	8 7	8 24	9 22	11 26	12 28	12 40	2 43		4 26		5 25	6 28		7 26	7 29	8 25		9 26	..	9 25	10 27	..	3 41	5 28	9 23

Miles	Up	Week Days a.m	a.m	a.m	a.m WO		p.m	p.m SO		p.m	p.m	p.m SO		p.m SX	p.m	p.m	p.m			Sundays a.m	a.m		p.m	p.m	p.m
—	Brighton.............. dep	6 30	8 0	9 30	1120	..	12 12	1 35	..	3 57	4 58	5 55	..	6 15	7 15	8 12	9 57	..	..	7 23	10 7	..	2 25	6 25	8 55
1½	Hove..................	6 34	8 4	9 34	1123	..	12 16	1 39	..	4 1	5 2	5 59	..	6 20	7 19	8 16	10 1	..	..	7 28	10 12	..	2 29	6 29	8 59
3	Portslade and West Hove..	6 38	8 8	9 38	1128	..	..	1 42	..	4 4	5 5	..	..	6 23	7 22	..	10 5	..	..	7 32	10 16	..	2 33	6 33	9 3
4½	Southwick..............	6 42	8 12	..	1131	..	..	..	..	4 8	5 9	..	..	6 27	—	..	10 8	..	..	7 36	10 20	..	2 37	6 37	9 7
6	Shoreham-by-Sea J......	6 46	8 16	9 44	1146	..	12 24	1 48	..	4 12	5 12	6 8	..	6 30	7 28	8 24	10 12	..	..	7 40	10 24	..	2 41	6 41	9 11
10	Bramber................	6 55	8 25	9 53	1154	—	12 32	1 56	..	4 20	5 21	6 17	..	6 39	7 37	8 33	10 21	..	..	7 49	10 33	..	2 50	6 50	9 20
10½	Steyning................	6 59	8 30	9 56	1157	..	12 36	1 59	..	4 24	5 25	6 20	..	6 42	7 41	8 38	10 24	..	..	7 53	10 38	..	2 54	6 54	9 24
14¼	Henfield................	7 7	8 39	10 3	..	..	12 44	2 7	..	4 32	5 33	6 28	..	6 50	7 50	8 48	..	..	..	8 1	10 48	..	3 1	7 2	9 32
16½	Partridge Green..........	7 13	8 45	10 8	..	..	12 49	2 12	..	4 37	5 38	6 33	..	6 55	7 56	8 55	..	..	..	8 7	10 55	..	3 6	7 7	9 37
18½	West Grinstead..........	7 20	8 52	10 14	..	..	12 55	2 17	..	4 42	5 44	6 39	..	7 0	8 3	9 2	..	..	..	8 13	11 2	..	3 12	7 14	9 43
21½	Southwater..............	7 28	8 59	10 21	..	..	1 2	2 24	..	4 49	5 50	6 45	..	7 7	8 10	9 9	..	..	..	8 20	11 10	..	3 18	7 21	9 50
23¾	Christ's Hospital K 159, 245	7 33	9 6	10 26	..	..	1 10	2 29	..	4 54	5 56	6 51	..	7 13	8 17	9 14	..	..	..	8 25	11 16	..	3 23	7 27	9 55
26	Horsham 196.......... arr	7 38	9 14	10 31	..	..	1 16	2 34	..	5 0	6 3	6 56	..	7 18	8 23	9 19	..	..	..	8 30	11 21	..	3 28	7 32	10 0
61½	427 Waterloo.......... arr	9③4	10③SO43	12③3	..	..	2③42	4③3	..	6③SX43	7③V43	9③3	..	9③3	10③ 3	11③ 3	..	..	..	9③50	12③59	..	5③9	8③59	12③6
62¾	427 London Bridge..... "	8*43	10SX21	..	..	..	2③ɨ38	..	..	6 36	7③L44	8③38	..	8③38	..	10③40	..	..	..	9③40	1③10	..	5③10	9③4	..
63¾	427 Victoria.......... "	8 37	10 26	11 32	..	..	2③Y50	3 40	..	6 40	7③45	8 40	..	8 40	9 40	10③44	..	..	..	9 31	1 6	..	5 7	8 43	..

③ Third class only. * Change at East Croydon. ɨ 7 mins. later Sats. J Station for Lancing College (2 miles).
K Christ's Hospital, West Horsham. L 5 mins. *earlier* on Sats. SO or SO Saturdays only. SX or SX Saturdays excepted. V Arr. 8③3 p.m on Sats.
WO Wednesdays only. Y Arr 2 40 p.m on Sats. 1st and 3rd class.

For **LOCAL TRAINS** and **intermediate Halts** between Shoreham-by-Sea and Brighton, see page 196
For **OTHER TRAINS** between Horsham and Christ's Hospital, see pages 159 and 245

HAVANT and HAYLING ISLAND

Miles	Down	Week Days only a.m		a.m		a.m		a.m		a.m		p.m		p.m		SO		p.m		p.m		SX		SO		SX		SO		SX		SO	
	Havant .... dep	6 35	..	7 17	..	8 16	..	9 7	..	1019	..	1250	..	1 34	..	2 20	..	4 42	..	5 33	..	6 20	—	6 34	..	7 20	..	7 34	..	8 20	..	8 34	..
	Langston	6 38	..	7 23	..	8 19	..	9 10	..	1022	..	1253	..	1 37	..	2 23	..	4 45	—	5 36	..	6 23	..	6 37	..	7 23	..	7 37	..	8 23	..	8 37	..
2¾	North Hayling..........	..	..	7 29	..	8 23	..	9 16	..	1026	..	1257	..	1 41	..	2 27	..	4 49	..	5 40	..	6 27	..	6 41	..	7 27	..	7 41	..	8 27	..	8 41	..
4½	Hayling Island.... arr	6 45	..	7 35	..	8 29	..	9 22	..	1032	..	1 3	..	1 47	..	2 33	..	4 55	..	5 46	..	6 33	..	6 47	..	7 33	..	7 47	..	8 33	..	8 47	..

SO Saturdays only. SX Saturdays excepted.

GUILDFORD and HORSHAM

Miles	Down	Week Days a.m		a.m	a.m		p.m SO	p.m		p.m		p.m		p.m SX		p.m		p.m		Sundays a.m		p.m			
	394 London (W.) ....dep	6 55	..	8③12	9 45	..	12③12	12 45	..	4Z20	..	5b20	..	5 45	..	6 45	..	7H27	..	7 25	..	6 27	..	..	..
—	**Guildford** ....dep	8 5	..	9 18	10 34	..	1 9	1 42	..	5 4	..	6 7	..	6 34	..	7 34	..	8 34	..	8 54	..	7 22	..	..	..
3¾	Bramley and Wonersh	8 12	..	9 26	10 41	..	1 16	1 50	..	5 12	..	6 15	..	6 42	..	7 41	..	8 42	..	9 2	..	7 29	..	..	..
8¾	Cranleigh	8 23	..	9 40	10 51	..	1 30	2 1	..	5 22	..	6 25	..	6 51	..	7 51	..	8 52	..	9 12	..	7 39	..	..	..
11½	Baynards	8 32	..	9 47	10 58	..	..	2 10	..	5 30	..	6 36	..	..	..	7 58	..	9 1	..	9 20	..	7 46	..	..	..
12½	Rudgwick	8 36	..	9 [illegible]	11 1	..	..	2 14	..	5 33	..	6 40	..	..	..	8 1	..	9 5	..	9 24	..	7 50	..	..	..
14¾	Slinfold	8 42	..	10 0	11 7	..	..	2 19	..	5 39	..	6 46	..	..	..	8 7	..	9 11	..	9 30	..	7 55	..	..	..
17½	Christ's Hospital K 159, 244..	8 49	..	10R11	11 15	..	..	2 26	..	5 45	..	6 53	..	..	..	8 13	..	9 19	..	9 37	..	8 1	..	..	..
41	244 Brighton ....arr	..	..	11 26	2Y43	..	..	4 26	..	7c29	..	8 25	..	..	..	9 26	..	..	..	..	..	9 23	..	..	..
19½	Horsham 198 ....arr	8 54	..	10 16	11 22	..	..	2 31	..	5 50	..	6 59	..	..	..	8 18	..	9 25	..	9 43	..	8 7	..	..	..
57¾	427 London Bridge ....arr	9‡57	..	11③B39	..	..	..	..	..	..	..	8③38	..	..	..	9③38	..	11③11	..	11③10	..	10 7	..	..	..
57¾	427 Victoria .... "	10③13	..	11 32	12 40	..	..	3 40	..	7③13	..	8 40	..	..	..	9 40	..	11 7	..	11 6	..	9 40	..	..	..

Miles	Up	Week Days a.m	a.m	a.m	a.m	a.m		p.m SO	p.m SX	p.m SO	p.m	p.m SO	p.m SX		p.m SX		p.m				Sundays a.m		p.m			
	394 Victoria ....dep	..	..	6③15	7 47	11 18	..	..	1 48	2 18	3 18	4③26	5 4	..	..	..	6U18	..	..	..	9 18	..	7 18	..	..	..
	394 London Bridge .... "	..	..	6③28	8③10	..	..	..	1③31	2③8	3③25	4③28	5 15	..	..	..	5U48	..	..	..	8③55	..	6③55	..	..	..
—	Horsham ....dep	6 36	..	7 59	9 30	12 22	..	..	3 23	3 23	4 53	6 0	6 16	..	..	..	7 12	..	..	..	10 19	..	8 23	..	..	..
—	244 Brighton ....dep	..	..	6 30	8 0	9 30	..	..	12 12	1 35	3 57	4 58	4 58	..	..	..	6V15	..	..	..	7 23	..	6 25	..	..	..
2¼	Christ's Hospital, West Horsham	..	..	8 3	9 35	12 26	..	..	3 27	3 27	4 58	6 4	6 20	..	..	..	7 16	..	..	..	10 23	..	8 27	..	..	..
4¾	Slinfold	..	..	8 9	9 41	12 32	..	..	3 33	3 33	5 4	6 10	6 26	..	..	..	7 22	..	..	..	10 29	..	8 32	..	..	..
7	Rudgwick	6 51	..	8 13	9 45	12 37	..	.	3 37	3 37	5 10	6 15	6 31	..	..	..	7 26	..	..	..	10 33	..	8 37	..	..	..
8¼	Baynards	6 57	..	8 17	9 49	12 42	..	..	3 41	3 41	5 14	6 20	6 35	..	.	..	7 30	..	..	..	10 37	..	8 40	..	..	..
11¼	Cranleigh	7 5	7 18	8 24	9 56	12 49	..	1 40	3 48	3 48	5 21	6 27	6L52	..	7 19	..	7T52	..	..	..	10 43	..	8 46	..	..	..
16¼	Bramley and Wonersh	..	7 27	8 36	10 6	12 59	..	1 50	3 58	3 58	5 35	6 39	7 3	..	7 28	..	8 2	..	..	..	10 53	..	8 56	..	..	..
19½	**Guildford** 246, 249, 359, 427..arr	..	7 36	8 45	10 14	1 7	..	2 1	4 6	4 6	5 47	6 51	7 11	..	7 36	..	8 10	..	..	..	11 5	..	9 4	..	..	..
50	427 London (W.) ....arr	..	8 29	9 30	11J16	2 1	..	3 1	5 3	5 3	6 48	8 16	8 16	..	8 46	..	9 1	..	..	..	12 1	..	10 1	..	..	..

③ Third class only
‡ 8 minutes later on Saturdays

B 3 minutes later on Saturdays
b Dep. 4 57 p.m. on Saturdays
c 3 minutes *earlier* on Saturdays

H Dep. 7 45 p.m. on Saturdays.
J Arr. 11 2 a.m. on Saturdays.
K Christ's Hospital, West Horsham
L Arr. 6 42 p.m.
R Arr. 10 6 a.m.
SO or S0 Saturdays only

SX Saturdays excepted
T Arr. 7 36 p.m.
U Dep. Victoria 5 48 and London Bridge 5③31 p.m. on Saturdays
V Dep. 5 55 p.m. on Saturdays
Y Arr. 12 28 p.m. on Saturdays
Z Dep. 3 57 p.m. on Saturdays

OTHER TRAINS BETWEEN Christ's Hospital and Horsham — PAGE 196 and 244

HAYLING ISLAND and HAVANT

Miles	Up	Week Days only a.m		a.m		a.m		a.m		p.m		p.m		SO		SX		SO		p.m		p.m		p.m		p.m		p.m			
	Hayling Island ....dep	6 58	..	7 46	..	8 40	..	9 45	..	12 27	..	1 12	..	1 57	..	3 18	..	3 22	..	5 6	..	5 57	..	6 52	..	7 52	..	8 52	..	..	..
2	North Hayling	7 2	..	7 50	..	8 44	..	9 49	..	12 31	..	1 16	..	2 1	..	3 24	..	3 26	..	5 10	..	6 1	..	6 56	..	7 56	..	8 56	..	..	..
3¼	Langston	7 7	..	7 55	..	8 49	..	9 54	..	12 36	..	1 21	..	2 6	..	3 30	..	3 31	..	5 15	..	6 6	..	7 1	..	8 1	..	9 1	..	..	..
4½	**Havant** 159, 196, 366...arr	7 13	..	7 59	..	8 53	..	9 58	..	12 40	..	1 25	..	2 10	..	3 35	..	3 35	..	5 19	..	6 10	..	7 5	..	8 5	..	9 5	..	..	.

SO Saturdays only SX Saturdays excepted

LONDON, REDHILL, ASH, ALDERSHOT, and READING

Miles from Redhill	Down	a.m	a.m	a.m	a.m	am	a.m	a.m	a.m	a.m	a.m	a.m	a.m	a.m	a.m	a.m	S O	am	a.m	a.m	a.m
	Victoria 252 .... dep	..	..	..	..	..	..	..	6 40	6 40	..	7 47	7 47	8 0	..	8NB48	9 18	918	..	9 28	9 48
	Clapham Junc. 252.. "	..	..	..	..	..	..	..	6 47	6 47	..	7 52	7 52	8 5	..	..	..	..	..	9 33	9 53
	London Bridge 252.. "	..	..	4 50	..	..	6 16	..	6B35	7 0	7 20	7B35	7B35	7B55	8 18	8 48	..	918	..	..	9B36
	East Croydon 252.. "	..	..	5 10	..	..	6 35	..	7 0	7 17	7 39	8 5	8 5	8 20	8 35	9 8	9 34	936	..	9 46	10 5
—	Redhill .... dep	..	..	5 58	..	..	6 56	..	7 22	7 47	7 59	8 25	8 30	8 45	8 55	9 28	9 50	956	..	10 17	10 26
1½	Reigate	..	..	6 6	..	..	7 (	..	7 26	7 51	8 3	8 29	8 34	8 50	8 59	9 32	9 54	101	..	10 21	10 30
4½	Betchworth	..	..	6 14	..	..	Stop	..	Stop	7 57	Stop	..	8 40	8 56	Stop	Stop	..	..	..	10 27	..
7½	Deepdene A	..	..	6 20	..	..		..		8 8		..	8 45	9 1			..	..	..	10 32	..
8	Dorking Town B	..	..	6 25	..	..	..	..	..	8 5	..	..	8 48	9 4	..	..	..	..	..	10 35	..
12¾	Gomshall and Shere	..	..	6 36	..	..	..	..	..	8 15	..	..	..	9 13	..	..	..	..	..	10 45	..
16¾	Chilworth and Albury	..	..	6 44	..	..	..	..	..	8 23	..	..	..	9 20	..	..	..	..	..	10 53	..
18½	Shalford	..	..	6 51	..	..	..	..	..	8 28	.	..	..	9 25	..	..	..	..	..	10 58	..
20½	Guildford 245,359,427 arr	..	..	6 58	..	..	a.m	..	..	8 34	a.m	..	..	9 32	a.m	a.m	..	..	..	11 4	..
—	394 London (W.) ...... dep	5 25	5 25	6B12	6 25	..	6B52	6 55	..	7 45	7B52	..	..	8 45	8 57	9 45	..	..	9 57	9 57	..
—	Guildford .... dep	6 35	6 54	7 7	7 30	..	7 50	8 3	..	8 38	8 55	..	..	9 34	10 0	10 32	..	..	11 2	11 6	..
24½	Wanborough, for	..	7 1	..	7 37	..	7 57	8 10	..	8 48	9 2	..	..	9 43	10 7	10 39	..	..	11 9	11 15	..
26½	Ash C ...... (Normandy.	6 47	7 5	7 18	7 41	..	8 2	8 14	p.m	8 54	9 6	..	..	9 48	1011	10 43	..	..	1113	11 20	..
—	Ash .... dep	7 0	7 5	7 34	7 41	8 0	..	8 14	8 31	..	9 6	..	..	..	1011	10 43	..	..	1113	..	..
29½	Aldershot D ...... arr	7 7	7 12	7 41	7 48	8 6	..	8 21	8 38	..	9 13	..	..	..	1018	10 50	..	..	1120	..	..
28¾	North Camp F	6 53	..	7 23	..	..	8 8	..	..	9 3	..	..	..	9 54	..	..	..	..	..	11 25	..
30½	Farnborough North G..	6 57	..	7 27	..	..	8 12	..	..	9 8	..	..	..	9 58	..	..	..	..	..	11 29	..
33	Blackwater (Hants) H..	7 2	..	7 32	..	..	8 18	..	..	9 14	..	..	..	10 3	..	..	..	..	..	11 34	..
34½	Sandhurst Halt	7 6	..	7 36	..	..	8 22	..	..	9 19	..	..	..	10 8	..	..	..	..	..	11 38	..
35½	Crowthorne I	7 11	..	7 41	..	..	8 27	..	..	9 25	..	..	..	10 12	..	..	..	..	..	11 43	..
39½	Wokingham 476	7 17	..	7 47	..	..	8 33	..	..	9 32	..	..	..	10 19	..	..	..	..	..	11 49	..
41½	Winnersh Halt L	7 21	..	..	..	..	..	..	..	..	..	..	..	10 24	..	..	..	..	..	..	..
43¾	Earley	7 26	..	..	..	..	8 41	..	..	..	..	..	..	10 28	..	..	..	..	..	..	..
46½	Reading .... arr	7 33	..	7 58	..	..	8 48	..	..	9 45	..	..	..	10 35	..	..	..	..	..	12 0	..

Week Days—*continued*

Down	a.m	a.m	a.m	a.m	SX	p.m	a.m	S O	S X	p.m	p.m	SX	p.m	p.m	SO	p.m	p.m	pm	p.m	p.m
Victoria 252 .... dep	..	10 43	10 48	11*8	11 48	SO	1148	12*3	12*3	S O	12 48	12 48	S O	SX	1 28	1 48	..	Sx	2 28	2 48
Clapham Junc. 252.. "	..	10 53	10 53	..	11 53	..	1153	..	..	..	12 53	12 53	..	..	1 34	1 53	..	..	2 34	2 53
London Bridge 252.. "	10 16	10B36	10B36	1118	11B31		11B37	1215	12 18	1240	12B31	12B31	1 9	1 18	1 32	1SO42	2 18	..	2 18	2SXB31
East Croydon 252.. "	10 32	11 5	11 5	1135	12 5	..	12 5	1230	12 36	..	1 5	1 5	1 24	1 35	1 49	2 5	2 34	..	2 46	3 5
Redhill .... dep	10 55	11 26	11 35	1155	12 26	..	1231	1252	12 56	1 18	1 26	1 30	1 42	1 55	2 9	2 26	2 55	..	3 4	3 26
Reigate	10 59	11 30	11 39	12 0	12 30	..	1236	1256	1 0	1 23	1 30	1 34	1 47	2 0	2 13	2 30	2 59	..	3 9	3 30
Betchworth	Stop	Stop	11 45	Stop	..	..	1242	Stop	Stop	1 29	..	1 40	..	Stop	Stop	Stop	Stop	..	3 16	Stop
Deepdene A			11 50		..	..	1247			1 35	..	1 46	..					..	3 21	
Dorking Town B	..	..	11 53	..	..	..	1250	..	..	1 38	..	1 50	..	..	..	..	..	..	3 24	..
Gomshall and Shere	..	..	12 3	..	..	..	1 0	..	..	1 48	..	2 0	..	..	..	..	..	..	3 34	..
Chilworth and Albury..	..	..	12 10	..	..	..	1 8	..	..	1 55	..	2 8	..	..	..	..	..	..	3 41	..
Shalford	..	a.m	12 15	..	..	..	1 15	..	..	2 2	..	2 14	..	..	p.m	..	p.m	..	3 45	..
Guildford 245,359,427 arr	a.m	S O	12 22	a.m	..	..	1 22	p.m	p.m	2 8	..	2 22	..	..	S O	p.m	S O	..	3 51	p.m
394 London (W.) .... dep	10 57	11 45	11 45	1157	..		12B12	1245	12g57	1 15	..	1B12	..	..	1 45	1 57	2 45		2B52	2 57
Guildford .... dep	12 0	12 30	12 37	1 0	..	..	1 23	1 30	2 0	2 14	..	2 23	..	..	2 30	3 0	3 30	..	3 53	4 0
Wanborough, for	12 7	12 37	..	1 7	..	..	1 32	1 37	2 7	2 24	..	2 32	..	p.m	2 37	3 7	3 37	..	4 2	4 7
Ash C ...... (Normandy.	12 11	12 41	12 48	1 11	..	1 16	1 37	1 41	2 11	2 30	..	2 37	..	SX	2 41	3 11	3 41	Sx	4 7	4 11
Ash .... dep	12 11	12 41	..	1 11	..	..	1 41	1 41	2 11	..	..	..	..	2 41	2 41	3 11	3 41	341	..	4 11
Aldershot D ...... arr	12 18	12 48	..	1 18	..	..	1 48	1 48	2 18	..	..	..	..	2 48	2 48	3 18	3 48	348	..	4 18
North Camp F	..	..	12 54	..	..	1 20	1 42	..	..	2 36	..	2 42	..	..	..	..	..	..	4 12	..
Farnborough North G..	..	..	12 59	..	..	1 25	1 47	..	..	2 41	..	2 47	..	..	..	..	..	..	4 17	..
Blackwater (Hants) H..	..	..	1 4	..	..	1 30	1 52	..	..	2 47	..	2 52	..	..	..	..	..	..	4 22	..
Sandhurst Halt	..	..	1 8	..	..	1 34	1 56	..	..	2 51	..	2 56	..	..	..	..	..	..	4 26	..
Crowthorne I	..	..	1 13	..	..	1 39	2 1	..	..	2 56	..	3 1	..	..	..	..	..	..	4 31	..
Wokingham 476	..	..	1 20	..	..	1 45	2 7	..	..	3 2	..	3 7	..	..	..	..	..	..	4 37	..
Winnersh Halt L	..	..	1 24	..	..	..	2 12	..	..	..	..	3 12	..	..	..	..	..	..	.	..
Earley	..	..	1 28	..	..	..	2 16	..	..	..	..	3 16	..	..	..	..	..	..	..	..
Reading .... arr	..	..	1 35	..	..	1 56	2 23	..	..	3 14	..	3 23	..	..	..	..	..	..	4 48	..

For Notes, see page 251

LONDON, REDHILL, EDENBRIDGE, and TONBRIDGE

Miles from Redhill	Down	a.m		a.m	a.m		a.m	a.m	a.m		p.m SX	p.m S O	p.m £0	p.m SX		p.m SO	p.m SO	p.m SX	p.m S O	p.m
	Victoria 252 .... dep	..	..	6 40	..	..	8 28	9 28	11 28	..	12 28	12*25	..	1 28	..	2 28	3 28	3 28	3 48	4 28
	Clapham Junc. 252.. "	..	..	6 47	..	..	8 33	9 33	11 34	..	12 34	..	..	1 34	..	2U34	3 34	3 34	3 53	4gL22
	London Bridge 252.. "	4 50	..	6B35	7 20	..	8 18	9 18	11 18	..	12 18	12 30	1 9	1 18	..	2 18	3 18	3 18	3B31	4*P20
	East Croydon 252.. "	5 10	..	7 0	7 39	..	8 44	9 46	11 46	..	12 46	12 47	1 24	1 46	..	2 46	3 46	3 46	4 5	4 46
—	Redhill .... dep	5 44	..	7 27	8 9	..	9 6	1018	12 6	..	1 4	1 4	1 50	2 10	..	3 6	4 5	4 15	4 36	5 5
2	Nutfield	5 51	..	7 31	..	..	9 10	1022	12 10	..	1 8	1 8	1 54	2 15	..	3 10	4 10	4 19	4 40	5 9
5½	Godstone	5 59	..	7 37	..	..	9 16	1029	12 17	..	1 15	1 15	2 1	2 21	..	3 17	4 19	4 25	4 47	5 17
10½	Edenbridge N	6 7	..	7 45	8 23	..	9 24	1037	12 26	..	1 24	1 24	2 10	2 29	..	3 25	4 29	4 33	4 55	5 25
15½	Penshurst	6 16	..	7 52	8 31	..	9 32	1045	12 34	..	1 32	1 32	2 20	2 37	..	3 33	4 38	4 41	5 3	5 33
17	Leigh Halt	..	..	7 57	8 35	..	9 36	1049	12 39	..	1 36	1 38	2 25	2 40	..	3 37	4 43	4 45	..	5 38
19½	Tonbridge 34, 43 .... arr	6 24	..	8 4	8 43	..	9 41	1057	12 48	..	1 42	1 46	2 33	2 46	..	3 43	4 50	4 51	5 12	5 46

For Notes, see page 247

LONDON, REDHILL, ASH, ALDERSHOT, and READING

Down	Week Days—continued																				
	p.m SX	p.m	p.m	p.m	p.m	p.m	p.m SO	SX	SX	p.m	SO	p.m SX	p.m		SO	p.m	p.m SX	SO	p.m SX	SO	SX
Victoria 252 .... dep		3 18	..	..	3 28	3 48		4 25	4*45	..	4 48		..	..	5* 9	..		5 28		5 48	6 4
Clapham Junc. 252.. "	..	..	..	..	3 34	3 53	..	4 21	4(3)40	..	4 53	..	..	..	..	..	..	5 34	..	5 53	6 9
London Bridge 252.. "	..	3 18	..	..	..	3(3)31	4 16	4*20	4 47	..	4(3)31	..	..	..	5 16	..	5 25	5*16	5 50	5(3)31	5(3)55
East Croydon 252.. "	..	3 36	..	..	3 46	4 5	4 34	4 46	5 2	..	5 5	..	..	..	5 34	..	..	5 46	6 f	6 5	6 21
Redhill .... dep	..	3 56	..	..	4 10	4 26	4 55	5 4	5 22	..	5 26	..	5 36	..	5 55	..	6 3	6 9	6 25	6 25	6 40
Reigate	..	4 0	..	..	4 16	4 30	4 59	5 8	5 26	..	5 30	..	5 40	..	5 59	..	6 7	6 13	6 30	6 30	6 44
Betchworth	..		..	..	4 23			..	..	..		..	5 46	..	..	..	6 13	6 19	..		
Deepdene A	..	Stop	..	..	4 28	Stop	Stop	..	..	..	Stop	..	5 51	..	..	..	6 19	6 24	..	Stop	Stop
Dorking Town B	..	..	..	..	4 33	..	..	..	..	..	..	..	5 54	..	..	..	6 23	6 27	..	..	..
Gomshall and Shere	..	..	..	..	4 45	..	..	..	..	..	..	..	6 4	..	..	..	6 35	6 37	..	..	..
Chilworth and Albury ..	..	..	..	..	4 55	..	..	..	..	..	..	..	6 11	..	..	..	6 43	6 45	..	..	..
Shalford	..	p.m	..	..	5 [illegible]	p.m	..	..	..	..	..	SX	6 15	..	..	..	6 48	6 50	..	..	p.m
Guildford 245, 359, 427 arr	..	SX	..	..	5 9	SX	..	..	..	..	..	—	6 21	..	..	..	6 54	6 56	..	..	SX
394 London (W.) .... dep	..	3 45	3(3)52	4l20	4l20	4 45	..	..	..	4 57	..	5 45	5 45	..	..	6t20	6 20	5 57	..	..	6 45
Guildford .... dep	..	4 30	4 54	5 0	5 24	5 30	..	..	..	6 0	..	6 30	6 35	..	..	7 0	7 3	7 3	..	..	7 30
Wanborough, for	..	4 37	5 2	5 7	5 32	5 37	p.m	..	..	6 7	p.m	6 37	6 43	..	..	7 7	7 13	7 13	..	p.m	7 37
Ash C ...... [Normandy.	SX	4 41	5 7	5 11	5 37	5 41	SO	..	..	6 11	SO	6 41	6 48	..	..	7 11	7 18	7 18	..	SO	7 41
Ash .... dep	4 33	4 41	..	5 11	..	5 41	5 41	..	..	6 11	6 41	6 41	..	..	..	7 11	..	..	..	7 41	7 41
Aldershot D ...... arr	4 40	4 48	..	5 18	..	5 48	5 48	..	..	6 18	6 48	6 48	..	..	..	7 18	..	..	..	7 48	7 48
North Camp F	..	..	5 12	..	5 42	..	..	..	..	..	..	..	6 53	..	..	..	7 23	7 23	..	..	..
Farnborough North G ..	..	..	5 17	..	5 47	..	..	..	..	..	..	..	6 58	..	..	..	7 28	7 28	..	..	..
Blackwater (Hants) H ..	..	..	5 22	..	5 52	..	..	..	..	..	..	..	7 3	..	..	..	7 33	7 33	..	..	..
Sandhurst Halt	..	..	5 26	..	5 56	..	..	..	..	..	..	..	7 7	..	..	..	7 37	7 37	..	..	..
Crowthorne I	..	..	5 31	..	6 1	..	..	..	..	..	..	..	7 12	..	..	..	7 42	7 42	..	..	..
Wokingham 476	..	..	5 37	..	6 7	..	..	..	..	..	..	..	7 21	..	..	..	7 48	7 48	..	..	..
Winnersh Halt L	..	..	..	..	..	..	..	..	..	..	..	..	..	..	..	..	..	..	..	..	..
Earley	..	..	..	..	..	..	..	..	..	..	..	..	..	..	..	..	..	..	..	..	..
Reading .... arr	..	..	5 48	..	6 18	..	..	..	..	..	..	..	7 34	..	..	..	7 59	7 59	..	..	..

Down	Week Days—continued																		
	SO	SX	p.m	p.m SX	SX	p.m	SO	p.m	p.m	p.m	p.m	p.m	p.m	p.m	p.m	p.m	p.m	p.m	p.m
Victoria 252 .... dep	6*10	6*10	6SO28		6*45	..	6 48	7SX5	7 48	7 48	8*2	8 48	..	8 48	..	9 48	..	10 48	11 15
Clapham Junc. 252.. "	6*16	..	6SO34	..	..	..	6 53	7SX10	7 53	7 53	..	8 53	..	8 53	..	9 53	..	10 53	11 21
London Bridge 252.. "	6 16	6 20	6SO16	..	6 48	..	6(3)31	7 18	7(3)v31	7(3)v31	8 16	8(3)31	..	8(3)31	9 16	9(3)31	1016	10(3)31	11(3)11
East Croydon 252.. "	6 34	6 35	6SO46	..	7 5	..	7 5	7 35	8 5	8 [illegible]	8 34	9 5	..	9 5	9 34	10 5	1034	11 5	11 33
Redhill .... dep	6 55	6 57	7 5	7 15	7 26	..	7 26	7 55	8 26	8 33	8 55	9 26	..	9 39	9 55	10 26	1055	11 26	11 54
Reigate	7 0	7 1	7 9	7 20	7 30	..	7 30	8 0	8 30	8 37	8 59	9 30	..	9 43	9 59	10 30	1059	11 30	11 58
Betchworth	..	..	7 15		..	..	..		..	8 43			..	9 50				..	..
Deepdene A	..	..	7 20	Stop	..	..	..	Stop	..	8 49	Stop	Stop	..	9 56	Stop	Stop	Stop	..	..
Dorking Town B	..	..	7 23	..	..	..	..	..	..	8 52	..	..	..	9 59	..	..	..	..	..
Gomshall and Shere ...	..	..	7 33	..	..	..	..	..	..	9 2	..	..	..	10 9	..	..	..	..	..
Chilworth and Albury ..	..	..	7 40	..	..	..	..	..	..	9 10	..	..	..	10 17	..	..	..	..	..
Shalford	..	..	7 45	..	..	..	..	..	..	9 14	..	..	..	10 22	..	..	..	..	..
Guildford 245, 359, 427 arr	..	..	7 51	p.m	..	..	..	p.m	..	9 21	..	p.m	..	10 28	p.m	..	..	..	..
394 London (W.) ..... dep	..	..	6P52	6 57	..	..	..	7 57	..	8(3)12	..	8 57	9 45	9 45	9 57	..	..	..	..
Guildford .... dep	..	..	7 54	8 3	..	..	..	9 2	..	9 23	..	10 0	1030	10 35	11 0	..	..	..	..
Wanborough, for	.	..	8 4	8 10	..	..	..	9 9	..	..	..	10 7	1037	10 45	11 7	ngt.	ngt.	..	..
Ash C ...... [Normandy.	..	..	8 9	8 15	..	..	..	9 13	..	9 36	p.m	10 11	1041	10 51	1111	SX	SO	..	..
Ash .... dep	..	..	..	8 15	..	8 41	..	9 13	..	..	9 41	10 11	1041	..	1111	12 0	1218	..	..
Aldershot D ...... arr	..	..	..	8 22	..	8 48	..	9 20	..	..	9 48	10 18	1048	..	1118	12 7	1225	..	..
North Camp F	..	..	8 14	..	..	..	..	..	..	9 42	..	..	..	10 57	..	..	..	..	..
Farnborough North G ..	..	..	8 19	..	..	..	..	..	..	9 47	..	..	..	11 1	..	..	..	..	..
Blackwater (Hants) H ..	..	..	8 24	..	.	..	..	..	..	9 52	..	..	..	11 6	..	..	..	..	...
Sandhurst Halt	..	..	8 28	..	..	..	..	..	..	9 56	..	..	..	11 13	..	..	..	..	..
Crowthorne I	..	..	8 33	..	..	..	..	..	..	10 1	..	..	..	11 18	..	..	..	..	..
Wokingham 476	..	..	8 39	..	..	..	..	..	..	10 7	..	..	..	11 25	..	..	..	..	..
Winnersh Halt L	..	..	..	..	..	..	..	..	..	10 12	..	..	..	..	..	..	..	..	..
Earley	..	..	..	..	..	..	..	..	..	10 16	..	..	..	11 32	..	..	..	..	..
Reading .... arr	..	..	8 50	..	..	..	..	..	..	10 23	..	..	..	11 39	..	..	..	..	..

For Notes, see page 251; for SUNDAY TRAINS, see page 248

LONDON, REDHILL, EDENBRIDGE, and TONBRIDGE

Down	Week Days—continued								
	p.m	p.m SX		p.m SX	p.m SO	p.m	p.m	p.m	p.m
Victoria 252 .... dep	5SO28	6 4	..	7 5	6 48	8 28	9 28	1028	..
Clapham Junc. 252...... "	5SO34	6 U9	..	7U10	6 53	8 34	9 34	1034	..
London Bridge 252...... "	5h25	6 9	..	6(3)55	6(3)31	8 16	9 16	1016	1150
East Croydon 252...... "	5h28	6 24	..	7 22	7 5	8 46	9 46	1046	1215
Redhill .... dep	6 7	6 51	..	7 44	7 44	9 5	1010	1111	1248
Nutfield	6 11	6 55	..	7 48	7 49	9 9	1014	1115	(3)
Godstone	6 18	7 1	..	7 55	7 55	9 16	1020	1121	
Edenbridge N	6 26	7 9	..	8 3	8 3	9 24	1028	1129	..
Penshurst	6 34	7 17	..	8 11	8 11	9 32	1036	1137	..
Lyghe Halt	6 38	7 21	..	8 16	8 16	9 37	1041	1145	..
Tonbridge 34, 43 .... arr	6 44	7 27	..	8 26	8 26	9 45	1048	1152	1 19

(3) Third class only
* Change at East Croydon.
g Dep. Clapham Junction 4 34 p.m on Sats.
h Dep. London Bridge 5 16 and East Croydon 5 46 p.m. on Sats.
N 1 mile to Edenbridge Town Sta.
P Dep. 6 1[illegible] p.m on Sats.
SO or SO Sats. only
SX or SX Sats. excepted.
l Calls to take up only.
Z Except on Sats. calls to take up only.

For SUNDAY TRAINS, see page 248

LONDON, REDHILL, ASH, ALDERSHOT, and READING

Down	Sundays																				
	am	am	a.m	am	a.m	a.m	a.m	a.m	a.m	a.m	a.m	a.m	a.m		p.m	a.m	p.m	p.m	p.m	p.m	p.m
Victoria 252 ....dep	..	..	6 40	..	7 46	..	8*28	..	9 28	9 48	10 18	10 48	10 48	..	..	11 48	..	..	12 48	1 28	1 48
Clapham Junc. 252.. "	..	..	6 46	..	7 51	..	8*33	..	9 33	9 53	..	10 53	10 53	..	..	11 53	..	..	12 53	1 33	1 53
London Bridge 252.. "	..	..	..	716	7 40	8 16	8 49	9 16	9 16	9③30	10 16	10③30	10③30	..	..	11③30	..	..	12③30	..	1③30
East Croydon 252.. "	..	..	7 2	735	8 5	8 35	9 6	9 35	9 46	10 5	10 35	11 5	11 5	..	..	12 5	..	..	1 5	1 46	2 5
Redhill ....dep	..	..	7 32	8 2	8 28	8 55	9 26	9 55	10 4	10 26	10 56	11 26	11 32	..	..	12 26	..	..	1 26	2 5	2 26
Reigate	..	..	7 38	8 6	8 32	9 0	9 30	9 59	10 8	10 30	11 0	11 30	11 36	..	..	12 30	..	..	1 30	2 9	2 30
Betchworth	..	..	7 44	..	—	..	—	..	1014	—	..	—	11 42	..	..	—	..	..	—	2 15	—
Deepdene A	..	..	7 50	..	Stop	..	Stop	..	1020	Stop	..	Stop	11 48	..	..	Stop	..	..	Stop	2 20	Stop
Dorking Town B	..	..	7 53	..	..	..	..	..	1023	..	..	..	11 51	..	..	..	..	..	..	2 23	..
Gomshall and Shere	..	..	8 3	..	..	..	..	..	1033	..	..	..	12 1	..	..	..	..	..	..	2 33	..
Chilworth and Albury ..	..	..	8 10	..	..	..	..	..	1040	..	..	..	12 8	..	..	..	..	..	..	2 40	..
Shalford	..	..	8 15	..	..	..	..	..	1045	..	..	..	12 14	..	..	..	..	..	..	2 44	..
Guildford 245, 359, 427 ar	..	..	8 21	..	a.m	..	a.m	..	1051	a.m	..	a.m	12 20	..	..	a.m	..	..	..	2 50	p.m
394 London (W.) ....dep	..	..	7 25	..	7 57	..	8 57	..	9 45	9 57	..	10 57	11③2	..	..	11 57	12 45	1257	..	1③38	1 57
Guildford ....dep	730	758	8 25	..	9 0	..	10 0	..	1052	11 0	..	12 0	12 21	..	..	1 0	1 30	2 0	..	2 53	3 0
Wanborough, for	737	8 5	8 34	..	9 7	..	10 7	..	11 1	11 7	..	12 7	12 30	..	..	1 7	1 37	2 7	..	..	3 7
Ash C ......[Normandy.	741	810	8 39	..	9 11	..	1011	..	11 6	11 11	..	12 11	12 35	..	..	1 11	1 41	2 11	p.m	3 5	3 11
Ash ....dep	741	811	8 43	..	9 11	..	1011	..	..	11 11	..	12 11	..	..	1241	1 11	1 41	2 11	2 41	..	3 11
Aldershot D ......arr	748	817	8 50	..	9 18	..	1018	..	..	11 18	..	12 18	..	..	1248	1 18	1 48	2 18	2 48	..	3 18
North Camp F	..	..	8 45	..	..	..	..	..	1111	..	..	..	12 40	..	..	..	..	..	..	3 10	..
Farnborough North G ..	..	..	8 49	..	..	..	..	..	1115	..	..	..	12 44	..	..	..	..	..	..	3 14	..
Blackwater (Hants) H ..	..	..	8 54	..	..	..	..	..	1120	..	..	..	12 49	..	..	..	..	..	..	3 19	..
Sandhurst Halt	..	..	8 59	..	..	..	..	..	1125	..	..	..	12 54	..	..	..	..	..	..	3 24	..
Crowthorne I	..	..	9 3	..	..	..	..	..	1129	..	..	..	12 58	..	..	..	..	..	..	3 28	..
Wokingham 476	..	..	9 9	..	..	..	..	..	1136	..	..	..	1 4	..	..	..	..	..	..	3 35	..
Winnersh Halt L	..	..	..	..	..	..	..	..	..	..	..	..	1 9	..	..	..	..	..	..	..	..
Earley	..	..	..	..	..	..	..	..	..	..	..	..	1 13	..	..	..	..	..	..	..	..
Reading ....arr	..	..	9 21	..	..	..	..	..	1148	..	..	..	1 20	..	..	..	..	..	..	3 48	..

Down	Sundays—*continued*																				
	p.m	p.m		p.m	p.m	p.m	p.m	p.m	p.m		p.m	p.m	p.m	p.m	p.m	p.m	p.m	p.m	p.m	p.m	p.m
Victoria 252 ....dep	2 28	2 48	..	3 48	..	4 28	4 48	5 48	..	..	6 28	6 48	7 28	7 48	7 48	..	8 48	8 48	..	9 48	1028
Clapham Junc. 252.. "	2 33	2 53	..	3 53	..	4 33	4 53	5 53	..	..	6 33	6 53	7 33	7 53	7 53	..	8 53	8 53	..	9 53	1033
London Bridge 252.. "	..	2③30	..	3③30	..	..	4③30	5③30	..	..	..	6*40	..	7③30	7③30	8 16	8③30	8③30	9 1	9③30	..
East Croydon 252.. "	2 46	3 5	..	4 5	..	4 46	5 5	6 5	..	..	6 46	7 5	7 46	8 5	8 5	8 35	9 5	9 5	9 35	10 5	1046
Redhill ....dep	3 4	3 26	..	4 26	..	5 5	5 26	6 26	..	..	7 5	7 26	8 8	8 26	8 35	8 55	9 26	9 39	10 4	10 26	11 5
Reigate	3 8	3 30	..	4 30	..	5 9	5 30	6 30	..	..	7 8	7 30	8 12	8 30	8 39	9 0	9 30	9 43	10 8	10 30	11 9
Betchworth	3 13	—	..	—	..	5 15	—	—	..	..	7 15	—	—	—	8 45	—	—	9 50	..	..	—
Deepdene A	3 19	Stop	..	Stop	..	5 20	Stop	Stop	..	..	7 21	Stop	Stop	Stop	8 51	Stop	Stop	9 56	..	..	Stop
Dorking Town B	3 22	..	..	..	..	5 23	..	..	..	..	7 24	..	..	..	8 55	..	..	9 59	..	..	..
Gomshall and Shere	3 32	..	..	..	..	5 33	..	..	..	..	7 34	..	..	..	9 5	..	..	10 9	..	..	..
Chilworth and Albury ..	3 39	..	..	..	..	5 40	..	..	..	..	7 41	..	..	..	9 12	..	..	10 17	..	..	..
Shalford	3 44	..	..	..	..	5 44	..	..	..	..	7 46	..	..	..	9 17	..	..	10 22	..	..	..
Guildford 245, 359, 427 ar	3 50	p.m	..	p.m	..	5 50	p.m	..	..	..	7 52	p.m	..	p.m	9 23	p.m	p.m	10 28	..	..	p.m
394 London (W.) ....dep	Stop	2 57	..	3 57	..	4 45	4 57	..	5 57	..	6 45	6 57	..	7 57	8③2	8 45	8 57	9 45	..	..	1027
Guildford ....dep		4 0	..	5 0	..	5 52	6 0	..	7 0	..	7 54	8 2	..	9 0	9 24	9 32	10 0	10 31	..	..	1130
Wanborough, for	..	4 7	..	5 7	..	6 1	6 7	..	7 7	..	..	8 9	..	9 7	..	9 39	10 7	10 41	..	..	1137
Ash C ......[Normandy.	p.m	4 11	..	5 11	..	6 6	6 11	p.m	7 11	..	8 6	8 13	p.m	9 11	9 35	9 43	10 11	10 47	..	..	1141
Ash ....dep	3 41	4 11	..	5 11	5 24	..	6 11	6 41	7 11	..	..	8 13	8 41	9 11	..	9 43	10 11	..	..	..	1147
Aldershot D ......arr	3 48	4 18	..	5 18	5 31	..	6 18	6 48	7 18	..	..	8 20	8 48	9 18	..	9 50	10 18	..	..	..	1154
North Camp F	..	..	..	..	..	6 11	..	..	..	..	8 13	..	..	..	9 42	..	..	10 54	..	..	..
Farnborough North G ..	..	..	..	..	..	6 15	..	..	..	..	8 18	..	..	..	9 47	..	..	10 58	..	..	..
Blackwater (Hants) H ..	..	..	..	..	..	6 20	..	..	..	..	8 24	..	..	..	9 52	..	..	11 3	..	..	..
Sandhurst Halt	..	..	..	..	..	6 25	..	..	..	..	8 29	..	..	..	9 57	..	..	11 8	..	..	..
Crowthorne I	..	..	..	..	..	6 29	..	..	..	..	8 35	..	..	..	10 2	..	..	11 14	..	..	..
Wokingham 476	..	..	..	..	..	6 35	..	..	..	..	8 42	..	..	..	10 8	..	..	11 21	..	..	..
Winnersh Halt L	..	..	..	..	..	..	..	..	..	..	..	..	..	..	..	..	..	..	..	..	..
Earley	..	..	..	..	..	..	..	..	..	..	..	..	..	..	..	..	..	..	..	..	..
Reading ....arr	..	..	..	..	..	6 46	..	..	..	..	8 53	..	..	..	10 19	..	..	11 32	..	..	..

For Notes, see page 251

LONDON, REDHILL, EDENBRIDGE, and TONBRIDGE

Down	Sundays											
	a.m	a.m		a.m		p.m	p.m		p.m	p.m	p.m	
Victoria 252 ....dep	..	8*28	..	11 48	..	2 28	4 28	..	6 48	8 28	8*48	..
Clapham Junc 252...... "	..	8*33	..	11 53	..	2 33	4 33	..	6 53	8 35	8*53	..
London Bridge 252...... "	7 16	8 49	..	11③30		2③0	4③0	..	6*40	8 16	9 5	..
East Croydon 252 ...... "	7 35	9 6	..	12 5	..	2 46	4 46	..	7 5	8 48	9 25	..
Redhill ....dep	7 59	9 41	..	12 32	..	3 10	5 5	..	7 43	9 6	9 50	..
Nutfield	8 3	9 45	..	12 35	..	3 14	5 9	..	7 49	9 10	9 54	..
Godstone	8 10	9 52	..	12 43	..	3 21	5 16	..	7 57	9 17	10 1	..
Edenbridge N	8 18	10 1	..	12 52	..	3 30	5 24	..	8 5	9 25	1010	..
Penshurst	8 26	10 10	..	1 0	..	3 38	5 32	..	8 13	9 33	1018	..
Lyghe Halt	8 30	10 14	..	1 4	..	3 44	5 36	..	8 18	9 37	1023	..
Tonbridge 34, 43 ....arr	8 38	10 20	..	1 10	..	3 50	5 43	..	8 24	9 45	1033	..

③ Third class only

* Change at East Croydon.

N 1 mile to Edenbridge Town Station.

OTHER TRAINS
BETWEEN

	PAGE
London and Edenbridge	234
London and Tonbridge	54

READING, ALDERSHOT, ASH, REDHILL, and LONDON

Miles	Up	Week Days																			
		a.m	a.m	am	a.m	a.m	a.m	a.m	a.m	a.m	a.m	a.m	a.m	a.m	a.m	a.m	a.m	a.m	a.m	a.m	a.m
	Reading ....dep	..	..	..	..	6 5	..	..	6 50	..	..	7 27	..	..	..	8 20	..	..	9 3	..	..
3	Earley	..	..	..	..	6 11	..	..	..	..	..	..	..	..	..	..	..	..	..	..	..
4¾	Winnersh Halt **L**	..	..	..	..	..	..	..	..	..	..	..	..	..	..	..	..	..	..	..	..
6¾	Wokingham	..	..	..	..	6 20	..	..	7 1	..	..	7 38	..	..	..	8 31	..	..	9 14	..	..
10½	Crowthorne **I**	..	..	..	..	6 27	..	..	7 8	..	..	7 45	..	..	..	8 37	..	..	9 21	..	..
12	Sandhurst Halt	..	..	..	..	..	..	..	7 12	..	..	7 49	..	..	..	8 41	..	..	9 25	..	..
13¾	Blackwater (Hants) **H** ..	..	..	..	..	6 34	..	..	7 16	..	..	7 53	..	..	..	8 45	..	..	9 29	..	..
15¾	Farnboro' North **G**	..	..	..	..	6 40	..	..	7 22	..	..	7 59	..	..	..	8 52	..	..	9 36	..	..
17½	North Camp **F**	..	..	..	..	6 45	..	..	7 26	..	..	8 3	..	..	..	8 56	..	..	9 41	..	..
—	Mls **Aldershot** ......dep	..	..	..	..	6 41	..	7 8	7 20	7 40	..	7 49	8 12	8 20	8 50	..	..	9 20	..	9 55	10 20
—	3 Ash **C** .... arr	..	..	..	..	6 47	..	7 14	7 26	7 46	..	7 55	8 18	8 26	8 56	..	..	9 26	..	10 1	10 26
19	Ash **C** ......[Normandy	..	..	..	..	6 51	..	7 14	7 32	7 46	..	8 9	..	8 28	8 56	9 2	..	9 28	9 47	10 1	10 26
21¼	Wanborough, for	..	..	..	..	6 57	..	7 19	7 36	7 51	..	8 13	..	8 35	9 1	9 8	..	9 35	..	10 6	10 31
26	Guildford 245, 359, 427ar	..	..	..	..	7 4	..	7 25	7 44	7 58	..	8 20	..	8 41	9 7	9 16	..	9 41	9 58	10 12	10 37
56	427London (W). ......arr	..	..	..	..	8Ⓐ5	..	8b22	8 29	8a52	..	9 13	..	9 30	10 5	10 5	..	10j28	11FⒶ5	11F16	11Ⓐ43
—	**Guildford** ....dep	..	..	..	..	7 8	..	Stop	7 45	Stop	..	8 22	..	Stop	Stop	9 20	..	Stop	10 2	Stop	Stop
27½	Shalford	..	..	..	..	7 14	..		7 52		..	8 30	..			9 27	..		10 9		
29½	Chilworth and Albury.	..	..	..	..	7 19	..	..	7 57	..	..	8 35	..	a.m	..	9 32	..	..	10 14	..	..
33½	Gomshall and Shere....	..	..	..	..	7 27	..	..	8 5	..	..	8 44	..	SX	..	9 40	..	..	10 22	..	..
38½	Dorking Town **B**	..	..	..	..	7 36	..	..	8 15	–	..	8 54	..	9 30	..	9 50	..	..	10 32	..	..
39	Deepdene **A**	..	..	..	..	7 38	..	..	8 18	..	..	8 57	..	9 32	a.m	9 53	..	..	10 34	..	..
41½	Betchworth..	..	..	..	..	7 44	..	a.m	8 24	a.m	..	9 2	..	9 37	SO	9 58	..	a.m	10 39	a.m	a.m
44½	**Reigate**	6 22	6 52	7 19	7 43	7 50	8 2	8 21	8 30	8 40	8 58	9 8	..	9 43	9 44	10 4	10 12	10 32	10 45	10 52	11 22
46½	**Redhill 158**, 246, 285ar	6 26	6 56	7 23	7 47	7 55	8 6	8 25	8 35	8 44	9 2	9 13	..	9 48	9 48	10 9	10 17	10 26	10 50	10 56	11 26
56½	East Croydon 285...arr	6 48	7 18	7 45	8 9	8 26	8 26	8 47	9 5	9 5	9 23	..	..	10 9	10 9	10 38	10 38	10 57	11 18	11 18	11 49
67	London Bridge 285.. "	7 7	7*39	8 0	8 26	8 43	8 43	9 3	9 20	9 20	9 38	9 48	..	10Ⓐ32	10*40	10 56	10 56	..	..		12Ⓐz11
64½	Clapham Junc. 285.. "	..	7 30	8*0	8*23	8*48	8*48	..	..	9U22	..	..	..	10 20	10 20	..	..	11 11	11 30	11 30	12SX1
67½	Victoria 285........ "	..	7 36	8*7	8*28	8*46	8*46	9* 8	..	9U27	9*42	..	..	10 26	10 26	10*57	10*57	11 17	11 37	11 37	12SX6

Up	Week Days—*continued*																	
	a.m	a.m	a.m	p.m	a.m		p.m	p.m	p.m	p.m	p.m	p.m	p.m	p.m	p.m	p.m	p.m	p.m
Reading ....dep	9 50	..	..	SO	11 0	..	..	..	..	12 15	..	..	..	..	1 50	..	..	2 50
Earley	..	..	..	..	11 6	..	..	..	..	12 21	..	..	..	..	..	..	..	..
Winnersh Halt **L**	..	..	..	..	11 11	..	..	..	..	..	..	..	..	..	..	..	..	..
Wokingham	10 2	..	..	..	11 16	..	..	..	..	12 28	..	..	..	..	2 2	..	..	3 2
Crowthorne **I**	10 9	..	..	..	11 23	..	..	..	..	12 35	..	..	..	..	2 9	..	..	3 9
Sandhurst Halt	10 14	..	..	..	11 27	..	..	..	..	12 39	..	..	..	..	2 14	..	..	3 14
Blackwater (Hants) **H** ..	10 19	..	..	..	11 31	..	..	..	..	12 42	..	..	..	..	2 18	..	..	3 18
Farnboro' North **G**	10 26	..	..	..	11 37	..	..	..	..	12 49	..	..	..	..	2 25	..	..	3 25
North Camp **F**	10 31	..	..	..	11 42	..	..	..	..	12 53	..	..	..	..	2 29	..	..	3 29
Aldershot ....dep	..	10 54	11 21	..	..	..	..	12 20	..	..	1 18	..	1J51	2 20	..	2 50	3 20	..
Ash **C** .... arr	..	11 0	11 27	..	..	..	..	12 26	..	..	1 24	..	1J57	2 26	..	2 56	3 26	..
Ash **C** ......[Normandy	10 37	11 0	11 27	..	11 48	..	..	12 26	..	12 59	1 24	..	2SO4	2 26	2 35	2SO56	3 26	3 35
Wanborough for	10 41	11 6	11 32	..	11 52	..	..	12 31	..	1 3	1 29	..	2SO9	2 31	2 40	3SO1	3 31	3 40
Guildford 245, 359, 427 ar	10 48	11 12	11 38	..	12 0	..	..	12 37	..	1 11	1 35	..	2SO15	2 37	2 47	3SO7	3 37	3 47
427London (W.) ......ar.	11 48	12 1	12Ⓐ43	..	1 1	..	..	1Ⓐ43	..	2 1	2Ⓐ43	..	3SO1	3Ⓐ43	3 46	4SO1	4Ⓐ44	4 46
Guildford ....dep	10 51	Stop	Stop	..	12 2	..	..	Stop	..	1 15	..	..	Stop	Stop	2 50	Stop	Stop	3 50
Shalford	11 1			..	..	..	..		..	1 20	..	..			2 59			3 58
Chilworth and Albury.	11 6	..	..	..	..	..	..	..	..	1 25	..	..	..	..	3 5	..	..	4 3
Gomshall and Shere....	11 14	..	..	SO	12 17	..	..	..	..	1 32	..	..	..	..	3 14	..	..	4 13
Dorking Town **B**	11 25	..	..	12 9	12 27	..	..	..	..	1 42	..	..	..	..	3 25	..	..	4 24
Deepdene **A**	11 28	..	p.m	12 11	12 29	..	..	..	..	1 45	..	..	..	..	3 28	..	..	4 27
Betchworth........	11 34	a.m	SX	..	12 35	..	..	p.m	..	1 51	..	..	p.m	p.m	3 34	p.m	p.m	4 33
Reigate	11 40	11 52	12 23	12 20	12 41	..	12 52	1 23	1 52	1 57	..	2 22	2 53	3 23	3 40	3 52	4 22	4 40
Redhill 158, 246.285 ar	11 45	11 56	12 27	12 25	12 46	..	12 56	1 27	1 56	2 2	..	2 27	2 57	3 27	3 45	3 56	4 26	4 45
East Croydon 285...arr	12 4	12 18	12 49	12 49	1 4	..	1 18	1 49	2 18	2 50	..	2 50	3 18	3 50	4 4	4 17	4 48	5 5
London Bridge 285.. "	12 25	12 38	1Ⓐ11	1Ⓐ11	1Ⓐ31	..	1 36	2Ⓐ11	2 36	3Ⓐ11	..	3Ⓐ11	3 35	4KⒶ8	..	4 36	5c 5	5Ⓐ30
Clapham Junc. 285.. "	12 16	12Ⓐ41	1 2	1 2	1 16	..	1Ⓐ41	2 1	2Ⓐ41	3 2	..	3 2	3*35	4 2	4 16	4Ⓐ40	5SO2	5 16
Victoria 285........ "	12 21	12Ⓐ47	1 8	1 8	1 21	..	1Ⓐ47	2 7	2Ⓐ47	3 8	..	3 9	3*42	4 7	4 22	4Ⓐ46	5SO7	5 22

For Notes see page 251

TONBRIDGE, EDENBRIDGE, REDHILL, and LONDON

Miles	Up	Week Days																		
		a.m	a.m	a.m	a.m	a.m	a.m	a.m	p.m SO	p.m SX	p.m	p.m SO	p.m SX	p.m SO	p.m SX	p.m SO	p.m SO	p.m SX	p.m	p.m
	Tonbridge ....dep	6 56	8 2	8 20	8 55	9 30	10 38	11 38	12 35	12 40	2 13	3 6	4 12	4 38	5 32	5 32	5 40	5 45	6 15	7 44
2½	Lyghe Halt........	7 4	8 7	8 27	9 1	9 38	10 43	11 43	12 40	12 45	2 18	3 10	4 17	4 43	..	..	5 45	5 50	6 20	7 49
4	Penshurst	7 8	8 12	8 33	9 8	9 42	10 48	11 48	12 44	12 49	2 23	3 14	4 23	4 48	..	..	5 50	5 55	6 25	7 53
9	Edenbridge **N**	7 16	8 20	8 42	9 19	9 50	10 56	11 56	12 52	12 57	2 31	3 22	4 32	4 56	..	..	5 58	6 3	6 34	8 1
14	Godstone	7 24	8 28	8 50	9 27	9 59	11 4	12 5	1 0	1 6	2 39	3 31	4 40	5 4	..	..	6 6	..	6 41	8 9
17½	Nutfield........	7 31	8 34	8 57	9 34	10 5	11 11	12 12	1 6	1 13	2 46	3 38	4 47	5 11	..	..	6 13	..	6 47	8 16
19½	Redhill **158**, 246, 285ar	7 37	8 39	9 2	9 39	10 10	11 16	12 18	1 12	1 19	2 52	3 43	4 52	5 16	6 0	6 3	6 18	..	6 52	8 21
30	East Croydon 285.. arr	8 9	9 5	9 22	10 9	10 38	11 47	12 49	1 49	1 49	3 18	4 4	5 18	5 50	6 27	6 27	6 50	..	7 19	8 48
40½	London Bridge 285.. "	8 26	9 20	9 38	..	10 56	12SO5	1Ⓐ11	2Ⓐ11	2Ⓐ11	3 35	4*36	5 38	6Ⓐ11	6 47	6 47	7Ⓐ11	..	7 38	9Ⓐ11
37½	Clapham Junc. 285. "	8*23	9Ⓐd22	..	10 20	..	12SX1	1 2	2 1	2 1	..	4 16	..	6 2	7 2	..	7 2	..	..	9 1
40½	Victoria 285........ "	8*28	9Ⓐd27	9*42	10 26	..	12SX6	1 8	2 7	2 7	..	4 22	..	6 8	7 8	..	7 8	..	..	9 7

For Notes see page 250

READING, ALDERSHOT, ASH, REDHILL, and LONDON

Up	Week Days—*continued*																		
	p.m	p.m	p.m	p.m		p.m	p.m	p.m	p.m	p.m	p.m		SX	p.m	p.m		p.m	p.m	p.m
Reading .... dep	..	3 20	SX	SO	..	..	..	SX	4 20	..	..	..	5 5	..	6 40	..	..	..	..
Earley	..	3 26	..	..	..	..	..	..	4 26	..	..	..	..	..	..	..	..	..	..
Winnersh Halt **L**	..	3 30	..	..	..	..	..	..	4 30	..	..	..	..	..	..	..	..	..	..
Wokingham	..	3 34	..	..	..	..	..	..	4 34	..	..	..	5 16	..	5 51	..	..	..	..
Crowthorne **I**	..	3 41	..	..	..	..	..	..	4 41	..	..	..	5 23	..	5 58	..	..	..	..
Sandhurst Halt	..	3 45	..	..	..	..	..	..	4 45	..	..	..	5 27	..	6 2	..	..	..	..
Blackwater (Hants) **H** ..	..	3 49	..	..	..	..	..	..	4 49	..	..	..	5 30	..	6 6	..	..	..	..
Farnboro' North **G**	..	3 56	..	..	..	..	..	..	4 56	..	..	..	5 36	..	6 12	..	..	..	..
North Camp **F**	SO	4 0	..	..	..	..	..	..	5 0	..	..	..	5 40	..	6 16	..	..	..	..
Aldershot .... dep	3 50	3 50	..	..	..	4 20	..	4 50	4 50	5 20	..	..	..	5y50	..	..	6 20	6 50	7 20
Ash C .... arr	3 56	3 56	..	..	..	4 26	..	4 56	4 56	5 26	..	..	..	5y56	..	..	6 26	6 56	7 26
Ash **C** ......(Normandy	3 56	4 6	..	..	..	4 26	..	4 56	5 6	5 26	..	..	5 46	5SX56	6 22	..	6 27	6SX56	7 26
Wanborough (for	4 1	4 10	..	..	..	4 31	..	5 1	5 10	5 31	..	..	5 50	6SX1	..	..	6 32	7SX1	7 31
Guildford 245, 359, 427 arr	4 7	4 17	..	..	..	4 37	..	5 7	5 17	5 37	..	..	5 58	6SX7	6 33	..	6 38	7SX7	7 37
427 London (W.) ...... arr	5 3	5 16	SX	SO	..	5(3)44	..	6 1	6 18	6(3)42	..	..	7 3	7SX3	7(3)43	..	7(3)43	8SX16	8 46
Guildford .... dep	..	Stop	4 34	4 34	..	Stop	..	..	5 20	Stop	..	..	Stop	Stop	6 40	..	Stop	Stop	Stop
Shalford	..		4 39	4 39	..		..	..	5 29		..	..			6 47	..			
Chilworth and Albury.	..	..	4 43	4 45	..	–	..	..	5 35	..	..	..	..	..	6 52	..	..	..	..
Gomshall and Shere	..	..	4 51	4 52	..	..	..	..	5 44	..	..	..	..	..	7 1	..	..	..	..
Dorking Town B	..	..	5 1	5 2	..	..	..	..	5 53	..	..	..	..	..	7 14	..	..	..	..
Deepdene **A**	..	..	5 4	5 5	..	p.m	..	..	5 58	p.m	..	..	..	..	7 17	..	p.m	p.m	..
Betchworth	..	p.m	5 9	5 10	..	SO	..	..	6 4	SO	SX	..	p.m	p.m	7 23	..	SX	SO	p.m
Reigate	..	4 50	5 15	5 16	..	5 23	5 52	..	6 11	6 23	6 30	..	6 53	7 23	7 29	..	7 48	7 52	8 21
Redhill **158**, 246, 285 arr	..	4 54	5 20	5 21	..	5 27	5 56	..	6 16	6 27	6 34	..	6 57	7 27	7 35	..	7 52	7 56	8 25
East Croydon 285 ... arr	..	5 20	5 50	5 50	..	5 59	6 18	..	6 50	6 50	7 4	..	7 20	7 50	8 4	..	8 18	8 18	8 50
London Bridge 285 .. "	..	5 38	6(3)11	6(3)11	..	6(3)11	6 36	..	7(3)10	7(3)11	..	..	7 38	8(3)11	8(3)31	..	8 36	8 36	9(3)11
Clapham Junc. 285 .. "	..	5(3)41	..	6 2	..	6 2	6(3)41	..	7 2	7 2	7 16	..	7(3)42	8 2	8 16	..	8(3)41	8(3)41	9 1
Victoria 285 .... "	..	5(3)47	6 6	6 8	..	6 8	6(3)47	..	7 8	7 8	7 22	..	7(3)49	8 8	8 22	..	8(3)47	8(3)47	9 7

Up	Week Days—*continued*																		
	p.m	p.m	p.m.		p.m	p.m	p.m		p.m	p.m	p.m		p.m	p.m	p.m		p.m	SX	SO
Reading .... dep	6 50	..	SX	..	..	7 50	..	..	..	..	..	..	..	9 34	..	..	..	11 10	11 10
Earley	..	..	..	..	..	..	..	..	..	..	..	..	..	..	..	..	..	11 16	11 17
Winnersh Halt **L**	..	..	..	..	..	..	..	..	..	..	..	..	..	..	..	..	..	11 20	11 23
Wokingham	7 2	..	..	..	..	8 2	..	..	..	..	..	..	..	9 45	..	..	..	11 25	11 28
Crowthorne **I**	7 9	..	..	..	..	8 9	..	..	..	..	..	..	..	9 52	..	..	..	11 31	11 37
Sandhurst Halt	7 14	..	..	..	..	8 14	..	..	..	..	..	..	..	9 56	..	..	..	11 37	11 43
Blackwater (Hants) **H** ..	7 18	..	..	..	..	8 18	..	..	..	..	..	..	..	10 0	..	..	..	11 41	11 50
Farnboro' North **G**	7 24	..	..	..	..	8 25	..	..	..	..	..	..	..	10 7	..	..	–	11 47	11 58
North Camp **F**	7 30	..	..	..	..	8 30	..	..	..	..	..	..	..	10 11	..	..	..	11 51	12 4
Aldershot .... dep	..	7 50	8 10	..	8 20	..	..	..	8 51	9 20	9 51	..	..	..	1020	..	1120	11 40	11 40
Ash **C** .... arr	..	7 56	8 16	..	8 26	..	..	..	8 57	9 26	9 57	..	..	..	1026	..	1126	11 46	11 46
Ash **C** ...... Normandy	7 36	7SX56	..	..	8 26	8 36	..	..	..	9 26	9 57	..	..	10 17	1026	..	1126	11 57	12 10
Wanborough, (for	7 40	8SX1	..	..	8 31	8 41	..	..	..	9 31	10 2	..	..	..	1031	..	1131	..	..
Guildford 245, 359, 427 arr	7 [illegible]8	8SX7	..	..	8 37	8 48	..	..	..	9 37	10 8	..	..	10 27	1037	..	1137	12 8	12 23
427 London (W.) ...... arr	[illegible] 46	9SX1	..	..	9 46	9 46	..	..	..	1046	1116	..	..	11(3)34	1146	..	..	..	..
Guildford .... dep	..	Stop	..	..	Stop	8 53	..	..	..	Stop	Stop	..	..	10 39	..	..	..	..	..
Shalford	..		..	..		9 1	..	..	..			..	..	10 44	..	..	..	..	..
Chilworth and Albury.	..	..	..	..	..	9 7	..	..	..	..	..	..	..	10 49	..	..	..	..	..
Gomshall and Shere	..	..	..	..	..	9 15	..	..	..	..	..	..	..	10 57	..	..	..	..	..
Dorking Town **B**	..	..	..	..	..	9 26	..	..	..	..	..	..	..	11 7	..	..	..	..	..
Deepdene **A**	..	..	..	..	..	9 29	..	..	..	..	..	..	..	11 10	..	..	..	..	..
Betchworth	..	p.m	..	..	p.m	9 35	..	..	..	p.m	p.m	..	..	11 16	..	..	..	..	..
Reigate	..	8 52	..	..	9 22	9 41	9 52	..	..	10 22	1042	..	1117	11 22	..	..	..	..	..
Redhill **158**, 246, 285 arr	..	8 56	..	..	9 26	9 46	9 56	..	..	10 26	1046	..	1121	11 27	..	..	..	..	..
East Croydon 285 .. arr	..	9 20	..	..	9 48	10 4	10 20	..	..	10 50	11 4	..	1150	12(3)59	..	..	..	..	..
London Bridge 285 .. "	..	9 36	..	..	10(3)11	..	10 39	..	..	11(3)11	..	..	..	1(3)19	..	..	..	..	..
Clapham Junc. 285 .. "	..	9(3)42	..	..	10 1	1016	10(3)42	..	..	11 2	1116	..	12 1	..	..	..	..	..	..
Victoria 285 .... "	..	9(3)48	..	..	10 7	1022	10(3)48	..	..	11 7	1121	..	12 7	..	..	..	..	..	..

For Notes, see page 251

TONBRIDGE, EDENBRIDGE, REDHILL, and LONDON

Up	Week Days—*Con*				Sundays								
	p.m	p.m	ngt.		a.m	a.m	a.m T	p.m	p.m	p.m	p.m	p.m V	ngt.
Tonbridge .... dep	8 34	9 45	12 7	..	8 40	9 7	10 37	2 5	6 5	7 45	8 43	10 9	12 7
Lyghe Halt	8 39	9 49	(3)	..	8 45	9 12	10 42	2 10	6 10	7 50	8 49	1014	(3)
Penshurst	8 44	9 54		..	8 49	9 17	10 46	2 16	6 16	7 55	8 54	1018	
Edenbridge **N**	8 54	10 2	..	..	8 57	9 25	10 54	2 24	6 25	8 3	9 2	1026	..
Godstone	9 3	10 10	..	..	9 5	9 33	11 2	2 32	6 33	8 11	9 10	1034	..
Nutfield	9 10	10 17	..	..	9 12	9 39	11 9	2 39	6 40	8 18	9 17	1040	..
Redhill **158**, 246, 285 arr	9 16	10 22	1236	..	9 17	9 44	11 14	2 44	6 45	8 23	9 22	1045	1236
East Croydon 285 .. arr	9 48	10 50	1259	..	9 48	10 3	11 49	3 3	7 4	8 52	9 48	..	1259
London Bridge 285 .. "	10(3)11	11(3)11	1 19	..	10(3)10	10(3)40	12(3)10	3(3)40	7 35	9*28	10 7	..	1 19
Clapham Junc. 285 .. "	10 1	11 2	..	..	10 0	10 15	12 1	3 15	7 16	9 7	1015	..	..
Victoria 285 .... "	10 7	11 7	..	..	10 [illegible]	10 20	12 7	3 20	7 21	9 13	1020	..	..

(3) Third class only
* Change at East Croydon
d 6 minutes later on Sats.
N 1 mile to Edenbridge Town Station
SO or SO Saturdays only
SX or SX Saturdays excepted
T Not after 21st March, 1948
V Commences 28th March, 1948

For **OTHER TRAINS** between Edenbridge and London, see page 237—Tonbridge and London, page 55

READING, ALDERSHOT, ASH, REDHILL, and LONDON

Sundays

Up	am	a.m	am	am	a.m	a.m	a.m	a.m	a.m	a.m	a.m	a.m	a.m	a.m	p.m	p.m	a.m	p.m	p.m	p.m	p.m
Reading ... dep	..	..	..	..	..	..	..	7 45	..	..	..	..	..	..	..	..	11 50	..	..	..	..
Earley	..	..	..	..	..	..	..	7 50	..	..	..	..	..	..	..	..	..	..	..	..	..
Winnersh Halt **L**	..	..	..	..	..	..	..	7 54	..	..	..	..	..	..	..	..	..	..	..	..	..
Wokingham	..	..	..	..	..	..	..	7 58	..	..	..	..	..	..	..	..	12 3	..	..	..	..
Crowthorne **I**	..	..	..	..	..	..	..	8 5	..	..	..	..	..	..	..	..	12 10	..	..	..	..
Sandhurst Halt	..	..	..	..	..	..	..	8 9	..	..	..	..	..	..	..	..	12 15	..	..	..	..
Blackwater (Hants) **H**	..	..	..	..	..	..	..	8 13	..	..	..	..	..	..	..	..	12 19	..	..	..	..
Farnboro North **G**	..	..	..	..	..	..	..	8 19	..	..	..	..	..	..	..	..	12 25	..	..	..	..
North Camp **F**	..	..	..	..	..	..	..	8 24	..	..	..	..	..	..	..	..	12 30	..	..	..	..
Aldershot ... dep	..	..	..	..	..	..	..	8 20	8 50	9 20	..	10 20	1050	1120	..	1220	..	1251	1 20	1 54	2 20
Ash **C** ... arr	..	..	..	..	..	..	..	8 26	8 56	9 26	..	10 26	1056	1126	..	1226	..	1257	1 26	2 1	2 26
Ash **C** ... Normandy,	..	..	..	..	..	..	..	8 29	8 56	9 26	..	10 26	Stop	1126	..	1226	12 36	1257	1 26	Stop	2 26
Wanborough, for	..	..	..	..	..	..	..	8 34	9 1	9 31	..	10 31		1131	..	1231	12 41	1 2	1 31		2 31
Guildford 245, 359, 427 ar	..	..	..	..	..	..	..	8 41	9 7	9 37	..	10 37	..	1137	..	1237	12 48	1 8	1 37	..	2 37
427 London (W.) ... arr	..	..	..	..	..	..	..	9 46	10 1	10 46	..	11 46	..	1246	..	1 46	1 46	2 [illegible]	2 46	..	3 46
Guildford ... dep	..	6 55	..	..	..	..	..	8 43	..	Stop	10 4	Stop	..	..	..	..	12 51	Stop	..	..	..
Shalford	..	7 0	..	..	..	..	..	8 50	..		10 9		..	..	..	..	1 0		..	..	..
Chilworth and Albury	..	7 5	..	..	..	..	..	8 55	..	..	10 13	..	..	..	..	..	1 6	..	..	..	..
Gomshall and Shere	..	7 13	..	..	..	..	..	9 3	..	..	10 21	..	..	..	..	..	1 14	..	..	..	..
Dorking Town **B**	..	7 24	..	..	..	..	..	9 13	..	..	10 30	..	..	..	..	..	1 25	..	..	..	..
Deepdene **A**	..	7 27	..	..	..	..	..	9 16	..	..	10 33	..	..	..	..	..	1 28	..	..	..	..
Betchworth	..	7 33	..	..	..	..	..	9 22	..	a.m	10 37	a.m	p.m	..	..	..	1 34	p.m	..	p.m	..
Reigate	720	7 40	755	812	8 20	8 50	9 22	9 29	..	10 22	10 42	11 22	1222	..	1 22	..	1 40	2 22	..	3 22	..
Redhill 158, 246, 285 ar	724	7 45	759	816	8 24	8 54	9 26	9 35	..	10 26	10 47	11 26	1226	..	1 26	..	1 45	2 26	..	3 26	..
East Croydon 285 ... arr	746	8 16	..	..	8 46	9 17	9 49	10 4	..	10 49	11 3	11 49	1249	..	1 49	..	2 4	2 4[illegible]	..	3 49	..
London Bridge 285 ... "	8 5	8 34	..	..	9③10	9 35	10③10	10③40	..	11③10	11③40	12③10	1③10		2③10	..	2③40	3③10		4③10	..
Clapham Junc. 285 ... "	..	..	..	..	8 59	9*36	10 0	10 14	..	11 0	11 14	12 2	1 0	..	2 2	..	2 14	3 0	..	4 1	..
Victoria 285 ... "	..	..	..	..	9 5	9*42	10 6	10 20	..	11 6	11 20	12 7	1 6	..	2 7	..	2 20	3 6	..	4 7	..

Sundays—*continued*

Up	p.m	p.m	p.m	p.m	p.m	p.m	p.m	p.m	p.m	p.m	p.m	p.m	p.m	p.m	p.m	p.m	p.m	p.m	p.m	p.m	p.m
Reading ... dep	1 50	..	..	..	..	4 20	..	..	..	5 46	..	..	7 20	..	..	..	8 50	..	..	..	10 35
Earley	..	..	..	..	..	4 25	..	..	..	..	..	..	7 25	..	..	..	..	..	..	..	10 43
Winnersh Halt **L**	..	..	..	..	..	4 29	..	..	..	..	..	..	7 29	..	..	..	..	..	..	..	10 49
Wokingham	2 2	..	..	..	..	4 33	..	..	..	5 58	..	..	7 33	..	..	..	9 2	..	..	..	10 53
Crowthorne **I**	2 9	..	..	..	..	4 40	..	..	..	6 5	..	..	7 40	..	..	..	9 9	..	..	..	11 6
Sandhurst Halt	2 14	..	..	..	..	4 44	..	..	..	6 9	..	..	7 44	..	..	..	9 15	..	..	..	11 14
Blackwater (Hants) **H**	2 18	..	..	..	..	4 48	..	..	..	6 14	..	..	7 48	..	..	..	9 19	..	..	..	11 21
Farnboro' North **G**	2 24	..	..	..	..	4 54	..	..	..	6 20	..	..	7 54	..	..	..	9 25	..	..	..	11 30
North Camp **F**	2 29	..	..	..	..	4 59	..	..	..	6 25	..	..	7 59	..	..	..	9 30	..	..	..	11 37
Aldershot ... dep	..	2 51	3 20	4 20	4 50	..	5 20	5 50	6 20	..	7 20	7 50	..	8 21	..	9 20	..	9 50	1020	1050	..
Ash **C** ... arr	..	2 58	3 26	4 26	4 57	..	5 26	5 57	6 26	..	7 26	7 57	..	8 27	..	9 26	..	9 56	1026	1056	..
Ash **C** ... (Normandy	2 35	Stop	3 26	4 26	..	5 5	5 26	Stop	6 26	6 31	7 26	Stop	8 5	8 27	..	9 26	9 36	9 56	1026	1056	11 44
Wanborough for	2 40		3 31	4 31	..	5 10	5 31		6 31	..	7 31		8 10	8 32	..	9 31	9 40	10 1	1031	11 1	11 50
Guildford 245, 359, 427 ar	2 47	..	3 37	4 37	..	5 17	5 37	..	6 37	6 43	7 37	..	8 17	8 38	..	9 37	9 47	10 7	1037	11 7	11 59
427 London (W.) ... arr	3 46	..	4 46	5 46	..	6 16	6 48	..	7 47	7 47	8 30	..	9 21	9 46	..	10 46	1046	11 1	1146	12 1	Stop
Guildford ... dep	2 50	..	..	Stop	..	5 20	Stop	..	Stop	6 45	Stop	..	8 20	Stop	..	Stop	10 0	..	..	..	
Shalford	3 0	..	..		..	5 25		..		6 51		..	8 28		..		10 5	..	..	..	..
Chilworth and Albury	3 6	..	..	..	..	5 30	..	..	..	6 56	..	..	8 33	..	..	..	1010	..	..	..	..
Gomshall and Shere	3 14	..	..	..	..	5 38	..	..	..	7 4	..	..	8 42	..	..	..	1019	..	..	..	..
Dorking Town **B**	3 25	..	..	..	..	5 48	..	..	..	7 15	..	..	8 53	..	..	..	1030	..	..	..	..
Deepdene **A**	3 28	..	..	..	..	5 51	..	..	..	7 18	..	..	8 56	..	..	..	1033	..	..	..	..
Betchworth	3 34	p.m	..	p.m	..	5 57	p.m	p.m	p.m	7 25	p.m	p.m	9 2	p.m	..	p.m	1040	..	..	..	p.m
Reigate	3 40	4 22	..	5 22	..	6 3	6 22	6 50	7 22	7 32	7 57	8 24	9 8	9 22	9 50	10 21	1047	..	..	..	10 54
Redhill 158, 246, 285 ar	3 45	4 26	..	5 26	..	6 8	6 26	6 54	7 26	7 37	8 1	8 28	9 13	9 26	9 54	10 25	1052	..	..	..	10 58
East Croydon 285 ... arr	4 3	4 49	..	5 49	..	6 49	6 49	7 16	7 49	8 4	8 24	8 53	9 48	9 48	1016	10 47	..	..	..	..	1③2
London Bridge 285 ... "	4③40	5③10		6③10		7③10	7③10	7 35	8③10	8③40	8 44	9*28	10 7	10 7	1035	11③10	..	..	..	..	1③19
Clapham Junc. 285 ... "	4 14	5 1	..	6 1	..	7 1	7 1	..	8 1	8 16	..	9 5	10 15	1015	..	10 59	..	..	..	..	..
Victoria 285 ... "	4 20	5 7	..	6 7	..	7 7	7 7	..	8 7	8 22	..	9 11	10 20	1020	..	11 4	..	..	..	..	..

③ Third class only
* Change at East Croydon
A Under ¼ mile to Dorking North Sta.
a Arr. 9③8 a.m. on Saturdays
B Nearly 1½ mls to Dorking North Sta
B Dep. 3 57 p.m. on Sats.
b Arr. 8③27 a.m. on Saturdays
C Station for Ash Green
c Arr. 5③12 p.m. on Saturdays
D Station for South Camp
F Station for Ash Vale and South Farnborough
f Arr. 11 2 a.m. on Sats. 1st & 3rd cl.
G Station for Frimley (1¼ miles), nearly 1 mile to Farnborough, and about 1 mile to Frimley Western Section Station
g 18 minutes later on Saturdays

H Nearly 1½ miles to Camberley Station, Western Section
I Station for Wellington College
J 7 minutes later on Saturdays
j Arr. 10③43 a.m. on Saturdays
K Arr. 4③11 p.m. on Saturdays
L Halt for Sindlesham and Hurst
L Dep. 4③12 p.m. on Saturdays
N Dep. 8*45 a.m. on Saturdays.
P 3rd class only. Dep. 6 45 p.m on Saturdays 1st and 3rd class
SO or SO Saturdays only
SX or SX Saturdays excepted
t Dep. 5 57 p.m. on Saturdays
U Saturdays excepted. 3rd class only
v Dep. 7 42 p.m. on Saturdays
y 1 min. later on Saturdays

Z 4 minutes *earlier* on Saturdays
z Arr. 12 5 p.m. on Saturdays 1st and 3rd class

For **OTHER TRAINS** between London & Dorking North, page 394—London & Guildford, 394—London & Aldershot, 388 & 390—London & Reading, 460—Chilworth & Albury and Guildford, 374—Guildford & Aldershot 390—Wokingham & Reading, 460

LONDON, CRYSTAL PALACE, CROYDON, SUTTON, DORKING NORTH,

For Notes, see page 284a

Miles from London Bridge	Miles from London Bridge	Miles from Victoria	Down	No.	a.m								Week Days						a.m				No.
			Victoria .... dep	1	..	..	..	..	5 14	..	..	..	..	..	..	..	5 20	..	5 34	..	..	..	1
			Charing Cross* .. "	2	3	..	..	..	3	..	3	..	3	..	3	..	..	3	3	3	3	3	2
			Waterloo* .... "	3		..	..	..		..		..		..		..	..						3
			London Bridge...... "	4	3 25	4 50	..	..	..	..	5 0	..	5 3	5 10	5 16	5 25	..	5 30	..	5 34	5 35	5 51	4
		1½	Battersea Park..........	5	..	..	..	..	5 17	..	..	..	..	..	..	..	..	..	..	..	..	..	5
		2¾	Clapham Junction......	6	..	..	..	..	5 21	..	..	..	..	..	..	..	5 28	..	5 40	..	..	..	6
		4	Wandsworth Common A	7	..	..	..	..	5 24	..	..	..	..	..	..	..	..	..	..	..	..	..	7
		4¾	Balham & Upper Tooting	8	..	..	..	..	5 26	..	..	..	..	..	..	..	..	..	5 44	..	..	..	8
1¼	—	—	South Bermondsey.......	9	..	..	..	..	..	..	..	..	..	..	..	..	..	..	..	..	5 38	..	9
2¼	—	—	Queen's Road, Peckham	10	..	..	..	..	..	..	..	..	..	..	..	..	..	..	..	..	5 41	..	10
3½	—	—	Peckham Rye...........	11	..	..	..	..	..	..	..	..	..	5 16	..	..	..	..	..	..	5 43	..	11
4¼	—	—	East Dulwich...........	12	..	..	..	..	..	..	..	..	..	5 20	..	..	..	..	..	..		..	12
4¾	—	—	North Dulwich	13	..	..	..	..	..	..	..	..	..	..	..	..	..	..	..	..	To Victoria, arr. 5 58 a.m	..	13
6½	—	—	Tulse Hill	14	..	..	..	..	..	..	..	..	..	5 27	..	..	..	..	..	..		..	14
7½	—	—	Streatham...............	15	..	..	..	..	..	..	..	..	..	5 32	..	..	..	..	..	..		..	15
—	2¾	—	New Cross Gate (for E.L	16	..	..	..	..	..	..	5 5	..	5 9	..	..	5 31	..	5 35	..	5 41		5 56	16
—	3¾	—	Brockley B ....[Line)	17	..	..	..	..	..	..	..	..	5 12	..	..	..	..	5 38	..	..		5 58	17
—	4¾	—	Honor Oak Park.........	18	..	..	..	..	..	..	..	..	5 15	..	..	..	..	5 41	..	..		6 1	18
—	5¾	—	Forest Hill, for Lordship	19	..	..	..	..	..	..	5 11	..	5 17	..	..	..	..	5 43	..	5 47		6 3	19
—	6½	—	Sydenham ....[Lane	20	..	..	..	..	..	..	5 14	..	5 20	..	..	..	..	5 46	..	5 52		6 6	20
—	7	—	Penge West C...........	21	..	..	..	..	..	..	5 17	..	5 22	..	..	..	..	5 48	..	5 54		6 8	21
—	7½	—	Anerley.................	22	..	..	..	..	..	..	5 20	..	5 23	..	..	..	..	5 49	..	5 55		6 9	22
8½	—	6½	Streatham Common.....	23	..	..	..	..	..	..	..	..	To London Bridge, via Streatham	..	..	..	..	To London Bridge, via Streatham	5 48	..	..	To London Bridge, via Streatham	23
9	—	7½	Norbury	24	..	..	..	..	..	..	..	..		..	..	..	..		5 51	..	..		24
10½	—	8¾	Thornton Heath.........	25	..	..	..	..	..	..	..	..		..	..	..	..		5 55	..	..		25
11	—	9½	Selhurst................	26	..	..	..	..	..	..	..	..		..	..	..	..		5 57	..	..		26
—	—	5¾	Streatham Hill........ ..	27	..	..	..	..	..	..	..	..		..	..	..	..		..	..	..		27
6¾	—	7	West Norwood (N'wood)	28	..	..	..	..	..	..	..	..		..	..	..	..		..	..	..		28
7½	—	8	Gipsy Hill (for Upper	29	..	..	..	..	..	..	..	..		..	..	..	..		..	..	..		29
8½	7½	8¾	Crystal Palace D........	30	..	..	..	..	..	..	..	..		..	..	..	..		..	..	..		30
—	—	10¾	Birkbeck	31	..	..	..	..	..	..	..	..		..	..	..	..		..	..	..		31
—	—	11¾	Beckenham Jn. arr	32	..	..	..	..	..	..	..	..		..	..	..	..		..	..	..		32
—	8½	10¼	Norwood Junction F..	33	..	..	..	..	..	..	5 24	..	5 26	..	5 29	5 40	..	5 52	..	5 59	..	6 12	33
—	10½	10½	East Croydon.... arr	34	..	5 7	..	..	..	..	..	..	Stop	..	5 33	5 44	5 42	Stop	..	..	..	..	34
			East Croydon.... dep	35	..	5 10	..	..	..	..	..	..		..	5 33	5 45	5 49		..	..	..	..	35
10½	—	8¾	Mitcham Junction......	36	..	..	..	..	5 32	..	..	..	..	5 38	..	..	..	..	..	..	..	..	36
11½	—	10	Hackbridge	37	..	..	..	..	5 35	..	..	..	..	5 42	..	..	..	a.m	..	..	..	..	37
12½	—	10¾	Carshalton	38	..	..	3	..	5 37	..	..	3	..	5 47	..	..	..	3	..	..	..	..	38
—	10½	10¼	West Croydon 319 arr	39	..	..		..	..	..	5 28		a.m	..	..	..	..		6 0	6 3	..	..	39
			West Croydon 319 dep	40	..	..	5 16	3	..	..	5 30	5 37	5 42	..	..	..	..	5 55	6 0	6 5	..	..	40
—	11½	11¾	Waddon G............	41	..	..	5 18		..	..	5 32	5 39	5 44	..	..	..	..	5 57	6 2	6 7	..	..	41
—	13	13¼	Wallington............	42	..	..	5 22	5 28	..	..	5 38	5 43	5 48	..	..	..	..	6 [illegible]	6 6	6 12	..	..	42
—	13¾	14	Carshalton Beeches.....	43	..	..	5 24	..	..	..	5 41	5 45	5 50	..	..	..	..	6 4	6 9	6 14	..	..	43
13¾	14¾	12	Sutton 322............	44	..	..	5 27	5 32	5 41	..	5 45	5 48	5 53	5 54	..	..	..	6 7	6 12	6 19	..	..	44
15	16	13¼	Belmont..............	45	..	..	..	..	..		..	Stop	3	..	..	..	..	..	..	..	..	..	45
16½	17½	14¾	Banstead..............	46	..	..	..	..	..	..	..			..	..	..	..	..	..	..	..	..	46
18	19	16¼	Epsom Downs...... arr	47	..	..	..	..	..	..	..	..	..	..	..	..	..	..	..	..	..	..	47
14¾	—	13	Cheam..................	48	..	..	..	..	5 44	3	5 50	..	..	5 59	..	..	..	..	..	6 22	..	..	48
16¼	—	14½	Ewell East H..........	49	..	..	..	..	5 47		5 53	a.m	..	6 3	..	..	..	..	..	6 25	..	..	49
17¼	—	16	Epsom.................	50	..	..	..	..	5 50	5 54	5 56	3	..	6 11	..	..	..	..	..	6 28	..	..	50
19¾	—	18	Ashtead................	51	..	..	..	..	..	5 58	..		..	6 18	..	..	..	..	..	..	..	..	51
21½	—	19¾	Leatherhead..[Bridge J	52	..	..	..	..	..	6 2	..	6 17	..	6 25	..	..	..	..	..	..	..	..	52
24¾	—	23	Boxhill and Burford	53	..	..	..	..	..	..	..	..	..	6 31	..	..	..	..	..	..	..	..	53
25½	—	23¾	Dorking North K.. arr	54	..	..	..	..	..	..	..	..	..	6 35	..	..	..	..	..	..	..	..	54
24	—	22¼	Bookham............[394	55	..	..	..	..	..	..	..	6 21	..	..	..	..	..	..	..	..	..	..	55
25¾	—	24	Effingham Junction arr	56	..	..	..	..	..	..	..	6 25	..	..	..	..	..	..	..	..	..	..	56
—	11¼	11½	South Croydon 234......	57	..	..	..	..	..	..	..	..	..	..	5 35	..	5 54	..	..	..	..	..	57
—	12¼	12½	Purley Oaks............	58	..	..	..	..	..	..	..	..	..	..	5 38	..	..	..	..	..	..	..	58
—	13¼	13½	Purley	59	..	5 19	..	..	..	..	..	..	..	..	5 41	5 50	..	..	..	..	..	..	59
—	14¾	15	Coulsdon North L.. arr	60	..	..	..	..	..	..	..	..	..	..	..	..	..	..	..	..	..	..	60
—	—	—	Purley .... dep	61	..	..	..	..	..	..	..	..	..	..	5 46	..	..	..	..	..	..	..	61
—	14½	14¾	Kenley.................	62	..	..	..	..	..	..	..	..	..	..	5 49	..	..	..	..	..	..	..	62
—	15¾	16	Whyteleafe.............	63	..	..	..	..	..	..	..	..	..	..	5 53	..	..	..	..	..	..	..	63
—	16½	16½	Warlingham.............	64	..	..	..	..	..	..	..	..	..	..	5 55	..	..	..	..	..	..	..	64
—	18	18½	Caterham.......... arr	65	..	..	..	..	..	..	..	..	..	..	5 59	..	..	..	..	..	..	..	65
—	—	—	Purley .... dep	66	..	..	..	..	..	..	..	..	..	..	5 42	§ Via Three Bridges	..	..	..	..	..	..	66
—	14	14½	Reedham................	67	..	..	..	..	..	..	..	..	..	..	5 44		..	..	..	..	..	..	67
—	14¾	15	Smitham	68	..	..	..	..	..	..	..	..	..	..	5 46		..	..	..	..	..	..	68
—	15½	15¾	Woodmansterne	69	..	..	..	..	..	..	..	..	..	..	5 49		..	..	..	..	..	..	69
—	16½	16¾	Chipstead	70	..	..	..	..	..	..	..	..	..	..	5 51		..	..	..	..	..	..	70
—	19	19½	Kingswood M	71	..	..	..	..	..	..	..	..	..	..	5 56		..	..	..	..	..	..	71
—	20½	20½	Tadworth N...........	72	..	..	..	..	..	..	..	..	..	..	6 0	..	..	..	..	..	..	..	72
—	21½	21¾	Tattenham Corner. arr	73	..	..	..	..	..	..	..	..	..	..	6 3	..	..	..	..	..	..	..	73
—	15½	15½	Coulsdon South.........	74	..	5 25	..	..	..	..	..	..	..	..	..	5 56	..	..	..	..	..	..	74
—	19	19½	Merstham	75	..	5 34	..	..	..	..	..	..	..	..	..	6 3	..	..	..	..	..	..	75
—	20¾	21	Redhill 158, 246 .... arr	76	3 58	5 39	..	..	..	..	..	..	..	..	..	6 7	..	..	..	..	..	..	76
—	22½	22¾	Reigate 246 ...... "	77	..	6 6	..	..	..	..	..	..	..	..	..	..	..	..	..	..	..	..	77
39	37¾	38	Horsham 159, 244, 245 "	78	..	..	..	..	..	..	..	..	..	7 7	..	7§ 4	..	..	..	..	..	..	78

CATERHAM, TATTENHAM CORNER, REDHILL, REIGATE, and HORSHAM

a.m — Week Days—*continued* — a.m

No.																												
1	5 51	..	6 0	..	5 56	..	..	..	..	..	..	6 11	6 15	..	..	..	6 18	6 20	..	..	..	..	..	..	6 30	6 31	6 33	..
2	3	3	3	3	3	..	3	..	3	3	3	3	3	..	3	3	3	3	..	3	3	3	3	3	..	3	3	3
3						..		6 4						..					6 27						..			
4	..	5 57	..	6 0	..	..	6 3	..	6 7	6 8	6 10	..	..	6 16	6 17	6 20	..	..	..	6 22	6 26	6 28	6 30	6 35	..	..	..	6 35
5	..	..	..	..	5 59	..	..	..	..	..	..	..	..	..	..	..	..	6 23	3	..	..	..	..	..	..	..	6 36	..
6	5 56	..	6 5	..	6 2	..	..	6 12	..	..	..	6 16	6 21	..	..	..	6 24	6 26		..	..	..	..	..	6 37	6 36	6 39	..
7	5 59	..	..	..	6 5	..	..	3	..	..	..	6 19	..	..	..	..	..	6 29	..	..	..	..	..	..	..	..	6 42	..
8	6 1	..	6 9	..	6 7	..	..		..	..	..	6 21	6 25	..	..	..	6 28	6 31	..	..	..	..	..	..	..	6 41	6 44	..
9	..	6 0	..	..	..	..	..	Via Worcester Park	..	..	6 13	..	..	..	6 21	..	..	..	Via Worcester Park	..	..	..	..	..	..	..	..	6 38
10	..	6 3	..	..	..	..	..		..	..	6 16	..	..	..	6 24	..	..	..		..	..	..	..	..	..	..	..	6 41
11	..	6 5	..	..	..	..	6 9		..	..	6 18	..	..	..	6 26	..	..	..		..	..	..	..	..	..	..	..	6 43
12	..	To Victoria, arr. 6 22 a.m	..	..	..	..	..		..	..	6 21	..	..	..	To Victoria, arr. 6 43 a.m	..	..	..		..	..	..	..	..	..	..	..	6 46
13	..		..	..	..	..	..		..	..	6 23	..	..	..		..	..	..		..	..	..	..	..	..	..	..	6 48
14	..		..	..	..	..	6 13		..	6 18	6 26	..	..	..		..	..	..		6 33	..	6 38	..	..	..	..	..	6 51
15	..		..	..	..	..	6 18		..	6 22	..	..	..	..		..	..	..		6 37	..	6 42	..	..	..	..	..	..
16	..		..	6 6	..	..	..		6 12	..	..	..	..	6 21		..	..	..	..	..	6 31	..	6 35	..	..	..	..	..
17	..		..	6 8	..	..	..		6 14	..	..	..	..	..		..	..	..	..	..	6 33	..	6 37	..	..	..	..	..
18	..		..	6 11	..	..	..		6 17	..	..	..	..	..		..	..	..	..	..	6 36	..	6 40	..	..	..	..	..
19	..		..	6 13	..	..	..		6 19	..	..	..	..	..		..	..	..	..	..	6 38	..	6 42	..	..	..	..	..
20	..		..	6 16	..	..	..		6 23	..	..	..	..	..		..	..	..	..	..	6 41	..	6 45	..	..	..	..	..
21	..		..	..	..	..	..		6 25	..	..	..	..	..		..	..	..	..	..	..	..	6 47	..	..	..	..	..
22	..		..	..	..	..	..		6 26	..	..	..	..	..		..	..	..	..	..	..	..	6 48	..	..	..	..	..
23	6 5		..	..	..	..	6 20		To London Bridge, via Streatham	..	..	6 25	..	..		..	6 32	..	..	6 41	..	..	To London Bridge via Streatham	..	..	6 45	..	..
24	6 7		..	..	..	..	6 24			..	..	6 27	..	..		..	6 34	..	..	6 43	..	..		..	..	6 47	..	..
25	6 10		..	..	..	..	6 28			..	..	6 30	..	..		..	6 37	..	..	6 47	..	..		..	..	6 50	..	..
26	6 12		..	..	..	..	6 30	..		..	..	6 32	..	..	Stop	..	6 39	..	..	6 49	..	..		..	..	6 52	..	..
27	..	Stop	..	..	6 10	..	..	..		..	..	..	..	..	..	..	..	6 34	..	..	..	..		..	..	..	6 46	..
28	..	..	..	..	6 14	3	..	..		..	6 28	..	..	..	..	..	..	6 37	..	..	..	..		..	..	..	6 49	6 53
29	..	..	..	..	6 16		..	..		..	6 31	..	..	..	..	..	..	6 39	..	..	..	..		..	..	..	6 52	6 56
30	..	..	..	6 19	6 20	6 30	..	..		..	6 34	..	..	..	..	..	..	6 42	..	..	6 44	..		..	..	..	6 54	6 59
31	..	..	..	Stop	..	6 33	..	..		..	..	..	..	..	..	..	..	..	..	..	Stop	..		..	..	..	6 58	..
32	..	..	..	..	..	6 37	..	..		..	..	..	..	..	..	..	..	..	..	..	..	..		..	..	..	7 2	..
33	..	..	..	..	6 26	..	6 33	..	6 30	..	..	..	..	6 29	..	6 33	..	6 47	..	6 53	..	..	6 51	6 49	..	..	..	..
34	6 16	..	..	..	..	..	..	..	Stop	..	..	6 36	..	6 33	..	..	..	..	..	..	..	..	..	6 53	6 51	6 56	..	..
35	6 16	..	..	..	..	..	..	..	..	..	..	6 36	..	6 35	..	..	..	..	..	..	..	..	..	6 53	..	6 56	..	..
36	..	..	6 15	..	..	..	To London Bridge, via Forest Hill	..	..	6 27	..	..	6 33	..	..	..	..	..	..	To London Bridge, via Forest Hill	..	6 47	..	..	..	..	..	..
37	..	a.m	6 18	..	..	..		..	..	6 29	..	..	6 35	..	a.m	..	..	..	..		..	6 49	..	..	..	..	..	..
38	..	3	6 20	..	..	..		..	..	6 32	..	..	6 38	..	3	..	..	..	..		..	6 52	..	..	..	..	..	..
39	..		..	a.m	6 30	..		..	..	..	..	..	..	..		6 37	6 42	6 51	..		..	..	..	..	..	..	..	..
40	..	6 15	..	3	..	..		..	..	..	..	..	..	..	6 33	6 38	6 42	..	..		..	..	..	..	..	..	..	..
41	..	6 17	..		..	..		..	..	..	..	..	..	..	6 35	6 40	6 45	..	..		..	..	..	..	..	..	..	..
42	..	6 21	..	6 24	..	..		..	..	..	..	..	..	..	6 39	6 44	6 48	..	..		..	..	..	..	..	..	..	..
43	..	6 23	..	6 26	..	..		..	..	..	..	..	..	..	6 42	6 46	6 51	..	..		..	..	..	..	..	..	..	..
44	..	6 26	6 27	6 29	..	..		..	..	6 35	..	..	6 42	..	6 45	6 49	6 54	..	..		..	6 57	..	..	..	..	..	..
45	..	..	6 32	..	..	..		..	..	..	..	..	..	..	..	6 53	6 57	..	..		..	..	..	..	..	..	..	..
46	..	..	6 35	..	..	..		..	..	..	..	..	..	..	..	6 56	7 0	..	..		..	..	..	..	..	..	..	..
47	..	..	6 38	..	..	..		..	..	..	..	..	..	..	..	6 59	7 3	..	..		a.m	..	..	..	..	..	..	..
48	..	..	Arr Sutton 6 24 a.m	..	..	..		..	..	6 38	..	..	6 46	..	..	..	..	..	..		3	7 0	..	..	..	..	..	..
49	..	..		..	..	..	..	..	a.m	6 41	..	..	6 49	..	..	..	..	..	..	..		7 3	..	..	..	..	..	..
50	..	..		..	..	..	..	6 36	3	6 46	..	..	6 52	..	..	..	..	..	6 55	..	7 3	7 7	..	..	..	..	..	..
51	..	..		..	..	..	..	6 40		6 50	..	..	..	..	..	..	..	..	6 59	..	7 7	7 11	..	..	..	..	..	..
52	..	..		..	..	..	..	6 44	6 50	6 55	..	..	..	..	..	..	..	..	7 3	..	7 11	7 15	..	..	..	..	..	..
53	..	..		..	..	..	..	6 49	..	..	..	..	..	..	..	..	..	..	7 8	..	..	7 20	..	..	..	..	..	..
54	..	..		..	..	..	..	6 52	..	..	..	..	..	..	..	..	..	..	7 11	..	..	7 23	..	..	..	..	..	..
55	..	..		..	..	..	..	..	6 54	6 59	..	..	..	..	..	..	..	..	..	..	7 16	..	..	..	..	..	..	..
56	..	..		..	..	..	..	..	6 58	7 3	..	..	..	..	..	..	..	..	..	..	7 19	..	..	..	..	..	..	..
57	6 18	..	..	..	..	..	..	..	..	..	..	6 38	..	..	..	..	..	..	..	..	..	..	..	6 55	..	6 58	..	..
58	6 21	..	..	..	..	..	..	..	..	..	..	6 41	..	..	..	..	..	..	..	..	..	..	..	6 58	..	7 1	..	..
59	6 23	..	..	..	..	..	..	..	..	..	..	6 43	..	6 40	..	..	..	..	..	..	..	..	..	7 1	..	7 3	..	..
60	6 27	..	..	..	..	..	..	..	..	..	..	6 47	..	..	..	..	..	..	..	..	..	..	..	..	..	7 7	..	..
61	..	..	..	..	..	..	..	..	..	..	..	..	..	..	..	..	..	..	..	..	..	..	..	7 6	..	..	..	..
62	..	..	..	..	..	..	..	..	..	..	..	..	..	..	..	..	..	..	..	..	..	..	..	7 9	..	..	..	..
63	..	..	..	..	..	..	..	..	..	..	..	..	..	..	..	..	..	..	..	..	..	..	..	7 12	..	..	..	..
64	..	..	..	..	..	..	..	..	..	..	..	..	..	..	..	..	..	..	..	..	..	..	..	7 14	..	..	..	..
65	..	..	..	..	..	..	..	..	..	..	..	..	..	..	..	..	..	..	..	..	..	..	..	7 18	..	..	..	..
66	..	..	..	..	..	..	..	..	..	..	..	..	..	§ Via Three Bridges	..	..	..	..	..	..	..	..	..	7 2	..	..	..	..
67	..	..	..	..	..	..	..	..	..	..	..	..	..		..	..	..	..	..	..	..	..	..	7 4	..	..	..	..
68	..	..	..	..	..	..	..	..	..	..	..	..	..		..	..	..	..	..	..	..	..	..	7 6	..	..	..	..
69	..	..	..	..	..	..	..	..	..	..	..	..	..		..	..	..	..	..	..	..	..	..	7 9	..	..	..	..
70	..	..	..	..	..	..	..	..	..	..	..	..	..		..	..	..	..	..	..	..	..	..	7 11	..	..	..	..
71	..	..	..	..	..	..	..	..	..	..	..	..	..		..	..	..	..	..	..	..	..	..	7 16	..	..	..	..
72	..	..	..	..	..	..	..	..	..	..	..	..	..		..	..	..	..	..	..	..	..	..	7 19	..	..	..	..
73	..	..	..	..	..	..	..	..	..	..	..	..	..	..	..	..	..	..	..	..	..	..	..	7 22	..	..	..	..
74	..	..	..	..	..	..	..	..	..	..	..	..	..	6 44	..	..	..	..	..	..	..	..	..	..	..	..	..	..
75	..	..	..	..	..	..	..	..	..	..	..	..	..	6 50	..	..	..	..	..	..	..	..	..	..	..	..	..	..
76	..	..	..	..	..	..	..	..	..	..	..	..	..	6 54	..	..	..	..	..	..	..	..	..	..	..	..	..	..
77	..	..	..	..	..	..	..	..	..	..	..	..	..	7 0	..	..	..	..	..	..	..	..	..	..	..	..	..	..
78	..	..	..	..	..	..	..	7 24	..	..	..	..	..	7§49	..	..	..	..	..	..	..	..	7 49	..	..	..	..	..

LONDON, CRYSTAL PALACE, CROYDON, SUTTON, DORKING NORTH,

For Notes, see page 284a

Down	No.	a.m							Week Days—continued										a.m		No.
Victoria .... dep	1	..	6 38	..	..	6 38	6 40	..	6 40	..	..	..	..	6 53	..	..	..	..	6 49	..	..	6 58	1
Charing Cross* ... "	2	3	3	..	3	3	3	..	..	3	3	3	3	3	..	3	3	3	3	3	..	3	2
Waterloo* .... "	3			..				6 47	..						..						..		3
London Bridge ..... "	4	6 37	..	..	6 41	..	..	..	..	6 45	6 46	6 48	6 50	..	..	6 50	6 54	6 55	..	6 57	7 0	..	4
Battersea Park	5		..	..	..	..	6 43	3	..	..	..	..	..	6 56	..	..	..	..	..	..	..	..	5
Clapham Junction	6	..	6 43	..	..	6 44	6 46		6 47	..	..	..	..	6 59	..	..	..	..	6 54	..	..	7 3	6
Wandsworth Common A	7	..	..	..	..	..	6 49	Via Worcester Park	..	..	..	..	..	7 2	..	..	..	..	..	..	..	..	7
Balham & Upper Tooting	8	..	6 47	..	..	6 48	6 51		..	..	..	..	..	7 4	..	..	..	..	6 59	..	..	7 7	8
South Bermondsey	9	6 41	..	..	..	..	..		..	..	..	..	..	..	..	..	..	6 58	..	7 1	..	..	9
Queen's Road, Peckham	10	6 44	..	..	..	..	..		..	..	..	..	6 55	..	..	..	..	7 1	..	7 4	..	..	10
Peckham Rye	11	6 46	..	..	..	..	..		..	..	..	6 54	6 57	..	..	..	..	7 3	..	7 6	..	..	11
East Dulwich	12		..	..	..	..	..		..	..	..	..	7 0	..	..	..	..	7 6	..	..	..	..	12
North Dulwich	13		..	..	..	..	..		..	..	..	..	7 2	..	..	..	..	7 8	..	To Victoria, arr. 7 23 a.m.	..	..	13
Tulse Hill	14	To Victoria, arr. 7 3 a.m.	..	..	..	..	..		..	6 55	..	6 58	7 5	..	..	..	..	7 11	..		..	..	14
Streatham	15		..	..	..	..	..		..	6 59	..	7 2	..	..	..	..	..	..	..		..	..	15
New Cross Gate (for E.L.	16		..	..	..	..	..	..	..	..	6 51	..	..	..	..	6 55	..	..	..		7 5	..	16
Brockley B .... [Line)	17		..	..	..	..	..	..	..	..	6 53	..	..	..	..	6 57	..	..	..		..	..	17
Honor Oak Park	18		..	..	..	..	..	..	..	..	6 56	..	..	..	..	7 0	..	..	..		..	..	18
Forest Hill, for Lordship	19		..	..	..	..	..	..	..	..	6 58	..	..	..	..	7 2	..	..	..		..	..	19
Sydenham .... [Lane	20		..	..	..	..	..	..	..	..	7 1	..	..	..	..	7 5	..	..	..	..	..	..	20
Penge West C	21		..	..	..	..	..	..	..	..	..	..	..	..	..	7 7	..	..	..	..	..	..	21
Anerley	22		..	..	..	..	..	..	..	..	..	..	..	..	..	7 8	..	..	..	..	..	..	22
Streatham Common	23	..	..	..	..	6 52	..	..	..	7 1	..	..	..	..	..	..	..	..	7 3	..	..	..	23
Norbury	24	..	..	..	..	6 54	..	..	..	7 4	..	..	..	..	..	..	..	..	7 5	..	..	..	24
Thornton Heath	25	..	..	..	..	6 57	..	..	..	7 7	..	..	..	..	..	..	..	..	7 8	..	..	..	25
Selhurst	26	..	..	..	..	6 59	..	..	..	7 10	..	..	..	..	..	..	..	..	7 10	..	..	..	26
Streatham Hill	27	..	..	..	..	..	6 54	..	..	..	..	..	7 8	7 6	..	..	..	..	..	..	..	..	27
West Norwood. [N'wood)	28	..	..	..	..	..	6 57	..	..	..	..	..	..	7 9	..	..	..	7 13	..	..	..	..	28
Gipsy Hill (for Upper	29	..	..	..	..	..	6 59	..	..	..	..	..	..	7 12	..	..	..	7 16	..	..	..	..	29
Crystal Palace D	30	..	..	..	..	..	7 2	..	..	..	7 4	..	..	7 14	..	..	..	7 19	..	..	..	..	30
Birkbeck	31	..	..	..	..	..	..	..	..	..	..	..	..	7 18	..	..	..	..	..	..	..	..	31
Beckenham Jn. arr	32	..	..	..	..	..	..	..	..	..	..	..	..	7 22	..	..	..	..	..	..	..	..	32
Norwood Junction F ..	33	..	..	..	6 54	..	7 7	..	..	7 13	..	..	..	..	..	7 11	7 7	..	..	..	..	..	33
East Croydon .... arr	34	..	..	..	..	..	..	..	6 59		..	..	..	..	..		7 10	..	7 14	..	7 16	..	34
East Croydon .... dep	35	..	..	..	..	..	..	..	7 0	To London Bridge, via Forest Hill	..	..	..	..	..	To London Bridge, via Streatham	7 10	..	7 14	..	7 17	..	35
Mitcham Junction	36	..	6 53	..	..	..	..	..	..		..	7 7	..	..	..		..	..	..	..	..	7 13	36
Hackbridge	37	..	6 56	..	..	..	..	..	..		..	7 9	..	..	..		..	..	..	..	..	7 16	37
Carshalton	38	..	6 58	..	..	..	..	..	..		..	7 12	..	..	..		..	..	..	..	..	7 18	38
West Croydon 319 arr	39	..	..	3	6 58	7 2	7 11	..	..		..	..	..	..	..		..	..	..	..	..	..	39
West Croydon 319 dep	40	..	..	6 54	6 58	7 2	..	..	..		..	..	..	..	..		..	..	..	..	..	..	40
Waddon G	41	..	..	6 56	7 0	7 5	..	..	..		..	..	..	..	..		..	..	..	..	..	..	41
Wallington	42	..	..	7 0	7 4	7 8	..	..	..		..	..	..	..	..		..	..	..	..	..	..	42
Carshalton Beeches	43	..	..	7 2	7 7	7 11	..	..	..		..	..	..	..	..		..	..	..	..	..	..	43
Sutton 322	44	..	7 1	7 5	7 10	7 14	..	..	..		..	7 15	..	..	..		..	..	..	..	..	7 21	44
Belmont	45	..	..	..	7 13	7 17	..	..	..	..	..	..	..	..	..	..	..	..	..	..	..	..	45
Banstead	46	..	..	..	7 16	7 20	..	..	..	..	..	..	..	..	..	..	..	..	..	..	..	..	46
Epsom Downs ...... arr	47	..	..	..	7 19	7 23	..	..	..	..	..	..	..	..	..	..	..	..	..	..	..	..	47
Cheam	48	..	7 4	..	..	..	..	..	..	..	..	7 18	..	..	3	..	..	..	..	..	..	7 24	48
Ewell East H	49	..	7 7	..	..	..	..	..	..	..	..	7 21	..	..		..	..	..	..	..	..	7 27	49
Epsom	50	..	7 11	..	..	..	..	7 15	..	..	..	7 24	..	..	7 28	..	..	..	..	..	..	7 31	50
Ashtead	51	..	..	..	..	..	..	7 19	..	..	..	7 28	..	..	7 32	..	..	..	..	..	..	..	51
Leatherhead .. [Bridge J	52	..	..	..	..	..	..	7 23	..	..	..	7 32	..	..	7 38	..	..	..	..	..	..	..	52
Boxhill and Burford	53	..	..	..	..	..	..	..	..	..	..	7 38	..	..	..	..	..	..	..	..	..	..	53
Dorking North K .. arr	54	..	..	..	..	..	..	..	..	..	..	7 40	..	..	..	..	..	..	..	..	..	..	54
Bookham .... [594	55	..	..	..	..	..	..	7 28	..	..	..	..	..	..	7L46	..	..	..	..	..	..	..	55
Effingham Junction arr	56	..	..	..	..	..	..	7 32	..	..	..	..	..	..	7 50	..	..	..	..	..	..	..	56
South Croydon 234	57	..	..	..	..	..	..	..	..	..	..	..	..	..	L Arrives Bookham 7 42 a.m	..	7 13	..	7 16	..	..	..	57
Purley Oaks	58	..	..	..	..	..	..	..	..	..	..	..	..	..		..	7 15	..	7 19	..	..	..	58
Purley	59	..	..	..	..	..	..	..	7 5	..	..	..	..	..		..	7 18	..	7 21	..	..	..	59
Coulsdon North L .. arr	60	..	..	..	..	..	..	..	..	..	..	..	..	..		..	..	..	7 25	..	..	..	60
Purley .... dep	61	..	..	..	..	..	..	..	..	..	..	..	..	..		..	7 24	..	..	..	..	..	61
Kenley	62	..	..	..	..	..	..	..	..	..	..	..	..	..		..	7 27	..	..	..	..	..	62
Whyteleafe	63	..	..	..	..	..	..	..	..	..	..	..	..	..		..	7 30	..	..	..	..	..	63
Warlingham	64	..	..	..	..	..	..	..	..	..	..	..	..	..		..	7 32	..	..	..	..	..	64
Caterham .... arr	65	..	..	..	..	..	..	..	..	..	..	..	..	..		..	7 36	..	..	..	..	..	65
Purley .... dep	66	..	..	..	..	..	..	..	§ Via Three Bridges	..	..	..	..	..		..	7 19	..	..	..	..	..	66
Reedham	67	..	..	..	..	..	..	..		..	..	..	..	..		..	7 21	..	..	..	..	..	67
Smitham	68	..	..	..	..	..	..	..		..	..	..	..	..		..	7 24	..	..	..	..	..	68
Woodmansterne	69	..	..	..	..	..	..	..		..	..	..	..	..		..	7 26	..	..	..	..	..	69
Chipstead	70	..	..	..	..	..	..	..		..	..	..	..	..	..	..	7 29	..	..	..	..	..	70
Kingswood M	71	..	..	..	..	..	..	..		..	..	..	..	..	..	..	7 33	..	..	..	..	..	71
Tadworth N	72	..	..	..	..	..	..	..		..	..	..	..	..	..	..	7 36	..	..	..	..	..	72
Tattenham Corner. arr	73	..	..	..	..	..	..	..		..	..	..	..	..	..	..	7 40	..	..	..	..	..	73
Coulsdon South	74	..	..	..	..	..	..	..	7 9	..	..	..	..	..	..	..	..	..	..	..	..	..	74
Merstham	75	..	..	..	..	..	..	..	7 15	..	..	..	..	..	..	..	..	..	..	..	..	..	75
Redhill 158, 246 ..... arr	76	..	..	..	..	..	..	..	7 19	..	..	..	..	..	..	..	..	..	..	..	7 31	..	76
Reigate 246 .... "	77	..	..	..	..	..	..	..	7 26	..	..	..	..	..	..	..	..	..	..	..	7 51	..	77
Horsham 159, 244, 245 "	78	..	..	..	..	..	..	..	8§ 5	..	..	..	..	..	..	..	..	..	..	..	..	..	78

CATERHAM, TATTENHAM CORNER, REDHILL, REIGATE, and HORSHAM

a.m — Week Days—continued — a.m

No.						SX																						
1	..	..	6 58	..	7 0	..	..	..	..	..	..	..	7 11	7 13	7 17	..	..	..	..	..	..	..	..	7 18	7 20	7 26	..	..
2	..	(3)	(3)	..	(3)	(3)	(3)	..	(3)	(3)	(3)	(3)	(3)	(3)	(3)	..	..	(3)	(3)	..	..	(3)	(3)	(3)	(3)	(3)	(3)	(3)
3	..			7 7				..								..	7 27			..	7 34							
4	..	7 1	..	..	..	7 5	7 6	..	7 8	7 10	7 10	7 15	..	..	..	..	..	7 15	7 17	7 20	..	7 21	7 24	..	..	..	7 25	7 27
5	..	..	..	(3)	7 3	..	..	..	..	..	..	..	..	7 16	..	..	(3)	..	..	..	(3)	..	..	..	7 23	..	..	..
6	..	..	7 4		7 6	..	..	..	..	..	..	..	7 16	7 19	7 22	..		..	..	..		..	..	7 24	7 26	..	..	..
7	..	..	..		7 9	..	..	..	..	..	..	..	..	7 22	..	..		..	..	..	..	..	..	..	7 29	..	..	..
8	..	..	7 8		7 11	..	..	..	..	..	..	..	7 21	7 24	7 26	..		..	..	..	..	..	..	7 28	7 31	7 36	..	..
9	..	..	..	Via Worcester Park	..	..	..	..	..	..	..	..	..	..	..	..	Via Worcester Park	7 18	7 21	..	..	..	..	..	..	..	..	..
10	..	..	..		..	..	..	..	..	7 15	..	..	..	..	..	..		7 21	7 24	..	..	..	..	..	..	..	..	..
11	..	..	..		..	..	..	..	7 14	7 17	..	..	..	..	..	..		7 23	7 26	..	..	..	..	..	..	..	..	..
12	..	..	..		..	..	..	..	..	7 20	..	..	..	..	..	..		7 26		..	..	..	..	..	..	..	..	..
13	..	..	..		..	..	..	..	..	7 22	..	..	..	..	..	..		7 28		..	..	..	..	..	..	..	..	..
14	..	..	..		..	7 15	..	..	7 18	7 25	..	..	..	..	..	..		7 31	To Victoria, arr. 7 42 a.m	..	..	..	..	..	..	..	7 35	..
15	..	..	..		..	7 19	..	..	7 22	..	..	..	..	..	..	..		..		..	..	..	..	..	..	..	7 39	..
16	..	..	..	..	..	..	7 11	..	..	..	7 15	..	..	..	..	..	..	..		..	..	..	7 29	..	..	..	..	7 32
17	..	..	..	..	..	..	7 13	..	..	..	7 17	..	..	..	..	..	..	..		..	..	..	..	..	..	..	..	7 34
18	..	..	..	..	..	..	7 16	..	..	..	7 20	..	..	..	..	..	..	..		..	..	..	..	..	..	..	..	7 37
19	..	..	..	..	..	..	7 18	..	..	..	7 22	..	..	..	..	..	..	..		..	..	..	..	..	..	..	..	7 39
20	..	..	..	..	..	..	7 21	..	..	..	7 25	..	..	..	..	..	..	..		..	..	..	..	..	..	..	..	7 42
21	..	..	..	..	..	..	..	..	..	..	7 27	..	..	..	..	..	..	..		..	..	..	..	..	..	..	..	..
22	..	..	..	..	..	..	..	..	..	..	7 28	..	..	..	..	..	..	..		..	..	..	..	..	..	..	..	..
23	..	..	7 12	..	..	7 21	..	..	..	..	..	..	7 25	..	..	..	..	..	..	..	..	..	..	7 32	..	..	7 41	..
24	..	..	7 14	..	..	7 24	..	..	..	..	..	..	7 27	..	..	..	..	..	..	..	..	..	..	7 34	..	7 41	7 44	..
25	..	..	7 17	..	..	7 27	..	..	..	..	..	..	7 30	..	..	..	..	..	..	..	..	..	..	7 37	..	7 44	7 47	..
26	..	..	7 19	..	..	7 30	..	..	..	..	..	..	7 32	..	..	..	..	..	..	..	..	..	..	7 39	..	7 46	7 50	..
27	..	..	..	..	7 14	..	..	..	..	7 28	..	..	..	7 26	..	..	..	..	..	..	..	..	..	..	7 34	..	..	..
28	..	..	..	..	7 17	..	..	..	..	..	..	..	..	7 29	..	..	..	7 33	..	..	..	..	..	..	7 37	..	..	..
29	..	..	..	..	7 19	..	..	..	..	..	..	..	..	7 32	..	..	..	7 36	..	..	..	..	..	..	7 39	..	..	..
30	..	..	..	..	7 22	..	7 24	..	..	..	..	..	..	7 34	..	..	..	7 39	..	..	..	..	..	..	7 42	..	..	7 45
31	..	..	..	..	..	..	..	..	..	..	..	..	..	7 38	..	..	..	..	..	..	..	..	..	..	..	..	..	..
32	..	..	..	..	..	..	..	..	..	..	..	..	..	7 42	..	..	..	..	..	..	..	..	..	..	..	..	..	..
33	..	7 14	..	..	7 27	7 33	..	..	..	..	7 31	7 28	..	..	..	..	..	..	..	7 32	..	7 34	7 38	..	7 47	..	7 53	..
34	..	..	..	..	..	To London Bridge, via Forest Hill	..	..	..	..		7 32	7 36	..	..	..	..	..	..	7 36	..	..	7 42	..	..	..		..
35	..	..	..	..	..		..	..	..	..	To London Bridge, via Streatham	7 32	7 36	..	..	..	..	..	..	7 39	..	..	7 42	..	..	..	To London Bridge, via Forest Hill	..
36	..	..	..	..	..		..	..	7 27	..		..	..	..	7 32	..	..	..	..	..	..	..	..	..	..	..		..
37	..	..	..	..	..		..	..	7 29	..		..	..	..	7 36	..	..	..	..	..	..	..	..	..	..	..		..
38	(3)	..	..	..	..		..	..	7 32	..		..	..	..	7 38	(3)	..	..	..	..	..	..	..	..	..	..		..
39		7 18	7 22	..	7 31		..	..	..	..		..	..	..	..		..	..	..	..	..	7 38	..	7 42	7 52	7 49		..
40	7 14	7 18	7 22	..	..		..	..	..	..		..	..	..	..	7 34	..	..	..	..	..	7 38	..	7 42	..	..		..
41	7 16	7 20	7 25	..	..		..	..	..	..		..	..	..	..	7 36	..	..	..	..	..	7 40	..	7 45	..	..		..
42	7 20	7 24	7 28	..	..		..	..	..	..		..	..	..	..	7 40	..	..	..	..	..	7 44	..	7 48	..	..		..
43	7 22	7 27	7 31	..	..		..	..	..	..		..	..	..	..	7 42	..	..	..	..	..	7 47	..	7 51	..	..		..
44	7 25	7 30	7 34	..	..		..	..	7 35	..		..	..	..	7 41	7 45	..	..	..	..	..	7 50	..	7 54	..	..		..
45	..	7 33	7 37	..	..	..	..	..	..	..	..	..	..	..	..	..	..	..	..	..	..	7 53	..	7 57	..	..	..	..
46	..	7 36	7 40	..	..	..	..	..	..	..	..	..	..	..	..	..	..	..	..	..	..	7 56	..	8 0	..	..	..	..
47	..	7 39	7 43	..	..	..	..	..	..	..	..	..	..	..	..	..	..	..	..	..	..	7 59	..	8 3	..	..	..	..
48	..	..	..	..	..	..	..	..	7 38	..	..	..	..	..	7 44	..	..	..	..	..	..	..	..	..	..	..	..	..
49	..	..	..	..	..	..	..	..	7 41	..	..	..	..	..	7 47	..	..	..	..	..	..	..	..	..	..	..	..	..
50	..	..	..	7 35	..	..	..	..	7 45	..	..	..	..	..	7 51	..	7 55	..	..	..	8 0	..	..	..	..	..	..	..
51	..	..	..	7 39	..	..	..	..	7 49	..	..	..	..	..	..	..	7 59	..	..	..	8 4	..	..	..	..	..	..	..
52	..	..	..	7 43	..	..	..	..	7 53	..	..	..	..	..	..	..	8 3	..	..	..	8 8	..	..	..	..	..	..	..
53	..	..	..	7 48	..	..	..	..	..	..	..	..	..	..	..	..	8 8	..	..	..	..	..	..	..	..	..	..	..
54	..	..	..	7 51	..	..	..	..	..	..	..	..	..	..	..	..	8 11	..	..	..	..	..	..	..	..	..	..	..
55	..	..	..	..	..	..	..	..	7 57	..	..	..	..	..	..	..	..	..	..	..	8 12	..	..	..	..	..	..	..
56	..	..	..	..	..	..	..	..	..	..	..	..	..	..	..	..	..	..	..	..	8 16	..	..	..	..	..	..	..
57	..	..	..	..	..	..	..	..	..	..	..	7 34	7 38	..	..	..	..	..	..	..	..	..	7 44	..	..	..	..	..
58	..	..	..	..	..	..	..	..	..	..	..	7 37	7 41	..	..	..	..	..	..	..	..	..	7 47	..	..	..	..	..
59	..	..	..	..	..	..	..	..	..	..	..	7 40	7 43	..	..	..	..	..	..	7 44	..	..	7 49	..	..	..	..	..
60	..	..	..	..	..	..	..	..	..	..	..	..	7 47	..	..	..	..	..	..	..	..	..	7 53	..	..	..	..	..
61	..	..	..	..	..	..	..	..	..	..	..	7 46	..	..	..	..	..	..	..	..	..	..	..	..	..	..	..	..
62	..	..	..	..	..	..	..	..	..	..	..	7 49	..	..	..	..	..	..	..	..	..	..	..	..	..	..	..	..
63	..	..	..	..	..	..	..	..	..	..	..	7 52	..	..	..	..	..	..	..		..	..	..	..	..	..	..	..
64	..	..	..	..	..	..	..	..	..	..	..	7 54	..	..	..	..	..	..	..		..	..	..	..	..	..	..	..
65	..	..	..	..	..	..	..	..	..	..	..	7 58	..	..	..	..	..	..	..		..	..	..	..	..	..	..	..
66	..	..	..	..	..	..	..	..	..	..	..	7 41	..	..	..	..	..	..	..	§ Via Three Bridges	..	..	..	..	..	..	..	..
67	..	..	..	..	..	..	..	..	..	..	..	7 43	..	..	..	..	..	..	..		..	..	..	..	..	..	..	..
68	..	..	..	..	..	..	..	..	..	..	..	7 45	..	..	..	..	..	..	..		..	..	..	..	..	..	..	..
69	..	..	..	..	..	..	..	..	..	..	..	7 48	..	..	..	..	..	..	..		..	..	..	..	..	..	..	..
70	..	..	..	..	..	..	..	..	..	..	..	7 50	..	..	..	..	..	..	..		..	..	..	..	..	..	..	..
71	..	..	..	..	..	..	..	..	..	..	..	7 55	..	..	..	..	..	..	..	..	..	..	..	..	..	..	..	..
72	..	..	..	..	..	..	..	..	..	..	..	7 58	..	..	..	..	..	..	..	..	..	..	..	..	..	..	..	..
73	..	..	..	..	..	..	..	..	..	..	..	8 0	..	..	..	..	..	..	..	..	..	..	..	..	..	..	..	..
74	..	..	..	..	..	..	..	..	..	..	..	..	..	..	..	..	..	..	..	7 48	..	..	..	..	..	..	..	..
75	..	..	..	..	..	..	..	..	..	..	..	..	..	..	..	..	..	..	..	7 54	..	..	..	..	..	..	..	..
76	..	..	..	..	..	..	..	..	..	..	..	..	..	..	..	..	..	..	..	7 58	..	..	..	..	..	..	..	..
77	..	..	..	..	..	..	..	..	..	..	..	..	..	..	..	..	..	..	..	8 3	..	..	..	..	..	..	..	..
78	..	..	..	8 16	..	..	..	..	..	..	..	..	..	..	..	..	..	..	..	8§49	..	..	..	..	..	..	..	..

For Notes, see page 284a

LONDON, CRYSTAL PALACE, CROYDON, SUTTON, DORKING NORTH,

Down	No.	a.m.									Week Days—*continued*							a.m.					No.
						SX													SX				
Victoria dep	1					7 31	7 33		7 38				7 38				7 40		7 41	7 47			1
Charing Cross* "	2	(3)	(3)	(3)	(3)	(3)	(3)	(3)	(3)			(3)	(3)		(3)	(3)	(3)	(3)	(3)		(3)		2
Waterloo* "	3										7 47											7 52	3
London Bridge "	4	7 28	7 30	7 31	7 35			7 35				7 42			7 37	7 44		7 47			7 45		4
Battersea Park	5						7 36				(3)						7 43						5
Clapham Junction	6					7 36	7 39		7 43				7 44				7 46		7 49	7 52		7 59	6
Wandsworth Common A	7						7 42				Via Worcester Park						7 49					(3)	7
Balham & Upper Tooting	8					7 41	7 44		7 47				7 48				7 51		7 54				8
South Bermondsey	9							7 38							7 41								9
Queen's Road, Peckham	10		7 35					7 41							7 44								10
Peckham Rye	11	7 34	7 37					7 43							7 46							Via Worcester Park	11
East Dulwich	12		7 40					7 46															12
North Dulwich	13		7 42					7 48															13
Tulse Hill	14	7 38	7 45					7 51													7 55		14
Streatham	15	7 42													To Victoria, arr. 8 1 a.m.						7 59		15
New Cross Gate (for E.L.	16			7 36												7 49		7 52					16
Brockley B [Line)	17			7 38														7 54					17
Honor Oak Park	18			7 41														7 57					18
Forest Hill, for Lordship	19			7 43														7 59					19
Sydenham [Lane	20			7 46														8 2					20
Penge West C	21			7 48																			21
Anerley	22			7 49																			22
Streatham Common	23					7 45							7 52								8 1		23
Norbury	24					7 47							7 54								8 4		24
Thornton Heath	25					7 50							7 57						8 1		8 7		25
Selhurst	26					7 52							7 59						8 3		8 10		26
Streatham Hill	27		7 48				7 46										7 54						27
West Norwood..[N'wood)	28		To Victoria, via Wandsworth Common				7 49	7 53									7 57						28
Gipsy Hill (for Upper	29						7 52	7 56									7 59						29
Crystal Palace D	30						7 54	7 59									8 2	8 5					30
Birkbeck	31						7 58																31
Beckenham Jn. arr	32						8 2																32
Norwood Junction F	33			7 52	7 48							7 55				7 58	8 7				8 13		33
East Croydon arr	34			To London Bridge, via Streatham	7 52	7 55										8 2				8 4			34
East Croydon dep	35				7 52	7 55										8 2				8 5	To London Bridge, via Forest Hill		35
Mitcham Junction	36	7 47							7 53														36
Hackbridge	37	7 49							7 56														37
Carshalton	38	7 52							7 58	(3)													38
West Croydon 319 arr	39											7 59	8 2				8 11						39
West Croydon 319 dep	40									7 54		7 59	8 2										40
Waddon G	41									7 56		8 1	8 5										41
Wallington	42									8 0		8 5	8 8										42
Carshalton Beeches	43									8 2		8 7	8 11										43
Sutton 322	44	7 55							8 1	8 5		8 10	8 14										44
Belmont	45											8 13	8 17										45
Banstead	46											8 16	8 20										46
Epsom Downs arr	47											8 19	8 23										47
Cheam	48	7 58							8 4														48
Ewell East H	49	8 1							8 7														49
Epsom	50	8 4							8 11		8 15											8 23	50
Ashtead	51	8 8									8 19											8 27	51
Leatherhead..[Bridge J	52	8 12									8 23											8 31	52
Boxhill and Burford	53	8 17									8 28												53
Dorking North K...arr	54	8 20									8 31												54
Bookham [394	55																					8 36	55
Effingham Junction arr	56																					8 40	56
South Croydon 234	57					7 58										8 4						Stop	57
Purley Oaks	58					8 0										8 7							58
Purley	59				7 57	8 3										8 9				8 10			59
Coulsdon North L.. arr	60					8 6										8 13							60
Purley dep	61				7 59																		61
Kenley	62				8 2																		62
Whyteleafe	63				8 5																		63
Warlingham	64				8 7																		64
Caterham arr	65				8 11																	a.m	65
Purley dep	66				7 58																		66
Reedham	67				8 0																		67
Smitham	68				8 3															§ Via Three Bridges			68
Woodmansterne	69				8 5																	d Departure time	69
Chipstead	70				8 8																		70
Kingswood M	71				8 12																		71
Tadworth N	72				8 15																		72
Tattenham Corner. arr	73				8 19																		73
Coulsdon South	74																			8 14			74
Merstham	75																			8 20			75
Redhill 158, 246 .... arr	76																			8 24		8d30	76
Reigate 246 "	77																			8 29		8 34	77
Horsham 159, 244, 245 "	78	8 44																		9§ 5			78

CATERHAM, TATTENHAM CORNER, REDHILL, REIGATE, and HORSHAM

Week Days—continued — a.m

No.												SX							SX									
1	..	..	..	7 51	7 53	..	..	..	7 56	..	..	..	7 58	8 0	..	..	..	8 0	8 4	8 4	..	..	8 7	..	..	..	..	..
2	3	3	3	3	3	3	3	3	3	..	..	3	3	..	..	3	..	3	3	3	3	3	3	3	3	..	3	3
3										..	8 7			..	..		..									..		
4	7 48	7 51	7 55	..	..	7 50	7 55	7 57	..	..	..	8 2	..	..	..	8 4	8 3	..	..	..	8 5	8 7	..	8 8	8 10	..	8 11	8 15
5	..	..	..	..	7 56	..	..	..	..	..	3	..	..	..	..	..	..	8 3	..	8 7	..	..	..	..	..	..	..	..
6	..	..	..	7 56	7 59	..	..	..	8 2	..		..	8 4	8 5	..	..	..	8 6	..	8 10	..	..	8 13	..	..	..	..	..
7	..	..	..	..	8 2	..	..	..	..	..	Via Worcester Park	..	..	..	..	..	..	8 9	..	8 13	..	..	..	..	..	..	..	..
8	..	..	..	8 1	8 4	..	..	..	8 6	..		..	8 8	..	..	..	..	8 11	..	8 15	..	..	8 17	..	..	..	..	..
9	..	..	..	..	..	..	7 58	8 1	..	..		..	..	..	..	..	..	..	..	..	..	..	..	..	..	..	..	..
10	..	..	..	..	..	7 55	8 1	8 4	..	..		..	..	..	..	..	..	..	..	..	..	..	..	..	..	..	..	..
11	7 54	..	..	..	..	7 57	8 3	8 6	..	..		..	..	..	..	..	..	..	..	..	..	..	..	8 14	..	..	..	..
12	..	..	..	..	..	8 0	8 6	To Victoria, arr. 8 21 a.m	..	..		..	..	..	..	..	..	..	..	..	..	..	..	..	..	..	..	..
13	..	..	..	..	..	8 2	8 8		..	..		..	..	..	..	..	..	..	..	..	..	..	..	..	..	..	..	..
14	7 58	..	..	..	..	8 5	8 11		..	..		..	..	..	..	..	..	..	..	..	8 15	..	..	8 18	..	..	..	..
15	8 2	..	..	..	..	..	..		..	..		..	..	..	..	..	..	..	..	..	8 19	..	..	8 22	..	..	..	..
16	..	7 56	..	..	..	..	..		..	..	..	..	..	..	..	8 9	..	..	..	..	..	8 12	..	..	8 15	..	8 16	..
17	..	7 58	..	..	..	..	..		..	..	..	..	..	..	..	..	..	..	..	..	..	8 14	..	..	..	..	8 18	..
18	..	8 1	..	..	..	..	..		..	..	..	..	..	..	..	..	..	..	..	..	..	8 17	..	..	..	..	8 21	..
19	..	8 3	..	..	..	..	..		..	..	..	..	..	..	..	..	..	..	..	..	..	8 19	..	..	8 19	..	8 23	..
20	..	8 6	..	..	..	..	..		..	..	..	..	..	..	..	..	..	..	..	..	..	8 22	..	..	..	..	8 26	..
21	..	8 8	..	..	..	..	..		..	..	..	..	..	..	..	..	..	..	..	..	..	..	..	..	..	..	8 28	..
22	..	8 9	..	..	..	..	..		..	..	..	..	..	..	..	..	..	..	..	..	..	..	..	..	..	..	8 29	..
23	..	..	..	8 5	..	..	..	..	..	..	..	..	8 12	..	..	..	..	..	..	..	8 21	..	..	..	..	..	..	..
24	..	..	..	8 7	..	..	..	..	..	..	..	..	8 14	..	..	..	..	..	8 17	..	8 24	..	..	..	..	..	..	..
25	..	..	..	8 10	..	..	..	..	..	..	..	..	8 17	..	..	..	..	..	8 20	..	8 27	..	..	..	..	..	..	..
26	..	..	..	8 12	..	..	..	..	..	..	..	..	8 19	..	..	..	..	..	8 22	..	8 30	..	..	..	..	..	..	..
27	..	..	..	..	8 6	8 9	..	..	..	..	..	..	..	..	..	..	..	8 14	..	8 18	..	..	..	..	..	..	..	..
28	..	..	..	..	8 9	To Victoria, via Wandsworth Common	8 13	..	..	..	..	..	..	..	..	..	..	8 17	..	To London Bridge, via Tulse Hill	..	..	..	..	..	..	..	..
29	..	..	..	..	8 12		8 16	..	..	..	..	..	..	..	..	..	..	8 19	..		..	..	..	..	..	..	..	..
30	..	..	..	..	8 14		8 19	..	..	..	..	..	..	..	..	..	..	8 22	..		..	8 25	..	..	..	..	..	..
31	..	..	..	..	8 18		..	..	..	..	..	..	..	..	..	..	..	..	..		..	..	..	..	..	..	..	..
32	..	..	..	..	8 22		..	..	..	..	..	..	..	..	..	..	..	..	..		..	..	..	..	..	..	..	..
33	..	8 12	8 8	..	..		..	..	..	..	..	8 15	..	..	..	8 18	8 18	8 27	..		8 33	..	..	..	8 24	..	8 32	..
34	..	To London Bridge, via Streatham	8 12	8 16	..		..	..	..	..	..	..	..	8 17	..	8 22	8 23	..	..		To London Bridge, via Forest Hill	..	..	..	..	..	..	8 30
35	..		8 12	8 16	..		..	..	..	..	..	..	..	8 20	..	8 22	8 25	..	..			..	..	..	..	..	To London Bridge, via Streatham	8 30
36	8 7		..	..	..		..	..	8 13	..	..	..	..	..	..	..	..	..	..			..	8 23	8 27	..	..		..
37	8 9		..	..	..		..	..	8 15	..	..	..	..	..	..	..	..	..	..			..	8 26	8 29	..	..		..
38	8 12		..	..	..		..	..	8 18	..	..	..	..	..	..	..	..	..	..			..	8 28	8 32	..	..		..
39	..		..	..	..		..	..	..	3	..	8 19	8 22	..	..	..	..	8 31	..	..		..	..	..	8 28	3		..
40	..		..	..	..		..	..	..	8 14	..	8 19	8 22	..	..	..	..	..	..	..		..	..	..	8 28	8 34		..
41	..		..	..	..		..	..	..	8 16	..	8 21	8 25	..	..	..	..	..	..	..		..	..	..	..	8 36		..
42	..		..	..	..		..	..	..	8 20	..	8 25	8 28	..	..	..	..	..	..	..		..	..	..	8 33	8 40		..
43	..		..	..	..		..	..	..	8 22	..	8 27	8 31	..	..	..	..	..	..	..		..	..	..	..	8 42		..
44	8 15		..	..	..		..	..	8 21	8 25	..	8 30	8 34	..	..	..	..	..	..	..		..	8 32	8 35	8 38	8 45		..
45	..	..	..	..	..	..	..	..	..	..	..	8 33	8 37	..	..	..	..	..	..	..	..	..	..	..	..	..	..	..
46	..	..	..	..	..	..	..	..	..	..	..	8 36	8 40	..	..	..	..	..	..	..	..	..	..	..	..	..	..	..
47	..	..	..	..	..	..	..	..	..	..	..	8 39	8 43	..	..	..	..	..	..	..	..	..	..	..	..	..	..	..
48	8 18	..	..	..	..	..	..	..	8 24	..	..	..	..	..	..	..	..	..	..	..	..	..	8 35	8 43	..	..	..	..
49	8 21	..	..	..	..	..	..	..	8 27	..	..	..	..	..	..	..	..	..	..	..	..	..	8 38	8 46	..	..	..	..
50	8 26	..	..	..	..	..	..	..	8 30	..	8 35	..	..	..	..	..	..	..	..	..	..	..	8 41	8 49	8 44	..	..	..
51	8 30	..	..	..	..	..	..	..	..	..	8 39	..	..	..	..	..	..	..	..	..	..	..	..	8 53	8 48	..	..	..
52	8 34	..	..	..	..	..	..	..	..	..	8 43	..	..	..	..	..	..	..	..	..	..	..	..	8 58	8 52	..	..	..
53	8 39	..	..	..	..	..	..	..	..	..	8 48	..	..	..	..	..	..	..	..	..	..	..	..	..	..	..	..	..
54	8 42	..	..	..	..	..	..	..	..	..	8 51	..	..	..	..	..	..	..	..	..	..	..	..	..	8 58	..	..	..
55	..	..	..	..	..	..	..	..	..	..	..	..	..	..	..	..	..	..	..	..	..	..	..	9 2	..	..	..	..
56	..	..	..	..	..	..	..	..	..	..	..	..	..	..	..	..	..	..	..	..	..	..	..	..	..	..	..	..
57	..	..	..	8 18	..	..	..	..	..	..	..	..	..	..	..	8 24	8 30	..	..	..	..	..	..	Arr. Cheam 8 39 a.m.	..	..	..	8 33
58	..	..	..	8 21	..	..	..	..	..	..	..	..	..	..	..	8 27	..	..	..	..	..	..	..		..	..	..	..
59	..	..	8 18	8 23	..	..	..	..	..	..	..	..	..	8 26	..	8 29	..	..	..	..	..	..	..		..	..	..	8 37
60	..	..	..	8 27	..	..	..	..	..	..	..	..	..	..	..	8 33	..	..	..	..	..	..	..		..	..	..	..
61	..	..	8 20	..	..	..	..	..	..	..	..	..	..	..	..	..	..	..	..	..	..	..	..		..	..	..	8 39
62	..	..	8 23	..	..	..	..	..	..	..	..	..	..	..	..	..	..	..	..	..	..	..	..		..	..	..	8 42
63	..	..	8 26	..	..	..	..	..	..	..	..	..	..	..	..	..	..	..	..	..	..	..	..		..	..	..	8 45
64	..	..	8 28	..	..	..	..	..	..	..	..	..	..	..	..	..	..	..	..	..	..	..	..		..	..	..	8 47
65	..	..	8 32	..	..	..	..	..	..	..	..	..	..	..	..	..	..	..	..	..	..	..	..		..	..	..	8 51
66	..	..	8 19	..	..	..	..	..	..	..	..	..	..	..	..	..	..	..	..	..	..	..	..	..	..	..	..	8 38
67	..	..	8 21	..	..	..	..	..	..	..	..	..	..	..	..	..	..	..	..	..	..	..	..	..	..	..	..	8 40
68	..	..	8 24	..	..	..	..	..	..	..	..	..	..	..	..	..	..	..	..	..	..	..	..	..	..	..	..	8 43
69	..	..	8 26	..	..	..	..	..	..	..	..	..	..	..	..	..	..	..	..	..	..	..	..	..	..	..	..	8 45
70	..	..	8 29	..	..	..	..	..	..	..	..	..	..	..	..	..	..	..	..	..	..	..	..	..	..	..	..	8 48
71	..	..	8 33	..	..	..	..	..	..	..	..	..	..	..	..	..	..	..	..	..	..	..	..	..	..	..	..	8 52
72	..	..	8 36	..	..	..	..	..	..	..	..	..	..	..	..	..	..	..	..	..	..	..	..	..	..	..	..	8 55
73	..	..	8 40	..	..	..	..	..	..	..	..	..	..	..	..	..	..	..	..	..	..	..	..	..	..	..	..	8 59
74	..	..	..	..	..	..	..	..	..	..	..	..	..	..	..	..	..	..	..	..	..	..	..	..	..	..	..	..
75	..	..	..	..	..	..	..	..	..	..	..	..	..	..	..	..	..	..	..	..	..	..	..	..	..	..	..	..
76	..	..	..	..	..	..	..	..	..	..	..	..	..	8 37	..	..	..	..	..	..	..	..	..	..	..	..	..	..
77	..	..	..	..	..	..	..	..	..	..	..	..	..	8 50	..	..	..	..	..	..	..	..	..	..	..	..	..	..
78	..	..	..	..	..	..	..	..	..	..	..	..	..	..	..	..	..	..	..	..	..	..	..	..	9 24	..	..	..

LONDON, CRYSTAL PALACE, CROYDON, SUTTON, DORKING NORTH,

For Notes, see page 284a

Down	No.	a.m							Week Days—continued								a.m						No.
													SX										
Victoria ..... dep	1	8 13	..	..	..	8 11	..	..	8 18	..	8 20	8 24	8 24	..	..	..	..	8 28	..	..	..	..	1
Charing Cross* ... "	2	3	3	3	..	3	3	3	3	..	3	3	3	..	3	3	..	..	..	3	3	3	2
Waterloo* ..... "	3	3	3	3	..	3	3	3	3	8 27	3	3	3	..	3	3	..	..	..	3	3	3	3
London Bridge .... "	4	..	8 15	8 17	8 18	..	8 22	8 24	..	..	..	..	..	..	8 25	8 27	..	..	8 27	8 28	8 30	8 31	4
Battersea Park	5	8 16	..	..	..	..	..	..	..	3	8 23	8 27	..	..	..	..	..	..	..	..	..	..	5
Clapham Junction	6	8 19	..	..	..	8 16	..	..	8 24		8 26	8 30	..	..	..	..	..	8 33	..	..	..	..	6
Wandsworth Common A	7	8 22	..	..	..	..	..	..	..		8 29	8 33	..	..	..	..	..	..	..	..	..	..	7
Balham & Upper Tooting	8	8 24	..	..	..	8 20	..	..	8 28		8 31	8 35	..	..	..	..	..	..	..	..	..	..	8
South Bermondsey	9	..	8 18	8 21	..	..	..	..	..	Via Worcester Park	..	..	..	..	..	..	..	..	..	..	..	..	9
Queen's Road, Peckham	10	..	8 21	8 24	..	..	..	..	..		..	..	..	..	..	..	..	..	..	..	8 35	..	10
Peckham Rye	11	..	8 23	8 26	..	..	..	..	..		..	..	..	..	..	..	..	..	..	8 34	8 37	..	11
East Dulwich	12	..	8 26		..	..	..	..	..		..	..	..	..	..	..	..	..	..	..	8 40	..	12
North Dulwich	13	..	8 28		..	..	..	..	..		..	..	..	..	..	..	..	..	..	..	8 42	..	13
Tulse Hill	14	..	8 31	To Victoria, arr. 8 42 a.m.	..	..	..	..	..		..	..	..	..	8 35	..	..	..	..	8 38	8 45	..	14
Streatham	15	..	..		..	..	..	..	..		..	..	..	..	8 39	..	..	..	..	8 42	..	..	15
New Cross Gate (for E.L.	16	..	..		..	..	..	8 29	..		..	..	..	..	..	8 32	..	..	8 32	..	..	8 36	16
Brockley B ...[Line)	17	..	..		..	..	..	..	..		..	..	..	..	..	8 34	..	..	..	..	..	8 38	17
Honor Oak Park	18	..	..		..	..	..	..	..	..	..	..	..	..	..	8 37	..	..	..	..	..	8 41	18
Forest Hill, for Lordship	19	..	..		..	..	..	..	..	..	..	..	..	..	..	8 39	..	..	..	..	..	8 43	19
Sydenham ...[Lane	20	..	..		..	..	..	..	..	..	..	..	..	..	..	8 42	..	..	..	..	..	8 46	20
Penge West C	21	..	..		..	..	..	..	..	..	..	..	..	..	..	..	..	..	..	..	..	8 48	21
Anerley	22	..	..		..	..	..	..	..	..	..	..	..	..	..	..	..	..	..	..	..	8 49	22
Streatham Common	23	..	..	..	..	8 25	..	..	8 32	..	..	..	..	..	8 41	..	..	..	..	..	..	..	23
Norbury	24	..	..	..	..	8 27	..	..	8 34	..	..	..	8 37	..	8 44	..	..	..	..	..	..	..	24
Thornton Heath	25	..	..	..	..	8 30	..	..	8 37	..	..	..	8 40	..	8 47	..	..	..	..	..	..	..	25
Selhurst	26	..	..	..	..	8 32	..	..	8 39	..	..	..	8 43	..	8 50	..	..	..	..	..	..	..	26
Streatham Hill	27	8 26	..	..	..	..	..	..	..	..	8 34	8 38	..	..	..	..	..	..	..	..	8 48	..	27
West Norwood..[N'wood)	28	8 29	8 33	..	..	..	..	..	..	..	8 37		..	..	..	..	..	..	..	..	..	..	28
Gipsy Hill (for Upper	29	8 32	8 36	..	..	..	..	..	..	..	8 39		..	..	..	..	..	..	..	..	..	..	29
Crystal Palace D	30	8 34	8 39	..	..	..	..	..	..	..	8 42		..	..	..	8 45	..	..	..	..		..	30
Birkbeck	31	8 38	..	..	..	..	..	..	..	..	..		..	..	..	..	..	..	..	..		..	31
Beckenham Jn. arr	32	8 42	..	..	..	..	..	..	..	..	..		..	..	..	..	..	..	..	..		..	32
Norwood Junction F	33	..	..	..	8 30	..	8 35	8 38	..	..	8 47		..	..	8 53	..	..	..	8 41	..		8 52	33
East Croydon ... arr	34	..	..	..	8 34	8 36	..	8 42	..	..	..		..	..	..	..	..	8 44	8 45	..		..	34
East Croydon ... dep	35	..	..	..	8 35	8 36	..	8 42	..	..	..		..	..	..	..	..	8 44	..	..		..	35
Mitcham Junction	36	..	..	..	..	..	..	..	..	..	..	To London Bridge, via Tulse Hill	..	..	To London Bridge, via Forest Hill	..	..	..	..	8 47	To Victoria, via Wandsworth Common	To London Bridge, via Streatham	36
Hackbridge	37	..	..	..	..	..	..	..	..	..	..		..	..		..	..	..	..	8 49			37
Carshalton	38	..	..	..	..	..	..	..	..	..	..		..	..		..	..	..	..	8 52			38
West Croydon 319 arr	39	..	..	..	..	..	8 39	..	8 42	..	8 51		..	..		..	..	..	..	..			39
West Croydon 319 dep	40	..	..	..	..	..	8 39	..	8 42	..	..		..	..		..	..	..	..	..			40
Waddon G	41	..	..	..	..	..	8 41	..	8 45	..	..		..	..		..	..	..	..	..			41
Wallington	42	..	..	..	..	..	8 45	..	8 48	..	..		..	..		..	..	..	..	..			42
Carshalton Beeches	43	..	..	..	..	..	8 47	..	8 51	..	..		..	..		..	..	..	..	..			43
Sutton 322	44	..	..	..	..	..	8 50	..	8 54	..	..		..	..		..	..	..	..	8 55			44
Belmont	45	..	..	..	..	..	8 53	..	8 57	..	..	..	..	..	..	..	..	..	..	..	..	..	45
Banstead	46	..	..	..	..	..	8 56	..	9 0	..	..	..	..	..	..	..	..	..	..	..	..	..	46
Epsom Downs ..... arr	47	..	..	..	..	..	8 59	..	9 3	..	..	..	..	..	..	..	..	..	..	..	..	..	47
Cheam	48	..	..	..	..	..	..	..	..	..	..	..	..	..	..	..	..	..	..	8 58	..	..	48
Ewell East H	49	..	..	..	..	..	..	..	..	..	..	..	..	..	..	..	..	..	..	9 1	..	..	49
Epsom	50	..	..	..	..	..	..	..	..	8 55	..	..	..	..	..	..	..	..	..	9 5	..	..	50
Ashtead	51	..	..	..	..	..	..	..	..	8 59	..	..	..	..	..	..	3	..	..	9 9	..	..	51
Leatherhead..[Bridge J	52	..	..	..	..	..	..	..	..	9 3	..	..	..	..	..	..	9 9	..	..	9 13	..	..	52
Boxhill and Burford	53	..	..	..	..	..	..	..	..	9 8	..	..	..	..	..	..	..	..	..	9 18	..	..	53
Dorking North K .. arr	54	..	..	..	..	..	..	..	..	9 11	..	..	..	..	..	..	..	..	..	9 21	..	..	54
Bookham ......[394	55	..	..	..	..	..	..	..	..	..	..	..	..	..	..	..	9 14	..	..	..	..	..	55
Effingham Junction arr	56	..	..	..	..	..	..	..	..	..	..	..	..	..	..	..	9 18	..	..	..	..	..	56
South Croydon 234	57	..	..	..	..	8 38	..	..	..	..	..	..	..	..	..	..	..	..	..	..	..	..	57
Purley Oaks	58	..	..	..	..	8 41	..	..	..	..	..	..	..	..	..	..	..	..	..	..	..	..	58
Purley	59	..	..	..	8 40	8 43	..	..	..	..	..	..	..	..	..	..	..	..	..	..	..	..	59
Coulsdon North L .. arr	60	..	..	..	..	8 47	..	8 49	..	..	..	..	..	..	..	..	..	..	..	..	..	..	60
Purley ..... dep	61	..	..	..	..	..	..	..	..	..	..	..	..	..	..	..	..	..	..	..	..	..	61
Kenley	62	..	..	..	..	..	..	..	..	..	..	..	..	..	..	..	..	..	..	..	..	..	62
Whyteleafe	63	..	..	..	..	..	..	..	..	..	..	..	..	..	..	..	..	..	..	..	..	..	63
Warlingham	64	..	..	..	..	..	..	..	..	..	..	..	..	..	..	..	..	..	..	..	..	..	64
Caterham ..... arr	65	..	..	..	..	..	..	..	..	..	..	..	..	..	..	..	..	..	..	..	..	..	65
Purley ..... dep	66	..	..	..	§ Via Three Bridges	..	..	..	..	..	..	..	..	..	..	..	..	§ Via Three Bridges	..	..	..	..	66
Reedham	67	..	..	..		..	..	..	..	..	..	..	..	..	..	..	..		..	..	..	..	67
Smitham	68	..	..	..		..	..	..	..	..	..	..	..	..	..	..	..		..	..	..	..	68
Woodmansterne	69	..	..	..		..	..	..	..	..	..	..	..	..	..	..	..		..	..	..	..	69
Chipstead	70	..	..	..		..	..	..	..	..	..	..	..	..	..	..	..		..	..	..	..	70
Kingswood M	71	..	..	..		..	..	..	..	..	..	..	..	..	..	..	..		..	..	..	..	71
Tadworth N	72	..	..	..		..	..	..	..	..	..	..	..	..	..	..	..		..	..	..	..	72
Tattenham Corner . arr	73	..	..	..		..	..	..	..	..	..	..	..	..	..	..	..		..	..	..	..	73
Coulsdon South	74	..	..	..	8 44	..	..	..	..	..	..	..	..	..	..	..	..	..	..	..	..	..	74
Merstham	75	..	..	..	8 51	..	..	..	..	..	..	..	..	..	..	..	..	..	..	..	..	..	75
Redhill 158, 248 ..... arr	76	..	..	..	8 54	..	..	..	..	..	..	..	..	..	..	..	..	8 59	..	..	..	..	76
Reigate 246 ..... "	77	..	..	..	8 59	..	..	..	..	..	..	..	..	..	..	..	..	..	..	..	..	..	77
Horsham 159, 244, 245 "	78	..	..	..	9§35	..	..	..	..	..	..	..	..	..	..	..	..	9§35	..	9 46	..	..	78

CATERHAM, TATTENHAM CORNER, REDHILL, REIGATE, and HORSHAM

Week Days—*continued* (a.m)

No.					SX							SX							SX			SX						
1	..	8 31	8 33	..	..	8 36	..	..	..	8 38	..	8 38	8 40	8 44	8 45	..	..	..	8 48	..	..	..	..	..	8 51	8 53	..	..
2	3	3	3	3	3	3	3	..	3	3	3	3	3	3	..	3	3	..	3	..	3	3	3	3	3	3	3	3
3								8 47							..			..		..								
4	8 35	..	..	8 35	8 38	..	8 37	..	8 42	..	8 44	..	..	..	..	8 47	8 45	..	..	8 48	8 48	8 50	8 50	8 55	..	..	8 55	8 57
5	..	..	8 36	..	..	..	..	3	..	..	..	..	8 44	8 47	..	..	..	..	..	..	..	..	..	..	..	8 56	..	..
6	..	8 36	8 39	..	..	8 41	..		..	8 43	..	..	8 47	8 50	..	..	..	..	..	..	..	..	..	..	8 56	8 59	..	..
7	..	..	8 42	..	..	..	..		..	..	..	..	8 50	8 53	..	..	..	..	..	..	..	..	..	..	..	9 2	..	..
8	..	8 40	8 44	..	..	8 45	..		..	8 47	..	..	8 52	8 55	..	..	..	..	..	..	..	..	..	..	9 1	9 4	..	..
9	..	..	..	8 38	..	..	8 41	Via Worcester Park	..	..	..	..	..	..	..	..	..	..	..	..	..	..	..	..	..	..	8 58	9 1
10	..	..	..	8 41	..	..	8 44		..	..	..	..	..	..	..	..	..	..	..	..	..	..	8 55	..	..	..	9 1	9 4
11	..	..	..	8 43	..	..	8 46		..	..	..	..	..	..	..	..	..	..	..	..	8 54	..	8 57	..	..	..	9 3	9 6
12	..	..	..	8 46	..	..	To Victoria, arr. 9 1 a.m		..	..	..	..	..	..	..	..	..	..	..	..	..	..	9 0	..	..	..	9 6	To Victoria, arr. 9 22 a.m
13	..	..	..	8 48	..	..			..	..	..	..	..	..	..	..	..	..	..	..	..	..	9 2	..	..	..	9 8	
14	..	..	..	8 51	..	..			..	..	..	..	..	..	..	..	8 55	..	..	..	8 58	..	9 5	..	..	..	9 11	
15	..	..	..	..	..	..			..	..	..	..	..	..	..	..	8 59	..	..	..	9 2	..	..	..	..	..	..	
16	..	..	..	..	..	..			8 47	..	8 49	..	..	..	..	8 52	..	..	..	..	..	8 56	..	..	..	..	..	
17	..	..	..	..	..	..			..	..	..	..	..	..	..	8 55	..	..	..	..	..	8 58	..	..	..	..	..	
18	..	..	..	..	..	..		..	..	..	..	..	..	..	..	8 58	..	..	..	..	..	9 1	..	..	..	..	..	
19	..	..	..	..	..	..		..	..	..	..	..	..	..	..	9 0	..	..	..	..	..	9 3	..	..	..	..	..	
20	..	..	..	..	..	..		..	..	..	..	..	..	..	..	9 3	..	..	..	..	..	9 6	..	..	..	..	..	
21	..	..	..	..	..	..		..	..	..	..	..	..	..	..	..	..	..	..	..	..	9 8	..	..	..	..	..	
22	..	..	..	..	..	..		..	..	..	..	..	..	..	..	..	..	..	..	..	..	9 9	..	..	..	..	..	
23	..	8 44	..	..	..	..		..	..	8 52	..	..	..	..	..	..	9 1	..	..	..	..	..	..	..	9 5	..	..	..
24	..	8 47	..	..	..	..		..	..	8 54	..	..	..	..	..	..	9 4	..	..	..	..	..	..	..	9 7	..	..	..
25	..	8 50	..	..	..	..	Stop	..	..	8 57	..	9 0	..	..	..	..	9 7	..	..	..	..	..	..	..	9 10	..	..	..
26	..	8 52	..	..	..	..	..	..	..	8 59	..	..	..	..	..	..	9 10	..	..	..	..	..	..	..	9 12	..	..	..
27	..	..	8 46	..	..	..	..	..	..	..	..	..	8 54	8 58	..	..	..	..	..	..	..	..	9 10	..	..	9 6	..	..
28	..	..	8 49	8 53	..	..	..	..	..	..	..	..	8 57		..	..	..	..	..	..	..	..	..	..	..	9 9	9 13	..
29	..	..	8 52	8 56	..	..	..	..	..	..	..	..	9 0		..	..	..	..	..	..	..	..	..	..	..	9 12	9 16	..
30	..	..	8 54	8 59	..	..	..	..	..	..	..	..	9 2		..	9 6	..	..	..	..	..	..	To Victoria, via Wandsworth Common	..	..	9 14	9 19	..
31	..	..	8 58	..	..	..	..	..	..	..	..	..	..		..	..	..	..	..	..	..	..		..	..	9 18	..	..
32	..	..	9 2	..	..	..	..	..	..	..	..	..	..	To London Bridge, via Tulse Hill	..	..	..	..	..	..	..	..		..	..	9 22	..	..
33	8 49	..	..	..	..	..	..	..	8 56	..	8 58	9 5	9 7		..	..	9 13	..	..	9 2	..	9 12		..	..	..	..	..
34	8 53	8 55	..	..	..	..	..	..	..	..	9 2	..	..		9 0	..		..	9 4	9 6	..	..		9 11	9 16	..	..	..
35	8 54	8 55	..	..	..	..	..	..	..	..	9 2	..	..		..	..		..	..	9 8	..	..		9 11	9 16	..	..	..
36	..	..	..	..	..	8 53	..	..	..	..	..	..	..		..	..	To London Bridge, via Forest Hill	..	..	..	9 7	..		..	..	..	..	..
37	..	..	..	..	..	8 56	a.m	..	..	..	..	..	..		..	..		..	..	..	9 9	To London Bridge, via Streatham		..	..	..	..	..
38	..	..	..	..	..	8 58	3	..	..	..	..	..	..		..	..		..	..	..	9 12			..	..	..	..	..
39	..	..	..	..	8 55	..		..	9 0	9 3	..	..	9 11		..	..		..	..	..	..			..	..	..	..	..
40	..	..	..	..	..	..	8 54	..	9 0	9 3	..	..	..		..	..		..	..	..	..			..	..	..	..	..
41	..	..	..	..	..	..	8 56	..	9 2	9 6	..	..	..		..	..		..	..	..	..			..	..	..	..	..
42	..	..	..	..	..	..	9 0	..	9 6	9 9	..	..	..		..	..		..	..	..	..			..	..	..	..	..
43	..	..	..	..	..	..	9 2	..	9 8	9 12	..	..	..		..	..		..	..	..	..			..	..	..	..	..
44	..	..	..	..	..	9 1	9 5	..	9 11	9 15	..	..	..		..	..		..	..	..	9 15			..	..	..	..	..
45	..	..	..	..	..	..	..	..	9 14	9 18	..	..	..	..	..	..		..	..	..	..	..	..	..	..	..	..	..
46	..	..	..	..	..	..	..	..	9 17	9 21	..	..	..	..	..	..		..	..	..	..	..	..	..	..	..	..	..
47	..	..	..	..	..	..	..	..	9 20	9 24	..	..	..	..	..	..		..	..	..	..	..	..	..	..	..	..	..
48	..	..	..	..	..	9 4	..	..	..	..	..	..	..	..	..	..	..	..	..	..	9 18	..	..	..	..	..	..	..
49	..	..	..	..	..	9 7	..	..	..	..	..	..	..	..	..	..	..	..	..	..	9 21	..	..	..	..	..	..	..
50	..	..	..	..	..	9 11	..	9 15	..	..	..	..	..	..	..	..	..	..	..	..	9 25	..	..	..	..	..	..	..
51	..	..	..	..	..	..	..	9 19	..	..	..	..	..	..	..	..	..	..	..	..	9 29	..	..	..	..	..	..	..
52	..	..	..	..	..	..	..	9 23	..	..	..	..	..	..	..	..	..	..	..	..	9 33	..	..	..	..	..	..	..
53	..	..	..	..	..	..	..	..	..	..	..	..	..	..	..	..	..	..	..	..	9 38	..	..	..	..	..	..	..
54	..	..	..	..	..	..	..	..	..	..	..	..	..	..	..	..	..	..	..	..	9 41	..	..	..	..	..	..	..
55	..	..	..	..	..	..	..	9 29	..	..	..	..	..	..	..	..	..	..	..	..	..	..	..	..	..	..	..	..
56	..	..	..	..	..	..	..	9 32	..	..	..	..	..	..	..	..	..	..	..	..	..	..	..	..	..	..	..	..
57	..	8 58	..	..	..	..	..	..	..	..	9 4	..	..	..	..	..	..	..	..	..	..	..	..	..	9 18	..	..	..
58	..	9 0	..	..	..	..	..	..	..	..	9 7	..	..	..	..	..	..	..	..	..	..	..	..	..	9 21	..	..	..
59	8 59	9 3	..	..	..	..	..	..	..	..	9 9	..	..	..	..	..	..	..	..	9 13	..	..	..	9 17	9 23	..	..	..
60	..	9 6	..	..	..	..	..	..	..	..	9 13	..	..	..	..	..	..	..	..	..	..	..	..	..	9 27	..	..	..
61	9 1	..	..	..	..	..	..	..	..	..	..	..	..	..	..	..	..	..	..	..	..	..	..	9 18	..	..	..	..
62	9 4	..	..	..	..	..	..	..	..	..	..	..	..	..	..	..	..	..	..	..	..	..	..	9 21	..	..	..	..
63	9 7	..	..	..	..	..	..	..	..	..	..	..	..	..	..	..	..	..	..	..	..	..	..	9 24	..	..	..	..
64	9 9	..	..	..	..	..	..	..	..	..	..	..	..	..	..	..	..	..	..	..	..	..	..	9 26	..	..	..	..
65	9 13	..	..	..	..	..	..	..	..	..	..	..	..	..	..	..	..	..	..	..	..	..	..	9 30	..	..	..	..
66	9 0	..	..	..	..	..	..	..	..	..	..	..	..	..	..	..	..	..	..	..	..	..	..	9 17	..	..	..	..
67	9 2	..	..	..	..	..	..	..	..	..	..	..	..	..	..	..	..	..	..	..	..	..	..	9 19	..	..	..	..
68	9 5	..	..	..	..	..	..	..	..	..	..	..	..	..	..	..	..	..	..	..	..	..	..	9 22	..	..	..	..
69	9 7	..	..	..	..	..	..	..	..	..	..	..	..	..	..	..	..	..	..	..	..	..	..	9 24	..	..	..	..
70	9 10	..	..	..	..	..	..	..	..	..	..	..	..	..	..	..	..	..	..	..	..	..	..	9 27	..	..	..	..
71	9 14	..	..	..	..	..	..	..	..	..	..	..	..	..	..	..	..	..	..	..	..	..	..	9 31	..	..	..	..
72	9 17	..	..	..	..	..	..	..	..	..	..	..	..	..	..	..	..	..	..	..	..	..	..	9 34	..	..	..	..
73	9 21	..	..	..	..	..	..	..	..	..	..	..	..	..	..	..	..	..	..	..	..	..	..	9 38	..	..	..	..
74	..	..	..	..	..	..	..	..	..	..	..	..	..	..	..	..	..	..	..	9 17	..	..	..	..	..	..	..	..
75	..	..	..	..	..	..	..	..	..	..	..	..	..	..	..	..	..	..	..	9 23	..	..	..	..	..	..	..	..
76	..	..	..	..	..	..	..	..	..	..	..	..	..	..	..	..	..	..	..	9 27	..	..	..	..	..	..	..	..
77	..	..	..	..	..	..	..	..	..	..	..	..	..	..	..	..	..	..	..	9 32	..	..	..	..	..	..	..	..
78	..	..	..	..	..	..	..	..	..	..	..	..	..	..	..	..	..	..	..	..	..	..	..	..	..	..	..	..

LONDON, CRYSTAL PALACE, CROYDON, SUTTON, DORKING NORTH,

Down	No.	a.m										Week Days—*continued*										a.m	No.
																	SX						
VICTORIA .... dep	1	8 55	..	..	..	..	..	8 58	9 0	9 4	..	9 8	..	..	9 8	..	..	..	..	..	..	..	1
CHARING CROSS* ... "	2	③	..	..	..	..	③	③	③	③	③	..	③	③	③	③	③	③	③	③	③	③	2
WATERLOO* .... "	3		9 7	..	..	..						..											3
LONDON BRIDGE..... "	4	..	..	..	..	9 0	9 2	..	..	..	9 4	..	9 5	9 7	..	9 8	9 10	9 11	9 12	9 15	9 15	9 17	4
Battersea Park.........	5	..	③	..	..	..	..	..	9 3	9 7	..	..	..	..	..	..	..	..	..	..	..	..	5
Clapham Junction.....	6	9 0		..	..	..	..	9 4	9 6	9 10	..	..	..	..	9 13	..	..	..	..	..	..	..	6
Wandsworth Common **A**	7	..	..	..	..	..	..	..	9 9	..	..	..	..	..	..	..	..	..	..	..	..	..	7
Balham & Upper Tooting	8	9 4	..	..	..	..	..	9 8	9 11	9 14	..	..	..	..	9 17	..	..	..	..	..	..	..	8
South Bermondsey......	9	..	Via Worcester Park	..	..	..	..	..	..	..	..	..	..	..	..	..	..	..	..	9 18	..	9 21	9
Queen s Road, Peckham	10	..		..	..	..	..	..	..	..	..	..	..	..	..	..	..	..	..	9 21	..	9 24	10
Peckham Rye...........	11	..		..	..	..	..	..	..	..	..	..	..	..	..	9 14	..	..	9 18	9 23	..	9 26	11
East Dulwich...........	12	..		..	..	..	..	..	..	..	..	..	..	..	..	..	..	..	9 20	9 26	..	To Victoria, arr. 9 41 a.m	12
North Dulwich	13	..		..	..	..	..	..	..	..	..	..	..	..	..	..	..	..	9 22	9 28	..		13
Tulse Hill..............	14	..		..	..	..	..	..	..	..	..	..	9 15	..	..	9 18	9 20	..	9 25	9 31	..		14
Streatham	15	..		..	..	..	..	..	..	..	..	..	9 19	..	..	9 22	9 25	..	..	..	..		15
New Cross Gate (for E.L.	16	..		..	..	9 5	..	..	..	..	9 9	..	..	9 12	..	..	..	9 16	..	..	..		16
Brockley **B**.......[Line)	17	..	..	..	..	..	..	..	..	..	..	..	..	9 14	..	..	..	9 18	..	..	..		17
Honor Oak Park.........	18	..	..	..	..	..	..	..	..	..	..	..	..	9 17	..	..	..	9 21	..	..	..		18
Forest Hill, for Lordship	19	..	..	..	..	..	..	..	..	..	..	..	..	9 19	..	..	..	9 23	..	..	..		19
Sydenham ....[Lane	20	..	..	..	..	..	..	..	..	..	..	..	..	9 22	..	..	..	9 26	..	..	..		20
Penge West **C**..........	21	..	..	..	..	..	..	..	..	..	..	..	..	..	..	..	..	9 28	..	..	..		21
Anerley.................	22	..	..	..	..	..	..	..	..	..	..	..	..	..	..	..	..	9 29	..	..	..		22
Streatham Common....	23	..	..	..	..	..	..	9 12	..	..	..	..	9 21	..	..	..	9 28	To London Bridge, via Streatham	..	..	..	..	23
Norbury	24	..	..	..	..	..	..	9 14	..	..	..	..	9 24	..	..	..	9 30		..	..	..	..	24
Thornton Heath........	25	..	..	..	..	..	..	9 17	..	..	..	..	9 27	..	..	..	9 33		..	..	..	..	25
Selhurst................	26	..	..	..	..	..	..	9 19	..	..	..	..	9 29	..	..	..	9 36		..	..	..	..	26
Streatham Hill..........	27	..	..	..	..	..	..	..	9 14	9 18	..	..	..	..	..	..	..		9 29	..	..	..	27
West Norwood.[N'wood)	28	..	..	..	..	..	..	..	9 17	..	..	..	..	..	..	..	..		..	9 33	..	..	28
Gipsy Hill (for Upper	29	..	..	..	..	..	..	..	9 19	..	..	..	..	..	..	..	..		..	9 36	..	..	29
Crystal Palace D......	30	..	..	..	..	..	..	..	9 22	..	..	..	..	9 25	..	..	..		..	9 39	..	..	30
Birkbeck	31	..	..	..	..	..	..	..	..	To London Bridge, via Tulse Hill	..	..	..	..	..	..	..		..	..	..	..	31
Beckenham Jn. arr	32	..	..	..	..	..	..	..	..		..	..	..	..	..	..	..		..	..	..	..	32
Norwood Junction F..	33	..	..	..	..	9 14	9 15	..	9 28		9 18	..	9SX33	..	..	..	..	9 32	To Victoria, via Wandsworth Common	..	..	..	33
East Croydon ... arr	34	..	..	..	..	9 18	..	..	..		9 22	9 27	..	..	..	..	..	Stop		..	9 29	..	34
East Croydon ... dep	35	..	..	..	..	9 18	..	..	..		9 22	9 28	..	..	..	..	..	Stop		..	9 30	..	35
Mitcham Junction......	36	9 13	..	..	..	..	..	..	..		..	..	To London Bridge (except Saturdays), via Forest Hill	..	9 23	9 27	..	..		..	..	..	36
Hackbridge	37	9 15	..	..	..	..	..	..	..		..	..		..	9 26	9 29	..	..		..	..	..	37
Carshalton.............	38	9 18	..	..	..	..	..	..	..		..	..		..	9 28	9 32	..	..		..	..	..	38
West Croydon 319 arr	39	..	..	③	..	..	9 19	9 22	9 33		..	..		..	..	..	..	a.m		..	..	..	39
West Croydon 319 dep	40	..	..	9 14	..	..	9 19	9 22	..		..	..		..	..	..	..	③		..	..	..	40
Waddon.. **G**..........	41	..	..	9 16	..	..	9 21	9 25	..		..	..		..	..	..	..			..	..	..	41
Wallington............	42	..	..	9 20	..	..	9 25	9 28	..		..	..		..	..	..	..	9 40		..	..	..	42
Carshalton Beeches	43	..	..	9 22	..	..	9 27	9 31	..		..	..		..	..	..	..	9 42		..	..	..	43
Sutton 322............	44	9 21	..	9 25	..	..	9 30	9 34	..		..	..		..	9 31	9 35	..	9 45		..	..	..	44
Belmont	45	..	..	..	..	..	9 33	9 37	..	..	..	..		..	..	..	..	..	..	..	..	..	45
Banstead..............	46	..	..	..	..	..	9 36	9 40	..	..	..	..		..	..	..	..	..	..	..	..	..	46
Epsom Downs...... arr	47	..	..	..	..	..	9 39	9 43	..	..	..	..		..	..	..	..	..	..	..	..	..	47
Cheam	48	9 24	..	..	..	..	..	..	..	..	..	..		..	9 34	9 38	..	..	..	..	..	..	48
Ewell East **H**..........	49	9 27	..	..	..	..	..	..	..	..	..	..		..	9 37	9 41	..	..	..	..	..	..	49
Epsom.................	50	9 30	9 35	..	..	..	..	..	..	..	..	..		..	9 40	9 45	..	..	..	..	..	..	50
Ashtead................	51	..	9 39	..	..	..	..	..	..	..	..	..		..	..	9 49	..	..	..	..	..	..	51
Leatherhead..[Bridge **J**	52	..	9 43	..	..	..	..	..	..	..	..	..		..	..	9 53	..	..	..	..	..	..	52
Boxhill and Burford	53	..	9 48	..	..	..	..	..	..	..	..	..		..	..	..	..	..	..	..	..	..	53
Dorking North K.. arr	54	..	9 51	..	..	..	..	..	..	..	..	..		..	..	..	..	..	..	..	..	..	54
Bookham...........[394	55	..	..	..	..	..	..	..	..	..	..	..	..	..	..	9 57	..	..	..	..	..	..	55
Effingham Junction arr	56	..	..	..	..	..	..	..	..	..	..	..	..	..	..	10 1	..	..	..	..	..	..	56
South Croydon 234......	57	..	..	..	..	..	..	..	..	..	9 24	9 32	..	..	..	..	..	..	..	..	..	..	57
Purley Oaks	58	..	..	..	..	..	..	..	..	..	9 27	..	..	..	..	..	..	..	..	..	..	..	58
Purley................	59	..	..	..	..	..	..	..	..	..	9 29	..	..	..	..	..	..	..	..	..	9 35	..	59
Coulsdon North **L**.. arr	60	..	..	..	..	..	..	..	..	..	9 33	..	..	..	..	..	..	..	..	..	..	..	60
Purley..............dep	61	..	..	..	..	..	..	..	..	..	..	..	..	..	..	..	..	..	..	..	9 38	..	61
Kenley..................	62	..	..	..	..	..	..	..	..	..	..	..	..	..	..	..	..	..	..	..	9 41	..	62
Whyteleafe............	63	..	..	..	..	..	..	..	..	..	..	..	..	..	..	..	..	..	..	..	9 44	..	63
Warlingham	64	..	..	..	..	..	..	..	..	..	..	..	..	..	..	..	..	..	..	..	9 46	..	64
Caterham.......... arr	65	..	..	..	..	..	..	..	..	..	..	..	..	..	..	..	..	..	..	..	9 50	..	65
Purley..............dep	66	..	..	..	..		..	..	..	..	..	..	..	..	..	..	..	..	..	..	9 37	..	66
Reedham...............	67	..	..	..	..	§ Via Three Bridges	..	..	..	..	..	..	..	..	..	..	..	..	..	..	9 39	..	67
Smitham	68	..	..	..	..		..	..	..	..	..	..	..	..	..	..	..	..	..	..	9 41	..	68
Woodmansterne........	69	..	..	..	..		..	..	..	..	..	..	..	..	..	..	..	..	..	..	9 44	..	69
Chipstead	70	..	..	..	..		..	..	..	..	..	..	..	..	..	..	..	..	..	..	9 46	..	70
Kingswood **M**..........	71	..	..	..	..		..	..	..	..	..	..	..	..	..	..	..	..	..	..	9 51	..	71
Tadworth **N**...........	72	..	..	..	..		..	..	..	..	..	..	..	..	..	..	..	..	..	..	9 54	..	72
Tattenham Corner. arr	73	..	..	..	..		..	..	..	..	..	..	..	..	..	..	..	..	..	..	9 57	..	73
Coulsdon South.........	74	..	..	..	..	..	..	..	..	..	..	..	..	..	..	..	..	..	..	..	..	..	74
Merstham	75	..	..	..	..	..	..	..	..	..	..	..	..	..	..	..	..	..	..	..	..	..	75
Redhill 158, 246 .... arr	76	..	..	..	..	..	..	..	..	..	..	..	..	..	..	..	..	..	..	..	..	..	76
Reigate 246....... "	77	..	..	..	..	..	..	..	..	..	..	..	..	..	..	..	..	..	..	..	..	..	77
Horsham 159, 244, 245 "	78	..	1020	..	..	10§5	..	..	..	..	..	..	..	..	..	..	..	..	..	..	..	..	78

For Notes, see page 284a

CATERHAM, TATTENHAM CORNER, REDHILL, REIGATE, and HORSHAM

a.m. — Week Days—continued — a.m.

No.											SX									SO	SX							
1	9 11	9 13		9 18			9 18			9 20	9 21		9 24		9 25	9 28			9 31	9 33					9 37			
2	3	3				3	3		3	3	3	3	3	3				3	3	3	3	3	3	3	3	3		3
3								9 27																			9 47	
4					9 18	9 22			9 24			9 25		9 27				9 28			9 30	9 21	9 35	9 36		9 37		9 42
5		9 16						3		9 23			9 27							9 36							3	
6	9 16	9 19					9 23			9 26			9 30			9 33			9 36	9 39					9 42			
7		9 22						Via Worcester Park		9 29			9 33							9 42								
8	9 21	9 24					9 27			9 31			9 35						9 41	9 44					9 46		Via Worcester Park	
9																							9 38			9 41		
10																					9 35		9 41			9 44		
11																		9 34			9 37		9 43			9 46		
12																					9 40		9 46					
13																					9 42		9 48					
14												9 35						9 38			9 45		9 51					
15												9 39						9 42										
16									9 29					9 32								9 36				To Victoria, arr. 10 1 a.m.		
17														9 34								9 38						
18														9 37								9 41						
19														9 39								9 43						
20														9 42								9 46						
21																						9 48						
22																						9 49						
23	9 25						9 32				9 35	9 41							9 45									
24	9 27						9 34				9 37	9 44							9 47									
25	9 30						9 37				9 40	9 47							9 50									
26	9 32						9 39				9 43	9 50							9 52									
27		9 26								9 34			9 38				SX			9 46	9 48					Stop		
28		9 29								9 37			To London Bridge, via Tulse Hill				3			9 49			9 53					
29		9 32								9 39										9 52			9 56					
30		9 34								9 42				9 45			9 53			9 54			9 59					
31		9 38															9 57			9 58								
32		9 42															10 0			10 2								
33					9 31	9 35			9 38	9 47		9 53										9 52						9 54
34	9 35			9 33	9 35				9 41			To London Bridge, via Forest Hill			9 41	9 45			9 56					9 50				
35	9 35			9 34	9 36				9 41							9 46			9 56			To London Bridge, via Streatham on Saturdays		9 50				
36																		9 47							9 53			
37																		9 49							9 55			
38																		9 52							9 58			
39						9 39	9 42			9 53																a.m		9 59
40						9 39	9 42																			3		9 59
41						9 41	9 45																					10 1
42						9 45	9 48																			10 1		10 5
43						9 47	9 51																			10 3		10 7
44						9 50	9 54											9 55							10 1	10 6		1010
45						9 53	9 57																					1013
46						9 56	10 0																					1016
47						9 59	10 3																					1019
48																		9 58							10 4			
49																		10 1							10 7			
50								9 55										10 5							1011		1015	
51								9 59										10 9									1019	
52								10 3										1013									1023	
53								10 8										1018										
54								1011										1021										
55																											1029	
56																											1032	
57	9 38								9 44										9 58									
58	9 40								9 46										10 0									
59	9 43				9 42				9 49										10 3					9 56				
60	9 46								9 53										10 6									
61																								9 58				
62																								10 1				
63																								10 4				
64																								10 6				
65																								1010				
66				§ Via Three Bridges	§ Via Three Bridges																			9 57				
67																								9 59				
68																								10 1				
69																								10 4				
70																								10 6				
71																								1011				
72																								1014				
73																								1017				
74					9 45																							
75					9 51																							
76				9 48	9 55											10 0												
77				9§54	10 1											1021												
78				10§13	10§35													1046										

LONDON, CRYSTAL PALACE, CROYDON, SUTTON, DORKING NORTH,

For Notes, see page 284a

Down	No.	a.m.	Week Days—continued																			a.m.	No.
					SX	SO	SX						SX	SO		SO	SX						
Victoria .... dep	1	9 38	9 40	9 45	..	..	9 44	..	9 48	..	..	..	..	..	9 51	9 53	9 53	..	9 55	..	..	..	1
Charing Cross* ... "	2	3	3	..	3	3	3	3	..	3	3	3	3	3	3	3	3	..	3	..	3	3	2
Waterloo* .... "	3			..					..									..		10 7			3
London Bridge ..... "	4	..	..	..	9 45	9 45	..	9 46	..	9 48	9 50	9H51	9 55	9 58	..	..	..	..	..	..	9 55	10 2	4
Battersea Park	5	..	9 43	..	..	..	9 47	..	..	..	..	..	..	..	..	9 56	9 56	..	..	3	..	..	5
Clapham Junction	6	9 44	9 47	..	..	..	9 51	..	9 53	..	..	H 1 min. earlier on Saturdays	..	..	9 56	9 59	9 59	..	10 0		..	..	6
Wandsworth Common A	7	..	9 50	..	..	..	9 54	..	..	..	..		..	..	..	10 2	10 2	..	..		..	..	7
Balham & Upper Tooting	8	9 48	9 52	..	..	..	9 56	..	..	..	..		..	..	10 1	10 4	10 4	..	10 4	Via Worcester Park	..	..	8
South Bermondsey	9	..	..	..	..	..	..	..	..	..	..		..	..	..	..	..	..	..		9 58	..	9
Queen's Road, Peckham	10	..	..	..	..	..	..	..	..	..	9 55		..	..	..	..	..	..	..		10 1	..	10
Peckham Rye	11	..	..	..	..	..	..	..	..	9 54	9 57		..	..	..	..	..	..	..		10 3	..	11
East Dulwich	12	..	..	..	..	..	..	..	..	..	10 0		..	..	..	..	..	..	..		10 6	..	12
North Dulwich	13	..	..	..	..	..	..	..	..	..	10 2		..	..	..	..	..	..	..		10 8	..	13
Tulse Hill	14	..	..	..	9 55	9 55	..	..	..	9 58	10 5		..	..	..	..	..	..	..		1011	..	14
Streatham	15	..	..	..	9 59	9 59	..	..	..	10 2	..		..	..	..	..	..	..	..		..	..	15
New Cross Gate (for E.L.	16	..	..	..	..	..	..	9 51	..	..	..	9 56	..	..	..	..	..	..	..	..	..	..	16
Brockley B .... [Line)	17	..	..	..	..	..	..	9 53	..	..	..	9 58	..	..	..	..	..	..	..	..	..	..	17
Honor Oak Park	18	..	..	..	..	..	..	9 56	..	..	..	10 1	..	..	..	..	..	..	..	..	..	..	18
Forest Hill for Lordship	19	..	..	..	..	..	..	9 58	..	..	..	10 3	..	..	..	..	..	..	..	..	..	..	19
Sydenham .... [Lane	20	..	..	..	..	..	..	10 1	..	..	..	10 6	..	..	..	..	..	..	..	..	..	..	20
Penge West C	21	..	..	..	..	..	..	..	..	..	..	10 8	..	..	..	..	..	..	..	..	..	..	21
Anerley	22	..	..	..	..	..	..	..	..	..	..	10 9	..	..	..	..	..	..	..	..	..	..	22
Streatham Common	23	9 52	..	..	10 1	10 2	..	..	..	..	..	..	..	..	10 5	..	..	..	..	..	..	..	23
Norbury	24	9 54	..	..	10 4	10 5	..	..	..	..	..	..	..	..	10 7	..	..	..	..	..	..	..	24
Thornton Heath	25	9 57	..	..	10 7	10 8	..	..	..	..	..	..	..	..	1010	..	..	..	..	..	..	..	25
Selhurst	26	9 59	..	..	1010	1010	..	..	..	..	..	..	..	..	1012	..	..	..	..	..	..	..	26
Streatham Hill	27	..	9 54	..	..	..	9 59	..	..	..	10 9	..	..	..	..	10 6	10 6	SX	..	..	..	..	27
West Norwood..[N'wood)	28	..	9 57	..	..	..	..	..	..	..	..	..	..	..	..	10 9	10 9	3	..	..	1013	..	28
Gipsy Hill (for Upper	29	..	10 0	..	..	..	..	..	..	..	..	..	..	..	..	1012	1012		..	..	1016	..	29
Crystal Palace D	30	..	10 3	..	..	..	..	10 4	..	..	..	..	..	..	..	1014	1015	1016	..	..	1019	..	30
Birkbeck	31	..	..	..	..	..	..	..	..	..	..	..	..	..	..	1018	..	1019	..	..	..	..	31
Beckenham Jn. arr	32	..	..	..	..	..	..	..	..	..	..	..	..	..	..	1022	..	1023	..	..	Stop	..	32
Norwood Junction F	33	..	10 8	..	..	1013	..	..	..	..	..	1012	10 7	1010	..	..	..	..	..	..	..	1015	33
East Croydon ... arr	34	..	..	10 0	..	..	..	..	10 5	..	..	..	1011	1014	1016	..	..	..	..	..	..	..	34
East Croydon ... dep	35	..	..	..	..		..	..	10 5	..	..		1011	1014	1016	..	..	..	..	..	..	..	35
Mitcham Junction	36	..	..	..	..		..	..	..	10 7	..		..	..	..	..	..	..	1013	..	..	..	36
Hackbridge	37	..	..	..	..		..	..	..	10 9	..		..	..	..	..	..	..	1015	..	..	..	37
Carshalton	38	..	..	..	..		..	..	..	1012	..		..	..	..	..	..	..	1018	..	a.m	..	38
West Croydon 319 arr	39	10 2	1012	..	..		..	..	..	..	..		..	..	..	..	..	..	..	..	SO	1019	39
West Croydon 319 dep	40	10 2	..	..	..	To London Bridge, via Forest Hill	..	..	..	..	..	To London Br'dge, via Streatham	..	..	..	..	..	..	..	..	3	1019	40
Waddon G	41	10 5	..	..	..		..	..	..	..	..		..	..	..	..	..	..	..	..		1021	41
Wallington	42	10 8	..	..	..		..	..	..	..	..		..	..	..	..	..	..	..	..	1020	1025	42
Carshalton Beeches	43	1011	..	..	..		..	..	..	..	..		..	..	..	..	..	..	..	..	1022	1027	43
Sutton 322	44	1014	..	..	..		..	..	..	1015	..		..	..	..	..	..	..	1021	..	1025	1030	44
Belmont	45	1017	..	..	..	..	..	..	..	..	..	..	..	..	..	..	..	..	..	..	..	1033	45
Banstead	46	1020	..	..	..	..	..	..	..	..	..	..	..	..	..	..	..	..	..	..	..	1036	46
Epsom Downs ..... arr	47	1023	..	..	..	..	..	..	..	..	..	..	..	..	..	..	..	..	..	..	..	1039	47
Cheam	48	..	..	..	..	..	..	..	..	1018	..	..	..	..	..	..	..	..	1024	..	..	..	48
Ewell East H	49	..	..	..	..	..	..	..	..	1021	..	..	..	..	..	..	..	..	1027	..	..	..	49
Epsom	50	..	..	..	..	..	..	..	..	1025	..	..	..	..	..	..	..	..	1030	1035	..	..	50
Ashtead	51	..	..	..	..	..	..	..	..	1029	..	..	..	..	..	..	..	..	..	1039	..	..	51
Leatherhead..[Bridge J	52	..	..	..	..	..	..	..	..	1033	..	..	..	..	..	..	..	..	..	1043	..	..	52
Boxhill and Burford	53	..	..	..	..	..	..	..	..	1038	..	..	..	..	..	..	..	..	..	1048	..	..	53
Dorking North K.. arr	54	..	..	..	..	..	..	..	..	1041	..	..	..	..	..	..	..	..	..	1051	..	..	54
Bookham .... [394	55	..	..	..	..	..	..	..	..	..	..	..	..	..	..	..	..	..	..	..	..	..	55
Effingham Junction arr	56	..	..	..	..	..	..	..	..	..	..	..	..	..	..	..	..	..	..	..	..	..	56
South Croydon 234	57	..	..	..	..	..	..	..	..	..	..	..	..	..	1020	..	..	..	..	..	..	..	57
Purley Oaks	58	..	..	..	..	..	..	..	..	..	..	..	..	..	1022	..	..	..	..	..	..	..	58
Purley	59	..	..	..	..	..	..	..	1011	..	..	..	1016	1019	1026	..	..	..	..	..	..	..	59
Coulsdon North L.. arr	60	..	..	..	..	..	..	..	..	..	..	..	..	..	1029	..	..	..	..	..	..	..	60
Purley .... dep	61	..	..	..	..	..	..	..	..	..	..	..	1019	1021	..	..	..	..	..	..	..	..	61
Kenley	62	..	..	..	..	..	..	..	..	..	..	..	1022	1024	..	..	..	..	..	..	..	..	62
Whyteleafe	63	..	..	..	..	..	..	..	..	..	..	..	1025	1027	..	..	..	..	..	..	..	..	63
Warlingham	64	..	..	..	..	..	..	..	..	..	..	..	1027	1029	..	..	..	..	..	..	..	..	64
Caterham .... arr	65	..	..	..	..	..	..	..	..	..	..	..	1031	1033	..	..	..	..	..	..	..	..	65
Purley .... dep	66	..	..	..	..	..	..	..		..	..	..	1017	1020	..	..	..	..	..	..	..	..	66
Reedham	67	..	..	..	..	..	..	..		..	..	..	1019	1022	..	..	..	..	..	..	..	..	67
Smitham	68	..	..	..	..	..	..	..		..	..	..	1022	1025	..	..	..	..	..	..	..	..	68
Woodmansterne	69	..	..	..	..	..	..	..	§ Via Three Bridges	..	..	..	1024	1027	..	..	..	..	..	..	..	..	69
Chipstead	70	..	..	..	..	..	..	..		..	..	..	1027	1030	..	..	..	..	..	..	..	..	70
Kingswood M	71	..	..	..	..	..	..	..		..	..	..	1031	1034	..	..	..	..	..	..	..	..	71
Tadworth N	72	..	..	..	..	..	..	..		..	..	..	1034	1037	..	..	..	..	..	..	..	..	72
Tattenham Corner. arr	73	..	..	..	..	..	..	..		..	..	..	1038	1041	..	..	..	..	..	..	..	..	73
Coulsdon South	74	..	..	..	..	..	..	..	1014	..	..	..	..	..	..	..	..	..	..	..	..	..	74
Merstham	75	..	..	..	..	..	..	..	1020	..	..	..	..	..	..	..	..	..	..	..	..	..	75
Redhill 158, 246 ..... arr	76	..	..	..	..	..	..	..	1024	..	..	..	..	..	..	..	..	..	..	..	..	..	76
Reigate 246 .... "	77	..	..	..	..	..	..	..	1030	..	..	..	..	..	..	..	..	..	..	..	..	..	77
Horsham 159, 244, 245 "	78	..	..	..	..	..	..	..	11§5	..	..	..	..	..	..	..	..	..	..	1124	..	..	78

CATERHAM, TATTENHAM CORNER, REDHILL, REIGATE, and HORSHAM

Week Days—*continued* (a.m)

No.			SX		SO	SO		SO			SO					SX										
1	9 58	10 0	..	..	..	..	..	1013	..	..	..	..	..	..	..	..	10 11	1018	..	1018	1020	10H24	..	1025	1028	1031
2	3	3	3	3	3	3	..	3	3	3	10 6	3	..	..	3	1011	3	..	3	3	3	3	3	..	..	3
3							..				10 8		..	..		1013		..						..	..	
4	..	..	10 5	10 8	10 5	10 7	..	..	1010	1011	1015	1015	10 16	..	1017	1018	..	..	1022	..	..	..	10 25	..	..	..
5	..	10 3	..	..	..	..	..	1016	..	..	3	..	..	..	..	3	..	..	..	..	1023	..	H 1 min. *earlier* on Saturdays	..	..	..
6	10 4	10 6	..	..	..	..	..	1019	..	..		..	..	..	..		10 16	..	..	1024	1026	10 30		..	1034	1036
7	..	10 9	..	..	..	..	..	1022	..	..	..	..	..	..	..	..	10SX19	..	..	..	1029	..		..	..	..
8	10 8	1011	..	..	..	..	..	1024	..	..	..	..	..	..	..	..	10 21	..	..	1028	1031	10 34		..	..	1041
9	..	..	..	..	..	..	..	..	..	..	..	1018	..	..	1021	..	..	..	..	..	..	H 1 minute *earlier* on Saturdays		..	..	..
10	..	..	..	..	..	..	..	..	1015	..	..	1021	..	..	1024	..	..	..	..	..	..			..	..	..
11	..	..	..	10 14	..	..	..	..	1017	..	..	1023	..	..	1026	..	..	..	..	..	..			..	..	..
12	..	..	..	..	..	..	..	..	1020	..	..	1026	..	..	}	..	..	..	..	..	..			..	..	..
13	..	..	..	..	..	..	..	..	1022	..	..	1028	..	..		..	..	..	..	..	..			..	..	..
14	..	..	1015	10 18	1015	..	..	..	1025	..	..	1031	..	..		..	..	..	..	..	..		10H36	..	..	..
15	..	..	1019	10 22	1019	..	..	..	..	..	..	..	..	..		..	..	..	..	..	..		10 39	..	..	..
16	..	..	..	..	..	1012	..	..	..	1016	..	..	..	..		..	..	..	..	..	..		..	..	..	..
17	..	..	..	..	..	1014	..	..	..	1018	..	..	..	..		..	..	..	..	..	..		..	..	..	..
18	..	..	..	..	..	1017	..	..	..	1021	..	..	..	..		..	..	..	..	..	..		..	..	..	..
19	..	..	..	..	..	1019	..	..	..	1023	..	..	..	..		..	..	..	..	..	..		..	..	..	..
20	..	..	..	..	..	1022	..	..	..	1026	..	..	..	..	To Victoria, arr. 10 43 a.m	..	..	..	..	..	..		..	..	..	..
21	..	..	..	..	..	..	..	..	..	1028	..	..	..	..		..	..	..	..	..	..		..	..	..	..
22	..	..	..	..	..	..	..	..	..	1029	..	..	..	..		..	..	..	..	..	..	..	..	..	..	..
23	1012	..	1021	..	1021	..	..	..	..	..	..	..	..	..		..	10 25	..	..	1032	..	..	10 41	..	..	1045
24	1014	..	1024	..	1024	..	..	..	..	..	..	..	..	..		..	10 27	..	..	1034	..	..	10 44	..	..	1047
25	1017	..	1027	..	1027	..	..	..	..	..	..	..	..	..		..	10 30	..	..	1037	..	..	10 47	..	..	1050
26	1019	..	1029	..	1030	..	..	..	..	..	..	..	..	..		..	10 32	..	..	1039	..	..	10 50	..	..	1052
27	..	1014	..	..	..	..	SX	1026	1029	..	..	..	..	..		..	..	..	..	..	1034	..	..	..	..	..
28	..	1017	..	..	..	..	3	1029	..	..	..	1033	..	..	Stop	..	..	..	..	..	1037	..	..	..	..	..
29	..	1019	..	..	..	..		1032	..	..	..	1036	..	..		..	..	..	..	..	1039	..	..	..	..	..
30	..	1022	..	..	..	1025	1032	1034	..	..	..	1039	..	..	..	..	..	..	..	..	1042	..	..	..	..	..
31	..	..	..	..	..	..	1035	1038	..	..	..	..	..	..	..	..	..	..	..	..	..	..	..	..	..	..
32	..	..	..	..	..	..	1039	1042	..	..	..	..	..	..	..	..	..	..	..	..	..	..	..	..	..	..
33	..	1027	..	..	1033	..	..	..	..	1032	1028	..	10 28	..	..	1031	..	..	1035	..	1046	..	10 53	..	..	..
34	..	..	..	..	..	..	..	..	..	..	1032	..	10 32	..	..	1035	10H37	..	..	..	..	..		1040	1045	1056
35	..	..	..	..	..	..	..	..	..	..	1032	..	10 32	..	..	1035	10H37	..	..	..	..	..		..	1046	1056
36	..	..	..	10 27	To London Bridge, via Forest Hill	..	..	..	..	To London Bridge via Streatham	..	..	..	..	..	..		..	..	..	..	10 40	To London Bridge, via Forest Hill	..	..	..
37	..	..	..	10 29		..	..	..	..		..	..	..	..	..	..		..	..	..	..	10 43		..	..	..
38	..	..	..	10 32		..	..	..	..		..	..	..	..	a.m	..		..	..	..	..	10 45		..	..	..
39	1022	1032	..	..		..	..	..	..		..	..	..	..	SX	..	H 1 minute *earlier* on Saturdays	..	1039	1042	1050	..		..	..	..
40	1022	..	..	..		..	..	..	..		..	..	..	..	3	..		..	1039	1042	..	..		..	..	..
41	1025	..	..	..		..	..	..	..		..	..	..	..		..		..	1041	1045	..	..		..	..	..
42	1028	..	..	..		..	..	..	..		..	..	..	..	1040	..		..	1045	1048	..	..		..	..	..
43	1031	..	..	..		..	..	..	..		..	..	..	..	1042	..		..	1047	1051	..	..		..	..	..
44	1034	..	..	10 35		..	..	..	..		..	..	..	..	1045	..		1039	1050	1054	..	10 49		..	..	..
45	1037	..	..	..		..	..	..	..		..	..	..	..	..	..		..	1053	1057	..	..		..	..	..
46	1040	..	..	..		..	..	..	..		..	..	..	..	..	..		..	1056	11 0	..	..		..	..	..
47	1043	..	..	..		..	..	..	..		..	..	..	..	..	..	..	..	1059	11 3	..	..		..	..	..
48	..	..	..	10 43	..	..	..	..	..	..	..	..	..	..	..	..	..	..	..	..	..	10 52	..	..	..	..
49	..	..	..	10 46	..	..	..	..	..	..	..	..	..	..	..	..	..	..	..	..	..	10 55	..	..	..	..
50	..	..	..	10 49	..	..	..	..	..	..	..	..	..	..	..	..	..	..	..	..	..	10 58	..	..	..	..
51	..	..	..	10 53	..	..	..	..	..	..	..	..	..	..	..	..	..	..	..	..	..	..	..	..	..	..
52	..	..	..	10 57	..	..	..	..	..	..	..	..	..	..	..	..	..	..	..	..	..	..	..	..	..	..
53	..	..	..	..	..	..	..	..	..	..	..	..	..	..	..	..	..	..	..	..	..	..	..	..	..	..
54	..	..	..	..	..	..	..	..	..	..	..	..	..	..	..	..	..	1055	..	..	..	..	..	..	..	..
55	..	..	..	11 1	..	..	..	..	..	..	..	..	..	..	..	..	..	..	..	..	..	..	..	..	..	..
56	..	..	..	11 5	..	..	..	..	..	..	..	..	..	..	..	..	..	..	..	..	..	..	..	..	..	..
57	..	..	..	Arr. Cheam 10 38 a.m	..	..	..	..	..	..	..	..	..	..	..	..	10 39	..	..	..	..	..	..	..	..	1058
58	..	..	..		..	..	..	..	..	..	..	..	..	..	..	..	10 41	..	..	..	..	..	..	..	..	11 1
59	..	..	..		..	..	..	..	..	..	1037	..	10 38	..	..	1040	10 44	..	..	..	..	..	..	..	..	11 3
60	..	..	..		..	..	..	..	..	..	..	..	..	..	..	..	10 47	..	..	..	..	..	..	..	..	11 7
61	..	..	..		..	..	..	..	..	..	1039	..	..	..	..	1042	..	..	..	..	..	..	..	..	..	..
62	..	..	..		..	..	..	..	..	..	1042	..	..	..	..	1045	..	..	..	..	..	..	..	..	..	..
63	..	..	..		..	..	..	..	..	..	1045	..	..	..	..	1048	..	..	..	..	..	..	..	..	..	..
64	..	..	..		..	..	..	..	..	..	1047	..	..	..	..	1050	..	..	..	..	..	..	..	..	..	..
65	..	..	..		..	..	..	..	..	..	1051	..	..	..	..	1054	..	..	..	..	..	..	..	..	..	..
66	..	..	..	..	..	..	..	..	..	..	1038	..	§ Via Three Bridges	..	..	1041	..	..	..	..	..	..	..	..	..	..
67	..	..	..	..	..	..	..	..	..	..	1040	..		..	..	1043	..	..	..	..	..	..	..	..	..	..
68	..	..	..	..	..	..	..	..	..	..	1043	..		..	..	1046	..	..	..	..	..	..	..	..	..	..
69	..	..	..	..	..	..	..	..	..	..	1045	..		..	..	1048	..	..	..	..	..	..	..	..	..	..
70	..	..	..	..	..	..	..	..	..	..	1048	..		..	..	1051	..	..	..	..	..	..	..	..	..	..
71	..	..	..	..	..	..	..	..	..	..	1052	..		..	..	1055	..	..	..	..	..	..	..	..	..	..
72	..	..	..	..	..	..	..	..	..	..	1055	..		..	..	1058	..	..	..	..	..	..	..	..	..	..
73	..	..	..	..	..	..	..	..	..	..	1059	..		..	..	11 2	..	..	..	..	..	..	..	..	..	..
74	..	..	..	..	..	..	..	..	..	..	..	..	10 41	..	..	..	..	..	..	..	..	..	..	..	..	..
75	..	..	..	..	..	..	..	..	..	..	..	..	10 47	..	..	..	..	..	..	..	..	..	..	..	..	..
76	..	..	..	..	..	..	..	..	..	..	..	..	10 53	..	..	..	..	..	..	..	..	..	..	..	11 0	..
77	..	..	..	..	..	..	..	..	..	..	..	..	10 59	..	..	..	..	..	..	..	..	..	..	..	..	..
78	..	..	..	..	..	..	..	..	..	..	..	..	11§35	..	..	..	..	1113	..	..	..	..	..	..	..	..

LONDON, CRYSTAL PALACE, CROYDON, SUTTON, DORKING NORTH,

For Notes, see page 284a

Down	No.	a.m. SX	SO	SO	SO	SX	SO		Week Days—continued SX	SO	SO	SO	SX		SO	SX	SX		a.m.		SX		No.
Victoria ....dep	1	..	..	..	1033	..	..	..	..	..	..	1038	1038	..	1040	1040	..	..	..	1045	..	1048	1
Charing Cross * .. "	2	3	3	3	3	3	3	10SX24	3	3	3	3	3	..	3	3	3	..	..	..	3	..	2
Waterloo * .... "	3							10SX28						..				..	1047	..		..	3
London Bridge ..... "	4	1027	1028	1029	..	1030	1030	10 36	1035	1037	1042	..	..	..	..	..	1043	..	..	..	1043	..	4
Battersea Park	5	..	..	..	1036	..	..	3	..	..	..	..	..	..	1043	1043	..	..	3	..	..	..	5
Clapham Junction	6	..	..	..	1039	..	..		..	..	..	1044	1044	..	1046	1047	..	..		..	..	1053	6
Wandsworth Common A	7	..	..	..	1042	..	..	..	..	..	..	..	..	..	1049	1050	..	..		..	..	..	7
Balham & Upper Tooting	8	..	..	..	1044	..	..	..	..	..	..	1048	1048	..	1051	1052	..	..	Via Worcester Park	..	..	..	8
South Bermondsey	9	..	..	..	..	..	..	..	1038	1041	..	..	..	..	..	..	..	..		..	..	..	9
Queen's Road, Peckham	10	..	..	..	..	1035	1035	..	1041	1044	..	..	..	..	..	..	..	..		..	..	..	10
Peckham Rye	11	1034	..	..	..	1037	1037	..	1043	1046	..	..	..	..	..	..	1049	..		..	..	..	11
East Dulwich	12	..	..	..	..	1040	1040	..	1046		..	..	..	..	..	..	..	..		..	..	..	12
North Dulwich	13	..	..	..	..	..	1042	..	1048		..	..	..	..	..	..	..	..		..	..	..	13
Tulse Hill	14	1038	1038	..	..	1044	1045	..	1051		..	..	..	..	..	..	1054	..		..	..	..	14
Streatham	15	1042	1042	..	..	1047	..	..	..		..	..	..	..	..	..	1057	..		..	..	..	15
New Cross Gate (for E.L.	16	..	..	1035	..	..	..	..	..		..	..	..	..	..	..	..	..	..	..	1048	..	16
Brockley B ....[Line)	17	..	..	1038	..	..	..	..	..		..	..	..	..	..	..	..	..	..	..	1050	..	17
Honor Oak Park	18	..	..	1040	..	..	..	..	..		..	..	..	..	..	..	..	..	..	..	1053	..	18
Forest Hill. for Lordship	19	..	..	1043	..	..	..	..	..	To Victoria, arr. 11 3 a.m.	..	..	..	..	..	..	..	..	..	..	1055	..	19
Sydenham ....[Lane	20	..	..	1045	..	..	..	..	..		..	..	..	..	..	..	..	..	..	..	1058	..	20
Penge West C	21	..	..	1047	..	..	..	..	..		..	..	..	..	..	..	..	..	..	..	11 0	..	21
Anerley	22	..	..	1049	..	..	..	..	..		..	..	..	..	..	..	..	..	..	..	11 1	..	22
Streatham Common	23	..	..	..	..	1049	..	..	..		..	1052	1052	..	..	..	1059	..	..	..	..	..	23
Norbury	24	..	..	..	..	..	..	..	..		..	1054	1054	..	..	..	11 2	..	..	..	..	..	24
Thornton Heath	25	..	..	..	..	..	..	..	..		..	1057	1057	..	..	..	11 5	..	..	..	..	..	25
Selhurst	26	..	..	..	..	1056	..	..	..		..	1059	1059	..	..	..	11 7	..	..	..	..	..	26
Streatham Hill	27	..	..	..	1046	..	1048	..	..		..	..	..	..	1054	1055	..	..	..	..	..	..	27
West Norwood [N'wood)	28	..	..	..	1049	..	..	..	1053	Stop	..	..	..	..	1057	1058	..	..	..	..	..	..	28
Gipsy Hill (for Upper	29	..	..	..	1052	..	..	..	1056	..	..	..	..	..	1059	11 0	..	..	..	..	..	..	29
Crystal Palace D	30	..	..	..	1054	..	..	..	1059	..	..	..	Arrive Sutton 11 14 a.m.	..	11 2	11 4	..	..	..	..	..	..	30
Birkbeck	31	..	..	..	1058	..	..	..	..	..	..	..		..	..	..	..	..	..	..	..	..	31
Beckenham Jn. arr	32	..	..	..	11 2	..	..	..	..	..	..	..		..	..	..	..	..	..	..	..	..	32
Norwood Junction F ..	33	..	..	1052	..	..	..	10 48	..	..	1055	..		..	11 7	11 9	..	..	..	..	11 4	..	33
East Croydon .... arr	34	..	..	..	..	..	..	10 52	..	..	..	..		..	..	..	..	..	..	11 0	..	11 5	34
East Croydon .... dep	35	..	..	..	..	..	..	10 52	..	..	..	..		..	..	..	..	..	..	..	..	11 5	35
Mitcham Junction	36	1047	1047	..	..	..	..	..	..	a.m SO	..	..		..	..	..	..	..	..	..	..	..	36
Hackbridge	37	1049	1049	To London Bridge, via Streatham	..	..	..	..	..		..	..	..	..	..	..	..	..	..	..	..	..	37
Carshalton	38	1052	1052		..	..	..	..	..		..	..	..	..	..	..	..	..	..	..	..	..	38
West Croydon 319 arr	39	..	..		..	..	..	..	..	3	1059	11 2	11 2	..	1111	1113	..	..	..	..	11 8	..	39
West Croydon 319 dep	40	..	..		..	..	..	..	..	1052	1059	11 2	11 2	..	..	..	..	..	..	..	11 8	..	40
Waddon G	41	..	..		..	..	..	..	..	1054	11 1	11 5	11 5	..	..	..	..	..	..	..	1111	..	41
Wallington	42	..	..		..	..	..	..	..	1058	11 5	11 9	11 8	..	..	..	..	..	..	..	1114	..	42
Carshalton Beeches	43	..	..		..	..	..	..	..	11 0	11 7	1111	1111	..	..	..	..	..	..	..	1117	..	43
Sutton 322	44	1055	1055		..	..	..	..	..	11 3	1110	1114	1117	..	..	..	..	..	..	..	1121	..	44
Belmont	45	..	..		..	..	..	..	..	..	1113	1117	1120	..	..	..	..	..	..	..	1124	..	45
Banstead	46	..	..		..	..	..	..	..	..	1116	1120	1123	..	..	..	..	..	..	..	1127	..	46
Epsom Downs ...... arr	47	..	..		..	..	..	..	..	..	1119	1123	1126	..	..	..	..	..	..	..	1130	..	47
Cheam	48	1058	1058	..	..	..	..	..	..	..	..	..	..	..	..	..	..	..	..	..	..	..	48
Ewell East H	49	11 1	11 1	..	..	..	..	‖1 minute *earlier* on Saturdays	..	..	..	..	..	..	..	..	..	..	..	..	..	..	49
Epsom	50	11 5	11 5	..	..	..	..		..	..	..	..	..	..	..	..	..	..	1115	..	..	..	50
Ashtead	51	11 9	11 9	..	..	..	..		..	..	..	..	..	..	..	..	..	..	1119	..	..	..	51
Leatherhead ..[Bridge J	52	1113	1113	..	..	..	..		..	..	..	..	..	..	..	..	..	..	1123	..	..	..	52
Boxhill and Burford	53	1118	1118	..	..	..	..		..	..	..	..	..	..	..	..	..	..	..	..	..	..	53
Dorking North K .. arr	54	1121	1121	..	..	..	..		..	..	..	..	..	..	..	..	..	..	..	..	..	..	54
Bookham ....[394	55	..	..	..	..	..	..		..	..	..	..	..	..	..	..	..	..	1128	..	..	..	55
Effingham Junction arr	56	..	..	..	..	..	..		..	..	..	..	..	..	..	..	..	..	1132	..	..	..	56
South Croydon 234	57	..	..	..	..	..	..		..	..	..	..	..	..	..	..	..	..	..	..	..	..	57
Purley Oaks	58	..	..	..	..	..	..		..	..	..	..	..	..	..	..	..	..	..	..	..	..	58
Purley	59	..	..	..	..	..	..	10 37	..	..	..	..	..	..	..	..	..	..	..	..	..	1111	59
Coulsdon North L .. arr	60	..	..	..	..	..	..	..	..	..	..	..	..	..	..	..	..	..	..	..	..	..	60
Purley ....dep	61	..	..	..	..	..	..	11‖ 0	..	..	..	..	..	..	..	..	..	..	..	..	..	..	61
Kenley	62	..	..	..	..	..	..	11‖ 3	..	..	..	..	..	..	..	..	..	..	..	..	..	..	62
Whyteleafe	63	..	..	..	..	..	..	11‖ 6	..	..	..	..	..	..	..	..	..	..	..	..	..	..	63
Warlingham	64	..	..	..	..	..	..	11‖ 8	..	..	..	..	..	..	..	..	..	..	..	..	..	..	64
Caterham .... arr	65	..	..	..	..	..	..	11‖12	..	..	..	..	..	..	..	..	..	..	..	..	..	..	65
Purley .... dep	66	..	..	..	..	..	..	10 58	..	..	..	..	..	..	..	..	..	..	..	..	..	§ Via Three Bridges	66
Reedham	67	..	..	..	..	..	..	11 0	..	..	..	..	..	..	..	..	..	..	..	..	..		67
Smitham	68	..	..	..	..	..	..	11 3	..	..	..	..	..	..	..	..	..	..	..	..	..		68
Woodmansterne	69	..	..	..	..	..	..	11 5	..	..	..	..	..	..	..	..	..	..	..	..	..		69
Chipstead	70	..	..	..	..	..	..	11 8	..	..	..	..	..	..	..	..	..	..	..	..	..		70
Kingswood M	71	..	..	..	..	..	..	11 12	..	..	..	..	..	..	..	..	..	..	..	..	..		71
Tadworth N	72	..	..	..	..	..	..	11 15	..	..	..	..	..	..	..	..	..	..	..	..	..		72
Tattenham Corner. arr	73	..	..	..	..	..	..	11 19	..	..	..	..	..	..	..	..	..	..	..	..	..		73
Coulsdon South	74	..	..	..	..	..	..	..	..	..	..	..	..	..	..	..	..	..	..	..	..	1114	74
Merstham	75	..	..	..	..	..	..	..	..	..	..	..	..	..	..	..	..	..	..	..	..	1120	75
Redhill 158, 246 ...... arr	76	..	..	..	..	..	..	..	..	..	..	..	..	..	..	..	..	..	..	..	..	1124	76
Reigate 246 .... "	77	..	..	..	..	..	..	..	..	..	..	..	..	..	..	..	..	..	..	..	..	1130	77
Horsham 159, 244, 245 "	78	1146	1146	..	..	..	..	..	..	..	..	..	..	..	..	..	..	..	..	..	..	12§5	78

CATERHAM, TATTENHAM CORNER, REDHILL, REIGATE, and HORSHAM

Week Days—*continued* (a.m)

No.	SX	SO	SO	SX	SX			SO	SO	SO	SX	SX	SX	SO		SO	SO	SO	SO	SO	SX	SO	SO	SO	SX	SO		SO
1	..	..	..	..	1051	10 51	..	1053	..	..	..	..	..	..	..	..	..	..	1055	..	..	1058	11 0	..	..	..	11 8	..
2	1044						..						..	..	..												..	
3	1046	③	③	③	③	③	..	③	③	③	③	③	..	..	11 7	③	③	③	③	③	③	③	③	③	③	③	..	③
4	1051	1045	1048	1047	..	..	..	..	1050	1051	1053	1053	..	..	..	1055	1057	1055	..	11 2	11 2	..	..	11 7	11 7	11 5	..	11 8
5	③	..	..	..	..	..	..	1056	..	..	..	..	..	..	③	..	..	..	..	..	..	..	11 3	..	..	..	..	..
6		..	..	..	1056	10 56	..	1059	..	..	..	..	..	..		..	..	..	11 0	..	..	11 4	11 6	..	..	..	..	..
7	..	..	..	..	..	10SX59	..	11 2	..	..	..	..	..	..		..	..	..	..	..	..	..	11 9	..	..	..	..	..
8	..	..	..	..	11 0	11 1	..	11 4	..	..	..	..	..	..		..	..	..	11 4	..	..	11 8	1111	..	..	..	..	..
9	..	..	..	1051	..	..	..	..	..	..	..	..	..	..		1058	11 1	..	..	..	..	..	..	..	..	..	..	..
10	..	..	..	1054	..	..	..	..	1055	..	..	..	..	..		11 1	11 4	..	..	..	..	..	..	..	..	..	..	..
11	..	..	1054	1056	..	..	..	..	1057	..	..	1059	..	..	Via Worcester Park	11 3	11 6	..	..	..	..	..	..	..	..	..	..	..
12	..	..	..		..	..	..	..	11 0	..	..	..	..	..		11 6	..	..	..	..	..	..	..	..	..	..	..	..
13	..	..	..		..	..	..	..	11 2	..	..	..	..	..		11 8	..	..	..	..	..	..	..	..	..	..	..	..
14	..	1055	1058		..	..	..	..	11 5	..	..	11 3	..	..		1111	..	..	..	..	..	..	..	..	..	1115	..	1118
15	..	1059	11 2		..	..	..	..	..	..	..	11 7	..	..		..	..	..	..	..	..	..	..	..	..	1119	..	1122
16	..	..	..		..	..	..	..	..	1056	1058	..	..	..	..	..	..	..	..	..	11 7	..	..	1112	1112	..	..	..
17	..	..	..	To Victoria arr 11 11 a.m	..	..	..	..	..	1058	11 0	..	..	..	..	..		..	..	..	..	..	..	1114	1114	..	..	..
18	..	..	..		..	..	..	..	..	11 1	11 3	..	..	..	..	..		..	..	..	..	..	..	1117	1117	..	..	..
19	..	..	..		..	..	..	..	..	11 3	11 5	..	..	..	..	..		..	..	..	1111	..	..	1119	1119	..	..	..
20	..	..	..		..	..	..	..	..	11 6	11 8	..	..	..	..	..		..	..	..	1114	..	..	1122	1122	..	..	..
21	..	..	..		..	..	..	..	..	11 8	..	..	..	..	..	..	To Victoria, arr. 11 23 a.m	..	..	..	1116	..	..	..	1124	..	..	..
22	..	..	..		..	..	..	..	..	11 9	..	..	..	..	..	..		..	..	..	1117	..	..	..	1125	..	..	..
23	..	11 1	..	..	..	11 5	..	..	..	..	..	..	..	..	..	..		..	..	..	..	1112	..	..	..	1121	..	..
24	..	11 4	..	..	..	11 7	..	..	..	..	..	..	..	..	..	..		..	..	..	..	1114	..	..	..	1124	..	..
25	..	11 7	..	..	..	11 10	..	..	..	..	..	..	..	..	..	..		..	..	..	..	1117	..	..	..	1127	..	..
26	..	1110	..	..	..	11 12	..	..	..	..	..	..	..	..	..	..		..	..	..	..	1119	..	..	..	1130	..	..
27	..	..	..	..	..	..	SX	11 6	11 8	..	..	..	..	..	..	..	..	..	..	..	..	..	1114	..	..	..	..	..
28	..	..	..	..	..	..	③	11 9	..	..	..	..	..	..	..	1113	..	..	..	..	..	..	1117	..	..	..	..	..
29	..	..	..	..	..	..		1112	..	..	..	..	..	..	..	1116	..	..	..	..	..	..	1119	..	..	..	..	..
30	..	..	..	..	..	..	1110	1114	..	..	1111	..	..	..	..	1119	..	..	..	..	..	..	1122	1125	..	..	..	..
31	..	..	..	..	..	..	1113	1118	..	..	..	..	..	..	..	..	..	..	..	..	..	..	..	..	..	..	..	..
32	..	..	..	..	..	..	1117	1122	..	..	..	..	..	..	..	..	..	..	..	..	..	..	..	..	..	..	..	..
33	11 4	1113	..	..	..	..		..	..	1112	..	..	..	..	..	..	..	11 7	..	1115	1120	..	1127	..	1129	1133	..	..
34	11 8		..	..	..	11 16	Stop	..	..		..	..	..	..	..	..	..	1111	..	..	..	..	..	..	..	..	1125	..
35	11 8		..	..	..	11 16	..	..	..		..	..	..	..	..	..	..	1111	..	..	..	..	..	..	..	..	..	..
36	..		11 7	..	11 6	..	..	..	..		..	1112	③	..	..	..	..	..	1113	..	..	..	..	..	..	..	..	1127
37	..		11 9	..	11 9	..	..	..	..		..	1114		..	..	..	..	..	1115	..	..	..	..	..	..	..	..	1129
38	..		1112	..	1111	..	..	..	..		..	1117	..	..	..	..	..	..	1118	..	..	..	..	..	..	..	..	1132
39	..		..	..	..	..	..	..	..		..	..	..	..	..	..	..	..	..	1119	1124	1123	1131	..			..	..
40	..	To London Bridge, via Forest Hill	..	..	..	..	..	..	..	To London Bridge, via Streatham	..	..	1113	③	..	..	..	..	..	1119	1124	1123	..	..			..	..
41	..		..	..	..	..	..	..	..		..	..	1115		..	..	..	..	..	1121	1127	1126	..	..			..	..
42	..		..	..	..	..	..	..	..		..	..	1119	1121	..	..	..	..	..	1125	1130	1129	..	..			..	..
43	..		..	..	..	..	..	..	..		..	..	1121	1123	..	..	..	..	..	1127	1133	1132	..	..	To London Bridge, via Streatham	To London Bridge, via Forest Hill	..	..
44	..		1115	..	1114	..	..	..	..		..	1121	1124	1126	..	..	..	..	1121	1130	1135	1135	..	..			..	1135
45	..		..	..	..	..	..	..	..		..	..	..	..	..	..	..	..	..	1133	1138	1138	..	..			..	..
46	..		..	..	..	..	..	..	..		..	..	..	..	..	..	..	..	..	1136	1141	1141	..	..			..	..
47	..		..	..	..	..	..	..	..		..	..	..	..	..	..	..	..	..	1139	1145	1144	..	..			..	..
48	..	..	1118	..	1117	..	..	..	..	..	..	1124	..	..	..	..	..	..	1124	..	..	..	..	..	..	..	..	1143
49	..	..	1121	..	1120	..	..	..	..	..	..	1127	..	..	..	..	..	..	1127	..	..	..	..	..	..	..	..	1146
50	..	..	1125	..	1124	..	..	..	..	..	..	1130	..	..	1135	..	..	..	1130	..	..	..	..	..	..	..	..	1149
51	..	..	1129	..	..	..	..	..	..	..	..	1134	..	..	1139	..	..	..	..	..	..	..	..	..	..	..	..	1153
52	..	..	1133	..	..	..	..	..	..	..	..	1138	..	..	1143	..	..	..	..	..	..	..	..	..	..	..	..	1157
53	..	..	1138	..	..	..	..	..	..	..	..	..	..	..	1148	..	..	..	..	..	..	..	..	..	..	..	..	..
54	..	..	1141	..	..	..	..	..	..	..	..	..	..	..	1151	..	..	..	..	..	..	..	..	..	..	..	..	..
55	..	..	..	..	..	..	..	..	..	..	..	1143	..	..	..	..	..	..	..	..	..	..	..	..	..	..	..	12 2
56	..	..	..	..	..	..	..	..	..	..	..	1146	..	..	..	..	..	..	..	..	..	..	..	..	..	..	..	..
57	1110	..	..	..	..	11 18	..	..	..	..	..	..	..	..	..	..	..	..	..	..	..	..	..	..	..	..	..	
58	1113	..	..	..	..	11 21	..	..	..	..	..	..	..	..	..	..	..	..	..	..	..	..	..	..	..	..	..	
59	1116	..	..	..	..	11 23	..	..	..	..	..	..	..	..	..	..	..	1116	..	..	..	..	..	..	..	..	..	
60	..	..	..	..	..	11 27	..	..	..	..	..	..	..	..	..	..	..	..	..	..	..	..	..	..	..	..	..	Arr. Cheam 11 38 a.m
61	1118	..	..	..	..	..	..	..	..	..	..	..	..	..	..	..	..	1119	..	..	..	..	..	..	..	..	..	
62	1121	..	..	..	..	..	..	..	..	..	..	..	..	..	..	..	..	1122	..	..	..	..	..	..	..	..	..	
63	1124	..	..	..	..	..	..	..	..	..	..	..	..	..	..	..	..	1125	..	..	..	..	..	..	..	..	..	
64	1126	..	..	..	..	..	..	..	..	..	..	..	..	..	..	..	..	1127	..	..	..	..	..	..	..	..	..	
65	1130	..	..	..	..	..	..	..	..	..	..	..	..	..	..	..	..	1131	..	..	..	..	..	..	..	..	..	
66	1117	..	..	..	..	..	..	..	..	..	..	..	..	..	..	..	..	1118	..	..	..	..	..	..	..	..	..	..
67	1119	..	..	..	..	..	a.m	..	..	..	..	..	..	..	..	..	..	1120	..	..	..	..	..	..	..	..	..	..
68	1121	..	..	..	..	..		..	..	..	..	..	..	..	..	..	..	1123	..	..	..	..	..	..	..	..	..	..
69	1124	..	..	..	..	..		..	..	..	..	..	..	..	..	..	..	1125	..	..	..	..	..	..	..	..	..	..
70	1126	..	..	..	..	..	*d* Departure time	..	..	..	..	..	..	..	..	..	..	1129	..	..	..	..	..	..	..	..	..	..
71	1131	..	..	..	..	..		..	..	..	..	..	..	..	..	..	..	1132	..	..	..	..	..	..	..	..	..	..
72	1134	..	..	..	..	..		..	..	..	..	..	..	..	..	..	..	1135	..	..	..	..	..	..	..	..	..	..
73	1137	..	..	..	..	..		..	..	..	..	..	..	..	..	..	..	1139	..	..	..	..	..	..	..	..	..	..
74	..	..	..	..	..	..		..	..	..	..	..	..	..	..	..	..	..	..	..	..	..	..	..	..	..	..	..
75	..	..	..	..	..	..	..	..	..	..	..	..	..	..	..	..	..	..	..	..	..	..	..	..	..	..	..	..
76	..	..	..	..	..	..	11*d*35	..	..	..	..	..	..	..	..	..	..	..	..	..	..	..	..	..	..	..	..	..
77	..	..	..	..	..	..	1139	..	..	..	..	..	..	..	..	..	..	..	..	..	..	..	..	..	..	..	..	..
78	..	..	..	..	..	..	..	..	..	..	..	..	..	..	1225	..	..	..	..	..	..	..	..	..	..	..	..	..

LONDON, CRYSTAL PALACE, CROYDON, SUTTON, DORKING NORTH,

For Notes, see page 284a

Down	No.	a.m							Week Days—continued							a.m							No.
		S X	S O	S O	S O	S O	S X				S O		S X		S O	S O		S O	S X	S X			
Victoria .... dep	1	11 8	1111	1113	..	..	1111	..	..	1118	..	..	..	..	..	1118	..	1120	1121	1124	..	1125	1
Charing Cross* ... "	2	3	3	3	..	3	3	3	..	..	3	..	3	..	3	3	..	3	3	3	..	..	2
Waterloo* .... "	3				1127				..	..		..		..			..				..	..	3
London Bridge ..... "	4	..	..	..	..	1115	..	11 15	..	..	1117	..	1119	11 18	11 20	..	..	..	..	..	..	..	4
Battersea Park	5	..	..	1116	3	..	1114	..	..	..	..	..	..	..	..	..	..	1123	..	..	..	..	5
Clapham Junction	6	1114	1116	1119		..	1117	..	..	..	..	..	..	..	..	1124	..	1126	1126	1129	..	..	6
Wandsworth Common A	7	..	..	1122	..	..	1120	..	..	..	..	..	..	..	..	..	..	1129	..	..	..	..	7
Balham & Upper Tooting	8	1118	1121	1124	..	..	1122	..	..	..	..	..	..	..	..	1128	..	1131	1130	1133	..	..	8
South Bermondsey	9	..	..	..	Via Worcester Park	..	..	11 18	..	..	1121	..	1122	..	..	..	..	..	..	..	..	..	9
Queen's Road, Peckham	10	..	..	..		..	..	11 21	..	..	1124	..	1125	..	..	..	..	..	..	..	..	..	10
Peckham Rye	11	..	..	..		..	..	11 23	..	..	1126	..	1127	..	..	..	..	..	..	..	..	..	11
East Dulwich	12	..	..	..		..	..	11 26	..	..		..		..	..	..	..	..	..	..	..	..	12
North Dulwich	13	..	..	..		..	..	11 28	..	..		..		..	..	..	..	..	..	..	..	..	13
Tulse Hill	14	..	..	..		..	..	11 31	..	..		..		..	..	..	..	..	..	..	..	..	14
Streatham	15	..	..	..		..	..	..	..	..		..		..	..	..	..	..	..	..	..	..	15
New Cross Gate (for E.L.	16	..	..	..		..	..	..	..	..	To Victoria, arr. 11 43 a.m.	..	To Victoria, arr. 11 43 a.m.	..	..	..	..	..	..	..	..	..	16
Brockley B .... [Line)	17	..	..	..		..	..	..	..	..		..		..	..	..	..	..	..	..	..	..	17
Honor Oak Park	18	..	..	..		..	..	..	..	..		..		..	..	..	..	..	..	..	..	..	18
Forest Hill, for Lordship	19	..	..	..		..	..	..	..	..		..		..	11 28	..	..	..	..	..	..	..	19
Sydenham .... [Lane	20	..	..	..		..	..	..	..	..		..		..	11 31	..	..	..	..	..	..	..	20
Penge West C	21	..	..	..		..	..	..	..	..		..		..	..	..	..	..	..	..	..	..	21
Anerley	22	..	..	..		..	..	..	..	..		..		..	..	..	..	..	..	..	..	..	22
Streatham Common	23	1122	1125	..	..	..	..	..	..	..		..		..	..	1132	..	..	1134	..	..	..	23
Norbury	24	1124	1127	..	..	..	..	..	..	..		..		..	..	1134	..	..	1136	..	..	..	24
Thornton Heath	25	1127	1130	..	..	..	..	..	..	..		..		..	..	1137	..	..	1139	..	..	..	25
Selhurst	26	1129	1132	..	..	..	..	..	..	..		..		..	..	1139	..	..	1141	..	..	..	26
Streatham Hill	27	Arr Sutton 11 44 a.m	..	1126	..	..	1124	..	..	..	Stop	S X	..	..	..	..	..	1134	..	..	..	..	27
West Norwood. [N'wood)	28		..	1129	..	..	1127	11 33	..	..	..	3	..	..	..	..	..	1137	..	..	..	..	28
Gipsy Hill (for Upper	29		..	1132	..	..	1130	11 36	..	..	..		..	..	..	..	..	1139	..	..	..	..	29
Crystal Palace D	30		..	1134	..	..	1132	11J38	..	..	..	1140	..	..	..	..	..	1142	..	..	..	..	30
Birkbeck	31		..	1138	..	..	..	..	..	..	..	1143	..	..	..	..	..	..	..	..	..	..	31
Beckenham Jn. arr	32		..	1142	..	..	..	..	..	..	..	1147	..	..	..	..	..	..	..	..	..	..	32
Norwood Junction F ..	33		..	..	..	1127	1136	J 1 minute later on Saturdays	..	..	..	..	..	11 30	11 35	..	..	1146	..	..	..	..	33
East Croydon .... arr	34		1136	..	..	1131	..		..	..	..	..	..	11 34	..	..	..	..	1145	..	..	1140	34
East Croydon .... dep	35		1136	..	..	1131	..		..	..	..	..	..	11 35	..	..	..	..	1145	..	..	..	35
Mitcham Junction	36	..	..	..	..	..	..		..	..	..	..	..	..	..	..	..	..	..	1140	..	..	36
Hackbridge	37	..	..	..	..	..	..		..	..	..	..	..	..	..	..	..	..	..	1143	..	..	37
Carshalton	38	..	..	..	..	..	..		..	..	a.m	..	..	..	..	..	..	..	..	1145	..	..	38
West Croydon 319 arr	39	1132	..	..	..	..	1141		..	..	S O	..	..	..	11 39	1142	..	1150	..	..	S X	..	39
West Croydon 319 dep	40	1132	..	..	..	..	..		..	..	3	..	..	..	11 39	1142	..	..	..	..	3	..	40
Waddon G	41	1135	..	..	..	..	..		..	..		..	..	..	11 41	1145	..	..	..	..		..	41
Wallington	42	1138	..	..	..	..	..	..	..	..	1141	..	..	..	11 45	1148	..	..	..	..	1148	..	42
Carshalton Beeches	43	1141	..	..	..	..	..	..	..	..	1143	..	..	..	11 47	1151	..	..	..	..	1151	..	43
Sutton 322	44	1147	..	..	..	..	..	..	..	1139	1147	..	..	..	11 50	1154	..	..	..	1149	1153	..	44
Belmont	45	1150	..	..	..	..	..	..	..	..	..	..	..	..	11 53	1157	..	..	..	..	..	..	45
Banstead	46	1153	..	..	..	..	..	..	..	..	..	..	..	..	11 56	12 0	..	..	..	..	..	..	46
Epsom Downs ...... arr	47	1156	..	..	..	..	..	..	..	..	..	..	..	..	11 59	12 3	..	..	..	..	..	..	47
Cheam	48	..	..	..	..	..	..	..	..	..	..	..	..	..	..	..	..	..	..	1152	..	..	48
Ewell East H	49	..	..	..	..	..	..	..	..	..	..	..	..	..	..	..	..	..	..	1155	..	..	49
Epsom	50	..	..	..	1155	..	..	..	..	..	..	..	..	..	..	..	..	..	..	1158	..	..	50
Ashtead	51	..	..	..	1159	..	..	..	..	..	..	..	..	..	..	..	..	..	..	..	..	..	51
Leatherhead .. [Bridge J	52	..	..	..	12 3	..	..	..	..	..	..	..	..	..	..	..	..	..	..	..	..	..	52
Boxhill and Burford	53	..	..	..	12 8	..	..	..	..	..	..	..	..	..	..	..	..	..	..	..	..	..	53
Dorking North K .. arr	54	..	..	..	1211	..	..	..	..	1155	..	..	..	..	..	..	..	..	..	..	..	..	54
Bookham .... [394	55	..	..	..	..	..	..	..	..	..	..	..	..	..	..	..	..	..	..	..	..	..	55
Effingham Junction arr	56	..	..	..	..	..	..	..	..	..	..	..	..	..	..	..	..	..	..	..	..	..	56
South Croydon 234	57	..	1138	..	..	..	..	..	..	..	..	..	..	..	..	..	..	..	1147	..	..	..	57
Purley Oaks	58	..	1141	..	..	..	..	..	..	..	..	..	..	..	..	..	..	..	1150	..	..	..	58
Purley	59	..	1143	..	..	1137	..	..	..	..	..	..	..	11 40	..	..	..	..	1152	..	..	..	59
Coulsdon North L .. arr	60	..	1147	..	..	..	..	..	..	..	..	..	..	..	..	..	..	..	1156	..	..	..	60
Purley .... dep	61	..	..	..	..	1139	..	..	..	..	..	..	..	..	..	..	..	..	..	..	..	..	61
Kenley	62	..	..	..	..	1142	..	..	..	..	..	..	..	..	..	..	..	..	..	..	..	..	62
Whyteleafe	63	..	..	..	..	1145	..	..	..	..	..	..	..	..	..	..	..	..	..	..	..	..	63
Warlingham	64	..	..	..	..	1147	..	..	..	..	..	..	..	..	..	..	..	..	..	..	..	..	64
Caterham .... arr	65	..	..	..	..	1151	..	..	..	..	..	..	..	..	..	..	..	..	..	..	..	..	65
Purley .... dep	66	..	..	..	..	1138	..	..	..	..	..	..	..	§ Via Three Bridges	..	..	..	..	..	..	..	..	66
Reedham	67	..	..	..	..	1140	..	..	..	..	..	..	..		..	..	..	..	..	..	..	..	67
Smitham	68	..	..	..	..	1143	..	..	..	..	..	..	..		..	..	..	..	..	..	..	..	68
Woodmansterne	69	..	..	..	..	1145	..	..	..	..	..	..	..		..	..	..	..	..	..	..	..	69
Chipstead	70	..	..	..	..	1148	..	..	..	..	..	..	..		..	..	..	..	..	..	..	..	70
Kingswood M	71	..	..	..	..	1152	..	..	..	..	..	..	..		..	..	..	..	..	..	..	..	71
Tadworth N	72	..	..	..	..	1155	..	..	..	..	..	..	..		..	..	..	..	..	..	..	..	72
Tattenham Corner. arr	73	..	..	..	..	1159	..	..	..	..	..	..	..	..	..	..	..	..	..	..	..	..	73
Coulsdon South	74	..	..	..	..	..	..	..	..	..	..	..	..	11 44	..	..	..	..	..	..	..	..	74
Merstham	75	..	..	..	..	..	..	..	..	..	..	..	..	11 50	..	..	..	..	..	..	..	..	75
Redhill 158, 246 ...... arr	76	..	..	..	..	..	..	..	..	..	..	..	..	11 54	..	..	..	..	..	..	..	..	76
Reigate 246 .... "	77	..	..	..	..	..	..	..	..	..	..	..	..	12 0	..	..	..	..	..	..	..	..	77
Horsham 159, 244, 245 "	78	..	..	..	..	..	..	..	..	1213	..	..	..	12§34	..	..	..	..	..	..	..	..	78

CATERHAM, TATTENHAM CORNER, REDHILL, REIGATE, and HORSHAM

a.m. — **Week Days**—*continued* — a.m.

No.	S X	S O		S O	S O	S X	S O	S X	S O	S O		S O	S O		S X	S O		S O	S O	S O	S X	S O	S X				S X
1	1127	..	1128	1131	..	..	..	..	..	1133	..	..	1136	..	..	..	..	..	..	1138	11 38	1140	..	..	..	1145	1140
2	3	3	..	3	3	3	3	1124	3	3	..	3	3	..	3	3	..	3	3	3	3	3	3	..	..	..	3
3			..					1126			..			..			..							..	1147	..	
4	..	1125	..	..	1127	1125	1128	1131	1131	..	..	1135	..	..	1129	1135	..	1137	1142	..	..	..	1136	..	..	..	..
5	..	..	..	..	..	..	..	3	..	1136	..	..	..	..	..	..	..	..	..	..	..	1143	..	..	3	..	1143
6	1132	..	1134	1136	..	..	..		..	1139	..	..	1141	..	..	..	..	..	..	1144	11 44	1146	..	..		..	1147
7	..	..	..	..	..	..	..	..	..	1142	..	..	..	..	..	..	..	..	..	..	..	1149	..	..	Via Worcester Park	..	1150
8	1136	..	..	1141	..	..	..	..	..	1144	..	..	1145	..	..	..	..	..	..	1148	11 48	1151	..	..		..	1152
9	..	..	..	..	..	..	..	..	..	..	..	..	..	..	..	1138	..	1141	..	..	..	..	1139	..		..	..
10	..	..	..	..	..	..	..	..	..	..	..	..	..	..	..	1141	..	1144	..	..	..	..	1142	..		..	..
11	..	..	..	..	..	1131	..	..	..	..	..	..	..	..	..	1143	..	1146	..	..	..	..	1144	..		..	..
12	..	..	..	..	..	..	..	..	..	..	..	..	..	..	..	1146	..	..	..	..	..	..	1147	..		..	..
13	..	..	..	..	..	..	..	..	..	..	..	..	..	..	..	1148	..		..	..	..	..	1149	..		..	..
14	..	1135	..	..	..	1136	1138	..	..	..	..	..	..	..	..	1151	..		..	..	..	..	1152	..		..	..
15	..	1139	..	..	..	1140	1142	..	..	..	..	..	..	..	..	..	..	To Victoria, arr. 12 3 p.m	..	..	..	..	1156	..		..	..
16	..	..	..	..	1132	..	..	..	1136	..	..	..	..	..	1134	..	..		..	..	..	..	..	..	..	..	..
17	..	..	..	..	1124	..	..	..	1138	..	..	..	..	..	1136	..	..		..	..	..	..	..	..	..	..	..
18	..	..	..	..	1137	..	..	..	1141	..	..	..	..	..	1140	..	..		..	..	..	..	..	..	..	..	..
19	..	..	..	..	1139	..	..	..	1143	..	..	..	..	..	1141	..	..		..	..	..	..	..	..	..	..	..
20	..	..	..	..	1142	..	..	..	1146	..	..	..	..	..	1144	..	..		..	..	..	..	..	..	..	..	..
21	..	..	..	..	..	..	..	..	1148	..	..	..	..	..	1146	..	..		..	..	..	..	..	..	..	..	..
22	..	..	..	..	..	..	..	..	1149	..	..	..	..	..	1147	..	..		..	..	..	..	..	..	..	..	..
23	1140	1141	..	1145	..	..	..	..	..	..	..	..	..	..	..	..	..		..	1152	11 52	..	1158	..	..	..	..
24	1142	1144	..	1147	..	..	..	..	..	..	..	..	..	..	..	..	..		..	1154	11 54	..	12 1	..	..	..	..
25	1145	1147	..	1150	..	..	..	..	..	..	..	..	..	..	..	..	..	..	..	1157	11 57	..	12 4	..	..	..	..
26	1147	1150	..	1152	..	..	..	..	..	..	..	..	..	..	..	..	..	..	..	1159	11 59	..	12 6	..	..	..	..
27	..	..	..	..	..	..	..	..	..	1146	..	..	..	..	..	..	..	..	..	..		1154	..	..	..	..	1154
28	..	..	..	..	..	..	..	..	..	1149	..	..	..	..	..	1153	..	..	..	..	Arr. Sutton 12 14 p.m.	1157	..	..	..	..	1157
29	..	..	..	..	..	..	..	..	..	1152	..	..	..	..	..	1156	..	..	..	..		1159	..	..	..	..	12 0
30	..	..	..	..	1145	..	..	..	..	1154	..	..	..	..	..	1159	..	..	..	..		12 2	..	..	..	..	12 2
31	..	..	..	..	Stop	..	..	..	..	1158	..	..	..	..	..	..	..	..	..	..		..	..	..	..	..	..
32	..	..	..	..		..	..	..	..	12 2	..	..	..	..	..	..	..	..	..	..		..	..	..	..	..	..
33	..	1153	..	..	..	..	..	1144	1152	..	..	1148	..	..	1150	..	..	..	1155	..		12 7	12 9	..	..	..	12 7
34	..	..	1145	1156	..	..	..	1148	To London Bridge, via Streatham	..	..	1152	..	..	..	..	..	..	..	..		..	To London Bridge via Forest Hill	..	..	12 0	..
35	..	To London Bridge, via Forest Hill	1146	1156	..	..	..	1148		..	..	1152	..	..	..	..	..	..	..	..		..		..	..	..	..
36	..		..	..	..	1146	1147	..		..	..	..	1152	..	..	..	..	..	..	..	..	..		..	..	..	..
37	..		..	..	..	1149	1149	..		..	..	..	1154	S O	..	..	..	..	..	..	..	..		..	..	..	..
38	..		..	..	..	1152	1152	..		..	..	..	1157	3	..	..	..	..	..	..	..	..		..	..	..	..
39	..		..	..	..	..	..	..		..	..	..	..		1154	..	..	..	1159	12 2	12 2	1211		..	..	..	1212
40	..		..	..	..	..	..	..		..	..	..	..	1150	1154	..	..	..	1159	12 2	12 2	..		..	..	..	..
41	..		..	..	..	..	..	..		..	..	..	..	1152	1157	..	..	..	12 1	12 5	12 5	..		..	..	..	..
42	..		..	..	..	..	..	..		..	..	..	..	1158	12 0	..	..	..	12 5	12 8	12 8	..		..	..	..	..
43	..		..	..	..	..	..	..		..	..	..	..	12 0	12 3	..	..	..	12 7	1211	12 11	..		..	..	..	..
44	..		..	..	..	1156	1155	..		..	..	..	12 0	12 3	12 5	..	..	..	1210	1214	12 17	..		..	..	..	..
45	..		..	..	..	..	..	..		..	..	..	..	..	12 8	..	..	..	1213	1217	12 20	..		..	..	..	..
46	..	..	..	..	..	..	..	..		..	..	..	..	..	1211	..	..	..	1216	1220	12 23	..		..	..	..	..
47	..	..	..	..	..	..	..	..	..	..	..	..	..	..	1215	..	..	..	1219	1223	12 26	..	..	..	..	..	..
48	..	..	..	..	p.m	1159	1158	..	..	..	..	..	12 3	..	..	..	..	..	..	..	..	..	..	..	..	..	..
49	..	..	..	..	S O	12 2	12 1	..	..	..	..	..	12 6	..	..	..	..	..	..	..	..	..	..	..	..	..	..
50	..	..	..	..	3	12 5	12 5	..	..	..	..	..	12 9	..	..	..	..	..	..	..	..	..	..	..	1215	..	..
51	..	..	..	..		12 9	12 9	..	..	..	..	..	..	..	..	..	..	..	..	..	..	..	..	..	1219	..	..
52	..	..	..	..	12 9	1213	1213	..	..	..	..	..	..	..	..	..	..	..	..	..	..	..	..	..	1223	..	..
53	..	..	..	..	..	1218	1218	..	..	..	..	..	..	..	..	..	..	..	..	..	..	..	..	..	..	..	..
54	..	..	..	..	..	1221	1221	..	..	..	..	..	..	..	..	..	..	..	..	..	..	..	..	..	..	..	..
55	..	..	..	..	1213	..	..	..	..	..	..	..	..	..	..	..	..	..	..	..	..	..	..	..	1228	..	..
56	..	..	..	..	1217	..	..	..	..	..	..	..	..	..	..	..	..	..	..	..	..	..	..	..	1232	..	..
57	..	..	..	1159	..	..	..	1151	..	..	..	..	..	..	..	..	..	..	..	..	..	..	..	..	..	..	..
58	..	..	..	12 1	..	..	..	1152	..	..	..	..	..	..	..	..	..	..	..	..	..	..	..	..	..	..	..
59	..	..	..	12 4	..	..	..	1156	..	..	..	1157	..	..	..	..	..	..	..	..	..	..	..	..	..	..	..
60	..	..	..	12 7	..	..	..	..	..	..	..	..	..	..	..	..	..	..	..	..	..	..	..	..	..	..	..
61	..	..	..	..	..	..	..	1159	..	..	..	1159	..	..	..	..	..	..	..	..	..	..	..	..	..	..	..
62	..	..	..	..	..	..	..	12 2	..	..	..	12 2	..	..	..	..	..	..	..	..	..	..	..	..	..	..	..
63	..	..	..	..	..	..	..	12 5	..	..	..	12 5	..	..	..	..	..	..	..	..	..	..	..	..	..	..	..
64	..	..	..	..	..	..	..	12 7	..	..	..	12 7	..	..	..	..	..	..	..	..	..	..	..	..	..	..	..
65	..	..	..	..	..	..	..	1211	..	..	..	1211	..	..	..	..	..	..	..	..	..	..	..	..	..	..	..
66	..	..	..	..	..	..	..	1157	..	..	..	1158	..	..	..	..	..	..	..	..	..	..	..	..	..	..	..
67	..	..	..	..	..	..	..	1159	..	..	..	12 0	..	..	..	..	..	..	..	..	..	..	..	..	..	..	..
68	..	..	..	..	..	..	..	12 1	..	..	..	12 3	..	..	..	..	..	..	..	..	..	..	..	..	..	..	..
69	..	..	..	..	..	..	..	12 4	..	..	..	12 5	..	..	..	..	..	..	..	..	..	..	..	..	..	..	..
70	..	..	..	..	..	..	..	12 6	..	..	..	12 8	..	..	..	..	..	..	..	..	..	..	..	..	..	..	..
71	..	..	..	..	..	..	..	1211	..	..	..	1212	..	..	..	..	..	..	..	..	..	..	..	..	..	..	..
72	..	..	..	..	..	..	..	1214	..	..	..	1215	..	..	..	..	..	..	..	..	..	..	..	..	..	..	..
73	..	..	..	..	..	..	..	1217	..	..	..	1219	..	..	..	..	..	..	..	..	..	..	..	..	..	..	..
74	..	..	..	..	..	..	..	..	..	..	..	..	..	..	..	..	..	..	..	..	..	..	..	..	..	..	..
75	..	..	..	..	..	..	..	..	..	..	..	..	..	..	..	..	..	..	..	..	..	..	..	..	..	..	..
76	..	..	12 0	..	..	..	..	..	..	..	..	..	..	..	..	..	..	..	..	..	..	..	..	..	..	..	..
77	..	..	..	..	..	..	..	..	..	..	..	..	..	..	..	..	..	..	..	..	..	..	..	..	..	..	..
78	..	..	..	..	..	1246	1246	..	..	..	..	..	..	..	..	..	..	..	..	..	..	..	..	..	..	..	..

For Notes, see page 284a

LONDON, CRYSTAL PALACE, CROYDON, SUTTON, DORKING NORTH,

Down	No.	a.m	Week Days—continued													a.m						No.
			S X	S O		S O	S X	S O	S X	S O	S O	S O	S X	S X	S O		S O		S O	S O	S O	
Victoria .... dep	1	11 48	..	..	..	..	11 51	..	..	1153	..	..	..	..	..	11 51	1155	..	..	..	1158	1
Charing Cross* ... "	2	..	1144	③	..	③	③	③	③	③	③	③	③	③	③	③	③	..	③	③	③	2
Waterloo* .... "	3	..	1146		..													..				3
London Bridge..... "	4	..	1151	1145	..	1147	.	1148	1148	..	1150	1151	1153	1153	1155		..	..	1157	12 2	..	4
Battersea Park..........	5	..	③	..	..	..	..	..	..	1156	..	..	..	..	..	..	..	..	..	..	..	5
Clapham Junction.....	6	11 53		..	..	..	11 56	..	..	1159	..	..	..	..	..	11 56	12 0	..	..	..	12 4	6
Wandsworth Common **A**	7	..	..	..	..	..	..	..	..	12 2	..	..	..	..	..	11SX59	..	..	..	..	..	7
Balham & Upper Tooting	8	..	..	..	..	..	12 0	..	..	12 4	..	..	..	..	..	12 1	12 4	..	..	..	12 8	8
South Bermondsey......	9	..	..	..	..	..	..	..	1151	..	..	..	..	..	..	..	..	..	12 1	..	..	9
Queen's Road, Peckham	10	..	..	..	..	..	..	..	1154	..	1155	..	..	..	..	..	..	..	12 4	..	..	10
Peckham Rye...........	11	..	..	..	..	..	..	..	1156	..	1157	..	..	1159	..	..	..	..	12 6	..	..	11
East Dulwich...........	12	..	..	..	..	..	..	..		..	12 0	..	..	..	..	..	..	..		..	..	12
North Dulwich..........	13	..	..	..	..	..	..	..		..	12 2	..	..	..	..	..	..	..		..	..	13
Tulse Hill...............	14	..	..	1155	..	..	..	1158		..	12 5	..	..	12 3	..	..	..	..		..	..	14
Streatham	15	..	..	1159	..	..	..	12 2		..	..	..	..	12 7	..	..	..	..		..	..	15
New Cross Gate (for E.L.	16	..	..	..	..	1152	..	..		..	..	1156	1158	..	..	..	..	..		..	..	16
Brockley **B**.......[Line)	17	..	..	..	..	1154	..	..	To Victoria, arr. 12 13 p.m	..	..	1158	12 0	..	..	..	..	..		..	..	17
Honor Oak Park........	18	..	..	..	..	1157	..	..		..	..	12 1	12 3	..	..	..	..	..		..	..	18
Forest Hill, for Lordship	19	..	..	..	..	1159	..	..		..	..	12 3	12 5	..	..	..	..	..	To Victoria arr. 12 22 p.m	..	..	19
Sydenham ....[Lane	20	..	..	..	..	12 2	..	..		..	..	12 6	12 8	..	..	..	..	..		..	..	20
Penge West **C**.	21	..	..	..	..	..	..	..		..	..	12 8	..	..	..	..	..	..		..	..	21
Anerley..................	22	..	..	..	..	..	..	..		..	..	12 9	..	..	..	..	..	..		..	..	22
Streatham Common....	23	J 1 minute later on Saturdays	..	12 1	..	..	..	..		..	..	..	..	..	..	12 5	..	..		..	1212	23
Norbury	24		..	12 4	..	..	..	..		..	..	..	..	..	..	12 7	..	..		..	1214	24
Thornton Heath........	25		..	12 7	..	..	..	..	Stop	..	..	..	..	..	..	12 10	..	..		..	1217	25
Selhurst.................	26		..	1210	..	..	..	..	p.m	..	..	..	..	..	..	12 12	..	..		..	1219	26
Streatham Hill..........	27		..	..	..	..	..	..	S X	12 6	12 8	..	..	..	..	..	..	..		..	..	27
West Norwood..[N'wood)	28		..	..	..	..	..	..	③	12 9	..	..	..	..	..	..	..	..	Stop	..	..	28
Gipsy Hill (for Upper	29		..	..	..	..	..	..		1212	..	..	..	..	..	..	..	..	..	..	..	29
Crystal Palace D.......	30		..	..	..	12 5	..	..	1210	1214		..	1211	..	..	..	..	..	..	..	..	30
Birkbeck	31		..	..	..	..	..	..	1213	1218	To Victoria, via Wandsworth Common	..	..	..	..	..	..	..	..	..	..	31
Beckenham Jn. arr	32		..	..	..	..	..	..	1217	1222		..	..	..	..	..	..	..	..	..	..	32
Norwood Junction F..	33		12 3	1213	..	..	..	..	..	..		1212	..	..	12 7	..	..	..	..	1215	..	33
East Croydon... arr	34	12J 4	12 7	..	..	..	..	..	..	..			..	..	1211	12 16	..	..	..	..	..	34
East Croydon... dep	35	12 5	12 7	..	..	..	..	..	..	..		To London Bridge, via Streatham	..	..	1211	12 16	..	..	..	..	..	35
Mitcham Junction......	36	..	..	To London Bridge, via Forest Hill	..	..	12 6	12 7	..	..			..	1212	..	..	1213	..	p.m	..	..	36
Hackbridge..............	37	..	..		..	..	12 9	12 9	..	..			..	1214	..	..	1215	..	S O	..	..	37
Carshalton	38	..	..		..	..	12 11	1212	..	..			..	1217	..	..	1218	..		..	..	38
West Croydon 319 arr	39	..	..		..	..	..	..	..	..			..	..	..	..	..	S X	③	1219	1222	39
West Croydon 319 dep	40	..	..		..	..	..	..	..	..			..	..	..	..	..	③	1214	1219	1222	40
Waddon **G**............	41	..	..		..	..	..	..	..	..			..	..	..	..	..		1216	1221	1225	41
Wallington..............	42	..	..		..	..	..	..	..	..			..	..	..	..	..	1219	1220	1225	1228	42
Carshalton Beeches.....	43	..	..		..	..	..	..	..	..			..	..	..	..	..	1221	1222	1227	1231	43
Sutton 322...............	44	..	..		..	..	12 14	1215	..	..			..	1220	..	..	1221	1224	1225	1230	1234	44
Belmont	45	..	..		..	..	..	..	..	..	..	..	..	..	..	..	..	..	..	1233	1237	45
Banstead.................	46	..	..		..	..	..	..	..	..	..	..	..	..	..	..	..	..	..	1236	1240	46
Epsom Downs...... arr	47	..	..		..	..	..	..	..	..	..	..	..	..	..	..	..	..	..	1239	1243	47
Cheam....................	48	..	..	..	..	..	12 17	1218	..	..	..	..	..	1223	..	..	1224	..	..	..	..	48
Ewell East **H**.........	49	..	..	..	..	..	12 20	1221	..	..	..	..	..	1226	..	..	1227	..	..	..	..	49
Epsom....................	50	..	..	..	..	..	12 24	1225	..	..	..	..	..	1229	..	..	1230	..	..	..	..	50
Ashtead..................	51	..	..	..	..	..	..	1229	..	..	..	..	..	1233	..	..	..	..	..	..	..	51
Leatherhead..[Bridge **J**	52	..	..	..	..	..	..	1233	..	..	..	..	..	1237	..	..	..	..	..	..	..	52
Boxhill and Burford	53	..	..	..	..	..	..	1238	..	..	..	..	..	..	..	..	..	..	..	..	..	53
Dorking North K.. arr	54	..	..	..	..	..	..	1241	..	..	..	..	..	..	..	..	..	..	..	..	..	54
Bookham........... [394	55	..	..	..	.	..	..	..	..	..	..	..	..	1242	..	..	..	..	..	..	..	55
Effingham Junction arr	56	..	..	..	..	..	..	..	..	..	..	..	..	1245	..	.	..	..	..	..	..	56
South Croydon 234......	57	..	1210	..	..	..	..	..	..	..	..	..	..	..	..	12 18	..	..	..	..	..	57
Purley Oaks............	58	..	1212	..	..	..	..	..	..	..	..	..	..	..	..	12 21	..	..	..	..	..	58
Purley..................	59	12 11	1215	..	..	..	..	..	..	..	..	..	..	..	1216	12 23	..	..	..	..	..	59
Coulsdon North **L**.. arr	60	..	..	..	..	..	..	..	..	..	..	..	..	..	..	12 27	..	..	..	..	..	60
Purley .... dep	61	K Arr. 12 36 p.m on Sats. § Via Three Bridges	1219	..	..	..	..	..	..	..	..	..	..	..	1219	..	..	..	..	..	..	61
Kenley..................	62		1222	..	..	..	..	..	..	..	..	..	..	..	1222	..	..	..	..	..	..	62
Whyteleafe..............	63		1225	..	..	..	..	..	..	..	..	..	..	..	1225	..	..	..	..	..	..	63
Warlingham............	64		1227	..	..	..	..	..	..	..	..	..	..	..	1227	..	..	..	..	..	..	64
Caterham........... arr	65		1231	..	..	..	..	..	..	..	..	..	..	..	1231	..	..	..	..	..	..	65
Purley .... dep	66		1217	..		..	..	..	..	..	..	..	..	..	1218	..	..	..	..	..	..	66
Reedham.................	67		1219	..	d Departure time	..	..	..	..	..	..	..	..	..	1220	..	..	..	..	..	..	67
Smitham	68		1221	..		..	..	..	..	..	..	..	..	..	1223	..	..	..	..	..	..	68
Woodmansterne	69		1224	..		..	..	..	..	..	..	..	..	..	1225	..	..	..	..	..	..	69
Chipstead	70		1226	..		..	..	..	..	..	..	..	..	..	1228	..	..	..	..	..	..	70
Kingswood **M**..........	71		1231	..		..	..	..	..	..	..	..	..	..	1232	..	..	..	..	..	..	71
Tadworth **N**...........	72		1234	..		..	..	..	..	..	..	..	..	..	1235	..	..	..	..	..	..	72
Tattenham Corner. arr	73		1237	..		..	..	..	..	..	..	..	..	..	1239	..	..	..	..	..	..	73
Coulsdon South.........	74	12 14	..	..		..	..	..	..	..	..	..	..	..	..	..	..	..	..	..	..	74
Merstham	75	12 20	..	..		..	..	..	..	..	..	..	..	..	..	..	..	..	..	..	..	75
Redhill...158,246.... arr	76	12 24	..	..	12d31	..	..	..	..	..	..	..	..	..	..	..	..	..	..	..	..	76
Reigate 246....... "	77	12K30	..	..	12 38	..	..	..	..	..	..	..	..	..	..	..	..	..	..	..	..	77
Horsham 159,244,245.. "	78	1 § 5	..	..	..	..	..	1 7	..	..	..	..	..	..	..	..	..	..	..	..	..	78

CATERHAM, TATTENHAM CORNER, REDHILL, REIGATE, and HORSHAM

p.m. — **Week Days**—*continued* — p.m.

No.	SO non	SO non		SX		SO	SO	SO	SX	SO	SX		SO	SO	SO	SO	SX		SX			SO	SO	SX	SO	SO	SO	
1	12 0	12 0	12 3	..	..	..	..	..	..	..	12 8	..	..	..	..	..	..	..	1210	..	..	..	12 18	..	1211	1213	..	..
2	..	3	..	3	..	3	3	3	3	3	3	..	3	3	..	3	3	..	3	..	3	3	..	..	3	3	..	..
3	..		..		12 7							..			..			..		..			..	..			..	..
4	..	..	..	12 2	..	12 5	12 5	12 7	12 7	12 8	.	..	1210	1211	1215	1217	1219	..	..	..	1215	1218	..	1218	..	..	1220	..
5	..	12 3	..	..	3	..	..	..	..	..	..	..	..	..	..	..	..	..	1213	..	..	..	..	..	..	1216	..	..
6	..	12 6	..	..		..	..	..	..	..	1214	..	..	..	..	..	..	..	1216	..	..	..	..	..	1216	1219	..	..
7	..	12 9	..	..	Via Worcester Park	..	..	..	..	..	..	..	..	..	..	..	..	..	1220	..	..	..	..	..	..	1222	..	..
8	..	1211	..	..		..	..	..	..	..	1218	..	..	..	..	..	..	..	1222	..	..	..	..	..	1221	1224	..	..
9	..	..	..	..		..	..	..	..	..	..	..	..	..	..	1221	1222	..	..	..	1218	..	..	..	..	..	..	..
10	..	..	..	..		..	..	..	..	..	..	..	1215	..	..	1224	1225	..	..	..	1221	..	..	..	..	..	..	..
11	..	..	..	..		..	..	..	..	..	..	..	1217	..	..	1226	1227	..	..	..	1223	..	..	..	..	..	..	..
12	..	..	..	..		..	..	..	..	..	..	..	1220	..	..	To Victoria, arr. 12 41 p.m	To Victoria, arr 12 43 p.m	..	..	..	1226	..	..	..	..	..	..	..
13	..	..	..	..		..	..	..	..	..	..	..	1222	..	..			..	..	..	1228	..	..	..	..	..	..	..
14	..	..	..	..		..	1215	..	..	1218	..	..	1225	..	..			..	..	..	1231	..	..	..	..	..	..	..
15	..	..	..	..		..	1219	..	..	1222	..	..	..	..	..			..	..	..	..	..	..	..	..	..	..	..
16	..	..	..	12 7	..	1210	..	1212	1212	..	..	..	..	1216	..			..	..	..	..	..	..	..	..	..	..	..
17	..	..	..	..	..	..	..	1214	1214	..	..	..	..	1218	..			..	..	..	..	..	..	..	..	..	..	..
18	..	..	..	..	..	..	..	1217	1217	..	..	..	..	1221	..			..	..	..	..	..	..	..	..	..	..	..
19	..	..	..	1211	..	..	..	1219	1219	..	..	..	..	1223	..			..	..	..	..	..	..	..	..	..	..	..
20	..	..	..	1214	..	..	..	1222	1222	..	..	..	..	1226	..			..	..	..	..	..	..	..	..	..	..	..
21	..	..	..	1216	..	..	..	..	1224	..	..	..	..	1228	..			..	..	..	..	..	..	..	..	..	..	..
22	..	..	..	1217	..	..	..	..	1225	..	..	..	..	1229	..			..	..	..	..	..	..	..	..	..	..	..
23	..	..	..	..	..	..	1221	..	..	..	1222	..	..	..	..	..	..	..	..	..	..	..	..	..	1225	..	..	..
24	..	..	..	..	..	..	1224	..	..	..	1224	..	..	..	..	..	..	..	..	..	..	..	..	..	1227	..	..	..
25	..	..	..	..	..	..	1227	..	..	..	1227	..	..	..	..	..	..	..	..	..	..	..	..	..	1230	..	..	..
26	..	..	..	..	..	..	1230	..	..	..	1229	..	..	..	..	..	..	..	..	..	..	..	..	..	1232	..	..	..
27	..	1214	..	..	..	..	..	..	..	..	Arr. Sutton 12 44 p.m	..	1229	..	..	..	..	..	1224	..	..	..	..	..	..	1226	..	SX
28	..	1217	..	..	..	..	..	..	..	..		..	To Victoria, via Wandsworth Common	..	..	..	..	..	1227	..	1233	..	..	..	..	1229	..	3
29	..	1219	..	..	..	..	..	..	..	..		..		..	..	..	..	..	1230	..	1236	..	..	..	..	1232	..	
30	..	1222	..	..	..	..	..	1225	..	..		..		..	..	..	..	..	1232	..	1238	..	..	..	..	1234	..	1240
31	..	..	..	..	..	..	..	..	..	..		..		..	..	..	..	..	..	..	..	..	..	..	..	1238	..	1243
32	..	..	..	..	..	..	..	..	..	..		..		..	..	..	..	..	..	..	..	..	..	..	..	1242	..	1247
33	..	1227	..	1220	..	1218	1233	..	1229	..		..		1232	..	..	..	..	1237	..	..	..	..	1230	..	..	..	..
34	1215	..	1220	..	..	1222		..		..		..		..	1230	..	..	..	..	..	..	1233	12 33	1234	1236	..	1237	..
35	..	..	1221	..	..	1222		..		..		..		..	1230	..	..	..	..	..	..	1233	12 34	1236	1236	..	1238	..
36	..	..	..	..	..	..	To London Bridge, via Forest Hill	..	To London Bridge, via Streatham	1227		..		To London Bridge, via Streatham	..	..	..	..	..	..	..	..	..	..	..	..	..	..
37	..	..	..	..	..	..		..		1229		..			..	..	..	..	..	..	..	..	..	..	..	..	..	..
38	..	..	..	..	..	..		..		1232		..			..	..	..	..	..	..	..	..	..	..	..	..	..	..
39	..	1231	..	1224	..	..		..		..	1232	..			..	..	..	..	1241	..	..	..	..	..	..	..	..	..
40	..	..	..	1224	..	..		..		..	1232	..			..	..	..	..	..	..	..	..	..	..	..	..	..	..
41	..	..	..	1227	..	..		..		..	1235	..			..	..	..	..	..	..	..	..	..	..	..	..	..	..
42	..	..	..	1230	..	..		..		..	1238	..			..	..	..	..	..	..	..	..	..	..	..	..	..	..
43	..	..	..	1233	..	..		..		..	1241	..			..	..	..	..	..	..	..	..	..	..	..	..	..	..
44	..	..	..	1235	..	..		..		1235	1247	..			..	..	..	..	..	..	..	..	..	..	..	..	..	..
45	..	..	..	1238	..	..		..		..	1250	..	..		..	..	..	..	..	..	..	..	..	..	..	..	..	..
46	..	..	..	1241	..	..		..		..	1253	..	..		..	..	..	..	..	..	..	..	..	..	..	..	..	..
47	..	..	..	1245	..	..		..		..	1256	..	..		..	..	..	..	..	..	..	..	..	..	..	..	..	..
48	..	..	..	..	..	..	..	..	..	1238	..	..	..	..	..	..	..	..	..	..	..	..	..	..	..	..	..	..
49	..	..	..	..	..	..	..	..	..	1241	..	..	..	..	..	..	..	..	..	..	..	..	..	..	..	..	..	..
50	..	..	..	..	1235	..	..	..	..	1245	..	..	..	..	..	..	..	..	..	..	..	..	..	..	..	..	..	..
51	..	..	..	..	1239	..	..	..	..	1249	..	..	..	..	..	..	..	..	..	..	..	..	..	..	..	..	..	..
52	..	..	..	..	1243	..	..	..	..	1253	..	..	..	..	..	..	..	..	..	..	..	..	..	..	..	..	..	..
53	..	..	..	..	1248	..	..	..	..	..	..	..	..	..	..	..	..	..	..	..	..	..	..	..	..	..	..	..
54	..	..	..	..	1251	..	..	..	..	..	..	..	..	..	..	..	..	..	..	..	..	..	..	..	..	..	..	..
55	..	..	..	..	..	..	..	..	..	1257	..	..	..	..	..	..	..	..	..	..	..	..	..	..	..	..	..	..
56	..	..	..	..	..	..	..	..	..	1 1	..	..	..	..	..	..	..	..	..	..	..	..	..	..	..	..	..	..
57	..	..	1225	..	..	1224	..	..	..	..	..	..	..	..	..	..	..	..	..	..	..	..	..	..	1238	..	1242	..
58	..	..	..	..	..	1227	..	..	..	..	..	..	..	..	..	..	..	..	..	..	..	..	..	..	1241	..	..	..
59	..	..	..	..	..	1229	..	..	..	..	..	..	..	..	1236	..	..	..	..	..	..	1238	..	1241	1243	..	..	..
60	..	..	..	..	..	1233	..	..	..	..	..	..	..	..	..	..	..	..	..	..	..	..	..	..	1247	..	..	..
61	..	..	..	..	..	..	..	..	..	..	..	..	..	..	§ Via Three Bridges	..	..	..	..	..	..	1241	§ Via Three Bridges	§ Via Three Bridges	..	..	..	..
62	..	..	..	..	..	..	..	..	..	..	..	..	..	..		..	..	..	..	..	..	1244			..	..	..	..
63	..	..	..	..	..	..	..	..	..	..	..	..	..	..		..	..	..	..	..	..	1247			..	..	..	..
64	..	..	..	..	..	..	..	..	..	..	..	..	..	..		..	..	..	..	..	..	1249			..	..	..	..
65	..	..	..	..	..	..	..	..	..	..	..	..	..	..		..	..	..	..	..	..	1253			..	..	..	..
66	..	..	..	..	..	..	..	..	..	..	..	..	..	..		..	..	..	..	..	..	1240			..	..	..	..
67	..	..	..	..	..	..	..	..	..	..	..	..	..	..		..	..	..	..	..	..	1243			..	..	..	..
68	..	..	..	..	..	..	..	..	..	..	..	..	..	..		..	..	..	..	..	..	1245			..	..	..	..
69	..	..	..	..	..	..	..	..	..	..	..	..	..	..		..	..	..	..	..	..	1248			..	..	..	..
70	..	..	..	..	..	..	..	..	..	..	..	..	..	..		..	..	..	..	..	..	1250			..	..	..	..
71	..	..	..	..	..	..	..	..	..	..	..	..	..	..		..	..	..	..	..	..	1255			..	..	..	..
72	..	..	..	..	..	..	..	..	..	..	..	..	..	..		..	..	..	..	..	..	1258			..	..	..	..
73	..	..	..	..	..	..	..	..	..	..	..	..	..	..		..	..	..	..	..	..	1 1			..	..	..	..
74	..	..	..	..	..	..	..	..	..	..	..	..	..	..	1240	..	..	..	..	..	..	..	..	1245	..	..	..	..
75	..	..	..	..	..	..	..	..	..	..	..	..	..	..	1246	..	..	..	..	..	..	..	..	1251	..	..	..	..
76	..	..	..	..	..	..	..	..	..	..	..	..	..	..	1250	..	..	..	..	..	..	..	..	1255	..	..	..	..
77	..	..	..	..	..	..	..	..	..	..	..	..	..	..	1256	..	..	..	..	..	..	..	..	1 0	..	..	..	..
78	..	..	..	..	1 24	..	..	..	..	..	..	..	..	..	1§35	..	..	..	..	..	..	..	1§ 13	1§35	..	..	..	..

For Notes, see page 284a

LONDON, CRYSTAL PALACE, CROYDON, SUTTON, DORKING NORTH,

Down	No.	p.m.					Week Days—continued										p.m.						No.
				SO	SO		SO	SX	SO	SO	SX		SO	SO	SO	SO	SX	SO	SO	SX		SO	
Victoria .... dep	1	1220	..	..	..	..	..	..	1218	1220	1221	..	1224	1228	..	..	1228	..	..	..	..	..	1
Charing Cross* ... "	2	3	..	3	..	..	3	3	3	3	3	..	3	3	3	3	..	3	..	1224	..	3	2
Waterloo* .... "	3		..		1227	..						..					..		..	1226	..		3
London Bridge ..... "	4	..	..	1222	..	..	1224	1225	..	..	..	..	..	..	1225	1227	..	1228	1230	1231	..	1231	4
Battersea Park	5	..	..	..	3	..	..	..	..	1223	..	..	1227	..	..	..	..	..	..	3	..	..	5
Clapham Junction	6	1225	..	..		..	..	..	1224	1226	1227	..	1230	..	..	..	1234	..	..		..	..	6
Wandsworth Common A	7	..	..	..	..	..	..	..	..	1229	..	..	1233	..	..	..	..	..	..	..	..	..	7
Balham & Upper Tooting	8	1229	..	..	Via Worcester Park	..	..	..	1228	1231	1231	..	1235	..	..	..	..	..	..	..	..	..	8
South Bermondsey	9	..	..	..		..	..	..	..	..	..	..	..	..	..	..	..	..	..	..	..	..	9
Queen's Road, Peckham	10	..	..	..		..	..	..	..	..	..	..	..	..	..	..	..	..	..	..	..	..	10
Peckham Rye	11	..	..	..		..	..	1231	..	..	..	..	..	..	..	..	..	..	..	..	..	..	11
East Dulwich	12	..	..	..		..	..	..	..	..	..	..	..	..	..	..	..	..	..	..	..	..	12
North Dulwich	13	..	..	..		..	..	..	..	..	..	..	..	..	..	..	..	..	..	..	..	..	13
Tulse Hill	14	..	..	..		..	..	1235	..	..	..	..	..	..	1235	..	..	1238	..	..	..	..	14
Streatham	15	..	..	..		..	..	1239	..	..	..	..	..	..	1239	..	..	1242	..	..	..	..	15
New Cross Gate (for E.L.	16	..	..	..	..	..	1229	..	..	..	..	..	..	..	..	1232	..	..	..	..	..	1236	16
Brockley B .... [Line)	17	..	..	..	..	..	..	..	..	..	..	..	..	..	..	1234	..	..	..	..	..	1238	17
Honor Oak Park	18	..	..	..	..	..	..	..	..	..	..	..	..	..	..	1237	..	..	..	..	..	1241	18
Forest Hill, for Lordship	19	..	..	..	..	..	..	..	..	..	..	..	..	..	..	1239	..	..	..	..	..	1243	19
Sydenham .... [Lane	20	..	..	..	..	..	..	..	..	..	..	..	..	..	..	1242	..	..	..	..	..	1246	20
Penge West C	21	..	..	..	..	..	..	..	..	..	..	..	..	..	..	..	..	..	..	..	..	1248	21
Anerley	22	..	..	..	..	..	..	..	..	..	..	..	..	..	..	..	..	..	..	..	..	1249	22
Streatham Common	23	..	..	..	..	..	..	..	1232	..	1235	..	..	..	1241	..	..	..	..	..	..	..	23
Norbury	24	..	..	..	..	..	..	..	1234	..	1237	..	..	1240	1244	..	..	..	..	..	..	..	24
Thornton Heath	25	..	..	..	..	..	..	..	1237	..	1240	..	..	1243	1247	..	..	..	..	..	..	..	25
Selhurst	26	..	..	..	..	..	..	..	1239	..	1242	..	..	1245	1250	..	..	..	..	..	..	..	26
Streatham Hill	27	..	..	..	..	..	..	..	..	1234	..	..	1238	..	..	..	..	..	..	..	..	..	27
West Norwood .. [N'wood)	28	..	..	..	..	..	..	..	..	1237	..	..	..	..	..	..	..	..	..	..	..	..	28
Gipsy Hill (for Upper	29	..	..	..	..	..	..	..	..	1239	..	..	..	..	..	..	..	..	..	..	..	..	29
Crystal Palace D	30	..	..	..	..	..	..	..	..	1242	..	..	..	..	..	1245	..	..	..	..	..	..	30
Birkbeck	31	..	..	..	..	..	..	..	..	..	..	..	..	..	..	..	..	..	..	..	..	..	31
Beckenham Jn. arr	32	..	..	..	..	..	..	..	..	..	..	..	..	..	..	..	..	..	..	..	..	..	32
Norwood Junction F ..	33	..	..	1235	..	..	1238	..	..	1247	..	..	..	..	1253	..	..	..	..	1243	..	1252	33
East Croydon .... arr	34	..	..	..	..	..	1242	..	..	..	1246	..	..	..	..	..	1245	..	1245	1247	..	..	34
East Croydon .... dep	35	..	..	..	..	..	1242	..	..	..	1246	..	..	..	..	..	1246	..	1247	1247	..	..	35
Mitcham Junction	36	1235	..	..	..	..	..	1244	..	..	..	..	..	..	To London Bridge, via Forest Hill	..	..	1247	..	..	..	To London Bridge, via Streatham	36
Hackbridge	37	1238	SO	..	..	..	..	1246	..	..	..	..	..	..		..	..	1249	..	..	..		37
Carshalton	38	1240	3	..	..	..	..	1249	..	..	..	..	..	..		..	..	1252	..	..	..		38
West Croydon 319 arr	39	..		1239	..	..	..	..	1242	1251	..	SX	..	..		..	..	..	..	..	..		39
West Croydon 319 dep	40	..	1234	1239	..	..	..	..	1242	..	..	3	..	..		..	..	..	..	..	..		40
Waddon G	41	..	1236	1241	..	..	..	..	1245	..	..		..	..		..	..	..	..	..	..		41
Wallington	42	..	1240	1245	..	..	..	..	1248	..	..	1249	..	..		..	..	..	..	..	..		42
Carshalton Beeches	43	..	1242	1247	..	..	..	..	1251	..	..	1251	..	..		..	..	..	..	..	..		43
Sutton 322	44	1243	1246	1250	..	..	..	1252	1254	..	..	1254	..	..		..	..	1255	..	..	..		44
Belmont	45	..	..	1253	..	..	..	..	1257	..	..	..	..	..	..	..	..	..	..	..	..		45
Banstead	46	..	..	1256	..	..	..	..	1 0	..	..	..	..	..	..	..	..	..	..	..	..		46
Epsom Downs ...... arr	47	..	..	1259	..	..	..	..	1 3	..	..	..	..	..	..	..	..	..	..	..	..		47
Cheam	48	1246	..	..	..	..	..	1255	..	..	..	..	..	..	..	..	..	1258	..	..	..	..	48
Ewell East H	49	1249	..	..	..	SO	..	1258	..	..	..	..	..	..	..	..	..	1 1	..	..	..	..	49
Epsom	50	1253	..	..	1255	3	..	1 3	..	..	..	..	..	..	..	..	..	1 5	..	..	..	..	50
Ashtead	51	..	..	..	1259		..	1 7	..	..	..	..	..	..	..	..	..	1 9	..	..	..	..	51
Leatherhead .. [Bridge J	52	..	..	..	1 3	1 9	..	1 11	..	..	..	..	..	..	..	..	..	1 13	..	..	..	..	52
Boxhill and Burford	53	..	..	..	1 8	..	..	1 17	..	..	..	..	..	..	..	..	..	1 18	..	..	..	..	53
Dorking North K .. arr	54	..	..	..	1 11	..	..	1 20	..	..	..	..	..	..	..	..	..	1 21	..	..	..	..	54
Bookham .... [394	55	..	..	..	..	1 14	..	..	..	..	..	..	..	..	..	..	..	..	..	..	..	..	55
Effingham Junction arr	56	..	..	..	..	1 18	..	..	..	..	..	..	..	..	..	..	..	..	..	..	..	..	56
South Croydon 234	57	..	..	..	..	..	1244	..	..	..	1248	..	..	..	..	..	..	..	..	1250	..	..	57
Purley Oaks	58	..	..	..	..	..	1247	..	..	..	1251	..	..	..	..	..	..	..	..	1252	..	..	58
Purley	59	..	..	..	..	..	1249	..	..	..	1253	..	..	..	..	..	..	..	..	1255	..	..	59
Coulsdon North L .. arr	60	..	..	..	..	..	1253	..	..	..	1257	..	..	..	..	..	..	..	..	..	..	..	60
Purley .... dep	61	..	..	..	..	..	..	..	..	..	..	..	..	..	..	..	..	..	..	1259	..	..	61
Kenley	62	..	..	..	..	..	..	..	..	..	..	..	..	..	..	..	..	..	..	1 2	..	..	62
Whyteleafe	63	..	..	..	..	..	..	..	..	..	..	..	..	..	..	..	..	..	..	1 5	..	..	63
Warlingham	64	..	..	..	..	..	..	..	..	..	..	..	..	..	..	..	..	..	..	1 7	..	..	64
Caterham .... arr	65	..	..	..	..	..	..	..	..	..	..	..	..	..	..	..	..	..	..	1 11	..	..	65
Purley .... dep	66	..	..	..	..	..	..	..	..	..	..	..	..	..	..	..	..	..	..	1257	..	..	66
Reedham	67	..	..	..	..	..	..	..	..	..	..	..	..	..	..	..	..	..	§ Via Three Bridges	1259	..	..	67
Smitham	68	..	..	..	..	..	..	..	..	..	..	..	..	..	..	..	..	..		1 1	..	..	68
Woodmansterne	69	..	..	..	..	..	..	..	..	..	..	..	..	..	..	..	..	..		1 4	..	..	69
Chipstead	70	..	..	..	..	..	..	..	..	..	..	..	..	..	..	..	..	..		1 6	..	..	70
Kingswood M	71	..	..	..	..	..	..	..	..	..	..	..	..	..	..	..	..	..		1 11	..	..	71
Tadworth N	72	..	..	..	..	..	..	..	..	..	..	..	..	..	..	..	..	..		1 14	..	..	72
Tattenham Corner. arr	73	..	..	..	..	..	..	..	..	..	..	..	..	..	..	..	..	..		1 17	..	..	73
Coulsdon South	74	..	..	..	..	..	..	..	..	..	..	..	..	..	..	..	..	..	..	..	..	..	74
Merstham	75	..	..	..	..	..	..	..	..	..	..	..	..	..	..	..	..	..	..	..	..	..	75
Redhill 158, 246 .... arr	76	..	..	..	..	..	..	..	..	..	..	..	..	..	..	..	1 0	..	1 1	..	..	..	76
Reigate 246 ...... "	77	..	..	..	..	..	..	..	..	..	..	..	..	..	..	..	..	..	..	..	..	..	77
Horsham 159, 244, 245 "	78	..	..	..	..	..	..	1 46	..	..	..	..	..	..	..	..	..	1 46	1§35	..	..	..	78

CATERHAM, TATTENHAM CORNER, REDHILL, REIGATE, and HORSHAM

p.m — **Week Days**—*continued* — p.m

No.	SO	SO	SO	SO		SX	SO	SO		SO	SO	SX	SX	SO	SO	SX	SX		SO	SO	SO	SO		SX	SO			SX
1	..	1231	1233	1237	..	..	..	..	..	..	1238	1238	1240	1240	..	..	1245	..	1244	..	..	..	1248	1251	..	..	..	..
2					..				..						..		..	..				..	..			..	..	
3	(3)	(3)	(3)	(3)	1247	(3)	(3)	(3)	..	(3)	(3)	(3)	(3)	(3)	..	(3)	..	..	(3)	(3)	(3)	..	..	(3)	(3)	..	..	(3)
4	1235	..	..	..	..	1229	1235	1237	..	1242	..	..	..	..	1240	1240	..	..	..	1247	1245	1247	..	..	1248	..	..	1248
5	..	..	1236	..		..	..	..	..	..	..	..	1243	1243	..	..	..	..	1247	..	..	..	..	..	..	..	..	..
6	..	1236	1239	1242	(3)	..	..	..	..	..	1244	1244	1247	1246	..	..	..	..	1250	..	..	..	12‖53	1256	..	..	..	..
7	..	..	1242	..	Via Worcester Park	..	..	..	..	..	..	..	1250	1249	..	..	..	..	1253	..	..	..	..	..	..	..	..	..
8	..	1241	1244	1246		..	..	..	..	..	1248	1248	1252	1251	..	..	..	..	1255	..	..	..	..	1 0	..	..	..	..
9	..	..	..	..		..	1238	1241	..	..	..	..	..	..	..	1243	..	..	..	..	..	..	‖ Takes up only	..	..	..	..	1251
10	..	..	..	..		..	1241	1244	..	..	..	..	..	..	..	1246	..	..	..	..	..	..		..	..	..	..	1254
11	..	..	..	..		..	1243	1246	..	..	..	..	..	..	..	1248	..	..	..	..	..	..		..	..	..	..	1256
12	..	..	..	..		..	1246	To Victoria arr. 1 2 p.m	..	..	..	..	..	..	..	1251	..	..	..	..	..	..		..	..	..	..	..
13	..	..	..	..		..	1248		..	..	..	..	..	..	..	1253	..	..	..	..	..	..		..	..	..	..	To Victoria, arr. 1 13 p.m
14	..	..	..	..		..	1251		..	..	..	..	..	..	..	1256	..	..	..	..	1255	..		..	1258	..	..	
15	..	..	..	..		..	..		..	..	..	..	..	..	..	1259	..	..	..	..	1259	..		..	1 2	..	..	
16	..	..	..	..	..	1234	..		..	..	..	..	..	..	..	..	..	..	..	1252	..	..	..	..	..	..	..	
17	..	..	..	..	..	1236	..		..	..	..	..	..	..	..	..	..	..	..	1254	..	..	..	..	..	..	..	
18	..	..	..	..	..	1239	..		..	..	..	..	..	..	..	..	..	..	..	1257	..	..	..	..	..	..	..	
19	..	..	..	..	..	1241	..		..	..	..	..	..	..	..	..	..	..	..	1259	..	..	..	..	..	..	..	
20	..	..	..	..	..	1244	..		..	..	..	..	..	..	..	..	..	..	..	1 2	..	..	..	..	..	..	..	
21	..	..	..	..	..	1246	..	..	..	..	..	..	..	..	..	..	..	..	..	..	..	..	..	..	..	..	..	
22	..	..	..	..	..	1247	..	..	..	..	..	..	..	..	..	..	..	..	..	..	..	..	..	..	..	..	..	..
23	..	1245	..	..	..	..	..	..	..	..	1252	1252	..	..	..	1 1	..	..	..	..	1 1	..	..	..	..	..	..	..
24	..	1247	..	..	..	..	..	..	..	..	1254	1254	..	..	..	1 4	..	..	..	..	1 4	..	..	..	..	..	..	..
25	..	1250	..	..	..	..	..	..	..	..	1257	1257	..	..	..	1 7	..	..	..	..	1 7	..	..	..	..	..	..	..
26	..	1252	..	..	..	..	..	..	..	..	1259	1259	..	..	..	1 9	..	..	..	..	1 10	..	..	..	..	..	..	..
27	..	..	1246	..	..	..	..	..	..	..	..	..	1254	1254	..	..	..	..	1258	..	..	..	..	..	..	SX	..	..
28	..	..	1249	..	..	..	1253	..	..	..	..	Arr Sutton 1 14 p.m	1257	1257	..	..	..	..	To London Bridge, via Tulse Hill	..	..	..	..	..	..		..	..
29	..	..	1252	..	..	..	1256	..	..	..	..		1 0	1259	..	..	..	..		..	..	..	..	..	..	(3)	..	..
30	..	..	1254	..	..	..	1259	..	..	..	..		1 2	1 2	..	..	..	..		1 5	..	..	..	..	..	1 10	..	..
31	..	..	1258	..	..	..		..	..	..	..		..	..	..	..	..	..		..	..	..	..	..	..	1 13	..	..
32	..	..	1 2	..	..	..	Stop	..	..	..	..		..	..	..	..	..	..		..	..	..	..	..	..	1 17	..	..
33	..	..	..	..	..	1250	..	..	..	1255	..		1 7	1 7	..	1 12	..	..		..	1 13	..	..	..	..		..	..
34	1250	1256	..	..	..	..	..	..	..	..	..		..	..	..	To London Bridge, via Forest Hill	1 0	..		..	To London Bridge, via Forest Hill	1 3	1 4	..	..	Stop	..	..
35	1250	1256	..	..	..	..	..	..	..	..	..		..	..	..		..	..		..		..	1 5	..	..	..	..	..
36	..	..	..	1253	..	..	p.m	..	..	..	..	..	..	..	..		..	..		..		..	..	1 6	1 7	..	..	..
37	..	..	..	1255	..	..	SO	..	..	..	..	..	..	..	..		..	..		..		..	..	1 9	1 9	..	..	..
38	..	..	..	1258	..	..	(3)	..	..	..	..	..	..	..	..		..	..		..		..	..	1 11	1 12	..	..	..
39	..	..	..	..	..	1254		..	..	1259	1 2	1 2	1 12	1 11	..		..	..	..	..		..	..	..	..	..	..	..
40	..	..	..	..	..	1254	1254	..	..	1259	1 2	1 2	..	..	..		..	..	..	..		..	..	..	..	..	..	..
41	..	..	..	..	..	1257	1256	..	..	1 1	1 5	1 5	..	..	..		..	..	..	..		..	..	..	..	..	..	..
42	..	..	..	..	..	1 0	1 0	..	..	1 5	1 8	1 8	..	..	..		..	..	..	..		..	..	..	..	..	..	..
43	..	..	..	..	..	1 3	1 3	..	..	1 7	1 11	1 11	..	..	..		..	..	..	..		..	..	..	..	..	..	..
44	..	..	..	1 1	..	1 5	1 6	..	..	1 10	1 14	1 17	..	..	..		..	..	..	..		..	..	1 14	1 15	..	..	..
45	..	..	..	..	..	1 8	..	..	..	1 13	1 17	1 20	..	..	..	..	..	..	..	..	..	..	..	..	..	..	..	..
46	..	..	..	..	..	1 11	..	..	..	1 16	1 20	1 23	..	..	..	..	..	..	..	..	..	..	..	..	..	..	..	..
47	..	..	..	..	..	1 15	..	..	..	1 19	1 23	1 26	..	..	..	..	..	..	..	..	..	..	..	..	..	..	..	..
48	..	..	..	1 4	..	..	..	..	..	..	..	..	..	..	..	..	..	..	..	..	..	..	..	1 17	1 18	..	..	..
49	..	..	..	1 7	..	..	..	..	..	..	..	..	..	..	..	..	..	..	..	..	..	..	..	1 20	1 21	..	..	..
50	..	..	..	1 10	1 15	..	..	..	..	..	..	..	..	..	..	..	..	..	..	..	..	..	..	1 24	1 25	..	..	..
51	..	..	..	..	1 19	..	..	..	..	..	..	..	..	..	..	..	..	..	..	..	..	..	..	..	1 29	..	..	..
52	..	..	..	..	1 23	..	..	..	..	..	..	..	..	..	..	..	..	..	..	..	..	..	..	..	1 33	..	..	..
53	..	..	..	..	..	..	..	..	..	..	..	..	..	..	..	..	..	..	..	..	..	..	..	..	1 38	..	..	..
54	..	..	..	..	..	..	..	..	..	..	..	..	..	..	..	..	..	..	..	..	..	..	..	..	1 41	..	..	..
55	..	..	..	..	1 28	..	..	..	..	..	..	..	..	..	..	..	..	..	..	..	..	..	..	..	..	..	..	..
56	..	..	..	..	1 31	..	..	..	..	..	..	..	..	..	..	..	..	..	..	..	..	..	..	..	..	..	..	..
57	..	1258	..	..	..	..	..	..	..	..	..	..	..	..	..	..	..	..	..	..	..	..	..	..	..	..	..	..
58	..	1 1	..	..	..	..	..	..	..	..	..	..	..	..	..	..	..	..	..	..	..	..	..	..	..	..	..	..
59	1256	1 3	..	..	..	..	..	..	..	..	..	..	..	..	..	..	..	..	..	..	..	..	1 11	..	..	..	..	..
60	..	1 7	..	..	..	..	..	..	..	..	..	..	..	..	..	..	..	..	..	..	..	..	..	..	..	..	..	..
61	1259	..	..	..	..	..	..	..	..	..	..	..	..	..	..	..	..	..	..	..	..	..	..	..	..	..	..	..
62	1 2	..	..	..	..	..	..	..	..	..	..	..	..	..	..	..	..	..	..	..	..	..	..	..	..	..	..	..
63	1 5	..	..	..	..	..	..	..	..	..	..	..	..	..	..	..	..	..	..	..	..	..	..	..	..	..	..	..
64	1 7	..	..	..	..	..	..	..	..	..	..	..	..	..	..	..	..	..	..	..	..	..	..	..	..	..	..	..
65	1 11	..	..	..	..	..	..	..	..	..	..	..	..	..	..	..	..	..	..	..	..	..	..	..	..	p.m	..	..
66	1258	..	..	..	..	..	..	..	..	..	..	..	..	..	..	..	..	..	..	..	..	..	§ Via Three Bridges	..	..	*d* Departure time.	..	..
67	1 0	..	..	..	..	..	..	..	..	..	..	..	..	..	..	..	..	..	..	..	..	..		..	..		..	..
68	1 3	..	..	..	..	..	..	..	..	..	..	..	..	..	..	..	..	..	..	..	..	..		..	..		..	..
69	1 5	..	..	..	..	..	..	..	..	..	..	..	..	..	..	..	..	..	..	..	..	..		..	..		..	..
70	1 8	..	..	..	..	..	..	..	..	..	..	..	..	..	..	..	..	..	..	..	..	..		..	..		..	..
71	1 12	..	..	..	..	..	..	..	..	..	..	..	..	..	..	..	..	..	..	..	..	..		..	..		..	..
72	1 15	..	..	..	..	..	..	..	..	..	..	..	..	..	..	..	..	..	..	..	..	..		..	..		..	..
73	1 19	..	..	..	..	..	..	..	..	..	..	..	..	..	..	..	..	..	..	..	..	..		..	..		..	..
74	..	..	..	..	..	..	..	..	..	..	..	..	..	..	1 4	..	..	..	..	..	..	..	1 14	..	..	..	..	..
75	..	..	..	..	..	..	..	..	..	..	..	..	..	..	1 12	..	..	..	..	..	..	..	1 20	..	..	SX	..	..
76	..	..	..	..	..	..	..	..	..	..	..	..	..	..	1 17	..	..	..	..	..	..	..	1 24	..	..	1*d*30	..	..
77	..	..	..	..	..	..	..	..	..	..	..	..	..	..	1 23	..	..	..	..	..	..	..	1 30	..	..	1 34	..	..
78	..	..	..	..	..	..	..	..	..	..	..	..	..	..	..	..	..	..	..	..	..	..	2§ 5	..	2 7	..	..	..

LONDON, CRYSTAL PALACE, CROYDON, SUTTON, DORKING NORTH,

For Notes, see page 284a

p.m — Week Days—continued — p.m

Down	No.	SX		SO	SO		SX	SX	SO		SO		SO	SO			SO	SO		SX	SO	SO	No.
Victoria.........dep	1	..		1253	..	..	..	..	..	..	..	1251	..	1255	..	..	..	1258	..	..	..	1 0	1
Charing Cross*... "	2	1244	..	3	3	..	3	3	3	..	3	3	3	3	..	..	3	3	..	3	3	3	2
Waterloo*........ "	3	1246	..			..				..					1 7	..			..				3
London Bridge..... "	4	1251	..	..	1251	..	1253	1253	1255	..	1255	..	1257	..	..	..	1 2	..	..	1 2	1 4	..	4
Battersea Park.........	5	3	..	1256	..	..	..	..	..	..	..	..	..	..	3	..	..	..	..	..	..	1 3	5
Clapham Junction.....	6		..	1259	..	..	..	..	..	..	..	1256	..	1 0		..	..	1 4	..	..	..	1 6	6
Wandsworth Common A	7	..	..	1 2	..	..	..	..	..	..	..	12SX59		..	Via Worcester Park	..	..	..	..	..	..	1 9	7
Balham & Upper Tooting	8	..	..	1 4	..	..	..	..	..	..	..	1 1	..	1 4		..	..	1 8	..	..	..	1 11	8
South Bermondsey......	9	..	..	..	..	..	..	..	..	..	1258	..	1 1	..		..	..	..	..	..	..	..	9
Queen's Road, Peckham	10	..	..	..	..	..	..	..	..	..	1 1	..	1 4	..		..	..	..	..	..	..	..	10
Peckham Rye...........	11	..	..	..	..	..	1259	..	..	..	1 3	..	1 6	..		..	..	..	..	..	..	..	11
East Dulwich..........	12	..	..	..	..	..	..	..	..	..	1 6	..	To Victoria arr. 1 23 p.m	..		..	..	..	..	..	..	..	12
North Dulwich.........	13	..	..	..	..	..	..	..	..	..	1 8	..		..		..	..	..	..	..	..	..	13
Tulse Hill..............	14	..	..	..	..	..	1 3	..	..	..	1 11	..		..		..	..	..	..	..	..	..	14
Streatham	15	..	..	..	..	..	1 7	..	..	..	..	..		..		..	..	..	..	..	..	..	15
New Cross Gate (for E.L.	16	..	..	..	1256	..	..	1258	..	..	..	..		..		..	..	..	..	1 7	1 9	..	16
Brockley B.......[Line)	17	..	..	..	1258	..	..	1 0	..	..	..	..		..		..	..	..	..	..	..	..	17
Honor Oak Park.........	18	..	..	..	1 1	..	..	1 3	..	..	..	..		..		..	..	..	..	..	..	..	18
Forest Hill, for Lordship	19	..	..	..	1 3	..	..	1 5	..	..	..	..		..		..	..	..	..	1 11	..	..	19
Sydenham ....[Lane	20	..	..	..	1 6	..	..	1 8	..	..	..	..		..	..	..	..	..	..	1 14	..	..	20
Penge West C...........	21	..	..	..	1 8	..	..	..	..	..	..	..		..	..	..	..	..	..	1 16	..	..	21
Anerley.................	22	..	..	..	1 9	..	..	..	..	..	..	..		..	..	..	..	..	..	1 17	..	..	22
Streatham Common....	23	..	..	..	..	..	..	..	..	..	..	1 5	..	..	..	..	..	1 12	..	..	..	..	23
Norbury.................	24	..	..	..	..	..	..	..	..	..	..	1 7	..	..	..	..	..	1 14	..	..	..	..	24
Thornton Heath........	25	..	..	..	..	..	..	..	..	..	..	1 10	..	..	..	..	..	1 17	..	..	..	..	25
Selhurst................	26	..	..	..	..	..	..	..	..	..	..	1 12	..	..	..	..	..	1 19	..	..	..	..	26
Streatham Hill..........	27	..	..	1 6	..	..	..	..	..	..	..	..	..	..	..	..	..	..	..	..	..	1 14	27
West Norwood..[N'wood)	28	..	..	1 9	..	..	..	..	..	..	1 13	..	..	..	..	..	..	..	..	..	..	1 17	28
Gipsy Hill (for Upper	29	..	..	1 12	..	..	..	..	..	..	1 16	..	..	..	..	..	..	..	..	..	..	1 19	29
Crystal Palace D.......	30	..	..	1 14	..	..	..	1 11	..	..	1 19	..	..	..	..	..	..	..	..	..	..	1 22	30
Birkbeck	31	..	..	1 18	..	..	..	..	..	..	..	..	..	..	..	..	..	..	..	..	..	..	31
Beckenham Jn. arr	32	..	..	1 22	..	..	..	..	..	..	..	..	..	..	..	..	..	..	..	..	..	..	32
Norwood Junction F..	33	1 3	..	..	1 12	..	..	..	..	..	..	..	..	..	..	..	1 15	..	..	1 20	1 18	1 28	33
East Croydon.... arr	34	1 7	..	..		..	..	..	1 10	..	..	1 16	..	..	..	..	..	..	..	..	1 22	..	34
East Croydon.... dep	35	1 8	..	..		..	..	..	1 10	..	..	1 16	..	..	..	..	..	..	..	..	1 22	..	35
Mitcham Junction......	36	..	..	..	To London Bridge, via Streatham	..	1 12	..	..	..	..	..	..	1 13	..	..	..	..	..	..	..	..	36
Hackbridge............	37	..	..	..		SO	1 14	..	..	..	..	..	..	1 15	..	..	..	..	..	..	..	..	37
Carshalton.............	38	..	..	..		3	1 17	..	..	..	..	..	..	1 18	..	..	..	..	..	..	..	..	38
West Croydon 319 arr	39	..	..	..			..	..	..	..	..	..	..	..	..	SX	1 19	1 22	..	1 24	..	1 32	39
West Croydon 319 dep	40	..	..	..		1 11	..	..	..	..	..	..	..	..	..	3	1 19	1 22	..	1 24	..	..	40
Waddon G.............	41	..	..	..		1 13	..	..	..	..	..	..	..	..	..		1 21	1 25	..	1 27	..	..	41
Wallington.............	42	..	..	..		1 19	..	..	..	..	..	..	..	..	..	1 19	1 25	1 28	..	1 30	..	..	42
Carshalton Beeches.....	43	..	..	..		1 21	..	..	..	..	..	..	..	..	..	1 21	1 27	1 31	..	1 33	..	..	43
Sutton 322.............	44	..	..	..		1 24	1 20	..	..	..	..	..	..	1 21	..	1 24	1 30	1 34	..	1 35	..	..	44
Belmont	45	..	..	..		..	..	..	..	..	..	..	..	..	..	..	1 33	1 37	..	1 38	..	..	45
Banstead...............	46	..	..	..	..	..	..	..	..	..	..	..	..	..	..	..	1 36	1 40	..	1 41	..	..	46
Epsom Downs...... arr	47	..	..	..	..	..	..	..	..	..	..	..	..	..	..	..	1 39	1 43	..	1 45	..	..	47
Cheam..................	48	..	..	..	..	..	1 23	..	..	..	..	..	..	1 24	..	..	..	..	..	..	..	..	48
Ewell East H.........	49	..	..	..	..	..	1 26	..	..	..	..	..	..	1 27	..	..	..	..	..	..	..	..	49
Epsom..................	50	..	..	..	..	..	1 29	..	..	..	..	..	..	1 30	1 35	..	..	..	..	..	..	..	50
Ashtead................	51	..	..	..	..	..	1 33	..	..	..	..	..	..	..	1 39	..	..	..	..	..	..	..	51
Leatherhead...[Bridge J	52	..	..	..	..	..	1 37	..	..	..	..	..	..	..	1 43	..	..	..	..	..	..	..	52
Boxhill and Burford	53	..	..	..	..	..	..	..	..	..	..	..	..	..	1 48	..	..	..	..	..	..	..	53
Dorking North K.. arr	54	..	..	..	..	..	..	..	..	..	..	..	..	..	1 51	..	..	..	..	..	..	..	54
Bookham...........[394	55	..	..	..	..	..	1 42	..	..	..	..	..	..	..	..	..	..	..	..	..	..	..	55
Effingham Junction arr	56	..	..	..	..	..	1 44	..	..	..	..	..	..	..	..	..	..	..	..	..	..	..	56
South Croydon 234.......	57	1 10	..	..	..	..	..	..	..	..	..	1 18	..	..	..	..	..	..	..	..	1 24	..	57
Purley Oaks............	58	1 13	..	..	..	..	..	..	..	..	..	1 21	..	..	..	..	..	..	..	..	1 27	..	58
Purley..................	59	1 16	..	..	..	..	..	..	1 16	..	..	1J23	..	..	..	..	..	..	..	..	1 29	..	59
Coulsdon North L.. arr	60	..	..	..	..	..	..	..	..	..	..	1 27	..	..	..	..	..	..	..	..	1 33	..	60
Purley .... dep	61	1 19	..	..	..	..	..	..	1 19	..	..	J 1 minute later on Saturdays	..	..	..	..	..	..	..	..	..	..	61
Kenley..................	62	1 22	..	..	..	..	..	..	1 22	..	..		..	..	..	..	..	..	..	..	..	..	62
Whyteleafe.............	63	1 25	..	..	..	..	..	..	1 25	..	..		..	..	..	..	..	..	..	..	..	..	63
Warlingham............	64	1 27	..	..	..	..	..	..	1 27	..	..		..	..	..	..	..	..	..	..	..	..	64
Caterham.......... arr	65	1 31	..	..	..	..	..	..	1 31	..	..		..	..	..	..	..	..	..	..	..	..	65
Purley .... dep	66	1 17	..	..	..	..	..	..	1 18	..	..		..	..	..	..	..	..	..	..	..	..	66
Reedham................	67	1 19	..	..	..	..	..	..	1 20	..	..		..	..	..	..	..	..	..	..	..	..	67
Smitham................	68	1 21	..	..	..	..	..	..	1 23	..	..		..	..	..	..	..	..	..	..	..	..	68
Woodmansterne.........	69	1 24	..	..	..	..	..	..	1 25	..	..		..	..	..	..	..	..	..	..	..	..	69
Chipstead	70	1 26	..	..	..	..	..	..	1 28	..	..		..	..	..	..	..	..	..	..	..	..	70
Kingswood M............	71	1 31	..	..	..	..	..	..	1 32	..	..	..	..	..	..	..	..	..	..	..	..	..	71
Tadworth N.............	72	1 34	..	..	..	..	..	..	1 35	..	..	..	..	..	..	..	..	..	..	..	..	..	72
Tattenham Corner. arr	73	1 37	..	..	..	..	..	..	1 39	..	..	..	..	..	..	..	..	..	..	..	..	..	73
Coulsdon South..	74	..	..	..	..	..	..	..	..	..	..	..	..	..	..	..	..	..	..	..	..	..	74
Merstham...............	75	..	..	..	..	..	..	..	..	..	..	..	..	..	..	..	..	..	..	..	..	..	76
Redhill 158, 246..... arr	76	..	..	..	..	..	..	..	..	..	..	..	..	..	..	..	..	..	..	..	..	..	78
Reigate 246........ "	77	..	..	..	..	..	..	..	..	..	..	..	..	..	..	..	..	..	..	..	..	..	75
Horsham 159,244,245 "	78	..	..	..	..	..	..	..	..	..	..	..	..	..	2 24	..	..	..	..	..	..	..	77

CATERHAM, TATTENHAM CORNER, REDHILL, REIGATE, and HORSHAM

Week Days—continued (p.m)

No.	SO	SO	SO	SX	SO	SO		SO	SO		SX	SX		SO	SO	SX	SO	SO		SO	SX	SO	SX	SO		SO	SO	SX
1	..	..	..	..	..	..	..	..	1 18	..	1 8	1 10	..	..	..	..	1 11	1 13	..	..	..	1 20	1 20	..	..	..	..	..
2	..	3	3	3	3	..	..	3	..	..	3	3	..	3	3	..	3	3	3	3	3	3	3	..	..	3	3	3
3	..					..	..		..	..			..			..								1 27	..			
4	1 5	1 5	1 7	1 7	1 8	1 9	..	1 11	..	..	..	..	..	1 10	1 16	1 18	..	..	1 15	1 17	1 19	..	..	..	..	1 22	1 24	1 25
5	..	..	..	..	..	..	..	..	..	..	..	1 13	..	..	..	..	..	1 16	..	..	..	..	..	3	..	..	..	..
6	..	..	..	..	..	..	..	..	..	..	1 14	1 16	..	..	..	..	1 16	1 19	..	..	..	1 25	1 25		..	..	..	..
7	..	..	..	..	..	..	..	..	..	..	..	1 20	..	..	..	..	..	1 22	..	..	..	..	..	Via Worcester Park	..	..	..	..
8	..	..	..	..	..	..	..	..	..	..	1 18	1 22	..	..	..	..	1 21	1 24	..	..	..	1 29	1 29		..	..	..	..
9	..	..	..	..	..	..	..	..	..	..	..	..	..	..	..	..	..	..	1 18	1 21	1 22	..	..		..	..	..	..
10	..	..	..	..	..	..	..	..	..	..	..	..	..	1 15	..	..	..	..	1 21	1 24	1 25	..	..		..	..	..	..
11	..	..	..	..	..	..	..	..	..	..	..	..	..	1 17	..	..	..	..	1 23	1 26	1 27	..	..		..	..	..	1 31
12	..	..	..	..	..	..	..	..	..	..	..	..	..	1 20	..	..	..	..	1 26	..	..	..	..		..	..	..	..
13	..	..	..	..	..	..	..	..	..	..	..	..	..	1 22	..	..	..	..	1 28	..	..	..	..		..	..	..	..
14	..	1 15	..	..	1 18	..	..	..	..	..	..	..	..	1 25	..	..	..	..	1 31	To Victoria arr. 1 41 p.m	☞ To Victoria arr. 1 43 p.m	..	..		..	..	..	1 35
15	..	1 19	..	..	1 22	..	..	..	..	..	..	..	..	..	..	..	..	..	..			..	..		..	..	..	1 39
16	..	..	1 12	1 12	..	..	..	1 16	..	..	..	..	..	..	..	..	..	..	..			..	..	..	..	..	1 29	..
17	..	..	1 14	1 14	..	..	..	1 18	..	..	..	..	..	..	..	..	..	..	..			..	..	..	..	..	..	..
18	..	..	1 17	1 17	..	..	..	1 21	..	..	..	..	..	..	..	..	..	..	..			..	..	..	..	..	..	..
19	..	..	1 19	1 19	..	..	..	1 23	..	..	..	..	..	..	..	..	..	..	..			..	..	..	..	..	..	..
20	..	..	1 22	1 22	..	..	..	1 26	..	..	..	..	..	..	..	..	..	..	..			..	..	..	..	..	..	..
21	..	..	..	1 24	..	..	..	1 28	..	..	..	..	..	..	..	..	..	..	..			..	..	..	..	..	..	..
22	..	..	..	1 25	..	..	..	1 29	..	..	..	..	..	..	..	..	..	..	..			..	..	..	..	..	..	..
23	..	1 21	..	..	..	..	..	..	..	..	1 22	..	..	..	..	..	1 25	..	..	..		..	..	..	..	..	..	..
24	..	1 24	..	..	..	..	..	..	..	..	1 24	..	..	..	..	..	1 27	..	..	..	Stop	..	..	..	..	..	..	..
25	..	1 27	..	..	..	..	..	..	..	..	1 27	..	..	..	..	..	1 30	..	..	..	..	..	..	..	..	..	..	..
26	..	1 30	..	..	..	..	..	..	..	..	1 29	..	..	..	..	..	1 32	..	..	..	p.m	..	..	..	..	..	..	..
27	‖ Takes up only	..	..	..	..	..	..	..	..	..	Arr. Sutton 1 44 p.m	1 24	..	1 29	..	..	..	1 26	..	..	SX	..	..	..	..	..	..	..
28		..	..	..	..	..	..	..	..	..		1 27	..	..	..	..	..	1 29	1 33	..	3	..	..	..	..	..	..	..
29		..	..	..	..	..	..	..	..	..		1 30	..	..	..	..	..	1 32	1 36	..		..	..	..	..	..	..	..
30		..	1 25	..	..	..	..	..	..	..		1 32	..	..	..	..	..	1 34	1 39	..	1 40	..	..	..	..	..	..	..
31		..	..	..	..	..	..	..	..	..		..	..	..	..	..	..	1 38	..	..	1 43	..	..	..	..	..	..	..
32		..	..	..	..	..	..	..	..	..		..	..	..	..	..	..	1 42	..	..	1 47	..	..	..	..	..	..	..
33		1 33	..	1 29	..	..	..	1 32	..	..		1 37	..	..	..	1 30	..	..	..	..	..	..	..	..	..	1 35	1 38	..
34		..	..	..	..	1 24	..	..	..	..		..	..	..	1 32	1 34	1 36	..	..	..	..	..	..	..	..	..	1 42	..
35	1‖20	To London Bridge, via Forest Hill	..	To London Bridge, via Streatham	..	1 24	..	To London Bridge, via Streatham	..	..	..	..	..	..	1 32	1 35	1 36	..	..	..	..	..	..	..	..	..	1 42	..
36	..		..		1 27	..	..		..	..	..	..	..	..	..	..	..	..	..	..	..	1 35	1 35	..	..	..	..	1 44
37	..		..		1 29	..	..		..	..	..	..	..	..	..	..	..	..	..	..	..	1 38	1 38	..	SO	..	..	1 46
38	..		..		1 32	..	..		..	..	..	..	..	..	..	..	..	..	..	..	..	1 40	1 40	..	3	..	..	1 49
39	..		..		..	..	..		..	..	1 32	1 41	..	..	..	..	..	..	..	..	..	..	..	..		1 39	..	..
40	..		..		..	..	..		..	..	1 32	..	..	..	..	..	..	..	..	..	..	..	..	..	1 34	1 39	..	..
41	..		..		..	..	..		..	..	1 35	..	..	..	..	..	..	..	..	..	..	..	..	..	1 36	1 41	..	..
42	..		..		..	..	..		..	..	1 38	..	..	..	..	..	..	..	..	..	..	..	..	..	1 40	1 45	..	..
43	..		..		..	..	..		..	..	1 41	..	..	..	..	..	..	..	..	..	..	..	..	..	1 43	1 47	..	..
44	..		..		1 35	..	..		1 39	..	1 47	..	..	..	..	..	..	..	..	..	..	1 43	1 44	..	1 46	1 50	..	1 52
45	..	..	..	..	..	..	..	..	..	..	1 50	..	..	..	..	..	..	..	..	..	..	..	..	..	..	1 53	..	..
46	..	..	..	..	..	..	..	..	..	..	1 53	..	..	..	..	..	..	..	..	..	..	..	..	..	..	1 56	..	..
47	..	..	..	..	..	..	..	..	..	..	1 56	..	..	..	..	..	..	..	..	..	..	..	..	..	..	1 59	..	..
48	..	..	..	..	1 43	..	..	..	..	..	..	..	..	..	..	..	..	..	..	..	..	1 46	1 47	..	..	..	..	1 55
49	..	..	..	..	1 46	..	..	..	..	..	..	..	..	..	..	..	..	..	..	..	..	1 49	1 50	..	..	..	..	1 58
50	..	..	..	..	1 49	..	..	..	..	..	..	..	..	..	..	..	..	..	..	..	..	1 53	1 53	1 55	..	..	..	2 3
51	..	..	..	..	1 53	..	..	..	..	..	..	..	..	..	..	..	..	..	..	..	..	..	..	1 59	..	..	..	2 7
52	..	..	..	..	1 57	..	..	..	..	..	..	..	..	..	..	..	..	..	..	..	..	..	..	2 3	..	..	..	2 11
53	..	..	..	..	..	..	..	..	..	..	..	..	..	..	..	..	..	..	..	..	..	..	..	2 8	..	..	..	2 17
54	..	..	..	..	..	..	..	..	1 55	..	..	..	..	..	..	..	..	..	..	..	..	..	..	2 11	..	..	..	2 20
55	..	..	..	..	2 1	..	..	..	..	..	..	..	..	..	..	..	..	..	..	..	..	..	..	..	..	..	..	..
56	..	..	..	..	2 4	..	..	..	..	..	..	..	..	..	..	..	..	..	..	..	..	..	..	..	..	..	..	..
57	..	..	..	..	Arr. Cheam 1 38 p.m	..	..	..	..	..	..	..	..	..	..	..	1 38	..	..	..	..	..	..	..	..	..	1 44	..
58	..	..	..	..		..	..	..	..	..	..	..	..	..	..	..	1 41	..	..	..	..	..	..	..	..	..	1 47	..
59	..	..	..	..		..	..	..	..	..	..	..	..	..	1 37	1 40	1 43	..	..	..	..	..	..	..	..	..	1 49	..
60	..	..	..	..		..	..	..	..	..	..	..	..	..	..	..	1 47	..	..	..	..	..	..	..	..	..	1 53	..
61	..	..	..	..		..	..	..	..	..	..	..	..	..	1 39	..	..	..	..	..	..	..	..	..	..	..	..	..
62	..	..	..	..		..	..	..	..	..	..	..	..	..	1 42	..	..	..	..	..	..	..	..	..	..	..	..	..
63	..	..	..	..		..	..	..	..	..	..	..	..	..	1 45	..	..	..	..	..	..	..	..	..	..	..	..	..
64	..	..	..	..		..	..	..	..	..	..	..	..	..	1 47	..	..	..	..	..	..	..	..	..	..	..	..	..
65	..	..	..	..	..	..	..	..	..	..	..	..	..	..	1 51	..	..	..	..	..	..	..	..	..	..	..	..	..
66	..	..	..	..	..	§ Via Three Bridges	..	..	..	..	..	..	..	..	1 38	§ Via Three Bridges	..	..	..	..	..	..	..	..	..	..	..	..
67	..	..	..	..	..		..	..	..	..	..	..	..	..	1 40		..	..	..	..	..	..	..	..	..	..	..	..
68	§ Via Three Bridges	..	..	..	..		..	..	..	..	..	..	..	..	1 43		..	..	..	..	..	..	..	..	..	..	..	..
69		..	..	..	..		..	..	..	..	..	..	..	..	1 45		..	..	..	..	..	..	..	..	..	..	..	..
70		..	..	..	..		..	..	..	..	..	..	..	..	1 48		..	..	..	..	..	..	..	..	..	..	..	..
71		..	..	..	..		..	..	..	..	..	..	..	..	1 52		..	..	..	..	..	..	..	..	..	..	..	..
72		..	..	..	..		..	..	..	..	..	..	..	..	1 55		..	..	..	..	..	..	..	..	..	..	..	..
73		..	..	..	..		..	..	..	..	..	..	..	..	1 59		..	..	..	..	..	..	..	..	..	..	..	..
74		..	..	..	..	1 31	..	..	..	..	..	..	..	..	..	1 44	..	..	..	..	..	..	..	..	..	..	..	..
75		..	..	..	..	1 37	..	..	..	..	..	..	..	..	..	1 50	..	..	..	..	..	..	..	..	..	..	..	..
76		..	..	..	..	1 41	..	..	..	..	..	..	..	..	..	1 54	..	..	..	..	..	..	..	..	..	..	..	..
77		..	..	..	..	1 47	..	..	..	..	..	..	..	..	..	2 0	..	..	..	..	..	..	..	..	..	..	..	..
78	2§ 5	..	..	..	..	2§32	..	..	2 13	..	..	..	..	..	..	2§35	..	..	..	..	..	..	..	..	..	..	..	2 46

LONDON, CRYSTAL PALACE, CROYDON, SUTTON, DORKING NORTH,

For Notes, see page 284a

Down	No.	p.m.							Week Days—continued									p.m.					No.
		SO		SO	SO	SX		SO	SO		SO	SO	SX	SO	SO	SO	SO	SO	SO		SX		
Victoria .... dep	1	1 18	..	1 20	..	1 21	..	1 25	..	1 28	..	..	..	1 32	..	..	..	1 31	1 37	..	..	..	1
Charing Cross* ... "	2	3	..	3	3	3	..	..	3	..	3	3	1 24	3	3	..	3	3	3	..	3	..	2
Waterloo* .... "	3		..				..	..		..			1 26			..				1 47		..	3
London Bridge ..... "	4	..	..	..	1 27	..	..	..	1 25	..	1 28	1 30	1 31	..	1 31	1 32	1 36	..	..	..	1 29	..	4
Battersea Park	5	..	..	1 23	..	..	..	..	..	..	..	..	3	1 36	..	..	..	..	..	3	..	..	5
Clapham Junction	6	1 24	..	1 26	..	1 27	..	..	..	§1 34	..	..		1 39	..	..	..	1 36	1 42		..	..	6
Wandsworth Common A	7	..	..	1 29	..	..	..	..	..	..	..	..	..	1 42	..	..	..	..	..	..	..	..	7
Balham & Upper Tooting	8	1 28	..	1 31	..	1 31	..	..	..	..	..	..	..	1 44	..	..	..	1 41	1 46	Via Worcester Park	..	..	8
South Bermondsey	9	..	..	..	..	..	..	..	..	§ On Mondays to Fridays stops unconditionally. On Saturdays calls to take up only.	..	1 33	..	..	..	..	..	..	..		..	..	9
Queen's Road, Peckham	10	..	..	..	..	..	..	..	..		..	1 36	..	..	..	..	..	..	..		..	..	10
Peckham Rye	11	..	..	..	..	..	..	..	..		..	1 38	..	..	..	..	..	..	..		..	..	11
East Dulwich	12	..	..	..	..	..	..	..	..		..	1 41	..	..	..	..	..	..	..		..	..	12
North Dulwich	13	..	..	..	..	..	..	..	..		..	1 43	..	..	..	..	..	..	..		..	..	13
Tulse Hill	14	..	..	..	..	..	..	..	1 35		1 38	1 46	..	..	..	..	..	..	..		..	..	14
Streatham	15	..	..	..	..	..	..	..	1 39		1 42	..	..	..	..	..	..	..	..		..	..	15
New Cross Gate (for E.L.	16	..	..	..	1 32	..	..	..	..		..	..	..	..	1 36	..	..	..	..	..	1 34	..	16
Brockley B .... [Line)	17	..	..	..	1 34	..	..	..	..		..	..	..	..	1 38	..	..	..	..	..	1 36	..	17
Honor Oak Park	18	..	..	..	1 37	..	..	..	..		..	..	..	..	1 41	..	..	..	..	..	1 39	..	18
Forest Hill, for Lordship	19	..	..	..	1 39	..	..	..	..		..	..	..	..	1 43	..	..	..	..	..	1 41	..	19
Sydenham .... [Lane	20	..	..	..	1 42	..	..	..	..		..	..	..	..	1 46	..	..	..	..	..	1 44	..	20
Penge West C	21	..	..	..	..	..	..	..	..		..	..	..	..	1 48	..	..	..	..	..	1 46	..	21
Anerley	22	..	..	..	..	..	..	..	..		..	..	..	..	1 49	..	..	..	..	..	1 47	..	22
Streatham Common	23	1 32	..	..	..	1 35	..	..	1 41		..	..	..	..	..	..	..	1 45	..	..	..	..	23
Norbury	24	1 34	..	..	..	1 37	..	..	1 44		..	..	..	..	..	..	..	1 47	..	..	..	..	24
Thornton Heath	25	1 37	..	..	..	1 40	..	..	1 47		..	..	..	..	..	..	..	1 50	..	..	..	..	25
Selhurst	26	1 39	..	..	..	1 42	..	..	1 50		..	..	..	..	..	..	..	1 52	..	..	..	..	26
Streatham Hill	27		..	1 34	..	..	..	..	..		..	..	..	1 48	..	..	..	..	..	..	..	..	27
West Norwood. [N'wood)	28	Arr. Sutton 1 54 p.m.	..	1 37	..	..	..	..	..		..	1 48	..	1 51	..	..	..	..	..	..	..	..	28
Gipsy Hill (for Upper	29		..	1 39	..	..	..	..	..		..	1 50	..	1 54	..	..	..	..	..	..	..	..	29
Crystal Palace D	30		..	1 42	1 45	..	..	..	..		..	1 53	..	1 56	..	..	..	..	..	..	..	..	30
Birkbeck	31		..	..	..	..	..	..	..		..	..	..	1 59	..	..	..	..	..	..	..	..	31
Beckenham Jn. arr	32		..	..	..	..	..	..	..		..	..	..	2 8	..	..	..	..	..	..	..	..	32
Norwood Junction F ..	33		..	1 47	..	..	..	..	1 53		..	..	1 43	..	1 52	..	..	..	..	..	1 50	..	33
East Croydon .... arr	34		..	..	..	1 46	..	1 42		1 45	..	..	1 47	..	..	1 47	1 51	1 56	..	..	..	..	34
East Croydon .... dep	35		..	..	..	1 46	..	..	To London Bridge via Forest Hill	1 46	..	..	1 47	..	..	1 48	1 52	1 56	..	..	..	..	35
Mitcham Junction	36	..	..	..	..	..	..	..		..	1 47	..	..	..		..	..	..	1 53	..	..	..	36
Hackbridge	37	..	..	..	..	..	..	..		..	1 49	..	..	..		..	..	..	1 55	..	..	SO	37
Carshalton	38	..	..	..	..	..	..	..		..	1 52	..	..	..	To London Bridge, via Streatham	..	..	..	1 58	..	..	3	38
West Croydon 319 arr	39	1 42	SX	1 51	..	..	..	..		..	..	..	..	..		..	..	..	..	..	1 54		39
West Croydon 319 dep	40	1 42	3	..	..	..	..	..		..	..	..	..	..		..	..	..	..	..	1 54	1 54	40
Waddon G	41	1 45		..	..	..	..	..		..	..	..	..	..		..	..	..	..	..	1 57	1 56	41
Wallington	42	1 48	1 49	..	..	..	..	..		..	..	..	..	..		..	..	..	..	..	2 0	2 0	42
Carshalton Beeches	43	1 51	1 51	..	..	..	..	..		..	..	..	..	..		..	..	..	..	..	2 3	2 2	43
Sutton 322	44	1 57	1 54	..	..	..	..	..		..	1 55	..	..	..		..	..	..	2 1	..	2 5	2 5	44
Belmont	45	2 0	..	..	..	..	..	..	..	..	..	..	..	..		..	..	..	..	..	2 8	..	45
Banstead	46	2 3	..	..	..	..	..	..	..	..	..	..	..	..		..	..	..	..	..	2 11	..	46
Epsom Downs ...... arr	47	2 6	..	..	..	..	..	..	..	..	..	..	..	..		..	..	..	..	..	2 15	..	47
Cheam	48	..	..	..	..	..	..	..	..	..	1 58	..	..	..	..	..	..	..	2 4	..	..	..	48
Ewell East H	49	..	..	..	..	..	..	..	..	..	2 1	..	..	..	..	..	..	..	2 7	..	..	..	49
Epsom	50	..	..	..	..	..	..	..	..	..	2 5	..	..	..	..	..	..	..	2 10	2 15	..	..	50
Ashtead	51	..	..	..	..	..	..	..	..	..	2 9	..	..	..	..	..	..	..	..	2 19	..	..	51
Leatherhead ... [Bridge J	52	..	..	..	..	..	..	..	..	..	2 13	..	..	..	..	..	..	..	..	2 23	..	..	52
Boxhill and Burford	53	..	..	..	..	..	..	..	..	..	2 18	..	..	..	..	..	..	..	..	..	..	..	53
Dorking North K .. arr	54	..	..	..	..	..	..	..	..	..	2 21	..	..	..	..	..	..	..	..	..	..	..	54
Bookham .... [394	55	..	..	..	..	..	..	..	..	..	..	..	..	..	..	..	..	..	..	2 28	..	..	55
Effingham Junction arr	56	..	..	..	..	..	..	..	..	..	..	..	..	..	..	..	..	..	..	2 31	..	..	56
South Croydon 234	57	..	..	..	..	1 48	..	..	..	..	..	..	1 50	..	..	..	..	1 58	..	..	..	..	57
Purley Oaks	58	..	..	..	..	1 51	..	..	..	..	..	..	1 52	..	..	..	..	2 1	..	..	..	..	58
Purley	59	..	..	..	..	1 53	..	..	..	..	..	..	1 55	..	..	1 54	1 57	2 3	..	..	..	..	59
Coulsdon North L .. arr	60	..	..	..	..	1 57	..	..	..	..	..	..	..	..	..	..	..	2 7	..	..	..	..	60
Purley .... dep	61	..	..	..	..	..	..	..	..	..	..	..	1 59	..	..	..	1 59	..	..	..	..	..	61
Kenley	62	..	..	..	..	..	..	..	..	..	..	..	2 2	..	..	..	2 2	..	..	..	..	..	62
Whyteleafe	63	..	..	..	..	..	..	..	..	..	..	..	2 5	..	..	..	2 5	..	..	..	..	..	63
Warlingham	64	..	..	..	..	..	..	..	..	..	..	..	2 7	..	..	..	2 7	..	..	..	..	..	64
Caterham .... arr	65	..	..	..	..	..	..	..	..	..	..	..	2 11	..	..	..	2 11	..	..	..	..	..	65
Purley .... dep	66	..	..	..	..	..	..	..	..	..	..	..	1 57	..	..	..	1 58	..	..	..	..	..	66
Reedham	67	..	..	..	..	..	..	..	..	..	..	..	1 59	..	..	..	2 0	..	..	..	..	..	67
Smitham	68		..	..	..	..	..	..	..	..	..	..	2 1	..	..	..	2 3	..	..	..	..	..	68
Woodmansterne	69	..	..	..	..	..	..	..	..	..	..	..	2 4	..	..	..	2 5	..	..	..	..	..	69
Chipstead	70	..	..	..	..	..	..	..	..	..	..	..	2 6	..	..	..	2 8	..	..	..	..	..	70
Kingswood M	71	..	..	..	..	..	..	..	..	..	..	..	2 11	..	..	..	2 12	..	..	..	..	..	71
Tadworth A	72	..	..	..	..	..	..	..	..	..	..	..	2 14	..	..	..	2 15	..	..	..	..	..	72
Tattenham Corner . arr	73	..	..	..	..	..	..	..	..	..	..	..	2 17	..	..	..	2 19	..	..	..	..	..	73
Coulsdon South	74	..	..	..	..	..	..	..	..	..	..	..	..	..	..	1 57	..	..	..	..	..	..	74
Merstham	75	..	..	..	..	..	..	..	..	..	..	..	..	..	..	2 3	..	..	..	..	..	..	75
Redhill .. 158, 246 .... arr	76	..	..	..	..	..	..	..	..	2 0	..	..	..	..	..	2 7	..	..	..	..	..	..	76
Reigate 246 ...... "	77	..	..	..	..	..	..	..	..	..	..	..	..	..	..	2 13	..	..	..	..	..	..	77
Horsham 159, 244, 245 "	78	..	..	..	..	..	..	..	..	..	2 46	..	..	..	..	..	..	..	..	..	..	..	78

CATERHAM, TATTENHAM CORNER, REDHILL, REIGATE, and HORSHAM

Week Days—continued (p.m)

No.	SO	SX		SO	SO	SO	SO	SX	SX	SO	SO	SX		SO	SO				SX	SO		SX	SO	SX	SO	SX	SX	SO
1	..	..	..	..	..	..	1 38	1 38	..	..	1 40	1 40	..	..	1 45	..	..	1 48	1 51	..	..	..	..	..	..	..	..	..
2	3	..	..	..	3	..	3	3	3	3	3	3	..	3	..	..	..	..	3	3	..	3	3	1 44	3	3	3	3
3		..	..	..		..							..		..	..	..	..			..			1 46				
4	1 36	..	..	1 40	1 42	1 42	..	..	1 37	1 44	..	..	..	1 45	..	..	..	..	..	1 48	..	1 48	1 50	1 51	1 51	1 53	1 53	1 55
5	..	..	..	..	..	..	..	..	..	..	1 43	1 43	..	..	..	..	..	..	..	..	..	..	..		..	..	..	..
6	..	..	..	..	..	..	1 44	1 44	..	..	1 46	1 47	..	..	..	..	..	1U53	1 56	..	..	..	..	3	..	..	..	..
7	..	..	..	..	..	..	..	..	..	..	1 49	1 50	..	..	..	..	..	..	..	..	..	..	..		..	..	..	..
8	..	..	..	..	..	..	1 48	1 48	..	..	1 51	1 52	..	..	..	..	..	..	2 0	..	..	..	..	..	..	..	..	..
9	1 39	..	..	..	..	..	..	..	1 40	..	..	..	..	..	..	..	..	U Takes up only	..	..	..	1 51	..	..	..	..	..	..
10	1 42	..	..	..	..	..	..	..	1 43	..	..	..	..	..	..	..	..		..	..	..	1 54	1 55	..	..	..	..	..
11	1 44	..	..	..	..	..	..	..	1 45	..	..	..	..	..	..	..	..		..	..	..	1 56	1 57	..	..	..	1 59	..
12	To Victoria arr. 2 1 p.m	..	..	..	..	..	..	..	1 48	..	..	..	..	..	..	..	..		..	..	..	To Victoria, arr. 2 13 p.m	2 0	..	..	..	..	..
13		..	..	..	..	..	..	..	1 50	..	..	..	..	..	..	..	..		..	..	..		2 2	..	..	..	..	..
14		..	..	..	..	..	..	..	1 53	..	..	..	..	1 55	..	..	..		..	1 58	..		2 5	..	..	..	2 3	..
15		..	..	..	..	..	..	..	1 57	..	..	..	..	1 59	..	..	..		..	2 2	..		..	..	..	..	2 7	..
16		..	..	..	..	..	..	..	..	1 49	..	..	..	..	..	..	..	..	..	..	..		..	..	1 56	1 58	..	..
17		..	..	..	..	..	..	..	..	..	..	..	..	..	..	..	..	..	..	..	..		..	..	1 58	2 0	..	..
18		..	..	..	..	..	..	..	..	..	..	..	..	..	..	..	..	..	..	..	..		..	..	2 1	2 3	..	..
19		..	..	..	..	..	..	..	..	..	..	..	..	..	..	..	..	..	..	..	..		..	..	2 3	2 5	..	..
20		..	..	..	..	..	..	..	..	..	..	..	..	..	..	..	..	..	..	..	..		..	..	2 6	2 8	..	..
21		..	..	..	..	..	..	..	..	..	..	..	..	..	..	..	..	..	..	..	..		..	..	2 8	..	..	..
22		..	..	..	..	..	..	..	..	..	..	..	..	..	..	..	..	..	..	..	..		..	..	2 9	..	..	..
23	..	..	..	..	..	..	1 52	1 53	1 59	..	..	..	..	2 1	..	..	..	..	..	..	..	..	..	..	..	..	..	..
24	..	..	..	..	..	..	1 54	1 55	2 1	..	..	..	..	2 4	..	..	..	..	..	..	..	..	..	..	..	..	..	..
25	..	..	..	..	..	..	1 57	1 58	2 4	..	..	..	..	2 7	..	..	..	..	..	..	..	..	..	..	..	..	..	..
26	..	..	..	..	..	..	1 59	2 0	2 6	..	..	..	..	2 9	..	..	..	..	..	..	..	..	..	..	..	..	..	..
27	..	..	..	..	..	..	..	..	..	..	1 54	1 54	..	..	..	SX	..	..	..	..	..	..	2 8	..	..	..	..	..
28	..	..	..	..	..	..	..	..	..	..	1 57	1 57	..	..	..	3	..	..	..	..	..	..	..	..	..	..	..	..
29	..	..	..	..	..	..	..	Arr. Sutton 2 15 p.m.	..	..	1 59	2 0	..	..	..		..	..	..	..	..	..	..	..	..	..	..	..
30	..	..	..	..	..	..	..		..	..	2 2	2 2	..	..	..	2 10	..	..	..	..	..	..	..	..	..	2 11	..	..
31	..	..	..	..	..	..	..		..	..	..	..	..	..	..	2 13	..	..	..	..	..	..	..	..	..	..	..	..
32	..	..	..	..	..	..	..		..	..	..	..	..	..	..	2 17	..	..	..	..	..	..	..	..	..	..	..	..
33	..	..	..	..	1 55	..	..		2 9	1 58	2 7	2 7	..	..	..	..	..	..	..	..	..	..	..	2 3	2 12	..	..	..
34	..	..	..	1 54	..	1 59	..		To London Bridge, via Forest Hill	2 2	..	..	..	..	2 0	..	..	2 5	..	..	..	..	..	2 7	To London Bridge, via Streatham	..	..	2 11
35	..	2 1	..	1 55	..	2 0	..			2 2	..	..	..	..	..	..	..	2 5	..	..	..	..	..	2 7		..	..	2 11
36	..	..	..	..	..	..	..			..	..	..	..	..	..	..	..	..	2 6	2 7	..	..	..	..		..	2 12	..
37	..	..	..	..	..	..	..	..		..	..	..	..	..	..	..	..	..	2 9	2 9	..	..	..	..		..	2 14	..
38	..	..	..	..	..	..	..	..		..	..	..	..	..	..	..	..	..	2 11	2 12	..	..	..	..		..	2 17	..
39	..	..	..	..	1 59	..	2 2	2 3		..	2 11	2 12	..	..	..	..	..	..	..	..	..	..	..	..		..	..	..
40	..	..	..	..	1 59	..	2 2	2 3		..	..	..	..	..	..	..	..	..	..	..	..	..	..	..		..	..	..
41	..	..	..	..	2 1	..	2 5	2 6		..	..	..	..	..	..	..	..	..	..	..	..	..	..	..		..	..	..
42	..	..	..	..	2 5	..	2 8	2 9		..	..	..	..	..	..	..	..	..	..	..	..	..	..	..		..	..	..
43	..	..	..	..	2 7	..	2 11	2 12		..	..	..	..	..	..	..	..	..	..	..	..	..	..	..		..	..	..
44	..	..	..	..	2 10	..	2 14	2 17		..	..	..	..	..	..	..	..	..	2 14	2 15	..	..	..	..		..	2 20	..
45	..	..	..	..	2 13	..	2 17	2 20		..	..	..	..	..	..	..	..	..	..	..	..	..	..	..		..	..	..
46	..	..	..	..	2 16	..	2 20	2 23		..	..	..	..	..	..	..	..	..	..	..	..	..	..	..		..	..	..
47	..	..	..	..	2 19	..	2 23	2 26		..	..	..	..	..	..	..	..	..	..	..	..	..	..	..		..	..	..
48	..	..	..	..	..	..	..	..	..	..	..	..	..	..	..	..	..	H 1 minute *earlier* on Saturdays	2 17	2 18	p.m	..	..	..	..	..	2 23	..
49	..	..	..	..	..	..	..	..	..	..	..	..	..	..	..	..	..		2 20	2 21	SO	..	..	..	..	..	2 26	..
50	..	..	..	..	..	..	..	..	..	..	..	..	..	..	..	..	..		2 24	2 25	3	..	..	..	..	..	2 29	..
51	..	..	..	..	..	..	..	..	..	..	..	..	..	..	..	..	..		..	2 29		..	..	..	..	..	2 33	..
52	..	..	..	..	..	..	..	..	..	..	..	..	..	..	..	..	..		..	2 33	2 36	..	..	..	..	..	2 37	..
53	..	..	..	..	..	..	..	..	..	..	..	..	..	..	..	..	..		..	2 38	..	..	..	..	..	..	..	..
54	..	..	..	..	..	..	..	..	..	..	..	..	..	..	..	..	..		..	2 41	..	..	..	..	..	..	..	..
55	..	..	..	..	..	..	..	..	..	..	..	..	..	..	..	..	..		..	..	2 40	..	..	..	..	..	2 42	..
56	..	..	..	..	..	..	..	..	..	..	..	..	..	..	..	..	..		..	..	2 44	..	..	..	..	..	2 45	..
57	..	2 3	..	..	..	2 3	..	..	..	2 4	..	..	..	..	..	..	..		..	..	..	..	..	2 10	..	..	..	..
58	..	..	..	..	..	..	..	..	..	2 7	..	..	..	..	..	..	..		..	..	..	..	..	2 12	..	..	..	..
59	..	..	..	..	..	..	..	..	..	2 9	..	..	..	..	..	..	..	2H11	..	..	..	..	..	2 15	..	..	..	2 16
60	..	..	..	..	..	..	..	..	..	2 13	..	..	..	..	..	..	..	..	..	..	..	..	..	..	..	..	..	..
61	..	..	..	..	..	..	..	..	..	..	..	..	..	..	..	..	..	..	..	..	..	..	..	2 19	..	..	..	2 19
62	..	..	..	..	..	..	..	..	..	..	..	..	..	..	..	..	..	..	..	..	..	..	..	2 22	..	..	..	2 22
63	..	..	..	..	..	..	..	..	..	..	..	..	..	..	..	..	..	..	..	..	..	..	..	2 25	..	..	..	2 25
64	..	..	..	..	..	..	..	..	..	..	..	..	..	..	..	..	..	..	..	..	..	..	..	2 27	..	..	..	2 27
65	..	..	..	..	..	..	..	..	..	..	..	..	..	..	..	..	..	..	..	..	..	..	..	2 31	..	..	..	2 31
66	..	..	..	§ Via Three Bridges	..	..	..	..	..	..	..	..	..	..	..	..	..	§ Via Three Bridges	..	..	..	..	..	2 17	..	..	..	2 18
67	..	..	..		..	..	..	..	..	..	..	..	..	..	..	..	..		..	..	..	..	..	2 19	..	..	..	2 20
68	..	..	..		..	..	..	..	..	..	..	..	..	..	..	..	..		..	..	..	..	..	2 21	..	..	..	2 23
69	..	..	..		..	..	..	..	..	..	..	..	..	..	..	..	..		..	..	..	..	..	2 24	..	..	..	2 25
70	..	..	..		..	..	..	..	..	..	..	..	..	..	..	..	..		..	..	..	..	..	2 26	..	..	..	2 28
71	..	..	..		..	..	..	..	..	..	..	..	..	..	..	..	..		..	..	..	..	..	2 31	..	..	..	2 32
72	..	..	..		..	..	..	..	..	..	..	..	..	..	..	..	..		..	..	..	..	..	2 34	..	..	..	2 35
73	..	..	..		..	..	..	..	..	..	..	..	..	..	..	..	..		..	..	..	..	..	2 37	..	..	..	2 39
74	..	..	..		..	..	..	..	..	..	..	..	..	..	..	..	..	2 14	..	..	..	..	..	..	..	..	..	..
75	..	..	..		..	..	..	..	..	..	..	..	..	..	..	..	..	2 20	..	..	..	..	..	..	..	..	..	..
76	..	..	..		..	..	..	..	..	..	..	..	..	..	..	..	..	2 24	..	..	..	..	..	..	..	..	..	..
77	..	..	..		..	..	..	..	..	..	..	..	..	..	..	..	..	2 30	..	..	..	..	..	..	..	..	..	..
78	..	..	..	2§32	..	..	..	..	..	..	..	..	..	..	..	..	..	3§ 5	..	..	..	..	..	..	..	..	..	..

LONDON, CRYSTAL PALACE, CROYDON, SUTTON, DORKING NORTH,

Down	No.	p.m				Week Days—*continued*												p.m					No.
		S O	S X	S O	S O		S O	S O	S O	S X		S O	S O			S X	S O	S O	S X		S O	S O	
VICTORIA ......dep	1	1 51	1 51	1 53	1 55	..	..	..	1 58	..	..	2 0	..	..	..	..	..	..	2 8	..	..	..	1
CHARING CROSS* ... "	2	3	3	3	3	..	3	3	3	3	..	3	3	..	..	3	3	3	3	..	3	3	2
WATERLOO* .... "	3					..					..			..	2 7					..			3
LONDON BRIDGE..... "	4	..	..	..	..	..	1 57	2 2	..	2 2	..	..	2 5	..	..	2 7	2 7	2 8	..	..	2 11	2 15	4
Battersea Park	5	..	..	1 56	..	..	..	..	..	..	..	2 3	..	..	3	..	..	..	..	..	..	..	5
Clapham Junction	6	1 56	1 57	1 59	2 0	..	..	..	2 4	..	..	2 6	..	..		..	..	..	2 14	..	..	..	6
Wandsworth Common **A**	7	..	2 0	2 2	..	..	..	..	..	..	..	2 9	..	..		..	..	..	..	..	..	..	7
Balham & Upper Tooting	8	2 1	2 2	2 4	2 4	..	..	..	2 8	..	..	2 11	..	..		..	..	..	2 18	..	..	..	8
South Bermondsey	9	..	..	..	..	..	2 1	..	..	..	..	..	..	..	Via Worcester Park	..	..	..	..	..	..	..	9
Queen's Road, Peckham	10	..	..	..	..	..	2 4	..	..	..	..	..	..	..		..	..	..	..	..	..	..	10
Peckham Rye	11	..	..	..	..	..	2 6	..	..	..	..	..	..	..		..	..	..	..	..	..	..	11
East Dulwich	12	..	..	..	..	..		..	..	..	..	..	..	..		..	..	..	..	..	..	..	12
North Dulwich	13	..	..	..	..	..		..	..	..	..	..	..	..		..	..	..	..	..	..	..	13
Tulse Hill	14	..	..	..	..	..		..	..	..	..	..	2 15	..		..	..	2 18	..	..	..	..	14
Streatham	15	..	..	..	..	..		..	..	..	..	..	2 19	..		..	..	2 22	..	..	..	..	15
New Cross Gate (for E.L.	16	..	..	..	..	..		..	..	2 7	..	..	..	..	..	2 12	2 12	..	..	..	2 16	..	16
Brockley **B**.......[Line)	17	..	..	..	..	..		..	..	..	..	..	..	..	..	2 14	2 14	..	..	..	2 18	..	17
Honor Oak Park	18	..	..	..	..	..		..	..	..	..	..	..	..	..	2 17	2 17	..	..	..	2 21	..	18
Forest Hill, for Lordship	19	..	..	..	..	..	To Victoria arr. 2 22 p.m	..	..	2 11	..	..	..	..	..	2 19	2 19	..	..	..	2 23	..	19
Sydenham ....[Lane	20	..	..	..	..	..		..	..	2 14	..	..	..	..	..	2 22	2 22	..	..	..	2 26	..	20
Penge West **C**..........	21	..	..	..	..	..		..	..	2 16	..	..	..	..	..	2 24	..	..	..	..	2 28	..	21
Anerley	22	..	..	..	..	..		..	..	2 17	..	..	..	..	..	2 25	..	..	..	..	2 29	..	22
Streatham Common	23	2 5	2 5	..	..	..		..	2 12	..	..	..	2 21	..	..	..	..	..	2 22	..	..	..	23
Norbury	24	2 7	2 7	..	..	..		..	2 14	..	..	..	2 24	..	..	..	..	..	2 24	..	..	..	24
Thornton Heath	25	2 10	2 10	..	..	..	Stop	..	2 17	..	..	..	2 27	..	..	..	..	..	2 27	..	..	..	25
Selhurst	26	2 12	2 12	..	..	..		..	2 19	..	..	..	2 30	..	..	..	..	..	2 29	..	..	..	26
Streatham Hill	27	..	..	2 6	..	..	..	..	..	..	..	2 14	..	..	..	..	..	..	..	..	..	..	27
West Norwood..[N'wood)	28	..	..	2 9	..	..	..	..	..	..	..	2 17	..	..	..	..	..	..	..	..	..	..	28
Gipsy Hill (for Upper	29	..	..	2 12	..	..	..	..	..	..	..	2 19	..	..	..	..	..	..	..	..	..	..	29
Crystal Palace D	30	..	..	2 14	..	..	..	..	..	..	..	2 22	..	..	..	..	2 25	..	..	..	..	..	30
Birkbeck	31	..	..	2 18	..	..	..	..	..	..	..	..	..	..	..	..	..	..	..	..	..	..	31
Beckenham Jn. arr	32	..	..	2 22	..	..	..	..	..	..	..	..	..	..	..	..	..	..	..	..	..	..	32
Norwood Junction F ..	33	..	..	..	..	..	..	2 15	..	2 20	..	2 27	2 33	..	..	2 29	..	..		..	2 32	2 27	33
East Croydon .... arr	34	2 16	2 17	..	..	..	..	..	..	..	..	..	..	..	..	..	..	..		..	..	2 31	34
East Croydon .... dep	35	2 16	2 17	..	..	..	..	..	..	..	..	..	..	..	..	..	..	..	Arr Sutton 244 p.m	..	..	2 31	35
Mitcham Junction	36	..	..	..	2 13	..	p.m S O	..	..	..	..	..		..	..		..	2 27		..		..	36
Hackbridge	37	..	..	..	2 15	..		..	..	..	..	..		..	..		..	2 29		..		..	37
Carshalton	38	..	..	..	2 18	..	3	..	..	..	..	..		..	..		..	2 32		..		..	38
West Croydon 319 arr	39	..	..	..	..	S X		2 19	2 22	2 24	..	2 31		..	..		..	..	2 32	..		..	39
West Croydon 319 dep	40	..	..	..	..	3	2 14	2 19	2 22	2 24	..	..		..	..		..	..	2 32	..		..	40
Waddon **G**	41	..	..	..	..		2 16	2 21	2 25	2 27	..	..	To London Bridge, via Forest Hill	..	..	To London Bridge, via Streatham	..	..	2 35	..	To London Bridge, via Streatham	..	41
Wallington	42	..	..	..	..	2 19	2 20	2 25	2 28	2 30	..	..		..	..		..	..	2 38	..		..	42
Carshalton Beeches	43	..	..	..	..	2 21	2 22	2 27	2 31	2 33	..	..		..	..		..	..	2 41	..		..	43
Sutton 322	44	..	..	..	2 21	2 24	2 25	2 30	2 34	2 35	..	..		..	..		..	2 35	2 47	..		..	44
Belmont	45	..	..	..	..	..	..	2 33	2 37	2 38	..	..		..	..		..	..	2 50	..		..	45
Banstead	46	..	..	..	..	..	..	2 36	2 40	2 41	..	..		..	..		..	..	2 53	..		..	46
Epsom Downs ...... arr	47	..	..	..	..	..	..	2 39	2 43	2 45	..	..		..	..		..	..	2 56	..		..	47
Cheam	48	..	..	..	2 24	..	..	..	..	..	..	..	..	..	..	..	..	2 43	..	..	..	..	48
Ewell East **H**	49	..	..	..	2 27	..	..	..	..	..	..	..	..	..	..	..	..	2 46	..	..	..	..	49
Epsom	50	..	..	..	2 31	..	..	..	..	..	..	..	..	..	2 35	..	..	2 49	..	..	..	..	50
Ashtead	51	..	..	..	..	..	..	..	..	..	..	..	..	..	2 39	..	..	2 53	..	..	..	..	51
Leatherhead...[Bridge **J**	52	..	..	..	..	..	..	..	..	..	..	..	..	..	2 43	..	..	2 57	..	..	..	..	52
Boxhill and Burford	53	..	..	..	..	..	..	..	..	..	..	..	..	..	2 48	..	..	..	..	..	..	..	53
Dorking North K .. arr	54	..	..	..	..	..	..	..	..	..	..	..	..	..	2 51	..	..	..	..	..	..	..	54
Bookham ....[394	55	..	..	..	..	..	..	..	..	..	..	..	..	..	..	..	..	3 1	..	..	..	..	55
Effingham Junction arr	56	..	..	..	..	..	..	..	..	..	..	..	..	..	..	..	..	3 4	..	..	..	..	56
South Croydon 234	57	2 18	2 19	..	..	..	..	..	..	..	..	..	..	..	..	..	..		..	..	..	2 33	57
Purley Oaks	58	2 21	2 22	..	..	..	..	..	..	..	..	..	..	..	..	..	..		..	..	..	..	58
Purley	59	2 23	2 24	..	..	..	..	..	..	..	..	..	..	..	..	..	..		..	..	..	2 37	59
Coulsdon North **L** .. arr	60	2 27	2 28	..	..	..	..	..	..	..	..	..	..	..	..	..	..		..	..	..	..	60
Purley .... dep	61	..	..	..	..	..	..	..	..	..	..	..	..	..	..	..	..	Arr. Cheam 2 38 p.m	..	..	..	2 39	61
Kenley	62	..	..	..	..	..	..	..	..	..	..	..	..	..	..	..	..		..	..	..	2 42	62
Whyteleafe	63	..	..	..	..	..	..	..	..	..	..	..	..	..	..	..	..		..	..	..	2 45	63
Warlingham	64	..	..	..	..	..	..	..	..	..	..	..	..	..	..	..	..		..	..	..	2 47	64
Caterham .... arr	65	..	..	..	..	..	..	..	..	..	..	..	..	..	..	..	..		..	..	..	2 51	65
Purley .... dep	66	..	..	..	..	..	..	..	..	..	..	..	..	..	..	..	..	..	..	..	..	2 38	66
Reedham	67	..	..	..	..	..	..	..	..	..	..	..	..	..	..	..	..	..	..	..	..	2 40	67
Smitham	68	..	..	..	..	..	..	..	..	..	..	..	..	..	..	..	..	..	..	..	..	2 43	68
Woodmansterne	69	..	..	..	..	..	..	..	..	..	..	..	..	..	..	..	..	..	..	..	..	2 45	69
Chipstead	70	..	..	..	..	..	..	..	..	..	..	..	..	..	..	..	..	..	..	..	..	2 48	70
Kingswood **M**	71	..	..	..	..	..	..	..	..	..	..	..	..	..	..	..	..	..	..	..	..	2 52	71
Tadworth **N**	72	..	..	..	..	..	..	..	..	..	..	..	..	..	..	..	..	..	..	..	..	2 55	72
Tattenham Corner. arr	73	..	..	..	..	..	..	..	..	..	..	..	..	..	..	..	..	..	..	..	..	2 59	73
Coulsdon South	74	..	..	..	..	..	..	..	..	..	..	..	..	..	..	..	..	..	..	..	..	..	74
Merstham	75	..	..	..	..	..	..	..	..	..	..	..	..	..	..	..	..	..	..	..	..	..	75
Redhill 158, 246 ..... arr	76	..	..	..	..	..	..	..	..	..	..	..	..	..	..	..	..	..	..	..	..	..	76
Reigate 246 .... "	77	..	..	..	..	..	..	..	..	..	..	..	..	..	..	..	..	..	..	..	..	..	77
Horsham 159, 244, 245 "	78	..	..	..	..	..	..	..	..	..	..	..	..	..	3 25	..	..	..	..	..	..	..	78

For Notes, see page 284a

CATERHAM, TATTENHAM CORNER, REDHILL, REIGATE, and HORSHAM

Week Days - *continued* — p.m

No.	SX	SO		SO		SX	SO		SO		SO		SO	SX	SO		SO	SX	SO	SO		SO		SX		SO	SO	
1	2 10	2 13	..	..	..	..	2 11	..	2 18	2 20	..	..	..	..	2 18	..	2 20	2 21	2 25	..	..	..	2 28	..	2 30	2 31	2 33	..
2	3	3	3	3	..	3	3	..	..	3	..	..	3	3	3	..	3	3	..	3	..	3	..	2 24	..	3	3	..
3					..			..	..		2 27	..				..			..		..		..	2 26	..			..
4	..	..	2 15	2 17	2 18	2 19	..	..	..	..	..	..	2 22	2 25	..	..	..	..	..	2 25	..	2 28	..	2 31	..	..	..	..
5	2 13	2 16	..	..	..	..	..	..	..	..	3	..	..	..	..	..	2 23	..	..	..	..	..	..	3	..	..	2 36	..
6	2 16	2 19	..	..	..	..	2 16	..	..	2 25		..	..	..	2 24	..	2 26	2 27	..	..	..	..	2U34		2U37	2 36	2 39	..
7	2 20	2 22	..	..	..	..	..	..	..	..	..	..	..	..	..	..	2 29	..	..	..	..	..	..	..	..	..	2 42	..
8	2 22	2 24	..	..	..	..	2 21	..	..	2 29	..	..	..	..	2 28	..	2 31	2 31	..	..	..	..	..	..	..	2 41	2 44	..
9	..	..	2 18	2 21	..	2 22	..	..	..	..	Via Worcester Park	..	..	..	..	..	..	..	..	..	..	..	U Takes up only	..	U Takes up only	..	..	..
10	..	..	2 21	2 24	..	2 25	..	..	..	..		..	..	..	..	..	..	..	..	..	..	..		..		..	..	..
11	..	..	2 23	2 26	..	2 27	..	..	..	..		..	..	2 31	..	..	..	..	..	..	..	2 34		..		..	..	..
12	..	..	2 26	To Victoria arr. 2 43 p.m	..		..	..	..	..		..	..	..	..	..	..	..	..	..	..	..		..		..	..	..
13	..	..	2 28		..	☞	..	..	..	..		..	..	..	..	..	..	..	..	..	..	..		..		..	..	..
14	..	..	2 31		..		..	..	..	..		..	..	2 35	..	..	..	..	..	2 35	..	2 38		..		..	..	..
15	..	..	..		..		..	..	..	..		..	..	2 39	..	..	..	..	..	2 39	..	2 42		..		..	..	..
16	..	..	..		..	To Victoria arr. 2 43 p.m	..	..	..	..	..	..	..	..	..	..	..	..	..	..	..	..	..	..	..	..	..	..
17	..	..	..		..		..	..	..	..	..	..	..	..	..	..	..	..	..	..	..	..	..	..	..	..	..	..
18	..	..	..		..		..	..	..	..	..	..	..	..	..	..	..	..	..	..	..	..	..	..	..	..	..	..
19	..	..	..		..		..	..	..	..	..	..	..	..	..	..	..	..	..	..	..	..	..	..	..	..	..	..
20	..	..	..	..	..		..	..	..	..	..	..	..	..	..	..	..	..	..	..	..	..	..	..	..	..	..	..
21	..	..	..	..	..		..	..	..	..	..	..	..	..	..	..	..	..	..	..	..	..	..	..	..	..	..	..
22	..	..	..	..	..		..	..	..	..	..	..	..	..	..	..	..	..	..	..	..	..	..	..	..	..	..	..
23	..	..	..	..	..		2 25	..	..	..	..	..	..	..	2 32	..	..	2 35	..	2 41	..	..	..	..	..	2 45	..	..
24	..	..	..	..	..	Stop	2 27	..	..	..	..	..	..	..	2 34	..	..	2 37	..	2 44	..	..	..	..	..	2 47	..	..
25	..	..	..	..	..		2 30	..	..	..	..	..	..	..	2 37	..	..	2 40	..	2 47	..	..	..	..	..	2 50	..	..
26	..	..	..	..	..	p.m	2 32	..	..	..	..	..	..	..	2 39	..	..	2 42	..	2 49	..	..	..	..	..	2 52	..	..
27	2 24	2 26	..	..	..	SX	..	..	..	J 1 minute later on Saturdays	..	..	..	..	..	..	2 34	..	..	..	..	..	..	..	..	..	2 46	..
28	2 27	2 29	2 33	..	..	3	..	..	..		..	..	..	..	..	..	2 37	..	..	..	..	..	..	..	..	..	2 49	..
29	2 30	2 32	2 36	..	..		..	..	..		..	..	..	..	..	..	2 39	..	..	..	..	..	..	..	..	..	2 52	..
30	2 32	2 35	2 39	..	..	2 40	..	..	..		..	..	..	..	..	..	2 44	..	..	..	..	..	..	..	..	..	2 54	..
31	..	2 40	..	..	..	2 43	..	..	..		..	..	..	..	..	..	..	..	..	..	..	..	..	..	..	..	2 58	..
32	..	2 44	..	..	..	2 47	..	..	..		..	..	..	..	..	..	..	..	..	..	..	..	..	..	..	..	3 2	..
33	2 37	..	..	..	2 30	..	..	..	..		..	..	2 35	..	..	..	2 50	..	..	..	..	..	..	2 43	..	..	..	..
34	..	..	..	..	2 34	..	2 36	..	..		..	..	..	..	..	..	..	2 46	2 40	..	..	..	2 45	2 47	2 51	2 56	..	..
35	..	..	..	..	2H35	..	2 36	..	..		..	..	..	..	..	..	..	2 46	..	..	..	..	2 46	2 47	2 52	2 56	..	..
36	..	..	..	..	H 1 minute earlier on Saturdays	..	..	..	..	2J35	..	SO	..	2 44	..	..	..	..	..	..	..	2 47	..	..	..	..	..	SO
37	..	..	..	..		..	..	..	..	2 38	..	3	..	2 46	..	..	..	..	..	..	..	2 49	..	..	..	..	..	3
38	..	..	..	..		..	..	..	..	2J40	..		..	2 49	..	..	..	..	..	..	..	2 52	..	..	..	..	..	
39	2 41	..	..	..		..	..	..	..	..	..	..	2 39	..	2 42	SX	2 54	..	..	..	..	..	..	..	..	..	..	..
40	..	..	..	..		..	..	..	..	..	..	2 34	2 39	..	2 42	3	..	..	..	..	..	..	..	..	..	..	..	2 54
41	..	..	..	..		..	..	..	..	..	..	2 36	2 41	..	2 45		..	..	..	..	..	..	..	..	..	..	..	2 56
42	..	..	..	..		..	..	..	..	..	..	2 40	2 45	..	2 48	2 49	..	..	..	..	..	..	..	..	..	..	..	3 0
43	..	..	..	..		..	..	..	..	..	..	2 42	2 47	..	2 51	2 51	..	..	..	..	..	..	..	..	..	..	..	..
44	..	..	..	..		..	..	..	2 39	2J43	..	2 46	2 50	2 52	2 54	2 54	..	..	..	..	..	2 55	..	..	..	..	..	..
45	..	..	..	..		..	..	..	..	..	..	..	2 53	..	2 57	..	..	..	..	..	..	..	..	..	..	..	..	..
46	..	..	..	..		..	..	..	..	..	..	..	2 56	..	3 0	..	..	..	..	..	..	..	..	..	..	..	..	..
47	..	..	..	..		..	..	..	..	..	..	..	2 59	..	3 3	..	..	..	..	..	..	..	..	..	..	..	..	..
48	..	..	..	..	..	..	..	..	..	2J46	..	..	..	2 55	..	..	..	..	..	..	..	2 58	..	..	..	..	..	..
49	..	..	..	..	..	..	..	..	..	2J49	..	..	..	2 58	..	..	..	..	..	..	..	3 1	..	..	..	..	..	..
50	..	..	..	..	..	..	..	..	..	2 53	2 55	..	..	3 2	..	..	..	..	..	..	..	3 5	..	..	..	..	..	..
51	..	..	..	..	..	..	..	..	..	..	2 59	..	..	3 6	..	..	..	..	..	..	..	3 9	..	..	..	..	..	..
52	..	..	..	..	..	..	..	..	..	..	3 3	..	..	3 11	..	..	..	..	..	..	..	3 13	..	..	..	..	..	..
53	..	..	..	..	..	..	..	..	..	..	3 8	..	..	3 17	..	..	..	..	..	..	..	3 18	..	..	..	..	..	..
54	..	..	..	..	..	..	..	..	2 55	..	3 11	..	..	3 20	..	..	..	..	..	..	..	3 21	..	..	..	..	..	..
55	..	..	..	..	..	..	..	..	..	..	..	..	..	..	..	..	..	..	..	..	..	..	..	..	..	..	..	..
56	..	..	..	..	..	..	..	..	..	..	..	..	..	..	..	..	..	..	..	..	..	..	..	..	..	..	..	..
57	..	..	..	..	..	..	2 38	..	..	..	..	..	..	..	..	..	..	2 49	..	..	..	..	..	2 50	2 56	2 58	..	..
58	..	..	..	..	..	..	2 41	..	..	..	..	..	..	..	..	..	..	2 51	..	..	..	..	..	2 52	..	3 1	..	..
59	..	..	..	..	2 40	..	2 43	..	..	..	..	..	..	..	..	..	..	2 53	..	..	..	..	..	2 55	..	3 3	..	..
60	..	..	..	..	..	..	2 47	..	..	..	..	..	..	..	..	..	..	2 57	..	..	..	..	..	..	..	3 7	..	..
61	..	..	..	..	..	..	..	..	..	..	..	..	..	..	..	..	..	..	..	..	..	..	..	2 59	..	..	..	..
62	..	..	..	..	..	..	..	..	..	..	..	..	..	..	..	..	..	..	..	..	..	..	..	3 2	..	..	..	..
63	..	..	..	..	..	..	..	..	..	..	..	..	..	..	..	..	..	..	..	..	..	..	..	3 5	..	..	..	..
64	..	..	..	..	§ Via Three Bridges	..	..	..	..	..	..	..	..	..	..	..	..	..	..	..	..	..	..	3 7	..	..	..	..
65	..	..	..	..		..	..	..	..	..	..	..	..	..	..	..	..	..	..	..	..	..	..	3 11	..	..	..	..
66	..	..	..	..		..	..	..	..	..	..	..	..	..	..	..	..	..	..	..	..	..	..	2 57	..	..	..	..
67	..	..	..	..		..	..	..	..	..	..	..	..	..	..	..	..	..	..	..	..	..	..	2 59	..	..	..	..
68	..	..	..	..		..	..	..	..	..	..	..	..	..	..	..	..	..	..	..	..	..	..	3 1	..	..	..	..
69	..	..	..	..		..	..	..	..	..	..	..	..	..	..	..	..	..	..	..	..	..	..	3 4	..	..	..	..
70	..	..	..	..		..	..	..	..	..	..	..	..	..	..	..	..	..	..	..	..	..	..	3 6	..	..	..	..
71	..	..	..	..		..	..	..	..	..	..	..	..	..	..	..	..	..	..	..	..	..	..	3 11	..	..	..	..
72	..	..	..	..	..	..	..	..	..	..	..	..	..	..	..	..	..	..	..	..	..	..	..	3 14	..	..	..	..
73	..	..	..	..	..	..	..	..	..	..	..	..	..	..	..	..	..	..	..	..	..	..	..	3 17	..	..	..	..
74	..	..	..	..	2 43	..	..	..	..	..	..	..	..	..	..	..	..	..	..	..	..	..	..	..	..	..	..	..
75	..	..	..	..	2 49	..	..	..	..	..	..	..	..	..	..	..	..	..	..	..	..	..	..	..	..	..	..	..
76	..	..	..	..	2H54	..	..	..	..	..	..	..	..	..	..	..	..	..	..	..	..	..	3 0	..	..	..	..	..
77	..	..	..	..	2 59	..	..	..	..	..	..	..	..	..	..	..	..	..	..	..	..	..	3 9	..	..	..	..	..
78	..	..	..	..	3§35	..	..	..	3 15	..	..	..	..	3 46	..	..	..	..	..	..	..	3 45	..	..	..	..	..	..

For Notes, see page 284a

LONDON, CRYSTAL PALACE, CROYDON, SUTTON, DORKING NORTH,

p.m. — **Week Days**—*continued* — p.m.

Down	No.	SO	SX	SO		SO	SO	SX			SX	SO	SO	SO		SO			SX	SO	SX	SO	No.
Victoria .... dep	1	2 37	..	..	..	..	2 38	2 38	2 40	..	..	..	2 45	..	..	..	..	2 48	..	..	..	..	1
Charing Cross* ... "	2	**3**	**3**	**3**	..	**3**	**3**	**3**	**3**	..	**3**	**3**	..	**3**	..	**3**	**3**	..	2 45	**3**	**3**	**3**	2
Waterloo* .... "	3				..					..			..		2 47			..	2 47				3
London Bridge ..... "	4	..	2 29	2 31	..	2 42	..	..	..	..	2 37	2 39	..	2 47	..	2 45	2 48	..	2 51	2 51	2 53	2 53	4
Battersea Park	5	..	..	..	..	..	..	..	2 43	..	..	..	..	..	**3**	..	..	..	**3**	..	..	..	5
Clapham Junction	6	2 42	..	..	..	..	2 44	2 44	2‖47	..	..	..	..	..		..	..	2U53		..	..	..	6
Wandsworth Common A	7	..	..	..	..	..	..	..	2 50	..	..	..	..	..	Via Worcester Park	..	..	..	..	..	..	..	7
Balham & Upper Tooting	8	2 46	..	..	..	..	2 48	2 48	2 52	..	..	..	..	..		..	..	..	..	..	..	..	8
South Bermondsey	9	..	..	..	..	..	..	..	‖ 1 minute *earlier* on Saturdays	..	2 40	2 42	..	..		2 48	2 51	U Takes up only	..	..	..	..	9
Queen's Road, Peckham	10	..	..	..	..	..	..	..		..	2 43	2 45	..	..		2 51	2 54		..	..	..	..	10
Peckham Rye	11	..	..	..	..	..	..	..		..	2 45	2 47	..	..		2 53	2 56		..	..	..	..	11
East Dulwich	12	..	..	..	..	..	..	..		..	2 48	2 50	..	..		2 56	..		..	..	..	..	12
North Dulwich	13	..	..	..	..	..	..	..		..	2 50	2 52	..	..		2 58	To Victoria arr. 3 13 p.m		..	..	..	..	13
Tulse Hill	14	..	..	..	..	..	..	..		..	2 53	2 55	..	..		3 1			..	..	..	..	14
Streatham	15	..	..	..	..	..	..	..		..	2 57	2 59	..	..		..			..	..	..	..	15
New Cross Gate (for E.L.	16	..	2 34	2 36	..	..	..	..		..	..	..	..	2 52	..	..		..	..	..	2 58	2 58	16
Brockley B ....[Line)	17	..	2 36	2 38	..	..	..	..		..	..	..	..	2 54	..	..		..	..	..	3 0	3 0	17
Honor Oak Park	18	..	2 39	2 41	..	..	..	..		..	..	..	..	2 57	..	..		..	..	..	3 3	3 3	18
Forest Hill, for Lordship	19	..	2 41	2 43	..	..	..	..		..	..	..	..	2 59	..	..		..	..	..	3 5	3 5	19
Sydenham .... [Lane	20	..	2 44	2 46	..	..	..	..		..	..	..	..	3 2	..	..		..	..	..	3 8	3 8	20
Penge West C	21	..	2 46	2 48	..	..	..	..		..	..	..	..	..	..	..		..	..	..	..	3 10	21
Anerley	22	..	2 47	2 49	..	..	..	..		..	..	..	..	..	..	..	Stop	..	..	..	..	3 11	22
Streatham Common	23	..	..	..	..	..	2 52	2 52	..	..	2 59	3 1	..	..	..	..	..	..	..	..	..	..	23
Norbury	24	..	..	..	..	..	2 54	2 54	..	..	3 1	3 3	..	..	..	..	..	..	..	..	..	..	24
Thornton Heath	25	..	..	..	..	..	2 57	2 57	..	..	3 4	3 6	..	..	..	..	..	..	..	..	..	..	25
Selhurst	26	..	..	..	..	..	2 59	2 59	..	..	3 6	3 8	..	..	..	..	..	..	..	..	..	..	26
Streatham Hill	27	..	..	..	..	..	..	Arr Sutton 3 14 p.m	2 54	..	..	..	..	..	..	..	p.m	..	..	..	..	..	27
West Norwood..[N'wood)	28	..	..	..	..	..	..		2 57	..	..	..	..	..	..	3 3	**3**	..	..	..	..	..	28
Gipsy Hill (for Upper	29	..	..	..	..	..	..		3 0	..	..	..	..	..	..	3 6		..	..	..	..	..	29
Crystal Palace D	30	..	..	..	..	..	..		3 2	..	..	..	..	3 5	..	3 9	3 10	..	..	..	3 11	..	30
Birkbeck	31	..	..	..	..	..	..		..	..	..	..	..	..	..	..	3 13	..	..	..	..	..	31
Beckenham Jn. arr	32	..	..	..	..	..	..		..	..	..	..	..	..	..	..	3 17	..	..	..	..	..	32
Norwood Junction F ..	33	..	2 50	2 52	..	2 55	..		3 7	..	3 9	3 11	..	..	..	..	..	..	3 3	3 3	..	3 14	33
East Croydon .... arr	34	..	..	..	..	..	..		..	..	..	..	3 0	..	..	..	..	3 5	3 7	3 7	..	..	34
East Croydon .... dep	35	..	..	..	..	..	..		..	..	..	..	..	..	..	..	..	3 5	3 7	3 7	..	To Selhurst arr. 3 18 p.m	35
Mitcham Junction	36	2 53	..	..	..	..	..		..	..	To London Bridge, via Forest Hill	To London Bridge, via Forest Hill	..	..	..	..	..	..	..	..	..		36
Hackbridge	37	2 55	..	To Selhurst arr. 2 56 p.m	..	..	..		..	..			..	..	..	..	..	..	..	..	..		37
Carshalton	38	2 58	..		..	..	..		..	..			..	..	..	..	..	..	..	..	..		38
West Croydon 319 arr	39	..	2 54		..	2 59	3 2	3 2	3 11	..			..	..	..	..	..	..	..	..	..		39
West Croydon 319 dep	40	..	2 54		..	2 59	3 2	3 2	..	..			..	..	..	..	..	..	..	..	..		40
Waddon G	41	..	2 57		..	3 1	3 5	3 5	..	..			..	..	..	..	..	..	..	..	..		41
Wallington	42	..	3 0		..	3 5	3 8	3 8	..	..			..	..	..	..	..	..	..	..	..		42
Carshalton Beeches	43	..	3 3		..	3 7	3 11	3 11	..	..			..	..	..	..	..	..	..	..	..	..	43
Sutton 322	44	3 1	3 5		..	3 10	3 14	3 17	..	..			..	..	..	..	..	..	..	..	..	..	44
Belmont	45	..	3 8	..	..	3 13	3 17	3 20	..	..			..	..	..	..	..	..	..	..	..	..	45
Banstead	46	..	3 11	..	..	3 16	3 20	3 23	..	..			..	..	..	..	..	..	..	..	..	..	46
Epsom Downs ...... arr	47	..	3 15	..	..	3 19	3 23	3 26	..	..			..	..	..	..	..	..	..	..	..	..	47
Cheam	48	3 4	..	..	..	..	..	..	..	..	..	..	..	..	..	..	..	..	..	..	..	..	48
Ewell East H	49	3 7	..	..	..	..	..	..	..	..	..	..	..	..	..	..	..	..	..	..	..	..	49
Epsom	50	3 10	..	..	..	..	..	..	..	..	..	..	..	..	3 15	..	..	..	..	..	..	..	50
Ashtead	51	..	..	..	..	..	..	..	..	..	..	..	..	..	3 19	..	..	..	..	..	..	..	51
Leatherhead ... [Bridge J	52	..	..	..	..	..	..	..	..	..	..	..	..	..	3 23	..	..	..	..	..	..	..	52
Boxhill and Burford	53	..	..	..	..	..	..	..	..	..	..	..	..	..	..	..	..	..	..	..	..	..	53
Dorking North K .. arr	54	..	..	..	..	..	..	..	..	..	..	..	..	..	..	..	..	..	..	..	..	..	54
Bookham .... [394	55	..	..	..	..	..	..	..	..	..	..	..	..	..	3 28	..	..	..	..	..	..	..	55
Effingham Junction arr	56	..	..	..	..	..	..	..	..	..	..	..	..	..	3 32	..	..	..	..	..	..	..	56
South Croydon 234	57	..	..	..	..	..	..	..	..	..	..	..	..	..	..	..	..	..	3 10	3 10	..	..	57
Purley Oaks	58	..	..	..	..	..	..	..	..	..	..	..	..	..	..	..	..	..	3 12	3 12	..	..	58
Purley	59	..	..	..	..	..	..	..	..	..	..	..	..	..	..	..	..	3 11	3 15	3 15	..	..	59
Coulsdon North L .. arr	60	..	..	..	..	..	..	..	..	..	..	..	..	..	..	..	..	..	..	..	..	..	60
Purley .... dep	61	..	..	..	..	..	..	..	..	..	..	..	..	..	..	..	..	..	3 19	3 19	..	..	61
Kenley	62	..	..	..	..	..	..	..	..	..	..	..	..	..	..	..	..	..	3 22	3 22	..	..	62
Whyteleafe	63	..	..	..	..	..	..	..	..	..	..	..	..	..	..	..	..	..	3 25	3 25	..	..	63
Warlingham	64	..	..	..	..	..	..	..	..	..	..	..	..	..	..	..	..	..	3 27	3 27	..	..	64
Caterham .... arr	65	..	..	..	..	..	..	..	..	..	..	..	..	..	..	..	..	..	3 31	3 31	..	..	65
Purley .... dep	66	..	..	..	..	..	..	..	..	..	..	..	..	..	..	..	..	§ Via Three Bridges	3 17	3 17	..	..	66
Reedham	67	..	..	..	..	..	..	..	..	..	..	..	..	..	..	..	..		3 19	3 19	..	..	67
Smitham	68	..	..	..	..	..	..	..	..	..	..	..	..	..	..	..	..		3 21	3 21	..	..	68
Woodmansterne	69	..	..	..	..	..	..	..	..	..	..	..	..	..	..	..	..		3 24	3 24	..	..	69
Chipstead	70	..	..	..	..	..	..	..	..	..	..	..	..	..	..	..	..		3 26	3 26	..	..	70
Kingswood M	71	..	..	..	..	..	..	..	..	..	..	..	..	..	..	..	..		3 31	3 31	..	..	71
Tadworth N	72	..	..	..	..	..	..	..	..	..	..	..	..	..	..	..	..		3 34	3 34	..	..	72
Tattenham Corner. arr	73	..	..	..	..	..	..	..	..	..	..	..	..	..	..	..	..		3 37	3 37	..	..	73
Coulsdon South	74	..	..	..	..	..	..	..	..	..	..	..	..	..	..	..	..	3 14	..	..	..	..	74
Merstham	75	..	..	..	..	..	..	..	..	..	..	..	..	..	..	..	..	3 20	..	..	..	..	75
Redhill 158, 246 ...... arr	76	..	..	..	..	..	..	..	..	..	..	..	..	..	..	..	..	3 24	..	..	..	..	76
Reigate 246 .... "	77	..	..	..	..	..	..	..	..	..	..	..	..	..	..	..	..	3 30	..	..	..	..	77
Horsham 159, 244, 245 "	78	..	..	..	..	..	..	..	..	..	..	..	..	..	..	..	..	4§ 5	..	..	..	..	78

CATERHAM, TATTENHAM CORNER, REDHILL, REIGATE, and HORSHAM

Week Days—continued (p.m.)

No.	SX	SO	SX	SO	SX			SO	SO			SO														SX	SO
1	2 51	2 51	2 51	2 55	..	..	..	3 0	..	..	..	..	3 8	3 10	..	..	3 18	..	..	..	3 21	3J24	..	3 25	3 28	3 30	3 30
2						..					..					..	..	..		..				..	..		
3	③	③	③	③	③	..	③	③	③	③	3 7	③	③	③	③	..	..	..	③	..	③	③	③	..	..	③	③
4	..	..	..	..	2 53	..	3 2	..	3 3	3 7	..	3 8	..	..	3 15	..	..	3 18	3 18	..	..	..	3 25	..	..	..	..
5	..	..	..	..	..	..	..	3 3	..	..		..	..	3 13	..	..	..	..	..	..	..	..	..	..	..	3 33	3 33
6	2 56	2 56	2 56	3 0	..	..	..	3 6	..	..	③	..	3 14	3 16	..	..	..	..	..	..	3H27	3 30	..	..	3 34	3 36	3 36
7	2 59	2 59	..	..	..	..	..	3 9	..	..		..	..	3 20	..	..	..	..	..	..	..	..	..	..	..	3 39	3 39
8	3 1	3 1	3 0	3 4	..	..	..	3 11	..	..	..	..	3 18	3 22	..	..	..	..	..	..	3H31	3 34	..	..	..	3 41	3 41
9	..	..	..	..	..	..	..	..	..	..	Via Worcester Park	..	..	..	3 18	..	..	..	3 21	..	..	..	..	..	..	..	..
10	..	..	..	..	..	..	..	..	3 9	..		..	..	..	3 21	..	..	..	3 24	..	..	..	..	..	..	..	..
11	..	..	..	..	2 59	..	..	..	3 11	..		3 14	..	..	3 23	..	..	..	3 26	..	..	..	3 31	..	..	..	..
12	..	..	..	..	..	..	..	..	..	..		..	..	..	3 26	..	..	..	To Victoria arr. 3 43 p.m	..	H 1 minute *earlier* on Saturdays	J 1 minute later on Saturdays	..	..	..	..	..
13	..	..	..	..	..	..	..	..	..	..		..	..	..	3 28	..	..	..		..			..	..	..	..	..
14	..	..	..	..	3 3	..	..	..	..	..		3 18	..	..	3 31	..	..	..		..			3 35	..	..	..	..
15	..	..	..	..	3 7	..	..	..	..	..		3 22	..	..	..	..	..	..		..			3 39	..	..	..	..
16	..	..	..	..	..	..	3 7	..	..	3 12		..	..	..	..	..	..	..		..			..	..	..	..	..
17	..	..	..	..	..	..	..	..	..	3 14		..	..	..	..	..	..	..		..			..	..	..	..	..
18	..	..	..	..	..	..	..	..	..	3 17		..	..	..	..	..	..	..		..			..	..	..	..	..
19	..	..	..	..	..	..	3 11	..	..	3 19	..	..	..	..	..	..	..	..		..			..	..	..	..	..
20	..	..	..	..	..	..	3 14	..	..	3 22	..	..	..	..	..	..	..	..	..	..			..	..	..	..	..
21	..	..	..	..	..	..	3 16	..	..	3 24	..	..	..	..	..	..	..	..	..	..			..	..	..	..	..
22	..	..	..	..	..	..	3 17	..	..	3 25	..	..	..	..	..	..	..	..	..	..	..	..	..	..	..	..	..
23	3 5	3 5	..	..	..	..	..	..	..	..	..	..	3 22	..	..	..	J 1 minute later on Saturdays	..	..	..	3 35	..	..	..	..	..	..
24	3 7	3 7	..	..	..	..	..	..	..	..	..	..	3 24	..	..	..		..	..	..	3 37	..	..	..	..	..	..
25	3 10	3 10	..	..	..	..	..	..	..	..	..	..	3 27	..	..	..		..	..	..	3 40	..	H 1 minute *earlier* on Saturdays	..	..	..	..
26	3 12	3 12	..	..	..	..	..	..	..	..	..	..	3 29	..	..	..		..	..	..	3 42	..		..	..	..	..
27	..	..	..	..	..	Runs 3 minutes later on Saturdays	..	3 13	..	..	..	..	Arr. Sutton 3 44 p.m	3 24	..	..		..	..	SO	..	..		..	..	3 43	3 43
28	..	..	..	..	..		..	3 16	..	..	..	..		3 27	3 33	..		..	..	③	..	..		..	..	3 46	3 46
29	..	..	..	..	..		..	3 19	..	..	..	..		3 30	3 36	..		..	..		..	..		..	..	3 49	3 49
30	..	..	..	..	..		..	3 22	..	..	..	..		3 32	3 39	..		..	..	3 40	..	..		..	..	3 51	3 52
31	..	..	..	..	..		..	..	..	..	..	..		..	..	..		..	..	3 43	..	..		..	..	3 55	..
32	..	..	..	..	..		..	..	..	..	..	..		..	..	..		..	..	3 47	..	..		..	..	3 59	..
33	..	..	..	..	..		3 20	..	..	3 29	..	..		3J37	..	..	..	3 30	..	..	..	..		..	..	..	..
34	3 16	3 16	..	..	..		..	..	..	..	..	..		..	..	..	3J33	3 34	..	..	3 46	..		3 40	3 45	..	..
35	3 16	3 16	..	..	..		..	..	..	..	..	..		..	..	..	3 34	3 36	..	..	3 46	..	..	—	3 46	..	..
36	..	..	3 6	3 10	3 12		..	..	..	To London Bridge, via Streatham	..	3 27		..	..	..	..	..	..	..	..	3 40	3 44	Stop	..	..	..
37	..	..	3 9	3 13	3 14		..	..	..		..	3 29		..	..	..	..	..	..	..	..	3 43	3 47	..	..	..	..
38	..	..	3 11	3 15	3 17		..	..	..		..	3 32		..	..	..	..	..	..	..	..	3 45	3 49	..	..	..	..
39	..	..	..	..	..	..	3 24	..	..		..	..	3 32	3J41	..	..	..	..	..	..	..	..	..	p.m	..	..	..
40	..	..	..	..	..	③	3 24	..	..		..	..	3 32	J 1 minute later on Saturdays	..	..	..	..	..	..	..	..	..	③	..	..	..
41	..	..	..	..	..		3 27	..	..		..	..	3 35		..	..	..	..	..	..	..	..	..		..	..	..
42	..	..	..	..	..	3 18	3 30	..	..		..	..	3 38		..	..	..	..	..	..	..	..	..	3 51	..	..	..
43	..	..	..	..	..	3 20	3 33	..	..		..	..	3 41		..	..	..	..	..	..	..	..	..	3 53	..	..	..
44	..	..	3 14	3 18	3 20	3 23	3 35	..	..		..	3 35	3 47		..	..	..	..	..	..	..	3 48	3H52	3 56	..	..	..
45	..	..	..	..	..	..	3 38	..	..	..	..	..	3 50		..	..	..	..	..	..	..	..	..	☞	..	..	..
46	..	..	..	..	..	..	3 41	..	..	..	..	..	3 53		..	..	..	..	..	..	..	..	..		..	..	..
47	..	..	..	..	..	..	3 45	..	..	..	..	..	3 56		..	..	..	..	..	..	..	..	..		..	..	..
48	..	..	3 17	3 21	3 23	..	..	..	..	..	..	3 38	..		..	..	..	..	..	..	..	3 51	3 56		..	..	..
49	..	..	3 20	3 24	3 26	..	..	..	..	..	..	3 41	..		..	..	..	..	..	..	..	3 54	3 59	Runs 1 minute *earlier* on Saturdays	..	..	..
50	..	..	3 24	3 28	3 29	..	..	..	..	..	3 35	3 45	..	..	..	..	..	..	..	..	..	3 58	4 4		..	..	..
51	..	..	..	..	3 33	..	..	..	..	..	3 39	3 49	..	..	..	..	..	..	..	..	..	..	4 8		..	..	..
52	..	..	..	..	3 37	..	..	..	..	..	3 43	3 54	..	..	..	..	..	..	..	..	..	..	4 13		..	..	..
53	..	..	..	..	..	..	..	..	..	..	3 48	..	..	..	..	..	..	..	..	..	..	..	4 18		..	..	..
54	..	..	..	..	..	..	..	..	..	..	3 51	..	..	..	..	..	..	..	..	..	..	..	4 21		..	..	..
55	..	..	..	..	3 42	..	..	..	..	..	..	3 58	..	..	..	..	..	..	..	..	..	..	..		..	..	..
56	..	..	..	..	3 44	..	..	..	..	..	..	4 2	..	..	..	..	..	..	..	..	..	..	..		..	..	..
57	3 18	3 19	..	..	..	..	..	..	..	..	..	..	..	..	..	..	..	..	..	..	3 48	..	..		..	..	..
58	3 21	3 22	..	..	..	..	..	..	..	..	..	..	..	..	..	..	..	..	..	..	3 51	..	..		..	..	..
59	3 23	3 26	..	..	..	..	..	..	..	..	..	..	..	..	..	..	..	3 41	..	..	3 53	..	..		..	..	..
60	3 27	3 29	..	..	..	..	..	..	..	..	..	..	..	..	..	..	..	..	..	..	3 57	..	..		..	..	..
61	..	..	..	..	..	..	..	..	..	..	..	..	..	..	..	..	..	..	..	..	..	..	..	..	..	..	..
62	..	..	..	..	..	..	..	..	..	..	..	..	..	..	..	..	..	..	..	..	..	..	..	..	..	..	..
63	..	..	..	..	..	..	..	..	..	..	..	..	..	..	..	..	..	..	..	..	..	..	..	..	..	..	..
64	..	..	..	..	..	..	..	..	..	..	..	..	..	..	..	..	..	..	..	..	..	..	..	..	..	..	..
65	..	..	..	..	..	..	..	..	..	..	..	..	..	..	..	..	..	..	..	..	..	..	..	..	..	..	..
66	..	..	..	..	..	..	..	..	..	..	..	..	..	..	..	..	§ Via Three Bridges	§ Via Three Bridges	..	..	..	..	..	..	..	..	..
67	..	..	..	..	..	..	..	..	..	..	..	..	..	..	..	..			..	..	..	..	..	..	..	..	..
68	..	..	..	..	..	..	..	..	..	..	..	..	..	..	..	..			..	..	..	..	..	..	..	..	..
69	..	..	..	..	..	..	..	..	..	..	..	..	..	..	..	..			..	..	..	..	..	..	..	..	..
70	..	..	..	..	..	..	..	..	..	..	..	..	..	..	..	..			..	..	..	..	..	..	..	..	..
71	..	..	..	..	..	..	..	..	..	..	..	..	..	..	..	..			..	..	..	..	..	..	..	..	..
72	..	..	..	..	..	..	..	..	..	..	..	..	..	..	..	..			..	..	..	..	..	..	..	..	..
73	..	..	..	..	..	..	..	..	..	..	..	..	..	..	..	..			..	..	..	..	..	..	..	..	..
74	..	..	..	..	..	..	..	..	..	..	..	..	..	..	..	..		3 45	..	..	..	..	..	..	..	..	..
75	..	..	..	..	..	..	..	..	..	..	..	..	..	..	..	..		3 51	..	..	..	..	..	..	..	..	..
76	..	..	..	..	..	..	..	..	..	..	..	..	..	..	..	..	3 48	3 55	..	..	..	..	..	..	4 0	..	..
77	..	..	..	..	..	..	..	..	..	..	..	..	..	..	..	..	..	4 0	..	..	..	..	..	..	4 16	..	..
78	..	..	..	..	..	..	..	..	..	..	4 24	..	..	..	..	..	4§13	4§35	..	..	..	..	4 46	..	..	..	..

LONDON, CRYSTAL PALACE, CROYDON, SUTTON, DORKING NORTH,

For Notes, see page 284a

Down	No.	p.m.							Week Days—continued								p.m						No.
			SX											SX	SO	SX		SO		SO		SX	
Victoria........dep	1	..	..	..	..	3 38	3 40	3 45	3 48	..	..	..	..	..	..	..	..	..	3 51	..	..	..	1
Charing Cross✻... "	2	3S024	③	③	..	③	③	..	..	..	③	..	③	③	3 44	③	..	③	③	③	..	..	2
Waterloo✻....... "	3	3S026			..			..	..	3 47		..			3 46		..				..	..	3
London Bridge..... "	4	3 31	3 30	3 29	..	..	..	..	..	..	3 37	..	3 48	3 49	3 51	3 51	..	3 53	..	3 53	..	4 0	4
Battersea Park.........	5	③	..	..	..	..	3 43	..	..	③	..	..	..	..	③	..	..	..	..	..	..	..	5
Clapham Junction.....	6		..	..	..	3 44	3‖47	..	3 53		..	..	..	..		..	..	..	3 56	..	..	..	6
Wandsworth Common **A**	7	..	..	..	..	..	3 50	..	..		..	..	..	..	..	..	..	..	..	..	..	..	7
Balham & Upper Tooting	8	..	..	..	..	3 48	3 52	..	..		..	..	..	..	..	..	..	..	4 0	..	..	..	8
South Bermondsey......	9	..	3 33	..	..	..	..	..	..	Via Worcester Park	3 40	..	3 51	..	..	..	..	..	..	..	..	..	9
Queen's Road, Peckham	10	..	3 36	..	..	..	..	..	..		3 43	..	3 54	..	..	..	..	..	..	..	..	..	10
Peckham Rye...........	11	..	3 38	..	..	..	..	..	..		3 45	..	3‖57	..	..	..	..	..	..	3 59	..	..	11
East Dulwich...........	12	..	3 41	..	..	..	..	..	..		3 48	..	‖ 1 minute *earlier* on Saturdays To Victoria arr. 4 13 p.m	..	..	..	..	..	..	..	..	..	12
North Dulwich..........	13	..	3 43	..	..	..	..	..	..		3 50	..		..	..	..	..	..	..	..	..	..	13
Tulse Hill..............	14	..	3 46	..	..	..	..	..	..		3 53	..		..	..	..	..	..	..	4 3	..	..	14
Streatham..............	15	..	..	..	..	..	..	..	..		3 57	..		..	..	..	..	..	..	4 7	..	..	15
New Cross Gate (for E.L.	16	..	..	3 34	..	..	..	..	..		..	..		3 54	..	..	..	3 58	..	..	..	..	16
Brockley **B**.......[Line)	17	..	..	3 36	..	..	‖ 1 minute *earlier* on Saturdays	..	..		..	..		3 56	..	..	..	4 0	..	..	..	..	17
Honor Oak Park........	18	..	..	3 39	..	..		..	..	..	..	..		3 59	..	..	..	4 3	..	..	..	..	18
Forest Hill, for Lordship	19	..	..	3 41	..	..		..	..	..	..	..		4 1	..	..	..	4 5	..	..	..	..	19
Sydenham ....[Lane	20	..	..	3 44	..	..		..	..	..	..	..		4 4	..	..	..	4 8	..	..	..	..	20
Penge West **C**..........	21	..	..	3 46	..	..		..	..	..	..	..		..	..	..	..	..	..	..	..	..	21
Anerley.................	22	..	..	3 47	..	..		..	..	..	..	..		..	..	..	..	..	..	..	..	..	22
Streatham Common....	23	..	..	..	..	3 52		..	..	..	3 59	..		..	..	..	..	..	..	..	..	..	23
Norbury................	24	..	..	..	..	3 54		..	..	..	4 1	..		..	..	..	..	..	..	..	..	..	24
Thornton Heath........	25	..	..	..	..	3 57		..	..	..	4 4	..		..	..	..	..	..	..	..	..	..	25
Selhurst................	26	..	..	..	..	3 59		..	..	..	4 6	..		..	..	..	..	..	..	..	..	..	26
Streatham Hill.........	27	..	3 49	..	..		3 54	..	..	..	..	..		..	..	..	SO	..	..	..	..	..	27
West Norwood.[N'wood)	28	..	..	..	..		3 57	..	..	..	..	..		..	..	..	③	..	..	..	..	..	28
Gipsy Hill (for Upper	29	..	..	..	..		4 0	..	..	..	..	..		..	..	..		..	..	..	..	..	29
Crystal Palace D......	30	..	..	..	..	Arr Sutton 4 14 p.m	4‖ 3	..	..	..	..	..		4 7	..	..	4 10	4 11	..	..	..	..	30
Birkbeck..............	31	..	..	..	..		..	..	..	..	..	..	..	—	..	..	4 13	..	..	..	..	..	31
Beckenham Jn. arr	32	..	..	..	..		..	..	..	..	..	..	..	Stop	..	..	4 17	..	..	..	..	..	32
Norwood Junction F..	33	3 43	..	3 50	..		4S07	..	..	..	4 9	..	..	..	4 3	4 3	..	..	..	..	..	..	33
East Croydon.... arr	34	3 47	..	..	..		..	4 0	4 5	..	..	..	..	..	4 7	4 7	..	..	..	..	..	4 14	34
East Croydon.... dep	35	3 47	..	..	..		..	..	4 5	..	..	..	..	..	4 7	4 7	..	..	..	..	..	4 16	35
Mitcham Junction......	36	..	..	..	..		..	..	..	..	To London Bridge, via Forest Hill	..	..	..	..	..	..	..	4 6	4 12	..	..	36
Hackbridge.............	37	..	..	..	..		..	..	..	..		..	..	..	..	..	..	..	4 9	4 14	..	..	37
Carshalton.............	38	..	..	..	..		..	..	..	..		..	..	..	..	..	..	..	4 11	4 17	..	..	38
West Croydon 319 arr	39	..	..	3 54	..	4 2	4S011	..	..	..		..	..	..	..	..	..	..	..	..	..	..	39
West Croydon 319 dep	40	..	..	3 54	..	4 2	..	..	..	..		..	..	..	..	..	..	..	..	..	③	..	40
Waddon **G**..............	41	..	..	3 57	..	4 5	..	..	..	..		..	..	..	..	..	..	..	..	..		..	41
Wallington.............	42	..	..	4 0	..	4 8	..	..	..	..		..	..	..	..	..	..	..	..	..	4 21	..	42
Carshalton Beeches	43	..	..	4 3	..	4 11	..	..	..	..		..	..	..	..	..	..	..	..	..	4 23	..	43
Sutton 322..............	44	..	..	4 5	..	4‖18	..	..	..	..		..	..	..	..	..	..	..	4 14	4 20	4 26	..	44
Belmont................	45	..	..	4 8	..	4‖21	..	..	..	..	..	..	..	..	..	..	..	..	..	..	..	..	45
Banstead...............	46	..	..	4 11	..	4‖24	..	..	..	..	..	..	..	..	..	..	..	..	..	..	..	..	46
Epsom Downs...... arr	47	..	..	4 15	..	4‖27	..	..	..	..	..	..	..	..	..	..	..	..	..	..	..	..	47
Cheam..................	48	..	..	..	..	‖ 1 minute *earlier* on Saturdays	..	..	..	..	..	..	..	p.m	..	..	..	..	4 17	4 23	..	..	48
Ewell East **H**..........	49	..	..	..	..		..	..	..	..	..	..	..	SX	..	..	..	..	4 20	4 26	..	..	49
Epsom.................	50	..	..	..	..		..	..	..	4 15	..	..	..	③	..	..	..	..	4 24	4 29	..	..	50
Ashtead................	51	..	..	..	..		..	..	..	4 19	..	..	..		..	..	..	..	..	4 33	..	..	51
Leatherhead..[Bridge **J**	52	..	..	..	..		..	..	..	4 23	..	..	..	4 31	..	..	..	..	..	4 37	..	..	52
Boxhill and Burford	53	..	..	..	..		..	..	..	..	..	..	..	4 36	..	..	..	..	..	..	..	..	53
Dorking North K.. arr	54	..	..	..	..		..	..	..	..	..	..	..	4 39	..	..	..	..	..	..	..	..	54
Bookham...........[394	55	..	..	..	..		..	..	..	4 28	..	..	..	..	..	..	..	..	..	4 41	..	..	55
Effingham Junction arr	56	..	..	..	..		..	..	..	4 31	..	..	..	..	..	..	..	..	..	4 44	..	..	56
South Croydon 234......	57	3 50	..	..	..		..	..	..	..	..	..	..	..	4 10	4 10	..	..	..	..	..	..	57
Purley Oaks............	58	3 52	..	..	..		..	..	..	..	..	..	..	..	4 12	4 12	..	..	..	..	..	..	58
Purley.................	59	3 55	..	..	..		..	..	4 11	..	..	..	..	..	4 15	4 15	..	..	..	..	..	..	59
Coulsdon North **L**.. arr	60	..	..	..	..		..	..	..	..	..	..	..	..	..	..	..	..	..	..	..	..	60
Purley..............dep	61	3 59	..	..	..	..	..	..		..	..	..	..	..	4 19	4 19	..	..	..	..	..	..	61
Kenley..................	62	4 2	..	..	..	..	..	..		..	..	..	..	..	4 22	4 22	..	..	..	..	..	..	62
Whyteleafe.............	63	4 5	..	..	..	..	..	..		..	..	..	..	..	4 25	4 25	..	..	..	..	..	..	63
Warlingham............	64	4 7	..	..	..	..	..	..		..	..	..	..	..	4 27	4 27	..	..	..	..	..	..	64
Caterham.......... arr	65	4 11	..	..	..	..	..	..		..	..	..	..	..	4 31	4 31	..	..	..	..	..	..	65
Purley..............dep	66	3 57	..	.	..	..	..	..		..	..	..	..	..	4 17	4 17	..	..	..	..	..	..	66
Reedham................	67	3 59	.	..	..	..	..	..		..	..	..	..	..	4 19	4 19	..	..	..	..	..		67
Smitham................	68	1	..	..	..	..	..	..	§ Via Three Bridges	..	..	..	..	..	4 21	4 21	..	..	..	..	..		68
Woodmansterne	69	4 4	..	..	..	..	..	..		..	..	..	..	..	4 24	4 24	..	..	..	..	..		69
Chipstead...............	70	4 6	..	..	..	..	..	..		..	..	..	..	..	4 26	4 26	..	..	..	..	..	§ Via Three Bridges	70
Kingswood **M**..........	71	4 11	..	..	..	..	..	..		..	..	..	..	..	4 31	4 31	..	..	..	..	..		71
Tadworth **N**............	72	4 14	..	..	..	..	..	..		..	..	..	..	..	4 34	4 34	..	..	..	..	..		72
Tattenham Corner. arr	73	4 17	..	..	..	..	..	..		..	..	..	..	..	4 37	4 37	..	..	..	..	..		73
Coulsdon South.........	74	..	..	..	..	..	..	..	4 14	..	..	..	..	..	..	..	..	..	..	..	..		74
Merstham...............	75	..	..	..	..	..	..	..	4 20	..	..	..	..	..	..	..	..	..	..	..	..		75
Redhill 158, 246..... arr	76	..	..	..	..	..	..	..	4 24	..	..	..	..	..	..	..	..	..	..	..	..	4 30	76
Reigate 246....... "	77	..	..	..	..	..	..	..	4 30	..	..	..	..	..	..	..	..	..	..	..	..	..	77
Horsham 159, 244, 245 "	78	..	..	..	..	..	..	..	5§ 5	..	..	..	..	..	..	..	..	..	..	..	..	5§ 5	78

CATERHAM, TATTENHAM CORNER, REDHILL, REIGATE, and HORSHAM

p.m — **Week Days**—*continued* — p.m

No.	SO	SX	SX		SX	SX	SO	SX	SO			SX		SX	SO	SO	SX		SX		SX	SO			SX		SO	SX
1	3 51	3 54	..	..	4 0	..	..	..	..	..	..	..	..	4 8	4 8	4 10	4 11	..	..	..	..	..	..	..	4 16	4 18	..	4 19
2	3	3	3	..	3	3	3	3	3	..	..	3	..	3	3	3	3	..	3	3	3	..	..	3	..	..	..	3
3				..						..	4 7		..					..				..	..		..	..	..	
4	..	..	4 0	..	..	4 2	4 2	4 5	4 7	..	..	4 7	..	..	..	..	..	..	4 10	4 15	4 16	4 16	..	4J17	..	..	4 18	..
5	..	..	..	..	4 3	..	..	..	..	..	3	..	..	..	..	4 13	4 14	..	..	..	..	..	..	..	..	..	..	..
6	3 56	3 59	..	..	4 6	..	..	..	..	..		..	..	4 14	4 14	4 16	4 18	..	..	..	..	..	..	..	4U21	..	..	4 24
7	3 59	..	..	..	4 9	..	..	..	..	..		..	..	..	..	4 20	4 21	..	..	..	..	..	..	..	..	..	..	..
8	4 1	4 3	..	..	4 11	..	..	..	..	..		..	..	4 18	4 18	4 22	4 23	..	..	..	..	..	..	..	..	..	..	4 28
9	..	..	..	..	..	..	..	..	..	..		..	..	..	..	..	..	..	..	4 18	..	..	..	4 21		..	..	..
10	..	..	4 5	..	..	..	..	..	..	..		..	..	..	..	..	..	..	4 15	4 21	..	..	..	4 24		..	..	..
11	..	..	4 7	..	..	..	..	..	..	..		4 13	..	..	..	..	..	..	4 17	4 23	..	..	..	4 26		..	..	..
12	..	..	4 9	..	..	..	..	..	..	..	Via Worcester Park	..	..	..	..	..	..	..	4 19	4 26	..	..	..	..	U Takes up only	..	..	..
13	..	..	..	..	..	..	..	..	..	..		..	..	..	..	..	..	..	4 21	4 28	..	..	..	..		..	..	..
14	..	..	4 13	..	..	..	..	..	..	..		4 18	..	..	..	..	..	..	4 24	4 31	..	..	..			..	..	..
15	..	..	4 16	..	..	..	..	..	..	..		4 22	..	..	..	..	..	..	..	..	..	..	..			..	..	..
16	..	..	..	..	..	..	4 7	4 10	4 12	..		..	..	..	..	..	..	..	..	..	..	..	..		..	..	..	..
17	..	..	..	..	..	..	..	4 12	4 14	..		..	..	..	..	..	..	..	..	..	..	..	..		..	..	..	..
18	..	..	..	..	..	..	..	4 15	4 17	..	..	..	..	..	..	..	..	..	..	..	..	..	..		..	..	..	..
19	..	..	..	..	..	..	4 11	4 18	4 19	..	..	..	..	..	..	..	..	..	..	..	..	..	..		..	..	..	..
20	..	..	..	..	..	..	4 14	4 21	4 22	..	..	..	..	..	..	..	..	..	..	..	..	..	..	J 1 min. later on Sats. To Victoria arr. 4J41 p.m	..	..	..	..
21	..	..	..	..	..	..	4 16	4 23	4 24	..	..	..	..	..	..	..	..	..	..	..	..	..	..		..	..	..	..
22	..	..	..	..	..	..	4 17	4 25	4 25	..	..	..	..	..	..	..	..	..	..	..	..	..	..		..	..	..	..
23	4 5	4 7	4 18	..	..	..	..	..	..	..	..	..	..	4 22	4 22	..	..	..	..	..	..	..	..		..	..	..	..
24	4 7	4 9	4 21	..	..	..	..	..	..	..	..	..	..	4 24	4 24	..	..	..	..	..	..	..	..		..	..	..	..
25	4 10	4 12	4 24	..	..	..	..	..	..	..	..	..	..	4 27	4 27	..	..	..	..	..	..	..	..		..	..	..	..
26	4 12	4 14	4 26	..	..	..	..	..	..	..	..	..	..	4 29	4 29	..	..	..	..	..	..	..	..	..	..	..	..	..
27	..	..	..	..	4 13	..	..	..	..	..	..	..	..	..		4 24	4 25	..	4 28	..	..	..	SO	..	..	..	..	..
28	..	..	..	..	4 16	..	..	..	..	..	..	..	..	..		4 27	4 28	..	..	4 33	..	..	3	..	..	..	..	..
29	..	..	..	..	4 19	..	..	..	..	..	..	..	..	..		4 30	4 31	..	..	4 36	..	..		..	..	..	..	..
30	..	..	..	..	4 25	..	..	..	..	..	..	..	..	..		4 32	4 33	..	..	4J38	..	..	4 40	..	..	..	..	..
31	..	..	..	..	4 29	..	..	..	..	..	..	..	..	..	Arr. Sutton 4 45 p.m	..	..	..	..		..	..	4 43	..	..	..	..	..
32	..	..	..	..	4 33	..	..	..	..	..	..	..	..	..		..	..	..	..		..	..	4 47	..	..	..	..	..
33	..	..	4 30	..	..	4 15	4 20	4 31	4 29	..	..	..	..	..		4 37	4 40	..	..		4 28	4 28	..	..	..	..	..	..
34	4 16	4 17		..	..	..	..			..	..	..	..	..		..	..	..	..		4 32	4 32	..	..	4 34	..	4 35	..
35	4 16	4 18		..	..	..	..			..	..	..	..	..		..	..	..	..		4 32	4 34	..	..	4 34	..	4 35	..
36	..	..		..	..	..	..			..	..	4 27	..	..	..	..	..	..	..		..	..	..	..	..	..	..	4 35
37	..	..		..	..	..	..			..	..	4 29	..	..	..	..	..	..	..		..	..	..	..	..	..	..	4 37
38	..	..		..	..	..	..			..	..	4 32	..	..	..	..	..	..	..	J 1 minute later on Saturdays	..	..	..	..	..	..	..	4 40
39	..	..		..	..	4 19	4 24			..	..	..	SX	4 32	4 32	4 41	4 46	..	..		..	..	..	..	..	..	..	..
40	..	..	To London Bridge, via Forest Hill	..	..	4 19	4 24	To London Bridge, via Streatham	To London Bridge, via Streatham	..	..	..	3	4 33	4 32	..	..	..	..		..	..	..	..	..	..	..	..
41	..	..		..	..	4 21	4 27			..	..	..		4 36	4 35	..	..	..	..		..	..	..	..	..	..	..	..
42	..	..		..	..	4 25	4 30			..	..	..	4 35	4 39	4 40	..	..	..	..		..	..	..	..	..	..	..	..
43	..	..		..	..	4 27	4 33			..	..	..	4 38	4 42	4 42	..	..	..	..		..	..	..	..	..	..	..	..
44	..	..		..	..	4 30	4 35			..	..	4 35	4 41	4 44	4 47	..	..	..	..		..	..	..	..	..	4 39	..	4 43
45	..	..		..	..	4 33	4 38	..		..	..	..	..	4 47	4 50	..	..	..	..	..	..	..	..	..	..	..	..	..
46	..	..		..	..	4 36	4 41	..		..	..	..	..	4 50	4 53	..	..	..	..	..	..	..	..	..	..	..	..	..
47	..	..		..	..	4 40	4 45	..		..	..	..	..	4 54	4 56	..	..	..	..	..	..	..	..	..	..	..	..	..
48	..	..	..	..	..	..	..	..	..	..	..	4 42	..	..	..	..	..	..	..	..	..	..	..	..	..	..	..	4 46
49	..	..	..	..	..	..	..	..	..	..	..	4 45	..	..	..	..	..	..	..	..	..	..	..	..	..	..	..	4 49
50	..	..	..	..	..	..	..	..	..	..	4 35	4 49	..	..	..	..	..	..	..	..	..	..	..	..	..	..	..	4 52
51	..	..	..	..	..	..	..	..	..	..	4 39	4 53	..	..	..	..	..	..	..	..	..	..	..	..	..	..	..	..
52	..	..	..	..	..	..	..	..	..	..	4 43	4 57	..	..	..	..	..	..	..	..	..	..	..	..	..	..	..	..
53	..	..	..	..	..	..	..	..	..	..	4 48	..	..	..	..	..	..	..	..	..	..	..	..	..	..	..	..	..
54	..	..	..	..	..	..	..	..	..	..	4 51	..	..	..	..	..	..	..	..	..	..	..	..	..	..	4 55	..	..
55	..	..	..	..	..	..	..	..	..	..	..	5 1	..	..	..	..	..	..	..	..	..	..	..	..	..	..	..	..
56	..	..	..	..	..	..	..	..	..	..	..	5 4	..	..	..	..	..	..	..	..	..	..	..	..	..	..	..	..
57	4 18	4 20	..	..	..	..	..	..	..	..	..		..	..	..	..	..	..	..	..	..	..	..	..	..	..	4 38	..
58	4 21	4 23	..	..	..	..	..	..	..	..	..		..	..	..	..	..	..	..	..	..	..	..	..	..	..	..	..
59	4 23	4 25	..	..	..	..	..	..	..	..	..		..	..	..	..	..	..	..	..	4 38	4 40	..	..	4 40	..	..	..
60	4 27	4 29	..	..	..	..	..	..	..	..	..		..	..	..	..	..	..	..	..	..	..	..	..	..	..	..	..
61	..	..	..	..	..	..	..	..	..	..	..	Arr. Cheam 4 38 p.m	..	..	..	..	..	..	..	..	4 40	..	..	..	..	..	..	..
62	..	..	..	..	..	..	..	..	..	..	..		..	..	..	..	..	..	..	..	4 43	..	..	..	..	..	..	..
63	..	..	..	..	..	..	..	..	..	..	..		..	..	..	..	..	..	..	..	4 46	..	..	..	..	..	..	..
64	..	..	..	..	..	..	..	..	..	..	..		..	..	..	..	..	..	..	..	4 48	..	..	..	..	..	..	..
65	..	..	..	..	..	..	..	..	..	..	..		..	..	..	..	..	..	..	..	4 52	..	..	..	..	..	..	..
66	..	..	..	..	..	..	..	..	..	..	..	..	..	..	..	..	..	..	..	..	4 39		..	..		..	..	..
67	..	..	..	..	..	..	..	..	..	..	..	..	..	..	..	..	..	..	..	..	4 41		..	..		..	..	..
68	..	..	..	..	..	..	..	..	..	..	..	..	..	..	..	..	..	..	..	..	4 43		..	..		..	..	..
69	..	..	..	..	..	..	..	..	..	..	..	..	..	..	..	..	..	..	..	..	4 46		..	..		..	..	..
70	..	..	..	..	..	..	..	..	..	..	..	..	..	..	..	..	..	..	..	..	4 48	§ Via Three Bridges	..	..	§ Via Three Bridges	..	..	..
71	..	..	..	..	..	..	..	..	..	..	..	..	..	..	..	..	..	..	..	..	4 53		..	..		..	..	..
72	..	..	..	..	..	..	..	..	..	..	..	..	..	..	..	..	..	..	..	..	4 56		..	..		..	..	..
73	..	..	..	..	..	..	..	..	..	..	..	..	..	..	..	..	..	..	..	..	4 59		..	..		..	..	..
74	..	..	..	..	..	..	..	..	..	..	..	..	..	..	..	..	..	..	..	..	..	4 43	..	..	4 44	..	..	..
75	..	..	..	..	..	..	..	..	..	..	..	..	..	..	..	..	..	..	..	..	..	4 49	..	..	4 50	..	..	..
76	..	..	..	..	..	..	..	..	..	..	..	..	..	..	..	..	..	..	..	..	..	4 53	..	..	4 54	..	..	..
77	..	..	..	..	..	..	..	..	..	..	..	..	..	..	..	..	..	..	..	..	..	4 59	..	..	..	..	..	..
78	..	..	..	..	..	..	..	..	..	..	5 24	..	..	..	..	..	..	..	..	..	..	5§32	..	..	5§32	5 13	..	..

For Notes, see page 284a

LONDON, CRYSTAL PALACE, CROYDON, SUTTON, DORKING NORTH,

Down	No.	p.m. SX	SX	SX	SX		SX	SX	SX	SO	SX	3X		SX		SO	SX	SX	SO	SX	SX	SO	No.
Victoria ... dep	1	..	..	4 25	..	4 21	..	..	..	4 26	4 26	4 25		..	..	..	..	..	..	4 35	4 38	..	1
Charing Cross * .. "	2	..	3	..	3	3	3	..	3	3	3	..	..	3	..	3	3	3	4 24	3	3	3	2
Waterloo * ... "	3	..		..				4 27				..	..		..				4 26				3
London Bridge ... "	4	4 20	4 22	..	4 25	..	4 25	..	4 26	..	..	..	..	4 28	..	4 28	4 30	4 31	4 31	..	..	4 29	4
Battersea Park	5	..	..	..	..	..	..	3	..	..	4 29	..	..	..	..	..	..	..	3	..	..	..	5
Clapham Junction	6	..	..	..	..	4 26	..		..	4 31	4 32	..	..	..	..	..	..	..		4 40	4 43	..	6
Wandsworth Common A	7	..	..	..	..		..		..	..	4 35	..	..	..	..	..	..	..		..	..	..	7
Balham & Upper Tooting	8	..	..	..	..	4‖31	..		..	4 35	4 37	..	..	..	..	..	..	..	..	..	4 47	..	8
South Bermondsey	9	..	..	..	..		..	Via Worcester Park	..	..	..	..	..	..	..	..	..	..	..	..	..	..	9
Queen's Road, Peckham	10	..	..	..	..		..		..	..	..	..	..	..	..	..	4 35	..	..	..	..	..	10
Peckham Rye	11	..	..	..	..		..		..	..	..	..	..	..	..	4 34	4 37	..	..	..	..	..	11
East Dulwich	12	..	..	..	..	‖1 minute *earlier* on Saturdays	..		..	..	..	..	..	..	..	..	4 40	..	..	..	..	..	12
North Dulwich	13	..	..	..	..		..		..	..	..	..	..	..	..	..	4 42	..	..	..	..	..	13
Tulse Hill	14	..	..	..	..		4 35		..	..	..	..	..	4 38	..	4 39	4 45	..	..	..	..	..	14
Streatham	15	..	..	..	..		4 39		..	..	..	..	..	4 42	..	4 42	..	..	..	..	..	..	15
New Cross Gate (for E.L.	16	..	..	..	..		..		4 31	..	..	..	..	..	..	..	..	4 36	..	..	..	4 34	16
Brockley B ... [Line)	17	..	..	..	..		..		..	..	..	..	..	..	..	..	..	4 38	..	..	..	4 36	17
Honor Oak Park	18	..	..	..	..		..		..	..	..	..	..	..	..	..	..	4 41	..	..	..	4 39	18
Forest Hill, for Lordship	19	..	..	..	..		..	..	4 35	..	..	..	..	..	..	..	..	4 43	..	..	..	4 41	19
Sydenham ... [Lane	20	..	..	..	..		..	..	4 38	..	..	..	..	..	..	..	..	4 46	..	..	..	4 44	20
Penge West C	21	..	..	..	..		..	..	..	..	..	..	..	..	..	..	..	4 48	..	..	..	4 46	21
Anerley	22	..	..	..	..		..	..	..	..	..	..	..	..	..	..	..	4 49	..	..	..	4 47	22
Streatham Common	23	..	..	..	..	4 35	4 41	..	..	..	..	..	..	..	..	..	..	..	..	..	..	..	23
Norbury	24	..	..	..	..	4 37	4 44	..	..	..	..	..	..	..	..	..	..	..	..	..	..	..	24
Thornton Heath	25	..	..	..	..	4 40	4 47	..	..	..	..	..	..	..	..	..	..	..	..	..	..	..	25
Selhurst	26	..	..	..	..	4 42	4 50	..	..	..	..	..	..	..	..	..	..	..	..	..	..	..	26
Streatham Hill	27	..	..	..	..	..	..	..	..	..	4 39	..	..	..	..	..	4 48	..	..	..	..	..	27
West Norwood [N'wood)	28	..	..	..	..	..	..	..	..	..	4 42	..	..	..	..	..		..	..	..	..	..	28
Gipsy Hill (for Upper	29	..	..	..	..	..	..	..	..	..	4 45	..	..	..	..	..		..	..	..	..	..	29
Crystal Palace D	30	..	..	..	..	..	..	..	4 41	..	4 48	..	..	..	..	..	To Victoria via Wandsworth Common.	..	..	..	..	..	30
Birkbeck	31	..	..	..	..	..	..	..	Stop	..	4 51	..	..	..	..	..		..	..	..	..	..	31
Beckenham Jn. arr	32	..	..	..	..	..	..	..		..	4 55	..	..	..	..	..		..	..	..	..	..	32
Norwood Junction F	33	..	4 35	..	4 38	..	4 53	..	..	..	..	..	..	..	..	..		4 52	4 43	..	..	4 50	33
East Croydon ... arr	34	4 38	..	4 40	4 42	4 46		..	..	..	..	4 45	..	..	..	..			4 47	4 52	..	..	34
East Croydon ... dep	35	4 42	..	..	4 42	4 46		..	..	..	..	4 46	..	..	..	..			4 47	4 52	..	..	35
Mitcham Junction	36	..	..	..	..	..		..	..	4 41	..	..	..	4 47	..	4 47			..	..	4 53	..	36
Hackbridge	37	..	..	..	..	..		..	..	4 44	..	..	..	4 49	..	4 50			..	..	4 56	..	37
Carshalton	38	..	..	..	..	..	To London Bridge, via Forest Hill	..	..	4 46	..	..	..	4 52	..	4 53		To London Bridge, via Streatham	..	..	4 58	..	38
West Croydon 319 arr	39	..	4 39	..	..	..		..	..	..	..	..	..	..	SO	..			..	..	..	4 54	39
West Croydon 319 dep	40	..	4 39	..	..	..		..	..	..	..	..	..	..	3	..			..	..	..	4 54	40
Waddon G	41	..	4 41	..	..	..		..	..	..	..	..	..	..		..			..	..	..	4 57	41
Wallington	42	..	4 45	..	..	..		..	..	..	..	..	..	..	4 48	..			..	..	..	5 0	42
Carshalton Beeches	43	..	4 47	..	..	..		..	..	..	..	..	..	..	4 50	..			..	..	..	5 3	43
Sutton 322	44	..	4 50	..	..	..		..	..	4 50	..	..	..	4 55	4 54	4 56			..	..	5 1	5 5	44
Belmont	45	..	4 53	..	..	..		..	..	..	..	..	..	..	..	..	..	..	..	..	..	5 8	45
Banstead	46	..	4 56	..	..	..	..	..	..	..	..	..	..	..	..	..	..	..	..	..	..	5 11	46
Epsom Downs ... arr	47	..	4 59	..	..	..	..	..	..	..	..	..	..	..	..	..	..	..	..	..	..	5 15	47
Cheam	48	..	..	..	..	..	..	..	p.m	4 53	..	..	..	4 58	..	4 59	..	..	..	..	5 4	..	48
Ewell East H	49	..	..	..	..	..	..	..	SX	4 56	..	..	..	5 1	..	5 2	..	..	..	..	5 7	..	49
Epsom	50	..	..	..	..	..	..	4 55	3	4 59	..	..	..	5 5	..	5 5	..	..	..	..	5 11	..	50
Ashtead	51	..	..	..	..	..	..	4 59		..	..	..	..	5 9	..	5 9	..	..	..	..	..	..	51
Leatherhead .. [Bridge J	52	..	..	..	..	..	..	5 3	5 9	..	..	..	..	5 13	..	5 13	..	..	..	..	..	..	52
Boxhill and Burford	53	..	..	..	..	..	..	5 8	..	..	..	..	..	5 18	..	5 18	..	..	..	..	..	..	53
Dorking North K .. arr	54	..	..	..	..	..	..	5 11	..	..	..	..	..	5 21	..	5 21	..	..	..	..	..	..	54
Bookham ... [394	55	..	..	..	..	..	..	..	5p22	..	..	..	..	..	..	..	..	..	..	..	..	..	55
Effingham Junction arr	56	..	..	..	..	..	..	..	5 25	..	..	..	..	..	..	..	..	..	..	..	..	..	56
South Croydon 234	57	4 46	..	..	..	4 48	..	..	..	..	..	..	..	..	..	..	..	..	4 50	..	..	..	57
Purley Oaks	58	..	..	..	..	4‖51	..	..	..	..	..	..	..	..	..	..	..	..	4 52	..	..	..	58
Purley	59	..	..	..	4 47	4 53	..	..	..	..	..	..	..	..	..	..	..	..	4 55	4 57	..	..	59
Coulsdon North L .. arr	60	..	..	..	4 50	4‖57	..	..	..	..	..	..	..	..	..	..	..	..	..	5 1	..	..	60
Purley ... dep	61	..	..	..	..	..	..	..	..	..	..	..	..	..	..	..	..	..	4 59	..	..	..	61
Kenley	62	..	..	..	..	..	..	..	..	..	..	..	..	..	..	..	..	..	5 2	..	..	..	62
Whyteleafe	63	..	..	..	..	..	..	..		..	..	..	..	..	..	..	..	..	5 5	..	..	..	63
Warlingham	64	..	..	..	..	..	..	..		..	..	..	..	..	..	..	..	..	5 7	..	..	..	64
Caterham ... arr	65	..	..	..	..	..	..	..		..	..	..	..	..	..	..	..	..	5 11	..	..	..	65
Purley ... dep	66	..	..	..	..	..	..	..	p Arr. Bookham 5 15 p.m	..	..		..	..	..	..	..	..	4 57	..	..	..	66
Reedham	67	..	..	..	..	..	..	..		..	..		..	..	..	..	..	..	4 59	..	..	..	67
Smitham	68	..	..	..	..	..	..	..		..	..		..	..	..	..	..	..	5 1	..	..	..	68
Woodmansterne	69	..	..	..	..	..	..	..		..	..	§ Via Three Bridges	..	..	..	..	..	..	5 4	..	..	..	69
Chipstead	70	..	..	..	..	..	..	..		..	..		..	..	..	..	..	..	5 6	..	..	..	70
Kingswood M	71	..	..	..	..	..	..	..		..	..		..	..	..	..	..	..	5 11	..	..	..	71
Tadworth N	72	..	..	..	..	..	..	..		..	..		..	..	..	..	..	..	5 14	..	..	..	72
Tattenham Corner . arr	73	..	..	..	..	..	..	..	..	..	..		..	..	..	..	..	..	5 17	..	..	..	73
Coulsdon South	74	..	..	..	..	..	..	..	..	..	..	..	..	..	..	..	..	..	..	..	..	..	74
Merstham	75	..	..	..	..	..	..	..	..	..	..	..	..	..	..	..	..	..	..	..	..	..	75
Redhill 158, 246 ... arr	76	..	..	..	..	..	..	..	..	..	..	5 0	..	..	..	..	..	..	..	..	..	..	76
Reigate 246 ... "	77	..	..	..	..	..	..	..	..	..	..	5 8	..	..	..	..	..	..	..	..	..	..	77
Horsham 159, 244, 245 "	78	..	..	..	..	..	..	..	..	..	..	5§32	..	5 56	..	5 46	..	..	..	..	..	..	78

CATERHAM, TATTENHAM CORNER, REDHILL, REIGATE, and HORSHAM

p.m — Week Days—*continued* — p.m

No.	S X	S X		S X	S X	S X	S X	S O		S O	S X	S O	S X	S X			S X	S O	S X	S O	S X	S O		S X	S X	S O	S X	S O
1							4 38	4 38	4 40									4 45	4Y45	4 48			4 50					4 51
2																						4 44						
3	3	3		3		3	3	3	3	3	3	4 47	4 47	3			3				3	4 46		4 52	3	3	3	3
4	4 35	4 35		4 37	4 40	4 42				4 37	4 44			4 45			4 47		4 47		4 54	4 51			4 48	4 48	4 50	
5									4 43																			
6							4 44	4 44	4 46			3	3							4 53		3		4 59				4 56
7									4 50																			4 59
8							4 48	4 48	4 52															3				5 1
9		4 38		4 41						4 40																4 51		
10		4 41		4 44						4 43																4 54		
11		4 43		4 46						4 45																4 56		
12		4 46								4 48		Via Worcester Park	Via Worcester Park															
13		4 48								4 50																		
14		4 51								4 53				4 55											4 58			
15				To Victoria, arr. 5 2 p.m						4 57				4 59					Y Does not convey local Passengers Victoria to East Croydon						5 2			
16											4 49						4 52										4 55	
17																	4 54									To Victoria arr. 5 11 p.m	4 58	
18																	4 57										5 0	
19																	4 59										5 3	
20																	5 2										5 5	
21																											5 7	
22																											5 9	
23							4 52	4 52		4 59				5 1														5 5
24							4 54	4 54		5 1				5 4														5 7
25							4 57	4 57		5 4				5 7														5 10
26							4 59	4 59		5 6				5 10														5 12
27									4 54						S O									Via Worcester Park				
28		4 53							4 57																			
29		4 56							5 0						3								J 1 minute later on Saturdays					
30		4 59							5 2						5 10		5 5											
31								Arr. Sutton 5 14 p.m							5 13													
32		Stop													5 17													
33	4 47					4 55			5 7	5 9	4 58			5 13								5 3					5 11	
34	4 51				4 57						5 1							5 0	5 1	5 5	5 8	5 7	5J 7					5 16
35	4 51										5 1								5 2	5 5	5 8	5 7						5 16
36																									5 7			
37																									5 9			
38		p.m																							5 12			
39		S X				4 59	5 2	5 2	5 11																			
40						4 59	5 2	5 2		To London Bridge, via Forest Hill				To London Bridge, via Forest Hill														
41		3				5 1	5 5	5 5																			To London Bridge, via Streatham	
42		5 1				5 5	5 8	5 8																				
43		5 3				5 7	5 11	5 11																				
44		5 6				5 10	5 14	5 17																	5 15			
45						5 13	5 17	5 20					Arr. Leatherhead 5 24 p.m															
46						5 16	5 20	5 23																				
47						5 19	5 24	5 26																				
48																									5 18			
49																									5 21			
50												5 15	5 15											5 23	5 24			
51												5 19	5 19												5 28			
52												5 23	5 28												5 32			
53																									5 37			
54																									5 40			
55												5 28	5 32															
56												5 31	5 36															
57	4 54										5 4											5 10						5 18
58											5 6											5 12						5 21
59	4 58										5 9								5 7	5 11	5 14	5 15						5 23
60											5 12																	5 27
61	5 0																				5 17	5 19						
62	5 3																				5 20	5 22						
63	5 6																				5 23	5 25						
64	5 8																				5 25	5 27						
65	5 12																				5 29	5 31						
66	4 59																				5 16	5 17						
67	5 1																				5 18	5 19						
68	5 4																				5 20	5 21						
69	5 6																				5 23	5 24						
70	5 9																		§ Via Three Bridges	§ Via Three Bridges	5 25	5 26						
71	5 13																				5 30	5 31						
72	5 16																				5 33	5 34						
73	5 20																				5 36	5 37						
74																			5 11	5 14								
75																			5 17	5 20								
76																			5 21	5 24								
77																			5 26	5 30								
78																			5§58	6§ 5								

LONDON, CRYSTAL PALACE, CROYDON, SUTTON, DORKING NORTH,

Week Days—continued (p.m)

Down	No.	SX	SO	SX	SX	SX	SO	SX	SO	SX	SX	SX	SX	SX	SO	SX	SX	SX	SO		SX	SX	No.
Victoria .... dep	1	..	..	4 51	5 0	4 53	4 54	4 55	..	..	..	5 4	..	4 58	..	5 0	..	5 4	5 8	..	..	..	1
Charing Cross* ... "	2											..								..			2
Waterloo* .... "	3	3	3	3	3	3	3	3	3	3	3	..	3	3	3	3	3	3	3	5 7	3	3	3
London Bridge ..... "	4	4 50	4 53	..	..	..	..	..	4 55	4 55	4 57	..	5 2	..	5 2	..	5 4	..	..	..	5 5	5 7	4
Battersea Park	5	..	..	..	..	4 56	..	..	..	..	..	..	..	..	..	5 3	..	5 7	..		..	..	5
Clapham Junction	6	..	..	4 56	..	4 59	4 59	5 0	..	..	..	..	..	5 3	..	5 6	..	5 10	5 14	3	..	..	6
Wandsworth Common A	7	..	..	..	..	5 2	..	..	..	..	..	..	..	..	..	5 9	..	5 13	..		..	..	7
Balham & Upper Tooting	8	..	..	5 1	..	5 4	5 3	5 4	..	..	..	..	..	5 7	..	5 11	..	5 15	5 18	Via Worcester Park	..	..	8
South Bermondsey	9	..	..	..	..	..	..	..	..	4 58	5 1	..	..	..	..	..	..	..	..		..	..	9
Queen's Road, Peckham	10	4 55	..	..	..	..	..	..	..	5 1	5 4	..	..	..	..	..	..	..	..		..	..	10
Peckham Rye	11	4 57	..	..	..	..	..	..	5 1	5 3	5 6	..	..	..	..	..	..	..	..		..	..	11
East Dulwich	12	5 0	..	..	..	..	..	..	..	5 6		..	..	..	..	..	..	..	..		..	..	12
North Dulwich	13	5 2	..	..	..	..	..	..	..	5 8		..	..	..	..	..	..	..	..		..	..	13
Tulse Hill	14	5 5	..	..	..	..	..	..	5 5	5 11		..	..	..	..	..	..	..	..		5 15	..	14
Streatham	15	..	..	..	..	..	..	..	5 9	..		..	..	..	..	..	..	..	..		5 19	..	15
New Cross Gate (for E.L.	16	..	4 58	..	..	..	..	..	..	..	To Victoria, arr. 5 21 p.m	..	..	..	5 7	..	5 9	..	..	..	..	5 12	16
Brockley B .... [Line)	17	..	5 0	..	..	..	..	..	..	..		..	..	..	..	..	..	..	..	..	..	5 14	17
Honor Oak Park	18	..	5 3	..	..	..	..	..	..	..		..	..	..	..	..	..	..	..	..	..	5 17	18
Forest Hill, for Lordship	19	..	5 5	..	..	..	..	..	..	..		..	..	..	5 11	..	..	..	..	..	..	5 19	19
Sydenham .... [Lane	20	..	5 8	..	..	..	..	..	..	..		..	..	..	5 14	..	..	..	..	..	..	5 22	20
Penge West C	21	..	..	..	..	..	..	..	..	..		..	..	..	5 16	..	..	..	..	..	..	..	21
Anerley	22	..	..	..	..	..	..	..	..	..		..	..	..	5 17	..	..	..	..	..	..	..	22
Streatham Common	23	..	..	5 6	..	..	..	..	..	..		..	..	5 12	..	..	..	..	5 22	..	5 21	..	23
Norbury	24	..	..	5 9	..	..	..	..	..	..		..	..	5 14	..	..	..	..	5 24	..	5 24	..	24
Thornton Heath	25	..	..	5 12	..	..	..	..	..	..	Stop	..	..	5 17	..	..	..	..	5 27	..	5 27	..	25
Selhurst	26	..	..	5 15	..	..	..	..	..	..	..	..	..	5 19	..	..	..	..	5 29	..	5 30	..	26
Streatham Hill	27	5 8	..	..	..	5 6	..	..	..	..	..	..	..	..	..	5 14	..	5 18	..	..	..	..	27
West Norwood .. [N'wood)	28	To Victoria, via Wandsworth Common	..	..	..	5 9	..	..	..	5 13	..	..	..	..	..	5 17	..	To London Bridge, via Tulse Hill	Arr. Sutton 5 44 p.m	..	..	..	28
Gipsy Hill (for Upper	29		..	..	..	5 12	..	..	..	5 16	..	..	..	..	..	5 19	..			..	..	..	29
Crystal Palace D	30		5 11	..	..	5 14	..	..	..	5 19	..	..	..	..	..	5 22	..			..	..	5 25	30
Birkbeck	31		..	..	..	5 18	..	..	..	Stop	..	..	..	..	..	..	..			..	..	..	31
Beckenham Jn. arr	32		..	..	..	5 22	..	..	..		..	..	..	..	..	..	..			..	..	..	32
Norwood Junction F ..	33		..	..	..	..	..	..	..	..	..	..	5 15	..	5 20	5 28	5 18			..	5 33	..	33
East Croydon .... arr	34		..	5 18	5 16	..	..	..	..	..	..	..	..	..	..	..	5 22			..	To London Bridge via Forest Hill	..	34
East Croydon .... dep	35		..	5 19	5 16	..	..	..	..	..	..	..	..	..	..	..	5 22			..		..	35
Mitcham Junction	36		..	..	..	..	5 9	5 11	5 14	p.m	..	..	..	..	..	..	..		..	..		..	36
Hackbridge	37		..	..	..	..	5 12	5 14	5 16	SX	..	Arr. Sutton 5 25 p.m	..	..	..	..	..		..	..		..	37
Carshalton	38		..	..	..	..	5 14	5 16	5 19		p.m		..	..	..	..	..		..	..		..	38
West Croydon 319 arr	39		..	..	..	..	..	..	..	3	SO		5 19	5 22	5 24	5 32	..		5 32	..		..	39
West Croydon 319 dep	40		..	..	..	..	..	..	..	5 11	3		5 19	5 22	5 24	..	..		5 32	..		..	40
Waddon G	41		..	..	..	..	..	..	..	5 14			5 21	5 25	5 27	..	..		5 35	..		..	41
Wallington	42		..	..	..	..	..	..	..	5 17	5 21		5 25	5 29	5 30	..	..		5 38	..		..	42
Carshalton Beeches	43		..	..	..	..	..	..	..	5 20	5 23		5 27	5 31	5 33	..	..		5 41	..		..	43
Sutton 322	44		..	..	..	..	5 17	5 19	5 22	5 22	5 26	5 27	5 30	5 35	5 35	..	..		5 47	..		..	44
Belmont	45	..	..	..	..	..	..	..	..	..	..	..	5 33	5 38	5 38	..	..	..	5 50	..	..	..	45
Banstead	46	..	..	..	..	..	..	..	..	..	..	..	5 36	5 41	5 41	..	..	..	5 53	..	..	..	46
Epsom Downs ...... arr	47	..	..	..	..	..	..	..	..	..	..	..	5 39	5 44	5 45	..	..	..	5 56	..	..	..	47
Cheam	48	..	..	..	..	..	5 20	5 22	5 25	..	..	..	..	..	..	..	..	..	..	..	..	..	48
Ewell East H	49	..	..	..	..	..	5 23	5 25	5 28	..	..	..	..	..	..	..	..	..	..	..	..	..	49
Epsom	50	..	..	..	..	..	5 27	5 29	5 32	..	..	..	..	..	..	..	..	..	..	5 35	..	..	50
Ashtead	51	..	..	..	..	..	..		5 36	..	..	..	..	..	..	..	..	..	..	5 39	..	..	51
Leatherhead .. [Bridge J	52	..	..	..	..	..	..	Stop	5 40	..	..	..	..	..	..	..	..	..	..	5 43	..	..	52
Boxhill and Burford	53	..	..	..	..	..	..	..	..	..	..	5 43	..	..	..	..	..	..	..	5 48	..	..	53
Dorking North K .. arr	54	..	..	..	..	..	..	..	..	..	..	5 46	..	..	..	..	..	..	..	5 51	..	..	54
Bookham .... [394	55	..	..	..	..	..	..	..	5 47	..	..	..	..	..	..	..	..	..	..	..	..	..	55
Effingham Junction arr	56	..	..	..	..	..	..	..	5 51	..	..	..	..	..	..	..	..	..	..	..	..	..	56
South Croydon 234	57	..	..	5 21	..	..	..	..	..	..	..	..	..	..	..	..	5 24	..	..	..	..	..	57
Purley Oaks	58	..	..	5 24	..	..	..	..	..	..	..	..	..	..	..	..	5 27	..	..	..	..	..	58
Purley	59	..	..	5 26	5 21	..	..	..	..	..	..	..	..	..	..	..	5 29	..	..	..	..	..	59
Coulsdon North L .. arr	60	..	..	5 30	5 25	..	..	..	..	..	..	..	..	..	..	..	5 33	..	..	..	..	..	60
Purley .... dep	61	..	..	..	..	..	..	..	..	..	..	..	..	..	..	..	..	..	..	..	..	..	61
Kenley	62	..	..	..	..	..	..	..	..	..	..	..	..	..	..	..	..	..	..	..	..	..	62
Whyteleafe	63	..	..	..	..	..	..	..	..	..	..	..	..	..	..	..	..	..	..	..	..	..	63
Warlingham	64	..	..	..	..	..	..	..	..	..	..	..	..	..	..	..	..	..	..	..	..	..	64
Caterham .... arr	65	..	..	..	..	..	..	p.m	..	..	..	..	..	..	..	..	..	..	..	..	..	..	65
Purley .... dep	66	..	..	..	..	..	..		..	..	..	..	..	..	..	..	..	..	..	..	..	..	66
Reedham	67	..	..	..	..	..	..	*d* Departure time	..	..	..	..	..	..	..	..	..	..	..	..	..	..	67
Smitham	68	..	..	..	..	..	..		..	..	..	..	..	..	..	..	..	..	..	..	..	..	68
Woodmansterne	69	..	..	..	..	..	..		..	..	..	..	..	..	..	..	..	..	..	..	..	..	69
Chipstead	70	..	..	..	..	..	..		..	..	..	..	..	..	..	..	..	..	..	..	..	..	70
Kingswood M	71	..	..	..	..	..	..		..	..	..	..	..	..	..	..	..	..	..	..	..	..	71
Tadworth N	72	..	..	..	..	..	..		..	..	..	..	..	..	..	..	..	..	..	..	..	..	72
Tattenham Corner. arr	73	..	..	..	..	..	..		..	..	..	..	..	..	..	..	..	..	..	..	..	..	73
Coulsdon South	74	..	..	..	..	..	..	..	..	..	..	..	..	..	..	..	..	..	..	..	..	..	74
Merstham	75	..	..	..	..	..	..	..	..	..	..	..	..	..	..	..	..	..	..	..	..	..	75
Redhill 158, 246 .... arr	76	..	..	..	..	..	..	5*d*36	..	..	..	..	..	..	..	..	..	..	..	..	..	..	76
Reigate 246 .... "	77	..	..	..	..	..	..	5 40	..	..	..	..	..	..	..	..	..	..	..	..	..	..	77
Horsham 159,244,245 "	78	..	..	..	..	..	..	..	..	..	..	6 10	..	..	..	..	..	..	..	..	..	..	78

For Notes, see page 284a

CATERHAM, TATTENHAM CORNER, REDHILL, REIGATE, and HORSHAM

Week Days—continued (p.m.)

No.	SX	SO	SX			SX	SO	SX	SX	SX	..	SO		SX
1	..	..	..	5 9	..	..	5 10	..	..	..	..	..	..	..
2	..	(3)	(3)	..	..	(3)	(3)	(3)	..	..	(3)	..	(3)	(3)
3	5 15			..	..				..	..		..		
4	..	5 7	5 8	..	..	5 10	..	5 11	5 15	5 12	5 15	5 16	5 17	5 18
5	(3)	..	..	..	..	..	5 13	..	..	..	..	..	..	..
6		..	..	..	..	..	5 16	..	..	..	..	..	..	..
7	Via Worcester Park	..	..	..	..	..	5 20	..	..	..	..	..	..	..
8		..	..	..	..	..	5 22	..	..	..	..	..	..	..
9		..	..	..	..	5 13	..	..	..	..	5 18	..	5 21	..
10		..	..	..	..	5 16	..	..	..	..	5 21	..	5 24	..
11		..	..	..	..	5 18	..	..	..	..	5 23	..	5 26	..
12		..	..	..	..	5 21	..	..	..	..	5 26	..		..
13		..	..	..	..	5 23	..	..	..	..	5 28	..		..
14		..	5 18	..	..	5 26	..	..	..	..	5 31	..		..
15		..	5 22	..	..	..	..	..	..	..	..	..		..
16	..	5 12	..	..	..	..	..	5 16	..	..	..	..		..
17	..	5 14	..	..	..	..	..	5 18	..	..	..	..		..
18	..	5 17	..	..	..	..	..	5 21	..	..	..	..		..
19	..	5 19	..	..	..	..	..	5 23	..	..	..	..	To Victoria arr. 5 42 p.m	..
20	..	5 22	..	..	..	..	..	5 26	..	..	..	..		..
21	..	5 24	..	..	..	..	..	5 28	..	..	..	..		..
22	..	5 25	..	..	..	..	..	5 29	..	..	..	..		..
23	..	..	..	..	..	..	..	..	..	..	..	..		..
24	..	..	..	..	..	..	..	..	..	..	..	..		..
25	..	..	..	..	..	..	..	..	..	..	..	..	Stop	..
26	..	..	..	..	..	..	..	..	..	..	..	..	p.m	..
27	..	..	..	..	..	5 30	5 24	..	..	..	..	..	SO	..
28	..	..	..	..	..		5 27	..	..	..	5 33	..	(3)	..
29	..	..	..	..	..		5 30	..	..	..	5 36	..		..
30	..	..	..	..	..		5 32	..	..	..	5 39	..	5 40	..
31	..	..	..	..	..		..	..	..	..	..	..	5 43	..
32	..	..	..	..	..		..	..	..	..	..	..	5 47	..
33	..	5 29	..	..	..		5 37	5 32	..	..	..	5 28	..	..
34	..		..	5 26	..		..		..	5 26	..	5 32	..	5 33
35	..		..	5 28	..		..		..	5 28	..	5 34	..	5 33
36	..		5 27	..	..	To Victoria, via Wandsworth Common	..		..	..	..	..	..	..
37	..		5 29	..	..		..		..	..	..	..	..	..
38	..	To London Bridge, via Streatham	5 32	..	..		..		..	..	..	..	..	..
39	..		..	..	..		5 41		..	..	..	..	..	..
40	..		..	..	..		..	To London Bridge, via Streatham	..	..	..	..	..	..
41	..		..	..	..		..		..	..	..	..	..	..
42	..		..	..	..		..		..	..	..	..	..	..
43	..		..	..	..		..		..	..	..	..	..	..
44	..		5 35	..	..		..		..	..	..	..	..	..
45	..	..	..	..	..	..	..	..	..	..	..	..	..	..
46	.	..	..	..	..	..	..	..	..	..	..	..	..	..
47	..	..	..	..	..	..	..	..	..	..	..	..	..	..
48	..	..	5 38	..	..	..	..	..	..	..	..	..	..	..
49	..	..	5 41	..	..	..	..	..	..	..	..	..	..	..
50	5 40	..	5 45	..	..	..	..	..	..	..	..	..	..	..
51	5 44	..	5 49	..	..	..	..	..	..	..	..	..	..	..
52	5 48	..	5 54	..	..	..	..	..	..	..	..	..	..	..
53	..	..	..	..	..	..	..	..	..	..	..	..	..	..
54	..	..	..	..	..	..	..	..	..	..	..	..	..	..
55	5 52	..	5 58	..	..	..	..	..	..	..	..	..	..	..
56	5 55	..	6 2	..	..	..	..	..	..	..	..	..	..	..
57	..	..	..	5 32	..	..	..	..	..	..	..	..	..	..
58	..	..	..	..	..	..	..	..	..	..	..	..	..	..
59	..	..	..	..	..	..	..	..	..	5 34	..	5 40	..	5 39
60	..	..	..	..	..	..	..	..	..	..	..	..	..	..
61	..	..	..	..	..	..	..	..	..	..	..	..	..	5 41
62	..	..	..	..	..	..	..	..	..	..	..	..	..	5 44
63	..	..	..	..	..	..	..	..	..	..	..	..	..	5 47
64	..	..	..	..	..	..	..	..	..	..	..	..	..	5 49
65	..	..	..	..	..	..	..	..	..	..	..	..	..	5 53
66	..	..	..	..	..	..	..	..	..		..	..	..	5 40
67	..	..	..	..	..	..	..	..	..		..	..	..	5 42
68	..	..	..	..	..	..	..	..	..		..	..	..	5 45
69	..	..	..	..	..	..	..	..	..		..	..	..	5 47
70	..	..	..	..	..	..	..	..		§ Via Three Bridges	..	..	..	5 50
71	..	..	..	..	..	..	..	..			..	..	..	5 54
72	..	..	..	..	..	..	..	..			..	..	..	5 57
73	..	..	..	..	..	..	..	..			..	..	..	6 1
74	..	..	..	..	..	..	..	..	§ Via Three Bridges	..	..	5 43	..	..
75	..	..	..	..	..	..	..	..		5 42	..	5 49	..	..
76	..	..	..	..	..	..	..	..		5 46	..	5 53	..	..
77	..	..	..	..	..	..	..	..		..	..	5 59	..	..
78	..	..	..	..	..	..	..	..	6§8	6§29	..	..	..	..

No.	SX	SX	SX	SX	SO	SO	..	SX	SX	SX		SX	SO	SX
1	5 11	5 13	..	5 15	5 18	5 20	..	..	5 18	5 20	..	..	5 21	..
2	(3)	(3)	..	(3)	..	(3)	..	(3)	(3)	(3)	..	(3)	(3)	..
3			..		..		..				..			..
4	..	..	5 20	..	..	..	..	5 22	..	..	..	5 24	..	5 25
5	..	5 16	..	..	..	..	..	..	..	5 23	..	..	..	..
6	5 16	5 19	..	5 20	..	5 25	..	..	5 24	5 26	..	..	5 26	..
7	..	5 22	..	..	..	..	..	..	..	5 29	..	..	..	..
8	5 21	5 24	..	5 24	..	5 29	..	..	5 28	5 31	..	..	5 30	..
9	..	..	..	..	..	..	..	..	..	..	..	..	..	..
10	..	..	..	..	..	..	..	..	..	..	..	..	..	..
11	..	..	..	..	..	..	..	..	..	..	..	..	..	..
12	..	..	..	..	..	..	..	..	..	..	..	..	..	..
13	..	..	..	..	..	..	..	..	..	..	..	..	..	..
14	..	..	..	..	..	..	..	..	..	..	..	..	..	..
15	..	..	..	..	..	..	..	..	..	..	..	..	..	..
16	..	..	..	..	..	..	..	..	..	..	..	5 29	..	..
17	..	..	..	..	..	..	..	..	..	..	..	..	..	..
18	..	..	..	..	..	..	..	..	..	..	..	..	..	..
19	..	..	..	..	..	..	..	..	..	..	..	..	..	..
20	..	..	..	..	..	..	..	..	..	..	..	..	..	..
21	..	..	..	..	..	..	..	..	..	..	..	..	..	..
22	..	..	..	..	..	..	..	..	..	..	..	..	..	..
23	5 25	..	..	..	..	..	..	..	5 32	..	..	..	5 35	..
24	5 27	..	..	..	..	..	..	..	5 34	..	..	..	5 37	..
25	5 30	..	..	..	..	..	..	..	5 37	..	..	..	5 40	..
26	5 32	..	..	..	..	..	..	..	5 39	..	..	..	5 42	..
27	..	5 26	..	..	..	..	..	..	..	5 34	..	..	..	..
28	..	5 29	..	..	..	..	..	..	..	5 37	..	..	..	..
29	..	5 32	..	..	..	..	..	..	..	5 39	..	..	..	..
30	..	5 34	..	..	..	..	..	..	..	5 42	..	..	..	..
31	..	5 38	..	..	..	..	..	..	..	..	..	..	..	..
32	..	5 42	..	..	..	..	..	..	..	..	..	..	..	..
33	..	..	..	..	..	..	..	5 35	..	5 47	..	5 38	..	..
34	5 36	..	5 37	..	..	..	..	..	..	..	..	5 42	5 46	..
35	5 37	..	5 38	..	..	..	..	..	..	..	..	5 42	5 46	..
36	..	..	..	5 32	..	5 35	..	..	..	..	..	..	..	..
37	..	..	..	5 35	..	5 38	SX	..	..	..	..	..	..	..
38	..	..	..	5 37	..	5 40	(3)	..	..	..	..	..	..	..
39	..	..	..	..	..	..		5 39	5 42	5 51	SO	..	..	..
40	..	..	..	..	..	..	5 34	5 39	5 42	..	(3)	..	..	..
41	..	..	..	..	..	..	5 36	5 41	5 45	..		..	..	..
42	..	..	..	..	..	..	5 40	5 45	5 48	..	5 47	..	..	..
43	..	..	..	..	..	..	5 42	5 47	5 51	..	5 49	..	..	..
44	..	..	..	5 40	5 39	5 43	5 46	5 50	5 54	..	5 52	..	..	..
45	..	..	..	..	..	..	..	5 53	5 57	..	..	..	..	..
46	..	..	..	..	..	..	..	5 56	6 0	..	..	..	..	..
47	..	..	..	..	..	..	..	5 59	6 4	..	..	..	..	..
48	..	..	..	5 43	..	5 46	..	..	..	..	..	..	..	..
49	..	..	..	5 46	..	5 49	..	..	..	..	..	..	..	..
50	..	..	..	5 50	..	5 53	..	..	..	..	..	..	..	..
51	..	..	..	..	..	..	..	..	..	..	..	..	..	..
52	..	..	..	..	..	..	..	..	..	..	..	..	..	..
53	..	..	..	..	..	..	..	..	..	..	..	..	..	..
54	..	..	..	..	5 55	..	..	..	..	..	..	..	..	..
55	..	..	..	..	..	..	..	..	..	..	..	..	..	..
56	..	..	..	..	..	..	..	..	..	..	..	..	..	..
57	5 39	..	5 42	..	..	..	..	..	..	..	..	5 44	5 48	..
58	5 42	..	..	..	..	..	..	..	..	..	..	5 47	5 51	..
59	5 44	..	..	..	..	..	..	..	..	..	..	5 49	5 53	..
60	5 48	..	..	..	..	..	..	..	..	..	..	5 53	5 57	..
61	..	..	..	..	..	..	..	..	..	..	..	..	..	..
62	..	..	..	..	..	..	..	..	..	..	..	..	..	..
63	..	..	..	..	..	..	..	..	..	..	..	..	..	..
64	..	..	..	..	..	..	..	..	..	..	..	..	..	..
65	..	..	..	..	..	..	..	..	..	..	..	..	..	..
66	..	..	..	..	..	..	..	..	..	..	..	..	..	..
67	..	..	..	..	..	..	..	..	..	..	..	..	..	..
68	..	..	..	..	..	..	..	..	..	..	..	..	..	..
69	..	..	..	..	..	..	..	..	..	..	..	..	..	..
70	..	..	..	..	..	..	..	..	..	..	..	..	..	..
71	..	..	..	..	..	..	..	..	..	..	..	..	..	..
72	..	..	..	..	..	..	..	..	..	..	..	..	..	..
73	..	..	..	..	..	..	..	..	..	..	..	..	..	..
74	..	..	..	..	..	..	..	..	..	..	..	..	..	5 48
75	..	..	..	..	..	..	..	..	..	..	..	..	..	5 56
76	..	..	..	..	..	..	..	..	..	..	..	..	..	6 1
77	..	..	..	..	..	..	..	..	..	..	..	..	..	6 7
78	..	..	..	..	6 13	..	..	..	..	..	..	..	..	..

LONDON, CRYSTAL PALACE, CROYDON, SUTTON, DORKING NORTH,

For Notes, see page 284a

Down	No.	p.m. S X	S O	S X	S X	S X	S X	S O	S X	S X	S X	S X	Week Days—continued S X	S O	S O	S X	S X	S X	S X	p.m. S X	S X	S X	No.
Victoria .... dep	1	5 24	5 28	5 29	5 30	..	..	..	..	..	..	..	..	..	..	..	5 31	5 32	5 33	5 38	..	..	1
Charing Cross✱ ... "	2	3	..	3	..	..	3	3	3	..	3	3	3	5 24	3	3	3	3	3	..	3	..	2
Waterloo✱ .... "	3		..		..	5 27				5 32				5 26						..		..	3
London Bridge ..... "	4	..	..	..	..	..	5 27	5 25	5 25	..	5 28	5 30	5 31	5 31	5 29	5 35	..	..	..	..	5 38	5 40	4
Battersea Park	5	..	..	..	..	3	..	..	..	..	..	..	..	3	..	..	..	..	5 36	..	..	..	5
Clapham Junction	6	5 29	5 34	..	..		..	..	..	5 39	..	..	..		..	..	5 36	..	5 39	..	..	..	6
Wandsworth Common A	7	..	..	..	..	Via Worcester Park	..	..	..	3	..	..	..	..	..	..	..	..	5 42	..	..	..	7
Balham & Upper Tooting	8	5 35	..	..	..		..	..	..		..	..	..	..	..	..	5 41	..	5 44	..	..	..	8
South Bermondsey	9	..	..	..	..		..	..	..	..	..	..	..	..	..	..	..	..	..	..	..	..	9
Queen's Road, Peckham	10	..	..	..	..		..	..	..	..	..	5 35	..	..	..	..	..	..	..	..	..	..	10
Peckham Rye	11	..	..	..	..		..	5 31	..	..	..	5 37	..	..	..	..	..	..	..	..	..	..	11
East Dulwich	12	..	..	..	..		..	..	..	..	..	5 40	..	..	..	..	..	..	..	..	..	..	12
North Dulwich	13	..	..	..	..		..	..	..	..	..	5 42	..	..	..	..	..	..	..	..	..	..	13
Tulse Hill	14	..	..	..	..		..	5 35	5 35	..	5 38	5 45	..	..	..	..	..	..	..	..	..	..	14
Streatham	15	..	..	..	..		..	5 39	5 39	..	5 44	..	..	..	..	..	..	..	..	..	..	..	15
New Cross Gate (for E.L.	16	..	..	..	..	..	5 32	..	..	..	..	..	5 36	..	5 34	..	..	..	..	..	..	..	16
Brockley B .... [Line)	17	..	..	..	..	..	5 34	..	..	..	..	..	5 38	..	5 36	..	..	..	..	..	..	..	17
Honor Oak Park	18	..	..	..	..	..	5 37	..	..	..	..	..	5 41	..	5 39	..	..	..	..	..	..	..	18
Forest Hill, for Lordship	19	..	..	..	..	..	5 39	..	..	..	..	..	5 43	..	5 41	..	..	..	..	..	..	..	19
Sydenham .... [Lane	20	..	..	..	..	..	5 42	..	..	..	..	..	5 46	..	5 44	..	..	..	..	..	..	..	20
Penge West C	21	..	..	..	..	..	..	..	..	..	..	..	5 48	..	5 46	..	..	..	..	..	..	..	21
Anerley	22	..	..	..	..	..	..	..	..	..	..	..	5 49	..	5 47	..	..	..	..	..	..	..	22
Streatham Common	23	..	..	..	..	..	..	..	5 41	..	..	..	..	..	..	..	5 45	..	..	..	..	..	23
Norbury	24	5 40	..	..	..	..	..	..	5 44	..	..	..	..	..	..	..	5 47	..	..	..	..	..	24
Thornton Heath	25	5 43	..	..	..	..	..	..	5 47	..	..	..	..	..	..	..	5 50	..	..	..	..	..	25
Selhurst	26	5 46	..	..	..	..	..	..	5 50	..	..	..	..	..	..	..	5 52	..	..	..	..	..	26
Streatham Hill	27	..	..	..	..	..	..	..	..	..	..	5 48	..	..	..	..	..	..	5 46	..	..	..	27
West Norwood.. [N'wood)	28	..	..	..	..	..	..	..	..	..	..	..	..	..	..	..	..	..	5 49	..	..	..	28
Gipsy Hill (for Upper	29	..	..	..	..	..	..	..	..	..	..	..	..	..	..	..	..	..	5 52	..	..	..	29
Crystal Palace D	30	..	..	..	..	..	5 45	..	..	Via Worcester Park	..	To Victoria, via Wandsworth Common	..	..	..	..	..	..	5 54	..	..	..	30
Birkbeck	31	..	..	..	..	..	..	..	..		..		..	..	..	..	..	..	5 58	..	..	..	31
Beckenham Jn. arr	32	..	..	..	..	..	Stop	..	..		..		..	..	..	..	..	..	6 2	..	..	..	32
Norwood Junction F ..	33	..	..	..	..	..	..	..	5 53		..		5 52	5 43	5 50	..	..	..	..	..	..	..	33
East Croydon .... arr	34	..	5 45	..	..	..	..	..	To London Bridge, via Forest Hill		..		..	5 47	..	5 50	5 56	5 48	..	..	..	5 56	34
East Croydon .... dep	35	..	5 46	..	..	..	..	..			..		..	5 47	..	5 52	5 56	5 48	..	..	..	..	35
Mitcham Junction	36	..	..	5 46	..	..	..	5 45			5 49		To London Bridge, via Streatham	..	..	..	..	..	..	..	..	..	36
Hackbridge	37	..	..	5 48	..	..	..	5 48			5 51			..	..	..	..	..	..	..	..	..	37
Carshalton	38	..	..	..	..	..	..	5 51			5 54			..	..	..	..	..	..	..	..	..	38
West Croydon 319 arr	39	..	..	..	..	..	..	..		..	..			..	5 54	..	..	..	..	..	5 54	..	39
West Croydon 319 dep	40	..	..	..	..	..	..	..		..	..			..	5 54	..	..	..	..	..	5 55	..	40
Waddon G	41	..	..	..	..	..	..	..		..	..			..	5 57	..	..	..	..	..	5 57	..	41
Wallington	42	..	..	..	..	..	..	..		..	..			..	6 0	..	..	..	..	..	6 1	..	42
Carshalton Beeches	43	..	..	..	..	..	..	..		..	..			..	6 3	..	..	..	..	..	6 3	..	43
Sutton 322	44	..	..	5 53	..	..	..	5 55		..	5 57			..	6 5	..	..	..	..	..	6 6	..	44
Belmont	45	..	..	..	..	..	..	..	..	..	..	..	..	..	6 8	..	..	..	..	..	..	..	45
Banstead	46	..	..	..	..	..	..	..	..	..	..	..	..	..	6 11	..	..	..	..	..	..	..	46
Epsom Downs ...... arr	47	..	..	..	..	..	..	..	..	..	..	..	..	..	6 15	..	..	..	..	..	..	..	47
Cheam	48	..	..	5 56	..	..	p.m	5 58	..	..	6 0	..	..	..	..	..	..	..	..	..	..	..	48
Ewell East H	49	..	..	..	..	..	S X	6 1	..	..	6 3	..	..	..	..	..	..	..	..	..	..	..	49
Epsom	50	..	..	6 1	..	5 56	3	6 5	..	6 3	6 7	..	..	..	..	..	..	..	..	..	..	..	50
Ashtead	51	..	..	..	..	6 0		6 9	..	..	6 11	..	..	..	..	..	..	..	..	..	..	..	51
Leatherhead... [Bridge J	52	..	..	..	..	6 4	6 9	6 13	..	..	6 15	..	..	..	..	..	..	..	..	..	..	..	52
Boxhill and Burford	53	..	..	..	..	6 9	..	6 18	..	..	6 20	..	..	..	..	..	..	..	..	..	..	..	53
Dorking North K .. arr	54	..	..	..	6 4	6 12	..	6 21	..	..	6 23	..	..	..	..	..	..	..	..	..	..	..	54
Bookham .... [394	55	..	..	..	..	..	6 13	..	..	..	..	..	..	..	..	..	..	..	..	..	..	..	55
Effingham Junction arr	56	..	..	..	..	..	6 16	..	..	..	..	..	..	..	..	..	..	..	..	..	..	..	56
South Croydon 234	57	..	..	..	..	..	..	..	..	..	..	..	..	5 50	..	..	5 58	..	..	..	..	..	57
Purley Oaks	58	..	..	..	..	..	..	..	..	..	..	..	..	5 52	..	..	6 1	..	..	..	..	..	58
Purley	59	..	..	..	..	..	..	..	..	..	..	..	..	5 55	..	5 57	6 3	5 53	..	5 58	..	..	59
Coulsdon North L .. arr	60	..	..	..	..	..	..	..	..	..	..	..	..	..	..	..	6 7	5 57	..	..	..	..	60
Purley .... dep	61	..	..	..	..	..	..	..	..	..	..	..	..	5 59	..	6 1	..	..	..	..	..	..	61
Kenley	62	..	..	..	..	..	..	..	..	..	..	..	..	6 2	..	6 4	..	..	..	..	..	..	62
Whyteleafe	63	..	..	..	..	..	..	..	..	..	..	..	..	6 5	..	6 7	..	..	..	..	..	..	63
Warlingham	64	..	..	..	..	..	..	..	..	..	..	..	..	6 7	..	6 9	..	..	..	..	..	..	64
Caterham .... arr	65	..	..	..	..	..	..	..	..	..	..	..	..	6 11	..	6 13	..	..	..	..	..	..	65
Purley .... dep	66	..	..	..	..	..	..	..	..	..	..	..	..	5 57	..	5 57	..	..	..	..	..	..	66
Reedham	67	..	..	..	..	..	..	..	..	..	..	..	..	5 59	..	5 59	..	..	..	..	..	..	67
Smitham	68	..	..	..	..	..	..	..	..	..	..	..	..	6 1	..	6 2	..	..	..	..	..	..	68
Woodmansterne	69	..	..	..	..	..	..	..	..	..	..	..	..	6 4	..	6 4	..	..	..	..	..	..	69
Chipstead	70	..	..	..	..	..	..	..	..	..	..	..	..	6 6	..	6 7	..	..	..	..	..	..	70
Kingswood M	71	..	..	..	..	..	..	..	..	..	..	..	..	6 11	..	6 11	..	..	..	..	..	..	71
Tadworth N	72	..	..	..	..	..	..	..	..	..	..	..	..	6 14	..	6 14	..	..	..	..	..	..	72
Tattenham Corner. arr	73	..	..	..	..	..	..	..	..	..	..	..	..	6 17	..	6 18	..	..	..	..	..	..	73
Coulsdon South	74	..	..	..	..	..	..	..	..	..	..	..	..	..	..	..	..	..	..	..	..	..	74
Merstham	75	..	..	..	..	..	..	..	..	..	..	..	..	..	..	..	..	..	..	..	..	..	75
Redhill 158, 246 ..... arr	76	..	6 0	..	..	..	..	..	..	..	..	..	..	..	..	..	..	..	..	..	..	..	76
Reigate 246 .... "	77	..	6 13	..	..	..	..	..	..	..	..	..	..	..	..	..	..	..	..	..	..	..	77
Horsham 159, 244, 245 "	78	..	..	..	6 21	6 36	..	6 46	..	..	6 49	..	..	..	..	..	..	..	..	..	..	..	78

CATERHAM, TATTENHAM CORNER, REDHILL, REIGATE, and HORSHAM

p.m — Week Days—continued — p.m

No.	SX	SX	SX	SX	SX	SO	SX		SX		SO	SX		SX	SX	SX	SX	SO	SX	SX	SO	SX	SX	SO	SX	SX		SO
1	5 40	..	..	..	5 38	5 38	..	5 40	5 47	..	..	5 44	..	..	..	..	5 47	5 48	..	..	..	..	..	..	..	..	5 50	..
2										..			..			..		..	..	..	5 44		..				..	
3	③	③	③	③	③	③	③	③	③	..	③	③	5 47	③	③	..	③	..	5 54	..	5 46	③	5 52	③	③	③	..	③
4	..	5 35	5 37	5 42	..	..	5 44	..	..	..	5 37	..	..	5 45	5 47	5 48	..	..	..	5 50	5 51	5 48	..	5 48	5 50	5 51	..	5 53
5	..	..	..	..	..	..	..	5 43	..	..	..	5 47		..	..	..	..	..		..		..	..	..	..	..	..	..
6	5 45	..	..	..	5 44	5 44	..	5 46	..	..	..	5 50	③	..	..	..	..	5 53	③	..	③	..	5 59	..	..	..	..	..
7	..	..	..	..	..	..	..	5J49	..	..	..	5 53		..	..	..	..	..		..	..	..		..	..	..	..	..
8	5 49	..	..	..	5 48	5 48	..	5J51	..	..	..	5 55		..	..	..	..	..	..	..	..	..	③	..	..	..	..	..
9	..	5 38	5 41	..	..	..	..		..	..	5 40	..		..	..	..	..	..		..	..	..		5 51	5 53	..	..	..
10	..	5 41	5 44	..	..	..	..		..	..	5 43	..		..	..	..	..	..		..	..	..		5 54	5 55	..	..	..
11	..	5 43	5 46	..	..	..	..		..	..	5 45	..	Via Worcester Park	..	..	..	..	..		..	..	..		5 56	5 57	..	..	..
12	..	5 46		..	..	..	..		..	..	5 48	..		..	..	..	..	..		..	..	..			6 0	..	..	..
13	..	5 48		..	..	..	..		..	..	5 50	..		..	..	..	..	..		..	..	..			6 2	..	..	..
14	..	5 51		..	..	..	..		..	..	5 53	..		5 55	..	..	..	..		..	..	5 58			6 5	..	..	..
15	..	..		..	..	..	..		..	..	5 57	..		5 59	..	..	..	..		..	..	6 2	Via Worcester Park		..	..	..	..
16	..	..	To Victoria arr 6 1 p.m	..	..	..	5 49	J 1 minute later on Saturdays	..	..	..	..	..	..	5 52	..	..	..		..	..	..			..	5 56	..	5 58
17	..	..		..	..	..	..		..	..	..	..	..	..	5 54	..	..	..	Via Worcester Park	..	..	..			..	5 58	..	6 0
18	..	..		..	..	..	..		..	..	..	..	..	..	5 57	..	..	..		..	..	..		To Victoria, arr. 6 13 p.m	..	6 1	..	6 3
19	..	..		..	..	..	..		..	..	..	..	..	..	5 59	..	..	..		..	..	..			..	6 3	..	6 5
20	..	..		..	..	..	..		..	..	..	..	..	..	6 2	..	..	..		..	..	..			..	6 6	..	6 8
21	..	..		..	..	..	..	..	..	..	..	..	..	..	..	..	..	..		..	..	..			..	6 8	..	..
22	..	..		..	..	..	..	..	..	..	..	..	..	..	..	..	..	..	..	..	..	..	..		..	6 9	..	..
23	..	..	..	..	5 52	5 52	..	..	..	..	5 59	..	..	6 1	..	..	..	..	..	..	..	..	..	..	..	..	..	..
24	..	..	..	..	5 54	5 54	..	..	..	..	6 1	..	..	6 4	..	..	..	..	..	..	..	..	..	..	..	..	..	..
25	..	..	..	..	5 57	5 57	..	..	..	..	6 4	..	..	6 7	..	..	..	..	..	..	..	..	..	..	..	..	..	..
26	..	..	..	..	5 59	5 59	..	..	..	..	6 6	..	..	6 10	..	..	..	..	..	..	..	..	..	..	..	..	..	..
27	..	..	..	..	..	..	..	5 54	..	SO	..	5 58	..	..	..	..	..	..	..	..	..	..	..	..	..	..	..	..
28	..	5 53	..	..	..		..	5 57	..		..		..	..	..	..	..	..	..	..	..	..	..	..	6 10	..	..	..
29	..	5 56	..	..	..		..	5J59	..	③	..		..	..	..	..	..	..	..	..	..	..	..	..		..	..	..
30	..	5 59	..	..	..		..	6 2	..	6 10	..		..	..	6 5	..	..	..	..	..	..	..	..	..		..	..	6 11
31	..	..	..	..	..		..	..	..	6 13	..		..	..	..	..	..	..	..	..	..	..	..	..		..	..	..
32	..	..	..	..	..		..	..	..	6 17	..		..	..	..	..	..	..	..	..	..	..	..	..		..	..	..
33	..	..	..	5 55	..	Arr Sutton 6 14 p.m	5 58	6 7	..	..	6 9	To London Bridge via Tulse Hill	..	6 13	..	..	..	..	..	..	6 3	..	..	..		6 12	..	..
34	..	..	..	..	..		6 2	..	6 4	..			..		..	..	6 4	6 5	..	6 5	6 7	..	..	..		..	6 8	..
35	..	..	..	..	..		6 2	..	6 5	..			..		..	..	..	6 5	..	6 5	6 7	..	..	..			..	..
36	5 56	..	..	..	..		..	..	..	..			..		..	..	..	..	..	..	..	6 7	..	..			..	..
37	5 58	..	..	..	..		..	..	..	..			..		..	..	..	..	..	..	..	6 9	..	..	To Victoria via Wandsworth Common		..	..
38	6 1	..	..	..	..		..	..	..	..			..		..	..	..	..	..	..	..	6 12	..	..			..	..
39	..	..	..	5 59	6 2	6 2	..	6 11	..	..	To London Bridge, via Forest Hill	..	..		..	..	..	..	..	..	..	..		..			..	..
40	..	..	..	5 59	6 2	6 2	..	..	..	..		..	..	To London Bridge, via Forest Hill	..	..	..	..	..	..	..	..		..		To London Bridge, via Streatham	..	..
41	..	..	..	6 1	6 5	6 5	..	..	..	..		..	..		..	..	..	..	..	..	..	..		..			..	..
42	..	..	..	6 5	6 8	6 8	..	..	..	..		..	..		..	..	..	..	..	..	..	..		..			..	..
43	..	..	..	6 7	6 11	6 11	..	..	..	..		..	..		..	..	..	..	..	..	..	..	Arr. Epsom 6 26 p.m	..			..	..
44	6 4	..	..	6 10	6 14	6 17	..	..	..	..		..	..		..	..	..	..	..	..	..	6 15		..			..	..
45	..	..	..	6 13	6 17	6 20	..	..	..	..	..	..	..	..	..	..	..	..	..	..	..	..		..	..	..	..	..
46	..	..	..	6 16	6 21	6 23	..	..	..	..	..	..	..	..	..	..	..	..	..	..	..	..		..	..	..	..	..
47	..	..	..	6 19	6 24	6 26	..	..	..	..	..	..	..	..	..	..	..	..	..	..	..	..		..	..	..	..	..
48	6 7	..	..	..	..	..	..	..	..	..	..	..	..	..	..	..	..	..	..	..	..	6 18	..	..	..	..	..	..
49	6 10	..	..	..	..	..	..	..	..	..	..	..	..	..	..	..	..	..	..	..	..	6 21	..	..	..	..	..	..
50	6 14	..	..	..	..	..	..	..	..	..	..	..	6 15	..	..	..	..	..	6 20	..	..	6 25	6 30	..	..	..	..	..
51	..	..	..	..	..	..	..	..	..	..	..	..	6 19	..	..	..	..	..	6 24	..	..	6 29	6 34	..	..	..	..	..
52	..	..	..	..	..	..	..	..	..	..	..	..	6 23	..	..	..	..	..	6 28	..	..	6 33	6 38	..	..	..	..	..
53	..	..	..	..	..	..	..	..	..	..	..	..	..	..	..	..	..	..	6 33	..	..	6 38	..	..	..	..	..	..
54	..	..	..	..	..	..	..	..	..	..	..	..	..	..	..	..	..	..	6 36	..	..	6 41	..	..	..	..	..	..
55	..	..	..	..	..	..	..	..	..	..	..	..	6 28	..	..	..	..	..	..	..	..	..	6 45	..	..	..	..	..
56	..	..	..	..	..	..	..	..	..	..	..	..	6 32	..	..	..	..	..	..	..	..	..	6 49	..	..	..	..	..
57	..	..	..	..	..	..	6 4	..	6 8	..	..	..	..	..	..	..	..	..	..	..	6 9	..	..	..	..	..	..	..
58	..	..	..	..	..	..	6 7	..	6 10	..	..	..	..	..	..	..	..	..	..	..	6 12	..	..	..	..	..	..	..
59	..	..	..	..	..	..	6 9	..	6 13	..	..	..	..	..	..	..	..	6 11	..	6 11	6 15	..	..	..	..	..	..	..
60	..	..	..	..	..	..	6 13	..	6 16	..	..	..	..	..	..	..	..	..	..	..	..	..	..	..	..	..	..	..
61	..	..	..	..	..	..	..	..	..	..	..	..	..	..	..	..	..	..	..	..	6 18	..	..	..	..	..	..	..
62	..	..	..	..	..	..	..	..	..	..	..	..	..	..	..	..	..	..	..	..	6 21	..	..	..	..	..	..	..
63	..	..	..	..	..	..	..	..	..	..	..	..	..	..	..	..	..	..	..	..	6 24	..	..	..	..	..	..	..
64	..	..	..	..	..	..	..	..	..	..	..	..	..	..	..	..	..	..	..	..	6 26	..	..	..	..	..	..	..
65	..	..	..	..	..	..	..	..	..	..	..	..	..	..	..	..	..	..	..	..	6 30	..	..	..	..	..	..	..
66	..	..	..	..	..	..	..	..	..	..	..	..	..	..	..		..		..	..	6 16	..	..	..	..	..	..	..
67	..	..	..	..	..	..	..	..	..	..	..	..	..	..	..		..		..	..	6 18	..	..	..	..	..	..	..
68	..	..	..	..	..	..	..	..	..	..	..	..	..	..	..		..		..	..	6 20	..	..	..	..	..	..	..
69	..	..	..	..	..	..	..	..	..	..	..	..	..	..	..		..		..	..	6 23	..	..	..	..	..	..	..
70	..	..	..	..	..	..	..	..	..	..	..	..	..	..	..	§ Via Three Bridges	..	§ Via Three Bridges	..	..	6 25	..	..	..	..	..	..	..
71	..	..	..	..	..	..	..	..	..	..	..	..	..	..	..		..		..	..	6 30	..	..	..	..	..	..	..
72	..	..	..	..	..	..	..	..	..	..	..	..	..	..	..		..		..	..	6 33	..	..	..	..	..	..	..
73	..	..	..	..	..	..	..	..	..	..	..	..	..	..	..		..		..	..	6 36	..	..	..	..	..	..	..
74	..	..	..	..	..	..	..	..	..	..	..	..	..	..	..	..	..	6 14	..	6 14	..	..	..	..	..	..	..	..
75	..	..	..	..	..	..	..	..	..	..	..	..	..	..	..	..	..	6 20	..	6 20	..	..	..	..	..	..	..	..
76	..	..	..	..	..	..	..	..	..	..	..	..	..	..	..	..	..	6 24	..	6 24	..	..	..	..	..	..	..	..
77	..	..	..	..	..	..	..	..	..	..	..	..	..	..	..	..	..	6 30	..	6 30	..	..	..	..	..	..	..	..
78	..	..	..	..	..	..	..	..	..	..	..	..	..	..	..	6§44	..	7§ 5	..	..	..	..	..	..	..	..	..	..

LONDON, CRYSTAL PALACE, CROYDON, SUTTON, DORKING NORTH,

For Notes, see page 284a

Down	No.	p.m.							Week Days—continued							p.m.							No.
		SX		SO	SX	SX	SO		SX	SX	SX	SX	..	SO	SX	SX	SX	SX	SX	SX	SO	SX	
Victoria ... dep	1	..	5 51	5 54	5 53	5 55	..	..	..	..	..	5 58	..	..	..	..	6 0	6 4	6 4	..	..	..	1
Charing Cross* ... "	2	3	3	3	3	3	3	..	3	3	3	3	..	3	3	3	3	..	3	3	3	3	2
Waterloo* ... "	3							..					6 7					..					3
London Bridge ... "	4	5 55	..	..	..	..	5 55	..	5 55	5 57	6 2	..	..	6 2	6 4	6 5	..	..	..	6 7	6 7	6 8	4
Battersea Park ...	5	..	..	..	5 56	..	..	..	..	..	..	..	3	..	..	..	6 3	..	6 7	..	..	..	5
Clapham Junction ...	6	..	5 56	5 59	5 59	6 0	..	..	..	..	..	6 4		..	..	..	6 6	6U 9	6 10	..	..	..	6
Wandsworth Common A	7	..	5SO59	..	6 2	..	..	..	..	..	..	..		..	..	..	6 9	..	6 13	..	..	..	7
Balham & Upper Tooting	8	..	6 1	6 3	6 4	6 4	..	..	..	..	..	6 8	Via Worcester Park	..	..	..	6 11		6 15	..	..	..	8
South Bermondsey ...	9	..	..	..	..	..	..	..	5 58	6 1	..	..		..	..	..	..	U Takes up only	..	..	..	..	9
Queen's Road, Peckham	10	..	..	..	..	..	..	..	6 1	6 4	..	..		..	..	..	..		..	..	..	..	10
Peckham Rye ...	11	..	..	..	..	..	6 1	..	6 3	6 6	..	..		..	..	..	..		..	..	..	..	11
East Dulwich ...	12	..	..	..	..	..	..	..	6 6		..	..		..	..	..	..		..	..	..	..	12
North Dulwich ...	13	..	..	..	..	..	..	..	6 8	To Victoria, arr. 6 22 p.m	..	..		..	..	..	..		..	..	..	..	13
Tulse Hill ...	14	..	..	..	..	..	6 5	..	6 11		..	..		..	..	6 15	..		..	..	..	6 18	14
Streatham ...	15	..	..	..	..	..	6 9	..	..		..	..		..	..	6 19	..		..	..	..	6 22	15
New Cross Gate (for E.L.	16	..	..	..	..	..	..	..	..		..	..	..	6 7	6 9	..	..	..	..	6 12	6 12	..	16
Brockley B ... [Line)	17	..	..	..	..	..	..	..	..		..	..	..	..	..	..	..	..	..	6 14	6 14	..	17
Honor Oak Park ...	18	..	..	..	..	..	..	..	..		..	..	..	..	..	..	..	..	..	6 17	6 17	..	18
Forest Hill, for Lordship	19	..	..	..	..	..	..	..	..		..	..	..	6 11	..	..	..	..	..	6 19	6 19	..	19
Sydenham ... [Lane	20	..	..	..	..	..	..	..	..		..	..	..	6 14	..	..	..	..	..	6 22	6 22	..	20
Penge West C ...	21	..	..	..	..	..	..	..	..		..	..	..	6 16	..	..	..	..	..	..	6 24	..	21
Anerley ...	22	..	..	..	..	..	..	..	..		..	..	..	6 17	..	..	..	..	..	..	6 25	..	22
Streatham Common ...	23	..	6 5	..	..	..	..	..	..	Stop	..	6 12	..	..	..	6 21	..	..	..	..	..	..	23
Norbury ...	24	..	6 7	..	..	..	..	..	..		..	6 14	..	..	..	6 24	..	..	..	..	..	..	24
Thornton Heath ...	25	..	6 10	..	..	..	..	..	..	..	..	6 17	..	..	..	6 27	..	..	..	..	..	..	25
Selhurst ...	26	..	6 12	..	..	..	..	..	..	..	..	6 19	..	..	..	6 30	..	..	..	..	..	..	26
Streatham Hill ...	27	..	..	..	6 6	..	..	..	..	..	..	..	..	..	..	..	6 14	..	6 18	..	..	..	27
West Norwood. [N'wood)	28	..	..	..	6 9	..	..	..	6 13	..	..	..	..	..	..	..	6 17	..	To London Bridge via Tulse Hill	..	..	..	28
Gipsy Hill (for Upper	29	..	..	..	6 12	..	..	..	6 16	..	..	..	..	..	..	..	6 19	..		..	..	..	29
Crystal Palace D ...	30	..	..	..	6 14	..	..	..	6 19	..	..	..	..	..	..	..	6 22	..		6 25	..	..	30
Birkbeck ...	31	..	..	..	6 18	..	..	..	..	..	..	..	..	..	..	..	..	..		..	..	..	31
Beckenham Jn. arr	32	..	..	..	6 22	..	..	..	..	..	..	..	..	..	..	..	..	..		..	..	..	32
Norwood Junction F ..	33	..	..	..	..	..	..	..	..	..	6 15	..	..	6 20	6 18	6 33	6 27	..		..	6 29	..	33
East Croydon .. arr	34	6 10	6 16	..	..	..	..	..	..	..	..	..	..	..	6 22	To London Bridge, via Forest Hill	..	6 21		..	..	..	34
East Croydon .. dep	35	6 10	6 16	..	..	..	..	..	..	..	..	..	..	..	6 22		..	6 21		..	To London Bridge via Streatham	..	35
Mitcham Junction ...	36	..	..	6 9	..	6 13	6 14	..	..	p.m	..	..	..	..	..		..	..		..		6 27	36
Hackbridge ...	37	..	..	6 12	..	6 15	6 16	..	..	SX	..	..	..	..	..		..	..		..		6 29	37
Carshalton ...	38	..	..	6 14	..	6 18	6 19	..	..		..	..	..	..	..		..	..		..		6 32	38
West Croydon 319 arr	39	..	..	..	..	..	..	SO	..	3	6 19	6 22	..	6 24	..		6 32	..	..	..		..	39
West Croydon 319 dep	40	..	..	..	..	..	..	3	..	6 14	6 19	6 22	..	6 24	..		..	..	..	..		..	40
Waddon G ...	41	..	..	..	..	..	..		..	6 16	6 21	6 25	..	6 27	..		..	..	..	..		..	41
Wallington ...	42	..	..	..	..	..	..	6 21	..	6 20	6 25	6 28	..	6 30	..		..	..	..	..		..	42
Carshalton Beeches ...	43	..	..	..	..	..	..	6 23	..	6 22	6 27	6 31	..	6 33	..		..	..	..	..		..	43
Sutton 322 ...	44	..	..	6 17	..	6 22	6 22	6 26	..	6 25	6 30	6 35	..	6 35	..		..	..	..	..		6 35	44
Belmont ...	45	..	..	..	..	..	..	..	..	..	6 33	6 38	..	6 38	..	..	..	..	..	..	..	..	45
Banstead ...	46	..	..	..	..	..	..	..	..	..	6 36	6 41	..	6 41	..	..	..	..	..	..	..	..	46
Epsom Downs ... arr	47	..	..	..	..	..	..	..	..	..	6 39	6 44	..	6 45	..	..	..	..	..	..	..	..	47
Cheam ...	48	..	..	6 20	..	6 25	6 25	..	..	..	..	..	..	..	..	..	..	..	..	..	..	6 38	48
Ewell East H ...	49	..	..	6 23	..	6 28	6 28	..	..	..	..	..	..	..	..	..	..	..	..	..	..	6 41	49
Epsom ...	50	..	..	6 27	..	6 31	6 31	..	..	..	..	..	6 35	..	..	..	..	..	..	..	..	6 45	50
Ashtead ...	51	..	..	..	..	..	6 35	..	..	..	..	..	6 39	..	..	..	..	..	..	..	..	6 49	51
Leatherhead ... [Bridge J	52	..	..	..	..	..	6 39	..	..	..	..	..	6 43	..	..	..	..	..	..	..	..	6 53	52
Boxhill and Burford	53	..	..	..	..	..	..	..	..	..	..	..	6 48	..	..	..	..	..	..	..	..	..	53
Dorking North K .. arr	54	..	..	..	..	..	..	..	..	..	..	..	6 51	..	..	..	..	..	..	..	..	..	54
Bookham ... [394	55	..	..	..	..	..	6 44	..	..	..	..	..	..	..	..	..	..	..	..	..	..	6 57	55
Effingham Junction arr	56	..	..	..	..	..	6 46	..	..	..	..	..	..	..	..	..	..	..	..	..	..	7 1	56
South Croydon 234 ...	57	..	6 18	..	..	..	..	..	..	..	..	..	..	..	6 24	..	..	..	..	..	..	..	57
Purley Oaks ...	58	..	6 21	..	..	..	..	..	..	..	..	..	..	..	6 27	..	..	..	..	..	..	..	58
Purley ...	59	6 15	6 23	..	..	..	..	..	..	..	..	..	..	..	6 29	..	..	..	..	..	..	..	59
Coulsdon North L .. arr	60	..	6 27	..	..	..	..	..	..	..	..	..	..	..	6 33	..	..	..	..	..	..	..	60
Purley ... dep	61	6 18	..	..	..	..	..	..	..	..	..	..	..	..	..	..	..	..	..	..	..	..	61
Kenley ...	62	6 21	..	..	..	..	..	..	..	..	..	..	..	..	..	..	..	..	..	..	..	..	62
Whyteleafe ...	63	6 24	..	..	..	..	..	..	..	..	..	..	..	..	..	..	..	..	..	..	..	..	63
Warlingham ...	64	6 26	..	..	..	..	..	..	..	..	..	..	..	..	..	..	..	..	..	..	..	..	64
Caterham ... arr	65	6 30	..	..	..	..	..	..	..	..	..	..	..	..	..	..	..	..	..	..	..	..	65
Purley ... dep	66	6 17	..	..	..	..	..	..	..	..	..	..	..	..	..	..	..	..	..	..	..	..	66
Reedham ...	67	6 19	..	..	..	..	..	..	..	..	..	..	B 8 minutes later on Saturdays	..	..	..	..	..	..	..	..	..	67
Smitham ...	68	6 21	..	..	..	..	..	..	..	..	..	..		..	..	..	..	..	..	..	..	..	68
Woodmansterne ...	69	6 24	..	..	..	..	..	..	..	..	..	..		..	..	..	..	..	..	..	..	..	69
Chipstead ...	70	6 26	..	..	..	..	..	..	..	..	..	..		..	..	..	..	..	..	..	..	..	70
Kingswood M ...	71	6 31	..	..	..	..	..	..	..	..	..	..		..	..	..	..	..	..	..	..	..	71
Tadworth N ...	72	6 34	..	..	..	..	..	..	..	..	..	..		..	..	..	..	..	..	..	..	..	72
Tattenham Corner. arr	73	6 37	..	..	..	..	..	..	..	..	..	..		..	..	..	..	..	..	..	..	..	73
Coulsdon South ...	74	..	..	..	..	..	..	..	..	..	..	..		..	..	..	..	..	..	..	..	..	74
Merstham ...	75	..	..	..	..	..	..	..	..	..	..	..		..	..	..	..	..	..	..	..	..	75
Redhill 158, 246 ... arr	76	..	..	..	..	..	..	..	..	..	..	..		..	..	..	..	6 36	..	..	..	..	76
Reigate 246 ... "	77	..	..	..	..	..	..	..	..	..	..	..		..	..	..	..	6 44	..	..	..	..	77
Horsham 159, 244, 245 "	78	..	..	..	..	..	..	..	..	..	..	..	7B16	..	..	..	..	..	..	..	..	..	78

CATERHAM, TATTENHAM CORNER, REDHILL, REIGATE, and HORSHAM

Week Days—continued (p.m)

No.	SX	SX	SO	SX	SO	SO		SX	SX	SX	SX	SO	..	SX	SX	SX	SX			SX		SX		SX	SX	SX	SO	SX
1	..	6 8	6 8	6 10	6 10	6 10	..	..	..	..	..	..	..	..	6 11	6 13	6 18	6 20	..	..	..	6 18	..	..	..	6 20	6 21	6 24
2	..			..	..		..					..		..			..				..		..		..			
3	..	3	3	..	..	3	..	3	3	3	3	..	3	..	3	3	..	3	3	3	..	3	..	3	6 27	3	3	3
4	6 9	..	..	..	..	..	..	6 10	6 11	6 12	6 16	6 16	6J17	6 20	..	..	..	..	6 15	6 22	..	..	..	6 24	..	..	..	..
5	..	..	..	..	..	6 13	..	..	..	..	..	..	..	..	..	6 16	..	..	..	..	..	..	..	..	3	6 23	..	6 27
6	..	..	6 14	..	6 16	6 16	..	..	..	..	..	..	..	..	6 16	6 19	..	6 25	..	..	..	6 24	..	..		6 26	6 26	6 30
7	..	..	..	..	..	6 20	..	..	..	..	..	..	..	..	..	6 22	..	..	..	..	..	..	..	..		6 29	..	6 33
8	..	..	6 18	..	..	6 22	..	..	..	..	..	..	..	..	6 21	6 24	..	6 29	..	..	..	6 28	..	..		6 31	6 30	6 35
9	..	..	..	..	..	..	..	..	..	..	..	..	6 21	..	..	..	..	..	6 18	..	..	..	..	..	Via Worcester Park	..	..	..
10	..	..	..	..	..	..	..	6 15	..	..	..	..	6 24	..	..	..	..	..	6 21	..	..	..	..	..		..	..	..
11	..	..	..	..	..	..	..	6 17	..	..	..	..	6 26	..	..	..	..	..	6 23	..	..	..	..	..		..	..	..
12	..	..	..	..	..	..	..	6 20	..	..	..	..	To Victoria, arr 6J42 p.m J1 min later on Sats	..	..	..	..	..	6 26	..	..	..	..	..		..	..	..
13	..	..	..	..	..	..	..	6 22	..	..	..	..		..	..	..	..	..	6 28	..	..	..	..	..		..	..	..
14	..	..	..	..	..	..	..	6 25	..	..	..	..		..	..	..	..	..	6 31	..	..	..	..	..		..	..	..
15	..	..	..	..	..	..	..	..	..	..	..	..		..	..	..	..	..	..	..	..	..	..	..		..	..	..
16	..	..	..	..	..	..	..	..	6 16	..	..	..		..	..	..	..	..	..	..	..	..	..	6 29	..	..	..	..
17	..	..	..	..	..	..	..	..	6 18	..	..	..		..	..	..	..	..	..	..	..	..	..	..	..	..	..	..
18	..	..	..	..	..	..	..	..	6 21	..	..	..		..	..	..	..	..	..	..	..	..	..	..	..	..	..	..
19	..	..	..	..	..	..	..	..	6 23	..	..	..		..	..	..	..	..	..	..	..	..	..	..	..	..	..	..
20	..	..	..	..	..	..	..	..	6 26	..	..	..		..	..	..	..	..	..	..	..	..	..	..	..	..	..	..
21	..	..	..	..	..	..	..	..	6 28	..	..	..		..	..	..	..	..	..	..	..	..	..	..	..	..	..	..
22	..	..	..	..	..	..	..	..	6 29	..	..	..		..	..	..	..	..	..	..	..	..	..	..	..	..	..	..
23	..	..	6 22	..	..	..	..	..	..	..	..	..		..	6 25	..	..	..	..	..	..	6 32	..	..	..	..	6 35	..
24	..	..	6 24	..	..	..	..	..	..	..	..	..		..	6 27	..	..	..	..	..	..	6 34	..	..	..	..	6 37	..
25	..	..	6 27	..	..	..	..	..	..	..	..	..	..	..	6 30	..	..	..	..	..	..	6 37	..	..	..	..	6 40	..
26	..	..	6 29	..	..	..	..	..	..	..	..	..	..	..	6 32	..	..	..	..	..	..	6 39	..	..	..	..	6 42	..
27	..	..		..	..	6 24	..	6 30	..	..	..	..	..	..	..	6 26	..	..	..	..	SO	..	..	..	..	6 34	..	6 38
28	..	..		..	..	6 27	..	..	..	..	..	..	..	..	..	6 29	..	..	6 33	..	3	Arr. Sutton 6 54 p.m.	..	..	..	6 37	..	To London Bridge, via Tulse Hill
29	..	..		..	..	6 30	..	..	..	..	..	..	..	..	..	6 32	..	..	6 36	..			..	..	..	6 39	..	
30	..	..	Arr Sutton 6 44 p.m	..	..	6 32	..	..	..	..	..	..	..	..	..	6 34	..	..	6 39	..	6 40		..	..	..	6 42	..	
31	..	..		..	..	..	..	..	..	..	..	..	..	..	..	6 38	..	..		..	6 43		..	..	..	..	..	
32	..	..		..	..	..	..	..	..	..	..	..	..	..	..	6 42	..	..	Stop	..	6 47		..	..	..	..	..	
33	..	..		..	..	6 37	..	..	6 32	..	..	6 28	..	..	..	..	..	..	..	6 35			..	6 38	..	6 47	..	
34	6 24	6 25		6 28	6 29	..	..	..	To London Bridge, via Streatham	..	6 31	6 32	..	6 35	6 35	..	..	..	..	..	Stop		..	6 42	..	..	6 46	
35	6 24	6 25		..	..	..	..	..		..	6 31	6 34	..	6 35	6 36	..	..	..	..	..	..		..	6 42	..	..	6 46	
36	..	..		..	..	..	..	..		..	..	..	..	..	..	..	..	6 35	p.m	..	..	..	..	..	..	..	..	
37	..	..		..	..	..	..	..		..	..	..	..	..	..	..	..	6 38	SX	..	..	..	..	..	..	..	..	
38	..	..		..	..	..	..	..		..	..	..	..	..	..	..	..	6 40	3	..	p.m	..	..	..	..	..	..	
39	..	..	6 32	..	..	6 41	..	..		6 27	..	..	..	..	..	..	..	..		6 39	SO	6 42	..	..	..	6 51	..	..
40	..	..	6 32	..	..	..	..	..		6 27	..	..	..	..	..	..	..	..	6 34	6 39	3	6 42	..	..	..	..	..	..
41	..	..	6 35	..	..	..	..	..		6 30	..	..	..	..	..	..	..	..	6 36	6 41		6 45	..	..	..	..	..	..
42	..	..	6 38	..	..	..	..	..		6 33	..	..	..	..	..	..	..	..	6 40	6 45	6 47	6 48	..	..	..	..	..	..
43	..	..	6 41	..	..	..	..	..		6 36	..	..	..	..	..	..	..	..	6 42	6 47	6 49	6 51	..	..	..	..	..	..
44	..	..	6 47	..	..	..	..	..		6 38	..	..	..	..	..	..	..	6 43	6 45	6 50	6 52	6 57	..	..	..	..	..	..
45	..	..	6 50	..	..	..	..	..	..	6 41	..	..	..	..	..	..	..	..	..	6 53	..	7 0	..	..	..	..	..	..
46	..	..	6 53	..	..	..	..	..	..	6 44	..	..	..	..	..	..	..	..	..	6 56	..	7 3	..	..	..	..	..	..
47	..	..	6 56	..	..	..	..	..	..	6 48	..	..	..	..	..	..	..	..	..	6 59	..	7 6	..	..	..	..	..	..
48	..	..	..	..	..	..	..	..	..	..	..	..	..	..	..	..	..	6 46	..	..	..	..	..	..	..	..	..	..
49	..	..	..	..	..	..	..	..	..	..	..	..	..	..	..	..	..	6 49	..	..	..	..	..	..	..	..	..	..
50	..	..	..	..	..	..	..	..	..	..	..	..	..	..	..	..	..	6 53	..	..	..	..	..	..	6 56	..	..	..
51	..	..	..	..	..	..	..	..	..	..	..	..	..	..	..	..	..	..	..	..	..	..	..	..	7 0	..	..	..
52	..	..	..	..	..	..	..	..	..	..	..	..	..	..	..	..	..	..	..	..	..	..	..	..	7 4	..	..	..
53	..	..	..	..	..	..	..	..	..	..	..	..	..	..	..	..	..	..	..	..	..	..	..	..	7 9	..	..	..
54	..	..	..	..	..	..	..	..	..	..	..	..	..	..	..	..	..	..	..	..	..	..	..	..	7 11	..	..	..
55	..	..	..	..	..	..	..	..	..	..	..	..	..	..	..	..	..	..	..	..	..	..	..	..	..	..	..	..
56	..	..	..	..	..	..	..	..	..	..	..	..	..	..	..	..	..	..	..	..	..	..	..	..	..	..	..	..
57	..	6 28	..	..	..	..	..	..	..	..	..	..	..	..	6 38	..	..	..	..	..	..	..	..	6 44	..	..	6 48	..
58	..	..	..	..	..	..	..	..	..	..	..	..	..	..	6 41	..	..	..	..	..	..	..	..	6 47	..	..	6 51	..
59	..	6 32	..	..	..	..	..	..	..	..	6 37	6 40	..	6 40	6 43	..	..	..	..	..	..	..	..	6 49	..	..	6 53	..
60	..	..	..	..	..	..	..	..	..	..	..	..	..	..	6 47	..	..	..	..	..	..	..	..	6 53	..	..	6 57	..
61	..	..	..	..	..	..	..	..	..	..	6 39	..	..	..	..	..	..	..	..	..	..	..	..	..	..	..	..	..
62	..	..	..	..	..	..	..	..	..	..	6 42	..	..	..	..	..	..	..	..	..	..	..	..	..	..	..	..	..
63	..	..	..	..	..	..	..	..	..	..	6 45	..	..	..	..	..	..	..	..	..	..	..	..	..	..	..	..	..
64	..	..	..	..	..	..	..	..	..	..	6 47	..	..	..	..	..	..	..	..	..	..	..	..	..	..	..	..	..
65	..	..	..	..	..	..	..	..	..	..	6 51	..	..	..	..	..	..	..	..	..	..	..	..	..	..	..	..	..
66	§ Via Three Bridges	..	..	..	..	..	..	..	..	..	6 38	..	..	§ Via Three Bridges	..	..	..	..	..	..	..	..	..	..	..	..	..	..
67		..	..	..	..	..	..	..	..	..	6 40	..	..		..	..	..	..	..	..	..	..	..	..	..	..	..	..
68		..	..	..	..	..	..	..	..	..	6 42	..	..		..	..	..	..	..	..	..	..	..	..	..	..	..	..
69		..	..	..	..	..	..	..	..	..	6 45	..	..		..	..	..	..	..	..	..	..	..	..	..	..	..	..
70		..	..	..	..	..	..	..	..	..	6 47	..	..		..	..	..	..	..	..	..	..	..	..	..	..	..	..
71		..	..	..	..	..	..	..	..	..	6 52	..	..		..	..	§ Via Three Bridges	..	..	..	..	..	..	..	..	..	..	..
72		..	..	..	..	..	..	..	..	..	6 55	..	..		..	..		..	..	..	..	..	..	..	..	..	..	..
73		..	..	..	..	..	..	..	..	..	6 58	..	..		..	..		..	..	..	..	..	..	..	..	..	..	..
74	6 32	..	..	..	..	..	..	..	..	..	..	6 43	..	6 44	..	..		..	..	..	..	..	..	..	..	..	..	..
75	6 38	..	..	..	..	..	..	..	..	..	..	6 49	..	6 50	..	..		..	..	..	..	..	..	..	..	..	..	..
76	6 42	..	..	..	..	..	..	..	..	..	..	6 53	..	6 54	..	..		..	..	..	..	..	..	..	..	..	..	..
77	..	..	..	..	..	..	..	..	..	..	..	7 0	..	7 1	..	..		..	..	..	..	..	..	..	..	..	..	..
78	7§23	..	..	..	..	..	..	..	..	..	..	..	..	7§34	..	..	7§5	..	..	..	..	..	..	..	..	..	..	..

LONDON, CRYSTAL PALACE, CROYDON, SUTTON, DORKING NORTH,

Down	No.	p.m.								Week Days—*continued*								p.m.					No.
		S X	S X	S O	S X	S X	S O			S X	S X	S X	S O	S X	S X	S X		S X	S X	S X	S X	S O	
Victoria .... dep	1	..	6 25	..	..	..	6 28	..	..	..	..	..	..	..	..	..		6 31	6 33	..	6 38	..	1
Charing Cross* ... "	2	..	3	3	3	3	..	..	..	3	..	3	6 24	3	3	3	..	3	3	3	3	3	2
Waterloo* .... "	3	6 32					..	..	..		..		6 26				..						3
London Bridge ..... "	4	..	..	6 25	6 25	6 27	..	..	..	6 28	6 30	6 30	6 31	6 31	6 35	6 35	..	..	..	6 37	..	6 29	4
Battersea Park	5	..	..	..	..	..	..	..	..	..	..	..	3	..	..	..	..	..	6 36	..	..	..	5
Clapham Junction	6	6 39	..	..	..	..	6U34	..	..	..	..	..		..	..	..	..	6 36	6 39	..	6 43	..	6
Wandsworth Common A	7	3	..	..	..	..	..	..	..	..	..	..	..	..	..	..	..	..	6 42	..	..	..	7
Balham & Upper Tooting	8		..	..	..	..	..	..	..	..	..	..	..	..	..	..	..	6 41	6 44	..	6 47	..	8
South Bermondsey	9	Via Worcester Park	..	..	..	..	U Takes up only	..	..	..	..	..	..	..	..	6 38	..	..	..	6 41	..	..	9
Queen's Road, Peckham	10		..	..	..	..		..	..	..	..	6 35	..	..	..	6 41	..	..	..	6 44	..	..	10
Peckham Rye	11		..	6 31	..	..		..	..	..	..	6 37	..	..	..	6 43	..	..	..	6 46	..	..	11
East Dulwich	12		..	..	..	..		..	..	..	..	6 40	..	..	..	6 46	..	..	..	}	..	..	12
North Dulwich	13		..	..	..	..		..	..	..	..	6 42	..	..	..	6 48	..	..	..		..	..	13
Tulse Hill	14		..	6 35	6 35	..		..	..	6 38	..	6 45	..	..	..	6 51	..	..	..	☞	..	..	14
Streatham	15		..	6 39	6 39	..		..	..	6 42	..	..	..	..	..	..	..	..	..		..	..	15
New Cross Gate (for E.L.	16		..	..	..	6 32	..	..	..	..	..	..	..	6 36	..	..	..	..	..		..	6 34	16
Brockley B ...... [Line)	17		..	..	..	6 34	..	..	..	..	..	..	..	6 38	..	..	..	..	..	To Victoria arr 7 1 p.m	..	6 36	17
Honor Oak Park	18		..	..	..	6 37	..	..	..	..	..	..	..	6 41	..	..	..	..	..		..	6 39	18
Forest Hill, for Lordship	19		..	..	..	6 39	..	..	..	..	..	..	..	6 43	..	..	..	..	..		..	6 41	19
Sydenham .... [Lane	20		..	..	..	6 42	..	..	..	..	..	..	..	6 46	..	..	..	..	..		..	6 44	20
Penge West C	21		..	..	..	..	..	..	..	..	..	..	..	6 48	..	..	..	..	..		..	6 46	21
Anerley	22		..	..	..	..	..	..	..	..	..	..	..	6 49	..	..	..	..	..		..	6 47	22
Streatham Common	23	..	6 37	..	6 41	..	..	..	..	..	..	..	..	..	..	..	..	6 45	..		..	..	23
Norbury	24	..	6 39	..	6 44	..	..	..	..	..	..	..	..	..	..	..	..	6 47	..		..	..	24
Thornton Heath	25	..	6 42	..	6 47	..	..	..	..	..	..	..	..	..	..	..	..	6 50	..		..	..	25
Selhurst	26	..	6 44	..	6 50	..	..	..	..	..	..	..	..	..	..	..	..	6 52	..	Stop	..	..	26
Streatham Hill	27	..	..	..	..	..	..	..	..	..	..	6 49	..	..	..	..	..	..	6 46	..	..	..	27
West Norwood..[N'wood)	28	..	..	..	..	..	..	..	..	..	..	..	..	..	..	6 53	..	..	6 49	..	..	..	28
Gipsy Hill (for Upper	29	..	..	..	..	..	..	..	..	..	..	..	..	..	..	6 56	..	..	6 52	..	..	..	29
Crystal Palace D	30	..	..	..	..	6 45	..	..	..	..	..	..	..	..	..	6 59	..	..	6 54	..	..	..	30
Birkbeck	31	..	..	..	..	..	..	..	..	..	..	..	..	..	..	..	..	..	6 58	..	..	..	31
Beckenham Jn. arr	32	..	..	..	..	..	..	..	..	..	..	To Victoria, via Wandsworth Common	..	..	..	..	..	..	7 2	..	..	..	32
Norwood Junction F ..	33	..	..	..	6 53	..	..	..	..	..	..		6 43	6 52	..	..	..	..	Stop	..	..	6 50	33
East Croydon .... arr	34	..	6 47	..	To London Bridge via Forest Hill	..	6 45	..	..	..	6 47		6 47	To London Bridge via Streatham	6 51	..	..	6 56		..	..	..	34
East Croydon .... dep	35	..	6 47	..		..	6 46	..	..	..	..		6 47		6 51	..	..	6 56	..	..	..	..	35
Mitcham Junction	36	..	..	6 45		..	..	..	..	6 47	..		..		..	..	..	..	..	p.m	6 54	..	36
Hackbridge	37	..	..	6 48		..	..	..	..	6 49	..		..		..	..	..	..	..	S X	6 56	..	37
Carshalton	38	..	..	6 51		..	..	..	..	6 52	..		..		..	..	..	..	..	3	6 59	..	38
West Croydon 319 arr	39	..	..	..		..	..	..	..	..	..		..		..	..	..	..	..		..	6 54	39
West Croydon 319 dep	40	..	..	..		..	..	..	..	..	..		..		..	..	..	..	..	6 54	..	6 54	40
Waddon G	41	..	..	..		..	..	..	..	..	..		..		..	..	..	..	..	6 56	..	6 57	41
Wallington	42	..	..	..		..	..	..	..	..	..		..		..	..	..	..	..	7 0	..	7 0	42
Carshalton Beeches	43	..	..	..		..	..	..	..	..	..		..		..	..	..	..	..	7 2	..	7 3	43
Sutton 322	44	..	..	6 55		..	..	..	..	6 55	..		..		..	..	..	..	..	7 5	7 2	7 5	44
Belmont	45	..	..	..	..	..	..	..	..	..	..	..	..	..	..	..	..	..	..	..	..	7 8	45
Banstead	46	..	..	..	..	..	..	..	..	..	..	..	..	..	..	..	..	..	..	..	..	7 11	46
Epsom Downs ...... arr	47	..	..	..	..	..	..	..	..	..	..	..	..	..	..	..	..	..	..	..	..	7 15	47
Cheam	48	..	..	6 58	..	..	..	..	..	6 58	..	..	..	..	..	..	..	..	..	..	7 5	..	48
Ewell East H	49	..	..	7 1	..	..	..	..	..	7 1	..	..	..	..	..	..	..	..	..	..	7 8	..	49
Epsom	50	7 3	..	7 5	..	..	..	..	..	7 7	..	..	..	..	..	..	..	..	..	..	7 11	..	50
Ashtead	51	7 7	..	7 9	..	..	..	..	..	7 11	..	..	..	..	..	..	..	..	..	..	..	..	51
Leatherhead..[Bridge J	52	7 11	..	7 13	..	..	..	..	..	7 15	..	..	..	..	..	..	..	..	..	..	..	..	52
Boxhill and Burford	53	..	..	7 18	..	..	..	..	..	7 20	..	..	..	..	..	..	..	..	..	..	..	..	53
Dorking North K .. arr	54	..	..	7 21	..	..	..	..	..	7 23	..	..	..	..	..	..	..	..	..	..	..	..	54
Bookham .... [394	55	7 16	..	..	..	..	..	..	..	..	..	..	..	..	..	..	..	..	..	..	..	..	55
Effingham Junction arr	56	7 19	..	..	..	..	..	..	..	..	..	..	..	..	..	..	..	..	..	..	..	..	56
South Croydon 234	57	..	6 50	..	..	..	..	..	..	..	..	..	6 50	..	..	..	..	6 58	..	..	..	..	57
Purley Oaks	58	..	6 53	..	..	..	..	..	..	..	..	..	6 52	..	..	..	..	7 1	..	..	..	..	58
Purley	59	..	6 56	..	..	..	..	..	..	..	..	..	6 55	..	6 56	..	..	7 3	..	..	..	..	59
Coulsdon North L .. arr	60	..	6 59	..	..	..	..	..	..	..	..	..	..	..	..	..	..	7 7	..	..	..	..	60
Purley .... dep	61	..	..	..	..	..	..	..	..	..	..	..	6 59	..	6 58	..	..	..	..	..	..	..	61
Kenley	62	..	..	..	..	..	..	..	..	..	..	..	7 2	..	7 1	..	..	..	..	..	..	..	62
Whyteleafe	63	..	..	..	..	..	..	..	..	..	..	..	7 5	..	7 4	..	..	..	..	..	..	..	63
Warlingham	64	..	..	..	..	..	..	..	..	..	..	..	7 7	..	7 6	..	..	..	..	..	..	..	64
Caterham .... arr	65	..	..	..	..	..	..	..	..	..	..	..	7 11	..	7 10	..	..	..	..	..	..	..	65
Purley .... dep	66	..	..	..	..	..	..	..	..	..	..	..	6 57	..	6 57	..	..	..	p.m	..	..	..	66
Reedham	67	..	..	..	..	..	..	*d* Departure time	..	..	..	..	6 59	..	6 59	..	..	..	*d* Departure time	..	..	..	67
Smitham	68	..	..	..	..	..	..		..	..	..	..	7 1	..	7 2	..	..	..		..	..	..	68
Woodmansterne	69	..	..	..	..	..	..		..	..	..	..	7 4	..	7 4	..	..	..		..	..	..	69
Chipstead	70	..	..	..	..	..	..		..	..	..	..	7 6	..	7 7	..	..	..		..	..	..	70
Kingswood M	71	..	..	..	..	..	..		..	..	..	..	7 11	..	7 11	..	..	..		..	..	..	71
Tadworth N	72	..	..	..	..	..	..		..	..	..	..	7 14	..	7 14	..	..	..		..	..	..	72
Tattenham Corner. arr	73	..	..	..	..	..	..		..	..	..	..	7 17	..	7 18	..	..	..		..	..	..	73
Coulsdon South	74	..	..	..	..	..	..	..	..	..	..	..	..	..	..	..	..	..		..	..	..	74
Merstham	75	..	..	..	..	..	..	..	..	..	..	..	..	..	..	..	..	..	S X	..	..	..	75
Redhill 158, 246 ...... arr	76	..	..	..	..	..	7 0	7*d*5	..	..	..	..	..	..	..	..	..	..	7*d*15	..	..	..	76
Reigate 246 .... "	77	..	..	..	..	..	7 9	7 9	..	..	..	..	..	..	..	..	..	..	7 20	..	..	..	77
Horsham 159, 244, 245 "	78	..	..	7 46	..	..	..	..	..	7 46	..	..	..	..	..	..	..	..	..	..	..	..	78

For Notes, see page 284a

CATERHAM, TATTENHAM CORNER, REDHILL, REIGATE, and HORSHAM

Week Days—continued (p.m)

No.	SX		SX	SO		SX		SX			SX	SO	SX	SO		SX		SO	SO	SX		SO	SX	SO	SX	SX	SO	SX
1	..	6J40	..	..	6 40	6 45	..	..	..	..	..	6 48	6 48	6 50	..	..	..	..	..	..	..	..	..	..	..	..	6 53	6 51
2	3	3	3	3	3	..	..	3	..	..	..	..	..	3	..	3	..	3	6 44	3	..	3	3	3	3	3	..	3
3						..	..		..	6 47	..	..	..		..		..		6 46		..						..	
4	6 42	..	6 44	6 37	..	..	..	6 45	..	..	6 48	..	..	..	..	6 48	..	6 48	6 51	6 50	..	6 53	6 51	6 53	6 55	6 57	..	..
5	..	..	..	..	6 43	..	..	..	..	3	..	..	..	..	..	..	..	..	3	..	..	..	..	..	..	..	..	..
6	..	6J46	..	..	6 46	..	..	..	..		..	6 53	6U54	6 55	..	..	..	..		..	..	..	..	..	..	..	..	6 56
7	..	..	..	..	6J49	..	..	..	..		..	..	..	..	..	..	..	..	..	..	..	..	..	..	..	..	..	..
8	..	6J50	..	..	6J51	..	..	..	..		..	..	..	6 59	..	..	..	..	..	..	..	..	..	..	..	..	..	7 1
9	..	..	..	6 40	..	..	..	..	..		..	..		..	..	..	..	6 51	..	..	..	..	..	..	..	7 1	..	..
10	..	..	..	6 43	..	..	..	..	..		..	..		..	..	..	..	6 54	..	6 55	..	..	..	..	..	7 4	..	..
11	..	..	..	6 45	..	..	..	..	..	Via Worcester Park	..	..		..	..	6 54	..	6 56	..	6 57	..	6 59	..	..	..	7 6	..	..
12	..	..	..	6 48	..	..	..	..	..		..	..	U Takes un only	..	..	..	..		..	7 0	..	..	..	..	..		..	..
13	..	..	..	6 50	..	..	..	..	..		..	..		..	..	..	..		..	7 2	..	..	..	..	..		..	..
14	..	..	..	6 53	..	..	..	6 55	..		..	..		..	..	6 58	..		..	7 5	..	7 3	..	..	..		..	..
15	..	..	..	6 57	..	..	..	6 59	..		..	..		..	..	7 2	..		..	..	..	7 7	..	..	..		..	..
16	..	..	6 49	..		..	..	..	..	..	..	..	..	..	..	..	..		..	..	..	..	6 56	6 58	..		..	..
17	..	..	..	..		..	..	..	..	..	..	..	..	..	..	..	..		..	..	..	..	6 58	7 0	..		..	..
18	..	..	..	..		..	..	..	..	..	..	..	..	..	..	..	..	To Victoria, arr. 7 13 p.m	..	..	..	..	7 1	7 3	..	To Victoria, arr. 7 21 p.m	..	..
19	..	..	..	..		..	..	..	..	..	..	..	..	..	..	..	..		..	..	..	..	7 3	7 5	..		..	..
20	..	..	..	..		..	..	..	..	..	..	..	..	..	..	..	..		..	..	..	..	7 6	7 8	..		..	..
21	..	..	..	..	J 1 minute later on Saturdays	..	..	..	..	..	..	..	..	..	..	..	..		..	..	..	..	7 8	..	..		..	..
22	..	..	..	..		..	..	..	..	..	..	..	..	..	..	..	..		..	..	..	..	7 9	..	..		..	..
23	..	6J54	..	6 59		..	..	7 1	..	..	..	..	..	..	..	..	..	..	..	..	..	..	..	..	..	..	..	7 5
24	..	6J56	..	7 1		..	..	7 4	..	..	..	..	..	..	..	..	..	..	..	..	..	..	..	..	..	..	..	7 7
25	..	6J59	..	7 4		..	..	7 7	..	..	..	..	..	..	..	..	..	..	..	..	..	..	..	..	..	..	..	7 10
26	..	7J 1	..	7 6		..	..	7 9	..	..	..	..	..	..	..	..	..	..	..	..	..	..	..	..	..	..	..	7 12
27	..		..	..	6 54	..	..	..	..	..	..	..	..	..	SO	..	..	..	..	7 9	..	..	..	..	..	..	..	..
28	..		..	..	6 57	..	..	..	..	..	..	..	..	..	3	..	..	..	..	..	..	..	..	..	..	..	..	..
29	..		..	..	6J59	..	..	..	..	..	..	..	..	..		..	..	..	..	..	..	..	..	..	..	..	..	..
30	..		..	..	7 2	..	..	..	..	..	..	..	..	..	7 10	..	..	..	..	..	..	..	..	7 11	..	..	..	..
31	..		..	..	..	..	..	..	..	..	..	..	..	..	7 13	..	..	..	..	..	..	..	..	..	..	..	..	..
32	..	J 2 minutes *earlier* on Saturdays	..	..	..	..	..	..	..	..	..	..	..	..	7 17	..	..	..	..	..	..	..	..	..	..	..	..	..
33	6 55		6 58	7 9	7 7	..	..	..	..	..	7 0	..	..	..	..	..	..	..	7 3	..	..	..	7 12	..	..	..	..	..
34	..		7 2		..	7 0	..	..	..	..	7 4	7 5	7 8	..	..	..	..	..	7 7	..	..	..	..	..	7 10	..	7 11	7 16
35	..		7 2		..	..	..	..	..	..	7 5	7 5	7 10	..	..	..	..	..	7 7	..	..	..	..	..	7 10	..	7 11	7 16
36	..		..		..	..	..	..	..	..	..	..	..	7 5	..	7 7	..	..	..	..	..	7 12		..	..	..	..	..
37	..		..		..	..	..	..	..	..	..	..	..	7 8	..	7 9	..	..	..	..	..	7 14		..	..	..	..	..
38	..		..		..	..	..	..	..	..	..	..	..	7 10	..	7 12	..	..	..	..	..	7 17		..	..	..	..	..
39	6 59	7J 4	..		7H12	..	..	..	..	..	..	..	..	..	..	..	..	..	..	..	..	..		..	..	..	..	..
40	6 59	7J 4	..	To London Bridge, via Forest Hill		..	..	..	..	..	..	..	..	..	..	..	..	..	..	..	..	..		..	..	..	..	..
41	7 1	7J 7	..			..	..	..	..	..	..	..	..	..	..	..	..	..	..	..	..	..		..	..	..	..	..
42	7 5	7J10	..			..	..	..	..	..	..	..	..	..	..	..	..	..	..	..	..	..	To London Bridge via Streatham	..	..	..	..	..
43	7 7	7J13	..			..	..	..	..	..	..	..	..	..	..	..	..	..	..	..	..	..		..	..	..	..	..
44	7 10	7J16	..			..	..	..	..	..	..	..	..	7 13	..	7 15	..	..	..	..	..	7 20		..	..	..	..	..
45	7 13	7 20	..		H 1 minute *earlier* on Saturdays	..	..	..	..	..	..	..	..	..	..	..	..	..	..	..	..	..		..	..	..	..	..
46	7 16	7 23	..	..		..	..	..	..	..	..	..	..	..	..	..	..	..	..	..	..	..		..	..	..	..	..
47	7 19	7 26	..	..		..	..	..	..	..	..	..	..	..	..	..	..	..	..	..	..	..		..	..	..	..	..
48	..	..	..	..		..	..	..	..	..	..	..	..	7 16	..	7 18	..	..	..	..	..	7 23	..	..	..	..	..	..
49	..	..	..	..		..	..	..	..	..	..	..	..	7 19	..	7 21	..	..	..	..	SX	7 26	..	..	..	..	..	..
50	..	..	..	..		..	..	..	..	7 15	..	..	..	7 23	..	7 25	..	..	..	..	3	7 29	..	..	..	..	..	..
51	..	..	..	..		..	..	..	..	7 19	..	..	..	..	..	7 29	..	..	..	..		7 33	..	..	..	..	..	..
52	..	..	..	..	..	..	..	..	..	7 23	..	..	..	..	..	7 33	..	..	..	..	7 36	7 37	..	..	..	..	..	..
53	..	..	..	..	..	..	..	..	..	..	..	..	..	..	..	7 38	..	..	..	..	..	..	..	..	..	..	..	..
54	..	..	..	..	..	..	..	..	..	..	..	..	..	..	..	7 41	..	..	..	..	..	..	..	..	..	..	..	..
55	..	..	..	..	..	..	..	..	..	7 28	..	..	..	..	..	..	..	..	..	..	7 40	7 42	..	..	..	..	..	..
56	..	..	..	..	..	..	..	..	..	7 31	..	..	..	..	..	..	..	..	..	..	7 43	7 45	..	..	..	..	..	..
57	..	..	7 4	..	..	..	..	..	..	..	..	..	7 15	..	..	..	..	..	7 10	..	..	..	..	..	..	..	7 15	7 19
58	..	..	7 7	..	..	..	..	..	..	..	..	..	..	..	..	..	..	..	7 12	..	..	..	..	..	..	..	..	7 21
59	..	..	7 9	..	..	..	..	..	..	..	7 11	7 11	..	..	..	..	..	..	7 16	..	..	..	..	..	7 16	..	..	7 24
60	..	..	7 13	..	..	..	..	..	..	..	..	..	..	..	..	..	..	..	..	..	..	..	..	..	..	..	..	7 27
61	..	..	..	..	..	..	..	..	..	..	..	..	..	..	..	..	..	..	7 19	..	..	..	..	..	7 18	..	..	..
62	..	..	..	..	..	..	..	..	..	..	..	..	..	..	..	..	..	..	7 22	..	..	..	..	..	7 21	..	..	..
63	..	..	..	..	..	..	..	..	..	..	..	..	..	..	..	..	..	..	7 25	..	..	..	..	..	7 24	..	..	..
64	..	..	..	..	..	..	..	..	..	..	..	..	..	..	..	..	..	..	7 27	..	..	..	..	..	7 26	..	..	..
65	..	..	..	..	..	..	..	..	..	..	..	..	..	..	..	..	..	..	7 31	..	..	..	..	..	7 30	..	..	..
66	..	..	..	..	..	..	..	..	..	..	..		..	..	..	..	..	..	7 17	..	..	..	..	..	7 17	..	..	..
67	..	..	..	..	..	..	..	..	..	..	..		..	..	..	..	..	..	7 19	..	..	..	..	..	7 19	..	..	..
68	..	..	..	..	..	..	..	..	..	..	..		..	..	..	..	..	..	7 21	..	..	..	..	..	7 21	..	..	..
69	..	..	..	..	..	..	..	..	..	..	..		..	..	..	..	..	..	7 24	..	..	..	..	..	7 24	..	..	..
70	..	..	..	..	..	..	..	..	..	..	..	§ Via Three Bridges	..	..	..	..	..	..	7 26	..	..	..	..	..	7 26	..	..	..
71	..	..	..	..	..	..	..	..	..	..	..		..	..	..	..	..	..	7 31	..	..	..	..	..	7 31	..	..	..
72	..	..	..	..	..	..	..	..	..	..	..		..	..	..	..	..	..	7 34	..	..	..	..	..	7 34	..	..	..
73	..	..	..	..	..	..	..	..	..	..	..		..	..	..	..	..	..	7 37	..	..	..	..	..	7 37	..	..	..
74	..	..	..	..	..	..	..	..	..	..	7 14	7 14	..	..	..	..	..	..	..	..	..	..	..	..	..	..	..	..
75	..	..	..	..	..	..	..	..	..	..	7 20	7 20	..	..	..	..	..	..	..	..	..	..	..	..	..	..	..	..
76	..	..	..	..	..	..	..	..	..	..	7 24	7 24	..	..	..	..	..	..	..	..	..	..	..	..	..	..	..	..
77	..	..	..	..	..	..	..	..	..	..	7 30	7 30	..	..	..	..	..	..	..	..	..	..	..	..	..	..	..	..
78	..	..	..	..	..	..	..	..	..	..	..	8§ 5	..	..	..	8 6	..	..	..	..	..	..	..	..	..	..	..	..

LONDON, CRYSTAL PALACE, CROYDON, SUTTON, DORKING NORTH,

For Notes, see page 284a

Week Days—continued (p.m.)

Down	No.	SO	SX	SX		SX	SX	SO	SX		SX	SX	SX	SO		SX	SX	SO		SO		SX	No.
Victoria .... dep	1	6 53	6 53	6 55	..	..	6 58	..	7 0	..	7 4	7 5	..	7 8	..	..	..	..	..	7 10	..	..	1
Charing Cross* ... "	2	3	3	3	..	3	3	3	3	..	3	..	3	3	..	3	3	3	..	3	..	3	2
Waterloo* .... "	3				..					..		..			7 7				..		..		3
London Bridge ..... "	4	..	..	..	..	7 2	..	7 2	..	..	..	..	7 4	..	..	7 5	7 7	7 7	..	..	..	7 10	4
Battersea Park	5	..	6 56	..	..	..	..	..	7 3	..	7 7	..	..	..	..	..	..	..	..	7 13	..	..	5
Clapham Junction	6	6 58	6 59	7 0	..	..	7 4	..	7 6	..	7 10	7U10	..	7 14	3	..	..	..	..	7 16	..	..	6
Wandsworth Common A	7	7 1	7 2	..	..	..	..	..	7 9	..	7 13	..	..	..		..	..	..	..	7 20	..	..	7
Balham & Upper Tooting	8	7 3	7 4	7 4	..	..	7 8	..	7 11	..	7 15	..	..	7 18	Via Worcester Park	..	..	..	..	7 22	..	..	8
South Bermondsey	9	..	..	..	..	..	..	..	..	..	..	U Takes up only	..	..		..	..	..	..	..	..	..	9
Queen's Road, Peckham	10	..	..	..	..	..	..	..	..	..	..		..	..		..	..	..	..	..	..	7 15	10
Peckham Rye	11	..	..	..	..	..	..	..	..	..	..		..	..		..	..	..	..	..	..	7 17	11
East Dulwich	12	..	..	..	..	..	..	..	..	..	..		..	..		..	..	..	..	..	..	7 20	12
North Dulwich	13	..	..	..	..	..	..	..	..	..	..		..	..		..	..	..	..	..	..	7 22	13
Tulse Hill	14	..	..	..	..	..	..	..	..	..	..		..	..		7 15	..	..	..	..	..	7 25	14
Streatham	15	..	..	..	..	..	..	..	..	..	..		..	..		7 19	..	..	..	..	..	..	15
New Cross Gate (for E.L.	16	..	..	..	..	..	..	7 7	..	..	..	..	7 9	..	..	..	7 12	7 12	..	..	..	..	16
Brockley B .... [Line)	17	..	..	..	..	..	..	..	..	..	..	..	..	..	..	..	7 14	7 14	..	..	..	..	17
Honor Oak Park	18	..	..	..	..	..	..	..	..	..	..	..	..	..	..	..	7 17	7 17	..	..	..	..	18
Forest Hill, for Lordship	19	..	..	..	..	..	..	7 11	..	..	..	..	..	..	..	..	7 19	7 19	..	..	..	..	19
Sydenham .... [Lane	20	..	..	..	..	..	..	7 14	..	..	..	..	..	..	..	..	7 22	7 22	..	..	..	..	20
Penge West C	21	..	..	..	..	..	..	7 16	..	..	..	..	..	..	..	..	..	7 24	..	..	..	..	21
Anerley	22	..	..	..	..	..	..	7 17	..	..	..	..	..	..	..	..	..	7 25	..	..	..	..	22
Streatham Common	23	7 7	..	..	..	..	7 12	..	..	..	..	..	..	7 22	..	7 21	..	..	..	..	..	..	23
Norbury	24	7 9	..	..	..	..	7 14	..	..	..	..	..	..	7 24	..	7 24	..	..	..	..	..	..	24
Thornton Heath	25	7 12	..	..	..	..	7 17	..	..	..	..	..	..	7 27	..	7 27	..	..	..	..	..	..	25
Selhurst	26	7 15	..	..	..	..	7 19	..	..	..	..	..	..	7 29	..	7 30	..	..	..	..	..	..	26
Streatham Hill	27	..	7 6	..	..	..	..	..	7 14	..	7 18	..	..	..	..	..	..	..	..	7 24	..	7 28	27
West Norwood..[N'wood)	28	..	7 9	..	..	..	..	..	7 17	..	To London Bridge, via Tulse Hill	..	..	..	..	..	..	..	..	7 27	..	..	28
Gipsy Hill (for Upper	29	..	7 12	..	..	..	..	..	7 19	..		..	..	..	..	..	..	..	..	7 30	..	..	29
Crystal Palace D	30	..	7 14	..	..	..	..	..	7 22	..		..	..	Arrive Sutton 7 44 p.m	..	..	7 25	..	..	7 32	..	..	30
Birkbeck	31	..	7 18	..	..	..	..	..	..	..		..	..		..	..	..	..	..	..	..	..	31
Beckenham Jn. arr	32	..	7 22	..	..	..	..	..	..	..		..	..		..	..	..	..	..	..	..	..	32
Norwood Junction F ..	33	..	..	..	..	7 15	..	7 20	7 26	..		..	7 18		..	7 33	..	7 29	..	7 37	..	..	33
East Croydon .... arr	34	7 18	..	..	..	..	..	..	..	..		7 22	7 22		..	..	..	..	..	..	..	..	34
East Croydon .... dep	35	7 18	..	..	..	..	..	..	..	..		7 23	7 22		..	..	..	..	..	..	..	..	35
Mitcham Junction	36	..	..	7 13	..	..	..	..	..	..		..	..		..	To London Bridge, via Forest Hill	..	To London Bridge, via Streatham	..	..	..	..	36
Hackbridge	37	..	..	7 15	..	..	..	..	..	..		..	..		..		..		..	..	..	..	37
Carshalton	38	..	..	7 18	..	..	..	..	..	..		..	..		..		..		..	..	..	..	38
West Croydon 319 arr	39	..	..	..	3	7 19	7 22	7 24	7 31	..	..	..	..	7 32	..		..		..	7 41	..	..	39
West Croydon 319 dep	40	..	..	..	7J14	7 19	7 22	7 24	..	..	..	..	..	7 32	..		..		..	..	..	..	40
Waddon G	41	..	..	..	7J16	7 21	7 25	7 27	..	..	..	..	..	7 35	..		..		..	..	..	..	41
Wallington	42	..	..	..	7J20	7 25	7 28	7 30	..	..	..	..	..	7 38	..		..		..	..	..	..	42
Carshalton Beeches	43	..	..	..	7J22	7 27	7 31	7 33	..	..	..	..	..	7 41	..		..		..	..	..	..	43
Sutton 322	44	..	..	7 21	7J25	7 30	7 34	7 35	..	..	..	..	..	7 47	..		..		..	..	..	..	44
Belmont	45	..	..	..	J 1 minute later on Saturdays	7 33	7 37	7 38	..	..	..	..	..	7 50	..	..	..	..	..	..	..	..	45
Banstead	46	..	..	..		7 36	7 40	7 41	..	..	..	..	..	7 53	..	..	..	..	..	..	..	..	46
Epsom Downs ...... arr	47	..	..	..		7 39	7 43	7 45	..	..	..	..	..	7 56	..	..	..	..	..	..	..	..	47
Cheam	48	..	..	7 24		..	..	..	..	..	..	..	..	..	..	..	..	..	..	..	..	..	48
Ewell East H	49	..	..	7 27		..	..	..	..	..	..	..	..	..	..	..	..	..	..	..	..	..	49
Epsom	50	..	..	7 31		..	..	..	..	..	..	..	..	..	7 35	..	..	..	..	..	..	..	50
Ashtead	51	..	..	..		..	..	..	..	..	..	..	..	..	7 39	..	..	..	..	..	..	..	51
Leatherhead ... [Bridge J	52	..	..	..		..	..	..	..	..	..	..	..	..	7 43	..	..	..	..	..	..	..	52
Boxhill and Burford	53	..	..	..		..	..	..	..	..	..	..	..	..	7 48	..	..	..	..	..	..	..	53
Dorking North K .. arr	54	..	..	..		..	..	..	..	..	..	..	..	..	7 51	..	..	..	..	..	..	..	54
Bookham .... [394	55	..	..	..	..	..	..	..	..	..	..	..	..	..	..	..	..	..	..	..	..	..	55
Effingham Junction arr	56	..	..	..	..	..	..	..	..	..	..	..	..	..	..	..	..	..	..	..	..	..	56
South Croydon 234	57	7 21	..	..	..	..	..	..	..	..	..	..	7 24	..	..	..	..	..	..	..	..	..	57
Purley Oaks	58	7 23	..	..	..	..	..	..	..	..	..	..	7 27	..	..	..	..	..	..	..	..	..	58
Purley	59	7 26	..	..	..	..	..	..	..	..	..	..	7 29	..	..	..	..	..	..	..	..	..	59
Coulsdon North L .. arr	60	7 29	..	..	..	..	..	..	..	..	..	..	7 33	..	..	..	..	..	..	..	..	..	60
Purley .... dep	61	..	..	..	..	..	..	..	..	..	..	..	..	..	..	..	..	..	..	..	..	..	61
Kenley	62	..	..	..	..	..	..	..	..	..	..	..	..	..	..	..	..	..	..	..	..	..	62
Whyteleafe	63	..	..	..	..	..	..	..	..	..	..	..	..	..	..	..	..	..	..	..	..	..	63
Warlingham	64	..	..	..	..	..	..	..	..	..	..	..	..	..	..	..	..	..	..	..	..	..	64
Caterham .... arr	65	..	..	..	..	..	..	..	..	..	..	..	..	..	..	..	..	..	..	..	..	..	65
Purley .... dep	66	..	..	..	..	..	..	..	..	..	..	§ Via Three Bridges	..	..	..	..	..	..	..	..	..	..	66
Reedham	67	..	..	..	..	..	..	..	..	..	..		..	..	..	..	..	..	..	..	..	..	67
Smitham	68	..	..	..	..	..	..	..	..	..	..		..	..	..	..	..	..	..	..	..	..	68
Woodmansterne	69	..	..	..	..	..	..	..	..	..	..		..	..	..	..	..	..	..	..	..	..	69
Chipstead	70	..	..	..	..	..	..	..	..	..	..		..	..	..	..	..	..	..	..	..	..	70
Kingswood M	71	..	..	..	..	..	..	..	..	..	..		..	..	..	..	..	..	..	..	..	..	71
Tadworth N	72	..	..	..	..	..	..	..	..	..	..		..	..	..	..	..	..	..	..	..	..	72
Tattenham Corner. arr	73	..	..	..	..	..	..	..	..	..	..		..	..	..	..	..	..	..	..	..	..	73
Coulsdon South	74	..	..	..	..	..	..	..	..	..	..	..	..	..	..	..	..	..	..	..	..	..	74
Merstham	75	..	..	..	..	..	..	..	..	..	..	..	..	..	..	..	..	..	..	..	..	..	75
Redhill 158,246 ..... arr	76	..	..	..	..	..	..	..	..	..	..	7 36	..	..	..	..	..	..	..	..	..	..	76
Reigate 246 .... "	77	..	..	..	..	..	..	..	..	..	..	..	..	..	..	..	..	..	..	..	..	..	77
Horsham 159,244,245 "	78	..	..	..	..	..	..	..	..	..	..	8§9	..	..	8 24	..	..	..	..	..	..	..	78

CATERHAM, TATTENHAM CORNER, REDHILL, REIGATE, and HORSHAM

p.m — **Week Days**—*continued* — p.m

No.	SX	SX				SX	SX		SX	SX		SX	SX		SO		SX		SX	SO					SO	SX		SX
1	..	7 13	..	..	..	7 11	7 18	7 18	7 20	..	..	..	7 20	..	7 21	7 25	..	..	..	7 25	..	..	728	..	..	..	..	7 33
2	③	③	③	③	..	③	③	..	③	③	..	③	③	..	③	..	③	..	..	③	..	③	..	7 24	③	③	..	③
3					..			..			..			..		..		..	7 27		..		..	7 26			..	
4	7 11	..	7 15	7J17	7 18	..	..	..	..	7 22	..	7 24	..	..	..	..	7 25	..	..	..	..	7 28	..	7 31	7 29	7 32	..	..
5	..	7 16	..	..	..	..	..	..	..	..	..	..	7 23	..	..	..	..	..	③	..	..	..	..	③	..	..	..	7 36
6	..	7 19	..	..	..	7 16	7 24	..	7 25	..	..	..	7 26	..	7 26	..	..	..		7 30	..	..	734		..	..	..	7 39
7	..	7 22	..	..	..	..	..	..	..	..	..	..	7 29	..	..	..	..	..	..	..	..	..	..	..	..	..	..	7 42
8	..	7 24	..	..	..	7 21	7 28	..	7 29	..	..	..	7 31	..	7 30	..	..	..	..	7 34	..	..	..	..	..	..	..	7 44
9	..	..	7 18	7 21	..	..	..	..	..	..	..	..	..	..	..	..	..	..	Via Worcester Park	..	..	..	..	..	..	..	..	..
10	..	..	7 21	7 24	..	..	..	..	..	..	..	..	..	..	..	..	..	..		..	..	..	..	..	..	..	..	..
11	..	..	7 23	7 26	..	..	..	..	..	..	..	..	..	..	..	..	..	..		..	..	7 34	..	..	..	..	..	..
12	..	..	7 26	To Victoria, arr 7 43 p.m; J 1 min. later on Sats.	..	..	..	..	..	..	..	..	..	..	..	..	..	..		..	..	..	..	..	..	..	..	..
13	..	..	7 28		..	..	..	..	..	..	..	..	..	..	..	..	..	..		..	..	..	..	..	..	..	..	..
14	..	..	7 31		..	..	..	..	..	..	..	..	..	..	..	..	7 35	..		..	..	7 38	..	..	..	..	..	..
15	..	..	..		..	..	..	..	..	..	..	..	..	..	..	..	7 39	..		..	..	7 42	..	..	..	..	..	..
16	7 16	..	..		..	..	..	..	..	..	..	7 29	..	..	..	..	..	..	..	..	..	..	..	7SO36	7 34	7 37	..	..
17	7 18	..	..		..	..	..	..	..	..	..	..	..	..	..	..	..	..	..	..	..	..	..	..	7 36	7 39	..	..
18	7 21	..	..		..	..	..	..	..	..	..	..	..	..	..	..	..	..	..	..	..	..	..	..	7 39	7 42	..	..
19	7 23	..	..		..	..	..	..	..	..	..	..	..	..	..	..	..	..	..	..	..	..	..	..	7 41	7 44	..	..
20	7 26	..	..		..	..	..	..	..	..	..	..	..	..	..	..	..	..	..	..	..	..	..	..	7 44	7 47	..	..
21	7 28	..	..		..	..	..	..	..	..	..	..	..	..	..	..	..	..	..	..	..	..	..	..	7 46	7 49	..	..
22	7 29	..	..		..	..	..	..	..	..	..	..	..	..	..	..	..	..	..	..	..	..	..	..	7 47	7 50	..	..
23	..	..	..		..	7 25	7 32	..	..	..	..	..	..	..	7 35	..	7 41	..	..	..	..	..	..	..	..	..	..	..
24	..	..	..		..	7 27	7 34	..	..	..	..	..	..	..	7 37	..	7 44	..	..	..	..	H 1 minute *earlier* on Saturdays	..	..	..	..	..	..
25	..	..	..	Stop	..	7 30	7 37	..	..	..	..	..	..	..	7 40	..	7 47	..	..	..	..		..	..	..	..	..	..
26	..	..	..	p.m	..	7 32	7 39	..	..	..	..	..	..	..	7 42	..	7 49	..	..	..	..		..	..	..	..	..	..
27	..	7 26	..	SO	..	..	..	..	..	..	..	..	7 34	..	..	..	..	..	..	..	..		..	..	..	..	..	7 46
28	..	7 29	7 33	③	..	..	..	..	..	..	..	..	7 37	..	..	..	..	..	..	..	..		..	..	..	..	..	7 49
29	..	7 32	7 36		..	..	..	..	..	..	..	..	7 39	..	..	..	..	..	..	..	..		..	..	..	..	..	7 52
30	..	7 36	7 39	7 40	..	..	..	..	..	..	..	..	7 42	..	..	..	..	..	..	..	..		..	..	..	..	..	7 54
31	..	7 39	..	7 43	..	..	..	..	..	..	..	..	..	..	..	..	..	..	..	..	..		..	..	..	..	..	7 58
32	..	7 45	..	7 47	..	..	..	..	..	..	..	..	..	..	..	..	..	..	..	..	..		..	..	..	..	..	8 2
33	7 32	..	..	..	7 30	..	..	..	..	7 35	..	7 38	7 47	..	..	..	..	..	..	..	..		..	7 44	7 50	7 53	..	..
34		..	..	..	7 34	7 35	..	..	..	..	..	7 42	..	..	7 46	7 40	..	..	..	..	..		745	7 47	..	..	..	..
35		..	..	..	7 35	7 36	..	..	..	..	..	7 42	..	..	7 46	..	..	..	..	..	..	..	746	7 48	..	..	..	..
36	To London Bridge, via Streatham	..	..	..	..	..	..	..	7 36	..	..	..	..	..	..	..	..	..	..	7 41	..	7 47	..	..	..	..	..	..
37		..	..	..	..	..	..	..	7 38	..	..	..	..	..	..	..	..	..	..	7 44	..	7 50	..	..	..	..	..	..
38		..	..	..	..	..	..	..	7 41	..	..	..	..	..	..	..	..	..	..	7 46	..	7H53	..	..	..	..	..	..
39		..	..	..	..	..	7 42	..	..	7 39	..	..	7 52	..	..	..	..	..	..	..	..	..	..	..	7 54	..	..	..
40		..	..	..	..	..	..	..	..	7 39	..	..	..	..	..	..	..	..	..	..	③	..	..	..	7 54	..	..	..
41		..	..	..	..	..	..	..	..	7 41	..	..	..	..	..	..	..	..	..	..		..	..	..	7 57	..	..	..
42		..	..	..	..	..	..	..	..	7 45	..	..	..	..	..	..	..	..	..	..	7 49	..	..	..	8 0	..	..	..
43		..	..	..	..	..	..	..	..	7 47	..	..	..	..	..	..	..	..	..	..	7 51	..	..	..	8 3	..	..	..
44		..	..	..	..	..	..	7 39	7 44	7 50	..	..	..	..	..	..	..	..	..	7 49	7 54	7 56	..	..	8 5	..	..	..
45		..	..	..	..	..	..	..	..	7 53	..	..	..	..	..	..	..	..	..	..	..	..	..	..	8 8	..	..	..
46	..	..	..	..	..	..	..	..	..	7 56	..	..	..	..	..	..	..	..	..	..	..	..	..	..	8 11	..	..	..
47	..	..	..	..	..	..	..	..	..	7 59	..	..	..	..	..	..	..	..	..	..	..	..	..	..	8 15	..	..	..
48	..	..	..	..	..	..	..	..	7 47	..	..	..	..	..	..	..	..	..	..	7 52	..	7 59	..	..	..	..	..	..
49	..	..	..	..	..	..	..	..	7 50	..	..	..	..	..	..	..	..	..	..	7 55	..	8 2	..	..	..	..	..	..
50	..	..	..	..	..	..	..	..	7 53	..	..	..	..	..	..	..	..	..	7 55	7 59	..	8 5	..	..	..	..	..	..
51	..	..	..	..	..	..	..	..	..	..	..	..	..	..	..	..	..	..	7 59	..	..	8 9	..	..	..	..	..	..
52	..	..	..	..	..	..	..	..	..	..	..	..	..	..	..	..	..	..	8 3	..	..	8 13	..	..	..	..	..	..
53	..	..	..	..	..	..	..	..	..	..	..	..	..	..	..	..	..	..	8 8	..	..	8 18	..	..	..	..	..	..
54	..	..	..	..	..	..	..	7 55	..	..	..	..	..	..	..	..	..	..	8 11	..	..	8 21	..	..	..	..	..	..
55	..	..	..	..	..	..	..	..	..	..	..	..	..	..	..	..	..	..	..	..	..	..	..	..	..	..	..	..
56	..	..	..	..	..	..	..	..	..	..	..	..	..	..	..	..	..	..	..	..	..	..	..	..	..	..	..	..
57	..	..	..	..	..	7 38	..	..	..	..	..	7 44	..	..	7 48	..	..	..	..	..	..	..	..	7 51	..	..	..	..
58	..	..	..	..	..	7 41	..	..	..	..	..	7 47	..	..	7 51	..	..	..	..	..	..	..	..	7 53	..	..	..	..
59	..	..	..	..	7 40	7 43	..	..	..	..	..	7 49	..	..	7 53	..	..	..	..	..	..	..	..	7 56	..	..	..	..
60	..	..	..	..	..	7 47	..	..	..	..	..	7 53	..	..	7 57	..	..	..	..	..	..	..	..	..	..	..	..	..
61	..	..	..	..	..	..	..	..	..	..	..	..	..	..	..	..	..	..	..	..	..	..	..	7 58	..	..	..	..
62	..	..	..	..	..	..	..	..	..	..	..	..	..	..	..	..	..	..	..	..	..	..	..	8 1	..	..	..	..
63	..	..	..	..	..	..	..	..	..	..	..	..	..	..	..	..	..	..	..	..	..	..	..	8 4	..	..	..	..
64		..	..	..	..	..	..	..	..	..	..	..	..	..	..	..	..	..	..	..	..	..	..	8 6	..	..	..	..
65		..	..	..	..	..	..	..	..	..	..	..	..	..	..	..	..	..	..	..	..	..	..	8 10	..	..	..	..
66	..	..	..	..	..	..	..	..	..	..	..	..	..	..	..	..	..	..	..	..	..	..	..	7 57	..	..	..	..
67	..	..	..	..	..	..	..	..	..	..	..	..	..	..	..	..	..	..	..	..	..	..	..	7 59	..	..	..	..
68	..	..	..	..	..	..	..	..	..	..	..	..	..	..	..	..	..	..	..	..	..	..	..	8 1	..	..	..	..
69	..	..	..	..	..	..	..	..	..	..	..	..	..	..	..	..	..	..	..	..	..	..	..	8 4	..	..	..	..
70	..	..	..	..	..	..	..	..	..	..	..	..	..	..	..	..	..	..	..	..	..	..	..	8 6	..	..	..	..
71	..	..	..	..	..	..	..	..	..	..	..	..	..	..	..	..	..	..	..	..	..	..	..	8 11	..	..	..	..
72	..	..	..	..	..	..	..	..	..	..	..	..	..	..	..	..	..	..	..	..	..	..	..	8 14	..	..	..	..
73	..	..	..	..	..	..	..	..	..	..	..	..	..	..	..	..	..	..	..	..	..	..	..	8 17	..	..	..	..
74	..	..	..	..	7 44	..	..	..	..	..	..	..	..	..	..	..	..	..	..	..	..	..	..	..	..	..	..	..
75	..	..	..	..	7 50	..	..	..	..	..	..	..	..	..	..	..	..	..	..	..	..	..	..	..	..	..	..	..
76	..	..	..	..	7 54	..	..	..	..	..	..	..	..	..	..	..	..	..	..	..	..	..	8 0	..	..	..	..	..
77	..	..	..	..	8 0	..	..	..	..	..	..	..	..	..	..	..	..	..	..	..	..	..	..	..	..	..	..	..
78	..	..	..	..	..	..	..	8 13	..	..	..	..	..	..	..	..	..	..	..	..	..	8 46	..	..	..	..	..	..

For Notes, see page 284a

LONDON, CRYSTAL PALACE, CROYDON, SUTTON, DORKING NORTH,

Down	No.	Week Days—continued p.m		SO	SO	SX		SX		SX							SO		SO	SX	SX	p.m	No.
VICTORIA .... dep	1	7 38	7 40				7 45					7 48		7 51		7 51							1
CHARING CROSS* ... "	2	3	3		3	3		3		3	3			3	7 44	3	3		3	3	3		2
WATERLOO* .... "	3												7 47		7 46								3
LONDON BRIDGE ..... "	4			7 42	7 37	7 43		7 47		7 45	7 48				7 51		7 53		7 53	7 53	7 53		4
Battersea Park	5		7 43										3		3								5
Clapham Junction	6	7 44	7 46									7U53		7 56		7 56							6
Wandsworth Common A	7		7 50													7SO59							7
Balham & Upper Tooting	8	7 48	7 52											8 0		8 1							8
South Bermondsey	9				7 40					7 48	7 51												9
Queen's Road, Peckham	10				7 43					7 51	7 54	U Takes up only	Via Worcester Park										10
Peckham Rye	11				7 45					7 53	7 56						7 59				8 0		11
East Dulwich	12				7 48					7 56													12
North Dulwich	13				7 50					7 58													13
Tulse Hill	14				7 53	7 53				8 1							8 3				8 4		14
Streatham	15				7 57	7 57					To Victoria, arr. 8 15 p.m						8 7				8 8		15
New Cross Gate (for E.L.	16							7 52											7 58	7 58			16
Brockley B .... [Line)	17							7 54											8 0	8 0			17
Honor Oak Park	18							7 57											8 3	8 3			18
Forest Hill, for Lordship	19							7 59											8 5	8 5			19
Sydenham .... [Lane	20							8 2											8 8	8 8			20
Penge West C	21																			8 10			21
Anerley	22																			8 11			22
Streatham Common	23	7 52			7 59	8 0										8 5							23
Norbury	24	7 54			8 1	8 3										8 7							24
Thornton Heath	25	7 57			8 4	8 6										8 10							25
Selhurst	26	7 59			8 6	8 8										8 12							26
Streatham Hill	27		7 54						SO														27
West Norwood. [N'wood)	28		7 57						3	8 3													28
Gipsy Hill (for Upper	29		8 0							8 6													29
Crystal Palace D	30		8 2					8 5	8 10	8 9									8 11				30
Birkbeck	31	Arrive Sutton 8 14 p.m							8 13														31
Beckenham Jn. arr	32								8 17														32
Norwood Junction F ..	33		8 7		8 9	8 10									8 3					8 14			33
East Croydon .... arr	34			7 59			8 0					8 5			8 7	8 16							34
East Croydon .... dep	35			8 0								8 5			8 7	8 16							35
Mitcham Junction	36													8 6			8 12				8 13		36
Hackbridge	37													8 9			8 14				8 15		37
Carshalton	38													8 11			8 17				8 18		38
West Croydon 319 arr	39	8 2	8 11																			3	39
West Croydon 319 dep	40	8H 3			To London Bridge, via Forest Hill	To London Bridge, via Forest Hill														To Selhurst arr. 8 19 p.m		8SX14	40
Waddon G	41	8 5																				8SX16	41
Wallington	42	8H 9																				8 20	42
Carshalton Beeches	43	8 11																				8 22	43
Sutton 322	44	8 17												8 14			8 20				8 21	8 25	44
Belmont	45	8 20																					45
Banstead	46	8 23																					46
Epsom Downs ...... arr	47	8 26																					47
Cheam	48													8 17			8 23				8 24		48
Ewell East H	49													8 20			8 26				8 27		49
Epsom	50												8 15	8 24			8 30				8 30		50
Ashtead	51												8 19	Stop			8 34				8 34		51
Leatherhead ... [Bridge J	52	H 1 minute earlier on Saturdays											8 23				8 38				8 38		52
Boxhill and Burford	53																						53
Dorking North K .. arr	54																						54
Bookham .... [394	55												8 28				8 42				8 42		55
Effingham Junction arr	56												8 32				8 46				8 46		56
South Croydon 234	57			8 3											8 10	8 18							57
Purley Oaks	58														8 12	8 21							58
Purley	59											8 11			8 15	8 23							59
Coulsdon North L .. arr	60															8 27							60
Purley .... dep	61														8 19								61
Kenley	62														8 22								62
Whyteleafe	63														8 25								63
Warlingham	64														8 27								64
Caterham .... arr	65													p.m	8 31								65
Purley .... dep	66														8 17								66
Reedham	67														8 19								67
Smitham	68											§ Via Three Bridges			8 21								68
Woodmansterne	69														8 24								69
Chipstead	70													d Departure time	8 26								70
Kingswood M	71														8 31								71
Tadworth N	72														8 34								72
Tattenham Corner. arr	73														8 37								73
Coulsdon South	74											8 14											74
Merstham	75											8 20											75
Redhill 158, 246 ..... arr	76											8 24		8d33									76
Reigate 246 .... "	77											8 30		8 37									77
Horsham 159, 244, 245 "	78											9§ 5											78

CATERHAM, TATTENHAM CORNER, REDHILL, REIGATE, and HORSHAM

p.m — **Week Days**–*continued* — p.m

No.	SX			SX																								
1	8 0	8 2	..	..	..	..	8 8	..	8 10	..	..	..	8 21	..	8 24	..	..	8 28	..	..	..	..	8 38	..	8 40	..	..	..
2		..				..		..			..			..			..	..	8 24		..	..		..		..		..
3	3	..	3	3	3	8 7	3	..	3	3	..	3	3	..	3	3	..	..	8 26	3	..	8 47	3	..	3	..	3	..
4	..	..	8 2	8 3	8 7	..	..	..	..	8 15	8 16	8 18	..	..	..	8 25	..	..	8 31	8 29	..	..	..	..	..	..	8 37	..
5	8 3	..	..	..	..	3	..	..	8 13	..	..	..	..	..	..	..	..	..	3	..	..	3	8 41	..	8 43	..	..	..
6	8 6	..	..	..	..		8 14	..	8 16	..	..	..	8 26	..	8 29	..	..	8 34		..	..		8 44	..	8H47	..	..	..
7	8 9	..	..	..	..	Via Worcester Park	..	..	8 20	..	..	..	..	..	..	..	..	..	..	..	..	Via Worcester Park.	..	..	8 50	..	..	..
8	8 11	..	..	..	..		8 18	..	8 22	..	..	..	8 30	..	8 33	..	..	..	..	..	..		8 48	..	8 52	..	..	..
9	..	..	..	8 6	..		..	..	..	8 18	..	8 21	..	..	..	..	..	..	..	..	..		..	..	H 1 minute *earlier* on Saturdays	..	8 40	..
10	..	..	..	8 9	..		..	..	..	8 21	..	8 24	..	..	..	..	..	..	..	..	..		..	..		..	8 43	..
11	..	..	..	8 12	..		..	..	..	8 23	..	8 26	..	..	..	8 31	..	..	..	..	..		..	..		..	8 45	..
12	..	..	..	..	..		..	..	..	8 26	..		..	..	..	..	..	..	..	..	..		..	..		..	8 48	..
13	..	..	..	..	..		..	..	..	8 28	..		..	..	..	..	..	..	..	..	..		..	..		..	8 50	..
14	..	..	..	..	..		..	..	..	8 31	..		..	..	..	8 35	..	..	..	..	..		..	..		..	8 53	..
15	..	..	..	..	..		..	..	..	..	..		..	..	..	8 39	..	..	..	..	..		..	..		..	8 57	..
16	..	..	8 7	..	8 12		..	..	..	..	..	To Victoria arr. 8 43 p.m	..	..	..	..	..	..	..	8 34	..		..	..		..	..	..
17	..	..	..	..	8 14		..	..	..	..	..		..	..	..	..	..	..	..	8 36	..		..	..		..	..	..
18	..	..	..	..	8 17	..	..	..	..	..	..		..	..	..	..	..	..	..	8 39	..	..	..	..		..	..	..
19	..	..	8 11	..	8 19	..	..	..	..	..	..		..	..	..	..	..	..	..	8 41	..	..	..	..		..	..	..
20	..	..	8 14	..	8 22	..	..	..	..	..	..		..	..	..	..	..	..	..	8 44	..	..	..	..		..	..	..
21	..	..	8 16	..	8 24	..	..	..	..	..	..		..	..	..	..	..	..	..	8 46	..	..	..	..		..	..	..
22	..	..	8 17	..	8 25	..	..	..	..	..	..		..	..	..	..	..	..	..	8 47	..	..	..	..		..	..	..
23	..	..	..	..	..	..	8 22	..	..	..	..		8 35	..	..	..	..	..	..	..	..	..	8 52	..	..	..	8 59	..
24	..	..	..	..	..	..	8 24	..	..	..	..		8 37	..	..	..	..	..	..	..	..	..	8 54	..	..	..	9 1	..
25	..	..	..	..	..	..	8 27	..	..	..	..		8 40	..	..	..	..	..	..	..	..	..	8 57	..	..	..	9 4	..
26	..	..	..	..	..	..	8 29	..	..	..	..	Stop	8 42	..	..	..	..	..	..	..	..	..	8 59	..	..	..	9 6	..
27	8 13	..	..	..	..	..	..	..	8 24	..	..	p.m	..	..	..	..	..	..	..	..	..	..	Arr Sutton 9 14 p.m	..	8 54	..	..	..
28	8 16	..	..	..	..	..	..	..	8 27	8 33	..	3	..	..	..	..	..	..	..	..	..	..		..	8 57	..	..	3
29	8 19	..	..	..	..	..	..	..	8 30	8 36	..		..	..	..	..	..	..	..	..	..	..		..	9 0	..	..	
30	8 21	..	..	..	..	..	..	..	8 32	8 39	..	8 40	..	..	..	..	..	..	..	..	..	..		..	9 2	..	..	9 10
31	8 25	..	..	..	..	..	..	..	..	..	..	8 43	..	..	..	..	..	..	..	..	..	..		..	..	..	..	9 13
32	8 29	..	..	..	..	..	..	..	..	..	..	8 47	..	..	..	..	..	..	..	..	..	..		..	..	..	..	9 17
33	..	..	8 20	..	8 29	..	..	..	8 37	..	8 28	..	..	..	..	..	..	..	8 44	8 51	..	..		..	9 7	..	9 9	..
34	..	8 20	..	..	..	..	..	..	..	..	8 32	..	8 46	..	..	..	..	8 45	8 48	..	..	..		..	..	..	..	..
35	..	8 23	..	..	..	..	..	..	..	..	8 34	..	8 46	..	..	..	..	8 46	8 48	..	..	..		..	..	..	To London Bridge, via Forest Hill	..
36	..	..	..	..	To London Bridge, via Streatham	..	..	..	..	..	..	..	..	..	8 40	8 44	..	..	..	..	..	..		..	..	..		..
37	..	..	..	..		..	..	..	..	..	..	..	..	..	8 42	8 46	..	..	..	..	..	..		..	..	..		..
38	..	..	..	..		..	..	..	..	..	..	..	..	..	8 45	8 49	..	..	..	..	..	..		..	..	..		..
39	..	..	8 24	..		..	8 32	..	8 41	..	..	..	..	..	..	..	..	..	..	8 55	..	..	9 2	..	9 12	..		..
40	..	..	8 24	..		..	8 32	..	..	..	..	..	..	..	..	..	3	..	..	8 55	..	..	9 2	..	..	..		..
41	..	..	8 27	..		..	8 35	..	..	..	..	..	..	..	..	..		..	..	8 58	..	..	9 5	..	..	..		..
42	..	..	8 30	..		..	8 38	..	..	..	..	..	..	..	..	..	8 49	..	..	9 1	..	..	9 8	..	..	..		..
43	..	..	8 33	..		..	8 41	..	..	..	..	..	..	..	..	..	8 51	..	..	9 4	..	..	9 11	..	..	..		..
44	..	..	8 35	..		..	8 45	..	..	..	..	..	..	..	8 48	8 52	8 54	..	..	9 6	..	..	9 17	..	..	..		..
45	..	..	8 38	..		..	8 48	..	..	..	..	..	..	..	..	..	..	..	..	9 9	..	..	9 20	..	..	..	..	..
46	..	..	8 41	..		..	8 51	..	..	..	..	..	..	..	..	..	..	..	..	9 12	..	..	9 23	..	..	..	..	..
47	..	..	8 45	..		..	8 54	..	..	..	..	..	..	..	..	..	..	..	..	9 16	..	..	9 26	..	..	..	..	..
48	..	..	..	..	..	..	..	..	..	..	..	..	..	..	8 51	8 56	..	..	..	..	..	..	..	..	..	..	..	..
49	..	..	..	..	..	..	..	..	..	..	..	..	..	..	8 54	8 59	..	..	..	..	..	..	..	..	..	..	..	..
50	..	..	..	..	..	8 35	..	..	..	..	..	..	..	..	8 57	9 3	..	..	..	..	..	9 15	..	..	..	..	..	..
51	..	..	..	..	..	8 39	..	..	..	..	..	..	..	..	..	9 7	..	..	..	..	..	9 19	..	..	..	..	..	..
52	..	..	..	..	..	8 43	..	..	..	..	..	..	..	..	..	9 12	..	..	..	..	..	9 23	..	..	..	..	..	..
53	..	..	..	..	..	8 48	..	..	..	..	..	..	..	..	..	9 17	..	..	..	..	..	..	..	..	..	..	..	..
54	..	..	..	..	..	8 51	..	..	..	..	..	..	..	..	..	9 20	..	..	..	..	..	..	..	..	..	..	..	..
55	..	..	..	..	..	..	..	..	..	..	..	..	..	..	..	..	..	..	..	..	..	9 28	..	..	..	..	..	..
56	..	..	..	..	..	..	..	..	..	..	..	..	..	..	..	..	..	..	..	..	..	9 32	..	..	..	..	..	..
57	..	8 27	..	..	..	..	..	..	..	..	..	..	8 48	..	..	..	..	..	8 51	..	..	..	..	..	..	..	..	..
58	..	..	..	..	..	..	..	..	..	..	..	..	8 51	..	..	..	..	..	8 53	..	..	..	..	..	..	..	..	..
59	..	..	..	..	..	..	..	..	..	..	8 40	..	8 53	..	..	..	..	..	8 56	..	..	..	..	..	..	..	..	..
60	..	..	..	..	..	..	..	..	..	..	..	..	8 57	..	..	..	..	..	..	..	..	..	..	..	..	..	..	..
61	..	..	..	..	..	..	..	..	..	..	..	..	..	..	..	..	..	..	8 59	..	..	..	..	..	..	..	..	..
62	..	..	..	..	..	..	..	..	..	..	..	..	..	..	..	..	..	..	9 2	..	..	..	..	..	..	..	..	..
63	..	..	..	..	..	..	..	..	..	..	..	..	..	..	..	..	..	..	9 5	..	..	..	..	..	..	..	..	..
64	..	..	..	..	..	..	..	..	..	..	..	..	..	..	..	..	..	..	9 7	..	..	..	..	..	..	..	..	..
65	..	..	..	..	..	..	..	..	..	..	..	..	..	..	..	..	..	..	9 11	..	..	..	..	..	..	..	..	..
66	..	..	..	..	..	..	..	..	..	..	..	..	..	..	..	..	..	..	8 57	..	..	..	..	..	..	..	..	..
67	..	..	..	..	..	..	..	..	..	..	..	..	..	..	..	..	..	..	8 59	..	..	..	..	..	..	..	..	..
68	..	..	..	..	..	..	..	..	..	..	..	..	..	..	..	..	..	..	9 2	..	..	..	..	..	..	..	..	..
69	..	..	..	..	..	..	..	..	..	..	..	..	..	..	..	..	..	..	9 4	..	..	..	..	..	..	..	..	..
70	..	..	..	..	..	..	..	..	..	..	..	..	..	..	..	..	..	..	9 7	..	..	..	..	..	..	..	..	..
71	..	..	..	..	..	..	..	..	..	..	..	..	..	..	..	..	..	..	9 11	..	..	..	..	..	..	..	..	..
72	..	..	..	..	..	..	..	..	..	..	..	..	..	..	..	..	..	..	9 14	..	..	..	..	..	..	..	..	..
73	..	..	..	..	..	..	..	..	..	..	..	..	..	..	..	..	..	..	9 18	..	..	..	..	..	..	..	..	..
74	..	..	..	..	..	..	..	..	..	..	8 43	..	..	..	..	..	..	..	..	..	..	..	..	..	..	..	..	..
75	..	..	..	..	..	..	..	..	..	..	8 49	..	..	..	..	..	..	..	..	..	..	..	..	..	..	..	..	..
76	..	..	..	..	..	..	..	..	..	..	8 53	..	..	..	..	..	..	9 0	..	..	..	..	..	..	..	..	..	..
77	..	..	..	..	..	..	..	..	..	..	8 59	..	..	..	..	..	..	..	..	..	..	..	..	..	..	..	..	..
78	..	..	..	..	..	9 24	..	..	..	..	..	..	..	..	..	9 46	..	..	..	..	..	..	..	..	..	..	..	..

LONDON, CRYSTAL PALACE, CROYDON, SUTTON, DORKING NORTH,

For Notes, see page 284a

Down	No.	p.m										Week Days—*continued*						p.m					No.
Victoria .... dep	1	8 48	..	..	..	8 51	8 51	..	..	..	..	9 8	..	9 10	..	..	..	..	..	9 18	9 20	9 20	1
Charing Cross* ... "	2	..	..	8 44	3	3	3	3	3	3	3	3	..	3	..	3	..	3	..	..	3	..	2
Waterloo* .... "	3	..	..	8 46									9 7		..		..		..	..		..	3
London Bridge ..... "	4	..	..	8 51	8 48	..	..	8 53	8 53	9 2	9 7	..	..	..	..	9 15	9 16	9 18	..	..	..	..	4
Battersea Park	5	..	..	3	..	..	..	..	..	..	..	..	3	9 13	..	..	..	..	..	..	..	..	5
Clapham Junction	6	8 53	..		..	8 56	8 56	..	..	..	..	9 14		9 16	..	..	..	..	..	..	9 25	9 26	6
Wandsworth Common A	7	..	..	..	..	..	8 59	..	..	..	..	..		9 20	..	..	..	..	..	..	..	..	7
Balham & Upper Tooting	8	..	..	..	..	9 0	9 1	..	..	..	..	9 18		9 22	..	..	..	..	..	..	9 29	..	8
South Bermondsey	9	..	..	..	8 51	..	..	..	..	..	..	..	Via Worcester Park	..	..	9 18	..	9 21	..	..	..	..	9
Queen's Road, Peckham	10	..	..	..	8 54	..	..	..	..	..	..	..		..	..	9 21	..	9 24	..	..	..	..	10
Peckham Rye	11	..	..	..	8 56	..	..	8 59	..	..	..	..		..	..	9 23	..	9 26	..	..	..	..	11
East Dulwich	12	..	..	..		..	..	..	..	..	..	..		..	..	9 26	..		..	..	..	..	12
North Dulwich	13	..	..	..		..	..	..	..	..	..	..		..	..	9 28	..		..	..	..	..	13
Tulse Hill	14	..	..	..	To Victoria, arr. 9 13 p.m	..	..	9 3	..	..	..	..		..	..	9 31	..		..	..	..	..	14
Streatham	15	..	..	..		..	..	9 7	..	..	..	..		..	..	..	..		..	..	..	..	15
New Cross Gate (for E.L.	16	..	..	..		..	..	..	8 58	9 7	9 12	..	..	..	..	..	..		..	..	..	..	16
Brockley B .... [Line)	17	..	..	..		..	..	..	9 0	..	9 14	..	..	..	..	..	..	To Victoria, arr. 9 43 p.m	..	..	..	..	17
Honor Oak Park	18	..	..	..		..	..	..	9 3	..	9 17	..	..	..	..	..	..		..	..	..	..	18
Forest Hill, for Lordship	19	..	..	..		..	..	..	9 5	9 11	9 19	..	..	..	..	..	..		..	..	..	..	19
Sydenham .... [Lane	20	..	..	..		..	..	..	9 8	9 14	9 22	..	..	..	..	..	..		..	..	..	..	20
Penge West C	21	..	..	..		..	..	..	..	9 16	9 24	..	..	..	..	..	..		..	..	..	..	21
Anerley	22	..	..	..		..	..	..	..	9 17	9 25	..	..	..	..	..	..		..	..	..	..	22
Streatham Common	23	..	..	..	..	..	9 5	..	..	..	..	9 22	..	..	..	..	..		..	..	..	..	23
Norbury ..	24	..	..	..	..	..	9 7	..	..	..	..	9 24	..	..	..	..	..		..	..	..	..	24
Thornton Heath	25	..	..	..	..	..	9 10	..	..	..	..	9 27	..	..	..	..	..		..	..	..	..	25
Selhurst ...	26	..	..	..	..	..	9 12	..	..	..	..	9 29	..	..	..	..	..	Stop	..	..	..	..	26
Streatham Hill	27	..	..	..	..	..	..	..	..	..	..		..	9 24	..	..	..	p.m	..	..	..	..	27
West Norwood .. [N'wood)	28	..	..	..	..	..	..	..	..	..	..		..	9 27	..	9 33	..	3	..	..	..	..	28
Gipsy Hill (for Upper	29	..	..	..	..	..	..	..	..	..	..		..	9 30	..	9 36	..		..	..	..	..	29
Crystal Palace D	30	..	..	..	..	..	..	..	9 11	..	..	Arr Sutton 9 44 p.m	..	9 32	..	9 39	..	9 40	..	..	..	..	30
Birkbeck	31	..	..	..	..	..	..	..		..	..		..	..	..	..	..	9 43	..	..	..	..	31
Beckenham Jn. arr	32	..	..	..	..	..	..	..	Stop	..	..		..	..	..	..	..	9 47	..	..	..	..	32
Norwood Junction F ..	33	..	..	9 3	..	..	..	..	..	9 20	9 29		..	9 37	..	..	9 28	..	..	..	..	..	33
East Croydon .. arr	34	9 5	..	9 7	..	..	9 16	..	..	..	..		..	..	..	..	9 32	..	..	..	..	9 40	34
East Croydon .. dep	35	9 5	..	9 7	..	..	9 16	..	..	..	..		..	..	..	..	9 34	..	..	..	..	..	35
Mitcham Junction	36	..	..	..	..	9 6	..	9 12	..	..	To London Bridge, via Streatham	..	..	..	..	..	..	..	..	..	9 36	..	36
Hackbridge	37	..	..	..	..	9 9	..	9 14	p.m	..		..	..	..	..	..	..	..	..	..	9 38	..	37
Carshalton	38	..	..	..	..	9 11	..	9 17	3	..		..	..	..	..	..	..	..	..	..	9 41	..	38
West Croydon 319 arr	39	..	..	..	..	..	..	..		9 24		9 32	..	9 41	..	..	..	..	..	..	..	..	39
West Croydon 319 dep	40	..	..	..	..	..	..	..	9 16	9 24		9 32	..	..	..	..	..	..	..	..	..	..	40
Waddon G	41	..	..	..	..	..	..	..	9 18	9 27		9 35	..	..	..	..	..	..	..	..	..	..	41
Wallington	42	..	..	..	..	..	..	..	9 22	9 30		9 38	..	..	..	..	..	..	..	..	..	..	42
Carshalton Beeches	43	..	..	..	..	..	..	..	9 24	9 33		9 41	..	..	..	..	..	..	..	..	..	..	43
Sutton 322	44	..	..	..	..	9 14	..	9 20	9 27	9 35		9 47	..	..	..	..	..	..	..	9 39	9 44	..	44
Belmont	45	..	..	..	..	..	..	..	..	9 38		9 50	..	..	..	..	..	..	..	..	..	..	45
Banstead	46	..	..	..	..	..	..	..	..	9 41		9 53	..	..	..	..	..	..	..	..	..	..	46
Epsom Downs ...... arr	47	..	..	..	..	..	..	..	..	9 45		9 56	..	..	..	..	..	..	..	..	..	..	47
Cheam	48	..	..	..	..	9 17	..	9 23	..	..	..	..	..	..	..	..	..	..	..	..	9 47	..	48
Ewell East H	49	..	..	..	..	9 20	..	9 26	..	..	..	..	..	..	..	..	..	..	..	..	9 50	..	49
Epsom	50	..	..	..	..	9 24	..	9 29	..	..	..	..	9 35	..	..	..	..	..	..	..	9 53	..	50
Ashtead	51	..	..	..	..	..	..	9 33	..	..	..	..	9 39	..	..	..	..	..	..	..	..	..	51
Leatherhead ... [Bridge J	52	..	..	..	..	..	..	9 37	..	..	..	..	9 43	..	..	..	..	..	..	..	..	..	52
Boxhill and Burford	53	..	..	..	..	..	..	..	..	..	..	..	9 48	..	..	..	..	..	..	..	..	..	53
Dorking North K ... arr	54	..	..	..	..	..	..	..	..	..	..	..	9 51	..	..	..	..	..	..	9 55	..	..	54
Bookham .... [394	55	..	..	..	..	..	..	9 42	..	..	..	..	..	..	..	..	..	..	..	..	..	..	55
Effingham Junction arr	56	..	..	..	..	..	..	9 46	..	..	..	..	..	..	..	..	..	..	..	..	..	..	56
South Croydon 234	57	..	..	9 10	..	..	9 18	..	..	..	..	..	..	..	..	..	..	..	..	..	..	..	57
Purley Oaks	58	..	..	9 12	..	..	9 21	..	..	..	..	..	..	..	..	..	..	..	..	..	..	..	58
Purley	59	9 11	..	9 15	..	..	9 23	..	..	..	..	..	..	..	..	..	9 40	..	..	..	..	..	59
Coulsdon North L .. arr	60	..	..	..	..	..	9 27	..	..	..	..	..	..	..	..	..	..	..	..	..	..	..	60
Purley .... dep	61	..	..	9 19	..	..	..	..	..	..	..	..	..	..	..	..	..	..	..	..	..	..	61
Kenley	62	..	..	9 22	..	..	..	..	..	..	..	..	..	..	..	..	..	..	..	..	..	..	62
Whyteleafe	63	..	..	9 25	..	..	..	..	..	..	..	..	..	..	..	..	..	..	..	..	..	..	63
Warlingham	64	..	..	9 27	..	..	..	..	..	..	..	..	..	..	..	..	..	..	..	..	..	..	64
Caterham .... arr	65	..	..	9 31	..	..	..	..	..	..	..	..	..	..	..	..	..	..	..	..	..	..	65
Purley .... dep	66	§ Via Three Bridges	*d* Departure time	9 17	..	..	..	..	..	..	..	..	..	..	..	..	§ Via Three Bridge	..	..	..	..	..	66
Reedham	67			9 19	..	..	..	..	..	..	..	..	..	..	..	..		..	..	..	..	..	67
Smitham	68			9 21	..	..	..	..	..	..	..	..	..	..	..	..		..	..	..	..	..	68
Woodmansterne	69			9 24	..	..	..	..	..	..	..	..	..	..	..	..		..	..	..	..	..	69
Chipstead	70			9 26	..	..	..	..	..	..	..	..	..	..	..	..		..	..	..	..	..	70
Kingswood M	71			9 31	..	..	..	..	..	..	..	..	..	..	..	..		..	..	..	..	..	71
Tadworth N	72			9 34	..	..	..	..	..	..	..	..	..	..	..	..		..	..	..	..	..	72
Tattenham Corner. arr	73			9 37	..	..	..	..	..	..	..	..	..	..	..	..		..	..	..	..	..	73
Coulsdon South	74	9 14	..	..	..	..	..	..	..	..	..	..	..	..	..	..	9 43	..	..	..	..	..	74
Merstham	75	9 20	..	..	..	..	..	..	..	..	..	..	..	..	..	..	9 49	..	..	..	..	..	75
Redhill 158, 246 ...... arr	76	9 24	9d39	..	..	..	..	..	..	..	..	..	..	..	..	..	9 53	..	..	..	..	..	76
Reigate 246 .... "	77	9 30	9 43	..	..	..	..	..	..	..	..	..	..	..	..	..	9 59	..	..	..	..	..	77
Horsham 159, 244, 245. "	78	10§8	..	..	..	..	..	..	..	..	..	..	1024	..	..	..	10§35	..	..	1013	..	..	78

CATERHAM, TATTENHAM CORNER, REDHILL, REIGATE, and HORSHAM

Week Days—continued — p.m.

No.								SO	SX		SO	SX																
1	9 22	..	..	9 28	..	..	9 38	..	..	..	9 40	9 40	..	..	..	9 48	..	9 51	9 51	..	..	..	..	..	..	..	10 8	1010
2	3	3	..	..	9 24	3	3	3	3	..	3	3	..	..	3	..	9 44	3	3	3	3	..	3	..	..	3	3	3
3			..	..	9 26					9 47			..	..		..	9 46					..		10 7	..			
4	..	9 24	..	..	9 31	9 33	..	9 38	9 38	..	..	..	..	..	9 48	..	9 51	..	..	9 53	9 53	..	10 2	..	..	10 7	..	..
5	..	..	..	..	3	..	9 41	..	..	3	9 43	9 43	..	..	..	..	3	..	9 54	..	..	..	..	3	..	..	..	1013
6	9 27	..	..	9 34		..	9 44	..	..		9 46	9 47	..	..	..	9 53		9 56	9 57	..	..	..	..		..	..	1014	1016
7	..	..	..	..	..	..	..	..	..	Via Worcester Park	9 50	9 50	..	..	..	..	..	..	10 0	..	..	..	..	Via Worcester Park	..	..	..	1020
8	9 31	..	..	..	..	..	9 48	..	..		9 52	9 52	..	..	..	..	..	10 0	10 2	..	..	..	..		..	..	1018	1022
9	..	..	..	..	..	..	..	9 41	9 41		..	..	..	..	9 51	..	..	..	..	..	..	..	..		..	..	..	..
10	..	..	..	..	..	..	..	9 44	9 44		..	..	..	..	9 54	..	..	..	..	..	..	..	..		..	..	..	..
11	..	9 30	..	..	..	..	..	9 46	9 46		..	..	..	..	9 56	..	..	..	..	..	9 59	..	..		..	..	..	..
12	..	..	..	..	..	..	..	9 48	9 49		..	..	..	..	To Victoria, arr. 10 13 p.m.	..	..	..	..	..	..	..	..		..	..	..	..
13	..	..	..	..	..	..	..	9 50	9 51		..	..	..	..		..	..	..	..	..	..	..	..		..	..	..	..
14	..	9 35	..	..	..	..	..	9 53	9 54		..	..	..	..		..	..	..	..	..	10 3	..	..		..	..	..	..
15	..	9 39	..	..	..	..	..	9 57	9 58		..	..	..	..		..	..	..	..	..	10 7	..	..		..	..	..	..
16	..	..	..	..	..	9 38	..	..	..	..	..	..	..	..		..	..	..	..	9 58	..	..	10 7	..	..	1012	..	..
17	..	..	..	..	..	9 40	..	..	..	..	..	..	..	..		..	..	..	..	10 0	..	..	..	..	..	1014	..	..
18	..	..	..	..	..	9 43	..	..	..	..	..	..	..	..		..	..	..	..	10 3	..	..	..	..	..	1017	..	..
19	..	..	..	..	..	9 45	..	..	..	..	..	..	..	..		..	..	..	..	10 5	..	..	1011	..	..	1019	..	..
20	..	..	..	..	..	9 48	..	..	..	..	..	..	..	..		..	..	..	..	10 8	..	..	1014	..	..	1022	..	..
21	..	..	..	..	..	9 50	..	..	..	..	..	..	..	..	..	..	..	..	..	..	..	..	1016	..	..	1024	..	..
22	..	..	..	..	..	9 51	..	..	..	..	..	..	..	..	..	..	..	..	..	..	..	..	1017	..	..	1025	..	..
23	9 35	..	..	..	..	..	9 52	9 59	10 0	..	..	..	..	..	..	..	..	..	10 6	..	..	..	..	..	..	To London Bridge via Streatham	1022	..
24	9 37	..	..	..	..	..	9 54	10 1	10 2	..	..	..	..	..	..	..	..	..	10 8	..	..	..	..	..	..		1024	..
25	9 40	..	..	..	..	..	9 57	10 4	10 5	..	..	..	..	..	..	..	..	..	1011	..	..	..	..	..	..		1027	..
26	9 44	..	..	..	..	..	9 59	10 6	10 7	..	..	..	..	..	..	..	..	..	1013	..	..	..	..	..	..		1029	..
27	..	..	..	..	..	..	Arr Sutton 10 14 p.m.	..	..	..	9 54	9 54	..	..	..	..	..	..	..	..	..	..	..	..	..		..	1024
28	..	..	..	..	..	..		..	..	..	9 57	9 57	3	..	..	..	..	..	..	..	..	..	..	..	..		Arr. Sutton 10 44 p.m.	1027
29	..	..	..	..	..	..		..	..	..	10 0	10 0		..	..	..	..	..	..	..	..	..	..	..	..			1030
30	..	..	..	..	..	..		..	..	..	10 2	10 3	1010	..	..	..	..	..	..	1011	..	..	..	..	..			1032
31	..	..	..	..	..	..		..	..	..	..	..	1013	..	..	..	..	..	..	..	..	..	..	..	..			..
32	..	..	..	..	..	..		..	..	..	..	..	1017	..	..	..	..	..	..	..	..	..	..	..	..			..
33	..	..	..	..	9 44	9 54		10 9	1010	..	10 7	10 8	..	..	..	..	10 3	..	..	..	..	..	1020	..	..	1029		1037
34	9 47	..	..	9 45	9 48	..		..	..	..	..	..	..	..	..	10 4	10 7	..	1017	..	..	..	..	..	..			..
35	9 47	..	..	9 46	9 48	..		..	..	..	..	..	..	..	..	10 5	10 7	..	1018	..	..	..	..	..	..	Stop		..
36	..	9 44	..	..	..	..		To London Bridge, via Forest Hill	To London Bridge, via Forest Hill	..	..	..	..	..	..	..	..	10 6	..	..	1012	..	..	..	..	..	..	..
37	..	9 46	..	..	..	..				..	..	..	..	..	..	..	..	10 9	..	..	1014	..	..	..	..	..	..	..
38	..	9 49	..	..	..	..				..	..	..	..	..	..	..	..	1011	..	..	1017	..	..	..	..	..	..	..
39	..	..	..	..	..	9 58	10 2			..	1012	1012	..	..	..	..	..	..	..	..	..	3	1024	..	..	..	1032	1041
40	..	..	3	..	..	9 58	10 2			..	..	..	..	..	..	..	..	..	..	..	..	1015	1024	..	..	..	1032	..
41	..	..		..	..	10 0	10 5			..	..	..	..	..	..	..	..	..	..	..	..	1017	1027	..	..	..	1035	..
42	..	..	9 50	..	..	10 4	10 8			..	..	..	..	..	..	..	..	..	..	..	..	1021	1030	..	..	..	1038	..
43	..	..	9 52	..	..	10 6	1011			..	..	..	..	..	..	..	..	..	..	..	..	1023	1033	..	..	..	1041	..
44	..	9 52	9 55	..	..	10 9	1018			..	..	..	..	..	..	..	..	1014	..	..	1020	1026	1035	..	..	..	1047	..
45	..	..	..	..	..	1012	1021			..	..	..	..	..	..	..	..	..	..	..	..	..	..	..	..	..	1050	..
46	..	..	..	..	..	1015	1024			..	..	..	..	..	..	..	..	..	..	..	..	..	..	..	..	..	1053	..
47	..	..	..	..	..	1018	1027			..	..	..	..	..	..	..	..	..	..	..	..	..	..	..	..	..	1056	..
48	..	9 55	..	..	..	..	..	..	..	..	..	..	..	..	..	..	..	1017	..	..	1023	..	..	..	..	..	..	..
49	..	9 58	..	..	..	..	..	..	..	..	..	..	..	..	..	..	..	1020	..	..	1026	..	..	..	..	p.m	..	..
50	..	10 3	..	..	..	..	..	..	..	1015	..	..	..	..	..	..	..	1024	..	..	1029	..	..	1035	..	3	..	..
51	..	10 7	..	..	..	..	..	..	..	1019	..	..	..	..	..	..	..	..	..	..	1033	..	..	1039	..		..	..
52	..	1011	..	..	..	..	..	..	..	1023	..	..	..	..	..	..	..	..	..	..	1037	..	..	1043	..	11 0	..	..
53	..	1017	..	..	..	..	..	..	..	..	..	..	..	..	..	..	..	..	..	..	..	..	..	1048	..	..	..	..
54	..	1020	..	..	..	..	..	..	..	..	..	..	..	..	..	..	..	..	..	..	..	..	..	1052	..	..	..	..
55	..	..	..	..	..	..	..	..	..	1028	..	..	..	..	..	..	..	..	..	..	1042	..	..	..	..	11 4	..	..
56	..	..	..	..	..	..	..	..	..	1032	..	..	..	..	..	..	..	..	..	..	1046	..	..	..	..	11 8	..	..
57	9 50	..	..	..	9 50	..	..	..	..	..	..	..	..	..	..	..	1010	..	1020	..	..	..	..	..	..	..	..	..
58	9 52	..	..	..	9 53	..	..	..	..	..	..	..	..	..	..	..	1013	..	1023	..	..	..	..	..	..	..	..	..
59	9 55	..	..	..	9 56	..	..	..	..	..	..	..	..	..	..	1011	1016	..	1025	..	..	..	..	..	..	..	..	..
60	9 58	..	..	..	..	..	..	..	..	..	..	..	..	..	..	..	..	..	1029	..	..	..	..	..	..	..	..	..
61	..	..	..	..	9 59	..	..	..	..	..	..	..	..	..	..	..	1019	..	..	..	..	..	..	..	..	..	..	..
62	..	..	..	..	10 2	..	..	..	..	..	..	..	..	..	..	..	1022	..	..	..	..	..	..	..	..	..	..	..
63	..	..	..	..	10 5	..	..	..	..	..	..	..	..	..	..	..	1025	..	..	..	..	..	..	..	..	..	..	..
64	..	..	..	..	10 7	..	..	..	..	..	..	..	..	..	..	..	1027	..	..	..	..	..	..	..	..	..	..	..
65	..	..	..		1011	..	..	..	..	..	..	..	..	..	..	..	1031	..	..	..	..	..	..	..	..	..	..	..
66	..	..	..	§ Via Three Bridges	9 57	..	..	..	..	..	..	..	..	..	..	..	1017	..	..	..	..	..	..	..	..	..	..	..
67	..	..	..		9 59	..	..	..	..	..	..	..	..	..	..	..	1019	..	..	..	..	..	..	..	..	..	..	..
68	..	..	..		10 1	..	..	..	..	..	..	..	..	..	..	..	1021	..	..	..	..	..	..	..	..	..	..	..
69	..	..	..		10 4	..	..	..	..	..	..	..	..	..	..	..	1024	..	..	..	..	..	..	..	..	..	..	..
70	..	..	..		10 6	..	..	..	..	..	..	..	..	..	..	..	1026	..	..	..	..	..	..	..	..	..	..	..
71	..	..	..		1011	..	..	..	..	..	..	..	..	..	..	..	1031	..	..	..	..	..	..	..	..	..	..	..
72	..	..	..		1014	..	..	..	..	..	..	..	..	..	..	..	1034	..	..	..	..	..	..	..	..	..	..	..
73	..	..	..		1017	..	..	..	..	..	..	..	..	..	..	..	1037	..	..	..	..	..	..	..	..	..	..	..
74	..	..	..	..	..	..	..	..	..	..	..	..	..	..	..	1014	..	..	..	..	..	..	..	..	..	..	..	..
75	..	..	..	..	..	..	..	..	..	..	..	..	..	..	..	1020	..	..	..	..	..	..	..	..	..	..	..	..
76	..	..	..	10 0	..	..	..	..	..	..	..	..	..	..	..	1024	..	..	..	..	..	..	..	..	..	..	..	..
77	..	..	..	..	..	..	..	..	..	..	..	..	..	..	..	1030	..	..	..	..	..	..	..	..	..	..	..	..
78	..	1046	..	10§35	..	..	..	..	..	..	..	..	..	..	..	..	..	..	..	..	..	..	..	1124	..	..	..	..

LONDON, CRYSTAL PALACE, CROYDON, SUTTON, DORKING NORTH,

For Notes, see page 284a

Down	No.	p.m.									Week Days—continued									p.m.			No.
																						S X	
VICTORIA .... dep	1	..	..	..	1020	..	..	1021	..	1025	..	1028	..	1030	..	1038	1040	..	..	1048	1051	..	1
CHARING CROSS✱ ... "	2	3	3	..	3	..	..	3	3	..	..	..	1024	..	3	3	3	..	3	..	3	3	2
WATERLOO✱ .... "	3			..		..	..			..	..	..	1026	..				1047		..			3
LONDON BRIDGE ..... "	4	1015	1018	..	..	1016	..	..	1024	..	..	..	1031	..	1032	..	..	..	1037	..	..	1045	4
Battersea Park	5	..	..	..	..	..	..	..	..	..	..	..	3	..	..	..	1043	3	..	..	..	..	5
Clapham Junction	6	..	..	..	1025	..	..	1026	..	..	..	1034		1037	..	1044	1046		..	1053	1056	..	6
Wandsworth Common A	7	..	..	..	..	..	..	1029	..	..	..	..	..	..	..	..	1050		..	..	..	..	7
Balham & Upper Tooting	8	..	..	..	1029	..	..	1031	..	..	..	..	..	..	..	1048	1052		..	..	11 0	..	8
South Bermondsey	9	1018	1021	..	..	..	..	..	..	..	..	..	..	..	..	..	..		..	..	..	..	9
Queen's Road, Peckham	10	1021	1024	..	..	..	..	..	..	..	..	..	..	..	..	..	..	Via Worcester Park	..	..	..	..	10
Peckham Rye	11	1023	1026	..	..	..	..	..	1030	..	..	..	..	..	..	..	..		..	..	..	..	11
East Dulwich	12	1026		..	..	..	..	..	..	..	..	..	..	..	..	..	..		..	..	..	..	12
North Dulwich	13	1028		..	..	..	..	..	..	..	..	..	..	..	..	..	..		..	..	..	..	13
Tulse Hill	14	1031		..	..	..	..	..	1035	..	..	..	..	..	..	..	..		..	..	..	..	14
Streatham	15	..		..	..	..	..	..	1039	..	..	..	..	..	..	..	..		..	..	..	..	15
New Cross Gate (for E.L.	16	..		..	..	..	..	..	..	..	..	..	..	..	1037	..	..	..	1042	..	..	1050	16
Brockley B .... [Line)	17	..		..	..	..	..	..	..	..	..	..	..	..	..	..	..	..	1044	..	..	..	17
Honor Oak Park	18	..		..	..	..	..	..	..	..	..	..	..	..	..	..	..	..	1047	..	..	..	18
Forest Hill, for Lordship	19	..		..	..	..	..	..	..	..	..	..	..	..	1041	..	..	..	1049	..	..	1054	19
Sydenham .... [Lane	20	..	To Victoria arr. 10 43 p.m	..	..	..	..	..	..	..	..	..	..	..	1044	..	..	..	1052	..	..	1057	20
Penge West C	21	..		..	..	..	..	..	..	..	..	..	..	..	1046	..	..	..	1054	..	..	1059	21
Anerley	22	..		..	..	..	..	..	..	..	..	..	..	..	1047	..	..	..	1055	..	..	11 0	22
Streatham Common	23	..		..	..	..	..	1035	..	..	..	..	..	..	..	1052	..	..	..	..	..	..	23
Norbury	24	..		..	..	..	..	1037	..	..	..	..	..	..	..	1054	..	..	..	..	..	..	24
Thornton Heath	25	..		..	..	..	..	1040	..	..	..	..	..	..	..	1057	..	..	..	..	..	..	25
Selhurst	26	..	Stop	..	..	..	..	1042	..	..	..	..	..	..	..	1059	..	..	..	..	..	..	26
Streatham Hill	27	..	p.m	..	..	..	..	..	..	..	..	..	..	..	..		1054	..	..	..	..	..	27
West Norwood..[N'wood)	28	1033	3	..	..	..	..	..	..	..	..	..	..	..	..		1057	..	..	..	..	..	28
Gipsy Hill (for Upper	29	1036		..	..	..	..	..	..	..	..	..	..	..	..		11 0	..	..	..	..	..	29
Crystal Palace D	30	1039	1040	..	..	..	..	..	..	..	..	..	..	..	..		11 2	..	..	..	..	..	30
Birkbeck	31	..	1043	..	..	..	..	..	..	..	..	..	..	..	..	Arr. Sutton 11 14 p.m	..	..	..	..	..	..	31
Beckenham Jn. arr	32	..	1047	..	..	..	..	..	..	..	..	..	..	..	..		..	..	..	..	..	..	32
Norwood Junction F ..	33	..	..	..	..	1028	..	..	..	..	..	..	1044	..	1050		11 7	..	1059	..	..	11 3	33
East Croydon .... { arr	34	..	..	..	..	1032	..	1046	..	1040	..	1045	1048	1051	..		..	..		11 4	..	..	34
East Croydon .... { dep	35	..	..	..	..	1034	..	1046	..	..	..	1046	1048	1052	..		..	..		11 5	..	..	35
Mitcham Junction	36	..	..	..	1036	..	..	..	1044	..	..	..	..	..	..	..	..	..		..	11 6	..	36
Hackbridge	37	..	..	..	1038	..	..	..	1046	..	..	..	..	..	..	..	..	..		..	11 9	..	37
Carshalton	38	..	..	..	1041	..	..	..	1049	..	..	..	..	..	..	..	..	..		..	1111	..	38
West Croydon 319 { arr	39	..	..	..	..	..	..	..	..	..	..	..	..	..	1054	11 2	1111	..		..	..	11 7	39
West Croydon 319 { dep	40	..	..	..	..	..	..	..	..	..	3	..	..	..	1054	11 2	..	..		..	..	11 7	40
Waddon G	41	..	..	..	..	..	..	..	..	..		..	..	..	1057	11 5	..	..	To London Bridge, via Streatham	..	..	1110	41
Wallington	42	..	..	..	..	..	..	..	..	..	1050	..	..	..	11 0	11 8	..	..		..	..	1113	42
Carshalton Beeches	43	..	..	..	..	..	..	..	..	..	1052	..	..	..	11 3	1111	..	..		..	..	1116	43
Sutton 322	44	..	..	..	1044	..	..	..	1052	..	1055	..	..	..	11 5	1117	11 X35			..	1114	1118	44
Belmont	45	..	..	..	..	..	..	..	..	..	..	..	..	..	11 8	1120	..	..		..	..	..	45
Banstead	46	..	..	..	..	..	..	..	..	..	..	..	..	..	1111	1123	..	..		..	..	..	46
Epsom Downs ...... arr	47	..	..	..	..	..	..	..	..	..	..	..	..	..	1115	1126	..	..		..	..	..	47
Cheam	48	..	..	..	1047	..	..	..	1056	..	..	..	..	..	..	..	..	..	..	..	1117	..	48
Ewell East H	49	..	..	..	1050	..	..	..	1059	..	..	..	..	..	..	..	..	..	..	..	1120	..	49
Epsom	50	..	..	..	1053	..	..	..	11 3	..	..	..	..	..	..	..	..	1115	..	..	1124	..	50
Ashtead	51	..	..	..	..	..	..	..	11 8	..	..	..	..	..	..	..	..	1119	..	..	..	..	51
Leatherhead..[Bridge J	52	..	..	..	..	..	..	..	1112	..	..	..	..	..	..	..	..	1123	..	..	..	..	52
Boxhill and Burford	53	..	..	..	..	..	..	..	1117	..	..	..	..	..	..	..	..	..	..	..	..	..	53
Dorking North K .. arr	54	..	..	..	..	..	..	..	1120	..	..	..	..	..	..	..	..	..	..	..	..	..	54
Bookham .... [394	55	..	..	..	..	..	..	..	..	..	..	..	..	..	..	..	..	1128	..	..	..	..	55
Effingham Junction arr	56	..	..	..	..	..	..	..	..	..	..	..	..	..	..	..	..	1132	..	..	..	..	56
South Croydon 234	57	..	..	..	..	..	..	1048	..	..	..	..	1050	1056	..	..	..	..	..	..	..	..	57
Purley Oaks	58	..	..	..	..	..	..	1051	..	..	..	..	1053	..	..	..	..	..	..	..	..	..	58
Purley	59	..	..	..	..	1040	..	1053	..	..	..	..	1056	..	..	..	..	..	..	1110	..	..	59
Coulsdon North L .. arr	60	..	..	..	..	..	..	1057	..	..	..	..	..	..	..	..	..	..	..	..	..	..	60
Purley .... dep	61	..	..	..	..	..	..	..	..	..	..	..	1059	..	..	..	..	..	..	..	..	..	61
Kenley	62	..	..	..	..	..	..	..	..	..	..	..	11 2	..	..	..	..	..	..	..	..	..	62
Whyteleafe	63	..	..	..	..	..	..	..	..	..	..	..	11 5	..	..	..	..	..	..	..	..	..	63
Warlingham	64	..	..	..	..	..	..	..	..	..	..	..	11 7	..	..	..	..	..	..	..	..	..	64
Caterham .... arr	65	..	..	..	..	..	..	..	..	..	..	..	1111	..	..	..	..	..	..	..	..	..	65
Purley .... dep	66	..	..	..	..	..	..	..	..	..	..	..	1057	..	..	..	..	..	..	..	..	..	66
Reednam	67	..	..	..	..	..	..	..	..	..	..	..	1059	..	..	..	..	..	..	..	..	..	67
Smitham	68	..	..	..	..	..	..	..	..	..	..	..	11 1	..	..	..	..	..	..	..	..	..	68
Woodmansterne	69	..	..	..	..	..	..	..	..	..	..	..	11 4	..	..	..	..	..	..	..	..	..	69
Chipstead	70	..	..	..	..	..	..	..	..	..	..	..	11 6	..	..	..	..	..	..	..	..	..	70
Kingswood M	71	..	..	..	..	..	..	..	..	..	..	..	1111	..	..	..	..	..	..	..	..	..	71
Tadworth N	72	..	..	..	..	..	..	..	..	..	..	..	1114	..	..	..	..	..	..	..	..	..	72
Tattenham Corner. arr	73	..	..	..	..	..	..	..	..	..	..	..	1117	..	..	..	..	..	..	..	..	..	73
Coulsdon South	74	..	..	..	..	1043	..	..	..	..	..	..	..	..	..	..	..	..	..	1114	..	..	74
Merstham	75	..	..	..	..	1049	..	..	..	..	..	..	..	..	..	..	..	..	..	1120	..	..	75
Redhill 158,246 ...... arr	76	..	..	..	..	1053	..	..	..	..	..	11 0	..	..	..	..	..	..	..	1123	..	..	76
Reigate 240 .... "	77	..	..	..	..	1059	..	..	..	..	..	..	..	..	..	..	..	..	..	1130	..	..	77
Horsham 159.244,245 "	78	..	..	..	..	..	..	..	..	..	..	..	..	..	..	..	..	..	..	..	..	..	78

CATERHAM, TATTENHAM CORNER, REDHILL, REIGATE, and HORSHAM

Week Days—continued — p.m

No.						S X					S X																
1	..	..	..	1051	..	..	..	..	..	11 8	..	..	1110	1115	..	11 20	11 21	..	..	1132	..	11 38	..	..	1146	..	..
2	3	..	3	3	3	..	3	..	..	3	3	11 5	3	..	3	3	3	3	3	3	3	3	1140	..	3	..	3
3		..				..		..	11 7			11 7		..									1142	..		1147	
4	1037	..	1048	..	1053	..	11 2	..	..	..	1111	1111	..	..	1115	..	..	1123	1123	..	1132	..	1146	..	..	..	1150
5	..	..	..	..	..	..	..	..	3	..	..	3	1113	..	..	..	..	..	..	1135	..	11 41	3	..	1149	..	..
6	..	..	..	1057	..	..	..	..		11 14	..		1117	1121	..	11 25	11J27	..	..	1138	..	11H44		..	1152	1154	..
7	..	..	..	..	..	..	..	..	..	..	..	..	1120	..	..	..	..	..	..	1141	..	..	..	..	1155	3	..
8	..	..	..	11 1	..	..	..	..	..	11 18	..	..	1122	..	..	11 29	11J31	..	..	1143	..	11H48	..	..	1157		..
9	1040	..	1051	..	..	..	..	..	Via Worcester Park	..	..	..	..	..	1118	..	J 1 minute later on Saturdays	..	..	..	..	H 1 minute earlier on Saturdays	..	..	..	Via Worcester Park	..
10	1043	..	1054	..	..	..	..	..		..	..	..	..	..	1121	..		..	..	..	..		..	..	..		..
11	1045	..	1056	..	..	..	..	..		..	1117	..	..	..	1123	..		..	1129	..	..		..	..	..		..
12	1048	..		..	..	..	..	..		..	1119	..	..	..	1126	..		..	..	..	..		..	..	..		..
13	1050	..		..	..	..	..	..		..	1121	..	..	..	1128	..		..	..	..	..		..	..	..		..
14	1053	..		..	..	..	..	..		..	1124	..	..	..	1131	..		..	1133	..	..		..	..	..		..
15	1057	..		..	..	..	..	..		..	1128	..	..	..	..	..		..	1137	..	..		..	..	..		..
16	..	..	To Victoria, arr. 11 13 p.m	..	1058	..	11 7	..	..	..	..	..	..	..	..	..		1128	..	..	1137		..	..	H 1 minute earlier on Saturdays		..
17	..	..		..	11 0	..	..	..	..	..	..	..	..	..	..	..		1130	..	..	1139		..	..			..
18	..	..		..	11 3	..	..	..	..	..	..	..	..	..	..	..		1133	..	..	1142		..	..		..	..
19	..	..		..	11 5	..	1111	..	..	..	..	..	..	..	..	..		1135	..	..	1144		..	..		..	..
20	..	..		..	11 8	..	1114	..	..	..	..	..	..	..	..	..		1138	..	..	1147		..	..		..	..
21	..	..		..	..	..	1116	..	..	..	..	..	..	..	..	..		..	..	..	1149		..	..		..	..
22	..	..		..	..	..	1117	..	..	..	..	..	..	..	..	..		..	..	..	1150		..	..		..	..
23	1059	..	..	11 5	..	..	..	..	..	11 22	1130	..	..	..	..	..	11J35	..	..	..	..	11H52	..	..		..	..
24	11 1	..	..	11 7	..	..	..	..	..	11 24	1132	..	..	..	..	..	11J37	..	..	..	..	11 54	..	..		..	..
25	11 4	..	..	1110	..	..	..	..	..	11 27	1135	..	..	..	..	..	11J40	..	..	..	..	11 57	..	..		..	..
26	11 6	..	..	1113	..	..	..	..	..	11 29	1137	..	..	..	..	..	11 43	..	..	..	..	11 59	..	..		..	..
27	..	..	..	..	..	..	..	..	..	..	..	..	1124	..	..	..	..	..	..	1146	..	Arr Sutton 12 14 ngt	..	..	1159	..	..
28	..	..	..	..	..	..	..	..	..	..	..	..	1127	..	1133	..	..	..	..	..	..		..	..	12H3	..	..
29	..	..	..	..	..	..	..	..	..	..	..	..	1130	..	1136	..	..	..	..	..	..		..	..	12H6	..	..
30	..	..	..	..	1111	..	..	..	..	..	..	..	1132	..	1139	..	..	1141	..	..	..		..	..	12 7	..	..
31	..	..	..	..		..	..	..	..	..	..	..	..	..		..	..	..	..	..	..		..	..	..	..	..
32	..	..	..	..	Stop	..	..	..	..	..	..	..	..	..	Stop	..	..	..	..	..	..		..	..	..	..	..
33	11 9	..	..	..	..	..	1120	..	..	..	..	1123	1137	..	..	..	..	..	..	..	1153		1158	..	1211	..	..
34	..	..	..	1117	..	..	..	..	..	..	..	1127	..	1132	..	..	11 47	..	..	..	..		12 2	..	..	..	..
35	..	..	..	1117	..	..	..	..	..	..	..	1127	..	1133	..	..	11 47	..	..	..	..		12 2	..	..	..	1215
36	To London Bridge, via Forest Hill	..	..	..	3	..	..	..	..	..	..	..	..	..	3	11 35	..	..	1142	..	..		..	..	..	..	..
37		..	..	..		..	..	..	..	..	..	..	..	..		11 38	..	..	1144	..	..		..	..	..	..	..
38		..	..	..	p.m	3	..	..	..	..	..	..	..	..	p.m	11 40	..	..	1147	..	..		..	..	..	..	..
39		..	..	..	S O		1124	..	..	11 33	..	..	1141	..	S O	..	..	..	..	..	1157	12 2	..	..	1216	..	..
40		..	..	..	1111	1111	1124	..	..	11 33	..	..	..	..	1143	..	..	..	..	..	..	12 2	..	..	..	..	..
41		..	..	..	1113	1113	1127	..	..	11 36	..	..	..	..	1145	..	..	..	..	..	..	12 5	..	..	..	..	..
42		..	..	..	1117	1117	1130	..	..	11 39	..	..	..	..	1149	..	..	..	..	..	..	12 8	..	..	..	..	..
43		..	..	..	1119	..	1133	..	..	11 42	..	..	..	..	..	..	..	..	..	..	..	12 11	..	..	..	..	..
44		..	..	..	1122	..	1135	..	..	11 47	..	..	..	..	..	11 43	..	..	1150	..	..	12 17	..	..	..	..	..
45	..	..	..	..	..	..	1138	..	..	11 50	..	..	..	..	..	..	..	..	..	..	..	12 20	..	..	..	..	..
46	..	..	..	..	..	..	1141	..	..	11 53	..	..	..	..	..	..	..	..	..	..	..	12 23	..	..	..	..	..
47	..	..	..	..	..	..	1145	..	..	11 56	..	..	..	..	..	..	..	..	..	..	..	12 26	..	..	..	..	..
48	..	..	..	..	..	..	..	..	..	Arr Sutton 11 45 p.m	..	..	..	..	..	11 46	..	..	1153	..	..	..	..	..	..	..	..
49	..	..	..	..	..	..	..	..	..		..	..	..	..	..	11 49	..	..	1156	..	..	..	..	..	..	..	..
50	..	..	..	..	..	..	..	..	1135		..	..	..	..	..	11 53	..	..	12 0	..	..	..	..	..	..	1218	..
51	..	..	..	..	..	..	..	..	1139		..	..	..	..	..	..	..	..	12 4	..	..	..	..	..	..	1222	..
52	..	..	..	..	..	..	..	..	1143		..	..	..	..	..	..	..	..	12 8	..	..	..	..	..	..	1228	..
53	..	..	..	..	..	..	..	..	1148		..	..	..	..	..	..	..	..	1213	..	..	..	..	..	..	1233	..
54	..	..	..	..	..	..	..	..	1152		..	..	..	..	..	..	..	..	1216	..	..	..	..	..	..	1236	..
55	..	..	..	..	..	..	..	..	..		..	..	..	..	..	..	..	..	..	..	..	..	..	..	..	..	..
56	..	..	..	..	..	..	..	..	..		..	..	..	..	..	..	..	..	..	..	..	..	..	..	..	..	..
57	..	..	..	1119	..	..	..	..	..	..	..	1130	..	..	..	..	11 49	..	..	..	..	..	12 4	..	..	..	..
58	..	..	..	1122	..	..	..	..	..	..	..	1132	..	..	..	..	11 52	..	..	..	..	..	12 7	..	..	..	..
59	..	..	..	1124	..	..	..	..	..	..	..	1135	..	1139	..	..	11 54	..	..	..	..	..	1210	..	..	..	..
60	..	..	..	1128	..	..	..	..	..	..	..	..	..	..	..	..	11 58	..	..	..	..	..	..	..	..	..	..
61	..	..	..	..	..	..	..	..	..	..	..	1141	..	..	..	..	..	..	..	..	..	..	1214	..	..	..	..
62	..	..	..	..	..	..	..	..	..	..	..	1144	..	..	..	..	..	..	..	..	..	..	1217	..	..	..	..
63	..	..	..	..	..	..	..	..	..	..	..	1147	..	..	..	..	..	..	..	..	..	..	1220	..	..	..	..
64	..	..	..	..	..	..	..	..	..	..	..	1149	..	..	..	..	..	..	..	..	..	..	1222	..	..	..	..
65	..	..	..	..	..	..	..	..	..	..	..	1153	..	..	..	..	..	..	..	..	..	..	1226	..	..	..	..
66	..	..	..	..	..	..	..	..	..	..	..	1140	..	..	..	..	..	..	..	..	..	..	1211	..	..	..	..
67	..	..	..	..	..	..	..	..	..	..	..	1142	..	..	..	..	..	..	..	..	..	..	1213	..	..	..	..
68	..	..	..	..	..	..	..	..	..	..	..	1145	..	..	..	..	..	..	..	..	..	..	1215	..	..	..	..
69	..	..	..	..	..	..	..	..	..	..	..	1147	..	..	..	..	..	..	..	..	..	..	1218	..	..	..	..
70	..	..	..	..	..	..	..	..	..	..	..	1150	..	..	..	..	..	..	..	..	..	..	1220	..	..	..	..
71	..	..	..	..	..	..	..	..	..	..	..	1154	..	..	..	..	..	..	..	..	..	..	1225	..	..	..	..
72	..	..	..	..	..	..	..	..	..	..	..	1157	..	..	..	..	..	..	..	..	..	..	1228	..	..	..	..
73	..	..	..	..	..	..	..	..	..	..	..	12 1	..	..	..	..	..	..	..	..	..	..	1231	..	..	..	..
74	..	..	..	..	..	..	..	..	..	..	..	..	..	1142	..	..	..	..	..	..	..	..	..	..	..	..	..
75	..	..	..	..	..	..	..	..	..	..	..	..	..	1148	..	..	..	..	..	..	..	..	..	..	..	..	..
76	..	..	..	..	..	..	..	..	..	..	..	..	..	1152	..	..	..	..	..	..	..	..	..	..	..	..	1238
77	..	..	..	..	..	..	..	..	..	..	..	..	..	1158	..	..	..	..	..	..	..	..	..	..	..	..	..
78	..	..	..	..	..	..	..	..	..	..	..	..	..	..	..	..	..	..	..	..	..	..	..	..	..	..	..

LONDON, CRYSTAL PALACE, CROYDON, SUTTON, DORKING NORTH,

For Notes, see page 284a

Down	No.	a.m								Sundays								a.m					No.
Victoria .... dep	1	4 45	..	6 40	..	..	..	7 15	..	..	..	..	7 40	7 45	7 46	7 48	..	..	..	..	..	..	1
Charing Cross* ... "	2	..	..	..	..	..	..	..	..	..	..	..	..	..	..	..	..	..	..	..	..	..	2
Waterloo* .... "	3	③	6 25	..	③	..	..	③	7 20	③	③	..	③	③	..	③	..	③	8 2	③	..	③	3
London Bridge ..... "	4	..	..	..	7 5	7 16	..	..	..	7 21	7 35	7 40	..	..	..	..	..	7 51	..	7 55	..	7 58	4
Battersea Park	5	..	..	6 43	..	..	..	..	..	..	..	..	7 43	..	..	..	..	..	..	..	..	..	5
Clapham Junction	6	..	6 32	6 46	..	..	..	7 20	7 27	..	..	..	7 46	7 50	7 51	7 54	..	..	8 9	..	..	..	6
Wandsworth Common A	7	..	..	..	..	..	..	7 23	..	..	..	..	7 49	7 53	..	7 57	..	..	..	..	..	..	7
Balham & Upper Tooting	8	..	③	6 50	..	..	..	7 25	③	..	..	..	7 51	7 55	..	7 59	..	..	③	..	..	..	8
South Bermondsey	9	..	Via Worcester Park Change at Wimbledon	..	..	..	..	..	Via Worcester Park	7 24	7 38	..	..	..	..	..	..	7 54	Via Worcester Park	7 58	..	..	9
Queen's Road, Peckham	10	..		..	..	..	..	..		7 27	7 41	..	..	..	..	..	..	7 57		8 1	..	..	10
Peckham Rye	11	..		..	..	..	..	..		7 29	7 43	..	..	..	..	..	..	7 59		8 3	..	..	11
East Dulwich	12	..		..	..	..	..	..		To Victoria, arr. 7 44 a.m	7 46	..	..	..	..	..	..	To Victoria, arr 8 14 a.m		8 6	..	..	12
North Dulwich	13	..		..	..	..	..	..			7 48	..	..	..	..	..	..			8 8	..	..	13
Tulse Hill	14	..		..	..	..	..	..			7 51	..	..	..	..	..	..			8 11	..	..	14
Streatham	15	..		..	..	..	..	..			..	..	..	..	..	..	..			8 14	..	..	15
New Cross Gate (for E.L.	16	..		..	7 10	7 21	..	..			..	7 45	..	..	..	..	..			..	..	8 3	16
Brockley B .... [Line)	17	..		..	7 12	..	..	..			..	..	..	..	..	..	..			..	..	8 5	17
Honor Oak Park	18	..		..	7 15	..	..	..	..		..	..	..	..	..	..	..		..	..	..	8 8	18
Forest Hill, for Lordship	19	..		..	7 17	..	..	..	..		..	..	..	..	..	..	..		..	..	..	8 10	19
Sydenham .... [Lane	20	..		..	7 20	..	..	..	..		..	..	..	..	..	..	..		..	..	..	8 13	20
Penge West C	21	..		..	..	..	..	..	..		..	..	..	..	..	..	..		..	..	..	8 15	21
Anerley	22	..		..	..	..	..	..	..		..	..	..	..	..	..	..		..	..	..	8 16	22
Streatham Common	23	..		6 54	..	..	..	..	..		..	..	..	..	..	8 3	..	..	..	..	..	..	23
Norbury	24	..		..	..	..	..	..	..		..	..	..	..	..	8 5	..	..	..	..	..	..	24
Thornton Heath	25	..		6 58	..	..	..	..	..		..	..	..	..	8 0	8 8	..	..	..	..	..	..	25
Selhurst	26	..		..	..	..	..	..	..	Stop	..	..	..	..	..	8 10	..	..	..	..	..	..	26
Streatham Hill	27	..	..	..	..	..	..	..	..	..	..	..	7 54	..	..	..	..	..	..	..	..	..	27
West Norwood. [N'wood)	28	..	..	..	..	..	..	..	..	..	7 53	..	7 57	..	..	..	..	..	..	..	..	..	28
Gipsy Hill (for Upper	29	..	..	..	..	..	..	..	..	..	7 55	..	7 59	..	..	..	③	..	..	..	..	..	29
Crystal Palace D	30	..	..	..	7 23	..	..	..	..	..	7 58	..	8 2	..	..	..	8 5	..	..	..	..	..	30
Birkbeck	31	..	..	..	..	..	..	..	..	..	..	..	..	..	..	..	8 8	..	..	..	..	..	31
Beckenham Jn. arr	32	..	..	..	Stop	..	..	..	..	..	..	..	..	..	..	..	8 12	..	..	..	..	..	32
Norwood Junction F ..	33	..	..	..	..	7 30	..	..	..	..	..	7 54	8 6	..	..	..	..	..	..	..	..	8 19	33
East Croydon .... arr	34	5 3	..	7 2	..	7 34	..	..	..	..	..	7 58	..	..	8 4	..	..	..	..	..	..	..	34
East Croydon .... dep	35	5 5	..	7 2	..	7 35	..	..	..	..	..	8 0	..	..	8 5	..	..	..	..	..	..	..	35
Mitcham Junction	36	..	..	..	..	..	..	7 31	..	..	..	..	..	8 1	..	..	..	..	..	8 19	..	..	36
Hackbridge	37	..	..	..	a.m	..	..	7 34	..	a.m	..	..	..	8 4	..	..	..	..	..	8 22	..	..	37
Carshalton	38	..	..	..	..	..	..	7 36	..	..	..	..	..	8 6	..	..	..	..	..	8 24	..	..	38
West Croydon 319 arr	39	..	..	..	③	..	③	..	..	③	..	..	8 11	..	..	8 13	..	..	..	..	③	8 23	39
West Croydon 319 dep	40	..	..	..	7 13	..	7 19	..	..	7 49	..	..	..	..	..	8 13	..	..	..	..	8 19	8 23	40
Waddon G	41	..	..	..	7 15	..	7 21	..	..	7 51	..	..	..	..	..	8 16	..	..	..	..	8 21	8 26	41
Wallington	42	..	..	..	7 19	..	7 25	..	..	7 55	..	..	..	..	..	8 19	..	..	..	..	8 25	8 29	42
Carshalton Beeches	43	..	..	..	7 21	..	7 27	..	..	7 57	..	..	..	..	..	8 22	..	..	..	..	8 27	8 32	43
Sutton 322	44	..	..	..	7 25	..	7 30	7 39	..	8 0	..	..	..	8 9	..	8 24	..	..	..	8 27	8 30	8 34	44
Belmont	45	..	..	..	7 28	..	..	..	..	..	..	..	..	..	..	8 27	..	..	..	..	..	8 37	45
Banstead	46	..	..	..	7 31	..	..	..	..	..	..	..	..	..	..	8 30	..	..	..	..	..	8 40	46
Epsom Downs ...... arr	47	..	..	..	7 34	..	..	..	..	..	..	..	..	..	..	8 34	..	..	..	..	..	8 44	47
Cheam	48	..	..	..	..	..	..	7 42	..	..	..	..	..	8 12	..	..	..	..	..	8 30	..	..	48
Ewell East H	49	..	..	..	..	..	..	7 45	..	..	..	..	..	8 15	..	..	..	..	..	8 33	..	..	49
Epsom	50	..	7 2	..	..	..	..	7 48	7 53	..	..	..	..	8 19	..	..	..	..	8 31	8 38	..	..	50
Ashtead	51	..	7 6	..	..	..	..	..	7 57	..	..	..	..	..	..	..	..	..	8 35	8 42	..	..	51
Leatherhead .. [Bridge J	52	..	7 10	..	..	..	..	..	8 1	..	..	..	..	..	..	..	..	..	8 39	8 46	..	..	52
Boxhill and Burford	53	..	7 15	..	..	..	..	..	8 6	..	..	..	..	..	..	..	..	..	..	8 51	..	..	53
Dorking North K .. arr	54	..	7 18	..	..	..	..	..	8 9	..	..	..	..	..	..	..	..	..	..	8 53	..	..	54
Bookham .... [394	55	..	..	..	..	..	..	..	..	..	..	..	..	..	..	..	..	..	8 45	..	..	..	55
Effingham Junction arr	56	..	..	..	..	..	..	..	..	..	..	..	..	..	..	..	..	..	8 49	..	..	..	56
South Croydon 234	57	..	..	..	..	..	..	..	..	..	..	..	..	..	..	..	..	..	..	..	..	..	57
Purley Oaks	58	..	..	..	..	..	..	..	..	..	..	..	..	..	..	..	..	..	..	..	..	..	58
Purley	59	..	..	7 8	..	7 40	..	..	..	..	..	..	..	..	8 10	..	..	..	..	..	..	..	59
Coulsdon North L .. arr	60	..	..	..	..	..	..	..	..	..	..	..	..	..	..	..	..	..	..	..	..	..	60
Purley .... dep	61	..	..	..	..	..	..	..	..	..	..	..	..	..	..	..	..	..	..	..	..	..	61
Kenley	62	..	..	..	..	..	..	..	..	..	..	..	..	..	..	..	..	..	..	..	..	..	62
Whyteleafe	63	..	..	..	..	..	..	..	..	..	..	..	..	..	..	..	..	..	..	..	..	..	63
Warlingham	64	..	..	..	..	..	..	..	..	..	..	..	..	..	..	..	..	..	..	..	..	..	64
Caterham .... arr	65	..	..		..	..	..	..	..	..	..	..	..	..		..	..	..	..	..	..	..	65
Purley .... dep	66	..	..	§ Via Three Bridges	..	..	..	..	..	..	..	..	..	..	§ Via Three Bridges	..	..	..	..	..	..	..	66
Reedham	67	..	..		..	..	..	..	..	..	..	..	..	..		..	..	..	..	..	..	..	67
Smitham	68	..	..		..	..	..	..	..	..	..	..	..	..		..	..	..	..	..	..	..	68
Woodmansterne	69	..	..		..	..	..	..	..	..	..	..	..	..		..	..	..	..	..	..	..	69
Chipstead	70	..	..		..	..	..	..	..	..	..	..	..	..		..	..	..	..	..	..	..	70
Kingswood M	71	..	..		..	..	..	..	..	..	..	..	..	..		..	..	..	..	..	..	..	71
Tadworth N	72	..	..		..	..	..	..	..	..	..	..	..	..		..	..	..	..	..	..	..	72
Tattenham Corner. arr	73	..	..		..	..	..	..	..	..	..	..	..	..		..	..	..	..	..	..	..	73
Coulsdon South	74	..	..	7 12	..	7 44	..	..	..	..	..	..	..	..	8 14	..	..	..	..	..	..	..	74
Merstham	75	..	..	7 18	..	7 50	..	..	..	..	..	..	..	..	8 20	..	..	..	..	..	..	..	75
Redhill 158, 246 ..... arr	76	5 23	..	7 22	..	7 54	..	..	..	..	..	8 14	..	..	8 24	..	..	..	..	..	..	..	76
Reigate 246 .... "	77	..	..	7 38	..	8 6	..	..	..	..	..	..	..	..	8 32	..	..	..	..	..	..	..	77
Horsham 159, 244, 245 "	78	..	..	8§ 5	..	..	..	..	8 33	..	..	..	..	..	9§ 5	..	..	..	..	9 17	..	..	78

CATERHAM, TATTENHAM CORNER, REDHILL, REIGATE, and HORSHAM

No.	a.m														Sundays										a.m			
1	8 2	..	..	8 10	..	..	8 15	8 18	..	..	..	..	..	..	..	8 28	..	..	..	..	..	8 40	..	..	8 45	..	8 48	..
2	3	3	..	3	..	3	3	3	..	..	3	..	3	..	..	..	3	8 23	..	..	3	3	..	..	3	..	3	3
3			..		..				..	..		8 20		..	..	..		8 25	..	..			..	..		..		
4	..	8 4	..	..	..	8 13	..	..	..	8 16	8 21	..	8 25	..	..	..	8 28	8 30	8 36	..	8 35	..	..	..	..	..	..	8 45
5	..	..	..	8 13	..	..	..	..	..	..	..	..	..	..	..	..	..	3	..	..	..	8 43	..	..	..	..	..	..
6	8 7	..	..	8 16	..	..	8 20	8 24	..	..	..	8 27	..	..	..	8 33	..		..	..	..	8 46	..	..	8 50	..	8 54	..
7	8 10	..	..	8 19	..	..	8 23	8 27	..	..	..	3	..	..	..	..	..	..	..	..	..	8 49	..	..	8 53	..	8 57	..
8	8 12	..	..	8 21	..	..	8 25	8 29	..	..	..		..	..	..	..	..	..	..	..	..	8 51	..	..	8 55	..	8 59	..
9	..	8 7	..	..	..	..	..	..	..	..	8 24		8 28	..	..	..	..	..	..	..	..	..	..	..	..	..	..	8 48
10	..	8 10	..	..	..	..	..	..	..	..	8 27		8 31	..	..	..	..	..	..	..	..	..	..	..	..	..	..	8 51
11	..	8 12	..	..	..	..	..	..	..	..	8 29		8 33	..	..	..	..	..	..	..	..	..	..	..	..	..	..	8 53
12	..	8 15	..	..	..	..	..	..	..	..	..	Via Worcester Park	8 36	..	..	..	..	..	..	..	..	..	..	..	..	..	..	8 56
13	..	8 17	..	..	..	..	..	..	..	..			8 38	..	..	..	..	..	..	..	..	..	..	..	..	..	..	8 58
14	..	8 20	..	..	..	..	..	..	..	..			8 41	..	..	..	..	..	..	..	..	..	..	..	..	..	..	9 1
15	..	..	..	..	..	..	..	..	..	..	To Victoria arr. 8 44 a.m		8 44	..	..	..	..	..	..	..	..	..	..	..	..	..	..	9 4
16	..	..	..	..	..	8 18	..	..	..	8 21			..	..	..	..	8 33	8 35	..	..	8 40	..	..	..	..	..	..	..
17	..	..	..	..	..	8 20	..	..	..	..			..	..	..	..	8 35	..	..	..	8 42	..	..	..	..	..	..	..
18	..	..	..	..	..	8 23	..	..	..	..		..	..	..	..	..	8 38	..	..	..	8 45	..	..	..	..	..	..	..
19	..	..	..	..	..	8 25	..	..	..	..		..	..	..	..	..	8 40	8 40	..	..	8 47	..	..	..	..	..	..	..
20	..	..	..	..	..	8 28	..	..	..	..	..	..	..	..	..	..	8 43	..	..	..	8 50	..	..	..	..	..	..	..
21	..	..	..	..	..	8 30	..	..	..	..	..	..	..	..	..	..	8 45	..	..	..	..	..	..	..	..	..	..	..
22	..	..	..	..	..	8 31	..	..	..	..	..	..	..	..	..	..	8 46	..	..	..	..	..	..	..	..	..	..	..
23	8 16	..	..	..	..	..	..	8 33	..	..	..	..	..	..	..	..	..	..	..	..	..	..	..	..	..	..	9 3	9 6
24	8 18	..	..	..	..	..	..	8 35	..	..	..	..	..	..	..	..	..	..	..	..	..	..	..	..	..	..	9 5	9 9
25	8 21	..	..	..	..	..	..	8 38	..	..	..	..	..	..	..	..	..	..	..	..	..	..	..	..	..	..	9 8	9 12
26	8 23	..	..	..	..	..	..	8 40	..	..	..	..	..	..	..	..	..	..	..	..	..	..	..	..	..	..	9 10	9 14
27	..	..	..	8 24	..	..	..	..	..	..	..	..	..	..	..	..	..	..	..	..	..	8 54	..	..	..	..	..	..
28	..	8 22	..	8 27	3	..	..	..	..	..	..	..	..	..	..	..	..	..	..	..	..	8 57	3	..	..	..	..	..
29	..	8 24	..	8 29		..	..	..	..	..	..	..	..	..	..	..	..	..	..	..	..	8 59		..	..	..	..	..
30	..	8 27	..	8 32	8 35	..	..	..	..	..	..	..	..	..	..	..	..	..	..	..	8 53	9 2	9 5	..	..	..	..	..
31	..		..	..	8 38	..	..	..	..	..	..	..	..	..	..	..	..	..	..	..	..	..	9 8	..	..	..	..	..
32	..	Stop	..	..	8 42	..	..	..	..	..	..	..	..	..	..	..	..	..	..	..	..	..	9 12	..	..	..	..	..
33	..	..	..	8 36	..	8 34	..	..	..	8 30	..	..	..	..	..	..	8 49	8 44	8 51	..	..	9 6	..	..	..	..	..	9 17
34	8 27	..	..	..	..	..	..	..	..	8 34	..	..	..	..	..	8 45	..	8 48	8 56	..	..	..	..	..	..	..	..	..
35	8 27	..	..	..	..		..	..	..	8 35	..	..	..	..	..	8 46	..	8 48	8 58	..	..	..	..	..	..	..	..	
36	..	..	..	..	..		8 31	..	..	..	..	..	8 49	..	..	..	..	..	..	..	..	..	..	..	9 1	..	..	
37	..	..	..	..	..		8 34	..	..	..	..	..	8 52	..	..	..	..	..	..	..	..	..	..	..	9 4	..	..	
38	..	..	..	..	..		8 36	..	..	..	..	..	8 54	..		..	..	..	..	..	..	..	..	..	9 6	..	..	
39	..	..	..	8 41	..	To London Bridge, via Streatham	..	8 43	..	..	..	..	..	..	3	..	8 52	..	..	..	..	9 11	..	..	..	..	9 13	To London Bridge via Forest Hill
40	..	..	..	..	..		..	8 43	..	..	..	..	..	..	8 49	..	8 53	..	..	..	..	..	..	..	..	..	9 13	
41	..	..	..	..	..		..	8 46	..	..	..	..	..	..	8 51	..	8 56	..	..	..	..	..	..	..	..	..	9 16	
42	..	..	..	..	..		..	8 49	..	..	..	..	..	..	8 55	..	8 59	..	..	..	..	..	..	..	..	..	9 19	
43	..	..	..	..	..		..	8 52	..	..	..	..	..	..	8 57	..	9 2	..	..	..	..	..	..	..	..	..	9 22	
44	..	..	..	..	..		8 39	8 54	..	..	..	..	8 58	..	9 0	..	9 4	..	..	..	..	..	..	..	9 9	..	9 24	
45	..	..	..	..	..	..	..	8 57	..	..	..	..	..	..	..	..	9 7	..	..	..	..	..	..	..	..	..	9 27	..
46	..	..	..	..	..	..	..	9 0	..	..	..	..	..	..	..	..	9 10	..	..	..	..	..	..	..	..	..	9 30	..
47	..	..	..	..	..	..	..	9 4	..	..	..	..	..	..	..	..	9 14	..	..	..	..	..	..	..	..	..	9 34	..
48	..	..	..	..	..	..	8 42	..	..	..	..	..	9 1	..	..	..	..	..	..	..	..	..	..	..	9 12	..	..	..
49	..	..	..	..	..	..	8 45	..	..	..	..	..	9 4	..	..	..	..	..	..	..	..	..	..	..	9 15	..	..	..
50	..	..	..	..	..	..	8 48	..	..	..	..	8 53	9 7	..	..	..	..	..	..	..	..	..	..	..	9 19	..	..	..
51	..	..	..	..	..	..	..	..	..	..	..	8 57	9 11	..	..	..	..	..	..	..	..	..	..	..	..	..	..	..
52	..	..	..	..	..	..	..	..	..	..	..	9 1	9 15	..	..	..	..	..	..	..	..	..	..	..	..	..	..	..
53	..	..	..	..	..	..	..	..	..	..	..	9 6	..	..	..	..	..	..	..	..	..	..	..	..	..	..	..	..
54	..	..	..	..	..	..	..	..	..	..	..	9 9	..	..	..	..	..	..	..	..	..	..	..	..	..	..	..	..
55	..	..	..	..	..	..	..	..	..	..	..	..	9 19	..	..	..	..	..	..	..	..	..	..	..	..	..	..	..
56	..	..	..	..	..	..	..	..	..	..	..	..	9 23	..	..	..	..	..	..	..	..	..	..	..	..	..	..	..
57	8 30	..	..	..	..	..	..	..	..	..	..	..	..	..	..	..	..	8 50	9 2	..	..	..	..	..	..	..	..	..
58	8 32	..	..	..	..	..	..	..	..	..	..	..	..	..	..	..	..	8 53	..	..	..	..	..	..	..	..	..	..
59	8 35	..	3	..	..	..	..	..	..	8 40	..	..	..	..	..	..	..	8 56	..	..	..	..	..	..	..	..	..	..
60	8 38	..		..	..	..	..	..	..	..	..	..	..	..	..	..	..	..	..	..	..	..	..	..	..	..	..	..
61	..	..	8 39	..	..	..	..	..	..	..	..	..	..	..	..	..	..	8 59	..	..	..	..	..	..	..	..	..	..
62	..	..	8 42	..	..	..	..	..	..	..	..	..	..	..	..	..	..	9 2	..	..	..	..	..	..	..	..	..	..
63	..	a.m	8 45	..	..	..	..	..	..	..	..	..	..	..	..	..	..	9 5	..	..	..	..	..	..	..	..	..	..
64	..	3	8 47	..	..	..	..	..	..	..	..	..	..	..	..	..	..	9 7	..	..	..	..	..	..	..	..	..	..
65	..		8 51	..	..	..	..	..	..	..	..	..	..	..	..	..	..	9 11	..	..	..	..	..	..	..	..	..	..
66	..	8 37	..	..	..	..	..	..	..	..	..	..	..	..	..	..	..	8 57	..	..	..	..	..	..	..	..	..	..
67	..	8 39	..	..	..	..	..	..	..	..	..	..	..	..	..	..	..	8 59	..	..	..	..	..	..	..	..	..	..
68	..	8 41	..	..	..	..	..	..	..	..	..	..	..	..	..	..	..	9 1	..	..	..	..	..	..	..	..	..	..
69	..	8 44	..	..	..	..	..	..	..	..	..	..	..	..	..	..	..	9 4	..	..	..	..	..	..	..	..	..	..
70	..	8 46	..	..	..	..	..	..	..	..	..	..	..	..	..	..	..	9 6	..	..	..	..	..	..	..	..	..	..
71	..	8 51	..	..	..	..	..	..	..	..	..	..	..	..	..	..	..	9 11	..	..	..	..	..	..	..	..	..	..
72	..	8 54	..	..	..	..	..	..	..	..	..	..	..	..	..	..	..	9 14	..	..	..	..	..	..	..	..	..	..
73	..	8 57	..	..	..	..	..	..	..	..	..	..	..	..	..	..	..	9 17	..	..	..	..	..	..	..	..	..	..
74	..	..	..	..	..	..	..	..	..	8 44	..	..	..	..	..	..	..	..	..	..	..	..	..	..	..	..	..	..
75	..	..	..	..	..	..	..	..	..	8 50	..	..	..	..	..	..	..	..	..	..	..	..	..	..	..	..	..	..
76	..	..	..	..	..	..	..	..	..	8 54	..	..	..	..	..	9 0	..	..	..	..	..	..	..	..	..	..	..	..
77	..	..	..	..	..	..	..	..	..	9 0	..	..	..	..	..	..	..	..	..	..	..	..	..	..	..	..	..	..
78	..	..	..	..	..	..	..	..	..	..	..	..	..	..	..	..	..	..	..	..	..	..	..	..	..	..	..	..

LONDON, CRYSTAL PALACE, CROYDON, SUTTON, DORKING NORTH,

For Notes, see page 284a

Down	No.	a.m								Sundays—*continued*								a.m					No.
Victoria............dep	1		8 50							9 2			9 10					9 18	9 18			9 24	1
Charing Cross*... "	2			(3)		(3)		(3)	8 53	(3)	(3)		(3)		(3)				(3)		(3)	(3)	2
Waterloo*......... "	3				9 2				8 55														3
London Bridge..... "	4	8 49		8 51		8 55		8 58	9 0		9 4				9 13		9 16				9 21		4
Battersea Park..........	5								(3)				9 13										5
Clapham Junction......	6		8 57		9 9					9 7			9 16						9 24			9 29	6
Wandsworth Common A	7				(3)					9 10			9 19						9 27				7
Balham & Upper Tooting	8									9 12			9 21						9 29			9 33	8
South Bermondsey......	9			8 54	Via Worcester Park	8 58					9 7										9 24		9
Queen's Road, Peckham	10			8 57		9 1					9 10										9 27		10
Peckham Rye...........	11			8 59		9 3					9 12										9 29		11
East Dulwich...........	12			To Victoria. arr. 9 14 a.m		9 6					9 15												12
North Dulwich..........	13					9 8					9 17												13
Tulse Hill...............	14					9 11					9 20										To Victoria, arr. 9 44 a.m		14
Streatham	15					9 14																	15
New Cross Gate (for E.L.	16							9 3	9 5						9 18		9 21						16
Brockley B.......[Line)	17							9 5							9 20								17
Honor Oak Park.........	18							9 8							9 23								18
Forest Hill, for Lordship	19							9 10	9 10						9 25								19
Sydenham ....[Lane	20							9 13							9 28								20
Penge West C...........	21							9 15							9 30								21
Anerley..................	22							9 16							9 31								22
Streatham Common....	23									9 16									9 33				23
Norbury..................	24									9 18									9 35				24
Thornton Heath.........	25									9 21									9 38				25
Selhurst..................	26									9 23									9 40				26
Streatham Hill..........	27												9 24										27
West Norwood..[N'wood)	28										9 22		9 27	(3)									28
Gipsy Hill (for Upper	29										9 24		9 29										29
Crystal Palace D......	30										9 27		9 32	9 35									30
Birkbeck	31													9 38									31
Beckenham Jn. arr	32													9 42									32
Norwood Junction F..	33	9 1						9 19	9 14				9 36		9 34		9 30						33
East Croydon.... arr	34	9 5	9 12						9 18	9 27							9 34						34
East Croydon.... dep	35	9 6							9 18	9 27					To London Bridge, via Streatham		9 35						35
Mitcham Junction......	36					9 19																9 39	36
Hackbridge..............	37					9 22																9 42	37
Carshalton......	38					9 24																9 45	38
West Croydon 319 arr	39						(3)	9 23					9 41						9 43				39
West Croydon 319 dep	40						9 19	9 23											9 43				40
Waddon G..............	41						9 21	9 26											9 46				41
Wallington.............	42						9 25	9 29											9 49				42
Carshalton Beeches.....	43						9 27	9 32											9 52				43
Sutton 322.............	44					9 27	9 30	9 34										9 39	9 54			9 48	44
Belmont	45							9 37											9 57				45
Banstead................	46							9 40											10 0				46
Epsom Downs...... arr	47							9 44											10 4				47
Cheam....................	48					9 30																9 51	48
Ewell East H..........	49					9 33																9 54	49
Epsom....................	50				9 31	9 36																9 58	50
Ashtead	51				9 35	9 40																	51
Leatherhead..[Bridge J	52				9 39	9 44																	52
Boxhill and Burford	53					9 49																	53
Dorking North K . arr	54					9 52												9 55					54
Bookham.......... [694	55				9 45																		55
Effingham Junction arr	56				9 49																		56
South Croydon 234......	57								9 20	9 30													57
Purley Oaks............	58								9 23	9 32													58
Purley....................	59	9 11							9 26	9 35							9 40						59
Coulsdon North L.. arr	60									9 38													60
Purley .... dep	61								9 29														61
Kenley..................	62								9 32														62
Whyteleafe.............	63								9 35														63
Warlingham	64								9 37														64
Caterham........... arr	65								9 41														65
Purley .... dep	66	§ Via Three Bridges							9 27														66
Reedham................	67								9 29														67
Smitham.................	68								9 31														68
Woodmansterne.........	69								9 34														69
Chipstead	70								9 36														70
Kingswood M..........	71								9 41														71
Tadworth N...........	72								9 44														72
Tattenham Corner. arr	73								9 47														73
Coulsdon South.........	74	9 15															9 44						74
Merstham	75	9 21															9 50						75
Redhill 158,246 ..... arr	76	9 25															9 54						76
Reigate 246....... "	77	9 30															9 59						77
Horsham 159,244,245 "	78	10§5																1013					78

CATERHAM, TATTENHAM CORNER, REDHILL, REIGATE, and HORSHAM

Sundays—continued (a.m)

No.	a.m																											a.m
1	9 25	9 28	..	..	..	..	..	..	9 32	..	..	9 40	..	..	9 45	..	9 45	9 48	9 48	..	..	..	..	..	..	..	..	..
2	..	..	9 23	..	..	..	..	..	..	..	..	..	..	..	..	..	..	..	..	..	..	..	..	..	..	9 53	..	..
3	..	..	9 25	(3)	..	..	(3)	..	(3)	(3)	..	(3)	..	9 42	(3)	..	..	..	(3)	(3)	(3)	..	(3)	..	(3)	9 55	(3)	10 2
4	..	..	9 30	9 25	..	..	9 28	..	..	9 35	..	..	..	..	..	..	..	..	..	9 45	9 51	..	9 55	..	9 58	10 0	10 4	..
5	..	..	(3)	..	..	..	..	..	..	..	..	9 43	..	..	..	..	..	..	..	..	..	..	..	..	..	..	..	..
6	..	9 33		..	..	..	..	..	9 37	..	..	9 46	..	9 49	9 50	..	..	9 53	9 54	..	..	..	..	..	..	(3)	..	10 9
7	..	..	..	..	..	..	..	..	9 40	..	..	9 49	..		9 53	..	..	..	9 57	..	..	..	..	..	..	..	..	
8	..	..	..	..	..	..	..	..	9 42	..	..	9 51	..	(3)	9 55	..	..	..	9 59	..	..	..	..	..	..	..	..	(3)
9	..	..	..	9 28	..	..	..	..	..	..	..	..	..	Via Worcester Park	..	..	..	..	..	9 48	9 54	..	9 58	..	..	..	10 7	..
10	..	..	..	9 31	..	..	..	..	..	..	..	..	..		..	..	..	..	..	9 51	9 57	..	10 1	..	..	..	1010	..
11	..	..	..	9 33	..	..	..	..	..	..	..	..	..		..	..	..	..	..	9 53	9 59	..	10 3	..	..	..	1012	..
12	..	..	..	9 36	..	..	..	..	..	..	..	..	..		..	..	..	..	..	9 56		..	10 6	..	..	..	1015	Via Worcester Park
13	..	..	..	9 38	..	..	..	..	..	..	..	..	..		..	..	..	..	..	9 58	To Victoria, arr. 10 14 a.m	..	10 8	..	..	..	1017	
14	..	..	..	9 41	..	..	..	..	..	..	..	..	..		..	..	..	..	..	10 1		..	1011	..	..	..	1020	
15	..	..	..	9 44	..	..	..	..	..	..	..	..	..		..	..	..	..	..	10 4		..	1014	..	..	..	..	
16	..	..	9 35	..	..	..	9 33	..	..	9 40	..	..	..		..	..	..	..	..	..		..	..	..	10 3	10 5	..	
17	..	..	..	..	..	..	9 35	..	..	9 42	..	..	..		..	..	..	..	..	..		..	..	..	10 5	..	..	
18	..	..	..	..	..	..	9 38	..	..	9 45	..	..	..	..	..	..	..	..	..	..		..	..	..	10 8	..	..	
19	..	..	9 40	..	..	..	9 40	..	..	9 47	..	..	..	..	..	..	..	..	..	..		..	..	..	1010	1010	..	
20	..	..	..	..	..	..	9 43	..	..	9 50	..	..	..	..	..	..	..	..	..	..		..	..	..	1013	..	..	
21	..	..	..	..	..	..	9 45	..	..	..	..	..	..	..	..	..	..	..	..	..	..	..	..	..	1015	..	..	..
22	..	..	..	..	..	..	9 46	..	..	..	..	..	..	..	..	..	..	..	..	..	..	..	..	..	1016	..	..	..
23	..	..	..	..	..	..	..	..	9 46	..	..	..	..	..	..	..	..	..	10 3	10 6	..	..	..	..	..	..	..	..
24	..	..	..	..	..	..	..	..	9 48	..	..	..	..	..	..	..	..	..	10 5	10 9	..	..	..	..	..	..	..	..
25	..	..	..	..	..	..	..	..	9 51	..	..	..	..	..	..	..	..	..	10 8	1012	..	..	..	..	..	..	..	..
26	..	..	..	..	..	..	..	..	9 53	..	..	..	..	..	..	..	..	..	1010	1014	..	..	..	..	..	..	..	..
27	..	..	..	..	..	..	..	..	..	..	..	9 54	..	..	..	..	..	..	..	..	..	..	..	..	..	..	..	..
28	..	..	..	..	..	..	..	..	..	..	..	9 57	..	..	..	..	..	..	..	..	..	..	..	..	..	..	1022	..
29	..	..	..	..	..	..	..	..	..	..	..	9 59	(3)	..	..	..	..	..	..	..	..	..	..	..	..	..	1024	..
30	..	..	..	..	..	..	..	..	..	9 53	..	10 2	10 5	..	..	..	..	..	..	..	..	..	..	..	..	..	1027	..
31	..	..	..	..	..	..	..	..	..	..	..	..	10 8	..	..	..	..	..	..	..	..	..	..	..	..	..	..	..
32	..	..	..	..	..	..	..	..	..	..	..	..	1012	..	..	..	..	..	..	..	..	..	..	..	..	..	..	..
33	..	..	9 44	..	..	..	9 49	..	..	..	..	10 6	..	..	..	..	..	..	..	1017	..	..	..	..	1019	1014	..	..
34	9 40	9 45	9 48	..	..	..	..	..	9 57	..	..	..	..	..	..	..	10 0	10 5	..	..	..	..	..	..	..	1018	..	..
35	..	9 46	9 48	..	..	..	..	..	9 57	..	..	..	..	..	..	..	..	10 5	..	..	..	..	..	..	..	1018	..	..
36	..	..	..	9 49	..	..	..	..	..	..	..	..	..	..	10 1	..	..	..	..	To London Bridge via Forest Hill	..	..	1019	..	..	..	..	..
37	..	..	..	9 52	..	..	..	..	..	..	..	..	..	..	10 4	..	..	..	..		..	..	1022	..	..	..	..	..
38	..	..	..	9 54	..	..	..	..	..	..	..	..	..	..	10 6	..	..	..	..		..	..	1024	..	..	..	..	..
39	..	..	..	..	..	(3)	9 53	..	..	..	..	1011	..	..	..	..	..	..	1013		..	..	..	(3)	1023	..	..	..
40	..	..	..	..	..	9 49	9 53	..	..	..	..	..	..	..	..	..	..	..	1013		..	..	..	1019	1023	..	..	..
41	..	..	..	..	..	9 51	9 56	..	..	..	..	..	..	..	..	..	..	..	1016		..	..	..	1021	1026	..	..	..
42	..	..	..	..	..	9 55	9 59	..	..	..	..	..	..	..	..	..	..	..	1019		..	..	..	1025	1029	..	..	..
43	..	..	..	..	..	9 57	10 2	..	..	..	..	..	..	..	..	..	..	..	1022		..	..	..	1027	1032	..	..	..
44	..	..	..	9 57	..	10 0	10 4	..	..	..	..	..	..	..	10 9	..	..	..	1024		..	..	1027	1030	1034	..	..	..
45	..	..	..	..	..	..	10 7	..	..	..	..	..	..	..	..	..	..	..	1027	..	..	..	..	..	1037	..	..	..
46	..	..	..	..	..	..	1010	..	..	..	..	..	..	..	..	..	..	..	1030	..	..	..	..	..	1040	..	..	..
47	..	..	..	..	..	..	1014	..	..	..	..	..	..	..	..	..	..	..	1034	..	..	..	..	..	1044	..	..	..
48	..	..	..	10 0	..	..	..	..	..	..	..	..	..	..	1012	..	..	..	..	..	..	..	1030	..	..	..	..	..
49	..	..	..	10 3	..	..	..	..	..	..	..	..	..	..	1015	..	..	..	..	..	..	..	1033	..	..	..	..	..
50	..	..	..	10 6	..	..	..	..	..	..	..	..	..	1012	1019	..	..	..	..	..	..	..	1036	..	..	..	..	1031
51	..	..	..	1010	..	..	..	..	..	..	..	..	..	1016	..	..	..	..	..	..	..	..	1040	..	..	..	..	1035
52	..	..	..	1014	..	..	..	..	..	..	..	..	..	1020	..	..	..	..	..	..	..	..	1044	..	..	..	..	1039
53	..	..	..	..	..	..	..	..	..	..	..	..	..	1025	..	..	..	..	..	..	..	..	1049	..	..	..	..	..
54	..	..	..	..	..	..	..	..	..	..	..	..	..	1028	..	..	..	..	..	..	..	..	1052	..	..	..	..	..
55	..	..	..	1019	..	..	..	..	..	..	..	..	..	..	..	..	..	..	..	..	..	..	..	..	..	..	..	1045
56	..	..	..	1023	..	..	..	..	..	..	..	..	..	..	..	..	..	..	..	..	..	..	..	..	..	..	..	1049
57	..	..	9 50	..	..	..	..	..	10 0	..	..	..	..	..	..	..	..	..	..	..	..	..	..	..	..	1020	..	..
58	..	..	9 53	..	..	..	..	..	10 2	..	..	..	..	..	..	..	..	..	..	..	..	..	..	..	..	1023	..	..
59	..	..	9 55	..	..	..	..	..	10 5	..	..	..	..	..	..	..	..	1011	..	..	..	..	..	..	..	1026	..	..
60	..	..	..	..	..	..	..	..	10 8	..	..	..	..	..	..	..	..	..	..	..	..	..	..	..	..	..	..	..
61	..	..	9 59	..	..	..	..	..	..	..	..	..	..	..	..	..	..	..	..	..	..	..	..	..	..	1029	..	..
62	..	..	10 2	..	..	..	..	..	..	..	..	..	..	..	..	..	..	..	..	..	..	..	..	..	..	1032	..	..
63	..	..	10 5	..	..	..	..	..	..	..	..	..	..	..	..	..	..	..	..	..	..	..	..	..	..	1035	..	..
64	..	..	10 7	..	..	..	..	..	..	..	..	..	..	..	..	..	..	..	..	..	..	..	..	..	..	1037	..	..
65	..	..	1011	..	..	..	..	..	..	..	..	..	..	..	..	..	..	..	..	..	..	..	..	..	..	1041	..	..
66	..	..	9 57	..	..	..	..	..	..	..	..	..	..	..	..	..	..	§ Via Three Bridges	..	..	..	..	..	..	..	1027	..	..
67	..	..	9 59	..	..	..	..	..	..	..	..	..	..	..	..	..	..		..	..	..	..	..	..	..	1029	..	..
68	..	..	10 1	..	..	..	..	..	..	..	..	..	..	..	..	..	..		..	..	..	..	..	..	..	1031	..	..
69	..	..	10 4	..	..	..	..	..	..	..	..	..	..	..	..	..	..		..	..	..	..	..	..	..	1034	..	..
70	..	..	10 6	..	..	..	..	..	..	..	..	..	..	..	..	..	..		..	..	..	..	..	..	..	1036	..	..
71	..	..	1011	..	..	..	..	..	..	..	..	..	..	..	..	..	..		..	..	..	..	..	..	..	1041	..	..
72	..	..	1014	..	..	..	..	..	..	..	..	..	..	..	..	..	..		..	..	..	..	..	..	..	1044	..	..
73	..	..	1017	..	..	..	..	..	..	..	..	..	..	..	..	..	..		..	..	..	..	..	..	..	1047	..	..
74	..	..	..	..	..	..	..	..	..	..	..	..	..	..	..	..	..	1014	..	..	..	..	..	..	..	..	..	..
75	..	..	..	..	..	..	..	..	..	..	..	..	..	..	..	..	..	1020	..	..	..	..	..	..	..	..	..	..
76	..	10 0	..	..	..	..	..	..	..	..	..	..	..	..	..	..	..	1024	..	..	..	..	..	..	..	..	..	..
77	..	10 8	..	..	..	..	..	..	..	..	..	..	..	..	..	..	..	1030	..	..	..	..	..	..	..	..	..	..
78	..	..	..	..	..	..	..	..	..	..	..	..	..	1033	..	..	..	11§5	..	..	..	..	..	..	..	..	..	..

For Notes, see page 284a

LONDON, CRYSTAL PALACE, CROYDON, SUTTON, DORKING NORTH,

Down	No.	a.m	Sundays—continued																	a.m	No.
Victoria .... dep	1	1010	..	..	..	1015	10 18	1018	..	..	..	1025	1028	..	..	..	..	1030	1032	..	..	1040	1
Charing Cross* ... "	2	3	..	3	..	3	..	3	..	..	3	..	..	1023	3	..	3	..	3	..	3	3	2
Waterloo* .... "	3		..		..		..		..	..		..	..	1025		..		..		..			3
London Bridge ..... "	4	..	.	1013	..	..	..	..	..	1016	1021	..	..	1030	1025	..	1028	..	..	..	1035	..	4
Battersea Park	5	1013	..	..	..	..	..	..	..	..	..	..	..		..	..	..	..	..	..	..	1043	5
Clapham Junction	6	1016	..	..	..	1020	..	1024	..	..	..	..	1033	3	..	..	..	1037	1037	..	..	1046	6
Wandsworth Common A	7	1019	..	..	..	1023	..	1027	..	..	..	..	..	..	..	..	..	..	1040	..	..	1049	7
Balham & Upper Tooting	8	1021	..	..	..	1025	..	1029	..	..	..	..	..	..	..	..	..	..	1042	..	..	1051	8
South Bermondsey	9	..	..	..	..	..	..	..	..	..	1024	..	..	..	1028	..	..	..	..	..	..	..	9
Queen's Road, Peckham	10	..	..	..	..	..	..	..	..	..	1027	..	..	..	1031	..	..	..	..	..	..	..	10
Peckham Rye	11	..	..	..	..	..	..	..	..	..	1029	..	..	..	1033	..	..	..	..	..	..	..	11
East Dulwich	12	..	..	..	..	..	..	..	..	..		..	..	..	1036	..	..	..	..	..	..	..	12
North Dulwich	13	..	..	..	..	..	..	..	..	..		..	..	..	1038	..	..	..	..	..	..	..	13
Tulse Hill	14	..	..	..	..	..	..	..	..	..		..	..	..	1041	..	..	..	..	..	..	..	14
Streatham	15	..	..	..	..	..	..	..	..	..		..	..	..	1044	..	..	..	..	..	..	..	15
New Cross Gate (for E.L.	16	..	..	1018	..	..	..	..	..	1021	To Victoria, arr. 10 44 a.m	..	..	1035	..	..	1033	..	..	..	1040	..	16
Brockley B .... [Line)	17	..	..	1020	..	..	..	..	..	..		..	..	..	..	..	1035	..	..	..	1042	..	17
Honor Oak Park	18	..	..	1023	..	..	..	..	..	..		..	..	..	..	..	1038	..	..	..	1045	..	18
Forest Hill, for Lordship	19	..	..	1025	..	..	..	..	..	..		..	..	1040	..	..	1040	..	..	..	1047	..	19
Sydenham .... [Lane	20	..	..	1028	..	..	..	..	..	..		..	..	..	..	..	1043	..	..	..	1050	..	20
Penge West C	21	..	..	1030	..	..	..	..	..	..		..	..	..	..	..	1045	..	..	..	..	..	21
Anerley	22	..	..	1031	..	..	..	..	..	..		..	..	..	..	..	1046	..	..	..	..	..	22
Streatham Common	23	..	..	..	..	..	..	1033	..	..	..	..	..	..	..	..	..	..	1046	..	..	..	23
Norbury	24	..	..	..	..	..	..	1035	..	..	..	..	..	..	..	..	..	..	1048	..	..	..	24
Thornton Heath	25	..	..	..	..	..	..	1038	..	..	..	..	..	..	..	..	..	..	1051	..	..	..	25
Selhurst	26	..	..	..	..	..	..	1040	..	..	..	..	..	..	..	..	..	..	1053	..	..	..	26
Streatham Hill	27	1024	..	..	..	..	..	..	..	..	..	..	..	..	..	..	..	..	..	..	..	1054	27
West Norwood..[N'wood)	28	1027	3	..	..	..	..	..	..	..	..	..	..	..	..	..	..	..	..	..	..	1057	28
Gipsy Hill (for Upper	29	1029		..	..	..	..	..	..	..	..	..	..	..	..	..	..	..	..	..	..	1059	29
Crystal Palace D	30	1032	1035	..	..	..	..	..	..	..	..	..	..	..	..	..	..	..	..	..	1053	11 2	30
Birkbeck	31	..	1038	..	..	..	..	..	..	..	..	..	..	..	..	..	..	..	..	..	..	..	31
Beckenham Jn. arr	32	..	1042	..	..	..	..	..	..	..	..	..	..	..	..	..	..	..	..	..	..	..	32
Norwood Junction F ..	33	1036	..	1034	..	..	..	..	..	1030	..	..	..	1044	..	..	1049	..	..	..	..	11 6	33
East Croydon .. arr	34	..	..	..	..	..	10 33	..	..	1034	..	1040	1045	1048	..	..	..	1050	1057	..	..	..	34
East Croydon .. dep	35	..	..	..	..	..	10 34	..	..	1035	..	..	1046	1048	..	..	..	1053	1057	..	..	..	35
Mitcham Junction	36	..	..	To London Bridge, via Streatham	..	1031	..	..	..	..	..	..	..	..	1049	..	..	..	..	..	..	..	36
Hackbridge	37	..	..		..	1034	..	..	..	..	..	..	..	..	1052	..	..	..	..	..	..	..	37
Carshalton	38	..	..		..	1036	..	..	..	..	..	..	..	..	1054	..	..	..	..	..	..	..	38
West Croydon 319 arr	39	1041	..		..	..	..	1043	..	..	..	..	..	..	..	3	1053	..	..	..	..	1111	39
West Croydon 319 dep	40	..	..		..	..	..	1043	..	..	..	..	..	..	..	1049	1053	..	..	..	..	..	40
Waddon G	41	..	..		..	..	..	1046	..	..	..	..	..	..	..	1051	1056	..	..	..	..	..	41
Wallington	42	..	..		..	..	..	1049	..	..	..	..	..	..	..	1055	1059	..	..	..	..	..	42
Carshalton Beeches	43	..	..		..	..	..	1052	..	..	..	..	..	..	..	1057	11 2	..	..	..	..	..	43
Sutton 322	44	..	..		..	1039	..	1054	..	..	..	..	..	..	1057	11 0	11 4	..	..	..	..	..	44
Belmont	45	..	..	..	..	..	..	1057	..	..	..	..	..	..	..	..	11 7	..	..	..	..	..	45
Banstead	46	..	..	..	..	..	..	11 0	..	..	..	..	..	..	..	..	1110	..	..	..	..	..	46
Epsom Downs ...... arr	47	..	..	..	..	..	..	11 4	..	..	..	..	..	..	..	..	1114	..	..	..	..	..	47
Cheam	48	..	..	..	..	1042	..	..	..	..	..	..	..	..	11 0	..	..	..	..	..	..	..	48
Ewell East H	49	..	..	..	..	1045	..	..	..	..	..	..	..	..	11 3	..	..	..	..	..	..	..	49
Epsom	50	..	..	..	..	1048	..	..	..	..	..	..	..	..	11 6	..	..	..	..	..	..	..	50
Ashtead	51	..	..	..	..	..	..	..	..	..	..	..	..	..	1110	..	..	..	..	..	..	..	51
Leatherhead ... [Bridge J	52	..	..	..	..	..	..	..	..	..	..	..	..	..	1114	..	..	..	..	..	..	..	52
Boxhill and Burford	53	..	..	..	..	..	..	..	..	..	..	..	..	..	..	..	..	..	..	..	..	..	53
Dorking North K ... arr	54	..	..	..	..	..	..	..	..	..	..	..	..	..	..	..	..	..	..	..	..	..	54
Bookham .... [394	55	..	..	..	..	..	..	..	..	..	..	..	..	..	1119	..	..	..	..	..	..	..	55
Effingham Junction arr	56	..	..	..	..	..	..	..	..	..	..	..	..	..	1123	..	..	..	..	..	..	..	56
South Croydon 234	57	..	..	..	..	..	..	..	..	..	..	..	..	1050	..	..	..	1057	11 0	..	..	..	57
Purley Oaks	58	..	..	..	..	..	..	..	..	..	..	..	..	1053	..	..	..	..	11 2	..	..	..	58
Purley	59	..	..	..	..	..	..	..	..	1040	..	..	..	1055	..	..	..	..	11 5	..	..	..	59
Coulsdon North L .. arr	60	..	..	..	..	..	..	..	..	..	..	..	..	..	..	..	..	..	11 8	..	..	..	60
Purley .... dep	61	..	..	..	..	..	..	..	..	..	..	..	..	1059	..	..	..	..	..	..	..	..	61
Kenley	62	..	..	..	..	..	..	..	..	..	..	..	..	11 2	..	..	..	..	..	..	..	..	62
Whyteleafe	63	..	..	..	..	..	..	..	..	..	..	..	..	11 5	..	..	..	..	..	..	..	..	63
Warlingham	64	..	..	..	..	..	..	..	..	..	..	..	..	11 7	..	..	..	..	..	..	..	..	64
Caterham .... arr	65	..	..	..	..	..	..	..	..	..	..	..	..	1111	..	..	..	..	..	..	..	..	65
Purley .... dep	66	..	..	..	..	..		..	..	..	..	..	..	1057	..	..	..	..	..	..	..	..	66
Reedham	67	..	..	..	..	..		..	..	..	..	..	..	1059	..	..	..	..	..	..	..	..	67
Smitham	68	..	..	..	..	..	§ Via Three Bridges	..	..	..	..	..	..	11 1	..	..	..	..	..	..	..	..	68
Woodmansterne	69	..	..	..	..	..		..	..	..	..	..	..	11 4	..	..	..	..	..	..	..	..	69
Chipstead	70	..	..	..	..	..		..	..	..	..	..	..	11 6	..	..	..	..	..	..	..	..	70
Kingswood M	71	..	..	..	..	..		..	..	..	..	..	..	1111	..	..	..	..	..	..	..	..	71
Tadworth N	72	..	..	..	..	..		..	..	..	..	..	..	1114	..	..	..	..	..	..	..	..	72
Tattenham Corner. arr	73	..	..	..	..	..		..	..	..	..	..	..	1117	..	..	..	..	..	..	..	..	73
Coulsdon South	74	..	..	..	..	..	..	..	..	1044	..	..	..	..	..	..	..	..	..	..	..	..	74
Merstham	75	..	..	..	..	..	..	..	..	1050	..	..	..	..	..	..	..	..	..	..	..	..	75
Redhill 158, 246 .... arr	76	..	..	..	..	..	10 49	..	..	1054	..	..	11 0	..	..	..	..	..	..	..	..	..	76
Reigate 246 .... "	77	..	..	..	..	..	..	..	..	11 0	..	..	..	..	..	..	..	..	..	..	..	..	77
Horsham 159, 244, 245 "	78	..	..	..	..	..	11§13	..	..	..	..	..	..	..	..	..	..	..	..	..	..	..	78

CATERHAM, TATTENHAM CORNER, REDHILL, REIGATE, and HORSHAM

a.m — **Sundays** —*continued* — a.m

No.																												
1	..	..	1045	..	1045	1048	1048	..	..	..	..	..	..	..	..	..	1110	..	..	1118	..	..	1124	1125	..	1128	..	..
2	..	..	..	..	(3)	..	(3)	(3)	(3)	(3)	..	(3)	1053	(3)	..	..	(3)	..	(3)	(3)	..	(3)	(3)	..	(3)	..	..	(3)
3	..	..	..	1042		..					..		1055		..	11 2		..			..			..		..	..	
4	..	..	..	..	..	..	..	1045	1051	1054	..	1058	11 0	11 4	..	..	..	..	1113	..	..	1121	..	..	1125	..	..	1128
5	..	..	..	..	..	..	..	..	..	..	..	..	(3)	..	..	..	1113	..	..	..	..	..	..	..	..	..	..	..
6	..	..	..	1049	1050	1053	1054	..	..	..	..	..		..	..	11 9	1116	..	..	1124	..	..	1129	..	..	1133	..	..
7	..	..	..	(3)	1053	..	1057	..	..	..	..	..	..	..	..	(3)	1119	..	..	1127	..	..	..	..	..	..	..	..
8	..	..	..		1055	..	1059	..	..	..	..	..	..	..	..		1121	..	..	1129	..	..	1133	..	..	..	..	..
9	..	..	..	Via Worcester Park	..	..	..	1048	1054	1057	..	..	..	11 7	..	Via Worcester Park	..	..	..	..	..	1124	..	..	1128	..	..	..
10	..	..	..		..	..	..	1051	1057	11 0	..	..	..	1110	..		..	..	..	..	..	1127	..	..	1131	..	..	..
11	..	..	..		..	..	..	1053	1059	11 2	..	..	..	1112	..		..	..	..	..	..	1129	..	..	1133	..	..	..
12	..	..	..		..	..	..	1056	☞ To Victoria, arr. 11 14 a.m	11 5	..	..	..	1115	..		..	..	..	..	..	To Victoria, arr. 11 44 a.m	..	..	1136	..	..	..
13	..	..	..		..	..	..	1058		11 7	..	..	..	1117	..		..	..	..	..	..		..	..	1138	..	..	..
14	..	..	..		..	..	..	11 1		1110	..	..	..	1120	..		..	..	..	..	..		..	..	1141	..	..	..
15	..	..	..		..	..	..	11 4		1113	..	..	..	..	..		..	..	..	..	..		..	..	1144	..	..	..
16	..	..	..		..	..	..	..		..	..	11 3	11 5	..	..		..	..	1118	..	..		..	..	..	..	..	1133
17	..	..	..		..	..	..	..		..	..	11 5	..	..	..		..	..	1120	..	..		..	..	..	..	..	1135
18	..	..	..		..	..	..	..		..	..	11 8	..	..	..		..	..	1123	..	..		..	..	..	..	..	1138
19	..	..	..		..	..	..	..		..	..	1110	1110	..	..		..	..	1125	..	..		..	..	..	..	..	1140
20	..	..	..		..	..	..	..		..	..	1113	..	..	..		..	..	1128	..	..		..	..	..	..	..	1143
21	..	..	..		..	..	..	..		..	..	1115	..	..	..		..	..	1130	..	..		..	..	..	..	..	1145
22	..	..	..		..	..	..	..		..	..	1116	..	..	..		..	..	1131	..	..		..	..	..	..	..	1146
23	..	..	..	..	..	..	11 3	11 6		..	..	..	..	..	..	..	..	..	..	1133	..	..	..	..	..	..	..	..
24	..	..	..	..	..	..	11 5	11 9		..	..	..	..	..	..	..	..	..	..	1135	..	..	..	..	..	..	..	..
25	..	..	..	..	..	..	11 8	1112		..	..	..	..	..	..	..	..	..	..	1138	..	..	..	..	..	..	..	..
26	..	..	..	..	..	..	1110	1114	Stop	..	..	..	..	..	..	..	..	..	..	1140	..	..	..	..	..	..	..	..
27	..	..	..	..	..	..	..	..	..	..	..	..	..	..	..	..	1124	..	..	..	..	..	..	..	..	..	..	..
28	(3)	..	..	..	..	..	..	..	..	..	..	..	..	1122	..	..	1127	(3)	..	..	..	..	..	..	..	..	..	..
29		..	..	..	..	..	..	..	..	..	..	..	..	1124	..	..	1129		..	..	..	..	..	..	..	..	..	..
30	11 5	..	..	..	..	..	..	..	..	..	..	..	..	1127	..	..	1132	1135	..	..	..	..	..	..	..	..	..	..
31	11 8	..	..	..	..	..	..	..	..	..	..	..	..	..	..	..	..	1138	..	..	..	..	..	..	..	..	..	..
32	1112	..	..	..	..	..	..	..	..	..	..	..	..	..	..	..	..	1142	..	..	..	..	..	..	..	..	..	..
33	..	..	..	..	..	..	..	1117	..	..	..	1119	1114	..	..	..	1136	..	1134	..	..	..	..	..	..	..	..	1149
34	..	..	11 0	..	..	11 5	..	To London Bridge, via Forest Hill	..	..	..	..	1118	..	..	..	..	..	To London Bridge, via Streatham	..	..	..	..	1140	..	1145	..	..
35	..	..	..	..	..	11 5	..		..	..	..	..	1119	..	..	..	..	..		..	..	..	..	..	..	1146	..	..
36	..	..	..	..	11 1	..	..		..	1118	..	..	..	..	..	..	..	..		..	..	..	1139	..	1149	..	..	..
37	.	..	..	..	11 4	..	..		..	1121	..	..	..	..	..	..	..	..		..	..	..	1142	..	1152	..	..	..
38	..	..	..	..	11 6	..	..		..	1123	(3)	..	..	..	..	..	..	..		..	..	..	1144	..	1154	..	(3)	..
39	..	..	..	..	..	..	1113		..	..		1123	..	..	..	..	1141	..		1143	..	..	..	..	..	..		1153
40	..	..	..	..	..	..	1113		..	..	1119	1123	..	..	..	..	..	..		1143	..	..	..	..	..	..	1149	1153
41	..	..	..	..	..	..	1116		..	..	1121	1126	..	..	..	..	..	..		1146	..	..	..	..	..	..	1151	1156
42	..	..	..	..	..	..	1119		..	..	1125	1129	..	..	..	..	..	..		1149	..	..	..	..	..	..	1155	1159
43	..	..	..	..	..	..	1122		..	..	1127	1132	..	..	..	..	..	..		1152	..	..	..	..	..	..	1157	12 2
44	..	..	..	..	11 9	..	1124		..	1127	1130	1134	..	..	..	..	..	..		1154	..	..	1148	..	1157	..	12 0	12 4
45	..	..	..	..	..	..	1127	..	..	..	..	1137	..	..	..	..	..	..	..	1157	..	..	..	..	..	..	..	12 7
46	..	..	..	..	..	..	1130	..	..	..	..	1140	..	..	..	..	..	..	..	12 0	..	..	..	..	..	..	..	1210
47	..	..	..	..	..	..	1134	..	..	..	..	1144	..	..	..	..	..	..	..	12 4	..	..	..	..	..	..	..	1214
48	..	..	..	..	1112	..	..	..	..	1130	..	..	..	..	..	..	..	..	..	..	..	..	1151	..	12 0	..	..	..
49	..	..	..	..	1115	..	..	..	..	1133	..	..	..	..	..	..	..	..	..	..	..	..	1154	..	12 3	..	..	..
50	..	..	..	1111	1119	..	..	..	..	1136	..	..	..	..	..	1131	..	..	..	..	..	..	1158	..	12 6	..	..	..
51	..	..	..	1115	..	..	..	..	..	1140	..	..	..	..	..	1135	..	..	..	..	..	..	..	..	1210	..	..	..
52	..	..	..	1119	..	..	..	..	..	1144	..	..	..	..	..	1139	..	..	..	..	..	..	..	..	1214	..	..	..
53	..	..	..	1124	..	..	..	..	..	1149	..	..	..	..	..	..	..	..	..	..	..	..	..	..	..	..	..	..
54	..	..	..	1128	..	..	..	..	..	1152	..	..	..	..	..	..	..	..	..	..	..	..	..	..	..	..	..	..
55	..	..	..	..	..	..	..	..	..	..	..	..	..	..	..	1145	..	..	..	..	..	..	..	..	1219	..	..	..
56	..	..	..	..	..	..	..	..	..	..	..	..	..	..	..	1149	..	..	..	..	..	..	..	..	1223	..	..	..
57	..	..	..	..	..	..	..	..	..	..	..	..	1121	..	..	..	..	..	..	..	..	..	..	..	..	..	..	..
58	..	..	..	..	..	..	..	..	..	..	..	..	1124	..	..	..	..	..	..	..	..	..	..	..	..	..	..	..
59	..	..	..	..	..	1111	..	..	..	..	..	..	1126	..	..	..	..	..	..	..	..	..	..	..	..	..	..	..
60	..	..	..	..	..	..	..	..	..	..	..	..	..	..	..	..	..	..	..	..	..	..	..	..	..	..	..	..
61	..	..	..	..	..	..	..	..	..	..	..	..	1130	..	..	..	..	..	..	..	..	..	..	..	..	..	..	..
62	..	..	..	..	..	..	..	..	..	..	..	..	1133	..	..	..	..	..	..	..	..	..	..	..	..	..	..	..
63	..	..	..	..	..	..	..	..	..	..	..	..	1136	..	..	..	..	..	..	..	..	..	..	..	..	..	..	..
64	..	..	..	..	..	..	..	..	..	..	..	..	1138	..	..	..	..	..	..	..	..	..	..	..	..	..	..	..
65	..	..	..	..	..	..	..	..	a.m	..	..	..	1142	..	..	..	..	..	..	..	..	..	..	..	..	..	..	..
66	..	..	..	..	..	§ Via Three Bridges	..	..	d Departure time	..	..	..	1128	..	..	..	..	..	..	..	..	..	..	..	..	..	..	..
67	..	..	..	..	..		..	..		..	..	..	1130	..	..	..	..	..	..	..	..	..	..	..	..	..	..	..
68	..	..	..	..	..		..	..		..	..	..	1132	..	..	..	..	..	..	..	..	..	..	..	..	..	..	..
69	..	..	..	..	..		..	..		..	..	..	1135	..	..	..	..	..	..	..	..	..	..	..	..	..	..	..
70	..	..	..	..	..		..	..		..	..	..	1137	..	..	..	..	..	..	..	..	..	..	..	..	..	..	..
71	..	..	..	..	..		..	..		..	..	..	1142	..	..	..	..	..	..	..	..	..	..	..	..	..	..	..
72	..	..	..	..	..		..	..		..	..	..	1145	..	..	..	..	..	..	..	..	..	..	..	..	..	..	..
73	..	..	..	..	..		..	..		..	..	..	1148	..	..	..	..	..	..	..	..	..	..	..	..	..	..	..
74	..	..	..	..	..	1114	..	..	..	..	..	..	..	..	..	..	..	..	..	..	..	..	..	..	..	..	..	..
75	..	..	..	..	..	1120	..	..	..	..	..	..	..	..	..	..	..	..	..	..	..	..	..	..	..	..	..	..
76	..	..	..	..	..	1124	..	..	11d32	..	..	..	..	..	..	..	..	..	..	..	..	..	..	..	..	12 0	..	..
77	..	..	..	..	..	1130	..	..	1136	..	..	..	..	..	..	..	..	..	..	..	..	..	..	..	..	..	..	..
78	..	..	..	1153	..	12§5	..	..	..	..	..	..	..	..	..	..	..	..	..	..	..	..	..	..	..	..	..	..

LONDON, CRYSTAL PALACE, CROYDON, SUTTON, DORKING NORTH,

Down	No.	a.m								Sundays—continued							a.m		p.m		p.m	No.
Victoria .... dep	1	..	1132	..		1140	..	..	..	1145	1148	1148	..	..	..	..	..	..	..		..	1210	1
Charing Cross* ... "	2	1123	3	..	3	3	..	..	..	3	..	3	..	3	3	3	..	3	1152	3	..	3	2
Waterloo* .... "	3	1125		..			..	..	1142		..		..				..		1155		..		3
London Bridge ..... "	4	1130	..	..	1135	..	..	..	..	..	..	..	..	1145	1151	1155	..	1158	12 0	12 4	..		4
Battersea Park	5	3	..	..	..	1143	..	..	..	..	..	..	..	..	..	..	..	..	3	..	..	1213	5
Clapham Junction.....	6		1137	..	..	1146	..	..	1149	1150	1153	1154	..	..	..	..	..	..		..	..	1216	6
Wandsworth Common A	7	..	1140	..	..	1149	..	..	3	1153	..	1157	..	..	..	..	..	..	..	..	..	1219	7
Balham & Upper Tooting	8	..	1142	..	..	1151	..	..		1155	..	1159	..	..	..	..	..	..	..	..	..	1221	8
South Bermondsey......	9	..	..	..	..	..	..	..	..	..	..	..	..	1148	1154	1158	..	..	..	12 7	..	..	9
Queen's Road, Peckham	10	..	..	..	..	..	..	..	..	..	..	..	..	1151	1157	12 1	..	..	..	1210	..	..	10
Peckham Rye...........	11	..	..	..	..	..	..	..		..	..	..	..	1153	1159	12 3	..	..	..	1212	..	..	11
East Dulwich............	12	..	..	..	..	..	..	..	Via Worcester Park	..	..	..	..	1156		12 6	..	..	..	1215	..	..	12
North Dulwich..........	13	..	..	..	..	..	..	..		..	..	..	..	1158		12 8	..	..	..	1217	..	..	13
Tulse Hill..............	14	..	..	..	..	..	..	..		..	..	..	..	12 1		1211	..	..	..	1220	..	..	14
Streatham	15	..	..	..	..	..	..	..		..	..	..	..	12 4		1214	..	..	..	..	..	..	15
New Cross Gate (for E.L.	16	1135	..	..	1140	..	..	..		..	..	..	..	..	To Victoria, arr 12 14 p.m	..	..	12 3	12 5	..	..	..	16
Brockley B........[Line)	17	..	..	..	1142	..	..	..		..	..	..	..	..		..	..	12 5	..	..	..	..	17
Honor Oak Park.........	18	..	..	..	1145	..	..	..		..	..	..	..	..		..	..	12 8	..	..	..	..	18
Forest Hill, for Lordship	19	1140	..	..	1147	..	..	..	..	..	..	..	..	..		..	..	1210	1210	..	..	..	19
Sydenham ....[Lane	20	..	..	..	1150	..	..	..	..	..	..	..	..	..		..	..	1213	..	..	..	..	20
Penge West C...........	21	..	..	..	..	..	..	..	..	..	..	..	..	..		..	..	1215	..	..	..	..	21
Anerley.................	22	..	..	..	..	..	..	..	..	..	..	..	..	..		..	..	1216	..	..	..	..	22
Streatham Common....	23	..	1146	..	..	..	..	..	..	..	..	12 3	..	12 6	..	..	..	..	..	..	..	..	23
Norbury................	24	..	1149	..	..	..	..	..	..	..	..	12 5	..	12 9	..	..	..	..	..	..	..	..	24
Thornton Heath........	25	..	1152	..	..	..	..	..	..	..	..	12 8	..	1212	..	..	..	..	..	..	..	..	25
Selhurst................	26	..	1154	..	..	..	..	..	..	..	..	1210	..	1214	..	..	..	..	..	..	..	..	26
Streatham Hill.........	27	..	..	..	..	1154	..	..	..	..	..	..	..	..	..	..	..	..	..	..	..	1224	27
West Norwood..[N'wood)	28	..	..	..	..	1157	3	..	..	..	..	..	..	..	..	..	..	..	..	1222	..	1227	28
Gipsy Hill, (for Upper	29	..	..	..	..	1159		..	..	..	..	..	..	..	..	..	..	..	..	1224	..	1229	29
Crystal Palace D......	30	..	..	..	1153	12 2	12 5	..	..	..	..	..	..	..	..	..	..	..	..	1227	..	1232	30
Birkbeck	31	..	..	..	..	..	12 8	..	..	..	..	..	..	..	..	..	..	..	..	..	..	..	31
Beckenham Jn. arr	37	..	..	..	..	..	1212	..	..	..	..	..	..	..	..	..	..	..	..	..	..	..	32
Norwood Junction F..	33	1144	..	..	..	12 6	..	..	..	..	..	..	..	1217	..	..	..	1219	1214	..	..	1236	33
East Croydon.... arr	34	1148	1157	..	..	..	..	..	..	..	12 5	..	..	..	..	..	..	..	1218	..	..	..	34
East Croydon.... dep	35	1149	1157	..	..	..	..	..	..	..	12 5	..	..	..	..	..	..	..	1218	..	..	..	35
Mitcham Junction......	36	..	..	..	..	..	..	..	..	12 1	..	..	..		..	1219	..	..	..	..	..	..	36
Hackbridge.............	37	..	..	..	..	..	..	..	..	12 4	..	..	..		..	1222	p.m	..	..	..	..	..	37
Carshalton.............	38	..	..	..	..	..	..	..	..	12 6	..	..	..		..	1224	3	..	..	..	..	..	38
West Croydon 319 arr	39	..	..	..	..	1211	..	..	..	..	..	1213	..		..	..		1223	..	..	..	1241	39
West Croydon 319 dep	40	..	..	..	..	..	..	..	..	..	..	1213	..	To London Bridge via Forest Hill	..	..	1219	1223	..	..	..	..	40
Waddon G...............	41	..	..	..	..	..	..	..	..	..	..	1216	..		..	..	1221	1226	..	..	..	..	41
Wallington.............	42	..	..	..	..	..	..	..	..	..	..	1219	..		..	..	1225	1229	..	..	..	..	42
Carshalton Beeches.....	43	..	..	..	..	..	..	..	..	..	..	1222	..		..	..	1227	1232	..	..	..	..	43
Sutton 322..............	44	..	..	..	..	..	..	..	..	12 9	..	1224	..		..	1227	1230	1234	..	..	..	..	44
Belmont................	45	..	..	..	..	..	..	..	..	..	..	1227	..		..	..	..	1237	..	..	..	..	45
Banstead...............	46	..	..	..	..	..	..	..	..	..	..	1230	..		..	..	..	1240	..	..	..	..	46
Epsom Downs...... arr	47	..	..	..	..	..	..	..	..	..	..	1234	..		..	..	..	1244	..	..	..	..	47
Cheam..................	48	..	..	..	..	..	..	..	..	1212	..	..	..	..	..	1230	..	..	..	..	..	..	48
Ewell East H...........	49	..	..	..	..	..	..	..	..	1215	..	..	..	..	..	1233	..	..	..	..	..	..	49
Epsom..................	50	..	..	..	..	..	..	..	1211	1219	..	..	..	..	..	1236	..	..	..	..	..	..	50
Ashtead................	51	..	..	..	..	..	..	..	1215	..	..	..	..	..	..	1240	..	..	..	..	..	..	51
Leatherhead...[Bridge J	52	..	..	..	..	..	..	..	1219	..	..	..	..	..	..	1244	..	..	..	..	..	..	52
Boxhill and Burford	53	..	..	..	..	..	..	..	1224	..	..	..	..	..	..	1249	..	..	..	..	..	..	53
Dorking North K ..arr	54	..	..	..	..	..	..	..	1228	..	..	..	..	..	..	1252	..	..	..	..	..	..	54
Bookham ....[394	55	..	..	..	..	..	..	..	..	..	..	..	..	..	..	..	..	..	..	..	..	..	55
Effingham Junction arr	56	..	..	..	..	..	..	..	..	..	..	..	..	..	..	..	..	..	..	..	..	..	56
South Croydon 234......	57	1150	12 0	..	..	..	..	..	..	..	..	..	..	..	..	..	..	..	1220	..	..	..	57
Purley Oaks............	58	1153	12 2	..	..	..	..	..	..	..	..	..	..	..	..	..	..	..	1223	..	..	..	58
Purley..................	59	1155	12 5	..	..	..	..	..	..	..	1211	..	..	..	..	..	..	..	1226	..	..	..	59
Coulsdon North L... arr	60	..	12 9	..	..	..	..	..	..	..	..	..	..	..	..	..	..	..	..	..	..	..	60
Purley .... dep	61	1159	..	..	..	..	..	..	..	..	..	..	..	..	..	..	..	..	1229	..	..	..	61
Kenley..................	62	12 2	..	..	..	..	..	..	..	..	..	..	..	..	..	..	..	..	1232	..	..	..	62
Whyteleafe.............	63	12 5	..	..	..	..	..	..	..	..	..	..	..	..	..	..	..	..	1235	..	..	..	63
Warlingham.............	64	12 7	..	..	..	..	..	..	..	..	..	..	..	..	..	..	..	..	1237	..	..	..	64
Caterham........... arr	65	1211	..	..	..	..	..	..	..	..	..	..	..	..	..	..	..	..	1241	..	..	..	65
Purley .... dep	66	1157	..	..	..	..	..	..	..	..		..	..	..	..	..	..	..	1227	..	..	..	66
Reedham................	67	1159	..	..	..	..	..	..	..	..		..	..	..	..	..	..	..	1229	..	..	..	67
Smitham................	68	12 1	..	..	..	..	..	..	..	..		..	..	..	..	..	..	..	1231	..	..	..	68
Woodmansterne.........	69	12 4	..	..	..	..	..	..	..	..	§ Via Three Bridges	..	..	..	..	..	..	..	1234	..	..	..	69
Chipstead..............	70	12 6	..	..	..	..	..	..	..	..		..	..	..	..	..	..	..	1236	..	..	..	70
Kingswood M...........	71	1211	..	..	..	..	..	..	..	..		..	..	..	..	..	..	..	1241	..	..	..	71
Tadworth N.............	72	1214	..	..	..	..	..	..	..	..		..	..	..	..	..	..	..	1244	..	..	..	72
Tattenham Corner. arr	73	1217	..	..	..	..	..	..	..	..		..	..	..	..	..	..	..	1247	..	..	..	73
Coulsdon South.........	74	..	..	..	..	..	..	..	..	..	1214	..	..	..	..	..	..	..	..	..	..	..	74
Merstham...............	75	..	..	..	..	..	..	..	..	..	1220	..	..	..	..	..	..	..	..	..	..	..	75
Redhill 158, 246 ..... arr	76	..	..	..	..	..	..	..	..	..	1224	..	..	..	..	..	..	..	..	..	..	..	76
Reigate 246........ "	77	..	..	..	..	..	..	..	..	..	1230	..	..	..	..	..	..	..	..	..	..	..	77
Horsham 159, 244, 245 "	78	..	..	..	..	..	..	..	1253	..	1§ 5	..	..	..	..	..	..	..	..	..	..	..	78

For Notes, see page 284a

CATERHAM, TATTENHAM CORNER, REDHILL, REIGATE, and HORSHAM

Sundays—*continued* (p.m)

No.																												
1				1215	1218					1228				1232				1240			1245	1248	1248					
2													1223															
3		3	12 2	3	3		3	3			3		1225	3		3		3		1242	3		3	3	3	3		3
4		1213					1221	1225			1228		1230			1235								1245	1251	1255		1258
5													3					1243										
6			12 9	1220	1224					1233				1237				1246		1249	1250	1253	1254					
7			3	1223	1227									1240				1249		3	1253		1257					
8				1225	1229									1242				1251			1255		1259					
9			Via Worcester Park				1224	1228												Via Worcester Park				1248	1254	1258		
10							1227	1231																1251	1257	1 1		
11							1229	1233																1253	1259	1 3		
12								1236																1256		1 6		
13								1238																1258		1 8		
14								1241																1 1		1 11		
15								1244																1 4		1 14		
16		1218					To Victoria, arr. 12 44 p.m				1233		1235			1240									To Victoria, arr. 1 14 p.m			1 3
17		1220									1235					1242												1 5
18		1223									1238					1245												1 8
19		1225									1240		1240			1247												1 10
20		1228									1243					1250												1 13
21		1230									1245																	1 15
22		1231									1246																	1 16
23					1233									1246									1 3	1 6				
24					1235									1248									1 5	1 9				
25					1238									1251									1 8	1 12				
26					1240									1253									1 10	1 14				
27																		1254										
28																		1257										
29	3																	1259	3									
30	1235															1253		1 2	1 5									
31	1238																		1 8									
32	1242																		1 12									
33		1234									1249		1244					1 6						1 17				1 19
34										1245			1248	1257								1 5						
35										1246			1249	1257								1 5						
36		To London Bridge, via Streatham		1231				1249													1 1			To London Bridge, via Forest Hill		1 19		
37				1234				1252													1 4					1 22		
38				1236				1254	3												1 6					1 24	3	
39					1243						1253							1 11					1 13					1 23
40					1243				1249		1253												1 13				1 19	1 23
41					1246				1251		1256												1 16				1 21	1 26
42					1249				1255		1259												1 19				1 25	1 29
43					1252				1257		1 2												1 22				1 27	1 32
44				1239	1254			1257	1 0		1 4										1 9		1 24			1 27	1 30	1 34
45					1257						1 7												1 27					1 37
46					1 0						1 10												1 30					1 40
47					1 4						1 14												1 34					1 44
48				1242				1 0													1 12					1 30		
49				1245				1 3													1 15					1 33		
50			1231	1248				1 6												1 11	1 19					1 36		
51			1235					1 10												1 15						1 40		
52			1239					1 14												1 19						1 44		
53																				1 24						1 49		
54																				1 28						1 52		
55			1245					1 19																				
56			1249					1 23																				
57													1250	1 0														
58													1253	1 2														
59													1255	1 5								1 11						
60														1 8														
61													1259															
62													1 2															
63													1 5															
64													1 7															
65													1 11															
66													1257									§ Via Three Bridges						
67													1259															
68													1 1															
69													1 4															
70													1 6															
71													1 11															
72													1 14															
73													1 17															
74																						1 14						
75																						1 20						
76										1 0												1 24						
77																						1 30						
78																				1 53		2§ 5						

LONDON, CRYSTAL PALACE, CROYDON, SUTTON, DORKING NORTH,

For Notes, see page 284a

Down	No.	p.m.										**Sundays**—*continued*						p.m.					No.
Victoria .... dep	1	..	..	..	..	1 10	..	..	1 15	1 18	..	..	..	..	1 28	..	..	..	1 32	..	..	1 40	1
Charing Cross* ... "	2	1253	3	..	..	3	..	3	3	3	..	3	3	..	..	3	..	1 23	3	..	3	3	2
Waterloo* .... "	3	1255		..	1 2		..				..			..	..		..	1 25		..			3
London Bridge ..... "	4	1 0	1 4	..	..	..	..	1 13	..	..	..	1 21	1 25	..	..	1 28	..	1 30	..	..	1 35	..	4
Battersea Park	5	3	..	..	..	1 13	..	..	..	..	..	..	..	..	..	..	..	3	..	..	..	1 43	5
Clapham Junction	6		..	..	1 9	1 16	..	..	1 20	1 24	..	..	..	..	1 33	..	..		1 37	..	..	1 46	6
Wandsworth Common **A**	7	..	..	..	3	1 19	..	..	1 23	1 27	..	..	..	..	..	..	..	..	1 40	..	..	1 49	7
Balham & Upper Tooting	8	..	..	..		1 21	..	..	1 25	1 29	..	..	..	..	..	..	..	..	1 42	..	..	1 51	8
South Bermondsey	9	..	1 7	..	Via Worcester Park	..	..	..	..	..	..	1 24	1 28	..	..	..	..	..	..	..	..	..	9
Queen's Road, Peckham	10	..	1 10	..		..	..	..	..	..	..	1 27	1 31	..	..	..	..	..	..	..	..	..	10
Peckham Rye.	11	..	1 12	..		..	..	..	..	..	..	1 29	1 33	..	..	..	..	..	..	..	..	..	11
East Dulwich	12	..	1 15	..		..	..	..	..	..	..	To Victoria arr. 1 44 p.m.	1 36	..	..	..	..	..	..	..	..	..	12
North Dulwich	13	..	1 17	..		..	..	..	..	..	..		1 38	..	..	..	..	..	..	..	..	..	13
Tulse Hill	14	..	1 20	..		..	..	..	..	..	..		1 41	..	..	..	..	..	..	..	..	..	14
Streatham	15	..	..	..		..	..	..	..	..	..		1 44	..	..	..	..	..	..	..	..	..	15
New Cross Gate (for E.L.	16	1 5	..	..		..	..	1 18	..	..	..		..	..	..	1 33	..	1 35	..	..	1 40	..	16
Brockley **B**.......[Line)	17	..	..	..		..	..	1 20	..	..	..		..	..	..	1 35	..	..	..	..	1 42	..	17
Honor Oak Park..........	18	..	..	..		..	..	1 23	..	..	..		..	..	..	1 38	..	..	..	..	1 45	..	18
Forest Hill, for Lordship	19	1 10	..	..	..	..	..	1 25	..	..	..	..	..	..	..	1 40	..	1 40	..	..	1 47	..	19
Sydenham ....[Lane	20	..	..	..	..	..	..	1 28	..	..	..	..	..	..	..	1 43	..	..	..	..	1 50	..	20
Penge West **C**..........	21	..	..	..	..	..	..	1 30	..	..	..	..	..	..	..	1 45	..	..	..	..	..	..	21
Anerley..................	22	..	..	..	..	..	..	1 31	..	..	..	..	..	..	..	1 46	..	..	..	..	..	..	22
Streatham Common....	23	..	..	..	..	..	..	..	..	1 33	..	..	..	..	..	..	..	..	1 46	..	..	..	23
Norbury	24	..	..	..	..	..	..	..	..	1 35	..	..	..	..	..	..	..	..	1 48	..	..	..	24
Thornton Heath........	25	..	..	..	..	..	..	..	..	1 38	..	..	..	..	..	..	..	..	1 51	..	..	..	25
Selhurst..........	26	..	..	..	..	..	..	..	..	1 40	..	..	..	..	..	..	..	..	1 53	..	..	..	26
Streatham Hill..........	27	..	..	..	..	1 24	..	..	..	..	..	..	..	..	..	..	..	..	..	..	..	1 54	27
West Norwood.[N'wood)	28	..	1 22	..	..	1 27	3	..	..	..	..	..	..	..	..	..	..	..	..	..	..	1 57	28
Gipsy Hill (for Upper	29	..	1 24	..	..	1 29		..	..	..	..	..	..	..	..	..	..	..	..	..	..	1 59	29
Crystal Palace D......	30	..	1 27	..	..	1 32	1 35	..	..	..	..	..	..	..	..	..	..	..	..	..	1 53	2 2	30
Birkbeck	31	..	..	..	..	..	1 38	..	..	..	..	..	..	..	..	..	..	..	..	..	..	..	31
Beckenham Jn. arr	32	..	..	..	..	..	1 42	..	..	..	..	..	..	..	..	..	..	..	..	..	..	..	32
Norwood Junction F..	33	1 14	..	..	..	1 36	..	1 34	..	..	..	..	..	..	..	1 49	..	1 44	..	..	..	2 6	33
East Croydon.. arr	34	1 18	..	..	..	..	..	..	..	..	..	..	..	..	1 45	..	..	1 48	1 57	..	..	..	34
East Croydon.. dep	35	1 18	..	..	..	..	..	To London Bridge, via Streatham	..	..	..	..	..	..	1 46	..	..	1 48	1 57	..	..	..	35
Mitcham Junction......	36	..	..	..	..	..	..		1 31	..	..	..	1 49	..	..	..	..	..	..	..	..	..	36
Hackbridge	37	..	..	..	..	..	..		1 34	..	..	..	1 52	..	..	..	..	..	..	..	..	..	37
Carshalton	38	..	..	..	..	..	..		1 36	..	..	..	1 54	3	..	..	..	..	..	..	..	..	38
West Croydon 319 arr	39	..	..	..	..	1 41	..		..	1 43	..	..	..		..	1 53	..	..	..	..	..	2 11	39
West Croydon 319 dep	40	..	..	..	..	..	..		..	1 43	..	..	..	1 49	..	1 53	..	..	..	..	..	..	40
Waddon **G**..........	41	..	..	..	..	..	..		..	1 46	..	..	..	1 51	..	1 56	..	..	..	..	..	..	41
Wallington..........	42	..	..	..	..	..	..		..	1 49	..	..	..	1 55	..	1 59	..	..	..	..	..	..	42
Carshalton Beeches	43	..	..	..	..	..	..		..	1 52	..	..	..	1 57	..	2 2	..	..	..	..	..	..	43
Sutton 322..........	44	..	..	..	..	..	..		1 39	1 54	..	..	1 57	2 0	..	2 4	..	..	..	..	..	..	44
Belmont	45	..	..	..	..	..	..	..	..	1 57	..	..	..	..	..	2 7	..	..	..	..	..	..	45
Banstead..........	46	..	..	..	..	..	..	..	..	2 0	..	..	..	..	..	2 10	..	..	..	..	..	..	46
Epsom Downs...... arr	47	..	..	..	..	..	..	..	..	2 4	..	..	..	..	..	2 14	..	..	..	..	..	..	47
Cheam..........	48	..	..	..	..	..	..	..	1 42	..	..	..	2 0	..	..	..	..	..	..	..	..	..	48
Ewell East **H**..........	49	..	..	..	..	..	..	..	1 45	..	..	..	2 3	..	..	..	..	..	..	..	..	..	49
Epsom..........	50	..	..	..	1 31	..	..	..	1 48	..	..	..	2 6	..	..	..	..	..	..	..	..	..	50
Ashtead..........	51	..	..	..	1 35	..	..	..	..	..	..	..	2 10	..	..	..	..	..	..	..	..	..	51
Leatherhead...[Bridge **J**	52	..	..	..	1 39	..	..	..	..	..	..	..	2 14	..	..	..	..	..	..	..	..	..	52
Boxhill and Burford	53	..	..	..	..	..	..	..	..	..	..	..	..	..	..	..	..	..	..	..	..	..	53
Dorking North K.. arr	54	..	..	..	..	..	..	..	..	..	..	..	..	..	..	..	..	..	..	..	..	..	54
Bookham..........[394	55	..	..	..	1 45	..	..	..	..	..	..	..	2 19	..	..	..	..	..	..	..	..	..	55
Effingham Junction arr	56	..	..	..	1 49	..	..	..	..	..	..	..	2 23	..	..	..	..	..	..	..	..	..	56
South Croydon 234......	57	1 20	..	..	..	..	..	..	..	..	..	..	..	..	..	..	..	1 50	2 0	..	..	..	57
Purley Oaks	58	1 23	..	..	..	..	..	..	..	..	..	..	..	..	..	..	..	1 53	2 2	..	..	..	58
Purley..........	59	1 26	..	..	..	..	..	..	..	..	..	..	..	..	..	..	..	1 55	2 5	..	..	..	59
Coulsdon North **L**.. arr	60	..	..	..	..	..	..	..	..	..	..	..	..	..	..	..	..	..	2 8	..	..	..	60
Purley..........dep	61	1 29	..	..	..	..	..	..	..	..	..	..	..	..	..	..	..	1 59	..	..	..	..	61
Kenley..........	62	1 32	..	..	..	..	..	..	..	..	..	..	..	..	..	..	..	2 2	..	..	..	..	62
Whyteleafe..........	63	1 35	..	..	..	..	..	..	..	..	..	..	..	..	..	..	..	2 5	..	..	..	..	63
Warlingham..........	64	1 37	..	..	..	..	..	..	..	..	..	..	..	..	..	..	..	2 7	..	..	..	..	64
Caterham.......... arr	65	1 41	..	..	..	..	..	..	..	..	..	..	..	..	..	..	..	2 11	..	..	..	..	65
Purley..........dep	66	1 27	..	..	..	..	..	..	..	..	..	..	..	..	..	..	..	1 57	..	..	..	..	66
Reedham..........	67	1 29	..	..	..	..	..	..	..	..	..	..	..	..	..	..	..	1 59	..	..	..	..	67
Smitham..........	68	1 31	..	..	..	..	..	..	..	..	..	..	..	..	..	..	..	2 1	..	..	..	..	68
Woodmansterne..........	69	1 34	..	..	..	..	..	..	..	..	..	..	..	..	..	..	..	2 4	..	..	..	..	69
Chipstead..........	70	1 36	..	..	..	..	..	..	..	..	..	..	..	..	..	..	..	2 6	..	..	..	..	70
Kingswood **M**..........	71	1 41	..	..	..	..	..	..	..	..	..	..	..	..	..	..	..	2 11	..	..	..	..	71
Tadworth **N**..........	72	1 44	..	..	..	..	..	..	..	..	..	..	..	..	..	..	..	2 14	..	..	..	..	72
Tattenham Corner. arr	73	1 47	..	..	..	..	..	..	..	..	..	..	..	..	..	..	..	2 17	..	..	..	..	73
Coulsdon South	74	..	..	..	..	..	..	..	..	..	..	..	..	..	..	..	..	..	..	..	..	..	74
Merstham..........	75	..	..	..	..	..	..	..	..	..	..	..	..	..	..	..	..	..	..	..	..	..	75
Redhill 158, 248...... arr	76	..	..	..	..	..	..	..	..	..	..	..	..	..	2 0	..	..	..	..	..	..	..	76
Reigate 246....... "	77	..	..	..	..	..	..	..	..	..	..	..	..	..	2 9	..	..	..	..	..	..	..	77
Horsham 159,244,245 "	78	..	..	..	..	..	..	..	..	..	..	..	..	..	..	..	..	..	..	..	..	..	78

CATERHAM, TATTENHAM CORNER, REDHILL, REIGATE, and HORSHAM

p.m — **Sundays**—*continued* — p.m

No.																												
1	..	..	..	1 45	1 48	1 48	..	..	..	..	..	..	..	..	..	..	..	2 10	..	2 15	2 18	..	..	..	..	2 28	..	..
2	..	..	..	3	..	3	3	3	3	..	3	..	1 53	3	..	..	3	3	..	3	3	..	3	3	..	..	3	2 23
3	..	1 42	..		..					..		..	1 55		..	2 2			..			..			..	..		2 25
4	..	..	..	..	..	..	1 45	1 51	1 55	..	1 58	..	2 0	2 4	..	..	2 13	..	..	..	..	..	2 21	2 25	..	..	2 28	2 30
5	..	..	..	..	..	..	..	..	..	..	..	..	3	..	..	..	..	2 13	..	..	..	..	..	..	..	..	..	3
6	..	1 49	..	1 50	1 53	1 54	..	..	..	..	..	..		..	..	2 9	..	2 16	..	2 20	2 24	..	..	..	..	2 33	..	
7	..	3	..	1 53	..	1 57	..	..	..	..	..	..	..	..	..	3	..	2 19	..	2 23	2 27	..	..	..	..	..	..	..
8	..		..	1 55	..	1 59	..	..	..	..	..	..	..	..	..		..	2 21	..	2 25	2 29	..	..	..	..	..	..	..
9	..	Via Worcester Park	..	..	..	..	1 48	1 54	1 58	..	..	..	..	2 7	..	Via Worcester Park	..	..	..	..	..	..	2 24	2 28	..	..	..	..
10	..		..	..	..	..	1 51	1 57	2 1	..	..	..	..	2 10	..		..	..	..	..	..	..	2 27	2 31	..	..	..	..
11	..		..	..	..	..	1 53	1 59	2 3	..	..	..	..	2 12	..		..	..	..	..	..	..	2 29	2 33	..	..	..	..
12	..		..	..	..	..	1 56	To Victoria, arr. 2 14 p.m	2 6	..	..	..	..	2 15	..		..	..	..	..	..	..	To Victoria, arr. 2 44 p.m	2 36	..	..	..	..
13	..		..	..	..	..	1 58		2 8	..	..	..	..	2 17	..		..	..	..	..	..	..		2 38	..	..	..	..
14	..		..	..	..	..	2 1		2 11	..	..	..	..	2 20	..		..	..	..	..	..	..		2 41	..	..	..	..
15	..		..	..	..	..	2 4		2 14	..	..	..	..	..	..		..	..	..	..	..	..		2 44	..	..	..	..
16	..		..	..	..	..	..		..	..	2 3	..	2 5	..	..		2 18	..	..	..	..	..		..	..	..	2 33	2 35
17	..		..	..	..	..	..		..	..	2 5	..	..	..	..		2 20	..	..	..	..	..		..	..	..	2 35	..
18	..		..	..	..	..	..		..	..	2 8	..	..	..	..		2 23	..	..	..	..	..		..	..	..	2 38	..
19	..	..	..	..	..	..	..		..	..	2 10	..	2 10	..	..	..	2 25	..	..	..	..	..		..	..	..	2 40	2 40
20	..	..	..	..	..	..	..		..	..	2 13	..	..	..	..	..	2 28	..	..	..	..	..		..	..	..	2 43	..
21	..	..	..	..	..	..	..		..	..	2 15	..	..	..	..	..	2 30	..	..	..	..	..		..	..	..	2 45	..
22	..	..	..	..	..	..	..		..	..	2 16	..	..	..	..	..	2 31	..	..	..	..	..		..	..	..	2 46	..
23	..	..	..	..	..	2 3	2 6	..	..	..	..	..	..	..	..	..	..	..	..	..	2 33	..	..	..	..	..	..	..
24	..	..	..	..	..	2 5	2 9	..	..	..	..	..	..	..	..	..	..	..	..	..	2 35	..	..	..	..	..	..	..
25	..	..	..	..	..	2 8	2 12	..	..	..	..	..	..	..	..	..	..	..	..	..	2 38	..	..	..	..	..	..	..
26	..	..	..	..	..	2 10	2 14	..	..	..	..	..	..	..	..	..	..	..	..	..	2 40	..	..	..	..	..	..	..
27	..	..	..	..	..	..	..	..	..	..	..	..	..	..	..	..	..	2 24	..	..	..	..	..	..	..	..	..	..
28	3	..	..	..	..	..	..	..	..	..	..	..	..	2 22	..	..	..	2 27	3	..	..	..	..	..	..	..	..	..
29		..	..	..	..	..	..	..	..	..	..	..	..	2 24	..	..	..	2 29		..	..	..	..	..	..	..	..	..
30	2 5	..	..	..	..	..	..	..	..	..	..	..	..	2 27	..	..	..	2 32	2 35	..	..	..	..	..	..	..	..	..
31	2 8	..	..	..	..	..	..	..	..	..	..	..	..	..	..	..	..	..	2 38	..	..	..	..	..	..	..	..	..
32	2 12	..	..	..	..	..	..	..	..	..	..	..	..	..	..	..	..	..	2 42	..	..	..	..	..	..	..	..	..
33	..	..	..	..	..	..	2 17	..	..	..	2 19	..	2 14	..	..	..	2 34	2 36	..	..	..	..	..	..	..	..	2 49	2 44
34	..	..	..	..	2 5	..	To London Bridge, via Forest Hill	..	..	..	..	..	2 18	..	..	..	To London Bridge, via Streatham	..	..	..	..	..	..	..	..	2 45	..	2 48
35	..	..	..	..	2 5	..		..	..	..	..	..	2 18	..	..	..		..	..	..	..	..	..	..	..	2 46	..	2 48
36	..	..	..	2 1	..	..		..	2 19	..	..	..	..	..	..	..		..	..	2 31	..	..	..	2 49	..	..	..	..
37	..	..	..	2 4	..	..		..	2 22	..	..	..	..	..	..	..		..	..	2 34	..	..	..	2 52	..	..	..	..
38	..	..	..	2 6	..	..		..	2 24	3	..	..	..	..	..	..		..	..	2 36	..	..	..	2 54	3	..	..	..
39	..	..	..	..	..	2 13		..	..		2 23	..	..	..	..	..		2 41	..	..	2 43	..	..	..		..	2 53	..
40	..	..	..	..	..	2 13		..	..	2 19	2 23	..	..	..	..	..		..	..	..	2 43	..	..	..	2 49	..	2 53	..
41	..	..	..	..	..	2 16		..	..	2 21	2 26	..	..	..	..	..		..	..	..	2 46	..	..	..	2 51	..	2 56	..
42	..	..	..	..	..	2 19		..	..	2 25	2 29	..	..	..	..	..		..	..	..	2 49	..	..	..	2 55	..	2 59	..
43	..	..	..	..	..	2 22		..	..	2 27	2 32	..	..	..	..	..		..	..	..	2 52	..	..	..	2 57	..	3 2	..
44	..	..	..	2 9	..	2 24		..	2 27	2 30	2 34	..	..	..	..	..		..	..	2 39	2 54	..	..	2 57	3 0	..	3 4	..
45	..	..	..	..	..	2 27		..	..	..	2 37	..	..	..	..	..		..	..	..	2 59	..	..	..	..	..	3 7	..
46	..	..	..	..	..	2 30		..	..	..	2 40	..	..	..	..	..		..	..	..	3 0	..	..	..	..	..	3 10	..
47	..	..	..	..	..	2 34		..	..	..	2 44	..	..	..	..	..		..	..	..	3 4	..	..	..	..	..	3 14	..
48	..	..	..	2 12	..	..	..	..	2 30	..	..	..	..	..	..	..	..	..	..	2 42	..	..	..	3 0	..	..	..	..
49	..	..	..	2 15	..	..	..	..	2 33	..	..	..	..	..	..	..	..	..	..	2 45	..	..	..	3 3	..	..	..	..
50	..	2 11	..	2 19	..	..	..	..	2 36	..	..	..	..	..	..	2 31	..	..	..	2 48	..	..	..	3 6	..	..	..	..
51	..	2 15	..	..	..	..	..	..	2 40	..	..	..	..	..	..	2 35	..	..	..	..	..	..	..	3 10	..	..	..	..
52	..	2 19	..	..	..	..	..	..	2 44	..	..	..	..	..	..	2 39	..	..	..	..	..	..	..	3 14	..	..	..	..
53	..	2 24	..	..	..	..	..	..	2 49	..	..	..	..	..	..	..	..	..	..	..	..	..	..	..	..	..	..	..
54	..	2 28	..	..	..	..	..	..	2 52	..	..	..	..	..	..	..	..	..	..	..	..	..	..	..	..	..	..	..
55	..	..	..	..	..	..	..	..	..	..	..	..	..	..	..	2 45	..	..	..	..	..	..	..	3 19	..	..	..	..
56	..	..	..	..	..	..	..	..	..	..	..	..	..	..	..	2 49	..	..	..	..	..	..	..	3 23	..	..	..	..
57	..	..	..	..	..	..	..	..	..	..	..	..	2 20	..	..	..	..	..	..	..	..	..	..	..	..	..	..	2 50
58	..	..	..	..	..	..	..	..	..	..	..	..	2 23	..	..	..	..	..	..	..	..	..	..	..	..	..	..	2 53
59	..	..	..	..	2 11	..	..	..	..	..	..	..	2 26	..	..	..	..	..	..	..	..	..	..	..	..	..	..	2 56
60	..	..	..	..	..	..	..	..	..	..	..	..	..	..	..	..	..	..	..	..	..	..	..	..	..	..	..	..
61	..	..	..	..	..	..	..	..	..	..	..	..	2 29	..	..	..	..	..	..	..	..	..	..	..	..	..	..	2 59
62	..	..	..	..	..	..	..	..	..	..	..	..	2 32	..	..	..	..	..	..	..	..	..	..	..	..	..	..	3 2
63	..	..	..	..	..	..	..	..	..	..	..	..	2 35	..	..	..	..	..	..	..	..	..	..	..	..	..	..	3 5
64	..	..	..	..	..	..	..	..	..	..	..	..	2 37	..	..	..	..	..	..	..	..	..	..	..	..	..	..	3 7
65	..	..	..	..	..	..	..	..	..	..	..	..	2 41	..	..	..	..	..	..	..	..	..	..	..	..	..	..	3 11
66	..	..	..	..	Via Three Bridges	..	..	..	..	..	..	..	2 27	..	..	..	..	..	..	..	..	..	..	..	..	..	..	2 57
67	..	..	..	..		..	..	..	..	..	..	..	2 29	..	..	..	..	..	..	..	..	..	..	..	..	..	..	2 59
68	..	..	..	..		..	..	..	..	..	..	..	2 31	..	..	..	..	..	..	..	..	..	..	..	..	..	..	3 1
69	..	..	..	..		..	..	..	..	..	..	..	2 34	..	..	..	..	..	..	..	..	..	..	..	..	..	..	3 4
70	..	..	..	..		..	..	..	..	..	..	..	2 36	..	..	..	..	..	..	..	..	..	..	..	..	..	..	3 6
71	..	..	..	..		..	..	..	..	..	..	..	2 41	..	..	..	..	..	..	..	..	..	..	..	..	..	..	3 11
72	..	..	..	..		..	..	..	..	..	..	..	2 44	..	..	..	..	..	..	..	..	..	..	..	..	..	..	3 14
73	..	..	..	..		..	..	..	..	..	..	..	2 47	..	..	..	..	..	..	..	..	..	..	..	..	..	..	3 17
74	..	..	..	..	2 14	..	..	..	..	..	..	..	..	..	..	..	..	..	..	..	..	..	..	..	..	..	..	..
75	..	..	..	..	2 20	..	..	..	..	..	..	..	..	..	..	..	..	..	..	..	..	..	..	..	..	..	..	..
76	..	..	..	..	2 24	..	..	..	..	..	..	..	..	..	..	..	..	..	..	..	..	..	..	..	..	3 0	..	..
77	..	..	..	..	2 30	..	..	..	..	..	..	..	..	..	..	..	..	..	..	..	..	..	..	..	..	3 8	..	..
78	..	2 53	..	..	3 § 5	..	..	..	..	..	..	..	..	..	..	..	..	..	..	..	..	..	..	..	..	..	..	..

LONDON, CRYSTAL PALACE, CROYDON, SUTTON, DORKING NORTH,

Down	No.	p.m								Sundays—continued								p.m					No.
Victoria .... dep	1	2 30	2 33	..	..	2 40	..	..	..	2 45	2 48	2 48	..	..	..	..	..	..	..	..	3 10	..	1
Charing Cross* ... "	2	..	③	..	③	③	..	..	..	③	..	③	③	③	③	..	③	2 53	③	..	③	..	2
Waterloo* .... "	3	..		..			..	..	2 42		..					..		2 55		..		..	3
London Bridge ..... "	4	..	..	..	2 35	..	..	..	..	..	..	..	2 45	2 51	2 55	..	2 58	3 0	3 4	..	..	..	4
Battersea Park	5	..	..	..	..	2 43	..	..	..	..	..	..	..	..	..	..	..	③	..	..	3 13	..	5
Clapham Junction	6	2 38	2 38	..	..	2 46	..	..	2 49	2 50	2 53	2 54	..	..	..	..	..		..	..	3 16	..	6
Wandsworth Common A	7	..	2 41	..	..	2 49	..	..	③	2 53	..	2 57	..	..	..	..	..	..	..	..	3 19	..	7
Balham & Upper Tooting	8	..	2 43	..	..	2 51	..	..		2 55	..	2 59	..	..	..	..	..	..	..	..	3 21	..	8
South Bermondsey	9	..	..	..	..	..	..	..	Via Worcester Park	..	..	..	2 48	2 54	2 58	..	..	..	3 7	..	..	..	9
Queen's Road, Peckham	10	..	..	..	..	..	..	..		..	..	..	2 51	2 57	3 1	..	..	..	3 10	..	..	..	10
Peckham Rye	11	..	..	..	..	..	..	..		..	..	..	2 53	2 59	3 3	..	..	..	3 12	..	..	..	11
East Dulwich	12	..	..	..	..	..	..	..		..	..	..	2 56	To Victoria arr 3 14 p.m	3 6	..	..	..	3 15	..	..	..	12
North Dulwich	13	..	..	..	..	..	..	..		..	..	..	2 58		3 8	..	..	..	3 17	..	..	..	13
Tulse Hill	14	..	..	..	..	..	..	..		..	..	..	3 1		3 11	..	..	..	3 20	..	..	..	14
Streatham	15	..	..	..	..	..	..	..		..	..	..	3 4		3 14	..	..	..	..	..	..	..	15
New Cross Gate (for E.L.	16	..	..	..	2 40	..	..	..		..	..	..	..		..	..	3 3	3 5	..	..	..	..	16
Brockley B ....[Line)	17	..	..	..	2 42	..	..	..		..	..	..	..		..	..	3 5	..	..	..	..	..	17
Honor Oak Park	18	..	..	..	2 45	..	..	..	..	..	..	..	..		..	..	3 8	..	..	..	..	..	18
Forest Hill, for Lordship	19	..	..	..	2 47	..	..	..	..	..	..	..	..		..	..	3 10	3 10	..	..	..	..	19
Sydenham ....[Lane	20	..	..	..	2 50	..	..	..	..	..	..	..	..		..	..	3 13	..	..	..	..	..	20
Penge West C	21	..	..	..	..	..	..	..	..	..	..	..	..		..	..	3 15	..	..	..	..	..	21
Anerley	22	..	..	..	..	..	..	..	..	..	..	..	..	..	..	..	3 16	..	..	..	..	..	22
Streatham Common	23	..	2 47	..	..	..	..	..	..	..	..	3 3	3 6	..	..	..	..	..	..	..	..	..	23
Norbury	24	..	2 50	..	..	..	..	..	..	..	..	3 5	3 9	..	..	..	..	..	..	..	..	..	24
Thornton Heath	25	2 49	2 53	..	..	..	..	..	..	..	..	3 8	3 12	..	..	..	..	..	..	..	..	..	25
Selhurst	26	..	2 55	..	..	..	..	..	..	..	..	3 10	3 14	..	..	..	..	..	..	..	..	..	26
Streatham Hill	27	..	..	..	..	2 54	..	..	..	..	..	..	..	..	..	..	..	..	..	..	3 24	..	27
West Norwood.[N'wood)	28	..	..	..	..	2 57	③	..	..	..	..	..	..	..	..	..	..	..	3 22	..	3 27	③	28
Gipsy Hill (for Upper	29	..	..	..	..	2 59		..	..	..	..	..	..	..	..	..	..	..	3 24	..	3 29		29
Crystal Palace D	30	..	..	..	2 53	3 2	3 5	..	..	..	..	..	..	..	..	..	..	..	3 27	..	3 32	3 35	30
Birkbeck	31	..	..	..	..	..	3 8	..	..	..	..	..	..	..	..	..	..	..	..	..	..	3 38	31
Beckenham Jn. arr	32	..	..	..	..	..	3 12	..	..	..	..	..	..	..	..	..	..	..	..	..	..	3 42	32
Norwood Junction F ..	33	..	..	..	..	3 6	..	..	..	..	..	..	3 17	..	..	..	3 19	3 14	..	..	3 36	..	33
East Croydon .... arr	34	2 56	2 58	..	..	..	..	..	..	..	3 5	..	..	..	..	..	..	3 18	..	..	..	..	34
East Croydon .... dep	35	3 0	2 58	..	..	..	..	..	..	..	3 5	..	..	..	..	..	..	3 18	..	..	..	..	35
Mitcham Junction	36	..	..	..	..	..	..	..	..	3 1	..	..	To London Bridge, via Forest Hill	..	3 19	..	..	..	..	..	..	..	36
Hackbridge	37	..	..	..	..	..	..	..	..	3 4	..	..		..	3 22	..	..	..	..	..	..	..	37
Carshalton	38	..	..	..	..	..	..	..	..	3 6	..	..		..	3 24	③	..	..	..	..	..	..	38
West Croydon 319 arr	39	..	..	..	..	3 11	..	..	..	..	..	3 13		..	..		3 23	..	..	..	3 41	..	39
West Croydon 319 dep	40	..	..	..	..	..	..	..	..	..	..	3 13		..	..	3 19	3 23	..	..	..	..	..	40
Waddon G	41	..	..	..	..	..	..	..	..	..	..	3 16		..	..	3 21	3 26	..	..	..	..	..	41
Wallington	42	..	..	..	..	..	..	..	..	..	..	3 19		..	..	3 25	3 29	..	..	..	..	..	42
Carshalton Beeches	43	..	..	..	..	..	..	..	..	..	..	3 22		..	..	3 27	3 32	..	..	..	..	..	43
Sutton 322	44	..	..	..	..	..	..	..	..	3 9	..	3 24		..	3 27	3 30	3 34	..	..	..	..	..	44
Belmont	45	..	..	..	..	..	..	..	..	..	..	3 27		..	..	..	3 37	..	..	..	..	..	45
Banstead	46	..	..	..	..	..	..	..	..	..	..	3 30	..	..	..	..	3 40	..	..	..	..	..	46
Epsom Downs ...... arr	47	..	..	..	..	..	..	..	..	..	..	3 34	..	..	..	..	3 44	..	..	..	..	..	47
Cheam	48	..	..	..	..	..	..	..	..	3 12	..	..	..	..	3 30	..	..	..	..	..	..	..	48
Ewell East H	49	..	..	..	..	..	..	..	..	3 15	..	..	..	..	3 33	..	..	..	..	..	..	..	49
Epsom	50	..	..	..	..	..	..	..	3 11	3 19	..	..	..	..	3 36	..	..	..	..	..	..	..	50
Ashtead	51	..	..	..	..	..	..	..	3 15	..	..	..	..	..	3 40	..	..	..	..	..	..	..	51
Leatherhead..[Bridge J	52	..	..	..	..	..	..	..	3 19	..	..	..	..	..	3 44	..	..	..	..	..	..	..	52
Boxhill and Burford	53	..	..	..	..	..	..	..	3 24	..	..	..	..	..	3 49	..	..	..	..	..	..	..	53
Dorking North K .. arr	54	..	..	..	..	..	..	..	3 28	..	..	..	..	..	3 52	..	..	..	..	..	..	..	54
Bookham ....[394	55	..	..	..	..	..	..	..	..	..	..	..	..	..	..	..	..	..	..	..	..	..	55
Effingham Junction arr	56	..	..	..	..	..	..	..	..	..	..	..	..	..	..	..	..	..	..	..	..	..	56
South Croydon 234	57	3 4	3 0	..	..	..	..	..	..	..	..	..	..	..	..	..	..	3 20	..	..	..	..	57
Purley Oaks	58	..	3 3	..	..	..	..	..	..	..	..	..	..	..	..	..	..	3 23	..	..	..	..	58
Purley	59	..	3 6	..	..	..	..	..	..	..	3 11	..	..	..	..	..	..	3 26	..	..	..	..	59
Coulsdon North L .. arr	60	..	3 9	..	..	..	..	..	..	..	..	..	..	..	..	..	..	..	..	..	..	..	60
Purley ....dep	61	..	..	..	..	..	..	..	..	..	..	..	..	..	..	..	..	3 29	..	..	..	..	61
Kenley	62	..	..	..	..	..	..	..	..	..	..	..	..	..	..	..	..	3 32	..	..	..	..	62
Whyteleafe	63	..	..	..	..	..	..	..	..	..	..	..	..	..	..	..	..	3 35	..	..	..	..	63
Warlingham	64	..	..	..	..	..	..	..	..	..	..	..	..	..	..	..	..	3 37	..	..	..	..	64
Caterham .... arr	65	..	..	..	..	..	..	..	..	..	..	..	..	..	..	..	..	3 41	..	..	..	..	65
Purley ....dep	66	..	..	..	..	..	..	..	..	..	§ Via Three Bridges	..	..	..	..	..	..	3 27	..	..	..	..	66
Reedham	67	..	..	..	..	..	..	..	..	..		..	..	..	..	..	..	3 29	..	..	..	..	67
Smitham	68	..	..	..	..	..	..	..	..	..		..	..	..	..	..	..	3 31	..	..	..	..	68
Woodmansterne	69	..	..	..	..	..	..	..	..	..		..	..	..	..	..	..	3 34	..	..	..	..	69
Chipstead	70	..	..	..	..	..	..	..	..	..		..	..	..	..	..	..	3 36	..	..	..	..	70
Kingswood M	71	..	..	..	..	..	..	..	..	..		..	..	..	..	..	..	3 41	..	..	..	..	71
Tadworth N	72	..	..	..	..	..	..	..	..	..		..	..	..	..	..	..	3 44	..	..	..	..	72
Tattenham Corner. arr	73	..	..	..	..	..	..	..	..	..		..	..	..	..	..	..	3 47	..	..	..	..	73
Coulsdon South	74	..	..	..	..	..	..	..	..	..	3 14	..	..	..	..	..	..	..	..	..	..	..	74
Merstham	75	..	..	..	..	..	..	..	..	..	3 20	..	..	..	..	..	..	..	..	..	..	..	75
Redhill 158, 246 ...... arr	76	..	..	..	..	..	..	..	..	..	3 24	..	..	..	..	..	..	..	..	..	..	..	76
Reigate 246 .... "	77	..	..	..	..	..	..	..	..	..	3 30	..	..	..	..	..	..	..	..	..	..	..	77
Horsham 159, 244, 245 "	78	..	..	..	..	..	..	..	3 53	..	4§5	..	..	..	..	..	..	..	..	..	..	..	78

For Notes, see page 284a

CATERHAM, TATTENHAM CORNER, REDHILL, REIGATE, and HORSHAM

Sundays – continued (p.m.)

No.																												
1		3 18		3 20	3 18							3 28		3 32				3 40			3 45		3 45	3 48	3 48			
2	③			③	③		③	③		③			3 23	③		③		③			③				③	③	③	③
3			3 2										3 25							3 42								
4	3 13						3 21	3 25		3 28			3 30			3 35										3 45	3 51	3 55
5													③					3 43										
6			3 9	3 25	3 24							3 33		3 37				3 46		3 49	3 50			3 53	3 54			
7			③		3 27									3 40				3 49		③	3 53				3 57			
8				3 29	3 29									3 42				3 51			3 55				3 59			
9			Via Worcester Park				3 24	3 28												Via Worcester Park						3 48	3 54	3 58
10							3 27	3 31																		3 51	3 57	4 1
11							3 29	3 33																		3 53	3 59	4 3
12							To Victoria arr. 3 44 p.m.	3 36																		3 56	To Victoria, arr. 4 14 p.m.	4 6
13								3 38																		3 58		4 8
14								3 41																		4 1		4 11
15								3 44																		4 4		4 14
16	3 18									3 33			3 35			3 40												
17	3 20									3 35						3 42												
18	3 23									3 38						3 45												
19	3 25									3 40			3 40			3 47												
20	3 28									3 43						3 50												
21	3 30									3 45																		
22	3 31									3 46																		
23					3 33									3 46											4 3	4 6		
24					3 35									3 48											4 5	4 9		
25					3 38									3 51											4 8	4 12		
26					3 40									3 53											4 10	4 14		
27																		3 54										
28																		3 57										
29																		3 59	③									
30																3 53		4 2	4 5									
31																			4 8									
32																			4 12									
33	3 34									3 49			3 44					4 6								4 17		
34	To London Bridge, via Streatham											3 45	3 48	3 57									4 0	4 5				
35												3 46	3 48	3 57										4 5		To London Bridge, via Forest Hill		
36				3 35				3 49													4 1							4 19
37				3 38				3 52													4 4							4 22
38				3 40				3 54													4 6							4 24
39					3 43				③	3 53								4 11							4 13			
40					3 43				3 49	3 53															4 13			
41					3 46				3 51	3 56															4 16			
42					3 49				3 55	3 59															4 19			
43					3 52				3 57	4 2															4 22			
44		3 39		3 44	3 54			3 57	4 0	4 4											4 9				4 24			4 27
45					3 57					4 7															4 27			
46					4 0					4 10															4 30			
47					4 4					4 14															4 34			
48				3 47				4 0													4 12							4 30
49				3 50				4 3													4 15							4 33
50			3 31	3 53				4 6												4 11	4 19							4 36
51			3 35					4 10												4 15								4 40
52			3 39					4 14												4 19								4 44
53																				4 24								4 49
54		3 55																		4 28								4 52
55			3 45					4 19																				
56			3 49					4 23																				
57													3 50	4 0														
58													3 53	4 2														
59													3 55	4 5										4 11				
60														4 8														
61													3 59															
62													4 2															
63													4 5															
64													4 7															
65													4 11															
66													3 57											§ Via Three Bridges				
67													3 59															
68													4 1															
69													4 4															
70													4 6															
71													4 11															
72													4 14															
73													4 17															
74																								4 14				
75																								4 20				
76												4 0												4 24				
77																								4 30				
78		4 13																		4 53				5§ 5				

LONDON, CRYSTAL PALACE, CROYDON, SUTTON, DORKING NORTH,

Down	No.	p.m							Sundays—continued							p.m							No.
Victoria ... dep	1	..	..	..	..	..	..	4 10	..	..	4 15	4 18	..	..	..	..	4 28	..	..	..	..	4 32	1
Charing Cross* ... "	2	..	3	3 53	3	..	..	3	..	3	3	3	..	3	3	..	..	..	..	3	4 23	3	2
Waterloo* ... "	3	..		3 55		..	4 2		..				..			..	..	..	..		4 25		3
London Bridge ... "	4	..	3 58	4 0	4 4	..	..	..	..	4 13	..	..	..	4 21	4 25	..	..	..	..	4 28	4 30	..	4
Battersea Park	5	..	..	3	..	..	..	4 13	..	..	..	..	..	..	..	..	..	..	..	..	3	..	5
Clapham Junction	6	..	..		..	..	4 9	4 16	..	..	4 20	4 24	..	..	..	..	4 33	..	..	..		4 37	6
Wandsworth Common **A**	7	..	..	..	..	..	3	4 19	..	..	4 23	4 27	..	..	..	..	..	..	..	..	..	4 40	7
Balham & Upper Tooting	8	..	..	..	..	..		4 21	..	..	4 25	4 29	..	..	..	..	..	..	..	..	..	4 42	8
South Bermondsey	9	..	..	..	4 7	..	Via Worcester Park	..	..	..	..	..	..	4 24	4 28	..	..	..	..	..	..	..	9
Queen's Road, Peckham	10	..	..	..	4 10	..		..	..	..	..	..	..	4 27	4 31	..	..	..	..	..	..	..	10
Peckham Rye	11	..	..	..	4 12	..		..	..	..	..	..	..	4 29	4 33	..	..	..	..	..	..	..	11
East Dulwich	12	..	..	..	4 15	..		..	..	..	..	..	..	To Victoria, arr. 4 44 p.m	4 36	..	..	..	..	..	..	..	12
North Dulwich	13	..	..	..	4 17	..		..	..	..	..	..	..		4 38	..	..	..	..	..	..	..	13
Tulse Hill	14	..	..	..	4 20	..		..	..	..	..	..	..		4 41	..	..	..	..	..	..	..	14
Streatham	15	..	..	..	..	..		..	..	..	..	..	..		4 44	..	..	..	..	..	..	..	15
New Cross Gate (for E.L.	16	..	4 3	4 5	..	..		..	..	4 18	..	..	..		..	..	..	..	..	4 33	4 35	..	16
Brockley **B** ...[Line)	17	..	4 5	..	..	..		..	..	4 20	..	..	..		..	..	..	..	..	4 35	..	..	17
Honor Oak Park	18	..	4 8	..	..	..		..	..	4 23	..	..	..		..	..	..	..	..	4 38	..	..	18
Forest Hill, for Lordship	19	..	4 10	4 10	..	..		..	..	4 25	..	..	..		..	..	..	..	..	4 40	4 40	..	19
Sydenham ...[Lane	20	..	4 13	..	..	..		..	..	4 28	..	..	..		..	..	..	..	..	4 43	..	..	20
Penge West **C**	21	..	4 15	..	..	..		..	..	4 30	..	..	..	..	..	..	..	..	..	4 45	..	..	21
Anerley	22	..	4 16	..	..	..		..	..	4 31	..	..	..	..	..	..	..	..	..	4 46	..	..	22
Streatham Common	23	..	..	..	..	..	..	..	..	..	..	4 33	..	..	..	..	..	..	..	..	..	4 46	23
Norbury	24	..	..	..	..	..	..	..	..	..	..	4 35	..	..	..	..	..	..	..	..	..	4 48	24
Thornton Heath	25	..	..	..	..	..	..	..	..	..	..	4 38	..	..	..	..	..	..	..	..	..	4 51	25
Selhurst	26	..	..	..	..	..	..	..	..	..	..	4 40	..	..	..	..	..	..	..	..	..	4 53	26
Streatham Hill	27	..	..	..	..	..	..	4 24	..	..	..	..	..	..	..	..	..	..	..	..	..	..	27
West Norwood..[N'wood)	28	..	..	..	4 22	..	..	4 27	3	..	..	..	..	..	..	..	..	..	..	..	..	..	28
Gipsy Hill (for Upper	29	..	..	..	4 24	..	..	4 29		..	..	..	..	..	..	..	..	..	..	..	..	..	29
Crystal Palace D	30	..	..	..	4 27	..	..	4 32	4 35	..	..	..	..	..	..	..	..	..	..	..	..	..	30
Birkbeck	31	..	..	..	..	..	..	..	4 38	..	..	..	..	..	..	..	..	..	..	..	..	..	31
Beckenham Jn. arr	32	..	..	..	..	..	..	..	4 42	..	..	..	..	..	..	..	..	..	..	..	..	..	32
Norwood Junction F	33	..	4 19	4 14	..	..	..	4 36	..	4 34	..	..	..	..	..	..	..	..	..	4 49	4 44	..	33
East Croydon arr	34	..	..	4 18	..	..	..	..	..	..	..	..	..	..	..	..	4 45	..	..	..	4 48	4 57	34
dep	35	..	..	4 18	..	..	..	..	..	..	..	..	..	..	..	..	4 46	..	..	..	4 48	4 57	35
Mitcham Junction	36	..	..	..	..	..	..	..	..	To London Bridge, via Streatham	4 31	..	..	..	4 49	..	..	..	..	..	..	..	36
Hackbridge	37	..	..	..	..	..	..	..	..		4 34	..	..	..	4 52	..	..	..	..	..	..	..	37
Carshalton	38	..	..	..	..	..	..	..	..		4 36	..	..	..	4 54	..	..	..	..	..	..	..	38
West Croydon 319 arr	39	3	4 23	..	..	..	..	4 41	..		..	4 43	..	..	..	3	..	..	..	4 53	..	..	39
dep	40	4 19	4 23	..	..	..	..	..	..		..	4 43	..	..	..	4 49	..	..	..	4 53	..	..	40
Waddon **G**	41	4 21	4 26	..	..	..	..	..	..		..	4 46	..	..	..	4 51	..	..	..	4 56	..	..	41
Wallington	42	4 25	4 29	..	..	..	..	..	..		..	4 49	..	..	..	4 55	..	..	..	4 59	..	..	42
Carshalton Beeches	43	4 27	4 32	..	..	..	..	..	..		..	4 52	..	..	..	4 57	..	..	..	5 2	..	..	43
Sutton 322	44	4 30	4 34	..	..	..	..	..	..		4 39	4 54	..	..	4 57	5 0	..	..	..	5 5	..	..	44
Belmont	45	..	4 37	..	..	..	..	..	..		..	4 57	..	..	..	..	..	..	..	5 7	..	..	45
Banstead	46	..	4 40	..	..	..	..	..	..		..	5 0	..	..	..	..	..	..	..	5 10	..	..	46
Epsom Downs arr	47	..	4 44	..	..	..	..	..	..	..	..	5 4	..	..	..	..	..	..	..	5 14	..	..	47
Cheam	48	..	..	..	..	..	..	..	..	..	4 42	..	..	..	5 0	..	..	..	..	..	..	..	48
Ewell East H	49	..	..	..	..	..	..	..	..	..	4 45	..	..	..	5 3	..	..	..	..	..	..	..	49
Epsom	50	..	..	..	..	..	4 31	..	..	..	4 48	..	..	..	5 6	..	..	..	..	..	..	..	50
Ashtead	51	..	..	..	..	..	4 35	..	..	..	..	..	..	..	5 10	..	..	..	..	..	..	..	51
Leatherhead...[Bridge **J**	52	..	..	..	..	..	4 39	..	..	..	..	..	..	..	5 14	..	..	..	..	..	..	..	52
Boxhill and Burford	53	..	..	..	..	..	..	..	..	..	..	..	..	..	..	..	..	..	..	..	..	..	53
Dorking North K.. arr	54	..	..	..	..	..	..	..	..	..	..	..	..	..	..	..	..	..	..	..	..	..	54
Bookham ...[394	55	..	..	..	..	..	4 45	..	..	..	..	..	..	..	5 19	..	..	..	..	..	..	..	55
Effingham Junction arr	56	..	..	..	..	..	4 49	..	..	..	..	..	..	..	5 23	..	..	..	..	..	..	..	56
South Croydon 234	57	..	..	4 20	..	..	..	..	..	..	..	..	..	..	..	..	..	..	..	..	4 50	5 0	57
Purley Oaks	58	..	..	4 23	..	..	..	..	..	..	..	..	..	..	..	..	..	..	..	..	4 53	5 2	58
Purley	59	..	..	4 26	..	..	..	..	..	..	..	..	..	..	..	..	..	..	..	..	4 55	5 5	59
Coulsdon North **L**.. arr	60	..	..	..	..	..	..	..	..	..	..	..	..	..	..	..	..	..	..	..	..	5 8	60
Purley ... dep	61	..	..	4 29	..	..	..	..	..	..	..	..	..	..	..	..	..	..	..	..	4 59	..	61
Kenley	62	..	..	4 32	..	..	..	..	..	..	..	..	..	..	..	..	..	..	..	..	5 2	..	62
Whyteleafe	63	..	..	4 35	..	..	..	..	..	..	..	..	..	..	..	..	..	..	..	..	5 5	..	63
Warlingham	64	..	..	4 37	..	..	..	..	..	..	..	..	..	..	..	..	..	..	..	..	5 7	..	64
Caterham arr	65	..	..	4 41	..	..	..	..	..	..	..	..	..	..	..	..	..	..	..	..	5 11	..	65
Purley ... dep	66	..	..	4 27	..	..	..	..	..	..	..	..	..	..	..	..	..	..	..	..	4 57	..	66
Reedham	67	..	..	4 29	..	..	..	..	..	..	..	..	..	..	..	..	..	..	..	..	4 59	..	67
Smitham	68	..	..	4 31	..	..	..	..	..	..	..	..	..	..	..	..	..	..	..	..	5 1	..	68
Woodmansterne	69	..	..	4 34	..	..	..	..	..	..	..	..	..	..	..	..	..	..	..	..	5 4	..	69
Chipstead	70	..	..	4 36	..	..	..	..	..	..	..	..	..	..	..	..	..	..	..	..	5 6	..	70
Kingswood M	71	..	..	4 41	..	..	..	..	..	..	..	..	..	..	..	..	..	..	..	..	5 11	..	71
Tadworth N	72	..	..	4 44	..	..	..	..	..	..	..	..	..	..	..	..	..	..	..	..	5 14	..	72
Tattenham Corner arr	73	..	..	4 47	..	..	..	..	..	..	..	..	..	..	..	..	..	..	..	..	5 17	..	73
Coulsdon South	74	..	..	..	..	..	..	..	..	..	..	..	..	..	..	..	..	..	..	..	..	..	74
Merstham	75	..	..	..	..	..	..	..	..	..	..	..	..	..	..	..	..	..	..	..	..	..	75
Redhill 158, 246 ... arr	76	..	..	..	..	..	..	..	..	..	..	..	..	..	..	..	5 0	..	..	..	..	..	76
Reigate 246 ... "	77	..	..	..	..	..	..	..	..	..	..	..	..	..	..	..	5 9	..	..	..	..	..	77
Horsham 159, 244, 245 "	78	..	..	..	..	..	..	..	..	..	..	..	..	..	..	..	..	..	..	..	..	..	78

For Notes, see page 284a

CATERHAM, TATTENHAM CORNER, REDHILL, REIGATE, and HORSHAM

p.m — **Sundays**—*continued* — p.m

No.																												
1	..	..	4 40	..	..	4 45	4 48	4 48	..	..	..	..	..	..	..	..	..	5 10	..	5 15	5 18	..	..	..	..	..	..	5 28
2	3	..	3	..	..	3	..	3	3	3	3	..	3	4 53	3	..	..	3	3	3	3	..	3	..	3	..	3	..
3		..		..	4 42		..					..		4 55		..	5 2					..		..		..		..
4	4 35	..	..	..	..	..	..	..	4 45	4 51	4 55	..	4 58	5 0	5 4	..	..	..	5 13	..	..	..	5 21	..	5 25	..	5 28	..
5	..	..	4 43	..	..	..	..	..	..	..	..	..	..	3	..	..	..	5 13	..	..	..	..	..	..	..	..	..	..
6	..	..	4 46	..	4 49	4 50	4 53	4 54	..	..	..	..	..		..	..	5 9	5 16	..	5 20	5 24	..	..	..	..	..	..	5 33
7	..	..	4 49	..	3	4 53	..	4 57	..	..	..	..	..	..	..	..	3	5 19	..	5 23	5 27	..	..	..	..	..	..	..
8	..	..	4 51	..		4 55	..	4 59	..	..	..	..	..	..	..	..		5 21	..	5 25	5 29	..	..	..	..	..	..	..
9	..	..	..	..	Via Worcester Park	..	..	..	4 48	4 54	4 58	..	..	..	5 7	..	Via Worcester Park	..	..	..	..	..	5 24	..	5 28	..	..	..
10	..	..	..	..		..	..	..	4 51	4 57	5 1	..	..	..	5 10	..		..	..	..	..	..	5 27	..	5 31	..	..	..
11	..	..	..	..		..	..	..	4 53	4 59	5 3	..	..	..	5 12	..		..	..	..	..	..	5 29	..	5 33	..	..	..
12	..	..	..	..		..	..	..	4 56	To Victoria, arr 5 14 p.m	5 6	..	..	..	5 15	..		..	..	..	..	..	☞ To Victoria, arr. 5 44 p.m	..	5 36	..	..	..
13	..	..	..	..		..	..	..	4 58		5 8	..	..	..	5 17	..		..	..	..	..	..		..	5 38	..	..	..
14	..	..	..	..		..	..	..	5 1		5 11	..	..	..	5 20	..		..	..	..	..	..		..	5 41	..	..	..
15	..	..	..	..		..	..	..	5 4		5 14	..	..	..	..	..		..	..	..	..	..		..	5 44	..	..	..
16	4 40	..	..	..		..	..	..	..		..	..	5 3	5 5	..	..		..	5 18	..	..	..		..	..	..	5 33	..
17	4 42	..	..	..		..	..	..	..		..	..	5 5	..	..	..		..	5 20	..	..	..		..	..	..	5 35	..
18	4 45	..	..	..		..	..	..	..		..	..	5 8	..	..	..		..	5 23	..	..	..		..	..	..	5 38	..
19	4 47	..	..	..		..	..	..	..		..	..	5 10	5 10	..	..		..	5 25	..	..	..		..	..	..	5 40	..
20	4 50	..	..	..		..	..	..	..		..	..	5 13	..	..	..		..	5 28	..	..	..		..	..	..	5 43	..
21	..	..	..	..		..	..	..	..		..	..	5 15	..	..	..		..	5 30	..	..	..		..	..	..	5 45	..
22	..	..	..	..		..	..	..	..		..	..	5 16	..	..	..		..	5 31	..	..	..		..	..	..	5 46	..
23	..	..	..	..	..	..	..	5 3	5 6	..	..	..	..	..	..	..	..	..	..	..	5 33	..		..	..	..	..	..
24	..	..	..	..	..	..	..	5 5	5 9	..	..	..	..	..	..	..	..	..	..	..	5 35	..		..	..	..	..	..
25	..	..	..	..	..	..	..	5 8	5 12	..	..	..	..	..	..	..	..	..	..	..	5 38	..		..	..	..	..	..
26	..	..	..	..	..	..	..	5 10	5 14	..	..	..	..	..	..	..	..	..	..	..	5 40	..	Stop	..	..	..	..	..
27	..	..	4 54	..	..	..	..	..	..	..	..	..	..	..	..	..	..	5 24	..	..	..	..	p.m	..	..	..	..	..
28	..	..	4 57	3	..	..	..	..	..	..	..	..	..	..	5 22	..	..	5 27	..	..	..	..	3	..	..	..	..	..
29	..	..	4 59		..	..	..	..	..	..	..	..	..	..	5 24	..	..	5 29	..	..	..	..		..	..	..	..	..
30	4 53	..	5 2	5 5	..	..	..	..	..	..	..	..	..	..	5 27	..	..	5 32	..	..	..	..	5 25	..	..	..	..	..
31	..	..	..	5 8	..	..	..	..	..	..	..	..	..	..	..	..	..	..	..	..	..	..	5 38	..	..	..	..	..
32	..	..	..	5 12	..	..	..	..	..	..	..	..	..	..	..	..	..	..	..	..	..	..	5 42	..	..	..	..	..
33	..	..	5 6	..	..	..	..	..	5 17	..	..	..	5 19	5 14	..	..	..	5 36	5 34	..	..	..	..	..	..	..	5 49	..
34	..	..	..	..	..	..	5 5	..		..	..	..	..	5 18	..	..	..	..	..	..	..	..	..	..	..	..	..	5 45
35	..	..	..	..	..	..	5 5	..		..	..	..	..	5 18	..	..	..	..	..	..	..	..	..	..	..	..	..	5 46
36	..	..	..	..	..	5 1	..	..	To London Bridge, via Fore.t Hill	..	5 19	..	..	..	..	..	..	..	To London Bridge, via Streatham	5 31	..	..	..	..	5 49	..	..	..
37	..	..	..	..	..	5 4	..	..		..	5 22	..	..	..	..	..	..	..		5 34	..	..	..	..	5 52	..	..	..
38	..	..	..	..	..	5 6	..	..		..	5 24	3	..	..	..	..	..	..		5 36	..	..	..	..	5 54	3	..	..
39	..	..	5 11	..	..	..	..	5 13		..	..		5 23	..	..	..	..	5 41		..	5 43	..	..	..	..		5 53	..
40	..	..	..	..	..	..	..	5 13		..	..	5 19	5 23	..	..	..	..	..		..	5 43	..	..	..	..	5 49	5 53	..
41	..	..	..	..	..	..	..	5 16		..	..	5 21	5 26	..	..	..	..	..		..	5 46	..	..	..	..	5 51	5 56	..
42	..	..	..	..	..	..	..	5 19		..	..	5 25	5 29	..	..	..	..	..		..	5 49	..	..	..	..	5 55	5 59	..
43	..	..	..	..	..	..	..	5 22		..	..	5 27	5 32	..	..	..	..	..		..	5 52	..	..	..	..	5 57	6 2	..
44	..	..	..	..	..	5 9	..	5 24		..	5 27	5 30	5 34	..	..	..	..	..		5 39	5 54	..	..	..	5 57	6 0	6 4	..
45	..	..	..	..	..	..	..	5 27		..	..	..	5 37	..	..	..	..	..		..	5 57	..	..	..	..	..	6 7	..
46	..	..	..	..	..	..	..	5 30		..	..	..	5 40	..	..	..	..	..		..	6 0	..	..	..	..	..	6 10	..
47	..	..	..	..	..	..	..	5 34		..	..	..	5 44	..	..	..	..	..		..	6 4	..	..	..	..	..	6 14	..
48	..	..	..	..	..	5 12	..	..	..	..	5 30	..	..	..	..	..	..	..	..	5 42	..	..	..	..	6 0	..	..	..
49	..	..	..	..	..	5 15	..	..	..	..	5 33	..	..	..	..	..	..	..	..	5 45	..	..	..	..	6 3	..	..	..
50	..	..	..	..	5 11	5 19	..	..	..	..	5 36	..	..	..	..	..	5 31	..	..	5 48	..	..	..	..	6 6	..	..	..
51	..	..	..	..	5 15	..	..	..	..	..	5 40	..	..	..	..	..	5 35	..	..	..	..	..	..	..	6 10	..	..	..
52	..	..	..	..	5 19	..	..	..	..	..	5 44	..	..	..	..	..	5 39	..	..	..	..	..	..	..	6 14	..	..	..
53	..	..	..	..	5 24	..	..	..	..	..	5 49	..	..	..	..	..	..	..	..	..	..	..	..	..	..	..	..	..
54	..	..	..	..	5 28	..	..	..	..	..	5 52	..	..	..	..	..	..	..	..	..	..	..	..	..	..	..	..	..
55	..	..	..	..	..	..	..	..	..	..	..	..	..	..	..	..	5 45	..	..	..	..	..	..	..	6 19	..	..	..
56	..	..	..	..	..	..	..	..	..	..	..	..	..	..	..	..	5 49	..	..	..	..	..	..	..	6 23	..	..	..
57	..	..	..	..	..	..	..	..	..	..	..	..	..	5 20	..	..	..	..	..	..	..	..	..	..	..	..	..	..
58	..	..	..	..	..	..	..	..	..	..	..	..	..	5 23	..	..	..	..	..	..	..	..	..	..	..	..	..	..
59	..	..	..	..	..	..	5 11	..	..	..	..	..	..	5 26	..	..	..	..	..	..	..	..	..	..	..	..	..	..
60	..	..	..	..	..	..	..	..	..	..	..	..	..	..	..	..	..	..	..	..	..	..	..	..	..	..	..	..
61	..	..	..	..	..	..	..	..	..	..	..	..	..	5 29	..	..	..	..	..	..	..	..	..	..	..	..	..	..
62	..	..	..	..	..	..	..	..	..	..	..	..	..	5 32	..	..	..	..	..	..	..	..	..	..	..	..	..	..
63	..	..	..	..	..	..	..	..	..	..	..	..	..	5 35	..	..	..	..	..	..	..	..	..	..	..	..	..	..
64	..	..	..	..	..	..	§ Via Three Bridges	..	..	..	..	..	..	5 37	..	..	..	..	..	..	..	..	..	..	..	..	..	..
65	..	..	..	..	..	..		..	..	..	..	..	..	5 41	..	..	..	..	..	..	..	..	..	..	..	..	..	..
66	..	..	..	..	..	..		..	..	..	..	..	..	5 27	..	..	..	..	..	..	..	..	..	..	..	..	..	..
67	..	..	..	..	..	..		..	..	..	..	..	..	5 29	..	..	..	..	..	..	..	..	..	..	..	..	..	..
68	..	..	..	..	..	..		..	..	..	..	..	..	5 31	..	..	..	..	..	..	..	..	..	..	..	..	..	..
69	..	..	..	..	..	..		..	..	..	..	..	..	5 34	..	..	..	..	..	..	..	..	..	..	..	..	..	..
70	..	..	..	..	..	..		..	..	..	..	..	..	5 36	..	..	..	..	..	..	..	..	..	..	..	..	..	..
71	..	..	..	..	..	..		..	..	..	..	..	..	5 41	..	..	..	..	..	..	..	..	..	..	..	..	..	..
72	..	..	..	..	..	..	..	..	..	..	..	..	..	5 44	..	..	..	..	..	..	..	..	..	..	..	..	..	..
73	..	..	..	..	..	..	..	..	..	..	..	..	..	5 47	..	..	..	..	..	..	..	..	..	..	..	..	..	..
74	..	..	..	..	..	..	5 14	..	..	..	..	..	..	..	..	..	..	..	..	..	..	..	..	..	..	..	..	..
75	..	..	..	..	..	..	5 20	..	..	..	..	..	..	..	..	..	..	..	..	..	..	..	..	..	..	..	..	..
76	..	..	..	..	..	..	5 24	..	..	..	..	..	..	..	..	..	..	..	..	..	..	..	..	..	..	..	..	6 0
77	..	..	..	..	..	..	5 20	..	..	..	..	..	..	..	..	..	..	..	..	..	..	..	..	..	..	..	..	..
78	..	..	..	..	5 53	..	6§ 5	..	..	..	..	..	..	..	..	..	..	..	..	..	..	..	..	..	..	..	..	..

LONDON, CRYSTAL PALACE, CROYDON, SUTTON, DORKING NORTH,

Down	No.	p.m.									Sundays—continued								p.m.				No.
Victoria .... dep	1	..	5 32	..	..	..	5 40	..	5 45	5 48	5 48	..	..	..	..	..	..	..	..	..	6 10	..	1
Charing Cross* ... "	2	5 23	**3**	..	**3**	..	**3**	..	**3**	..	**3**	**3**	**3**	**3**	..	**3**	5 53	**3**	..	..	**3**	..	2
Waterloo* .... "	3	5 25		..		..		5 42		..					..		5 55		6 2	..		..	3
London Bridge ..... "	4	5 30	..	..	5 35	..	..	..	..	..	..	5 45	5 51	5 55	..	5 58	6 0	6 4	..	..	..	..	4
Battersea Park	5	**3**	..	..	..	..	5 43	..	..	..	..	..	..	..	..	..	**3**	..	..	..	6 13	..	5
Clapham Junction	6		5 37	..	..	..	5 46	5 49	5 50	5 53	5 54	..	..	..	..	..		..	6 9	..	6 16	..	6
Wandsworth Common **A**	7	..	5 40	..	..	..	5 49	**3**	5 53	..	5 57	..	..	..	..	..	..	..	**3**	..	6 19	..	7
Balham & Upper Tooting	8	..	5 42	..	..	..	5 51		5 55	..	5 59	..	..	..	..	..	..	..		..	6 21	..	8
South Bermondsey	9	..	..	..	..	..	..	Via Worcester Park	..	..	..	5 48	5 54	5 58	..	..	..	6 7	Via Worcester Park	..	..	..	9
Queen's Road, Peckham	10	..	..	..	..	..	..		..	..	..	5 51	5 57	6 1	..	..	..	6 10		..	..	..	10
Peckham Rye	11	..	..	..	..	..	..		..	..	..	5 53	5 59	6 3	..	..	..	6 12		..	..	..	11
East Dulwich	12	..	..	..	..	..	..		..	..	..	5 56		6 6	..	..	..	6 15		..	..	..	12
North Dulwich	13	..	..	..	..	..	..		..	..	..	5 58		6 8	..	..	..	6 17		..	..	..	13
Tulse Hill	14	..	..	..	..	..	..		..	..	..	6 1	☝	6 11	..	..	..	6 20		..	..	..	14
Streatham	15	..	..	..	..	..	..		..	..	..	6 4		6 14	..	..	..	..		..	..	..	15
New Cross Gate (for E.L.	16	5 35	..	..	5 40	..	..		..	..	..	..	To Victoria, arr. 6 14 p.m	..	..	6 3	6 5	..		..	..	..	16
Brockley **B** .... [Line)	17	..	..	..	5 42	..	..		..	..	..	..		..	..	6 5	..	..		..	..	..	17
Honor Oak Park	18	..	..	..	5 45	..	..	..	..	..	..	..		..	..	6 8	..	..	..	..	..	..	18
Forest Hill for Lordship	19	5 40	..	..	5 47	..	..	..	..	..	..	..		..	..	6 10	6 10	..	..	..	..	..	19
Sydenham .... [Lane	20	..	..	..	5 50	..	..	..	..	..	..	..		..	..	6 13	..	..	..	..	..	..	20
Penge West **C**	21	..	..	..	..	..	..	..	..	..	..	..		..	..	6 15	..	..	..	..	..	..	21
Anerley	22	..	..	..	..	..	..	..	..	..	..	..		..	..	6 16	..	..	..	..	..	..	22
Streatham Common	23	..	5 46	..	..	..	..	..	..	..	6 3	6 6		..	..	..	..	..	..	..	..	..	23
Norbury	24	..	5 48	..	..	..	..	..	..	..	6 5	6 9		..	..	..	..	..	..	..	..	..	24
Thornton Heath	25	..	5 51	..	..	..	..	..	..	..	6 8	6 12		..	..	..	..	..	..	..	..	..	25
Selhurst	26	..	5 53	..	..	..	..	..	..	..	6 10	6 14	Stop	..	..	..	..	..	..	..	..	..	26
Streatham Hill	27	..	..	..	..	..	5 54	..	..	..	..	..	p.m	..	..	..	..	..	..	..	6 24	..	27
West Norwood..[N'wood)	28	..	..	..	..	..	5 57	..	..	..	..	..	**3**	..	..	..	..	6 22	..	..	6 27	**3**	28
Gipsy Hill (for Upper	29	..	..	..	..	..	5 59	..	..	..	..	..		..	..	..	..	6 24	..	..	6 29		29
Crystal Palace **D**	30	..	..	..	5 53	..	6 2	..	..	..	..	..	6 5	..	..	..	..	6 27	..	..	6 32	6 35	30
Birkbeck	31	..	..	..	..	..	..	..	..	..	..	..	6 8	..	..	..	..	..	..	..	..	6 38	31
Beckenham Jn. arr	32	..	..	..	..	..	..	..	..	..	..	..	6 12	..	..	..	..	..	..	..	..	6 42	32
Norwood Junction **F** ..	33	5 44	..	..	..	..	6 6	..	..	..	..	..	..	..	..	6 19	6 14	..	..	..	6 36	..	33
East Croydon .... arr	34	5 48	5 57	..	..	..	..	..	..	6 5	..	6 17	..	..	..	..	6 18	..	..	..	..	..	34
East Croydon .... dep	35	5 48	5 57	..	..	..	..	..	..	6 5	..	To London Bridge via Forest Hill	..	..	..	..	6 18	..	..	..	..	..	35
Mitcham Junction	36	..	..	..	..	..	..	..	6 1	..	..		..	6 19	..	..	..	..	..	..	..	..	36
Hackbridge	37	..	..	..	..	..	..	..	6 4	..	..		..	6 22	..	..	..	..	..	..	..	..	37
Carshalton	38	..	..	..	..	..	..	..	6 6	..	..		..	6 24	**3**	..	..	..	..	..	..	..	38
West Croydon 319 arr	39	..	..	..	..	..	6 11	..	..	..	6 13		..	..		6 23	..	..	..	..	6 41	..	39
West Croydon 319 dep	40	..	..	..	..	..	..	..	..	..	6 13		..	..	6 19	6 23	..	..	..	..	..	..	40
Waddon **G**	41	..	..	..	..	..	..	..	..	..	6 16		..	..	6 21	6 26	..	..	..	..	..	..	41
Wallington	42	..	..	..	..	..	..	..	..	..	6 19		..	..	6 25	6 29	..	..	..	..	..	..	42
Carshalton Beeches	43	..	..	..	..	..	..	..	..	..	6 22		..	..	6 27	6 32	..	..	..	..	..	..	43
Sutton 322	44	..	..	..	..	..	..	..	6 9	..	6 24		..	6 27	6 30	6 34	..	..	..	..	..	..	44
Belmont	45	..	..	..	..	..	..	..	..	..	6 27	..	..	..	..	6 37	..	..	..	..	..	..	45
Banstead	46	..	..	..	..	..	..	..	..	..	6 30	..	..	..	..	6 40	..	..	..	..	..	..	46
Epsom Downs ...... arr	47	..	..	..	..	..	..	..	..	..	6 34	..	..	..	..	6 44	..	..	..	..	..	..	47
Cheam	48	..	..	..	..	..	..	..	6 12	..	..	..	..	6 30	..	..	..	..	..	..	..	..	48
Ewell East **H**	49	..	..	..	..	..	..	..	6 15	..	..	..	..	6 33	..	..	..	..	..	..	..	..	49
Epsom	50	..	..	..	..	..	..	6 11	6 19	..	..	..	..	6 36	..	..	..	..	6 31	..	..	..	50
Ashtead	51	..	..	..	..	..	..	6 15	..	..	..	..	..	6 40	..	..	..	..	6 35	..	..	..	51
Leatherhead ... [Bridge **J**	52	..	..	..	..	..	..	6 19	..	..	..	..	..	6 44	..	..	..	..	6 39	..	..	..	52
Boxhill and Burford	53	..	..	..	..	..	..	6 24	..	..	..	..	..	6 49	..	..	..	..	..	..	..	..	53
Dorking North **K** .. arr	54	..	..	..	..	..	..	6 28	..	..	..	..	..	6 52	..	..	..	..	..	..	..	..	54
Bookham .... [394	55	..	..	..	..	..	..	..	..	..	..	..	..	..	..	..	..	..	6 45	..	..	..	55
Effingham Junction arr	56	..	..	..	..	..	..	..	..	..	..	..	..	..	..	..	..	..	6 49	..	..	..	56
South Croydon 234	57	5 50	6 0	..	..	..	..	..	..	..	..	..	..	..	..	..	6 20	..	..	..	..	..	57
Purley Oaks	58	5 53	6 2	..	..	..	..	..	..	..	..	..	..	..	..	..	6 23	..	..	..	..	..	58
Purley	59	5 55	6 5	..	..	..	..	..	..	6 11	..	..	..	..	..	..	6 26	..	..	..	..	..	59
Coulsdon North **L** .. arr	60	..	6 8	..	..	..	..	..	..	..	..	..	..	..	..	..	..	..	..	..	..	..	60
Purley .... dep	61	5 59	..	..	..	..	..	..	..	..	..	..	..	..	..	..	6 29	..	..	..	..	..	61
Kenley	62	6 2	..	..	..	..	..	..	..	..	..	..	..	..	..	..	6 32	..	..	..	..	..	62
Whyteleafe	63	6 5	..	..	..	..	..	..	..	..	..	..	..	..	..	..	6 35	..	..	..	..	..	63
Warlingham	64	6 7	..	..	..	..	..	..	..	..	..	..	..	..	..	..	6 37	..	..	..	..	..	64
Caterham .... arr	65	6 11	..	..	..	..	..	..	..	..	..	..	..	..	..	..	6 41	..	..	..	..	..	65
Purley .... dep	66	5 57	..	..	..	..	..	..	..	§ Via Three Bridges	..	..	..	..	..	..	6 27	..	..	..	..	..	66
Reedham	67	5 59	..	..	..	..	..	..	..		..	..	..	..	..	..	6 29	..	..	..	..	..	67
Smitham	68	6 1	..	..	..	..	..	..	..		..	..	..	..	..	..	6 31	..	..	..	..	..	68
Woodmansterne	69	6 4	..	..	..	..	..	..	..		..	..	..	..	..	..	6 34	..	..	..	..	..	69
Chipstead	70	6 6	..	..	..	..	..	..	..		..	..	..	..	..	..	6 36	..	..	..	..	..	70
Kingswood **M**	71	6 11	..	..	..	..	..	..	..		..	..	..	..	..	..	6 41	..	..	..	..	..	71
Tadworth **N**	72	6 14	..	..	..	..	..	..	..		..	..	..	..	..	..	6 44	..	..	..	..	..	72
Tattenham Corner. arr	73	6 17	..	..	..	..	..	..	..		..	..	..	..	..	..	6 47	..	..	..	..	..	73
Coulsdon South	74	..	..	..	..	..	..	..	..	6 14	..	..	..	..	..	..	..	..	..	..	..	..	74
Merstham	75	..	..	..	..	..	..	..	..	6 20	..	..	..	..	..	..	..	..	..	..	..	..	75
Redhill 158,246 ...... arr	76	..	..	..	..	..	..	..	..	6 24	..	..	..	..	..	..	..	..	..	..	..	..	76
Reigate 246 .... "	77	..	..	..	..	..	..	..	..	6 30	..	..	..	..	..	..	..	..	..	..	..	..	77
Horsham 159,244,245 "	78	..	..	..	..	..	..	6 53	..	7§ 5	..	..	..	..	..	..	..	..	..	..	..	..	78

For Notes, see page 284a

CATERHAM, TATTENHAM CORNER, REDHILL, REIGATE, and HORSHAM

p.m — **Sundays** —*continued* — p.m

No.																												
1	..	6 15	6 18	..	..	..	6 28	..	..	..	..	6 32	..	..	..	6 40	..	6 45	..	6 45	..	6 48	6 48	..	..	..	..	..
2	3	3	3	..	..	3	..	3	..	3	6 23	3	..	3	..	3	..	3	..	..	..	..	3	3	3	3	..	3
3				..	..		..		..		6 25		..		..		6 42		..	..	..	..					..	
4	6 13	..	..	..	..	6 21	..	6 25	..	6 28	6 30	..	..	6 35	6 40	..	..	..	..	..	..	..	..	6 45	6 51	6 55	..	6 58
5	..	..	..	..	..	..	..	..	..	..	3	..	..	..	..	6 43	..	..	..	..	..	..	..	..	..	..	..	..
6	..	6 20	6 24	..	..	..	6 33	..	..	..		6 37	..	..	..	6 46	6 49	6 50	..	..	..	6 53	6 54	..	..	..	..	..
7	..	6 23	6 27	..	..	..	..	..	..	..	..	6 40	..	..	..	6 49	3	6 53	..	..	..	..	6 57	..	..	..	..	..
8	..	6 25	6 29	..	..	..	..	..	..	..	..	6 42	..	..	..	6 51		6 55	..	..	..	..	6 59	..	..	..	..	..
9	..	..	..	..	..	6 24	..	6 28	..	..	..	..	..	..	..	..	Via Worcester Park	..	..	..	..	..	..	6 48	6 54	6 58	..	..
10	..	..	..	..	..	6 27	..	6 31	..	..	..	..	..	..	..	..		..	..	..	..	..	..	6 51	6 57	7 1	..	..
11	..	..	..	..	..	6 29	..	6 33	..	..	..	..	..	..	..	..		..	..	..	..	..	..	6 53	6 59	7 3	..	..
12	..	..	..	..	..	To Victoria, arr. 6 44 p.m	..	6 36	..	..	..	..	..	..	..	..		..	..	..	..	..	..	6 56	To Victoria, arr. 7 14 p.m	7 6	..	..
13	..	..	..	..	..		..	6 38	..	..	..	..	..	..	..	..		..	..	..	..	..	..	6 58		7 8	..	..
14	..	..	..	..	..		..	6 41	..	..	..	..	..	..	..	..		..	..	..	..	..	..	7 1		7 11	..	..
15	..	..	..	..	..		..	6 44	..	..	..	..	..	..	..	..		..	..	..	..	..	..	7 4		7 14	..	..
16	6 18	..	..	..	..		..	..	..	6 33	6 35	..	..	6 40	6 47	..		..	..	..	..	..	..	..		..	..	7 3
17	6 20	..	..	..	..		..	..	..	6 35	..	..	..	6 42	..	..		..	..	..	..	..	..	..		..	..	7 5
18	6 23	..	..	..	..		..	..	..	6 38	..	..	..	6 45	..	..	..	..	..	..	..	..	..	..		..	..	7 8
19	6 25	..	..	..	..		..	..	..	6 40	6 40	..	..	6 47	..	..	..	..	..	..	..	..	..	..		..	..	7 10
20	6 28	..	..	..	..		..	..	..	6 43	..	..	..	6 50	..	..	..	..	..	..	..	..	..	..		..	..	7 13
21	6 30	..	..	..	..		..	..	..	6 45	..	..	..	..	..	..	..	..	..	..	..	..	..	..		..	..	7 15
22	6 31	..	..	..	..		..	..	..	6 46	..	..	..	..	..	..	..	..	..	..	..	..	..	..		..	..	7 16
23	..	..	6 33	..	..	..	..	..	..	..	..	6 46	..	..	..	..	..	..	..	..	..	..	7 3	7 6	..	..	..	..
24	..	..	6 35	..	..	..	..	..	..	..	..	6 48	..	..	..	..	..	..	..	..	..	..	7 5	7 9	..	..	..	..
25	..	..	6 38	..	..	..	..	..	..	..	..	6 51	..	..	..	..	..	..	..	..	..	..	7 8	7 12	..	..	..	..
26	..	..	6 40	..	..	..	..	..	..	..	..	6 53	..	..	..	..	..	..	..	..	..	..	7 11	7 14	..	..	..	..
27	..	..	..	..	..	..	..	..	..	..	..	..	..	..	..	6 54	..	..	..	..	..	..	..	..	..	..	..	..
28	..	..	..	..	..	..	..	..	..	..	..	..	..	..	..	6 57	..	..	3	..	..	..	..	..	..	..	..	..
29	..	..	..	..	..	..	..	..	..	..	..	..	..	..	..	6 59	..	..		..	..	..	..	..	..	..	..	..
30	..	..	..	..	..	..	..	..	..	..	..	..	..	6 53	..	7 2	..	..	7 5	..	..	..	..	..	..	..	..	..
31	..	..	..	..	..	..	..	..	..	..	..	..	..	..	..	..	..	..	7 8	..	..	..	..	..	..	..	..	..
32	..	..	..	..	..	..	..	..	..	..	..	..	..	..	..	..	..	..	7 12	..	..	..	..	..	..	..	..	..
33	6 34	..	..	..	..	..	..	..	..	6 49	6 44	..	..	..	6 59	7 6	..	..	..	..	..	..	..	7 17	..	..	..	7 19
34	To London Bridge via Streatham	..	..	..	..	..	6 45	..	..	..	6 48	6 57	..	..	7 4	..	..	..	..	7 1	..	7 5	..	..	..	..	..	..
35		..	..	..	..	..	6 46	..	..	..	6 48	6 57	..	..	7 6	..	..	..	..	..	..	7 5	..	To London Bridge, via Forest Hill	..	..	..	..
36		6 31	..	..	..	..	..	6 49	..	..	..	..	..	..	..	..	..	7 1	..	..	..	..	..		..	7 19	..	..
37		6 34	..	..	..	..	..	6 52	..	..	..	..	..	..	..	..	..	7 4	..	..	..	..	..		..	7 22	..	..
38		6 36	..	..	..	..	..	6 54	3	..	..	..	..	..	..	..	..	7 6	..	..	..	..	..		..	7 24	3	..
39		..	6 43	..	..	..	..	..		6 53	..	..	..	..	..	7 11	..	..	..	..	..	..	7 13		..	..		7 28
40		..	6 43	..	..	..	..	..	6 49	6 53	..	..	..	..	..	..	..	..	..	..	..	..	7 13		..	..	7 19	7 23
41		..	6 46	..	..	..	..	..	6 51	6 56	..	..	..	..	..	..	..	..	..	..	..	..	7 16		..	..	7 21	7 26
42		..	6 49	..	..	..	..	..	6 55	6 59	..	..	..	..	..	..	..	..	..	..	..	..	7 19		..	..	7 25	7 29
43		..	6 52	..	..	..	..	..	6 57	7 2	..	..	..	..	..	..	..	..	..	..	..	..	7 22		..	..	7 27	7 32
44		6 39	6 54	..	..	..	..	6 57	7 0	7 4	..	..	..	..	..	..	..	7 9	..	..	..	..	7 24		..	7 27	7 30	7 34
45	..	..	6 57	..	..	..	..	..	..	7 7	..	..	..	..	..	..	..	..	..	..	..	..	7 27	..	..	..	..	7 37
46	..	..	7 0	..	..	..	..	..	..	7 10	..	..	..	..	..	..	..	..	..	..	..	..	7 30	..	..	..	..	7 40
47	..	..	7 4	..	..	..	..	..	..	7 14	..	..	..	..	..	..	..	..	..	..	..	..	7 34	..	..	..	..	7 44
48	..	6 42	..	..	..	..	..	7 0	..	..	..	..	..	..	..	..	..	7 12	..	..	..	..	..	..	..	7 30	..	..
49	..	6 45	..	..	..	..	..	7 3	..	..	..	..	..	..	..	..	..	7 15	..	..	..	..	..	..	..	7 33	..	..
50	..	6 48	..	..	..	..	..	7 6	..	..	..	..	..	..	..	..	7 11	7 19	..	..	..	..	..	..	..	7 36	..	..
51	..	..	..	..	..	..	..	7 10	..	..	..	..	..	..	..	..	7 15	..	..	..	..	..	..	..	..	7 40	..	..
52	..	..	..	..	..	..	..	7 14	..	..	..	..	..	..	..	..	7 19	..	..	..	..	..	..	..	..	7 44	..	..
53	..	..	..	..	..	..	..	..	..	..	..	..	..	..	..	..	7 24	..	..	..	..	..	..	..	..	7 49	..	..
54	..	..	..	..	..	..	..	..	..	..	..	..	..	..	..	..	7 28	..	..	..	..	..	..	..	..	7 52	..	..
55	..	..	..	..	..	..	..	7 19	..	..	..	..	..	..	..	..	..	..	..	..	..	..	..	..	..	..	..	..
56	..	..	..	..	..	..	..	7 23	..	..	..	..	..	..	..	..	..	..	..	..	..	..	..	..	..	..	..	..
57	..	..	..	..	..	..	..	..	..	..	6 50	7 0	..	..	7 9	..	..	..	..	..	..	..	..	..	..	..	..	..
58	..	..	..	..	..	..	..	..	..	..	6 53	7 2	..	..	..	..	..	..	..	..	..	..	..	..	..	..	..	..
59	..	..	..	..	..	..	..	..	..	..	6 55	7 5	..	..	..	..	..	..	..	..	..	7 11	..	..	..	..	..	..
60	..	..	..	..	..	..	..	..	..	..	..	7 8	..	..	..	..	..	..	..	..	..	..	..	..	..	..	..	..
61	..	..	..	..	..	..	..	..	..	..	6 59	..	..	..	..	..	..	..	..	..	..	..	..	..	..	..	..	..
62	..	..	..	..	..	..	..	..	..	..	7 2	..	..	..	..	..	..	..	..	..	..	..	..	..	..	..	..	..
63	..	..	..	..	..	..	..	..	..	..	7 5	..	..	..	..	..	..	..	..	..	..	..	..	..	..	..	..	..
64	..	..	..	..	..	..	..	..	..	..	7 7	..	..	..	..	..	..	..	..	..	..	..	..	..	..	..	..	..
65	..	..	..	..	..	..	..	..	..	..	7 11	..	..	..	..	..	..	..	..	..	..	..	..	..	..	..	..	..
66	..	..	..	..	..	..	..	..	..	..	6 57	..	..	..	..	..	..	..	..	..	..	§ Via Three Bridges	..	..	..	..	..	..
67	..	..	..	..	..	..	..	..	..	..	6 59	..	..	..	..	..	..	..	..	..	..		..	..	..	..	..	..
68	..	..	..	..	..	..	..	..	..	..	7 1	..	..	..	..	..	..	..	..	..	..		..	..	..	..	..	..
69	..	..	..	..	..	..	..	..	..	..	7 4	..	..	..	..	..	..	..	..	..	..		..	..	..	..	..	..
70	..	..	..	..	..	..	..	..	..	..	7 6	..	..	..	..	..	..	..	..	..	..		..	..	..	..	..	..
71	..	..	..	..	..	..	..	..	..	..	7 11	..	..	..	..	..	..	..	..	..	..		..	..	..	..	..	..
72	..	..	..	..	..	..	..	..	..	..	7 14	..	..	..	..	..	..	..	..	..	..		..	..	..	..	..	..
73	..	..	..	..	..	..	..	..	..	..	7 17	..	..	..	..	..	..	..	..	..	..		..	..	..	..	..	..
74	..	..	..	..	..	..	..	..	..	..	..	..	..	..	..	..	..	..	..	..	..	7 14	..	..	..	..	..	..
75	..	..	..	..	..	..	..	..	..	..	..	..	..	..	..	..	..	..	..	..	..	7 20	..	..	..	..	..	..
76	..	..	..	..	..	..	7 0	..	..	..	..	..	..	..	..	..	..	..	..	..	..	7 24	..	..	..	..	..	..
77	..	..	..	..	..	..	7 9	..	..	..	..	..	..	..	..	..	..	..	..	..	..	7 30	..	..	..	..	..	..
78	..	..	..	..	..	..	..	..	..	..	..	..	..	..	..	..	7 53	..	..	..	..	8 §5	..	..	..	..	..	..

LONDON, CRYSTAL PALACE, CROYDON, SUTTON, DORKING NORTH,

For Notes, see page 284a

Down	No.				p.m					Sundays—continued									p.m				No.
VICTORIA .... dep	1	..	..	..	..	7 8	7 11	..	7 18	7 24	7 18	..	..	7 25	..	..	7 28	..	..	..	..	7 32	1
CHARING CROSS* ... "	2	6 53	3	..	..	..	3	3	..	3	3	..	3	..	3	..	..	..	3	..	7 23	3	2
WATERLOO* .... "	3	6 55		..	7 2	..			..			..		..		..	..	..		..	7 25		3
LONDON BRIDGE ..... "	4	7 0	7 4	..	..	..	..	7 13	..	..	..	..	7 21	..	7 25	..	..	..	7 28	..	7 30	..	4
Battersea Park	5	3	..	..	..	..	7 14	..	..	..	..	..	..	..	..	..	..	..	..	..	3	..	5
Clapham Junction	6		..	..	7 9	7 15	7 17	..	..	7 29	7 24	..	..	..	..	..	7 33	..	..	..		7 37	6
Wandsworth Common A	7	..	..	..	3	..	7 20	..	..	..	7 27	..	..	..	..	..	..	..	..	..	..	7 40	7
Balham & Upper Tooting	8	..	..	..		..	7 22	..	..	7 33	7 29	..	..	..	..	..	..	..	..	..	..	7 42	8
South Bermondsey	9	..	7 7	..	Via Worcester Park	..	..	..	..	..	..	..	7 24	..	7 28	..	..	..	..	..	..	..	9
Queen's Road, Peckham	10	..	7 10	..		..	..	..	..	..	..	..	7 27	..	7 31	..	..	..	..	..	..	..	10
Peckham Rye	11	..	7 12	..		..	..	..	..	..	..	..	7 29	..	7 33	..	..	..	..	..	..	..	11
East Dulwich	12	..	7 15	..		..	..	..	..	..	..	..		..	7 36	..	..	..	..	..	..	..	12
North Dulwich	13	..	7 17	..		..	..	..	..	..	..	..	To Victoria, arr. 7 44 p.m	..	733	..	..	..	..	..	..	..	13
Tulse Hill	14	..	7 20	..		..	..	..	..	..	..	..		..	7 41	..	..	..	..	..	..	..	14
Streatham	15	..	..	..		..	..	..	..	..	..	..		..	7 44	..	..	..	..	..	..	..	15
New Cross Gate (for E.L.	16	7 5	..	..		..	..	7 18	..	..	..	..		..	..	..	..	..	7 33	..	7 35	..	16
Brockley B .... [Line)	17	..	..	..	..	..	..	7 20	..	..	..	..		..	..	..	..	..	7 35	..	..	..	17
Honor Oak Park	18	..	..	..	..	..	..	7 23	..	..	..	..		..	..	..	..	..	7 38	..	..	..	18
Forest Hill, for Lordship	19	7 10	..	..	..	..	..	7 25	..	..	..	..		..	..	..	..	..	7 40	..	7 40	..	19
Sydenham .... [Lane	20	..	..	..	..	..	..	7 28	..	..	..	..		..	..	..	..	..	7 43	..	..	..	20
Penge West C	21	..	..	..	..	..	..	7 30	..	..	..	..		..	..	..	..	..	7 45	..	..	..	21
Anerley	22	..	..	..	..	..	..	7 31	..	..	..	..		..	..	..	..	..	7 46	..	..	..	22
Streatham Common	23	..	..	..	..	..	..	..	..	..	7 33	..		..	..	..	..	..	..	..	..	7 46	23
Norbury	24	..	..	..	..	..	..	..	..	..	7 35	..		..	..	..	..	..	..	..	..	7 48	24
Thornton Heath	25	..	..	..	..	..	..	..	..	..	7 38	..		..	..	..	..	..	..	..	..	7 51	25
Selhurst	26	..	..	..	..	..	..	..	..	..	7 40	..	Stop	..	..	..	..	..	..	..	..	7 53	26
Streatham Hill	27	..	..	..	..	..	7 24	..	..	..	..	..	p.m	..	..	..	..	..	..	..	..	..	27
West Norwood..[N'wood)	28	..	7 22	..	..	..	7 27	..	..	..	..	..	3	..	..	..	..	..	..	..	..	..	28
Gipsy Hill (for Upper	29	..	7 24	..	..	..	7 30	..	..	..	..	..		..	..	..	..	..	..	..	..	..	29
Crystal Palace D	30	..	7 27	..	..	..	7 32	..	..	..	..	..	7 35	..	..	..	..	..	..	..	..	..	30
Birkbeck	31	..	..	..	..	..	..	..	..	..	..	..	7 38	..	..	..	..	..	..	..	..	..	31
Beckenham Jn. arr	32	..	..	..	..	..	..	..	..	..	..	..	7 42	..	..	..	..	..	..	..	..	..	32
Norwood Junction F ..	33	7 14	..	..	..	..	7 36	7 34	..	..	..	..	..	..	..	..	..	..	7 49	..	7 44	..	33
East Croydon .. arr	34	7 18	..	..	..	7 29	..	..	..	..	..	..	..	7 40	..	..	7 45	..	..	..	7 48	7 57	34
East Croydon .. dep	35	7 18	..	..	..	7 31	..	..	..	..	..	..	..	..	..	..	7 46	..	..	..	7 48	7 57	35
Mitcham Junction	36	..	..	..	..	..	..	To London Bridge, via Streatham	..	7 39	..	..	..	..	7 49	..	..	..	..	..	..	..	36
Hackbridge	37	..	..	..	..	..	..		..	7 42	..	..	..	..	7 52	..	..	..	..	..	..	..	37
Carshalton	38	..	..	..	..	..	..		..	7 44	..	..	..	..	7 54	3	..	..	..	..	..	..	38
West Croydon 319 arr	39	..	..	..	..	..	7 41		..	..	7 43	..	..	..	..		..	..	7 53	..	..	..	39
West Croydon 319 dep	40	..	..	..	..	..	..		..	..	7 43	..	..	..	..	7 49	..	..	7 53	..	..	..	40
Waddon G	41	..	..	..	..	..	..		..	..	7 46	..	..	..	..	7 51	..	..	7 56	..	..	..	41
Wallington	42	..	..	..	..	..	..		..	..	7 49	..	..	..	..	7 55	..	..	7 59	..	..	..	42
Carshalton Beeches	43	..	..	..	..	..	..		..	..	7 52	..	..	..	..	7 57	..	..	8 2	..	..	..	43
Sutton 322	44	..	..	..	..	..	..		7 39	7 48	7 54	..	..	..	7 57	8 0	..	..	8 4	..	..	..	44
Belmont	45	..	..	..	..	..	..		..	..	7 57	..	..	..	..	..	..	..	8 7	..	..	..	45
Banstead	46	..	..	..	..	..	..		..	..	8 0	..	..	..	..	..	..	..	8 10	..	..	..	46
Epsom Downs ...... arr	47	..	..	..	..	..	..		..	..	8 4	..	..	..	..	..	..	..	8 14	..	..	..	47
Cheam	48	..	..	..	..	..	..	..	..	7 51	..	..	..	..	8 0	..	..	..	..	..	..	..	48
Ewell East H	49	..	..	..	..	..	..	..	..	7 54	..	..	..	..	8 3	..	..	..	..	..	..	..	49
Epsom	50	..	..	..	7 31	..	..	..	..	7 58	..	..	..	..	8 6	..	..	..	..	..	..	..	50
Ashtead	51	..	..	..	7 35	..	..	..	..	..	..	..	..	..	8 10	..	..	..	..	..	..	..	51
Leatherhead..[Bridge J	52	..	..	..	7 39	..	..	..	..	..	..	..	..	..	8 14	..	..	..	..	..	..	..	52
Boxhill and Burford	53	..	..	..	..	..	..	..	..	..	..	..	..	..	..	..	..	..	..	..	..	..	53
Dorking North K .. arr	54	..	..	..	..	..	..	..	7 53	..	..	..	..	..	..	..	..	..	..	..	..	..	54
Bookham .... [594	55	..	..	..	7 45	..	..	..	..	..	..	..	..	..	8 19	..	..	..	..	..	..	..	55
Effingham Junction arr	56	..	..	..	7 49	..	..	..	..	..	..	..	..	..	8 23	..	..	..	..	..	..	..	56
South Croydon 234	57	7 20	..	..	..	7 34	..	..	..	..	..	..	..	..	..	..	..	..	..	..	7 50	8 0	57
Purley Oaks	58	7 23	..	..	..	..	..	..	..	..	..	..	..	..	..	..	..	..	..	..	7 53	8 2	58
Purley	59	7 26	..	..	..	..	..	..	..	..	..	..	..	..	..	..	7 51	..	..	..	7 55	8 5	59
Coulsdon North L .. arr	60	..	..	..	..	..	..	..	..	..	..	..	..	..	..	..	..	..	..	..	..	8 8	60
Purley .... dep	61	7 29	..	..	..	..	..	..	..	..	..	..	..	..	..	..	..	..	..	..	7 59	..	61
Kenley	62	7 32	..	..	..	..	..	..	..	..	..	..	..	..	..	..	..	..	..	..	8 2	..	62
Whyteleafe	63	7 35	..	..	..	..	..	..	..	..	..	..	..	..	..	..	..	..	..	..	8 5	..	63
Warlingham	64	7 37	..	..	..	..	..	..	..	..	..	..	..	..	..	..	..	..	..	..	8 7	..	64
Caterham .... arr	65	7 41	..	..	..	..	..	..	..	..	..	..	..	..	..	..	..	..	..	..	8 11	..	65
Purley .... dep	66	7 27	..	..	..	..	..	..	..	..	..	..	..	..	..	..	..	..	..	..	7 57	..	66
Reedham	67	7 29	..	..	..	..	..	..	..	..	..	..	..	..	..	..	..	..	..	..	7 59	..	67
Smitham	68	7 31	..	..	..	..	..	..	..	..	..	..	..	..	..	..	..	..	..	..	8 1	..	68
Woodmansterne	69	7 34	..	..	..	..	..	..	..	..	..	..	..	..	..	..	..	..	..	..	8 4	..	69
Chipstead	70	7 36	..	..	..	..	..	..	..	..	..	..	..	..	..	..	..	..	..	..	8 6	..	70
Kingswood M	71	7 41	..	..	..	..	..	..	..	..	..	..	..	..	..	..	..	..	..	..	8 11	..	71
Tadworth N	72	7 44	..	..	..	..	..	..	..	..	..	..	..	..	..	..	..	..	..	..	8 14	..	72
Tattenham Corner. arr	73	7 47	..	..	..	..	..	..	..	..	..	..	..	..	..	..	..	..	..	..	8 17	..	73
Coulsdon South	74	..	..	..	..	..	..	..	..	..	..	..	..	..	..	..	..	..	..	..	..	..	74
Merstham	75	..	..	..	..	..	..	..	..	..	..	..	..	..	..	..	..	..	..	..	..	..	75
Redhill 158,246 ...... arr	76	..	..	..	..	..	..	..	..	..	..	..	..	..	..	..	8 2	..	..	..	..	..	76
Reigate 246 .... "	77	..	..	..	..	..	..	..	..	..	..	..	..	..	..	..	8 12	..	..	..	..	..	77
Horsham 159,244,245 "	78	..	..	..	..	..	..	..	8 13	..	..	..	..	..	..	..	..	..	..	..	..	..	78

CATERHAM, TATTENHAM CORNER, REDHILL, REIGATE, and HORSHAM

No.	p.m.													Sundays—continued									p.m.					
1	..	..	7 40	..	7 45	..	7 48	7 48	..	..	..	..	..	..	..	..	..	8 10	..	8 15	8 18	..	..	..	..	..	..	8 28
2	3	..	3	..	3	..	..	3	3	3	3	..	3	7 53	3	..	..	3	3	3	3	3	..	3	3	..	3	..
3		..		7 42		..	..					..		7 55		..	8 2						..			..		..
4	7 35	..	..	..	..	..	..	..	7 45	7 51	7 55	..	7 58	8 0	8 4	..	..	..	8 14	..	..	8 15	8 16	8 21	8 25	..	8 28	..
5	..	..	7 43	..	..	..	..	..	..	..	..	..	..	3	..	..	..	8 13	..	..	..	..	..	..	..	..	..	..
6	..	..	7 46	7 40	7 50	..	7 53	7 53	..	..	..	..	..		..	..	8 9	8 16	..	8 20	8 24	..	..	..	..	..	..	8 35
7	..	..	7 49	3	7 53	..	..	7 56	..	..	..	..	..	..	..	..	3	8 19	..	8 23	8 27	..	..	..	..	..	..	..
8	..	..	7 51		7 56	..	..	7 58	..	..	..	..	..	..	..	..		8 21	..	8 25	8 29	..	..	..	..	..	..	..
9	..	..	..	Via Worcester Park	..	..	..	..	7 48	7 54	7 58	..	..	..	8 7	..	Via Worcester Park	..	..	..	..	8 18	..	8 24	8 28	..	..	..
10	..	..	..		..	..	..	..	7 51	7 57	8 1	..	..	..	8 10	..		..	..	..	..	8 21	..	8 27	8 31	..	..	..
11	..	..	..		..	..	..	..	7 53	7 59	8 3	..	..	..	8 12	..		..	..	..	..	8 23	..	8 29	8 33	..	..	..
12	..	..	..		..	..	..	..	7 56		8 6	..	..	..	8 15	..		..	..	..	..	8 26	..		8 36	..	..	..
13	..	..	..		..	..	..	..	7 58		8 8	..	..	..	8 17	..		..	..	..	..	8 28	..		8 38	..	..	..
14	..	..	..		..	..	..	..	8 1		8 11	..	..	..	8 20	..		..	..	..	..	8 31	..		8 41	..	..	..
15	..	..	..		..	..	..	..	8 4		8 14	..	..	..	..	..		..	..	..	..	8 34	..		8 44	..	..	..
16	7 40	..	..		..	..	..	..	..	To Victoria, arr. 8 14 p.m	..	..	8 3	8 5	..	..		..	8 19	..	..	..	8 21	To Victoria, arr. 8 44 p.m	..	..	8 33	..
17	7 42	..	..		..	..	..	..	..		..	..	8 5	..	..	..		..	8 21	..	..	..	..		..	..	8 35	..
18	7 45	..	..		..	..	..	..	..		..	..	8 8	..	..	..		..	8 24	..	..	..	..		..	..	8 38	..
19	7 47	..	..	..	..	..	..	..	..		..	..	8 10	8 10	..	..	..	..	8 26	..	..	..	..		..	..	8 40	..
20	7 50	..	..	..	..	..	..	..	..		..	..	8 13	..	..	..	..	..	8 29	..	..	..	..		..	..	8 43	..
21	..	..	..	..	..	..	..	..	..		..	..	8 15	..	..	..	..	..	8 31	..	..	..	..		..	..	8 45	..
22	..	..	..	..	..	..	..	..	..		..	..	8 16	..	..	..	..	..	8 32	..	..	..	..		..	..	8 46	..
23	..	..	..	..	..	..	..	8 2	8 6		..	..	..	..	..	..	..	..	..	..	8 33	8 36	..		..	..	..	..
24	..	..	..	..	..	..	..	8 4	8 9		..	..	..	..	..	..	..	..	..	..	8 35	8 39	..		..	..	..	..
25	..	..	..	..	..	..	..	8 7	8 12		..	..	..	..	..	..	..	..	..	..	8 38	8 42	..		..	..	..	..
26	..	..	..	..	..	..	..	8 9	8 14	Stop	..	..	..	..	..	..	..	..	..	..	8 40	8 44	..	Stop	..	..	..	..
27	..	..	7 54	..	..	..	..	..	..	p.m	..	..	..	..	..	..	..	8 24	..	..	..	..	..	p.m	..	..	..	..
28	..	..	7 57	..	..	..	..	..	..	3	..	..	..	..	8 22	..	..	8 27	..	..	..	..	..	3	..	..	..	..
29	..	..	7 59	..	..	..	..	..	..		..	..	..	..	8 24	..	..	8 29	..	..	..	..	..		..	..	..	..
30	7 53	..	8 2	..	..	..	..	..	..	8 5	..	..	..	..	8 27	..	..	8 32	..	..	..	..	..	8 35	..	..	..	..
31	..	..	..	..	..	..	..	..	..	8 8	..	..	..	..	..	..	..	..	..	..	..	..	..	8 38	..	..	..	..
32	..	..	..	..	..	..	..	..	..	8 12	..	..	..	..	..	..	..	..	..	..	..	..	..	8 42	..	..	..	..
33	..	..	8 6	..	..	..	..	..	8 17	..	..	..	8 19	8 14	..	..	..	8 37	8 35	..	..	8 47	8 30	..	..	..	8 49	..
34	..	..	..	..	..	..	8 5	..	To London Bridge, via Forest Hill	..	..	..	..	8 18	..	..	..	..	To London Bridge, via Streatham	..	..	To London Bridge, via Forest Hill	8 34	..	..	..	..	8 47
35	..	..	..	..	..	..	8 5	..		..	..	..	..	8 18	..	..	..	..		..	..		8 35	..	..	..	..	8 48
36	..	..	..	..	8 1	..	..	..		..	8 19	..	..	..	..	..	..	..		8 31	..		..	..	8 49	..	..	..
37	..	..	..	..	8 4	..	..	..		..	8 22	..	..	..	..	..	..	..		8 34	..		..	..	8 52	..	..	..
38	..	..	..	..	8 6	..	..	..		..	8 24	3	..	..	..	..	..	..		8 36	..		..	..	8 54	3	..	..
39	..	..	8 11	..	..	..	..	8 13		..	..		8 23	..	..	..	..	8 41		..	8 43		..	..	..		8 52	..
40	..	..	..	..	..	..	..	8 13		..	..	8 19	8 23	..	..	..	..	..		..	8 43		..	..	..	8 49	8 53	..
41	..	..	..	..	..	..	..	8 16		..	..	8 21	8 26	..	..	..	..	..		..	8 46		..	..	..	8 51	8 56	..
42	..	..	..	..	..	..	..	8 19		..	..	8 25	8 29	..	..	..	..	..		..	8 49		..	..	..	8 55	8 59	..
43	..	..	..	..	..	..	..	8 22		..	..	8 27	8 32	..	..	..	..	..		..	8 52		..	..	..	8 57	9 2	..
44	..	..	..	..	8 9	..	..	8 24		..	8 27	8 30	8 34	..	..	..	..	..		8 39	8 54		..	..	8 57	9 0	9 4	..
45	..	..	..	..	..	..	..	8 27		..	..		8 37	..	..	..	..	..		..	8 57		..	..	..	..	9 7	..
46	..	..	..	..	..	..	..	8 30		..	..	Stop	8 40	..	..	..	..	..		..	9 0		..	..	..	..	9 10	..
47	..	..	..	..	..	..	..	8 34		..	..	..	8 44	..	..	..	..	..		..	9 4		..	..	..	..	9 14	..
48	..	..	..	..	8 12	..	..	..	..	..	8 30	..	..	..	..	..	..	..	..	8 42	..	..	..	..	9 0	..	..	..
49	..	..	..	..	8 15	..	..	..	..	..	8 33	..	..	..	..	..	..	..	..	8 45	..	..	..	..	9 3	..	..	..
50	..	..	..	8 11	8 19	..	..	..	..	..	8 36	..	..	..	..	..	8 31	..	..	8 48	..	..	..	..	9 6	..	..	..
51	..	..	..	8 15	..	..	..	..	..	..	8 40	..	..	..	..	..	8 35	..	..	..	..	..	..	..	9 10	..	..	..
52	..	..	..	8 19	..	..	..	..	..	..	8 44	..	..	..	..	..	8 39	..	..	..	..	..	..	..	9 14	..	..	..
53	..	..	..	8 24	..	..	..	..	..	..	8 49	..	..	..	..	..	..	..	..	..	..	..	..	..	..	..	..	..
54	..	..	..	8 28	..	..	..	..	..	..	8 52	..	..	..	..	..	..	..	..	..	..	..	..	..	..	..	..	..
55	..	..	..	..	..	..	..	..	..	..	..	..	..	..	..	..	8 45	..	..	..	..	..	..	..	9 19	..	..	..
56	..	..	..	..	..	..	..	..	..	..	..	..	..	..	..	..	8 49	..	..	..	..	..	..	..	9 23	..	..	..
57	..	..	..	..	..	..	..	..	..	..	..	..	..	8 20	..	..	..	..	..	..	..	..	..	..	..	..	..	..
58	..	..	..	..	..	..	..	..	..	..	..	..	..	8 23	..	..	..	..	..	..	..	..	..	..	..	..	..	..
59	..	..	..	..	..	..	8 11	..	..	..	..	..	..	8 26	..	..	..	..	..	..	..	..	8 40	..	..	..	..	..
60	..	..	..	..	..	..	..	..	..	..	..	..	..	..	..	..	..	..	..	..	..	..	..	..	..	..	..	..
61	..	..	..	..	..	..	..	..	..	..	..	d Departure time	..	8 29	..	..	..	..	..	..	..	..	..	..	..	..	..	..
62	..	..	..	..	..	..	..	..	..	..	..		..	8 32	..	..	..	..	..	..	..	..	..	..	..	..	..	..
63	..	..	..	..	..	..	..	..	..	..	..		..	8 35	..	..	..	..	..	..	..	..	..	..	..	..	..	..
64	..	..	..	..	..	..	..	..	..	..	..		..	8 37	..	..	..	..	..	..	..	..	..	..	..	..	..	..
65	..	..	..	..	..	..	..	..	..	..	..		..	8 41	..	..	..	..	..	..	..	..	..	..	..	..	..	..
66	..	..	..	..	..	..	§ Via Three Bridges	..	..	..	..		..	8 27	..	..	..	..	..	..	..	..	..	..	..	..	..	‡ Via Three Bridges
67	..	..	..	..	..	..		..	..	..	..		..	8 29	..	..	..	..	..	..	..	..	..	..	..	..	..	
68	..	..	..	..	..	..		..	..	..	..		..	8 31	..	..	..	..	..	..	..	..	..	..	..	..	..	
69	..	..	..	..	..	..		..	..	..	..		..	8 34	..	..	..	..	..	..	..	..	..	..	..	..	..	
70	..	..	..	..	..	..		..	..	..	..		..	8 36	..	..	..	..	..	..	..	..	..	..	..	..	..	
71	..	..	..	..	..	..		..	..	..	..		..	8 41	..	..	..	..	..	..	..	..	..	..	..	..	..	
72	..	..	..	..	..	..		..	..	..	..		..	8 44	..	..	..	..	..	..	..	..	..	..	..	..	..	
73	..	..	..	..	..	..		..	..	..	..		..	8 47	..	..	..	..	..	..	..	..	..	..	..	..	..	
74	..	..	..	..	..	..	8 14	..	..	..	..		..	..	..	..	..	..	..	..	..	..	8 44	..	..	..	..	..
75	..	..	..	..	..	..	8 20	..	..	..	..	p.m	..	..	..	..	..	..	..	..	..	..	8 50	..	..	..	..	..
76	..	..	..	..	..	..	8 24	..	..	..	..	8d35	..	..	..	..	..	..	..	..	..	..	8 54	..	..	..	..	9 2
77	..	..	..	..	..	..	8 30	..	..	..	..	8 39	..	..	..	..	..	..	..	..	..	..	9 0	..	..	..	..	..
78	..	..	..	8 53	..	..	9§ 5	..	..	..	..	..	..	..	..	..	..	..	..	..	..	..	..	..	..	..	..	9‡40

LONDON, CRYSTAL PALACE, CROYDON, SUTTON, DORKING NORTH,

For Notes, see page 284a

Down	No.	p.m								Sundays—continued							p.m						No.
VICTORIA .... dep	1	..	8 32	..	..	..	8 40	..	8 45	8 45	8 48	8 48	..	..	..	..	..	..	..	..	..	9 10	1
CHARING CROSS✱ ... "	2	8 23	3	..	3	..	3		3	..	..	3	3	3	3	..	3	8 53	3	..	..	3	2
WATERLOO✱ .... "	3	8 25		..		..		8 42		..	..					..		8 55		..	..		3
LONDON BRIDGE ..... "	4	8 30	..	..	8 35	..	..	..	..	..	..	..	8 45	8 51	8 55	..	8 58	9 0	9 4	..	9 5	..	4
Battersea Park	5	3	..	..	..	..	8 43	..	..	..	..	..	..	..	..	..	..	3	..	..	..	9 13	5
Clapham Junction ...	6		8 37	..	..	..	8 46	8 49	8 50	..	8 53	8 54	..	..	..	..	..		..	..	..	9 16	6
Wandsworth Common A	7	..	8 40	..	..	..	8 49	3	8 53	..	..	8 57	..	..	..	..	..	..	..	..	..	9 19	7
Balham & Upper Tooting	8	..	8 42	..	..	..	8 51		8 55	..	..	8 59	..	..	..	..	..	..	..	..	..	9 21	8
South Bermondsey	9	..	..	..	..	..	..	Via Worcester Park	..	..	..	..	8 48	8 54	8 58	..	..	..	9 7	..	..	..	9
Queen's Road, Peckham	10	..	..	..	..	..	..		..	..	..	..	8 51	8 57	9 1	..	..	..	9 10	..	..	..	10
Peckham Rye	11	..	..	..	..	..	..		..	..	..	..	8 53	8 59	9 3	..	..	..	9 12	..	..	..	11
East Dulwich	12	..	..	..	..	..	..		..	..	..	..	8 56	To Victoria, arr. 9 14 p.m	9 6	..	..	..	9 15	..	..	..	12
North Dulwich	13	..	..	..	..	..	..		..	..	..	..	8 58		9 8	..	..	..	9 17	..	..	..	13
Tulse Hill	14	..	..	..	..	..	..		..	..	..	..	9 1		9 11	..	..	..	9 20	..	..	..	14
Streatham	15	..	..	..	..	..	..		..	..	..	..	9 4		9 14	..	..	..	..	..	..	..	15
New Cross Gate (for E.L.	16	8 35	..	..	8 40	..	..		..	..	..	..	..		..	..	9 3	9 5	..	..	..	..	16
Brockley B .... [Line)	17	..	..	..	8 42	..	..	..	..	..	..	..	..		..	..	9 5	..	..	..	..	..	17
Honor Oak Park	18	..	..	..	8 45	..	..	..	..	..	..	..	..		..	..	9 8	..	..	..	..	..	18
Forest Hill, for Lordship	19	8 40	..	..	8 47	..	..	..	..	..	..	..	..		..	..	9 10	9 10	..	..	..	..	19
Sydenham .... [Lane	20	..	..	..	8 50	..	..	..	..	..	..	..	..		..	..	9 13	..	..	..	..	..	20
Penge West C	21	..	..	..	..	..	..	..	..	..	..	..	..		..	..	9 15	..	..	..	..	..	21
Anerley	22	..	..	..	..	..	..	..	..	..	..	..	..		..	..	9 16	..	..	..	..	..	22
Streatham Common	23	..	8 46	..	..	..	..	..	..	..	..	9 3	9 6		..	..	..	..	..	..	..	..	23
Norbury	24	..	8 48	..	..	..	..	..	..	..	..	9 5	9 9		..	..	..	..	..	..	..	..	24
Thornton Heath	25	..	8 51	..	..	..	..	..	..	..	..	9 8	9 12		..	..	..	..	..	..	..	..	25
Selhurst	26	..	8 53	..	..	..	..	..	..	..	..	9 11	9 14	Stop	..	..	..	..	..	..	..	..	26
Streatham Hill	27	..	..	..	..	..	8 54	..	..	..	..	..	..	p.m	..	..	..	..	..	..	..	9 24	27
West Norwood. [N'wood)	28	..	..	..	..	..	8 57	..	..	..	..	..	..	3	..	..	..	..	9 22	..	..	9 27	28
Gipsy Hill (for Upper	29	..	..	..	..	..	8 59	..	..	..	..	..	..		..	..	..	..	9 24	..	..	9 29	29
Crystal Palace D	30	..	..	..	8 53	..	9 2	..	..	..	..	..	..	9 5	..	..	..	..	9 27	..	..	9 32	30
Birkbeck	31	..	..	..	..	..	..	..	..	..	..	..	..	9 8	..	..	..	..	..	..	..	..	31
Beckenham Jn. arr	32	..	..	..	..	..	..	..	..	..	..	..	..	9 12	..	..	..	..	..	..	..	..	32
Norwood Junction F ..	33	8 44	..	..	..	..	9 6	..	..	..	..	..	9 17	..	..	..	9 19	9 14	..	..	..	9 36	33
East Croydon .... arr	34	8 48	8 57	..	..	..	..	..	..	9 0	9 5	..	..	..	..	..	..	9 18	..	..	9 23	..	34
East Croydon .... dep	35	8 48	8 57	..	..	..	..	..	..	..	9 5	..	To London Bridge, via Forest Hill	..	..	..	..	9 18	..	..	9 25	..	35
Mitcham Junction	36	..	..	..	..	..	..	..	9 1	..	..	..		..	9 19	..	..	..	..	..	..	..	36
Hackbridge	37	..	..	..	..	..	..	..	9 4	..	..	..		..	9 22	..	..	..	..	..	..	..	37
Carshalton	38	..	..	..	..	..	..	..	9 6	..	..	..		..	9 24	..	..	..	..	..	..	..	38
West Croydon 319 arr	39	..	..	..	..	..	9 11	..	..	..	..	9 13		..	..	3	9 23	..	..	..	..	9 41	39
West Croydon 319 dep	40	..	..	..	..	..	..	..	..	..	..	9 13		..	..	9 19	9 23	..	..	..	..	..	40
Waddon G	41	..	..	..	..	..	..	..	..	..	..	9 16		..	..	9 21	9 26	..	..	..	..	..	41
Wallington	42	..	..	..	..	..	..	..	..	..	..	9 19		..	..	9 25	9 29	..	..	..	..	..	42
Carshalton Beeches	43	..	..	..	..	..	..	..	..	..	..	9 22		..	..	9 27	9 32	..	..	..	..	..	43
Sutton 322	44	..	..	..	..	..	..	..	9 9	..	..	9 24		..	9 27	9 30	9 34	..	..	..	..	..	44
Belmont	45	..	..	..	..	..	..	..	..	..	..	9 27	..	..	..	Stop	9 37	..	..	..	..	..	45
Banstead	46	..	..	..	..	..	..	..	..	..	..	9 30	..	..	..		9 40	..	..	..	..	..	46
Epsom Downs ...... arr	47	..	..	..	..	..	..	..	..	..	..	9 34	..	..	..	..	9 44	..	..	..	..	..	47
Cheam	48	..	..	..	..	..	..	..	9 12	..	..	..	..	..	9 30	..	..	..	..	..	..	..	48
Ewell East H	49	..	..	..	..	..	..	..	9 15	..	..	..	..	..	9 33	..	..	..	..	..	..	..	49
Epsom	50	..	..	..	..	..	..	9 11	9 19	..	..	..	..	..	9 36	..	..	..	..	..	..	..	50
Ashtead	51	..	..	..	..	..	..	9 15	..	..	..	..	..	..	9 40	..	..	..	..	..	..	..	51
Leatherhead .. [Bridge J	52	..	..	..	..	..	..	9 19	..	..	..	..	..	..	9 44	..	..	..	..	..	..	..	52
Boxhill and Burford	53	..	..	..	..	..	..	9 24	..	..	..	..	..	..	9 49	..	..	..	..	..	..	..	53
Dorking North K .. arr	54	..	..	..	..	..	..	9 28	..	..	..	..	..	..	9 52	..	..	..	..	..	..	..	54
Bookham .... [394	55	..	..	..	..	..	..	..	..	..	..	..	..	..	..	..	..	..	..	..	..	..	55
Effingham Junction arr	56	..	..	..	..	..	..	..	..	..	..	..	..	..	..	..	..	..	..	..	..	..	56
South Croydon 234	57	8 50	9 0	..	..	..	..	..	..	..	..	..	..	..	..	..	..	9 20	..	..	..	..	57
Purley Oaks	58	8 53	9 2	..	..	..	..	..	..	..	..	..	..	..	..	..	..	9 23	..	..	..	..	58
Purley	59	8 55	9 5	..	..	..	..	..	..	..	9 11	..	..	..	..	..	..	9 26	..	..	..	..	59
Coulsdon North L .. arr	60	..	9 9	..	..	..	..	..	..	..	..	..	..	..	..	..	..	..	..	..	..	..	60
Purley .... dep	61	8 59	..	..	..	..	..	..	..	..	..	..	..	..	..	..	..	9 29	..	..	..	..	61
Kenley	62	9 2	..	..	..	..	..	..	..	..	..	..	..	..	..	..	..	9 32	..	..	..	..	62
Whyteleafe	63	9 5	..	..	..	..	..	..	..	..	..	..	..	..	..	..	..	9 35	..	..	..	..	63
Warlingham	64	9 7	..	..	..	..	..	..	..	..	..	..	..	..	..	..	..	9 37	..	..	..	..	64
Caterham .... arr	65	9 11	..	..	..	..	..	..	..	..	..	..	..	..	..	p.m	..	9 41	..	..	..	..	65
Purley .... dep	66	8 57	..	..	..	..	..	..	..	..	..	..	..	..	..	d Departure time	..	9 27	..	..	..	..	66
Reedham	67	8 59	..	..	..	..	..	..	..	..	..	..	..	..	..		..	9 29	..	..	..	..	67
Smitham	68	9 1	..	..	..	..	..	..	..	..	..	..	..	..	..		..	9 31	..	..	..	..	68
Woodmansterne	69	9 4	..	..	..	..	..	..	..	..	..	..	..	..	..		..	9 34	..	..	..	..	69
Chipstead	70	9 6	..	..	..	..	..	..	..	..	..	..	..	..	..		..	9 36	..	..	..	..	70
Kingswood M	71	9 11	..	..	..	..	..	..	..	..	..	..	..	..	..		..	9 41	..	..	..	..	71
Tadworth N	72	9 14	..	..	..	..	..	..	..	..	..	..	..	..	..		..	9 44	..	..	..	..	72
Tattenham Corner. arr	73	9 17	..	..	..	..	..	..	..	..	..	..	..	..	..		..	9 47	..	..	..	..	73
Coulsdon South	74	..	..	..	..	..	..	..	..	..	9 14	..	..	..	..	..	..	..	..	..	..	..	74
Merstham	75	..	..	..	..	..	..	..	..	..	9 20	..	..	..	..	..	..	..	..	..	..	..	75
Redhill 158, 246 .... arr	76	..	..	..	..	..	..	..	..	..	9 24	..	..	..	..	9d39	..	..	..	..	9 42	..	76
Reigate 246 .... "	77	..	..	..	..	..	..	..	..	..	9 30	..	..	..	..	9 43	..	..	..	..	..	..	77
Horsham 159, 244, 245 "	78	..	..	..	..	..	..	9 53	..	..	..	..	..	..	..	..	..	..	..	..	..	..	78

CATERHAM, TATTENHAM CORNER, REDHILL, REIGATE, and HORSHAM

No.						p.m						Sundays—continued											p.m					
1	..	..	9 18	..	..	9 20	9 24	9 18	..	..	..	9 25	9 28	..	..	9 32	..	..	..	9 40	..	9 45	9 45	9 48	9 48	..	..	..
2	..	..	..	..	..	..	..	..	..	..	..	..	..	..	9 23	..	..	..	..	..	..	..	..	..	..	..	..	..
3	3	..	..	9 2	..	..	3	3	..	3	3	..	..	3	9 25	3	..	3	..	3	9 42	3	..	..	3	3	3	3
4	9 13	..	..	..	9 16	..	..	..	..	9 21	9 25	..	..	9 28	9 30	..	..	9 35	..	..	..	..	..	..	..	9 45	9 51	9 55
5	..	..	..	..	..	..	..	..	..	..	..	..	..	..	..	..	..	..	..	9 43	..	..	..	..	..	..	..	..
6	..	..	..	9 9	..	9 26	9 29	9 24	..	..	..	..	9 34	..	3	9 27	..	..	..	9 46	9 49	9 50	..	9 53	9 54	..	..	..
7	..	..	..	3	..	..	..	9 27	..	..	..	..	..	..	..	9 40	..	..	..	9 49	3	9 53	..	..	9 57	..	..	..
8	..	..	..	..	..	..	9 33	9 29	..	..	..	..	..	..	..	9 42	..	..	..	9 51	..	9 55	..	..	9 59	..	..	..
9	..	..	..		..	..	..	..	..	9 24	9 28	..	..	..	..	..	..	..	..	..		..	..	..	..	9 48	9 54	9 58
10	..	..	..		..	..	..	..	..	9 27	9 31	..	..	..	..	..	..	..	..	..		..	..	..	..	9 51	9 57	10 1
11	..	..	..		..	..	..	..	..	9 29	9 33	..	..	..	..	..	..	..	..	..		..	..	..	..	9 53	10 0	10 3
12	..	..	..		..	..	..	..	..		9 36	..	..	..	..	..	..	..	..	..		..	..	..	..	9 56	—	10 6
13	..	..	..	Via Worcester Park	..	..	..	..	..		9 38	..	..	..	..	..	..	..	..	..		..	..	..	..	9 58	Stop	10 8
14	..	..	..		..	..	..	..	..		9 41	..	..	..	..	..	..	..	..	..	Via Worcester Park	..	..	..	..	10 1	..	1011
15	..	..	..		..	..	..	..	..		9 44	..	..	..	..	..	..	..	..	..		..	..	..	..	10 4	..	1014
16	9 18	..	..		9 21	..	..	..	..	To Victoria. arr. 9 44 p.m	..	..	..	9 33	9 35	..	..	9 40	..	..		..	..	..	..	..	..	..
17	9 20	..	..		..	..	..	..	..		..	..	..	9 35	..	..	..	9 42	..	..		..	..	..	..	..	..	..
18	9 23	..	..		..	..	..	..	..		..	..	..	9 38	..	..	..	9 45	..	..		..	..	..	..	..	..	..
19	9 25	..	..	..	..	..	..	..	..		..	..	..	9 40	9 40	..	..	9 47	..	..		..	..	..	..	..	..	..
20	9 28	..	..	..	..	..	..	..	..		..	..	..	9 43	..	..	..	9 50	..	..		..	..	..	..	..	..	..
21	9 30	..	..	..	..	..	..	..	..		..	..	..	9 45	..	..	..	..	..	..	..	..	..	..	..	..	..	..
22	9 31	..	..	..	..	..	..	..	..		..	..	..	9 46	..	..	..	..	..	..	..	..	..	..	..	..	..	..
23	..	..	..	..	..	..	..	9 33	..	..	..	..	..	..	..	9 46	..	..	..	..	..	..	..	..	10 3	10 6	..	..
24	..	..	..	..	..	..	..	9 35	..	..	..	..	..	..	..	9 48	..	..	..	..	..	..	..	..	10 5	10 9	..	..
25	..	..	..	..	..	..	..	9 38	..	..	..	..	..	..	..	9 51	..	..	..	..	..	..	..	..	10 8	1012	..	..
26	..	..	..	..	..	..	..	9 40	..	..	..	..	..	..	..	9 53	..	..	..	..	..	..	..	..	1010	1014	..	..
27	..	..	..	..	..	..	..	..	..	..	..	..	..	..	..	..	..	..	..	9 54	..	..	..	..	..	..	p.m	..
28	..	..	..	..	..	..	..	..	..	..	..	..	..	..	..	..	..	..	..	9 57	..	..	..	..	..	..	..	..
29	..	3	..	..	..	..	..	..	..	..	..	..	..	..	..	..	..	..	..	9 59	..	..	..	..	..	..	3	..
30	..	9 35	..	..	..	..	..	..	..	..	..	..	..	..	..	..	..	9 53	..	10 2	..	..	..	..	..	..	10 5	..
31	..	9 38	..	..	..	..	..	..	..	..	..	..	..	..	..	..	..	..	..	..	..	..	..	..	..	..	10 8	..
32	..	9 42	..	..	..	..	..	..	..	..	..	..	..	..	..	..	..	..	..	..	..	..	..	..	..	..	1012	..
33	9 34	..	..	..	9 30	..	..	..	..	..	..	..	..	9 49	9 44	..	..	..	..	10 6	..	..	..	..	..	1017	..	..
34		..	..	..	9 34	9 40	..	..	..	..	..	9 43	9 46	..	9 48	9 57	..	..	..	..	..	..	10 0	10 5	..	..	..	..
35		..	..	..	9 35	..	..	..	..	..	..	—	9 47	..	9 48	9 57	..	..	..	..	..	..	..	10 5	..	..	..	..
36		..	..	..	..	..	9 39	..	..	..	9 49	Stop	..	..	..	..	..	..	..	..	..	10 1	..	..	..		..	1019
37		..	..	..	..	..	9 42	..	..	..	9 52	p.m	..	..	..	..	..	..	..	..	..	10 4	..	..	..		..	1022
38		..	..	..	..	..	9 44	..	..	..	9 54	3	..	..	..	..	..	..	..	..	..	10 6	..	..	..		..	1024
39	To London Bridge, via Streatham	..	..	..	..	..	..	9 43	..	..	..	..	..	9 53	..	..	..	..	..	1011	..	..	..	..	1013		..	..
40		..	..	..	..	..	..	9 43	..	..	..	9 49	..	9 53	..	..	..	..	..	..	..	..	..	..	1013		..	..
41		..	..	..	..	..	..	9 46	..	..	..	9 51	..	9 56	..	..	..	..	..	..	..	..	..	..	1016	To London Bridge, via Forest Hill	..	..
42		..	..	..	..	..	..	9 49	..	..	..	9 55	..	9 59	..	..	..	..	..	..	..	..	..	..	1019		..	..
43		..	..	..	..	..	..	9 52	..	..	..	9 57	..	10 2	..	..	..	..	..	..	..	..	..	..	1022		..	..
44		..	9 39	..	..	..	9 48	9 54	..	..	9 57	10 0	..	10 4	..	..	..	..	..	..	..	10 9	..	..	1024		..	1027
45	..	..	..	..	..	..	..	9 57	..	..	..	..	..	10 7	..	..	..	..	..	..	..	..	..	..	1027		..	..
46	..	..	..	..	..	..	..	10 0	..	..	..	..	..	1010	..	..	..	..	..	..	..	..	..	..	1030		..	..
47	..	..	..	..	..	..	..	10 4	..	..	..	..	..	1014	..	..	..	..	..	..	..	..	..	..	1034		..	..
48	..	..	..	..	..	..	9 51	..	..	..	10 0	..	..	..	..	..	..	..	..	..	..	1012	..	..	..	..	..	1030
49	..	..	..	..	..	..	9 54	..	..	..	10 3	..	..	..	..	..	..	..	..	..	..	1015	..	..	..	..	..	1033
50	..	..	..	9 31	..	..	10 0	..	..	..	10 6	..	..	..	..	..	..	..	..	..	1011	1019	..	..	..	..	..	1036
51	..	..	..	9 35	..	..	10 4	..	..	..	1010	..	..	..	..	..	..	..	..	..	1015	●	..	..	..	..	..	1040
52	..	..	..	9 39	..	..	10 8	..	..	..	1014	..	..	..	..	..	..	..	..	..	1019	..	..	..	..	..	..	1044
53	..	..	..	..	..	..	1013	..	..	..	..	..	..	..	..	..	..	..	..	..	1024	..	..	..	..	..	..	1049
54	..	..	9 55	..	..	..	1016	..	..	..	..	..	..	..	..	..	..	..	..	..	1028	..	..	..	..	..	..	1052
55	..	..	..	9 45	..	..	..	..	..	..	1019	..	..	..	..	..	..	..	..	..	..	..	..	..	..	..	..	..
56	..	..	..	9 49	..	..	..	..	..	..	1023	..	..	..	..	..	..	..	..	..	..	..	..	..	..	..	..	..
57	..	..	..	..	..	..	..	..	..	..	..	..	..	..	9 50	10 0	..	..	..	..	..	..	..	..	..	..	..	..
58	..	..	..	..	..	..	..	..	..	..	..	..	..	..	9 53	10 2	..	..	..	..	..	..	..	..	..	..	..	..
59	..	..	..	..	9 40	..	..	..	..	..	..	..	..	..	9 55	10 5	..	..	..	..	..	..	..	1011	..	..	..	..
60	..	..	..	..	..	..	..	..	..	..	..	..	..	..	..	10 8	..	..	..	..	..	..	..	..	..	..	..	..
61	..	..	..	..	..	..	..	..	..	..	..	..	..	..	9 59	..	..	..	..	..	..	..	..	..	..	..	..	..
62	..	..	..	..	..	..	..	..	..	..	..	..	..	..	10 2	..	..	..	..	..	..	..	..	..	..	..	..	..
63	..	..	..	..	..	..	..	..	..	..	..	..	..	..	10 5	..	..	..	..	..	..	..	..	..	..	..	..	..
64	..	..	..	..	..	..	..	..	..	..	..	..	..	..	10 7	..	..	..	..	..	..	..	..	..	..	..	..	..
65	..	..	..	..	..	..	..	..	..	..	..	..	..	..	1011	..	..	..	..	..	..	..	..	..	..	..	..	..
66	..	..	..	..	..	..	..	..	..	..	..	..	..	..	9 57	..	..	..	..	..	..	..	..	..	..	..	..	..
67	..	..	..	..	..	..	..	..	..	..	..	..	..	..	9 59	..	..	..	..	..	..	..	..	..	..	..	..	..
68	..	..	..	..	..	..	..	..	..	..	..	..	..	..	10 1	..	..	..	..	..	..	..	..	..	..	..	..	..
69	..	..	..	..	..	..	..	..	..	..	..	..	..	..	10 4	..	..	..	..	..	..	..	..	..	..	..	..	..
70	..	..	..	..	..	..	..	..	..	..	..	..	..	..	10 6	..	..	..	..	..	..	..	..	..	..	..	..	..
71	..	..	..	..	..	..	..	..	..	..	..	..	..	..	1011	..	..	..	..	..	..	..	..	..	..	..	..	..
72	..	..	..	..	..	..	..	..	..	..	..	..	..	..	1014	..	..	..	..	..	..	..	..	..	..	..	..	..
73	..	..	..	..	..	..	..	..	..	..	..	..	..	..	1017	..	..	..	..	..	..	..	..	..	..	..	..	..
74	..	..	..	..	9 44	..	..	..	..	..	..	..	..	..	..	..	..	..	..	..	..	..	..	1014	..	..	..	..
75	..	..	..	..	9 50	..	..	..	..	..	..	..	..	..	..	..	..	..	..	..	..	..	..	1020	..	..	..	..
76	..	..	..	..	9 54	..	..	..	..	..	..	..	10 1	..	..	..	..	..	..	..	..	..	..	1024	..	..	..	..
77	..	..	..	..	10 8	..	..	..	..	..	..	..	..	..	..	..	..	..	..	..	..	..	..	1030	..	..	..	..
78	..	..	1013	..	..	..	1042	..	..	..	..	..	..	..	..	..	..	..	..	..	1053	..	..	..	..	..	..	..

LONDON, CRYSTAL PALACE, CROYDON, SUTTON, DORKING NORTH,

For Notes, see page 284a

Down	No.	p.m								Sundays—*continued*							p.m						No.
Victoria .... dep	1	..	..	..	..	..	..	1010	..	1015	..	..	1018	..	..	..	..	1028	..	..	..	1032	1
Charing Cross* ... "	2	..		9 53	..		..				..	..		..		..		..		..	1023		2
Waterloo* .... "	3	..	(3)	9 55	10 2	(3)	..	(3)	(3)	(3)	..	..	(3)	..	(3)	..	(3)	..	(3)	..	1025	(3)	3
London Bridge ..... "	4	..	9 58	10 0	..	10 4	..	..	1013	..	..	..	..	..	1021	..	1025	..	1028	..	1030	..	4
Battersea Park	5	..	..		..	..	..	1012	..	..	..	..	..	..	..	..	..	..	..	..		..	5
Clapham Junction	6	..	..	(3)	10 9	..	..	1016	..	1020	..	..	1024	..	..	..	..	1033	..	..	(3)	1037	6
Wandsworth Common A	7	..	..	..		..	..	1019	.	1024	..	..	1027	..	..	..	..	..	..	..	..	1040	7
Balham & Upper Tooting	8	..	..	..	(3)	..	..	1021	.	1026	..	..	1029	..	..	..	..	..	..	..	..	1042	8
South Bermondsey	9	..	..	..		10 7	..	..	..	..	..	..	..	..	1024	..	1028	..	..	..	..	..	9
Queen's Road, Peckham	10	..	..	..		1010	..	..	..	..	..	..	..	..	1027	..	1031	..	..	..	..	..	10
Peckham Rye	11	..	..	..		1012	..	..	..	..	..	..	..	..	1029	..	1033	..	..	..	..	..	11
East Dulwich	12	..	..	..	Via Worcester Park	1015	..	..	..	..	..	..	..	..	..	..	1036	..	..	..	..	..	12
North Dulwich	13	..	..	..		1017	..	..	..	..	..	..	..	..	..	..	1038	..	..	..	..	..	13
Tulse Hill	14	..	..	..		1020	..	..	..	..	..	..	..	..	..	..	1041	..	..	..	..	..	14
Streatham	15	..	..	..		..	..	..	..	..	..	..	..	..	..	..	1044	..	..	..	..	..	15
New Cross Gate (for E.L.	16	..	10 3	10 5		..	..	..	1018	..	..	..	..	..	..	..	..	..	1033	..	1035	..	16
Brockley B ....[Line)	17	..	10 5	..		..	..	..	1020	..	..	..	..	..	..	..	..	..	1035	..	..	..	17
Honor Oak Park	18	..	10 8	..		..	..	..	1023	..	..	..	..	..	..	..	..	..	1038	..	..	..	18
Forest Hill, for Lordship	19	..	1010	1010		..	..	..	1025	..	..	..	..	..	..	..	..	..	1040	..	1040	..	19
Sydenham ....[Lane	20	..	1013	..	..	..	..	..	1028	..	..	..	..	..	..	..	..	..	1043	..	..	..	20
Penge West C	21	..	1015	..	..	..	..	..	1030	..	..	..	..	..	..	..	..	..	1045	..	..	..	21
Anerley	22	..	1016	..	..	..	..	..	1031	..	..	..	..	..	..	..	..	..	1046	..	..	..	22
Streatham Common	23	..	..	..	..	..	..	..	..	..	..	..	1033	..	..	..	..	..	..	..	..	1046	23
Norbury	24	..	..	..	..	..	..	..	..	..	..	..	1035	..	..	..	..	..	..	..	..	1048	24
Thornton Heath	25	..	..	..	..	..	..	..	..	..	..	..	1038	..	..	..	..	..	..	..	..	1051	25
Selhurst	26	..	..	..	..	..	..	..	..	..	..	..	1040	..	..	..	..	..	..	..	..	1053	26
Streatham Hill	27	..	..	..	..	..	..	1024	..	..	..	..	..	..	..	..	..	..	..	..	..	..	27
West Norwood..[N'wood)	28	..	..	..	..	1022	..	1027	..	..	..		..	..	..	..	..	..	..	..	..	..	28
Gipsy Hill (for Upper	29	..	..	..	..	1024	..	1029	..	..	..	(3)	..	..	..	..	..	..	..	..	..	..	29
Crystal Palace D	30	..	..	..	..	1027	..	1032	..	..	..	1035	..	..	..	..	..	..	..	..	..	..	30
Birkbeck	31	..	..	..	..	..	..	..	..	..	..	1038	..	..	..	..	..	..	..	..	..	..	31
Beckenham Jn. arr	32	..	..	..	..	..	..	..	..	..	..	1042	..	..	..	..	..	..	..	..	..	..	32
Norwood Junction F ..	33	..	1019	1014	..	..	..	1036	1034	..	..	..	..	..	..	..	..	..	1049	..	1044	..	33
East Croydon .... arr	34	..	..	1018	..	..	..	..	..	..	..	..	..	..	..	..	..	1045	..	..	1048	1057	34
East Croydon .... dep	35	..	..	1018	..	..	..	..	..	..	..	..	..	..	..	..	..	1046	..	..	1048	1057	35
Mitcham Junction	36	..	..	..	..	..	..	..		1032	..	..	..	..	..	..	1049	..	..	..	..	..	36
Hackbridge	37	..	..	..	..	..	..	..		1035	..	..	..	..	..	..	1052	..	..	..	..	..	37
Carshalton	38		..	..	..	..	..	..		1037		..	..	..	..	..	1054	..	..	..	..	..	38
West Croydon 319 arr	39	(3)	1023	..	..	..	..	1040		..	(3)	..	1044	..	..	..	..	..	1053	..	..	..	39
West Croydon 319 dep	40	1019	1023	..	..	..	..	..	To London Bridge, via Streatham	..	1042	..	1045	..	..	..	..	..	1053	..	..	..	40
Waddon G	41	1021	1026	..	..	..	..	..		..	1044	..	1047	..	..	..	..	..	1056	..	..	..	41
Wallington	42	1025	1029	..	..	..	..	..		..	1048	..	1051	..	..	..	..	..	1059	..	..	..	42
Carshalton Beeches	43	1027	1032	..	..	..	..	..		.	1050	..	1053	..	..	..	..	..	11 2	..	..	..	43
Sutton 322	44	1030	1034	..	..	..	..	..		1040	1053	..	1056	..	..	..	1059	..	11 6	..	..	..	44
Belmont	45	..	1037	..	..	..	..	..	..	..	..	..	1059	..	..	..	..	..	11 9	..	..	..	45
Banstead	46	..	1040	..	..	..	..	..	..	..	..	..	11 2	..	..	..	..	..	1112	..	..	..	46
Epsom Downs ...... arr	47	..	1044	..	..	..	..	..	..	..	..	..	11 5	..	..	..	..	..	1115	..	..	..	47
Cheam	48	..	..	..	..	..	..	..	..	1043	..	..	..	..	..	..	11 2	..	..	..	..	..	48
Ewell East H	49	..	..	..	..	..	..	..	..	1046	..	..	..	..	..	..	11 5	..	..	..	..	..	49
Epsom	50	..	..	..	1031	..	..	..	..	1050	..	..	..	..	..	..	11 8	..	..	..	..	..	50
Ashtead	51	..	..	..	1035	..	..	..	..	..	..	..	..	..	..	..	1112	..	..	..	..	..	51
Leatherhead...[Bridge J	52	..	..	..	1040	..	..	..	..	..	..	..	..	..	..	..	1116	..	..	..	..	..	52
Boxhill and Burford	53	..	..	..	..	..	..	..	..	..	..	..	..	..	..	..	..	..	..	..	..	..	53
Dorking North K .. arr	54	..	..	..	..	..	..	..	..	..	..	..	..	..	..	..	..	..	..	..	..	..	54
Bookham ....[394	55	..	..	..	1045	..	..	..	..	..	..	..	..	..	..	..	1120	..	..	..	..	..	55
Effingham Junction arr	56	..	..	..	1049	..	..	..	..	..	..	..	..	..	..	..	1124	..	..	..	..	..	56
South Croydon 234	57	..	..	1020	..	..	..	..	..	..	..	..	..	..	..	..	..	..	..	..	1050	11 0	57
Purley Oaks	58	..	..	1023	..	..	..	..	..	..	..	..	..	..	..	..	..	..	..	..	1053	11 2	58
Purley	59	..	..	1026	..	..	..	..	..	..	..	..	..	..	..	..	..	..	..	..	1055	11 5	59
Coulsdon North L .. arr	60	..	..	..	..	..	..	..	..	..	..	..	..	..	..	..	..	..	..	..	..	11 8	60
Purley .... dep	61	..	..	1029	..	..	..	..	..	..	..	..	..	..	..	..	..	..	..	..	1059	..	61
Kenley	62	..	..	1032	..	..	..	..	..	..	..	..	..	..	..	..	..	..	..	..	11 2	..	62
Whyteleafe	63	..	..	1035	..	..	..	..	..	..	..	..	..	..	..	..	..	..	..	..	11 5	..	63
Warlingham	64	..	..	1037	..	..	..	..	..	..	..	..	..	..	..	..	..	..	..	..	11 7	..	64
Caterham .... arr	65	..	..	1041	..	..	..	..	..	..	..	..	..	..	..	..	..	..	..	..	1111	..	65
Purley .... dep	66	..	..	1027	..	..	..	..	..	..	..	..	..	..	..	..	..	..	..	..	1057	..	66
Reedham	67	..	..	1029	..	..	..	..	..	..	..	..	..	..	..	..	..	..	..	..	1059	..	67
Smitham	68	..	..	1031	..	..	..	..	..	..	..	..	..	..	..	..	..	..	..	..	11 1	..	68
Woodmansterne	69	..	..	1034	..	..	..	..	..	..	..	..	..	..	..	..	..	..	..	..	11 4	..	69
Chipstead	70	..	..	1036	..	..	..	..	..	..	..	..	..	..	..	..	..	..	..	..	11 6	..	70
Kingswood M	71	..	..	1041	..	..	..	..	..	..	..	..	..	..	..	..	..	..	..	..	1111	..	71
Tadworth N	72	..	..	1044	..	..	..	..	..	..	..	..	..	..	..	..	..	..	..	..	1114	..	72
Tattenham Corner. arr	73	..	..	1047	..	..	..	..	..	..	..	..	..	..	..	..	..	..	..	..	1117	..	73
Coulsdon South	74	..	..	..	..	..	..	..	..	..	..	..	..	..	..	..	..	..	..	..	..	..	74
Merstham	75	..	..	..	..	..	..	..	..	..	..	..	..	..	..	..	..	..	..	..	..	..	75
Redhill 158, 246 ..... arr	76	..	..	..	..	..	..	..	..	..	..	..	..	..	..	..	..	11 0	..	..	..	..	76
Reigate 246 .... "	77	..	..	..	..	..	..	..	..	..	..	..	..	..	..	..	..	11 9	..	..	..	..	77
Horsham 159,244,245 "	78	..	..	..	..	..	..	..	..	..	..	..	..	..	..	..	..	..	..	..	..	..	78

CATERHAM, TATTENHAM CORNER, REDHILL, REIGATE, and HORSHAM

No.	p.m — Sundays—continued — p.m																				
1		1040			1045	1048				11 2			1110	1115	1116	1118		1140	1145		
2									1053								1123				
3	3	3	3	1042	3	3	3	3	1055	3	3	11 7	3	3		3	1125	3	3	1147	
4	1035		1043				1045	1058	11 0		11 4						1130				
5		1043							3				1113				3	1143			
6		1046		1049	1050	1054				11 7		1114	1116	1120	1122	1124		1146	1150	1154	
7		1049		3	1053	1057				1110		3	1119	1123		1127		1149	1153	3	
8		1051			1055	1059				1112			1121	1125		1129		1151	1155		
9							1048				11 7										
10							1051				1110										
11							1053				1112										
12				Via Worcester Park			1056				1115	Via Worcester Park								Via Worcester Park	
13							1058				1117										
14							11 1				1120										
15							11 4														
16	1040		1048					11 3	11 5								1135				
17	1042		1050					11 5													
18	1045		1053					11 8													
19	1047		1055					1110	1110								1140				
20	1050		1058					1113													
21			11 0					1115													
22			11 1					1116													
23						11 3	11 6			1116						1133					
24						11 5	11 9			1118						1135					
25						11 8	1112			1121						1138					
26						1110	1114			1123						1140					
27		1054											1124					1154			
28		1057					Stop				1122		1127					1157			
29		1059					p.m				1124		1129					1159			
30	1053	11 2					11 5				1127		1132					12 2			
31							11 8														
32							1112														
33		11 6	11 4				3	1119	1114				1136				1144	12 6			
34									1118	1127					1134		1148				
35									1118	1127					1135		1148				
36					11 1									1131					12 1		
37					11 4									1134					12 4		
38					11 6									1136					12 6		
39		1111				1113		1123					1140			1144		1211			
40			To Selhurst, arr. 11 8 p.m			1113		1123								1145					
41						1116		1126								1147					
42						1119		1129								1151					
43						1122		1132								1153					
44					11 9	1124		1134						1139		1156			12 9		
45						1127		1137								1159					
46						1130		1140								12 2					
47						1134		1144								12 6					
48					1112									1142					1212		
49					1115									1145					1215		
50				1113	1119							1137		1149					1219	1220	
51				1117								1141								1224	
52				1121								1145								1228	
53				1126																1233	
54				1129																1236	
55												1149									
56												1155									
57									1120	1130							1150				
58									1123	1132							1153				
59									1125	1136					1140		1156				
60										1139											
61									1129								1159				
62									1132								12 2				
63									1135								12 5				
64									1137								12 7				
65									1141								1211				
66									1127								1157				
67									1129								1159				
68									1131								12 1				
69									1134								12 4				
70									1136								12 6				
71									1141								1211				
72									1144								1214				
73									1147								1217				
74															1144						
75															1150						
76															1154						
77																					
78				1153																	

NOTES

3 Third Class only
* Trains run between Charing Cross, Waterloo, and London Bridge at frequent intervals
§ Via Three Bridges

A Station for Clapham (Nightingale Lane)
B Station for Upper New Cross and Nunhead
B 8 minutes later on Sats.
C Under ½ mile to Penge East Station.
C On Mondays to Fridays stops unconditionally, on Saturdays calls to take up only
D Low Level, nearly ¾ mile to High Level Station
d Departure time
F Norwood Junction and South Norwood for Woodside
G Station for Beddington (¾ mile), Bandon Hill (¾ mile) and Beddington Lane 1¼ miles from Beddington
H 1 mile to Ewell West Station
H 1 minute *earlier* on Sats.
J Station for Mickleham 1¼ miles.
J 1 minute later on Sats.
K Nearly 1½ miles to Dorking Town and under ¼ mile to Deepdene Stas.
K Arr. 12 36 pm on Sats.
L Station for Cane Hill (1 mile)
L Arr. Bookham 7 42 a.m.
M Kingswood and Burgh Heath
N Tadworth and Walton-on-the-Hill
P Arr 5 15 p.m.
SO or SO Saturdays only
SX or SX Saturdays excepted
U Calls to take up only
X Arr 11 22 p.m on Sats.

LOCAL TRAINS and Intermediate Stations

BETWEEN — PAGE

Dorking North and Horsham 394

For OTHER TRAINS

BETWEEN — PAGE

Victoria and Battersea Park 318
London, Tulse Hill, and Streatham 320
London and Beckenham Junction 136
London and Sutton 320
London and Epsom..... 394
London and Effingham Junction 394

HORSHAM, REIGATE, REDHILL, TATTENHAM CORNER, CATERHAM,

For Notes, see page 317a

Up	No.	a.m. Week Days 3	3	3	3	3	3	3	3	3	3	3	3	3	3	3	..	a.m. 3	3	3	3	3	No.
Horsham .... dep	1																						1
Reigate .... "	2	..	..	..	..	..	..	..	..	..	..	..	..	..	..	..	..	..	..	..	..	..	2
Redhill .... "	3	..	..	..	..	..	..	..	..	..	..	..	..	..	..	..	..	..	..	..	..	..	3
Merstham	4	..	..	..	..	..	..	..	..	..	..	..	..	..	..	..	..	..	..	..	..	..	4
Coulsdon South	5	..	..	..	..	..	..	..	..	..	..	..	..	..	..	..	..	..	..	..	..	..	5
Tattenham Corner. dep	6	..	..	..	..	..	..	..	..	..	..	..	..	..	..	..	..	..	..	..	..	..	6
Tadworth **N**	7	..	..	..	..	..	..	..	..	..	..	..	..	..	..	..	..	..	..	..	..	..	7
Kingswood **M**	8	..	..	..	..	..	..	..	..	..	..	..	..	..	..	..	..	..	..	..	..	..	8
Chipstead	9	..	..	..	..	..	..	..	..	..	..	..	..	..	..	..	..	..	..	..	..	..	9
Woodmansterne	10	..	..	..	..	..	..	..	..	..	..	..	..	..	..	..	..	..	..	..	..	..	10
Smitham	11	..	..	..	..	..	..	..	..	..	..	..	..	..	..	..	..	..	..	..	..	..	11
Reedham	12	..	..	..	..	..	..	..	..	..	..	..	..	..	..	..	..	..	..	..	..	..	12
Purley 252 .... arr	13	..	..	..	..	..	..	..	..	..	..	..	..	..	..	..	..	..	..	..	..	..	13
Caterham .... dep	14	..	..	..	..	..	..	..	..	..	..	..	..	..	..	..	..	..	..	..	..	..	14
Warlingham	15	..	..	..	..	..	..	..	..	..	..	..	..	..	..	..	..	..	..	..	..	..	15
Whyteleafe	16	..	..	..	..	..	..	..	..	..	..	..	..	..	..	..	..	..	..	..	..	..	16
Kenley	17	..	..	..	..	..	..	..	..	..	..	..	..	..	..	..	..	..	..	..	..	..	17
Purley 252 .... arr	18	..	..	..	..	..	..	..	..	..	..	..	..	..	..	..	..	..	..	..	..	..	18
Coulsdon North ..... dep	19	..	..	..	..	..	5 8	..	..	..	..	..	..	..	5 31	..	..	..	..	..	..	..	19
Purley 252	20	..	..	..	..	..	5 11	..	..	..	..	..	..	..	5 34	..	..	..	..	..	..	..	20
Purley Oaks	21	..	..	..	..	..	5 13	..	..	..	..	..	..	..	5 36	..	..	..	..	..	..	..	21
South Croydon 234	22	..	..	..	..	..	5 16	..	..	..	..	..	..	..	5 39	..	..	..	..	..	..	..	22
Effingham Junction dep	23	..	..	..	..	..	..	..	..	..	..	..	4 57	..	..	..	..	..	..	5 14	..	..	23
Bookham	24	..	..	..	..	..	..	..	..	..	..	..	5 0	..	..	..	..	..	..	5 17	..	..	24
Dorking North ..... dep	25	..	..	..	..	..	..	..	..	..	..	..	..	..	..	..	..	..	..	..	..	..	25
Boxhill and Burford	26	..	..	..	..	..	..	..	..	..	..	..	..	..	..	..	..	..	..	..	..	..	26
Leatherhead ...[Bridge **J**	27	..	..	..	..	..	..	..	..	..	..	..	5 5	..	..	..	..	..	..	5 22	..	..	27
Ashtead	28	..	..	..	..	..	..	..	..	..	..	..	5 9	..	..	..	..	..	..	5 26	..	..	28
Epsom 427	29	..	..	..	..	..	..	..	..	..	..	..	5 13	5 20	..	..	..	..	..	5 30	..	..	29
Ewell East **H**	30	..	..	..	..	..	..	..	..	..	..	..	..	5 23	..	..	..	..	..	..	..	..	30
Cheam	31	..	..	..	..	..	..	..	..	..	..	..	..	5 26	..	..	..	..	..	..	..	..	31
Epsom Downs ...... dep	32	..	..	..	..	..	..	5 15	..	..	..	..	..	..	..	..	..	..	..	..	..	..	32
Banstead	33	..	..	..	..	..	..	5 18	..	..	..	..	..	..	..	..	..	..	..	..	..	..	33
Belmont	34	..	..	..	..	..	..	5 21	..	..	..		..	..	..	..	..	..	..	..	..	..	34
Sutton 322	35	..	..	..	..	..	..	5 24	..	..	5 17		..	5 30	..	..	..	..	..	..	5 38	5 42	35
Carshalton Beeches	36	..	..	..	..	..	..	..	..	..	5 20		..	..	..	..	..	..	..	..	5 40	5 44	36
Wallington	37	..	..	..	..	5 14	..	..	..	..	5 23		..	..	..	..	..	..	..	..	5 43	5 49	37
Waddon **G**	38	..	..	..	..	5 17	..	..	..	..	5 26		..	..	..	..	..	..	..	..	5 46	5 52	38
West Croydon 319 arr	39	..	..	..	..	5 20	..	..	..	..	5 29		..	..	..	..	..	..	..	..	5 49	5 55	39
West Croydon 319 dep	40	..	..	..	..	..	..	..	5 20	..	5 29		..	..	..	5 40	..	..	..	..	5 49	..	40
Carshalton	41	..	..	..	..	..	..	5 27	..	..	..	From London Bridge via Forest Hill	..	5 34	..	..	..	..	..	..	..	..	41
Hackbridge	42	..	..	..	..	..	..	5 30	..	..	..		..	5 36	..	..	..	..	..	..	..	..	42
Mitcham Junction	43	..	..	..	..	..	..	5 32	..	..	..		..	5 39	..	..	..	..	..	..	..	..	43
East Croydon .... arr	44	..	..	..	..	..	5 19	..	..	..	..	..	..	..	5 42	..	..	..	..	..	..	..	44
East Croydon .... dep	45	..	..	..	..	..	5 19	..	..	..	..	..	..	..	5 42	..	..	..	..	..	..	..	45
Norwood Junction F ..	46	..	..	..	5 15	..	..	..	5 24	..	5 33	5 26	..	..	..	5 44	..	..	..	..	..	..	46
Beckenham Jn. dep	47	..	..	..	..	..	..	..	..	..	..	..	..	..	..	..	..	..	..	..	..	..	47
Birkbeck	48	..	..	..	..	..	..	..	..	..	..	..	..	..	..	..	..	..	..	..	..	..	48
Crystal Palace D	49	..	..	..	..	..	..	..	5 28	..	..	..	..	..	..	5 48	..	5 55	..	..	..	..	49
Gipsy Hill (for Upper	50	..	..	..	..	..	..	..	5 31	..	..	..	..	..	..	5 51	..	..	..	..	..	..	50
West Norwood.[N'wood)	51	..	..	..	..	..	..	..	5 33	..	..	..	..	..	..	5 53	..	..	..	..	..	..	51
Streatham Hill	52	..	..	..	..	..	..	..	5 36	..	..	..	..	..	..	5 56	..	..	..	..	..	..	52
Selhurst	53	..	5 7	..	..	..	5 22	..	..	..	..	5 29	..	..	5 45	..	..	..	..	..	5 52	..	53
Thornton Heath	54	..	5 9	..	..	..	5 24	..	..	..	..	5 31	..	..	5 47	..	..	..	..	..	5 54	..	54
Norbury	55	..	5 12	..	..	..	5 27	..	..	..	..	5 34	..	..	5 50	..	..	..	..	..	5 57	..	55
Streatham Common	56	..	5 14	..	..	..	5 29	..	..	..	..	5 37	..	..	5 52	..	..	..	..	..	5 59	..	56
Anerley	57	..	..	..	5 17	..	..	..	..	..	5 36	..	..	..	..	..	..	..	..	..	..	..	57
Penge West **C**	58	..	..	..	5 19	..	..	..	..	..	5 37	..	..	..	..	..	..	..	..	..	..	..	58
Sydenham ....[Lane	59	..	..	..	5 21	..	..	..	..	..	5 39	..	..	..	..	..	..	5 58		..	..	..	59
Forest Hill, for Lordship	60	..	..	..	5 23	..	..	..	..	..	5 42	..	..	..	..	..	..	6 0		..	..	..	60
Honor Oak Park	61	..	..	..	5 26	..	..	..	..	..	5 44	..	..	..	..	..	..	6 3		..	..	..	61
Brockley **B** ....[Line)	62	..	..	..	5 28	..	..	..	..	..	5 47	..	..	..	..	..	..	6 5		..	..	..	62
New Cross Gate (for E.L.	63	..	..	..	5 31	..	..	..	..	..	5 49	..	..	..	..	..	..	6 8		..	..	..	63
Streatham	64	..	..	..	..	..	..	..	..	..	..	5 39		5 45	..	..	..	..	From Victoria dep. 5 48 a.m	..	..	..	64
Tulse Hill	65	..	..	..	..	..	..	..	..	..	..	5 42		5 49	..	..	..	..			..	..	65
North Dulwich	66	..	..	..	..	..	..	..	..	..	..	5 45		..	..	..	..	..			..	..	66
East Dulwich	67	..	..	..	..	..	..	..	..	..	..	5 47		..	..	..	..	..			..	..	67
Peckham Rye	68	..	..	5 23	..	..	..	..	..	5 44	..	5 50	Via Worcester Park	..	..	..	..	..	6 4	Via Worcester Park	..	..	68
Queen's Road, Peckham	69	..	..	5 25	..	..	..	..	..	5 46	..	5 52		..	..	..	..	..	6 6		..	..	69
South Bermondsey	70	..	..	5 28	..	..	..	..	..	5 49	..	..		..	..	..	..	..	6 9		..	..	70
Balham & Upper Tooting	71	..	5 18	..	..	..	5 33	5 39	5 39	..	..	..		..	5 56	5 59	..	..	..		6 3	..	71
Wandsworth Common **A**	72	..	..	..	..	..	5 35	..	5 41	..	..	..		..	5 58	6 1	..	..	..		..	..	72
Clapham Junction	73	4 48	5 22	..	..	..	5 38	5 43	5 44	..	..	..	5 37	..	6 1	6 4	..	..	..	5 54	6 7	..	73
Battersea Park	74	..	..	..	..	..	..	..	5 47	..	..	..	..	..	..	6 7	..	..	..	..	..	..	74
London Bridge ..... arr	75	..	..	5 32	5 37	..	..	..	..	5 53	5 55	5 57	..	6 0	..	..	..	6 13	6 13	..	..	..	75
Waterloo * .... "	76	..	..	..	..	..	..	..	..	..	..	..	5 46	..	..	..	..	..	..	6 3	..	..	76
Charing Cross * .. "	77	..	..	..	..	..	..	..	..	..	..	..	..	..	..	..	..	..	..	..	..	..	77
Victoria .... "	78	4 55	5 28	..	..	..	5 44	5 49	5 51	..	..	..	..	..	6 7	6 11	..	..	..	..	6 14	..	78

DORKING NORTH, SUTTON, CROYDON, CRYSTAL PALACE, and LONDON

No.							a.m.							Week Days									a.m.					
1	3	3	3	..	3	3	3	3	3	3	3	3	3	3	3	3	3	3	3	3	3	3	3	3	3	3	3	3
2	..	..	..	..	..	..	..	..	..	..	..	..	..	..	..	..	..	..	..	..	..	..	..	..	..	..	..	..
3	..	..	..	..	..	..	..	..	..	..	..	..	..	..	..	..	..	..	..	..	..	..	..	..	..	..	..	..
4	..	..	..	..	..	..	..	..	..	..	..	..	..	..	..	..	..	..	..	..	..	..	..	..	..	..	..	..
5	..	..	..	..	..	..	..	..	..	..	..	..	..	..	..	..	..	..	..	..	..	..	..	..	..	..	..	..
6	..	..	..	..	..	..	..	..	..	..	..	..	5 40	..	..	..	..	..	..	..	..	..	..	..	6 0	..	..	..
7	..	..	..	..	..	..	..	..	..	..	..	..	5 43	..	..	..	..	..	..	..	..	..	..	..	6 3	..	..	..
8	..	..	..	..	..	..	..	..	..	..	..	..	5 46	..	..	..	..	..	..	..	..	..	..	..	6 6	..	..	..
9	..	..	..	..	..	..	..	..	..	..	..	..	5 51	..	..	..	..	..	..	..	..	..	..	..	6 10	..	..	..
10	..	..	..	..	..	..	..	..	..	..	..	..	5 54	..	..	..	..	..	..	..	..	..	..	..	6 13	..	..	..
11	..	..	..	..	..	..	..	..	..	..	..	..	5 57	..	..	..	..	..	..	..	..	..	..	..	6 15	..	..	..
12	..	..	..	..	..	..	..	..	..	..	..	..	6 0	..	..	..	..	..	..	..	..	..	..	..	6 18	..	..	..
13	..	..	..	..	..	..	..	..	..	..	..	..	6 2	..	..	..	..	..	..	..	..	..	..	..	6 20	..	..	..
14	..	..	..	..	..	..	..	..	..	..	..	..	5 51	..	..	..	..	..	..	..	..	..	..	..	6 11	..	..	..
15	..	..	..	..	..	..	..	..	..	..	..	..	5 55	..	..	..	..	..	..	..	..	..	..	..	6 14	..	..	..
16	..	..	..	..	..	..	..	..	..	..	..	..	5 57	..	..	..	..	..	..	..	..	..	..	..	6 16	..	..	..
17	..	..	..	..	..	..	..	..	..	..	..	..	6 1	..	..	..	..	..	..	..	..	..	..	..	6 19	..	..	..
18	..	..	..	..	..	..	..	..	..	..	..	..	6 4	..	..	..	..	..	..	..	..	..	..	..	6 23	..	..	..
19	..	..	..	..	..	..	..	..	5 51	..	..	..	..	..	..	..	..	..	..	..	..	..	..	6 8	..	..	..	..
20	..	..	..	..	..	..	..	..	5 54	..	..	..	6 7	..	..	..	..	..	..	..	..	..	..	6 12	6 25	..	..	..
21	..	..	..	..	..	..	..	..	5 56	..	..	..	6 10	..	..	..	..	..	..	..	..	..	..	6 15	6 28	..	..	..
22	..	..	..	..	..	..	..	..	5 59	..	..	..	6 12	..	..	..	..	..	..	..	..	..	..	6 18	6 30	..	..	..
23	..	..	..	..	..	..	..	..	..	..	..	..	..	..	..	..	..	..	..	..	..	..	5 56	..	..	..	..	..
24	..	..	..	..	..	..	..	..	..	..	..	..	..	..	..	..	..	..	..	..	..	..	5 59	..	..	..	..	..
25	..	..	..	..	..	..	..	..	..	..	..	..	..	..	..	..	..	..	..	..	..	..	..	..	..	..	..	..
26	..	..	..	..	..	..	..	..	..	..	..	..	..	..	..	..	..	..	..	..	..	..	..	..	..	..	..	..
27	..	..	..	..	..	..	..	..	..	..	..	..	..	..	..	..	..	..	..	..	..	..	6 4	..	..	..	..	..
28	..	..	..	..	..	..	..	..	..	..	..	..	..	..	..	..	..	..	..	..	..	..	6 8	..	..	..	..	..
29	5 34	..	..	..	..	..	..	..	..	..	..	5 56	..	..	..	..	..	..	..	..	..	6 3	6 12	..	..	..	..	..
30	5 37	..	..	..	..	..	..	..	..	..	..	5 59	..	..	..	..	..	..	..	..	..	6 6	..	..	..	..	..	..
31	5 41	..	..	..	..	..	..	..	..	..	..	6 2	..	..	..	..	..	..	..	..	..	6 9	..	..	..	..	..	..
32	..	..	..	..		..	5 44	..	..	..	..	..	..	..	..	..	..		..	..	6 0	..	..	..	..	..	..	..
33	..	..	..	..		..	5 47	..	..	..	..	..	..	..	..	..	..		..	..	6 3	..	..	..	..	..	..	..
34	..	..	..	..		..	5 50	..	..	..	..	..	..	..	..	..	..		..	..	6 7	..	..	..	..	..	..	..
35	5 45	..	..	..		..	5 53	..	..	5 58	6 2	6 5	..	..	..	..	..		..	..	6 11	6 13	..	..	..	..	6 18	6 22
36	..	..	..	..		..	5 55	..	..	6 0	6 5	..	..	..	..	..	..		..	..	6 13	..	..	..	..	..	6 20	6 24
37	..	..	..	..		..	5 58	..	..	6 3	6 9	..	..	..	..	..	..		..	..	6 16	..	..	..	..	..	6 23	6 29
38	..	..	..	..	From London Bridge, via Forest Hill	..	6 1	..	..	6 6	6 12	..	..	..	..	..	..	From London Bridge, via Forest Hill	..	..	6 19	..	..	..	..	..	6 26	6 32
39	..	..	..	..		..	6 4	..	..	6 9	6 15	..	..	..	..	..	..		..	..	6 23	..	..	..	..	..	6 29	6 35
40	..	..	..	..		6 0	6 4	..	..	6 9	..	..	..	..	..	..	..		..	6 20	6 23	..	..	..	..	..	6 29	..
41	5 48	..	..	..		..	..	..	..	..	..	6 8	..	..	..	..	..		..	..	..	6 16	..	..	..	..	..	..
42	5 51	..	..	..		..	..	..	..	..	..	6 11	..	..	..	..	..		..	..	..	6 19	..	..	..	..	..	..
43	5 53	..	..	..		..	..	..	..	..	..	6 13	..	..	..	..	..		..	..	..	6 22	..	..	..	..	..	..
44	..	..	..	..		..	..	..	6 2	..	..	..	6 15	..	..	..	..		..	..	..	..	..	6 21	6 33	..	..	..
45	..	..	..	..		..	..	..	6 2	..	..	..	6 15	..	..	..	..		..	..	..	..	..	6 21	6 33	..	..	..
46	..	..	..	..	5 52	6 4	6 8	6 1	..	..	..	..	6 18	..	..	..	..	6 12	6 15	6 24	6 28	..	..	..	6 36	..	..	..
47	..	..	..	..	..	..	..	..	..	..	..	..	..	..	..	..	..	..	..	..	..	..	..	..	..	..	..	..
48	..	..	..	..	..	..	..	..	..	..	..	..	..	..	..	..	..	..	..	..	..	..	..	..	..	..	..	..
49	..	5 52	5 56	..	..	6 8	..	..	..	..	..	..	..	..	6 15	..	6 16	..	..	6 29	..	..	..	..	..	6 25	..	..
50	..	5 54	5 58	..	..	6 11	..	..	..	..	..	..	..	..	..	..	6 18	..	..	6 31	..	..	..	..	..	6 28	..	..
51	..	5 57	6 1	..	..	6 13	..	..	..	..	..	..	..	..	..	..	6 21	..	..	6 34	..	..	..	..	..	6 30	..	..
52	..	..	6 4	..	..	6 16	..	..	..	..	..	..	..	..	..	6 18	6 24	..	..	6 37	..	..	..	..	..	..	..	..
53	..	..	..	..	5 55	..	..	..	6 5	6 12	..	..	..	..	..	..	..	6 15	..	..	..	..	..	6 25	..	..	6 32	..
54	..	..	..	..	5 57	..	..	..	6 7	6 14	..	..	..	..	..	..	..	6 17	..	..	..	..	..	6 27	..	..	6 34	..
55	..	..	..	..	6 0	..	..	..	6 10	6 17	..	..	..	..	..	..	..	6 20	..	..	..	..	..	6 30	..	..	6 37	..
56	..	..	..	..	6 3	..	..	..	6 12	6 19	..	..	..	..	..	..	..	6 23	..	..	..	..	..	6 32	..	..	6 40	..
57	..	..	..	..	..	..	..	6 4	..	..	..	..	..		..	..	..	..	6 18	..	..	..	..	..	..	..	..	..
58	..	..	..	..	..	..	..	6 6	..	..	..	..	..		..	..	..	..	6 20	..	..	..	..	..	..	..	..	..
59	..	..	..	..	..	..	..	6 8	..	..	..	..	..		6 18	..	..	..	6 23	..	..	..	..	..	..	..	..	..
60	..	..	..	..	..	..	..	6 11	..	..	..	..	..		6 21	..	..	..	6 26	..	..	..	..	..	..	..	..	..
61	..	..	..	..	..	..	..	6 13	..	..	..	..	..		6 24	..	..	..	6 29	..	..	..	..	..	..	..	..	..
62	..	..	..	..	..	..	..	6 16	..	..	..	..	..	From Victoria, dep. 6 7 a.m	6 27	..	..	..	6 32	..	..	..	..	..	..	..	..	..
63	..	..	..	..	..	..	6 17	6 18	..	..	..	..	..		6 30	..	..	..	6 35	..	6 37	..	..	..	6 45	..	..	..
64	..	..	..	..	6 5	..	..	..	..	..	..	..	..		..	..	..	6 25	..	..	..	6 28		..	..	..	..	..
65	..	6 0	..	..	6 8	..	..	..	..	..	..	..	..		..	6 21	..	6 28	..	..	..	6 31		..	..	6 33	..	..
66	..	6 3	..	..	..	..	..	..	..	..	..	..	..		..	6 24	..	..	..	..	..	..		..	..	6 36	..	..
67	..	6 6	..	..	..	..	..	..	..	..	..	..	..		..	6 26	..	..	..	..	..	..		..	..	6 38	..	..
68	..	6 8	..	..	..	..	..	..	..	..	..	..	..	6 24	..	6 28	..	..	..	..	..	..		..	..	6 41	..	..
69	..	6 10	..	..	..	..	..	..	..	..	..	..	..	6 26	..	6 30	..	..	..	..	..	..	Via Worcester Park	..	..	6 43	..	..
70	..	6 13	..	..	..	..	..	..	..	..	..	..	..	6 29	..	6 33	..	..	..	..	..	..		..	..	6 46	..	..
71	6 0	..	6 6	..	..	6 19	..	..	6 16	6 23	..	6 20	..	..	..	..	6 26	..	..	6 39	..	..		6 36	..	..	6 44	..
72	..	..	6 8	..	..	6 21	..	..	6 18	..	..	..	..	..	..	..	6 28	..	..	6 41	..	..		..	..	..	..	..
73	6 5	..	6 11	..	..	6 24	..	..	6 21	6 27	..	6 24	..	..	..	..	6 31	..	..	6 44	..	..		6 40	..	..	6 48	..
74	..	..	6 14	..	..	6 27	..	..	..	..	..	..	..	..	..	..	6 34	..	..	6 47	..	..		..	..	..	..	..
75	..	6 17	..	..	6 19	..	6 22	6 24	..	..	..	..	6 31	6 33	6 36	6 37	..	6 39	6 40	..	6 42	6 42	..	..	6 50	6 50	..	..
76	..	..	..	..	..	..	..	..	..	..	..	..	..	..	..	..	..	..	..	..	..	..	6 41	..	..	..	..	..
77	..	..	..	..	..	..	..	..	..	..	..	..	..	..	..	..	..	..	..	..	..	..	..	..	..	..	..	..
78	6 10	..	6 18	..	..	6 31	..	..	6 27	6 34	..	6 29	..	..	..	..	6 38	..	..	6 51	..	..	..	6 46	..	..	6 54	..

HORSHAM, REIGATE, REDHILL, TATTENHAM CORNER, CATERHAM,

For Notes, see page 317a

Up	No.	a.m. 3	3	3	3	3	3	3	Week Days—continued 3	3	3	3		3	3	3	3	3	a.m. 3	3	3	3	No.
Horsham........dep	1	..	..	..	..	..	..	..	..	..	..	..	..	..	..	..	..	..	..	..	..	..	1
Reigate........ "	2	..	..	..	..	..	..	..	..	..	..	..	6 22	..	..	..	..	..	..	..	..	..	2
Redhill........ "	3	..	..	..	..	..	..	..	..	..	..	..	6 29	..	..	..	..	..	..	..	..	..	3
Merstham........	4	..	..	..	..	..	..	..	..	..	..	..	6 33	..	..	..	..	..	..	..	..	..	4
Coulsdon South........	5	..	..	..	..	..	..	..	..	..	..	..	6 39	..	..	..	..	..	..	..	..	..	5
Tattenham Corner dep	6	..	..	..	..	..	..	..	..	..	..	..	..	..	..	..	..	..	6 22	..	..	..	6
Tadworth **N**........	7	..	..	..	..	..	..	..	..	..	..	..	..	..	..	..	..	..	6 25	..	..	..	7
Kingswood **M**........	8	..	..	..	..	..	..	..	..	..	..	..	..	..	..	..	..	..	6 28	..	..	..	8
Chipstead........	9	..	..	..	..	..	..	..	..	..	..	..	..	..	..	..	..	..	6 32	..	..	..	9
Woodmansterne........	10	..	..	..	..	..	..	..	..	..	..	..	..	..	..	..	..	..	6 35	..	..	..	10
Smitham........	11	..	..	..	..	..	..	..	..	..	..	..	..	..	..	..	..	..	6 37	..	..	..	11
Reedham........	12	..	..	..	..	..	..	..	..	..	..	..	..	..	..	..	..	..	6 40	..	..	..	12
Purley 252........ arr	13	..	..	..	..	..	..	..	..	..	..	..	..	..	..	..	..	..	6 42	..	..	..	13
Caterham........ dep	14	..	..	..	..	..	..	..	..	..	..	..	..	..	..	..	..	..	6 33	..	..	..	14
Warlingham........	15	..	..	..	..	..	..	..	..	..	..	..	..	..	..	..	..	..	6 36	..	..	..	15
Whyteleafe........	16	..	..	..	..	..	..	..	..	..	..	..	..	..	..	..	..	..	6 38	..	..	..	16
Kenley........	17	..	..	..	..	..	..	..	..	..	..	..	..	..	..	..	..	..	6 41	..	..	..	17
Purley 252........ arr	18	..	..	..	..	..	..	..	..	..	..	..	..	..	..	..	..	..	6 45	..	..	..	18
Coulsdon North..... dep	19	..	..	..	..	..	..	..	..	..	..	6 31	..	..	..	..	..	..	..	..	..	..	19
Purley 252........	20	..	..	..	..	..	..	..	..	..	..	6 34	6 43	..	..	..	..	..	6 47	..	..	..	20
Purley Oaks........	21	..	..	..	..	..	..	..	..	..	..	6 36	..	..	..	..	..	..	6 50	..	..	..	21
South Croydon 234......	22	..	..	..	..	..	..	..	..	..	..	6 39	..	..	..	..	..	..	6 52	..	..	..	22
Effingham Junction dep	23	..	..	..	..	..	..	..	..	6 9	..	..	..	..	..	..	..	..	..	..	..	..	23
Bookham........	24	..	..	..	..	..	..	..	..	6 12	..	..	..	..	..	..	..	..	..	..	..	..	24
Dorking North...... dep	25	..	..	..	..	..	..	..	..	..	6 18	..	..	..	..	..	..	..	..	..	..	..	25
Boxhill and Burford	26	..	..	..	..	..	..	..	..	..	6 21	..	..	..	..	..	..	..	..	..	..	..	26
Leatherhead...[Bridge **J**	27	..	..	..	..	..	..	..	..	6 17	6 26	..	..	..	..	..	..	..	..	..	..	..	27
Ashtead........	28	..	..	..	..	..	..	..	..	6 21	6 30	..	..	..	..	..	..	..	..	..	..	..	28
Epsom 427........	29	6 17	..	..	..	..	..	..	..	6 25	6 34	..	..	..	..	..	..	6 37	..	..	..	..	29
Ewell East **H**........	30	6 20	..	..	..	..	..	..	..	6 28	..	..	..	..	..	..	..	6 40	..	..	..	..	30
Cheam........	31	6 23	..	..	..	..	..	..	..	6 31	..	..	..	..	..	..	..	6 43	..	..	..	..	31
Epsom Downs...... dep	32	..	..	..		..	..		6 24	..	..	..	..	..	..	..	..	..	..	..		..	32
Banstead........	33	..	..	..		..	..		6 27	..	..	..	..	..	..	..	..	..	..	..		..	33
Belmont........	34	..	..	..		..	..		6 30	..	..	..	..	..	..	..	..	..	..	..		..	34
Sutton 322........	35	6 26	..	..		..	..		6 33	6 35	..	..	..	..	..	6 38	6 42	6 46	..	..		..	35
Carshalton Beeches.....	36	..	..	..		..	..		6 35	..	..	..	..	..	..	6 40	6 44	..	..	..		..	36
Wallington........	37	..	..	..		..	..		6 38	..	..	..	..	..	..	6 43	6 49	..	..	..		..	37
Waddon **G**........	38	..	..	..		..	..		6 41	..	..	..	..	..	..	6 46	6 52	..	..	..		..	38
West Croydon 319 arr	39	..	..	..		..	..		6 44	..	..	..	..	..	..	6 49	6 55	..	..	..		..	39
dep	40	..	..	..	From London Bridge, via Streatham	..	..	From London Bridge, via Forest Hill	6 44	..	..	..	..	..	6 41	6 49	..	..	..	..	From London Bridge, via Streatham	..	40
Carshalton........	41	6 29	..	..		..	..		..	6 38	..	..	..	..	..	..	..	6 49	..	..		..	41
Hackbridge........	42	6 31	..	..		..	..		..	6 40	..	..	..	..	..	..	..	6 51	..	..		..	42
Mitcham Junction.......	43	6 34	..	..		..	..		..	6 43	..	..	..	..	..	..	..	6 54	..	..		..	43
East Croydon arr	44	..	..	..		..	..		..	..	..	6 42	6 48	..	..	..	..	..	6 55	..		..	44
dep	45	..	..	..		..	..		..	..	..	6 42	6 50	..	..	..	..	..	6 55	..		..	45
Norwood Junction F..	46	..	..	..	6 33	..	..	6 30	6 48	..	..	..	..	..	6 45	..	..	..	6 58	..	6 53	..	46
Beckenham Jn. dep	47	..	..	6 29	..	..	..	..	..	..	..	..	..	..	..	..	..	..	..	..	..	..	47
Birkbeck........	48	..	..	6 32	..	..	..	..	..	..	..	..	..	..	..	..	..	..	..	..	..	..	48
Crystal Palace D......	49	..	..	6 36	..	..	6 39	..	..	..	..	..	..	6 45	6 49	..	..	..	..	..	..	..	49
Gipsy Hill (for Upper	50	..	..	6 38	..	..	..	..	..	..	..	..	..	6 47	6 51	..	..	..	..	..	..	..	50
West Norwood.[N'wood)	51	..	..	6 41	..	SX	..	..	..	..	..	..	..	6 50	6 54	..	..	..	..	..	..	..	51
Streatham Hill........	52	..	..	6 44	..	6 38	..	..	..	..	..	..	..	..	6 57	..	..	..	..	..	..	6 58	52
Selhurst........	53	..		..	..	..	..	6 33	..	..	..	6 45	..	..	..	6 52	..	..	..		..	..	53
Thornton Heath........	54	..		..	..	..	..	6 36	..	..	..	6 47	..	..	..	6 54	..	..	..		..	..	54
Norbury........	55	..		..	..	..	..	6 40	..	..	..	6 50	..	..	..	6 57	..	..	..		..	..	55
Streatham Common....	56	..		..	..	..	..	6 43	..	..	..	6 52	..	..	..	6 59	..	..	..		..	..	56
Anerley........	57	..		..	6 36	..	..	..	..	..	..	..	..	..	..	..	..	..	..		6 56	..	57
Penge West C........	58	..		..	6 37	..	..	..	..	..	..	..	..	..	..	..	..	..	..		6 57	..	58
Sydenham........[Lane	59	..		..	6 39	..	6 42	..	..	..	..	..	..	..	..	..	..	..	..		6 59	..	59
Forest Hill, for Lordship	60	..	From Victoria, dep. 6 28 a.m	..	6 42	..	6 45	..	..	..	..	..	..	..	..	..	..	..	..	From Victoria dep. 6 48 a.m	7 2	..	60
Honor Oak Park........	61	..		..	6 44	..	6 47	..	..	..	..	..	..	..	..	..	..	..	..		7 4	..	61
Brockley **B**........[Line)	62	..		..	6 47	..	6 50	..	..	..	..	..	..	..	..	..	..	..	..		7 7	..	62
New Cross Gate (for E.L.	63	..		..	6 49	..	6 52	..	..	..	..	..	7 1	..	..	..	..	..	..		7 9	..	63
Streatham........	64	..		..	..	..	..	6 45	..	6 48		..	..	..	..	..	..	..	..		..	..	64
Tulse Hill........	65	..		..	..	6 41	..	6 48	..	6 51		..	..	6 53	..	..	..	..	..		..	7 1	65
North Dulwich........	66	..		..	..	6 44	..	..	..	..		..	..	6 56	..	..	..	..	..		..	7 4	66
East Dulwich........	67	..		..	..	6 46	..	..	..	..		..	..	6 58	..	..	..	..	..		..	7 6	67
Peckham Rye........	68	..	6 44	..	..	6 48	..	..	..	..		..	..	7 1	..	..	..	..	..	7 4	..	7 8	68
Queen's Road, Peckham	69	..	6 46	..	..	6 50	..	..	..	..	Via Worcester Park	..	..	7 3	..	..	..	..	..	7 6	..	7 10	69
South Bermondsey.......	70	..	6 49	..	..	6 53	..	..	..	..		..	..	7 6	..	..	..	..	..	7 9	..	7 13	70
Balham & Upper Tooting	71	6 41	..	6 46	..	..	..	..	..	..		6 56	..	..	6 59	7 3	..	7 1	..	..	..	..	71
Wandsworth Common **A**	72	..	..	6 48	..	..	..	..	..	..		..	..	..	7 1	..	..	..	..	..	..	..	72
Clapham Junction.....	73	6 45	..	6 51	..	..	..	..	..	..		7 0	..	..	7 4	7 7	..	7 5	..	..	..	..	73
Battersea Park........	74	..	..	6 54	..	..	..	..	..	..		..	..	..	7 7	..	..	..	..	..	..	..	74
LONDON BRIDGE..... arr	75	..	6 53	..	6 55	6 57	6 58	6 59	7 0	7 2	..	..	7 7	7 10	..	..	..	..	7 11	7 13	7 15	7 17	75
WATERLOO ✱...... "	76	..	..	..	..	..	..	..	..	..	7 2	..	..	..	..	..	..	..	..	..	..	..	76
CHARING CROSS ✱.. "	77	..	..	..	..	..	..	..	..	..	..	..	..	..	..	..	..	..	..	..	..	..	77
VICTORIA........ "	78	6 51	..	6 58	..	..	..	..	..	..	..	7 6	..	..	7 11	7 13	..	7 10	..	..	..	..	78

DORKING NORTH, SUTTON, CROYDON, CRYSTAL PALACE, and LONDON

a.m. — **Week Days**—*continued* — a.m.

No.	3	3	3	3	3	3	3	3	3	3	3	..	3	3	3	3	3		3	3	3	..	3	..	3	3	3	3
1																		6§17										
2	..	..	..	..	..	..	..	..	..	..	..	..	..	..	..	..	..	6 52	..	..	..	..	..	..	..	..	..	..
3	..	..	..	..	..	..	..	..	..	..	..	..	..	..	..	..	..	6 59	..	..	..	7 7	..	..	..	..	..	..
4	..	..	..	..	..	..	..	..	..	..	..	..	..	..	..	..	..	7 3	..	..	..	..	..	..	..	..	..	..
5	..	..	..	..	..	..	..	..	..	..	..	..	..	..	..	..	..	7 9	..	..	..	..	..	..	..	..	..	..
6	..	..	..	..	..	..	..	..	..	..	..	..	..	..	6 42	..	..	§ Via Three Bridges	..	..	..	..	..	..	..	..	..	..
7	..	..	..	..	..	..	..	..	..	..	..	..	..	..	6 45	..	..		..	..	..	..	..	..	..	..	..	..
8	..	..	..	..	..	..	..	..	..	..	..	..	..	..	6 48	..	..		..	..	..	..	..	..	..	..	..	..
9	..	..	..	..	..	..	..	..	..	..	..	..	..	..	6 52	..	..		..	..	..	..	..	..	..	..	..	..
10	..	..	..	..	..	..	..	..	..	..	..	..	..	..	6 55	..	..		..	..	..	..	..	..	..	..	..	..
11	..	..	..	..	..	..	..	..	..	..	..	..	..	..	6 57	..	..		..	..	..	..	..	..	..	..	..	..
12	..	..	..	..	..	..	..	..	..	..	..	..	..	..	7 0	..	..		..	..	..	..	..	..	..	..	..	..
13	..	..	..	..	..	..	..	..	..	..	..	..	..	..	7 2	..	..		..	..	..	..	..	..	..	..	..	..
14	..	..	..	..	..	..	..	..	..	..	..	..	..	..	6 53	..	..		..	..	..	..	..	..	..	..	..	..
15	..	..	..	..	..	..	..	..	..	..	..	..	..	..	6 56	..	..		..	..	..	..	..	..	..	..	..	..
16	..	..	..	..	..	..	..	..	..	..	..	..	..	..	6 58	..	..		..	..	..	..	..	..	..	..	..	..
17	..	..	..	..	..	..	..	..	..	..	..	..	..	..	7 1	..	..		..	..	..	..	..	..	..	..	..	..
18	..	..	..	..	..	..	..	..	..	..	..	..	..	..	7 5	..	..		..	..	..	..	..	..	..	..	..	..
19	..	..	..	..	..	..	6 51	..	..	..	..	..	..	..	..	..	..	..	..	..	..	..	..	..	..	..	..	..
20	..	..	..	..	..	..	6 54	..	..	..	..	..	..	..	7 7	..	..	7 13	..	..	..	..	..	..	..	..	..	..
21	..	..	..	..	..	..	6 56	..	..	..	..	..	..	..	7 10	..	..	..	..	..	..	..	..	..	..	..	..	..
22	..	..	..	..	..	..	6 59	..	..	..	..	..	..	..	7 12	..	..	..	..	..	..	..	..	..	..	..	..	..
23	..	..	..	..	..	..	..	..	..	..	..	..	6 38	..	..	..	..	..	..	..	..	..	..	..	..	..	..	..
24	..	..	..	..	..	..	..	..	..	..	..	..	6 41	..	..	..	..	..	..	..	..	..	..	..	..	..	..	..
25	..	..	..	..	..	6 29	..	..	..	..	..	..	..	..	..	..	..	..	..	..	..	..	..	..	..	..	..	..
26	..	..	..	..	..	6 32	..	..	..	..	..	..	..	..	..	..	..	..	..	..	..	..	..	..	..	..	..	..
27	..	..	..	..	..	6 37	..	..	..	..	..	..	6 46	..	..	..	..	..	..	..	..	..	..	..	..	..	..	..
28	..	..	..	..	..	6 41	..	..	..	..	..	..	6 50	..	..	..	..	..	..	..	..	..	..	..	..	..	..	..
29	..	..	..	..	..	6 45	..	..	..	..	..	..	6 54	6 57	..	..	..	..	..	..	..	..	..	..	..	..	..	..
30	..	..	..	..	..	6 48	..	..	..	..	..	..	..	7 0	..	..	..	..	..	..	..	..	..	..	..	..	..	..
31	..	..	..	..	..	6 51	..	..	..	..	..	..	..	7 3	..	..	..	..	..	..	..	..	..	..	..	..	..	..
32	..	..	From London Bridge, via Forest Hill	..	6 44	..	..	..	..	6 49	..	..	..	..	..	..	..	..	..	..	..	..	..	..	..	..	..	7 4
33	..	..		..	6 47	..	..	..	..	6 52	..	..	..	..	..	..	..	..	..	..	..	..	..	..	..	..	..	7 7
34	..	..		..	6 50	..	..	..	..	6 55	..	..	..	..	..	..	..	..	..	..	..	..	..	..	..	..	..	7 10
35	..	..		..	6 53	6 55	..	..	..	6 58	7 2	..	..	7 6	..	..	From London Bridge, via Streatham	..	..	..	..	..	From London Bridge, via Forest Hill	..	..	..	..	7 13
36	..	..		..	6 55	..	..	..	..	7 0	7 4	..	..	..	..	..		..	..	..	..	..		..	..	..	..	7 15
37	..	..		..	6 58	..	..	..	..	7 3	7 7	..	..	..	..	..		..	..	..	..	..		..	..	..	..	7 18
38	..	..		..	7 1	..	..	..	..	7 6	7 10	..	..	..	..	..		..	..	..	..	..		..	..	..	..	7 21
39	..	..		..	7 4	..	..	..	..	7 9	7 13	..	..	..	..	..		..	..	..	..	..		..	..	..	..	7 24
40	..	..		..	7 4	..	..	..	7 0	7 9	..	..	..	..	..	..		..	..	..	..	..		..	..	..	7 20	7 24
41	..	..		..	..	6 58	..	..	..	..	..	..	..	7 9	..	..		..	..	..	..	..		..	..	..	..	..
42	..	..		..	..	7 0	..	..	..	..	..	..	..	7 11	..	..		..	..	..	..	..		..	..	..	..	..
43	..	..		..	..	7 3	..	..	..	..	..	..	..	7 14	..	..		..	..	..	..	..		..	..	..	..	..
44	..	..		..	..	..	7 2	..	..	..	..	..	..	..	7 15	..		7 18	..	..	..	7 22		..	..	..	..	..
45	..	..		..	..	..	7 2	..	..	..	..	..	..	..	7 15	..		7 19	..	..	..	7 22		..	..	..	..	..
46	..	..	6 51	..	7 8	..	..	..	7 4	..	..	..	..	..	7 18	..	7 13	..	..	..	..	..	7 11	..	..	..	7 24	7 28
47	6 49	..	..	..	..	..	..	..	..	..	..	..	..	..	..	..	..	..	7 9	..	..	..	..	..	..	..	..	..
48	6 52	..	..	..	..	..	..	..	..	..	..	..	..	..	..	..	..	..	7 12	..	..	..	..	..	..	..	..	..
49	6 56	6 59	..	..	..	..	..	7 5	7 9	..	..	..	..	..	..	..	..	..	7 16	7 19	..	..	..	..	..	7 25	7 29	..
50	6 58	..	..	..	..	..	..	7 8	7 11	..	..	..	..	..	..	..	..	..	7 18	..	..	..	..	..	..	7 28	7 31	..
51	7 1	..	..	..	..	..	..	7 10	7 14	..	..	..	..	..	..	..	..	..	7 21	..	..	..	..	..	..	7 30	7 34	..
52	7 4	..	..	S X	..	..	..	..	7 17	..	..	..	..	..	..	..	..	..	7 24	..	7 18	..	..	..	S X	..	7 37	..
53	..	..	6 55	6 59	..	..	7 5	..	..	7 12	..	..	..	..	..	From Victoria, dep. 7 8 a.m	..	..	..	..	..	..	7 15	..	7 20	..	..	..
54	..	..	6 57	7 1	..	..	7 7	..	..	7 14	..	..	..	..	..		..	..	..	..	..	..	7 17	..	7 22	..	..	..
55	..	..	7 0	7 4	..	..	7 10	..	..	7 17	..	..	..	..	..		..	..	..	..	..	..	7 20	..	7 25	..	..	..
56	..	..	7 3	7 7	..	..	7 12	..	..	7 19	..	..	..	..	..		..	..	..	..	..	..	7 23	..	..	..	..	..
57	..	..	..	..	..	..	..	..	..	..	..	..	..	..	..		7 16	..	..	..	..	..	..	..	..	..	..	..
58	..	..	..	..	..	..	..	..	..	..	..	..	..	..	..		7 17	..	..	..	..	..	..	..	..	..	..	..
59	..	7 2	..	..	..	..	..	..	..	..	..	..	..	..	..		7 19	..	..	7 22	..	..	..	..	..	..	..	..
60	..	7 5	..	..	..	..	..	..	..	..	..	..	..	..	..		7 22	..	..	7 25	..	..	..	..	..	..	..	..
61	..	7 7	..	..	..	..	..	..	..	..	..	..	..	..	..		7 24	..	..	7 27	..	..	..	..	..	..	..	..
62	..	7 10	..	..	..	..	..	..	..	..	..	..	..	..	..		7 27	..	..	7 30	..	..	..	..	..	..	..	..
63	..	7 12	..	..	..	..	..	..	..	..	..	..	..	..	..		7 29	..	..	7 32	..	..	..	..	..	..	..	..
64	..	..	7 5	..	..	7 8	..	..	..	..	..	..	Via Worcester Park	..	..		..	..	..	..	..	..	7 25	..	..	..	..	..
65	..	..	7 8	..	..	7 11	..	7 13	..	..	..	..		..	..		..	..	..	..	7 21	..	7 28	..	..	7 33	..	..
66	..	..	..	..	..	..	..	7 16	..	..	..	..		..	..		..	..	..	..	7 24	..	..	..	..	7 36	..	..
67	..	..	..	..	..	..	..	7 18	..	..	..	..		..	..		..	..	..	..	7 26	..	..	..	..	7 38	..	..
68	..	..	..	..	..	..	..	7 21	..	..	..	..		..	..	7 24	..	..	..	..	7 28	..	..	..	..	7 41	..	..
69	..	..	7 14	..	..	..	..	7 23	..	..	..	..		..	..	7 26	..	..	..	..	7 30	..	..	..	..	7 43	..	..
70	..	..	..	..	..	..	..	7 26	..	..	..	..		..	..	7 29	..	..	..	..	7 33	..	..	..	..	7 46	..	..
71	7 6	..	..	..	..	..	7 16	..	7 19	7 23	..	..		7 21	..	..	..	..	7 26	..	..	..	..	..	..	..	7 39	..
72	7 8	..	..	..	..	..	..	..	7 21	..	..	..		..	..	..	..	..	7 28	..	..	..	..	..	..	..	7 41	..
73	7 11	..	..	..	..	..	7 20	..	7 24	7 27	..	..		7 25	..	..	..	7 30	7 31	..	..	..	..	..	7 34	..	7 44	..
74	7 14	..	..	..	..	..	..	..	7 27	..	..	..		..	..	..	..	..	7 34	..	..	..	..	..	..	..	7 47	..
75	..	7 18	7 20	..	7 22	7 22	..	7 30	..	..	..	..	..	..	7 31	7 33	7 35	..	..	7 38	7 37	7 39	7 39	..	..	7 50	..	7 41
76	..	..	..	..	..	..	..	..	..	..	..	..	7 23	..	..	..	..	..	..	..	..	..	..	..	..	..	..	..
77	..	..	..	..	..	..	..	..	..	..	..	..	..	..	..	..	..	..	..	..	..	..	..	..	..	..	..	..
78	7 18	..	..	7 21	..	..	7 26	..	7 31	7 33	..	..	..	7 30	..	..	..	7 36	7 38	..	..	..	..	..	7 40	..	7 51	..

For Notes, see page 317a

HORSHAM, REIGATE, REDHILL, TATTENHAM CORNER, CATERHAM,

Up	No.	a.m.							Week Days—continued										a.m.			No.
Horsham .... dep	1	6 23	3	3	..	3	3	3	3	3	3	3	3	3	3	..	3	3	3	3	6§45	3	1
Reigate .... "	2	3	..	..	..	..	..	..	..	..	..	..	..	..	..	..	..	..	..	..	7 19	..	2
Redhill .... "	3		..	..	..	..	..	..	..	..	..	..	..	..	..	..	..	..	..	..	7 26	..	3
Merstham	4	..	..	..	..	..	..	..	..	..	..	..	..	..	..	..	..	..	..	..	7 30	..	4
Coulsdon South	5	..	..	..	..	..	..	..	..	..	..	..	..	..	..	..	..	..	..	..	7 36	..	5
Tattenham Corner. dep	6	..	..	..	..	..	7 4	..	..	..	..	..	..	..	..	..	..	..	..	..	§ Via Three Bridges	..	6
Tadworth N	7	..	..	..	..	..	7 7	..	..	..	..	..	..	..	..	..	..	..	..	..		..	7
Kingswood M	8	..	..	..	..	..	7 10	..	..	..	..	..	..	..	..	..	..	..	..	..		..	8
Chipstead	9	..	..	..	..	..	7 14	..	..	..	..	..	..	..	..	..	..	..	..	..		..	9
Woodmansterne	10	..	..	..	..	..	7 17	..	..	..	..	..	..	..	..	..	..	..	..	..		..	10
Smitham	11	..	..	..	..	..	7 19	..	..	..	..	..	..	..	..	..	..	..	..	..		..	11
Reedham	12	..	..	..	..	..	7 22	..	..	..	..	..	..	..	..	..	..	..	..	..		..	12
Purley 252 .... arr	13	..	..	..	..	..	7 24	..	..	..	..	..	..	..	..	..	..	..	..	..		..	13
Caterham .... dep	14	..	..	..	..	..	7 14	..	..	..	..	..	..	..	..	..	..	..	..	..	..	..	14
Warlingham	15	..	..	..	..	..	7 18	..	..	..	..	..	..	..	..	..	..	..	..	..	..	..	15
Whyteleafe	16	..	..	..	..	..	7 20	..	..	..	..	..	..	..	..	..	..	..	..	..	..	..	16
Kenley	17	..	..	..	..	..	7 23	..	..	..	..	..	..	..	..	..	..	..	..	..	..	..	17
Purley 252 .... arr	18	..	..	..	..	..	7 26	..	..	..	..	..	..	..	..	..	..	..	..	..	..	..	18
Coulsdon North ..... dep	19	..	..	7 11	..	7 16	..	..	..	..	..	..	..	..	..	..	..	..	..	7 31	..	..	19
Purley 252	20	..	..	7 14	..	7 19	7 29	..	..	..	..	..	..	..	..	..	..	..	..	7 34	7 39	..	20
Purley Oaks	21	..	..	7 16	..	7 22	..	..	..	..	..	..	..	..	..	..	..	..	..	7 36	..	..	21
South Croydon 234	22	..	..	7 19	7 21	7 24	..	..	..	..	..	..	..	..	..	..	..	..	..	7 39	..	..	22
Effingham Junction dep	23	..	..	..	..	..	..	..	..	..	..	..	..	..	..	..	..	..	..	..	..	..	23
Bookham	24	..	..	..	..	..	..	..	..	..	..	..	..	..	..	..	..	..	..	..	..	..	24
Dorking North ..... dep	25	6 49	6 58	..	..	..	..	..	..	..	..	..	..	..	..	..	..	..	..	..	..	..	25
Boxhill and Burford	26	6 52	7 1	..	..	..	..	..	..	..	..	..	..	..	..	..	..	..	..	..	..	..	26
Leatherhead ...[Bridge J	27	6 57	7 6	..	..	..	..	..	..	..	..	..	..	..	..	..	..	..	..	..	..	..	27
Ashtead	28	7 1	7 10	..	..	..	..	..	..	..	..	..	..	..	..	..	..	..	..	..	..	..	28
Epsom 427	29	7 5	7 14	..	..	..	..	..	..	..	7 17	..	..	..	..	..	..	..	..	..	..	..	29
Ewell East H	30	7 8	..	..	..	..	..	..	..	..	7 20	..	..	..	..	..	..	..	..	..	..	..	30
Cheam	31	7 11	..	..	..	..	..	..	..	..	7 23	..	..	..	..	..	..	..	..	..	..	..	31
Epsom Downs ...... dep	32	..	..	..	..	..	..	..	7 9	..	..	..	From London Bridge, via Streatham	..	..	..	..	..	..	..	..	..	32
Banstead	33	..	..	..	..	..	..	..	7 12	..	..	..		..	..	..	..	..	..	..	..	..	33
Belmont	34	..	..	..	..	..	..	..	7 15	..	..	..		..	..	..	..	..	..	..	..	..	34
Sutton 322	35	7 15	..	..	..	..	..	..	7 18	7 22	7 26	..		..	..	..	From London Bridge, via Forest Hill	..	..	..	..	..	35
Carshalton Beeches	36	..	..	..	..	..	..	..	7 20	7 25	..	..		..	..	..		..	..	..	..	..	36
Wallington	37	..	..	..	..	..	..	..	7 23	7 28	..	..		..	..	..		..	..	..	..	..	37
Waddon G	38	..	..	..	..	..	..	..	7 26	7 32	..	..		..	..	..		..	..	..	..	..	38
West Croydon 319 arr	39	..	..	..	..	..	..	..	7 29	7 35	..	..		..	..	..		..	..	..	..	..	39
West Croydon 319 dep	40	..	..	..	..	..	..	..	7 29	..	..	..		..	..	..		..	..	..	..	..	40
Carshalton	41	7 18	..	..	..	..	..	..	..	..	7 29	..		..	..	..		..	From London Bridge, via Tulse Hill	..	..	..	41
Hackbridge	42	7 20	..	..	..	..	..	..	..	..	7 31	..		..	..	..		..		..	..	..	42
Mitcham Junction	43	7 23	..	..	..	..	..	..	..	..	7 34	..	..	..	..	..		..		..	..	..	43
East Croydon ... arr	44	..	..	7 23	7 25	7 27	7 34	..	..	..	..	..	..	..	..	..		..		7 42	7 45	..	44
East Croydon ... dep	45	..	..	7 23	7 25	7 27	7 34	..	..	..	..	..	S X	..	..	..		..		7 42	7 45	..	45
Norwood Junction F ..	46	..	..	..	..	7 31	..	..	..	..	..	..	7 33	..	..	..	7 31	..		..	..	..	46
Beckenham Jn. dep	47	..	..	..	..	..	..	..	..	..	..	..	..	7 29	..	..	..	..		..	..	..	47
Birkbeck	48	..	..	..	..	..	..	..	..	..	..	..	..	7 32	..	..	..	..		..	..	..	48
Crystal Palace D	49	..	..	..	..	..	..	..	..	..	..	..	..	7 36	7 39	..	..	..		..	..	7 45	49
Gipsy Hill (for Upper	50	..	..	..	..	..	..	..	..	..	..	..	..	7 38	..	..	..	..		..	..	7 48	50
West Norwood.[N'wood)	51	..	..	..	..	..	..	..	..	..	..	..	..	7 41	..	..	..	..		..	..	7 50	51
Streatham Hill	52	..	..	..	..	..	..	..	..	..	..	7 38	..	7 44	..	..	..	S X	7 49	..	..	..	52
Selhurst	53	..	..	7 26	..	..	..	..	7 32	..	..	..	..	..	..	..	7 35	7 39	..	7 45	..	..	53
Thornton Heath	54	..	..	7 28	..	..	..	..	7 34	..	..	..	..	..	..	..	7 37	7 41	..	7 47	..	..	54
Norbury	55	..	..	7 31	..	..	..	..	7 37	..	..	..	..	..	..	..	7 40	7 44	..	7 50	..	..	55
Streatham Common	56	..	..	7 33	..	..	..	..	7 39	..	..	..	..	..	..	..	7 43	7 46	..	7 52	..	..	56
Anerley	57	..	..	..	..	..	..	From Victoria, dep 7 28 a.m.	..	..	..	..	7 36	..	..	..	..	..	..	..	..	..	57
Penge West C	58	..	..	..	..	..	..		..	..	..	..	7 37	..	..	..	..	..	..	..	..	..	58
Sydenham ....[Lane	59	..	..	..	..	..	..		..	..	..	..	7 39	..	7 42	..	..	..	..	..	..	..	59
Forest Hill, for Lordship	60	..	..	..	..	..	..		..	..	..	..	7 42	..	7 45	..	..	..	..	..	..	..	60
Honor Oak Park	61	..	..	..	..	..	..		..	..	..	..	7 44	..	7 47	..	..	..	..	..	..	..	61
Brockley B ....[Line)	62	..	..	..	..	..	..		..	..	..	..	7 47	..	7 50	..	..	..	..	..	..	..	62
New Cross Gate (for E.L.	63	..	..	..	7 37	7 40	..		..	..	..	..	7 49	..	7 53	..	..	..	..	..	..	..	63
Streatham	64	7 28	Via Worcester Park	..	..	..	..		..	..	..	..	..	..	..	..	7 45	..	..	..	..	..	64
Tulse Hill	65	7 21		..	..	..	..		..	..	..	7 41	..	..	..	..	7 48	..	..	..	..	7 53	65
North Dulwich	66	..		..	..	..	..		..	..	..	7 44	..	..	..	..	..	..	..	..	..	7 56	66
East Dulwich	67	..		..	..	..	..		..	..	..	7 46	..	..	..	..	..	..	..	..	..	7 58	67
Peckham Rye	68	..		..	..	..	..	7 44	..	..	..	7 48	..	..	..	..	..	..	..	..	..	8 1	68
Queen's Road, Peckham	69	..		..	..	..	..	7 46	..	..	..	7 50	..	..	..	..	..	..	..	..	..	8 3	69
South Bermondsey	70	..		..	..	..	..	7 49	..	..	..	7 53	..	..	..	..	..	..	..	..	..	8 6	70
Balham & Upper Tooting	71	..		7 37	..	..	..	..	7 43	..	7 41	..	..	7 46	..	..	..	..	7 52	7 56	..	..	71
Wandsworth Common A	72	..		..	..	..	..	..	..	..	..	..	..	7 48	..	..	..	..	7 54	..	..	..	72
Clapham Junction	73	..		7 42	..	..	..	..	7 47	..	7 45	..	..	7 51	..	..	..	..	7 57	8 0	..	..	73
Battersea Park	74	..		..	..	..	..	..	..	..	..	..	..	7 54	..	..	..	..	8 0	..	..	..	74
LONDON BRIDGE ..... arr	75	7 42	..	..	7 43	7 46	7 50	7 53	..	..	..	7 57	7 55	..	7 58	..	7 59	..	..	..	8 0	8 10	75
WATERLOO * .... "	76	..	7 43	..	..	..	..	..	..	..	..	..	..	..	..	..	..	..	..	..	..	..	76
CHARING CROSS * .... "	77	..	..	..	..	..	..	..	..	..	..	..	..	..	..	..	..	..	..	..	..	..	77
VICTORIA .... "	78	..	..	7 47	..	..	..	..	7 53	..	7 50	..	..	7 58	..	..	..	7 59	8 4	8 6	..	..	78

DORKING NORTH, SUTTON, CROYDON, CRYSTAL PALACE, and LONDON

No.					a.m.								Week Days—continued										a.m.					
1	3	3	3	3	..	6 52	3	3	3	3	..	..	3	3	..	..	3	3	3	3	3	3	3	3	3	..	7 3	3
2	..	..	..	..	..	3	..	..	..	..	..	..	..	..	..	..	..	..	..	..	..	..	..	..	..	..	..	..
3	..	..	..	..	..	..	..	..	..	..	..	..	..	..	..	..	..	..	..	..	..	..	..	..	..	..	3	..
4	..	..	..	..	..	..	..	..	..	..	..	..	..	..	..	..	..	..	..	..	..	..	..	..	..	..	..	..
5	..	..	..	..	..	..	..	..	..	..	..	..	..	..	..	..	..	..	..	..	..	..	..	..	..	..	..	..
6	..	..	..	..	..	..	7 24	..	..	..	..	..	..	..	..	..	..	..	..	..	..	..	..	..	..	..	..	..
7	..	..	..	..	..	..	7 27	..	..	..	..	..	..	..	..	..	..	..	..	..	..	..	..	..	..	..	..	..
8	..	..	..	..	..	..	7 30	..	..	..	..	..	..	..	..	..	..	..	..	..	..	..	..	..	..	..	..	..
9	..	..	..	..	..	..	7 34	..	..	..	..	..	..	..	..	..	..	..	..	..	..	..	..	..	..	..	..	..
10	..	..	..	..	..	..	7 37	..	..	..	..	..	..	..	..	..	..	..	..	..	..	..	..	..	..	..	..	..
11	..	..	..	..	..	..	7 39	..	..	..	..	..	..	..	..	..	..	..	..	..	..	..	..	..	..	..	..	..
12	..	..	..	..	..	..	7 42	..	..	..	..	..	..	..	..	..	..	..	..	..	..	..	..	..	..	..	..	..
13	..	..	..	..	..	..	7 44	..	..	..	..	..	..	..	..	..	..	..	..	..	..	..	..	..	..	..	..	..
14	..	..	..	..	..	..	7 34	..	..	..	..	..	..	..	..	..	..	..	..	..	..	..	..	..	..	..	..	..
15	..	..	..	..	..	..	7 38	..	..	..	..	..	..	..	..	..	..	..	..	..	..	..	..	..	..	..	..	..
16	..	..	..	..	..	..	7 40	..	..	..	..	..	..	..	..	..	..	..	..	..	..	..	..	..	..	..	..	..
17	..	..	..	..	..	..	7 43	..	..	..	..	..	..	..	..	..	..	..	..	..	..	..	..	..	..	..	..	..
18	..	..	..	..	..	..	7 46	..	..	..	..	..	..	..	..	..	..	..	..	..	..	..	..	..	..	..	..	..
19	..	..	..	7 36	..	..	..	..	..	..	..	..	..	..	..	..	..	..	..	..	..	..	..	..	..	..	..	..
20	..	..	..	7 39	..	..	7 49	..	..	..	..	..	..	..	..	..	..	..	..	..	..	..	..	..	..	..	..	..
21	..	..	..	7 42	..	..	..	..	..	..	..	..	..	..	..	..	..	..	..	..	..	..	..	..	..	..	..	..
22	..	..	..	7 44	7 45	..	..	..	..	..	..	..	..	..	..	..	..	..	..	..	..	..	..	..	..	..	..	..
23	..	..	7 10	..	..	..	..	..	..	..	..	..	..	..	..	..	..	..	..	..	..	..	..	..	..	..	..	7 38
24	..	..	7 13	..	..	..	..	..	..	..	..	..	..	..	..	..	..	..	..	..	..	..	..	..	..	..	..	7 41
25	..	..	..	..	..	7 18	..	..	..	..	..	..	..	..	..	..	..	..	..	..	..	..	..	..	..	..	7 29	..
26	..	..	..	..	..	7 21	..	..	..	..	..	..	..	..	..	..	..	..	..	..	..	..	..	..	..	..	7 32	..
27	..	..	7 18	..	..	7 26	..	..	..	..	..	..	..	..	..	..	..	..	..	..	..	..	..	..	..	..	7 37	7 45
28	..	..	7 22	..	..	7 30	..	..	..	..	..	..	..	..	..	..	..	..	..	..	..	..	..	..	..	..	7 41	7 49
29	..	..	7 26	..	..	7 34	..	..	..	7 37	..	..	..	..	..	..	..	..	..	..	..	..	..	..	..	..	7 45	7 53
30	..	..	7 29	..	..	..	..	..	..	7 40	..	..	..	..	..	..	..	..	..	..	..	..	..	..	..	..	7 48	..
31	..	..	7 32	..	..	..	..	..	..	7 43	..	..	..	..	..	..	..	..	..	..	..	..	..	..	..	..	7 51	..
32	..	7 24	..	..	..	..	..	7 29	..	..	..	..	..	..	..	..	..	..	..	..	..	..	..	..	7 44	..	..	..
33	..	7 27	..	..	..	..	..	7 32	..	..	..	..	..	..	..	..	..	..	..	..	..	..	..	..	7 47	..	..	..
34	..	7 30	..	..	..	..	..	7 35	..	..	..	..	..	..	..	..	..	..	..	..	..	..	..	..	7 50	..	..	..
35	..	7 33	7 35	..	..	..	..	7 38	7 43	7 46	..	..	..	..	..	..	..	..	..	..	..	..	..	..	7 53	..	7 55	..
36	..	7 35	..	..	..	..	..	7 40	7 45	..	..	..	..	..	..	..	..	..	..	..	..	..	..	..	7 55	..	..	..
37	..	7 38	..	..	..	..	..	7 43	7 49	..	..	..	..	..	..	..	..	..	..	..	..	..	..	..	7 58	..	..	..
38	..	7 41	..	..	..	..	..	7 46	7 52	..	..	..	..	..	..	..	..	..	..	..	..	..	..	..	8 1	..	..	..
39	..	7 44	..	..	..	..	..	7 49	7 55	..	..	..	..	..	..	..	..	..	..	..	..	..	..	..	8 4	..	..	..
40	7 40	7 44	..	..	..	..	..	7 49	..	..	..	..	..	From London Bridge, via Streatham	..	..	..	..	..	From London Bridge, via Forest Hill	..	..	..	8 0	8 4	..	..	..
41	..	..	7 38	..	..	..	..	..	..	7 49	..	..	..	..	..	..	..	..	..	..	..	..	..	..	..	..	7 58	..
42	..	..	7 40	..	..	..	..	..	..	7 51	..	..	..	..	..	..	..	..	..	..	..	..	..	..	..	..	8 0	..
43	..	..	7 43	..	..	..	..	..	..	7 54	..	..	..	..	..	..	..	..	..	..	..	..	..	..	..	..	8 3	..
44	..	..	..	7 47	7 49	..	7 54	..	..	..	..	..	..	..	..	..	..	..	..	..	..	..	..	..	..	..	..	..
45	..	..	..	7 47	7 49	..	7 54	..	..	..	7 58	..	..	..	8 0	..	..	..	..	..	..	..	..	..	..	..	..	..
46	7 44	7 48	..	7 51	..	..	..	..	..	..	..	..	..	7 53	..	..	..	..	..	7 52	From London Bridge, via Tulse Hill	..	..	8 4	8 8	..	..	..
47	..	..	..	..	..	..	..	..	..	..	..	..	..	..	..	..	..	7 49	..	..	..	..	..	..	..	..	..	..
48	..	..	..	..	..	..	..	..	..	..	..	..	..	..	..	..	..	7 52	..	..	..	..	..	..	..	..	..	..
49	7 49	..	..	..	..	..	..	..	..	..	..	..	..	..	..	..	..	7 56	7 59	..	..	..	8 5	8 9	..	..	..	..
50	7 51	..	..	..	..	..	..	..	..	..	..	..	..	..	..	..	..	7 58	..	..	..	..	8 8	8 11	..	..	..	..
51	7 54	..	..	..	..	..	..	..	..	..	..	..	..	..	..	..	..	8 1	..	..	..	..	8 10	8 14	..	..	..	..
52	7 57	..	..	..	..	..	..	..	..	..	..	..	..	..	..	..	7 58	8 4	..	..	8 9	S X	..	8 17	..	..	..	..
53	..	..	..	..	..	..	..	7 52	..	..	..	..	..	..	..	..	..	..	..	7 55	..	7 59	..	..	..	..	..	..
54	..	..	..	..	..	..	..	7 54	..	..	..	..	..	..	..	..	..	..	..	7 57	..	8 1	..	..	..	..	..	..
55	..	..	..	..	..	..	..	7 57	..	..	..	..	..	..	..	..	..	..	..	8 0	..	8 4	..	..	..	..	..	..
56	..	..	..	..	..	..	..	7 59	..	..	..	..	..	..	..	..	..	..	..	8 3	..	8 6	..	..	..	..	..	..
57	..	..	..	..	..	..	..	..	..	..	..	..	..	7 56	..	..	..	..	..	..	..	..	..	..	..	..	..	..
58	..	..	..	..	..	..	..	..	..	..	..	..	..	7 57	..	..	..	..	..	..	..	..	..	..	..	..	..	..
59	..	..	..	..	..	..	..	..	..	..	..	..	..	7 59	..	..	..	..	8 2	..	..	..	..	..	..	..	..	..
60	..	..	..	..	..	..	..	..	..	..	..	..	..	8 2	..	..	..	..	8 5	..	..	..	..	..	..	..	..	..
61	..	..	..	..	..	..	..	..	..	..	..	..	..	8 4	..	..	..	..	8 7	..	..	..	..	..	..	..	..	..
62	..	..	..	..	..	..	..	..	..	..	..	..	From Victoria, dep. 7 48 a.m	8 7	..	..	..	..	8 10	..	..	..	..	..	..	..	..	..
63	..	..	..	8 0	..	..	..	..	..	..	..	..	..	8 9	..	..	..	..	8 12	..	..	..	..	..	..	..	..	..
64	..	..	7 48	..	..	..	..	..	..	..	..	..	..	..	..	..	..	..	..	8 5	..	..	..	..	..	..	8 8	..
65	..	..	7 51	..	..	..	..	..	..	..	..	..	..	..	..	..	8 1	..	..	8 8	..	..	8 13	..	..	..	8 11	..
66	..	..	..	..	..	..	..	..	..	..	..	..	..	..	..	..	8 4	..	..	..	..	..	8 16	..	..	..	..	..
67	..	..	..	..	..	..	..	..	..	..	..	..	..	..	..	..	8 6	..	..	..	..	..	8 18	..	..	..	..	..
68	..	..	..	..	..	..	..	..	..	..	..	..	8 4	..	..	..	8 8	..	..	..	..	..	8 21	..	..	..	..	..
69	..	..	..	..	..	..	..	..	..	..	..	..	8 6	..	..	..	8 10	..	..	..	..	..	8 23	..	..	..	..	..
70	..	..	..	..	..	Via Worcester Park	..	..	..	..	..	..	8 9	..	..	..	8 13	..	..	..	..	..	8 26	..	..	..	..	Via Worcester Park
71	7 59	..	..	..	..	..	..	8 3	..	8 1	..	..	..	..	..	..	..	8 6	..	..	8 12	..	..	8 19	..	..	..	..
72	8 1	..	..	..	..	..	..	..	..	..	..	..	..	..	..	..	..	8 8	..	..	8 14	..	..	8 21	..	..	..	..
73	8 5	..	..	..	8 0	..	..	8 7	..	8 5	..	..	..	..	..	..	..	8 11	..	..	8 17	..	..	8 24	..	..	..	..
74	8 7	..	..	..	..	..	..	..	..	..	..	..	..	..	..	..	..	8 14	..	..	8 20	..	..	8 27	..	..	..	..
75	..	8 1	8 2	8 6	..	..	8 10	..	..	..	8 13	..	8 13	8 15	..	..	8 17	..	8 18	8 19	..	..	8 30	..	8 21	..	8 22	..
76	..	..	..	..	..	8 3	..	..	..	..	..	..	..	..	..	..	..	..	..	..	..	..	..	..	..	..	..	8 22
77	..	..	..	..	..	..	..	..	..	..	..	..	..	..	..	..	..	..	..	..	..	..	..	..	..	..	..	..
78	8 11	..	..	..	8 7	..	..	8 13	..	8 10	..	..	..	..	8 15	..	..	8 18	..	..	8 24	8 19	..	8 31	..	..	..	..

HORSHAM, REIGATE, REDHILL, TATTENHAM CORNER, CATERHAM,

For Notes, see page 317a

Up	No.	a.m.						Week Days—continued												a.m.			No.
		3	..	3		..	3	3	3	3	3	3	..	3		3	3	3	3	3	..	3	
Horsham .... dep	1	..	..	..	7§ 7	..	..	..	..	..	..	..	..	..	7§46	..	..	..	..	..	..	..	1
Reigate .... "	2	..	..	..	7 43	..	..	..	..	..	..	..	..	..	..	..	..	..	..	..	..	..	2
Redhill .... "	3	..	..	..	7 50	..	..	..	..	..	..	..	..	..	..	..	..	..	..	..	..	..	3
Merstham	4	..	..	..	7 54	..	..	..	..	..	..	..	..	..	..	..	..	..	..	..	..	..	4
Coulsdon South	5	..	..	..	8 0	..	..	..	..	..	..	..	..	..	§ Via Three Bridges	..	..	..	..	..	..	..	5
Tattenham Corner. dep	6	..	..	..	§ Via Three Bridges	..	7 44	..	..	..	..	..	..	..		..	..	..	..	..	..	..	6
Tadworth **N**	7	..	..	..		..	7 47	..	..	..	..	..	..	..		..	..	..	..	..	..	..	7
Kingswood **M**	8	..	..	..		..	7 50	..	..	..	..	..	..	..		..	..	..	..	..	..	..	8
Chipstead	9	..	..	..		..	7 54	..	..	..	..	..	..	..		..	..	..	..	..	..	..	9
Woodmansterne	10	..	..	..		..	7 57	..	..	..	..	..	..	..		..	..	..	..	..	..	..	10
Smitham	11	..	..	..		..	7 59	..	..	..	..	..	..	..		..	..	..	..	..	..	..	11
Reedham	12	..	..	..		..	8 2	..	..	..	..	..	..	..		..	..	..	..	..	..	..	12
Purley 252 .... arr	13	..	..	..		..	8 4	..	..	..	..	..	..	..	..	..	..	..	..	..	..	..	13
Caterham .... dep	14	..	..	..	..	..	7 54	..	..	..	..	..	..	..	..	..	..	..	..	..	..	..	14
Warlingham	15	..	..	..	..	..	7 58	..	..	..	..	..	..	..	..	..	..	..	..	..	..	..	15
Whyteleafe	16	..	..	..	..	..	8 0	..	..	..	..	..	..	..	..	..	..	..	..	..	..	..	16
Kenley	17	..	..	..	..	..	8 3	..	..	..	..	..	..	..	..	..	..	..	..	..	..	..	17
Purley 252 .... arr	18	..	..	..	..	..	8 6	..	..	..	..	..	..	..	..	..	..	..	..	..	..	..	18
Coulsdon North ..... dep	19	7 51	..	7 56	..	..	..	..	..	..	..	..	..	..	..	..	..	..	..	..	..	..	19
Purley 252	20	7 54	..	7 59	8 4	8 6	8 9	..	..	..	..	..	..	..	..	..	..	..	..	..	..	..	20
Purley Oaks	21	7 56	..	8 2	..	..	..	..	..	..	..	..	..	..	..	..	..	..	..	..	..	..	21
South Croydon 234	22	7 59	..	8 4	..	..	..	..	..	..	..	..	..	..	..	..	..	..	..	..	8 20	..	22
Effingham Junction dep	23	..	..	..	..	..	..	..	..	..	..	..	..	..	..	..	..	..	..	..	..	..	23
Bookham	24	..	..	..	..	..	..	..	..	..	..	..	..	..	..	..	..	..	..	..	..	..	24
Dorking North ..... dep	25	..	..	..	..	..	..	..	..	..	..	..	..	..	..	..	..	..	..	..	..	..	25
Boxhill and Burford	26	..	..	..	..	..	..	..	..	..	..	..	..	..	..	..	..	..	..	..	..	..	26
Leatherhead ...[Bridge **J**	27	..	..	..	..	..	..	..	..	..	..	..	..	..	..	..	..	..	..	..	..	..	27
Ashtead	28	..	..	..	..	..	..	..	..	..	..	..	..	..	..	..	..	..	..	..	..	..	28
Epsom 427	29	..	..	..	..	..	..	..	..	..	7 57	..	..	..	..	..	..	..	..	..	..	..	29
Ewell East **H**	30	..	..	..	..	..	..	..	..	..	8 0	..	..	..	..	..	..	..	..	..	..	..	30
Cheam	31	..	..	..	..	..	..	..	..	..	8 3	..	..	..	..	..	..	..	..	..	..	..	31
Epsom Downs ...... dep	32	..	..	..	..	..	..	7 49	..	..	..	..	..	..	..	..	..	..	..	..	..	..	32
Banstead	33	..	..	..	..	..	..	7 52	..	..	..	..	..	..	..	..	..	..	..	..	..	..	33
Belmont	34	..	..	..	..	..	..	7 55	SX	SO	..	..	..	..	..	..	..	..	..	..	..	..	34
Sutton 322	35	..	..	..	..	..	..	7 58	8 3	8 3	8 6	..	..	From London Bridge, via Streatham	..	..	..	..	From London Bridge, via Forest Hill	..	..	..	35
Carshalton Beeches	36	..	..	..	..	..	..	8 0	8 7	8 7	..	..	..		..	..	..	..		..	..	..	36
Wallington	37	..	..	..	..	..	..	8 3	8 11	8 11	..	..	..		..	From Victoria, via Wandsworth Common	..	..		..	..	..	37
Waddon **G**	38	..	..	..	..	..	..	8 6	8 14	8 14	..	..	..		..		..	..		..	..	..	38
West Croydon 319 arr	39	..	..	..	..	..	..	8 9	8 17	8 17	..	..	..		..		..	..		..	..	..	39
West Croydon 319 dep	40	..	..	..	..	..	..	8 9	8 17	..	..	..	..		..		..	..		..	..	..	40
Carshalton	41	..	..	..	..	..	..	..	..	..	8 9	..	..		..		..	..		..	..	..	41
Hackbridge	42	..	..	..	..	..	..	..	..	..	8 11	..	..		..		..	..		..	..	..	42
Mitcham Junction	43	..	..	..	..	..	..	..	..	..	8 14	..	..		..		..	..		..	..	..	43
East Croydon ... arr	44	8 2	SX	8 7	8 9	8 12	8 15	..	..	..	..	..	..		8 20		..	..		..	8 23	..	44
East Croydon ... dep	45	8 2	8 5	8 7	8 10	8 12	8 15	..	..	..	..	..	8 18		8 20		..	..	..	..	8 23	..	45
Norwood Junction F ..	46	..	..	8 11	..	..	..	..	8 21	..	..	..	..	8 13	..		..	..	8 12	..	..	..	46
Beckenham Jn. dep	47	..	..	..	..	..	..	..	..	..	..	..	..	..	..		8 9	..	..	..	..	..	47
Birkbeck	48	..	..	..	..	..	..	..	..	..	..	..	..	..	..		8 12	..	..	..	..	..	48
Crystal Palace D	49	..	..	..	..	..	..	..	..	..	..	..	..	..	..		8 16	8 19	..	..	..	8 25	49
Gipsy Hill (for Upper	50	..	..	..	..	..	..	..	..	..	..	..	..	..	..		8 18	..	..	..	..	8 28	50
West Norwood. [N'wood)	51	..	..	..	..	..	..	..	..	..	..	..	..	..	..		8 21	..	..	..	..	8 30	51
Streatham Hill	52	..	..	..	..	..	..	..	..	..	..	..	..	..	..	8 18	8 24	..	..	..	..	..	52
Selhurst	53	8 5	..	..	..	..	..	8 12	..	..	..	..	..	..	..	..	..	..	8 15	8 19	..	..	53
Thornton Heath	54	8 7	..	..	..	..	..	8 14	..	..	..	..	..	..	..	..	..	..	8 17	8 21	..	..	54
Norbury	55	8 10	..	..	..	..	..	8 17	..	..	..	..	..	..	..	..	..	..	8 20	8 24	..	..	55
Streatham Common	56	8 12	..	..	..	..	..	8 19	..	..	..	..	..	..	..	..	..	..	8 23	8 26	..	..	56
Anerley	57	..	..	..	..	..	..	..	..	..	..	..	..	8 16	..	..	..	..	..	..	..	..	57
Penge West **C**	58	..	..	..	..	..	..	..	..	..	..	From Victoria, dep. 8 7 a.m.	..	8 17	..	..	..	..	..	..	..	..	58
Sydenham .... [Lane	59	..	..	..	..	..	..	..	..	..	..		..	8 19	..	..	..	8 22	..	..	..	..	59
Forest Hill, for Lordship	60	..	..	..	..	..	..	..	..	..	..		..	8 22	..	..	..	8 25	..	..	..	..	60
Honor Oak Park	61	..	..	..	..	..	..	..	..	..	..		..	8 24	..	..	..	8 27	..	..	..	..	61
Brockley B .... [Line)	62	..	..	..	..	..	..	..	..	..	..		..	8 27	..	..	..	8 30	..	..	..	..	62
New Cross Gate (for E.L.	63	..	..	8 20	..	..	..	..	..	..	..		..	8 29	..	..	..	8 32	..	..	..	..	63
Streatham	64	..	..	..	..	..	..	..	..	..	..		..	..	..	..	..	..	8 25	..	..	..	64
Tulse Hill	65	..	..	..	..	..	..	..	..	..	..		..	..	..	8 21	..	..	8 28	..	..	8 33	65
North Dulwich	66	..	..	..	..	..	..	..	..	..	..		..	..	..	8 24	..	..	..	..	..	8 36	66
East Dulwich	67	..	..	..	..	..	..	..	..	..	..	..	..	..	..	8 26	..	..	..	..	..	8 38	67
Peckham Rye	68	..	..	..	..	..	..	..	..	..	..	8 24	..	..	..	8 28	..	..	..	..	..	8 41	68
Queen's Road, Peckham	69	..	..	..	..	..	..	..	..	..	..	8 26	..	..	..	8 30	..	..	..	..	..	8 43	69
South Bermondsey	70	..	..	..	..	..	..	..	..	..	..	8 29	..	..	..	8 33	..	..	..	..	..	8 46	70
Balham & Upper Tooting	71	8 16	..	..	..	..	..	8 24	..	..	8 21	..	..	..	..	..	8 26	..	..	..	..	..	71
Wandsworth Common **A**	72	..	..	..	..	..	..	..	..	..	..	..	..	..	..	..	8 28	..	..	..	..	..	72
Clapham Junction	73	8 21	..	..	..	8 23	..	8 28	..	..	8 25	..	..	..	8 31	..	8 31	..	..	8 33	8 36	..	73
Battersea Park	74	..	..	..	..	..	..	..	..	..	..	..	..	..	..	..	8 34	..	..	..	..	..	74
LONDON BRIDGE ..... arr	75	..	8 20	8 26	8 26	..	8 30	..	8 37	..	..	8 33	8 33	8 35	..	8 37	..	8 38	8 39	..	..	8 50	75
WATERLOO ✻ .... "	76	..	..	..	..	..	..	..	..	..	..	..	..	..	..	..	..	..	..	..	..	..	76
CHARING CROSS ✻ .. "	77	..	..	..	..	..	..	..	..	..	..	..	..	..	..	..	..	..	..	..	..	..	77
VICTORIA .... "	78	8 27	..	..	..	8 28	..	8 33	..	..	8 31	..	..	..	8 37	..	8 38	..	..	8 40	8 43	..	78

DORKING NORTH, SUTTON, CROYDON, CRYSTAL PALACE, and LONDON

No.	a.m											Week Days—continued											a.m					
1	3	3	..	3	7 23	3	3	7§27	3	..	..	3	..	3	3	3	3	3	3	..	3	..	3	3	3	3	3	3
2			7 50		3			8 2																				
3			7a55					8 9																				
4								8 13																				
5								8 19																				
6			a Arrival time					§ Via Three Bridges				8 4																
7												8 7																
8												8 10																
9												8 14																
10												8 17																
11												8 19																
12												8 22																
13												8 24																
14												8 14																
15												8 18																
16												8 20																
17												8 23																
18									SX			8 26																
19							8 11		8 16																			8 31
20							8 14		8 19			8 29	8 31									8 35						8 34
21							8 16		8 21																			8 36
22							8 19		8 24																			8 39
23				7 42																								
24				7 48																								
25					7 49											7 58												
26					7 52											8 1												
27				7 52	7 57											8 6												
28				7 56	8 1	SX										8 10												
29				8 0	8 5	8 9										8 14	8 17											
30					8 8												8 20											
31					8 11	8 14											8 23											
32		8 4												8 9														
33		8 7												8 12														
34		8 10												8 15														
35		8 13			8 14	8 17								8 18	8 22		8 26		From London Bridge, via Streatham						From London Bridge, via Forest Hill			
36		8 15												8 20	8 26													
37		8 18												8 23	8 30						From Victoria, via Wandsworth Common							
38		8 21												8 26	8 33												From London Bridge, via Tulse Hill	
39		8 24												8 29	8 36													
40	8 20	8 24												8 29	8 36													
41					8 17	8 20											8 29											
42					8 19	8 22											8 31											
43					8 22	8 25											8 34											
44							8 22	8 26	8 27			8 34	8 36									8 41						8 42
45							8 22	8 27	8 27	8 30	8 31	8 34	8 36									8 41						8 42
46	8 24	8 28							8 31						8 40				8 33						8 32			
47																							8 29					
48																							8 32					
49	8 29																						8 36	8 39				
50	8 31																						8 38					
51	8 34																						8 41					
52	8 37																				8 38		8 44				8 48	
53							8 25							8 32											8 35	8 39		8 45
54							8 27							8 34											8 37	8 41		8 47
55							8 30							8 37											8 40	8 44		8 50
56							8 33							8 39											8 43			8 52
57																		From Victoria, dep. 8 28 a.m	8 36									
58																			8.37									
59																			8 39					8 42				
60																			8 42					8 45				
61																			8 44					8 47				
62																			8 47					8 50				
63								8 38	8 40										8 49					8 52				
64				Via Worcester Park	8 28																				8 45			
65					8 31																8 41				8 48			
66																Via Worcester Park					8 44							
67																					8 46							
68																		8 44			8 48							
69																		8 46			8 50							
70																		8 49			8 53							
71	8 39					8 32	8 37							8 43			8 41						8 46				8 51	8 56
72	8 41					8 34																	8 48				8 53	
73	8 44			8 26		8 37	8 41						8 48	8 47			8 45						8 51			8 52	8 57	9 1
74	8 47					8 41																	8 54				9 0	
75		8 41			8 42			8 43	8 46		8 47	8 50			8 53			8 53	8 55		8 57	8 55		8 58	8 59			
76				8 36												8 43												
77																												
78	8 51					8 45	8 48			8 46			8 53	8 54			8 50						8 58			8 57	9 3	9 7

For Notes, see page 317a

HORSHAM, REIGATE, REDHILL, TATTENHAM CORNER, CATERHAM,

Week Days—*continued* (a.m.)

Up	No.	3	3		3	3	3	7§46	3	3	3	3	7 52	3	7§59			3	3		3	3	No.
Horsham .... dep	1																						1
Reigate .... "	2							8 21							§ Via Three Bridges								2
Redhill .... "	3							8 28					3										3
Merstham	4							8 32															4
Coulsdon South	5							8 38															5
Tattenham Corner. dep	6							§ Via Three Bridges										8 24					6
Tadworth N	7																	8 27					7
Kingswood M	8																	8 30					8
Chipstead	9																	8 34					9
Woodmansterne	10																	8 37					10
Smitham	11																	8 39					11
Reedham	12																	8 42					12
Purley 252 .... arr	13																	8 44					13
Caterham .... dep	14																	8 34					14
Warlingham	15																	8 38					15
Whyteleafe	16																	8 40					16
Kenley	17																	8 43					17
Purley 252 .... arr	18																	8 46					18
Coulsdon North ..... dep	19								8 36												8 47		19
Purley 252	20								8 39						8 44			8 49			8 50		20
Purley Oaks	21								8 41												8 53		21
South Croydon 234	22								8 44											8 54	8 55		22
Effingham Junction dep	23											8 12											23
Bookham	24						8 10					8 15											24
Dorking North ..... dep	25												8 18										25
Boxhill and Burford	26												8 21										26
Leatherhead ...[Bridge J	27						8 14					8 19	8 26										27
Ashtead	28					8 15	8 19					8 23	8 30										28
Epsom 427	29					8 20	8 25					8 27	8 35	8 38									29
Ewell East H	30						8 28							8 41									30
Cheam	31						8 31							8 44									31
Epsom Downs ...... dep	32				8 24					8 29													32
Banstead	33				8 27					8 32													33
Belmont	34				8 30					8 35													34
Sutton 322	35				8 33		8 35			8 38	8 43			8 47								From London Bridge, via Streatham	35
Carshalton Beeches	36				8 35					8 40	8 48												36
Wallington	37				8 38					8 43	8 51												37
Waddon G	38				8 41					8 46	8 54												38
West Croydon 319 arr	39				8 44					8 49	8 57												39
West Croydon 319 dep	40		8 40		8 44					8 49	8 57												40
Carshalton	41						8 38							8 50									41
Hackbridge	42						8 40							8 52									42
Mitcham Junction	43						8 43							8 55									43
East Croydon .... arr	44							8 47	8 47						8 51			8 54		8 58	8 58		44
East Croydon .... dep	45			8 45				8 48	8 47						8 51	8 52		8 54		8 58	8 58		45
Norwood Junction F	46		8 44		8 48				8 51		9 2											8 53	46
Beckenham Jn. dep	47																						47
Birkbeck	48																						48
Crystal Palace D	49	8 45	8 49																				49
Gipsy Hill (for Upper	50	8 48	8 51																				50
West Norwood.[N'wood)	51	8 50	8 54																				51
Streatham Hill	52		8 57																				52
Selhurst	53									8 52													53
Thornton Heath	54									8 54													54
Norbury	55									8 57													55
Streatham Common	56									8 59													56
Anerley	57																					8 56	57
Penge West C	58																					8 57	58
Sydenham ......[Lane	59																		From Victoria, dep. 8 48 a.m.			8 59	59
Forest Hill, for Lordship	60																					9 2	60
Honor Oak Park	61																					9 4	61
Brockley B ....[Line)	62																					9 7	62
New Cross Gate (for E.L.	63								8 59													9 9	63
Streatham	64					Via Worcester Park	8 48					Via Worcester Park											64
Tulse Hill	65	8 53					8 51																65
North Dulwich	66	8 56											Via Worcester Park										66
East Dulwich	67	8 58																					67
Peckham Rye	68	9 1																	9 4				68
Queen's Road, Peckham	69	9 3																	9 6				69
South Bermondsey	70	9 6																	9 9				70
Balham & Upper Tooting	71		8 59							9 3				9 1									71
Wandsworth Common A	72		9 1																				72
Clapham Junction	73		9 4			8 44				9 7		8 47		9 6							9 10		73
Battersea Park	74		9 7																				74
LONDON BRIDGE ..... arr	75	9 10		9 0	9 1		9 2	9 3	9 5		9 16				9 6			9 10	9 13	9 14		9 15	75
WATERLOO * .... "	76					8 53						8 54	9 4										76
CHARING CROSS * .. "	77																						77
VICTORIA .... "	78		9 11							9 14				9 11		9 8					9 15		78

DORKING NORTH, SUTTON, CROYDON, CRYSTAL PALACE, and LONDON

Week Days—continued (a.m.)

No.		3		3	3	3	3	3	3		3	3	3	3		3	3	3	3	3		3	3		3			3
1										7§59																8§39		
2			8 30							8 40																		
3			8a35							8 47																§ Via Three Bridges		
4										8 51																		
5										8 57																		
6			a Arrival time							§ Via Three Bridges															8 44			
7																									8 47			
8																									8 50			
9																									8 54			
10																									8 57			
11																									8 59			
12																									9 2			
13																									9 4			
14																									8 54			
15																									8 58			
16																									9 0			
17																									9 3			
18																									9 6			
19									8 51							8 56												
20									8 54							8 59									9 9			
21									8 56							9 2												
22									8 59							9 4												
23																						8 38						
24																						8 41						
25														8 29														
26														8 32														
27														8 37								8 46						
28														8 41								8 50						
29														8 45								8 54	8 57					
30														8 48									9 0					
31													SX	8 51									9 3					
32													8 44					8 49										
33													8 47					8 52										
34													8 50					8 55	SO	SX								
35		From Victoria, via Wandsworth Common				From London Bridge, via Forest Hill						From Victoria, dep. 8 38 a.m.	8 53	8 55				8 53	9 2	9 2			9 6					
36													8 55					9 0	9 5	9 5								
37													8 58					9 3	9 7	9 11								
38													9 1					9 6	9 11	9 14								
39													9 4					9 9	9 14	9 17								
40													9 4					9 9		9 17								
41								From London Bridge, via Tulse Hill						8 58									9 9					
42														9 0									9 11					
43														9 3									9 14					
44	SX								9 2	9 5						9 7	SX								9 14	9 16		
45	9 1								9 2	9 6		SX			9 9	9 7	9 11				9 12				9 14	9 17	9 18	
46						8 52						9 5	9 8			9 11				9 22								
47				8 49																								
48				8 52																								
49				8 56	8 59						9 6	9 9																
50				8 58							9 8	9 11																
51				9 1							9 11	9 14																
52		8 58		9 4			SX	9 10				9 17																
53						8 55	8 58		9 5									9 12										
54						8 57	9 0		9 7									9 14										
55						9 0	9 3		9 10									9 17										
56						9 J2	9 5		9 12									9 19										
57																												From Victoria, dep. 9 10 a.m
58																												
59					9 2																							
60					9 5																							
61					9 7																							
62					9 10																							
63					9 12											9 20												
64						9 5								9 8														
65		9 1				9 8					9 14			9 11								Via Worcester Park						
66		9 4				J 1 min later on Saturdays					9 17																	
67		9 6									9 19																	
68		9 8									9 21																	9 24
69		9 10									9 23																	9 26
70		9 13									9 26																	9 29
71				9 6				9 12	9 16			9 19						9 23					9 21					
72				9 8				9 14				9 21																
73				9 11			9 14	9 17	9 21			9 24					9 22	9 27					9 25			9 28		
74				9 14				9 20				9 27																
75		9 17			9 18	9 19				9 20	9 30		9 21	9 22	9 23	9 26				9 35	9 28				9 30		9 33	9 33
76																						9 23						
77																												
78	9 18			9 18			9 20	9 24	9 27			9 31					9 27	9 34					9 30			9 34		

HORSHAM, REIGATE, REDHILL, TATTENHAM CORNER, CATERHAM,

Up	No.	a.m. Week Days—continued																				a.m.	No.
Horsham dep	1	3	3	3	3	3	..	3	3	8§26	3	..	3	3	8 22	3	..	..	..	3	..	3	1
Reigate "	2	..	..	..	..	..	..	..	..	8 58	..	..	..	..	..	..	..	..	9 8	..	..	..	2
Redhill "	3	..	..	..	..	..	..	..	..	9 4	..	..	..	..	3	..	..	..	9 14	..	..	..	3
Merstham	4	..	..	..	..	..	..	..	..	9 8	..	..	..	..	..	..	..	..	9 19	..	..	..	4
Coulsdon South	5	..	..	..	..	..	..	..	..	9 14	..	..	..	..	..	..	..	..	9 27	..	..	..	5
Tattenham Corner dep	6	..	..	..	..	..	..	..	..	§ Via Three Bridges	..	..	..	..	..	..	..	..	..	..	..	..	6
Tadworth **N**	7	..	..	..	..	..	..	..	..		..	..	..	..	..	..	..	..	..	..	..	..	7
Kingswood **M**	8	..	..	..	..	..	..	..	..		..	..	..	..	..	..	..	..	..	..	..	..	8
Chipstead	9	..	..	..	..	..	..	..	..		..	..	..	..	..	..	..	..	..	..	..	..	9
Woodmansterne	10	..	..	..	..	..	..	..	..		..	..	..	..	..	..	..	..	..	..	..	..	10
Smitham	11	..	..	..	..	..	..	..	..		..	..	..	..	..	..	..	..	..	..	..	..	11
Reedham	12	..	..	..	..	..	..	..	..		..	..	..	..	..	..	..	..	..	..	..	..	12
Purley 252 arr	13	..	..	..	..	..	..	..	..		..	..	..	..	..	..	..	..	..	..	..	..	13
Caterham dep	14	..	..	..	..	..	..	..	..	..	..	..	..	..	..	..	..	..	..	..	..	..	14
Warlingham	15	..	..	..	..	..	..	..	..	..	..	..	..	..	..	..	..	..	..	..	..	..	15
Whyteleafe	16	..	..	..	..	..	..	..	..	..	..	..	..	..	..	..	..	..	..	..	..	..	16
Kenley	17	..	..	..	..	..	..	..	..	..	..	..	..	..	..	..	..	..	..	..	..	..	17
Purley 252 arr	18	..	..	..	..	..	..	..	..	..	..	..	..	..	..	S X	..	..	..	..	..	..	18
Coulsdon North dep	19	..	..	..	..	..	..	..	9 11	..	..	..	..	..	..	9 16	..	..	..	..	..	..	19
Purley 252	20	..	..	..	..	..	..	..	9 14	9 17	..	..	..	..	..	9 19	..	..	..	..	..	..	20
Purley Oaks	21	..	..	..	..	..	..	..	9 17	..	..	..	..	..	..	9 21	..	..	..	..	..	..	21
South Croydon 234	22	..	..	..	..	..	..	..	9 19	..	..	..	..	..	..	9 24	..	..	..	..	..	..	22
Effingham Junction dep	23	..	..	..	..	..	..	..	..	..	..	..	..	..	..	..	..	..	..	..	..	..	23
Bookham	24	..	..	..	..	..	..	..	..	..	..	..	..	..	..	..	..	..	..	..	..	..	24
Dorking North dep	25	..	..	..	..	..	..	..	..	..	..	..	..	..	8 49	..	..	..	..	..	..	..	25
Boxhill and Burford	26	..	..	..	..	..	..	..	..	..	..	..	..	..	8 52	..	..	..	..	..	..	..	26
Leatherhead...[Bridge **J**	27	..	..	..	..	..	..	..	..	..	..	..	..	..	8 57	..	..	..	..	..	..	..	27
Ashstead	28	..	..	..	..	..	..	..	..	..	..	..	..	..	9 1	..	..	..	..	..	..	..	28
Epsom 427	29	..	..	..	..	..	..	..	..	..	..	..	..	..	9 5	..	..	..	..	..	..	..	29
Ewell East **H**	30	..	..	..	..	..	..	..	..	..	..	..	..	..	9 8	..	..	..	..	..	..	..	30
Cheam	31	..	..	..	..	..	..	..	..	..	..	..	..	..	9 11	..	..	..	..	..	..	..	31
Epsom Downs dep	32	From London Bridge, via Streatham	..	..	..	From London Bridge, via Forest Hill	..	..	..	..	..	..	..	9 4	..	..	..	..	..	..	..	9 9	32
Banstead	33		..	..	..		..	..	..	..	..	..	..	9 7	..	..	..	..	..	..	..	9 12	33
Belmont	34		..	..	..		..	..	..	..	..	..	..	9 10	..	..	..	..	..	..	..	9 15	34
Sutton 322	35		From Victoria via Wandsworth Common	..	..		..	..	..	..	..	..	..	9 13	9 15	..	..	..	..	..	..	9 18	35
Carshalton Beeches	36			..	..		..	..	..	..	..	..	..	9 15	..	..	..	..	..	..	..	9 20	36
Wallington	37			..	..		..	..	..	..	..	..	..	9 18	..	..	..	..	..	..	..	9 23	37
Waddon **G**	38			..	..		..	..	..	..	..	..	..	9 21	..	..	..	..	..	..	..	9 26	38
West Croydon 319 arr	39			..	..		..	..	..	..	..	..	..	9 24	..	..	..	..	..	..	..	9 29	39
West Croydon 319 dep	40			..	..		..	..	..	..	..	..	9 20	9 24	..	..	..	..	..	..	..	9 29	40
Carshalton	41			..	..		..	From London Bridge via Tulse Hill	..	..	..	..	..	..	9 18	..	..	..	..	..	..	..	41
Hackbridge	42			..	..		..		..	..	..	..	..	..	9 20	..	..	..	..	..	..	..	42
Mitcham Junction	43			..	..		..		..	..	..	..	..	..	9 23	..	..	..	..	..	..	..	43
East Croydon arr	44	..		..	..	..	..		9 22	9 23	..	..	..	..	..	9 26	..	S X	..	..	..	..	44
East Croydon dep	45	..		..	..	S X	9 21		9 22	9 23	..	..	..	..	..	9 26	9 27	9 29	..	..	..	..	45
Norwood Junction F	46	9 13		..	..	9 12	..		..	..	..	..	9 24	9 28	..	9 31	..	..	..	..	..	..	46
Beckenham Jn. dep	47	..		9 9	..	..	..		..	..	..	..	..	..	..	..	..	..	..	..	..	..	47
Birkbeck	48	..		9 12	..	..	..		..	..	S O	..	..	..	..	..	..	..	..	..	..	..	48
Crystal Palace D	49	..		9 16	9 20	..	..		..	..	9 25	..	9 29	..	..	..	..	..	..	..	..	..	49
Gipsy Hill (for Upper	50	..		9 18	..	..	..		..	..	9 28	..	9 31	..	..	..	..	..	..	..	..	..	50
West Norwood.[N'wood)	51	..		9 21	..	..	..		..	..	9 30	..	9 34	..	..	..	..	..	..	..	..	..	51
Streatham Hill	52	..	9 18	9 24	..	..	..	9 29	..	..	..	..	9 37	..	..	..	..	..	..	..	..	..	52
Selhurst	53	..	..	..	..	9 15	..	..	9 25	..	..	..	..	..	..	..	..	..	..	..	..	9 32	53
Thornton Heath	54	..	..	..	..	9 17	..	..	9 27	..	..	..	..	..	..	..	..	..	..	..	..	9 34	54
Norbury	55	..	..	..	..	9 20	..	..	9 30	..	..	..	..	..	..	..	..	..	..	..	..	9 37	55
Streatham Common	56	..	..	..	..	9 23	..	..	9 32	..	..	..	..	..	..	..	..	..	..	..	..	9 39	56
Anerley	57	9 16	..	..	..	..	..	..	..	..	..	..	..	..	..	..	..	..	..	..	..	..	57
Penge West **C**	58	9 17	..	..	..	..	..	..	..	..	..	..	..	..	..	..	..	..	..	From Victoria, dep. 9 28 a.m	..	..	58
Sydenham [Lane	59	9 19	..	..	9 23	..	..	..	..	..	..	..	..	..	..	..	..	..	..		..	..	59
Forest Hill, for Lordship	60	9 22	..	..	9 25	..	..	..	..	..	..	..	..	..	..	..	..	..	..		..	..	60
Honor Oak Park	61	9 24	..	..	9 28	..	..	..	..	..	..	..	..	..	..	..	..	..	..		..	..	61
Brockley **B** [Line)	62	9 27	..	..	9 30	..	..	..	..	..	..	..	..	..	..	..	..	..	..		..	..	62
New Cross Gate (for E.L.	63	9 29	..	..	9 33	..	..	..	..	..	..	..	..	..	..	9 40	..	..	..		..	..	63
Streatham	64	..	..	..	..	9 25	..	..	..	..	..	..	..	..	9 28	..	..	..	..		..	..	64
Tulse Hill	65	..	9 21	..	..	9 28	..	..	..	..	9 33	..	..	..	9 31	..	..	..	..		..	..	65
North Dulwich	66	..	9 24	..	..	..	..	..	..	..	9 36	..	..	..	..	..	..	..	..		..	..	66
East Dulwich	67	..	9 26	..	..	..	..	..	..	..	9 38	..	..	..	..	..	..	..	..	..	..	..	67
Peckham Rye	68	..	9 28	..	..	..	..	..	..	..	9 41	..	..	..	..	..	..	..	..	9 44	..	..	68
Queen's Road, Peckham	69	..	9 30	..	..	..	..	..	..	..	9 43	..	..	..	..	..	..	..	..	9 46	..	..	69
South Bermondsey	70	..	9 33	..	..	..	..	..	..	..	9 46	..	..	..	..	..	..	..	..	9 49	..	..	70
Balham & Upper Tooting	71	..	..	9 26	..	..	..	9 32	9 36	..	..	..	9 39	..	..	..	..	..	..	..	..	9 43	71
Wandsworth Common **A**	72	..	..	9 28	..	..	..	9 34	..	..	..	..	9 41	..	..	..	..	..	..	..	..	..	72
Clapham Junction	73	..	..	9 31	..	..	..	9 37	9 41	..	..	..	9 44	..	..	..	..	..	..	..	..	9 47	73
Battersea Park	74	..	..	9 34	..	..	..	9 40	..	..	..	..	9 47	..	..	..	..	..	..	..	..	..	74
LONDON BRIDGE arr	75	9 35	9 37	..	9 38	9 39	..	..	..	9 38	9 50	..	..	9 41	9 42	9 45	..	..	9 48	9 53	..	..	75
WATERLOO ✻ "	76	..	..	..	..	..	..	..	..	..	..	..	..	..	..	..	..	..	..	..	..	..	76
CHARING CROSS ✻ "	77	..	..	..	..	..	..	..	..	..	..	..	..	..	..	..	..	..	..	..	..	..	77
VICTORIA "	78	..	..	9 38	..	..	9 37	9 44	9 46	..	..	..	9 51	..	..	..	9 42	9 46	..	..	..	9 54	78

For Notes, see page 317a

DORKING NORTH, SUTTON, CROYDON, CRYSTAL PALACE, and LONDON

a.m. — **Week Days**—*continued* — a.m.

No.																											
1	3	3	3	8§46	3	SX 9§ 9	3	3	3	3	8 34	3	3	3	3	3	3	..	..	..	..	3	3	3	3	9 1	3
2	..	..	..	§ Via Three Bridges	..	§ Via Three Bridges	..	..	..	..	3	..	..	..	..	..	..	..	..	..	..	..	..	..	..	..	..
3	..	..	..		..		..	..	..	..		..	..	..	..	..	..	..	..	..	..	..	..	..	..	..	..
4	..	..	..		..		..	..	..	..	..	..	..	..	..	..	..	..	..	..	..	..	..	..	..	..	..
5	..	..	..		..		..	..	..	..	..	..	..	..	..	..	..	..	..	..	..	..	..	..	..	..	..
6	..	..	..		9 10		..	..	..	..	..	..	..	..	..	..	..	..	..	..	..	..	..	..	..	..	9 24
7	..	..	..		9 13		..	..	..	..	..	..	..	..	..	..	..	..	..	..	..	..	..	..	..	..	9 27
8	..	..	..		9 16		..	..	..	..	..	..	..	..	..	..	..	..	..	..	..	..	..	..	..	..	9 30
9	..	..	..		9 20		..	..	..	..	..	..	..	..	..	..	..	..	..	..	..	..	..	..	..	..	9 34
10	..	..	..		9 23		..	..	..	..	..	..	..	..	..	..	..	..	..	..	..	..	..	..	..	..	9 37
11	..	..	..		9 25		..	..	..	..	..	..	..	..	..	..	..	..	..	..	..	..	..	..	..	..	9 39
12	..	..	..		9 28		..	..	..	..	..	..	..	..	..	..	..	..	..	..	..	..	..	..	..	..	9 42
13	..	..	..		9 30		..	..	..	..	..	..	..	..	..	..	..	..	..	..	..	..	..	..	..	..	9 44
14	..	..	..	..	9 20	..	..	..	..	..	..	..	..	..	..	..	..	..	..	..	..	..	..	..	..	..	9 34
15	..	..	..	..	9 24	..	..	..	..	..	..	..	..	..	..	..	..	..	..	..	..	..	..	..	..	..	9 38
16	..	..	..	..	9 26	..	..	..	..	..	..	..	..	..	..	..	..	..	..	..	..	..	..	..	..	..	9 40
17	..	..	..	..	9 29	..	..	..	..	..	..	..	..	..	..	..	..	..	..	..	..	..	..	..	..	..	9 43
18	..	..	SO	..	9 32	..	..	..	..	..	..	..	..	..	..	..	..	..	..	..	..	..	..	..	..	..	9 46
19	..	..	9 20	..	..	..	..	..	..	..	..	..	9 31	..	..	9 36	..	..	..	..	..	..	..	..	..	..	..
20	..	..	9 23	9 31	9 35	..	..	..	..	..	..	..	9 34	..	..	9 39	..	..	..	..	..	..	..	..	..	..	9 49
21	..	..	9 25	..	..	..	..	..	..	..	..	..	9 36	..	..	9 42	..	..	..	..	..	..	..	..	..	..	..
22	..	..	9 28	..	..	..	..	..	..	..	..	..	9 39	..	..	9 44	..	..	..	..	..	..	..	..	..	..	..
23	..	..	..	..	..	..	..	..	..	8 54	..	..	..	..	..	..	..	..	..	..	..	..	..	..	..	..	..
24	..	..	..	..	..	..	..	..	..	8 57	..	..	..	..	..	..	9 12	..	..	..	..	..	..	..	..	..	..
25	From London Bridge, via Streatham	..	..	..	..	..	..	..	..	..	8 59	..	..	..	..	..	..	..	..	..	..	..	..	..	9 18	9 26	..
26		..	..	..	..	..	..	..	..	..	9 2	..	..	..	..	..	..	..	..	..	..	..	..	..	9 20	..	..
27		..	..	..	..	..	..	..	..	9 2	9 7	..	..	..	..	..	9 17	..	..	..	..	..	..	..	9 25	..	..
28		..	..	..	..	..	..	..	..	..	9 11	..	..	..	..	..	9 21	..	..	..	..	..	..	..	9 29	..	..
29		..	..	..	..	..	..	..	..	..	9 15	9 17	..	..	..	..	9 25	..	..	..	..	..	..	..	9 34	..	..
30		..	..	..	..	..	..	..	..	..	..	9 20	..	..	..	..	9 28	..	..	..	..	..	..	..	..	..	..
31		..	..	..	..	..	..	..	..	..	..	9 23	..	..	..	..	9 31	..	..	..	..	..	..	..	..	..	..
32		..	..	..	..	..	..	..	..	..	..	..	..	..	9 24	..	..	..	..	..	..	..	..	9 29	..	..	..
33		..	..	..	..	..	..	..	..	..	..	..	..	..	9 27	..	..	..	..	..	..	..	..	9 32	..	..	..
34		..	..	..	..	..	..	..	..	..	..	..	..	..	9 30	..	..	..	..	..	..	..	..	9 35	..	..	..
35		9 22	..	..	..	..	From Victoria via Wandsworth Common	..	From London Bridge, via Forest Hill	..	..	9 26	..	..	9 33	..	9 35	..	..	..	..	..	..	9 38	..	9 43	..
36		9 24	..	..	..	..		..		..	..	..	..	..	9 35	..	..	..	..	..	..	..	..	9 40	..	..	..
37		9 27	..	..	..	..		..		..	..	..	..	..	9 38	..	..	..	..	..	..	..	..	9 43	..	..	..
38		..	..	..	..	..		..		..	..	..	..	..	9 41	..	..	..	..	..	..	..	..	9 46	..	..	..
39		..	..	..	..	..		..		..	..	..	..	..	9 44	..	..	..	..	..	..	..	..	9 49	..	..	..
40		..	..	..	..	..		..		..	..	..	..	9 39	9 44	..	..	..	..	..	..	..	..	9 49	..	..	..
41		..	..	..	..	..		..		..	..	9 29	..	..	..	..	9 38	..	..	..	..	..	..	..	..	..	..
42		..	..	..	..	..		..		..	..	9 31	..	..	..	..	9 40	..	..	..	..	..	..	..	..	..	..
43		..	..	..	..	..		..		..	..	9 34	..	..	..	..	9 43	..	..	..	..	..	..	..	..	..	..
44	..	..	9 30	9 37	9 40	..		..		..	..	..	9 42	..	..	9 47	..	SX	SO	..	..	..	..	..	..	..	9 55
45	SX	..	9 30	9 37	9 40	..		..		..	..	..	9 42	..	..	9 47	..	9 48	9 48	9 51	9 54	..	..	..	..	..	9 55
46	9 33	..	9 34	..	..	..		..	9 32	..	..	..	..	9 43	9 48	9 51	..	..	..	..	..	..	..	..	..	..	9 58
47	..	..	..	..	..	..		9 29	..	..	..	..	..	..	..	..	..	..	..	..	..	..	..	..	..	..	..
48	..	..	..	..	..	..		9 32	..	..	..	..	..	..	..	..	..	..	..	..	..	..	..	..	..	..	..
49	..	..	..	..	..	..		9 36	..	..	..	..	..	9 47	..	..	..	..	..	..	..	..	9 50	..	..	..	..
50	..	..	..	..	..	..		9 38	..	..	..	..	..	9 49	..	..	..	..	..	..	..	..	9 52	..	..	..	..
51	..	..	..	..	..	..		9 41	..	..	..	..	..	9 52	..	..	..	..	..	..	..	..	9 55	..	..	..	..
52	..	..	..	..	..	..	9 38	9 44	..	..	..	..	..	9 56	..	..	..	..	..	..	..	..	..	..	..	..	..
53	..	..	..	..	..	..	..	..	9 35	..	..	..	9 45	..	..	..	..	..	..	..	..	..	..	9 52	..	..	..
54	..	..	..	..	..	..	..	..	9 37	..	..	..	9 47	..	..	..	..	..	..	..	..	..	..	9 54	..	..	..
55	..	..	..	..	..	..	..	..	9 40	..	..	..	9 50	..	..	..	..	..	..	..	..	..	..	9 57	..	..	..
56	..	..	..	..	..	..	..	..	9 43	..	..	..	9 52	..	..	..	..	..	..	..	..	..	..	9 59	..	..	..
57	9 36	..	9 37	..	..	..	..	..	..	..	..	..	..	..	..	..	..	..	..	..	..	From Victoria, dep 9 46 a.m.	..	H 1 minute *earlier* on Saturdays	..	..	..
58	9 37	..	9 39	..	..	..	..	..	..	..	..	..	..	..	..	..	..	..	..	..	..		..		..	..	..
59	9 39	..	9 41	..	..	..	..	..	..	..	..	..	..	..	..	..	..	..	..	..	..		..		..	..	..
60	9 42	..	9 44	..	..	..	..	..	..	..	..	..	..	..	..	9 55	..	..	..	..	..		..		..	..	..
61	9 44	..	9 46	..	..	..	..	..	..	..	..	..	..	..	..	..	..	..	..	..	..		..		..	..	..
62	9 47	..	9 49	..	..	..	..	..	..	..	..	..	..	..	..	..	..	..	..	..	..		..		..	..	..
63	9 49	..	9 52	..	..	..	..	..	..	..	..	..	..	..	..	10 1	..	..	..	..	..		..		..	..	..
64	..	..	..	..	..	..	..	..	9 45	..	Via Worcester Park	..	..	..	..	..	9 48	..	..	..	..	..	..		Via Worcester Park	..	..
65	..	..	..	..	..	..	9 41	..	9 48	..		..	..	..	..	..	9 51	..	..	..	..	..	9 58			..	..
66	..	..	..	..	..	..	9 44	..	..	..		..	..	..	..	..	..	..	..	..	..	..	10 1			..	..
67	..	..	..	..	..	..	9 46	..	..	..		..	..	..	..	..	..	..	..	..	..	..	10 3			..	..
68	..	..	..	..	..	..	9 48	..	..	..		..	..	..	..	..	..	..	..	..	..	10 1	10 5			..	..
69	..	..	..	..	..	..	9 50	..	..	..		..	..	..	..	..	..	..	..	..	..	10 3	..			..	..
70	..	..	..	..	..	..	9 53	..	..	..		..	..	..	..	..	..	..	..	..	..	10 6	..			..	..
71	..	..	..	..	..	..	..	9 46	..	..		9 41	9 56	9 59	..	..	..	..	..	..	..	..	..	10 3		..	..
72	..	..	..	..	..	..	..	9 48	..	..		..	..	10 1	..	..	..	..	..	..	..	..	..	..		..	..
73	..	..	..	9 49	..	..	..	9 51	..	..		9 45	10 0	10 4	..	..	..	..	..	..	10 5	..	..	10 7		..	..
74	..	..	..	..	..	..	..	9 54	..	..		..	..	10 7	..	..	..	..	..	..	..	..	..	..		..	..
75	9 55	..	9 57	..	9 55	9 57	9 57	..	9 59	..	..	..	..	..	10 2	10 6	10 2	10 2	..	10 8	..	1010	1012	..	..	10 4	10 12
76	..	..	..	..	9 59	..	..	..	..	..	9 43	..	..	..	..	..	..	..	..	..	..	..	..	..	10 4	..	10SX15
77	..	..	..	..	10 2	..	..	..	..	..	..	..	..	..	..	..	..	..	..	..	..	..	..	..	..	..	10SX18
78	..	..	..	9 55	..	..	..	9 58	..	..	..	9 50	10 6	1010	..	..	..	..	10 3	..	1010	..	..	10H14	..	..	..

HORSHAM, REIGATE, REDHILL, TATTENHAM CORNER, CATERHAM,

For Notes, see page 317a

Up — Week Days—*continued* (a.m)

Up	No.	3	3	3		3	3		3			3	3	3	3		3	3		3	3	No.
Horsham ... dep	1	..	..	..	..	..	..	..	..	..	..	..	..	..	..	..	..	..	9§16	..	..	1
Reigate ... "	2	..	..	..	..	..	..	..	..	..	..	..	..	..	..	..	..	..	9 43	..	..	2
Redhill ... "	3	..	..	..	..	..	..	..	..	..	..	..	..	..	..	..	..	..	9 50	..	..	3
Merstham	4	..	..	..	..	..	..	..	..	..	..	..	..	..	..	..	..	..	9 54	..	..	4
Coulsdon South	5	..	..	..	..	..	..	..	..	..	..	..	..	..	..	..	..	..	10 0	..	..	5
Tattenham Corner dep	6	..	..	..	..	..	..	..	..	..	..	..	..	..	..	..	..	..		..	..	6
Tadworth N	7	..	..	..	..	..	..	..	..	..	..	..	..	..	..	..	..	..		..	..	7
Kingswood M	8	..	..	..	..	..	..	..	..	..	..	..	..	..	..	..	..	..		..	..	8
Chipstead	9	..	..	..	..	..	..	..	..	..	..	..	..	..	..	..	..	..	§ Via Three Bridges	..	..	9
Woodmansterne	10	..	..	..	..	..	..	..	..	..	..	..	..	..	..	..	..	..		..	..	10
Smitham	11	..	..	..	..	..	..	..	..	..	..	..	..	..	..	..	..	..		..	..	11
Reedham	12	..	..	..	..	..	..	..	..	..	..	..	..	..	..	..	..	..		..	..	12
Purley 252 ... arr	13	..	..	..	..	..	..	..	..	..	..	..	..	..	..	..	..	..		..	..	13
Caterham ... dep	14	..	..	..	..	..	..	..	..	..	..	..	..	..	..	..	..	..	..	..	..	14
Warlingham	15	..	..	..	..	..	..	..	..	..	..	..	..	..	..	..	..	..	..	..	..	15
Whyteleafe	16	..	..	..	..	..	..	..	..	..	..	..	..	..	..	..	..	..	..	..	..	16
Kenley	17	..	..	..	..	..	..	..	..	..	..	..	..	..	..	..	..	..	..	..	..	17
Purley 252 ... arr	18	..	..	..	..	..	..	..	..	..	..	..	..	..	..	..	..	..	..	..	..	18
Coulsdon North ... dep	19	..	..	..	..	..	..	..	..	..	..	..	..	..	9 51	..	..	..	..	..	..	19
Purley 252	20	..	..	..	..	..	..	..	..	..	..	..	..	..	9 54	..	..	..	10 4	..	..	20
Purley Oaks	21	..	..	..	..	..	..	..	..	..	..	..	..	..	9 57	..	..	..	..	..	..	21
South Croydon 234	22	..	..	..	..	..	..	..	..	..	..	..	..	..	10 0	..	..	..	..	..	..	22
Effingham Junction dep	23	..	..	..	..	..	..	..	..	..	..	..	..	..	..	..	..	..	..	..	..	23
Bookham	24	..	..	..	..	..	..	..	..	..	..	..	..	..	..	..	..	..	..	..	..	24
Dorking North ... dep	25	..	..	..	..	..	..	..	..	..	..	..	..	..	..	..	..	9 30	..	..	..	25
Boxhill and Burford	26	..	..	..	..	..	..	..	..	..	..	..	..	..	..	..	..	9 33	..	..	..	26
Leatherhead ... [Bridge J	27	..	..	..	..	..	..	..	..	..	..	..	..	..	..	..	..	9 38	..	..	..	27
Ashtead	28	..	..	..	..	..	..	..	..	..	..	..	..	..	..	..	..	9 42	..	..	..	28
Epsom 427	29	..	..	..	..	..	..	..	9 40	..	..	..	..	..	..	..	..	9 46	..	..	..	29
Ewell East H	30	..	..	..	..	..	..	..	9 43	..	..	..	..	..	..	..	..	9 49	..	..	..	30
Cheam	31	..	..	..	..	..	..	..	9 46	..	..	..	..	..	..	..	..	9 52	..	..	..	31
Epsom Downs ... dep	32	..	..	..	..	..	..	..	..	..	..	..	..	..	..	..	9 44	..	..	..	..	32
Banstead	33	..	..	..	..	..	..	..	..	..	..	..	..	..	..	..	9 47	..	..	..	..	33
Belmont	34	..	..	..	..	..	..	..	..	..	..	..	..	..	..	..	9 50	..	..	..	..	34
Sutton 322	35		..	..	..		9 46	..	9 49	..	..	..	..	..	..	..	9 53	9 55	..	..		35
Carshalton Beeches	36		..	..	..		9 48	..	..	..	..	..	..	..	..	..	9 55	..	..	..		36
Wallington	37		..	..	..		9 51	..	..	..	..	..	..	..	..	..	9 58	..	..	..		37
Waddon G	38		..	..	..		..	..	..	..	..	..	..	..	..	..	10 1	..	..	..		38
West Croydon 319 arr	39		..	..	..	From London Bridge, via Forest Hill	..	..	..	..	..	..	..	..	..	..	10 4	..	..	..	From London Bridge, via Streatham	39
West Croydon 319 dep	40	From London Bridge, via Streatham	..	..	..		..	..	..	..	..	..	..	10 0	..	..	10 4	..	..	..		40
Carshalton	41		..	..	..		..	..	9 52	..	..	..	..	..	..	..	..	9 58	..	..		41
Hackbridge	42		..	..	..		..	..	9 54	..	..	..	..	..	..	..	..	10 0	..	..		42
Mitcham Junction	43		..	..	..		..	..	9 57	..	..	..	..	..	..	..	..	10 3	..	..		43
East Croydon ... arr	44		..	..	..		..	..	..	..	S X	..	..	..	10 2	..	..	..	10 9	..		44
East Croydon ... dep	45		..	..	..	S O	..	10 5	..	..	10 7	..	..	..	10 2	..	..	..	1010	..	S O	45
Norwood Junction F	46	9 53	S O	..	..	9 52	..	..	..	..	..	S X	..	10 4	..	..	10 8	..	..	..	1013	46
Beckenham Jn. dep	47	..	9 49	..	..	..	..	..	..	..	..	9 52	..	..	..	..	..	..	..	..	..	47
Birkbeck	48	..	9 52	S O	..	..	..	..	..	..	..	9 55	S X	..	..	..	..	..	..	..	..	48
Crystal Palace D	49	..	9 56	9 59	..	..	..	..	..	..	..	9 59	10 5	10 9	..	..	..	..	..	..	..	49
Gipsy Hill (for Upper	50	..	9 58	..	..	..	..	..	..	..	..	..	10 8	10 11	..	..	..	..	..	..	..	50
West Norwood. [N'wood)	51	..	10 1	..	..	..	..	..	..	..	..	..	1010	10 14	..	..	..	..	..	..	..	51
Streatham Hill	52	..	10 4	..	..	..	..	..	..	..	..	..	..	10 17	..	..	..	..	..	..	..	52
Selhurst	53	..	..	..	..	9 55	..	..	..	..	..	..	..	..	10 6	..	..	..	..	..	..	53
Thornton Heath	54	..	..	..	..	9 57	..	..	..	..	..	..	..	..	10 8	..	..	..	..	..	..	54
Norbury	55	..	..	..	..	10 0	..	..	..	..	..	..	..	..	10H11	..	..	..	..		..	55
Streatham Common	56	..	..	..	..	10 3	..	..	..	..	..	..	..	..	10 13	..	..	..	..		..	56
Anerley	57	9 56	..	..	..	..	..	..	..	..	..	..	..			..	..	..	..		1016	57
Penge West C	58	9 57	..	..	..	..	..	..	..	..	..	..	..			..	..	..	..		1017	58
Sydenham ... [Lane	59	9 59	..	10 2	..	..	..	..	..	..	..	..	..			..	..	..	..	From Victoria, dep. 10 8 a.m	1019	59
Forest Hill, for Lordship	60	10 2	..	10 5	..	..	..	..	..	..	..	..	..			..	..	..	..		1022	60
Honor Oak Park	61	10 4	..	10 7	..	..	..	..	..	..	..	..	..			..	..	..	..		1024	61
Brockley B ... [Line)	62	10 7	..	1010	..	..	..	..	..	..	..	..	..			..	..	..	..		1027	62
New Cross Gate (for E.L.	63	10 9	..	1012	..	..	..	..	..	..	..	..	..			..	10 17	..	..		1029	63
Streatham	64	..	..	..	..	10 5	..	..	..	..	..	..	..			..		10 8	..	..	..	64
Tulse Hill	65	..	..	..	..	10 8	..	..	..	..	..	..	1013	J 1 minute later on Saturdays	H 1 minute *earlier* on Saturdays	..		1011	..	..	..	65
North Dulwich	66	..	..	..	..	..	..	..	..	..	..	..	1016			..		..	..	..	..	66
East Dulwich	67	..	..	..	..	..	..	..	..	..	..	..	1018			..		..	..	..	..	67
Peckham Rye	68	..	..	..	..	..	..	..	..	..	..	..	1021			..		..	..	1024	..	68
Queen's Road, Peckham	69	..	..	..	..	..	..	..	..	..	..	..	1023			..		..	..	1026	..	69
South Bermondsey	70	..	..	..	..	..	..	..	..	..	..	..	1026			..	H 1 minute *earlier* on Saturdays	..	..	1029	..	70
Balham & Upper Tooting	71	..	10 6	..	..	..	..	..	10 4	..	..	..	..	10J19	10 17	..		..	..	..	..	71
Wandsworth Common A	72	..	10 8	..	..	..	..	..	..	..	..	..	..	10J21	..	..		..	..	..	..	72
Clapham Junction	73	..	1011	..	..	..	..	..	10 8	..	..	..	..	10J24	10 21	..		..	1020	..	..	73
Battersea Park	74	..	1014	..	..	..	..	..	..	..	..	..	..	10J27	..	..		..	..	..	..	74
London Bridge ... arr	75	1015	..	1018	..	1021	..	..	..	..	1021	..	1030	..	..	..	10H23	1023	..	1033	1035	75
Waterloo* ... "	76	..	..	..	..	..	..	..	..	..	..	..	..	..	..	..	..	..	..	..	..	76
Charing Cross * .. "	77	..	..	..	..	..	..	..	..	..	..	..	..	..	..	..	..	..	..	..	..	77
Victoria ... "	78	..	1018	..	..	..	..	1021	1013	..	..	..	..	10 31	10 27	..	..	..	1026	..	..	78

DORKING NORTH, SUTTON, CROYDON, CRYSTAL PALACE, and LONDON

No.	a.m									Week Days—*continued*										a.m						
1	3	3	3	3	3	3	3	3	9§42	3	3	3	..	SX 9 23	SO 9 23	3	..	3	3	3	--	--	..	3	9 37	3
2	..	..	..	..	..	..	..	..		..	..	..	..	3	3	..	..	..	..	..	..	..	10 4	..	..	..
3	..	..	..	..	..	..	..	..		..	..	..	..			..	..	..	..	..	..	..	10a9	..	..	..
4	..	..	..	..	..	..	..	..		..	..	..	..	..	..	..	..	..	..	..	..	..	..	..	..	..
5	..	..	..	..	..	..	..	..		SX	..	..	..	..	..	..	..	..	..	..	..	..	..	..	..	..
6	..	..	..	..	..	..	..	..	§ Via Three Bridges	9 45	..	..	..	..	..	..	..	..	..	..	..	..	*a* Arrival time	..	..	..
7	..	..	..	..	..	..	..	..		9 48	..	..	..	..	..	..	..	..	..	..	..	..		..	..	..
8	..	..	..	..	..	..	..	..		9 51	..	..	..	..	..	..	..	..	..	..	..	..		..	..	..
9	..	..	..	..	..	..	..	..		9 55	..	..	..	..	..	..	..	..	..	..	..	..		..	..	..
10	..	..	..	..	..	..	..	..		9 58	..	..	..	..	..	..	..	..	..	..	..	..		..	..	..
11	..	..	..	..	..	..	..	..		10 0	..	..	..	..	..	..	..	..	..	..	..	..		..	..	..
12	..	..	..	..	..	..	..	..		10 3	..	..	..	..	..	..	..	..	..	..	..	..		..	..	..
13	..	..	..	..	..	..	..	..		10 5	..	..	..	..	..	..	..	..	..	..	..	..		..	..	..
14	..	..	..	..	..	..	..	..	..	9 55	..	..	..	..	..	..	..	..	..	..	..	..	Stop	..	..	..
15	..	..	..	..	..	..	..	..	..	9 59	..	..	..	..	..	..	..	..	..	..	..	..		..	..	..
16	..	..	..	..	..	..	..	..	..	10 1	..	..	..	..	..	..	..	..	..	..	..	..	..	..	..	..
17	..	..	..	..	..	..	..	..	..	10 4	..	..	..	..	..	..	..	..	..	..	..	..	..	..	..	..
18	..	..	..	..	..	..	..	..	..	10 7	..	..	..	..	..	..	..	..	..	..	..	..	..	..	..	..
19	..	..	..	..	..	..	..	..	..	..	..	..	..	..	..	10 11	..	..	..	..	..	..	..	..	..	..
20	..	..	..	..	..	..	..	..	..	1010	..	..	..	..	..	10 14	..	..	..	..	..	..	..	..	..	..
21	..	..	..	..	..	..	..	..	..	..	..	..	..	..	..	10 16	..	..	..	..	..	..	..	..	..	..
22	..	..	..	..	..	..	..	..	..	1014	..	..	..	..	..	10 19	..	..	..	..	..	..	..	..	..	..
23	..	..	..	..	..	..	9 38	..	..	..	..	..	..	..	..	..	..	..	..	..	..	..	..	..	..	..
24	..	..	..	..	..	..	9 41	..	..	..	..	..	..	..	..	..	..	..	..	..	..	..	..	SO	..	..
25	..	..	..	..	..	..	..	..	..	..	..	..	..	9 49	9 49	..	..	..	..	..	..	..	..	9 55	10 3	..
26	..	..	..	..	..	..	..	..	..	..	..	..	..	9 52	9 52	..	..	..	..	..	..	..	..	9 58	..	..
27	..	..	..	..	..	..	9 46	..	..	..	..	..	..	9 57	9 57	..	..	..	..	..	..	..	..	10 3	..	..
28	..	..	..	..	..	..	9 50	..	..	..	..	..	..	10 1	10 1	..	..	..	..	..	..	..	..	10 7	..	..
29	..	..	..	..	..	9 56	9 54	..	..	..	..	..	..	10 5	10 5	..	..	..	..	..	..	..	a.m	1014	1015	..
30	..	..	..	..	..	9 59	..	..	..	..	..	..	..	10 8	10 8	..	..	..	..	..	..	..	3	..	..	..
31	..	..	..	..	..	10 2	..	SO	..	..	..	SX	..	1011	1011	..	..	..	..	..	..	..		..	..	..
32	..	..	..	9 49	..	..	..	10 4	..	..	..	10 4	..	..	..	..	..	..	..	..	From London Bridge via Streatham	..	10 9	..	..	..
33	..	..	..	9 52	..	..	..	10 7	..	..	..	10 7	..	..	..	..	..	..	..	..		..	10 12	..	..	..
34	..	..	From London Bridge, via Forest Hill	9 55	..	..	..	1010	..	..	..	1010	..	..	..	..	..	..	..	..		..	10 15	..	..	..
35	..	..		9 58	10 1	10 5	..	1013	..	..	..	1013	..	1014	1014	..	..	..	..	..		..	10 18	..	1022	1026
36	..	..		10 0	10 4	..	..	1015	..	..	..	1015	..	..	..	..	..	..	..	..		..	10 20	..	..	1029
37	..	..		10 3	10 7	..	..	1018	..	..	..	1018	..	..	..	..	..	..	..	..		..	10 23	..	..	1032
38	..	..		10 6	..	..	..	1021	..	..	..	1021	..	..	..	..	..	..	..	..		..	10 26	..	..	1035
39	..	..		10 9	..	..	..	1024	..	..	..	1024	..	..	..	..	..	..	..	..		..	10 29	..	..	1038
40	..	..		10 9	..	..	..	1024	..	..	..	1024	..	..	..	..	..	..	..	1020		..	10 29	..	..	..
41	..	..		..	..	10 8	..	..	..	..	..	..	..	1017	1017	..	..	..	..	..		..	..	..	..	..
42	..	..		..	..	1010	..	..	..	..	..	..	..	1020	1020	..	..	..	..	..		..	..	..	..	..
43	..	..		..	..	1013	..	..	..	..	..	..	..	1022	1022	..	..	..	..	..		..	..	..	..	..
44	..	..		..	..	..	..	..	10 15	1016	..	..	..	..	..	10 22	..	..	..	..		--	..	..	..	..
45	..	..	..	..	..	..	..	..	10J15	1016	..	..	1024	..	..	10 22	1028	..	..	..	SO	..	..	..	..	..
46	..	SO	1012	..	..	..	..	1028		1020	..	1028	..	..	..	..	..	SX	..	1024	1033	..	..	..	..	..
47	..	10 9	..	..	..	..	..	..	J1 minute later on Saturdays	..	..	..	..	..	..	..	..	1012	..	..	..	..	..	..	..	..
48	..	1012	..	..	..	..	..	..		..	SX	..	..	..	..	..	..	1015	SO	..	..	..	..	..	..	..
49	..	1016	..	..	..	..	..	..		..	1020	..	..	..	..	..	..	1019	1025	1029	..	..	..	..	..	..
50	..	1018	..	..	..	..	..	..		..	..	..	..	..	..	..	..	..	1028	1031	..	..	..	..	..	..
51	SO	1021	..	..	..	..	..	..		..	..	..	..	..	..	..	..	..	1030	1034	..	..	..	..	..	..
52	1018	1024	..	..	..	..	..	..		..	..	..	..	..	..	..	..	..	..	1037	..	..	..	..	..	..
53	..	..	1015	10 12	..	..	..	..		..	..	..	..	..	..	10 25	..	..	..	..	..	..	10 32	..	..	..
54	..	..	1017	10 14	..	..	..	..		..	..	..	..	..	..	10 27	..	..	..	..	..	..	10 34	..	..	..
55	..	..	1020	10 17	..	..	..	..		..	..	..	..	..	..	10 30	..	..	..	..	..	..	10 37	..	..	..
56	..	..	1022	10 19	..	..	..	..		..	..	..	..	..	..	10 32	..	..	..	..	..	..	10 39	..	..	..
57	..	..	..	J1 minute later on Saturdays	..	..	..	..	..	..	..	1031	..	..	..	H 1 minute *earlier* on Saturdays	..	..	..	..	1036	..	H 1 minute *earlier* on Saturdays	..	..	..
58	..	..	..		..	..	..	..	..	..	..	1032	..	..	..		..	..	..	..	1037	..		..	..	..
59	..	..	..		..	..	..	..	..	..	1023	1034	..	..	..		..	..	..	..	1039	..		..	..	..
60	..	..	..		..	..	..	..	..	..	1026	1037	..	..	..		..	..	..	..	1042	..		..	..	..
61	..	..	..		..	..	..	..	..	..	1028	1039	..	..	..		..	..	..	..	1044	..		..	..	..
62	..	..	..		..	..	..	..	..	..	1031	1042	..	..	..		..	..	..	..	1047	..		..	..	..
63	..	..	..		..	..	..	..	..	..	1033	1044	..	..	..		..	..	..	..	1049	..		..	..	..
64	..	..	1025		..	..	Via Worcester Park	..	..	..	..	..	..	1028	1028		..	..	..	..	..	..		Via Worcester Park	..	..
65	1021	..	1028		..	..		..	..	..	..	..	..	1031	1032		..	..	1034	..	..	..			..	..
66	1024	..	..		..	..		..	..	..	..	..	..	..	..		..	..	1037	..	..	..			..	..
67	1026	..	..		..	..		..	..	..	..	..	..	..	..		..	..	1039	..	..	..			..	..
68	1028	..	..		..	..		..	..	..	..	..	..	1036	..		..	..	1041	..	..	..			..	..
69	1030	..	..		..	..		..	..	..	..	..	..	..	..		..	..	1043	..	..	..			..	..
70	1033	..	..		..	..		..	..	..	..	..	..	..	..		..	..	1046	..	..	..			..	..
71	..	1026	..	10 23	..	1019		..	..	..	..	..	..	..	..	10 36	..	..	..	1039	..	..	10 43		..	..
72	..	1028	..	..	..	..		..	..	..	..	..	..	..	..	10SX38	..	..	..	1041	..	..	..		..	..
73	..	1031	..	10J27	..	1023		..	..	..	..	..	..	..	..	10H41	1042	..	..	1044	..	..	10 47		..	..
74	..	1034	..	..	..	..		..	..	..	..	..	..	..	..	..	..	..	..	1047	..	..	..		..	..
75	1037	..	1039	..	..	..	..	1042	..	1032	1038	1050	1040	1042	1042	..	..	..	1050	..	1055	..	..	..	..	..
76	..	..	..	..	..	..	1023	..	..	1037	..	..	..	..	..	..	..	..	..	..	..	..	..	1043	..	..
77	..	..	..	..	..	..	..	..	..	1040	..	..	..	..	..	..	..	..	..	..	..	..	..	..	..	..
78	..	1038	..	10J33	..	1029	..	..	10 31	..	..	..	..	..	..	10H47	1050	..	..	1051	..	..	10H54	..	1042	..

For Notes, see page 317a

HORSHAM, REIGATE, REDHILL, TATTENHAM CORNER, CATERHAM,

Up	No.	a.m. Week Days—*continued*																	a.m.			No
		3		3		3	3	3	3	3	3			3	3	3	3	3	3	3	3	3	
Horsham .... dep	1																				9 52		1
Reigate .... "	2		1012																				2
Redhill .... "	3		1019																				3
Merstham	4		1023																				4
Coulsdon South	5	S O	1029																				5
Tattenham Corner. dep	6	10 3																					6
Tadworth N	7	10 6																					7
Kingswood M	8	10 9																					8
Chipstead	9	1013																					9
Woodmansterne	10	1016																					10
Smitham	11	1018																					11
Reedham	12	1021																					12
Purley 252 .... arr	13	1023																					13
Caterham .... dep	14	1013																					14
Warlingham	15	1017																					15
Whyteleafe	16	1019																					16
Kenley	17	1022																					17
Purley 252 .... arr	18	1025						S O															18
Coulsdon North ..... dep	19							1031															19
Purley 252	20	1028	1032					1034															20
Purley Oaks	21							1036															21
South Croydon 234	22							1039															22
Effingham Junction dep	23	—															10 13						23
Bookham	24																10 16						24
Dorking North ..... dep	25																				1018		25
Boxhill and Burford	26																				1021		26
Leatherhead ..[Bridge J	27																10 20				1026		27
Ashtead	28																10 24				1030		28
Epsom 427	29																10 28				1034		29
Ewell East H	30																10 31						30
Cheam	31														S O	S X	10 34						31
Epsom Downs ...... dep	32														1024	1024		1029					32
Banstead	33														1027	1027		1032					33
Belmont	34														1030	1030		1035	S O	S X			34
Sutton 322	35														1033	1033	10 37	1038	1041	1042			35
Carshalton Beeches	36														1035	1035		1040	1043	1045			36
Wallington	37														1038	1038		1043	1046	1047			37
Waddon G	38					From London Bridge, via Forest Hill	From London Bridge, via Forest Hill								1041	1041		1046					38
West Croydon 319 arr	39													S O	1044	1044		1049					39
West Croydon 319 dep	40													1040	1044	1044		1049					40
Carshalton	41																10 40					—	41
Hackbridge	42																10 43						42
Mitcham Junction	43																10 45						43
East Croydon .... arr	44	1034	1038					1042															44
East Croydon .... dep	45	1034	1088		1041	S O	S X	1042				1047											45
Norwood Junction F ..	46	1038	1043			1032	1032		S O					1044	1048	1048							46
Beckenham Jn. dep	47								1029														47
Birkbeck	48								1032	S O	S X												48
Crystal Palace D	49								1036	1039	1042			1049				—					49
Gipsy Hill (for Upper	50								1038					1051									50
West Norwood. [N'wood)	51			S O					1041					1054									51
Streatham Hill	52			1038					1044					1057									52
Selhurst	53					1035	1035	1045										1052					53
Thornton Heath	54					1037	1037	1047										1054					54
Norbury	55					1040	1040	1050										1057					55
Streatham Common	56					1042	1042	1052										1059					56
Anerley	57															1051							57
Penge West C	58															1052							58
Sydenham .... [Lane	59									1042	1045					1054							59
Forest Hill for Lordship	60									1045	1048					1057							60
Honor Oak Park	61									1047	1050					1059							61
Brockley B .... [Line)	62									1050	1053					11 2						From Victoria dep. 10 47 a.m.	62
New Cross Gate (for E.L.	63									1052	1055					11 4							63
Streatham	64					1044	1044										10 51						64
Tulse Hill	65			1041		1048	1048										10 54						65
North Dulwich	66			1044			1051						—										66
East Dulwich	67			1046			1053															S X	67
Peckham Rye	68			1048		1053	1055										10SX59					11 1	68
Queen's Road Peckham	69			1050																	Via Worcester Park	11 3	69
South Bermondsey	70			1053																		11 6	70
Balham & Upper Tooting	71							1056	1046					1059				11 3					71
Wandsworth Common A	72								1048					11 1									72
Clapham Junction	73							11 0	1051					11 4				11 7					73
Battersea Park	74								1054					11 7									74
London Bridge ..... arr	75	1050	1056	1057		11 0	11 2			1058	11 0		—		11 1	1110	11 5					1110	75
Waterloo* .... "	76																				11 3		76
Charing Cross* ... "	77																						77
Victoria .... "	78				1057			11 6	1058			11 3		1111				1114					78

DORKING NORTH, SUTTON, CROYDON, CRYSTAL PALACE, and LONDON

a.m. — **Week Days**—*continued* — a.m.

No.	3	3	3	3	3	3		..	3	3	3	..	3	3	..	..	3	3	..	..	3	3	3	3	3	3	3	3
1	..	..	..	..	..	..	9§48	..	..	..	..	..	..	..	..	..	..	..	..	..	..	..	..	..	..	..	..	..
2	..	..	..	..	..	..	1032	..	..	..	..	..	..	..	..	..	..	..	..	..	..	..	..	..	..	..	..	..
3	..	..	..	..	..	..	1038	..	..	..	..	..	..	..	1050	..	..	..	..	..	..	..	..	..	..	..	..	..
4	..	..	..	..	..	..	1042	..	..	..	..	..	..	..	..	..	..	..	..	..	..	..	..	..	..	..	..	..
5	..	..	S X	S O	..	..	1048	..	..	..	..	..	..	..	..	..	..	..	..	..	..	..	..	..	..	..	..	..
6	..	..	1023	1024	..	..	§ Via Three Bridges	..	..	..	..	..	..	..	..	..	..	..	..	..	..	..	..	..	..	..	..	..
7	..	..	1026	1027	..	..		..	..	..	..	..	..	..	..	..	..	..	..	..	..	..	..	..	..	..	..	..
8	..	..	1029	1030	..	..		..	..	..	..	..	..	..	..	..	..	..	..	..	..	..	..	..	..	..	..	..
9	..	..	1033	1034	..	..		..	..	..	..	..	..	..	..	..	..	..	..	..	..	..	..	..	..	..	..	..
10	..	..	1035	1037	..	..		..	..	..	..	..	..	..	..	..	..	..	..	..	..	..	..	..	..	..	..	..
11	..	..	1038	1039	..	..		..	..	..	..	..	..	..	..	..	..	..	..	..	..	..	..	..	..	..	..	..
12	..	..	1041	1042	..	..		..	..	..	..	..	..	..	..	..	..	..	..	..	..	..	..	..	..	..	..	..
13	..	..	1043	1044	..	..		..	..	..	..	..	..	..	..	..	..	..	..	..	..	..	..	..	..	..	..	..
14	..	..	1033	1034	..	..	..	..	..	..	..	..	..	..	..	..	..	..	..	..	..	..	..	..	..	..	..	..
15	..	..	1037	1038	..	..	..	..	..	..	..	..	..	..	..	..	..	..	..	..	..	..	..	..	..	..	..	..
16	..	..	1039	1040	..	..	..	..	..	..	..	..	..	..	..	..	..	..	..	..	..	..	..	..	..	..	..	..
17	..	..	1042	1043	..	..	..	..	..	..	..	..	..	..	..	..	..	..	..	..	..	..	..	..	..	..	..	..
18	..	S X	1045	1046	..	..	..	..	..	..	..	..	..	..	..	..	..	..	..	..	..	..	..	..	S O	..	..	..
19	..	1041	..	..	..	..	..	..	..	..	..	..	..	..	..	..	..	..	..	..	..	..	..	..	1051	..	..	..
20	..	1044	1047	1049	..	..	1052	..	..	..	..	..	..	..	..	..	..	..	..	..	..	..	..	..	1054	..	..	..
21	..	1046	1050	..	..	..	..	..	..	..	..	..	..	..	..	..	..	..	..	..	..	..	..	..	1056	..	..	..
22	..	1049	1052	..	..	..	..	..	..	..	..	..	..	..	..	..	..	..	..	..	..	..	..	..	1059	..	..	S O
23	..	..	..	..	..	..	..	..	..	..	..	..	..	..	..	..	..	..	..	..	..	..	..	..	..	..	..	1038
24	..	..	..	..	..	..	..	..	..	..	..	..	..	..	..	..	..	..	..	..	..	..	S O	..	..	..	..	1041
25	..	..	..	..	..	..	..	..	..	..	..	..	..	..	..	..	..	..	..	..	..	..	1029	..	..	..	..	..
26	..	..	..	..	..	..	..	..	..	..	..	..	..	..	..	..	..	..	..	..	..	..	1032	..	..	..	..	..
27	..	..	..	..	..	..	..	..	..	..	..	..	..	..	..	..	..	..	..	..	..	..	1037	..	..	..	..	1046
28	..	..	..	..	..	S O	..	..	..	..	..	..	..	..	..	..	..	..	..	..	..	..	1041	S X	..	..	..	1050
29	..	..	..	..	..	1040	..	..	..	..	..	..	..	..	..	..	..	..	..	..	..	..	1045	1047	..	..	..	1054
30	..	..	..	..	..	1043	..	..	..	..	..	..	..	..	..	..	..	..	..	..	..	..	1048	1050	..	..	..	..
31	..	..	..	..	..	1046	..	..	..	..	..	..	..	..	..	..	..	..	..	..	..	S O	1051	1053	..	..	..	..
32	..	..	..	..	From London Bridge, via Streatham	..	..	..	..	..	From London Bridge, via Forest Hill	..	..	..	..	..	..	..	..	..	..	1044	..	..	..	10 49	..	..
33	..	..	..	..		..	..	..	..	..		..	..	..	..	..	..	..	..	..	..	1047	..	..	..	10 52	..	..
34	..	..	..	..		..	..	..	..	..		..	..	..	..	..	..	..	..	..	..	1050	..	..	..	10 55	S X	..
35	..	..	..	..		1049	..	..	..	..		..	..	..	..	..	..	..	..	..	..	1053	1054	1057	..	10 58	11 2	..
36	..	..	..	..		..	..	..	..	..		..	..	..	..	..	..	..	..	..	..	1055	..	..	..	11 0	11 4	..
37	..	..	..	..		..	..	..	..	..		..	..	..	..	..	..	..	..	..	..	1058	..	..	..	11 3	11 7	..
38	..	..	..	..		..	..	..	..	..		..	..	..	..	..	..	..	..	..	..	11 1	..	..	..	11 6	1110	..
39	..	..	..	..		..	..	..	..	..		..	..	S X	..	..	..	S O	..	..	..	11 4	..	..	..	11 9	1113	..
40	..	..	..	..		..	..	..	..	..		..	..	1055	..	..	..	11 0	..	..	..	11 4	..	..	..	11 9	..	..
41	..	..	..	..		1052	..	..	..	..		..	..	..	..	..	..	..	..	..	..	..	1057	11 0	..	..	..	..
42	..	..	..	..		1055	..	..	..	..		..	..	..	..	..	..	..	..	..	..	..	1059	11 2	..	..	..	..
43	..	..	..	..		1057	..	..	..	..		..	..	..	..	..	..	..	..	..	..	..	11 2	11 5	..	..	..	..
44	..	1052	1055	1055		..	1057	..	..	..		..	..	..	11 5	..	..	..	..	..	..	..	..	..	11 2	..	..	..
45	..	1052	1055	1055		..	1059	..	..	..	S O	..	..	..	11 5	..	..	..	..	..	..	..	..	..	11 2	..	..	..
46	..	..	1058	1058	1053	..	..	..	S O	..	1052	..	S X	1059	..	..	..	11 4	..	..	..	11 8	..	..	..	..	..	..
47	..	..	..	..	..	..	..	..	1049	..	..	..	1050	..	..	..	..	..	..	..	..	..	..	..	..	..	..	..
48	..	..	..	..	..	..	..	..	1052	S O	..	..	1053	..	..	..	S O	..	..	..	S X	..	..	..	..	..	..	..
49	..	..	..	..	..	..	..	..	1056	1059	..	..	1057	11 3	..	..	11 5	11 9	..	..	1111	..	..	..	..	..	..	..
50	..	..	..	..	..	..	..	..	1058	..	..	..	..	11 6	..	..	11 8	1111	..	..	1113	..	..	..	..	..	..	..
51	..	..	..	..	..	..	..	..	11 1	..	..	..	..	11 8	..	..	1110	1114	..	..	1116	..	..	..	..	..	..	..
52	..	..	..	..	..	..	..	..	11 4	..	..	..	..	1111	..	..	..	1117	..	..	..	..	..	..	..	..	..	..
53	..	1055	..	..	..	..	..	..	..	..	1055	..	..	..	..	..	..	..	..	..	..	..	..	..	11 5	11 12	..	..
54	..	1057	..	..	..	..	..	..	..	..	1057	..	..	..	..	..	..	..	..	..	..	..	..	..	11 7	11 14	..	..
55	..	11 0	..	..	..	..	..	..	..	..	11 0	..	..	..	..	..	..	..	..	..	..	..	..	..	1110	11 17	..	..
56	..	11 2	..	..	..	..	..	..	..	..	11 3	..	..	..	..	..	..	..	..	..	..	..	..	..	1112	11 19	..	..
57	From Victoria dep. 10 47 a.m.	..	..	..	1056	..	..	..	..	..	..	..	..	..	..	..	..	..	..	..	..	..	..	..	..	..	..	..
58		..	..	..	1057	..	..	..	..	..	..	..	..	..	..	..	..	..	..	..	..	..	..	..	..	..	..	..
59		..	..	..	1059	..	..	..	..	11 2	..	..	..	..	..	..	..	..	..	..	..	..	..	..	..	..	..	..
60		..	..	..	11 2	..	..	..	..	11 5	..	..	..	..	..	..	..	..	..	..	..	..	..	..	..	..	..	..
61		..	..	..	11 4	..	..	..	..	11 7	..	..	..	..	..	..	..	..	..	..	..	..	..	..	..	..	..	..
62		..	..	..	11 7	..	..	..	..	1110	..	..	..	..	..	..	..	..	..	..	..	..	..	..	..	J 1 minute later on Saturdays	..	..
63		..	..	..	11 9	..	..	..	..	1112	..	..	..	..	..	..	..	..	..	..	..	..	..	..	..		..	..
64		..	..	..	..	..	..	..	..	..	11 5	..	..	..	..	..	..	..	..	..	..	..	11 8	..	..		..	..
65		..	..	..	..	..	..	..	..	..	11 8	..	..	..	..	..	1113	..	..	..	1118	..	1111	..	..		..	..
66		..	..	..	..	..	..	..	..	..	..	..	..	..	..	..	1116	..	..	..	1121	..	..	..	..		..	..
67	S O	..	..	..	..	..	..	..	..	..	..	..	..	..	..	..	1118	..	..	..	1123	..	..	..	..		..	Via Worcester Park
68	11 2	..	..	..	..	..	..	..	..	..	..	..	..	..	..	..	1121	..	..	..	1126	..	..	..	..		..	
69	11 4	..	..	..	..	..	..	..	..	..	..	..	..	..	..	..	1123	..	..	..	1128	..	..	..	..		..	
70	11 7	..	..	..	..	..	..	..	..	..	..	..	..	..	..	..	1126	..	..	..	1131	..	..	..	..		..	
71	..	11 6	..	..	..	11 4	..	..	11 6	..	..	..	..	1114	..	..	..	1119	..	..	..	..	..	1111	1116	11 23	..	
72	..	..	..	..	..	..	..	..	11 8	..	..	..	..	1116	..	..	..	1121	..	..	..	..	..	..	..	..	..	
73	..	1110	..	..	..	11 8	1111	..	1111	..	..	..	..	1119	1116	..	..	1124	..	..	..	..	..	1115	1120	11 27	..	
74	..	..	..	..	..	..	..	..	1114	..	..	..	..	1123	..	..	..	1127	..	..	..	..	..	..	..	..	..	
75	1111	..	1111	1111	1115	..	..	..	..	1118	1119	..	..	..	..	..	1130	..	..	..	1135	1121	1122	..	..	..	..	..
76	..	..	1115	..	..	..	..	..	..	..	..	..	..	..	..	..	..	..	..	..	..	..	..	..	..	..	..	1122
77	..	..	1117	..	..	..	..	..	..	..	..	..	..	..	..	..	..	..	..	..	..	..	..	..	..	..	..	..
78	..	1116	..	..	..	1113	1117	..	1118	..	..	..	..	1126	1121	..	..	1131	..	..	..	..	..	1121	1126	11J33	..	..

HORSHAM, REIGATE, REDHILL, TATTENHAM CORNER, CATERHAM,

Up	No.	a.m. — Week Days—*continued*																			a.m.	No.
Horsham ... dep	1	3	3	3	10§43	..	3	3	3	3	10§15	SX 1020	3	3	3	..	3	3	3	SO 1022	3	1
Reigate ... "	2	..	..	..	§ Via Three Bridges	10 45	..	..	..	..	10 52	3	..	..	..	..	..	..	..	3	..	2
Redhill ... "	3	..	..	..		10a50	..	..	..	..	10 59		..	..	..	..	..	..	..		..	3
Merstham ...	4	..	..	..		a Arrival time	..	..	..	..	11 3	..	..	..	..	..	..	..	..	..	..	4
Coulsdon South ...	5	..	SX	SO			..	..	..	..	11 9	..	..	..	..	..	..	..	..	..	..	5
Tattenham Corner. dep	6	..	1043	1044			..	..	..	..	§ Via Three Bridges	..	..	..	..	..	..	..	..	..	..	6
Tadworth N ...	7	..	1046	1047			..	..	..	..		..	..	..	..	..	..	..	..	..	..	7
Kingswood M ...	8	..	1049	1050			..	..	..	..		..	..	..	..	..	..	..	..	..	..	8
Chipstead ...	9	..	1053	1054			..	..	..	..		..	..	..	..	..	..	..	..	..	..	9
Woodmansterne ...	10	..	1055	1057	..		..	..	..	..		..	..	..	..	..	..	..	..	..	..	10
Smitham ...	11	..	1058	1059	..		..	..	..	..		..	..	..	..	..	..	..	..	..	..	11
Reedham ...	12	..	11 1	11 2	..	..	..	..	..	..		..	..	..	..	..	..	..	..	..	..	12
Purley 252 ... arr	13	..	11 3	11 4	..	..	..	..	..	..		..	..	..	..	..	..	..	..	..	..	13
Caterham ... dep	14	..	1053	1054	..	..	..	..	..	..	..	..	..	..	..	..	..	..	..	..	..	14
Warlingham ...	15	..	1057	1058	..	..	..	..	..	..	..	..	..	..	..	..	..	..	..	..	..	15
Whyteleafe ...	16	..	1059	11 0	..	..	..	..	..	..	..	..	..	..	..	..	..	..	..	..	..	16
Kenley ...	17	..	11 2	11 3	..	..	..	..	..	..	..	..	..	..	..	..	..	..	..	..	..	17
Purley 252 ... arr	18	..	11 5	11 6	..	..	..	..	..	..	..	..	..	SO	SX	..	..	..	..	..	..	18
Coulsdon North ... dep	19	..	..	..	..	..	..	..	..	..	..	..	..	1111	1111	..	..	..	..	..	..	19
Purley 252 ...	20	..	11 7	11 8	..	..	..	..	..	..	11 12	..	..	1114	1114	..	..	..	..	..	..	20
Purley Oaks ...	21	..	1110	..	..	..	..	..	..	..	..	..	..	1116	1116	..	..	..	..	..	..	21
South Croydon 234 ...	22	..	1112	..	..	..	..	..	..	..	..	..	..	1119	1119	..	..	..	..	..	..	22
Effingham Junction dep	23	..	..	..	..	..	..	..	..	..	..	..	..	..	..	..	..	..	..	..	..	23
Bookham ...	24	..	..	..	..	..	..	..	..	..	..	..	..	..	..	..	..	..	..	..	..	24
Dorking North ... dep	25	..	..	..	..	..	..	..	..	..	..	1046	..	..	..	..	..	..	..	1048	..	25
Boxhill and Burford	26	..	..	..	..	..	..	..	..	..	..	1048	..	..	..	..	..	..	..	1051	..	26
Leatherhead ... [Bridge J	27	..	..	..	..	..	..	..	..	..	..	1053	..	..	..	..	..	..	..	1056	..	27
Ashtead ...	28	..	..	..	..	..	..	..	..	..	..	1057	..	..	..	..	..	..	..	11 0	..	28
Epsom 427 ...	29	..	..	..	..	..	..	..	..	..	..	11 2	..	..	..	..	..	..	..	11 5	..	29
Ewell East H ...	30	..	..	..	..	..	..	..	..	..	..	11 5	..	..	..	..	..	..	..	11 8	..	30
Cheam ...	31	..	..	..	..	..	..	..	..	..	..	11 8	..	..	..	..	..	SX	SO	1111	..	31
Epsom Downs ... dep	32	From London Bridge, via Streatham	..	..	..	..	..	..	..	..	..	..	..	..	..	..	..	11 0	11 4	..	..	32
Banstead ...	33		..	..	..	..	..	..	..	..	..	..	..	..	..	..	..	11 3	11 7	..	..	33
Belmont ...	34		..	..	..	..	..	..	..	..	..	..	..	..	..	..	..	11 6	1110	..	..	34
Sutton 322 ...	35		..	..	..	..	..	..	..	..	..	1111	From London Bridge, via Forest Hill	..	..	..	..	11 9	1113	1114	..	35
Carshalton Beeches ...	36		..	..	..	..	..	..	..	..	..	..		..	..	..	..	1111	1115	..	..	36
Wallington ...	37		..	..	..	..	..	..	..	..	..	..		..	..	..	..	1114	1118	..	..	37
Waddon G ...	38		..	..	..	..	..	..	..	..	..	..		..	..	..	..	1117	1121	..	..	38
West Croydon 319 arr	39		..	..	..	..	..	..	..	..	..	..		..	..	..	SO	1120	1124	..	..	39
West Croydon 319 dep	40		..	..	..	..	..	..	..	..	..	..		..	..	..	1120	1120	1124	..	..	40
Carshalton ...	41		..	..	..	..	..	..	..	..	..	1114		..	..	..	..	..	..	1117	..	41
Hackbridge ...	42		..	..	..	..	..	..	..	..	..	1116		..	..	..	..	..	..	1120	..	42
Mitcham Junction ...	43		..	..	..	..	..	..	..	..	..	1119		..	..	..	..	..	..	1122	..	43
East Croydon ... arr	44		1115	1114	11 15	..	..	..	..	..	11 18	..		1122	1122	..	..	..	..	..	..	44
East Croydon ... dep	45	SO	1115	1114	11 16	..	..	..	..	..	11 18	..	SO	1122	1122	1128	..	..	..	..	..	45
Norwood Junction F ..	46	1113	1118	1118	..	..	..	..	SO	..	..	..	1112	..	..	..	1124	1124	1128	..	..	46
Beckenham Jn. dep	47	..	..	..	..	..	..	..	11 9	..	..	..	..	..	..	..	..	..	..	..	..	47
Birkbeck ...	48	..	..	..	..	..	..	..	11 12	SO	..	..	..	..	..	..	..	..	..	..	..	48
Crystal Palace D ...	49	..	..	..	..	..	..	..	11 16	11 19	..	..	..	..	..	..	1129	..	..	..	..	49
Gipsy Hill (for Upper	50	..	..	..	..	..	..	..	11 18	..	..	..	..	..	..	..	1131	..	..	..	..	50
West Norwood. [N'wood)	51	..	..	..	..	..	..	SO	11 21	..	..	..	..	..	..	..	1134	..	..	..	..	51
Streatham Hill ...	52	..	..	..	..	..	..	1118	11 24	..	..	..	..	..	..	..	1137	..	..	..	..	52
Selhurst ...	53	..	..	..	..	..	..	..	..	..	..	..	1115	1125	1125	..	..	..	..	..	..	53
Thornton Heath ...	54	..	..	..	..	..	..	..	..	..	..	..	1117	1127	1127	..	..	..	..	..	..	54
Norbury ...	55	..	..	..	..	..	..	..	..	..	..	..	1120	1130	1130	..	..	..	..	..	..	55
Streatham Common ...	56	..	..	..	..	..	..	..	..	..	..	..	1123	1132	1133	..	..	..	..	..	..	56
Anerley ...	57	1116	..	..	‖ 1 minute *earlier* on Saturdays	..	From Victoria, dep. 11 8 a.m.	..	..	..	‖ 2 minutes *earlier* on Saturdays	..	..	..	..	..	..	1127	..	..	From Victoria dep. 11 18 a.m.	57
Penge West C ...	58	1117	..	..		..		..	..	..		..	..	..	..	..	..	1128	..	..		58
Sydenham ... [Lane	59	1119	..	..		..		..	..	11 22		..	..	..	..	..	..	1130	..	..		59
Forest Hill, for Lordship	60	1122	..	..		..		..	..	11 25		..	..	..	..	..	..	1133	..	..		60
Honor Oak Park ...	61	1124	..	..		..		..	..	11 27		..	..	..	..	..	..	1135	..	..		61
Brockley B ... [Line	62	1127	..	..		..		..	..	11 30		..	..	..	..	..	..	1138	..	..		62
New Cross Gate (for E.L.	63	1129	..	..		..		..	..	11 32		..	..	..	..	..	..	1140	..	..		63
Streatham ...	64	..	..	..		..		..	..	..		1124	1125	..	..	..	..	..	..	1128		64
Tulse Hill ...	65	..	..	..		..		1121	..	..		1127	1128	..	..	..	..	..	..	1131		65
North Dulwich ...	66	..	..	..		..		1124	..	..		..	..	..	..	..	..	..	..	..		66
East Dulwich ...	67	..	..	..		..	SO	1126	..	..		..	..	..	..	..	..	..	..	..	SX	67
Peckham Rye ...	68	..	..	..		..	1124	1128	..	..		1132	..	..	..	..	..	..	..	..	1135	68
Queen's Road, Peckham	69	..	..	..		..	1126	1130	..	..		..	..	..	..	..	..	..	..	..	1137	69
South Bermondsey ...	70	..	..	..		..	1129	1133	..	..		..	..	..	..	..	..	..	..	..	1140	70
Balham & Upper Tooting	71	..	..	..	..	..	..	..	11 26	..	..	..	..	1136	1137	..	1139	..	..	..	..	71
Wandsworth Common A	72	..	..	..	..	..	..	..	11 28	..	..	..	..	..	1139	..	1141	..	..	..	..	72
Clapham Junction ...	73	..	..	..	..	..	..	..	11 31	..	11 30	..	..	1140	1142	1140	1144	..	..	..	..	73
Battersea Park ...	74	..	..	..	..	..	..	..	11 34	..	..	..	..	..	..	..	1147	..	..	..	..	74
London Bridge ... arr	75	1135	1131	1130	..	..	1133	1137	..	11 38	..	1139	1139	..	..	..	..	1146	1141	1142	1144	75
Waterloo * ... "	76	..	1135	..	..	..	..	..	..	..	..	..	..	..	..	..	..	..	..	..	..	76
Charing Cross * .. "	77	..	1137	..	..	..	..	..	..	..	..	..	..	..	..	..	..	..	..	..	..	77
Victoria ... "	78	..	..	..	11‖32	..	..	..	11 38	..	11‖37	..	..	1146	1147	1147	1151	..	..	..	..	78

For Notes, see page 317a

DORKING NORTH, SUTTON, CROYDON, CRYSTAL PALACE, and LONDON

a.m — **Week Days**—*continued* — a.m

No.	3	3	3	3	3	3	3	3	3	3	..	3	3	..	3	3	3	3	..	3	..	3	3	3	..	3	3	..
1																												
2																												
3																												
4																												
5				S O																								
6				11 3																								
7				11 6																								
8				11 9																								
9				1113																								
10				1116																								
11				1118																								
12				1121																								
13				1123																								
14				1113																								
15				1117																								
16				1119																								
17				1122																								
18				1125																S O								
19																				1131								
20				1128																1134								
21																				1136								
22							S X													1139							S O	
23							1055																				1110	
24							1058	S O																			1113	
25								1055																				
26								1057																				
27							11 2	11 2																			1117	
28							11 6	11 6																			1121	
29							1114	1114		1117																	1125	
30										1120																	1128	
31					S O					1123								S X								S O	1131	
32					11 9		Arr. Epsom 11 10 a.m	Arr. Epsom 11 10 a.m	From London Bridge, via Streatham									1119								1124		
33					1112								From London Bridge, via Forest Hill					1122								1127		
34	S O				1115													1125				S X				1130		
35	1123				1118					1126								1128				1132				1133	1134	
36	1125				1120													1130				1134				1135		
37	1128				1123													1133				1137				1138		
38					1126													1136								1141		
39			S X		1129													1139						S O		1144		
40			1125		1129													1139						1140		1144		
41										1129																	1137	
42										1131																	1140	
43										1134																	1142	
44				1134																1142								
45				1134					S O				S X	1142						1142								1147
46		S X	1129	1138					1133				1129			S O								1144		1148		
47		1120														1129												
48		1123													S X	1132	S O						S O					
49		1127	1133												1138	1136	1139						1145	1149				
50			1136													1138							1148	1151				
51			1138									S O				1141							1150	1154				
52			1141									1138				1144								1157				
53					1132	From Victoria, dep. 11 23 a.m							1132					1142		1145								
54					1134								1134					1144		1147								
55					1137								1137					1147		1150								
56					1139								1140					1149		1152								
57									1136																			
58									1137																			
59									1139						1141		1142											
60									1142						1144		1145											
61									1144						1146		1147											
62									1147						1149		1150											
63									1149						1151		1152									1157		
64							Via Worcester Park	Via Worcester Park					1142														1148	
65												1141	1146										1153				1151	
66												1144	1149										1156					
67						S O						1146	1151										1158					
68						1144						1148	1153										12 1					
69						1146						1150	1154										12 3					
70						1149						1153	1158										12 6					
71			1144		1143					1141						1146		1153		1156				1159				
72			1146													1148								12 1				
73			1149		1147					1145						1151		1157		12 0				12 4				
74			1153													1154								12 7				
75				1150		1153			1155			1157	12 2		1157		1158						1210			12 2	12 2	
76							1142	1142																				
77																												
78			1157		1154					1150				1157		1158		12 3		12 6				1211				12 8

HORSHAM, REIGATE, REDHILL, TATTENHAM CORNER, CATERHAM,

For Notes, see page 317a

Up	No.	a.m. Week Days—*continued*																a.m.				No.
		S O	S X	3	3	3	3	3	3	3	3	3		3	3	3		3	3	3	3	
Horsham............dep	1	10§48	10§48										1052				..					1
Reigate .... "	2	11 22	11 22	..	..	..	..	..	..	..	..	..		..	..	..	..	..	..	..	..	2
Redhill............. "	3	11 28	11 28	..	..	..	..	..	..	..	..	..	3	..	..	..	..	..	..	..	..	3
Merstham..............	4	11 32	11 32	..	..	..	..	..	..	..	..	..		..	..	..	..	..	..	..	..	4
Coulsdon South.........	5	11 38	11 38	..	..	..	S X	..	..	..	..	S O	..	..	..	..	..	..	..	..	..	5
Tattenham Corner. dep	6	§ Via Three Bridges	§ Via Three Bridges	..	..	..	1123	..	..	..	..	1124	..	..	..	..	..	..	..	..	..	6
Tadworth N..........	7			..	..	..	1126	..	..	..	..	1127	..	..	..	..	..	..	..	..	..	7
Kingswood M..........	8			..	..	..	1129	..	..	..	..	1130	..	..	..	..	..	..	..	..	..	8
Chipstead............	9			..	..	..	1133	..	..	..	..	1134	..	..	..	..	..	..	..	..	..	9
Woodmansterne	10			..	..	..	1136	..	..	..	..	1137	..	..	..	..	..	..	..	..	..	10
Smitham..............	11			..	..	..	1138	..	..	..	..	1139	..	..	..	..	..	..	..	..	..	11
Reedham..............	12			..	..	..	1141	..	..	..	..	1142	..	..	..	..	..	..	..	..	..	12
Purley 252.......... arr	13			..	..	..	1143	..	..	..	..	1144	..	..	..	..	..	..	..	..	..	13
Caterham........... dep	14	..	..	..	..	..	1133	..	..	..	..	1134	..	..	..	..	..	..	..	..	..	14
Warlingham............	15	..	..	..	..	..	1137	..	..	..	..	1138	..	..	..	..	..	..	..	..	..	15
Whyteleafe............	16	..	..	..	..	..	1139	..	..	..	..	1140	..	..	..	..	..	..	..	..	..	16
Kenley................	17	..	..	..	..	..	1142	..	..	..	..	1143	..	..	..	..	..	..	..	..	..	17
Purley 252......... arr	18	..	..	..	..	S X	1145	..	..	..	..	1146	..	..	..	..	..	..	..	..	..	18
Coulsdon North..... dep	19	..	..	..	..	1142	..	..	..	..	..	..	..	..	..	..	..	..	..	..	..	19
Purley 252............	20	11 42	11 42	..	..	1145	1147	..	..	..	..	1148	..	..	..	..	..	..	..	..	..	20
Purley Oaks...........	21	..	..	..	..	1147	1150	..	..	..	..	..	..	..	..	..	..	..	..	..	..	21
South Croydon 234......	22	..	..	S X	..	1150	1152	..	..	..	..	..	..	..	..	..	..	..	..	..	..	22
Effingham Junction dep	23	..	..	1113	..	..	..	..	..	..	..	..	..	..	..	..	..	..	..	..	..	23
Bookham..............	24	..	..	1116	..	..	..	..	..	..	..	..	..	..	..	..	..	..	..	..	..	24
Dorking North..... dep	25	..	..	..	..	..	..	..	..	..	..	..	1118	..	..	..	..	..	..	..	..	25
Boxhill and Burford	26	..	..	..	..	..	..	..	..	..	..	..	1121	..	..	..	..	..	..	..	..	26
Leatherhead...[Bridge J	27	..	..	1120	..	..	..	..	..	..	..	..	1126	..	..	..	..	..	..	..	..	27
Ashtead..............	28	..	..	1124	..	..	..	..	..	..	..	..	1130	S O	S X	..	..	..	..	..	..	28
Epsom 427............	29	..	..	1128	..	..	..	..	..	..	..	..	1134	1138	1140	..	..	..	..	..	..	29
Ewell East H.........	30	..	..	1131	..	..	..	..	..	..	..	..	..	1141	1143	..	..	..	..	..	..	30
Cheam................	31	..	..	1134	S O	..	..	..	..	S X	..	..	..	1144	1146	..	..	..	..	..	..	31
Epsom Downs...... dep	32	..	..	..	1129	..	..	..	..	1139	..	..	..	..	..	..	..	..	..	..	..	32
Banstead.............	33	..	..	..	1132	..	..	..	..	[illegible]	..	..	..	..	..	From London Bridge, via Streatham	..	..	..	..	..	33
Belmont..............	34	..	..	..	1135	..	..	..	..	1138	S O	..	..	..	..		..	..	..	From London Bridge, via Forest Hill	..	34
Sutton 322...........	35	..	..	1138	1138	..	..	..	..	1129	1144	..	..	1148	1149		..	..	..		..	35
Carshalton Beeches.....	36	..	..	..	1140	..	..	..	..	1141	1146	..	..	..	..		..	..	..		From London Bridge, via Tulse Hill	36
Wallington............	37	..	..	..	1143	..	..	..	..	1144	1150	..	..	..	..		..	..	..			37
Waddon G.............	38	..	..	..	1146	..	..	..	..	1148	1153	..	..	..	..		..	..	..			38
West Croydon 319 arr	39	..	..	..	1149	..	..	..	..	1150	1156	..	..	..	..		..	..	..			39
West Croydon 319 dep	40	..	..	..	1149	..	..	..	..	1150	1156	..	..	..	..		..	..	..			40
Carshalton............	41	..	..	1141	..	..	..	..	..	..	..	..	..	1151	1152		..	..	..			41
Hackbridge............	42	..	..	1144	..	..	..	..	..	..	..	..	..	1153	1155		..	..	..			42
Mitcham Junction......	43	..	..	1146	..	..	..	..	..	..	..	..	..	1156	1157		..	..	..			43
East Croydon .. arr	44	11 49	11 49	..	..	1152	1155	..	..	..	..	1154	..	..	..	..	..	..	..	..		44
East Croydon .. dep	45	11 49	11 49	..	..	1152	1155	..	..	..	..	1154	..	..	..	S O	..	..	..	S O		45
Norwood Junction F..	46	11 53	..	..	..	..	1158	..	..	1154	12 1	1157	..	..	..	1153	..	S O	..	1152		46
Beckenham Jn. dep	47	..	..	..	..	..	..	..	..	..	..	..	..	..	..	..	..	11 49	..	..		47
Birkbeck............	48	..	..	..	..	..	..	..	..	..	..	..	..	..	..	..	..	11 52	S O	..		48
Crystal Palace D......	49	..	..	..	..	..	..	..	..	..	..	..	..	..	..	..	..	11 56	1159	..		49
Gipsy Hill (for Upper	50	..	..	..	..	..	..	..	..	..	..	..	..	..	..	..	..	11 58	..	..	p.m	50
West Norwood.[N'wood)	51	..	..	..	..	..	..	..	..	..	..	..	..	..	..	..	..	12 1	..	..	S O	51
Streatham Hill.........	52	..	..	..	..	..	..	..	..	..	..	..	..	..	..	..	..	12 4	..	..	12 8	52
Selhurst..............	53	..	..	..	1152	1155	..	..	..	..	..	..	..	..	..	..	..	..	..	1155	..	53
Thornton Heath........	54	..	..	..	1154	1157	..	..	..	..	..	..	..	..	..	..	..	..	..	1157	..	54
Norbury..............	55	..	..	..	1157	12 0	..	..	..	..	..	..	..	..	..	..	..	..	..	12 0	..	55
Streatham Common....	56	..	..	..	1159	12 3	..	..	..	..	..	..	..	..	..	..	..	..	..	12 2	..	56
Anerley..............	57	..	..	..	..	..	..	..	..	1157	..	..	..	..	..	1156	..	..	..	..	..	57
Penge West C.........	58	..	..	..	..	..	..	From Victoria, dep. 11 47 a.m	From Victoria, dep. 11 56 a.m	1158	..	..	..	..	..	1157	..	..	..	..	..	58
Sydenham ....[Lane	59	..	..	..	..	..	..			12 0	..	..	..	..	..	1159	..	..	12 2	..	..	59
Forest Hill, for Lordship	60	..	..	..	..	..	..			12 3	..	..	..	..	..	12 2	..	..	12 5	..	..	60
Honor Oak Park........	61	..	..	..	..	..	..			12 5	..	..	..	..	..	12 4	..	..	12 7	..	..	61
Brockley B.......[Line)	62	..	..	..	..	..	..			12 8	..	..	..	..	..	12 7	..	..	1210	..	..	62
New Cross Gate (for E.L.	63	..	..	..	..	..	..			1210	..	..	..	..	..	12 9	..	..	1212	..	..	63
Streatham............	64	..	..	1151	..	..	..			..	..	..	..	..	..	..	..	..	..	12 5	..	64
Tulse Hill............	65	..	..	1155	..	..	..			..	..	..	..	..	..	..	..	..	..	12 8	..	65
North Dulwich.........	66	..	..	..	..	..	..			..	..	..	Via Worcester Park	..	..	..	..	..	..	..	..	66
East Dulwich..........	67	..	..	..	..	..	..	SX	S O	..	..	..		..	..	..	..	..	..	..	..	67
Peckham Rye..........	68	..	..	12 0	..	..	..	12 4	12 4	..	..	..		..	..	..	..	..	..	..	..	68
Queen's Road, Peckham	69	..	..	..	..	..	..	12 6	12 6	..	..	..		..	..	..	..	..	..	..	..	69
South Bermondsey.....	70	..	..	..	..	..	..	12 9	12 9	..	..	..		..	..	..	..	..	..	..	..	70
Balham & Upper Tooting	71	..	..	..	12 3	12 7	..	..	..	..	..	..		12 4	12 5	..	..	12 6	..	..	12 10	71
Wandsworth Common A	72	..	..	..	..	..	..	..	..	..	..	..		..	..	..	..	12 8	..	..	12 12	72
Clapham Junction.....	73	..	12 1	..	12 7	1211	..	..	..	..	..	..		12 8	12 9	..	..	12 11	..	..	12 17	73
Battersea Park........	74	..	..	..	..	..	..	..	..	..	..	..		..	..	..	..	12 14	..	..	12 20	74
London Bridge..... arr	75	12 5	..	12 7	..	..	1211	1213	1213	1216	1216	1210	..	..	..	1215	..	..	1218	1219	..	75
Waterloo *........ "	76	..	..	..	..	..	1215	..	..	..	..	..	12 3	..	..	..	..	..	..	..	..	76
Charing Cross*... "	77	..	..	..	..	..	1217	..	..	..	..	..	..	..	..	..	..	..	..	..	..	77
Victoria........... "	78	..	12 6	..	1214	1216	..	..	..	..	..	..	..	1214	1214	..	..	12 18	..	..	12 24	78

DORKING NORTH, SUTTON, CROYDON, CRYSTAL PALACE, and LONDON

Week Days—continued (a.m … a.m … p.m)

No. 1	3	3	3		3	3	3			3		3	3	3		3		3	3	3	3	3			3	3		3
2									1140																			
3									1150																			
4																												
5																					S X	S O						
6																					1143	1144						
7																					1146	1147						
8																					1149	1150						
9																					1153	1154						
10																					1156	1157						
11																					1158	1159						
12																					12 1	12 2						
13																					12 3	12 4						
14																					1153	1154						
15																					1157	1158						
16																					1159	12 0						
17																					12 2	12 3						
18										S O											12 5	12 6						
19										1151																		
20										1154											12 7	12 8						
21										1156											1210							
22										1159					1157			S O			1212							
23																		1138										
24							S O											1141										
25							1129																					
26							1132																					
27							1137											1146										
28							1141											1150	S O									
29							1145											1154	1157									
30							1148												12 0									
31						S O	1151												12 3									
32						1144						11 49																
33						1147						11 52	p.m	p.m														
34						1150						11 55	S X	S O														
35						1153	1155					11 58	12 2	12 3					12 6									
36						1155						12 0	12 5	12 5														
37						1158						12 3	12 8	12 8														
38					non	12 1						12 6		1211		From London Bridge via Streatham										From London Bridge via Streatham		
39		S X			S O	12 4						12 9		1214														
40		1155			12 0	12 4						12 9																
41							1158												12 9									
42							12 0												1211									
43							12 3										p.m		1214									
44									12 4	12 2					12 2	p.m	S X				1215	1214		S O				
45									12 5	12 2					12 2	S X	1212				1215	1214		1216		S O		
46	S X	1159			12 4	12 8									12 7	12 9					1218	1218				1213		S O
47	1150		p.m																									12 9
48	1153		S O																						S X			1212
49	1157	12 3	12 5		12 9																				1211			1216
50		12 6	12 8		1211																				1213			1218
51		12 8	1210		1214																				1216			1221
52		1211			1217																							1224
53										12 5		12 12																
54										12 7		12 14																
55										1210		12 17																
56										1212		12 19																
57																1212										1216		
58																1213										1217		
59																1215										1219		
60																1218										1222		
61																1220				From Victoria dep. 12 7 p.m						1224		
62																1223										1227		
63															1218	1225										1229		
64							12 8																					
65			1213				1211																		1218			
66			1216									J 1 minute later on Saturdays								p.m					1221			
67			1218																	S O					1223			
68			1221																	1224					1226			
69			1223															Via Worcester Park		1226					1228			
70			1226																	1229					1231			
71		1214			1219					1217		12 23							1220									1226
72		1216			1221																							1228
73		1219			1224				1216	1221		12 27					1226		1224					1230				1231
74		1222			1227																							1234
75			1230			1222	1222								1225	1231				1233	1231	1230			1235	1235		
76																		1223			1235							
77																					1237							
78		1226			1231				1221	1226		12J33					1233		1230					1237				1238

For Notes, see page 317a

HORSHAM, REIGATE, REDHILL, TATTENHAM CORNER, CATERHAM,

Up	No.	p.m.							Week Days—continued						p.m							No.
		3	3	S X	3	a.m	3	3	3		S O	3	3		3	3	3	3	3	3	a.m	
Horsham.........dep	1	..	..	1120	..	11§15	..	..	..	..	1122	..	..	..	..	..	..	..	..	..	1143	1
Reigate........ "	2	..	..	a.m	..	11 52	..	..	..	..	a.m	..	..	..	..	..	..	..	..	..	..	2
Redhill........ "	3	..	..	3	..	11 59	..	..	..	..	3	..	..	..	..	..	..	..	..	..	..	3
Merstham..........	4	..	..	..	..	12 3	..	..	..	..	..	..	..	..	..	..	..	..	..	..	..	4
Coulsdon South.........	5	..	..	..	..	12 9	..	..	..	..	..	..	..	..	S O	..	..	..	..	..	..	5
Tattenham Corner. dep	6	..	..	..	..	§ Via Three Bridges	..	..	..	..	..	..	..	..	12 4	..	..	..	..	..	..	6
Tadworth N..........	7	..	..	..	..		..	..	..	..	..	..	..	..	12 7	..	..	..	..	..	..	7
Kingswood M..........	8	..	..	..	..		..	..	..	..	..	..	..	..	1210	..	..	..	..	..	..	8
Chipstead..........	9	..	..	..	..		..	..	..	..	..	..	..	..	1214	..	..	..	..	..	..	9
Woodmansterne........	10	..	..	..	..		..	..	..	..	..	..	..	..	1217	..	..	..	..	..	..	10
Smitham..........	11	..	..	..	..		..	..	..	..	..	..	..	..	1219	..	..	..	..	..	..	11
Reedham..........	12	..	..	..	..		..	..	..	..	..	..	..	..	1222	..	..	..	..	..	..	12
Purley 252.........arr	13	..	..	..	..		..	..	..	..	..	..	..	..	1224	..	..	..	..	..	..	13
Caterham.........dep	14	..	..	..	..	..	..	..	..	..	..	..	..	..	1214	..	..	..	..	..	..	14
Warlingham..........	15	..	..	..	..	..	..	..	..	..	..	..	..	..	1218	..	..	..	..	..	..	15
Whyteleafe..........	16	..	..	..	..	..	..	..	..	..	..	..	..	..	1220	..	..	..	..	..	..	16
Kenley..........	17	..	..	..	..	..	..	..	..	..	..	..	..	..	1223	..	..	..	..	..	..	17
Purley 252.........arr	18	..	..	..	..	..	..	..	..	..	..	..	..	..	1226	..	..	..	..	..	..	18
Coulsdon North..... dep	19	..	..	..	..	..	..	12 11	..	..	..	..	..	..	..	..	..	..	..	..	..	19
Purley 252..........	20	..	..	..	..	12 13	..	12 14	..	..	..	..	..	..	1229	..	..	..	..	..	..	20
Purley Oaks..........	21	..	..	..	..	..	..	12 16	..	..	..	..	..	..	..	..	..	..	..	a.m	..	21
South Croydon 234.....	22	..	..	..	..	..	..	12 19	..	..	..	..	..	..	..	..	..	..	..	S O	..	22
Effingham Junction dep	23	..	..	..	..	..	..	..	..	..	..	..	..	..	..	..	..	..	..	1151	..	23
Bookham..........	24	..	..	..	..	..	..	..	..	..	..	..	..	..	..	..	..	..	..	1154	..	24
Dorking North..... dep	25	..	..	1146	..	..	..	..	..	..	1148	..	..	..	..	..	..	..	..	..	12 2	25
Boxhill and Burford	26	..	..	1148	..	..	..	..	..	..	1151	..	..	..	..	..	..	..	..	..	..	26
Leatherhead...[Bridge J	27	..	..	1153	..	..	..	..	..	..	1156	..	..	..	..	..	..	..	..	1159	..	27
Ashtead	28	..	..	1157	..	..	..	..	..	..	12 0	..	..	..	..	..	..	..	..	..	..	28
Epsom 427..........	29	..	..	12 1	..	..	..	..	..	..	12 5	..	..	..	..	..	..	..	..	..	..	29
Ewell East H..........	30	..	non	12 4	..	..	..	..	..	..	12 8	..	..	..	..	..	..	..	..	..	..	30
Cheam..........	31	..	S X	12 7	..	..	..	..	S O	..	1211	..	..	..	..	..	S O	..	..	..	..	31
Epsom Downs...... dep	32	..	12 0	..	From London Bridge, via Forest Hill	..	..	..	12 4	..	..	..	..	..	..	..	12 9	..	..	..	..	32
Banstead..........	33	..	12 3	..		..	..	..	12 7	..	..	..	..	..	..	..	1212	..	..	..	..	33
Belmont..........	34	..	12 6	..		..	..	..	1210	..	..	..	..	..	..	..	1215	..	..	..	..	34
Sutton 322..........	35	..	12 9	1210		..	..	..	1213	..	1214	..	..	..	..	..	1218	..	..	..	1220	35
Carshalton Beeches.....	36	..	1211	..		..	..	..	1215	..	..	..	..	..	..	..	1220	..	..	..	..	36
Wallington..........	37	..	1214	..		..	..	..	1218	..	..	..	..	..	..	..	1223	..	..	..	..	37
Waddon G..........	38	..	1217	..		..	..	..	1221	..	..	..	..	..	..	..	1226	..	..	..	..	38
West Croydon 319 arr	39	..	1220	..		..	..	..	1224	..	..	..	..	..	..	..	1229	..	SX	..	..	39
West Croydon 319 dep	40	..	1220	..		..	..	..	1224	..	..	..	..	..	..	..	1229	..	1225	..	..	40
Carshalton..........	41	..	..	1213		..	From London Bridge, via Tulse Hill	..	..	..	1217	..	..	..	..	..	..	..	..	..	..	41
Hackbridge..........	42	..	..	1216		..		..	..	..	1220	..	..	..	..	..	..	..	..	..	..	42
Mitcham Junction......	43	..	..	1218		..		..	..	..	1222	..	..	..	..	..	..	..	..	..	..	43
East Croydon .. arr	44	..	..	..	..	12 18		12 22	..	..	..	..	..	..	1234	..	..	..	..	..	..	44
East Croydon .. dep	45	..	..	..	S O	12 20		12 22	..	..	..	..	..	..	1234	..	..	..	..	..	..	45
Norwood Junction F..	46	..	1224	..	1212	12 24		..	1228	..	..	..	..	..	1238	..	..	S X	1229	..	..	46
Beckenham Jn. dep	47	..	..	..	..	..		..	..	..	..	..	..	..	..	..	..	1220	..	..	..	47
Birkbeck..........	48	S O	..	..	..	..		..	..	..	..	..	S O	..	..	..	..	1223	..	..	..	48
Crystal Palace D......	49	1219	..	..	..	..		..	..	..	..	..	1225	..	..	..	..	1227	1233	..	..	49
Gipsy Hill (for Upper	50	..	..	..	..	..		..	..	..	..	..	1228	..	..	..	..	..	1236	..	..	50
West Norwood.[N'wood)	51	..	..	..	..	..	S O	..	..	..	..	..	1230	..	..	..	..	..	1238	..	..	51
Streatham Hill........	52	..	..	..	..	..	1229	..	..	..	..	..	..	..	..	..	..	..	1241	..	..	52
Selhurst..........	53	..	..	..	1215	..	..	12 25	..	..	..	..	..	..	..	..	1232	..	..	..	..	53
Thornton Heath........	54	..	..	..	1217	..	..	12 27	..	..	..	..	..	..	..	..	1234	..	..	..	..	54
Norbury..........	55	..	..	..	1220	..	..	12 30	..	..	..	..	..	..	..	..	1237	..	..	..	..	55
Streatham Common....	56	..	..	..	1223	..	..	12 32	..	..	..	..	..	..	..	..	1239	..	..	..	..	56
Anerley..........	57	..	1227	..	..	..	..	..	..	..	..	..	..	..	..	..	..	..	..	..	..	57
Penge West C..........	58	..	1228	..	..	..	..	..	..	..	..	From Victoria, dep. 12 18 p.m	..	..	..	From Victoria, dep. 12 27 p.m	..	..	..	..	..	58
Sydenham ....[Lane	59	1222	1230	..	..	..	..	..	..	..	..		..	..	..		..	..	..	..	..	59
Forest Hill, for Lordship	60	1225	1233	..	..	..	..	..	..	..	..		..	..	..		..	..	..	..	..	60
Honor Oak Park........	61	1227	1235	..	..	..	..	..	..	..	..		..	..	..		..	..	..	..	..	61
Brockley B.......[Line)	62	1230	1238	..	..	..	..	..	..	..	..		..	..	..		..	..	..	..	..	62
New Cross Gate (for E.L.	63	1232	1240	..	..	..	..	..	..	..	..		..	..	..		..	..	..	..	..	63
Streatham..........	64	..	..	1224	1225	..	..	..	..	..	1228		..	..	..		..	..	..	..	..	64
Tulse Hill...	65	..	..	1227	1228	..	..	..	..	..	1231		1233	..	..		..	..	..	..	..	65
North Dulwich..........	66	..	..	..	..	..	..	..	..	..	..	..	1236	..	..	..	..	..	..	..	..	66
East Dulwich..........	67	..	..	..	..	..	..	..	..	..	..	S X	1238	..	..	S O	..	..	..	..	..	67
Peckham Rye..........	68	..	..	1232	..	..	..	..	..	..	..	1235	1241	..	..	1244	..	..	..	..	..	68
Queen's Road, Peckham	69	..	..	..	..	..	..	..	..	..	..	1237	1243	..	..	1246	..	..	..	..	..	69
South Bermondsey......	70	..	..	..	..	..	..	..	..	..	..	1240	1246	..	..	1249	..	..	..	..	..	70
Balham & Upper Tooting	71	..	..	..	..	..	1232	12 36	..	..	..	..	..	..	..	..	1243	..	1244	..	..	71
Wandsworth Common A	72	..	..	..	..	..	1234	12SX38	..	..	..	..	..	..	..	..	..	..	1246	..	..	72
Clapham Junction.....	73	..	..	..	..	..	1237	12 41	..	..	..	..	..	..	..	..	1247	..	1249	..	..	73
Battersea Park........	74	..	..	..	..	..	1240	..	..	..	..	..	..	..	..	..	..	..	1252	..	..	74
London Bridge..... arr	75	1238	1246	1238	1239	12 38	..	..	1241	..	1242	1244	1250	..	1250	1253	..	..	..	..	..	75
Waterloo *........ "	76	..	..	..	..	..	..	..	..	..	..	..	..	..	..	..	..	..	..	..	..	76
Charing Cross *.. "	77	..	..	..	..	..	..	..	..	..	..	..	..	..	..	..	..	..	..	..	..	77
Victoria.......... "	78	..	..	..	..	..	1244	12 47	..	..	..	..	..	..	..	..	1254	..	1256	..	1240	78

DORKING NORTH, SUTTON, CROYDON, CRYSTAL PALACE, and LONDON

p.m — **Week Days**—*continued* — p.m

No.	3	3	3	3	3	..	3	3	..	3	3	..	3	3	3	3	3	..	3	..	3	3	3	3	3	a.m	3	3
1	..	..	..	..	..	..	..	..	..	..	..	..	..	..	..	..	..	..	..	..	..	..	..	..	..	11§48	..	..
2	..	..	..	..	..	..	..	..	..	..	..	..	..	..	..	..	..	..	..	..	..	..	..	..	..	12‖23	..	..
3	..	..	..	..	..	..	..	..	..	..	..	..	..	..	..	..	..	..	..	..	..	..	..	..	..	12 30	..	..
4	..	..	..	..	..	..	..	..	..	..	..	..	..	..	..	..	..	..	..	..	..	..	..	..	..	12 34	..	..
5	..	..	..	..	..	..	..	..	..	..	..	..	..	..	..	..	..	..	..	..	..	..	..	..	..	12 40	..	S X
6	..	..	..	..	..	..	..	..	..	..	..	..	..	..	..	..	..	..	..	..	..	..	..	..	..	§ Via Three Bridges	..	1223
7	..	..	..	..	..	..	..	..	..	..	..	..	..	..	..	..	..	..	..	..	..	..	..	..	..		..	1226
8	..	..	..	..	..	..	..	..	..	..	..	..	..	..	..	..	..	..	..	..	..	..	..	..	..		..	1229
9	..	..	..	..	..	..	..	..	..	..	..	..	..	..	..	..	..	..	..	..	..	..	..	..	..		..	1233
10	..	..	..	..	..	..	..	..	..	..	..	..	..	..	..	..	..	..	..	..	..	..	..	..	..		..	1236
11	..	..	..	..	..	..	..	..	..	..	..	..	..	..	..	..	..	..	..	..	..	..	..	..	..		..	1238
12	..	..	..	..	..	..	..	..	..	..	..	..	..	..	..	..	..	..	..	..	..	..	..	..	..		..	1241
13	..	..	..	..	..	..	..	..	..	..	..	..	..	..	..	..	..	..	..	..	..	..	..	..	..		..	1243
14	..	..	..	..	..	..	..	..	..	..	..	..	..	..	..	..	..	..	..	..	..	..	..	..	..	..	..	1233
15	..	..	..	..	..	..	..	..	..	..	..	..	..	..	..	..	..	..	..	..	..	..	..	..	..	..	..	1237
16	..	..	..	..	..	..	..	..	..	..	..	..	..	..	..	..	..	..	..	..	..	..	..	..	..	..	..	1239
17	..	..	..	..	..	..	..	..	..	..	..	..	..	..	..	..	..	..	..	..	..	..	..	..	..	..	..	1242
18	..	..	..	..	..	..	..	..	..	..	..	..	..	..	..	..	..	..	S O	..	..	..	S O	..	..	..	S X	1245
19	..	..	..	..	..	..	..	..	..	..	..	..	..	..	..	..	..	..	1231	..	..	..	1236	..	..	..	1241	..
20	..	..	..	..	..	..	..	..	..	..	..	..	..	..	..	..	..	..	1234	..	..	..	1239	..	..	12 44	1244	1247
21	a.m	..	..	..	..	..	..	..	..	..	..	..	..	..	..	..	..	..	1236	..	..	..	1242	..	..	..	1246	1250
22	S X	..	..	..	..	..	..	..	..	..	..	..	..	..	..	..	..	..	1239	..	..	..	1244	..	S X	..	1249	1252
23	1155	..	..	..	..	..	..	..	..	..	..	..	..	..	..	..	S O	..	..	..	..	..	..	..	1213	..	..	..
24	1158	..	..	..	..	..	..	..	..	..	..	..	..	S O	..	..	1213	..	..	..	..	..	..	..	1216	..	..	..
25	..	..	..	..	..	..	..	..	..	..	..	..	..	12 8	..	..	..	..	..	..	..	..	..	..	..	L 3 minutes *earlier* on Saturdays.	..	..
26	..	..	..	..	..	..	..	..	..	..	..	..	..	..	..	..	..	..	..	..	..	..	..	..	..		..	..
27	12 2	..	..	..	..	..	..	..	..	..	..	..	..	1214	..	..	1217	..	..	..	..	..	..	..	1220		..	..
28	12 6	..	..	..	..	..	..	..	..	..	..	..	..	..	..	..	1221	..	..	..	..	..	..	..	1224		..	..
29	1214	..	12 17	..	..	..	..	..	..	..	..	..	..	1220	..	..	1225	..	..	..	..	..	..	..	1228		..	..
30	..	..	12 20	..	..	..	..	..	..	..	..	..	..	1223	..	..	1228	..	..	..	..	..	..	..	1231		..	..
31	..	..	12 23	..	..	..	..	..	..	..	..	..	S X	1226	..	S O	1231	..	..	..	..	..	..	S O	1234		..	..
32	Arr. Epsom 12 10 p.m	..	..	..	..	..	..	..	..	..	..	..	1219	..	..	1224	..	..	..	..	..	..	..	1229	..		..	..
33		..	..	From London Bridge, via Forest Hill	From London Bridge, via Streatham	..	..	..	..	..	From London Bridge, via Forest Hill	..	1222	..	..	1227	..	..	..	..	..	..	..	1232	..		..	..
34		S O	..			..	..	..	..	..		..	1225	..	S X	1230	..	—	..	..	..	..	..	1235	..		..	..
35		1222	12 26			..	..	..	..	..		..	1228	1229	1232	1233	1235	..	..	..	..	..	..	1238	1238	..	..	..
36		1225	..			..	..	..	..	..		..	1230	..	1234	1235	..	..	..	..	..	..	..	1240	..	..	..	..
37		1227	..			..	..	..	..	..		..	1233	1233	1237	1238	..	..	..	..	..	..	..	1243	..	..	..	..
38		..	..			..	..	..	..	..		..	1236	..	..	1241	..	..	..	..	..	..	..	1246	..	..	..	..
39		1233	..			..	..	..	..	..		..	1239	1238	..	1244	..	..	..	..	..	S O	..	1249	..	..	..	..
40		..	..			..	..	..	..	..		..	1239	1238	..	1244	..	..	..	..	..	1240	..	1249	..	..	..	..
41	..	..	12 29			..	..	..	..	..		..	..	..	..	..	1238	..	..	..	..	..	..	..	1241	..	..	..
42	..	..	12‖32			..	..	..	..	..		..	..	..	..	..	1240	..	..	..	..	..	..	..	1244	..	..	..
43	..	..	12 34			..	..	..	..	..		..	..	..	..	..	1243	..	..	..	..	..	..	..	1246	..	..	..
44	..	..	‖ 1 minute *earlier* on Saturdays			..	..	..	..	..	..	..	..	..	..	..	..	..	1242	S O	..	..	1247	..	..	12 49	1252	1255
45	..	..		S X	S O	..	..	..	..	..	S O	..	..	..	..	..	..	..	1242	1247	..	..	1247	..	..	12 51	1252	1255
46	..	..		1229	1233	..	..	S O	..	..	1232	..	..	1242	..	1248	..	..	..	..	..	1244	1251	..	..	..	..	1258
47	..	..		..	..	..	..	1229	..	..	..	..	..	..	..	..	..	..	..	..	..	..	..	..	..	..	..	..
48	..	..		..	..	..	S X	1232	..	S O	..	..	..	..	..	..	..	..	..	..	S O	..	..	..	..	..	..	..
49	..	..		..	..	..	1238	1236	..	1239	..	..	..	..	..	..	..	..	..	..	1245	1249	..	..	..	..	..	..
50	..	..		..	..	..	..	1238	..	..	..	..	..	..	..	..	..	..	..	..	1248	1251	..	..	..	..	..	..
51	..	..		..	..	..	..	1241	..	..	..	..	..	..	..	..	..	..	..	..	1250	1254	..	..	..	..	..	..
52	..	..		..	..	..	..	1244	..	..	..	..	..	..	..	..	..	..	..	..	..	1257	..	..	..	..	..	..
53	..	..		1232	..	..	..	..	..	..	1235	..	1242	..	..	..	..	..	1245	..	..	..	..	1252	..	..	1255	..
54	..	..		1234	..	..	..	..	..	..	1237	..	1244	..	..	..	..	..	1247	..	..	..	..	1254	..	..	1257	..
55	..	..		1237	..	..	..	..	..	..	1240	..	1247	..	..	..	..	..	1250	..	..	..	..	1257	..	..	1 0	..
56	..	..	..	1240	..	..	..	..	..	..	1243	..	1249	..	..	..	..	..	1252	..	..	..	..	1259	..	..	1 2	..
57	..	..	..	..	1236	..	..	..	..	..	..	..	..	..	..	..	..	..	..	..	..	..	..	..	..	..	..	..
58	..	..	..	..	1237	..	..	..	..	..	..	..	..	..	..	..	..	..	..	..	..	..	..	..	..	..	..	..
59	..	..	..	..	1239	..	1241	..	..	1242	..	..	..	..	..	..	..	..	..	..	..	..	..	..	..	..	..	..
60	..	..	..	..	1242	..	1244	..	..	1245	..	..	..	1249	..	..	..	..	..	..	..	..	..	..	..	..	..	..
61	..	..	..	..	1244	..	1246	..	..	1247	..	..	..	..	..	..	..	..	..	..	..	..	..	..	..	..	..	..
62	..	..	..	..	1247	..	1249	..	..	1250	..	..	..	..	..	..	..	..	..	..	..	..	..	..	..	..	..	..
63	..	..	..	..	1249	..	1251	..	..	1252	..	..	..	1255	..	..	..	..	..	..	..	..	1 0	..	..	..	..	..
64	..	..	..	1242	..	..	..	..	..	..	1245	..	..	..	..	..	1248	..	..	..	..	..	..	..	1251	..	..	..
65	..	..	..	1245	..	..	..	..	..	..	1248	..	..	..	..	..	1251	..	..	..	1253	..	..	..	1255	..	..	..
66	Via Worcester Park	..	..	1248	..	..	..	..	..	..	..	..	..	..	..	..	..	..	..	..	1256	..	..	..	..	..	..	..
67		..	..	1250	..	..	..	..	..	..	..	..	..	..	..	..	..	..	..	..	1258	..	..	..	..	..	..	..
68		..	..	1253	..	..	..	..	..	..	..	..	..	..	..	..	..	..	..	..	1 1	..	..	..	1 0	..	..	..
69		..	..	1255	..	..	..	..	..	..	..	..	..	..	..	..	..	..	..	..	1 3	..	..	..	..	..	..	..
70		..	..	1258	..	..	..	..	..	..	..	..	..	..	..	..	..	..	..	..	1 6	..	..	..	..	..	..	..
71		..	12‖41	..	..	..	..	1246	..	..	..	..	1253	..	..	..	..	..	1256	..	..	1259	..	1 3	..	..	1 6	..
72		..	..	..	..	..	..	1248	..	..	..	..	..	..	..	..	..	..	..	..	..	1 1	..	..	..	..	..	..
73		..	12‖45	..	..	..	..	1251	..	..	..	..	1257	..	..	..	..	..	1 1	..	..	1 4	..	1 7	..	1 2	1 10	..
74		..	..	..	..	..	..	1254	..	..	..	..	..	..	..	..	..	..	..	..	..	1 7	..	..	..	..	..	..
75	..	..	..	1 2	1255	..	1257	..	..	1258	1259	..	..	1 0	..	1 4	1 2	..	..	..	1 10	..	1 6	..	1 7	..	..	1 11
76	1242	..	..	..	..	..	..	..	..	..	..	..	..	..	..	..	..	..	..	..	..	..	..	..	..	..	..	1 15
77	..	..	..	..	..	..	..	..	..	..	..	..	..	..	..	..	..	..	..	..	..	..	..	..	..	..	..	1 17
78	..	..	12 50	..	..	..	..	1258	..	..	..	..	1 3	..	..	..	..	..	1 7	1 3	..	1 11	..	1 14	..	1 8	1 16	..

HORSHAM, REIGATE, REDHILL, TATTENHAM CORNER, CATERHAM,

For Notes, see page 317a

Up	No.	p.m					Week Days—*continued*										p.m					No.
		3	3	3	3	3		3	3	3		a.m	3	3	3			3	3	3		3	
Horsham dep	1											1152				12§15							1
Reigate "	2															12 41							2
Redhill "	3											3				12 50							3
Merstham	4																						4
Coulsdon South	5	S O														§ Via Three Bridges							5
Tattenham Corner dep	6	1224																					6
Tadworth N	7	1227																					7
Kingswood M	8	1230																					8
Chipstead	9	1234																					9
Woodmansterne	10	1237																					10
Smitham	11	1239																					11
Reedham	12	1242																					12
Purley 252 arr	13	1244																					13
Caterham dep	14	1234																					14
Warlingham	15	1238																					15
Whyteleafe	16	1240																					16
Kenley	17	1243																					17
Purley 252 arr	18	1246																S O				S O	18
Coulsdon North dep	19																	1251				1256	19
Purley 252	20	1249																1254				1259	20
Purley Oaks	21																	1256				1 2	21
South Croydon 234	22																	1259				1 4	22
Effingham Junction dep	23																						23
Bookham	24														S O								24
Dorking North dep	25											1218			1229								25
Boxhill and Burford	26											1221			1232								26
Leatherhead...[Bridge J	27											1226			1237								27
Ashtead	28											1230			1241								28
Epsom 427	29											1234	1240		1245								29
Ewell East **H**	30												1243		1248								30
Cheam	31					S X							1246	S O	1251								31
Epsom Downs dep	32					1230								1244									32
Banstead	33		From London Bridge, via Streatham			1233								1247									33
Belmont	34					1236			S O	From London Bridge, via Forest Hill				1250									34
Sutton 322	35					1239			1240				1249	1253	1255								35
Carshalton Beeches	36					1241			1244					1255									36
Wallington	37					1244			1247					1258									37
Waddon **G**	38					1247			1251					1 1									38
West Croydon 319 arr	39					1250			1254					1 4						S X			39
West Croydon 319 dep	40				From Victoria, via Wandsworth Common	1250			—					1 4						1255			40
Carshalton	41								Stop				1252		1258								41
Hackbridge	42												1254		1 0								42
Mitcham Junction	43												1257		1 3								43
East Croydon arr	44	1255														1 4		1 2				1 7	44
East Croydon dep	45	1255	S O						p.m	S O						1 5		1 2				1 7	45
Norwood Junction F	46	1258	1253			1254		S O	3	1252				1 8					S X	1259		1 11	46
Beckenham Jn. dep	47							1249											1250				47
Birkbeck	48							1252	S O										1253				48
Crystal Palace D	49							1256	1259										1257	1 3			49
Gipsy Hill (for Upper	50							1258												1 6			50
West Norwood. [N'wood)	51				S O			1 1												1 8			51
Streatham Hill	52				1258			1 4												1 11			52
Selhurst	53									1255								1 5					53
Thornton Heath	54									1257								1 7					54
Norbury	55									1 0								1 10					55
Streatham Common	56									1 3								1 12					56
Anerley	57		1256			1257																	57
Penge West **C**	58		1257			1258																	58
Sydenham [Lane	59		1259	From Victoria dep. 12 47 p.m		1 0			1 2														59
Forest Hill, for Lordship	60		1 2			1 3			1 5														60
Honor Oak Park	61		1 4			1 5			1 7														61
Brockley **B** [Line)	62		1 7			1 8			1 10														62
New Cross Gate (for E.L.	63		1 9			1 10			1 12													1 20	63
Streatham	64									1 5					1 8								64
Tulse Hill	65				1 1					1 8					1 11								65
North Dulwich	66				1 4							Via Worcester Park											66
East Dulwich	67				1 6																		67
Peckham Rye	68			1 4	1 8										1 16								68
Queen's Road, Peckham	69			1 6	1 10																		69
South Bermondsey	70			1 9	1 13																		70
Balham & Upper Tooting	71							1 6					1 4					1 16		1 14			71
Wandsworth Commo.. **A**	72							1 8												1 16			72
Clapham Junction	73							1 11					1 8			1 16		1 20		1 19			73
Battersea Park	74							1 14												1 22			74
LONDON BRIDGE arr	75	1 11	1 15	1 13	1 17	1 16			1 18	1 19				1 22	1 22							1 26	75
WATERLOO * "	76											1 3											76
CHARING CROSS * "	77																						77
VICTORIA "	78							1 18					1 13			1 21		1 27		1 26			78

DORKING NORTH, SUTTON, CROYDON, CRYSTAL PALACE, and LONDON

Week Days—*continued* (p.m)

No.	3	3	3	3	3	3	3	3	3	3	3	3			3	3	3	3	3		3	3			3		3
1													..	12§15						SX 1220			SO 1220	..		SO 12§43	
2	..	..	..	..	..	..	..	..	..	..	..	..	..	12 52	..	..	..	..	..	3	..	..	3	..	..	..	..
3	..	..	..	..	..	..	..	..	..	..	..	..	..	12 59	..	..	..	..	..		..	..		..	..	1 9	..
4	..	..	..	..	..	..	..	..	..	..	..	..	..	1 3	..	..	..	..	..	..	..	..	..	..	..	..	..
5	..	..	..	SX	SO	..	..	..	..	..	..	..	..	1 9	..	..	..	..	..	..	..	..	..	..	..	..	..
6	..	..	..	1243	1244	..	..	..	..	..	..	..	..		..	..	..	..	..	..	..	..	..	..	..		..
7	..	..	..	1246	1247	..	..	..	..	..	..	..	..		..	..	..	..	..	..	..	..	..	..	..		..
8	..	..	..	1249	1250	..	..	..	..	..	..	..	..		..	..	..	..	..	..	..	..	..	..	..		..
9	..	..	..	1253	1254	..	..	..	..	..	..	..	..	§ Via Three Bridges	..	..	..	..	..	..	..	..	..	..	..	§ Via Three Bridges	..
10	..	..	..	1256	1257	..	..	..	..	..	..	..	..		..	..	..	..	..	..	..	..	..	..	..		..
11	..	..	..	1258	1259	..	..	..	..	..	..	..	..		..	..	..	..	..	..	..	..	..	..	..		..
12	..	..	..	1 1	1 2	..	..	..	..	..	..	..	..		..	..	..	..	..	..	..	..	..	..	..		..
13	..	..	..	1 3	1 4	..	..	..	..	..	..	..	..		..	..	..	..	..	..	..	..	..	..	..		..
14	..	..	..	1253	1254	..	..	..	..	..	..	..	..	..	..	..	..	..	..	..	..	..	..	..	..	..	..
15	..	..	..	1257	1258	..	..	..	..	..	..	..	..	..	..	..	..	..	..	..	..	..	..	..	..	..	..
16	..	..	..	1259	1 0	..	..	..	..	..	..	..	..	..	..	..	..	..	..	..	..	..	..	..	..	..	..
17	..	..	..	1 2	1 3	..	..	..	..	..	..	..	..	..	..	..	..	..	..	..	..	..	..	..	..	..	..
18	..	..	..	1 5	1 6	..	..	..	..	..	..	..	..	..	..	..	..	..	..	..	..	..	..	..	..	..	..
19	..	..	..	..	..	..	..	..	..	..	..	..	..	..	..	..	..	..	..	..	..	..	..	..	1 11	..	..
20	..	..	..	1 7	1 9	..	..	..	..	..	..	..	..	1 13	..	..	..	..	..	..	..	..	..	..	1 14	..	..
21	..	..	..	1 10	..	..	..	..	..	..	..	..	..	..	..	..	..	..	..	..	..	..	..	..	1 16	..	..
22	..	..	..	1 12	..	..	..	..	..	..	SO	..	..	..	..	..	..	..	..	..	..	..	..	..	1 19	..	..
23	..	..	..	..	..	..	..	..	..	..	1238	..	..	..	..	..	..	..	..	..	..	..	..	..	..	..	..
24	..	..	..	..	..	..	..	..	..	..	1241	..	..	..	..	..	..	..	..	..	..	..	..	..	..	..	..
25	..	..	..	..	..	..	..	..	..	..	..	..	..	..	..	..	..	..	..	1246	..	..	1248	..	..	..	..
26	..	..	..	..	..	..	..	..	..	..	..	..	..	..	..	..	..	..	..	1248	..	..	1251	..	..	..	..
27	..	..	..	..	..	..	..	..	..	..	1246	..	..	..	..	..	..	..	..	1253	..	..	1256	..	..	..	..
28	..	..	..	..	..	..	..	..	..	..	1250	SO	..	..	..	..	..	..	..	1257	..	..	1 0	..	..	..	..
29	..	..	..	..	..	..	..	..	..	..	1254	1257	..	..	..	..	..	..	..	1 2	..	..	1 4	..	..	..	..
30	..	..	..	..	..	..	..	..	..	..	..	1 0	..	..	..	..	..	..	..	1 5	..	..	1 7	..	..	..	..
31	..	..	..	..	..	..	..	..	..	..	..	1 3	..	..	..	..	..	..	SX	1 8	..	SO	1 10	..	..	..	..
32	..	..	..	..	..	..	..	1249	..	..	..	..	..	..	..	..	..	..	1 0	..	..	1 4	..	..	..	..	..
33	..		..	..	..	..		1252	..	..	..	..	..	..	..	..	..	..	1 3	..	..	1 7	..	..		..	..
34	..		..	..	..	..		1255	SX	SO	..	..	..	..	..	..	..		1 6	..	..	1 10	..	..		..	..
35	..		..	..	..	..		1258	1 2	1 3	..	1 6	..	..	..	..	..		1 9	1 11	..	1 13	1 14	..		..	..
36	..		..	..	..	..		1 0	1 4	1 5	..	..	..	..	..	..	..		1 11	..	..	1 15	..	..		..	..
37	..		..	..	..	..		1 3	1 7	1 8	..	..	..	..	..	..	..		1 14	..	..	1 18	..	..		..	..
38	..	From London Bridge, via Streatham	..	..	..	..	From London Bridge, via Streatham	1 6	..	1 11	..	..	..	..	..	..	..		1 17	..	..	1 21	..	..	H 1 minute *earlier* on Saturdays	..	..
39	..		SO	..	..	..		1 9	..	1 14	..	..	..	..	..	..	..	From London Bridge, via Forest Hill	1 20	..	..	1 24	..	..		..	..
40	..		1 0	..	..	..		1 9	..	..	..	..	..	..	..	..	..		1 20	..	..	1 24	..	..		..	..
41	..		..	..	..	..		..	..	..	..	1 9	..	..	..	..	..		..	1 14	..	..	1 17	..		..	..
42	..		..	..	..	..		..	..	..	..	1 12	..	..	..	..	..		..	1 16	..	..	1 20	..		..	..
43	..		..	..	..	..		..	..	..	..	1 14	..	..	..	..	..		..	1 19	..	..	1 22	..		..	..
44	..		..	1 15	1 14	..		..	..	..	..	..	..	1 18	..	..	..		..	..	..	..	..	..	..	..	..
45	..	SX	..	1 15	1 14	..	SO	..	..	..	..	..	..	1 20	..	..	..	SO	..	..	..	..	..	..	1 22	1 23	..
46	..	1 12	1 4	1 18	1 18	..	1 13	..	..	..	..	..	1 15	1 24	..	SO	..	1 12	1 24	..	..	1 28	..	..	1 22	1 25	..
47	..	..	..	..	..	..	..	..	..	..	..	..	..	..	..	1 9	..	..	..	..	..	..	..	..	..	..	..
48	..	..	..	..	..	SX	..	..	..	..	..	..	..	..	SO	1 12	SO	..	..	..	..	..	..	..	..	..	SO
49	..	..	1 9	..	..	1 11	..	..	..	..	..	..	..	..	1 12	1 16	1 19	..	..	..	..	..	..	..	..	..	1 26
50	..	..	1 11	..	..	1 13	..	..	..	..	..	..	..	..	1 15	1 18	..	..	..	..	..	..	..	..	..	..	1 28
51	..	..	1 14	..	..	1 16	..	..	..	..	..	..	..	..	1 18	1 21	..	..	..	..	..	..	..	..	..	..	1 31
52	..	..	1 17	..	..	..	..	..	..	..	..	..	..	..	..	1 24	..	..	..	..	..	..	..	..	..	..	..
53	..	..	..	..	..	..	..	1 12	..	..	..	..	..	..	..	..	..	1 15	..	..	..	..	..	..	1 25	..	..
54	..	..	..	..	..	..	..	1 14	..	..	..	..	..	..	..	..	..	1 17	..	..	..	..	..	..	1 27	..	..
55	..	..	..	..	..	..	..	1 17	..	..	..	..	..	..	..	..	..	1 20	..	..	..	..	..	..	1 30	..	..
56	..	..	..	..	..	..	..	1 19	..	..	..	..	..	..	..	..	..	1 23	..	..	..	..	..	..	1J32	..	..
57		1 14	..	..	..	..	1 16	..	..	..	..	..	..	..	..	..	..	..	1 27	..		..	..	..	..	..	..
58		1 16	..	..	..	..	1 17	..	..	..	..	..	..	..	..	..	..	..	1 28	..		..	..	..	..	..	..
59		1 18	..	..	..	..	1 19	..	..	..	..	..	..	..	..	..	1 22	..	1 30	..		..	..	..		..	..
60		1 20	..	..	..	..	1 22	..	..	..	..	..	..	..	..	..	1 25	..	1 33	..		..	..	..		..	..
61	From Victoria, dep. 1 7 p.m	1 23	..	..	..	..	1 24	..	..	..	..	..	..	..	..	..	1 27	..	1 35	..	From Victoria, dep. 1 18 p.m	..	..	..		..	..
62		1 25	..	..	..	..	1 27	..	..	..	..	..	..	..	..	..	1 30	..	1 38	..		..	..	..		..	..
63		1 28	..	..	..	..	1 29	..	..	..	..	..	..	..	..	..	1 32	..	1 40	..		..	..	..		..	..
64		..	..	..	..	..	..	..	..	..		..	..	..	..	..	..	1 25	..	1 24		..	1 28	..		..	..
65		..	..	..	..	1 18	..	..	..	..		..	..	..	1 21	..	..	1 28	..	1 27		..	1 31	..	J 1 minute later on Saturdays	..	1 33
66		..	..	..	..	1 21	..	..	..	..		..	..	..	1 24	..	..	..	..	..		..	..	..		..	1 36
67	SO	..	..	..	..	1 23	..	..	..	..		..	..	..	1 26	..	..	..	..	..	SX	..	..	..		..	1 38
68	1 22	..	..	..	..	1 26	..	..	..	..		..	..	..	1 28	..	..	..	..	1 32	1 35	..	..	..		..	1 41
69	1 24	..	..	..	..	1 28	..	..	..	..	Via Worcester Park	..	..	..	1 30	..	..	..	..	..	1 37	..	..	..		..	1 43
70	1 27	..	..	..	..	1 31	..	..	..	..		..	..	..	1 33	..	..	..	..	..	1 40	..	..	..		..	1 46
71	..	..	1 19	..	..	..	..	1 23	..	..		1 21	..	..	..	1 26	..	..	..	..	..	..	..	..	1J36	..	..
72	..	..	1 21	..	..	..	..	..	..	..		..	..	..	..	1 28	..	..	..	..	..	..	..	..	1SX38	..	..
73	..	..	1 24	..	..	..	..	1 27	..	..		1 25	1 29	..	..	1 31	..	..	..	..	..	..	..	..	1 41	..	..
74	..	..	1 27	..	..	..	..	..	..	..		..	..	..	..	1 34	..	..	..	..	..	..	..	..	1SX44	..	..
75	1 32	1 36	..	1 31	1 30	1 35	1 35	..	..	..	..	..	..	1 36	1 37	..	1 38	1 39	1 46	1 38	1 44	1 41	1 42	..	..	..	1 50
76	..	..	..	1 35	..	..	..	..	..	..	1 22	..	..	..	..	..	..	..	..	..	..	..	..	..	..	..	..
77	..	..	..	1 37	..	..	..	..	..	..	..	..	..	..	..	..	..	..	..	..	..	..	..	..	..	..	..
78	..	..	1 31	..	..	..	..	1 33	..	..	..	1 31	1 36	..	..	1 38	..	..	..	..	..	..	..	..	1H47	1 40	..

HORSHAM, REIGATE, REDHILL, TATTENHAM CORNER, CATERHAM,

For Notes, see page 317a

Up	No.	p.m							Week Days—continued									p.m					No.
		3	3	3	3	3	3	3	3		3	3	3	3	3	3	3			3		3	
Horsham .... dep	1																	..	..		..		1
Reigate .... "	2	..	..	..	..	..	..	..	..	..	..	..	..	..	..	..	..	..	..	..	..	..	2
Redhill .... "	3	..	..	..	..	..	..	..	..	..	..	..	..	..	..	..	..	..	..	..	..	..	3
Merstham	4	..	..	..	..	..	..	..	..	..	..	..	..	..	..	..	..	..	..	..	..	..	4
Coulsdon South	5	..	S O	..	..	..	..	..	..	..	..	..	..	..	..	..	..	..	..	..	..	..	5
Tattenham Corner dep	6	..	1 5	..	..	..	..	..	..	..	..	..	..	..	..	..	..	..	..	..	..	..	6
Tadworth **N**	7	..	1 8	..	..	..	..	..	..	..	..	..	..	..	..	..	..	..	..	..	..	..	7
Kingswood **M**	8	..	1 11	..	..	..	..	..	..	..	..	..	..	..	..	..	..	..	..	..	..	..	8
Chipstead	9	..	1 15	..	..	..	..	..	..	..	..	..	..	..	..	..	..	..	..	..	..	..	9
Woodmansterne	10	..	1 18	..	..	..	..	..	..	..	..	..	..	..	..	..	..	..	..	..	..	..	10
Smitham	11	..	1 20	..	..	..	..	..	..	..	..	..	..	..	..	..	..	..	..	..	..	..	11
Reedham	12	..	1 23	..	..	..	..	..	..	..	..	..	..	..	..	..	..	..	..	..	..	..	12
Purley 252 .... arr	13	..	1 25	..	..	..	..	..	..	..	..	..	..	..	..	..	..	..	..	..	..	..	13
Caterham .... dep	14	..	1 15	..	..	..	..	..	..	..	..	..	..	..	..	..	..	..	..	..	..	..	14
Warlingham	15	..	1 19	..	..	..	..	..	..	..	..	..	..	..	..	..	..	..	..	..	..	..	15
Whyteleafe	16	..	1 21	..	..	..	..	..	..	..	..	..	..	..	..	..	..	..	..	..	..	..	16
Kenley	17	..	1 24	..	..	..	..	..	..	..	..	..	..	..	..	..	..	..	..	..	..	..	17
Purley 252 .... arr	18	..	1 27	..	..	..	..	..	..	..	..	..	..	..	..	..	..	..	..	..	..	..	18
Coulsdon North ..... dep	19	..	..	..	..	..	..	..	..	..	..	..	..	..	..	..	..	..	..	..	..	..	19
Purley 252	20	..	1 29	..	..	..	..	..	..	..	..	..	..	..	..	..	..	..	..	..	..	..	20
Purley Oaks	21	..	..	..	..	..	..	..	..	..	..	..	..	..	..	..	..	..	..	..	..	..	21
South Croydon 234	22	..	..	..	..	..	S O	S X	..	..	..	..	..	..	..	..	..	..	..	..	..	..	22
Effingham Junction dep	23	..	..	..	..	..	1252	1255	..	..	..	..	..	..	..	..	..	..	..	..	..	..	23
Bookham	24	..	..	..	..	..	1255	1258	S O	..	..	..	..	..	..	..	..	..	..	..	..	..	24
Dorking North ...... dep	25	..	..	..	..	..	..	..	1258	..	..	..	..	..	..	..	..	..	..	..	..	..	25
Boxhill and Burford	26	..	..	..	..	..	..	..	1 1	..	..	..	..	..	..	..	..	..	..	..	..	..	26
Leatherhead ...[Bridge **J**	27	..	..	..	..	..	1 0	1 2	1 6	..	..	..	..	..	..	..	..	..	..	..	..	..	27
Ashtead	28	..	..	..	S X	..	..	1 6	1 10	..	S O	..	..	..	..	..	..	..	..	..	..	..	28
Epsom 427	29	..	..	..	1 10	..	..	1 14	1 14	..	1 17	..	..	..	..	..	..	..	..	..	..	..	29
Ewell East **H**	30	..	..	..	1 13	..	..		..	..	1 20	..	..	..	..	..	..	..	..	..	..	..	30
Cheam	31	..	..	S O	1 16	..	..		..	..	1 23	..	..	..	..	..	..	..	..	..	..	S X	31
Epsom Downs ...... dep	32	..	..	1 9	..	..	..		..	..	..	..	..	..	..	..	..	..	..	..	..	1 19	32
Banstead	33	..	..	1 12	..	..	..		..	..	..	..	..	..	..	..	..	..	..	..	..	1 22	33
Belmont	34	..	..	1 15	..	S O	..		..	..	..	..	..	..				..	..	..	..	1 25	34
Sutton 322	35	..	..	1 18	1 20	1 22	..	Arr. Epsom 1 10 p.m	..	..	1 26	..	..	..				..	..	..	..	1 28	35
Carshalton Beeches	36	..	..	1 20	..	1 25	..		..	..	..	..	..	..				..	..	..	..	1 30	36
Wallington	37	..	..	1 23	..	1 27	..		..	..	..	..	..	..				..	..	..	..	1 33	37
Waddon **G**	38	..	..	1 26	..	1 31	..		..	..	..	..	..	..				..	..	..	..	1 36	38
West Croydon 319 arr	39	S O	..	1 29	..	1 34	..		..	..	..	..	..	S X	From London Bridge, via Forest Hill	From London Bridge, via Forest Hill	From London Bridge, via Streatham	..	..	..	..	1 39	39
West Croydon 319 dep	40	1 20	..	1 29	..	..	..		..	..	..	..	..	1 25				..	..	..	..	1 39	40
Carshalton	41	..	..	..	1 23	..	..	..	..	..	1 29	..	..	..				..	..	..	..	..	41
Hackbridge	42	..	..	..	1 25	..	..	..	..	..	1 32	..	..	..				..	..	..	..	..	42
Mitcham Junction	43	..	..	..	1 28	..	..	..	..	..	1 34	..	..	..				..	..	..	..	..	43
East Croydon .... arr	44	..	1 35	..	..	..	..	..	..	..	..	..	..	..				..	..	..	S O	..	44
East Croydon .... dep	45	..	1 35	..	..	..	..	..	..	..	..	..	..	..	S X	S O	S O	..	1 42	..	1 46	..	45
Norwood Junction F	46	1 24	1 38	..	..	..	..	..	..	..	..	..	S X	1 29	1 29	1 32	1 33	..	..	S O	..	..	46
Beckenham Jn. dep	47	..	..	..	..	..	..	..	..	..	..	..	1 20	..	..	..	..	..	..	1 29	..	..	47
Birkbeck	48	..	..	..	..	..	..	..	..	..	..	..	1 23	..	..	..	..	..	..	1 32	..	..	48
Crystal Palace D	49	1 29	..	..	..	..	..	..	..	..	..	..	1 27	1 33	..	..	..	..	..	1 36	..	..	49
Gipsy Hill (for Upper	50	1 31	..	..	..	..	..	..	..	..	..	..	..	1 36	..	..	..	..	..	1 38	..	..	50
West Norwood. [N'wood)	51	1 34	..	..	..	..	..	..	..	..	..	..	..	1 38	..	..	..	..	..	1 41	..	..	51
Streatham Hill	52	1 37	..	..	..	..	..	..	..	..	..	..	..	1 41	..	..	..	..	..	1 44	..	..	52
Selhurst	53	..	..	1 32	..	..	..	..	..	..	..	..	..	..	1 32	1 35	..	..	..	..	..	1 42	53
Thornton Heath	54	..	..	1 34	..	..	..	..	..	..	..	..	..	..	1 34	1 37	..	..	..	..	..	1 44	54
Norbury	55	..	..	1 37	..	..	..	..	..	..	..	..	..	..	1 37	1 40	..	..	..	..	..	1 47	55
Streatham Common	56	..	..	1 39	..	..	..	..	..	..	..	..	..	..	1 40	1 43	..	..	..	..	..	1 49	56
Anerley	57	..	..	..	..	..	..	..	..	..	..	..	..	..	..	..	1 36	..	..	..	..	..	57
Penge West **C**	58	..	..	..	..	..	..	..	..	..	..		..	..	..	..	1 37	..	..	..	..	..	58
Sydenham .... [Lane	59	..	..	..	..	..	..	..	..	..	..		..	..	..	..	1 39	..	..	..	..	..	59
Forest Hill, for Lordship	60	..	..	..	..	..	..	..	..	..	..		..	..	..	..	1 42	..	..	..	..	..	60
Honor Oak Park	61	..	..	..	..	..	..	..	..	..	..	From Victoria, dep. 1 27 p.m	..	..	..	..	1 44	..	..	..	..	..	61
Brockley **B** .... [Line)	62	..	..	..	..	..	..	..	..	..	..		..	..	..	..	1 47	..	..	..	..	..	62
New Cross Gate (for E.L.	63	..	..	..	..	..	..	..	..	..	..		..	..	..	..	1 49	..	..	..	..	..	63
Streatham	64	..	..	..	..	..	..	..	..	..	..		..	..	1 42	1 45	..	..	..	..	..	..	64
Tulse Hill	65	..	..	..	..	..	..	..	..	..	..		..	..	1 45	1 48	..	..	..	..	..	..	65
North Dulwich	66	..	..	..	..	..	..			..	..		..	..	1 48	..	..	..	..	..	..	..	66
East Dulwich	67	..	..	..	..	..	..			..	..	S O	..	..	1 50	..	..	..	..	..	..	..	67
Peckham Rye	68	..	..	..	..	..	..			..	..	1 44	..	..	1 53	..	..	..	..	..	..	..	68
Queen's Road, Peckham	69	..	..	..	..	..	..	Via Worcester Park	Via Worcester Park	..	..	1 46	..	..	1 55	..	..	..	..	..	..	..	69
South Bermondsey	70	..	..	..	..	..	..			..	..	1 49	..	..	1 58	..	..	..	..	..	..	..	70
Balham & Upper Tooting	71	1 40	..	1 43	1 34	..	..			..	1 41	..	..	1 44	..	..	..	..	..	1 46	..	1 53	71
Wandsworth Common **A**	72	1 42	..	..	..	..	..			..	..	..	..	1 46	..	..	..	..	..	1 48	..	..	72
Clapham Junction	73	1 45	..	1 48	1 39	..	..			..	1 45	..	..	1 49	..	..	..	..	..	1 51	..	1 57	73
Battersea Park	74	1 48	..	..	..	..	..			..	..	..	..	1 52	..	..	..	..	..	1 54	..	..	74
London Bridge ..... arr	75	..	1 51	..	..	..	..	..	..	..	..	1 53	..	..	2 2	1 59	1 55	..	..	..	..	..	75
Waterloo* .... "	76	..	..	..	..	..	..	1 42	1 42	..	..	..	..	..	..	..	..	..	..	..	..	..	76
Charing Cross * .. "	77	..	..	..	..	..	..	..	..	..	..	..	..	..	..	..	..	..	..	..	..	..	77
Victoria .... "	78	1 51	..	1 53	1 45	..	..	..	..	..	1 50	..	..	1 56	..	..	..	..	1 57	1 58	2 2	2 3	78

DORKING NORTH, SUTTON, CROYDON, CRYSTAL PALACE, and LONDON

p.m — Week Days—continued — p.m

No. 1	3	3	3		3	3	3	3	3	12§48	3	3		3	3	3	3	3	3	3	1252	3	3		3	3	3	..
2										1 23											3							
3										1 30																		1 50
4										1 34																		
5										1 40		S X		S O														
6												1 23		1 24														
7												1 26		1 27														
8												1 29		1 30														
9										§ Via Three Bridges		1 33		1 34														
10												1 36		1 37														
11												1 38		1 39														
12												1 41		1 42														
13												1 43		1 44														
14												1 33		1 34														
15												1 37		1 38														
16												1 39		1 40														
17												1 42		1 43														
18		S O							S O			1 45		1 46											S X			
19		1 31							1 36																1 41			
20		1 34							1 39	1 43		1 47		1 49											1 44			
21		1 36							1 42			1 50													1 46			
22		1 39				S O		S X	1 44			1 52													1 49			
23						1 10		1 13																				
24						1 13		1 16																				
25																					1 18							
26																					1 21							
27						1 17		1 20													1 26							
28						1 21		1 24													1 30	S O	S X					
29						1 25		1 28													1 34	1 37	1 40					
30						1 28		1 31														1 40	1 43					
31					S O	1 31		1 34										S O	S X			1 43	1 46					
32					1 24													1 29	1 30									
33					1 27													1 32	1 33									
34	S X				1 30													1 35	1 36	S O								
35	1 32				1 33	1 35		1 38										1 38	1 39	1 43		1 46	1 49					
36	1 34				1 35													1 40	1 41	1 46								
37	1 37				1 38													1 43	1 44	1 48								
38					1 41												From London Bridge, via Streatham	1 46	1 47	1 52							From London Bridge, via Forest Hill	
39					1 44						S O							1 49	1 50	1 55								
40					1 44						1 40							1 49	1 50									
41						1 38		1 41														1 49	1 52					
42						1 40		1 44														1 52	1 55					
43						1 43		1 46														1 54	1 57					
44		1 42							1 47	1 49		1 55		1 54											1 52			2 5
45		1 42							1 47	1 50		1 55		1 54			S O								1 52		S O	2 5
46					1 48				1 51		1 44	1 58		1 58			1 53		1 54							S O	1 52	
47																										1 49		
48							S O								S O											1 52		
49			1 39				1 45				1 49				1 53											1 56		
50							1 48				1 51															1 58		
51							1 50				1 54															2 1		
52											1 57															2 4		
53		1 45																1 52							1 55		1 55	
54		1 47																1 54							1 57		1 57	
55		1 50																1 57							2 0		2 0	
56		1 52																2 0							2 2		2 3	
57																	1 56		1 57									
58																	1 57		1 58									
59			1 42												1 56		1 59		2 0									
60			1 44												1 58		2 2		2 3									
61			1 47												2 1		2 4		2 5									
62			1 49												2 3	From Victoria, dep. 1 47 p.m.	2 7		2 8									
63			1 52						2 0						2 6		2 9		2 10									
64						1 48		1 51																			2 5	
65						1 51	1 53	1 55																			2 8	
66							1 56																					
67							1 58																					
68							2 1	2 0								2 4					Via Worcester Park							
69							2 3									2 6												
70							2 6									2 9												
71		1 56									1 59							2 4				2 1	2 4		2 6	2 6		
72											2 1															2 8		
73		2 0								2 1	2 4							2 8				2 6	2 8		2 11	2 11		2 16
74											2 7															2 14		
75			1 58		2 2	2 2	2 10	2 7	2 6			2 11		2 10	2 11	2 13	2 15		2 16								2 19	
76												2 15									2 3							
77												2 17																
78		2 6								2 7	2 11							2 14				2 11	2 13		2 17	2 18		2 21

HORSHAM, REIGATE, REDHILL, TATTENHAM CORNER, CATERHAM,

Up	No.	p.m						Week Days—continued										p.m					No.
		3	3	3		3	3	S O	3	3	3	3	3	3		3	3	3	3	3			
Horsham........dep	1	..	..	..	..	..	..	1 3	..	..	..	..	..	..	..	..	..	..	..	..	..	1§15	1
Reigate........ "	2	..	–	..	..	..	..	..	..	..	..	..	..	..	..	..	..	..	..	..	..	1 52	2
Redhill........ "	3	..	..	..	..	..	..	3	..	..	..	..	..	..	..	..	..	..	..	..	..	1 59	3
Merstham........	4	..	..	..	..	..	..	..	..	..	..	..	..	..	..	..	..	..	..	..	..	2 3	4
Coulsdon South........	5	..	..	..	..	..	..	..	..	..	..	..	..	..	..	..	..	..	..	..	..	2 9	5
Tattenham Corner. dep	6	..	..	..	..	..	..	..	..	..	..	..	..	..	..	..	..	..	..	1 43	..	§ Via Three Bridges	6
Tadworth N........	7	..	..	..	..	..	..	..	..	..	..	..	..	..	..	..	..	..	..	1 46	..		7
Kingswood M........	8	..	..	..	..	..	..	..	..	..	..	..	..	..	..	..	..	..	..	1 49	..		8
Chipstead........	9	..	..	..	..	..	..	..	..	..	..	..	..	..	..	..	..	..	..	1 53	..		9
Woodmansterne........	10	..	..	..	..	..	..	..	..	..	..	..	..	..	..	..	..	..	..	1 56	..		10
Smitham........	11	..	..	..	..	..	..	..	..	..	..	..	..	..	..	..	..	..	..	1 58	..		11
Reedham........	12	..	..	..	..	..	..	..	..	..	..	..	..	..	..	..	..	..	..	2 1	..		12
Purley 252........arr	13	..	..	..	..	..	..	..	..	..	..	..	..	..	..	..	..	..	..	2 3	..		13
Caterham........dep	14	..	..	..	..	..	..	..	..	..	..	..	..	..	..	..	..	..	..	1 53	..	..	14
Warlingham........	15	..	..	..	..	..	..	..	..	..	..	..	..	..	..	..	..	..	..	1 57	..	..	15
Whyteleafe........	16	..	..	..	..	..	..	..	..	..	..	..	..	..	..	..	..	..	..	1 59	..	..	16
Kenley........	17	..	..	..	..	..	..	..	..	..	..	..	..	..	..	..	..	..	..	2 2	..	..	17
Purley 252........arr	18	S O	..	..	..	..	..	..	..	..	..	..	..	..	..	..	..	..	..	2 5	..	..	18
Coulsdon North.....dep	19	1 51	..	..	..	..	..	..	..	..	..	..	..	..	..	..	..	..	..	..	..	..	19
Purley 252........	20	1 54	..	..	..	..	..	..	..	..	..	..	..	..	..	..	..	..	..	2 7	..	2 13	20
Purley Oaks........	21	1 56	..	..	..	..	..	..	..	..	..	..	..	..	..	..	..	..	..	2 10	..	..	21
South Croydon 234.....	22	1 59	..	..	..	..	..	..	S O	..	..	..	..	..	..	..	..	..	..	2 12	..	..	22
Effingham Junction dep	23	..	..	..	..	..	..	..	1 38	..	..	..	..	..	..	..	..	..	..	..	..	..	23
Bookham........	24	..	..	..	..	..	..	..	1 41	..	..	..	..	..	..	..	..	..	..	..	..	..	24
Dorking North.....dep	25	..	..	..	..	..	..	1 29	..	..	..	..	..	..	..	..	..	..	..	..	..	..	25
Boxhill and Burford	26	..	..	..	..	..	..	1 32	..	..	..	..	..	..	..	..	..	..	..	..	..	..	26
Leatherhead...[Bridge J	27	..	..	..	..	..	..	1 37	1 46	..	..	..	..	..	..	..	..	..	..	..	..	..	27
Ashtead........	28	..	..	..	..	..	..	1 41	..	..	..	..	..	..	..	..	S O	..	..	..	..	..	28
Epsom 427........	29	..	..	..	..	..	..	1 45	..	..	..	..	..	..	..	..	1 57	..	..	..	..	..	29
Ewell East H........	30	..	..	..	..	..	..	1 48	..	..	..	..	..	..	..	..	2 0	..	..	..	..	..	30
Cheam........	31	..	..	..	..	..	S O	1 51	..	..	..	..	S X	S O	..	..	2 3	..	..	..	..	..	31
Epsom Downs......dep	32	..	..	..	..	..	1 44	..	..	..	..	..	1 49	1 49	..	..	..	..	..	..	..	..	32
Banstead........	33	..	..	..	..	..	1 47	..	..	..	..	..	1 52	1 52	..	..	..	..	..	..	..	..	33
Belmont........	34	..	..	..	..	..	1 50	..	..	..	..	..	1 55	1 55	..	..	..	..	..	..	..	..	34
Sutton 322........	35	..	..	..	..	..	1 53	1 55	..	From London Bridge, via Streatham	..	..	1 58	1 58	..	2 2	2 6	..	From London Bridge, via Forest Hill	..	..	..	35
Carshalton Beeches.....	36	..	..	..	..	..	1 55	..	..		..	..	2 0	2 1	..	2 4	..	..		..	..	..	36
Wallington........	37	..	..	..	..	..	1 58	..	..		..	..	2 3	2 3	..	2 7	..	..		..	..	..	37
Waddon G........	38	..	..	..	..	..	2 1	..	..		..	..	2 6	2 7	..	2SO10	..	..		..	..	..	38
West Croydon 319 arr	39	..	..	S X	..	S O	2 4	..	..		..	..	2 9	2 9	..	2SO13	..	..		..	..	..	39
West Croydon 319 dep	40	..	..	1 55	..	2 0	2 4	..	..		..	..	2 9	2 9	..	..	..	..		..	..	..	40
Carshalton........	41	..	..	..	..	..	..	1 58	..		..	..	..	..	..	..	2 9	..		..	..	..	41
Hackbridge........	42	..	..	..	..	..	..	2 0	..		..	..	..	..	..	..	2 11	..		..	..	..	42
Mitcham Junction......	43	..	..	..	..	..	..	2 3	..		..	..	..	..	..	..	2 14	..		..	..	..	43
East Croydon.... arr	44	2 2	..	..	..	..	..	..	..	..	..	..	..	..	..	..	..	..	..	2 15	..	2 18	44
East Croydon.... dep	45	2 2	..	..	..	..	..	..	..	S X	..	..	..	..	..	..	..	..	S O	2 15	..	2 20	45
Norwood Junction F..	46	..	S X	1 59	..	2 4	2 8	..	..	2 9	..	..	..	..	..	..	..	S O	2 12	2 18	..	2 24	46
Beckenham Jn. dep	47	..	1 50	..	..	..	..	..	..	..	..	..	..	..	..	..	..	2 9	..	..	..	..	47
Birkbeck........	48	..	1 53	..	..	..	..	..	..	..	..	S X	..	..	..	..	..	2 12	..	..	..	..	48
Crystal Palace D......	49	..	1 57	2 3	..	2 9	..	..	..	..	..	2 11	..	..	..	..	..	2 16	..	..	..	..	49
Gipsy Hill (for Upper	50	..	..	2 6	..	2 11	..	..	..	..	..	2 13	..	..	..	..	..	2 18	..	..	..	..	50
West Norwood,[N'wood)	51	..	..	2 8	..	2 14	..	..	..	..	..	2 16	..	..	..	..	..	2 21	..	..	..	..	51
Streatham Hill........	52	..	..	2 11	..	2 17	..	..	..	..	..	..	..	..	..	..	..	2 24	..	..	..	..	52
Selhurst........	53	2 5	..	..	..	..	..	..	..	..	..	..	2 12	2 12	..	..	..	..	2 15	..	..	..	53
Thornton Heath........	54	2 7	..	..	..	..	..	..	..	..	..	..	2 14	2 14	..	..	..	..	2 17	..	..	..	54
Norbury........	55	2 10	..	..	..	..	..	..	..	..	..	..	2 17	2 17	..	..	..	..	2 20	..	..	..	55
Streatham Common....	56	2 12	..	..	..	..	..	..	..	..	..	..	2 19	2 20	..	..	..	..	2 23	..	..	..	56
Anerley........	57	..	..	..	..	..	..	..	..	2 12	..	..	..	..	..	..	..	..	..	..	..	..	57
Penge West C........	58	..	..	..	..	..	..	..	..	2 13	From Victoria, dep 2 7 p.m	..	..	..	..	..	..	..	..	..	..	..	58
Sydenham........[Lane	59	..	..	..	..	..	..	..	..	2 15		..	..	..	..	..	..	..	..	..	..	..	59
Forest Hill, for Lordship	60	..	..	..	..	..	..	..	..	2 18		..	..	..	..	..	..	..	..	..	..	..	60
Honor Oak Park........	61	..	..	..	..	..	..	..	..	2 20		..	..	..	..	..	..	..	..	..	..	..	61
Brockley B.......[Line)	62	..	..	..	..	..	..	..	..	2 23		..	..	..	..	..	..	..	..	..	..	..	62
New Cross Gate (for E.L.	63	..	..	..	..	..	..	..	..	2 25		..	..	..	..	..	..	..	..	..	..	..	63
Streatham........	64	..	..	..	..	..	..	2 8	..	..		..	..	..	..	..	..	..	2 25	..	..	..	64
Tulse Hill........	65	..	..	..	..	..	..	2 11	..	..		2 18	..	..	..	..	..	..	2 28	..	..	..	65
North Dulwich........	66	..	..	..	..	..	..	..	..	..		2 21	..	..	..	..	..	..	2 34	..	..	..	66
East Dulwich........	67	..	..	..	..	..	..	..	..	..	S O	2 23	..	..	..	..	..	..	2 36	..	..	..	67
Peckham Rye........	68	..	..	..	..	..	..	..	..	..	2 24	2 26	..	..	..	..	..	..	2 39	..	..	..	68
Queen's Road, Peckham	69	..	..	..	..	..	..	..	..	..	2 26	2 28	..	..	..	..	..	..	..	..	..	..	69
South Bermondsey......	70	..	..	..	..	..	..	..	..	..	2 29	2 31	..	..	..	..	..	..	..	..	..	..	70
Balham & Upper Tooting	71	2 16	..	2 14	..	2 19	..	..	..	..	..	..	2 23	2 24	..	..	2 20	2 26	..	..	..	..	71
Wandsworth Common A	72	..	..	2 16	..	2 21	..	..	..	..	..	..	..	..	..	..	..	2 28	..	..	..	..	72
Clapham Junction.....	73	2 20	..	2 19	..	2 24	..	..	..	..	..	..	2 27	2 28	..	..	2 24	2 31	..	..	..	..	73
Battersea Park........	74	..	..	2 22	..	2 27	..	..	..	..	..	..	..	..	..	..	..	2 34	..	..	..	..	74
London Bridge..... arr	75	..	..	..	..	..	2 22	2 22	..	2 31	2 33	2 35	..	..	..	..	..	..	2 45	2 31	..	2 36	75
Waterloo *........ "	76	..	..	..	..	..	..	..	..	..	..	..	..	..	..	..	..	..	..	2SX35	..	..	76
Charing Cross *.. "	77	..	..	..	..	..	..	..	..	..	..	..	..	..	..	..	..	..	..	2SX37	..	..	77
Victoria........ "	78	2 26	..	2 26	..	2 31	..	..	..	..	..	..	2 33	2 34	..	..	2 30	2 38	..	..	..	..	78

For Notes, see page 317a

DORKING NORTH, SUTTON, CROYDON, CRYSTAL PALACE, and LONDON

No.	p.m										Week Days—*continued*												p.m					
1	3	3	SX 1 20	3	3	SO 1 20	3	3	SO 1 43	..	3	3	3	3	3	3	..	3	3	..	3	..	3	3	..	..	3	3
2	..	..	3	..	..	3	..	..	..	..	..	..	..	..	..	..	1 57	..	..	..	..	..	..	..	..	..	..	..
3	..	..		..	..		..	..	..	..	..	..	..	..	..	..	2 a 2	..	..	..	..	..	..	..	..	..	..	..
4	..	..	..	..	..	..	..	..	..	..	..	..	..	..	..	..		..	..	..	..	..	..	..	..	..	..	..
5	..	..	..	..	..	..	..	..	..	..	..	..	..	..	..	..		..	..	..	..	..	..	..	..	..	..	..
6	..	..	..	..	..	..	..	..	..	..	..	..	..	..	..	..	*a* Arrival time	..	..	..	..	..	..	..	..	..	..	..
7	..	..	..	..	..	..	..	..	..	..	..	..	..	..	..	..		..	..	..	..	..	..	..	..	..	..	..
8	..	..	..	..	..	..	..	..	..	..	..	..	..	..	..	..		..	..	..	..	..	..	..	..	..	..	..
9	..	..	..	..	..	..	..	..	..	..	..	..	..	..	..	..		..	..	..	..	..	..	..	..	..	..	..
10	..	..	..	..	..	..	..	..	..	..	..	..	..	..	..	..		..	..	..	..	..	..	..	..	..	..	..
11	..	..	..	..	..	..	..	..	..	..	..	..	..	..	..	..		..	..	..	..	..	..	..	..	..	..	..
12	..	..	..	..	..	..	..	..	..	..	..	..	..	..	..	..		..	..	..	..	..	..	..	..	..	..	..
13	..	..	..	..	..	..	..	..	..	..	..	..	..	..	..	..		..	..	..	..	..	..	..	..	..	..	..
14	..	..	..	..	..	..	..	..	..	..	..	..	..	..	..	..	..	..	..	..	..	..	..	..	..	..	..	..
15	..	..	..	..	..	..	..	..	..	..	..	..	..	..	..	..	..	..	..	..	..	..	..	..	..	..	..	..
16	..	..	..	..	..	..	..	..	..	..	..	..	..	..	..	..	..	..	..	..	..	..	..	..	..	..	..	..
17	..	..	..	..	..	..	..	..	..	..	..	..	..	..	..	..	..	..	..	..	..	..	..	..	..	..	..	..
18	..	..	..	..	..	..	..	..	..	..	..	..	..	..	..	..	..	..	..	..	..	..	..	..	..	..	..	..
19	2 11	..	..	..	..	..	..	..	..	..	..	..	..	..	..	..	..	..	..	..	..	..	..	..	..	..	..	..
20	2 14	..	..	..	..	..	..	..	..	..	..	..	..	..	..	..	..	..	..	..	..	..	..	..	..	..	..	..
21	2 16	..	..	..	..	..	..	..	..	..	..	..	..	..	..	..	..	..	..	..	..	..	..	..	..	..	..	..
22	2 19	..	..	..	..	..	..	SX	..	..	..	..	..	..	..	..	..	..	..	..	..	..	..	..	..	..	..	..
23	..	..	..	..	..	..	..	1 55	..	..	..	..	..	..	..	..	..	..	..	..	..	..	..	..	..	..	..	..
24	..	..	..	..	..	..	SO	1 58	..	..	..	..	..	..	..	..	..	..	..	..	..	..	..	..	..	..	..	..
25	..	..	1 46	..	..	1 48	1 55	..	2 2	..	..	..	..	..	..	..	..	..	..	..	..	..	..	..	..	..	..	..
26	..	..	1 48	..	..	1 51	1 57	..	..	..	..	..	..	..	..	..	..	..	..	..	..	..	..	..	..	..	..	..
27	..	..	1 53	..	..	1 56	2 2	2 2	..	..	..	..	..	..	..	..	..	..	..	..	..	..	..	..	..	..	..	..
28	..	..	1 57	..	..	2 0	2 6	2 6	..	..	..	..	..	..	..	..	..	..	..	..	..	..	..	..	..	..	..	..
29	..	..	2 2	..	..	2 5	2 14	2 14	..	..	..	2 17	..	..	..	..	..	..	..	..	..	..	..	..	..	..	..	..
30	..	..	2 5	..	..	2 8			..	..	..	2 20	..	..	..	..	..	..	..	..	..	..	..	..	..	..	..	..
31	..	SX	2 8	..	SO	2 11			..	..	..	2 23	..	..	..	..	..	..	..	..	..	..	..	..	..	..	..	..
32	..	2 0	..	..	2 4	..	Arr. Epsom 2 10 p.m	Arr. Epsom 2 10 p.m	..	..	..	..	..	..	..	..	..	..	..	..	..	..	..	..	..	..	2 19	..
33	..	2 3	..	..	2 7	..			..	..	..	..	..	..	..	..	..	..	..	..	..	..	..	..	..	..	2 22	..
34	..	2 6	..	..	2 10	..			..	..	SO	..	..	..	..	..	..	..	..	..	..	..	..	..	..	..	2 25	SX
35	..	2 9	2 11	..	2 13	2 14			2 20	..	2 23	2 26	..	From London Bridge, via Forest Hill	From London Bridge, via Forest Hill	From London Bridge, via Streatham	..	..	..	..	..	..	..	..	..	..	2 28	2 32
36	..	2 11	..	..	2 15	..			..	..	2 25	..	..				..	..	..	..	..	..	..	..	..	..	2 30	2 34
37	..	2 14	..	..	2 18	..			..	..	2 28	..	..				..	..	..	..	..	..	..	..	..	..	2 33	2 37
38	..	2 17	..	..	2 21	..			..	..	2 31	..	..				..	..	..	..	..	..	..	..	..	..	2 36	..
39	..	2 20	..	..	2 24	..	..	..	..	..	2 34	..	..				..	..	SX	..	SO	..	..	..	..	..	2 39	..
40	..	2 20	..	..	2 24	..	..	..	..	..	..	..	..				..	..	2 25	..	2 27	..	..	..	..	..	2 39	..
41	..	..	2 14	..	..	2 17	..	..	..	..	..	2 29	..				..	..	..	..	..	..	..	..	..	..	..	..
42	..	..	2 16	..	..	2 20	..	..	..	..	..	2‡32	..				..	..	..	..	..	..	..	..	..	..	..	..
43	..	..	2 19	..	..	2 22	..	..	..	..	..	2 34	..				..	..	..	..	..	..	..	..	..	..	..	..
44	2 22	..	..	..	..	..	..	..	..	..	..	‡ 1 minute *earlier* on Saturdays	..				..	..	..	SX	..	..	..	..	..	..	..	..
45	2 22	..	..	..	..	..	..	..	..	..	..		..	SX	SO	SO	..	..	..	2 42	..	..	..	..	..	..	..	..
46	..	2 24	..	..	2 28	..	..	..	..	..	..		..	2 29	2 32	2 33	..	SX	2 29	..	2 31	..	..	..	..	..	..	..
47	..	..	..	..	..	..	..	..	..	..	..		..	..	..	..	..	2 20	..	..	..	..	..	..	..	..	..	..
48	..	..	..	..	..	..	..	..	..	..	..		..	..	..	..	..	2 23	..	..	..	..	SX	SO	..	..	..	..
49	..	..	..	..	..	..	..	..	..	..	..		..	..	..	..	..	2 27	2 33	..	2 35	..	2 39	2 39	..	..	..	..
50	..	..	..	..	..	..	..	..	..	..	..		..	..	..	..	..	..	2 36	..	2 38	..	..	..	..	..	..	..
51	..	..	..	..	..	..	..	..	..	..	..		..	..	..	..	..	..	2 38	..	2 40	..	..	..	..	..	..	..
52	..	..	..	..	..	..	..	..	..	..	..		..	..	..	..	..	..	2 41	..	2 43	..	..	..	..	..	..	..
53	2 25	..	..	..	..	..	..	..	..	..	..	..	..	2 32	2 35	..	..	..	..	..	..	..	..	..	..	..	2 42	..
54	2 27	..	..	..	..	..	..	..	..	..	..	..	..	2 34	2 37	..	..	..	..	..	..	..	..	..	..	..	2 44	..
55	2 30	..	..	..	..	..	..	..	..	..	..	..	..	2 37	2 40	..	..	..	..	..	..	..	..	..	..	..	2 47	..
56	2 32	..	..	..	..	..	..	..	..	..	..	..	..	2 40	2 43	..	..	..	..	..	..	..	..	..	..	..	2 49	..
57	‡ 1 minute *earlier* on Saturdays	2 27	..	From Victoria, dep. 2 18 p.m	2 31	..	..	..	..	..	..	..	From Victoria, dep 2 28 p.m	..	..	2 36	..	..	..	..	..	..	..	..	..	..	..	..
58		2 28	..		2 32	..	..	..	..	..	..	..		..	..	2 37	..	..	..	..	..	..	..	..	..	..	..	..
59		2 30	..		2 34	..	..	..	..	..	..	..		..	..	2 39	..	..	..	..	..	..	2 42	2 42	..	..	..	..
60		2 33	..		2 37	..	..	..	..	..	..	..		..	..	2 42	..	..	..	..	..	..	2 45	2 45	..	..	..	..
61		2 35	..		2 39	..	..	..	..	..	..	..		..	..	2 44	..	..	..	..	..	..	2 47	2 47	..	..	..	..
62		2 38	..		2 42	..	..	..	..	..	..	..		..	..	2 47	..	..	..	..	..	..	2 49	2 50	..	..	..	..
63		2 40	..		2 44	..	..	..	..	..	..	..		..	..	2 49	..	..	..	..	..	..	2 52	2 52	..	..	..	..
64		..	2 24		..	2 28	Via Worcester Park	Via Worcester Park	..	..	..	..		2 42	2 45	..	..	..	..	..	..	..	..	..	..	..	..	..
65		..	2 27		..	2 31			..	..	..	..		2 45	2 48	..	..	..	..	..	..	..	..	..	..	..	..	..
66		..	..		..	..			..	..	..	..		2 48	..	..	..	..	..	..	..	..	..	..	..	..	..	..
67		..	..	SX	..	..			..	..	..	..	SO	2 50	..	..	..	..	..	..	..	..	..	..	..	..	..	..
68		..	2 32	2 35	..	..			..	..	..	..	2 44	2 53	2 53	..	..	..	..	..	..	..	..	..	..	..	..	..
69		..	..	2 37	..	..			..	..	..	..	2 46	2 55	..	..	..	..	..	..	..	..	..	..	..	..	..	..
70		..	..	2 40	..	..			..	..	..	..	2 49	2 58	..	..	..	..	..	..	..	..	..	..	..	..	..	..
71	2 36	..	..	..	..	..			..	..	..	2 41	..	..	..	..	..	..	2 44	..	2 46	..	..	..	..	..	2 53	..
72	2SX38	..	..	..	..	..			..	..	..	..	..	..	..	..	..	..	2 46	..	2 48	..	..	..	..	..	..	..
73	2 ‡41	..	..	..	..	..			..	..	..	2 45	..	..	..	..	..	..	2 49	..	2 51	..	..	..	..	..	2 57	..
74	..	..	..	..	..	..			..	..	..	..	..	..	..	..	..	..	2 52	..	2 54	..	..	..	..	..	..	..
75	..	2 46	2 38	2 44	2 50	2 45	..	..	..	..	..	..	2 53	3 2	2 59	2 55	..	..	..	..	..	..	2 58	2 58	..	..	..	..
76	..	..	..	..	..	..	2 42	2 42	..	..	..	..	..	..	..	..	..	..	..	..	..	..	..	..	..	..	..	..
77	..	..	..	..	..	..	..	..	..	..	..	..	..	..	..	..	..	..	..	..	..	..	..	..	..	..	..	..
78	2 ‡47	..	..	..	..	..	..	..	2 40	..	..	2 50	..	..	..	..	..	..	2 56	2 57	2 58	..	..	..	..	..	3 3	..

HORSHAM, REIGATE, REDHILL, TATTENHAM CORNER, CATERHAM,

For Notes, see page 317a

Week Days—continued (p.m.)

Up	No.	3			3	3		3	3	3	3	3		3	3	3				3	3		No.
Horsham ... dep	1						1§48											1 52					1
Reigate ... "	2						2 23											3					2
Redhill ... "	3						2 31															2 50	3
Merstham	4						2 35																4
Coulsdon South	5						2 41																5
Tattenham Corner dep	6						§ Via Three Bridges					2 23											6
Tadworth N	7											2 26											7
Kingswood M	8											2 29											8
Chipstead	9											2 33											9
Woodmansterne	10											2 36											10
Smitham	11											2 38											11
Reedham	12											2 41											12
Purley 252 ... arr	13											2 43											13
Caterham ... dep	14											2 33											14
Warlingham	15											2 37											15
Whyteleafe	16											2 39											16
Kenley	17											2 42											17
Purley 252 ... arr	18											2 45											18
Coulsdon North ... dep	19								2 42														19
Purley 252	20						2 45		2 45			2 47											20
Purley Oaks	21								2 47			2 50											21
South Croydon 234	22	S O	2 41		S X				2 50			2 52											22
Effingham Junction dep	23	2 10			2 13																		23
Bookham	24	2 13			2 16																		24
Dorking North ... dep	25																	2 18					25
Boxhill and Burford	26																	2 21					26
Leatherhead ... [Bridge J	27	2 17			2 20													2 26					27
Ashtead	28	2 21			2 24													2 30		S O	S X		28
Epsom 427	29	2 25			2 28													2 34		2 38	2 40		29
Ewell East H	30	2 28			2 31															2 41	2 43		30
Cheam	31	2 31			2 34															2 44	2 46		31
Epsom Downs ... dep	32													2 30									32
Banstead	33													2 33									33
Belmont	34													2 36	S O								34
Sutton 322	35	2 35			2 38									2 39	2 44					2 48	2 49		35
Carshalton Beeches	36													2 41	2 46								36
Wallington	37													2 44	2 49								37
Waddon G	38													2 47	2 52								38
West Croydon 319 arr	39													2 50	2 55								39
West Croydon 319 dep	40													2 50									40
Carshalton	41	2 38			2 41															2 51	2 52		41
Hackbridge	42	2 40			2 44															2 53	2 55		42
Mitcham Junction	43	2 43			2 46															2 56	2 57		43
East Croydon ... arr	44		2 45				2 50		2 52			2 55										3 5	44
East Croydon ... dep	45		2 45	2 47			2 51		2 52			2 55										3 5	45
Norwood Junction F	46		2 50					S O				2 58		2 54									46
Beckenham Jn. dep	47							2 38															47
Birkbeck	48					S X		2 41															48
Crystal Palace D	49					2 46		2 45															49
Gipsy Hill (for Upper	50					2 48		2 48															50
West Norwood. [N'wood)	51					2 51		2 50								S X							51
Streatham Hill	52					2 54		2 55								2 58							52
Selhurst	53								2 55														53
Thornton Heath	54								2 57														54
Norbury	55								3 0														55
Streatham Common	56								3 3														56
Anerley	57								H 1 minute *earlier* on Saturdays	From Victoria, dep. 2 46 p.m.	From Victoria, dep. 2 47 p.m.			2 57									57
Penge West C	58													2 58									58
Sydenham ... [Lane	59													3 0									59
Forest Hill, for Lordship	60													3 3									60
Honor Oak Park	61													3 5									61
Brockley B ... [Line)	62													3 8									62
New Cross Gate (for E.L.	63													3 10									63
Streatham	64	2 48			2 51																		64
Tulse Hill	65	2 51			2 55											3 1		Via Worcester Park					65
North Dulwich	66	2 54														3 4							66
East Dulwich	67	2 56								S O	S X					3 6							67
Peckham Rye	68	2 59			3 0					3 1	3 4					3 9							68
Queen's Road, Peckham	69									3 3	3 6					3 11							69
South Bermondsey	70									3 6	3 9					3 14							70
Balham & Upper Tooting	71					2 56		2 58	3 7											3 2	3 4		71
Wandsworth Common A	72					2 58		3 0															72
Clapham Junction	73					3 1	3 2	3 3	3H12											3 7	3 8	3 16	73
Battersea Park	74					3 4		3 6															74
London Bridge ... arr	75	3 5	3 5		3 7					3 10	3 13	3 11		3 16		3 18							75
Waterloo * ... "	76											3SO14						3 3					76
Charing Cross * ... "	77											3SO17											77
Victoria ... "	78			3 3		3 8	3 8	3 9	3H17											3 12	3 13	3 22	78

DORKING NORTH, SUTTON, CROYDON, CRYSTAL PALACE, and LONDON

Week Days—*continued* (p.m.)

No	1	2	3	4	5	6	7	8	9	10	11	12	13	14	15	16	17	18	19	20	21	22	23	24	25	26	27	28
1	3	3	..	3	3	..	3	3	3	3	..	3	3	3	3	..	2§15	3	2 20	3	..	3	3	2 43	..	3	3	3
2	..	..	..	..	..	..	..	..	..	..	..	..	..	..	..	..	2 53	..	..	..	..	..	..	..	..	..	..	..
3	..	..	..	..	..	..	..	..	..	..	..	..	..	..	..	..	2 59	..	3	..	..	..	..	..	..	..	..	..
4	..	..	..	..	..	..	..	..	..	..	..	..	..	..	..	..	3 3	..	..	..	..	..	..	..	..	..	..	..
5	..	..	..	..	..	..	..	..	..	..	..	..	SX	SO	..	..	3 9	..	..	..	..	..	..	..	..	..	..	..
6	..	..	..	..	..	..	..	..	..	..	..	..	2 42	2 43	..	..	..	..	..	..	..	..	..	..	..	..	..	..
7	..	..	..	..	..	..	..	..	..	..	..	..	2 45	2 46	..	..	..	..	..	..	..	..	..	..	..	..	..	..
8	..	..	..	..	..	..	..	..	..	..	..	..	2 48	2 49	..	..	§ Via Three Bridges	..	..	..	..	..	..	..	..	..	..	..
9	..	..	..	..	..	..	..	..	..	..	..	..	2 52	2 53	..	..	..	..	..	..	..	..	..	..	..	..	..	..
10	..	..	..	..	..	..	..	..	..	..	..	..	2 55	2 56	..	..	..	..	..	..	..	..	..	..	..	..	..	..
11	..	..	..	..	..	..	..	..	..	..	..	..	2 57	2 58	..	..	..	..	..	..	..	..	..	..	..	..	..	..
12	..	..	..	..	..	..	..	..	..	..	..	..	3 0	3 1	..	..	..	..	..	..	..	..	..	..	..	..	..	..
13	..	..	..	..	..	..	..	..	..	..	..	..	3 2	3 3	..	..	..	..	..	..	..	..	..	..	..	..	..	..
14	..	..	..	..	..	..	..	..	..	..	..	..	2 52	2 53	..	..	..	..	..	..	..	..	..	..	..	..	..	..
15	..	..	..	..	..	..	..	..	..	..	..	..	2 56	2 57	..	..	..	..	..	..	..	..	..	..	..	..	..	..
16	..	..	..	..	..	..	..	..	..	..	..	..	2 58	2 59	..	..	..	..	..	..	..	..	..	..	..	..	..	..
17	..	..	..	..	..	..	..	..	..	..	..	..	3 1	3 2	..	..	..	..	..	..	..	..	..	..	..	..	..	..
18	..	..	..	..	..	..	..	..	..	..	..	..	3 4	3 5	..	..	..	..	..	..	..	..	..	..	..	..	..	..
19	..	..	..	..	..	..	..	..	..	..	..	..	..	..	..	..	..	..	..	..	..	3 11	..	..	..	..	..	..
20	..	..	..	..	..	..	..	..	..	..	..	..	3 7	3 7	..	..	3 13	..	..	..	..	3 14	..	..	..	..	..	..
21	..	..	..	..	..	..	..	..	..	..	..	..	3 9	3 10	..	..	..	..	..	..	..	3 16	..	..	..	..	..	..
22	..	..	..	..	..	..	..	..	..	..	..	..	3 12	3 12	..	..	..	..	..	..	..	3 19	..	..	..	..	..	..
23	..	..	..	..	..	..	..	..	..	..	..	..	..	..	..	..	..	..	..	..	..	..	2 55	..	..	..	..	..
24	..	..	..	..	..	..	..	..	..	SO	..	..	..	..	..	..	..	..	..	..	..	..	2 58	..	..	..	..	..
25	..	..	..	..	..	..	..	..	..	2 38	..	..	..	..	..	..	..	..	2 46	..	..	..	..	3 2	..	..	..	..
26	..	..	..	..	..	..	..	..	..	2 41	..	..	..	..	..	..	..	..	2 48	..	..	..	..	..	..	..	..	..
27	..	..	..	..	..	..	..	..	..	2 46	..	..	..	..	..	..	..	..	2 53	..	..	..	3 2	..	..	..	..	..
28	..	..	..	..	..	..	..	..	..	2 50	..	SO	..	..	..	..	..	..	2 57	..	..	..	3 6	..	..	..	..	..
29	..	..	..	..	..	..	..	..	..	2 54	..	2 57	..	..	..	..	..	..	3 2	..	..	..	3 14	..	..	3 17	..	..
30	..	..	..	..	..	..	..	..	..	..	..	3 0	..	..	..	..	..	..	3 5	..	..	..	..	..	..	3 20	..	..
31	..	..	..	..	..	..	..	..	..	..	..	3 3	..	..	..	..	..	..	3 8	..	..	..	..	..	..	3 23	..	..
32	..	..	..	..	..	..	..	2 49	..	..	..	..	..	..	..	..	..	3 0	..	..	..	..	..	..	..	..	..	..
33	..	..	..	..	..	..	..	2 52	..	..	..	..	..	..	..	..	..	3 3	..	..	..	..	Arr. Epsom 3 10 p.m.	..	..	..	..	..
34	..	..	..	..	..	..	..	2 55	..	..	..	..	..	..	..	..	..	3 6	..	..	..	..	..	..	..	..	..	..
35	..	..	..	..	..	..	..	2 58	3 2	..	..	3 6	..	..	..	..	..	3 9	3 11	..	..	..	..	3 20	..	3‖27	..	..
36	..	..	..	..	..	..	..	3 0	3‖5	..	..	..	..	..	..	..	..	3 11	..	..	..	..	..	..	..	..	..	..
37	..	..	..	..	..	..	..	3 3	3‖8	..	..	..	..	..	..	..	..	3 14	..	..	..	..	..	..	..	..	..	..
38	..	..	..	..	..	..	From London Bridge, via Streatham	3 6	..	..	..	..	..	..	From London Bridge, via Streatham	..	..	3 17	..	..	..	..	..	..	..	..	..	..
39	..	..	..	..	..	..	..	3 9	..	..	..	..	..	..	..	..	..	3 20	..	..	..	..	..	..	..	..	..	..
40	..	2 55	..	..	..	..	..	3 9	..	..	..	..	..	..	..	..	..	3 20	..	..	..	..	..	..	..	..	..	3 25
41	..	..	..	..	..	..	..	..	‖ 1 minute *earlier* on Saturdays	..	..	3 9	..	..	..	..	..	..	3 14	..	..	..	..	..	..	3‖30	..	..
42	..	..	..	..	..	..	..	..	..	..	..	3 11	..	..	..	..	..	..	3 16	..	..	..	..	..	..	3‖32	..	..
43	..	..	..	..	..	..	..	..	..	..	..	3 14	..	..	..	..	..	..	3 19	..	..	..	..	..	..	3‖35	..	..
44	..	..	..	..	..	..	..	..	..	..	..	..	3 14	3 15	..	..	3 18	..	..	..	..	3 22	..	..	..	..	..	..
45	..	..	..	..	..	..	SX	..	..	..	..	..	3 14	3 15	SO	..	3 19	..	..	..	..	3 22	..	..	3 23	..	..	..
46	..	2 59	..	..	..	..	3 9	..	..	..	..	..	3 18	3 18	3 11	..	3 23	3 24	..	..	..	..	..	..	..	..	SO	3 29
47	2 50	..	..	..	..	..	..	..	..	..	..	..	..	..	..	..	..	..	..	..	..	..	..	..	..	..	3 20	..
48	2 53	..	..	SO	SX	..	..	..	..	..	..	..	..	..	..	..	..	..	..	..	..	..	..	..	..	..	3 23	..
49	2 57	3 3	..	3 7	3 11	..	..	..	..	..	..	..	..	..	..	..	..	..	..	..	..	..	..	..	..	..	3 27	3 33
50	..	3 6	..	3 9	3 13	..	..	..	..	..	..	..	..	..	..	..	..	..	..	..	..	..	..	..	..	‖ 1 minute *earlier* on Saturdays	..	3J35
51	..	3 8	..	3 12	3 16	..	..	..	..	..	..	..	..	..	..	..	..	..	..	..	..	..	..	..	..	..	..	3 38
52	..	3 11	..	..	..	..	..	..	..	..	..	..	..	..	..	..	..	..	..	..	..	..	..	..	..	..	..	3J40
53	..	..	..	..	..	..	..	3 12	..	..	..	..	..	..	..	..	..	..	..	..	..	3 25	..	..	..	..	..	..
54	..	..	..	..	..	..	..	3 14	..	..	..	..	..	..	..	..	..	..	..	..	..	3 27	..	..	..	..	..	..
55	..	..	..	..	..	..	..	3 17	..	..	..	..	..	..	..	..	..	..	..	..	..	3 30	..	..	..	..	..	..
56	..	..	..	..	..	..	..	3 19	..	..	..	..	..	..	..	..	..	..	..	..	..	3 32	..	..	..	..	..	..
57	..	..	..	..	..	..	3 12	..	..	..	..	..	..	..	3 14	..	..	3 27	..	..	..	..	..	..	..	..	..	J 1 minute later on Saturdays
58	..	..	..	..	..	..	3 13	..	..	..	..	..	..	..	3 15	..	..	3 28	..	..	..	..	..	..	..	..	..	..
59	..	..	..	..	..	..	3 15	..	..	..	..	..	..	..	3 17	..	..	3 30	..	..	..	..	..	..	..	..	..	..
60	..	..	..	..	..	..	3 18	..	..	..	..	..	..	..	3 20	..	..	3 33	..	..	..	..	..	..	..	..	..	..
61	..	..	..	..	..	..	3 20	..	..	..	..	..	..	..	3 22	..	..	3 35	..	From Victoria, dep 3 18 p.m.	..	..	..	..	..	..	..	..
62	..	..	..	..	..	..	3 23	..	..	..	..	..	..	..	3 25	..	..	3 38	..	..	..	..	..	..	..	..	..	..
63	..	..	..	..	..	..	3 25	..	..	..	..	..	..	..	3 27	..	..	3 40	..	..	..	..	..	..	..	..	..	..
64	..	..	..	..	..	..	..	..	..	..	..	..	..	..	..	..	..	..	3 24	..	..	..	..	..	..	..	..	..
65	..	..	..	3 14	3 18	..	..	..	..	..	..	..	..	..	..	..	..	..	3 27	..	..	..	..	..	..	..	..	..
66	..	..	..	3 17	3 21	..	..	..	..	..	..	..	..	..	..	..	..	..	..	..	..	..	..	..	..	..	..	..
67	..	..	..	3 19	3 23	..	..	..	..	..	..	..	..	..	..	..	..	..	..	..	..	..	..	..	..	..	..	..
68	..	..	..	3 22	3 26	..	..	..	..	Via Worcester Park	..	..	..	..	..	..	..	..	3 32	3 35	..	..	Via Worcester Park	..	..	..	..	..
69	..	..	..	3 24	3 28	..	..	..	..	..	..	..	..	..	..	..	..	..	..	3 37	..	..	..	..	..	..	..	..
70	..	..	..	3 27	3 31	..	..	..	..	..	..	..	..	..	..	..	..	..	..	3 40	..	..	..	..	..	..	..	..
71	..	3 14	..	..	..	..	..	3 23	..	..	..	3 20	..	..	..	..	..	..	..	..	..	3 36	..	..	..	3 41	..	3J43
72	..	3 16	..	..	..	..	..	..	..	..	..	..	..	..	..	..	..	..	..	..	..	3 38	..	..	..	..	..	3J45
73	..	3 20	..	..	..	..	..	3 27	..	..	..	3 24	..	..	..	..	..	..	..	..	..	3 41	..	..	3 35	3 45	..	3J48
74	..	3 23	..	..	..	..	..	..	..	..	..	..	..	..	..	..	..	..	..	..	..	..	..	..	..	..	..	3J51
75	..	..	..	3 31	3 35	..	3 31	..	..	..	..	..	3 30	3 31	3 33	..	3 35	3 46	3 38	3 44	..	..	..	..	..	..	..	..
76	..	..	..	..	..	..	..	..	..	3 23	..	..	..	3 35	..	..	..	..	..	..	..	..	3 41	..	..	..	..	..
77	..	..	..	..	..	..	..	..	..	..	..	..	..	3 37	..	..	..	..	..	..	..	..	..	..	..	..	..	..
78	..	3 27	..	..	..	..	..	3 33	..	..	..	3 30	..	..	..	..	..	..	..	..	..	3 47	..	3 40	3 42	3‖51	..	3J54

HORSHAM, REIGATE, REDHILL, TATTENHAM CORNER, CATERHAM,

For Notes, see page 317a

Up	No.	p.m							Week Days—continued							p.m							No.
		3	3	3	..	3	..	3	3	3	..	3	3	..	3	..		3	3	3	3	3	
Horsham ....dep	1																2§48						1
Reigate........... "	2																3 23						2
Redhill........... "	3																3 30						3
Merstham	4																3 34						4
Coulsdon South	5																3 41		SX		SO		5
Tattenham Corner. dep	6																§ Via Three Bridges		3 23		3 23		6
Tadworth N	7																		3 26		3 26		7
Kingswood M	8																		3 29		3 29		8
Chipstead	9																		3 33		3 33		9
Woodmansterne	10																		3 36		3 36		10
Smitham	11																		3 38		3 38		11
Reedham	12																		3 41		3 41		12
Purley 252.......... arr	13																		3 43		3 43		13
Caterham.......... dep	14																		3 33		3 33		14
Warlingham	15																		3 37		3 37		15
Whyteleafe	16																		3 39		3 39		16
Kenley	17																		3 42		3 42		17
Purley 252.......... arr	18																		3 45		3 45		18
Coulsdon North..... dep	19																	3J41					19
Purley 252	20																3 44	3J44	3 47		3 47		20
Purley Oaks	21																	3J46			3 50		21
South Croydon 234	22											SX			SO			3J49			3 52		22
Effingham Junction dep	23											3 10			3 12								23
Bookham	24											3 13			3 15								24
Dorking North..... dep	25																						25
Boxhill and Burford	26																						26
Leatherhead...[Bridge J	27											3 17			3 19								27
Ashtead	28											3 21			3 23								28
Epsom 427	29											3 26			3 28								29
Ewell East H	30											3 29			3 31								30
Cheam	31											3 32			3 34								31
Epsom Downs...... dep	32	From London Bridge, via Forest Hill	From London Bridge, via Forest Hill						3 19														32
Banstead	33								3 22														33
Belmont	34								3 25														34
Sutton 322	35								3 28	3 32		3 35			3 37								35
Carshalton Beeches	36								3 30	3 34													36
Wallington	37								3 33	3 37													37
Waddon G	38								3 36														38
West Croydon 319 arr	39								3 39														39
West Croydon 319 dep	40								3 39														40
Carshalton	41											3 38			3 40								41
Hackbridge	42											3 41			3 43								42
Mitcham Junction	43											3 43			3 45								43
East Croydon .. arr	44																3 50	3 52	3 53		3 55		44
East Croydon .. dep	45	SO	SX				3 43									3 47	3 51	3 52	3 53		3 55		45
Norwood Junction F	46	3 29	3 29										SX								3 58		46
Beckenham Jn. dep	47												3 38										47
Birkbeck	48			SO		SX							3 41							SX			48
Crystal Palace D	49			3 39		3 40							3 45							3 48			49
Gipsy Hill (for Upper	50												3 47							3 50			50
West Norwood.[N'wood)	51							SX					3 50							3 53			51
Streatham Hill	52							3 46					3 53										52
Selhurst	53	3 32	3 32						3 42									3 55					53
Thornton Heath	54	3 34	3 34						3 44									3 57					54
Norbury	55	3 37	3 37						3 47									4 0					55
Streatham Common	56	3 39	3 40						3 49									4 J2					56
Anerley	57																	J 1minute later on Saturdays				From Victoria, dep. 3 47 p.m	57
Penge West C	58																						58
Sydenham ....[Lane	59			3 42		3 43																	59
Forest Hill, for Lordship	60			3 44		3 46																	60
Honor Oak Park	61			3 47		3 48																	61
Brockley B.......[Line)	62			3 50		3 51																	62
New Cross Gate (for E.L.	63			3 52		3 53																	63
Streatham	64	3 41	3 42									3 48			3 51								64
Tulse Hill	65	3 45	3 45					3 49				3 52			3 55					3 55			65
North Dulwich	66	3 48																		3 58			66
East Dulwich	67	3 50																		4 0		SO	67
Peckham Rye	68	3 52	3 50					3 54				3 56			4 0					4 2		4 3	68
Queen's Road, Peckham	69	3 54																		4 4		4 5	69
South Bermondsey	70	3 57																		4 7		4 8	70
Balham & Upper Tooting	71								3 53				3 56					4 J6					71
Wandsworth Common A	72												3 58										72
Clapham Junction	73								3 57				4 1				4 2	4J10					73
Battersea Park	74												4 4										74
London Bridge..... arr	75	4 1	3 56	3 58		3 59		4 0				4 4			4 7				4 8	4 11	4 11	4 12	75
Waterloo * .... "	76																				4 15		76
Charing Cross * .. "	77																				4 17		77
Victoria.......... "	78						3 58		4 3				4 7			4 3	4 7	4 16					78

DORKING NORTH, SUTTON, CROYDON, CRYSTAL PALACE, and LONDON

p.m. — **Week Days**—*continued* — p.m.

No.																												
1	3	2 52	3	3	3		3		3		3	3	3	3	3	3	3	3	3	3	3§15		3	3	3	SO 3 20	SX 3 20	3
2		3				3 40															3 52							
3						3 50															3 58					3	3	
4																					4 2							
5																			SX	SO	4 8							
6																			3 42	3 43								
7																			3 45	3 46	§ Via Three Bridges							
8																			3 48	3 49								
9																			3 52	3 53								
10																			3 55	3 56								
11																			3 57	3 58								
12																			4 0	4 1								
13																			4 2	4 3								
14																			3 52	3 53								
15																			3 56	3 57								
16																			3 58	3 59								
17																			4 1	4 2								
18				SX															4 4	4 5								
19			J 1 minute later on Saturdays	3 51																								
20				3 54															4 7	4 7	4 12							
21				3 56															4 9	4 9								
22				3 59													SX		4 12	4 12								
23																	3 38											
24																	3 41											
25		3 18																								3 46	3 46	
26		3 21																								3 48	3 48	
27		3 26															3 46									3 53	3 53	
28		3 30															3 50	SX								3 57	3 57	
29		3 34	3 40														3 54	3 56								4 1	4 2	
30			3 43															3 59								4 4	4 5	
31			3 46															4 2							SO	4 7	4 8	
32	3 28														3 49										4 0			
33	3 31														3 52										4 3			
34	3 34													From London Bridge, via Streatham	3 55										4 6			
35	3 39		3J49												3 58	4 2		4 5							4 9	4 11	4 11	
36	3 41														4 0	4 4									4 11			
37	3 44														4 3	4 7									4 14			
38	3 47														4 6										4 17			
39	3 50														4 9										4 20			
40	3 50											3 55			4 9										4 20			
41			3 53															4 8								4 14	4 15	
42			3 55															4 10								4 16	4 17	
43			3 58															4 13								4 19	4 20	
44				4 2		4 4													4 14	4 14	4 17							
45				4 2		4 5			SX										4 14	4 14	4 18							
46	3 54			4 6					4 13		SO	3 59		4 9					4 18	4 18	4 22			SX	4 24			
47											3 50													4 7				
48											3 53		SX											4 10				SX
49											3 57	4 3	4 9										4 11	4 14				4 24
50												4 6											4 13	4 16				4 26
51							SX					4 8											4 16	4 19				4 29
52							4 5					4 11												4 22				
53															4 12													
54															4 14								H 1 minute earlier on Saturdays					
55															4 17													
56															4 19													
57	3 57													4 12											4 27			
58	3 58				From Victoria, dep. 3 56 p.m									4 13											4 28			
59	4 0												4 12	4 15											4 30			
60	4 3												4 14	4 18											4 33			
61	4 5												4 16	4 20											4 35			
62	4 8												4 19	4 23											4 38			
63	4 10												4 22	4 25											4 40			
64																										4 24	4 25	
65							4 8																4 18			4 27	4 28	4 31
66							4 11										Via Worcester Park						4 21					4 34
67		Via Worcester Park			SX		4 13																4 23					4 36
68					4 11		4 15																4 26			4 32	4 33	4 38
69					4 13		4 17																4 28					
70					4 16		4 20																4H32					
71			4 5									4 14			4 23			4 19						4 24				
72												4 16												4 26				
73			4 9			4 16						4 19			4 27			4 24						4 29				
74												4 22												4 32				
75	4 16			4 19	4 20		4 24		4 26				4 27	4 31					4 30	4 31	4 36		4H36		4 46	4 40	4 39	4 44
76		4 3															4 23			4 35								
77																				4 37								
78			4 14			4 22						4 26			4 33			4 30						4 36				

HORSHAM, REIGATE, REDHILL, TATTENHAM CORNER, CATERHAM,

For Notes, see page 317a

Up	No.	p.m.							Week Days—*continued*								p.m.						No.
		3	3	3	3	3	3	3	..	..	3	3	3	3	3	..	3	3	3	3	..	3	
Horsham .... dep	1	..	..	..	..	..	..	..	..	..	..	..	..	..	..	..	..	..	..	..	..	..	1
Reigate .... "	2	..	..	..	..	..	..	..	..	..	..	..	..	..	..	..	..	..	..	..	..	..	2
Redhill .... "	3	..	..	..	..	..	..	..	..	..	..	..	..	..	..	..	..	..	..	..	..	..	3
Merstham	4	..	..	..	..	..	..	..	..	..	..	..	..	..	..	..	..	..	..	..	..	..	4
Coulsdon South	5	..	..	..	..	..	..	..	..	..	..	..	..	..	..	..	S X	..	..	..	..	..	5
Tattenham Corner dep	6	..	..	..	..	..	..	..	..	..	..	..	..	..	..	..	4 2	..	..	..	..	..	6
Tadworth N	7	..	..	..	..	..	..	..	..	..	..	..	..	..	..	..	4 5	..	..	..	..	..	7
Kingswood M	8	..	..	..	..	..	..	..	..	..	..	..	..	..	..	..	4 8	..	..	..	..	..	8
Chipstead	9	..	..	..	..	..	..	..	..	..	..	..	..	..	..	..	4 12	..	..	..	..	..	9
Woodmansterne	10	..	..	..	..	..	..	..	..	..	..	..	..	..	..	..	4 15	..	..	..	..	..	10
Smitham	11	..	..	..	..	..	..	..	..	..	..	..	..	..	..	..	4 17	..	..	..	..	..	11
Reedham	12	..	..	..	..	..	..	..	..	..	..	..	..	..	..	..	4 20	..	..	..	..	..	12
Purley 252 .... arr	13	..	..	..	..	..	..	..	..	..	..	..	..	..	..	..	4 22	..	..	..	..	..	13
Caterham .... dep	14	..	..	..	..	..	..	..	..	..	..	..	..	..	..	..	4 8	..	..	..	..	..	14
Warlingham	15	..	..	..	..	..	..	..	..	..	..	..	..	..	..	..	4 12	..	..	..	..	..	15
Whyteleafe	16	..	..	..	..	..	..	..	..	..	..	..	..	..	..	..	4 14	..	..	..	..	..	16
Kenley	17	..	..	..	..	..	..	..	..	..	..	..	..	..	..	..	4 17	..	..	..	..	..	17
Purley 252 .... arr	18	..	..	..	..	..	..	..	..	..	..	..	..	..	..	..	4 20	..	..	..	..	..	18
Coulsdon North ..... dep	19	..	..	..	..	4 11	..	..	..	..	..	..	..	..	..	..	..	..	..	..	..	..	19
Purley 252	20	..	..	..	..	4 14	..	..	..	..	..	..	..	..	..	..	4 24	..	..	..	..	..	20
Purley Oaks	21	..	..	..	..	4 16	..	..	S X	S O	..	..	..	..	..	..	..	..	..	..	..	..	21
South Croydon 234	22	..	..	..	..	4 19	..	..	4 24	4 24	..	..	..	S O	..	..	4 28	..	..	..	..	..	22
Effingham Junction dep	23	..	..	..	..	..	..	..	..	..	..	..	..	3 55	..	..	..	..	..	..	..	..	23
Bookham	24	..	..	..	..	..	..	..	..	..	..	..	S X	3 58	..	..	..	..	..	..	..	..	24
Dorking North ...... dep	25	..	..	..	..	..	..	..	..	..	..	..	3 58	..	..	..	..	..	..	..	..	..	25
Boxhill and Burford	26	..	..	..	..	..	..	..	..	..	..	..	4 1	..	..	..	..	..	..	..	..	..	26
Leatherhead ...[Bridge J	27	..	..	..	..	..	..	..	..	..	..	..	4 6	4 2	..	..	..	..	..	..	..	..	27
Ashtead	28	..	..	..	..	..	..	..	..	..	..	S X	4 10	4 6	S O	..	..	..	..	..	..	..	28
Epsom 427	29	..	..	..	..	..	..	..	..	..	..	4 16	4 14	4 14	4 16	..	..	..	..	..	..	..	29
Ewell East H	30	..	..	..	..	..	..	..	..	..	..	4 19	..	..	4 19	..	..	..	..	..	..	..	30
Cheam	31	..	..	S X	..	..	..	..	..	..	S X	4 22	..	..	4 22	..	..	..	..	..	..	..	31
Epsom Downs ...... dep	32	..	..	4 4	..	..	..	..	..	..	4 9	..	..		..	..	..	..	..	..	..	..	32
Banstead	33	..	..	4 7	..	..	..	..	..	..	4 12	..	..		..	..	..	..	..	..	..	..	33
Belmont	34	..	..	4 10	..	..	..	..	..	..	4 15	..	..		..	..	..	..			..	..	34
Sutton 322	35	..	..	4 13	..	..	..	..	..	..	4 18	4 25	..	Arr. Epsom 4 10 p.m	4 25	..	..	..	From London Bridge, via Streatham	From London Bridge, via Forest Hill	..	..	35
Carshalton Beeches	36	..	..	4 15	..	..	..	..	..	..	4 20	..	..		..	..	..	..			..	..	36
Wallington	37	..	..	4 18	..	..	..	..	..	..	4 23	..	..		..	..	..	..			..	..	37
Waddon G	38	..	..	4 21	..	..	..	..	..	..	4 26	..	..		..	..	..	..			..	..	38
West Croydon 319 arr	39	..	S X	4 24	..	..	..	S O	..	..	4 29	..	..		..	..	..	..			..	..	39
West Croydon 319 dep	40	..	4 20	4 24	..	..	..	4 25	..	..	4 29	..	..		..	..	..	..			..	..	40
Carshalton	41	..	..	..	..	..	..	..	..	..	..	4 28	..	..	4 28	..	..	..			..	..	41
Hackbridge	42	..	..	..	..	..	..	..	..	..	..	4 30	..	..	4 30	..	..	..			..	..	42
Mitcham Junction	43	..	..	..	..	..	..	..	..	..	..	4 33	..	..	4 33	..	..	..			..	..	43
East Croydon ... arr	44	..	..	..	..	4 22	..	..	4 27	4 28	..	..	..	..	..	..	4 32	..			..	..	44
East Croydon ... dep	45	..	..	..	..	4 22	..	..	..	4 28	..	..	..	..	..	..	4 32	..	S X	S O	..	..	45
Norwood Junction F ..	46	..	4 24	4 28	..	..	S O	4 29	..	..	..	..	..	..	..	..	4 35	..	4 31	4 29	..	S X	46
Beckenham Jn. dep	47	..	..	..	..	..	4 20	..	..	..	..	..	..	..	..	..	..	..	..	..	..	4 29	47
Birkbeck	48	..	..	..	..	..	4 23	..	..	..	..	..	..	..	..	..	..	..	..	..	..	4 32	48
Crystal Palace D	49	..	4 29	..	..	..	4 27	4 33	..	..	..	..	..	..	..	..	..	..	..	..	..	4 36	49
Gipsy Hill (for Upper	50	..	4 31	..	..	..	..	4 36	..	..	..	..	..	..	..	..	..	..	..	..	..	4 38	50
West Norwood. [N'wood)	51	S X	4 34	..	..	..	..	4 38	..	..	..	..	..	..	..	..	..	..	..	..	..	4 41	51
Streatham Hill	52	4 31	4 37	..	..	..	..	4 41	..	..	..	..	..	..	..	..	..	..	..	..	..	4 44	52
Selhurst	53	..	..	..	..	4 25	..	..	..	..	4 32	..	..	..	..	..	..	..	..	4 32	..	..	53
Thornton Heath	54	..	..	..	..	4 27	..	..	..	..	4 34	..	..	..	..	..	..	..	..	4 34	..	..	54
Norbury	55	..	..	..	..	4 30	..	..	..	..	4 37	..	..	..	..	..	..	..	..	4 37	..	..	55
Streatham Common	56	..	..	..	..	4J32	..	..	..	..	4 39	..	..	..	..	..	..	..	..	4 39	..	..	56
Anerley	57	..	..	..	..	..	..	..	..	..	..	..	..	..	..	..	..	..	4 34	..	..	..	57
Penge West C	58	..	..	..		..	..	..	..	..	..	..	..	..	..	..	..		4 36	..	..	..	58
Sydenham ....[Lane	59	..	..	..			..	..	..	..	..	..	..	..	..	..	..		4 38	..	..	..	59
Forest Hill, for Lordship	60	..	..	..	From Victoria, dep. 4 18 p.m		..	..	..	..	..	..	..	..	..	..	..	From Victoria, dep. 4 28 p.m	4 41	..	..	..	60
Honor Oak Park	61	..	..	..		J 1 minute later on Saturdays	..	..	..	..	..	..	..	..	..	..	..		4 44	..	..	..	61
Brockley B ......[Line)	62	..	..	..			..	..	..	..	..	..	..	..	..	..	..		4 46	..	..	..	62
New Cross Gate (for E.L.	63	..	..	4 37			..	..	..	..	..	..	..	..	..	..	..		4 49	..	..	..	63
Streatham	64	..	..	..			..	..	..	..	..	..	..	..	..	..	..		..	4 41	..	..	64
Tulse Hill	65	4 34	..	..			..	..	..	..	..	..			..	..	..		..	4 45	..	..	65
North Dulwich	66	4 37	..	..			..	..	..	..	..	..			..	..	..		..	4 48	..	..	66
East Dulwich	67	4 39	..	..	S O		..	..	..	..	..	..			..	..	..	S X	..	4 50	..	..	67
Peckham Rye	68	4 41	..	..	4 35		..	..	..	..	..	..	Via Worcester Park	Via Worcester Park	..	..	..	4 44	..	4 52	..	..	68
Queen's Road, Peckham	69	4 43	..	..	4 37		..	..	..	..	..	..			..	..	..	4 46	..	4 54	..	..	69
South Bermondsey	70	4 46	..	..	4 40		..	..	..	..	..	..			..	..	..	4 49	..	4 57	..	..	70
Balham & Upper Tooting	71	..	4 39	..	..	4J36	..	4 44	..	..	4 43	4 39			4 40	..	..	..	..	..	..	4 46	71
Wandsworth Common A	72	..	4 41	..	..	4SO39	..	4 46	..	..	..	..			..	..	..	..	..	..	..	4 48	72
Clapham Junction	73	..	4 44	..	..	4J40	..	4 49	..	4 41	4 47	4 43			4 44	..	..	..	..	..	..	4 51	73
Battersea Park	74	..	4 47	..	..	..	..	4 52	..	..	..	..			..	..	..	..	..	..	..	4 54	74
LONDON BRIDGE ..... arr	75	4 50	..	4 44	4 44	..	..	..	..	..	..	..	..	..	..	..	4 49	4 53	4 54	5 1	..	..	75
WATERLOO* .... "	76	..	..	..	..	..	..	..	..	..	..	..	4 43	4 43	..	..	..	..	..	..	..	..	76
CHARING CROSS * .. "	77	..	..	..	..	..	..	..	..	..	..	..	..	..	..	..	..	..	..	..	..	..	77
VICTORIA .... "	78	..	4 51	..	..	4J46	..	4 56	..	4 48	4 54	4 49	..	..	4 50	..	..	..	..	..	..	4 58	78

DORKING NORTH, SUTTON, CROYDON, CRYSTAL PALACE, and LONDON

Week Days—*continued* (p.m.)

No.	3	3	..	3	3	3	3	..	3	3	–	3	..	3	S X	3	S O	3	3	3	3	3	3	..	3	3	3	3
1															3§48		3§48											
2	..	..	..	..	..	..	..	..	..	..	..	..	..	..	4 22	..	4 22	..	..	..	..	..	..	..	..	..	..	..
3	..	..	..	..	..	..	..	..	..	..	..	..	..	..	4 29	..	4 29	..	..	..	..	..	..	..	..	..	..	..
4	..	..	..	..	..	..	..	..	..	..	..	..	..	..	4 33	..	4 33	..	..	..	..	..	..	..	..	..	..	..
5	..	..	..	..	..	..	..	..	..	..	..	..	..	..	4 39	..	4 39	..	..	..	S X	S O	..	..	..	..	..	..
6	..	..	..	..	..	..	..	..	..	..	..	..	..	..		..		..	..	..	4 23	4 23	..	..	..	..	..	..
7	..	..	..	..	..	..	..	..	..	..	..	..	..	..		..		..	..	..	4 26	4 26	..	..	..	..	..	..
8	..	..	..	..	..	..	..	..	..	..	..	..	..	..		..		..	..	..	4 29	4 29	..	..	..	..	..	..
9	..	..	..	..	..	..	..	..	..	..	..	..	..	..	§ Via Three Bridges	..	§ Via Three Bridges	..	..	..	4 33	4 33	..	..	..	..	..	..
10	..	..	..	..	..	..	..	..	..	..	..	..	..	..		..		..	..	..	4 36	4 36	..	..	..	..	..	..
11	..	..	..	..	..	..	..	..	..	..	..	..	..	..		..		..	..	..	4 38	4 38	..	..	..	..	..	..
12	..	..	..	..	..	..	..	..	..	..	..	..	..	..		..		..	..	..	4 41	4 41	..	..	..	..	..	..
13	..	..	..	..	..	..	..	..	..	..	..	..	..	..		..		..	..	..	4 43	4 43	..	..	..	..	..	..
14	..	..	..	..	..	..	..	..	..	..	..	..	..	..	..	..	..	..	..	..	4 33	4 33	..	..	..	..	..	..
15	..	..	..	..	..	..	..	..	..	..	..	..	..	..	..	..	..	..	..	..	4 37	4 37	..	..	..	..	..	..
16	..	..	..	..	..	..	..	..	..	..	..	..	..	..	..	..	..	..	..	..	4 39	4 39	..	..	..	..	..	..
17	..	..	..	..	..	..	..	..	..	..	..	..	..	..	..	..	..	..	..	..	4 42	4 42	..	..	..	..	..	..
18	..	..	..	..	..	..	S X	..	..	..	..	..	..	S X	..	..	..	S O	..	..	4 45	4 45	..	..	..	..	..	..
19	..	..	..	..	..	..	4 31	..	..	..	..	..	..	4 36	..	..	..	4 42	..	..	..	..	..	..	..	..	..	..
20	..	..	..	..	..	..	4 34	..	..	..	..	..	..	4 39	4 43	..	4 43	4 45	..	..	4 48	4 47	..	..	..	..	..	..
21	..	..	..	..	..	..	4 36	..	..	..	..	..	..	4 42	..	..	..	4 47	..	..	..	4 50	..	..	..	..	..	..
22	..	..	..	..	..	..	4 39	..		..	..	S X	..	4 44	..	S O	..	4 50	..	..	..	4 52	..	..	..	..	..	..
23	..	..	..	..	..	..	..	..		..	..	4 10	..	..	..	4 12	..	..	..	..	..	..	..	..	..	..	..	..
24	..	..	..	..	..	..	..	..		S O	..	4 13	..	..	..	4 15	..	..	..	..	..	..	..	..	..	..	..	..
25	..	..	..	..	..	..	..	..	Arr Sutton 4 30 p.m.	4 3	..	..	..	..	..	..	..	..	..	..	..	..	..	..	..	..	..	..
26	..	..	..	..	..	..	..	..		4 6	..	..	..	..	..	..	..	..	..	..	..	..	..	..	..	..	..	..
27	..	..	..	..	..	..	..	..		4 10	..	4 17	..	..	..	4 20	..	..	..	..	..	..	..	..	..	..	..	..
28	..	..	..	..	..	..	..	..		..	..	4 21	..	..	..	4 24	..	..	..	..	..	..	..	..	..	..	..	..
29	..	..	..	..	..	..	..	..	..	..	..	4 25	..	..	..	4 28	..	..	..	..	..	..	..	..	..	..	..	..
30	..	..	..	..	..	..	..	..	..	..	..	4 28	..	..	..	4 31	..	..	..	..	..	..	..	..	..	..	..	..
31	..	..	..	S O	..	..	..	..	S X	..	..	4 31	..	..	..	4 34	..	..	..	..	..	..	S X	..	..	..	S O	..
32	..	..	..	4 19	..	..	..	..	4 21	..	..	..	..	..	..	..	..	..	..	..	..	..	4 28	..	..	..	4 30	..
33	..	..	..	4 22	..	..	..	..	4 24	..	..	..	..	..	..	..	..	..	..	..	..	..	4 31	..	..	..	4 33	..
34	..		..	4 25	S O	..	..	..	4 27	..	..	..	..	..	..	..	..	..	..	..	..	..	4 34	..	..		4 36	S X
35	..		..	4 28	4 32	..	..	..	4 33	..	..	4 34	..	..	..	4 37	..	..	..	..	..	..	4 37	..	..		4 39	4 42
36	..		..	4 30	4 34	..	..	..	4 35	..	..	..	..	..	..	..	..	..	..	..	..	..	4 39	..	..		4 41	4 44
37	..		..	4 33	4 37	..	..	..	4 38	..	..	..	..	..	..	..	..	..	..	..	..	..	4 42	..	..		4 44	4 46
38	..	From London Bridge, via Forest Hill	..	4 36	..	..	..	..	4 41	..	..	..	..	..	..	..	..	..	..	..	..	..	4 45	..	..		4 47	..
39	..		..	4 39	..	..	..	..	4 44	..	..	..	..	..	..	..	..	..	..	S X	..	..	4 48	..	..		4 50	..
40	..		..	4 39	..		..	..	4 44	..	..	..	..	..	..	..	..	..	..	4 40	..	..	4 48	..	..	From London Bridge, via Streatham	4 50	..
41			..	..	..		..	..	..	..	..	4 37	..	..	..	4 40	..	..	..	..	..	..	..	..	..		..	..
42			..	..	..		..	..	..	..	..	4 40	..	..	..	4 43	..	..	..	..	..	..	..	..	..		..	..
43			..	..	..		..	..	..	..	..	4 42	..	..	..	4 45	..	..	..	..	..	..	..	..	..		..	..
44	J 1 minute later on Saturdays		..	..	..		4 42	S O	..	..	..	..	..	4 47	4 48	..	4 48	4 52	..	..	4 53	4 55	..	..	..		..	..
45		S X	..	..	..	From London Bridge, via Tulse Hill	4 42	4 42	..	..	..	..	4 46	4 47	4 48	..	4 50	4 52	..	..	4 53	4 55	..	..	..	S X	..	..
46		4 31	..	..	..		..	..	4 48	..	..	..	..	4 51	..	..	..	..	..	4 44	4 57	4 58	..	..	..	4 53	4 54	..
47		..	..	..	..		..	..	..	..	..	..	..	..	..	..	..	..	..	..	..	..	..	..	..	..	..	..
48		..	..	..	..		..	..	..	..	..	..	..	..	..	..	..	..	S X	..	..	..	..	..	..	..	..	..
49	4J38	..	..	..	..		..	..	..	..	..	..	..	..	..	..	..	..	4 45	4 49	..	..	..	..	..	..	..	..
50	..	..	..	..	..		..	..	..	..	..	..	..	..	..	..	..	..	4 48	4 51	..	..	..	..	..	..	..	..
51	..	..	..	..	..	S X	..	..	..	..	..	..	..	..	..	..	..	..	4 51	4 54	..	..	..	..	..	..	..	..
52	..	..	..	..	..	4 50	..	..	..	..	..	..	..	..	..	..	..	..	..	4 57	..	..	..	..	..	..	..	..
53	..	4 35	..	4 42	..	..	4 45	..	..	..	..	..	..	..	..	..	..	4 55	..	..	..	..	4 51	..	..	..	..	..
54	..	4 37	..	4 44	..	..	4 47	..	..	..	..	..	..	..	..	..	..	4 57	..	..	..	..	4 53	..	..	..	..	..
55	..	4 40	..	4 47	..	..	4 50	..	..	..	..	..	..	..	..	..	..	5 0	..	..	..	..	4 56	..		..	..	..
56	..	4 43	..	4 49	..	..	4 52	..	..	..	..	..	..	..	..	..	..	5 3	..	..	..	..	4 58	..		..	..	..
57	..	..	..	..	..	..	..	..	..	..	..	..	..	..	..	..	..	..	..	..	..	..	..	..		4 56	4 57	..
58	..	..	..	..	..	..	..	..	..	..	..	..	..	..	..	..	..	..	..	..	..	..	..	..		4 57	4 58	..
59	4 42	..	..	..	..	..	..	..	..	..	..	..	..	..	..	..	..	..	..	..	..	..	..	..		4 59	5 0	..
60	4H45	..	..	..	..	..	..	..	..	..	..	..	..	..	..	..	..	..	..	..	..	..	..	..		5 2	5 3	..
61	4 47	..	..	..	..	..	..	..	..	..	..	..	..	..	..	..	..	..	..	..	..	..	..	..		5 4	5 5	..
62	4H50	..	..	..	..	..	..	..	..	..	..	..	..	..	..	..	..	..	..	..	..	..	..	..	From Victoria, dep. 4S§47, 4SX48 p.m.	5 7	5 8	..
63	4 52	..	..	..	..	..	..	..	..	..	..	..	..	5 1	..	..	..	..	..	..	..	..	..	..		5 9	5 10	..
64		4 45	..	..	..	..	..	..	..	..	..	4 48		..	..	4 51	..	..	..	..	..	..	..	..		..	..	..
65		4 48	..	..	..	..	..	..	..	..	..	4 52		..	..	4 55	..	..	4 54	..	..	..	..	..		..	..	..
66		..	..	..	..	..	..	..	..	..	..	..		..	..	..	..	..	4 57	..	..	..	..	..		..	..	..
67		..	..	..	..	..	..	..	..	..	..	..		..	..	..	..	..	4 59	..	..	..	..	..		..	..	..
68	H 1 minute *earlier* on Saturdays	..	..	..	..	..	..	..	..	..	..	..	J 1 minute later on Saturdays	..	..	5 0	..	..	5 1	..	..	..	..	..	5 4	..	..	..
69		..	..	..	..	..	..	..	..	..	..	..		..	..	..	..	..	5 3	..	..	..	..	..	5 6	..	..	..
70		..	..	..	..	..	..	..	..	..	..	..		..	..	..	..	..	5 6	..	..	..	..	..	5 9	..	..	..
71		..	..	4 53	..	4 52	4 56	..	..	..	..	..		..	..	..	..	5 7	..	4 59	..	..	5 2	..	..	..	..	..
72		..	..	..	..	4 54	..	..	..	..	..	..		..	..	..	..	..	..	5 1	..	..	..	..	..	..	..	..
73		..	..	4 57	..	4 57	5 1	..	..	..	..	..		..	..	..	5 2	5 11	..	5 4	..	..	5 7	..	..	..	..	..
74		..	..	..	..	5 1	..	..	..	..	..	..		..	..	..	..	..	..	5 7	..	..	..	..	..	..	..	..
75	4H58	4 59	..	..	..	..	..	..	5 0	..	..	5 2	..	5 6	5 3	5 7	..	..	5 10	..	5 10	5 12	..	..	5 13	5 15	5 16	..
76	..	..	..	..	..	..	..	..	..	..	..	..	..	..	..	..	..	..	..	..	..	5 16	..	..	..	..	..	..
77	..	..	..	..	..	..	..	..	..	..	..	..	..	..	..	..	..	..	..	..	..	5 18	..	..	..	..	..	..
78	..	..	..	5 3	..	5 4	5 7	4 58	..	..	..	..	5 J1	..	..	..	5 7	5 16	..	5 11	..	..	5 13	..	..	..	..	..

HORSHAM, REIGATE, REDHILL, TATTENHAM CORNER, CATERHAM,

For Notes, see page 317a

Up	No.	p.m. —— Week Days—*continued* —— p.m.																					No
Horsham .... dep	1	3 52	③	③	..	③	③	③	③	..	..	③	..	③	③	③	..	③	③	③	③	③	1
Reigate .... "	2	③	..	..	..	..	..	..	..	..	..	..	4 40	..	..	..	..	..	..	..	..	..	2
Redhill .... "	3		..	..	..	..	..	..	..	..	..	..	4 50	..	..	..	..	..	..	..	..	..	3
Merstham	4	..	..	..	..	..	..	..	..	..	..	..	..	..	..	..	..	..	..	..	..	..	4
Coulsdon South	5	..	..	..	..	..	..	..	..	..	..	..	..	..	..	..	..	..	..	..	..	..	5
Tattenham Corner . dep	6	..	..	..	..	..	..	..	..	..	..	..	..	..	..	..	..	..	..	..	..	..	6
Tadworth **N**	7	..	..	..	..	..	..	..	..	..	..	..	..	..	..	..	..	..	..	..	..	..	7
Kingswood **M**	8	..	..	..	..	..	..	..	..	..	..	..	..	..	..	..	..	..	..	..	..	..	8
Chipstead	9	..	..	..	..	..	..	..	..	..	..	..	..	..	..	..	..	..	..	..	..	..	9
Woodmansterne	10	..	..	..	..	..	..	..	..	..	..	..	..	..	..	..	..	..	..	..	..	..	10
Smitham	11	..	..	..	..	..	..	..	..	..	..	..	..	..	..	..	..	..	..	..	..	..	11
Reedham	12	..	..	..	..	..	..	..	..	..	..	..	..	..	..	..	..	..	..	..	..	..	12
Purley 252 .... arr	13	..	..	..	..	..	..	..	..	..	..	..	..	..	..	..	..	..	..	..	..	..	13
Caterham .... dep	14	..	..	..	..	..	..	..	..	..	..	..	..	..	..	..	..	..	..	..	..	..	14
Warlingham	15	..	..	..	..	..	..	..	..	..	..	..	..	..	..	..	..	..	..	..	..	..	15
Whyteleafe	16	..	..	..	..	..	..	..	..	..	..	..	..	..	..	..	..	..	..	..	..	..	16
Kenley	17	..	..	..	..	..	..	..	..	..	..	..	..	..	..	..	..	..	..	..	..	..	17
Purley 252 .... arr	18	..	..	..	..	..	..	..	..	..	..	..	..	..	..	..	..	S X	S X	..	..	..	18
Coulsdon North ..... dep	19	..	..	..	..	..	..	..	..	..	..	..	..	..	..	..	..	4 51	4 56	..	..	..	19
Purley 252	20	..	..	..	..	..	..	..	..	..	..	..	..	..	..	..	..	4 54	4 59	..	..	..	20
Purley Oaks	21	..	..	..	..	..	..	..	..	..	..	..	..	..	..	..	..	4 56	5 2	..	..	..	21
South Croydon 234	22	..	..	..	..	..	..	..	..	4 57	..	..	..	..	..	..	..	4 59	5 4	..	..	..	22
Effingham Junction dep	23	..	..	..	..	..	..	..	..	..	..	..	..	..	..	..	..	..	..	..	..	..	23
Bookham	24	..	..	..	..	..	..	..	..	..	..	..	..	S X	..	..	..	..	..	..	..	..	24
Dorking North ..... dep	25	4 18	..	..	..	..	..	..	..	..	..	..	..	4 29	..	..	..	..	..	..	..	..	25
Boxhill and Burford	26	4 21	..	..	..	..	..	..	..	..	..	..	..	4 32	..	..	..	..	..	..	..	..	26
Leatherhead ... [Bridge **J**	27	4 26	..	..	..	..	..	..	..	..	..	..	..	4 37	..	..	..	..	..	..	..	..	27
Ashtead	28	4 30	S X	S O	..	..	..	..	..	..	..	..	..	4 41	..	..	..	..	..	..	..	..	28
Epsom 427	29	4 34	4 36	4 40	..	..	..	..	..	..	..	..	..	4 45	..	..	..	..	..	..	..	..	29
Ewell East **H**	30	..	4 39	4 43	..	..	..	..	..	..	..	..	..	4 48	..	..	..	..	..	..	..	..	30
Cheam	31	..	4 42	4 46	..	..	..	..	..	..	..	S X	..	4 51	..	..	..	..	..	..	..	..	31
Epsom Downs ...... dep	32	..	..	..	..	..	..	..	..	..	..	4 44	..	..	..	..	..	..	..	..	..	..	32
Banstead	33	..	..	..	..	..	..	..	..	..	..	4 47	..	..	..	..	..	..	..	..	..	..	33
Belmont	34	..	..	..	..	..	..	..	..	..	..	4 50	..	..	..	..	..	..	..	..	..	..	34
Sutton 322	35	..	4 45	4 49	..	..	..	..	From London Bridge, via Forest Hill	J 1 minute later on Saturdays	..	4 53	..	4 55	..	..	..	..	..	..	..	..	35
Carshalton Beeches	36	..	..	..	..	..	..	..			..	4 55	..	..	..	..	..	..	..	..	..	..	36
Wallington	37	..	..	..	..	..	..	..			..	4 58	..	..	..	..	..	..	..	..	..	..	37
Waddon **G**	38	..	..	..	..	..	..	..			..	5 1	..	..	..	..	..	..	..	..	..	..	38
West Croydon 319 arr	39	..	..	..	..	..	..	..			..	5 4	..	..	..	..	..	S O	..	..	..	S X	39
West Croydon 319 dep	40	..	..	..	..	..	..	..			..	5 4	..	..	..	..	..	4 55	..	..	..	5 0	40
Carshalton	41	..	4 48	4 52	..	..	..	..			..	..	..	4 58	From London Bridge, via Tulse Hill	..	..	..	..	..	..	..	41
Hackbridge	42	..	4 50	4 54	..	..	..	..			..	..	..	5 0		..	..	..	..	..	..	..	42
Mitcham Junction	43	..	4 53	4 57	..	..	..	..			..	..	..	5 3		..	..	..	..	..	..	..	43
East Croydon .... arr	44	..	..	..	..	..	..	..		5J 1	..	..	5 5	..		..	..	..	5 2	5 7	..	..	44
East Croydon .... dep	45	..	..	..	..	..	..	..	S X	5J 1	..	..	5 5	..		..	..	..	5 2	5 7	..	..	45
Norwood Junction F ..	46	..	..	..	..	..	S X	..	4 52	..	..	5 8	..	..		S O	..	4 59	..	5 11	..	5 4	46
Beckenham Jn. dep	47	..	..	..	..	..	4 49	..	..	..	..	..	..	..		4 50	..	..	..	..	..	..	47
Birkbeck	48	..	..	..	..	..	4 52	S X	..	..	..	..	..	..		4 53	..	..	..	..	S X	..	48
Crystal Palace D	49	..	..	..	..	..	4 56	4 59	..	..	..	..	..	..		4 57	..	5 3	..	..	5 5	5 9	49
Gipsy Hill (for Upper	50	..	..	..	..	..	4 58	..	..	..	..	..	..	..		..	..	5 6	..	..	5 8	5 11	50
West Norwood. [N'wood)	51	..	..	..	..	S X	5 1	..	..	..	..	..	..	..	S X	..	..	5 8	..	..	5 10	5 14	51
Streatham Hill	52	..	..	..	..	4 58	5 4	..	..	..	..	..	..	..	5 9	..	..	5 11	..	..	..	5 17	52
Selhurst	53	..	..	..	..	..	..	..	4 55	..	..	..	..	..	..	..	..	..	5 5	..	..	..	53
Thornton Heath	54	..	..	..	..	..	..	..	4 57	..	..	..	..	..	..	..	..	..	5 7	..	..	..	54
Norbury	55	..	..	..	..	..	..	..	5 0	..	..	..	..	..	..	..	..	..	5 10	..	..	..	55
Streatham Common	56	..	..	..	..	..	..	..	5 2	..	..	..	..	..	..	..	..	..	5 12	..	..	..	56
Anerley	57	..	..	..	..	..	..	..	..	..	..	..	..	..	..	..	..	..	..	..	..	..	57
Penge West C	58	..	..	..	..	..	..	..	..	..	..	..	..	..	..	..	..	..	..	..	..	..	58
Sydenham .... [Lane	59	..	..	..	..	..	..	5 2	..	..	..	..	..	..	..	..	..	..	..	..	..	..	59
Forest Hill, for Lorship	60	..	..	..	..	..	..	5 5	..	..	..	..	..	..	..	..	..	..	..	..	..	..	60
Honor Oak Park	61	..	..	..	..	..	..	5 7	..	..	..	..	..	..	..	..	..	..	..	..	..	..	61
Brockley **B** .... [Line)	62	..	..	..	..	..	..	5 10	..	..	..	..	..	..	..	..	..	..	..	..	..	..	62
New Cross Gate (for E.L	63	..	..	..	..	..	..	5 12	..	..	..	..	..	..	..	..	..	..	..	..	..	..	63
Streatham	64	Via Worcester Park	..	..	..	..	..	..	5 4	..	..	..	..	5 8	..	..	..	..	..	..	..	..	64
Tulse Hill	65		..	..	..	5 1	..	..	5 8	..	..	..	..	5 11	..	..	..	..	..	..	5 13	..	65
North Dulwich	66		..	..	..	5 4	..	..	..	..	..	..	..	..	..	..	..	..	..	..	5 16	..	66
East Dulwich	67		..	..	..	5 6	..	..	..	..	..	..	..	..	..	..	..	..	..	..	5 18	..	67
Peckham Rye	68		..	..	..	5 8	..	..	..	..	..	..	..	..	..	..	..	..	..	..	5 21	..	68
Queen's Road. Peckham	69		..	..	..	5 10	..	..	..	..	..	..	..	..	..	..	..	..	..	..	5 23	..	69
South Bermondsey	70		..	..	..	5 13	..	..	..	..	..	..	..	..	..	..	..	..	..	..	5 26	..	70
Balham & Upper Tooting	71		4 59	5 4	..	..	5 6	..	..	..	..	..	..	..	5 12	..	..	5 14	5 16	..	..	5 19	71
Wandsworth Common **A**	72		..	..	..	..	5 8	..	..	..	..	..	..	..	5 14	..	..	5 16	..	..	..	5 21	72
Clapham Junction	73		5 3	5 8	..	..	5 11	..	..	..	..	..	5 16	..	5 17	..	..	5 19	5 21	..	..	5 24	73
Battersea Park	74		..	..	..	..	5 14	..	..	..	..	..	..	..	5 20	..	..	5 22	..	..	..	5 27	74
London Bridge ..... arr	75	..	..	..	..	5 17	..	5 18	5 19	5 20	..	5 21	..	5 22	..	..	—	..	..	5 24	5 30	..	75
Waterloo * .... "	76	5 4	..	..	..	..	—	..	..	..	..	..	..	..	..	..	..	..	..	..	..	..	76
Charing Cross * .. "	77	..	..	..	..	..	—	..	..	..	..	..	..	..	..	..	..	..	..	..	..	..	77
Victoria .... "	78	..	5 9	5 13	..	..	5 18	..	..	..	..	..	5 22	..	5 24	..	..	5 26	5 27	..	..	5 31	78

DORKING NORTH, SUTTON, CROYDON, CRYSTAL PALACE, and LONDON

Week Days—continued (p.m)

No.																									
1	3	3	3	3	3	3	3	3	3	3	3	3	3	3	3	4§15	3	SO 4 20	3	3	3	SX 4 20	3	3	3
2																4 50		3				3			
3																4 59									
4																5 3									
5		SX								SO						5 9									
6		4 42								4 43															
7		4 45								4 46															
8		4 48								4 49															
9		4 52								4 53						§ Via Three Bridges									
10		4 55								4 56															
11		4 57								4 58															
12		5 0								5 1															
13		5 2								5 3															
14		4 52								4 53															
15		4 56								4 57															
16		4 58								4 59															
17		5 1								5 2															
18		5 4								5 5	SX													SX	SO
19											5 8													5 11	5 12
20		5 8								5 8						5 13								5 14	5 15
21										5 11														5 16	5 17
22						SX				5 13														5 19	5 20
23						4 38																			
24						4 41																			
25																		4 46				4 48			
26																		4 48				4 50			
27						4 46												4 53				4 55			
28						4 50	SX											4 57				5 0			
29						4 54	4 58											5 1				5 5			
30							5 1											5 4				5 8			
31							5 4										SO	5 7		SX		5 11			
32			4 49														5 0			5 4					
33			4 52														5 3			5 7					
34			4 55	SO	SX												5 6			5 10					
35			4 58	5 2	5 2		5 7										5 9	5 11		5 13		5 15			
36			5 0	5 4	5 5												5 11			5 15					
37			5 3	5 7	5 7												5 14			5 18					
38	From London Bridge, via Streatham		5 6		5 11				From London Bridge, via Streatham								5 17		From London Bridge, via Forest Hill	5 21					
39			5 9		5 14												5 20			5 24					
40			5 9														5 20			5 24					
41							5 10											5 14				5 18			
42							5 12											5 16				5 20			
43							5 15						From Victoria via Wandsworth Common					5 19				5 23			
44		5 14								5 15	5 16					5 20								5 22	5 22
45	SO	5 14							SX	5 15	5 16					5 20			SX				From London Bridge, via Tulse Hill	5 22	5 22
46	5 9								5 13	5 18	5 20			SX		5 24	5 24		5 11	5 28					
47														5 9											
48												SO		5 12	SX										
49												5 11		5 16	5 19										
50												5 13		5 18											
51												5 16	SX	5 21									SX		
52													5 18	5 24									5 30		
53			5 12																5 14					5 25	5 25
54			5 14																5 16					5 27	5 27
55			5 17																5 20					5 30	5 30
56			5 19																5 23					5 33	5 33
57	5 12								5 15								5 27								
58	5 13								5 17								5 28								
59	5 15								5 19						5 22		5 30								
60	5 18								5 21						5 25		5 33								
61	5 20							From Victoria, dep. 5 7 p.m	5 24						5 27		5 35				From Victoria, dep. 5 18 p.m				
62	5 23								5 26						5 30		5 38								
63	5 25								5 29						5 32		5 40								
64			H 1 minute *earlier* on Saturdays															5 24	5 25			5 28			
65												5 18	5 21					5 27	5 28			5 31			
66												5 21	5 24												
67								SX				5 23	5 26								SO				
68								5 24				5 26	5 28					5 32			5 35	5 36			
69						Via Worcester Park		5 28				5 28	5 30								5 37				
70								5 29				5 31	5 33								5 40				
71			5 23				5 22							5 26									5 32	5 37	5 37
72														5 28									5 34		5 39
73			5 27				5 26							5 31									5 37	5 41	5 42
74														5 34									5 40		
75	5 31	5 30						5 33	5 34	5 31	5 33	5 35	5 37		5 38	5 38	5 46	5 38	5 39	5 42	5 44	5 42			
76						5 23				5 35															
77										5 37															
78			5H34				5 31							5 38									5 44	5 47	5 47

HORSHAM, REIGATE, REDHILL, TATTENHAM CORNER, CATERHAM,

For Notes, see page 317a

Up	No.	Week Days—continued p.m.																					No.
		3	3	3	3	3	3	3	3	3	3	3		3	3		3	3	3	3	3	3	
Horsham............dep	1												4 43			..							1
Reigate.......... "	2	..	..	..	..	..	..	..	..	..	..	..	..	..	..	..	..	..	..	..	..	..	2
Redhill............ "	3	..	..	..	..	..	..	..	..	..	..	..	..	..	..	..	..	..	..	..	..	..	3
Merstham..............	4	..	..	..	..	..	..	..	..	..	..	..	..	..	..	..	..	..	..	..	..	..	4
Coulsdon South.........	5	..	..	..	..	..	..	S X	..	..	..	..	..	..	..	..	..	..	..	..	..	..	5
Tattenham Corner. dep	6	..	..	..	..	..	..	5 4	..	..	..	..	..	..	..	..	..	..	..	..	..	..	6
Tadworth **N**............	7	..	..	..	..	..	..	5 7	..	..	..	..	..	..	..	..	..	..	..	..	..	..	7
Kingswood **M**..........	8	..	..	..	..	..	..	5 10	..	..	..	..	..	..	..	..	..	..	..	..	..	..	8
Chipstead..............	9	..	..	..	..	..	..	5 14	..	..	..	..	..	..	..	..	..	..	..	..	..	..	9
Woodmansterne..........	10	..	..	..	..	..	..	5 17	..	..	..	..	..	..	..	..	..	..	..	..	..	..	10
Smitham...............	11	..	..	..	..	..	..	5 19	..	..	..	..	..	..	..	..	..	..	..	..	..	..	11
Reedham...............	12	..	..	..	..	..	..	5 22	..	..	..	..	..	..	..	..	..	..	..	..	..	..	12
Purley 252..........arr	13	..	..	..	..	..	..	5 24	..	..	..	..	..	..	..	..	..	..	..	..	..	..	13
Caterham...........dep	14	..	..	..	..	..	..	5 14	..	..	..	..	..	..	..	..	..	..	..	..	..	..	14
Warlingham............	15	..	..	..	..	..	..	5 18	..	..	..	..	..	..	..	..	..	..	..	..	..	..	15
Whyteleafe............	16	..	..	..	..	..	..	5 20	..	..	..	..	..	..	..	..	..	..	..	..	..	..	16
Kenley................	17	..	..	..	..	..	..	5 23	..	..	..	..	..	..	..	..	..	..	..	..	..	..	17
Purley 252..........arr	18	..	..	..	..	..	S X	5 26	..	..	..	..	..	..	..	..	..	..	..	..	..	..	18
Coulsdon North.....dep	19	..	..	..	..	..	5 16	..	..	..	..	..	..	..	..	..	..	..	..	..	..	..	19
Purley 252............	20	..	..	..	..	..	5 19	5 29	..	..	..	..	..	..	..	..	..	..	..	..	..	..	20
Purley Oaks............	21	..	..	..	..	..	5 22	..	..	..	..	..	..	..	..	..	..	..	..	..	..	..	21
South Croydon 234......	22	..	..	..	..	..	5 24	..	..	S X	..	S O	..	..	..	..	..	..	..	..	..	..	22
Effingham Junction dep	23	..	..	..	..	..	..	..	..	4 51	..	4 55	..	..	..	..	..	..	..	..	..	..	23
Bookham...............	24	..	..	..	..	..	..	..	..	4 54	S X	4 58	..	..	..	..	..	..	..	..	..	..	24
Dorking North.....dep	25	..	..	..	..	..	..	..	..	..	4 55	..	5 2	..	..	..	..	..	..	..	..	..	25
Boxhill and Burford	26	..	..	..	..	..	..	..	..	..	4 57	..	..	..	..	..	..	..	..	..	..	..	26
Leatherhead...[Bridge **J**	27	..	..	..	..	..	..	..	..	4 59	5 2	5 2	..	..	..	..	..	..	..	..	..	..	27
Ashtead...............	28	..	..	..	..	..	..	..	..	..	5 6	5 6	..	..	..	..	..	..	..	..	..	..	28
Epsom 427............	29	..	..	..	..	..	..	..	..	..	5 14	5 14	..	..	5 17	..	..	..	..	..	..	..	29
Ewell East **H**..........	30	..	..	..	..	..	..	..	..	..	..	..	..	..	5 20	..	..	..	..	..	..	..	30
Cheam.................	31	..	..	..	..	..	..	..	S X	..	..	..	..	..	5 23	..	..	..	..	..	..	..	31
Epsom Downs......dep	32	..	..	..	..	..	..	..	5 9	..			..	..	..	..	..	..	..	..	..	..	32
Banstead...............	33	..	..	..	..	..	..	..	5 12	..			..	..	..	..	..	..	..			..	33
Belmont................	34	..	..	..	..	..	..	..	5 15	..			..	S X	..	..	..	..	..			..	34
Sutton 322............	35	..	..	..	..	..	..	..	5 18	..	Arr. Epsom 5 10 p.m	Arr. Epsom 5 10 p.m	5 20	5 22	5 26	..	..	..	..			..	35
Carshalton Beeches.....	36	..	..	..	..	..	..	..	5 20	..			..	5 25	..	..	..	..	..			..	36
Wallington.............	37	..	..	..	..	..	..	..	5 23	..			..	5 27	..	..	..	..	..			..	37
Waddon **G**.............	38	..	..	..	..	..	..	..	5 26	..			..	..	..	..	..	..	..	From London Bridge, via Streatham	From London Bridge, via Forest Hill	..	38
West Croydon 319 arr	39	..	..	S X	..	S O	..	..	5 29	..	..	..	..	5 33	..	..	..	..	..			..	39
dep	40	..	..	5 20	..	5 25	..	..	5 29	..	..	..	..	..	..	..	..	..	..			..	40
Carshalton.............	41	..	..	..	..	..	..	..	..	..	..	..	..	..	5 29	..	..	..				..	41
Hackbridge.............	42	..	..	..	..	..	..	..	..	..	..	..	..	..	5 31	..	..	..				..	42
Mitcham Junction.......	43	..	..	..	..	..	..	..	..	..	..	..	..	..	5 34	..	..	..				..	43
East Croydon.... arr	44	..	..	..	..	..	5 27	5 34	..	..	..	..	..	..	..	..	..	..		..	..	..	44
dep	45	..	..	..	..	..	5 27	5 34	..	..	..	..	..	..	..	..	S X	..	From London Bridge via Tulse Hill	S X	S O	..	45
Norwood Junction F..	46	..	..	5 24	S O	5 29	5 31	..	..	..	..	..	..	..	..	..	5 40	S X		5 33	5 29	..	46
Beckenham Jn. dep	47	..	..	..	5 20	..	..	..	..	..	..	..	..	..	..	..	..	5 29		..	..	..	47
Birkbeck..............	48	S X	..	..	5 23	..	..	..	..	..	..	..	..	..	..	..	..	5 32		..	..	..	48
Crystal Palace D......	49	5 25	..	5 29	5 27	5 33	..	..	..	..	..	..	..	..	..	..	..	5 36		..	..	5 39	49
Gipsy Hill (for Upper	50	5 28	..	5 31	..	5 36	..	..	..	..	..	..	..	..	..	..	..	5 38		..	..	..	50
West Norwood. [N'wood)	51	5 30	..	5 34	..	5 38	..	..	..	..	..	..	..	..	..	..	..	5 41	S X	..	..	..	51
Streatham Hill.........	52	..	..	5 37	..	5 41	..	..	..	..	..	..	..	..	..	..	..	5 44	5 49	..	..	..	52
Selhurst..............	53	..	..	..	..	..	..	..	5 32	..	..	..	..	..	..	..	..	..	..	..	5 32	..	53
Thornton Heath........	54	..	..	..	..	..	..	..	5 34	..	..	..	..	..	..	..	..	..	..	..	5 34	..	54
Norbury...............	55	..	..	..	..	..	..	..	5 37	..	..	..	..	..	..	..	..	..	..	..	5 37	..	55
Streatham Common......	56	..	..	..	..	..	..	..	5 39	..	..	..	..	..	..	..	..	..	..	..	5 39	..	56
Anerley................	57	..		..	..	..	..	..	..	..	..	..	..	..	..	..	..	..	..	5 36	..	..	57
Penge West **C**..........	58	..		..	..	..	..	..	..	..	..	..	..	..		..	..	..	..	5 37	..	..	58
Sydenham ....[Lane	59	..		..	..	..	..	..	..	..	..	..	..	..		..	..	..	..	5 39	..	5 42	59
Forest Hill, for Lordship	60	..		..	..	..	..	..	..	..	..	..	..	..		..	..	..	..	5 42	..	5 45	60
Honor Oak Park.........	61	..	From Victoria, dep. 5 27 p.m	..	..	..	..	..	..	..	..	..	..	..		..	..	..	..	5 44	..	5 47	61
Brockley **B**.......[Line)	62	..		..	..	..	..	..	..	..	..	..	..	..		..	..	..	..	5 47	..	5 50	62
New Cross Gate (for E.L.	63	..		..	..	..	5 39	..	..	..	..	..	..	..		..	..	..	..	5 49	..	5 52	63
Streatham..............	64	..		..	..	..	..	..	..	..			..	..	J 1 minute later on Saturdays	..	..	..	..	..	5 41	..	64
Tulse Hill.............	65	5 33		..	..	..	..	..	..	..			..	..		..	..	..	..	..	5 45	..	65
North Dulwich..........	66	5 36		..	..	..	..	..	..	..			..	..		..	..	..	..	..	5 48	..	66
East Dulwich...........	67	5 38	S X	..	..	..	..	..	..	..			..	..		..	..	..	..	..	5 50	..	67
Peckham Rye............	68	5 41	5 44	..	..	..	..	..	..	..			..	..		..	..	..	..	..	5 52	..	68
Queen's Road, Peckham	69	5 43	5 46	..	..	..	..	..	..	..	Via Worcester Park	Via Worcester Park	..	..		..	..	..	..	..	5 54	..	69
South Bermondsey......	70	5 46	5 49	..	..	..	..	..	..	..			..	..		..	..	..	..	..	5 57	..	70
Balham & Upper Tooting	71	..	..	5 39	..	5 44	..	..	5 43	..			..	..	5J40	..	..	5 46	5 52	..	..	..	71
Wandsworth Common **A**	72	..	..	5 41	..	5 46	..	..	..	..			..	..	..	..	..	5 48	5 54	..	..	..	72
Clapham Junction.....	73	..	..	5 44	..	5 49	..	..	5 47	..			5 37	..	5J44	..	..	5 51	5 57	..	..	..	73
Battersea Park.........	74	..	..	5 47	..	5 52	..	..	..	..			..	..	..	..	..	5 54	6 0	..	..	..	74
London Bridge..... arr	75	5 50	5 53	..	..	..	5 45	5 50	..	..	..	..	..	..	..	..	5 57	..	..	5 55	6 1	5 58	75
Waterloo *........ "	76	..	..	..	..	..	..	..	..	..	5 43	5 43	..	..	..	..	..	..	..	..	..	..	76
Charing Cross *... "	77	..	..	..	..	..	..	..	..	..	..	..	..	..	..	..	..	..	..	..	..	..	77
Victoria........... "	78	..	..	5 51	..	5 57	..	..	5 54	..	..	..	5 43	..	5 50	..	..	5 58	6 4	..	..	..	78

DORKING NORTH, SUTTON, CROYDON, CRYSTAL PALACE, and LONDON

Week Days—continued (p.m)

No.	3	3	SX	3	SO	3	3	3		3	3	SO	SX	3	3		3	3		3	3	3	3	3		3	3	3
1			4 48									4§47	4§47												4S052			
2			3		5 16							5 23	5 15												3			
3					5a21							5 30	5 31															
4												5 34	5 35															
5												5 40	5 41							S O	S X							
6					a Arrival time							§ Via Three Bridges	§ Via Three Bridges							5 23	5 24							
7																				5 26	5 27							
8																				5 29	5 30							
9																				5 33	5 34							
10																				5 36	5 37							
11																				5 38	5 39							
12																				5 41	5 42							
13																				5 43	5 44							
14																				5 33	5 34							
15																				5 37	5 38							
16																				5 38	5 40							
17																				5 42	5 43							
18								S X		S X								S O		5 45	5 46							
19								5 31		5 36								5 41										
20								5 34		5 39		5 44	5 44					5 44		5 47	5 50							
21								5 36		5 42								5 46		5 50								
22							S X	5 39		5 44	S O							5 49		5 52								
23							5 12				5 12																	
24							5 15				5 15																	
25			5 8																						5 18			
26																									5 21			
27			5 14				5 19				5 19														5 26			
28							5 23				5 23														5 30			
29			5 20				5 27				5 28														5 34		5 37	
30			5 23								5 31																5 40	
31		S O	5 26			SX					5 34						S X							S O			5 43	
32	From London Bridge, via Forest Hill	5 19				5 24											5 29						From London Bridge, via Streatham	5 30				
33		5 22				5 27											5 32							5 33				
34		5 25		S O		5 30											5 35							5 36		S X		
35		5 28	5 29	5 32		5 33	5 35				5 37						5 38							5 39		5 42	5 46	From Victoria, via Wandsworth Common
36		5 30		5 34		5 35											5 40							5 41		5 44		
37		5 33	5 33	5 37		5 38											5 43							5 44		5 47		
38		5 36				5 41											5 46							5 47		5 50		
39		5 39	5 38			5 44									S X		5 49							5 50		5 53		
40		5 39	5 38			5 45									5 40		5 49							5 50				
41							5 38				5 40																5 49	
42							5 40				5 43																5 51	
43							5 43				5 45																5 54	
44								5 42		5 47		5 50	5 50					5 52		5 55	5 56							
45	S X							5 42		5 47		5 50	5 50					5 52		5 55	5 56		S X					
46	5 32		5 42			5 49				5 51					5 44					5 58			5 53	5 54				
47																												
48														S X														
49														5 45	5 49													
50														5 48	5 51													
51														5 50	5 54													S X
52															5 57													5 58
53	5 35	5 42						5 45									5 52	5 55										
54	5 37	5 44						5 47									5 54	5 57										
55	5 40	5 47						5 50									5 57	6 0										
56	5 43	5 49						5 52									5 59	6 2										
57																						From Victoria, dep. 5 47 p.m	5 56	5 57			J1 minute later on Saturdays	
58																							5 57	5 58				
59																							5 59	6 0				
60			5 49																				6 2	6 3				
61																							6 4	6 5				
62																							6 7	6 8				
63			5 55							6 0													6 10	6 10				
64	5 45						5 48				5 51														Via Worcester Park			
65	5 48						5 51				5 55			5 53														6 1
66														5 56														6 4
67														5 58														6 6
68											6 0			6 1								6 4						6 8
69														6 3								6 6						6 10
70														6 6								6 9						6 13
71		5 53						5 56							5 59		6 3	6 6									6 J0	
72															6 1													
73		5 57						6 1				6 2			6 4		6 7	6 10									6 J4	
74															6 7													
75	5 59		6 0			6 4	6 2			6 6	6 7			6 10						6 11	6 11	6 13	6 15	6 16				6 17
76																				6 15					6 3			
77																				6 17								
78		6 8						6 7				6 8	6 6		6 11		6 14	6 16									6 10	

For Notes, see page 317a

HORSHAM, REIGATE, REDHILL, TATTENHAM CORNER, CATERHAM,

Up	No.	Week Days—continued p.m.																p.m.					No.
		(3)	(3)	(3)	..	(3)	..	(3)	(3)	..	..	(3)	..	(3)	S X	(3)	..	(3)	..	(3)	(3)	(3)	
Horsham............dep	1	..	..	..	..	..	..	..	..	..	..	..	..	..	5 2	..	..	..	..	..	..	..	1
Reigate............ "	2	..	..	..	..	..	..	..	..	..	..	..	..	..	..	..	..	..	..	..	..	..	2
Redhill............ "	3	..	..	..	..	..	..	..	..	..	..	..	5 50	..	(3)	..	..	..	..	..	..	..	3
Merstham............	4	..	..	..	..	..	..	..	..	..	..	..	..	..	..	..	..	..	..	..	..	..	4
Coulsdon South.........	5	..	..	..	..	..	..	..	..	..	..	..	..	..	..	..	..	..	..	..	..	..	5
Tattenham Corner. dep	6	..	..	..	..	..	..	..	..	..	..	..	..	..	..	..	..	..	..	..	..	..	6
Tadworth **N**........	7	..	..	..	..	..	..	..	..	..	..	..	..	..	..	..	..	..	..	..	..	..	7
Kingswood **M**.........	8	..	..	..	..	..	..	..	..	..	..	..	..	..	..	..	..	..	..	..	..	..	8
Chipstead	9	..	..	..	..	..	..	..	..	..	..	..	..	..	..	..	..	..	..	..	..	..	9
Woodmansterne	10	..	..	..	..	..	..	..	..	..	..	..	..	..	..	..	..	..	..	..	..	..	10
Smitham	11	..	..	..	..	..	..	..	..	..	..	..	..	..	..	..	..	..	..	..	..	..	11
Reedham.............	12	..	..	..	..	..	..	..	..	..	..	..	..	..	..	..	..	..	..	..	..	..	12
Purley 252.......... arr	13	..	..	..	..	..	..	..	..	..	..	..	..	..	..	..	..	..	..	..	..	..	13
Caterham.......... dep	14	..	..	..	..	..	..	..	..	..	..	..	..	..	..	..	..	..	..	..	..	..	14
Warlingham	15	..	..	..	..	..	..	..	..	..	..	..	..	..	..	..	..	..	..	..	..	..	15
Whyteleafe...........	16	..	..	..	..	..	..	..	..	..	..	..	..	..	..	..	..	..	..	..	..	..	16
Kenley...............	17	..	..	..	..	..	..	..	..	..	..	..	..	..	..	..	..	..	..	..	..	..	17
Purley 252.......... arr	18	..	..	..	..	..	..	..	..	..	..	S X	..	..	..	S X	..	..	..	..	..	..	18
Coulsdon North..... dep	19	..	..	..	..	..	..	..	..	..	..	5 51	..	..	..	5 56	..	..	..	..	..	..	19
Purley 252..........	20	..	..	..	..	..	..	..	..	..	..	5 54	..	..	..	5 59	..	..	..	..	..	..	20
Purley Oaks...........	21	..	..	..	..	..	..	..	..	..	..	5 57	..	..	..	6 2	..	..	..	..	..	..	21
South Croydon 234......	22	..	..	..	..	..	..	..	..	..	..	5 59	..	..	..	6 4	..	..	..	..	..	..	22
Effingham Junction dep	23	..	..	..	..	..	..	..	..	..	..	..	..	..	..	..	..	..	..	..	..	..	23
Bookham..............	24	..	..	..	..	..	..	..	..	..	..	..	..	..	..	..	..	..	..	..	..	..	24
Dorking North..... dep	25	..	..	..	..	..	..	..	..	..	..	..	..	..	5 29	..	..	..	..	..	..	..	25
Boxhill and Burford	26	..	..	..	..	..	..	..	..	..	..	..	..	..	5 32	..	..	..	..	..	..	..	26
Leatherhead..[Bridge **J**	27	..	..	..	..	..	..	..	..	..	..	..	..	..	5 37	..	..	..	..	..	..	..	27
Ashtead..............	28	..	..	..	..	..	..	..	..	..	..	..	..	..	5 41	..	..	..	..	..	..	..	28
Epsom 427............	29	..	..	..	..	..	..	..	..	..	..	..	..	..	5 45	..	..	..	..	..	..	..	29
Ewell East **H**.........	30	..	..	..	..	..	..	..	..	..	..	..	..	..	5 48	..	..	..	..	..	..	..	30
Cheam	31	..	..	..	..	..	..	..	..	..	..	..	..	S X	5 51	..	..	..	..	..	..	..	31
Epsom Downs...... dep	32	..	..	..	..	..	..	..	..	..	..	..	..	5 44	..	..	..	..	..	..	..	..	32
Banstead..............	33	..	..	..	..	..	..	..	..	..	..	..	..	5 47	..	..	..	..	..	..	..	..	33
Belmont	34	..	..	..	..	..	..	..	..	..	..	..	..	5 50	..	..	..	..	..	..	..	..	34
Sutton 322............	35	..	..	..	..	..	..	..	..	..	..	..	..	5 53	5 55	..	..	..	..	..	..	..	35
Carshalton Beeches.....	36	..	..	..	..	..	..	..	..	..	..	..	..	5 55	..	..	..	..	..	..	..	..	36
Wallington............	37	..	..	..	..	..	..	..	..	..	..	..	..	5 58	..	..	..	..	..	..	..	..	37
Waddon **G**............	38	..	..	..	..	..	..	..	..	..	..	..	..	6 1	..	..	..	..	..	..	..	..	38
West Croydon 319 arr	39	..	..	From London Bridge, via Forest Hill	..	From London Bridge, via Tulse Hill	..	..	S O	..	..	..	..	6 4	..	..	..	..	..	From London Bridge, via Streatham	..	S X	39
West Croydon 319 dep	40	..	..	..	..	..	..	..	5 55	..	..	..	..	6 4	..	..	..	..	..	..	..	6 0	40
Carshalton.............	41	..	..	..	..	..	..	..	..	..	..	..	..	..	5 58	..	..	..	..	..	..	..	41
Hackbridge.............	42	..	..	..	..	..	..	..	..	..	..	..	..	..	6 0	..	..	..	..	..	..	..	42
Mitcham Junction.......	43	..	..	..	..	..	..	..	..	..	..	..	..	..	6 3	..	..	..	..	..	..	..	43
East Croydon.... arr	44	..	..	..	..	..	..	..	..	..	..	6 2	6 5	..	..	6 7	..	..	..	..	..	..	44
East Croydon.... dep	45	..	..	S X	..	..	..	..	..	..	6 1	6 2	6 5	..	..	6 7	..	..	..	S O	..	..	45
Norwood Junction F..	46	S X	..	5 52	..	..	..	S O	5 59	..	..	..	..	6 8	..	6 11	..	..	..	6 9	..	6 4	46
Beckenham Jn. dep	47	5 49	..	..	..	..	..	5 50	..	..	..	..	..	..	..	..	..	..	..	..	..	..	47
Birkbeck	48	5 52	S X	..	..	..	..	5 53	..	..	..	..	..	..	..	..	..	S X	..	..	..	..	48
Crystal Palace D......	49	5 56	5 59	..	..	..	..	5 57	6 3	..	..	..	..	..	..	..	..	6 5	..	..	..	6 9	49
Gipsy Hill (for Upper	50	5 58	..	..	..	..	..	..	6 6	..	..	..	..	..	..	..	..	6 8	..	..	..	6 11	50
West Norwood.[N'wood)	51	6 1	..	..	..	S X	..	..	6 8	..	..	..	..	..	..	..	..	6 10	..	..	..	6 14	51
Streatham Hill.........	52	6 4	..	..	..	6 10	..	..	6 11	..	..	..	..	..	..	..	..	..	..	..	..	6 17	52
Selhurst.............	53	..	..	5 55	..	..	..	..	..	..	..	6 5	..	..	..	..	..	..	..	..	..	..	53
Thornton Heath........	54	..	..	5 57	..	..	..	..	..	..	..	6 7	..	..	..	..	..	..	..	..	..	..	54
Norbury	55	..	..	6 0	..	..	..	..	..	..	..	6 10	..	..	..	..	..	..	..	..	..	..	55
Streatham Common......	56	..	..	6 3	..	..	..	..	..	..	..	6 13	..	..	..	..	..	..	..	..	..	..	56
Anerley..............	57	..	..	..	..	..	..	..	..	..	..	..	..	..	..	..	..	..	..	6 12	..	..	57
Penge West **C**........	58	..	..	..	..	..	..	..	..	..	..	..	..	..	..	..	..	..	..	6 13	..	..	58
Sydenham ....[Lane	59	..	6 2	..	..	..	..	..	..	..	..	..	..	..	..	..	..	..	..	6 15	..	..	59
Forest Hill for Lordship	60	..	6 5	..	..	..	..	..	..	..	..	..	..	..	..	..	..	..	..	6 18	From Victoria, dep. 6 7 p.m.	..	60
Honor Oak Park.........	61	..	6 7	..	..	..	..	..	..	..	..	..	..	..	..	..	..	..	..	6 20	..	..	61
Brockley **B**.......[Line)	62	..	6 10	..	..	..	..	..	..	..	..	..	..	..	..	..	..	..	..	6 23	..	..	62
New Cross Gate (for E.L.	63	..	6 12	..	..	..	..	..	..	..	..	..	..	..	..	6 20	..	..	..	6 25	..	..	63
Streatham	64	..	..	6 5	..	..	..	..	..	..	..	..	..	..	6 8	..	..	..	..	..	..	..	64
Tulse Hill............	65	..	..	6 8	..	..	..	..	..	..	..	..	..	..	6 11	..	..	6 13	..	..	..	..	65
North Dulwich.........	66	..	..	..	..	..	..	..	..	..	..	..	..	..	..	..	..	6 16	..	..	..	..	66
East Dulwich..........	67	..	..	..	..	..	..	..	..	..	..	..	..	..	..	..	..	6 18	..	..	S X	..	67
Peckham Rye..........	68	..	..	..	..	..	..	..	..	..	..	..	..	..	..	..	..	6 21	..	..	6 24	..	68
Queen's Road, Peckham	69	..	..	..	..	..	..	..	..	..	..	..	..	..	..	..	..	6 23	..	..	6 26	..	69
South Bermondsey......	70	..	..	..	..	..	..	..	..	..	..	..	..	..	..	..	..	6 26	..	..	6 29	..	70
Balham & Upper Tooting	71	6 6	..	..	..	6 12	..	..	6 14	..	..	6 17	..	..	..	..	..	..	..	..	..	6 19	71
Wandsworth Common **A**	72	6 8	..	..	..	6 14	..	..	6 16	..	..	..	..	..	..	..	..	..	..	..	..	6 21	72
Clapham Junction.....	73	6 11	..	..	..	6 17	..	..	6 19	..	..	6 21	6 16	..	..	..	..	..	..	..	..	6 24	73
Battersea Park.........	74	6 14	..	..	..	6 20	..	..	6 22	..	..	..	..	..	..	..	..	..	..	..	..	6 27	74
LONDON BRIDGE..... arr	75	..	6 18	6 19	..	..	..	..	..	..	..	..	..	6 21	6 22	6 26	..	6 30	..	6 31	6 33	..	75
WATERLOO*........ "	76	..	..	..	..	..	..	..	..	..	..	..	..	..	..	..	..	..	..	..	..	..	76
CHARING CROSS*... "	77	..	..	..	..	..	..	..	..	..	..	..	..	..	..	..	..	..	..	..	..	..	77
VICTORIA............ "	78	6 18	..	..	..	6 24	..	..	6 26	..	6 18	6 27	6 22	..	..	..	..	..	..	..	..	6 31	78

DORKING NORTH, SUTTON, CROYDON, CRYSTAL PALACE, and LONDON

Week Days—continued (p.m.)

No.																												
1	3	3	3	3	3	3	3	3	5§15	3	3	..	3	3	3	3	3	S O 5 20	3	S X 5 20	..	3	3	3	3	3	5 43	3
2	..	..	..	..	..	..	..	..	5 52	..	..	..	..	..	..	..	..	3	..	3	..	..	..	..	..	..	..	..
3	..	..	..	..	..	..	..	..	5 59	..	..	..	..	..	..	..	..		..		..	..	..	..	..	..	..	..
4	..	..	..	..	..	..	..	..	6 2	..	..	..	..	..	..	..	..	..	..	..	..	..	..	..	..	..	..	..
5	S O	S X	..	..	..	..	..	..	6 8	..	..	..	..	..	..	..	..	..	..	..	..	..	..	..	..	..	..	..
6	5 43	5 44	..	..	..	..	..	..	§ Via Three Bridges	..	..	..	..	..	..	..	..	..	..	..	..	..	..	..	..	..	..	..
7	5 46	5 47	..	..	..	..	..	..		..	..	..	..	..	..	..	..	..	..	..	..	..	..	..	..	..	..	..
8	5 49	5 50	..	..	..	..	..	..		..	..	..	..	..	..	..	..	..	..	..	..	..	..	..	..	..	..	..
9	5 53	5 54	..	..	..	..	..	..		..	..	..	..	..	..	..	..	..	..	..	..	..	..	..	..	..	..	..
10	5 56	5 57	..	..	..	..	..	..		..	..	..	..	..	..	..	..	..	..	..	..	..	..	..	..	..	..	..
11	5 58	5 59	..	..	..	..	..	..		..	..	..	..	..	..	..	..	..	..	..	..	..	..	..	..	..	..	..
12	6 1	6 2	..	..	..	..	..	..		..	..	..	..	..	..	..	..	..	..	..	..	..	..	..	..	..	..	..
13	6 3	6 4	..	..	..	..	..	..		..	..	..	..	..	..	..	..	..	..	..	..	..	..	..	..	..	..	..
14	5 53	5 54	..	..	..	..	..	..	..	..	..	..	..	..	..	..	..	..	..	..	..	..	..	..	..	..	..	..
15	5 57	5 58	..	..	..	..	..	..	..	..	..	..	..	..	..	..	..	..	..	..	..	..	..	..	..	..	..	..
16	5 59	6 0	..	..	..	..	..	..	..	..	..	..	..	..	..	..	..	..	..	..	..	..	..	..	..	..	..	..
17	6 2	6 3	..	..	..	..	..	..	..	..	..	..	..	..	..	..	..	..	..	..	..	..	..	..	..	..	..	..
18	6 5	6 6	..	..	..	..	..	..	..	..	..	..	..	..	..	..	..	..	..	..	..	S O	S X	..	..	S X	..	..
19	..	..	..	..	..	..	..	..	..	..	..	..	..	..	..	..	..	..	..	..	..	6 11	6 12	..	..	6 16	..	..
20	6 7	6 9	..	..	..	..	..	..	6 12	..	..	..	..	..	..	..	..	..	..	..	..	6 14	6 15	..	..	6 19	..	..
21	6 10	..	..	..	..	..	..	..	..	..	..	..	..	..	..	..	..	..	..	..	..	6 16	6 17	..	..	6 22	..	..
22	6 12	..	..	..	..	..	..	..	..	..	..	..	..	..	..	..	..	..	..	..	..	6 19	6 20	..	..	6 24	..	..
23	..	..	..	..	..	..	5 38	..	..	..	..	..	..	..	..	..	..	..	..	..	..	..	..	..	..	..	..	..
24	..	..	..	..	..	..	5 41	..	..	..	..	..	..	..	..	..	..	..	..	..	..	..	..	..	..	..	..	..
25	..	..	..	..	..	..	..	..	..	..	..	..	..	..	..	..	..	5 46	..	5 48	..	..	..	..	..	..	6 2	..
26	..	..	..	..	..	..	..	..	..	..	..	..	..	..	..	..	..	5 48	..	5 50	..	..	..	..	..	..	..	..
27	..	..	..	..	..	..	5 46	..	..	..	..	..	..	..	..	..	..	5 53	..	5 55	..	..	..	..	..	..	..	..
28	..	..	..	..	..	..	5 50	S X	..	..	..	..	..	..	..	..	..	5 57	..	6 0	..	..	..	..	..	..	..	..
29	..	..	..	..	..	..	5 54	5 57	..	..	..	..	..	..	..	..	..	6 2	..	6 5	..	..	..	..	..	..	..	..
30	..	..	..	..	..	..	..	6 0	..	..	..	..	..	..	..	..	..	6 5	..	6 8	..	..	..	..	..	..	..	..
31	..	..	..	..	..	..	..	6 3	..	..	..	..	..	..	..	S O	..	6 8	S X	6 11	..	..	..	..	S X	..	..	..
32	..	..	..	5 49	..	..	..	..	..	From London Bridge, via Streatham	..	..	..	..	..	6 0	..	..	6 4	..	..	..	..	..	6 9	..	..	..
33	..	..	..	5 52	..	..	..	..	..		..	..	..	..	..	6 3	..	..	6 7	..	..	..	..	..	6 12	..	..	..
34	..	..	..	5 55	S O	S X	..	..	..		..	..	..	..	..	6 6	..	..	6 10	..	..	..	..	..	6 15	..	..	S X
35	..	..	..	5 58	6 2	6 1	..	6 6	..		From Victoria, via Wandsworth Common	..	..	..	From London Bridge, via Forest Hill	6 9	..	6 11	6 13	6 14	..	..	..	..	6 18	..	6 20	6 23
36	..	..	..	6 0	6 4	6 4	..	..	..			..	..	..		6 11	..	..	6 15	..	..	..	..	..	6 20	..	..	6 25
37	..	..	..	6 3	6 7	6 9	..	..	..			..	..	..		6 14	..	..	6 18	..	..	..	..	..	6 23	..	..	6 28
38	..	..	..	6 6	..	6 12	..	..	..			..	..	..		6 17	..	..	6 21	..	..	..	..	..	6 26	..	..	6 31
39	..	..	..	6 9	..	6 15	..	..	..			..	..	..		6 20	..	..	6 24	..	..	..	..	S X	6 29	..	..	6 34
40	..	..	..	6 9	..	6 15	..	..	..			..	..	..		6 20	..	..	6 24	..	..	..	..	6 20	6 29	..	..	..
41	..	..	..	..	..	..	..	6 9	..			..	..	..		..	..	6 14	..	6 17	..	..	..	..	..	..	..	..
42	..	..	..	..	..	..	..	6 12	..			..	..	..		..	..	6 16	..	6 19	..	..	..	..	..	..	..	..
43	..	..	..	..	..	..	..	6 14	..			..	..	..		..	..	6 19	..	6 22	..	..	..	..	..	..	..	..
44	6 15	6 14	..	..	..	..	..	..	6 18			..	..	..		..	..	..	..	..	..	6 22	6 22	..	..	6 27	..	..
45	6 15	6 14	..	..	..	..	..	..	6 19	S X		..	..	..	S X	..	..	..	..	..	..	6 22	6 22	..	..	6 27	..	..
46	6 18	..	..	..	..	6 20	..	..	6 23	6 13		..	S X	..	6 12	6 24	..	..	6 28	..	..	..	..	6 24	..	6 31	..	..
47	..	..	..	..	..	..	..	..	..	..		..	6 9	..	..	..	..	..	..	..	..	..	..	..	..	..	..	..
48	..	..	S O	..	..	..	..	..	..	..		..	6 12	S X	..	..	..	..	..	..	..	..	..	..	..	..	..	..
49	..	..	6 11	..	..	..	..	..	..	..		..	6 16	6 19	..	..	..	..	..	..	..	..	..	6 29	..	..	..	..
50	..	..	6 13	..	..	..	..	..	..	..		..	6 18	..	..	..	..	..	..	..	..	..	..	6 31	..	..	..	..
51	..	..	6 16	..	..	..	..	..	..	..	S X	..	6 21	..	..	..	..	..	..	..	..	..	..	6 34	..	..	..	..
52	..	..	..	..	..	..	..	..	..	..	6 18	..	6 24	..	..	..	..	..	..	..	..	..	..	6 37	..	..	..	..
53	..	..	..	6 12	..	..	..	..	..	..	..	..	..	..	6 15	..	..	..	..	..	..	6 25	6 25	..	6 32	..	..	..
54	..	..	..	6 14	..	..	..	..	..	..	..	..	..	..	6 17	..	..	..	..	..	..	6 27	6 27	..	6 34	..	..	..
55	..	..	..	6 17	..	..	..	..	..	..	..	..	..	..	6 20	..	..	..	..	..	..	6 30	6 30	..	6 37	..	..	..
56	..	..	..	6 19	..	..	..	..	..	..	..	..	..	..	6 22	..	..	..	..	..	..	6 33	6 33	..	6 39	..	..	..
57	..	..	..	‖ 1 minute *earlier* on Saturdays	..	..	..	..	..	6 16	..	..	..	..	..	6 27	From Victoria dep 6 18 p.m.	..	..	..	..	..	..	..	..	..	..	..
58	..	..	..		..	..	..	..	..	6 17	..	..	..	..	..	6 28		..	..	..	..	..	..	..	..	..	..	..
59	..	..	..		..	..	..	..	..	6 19	..	..	..	6 22	..	6 30		..	..	..	..	..	..	..	..	..	..	..
60	..	..	..		..	..	..	..	..	6 22	..	..	..	6 25	..	6 33		..	..	..	..	..	..	..	..	..	..	..
61	..	..	..		..	..	..	..	..	6 24	..	..	..	6 27	..	6 35		..	..	..	..	..	..	..	..	..	..	..
62	..	..	..		..	..	..	..	..	6 27	..	..	..	6 30	..	6 38		..	..	..	..	..	..	..	..	..	..	..
63	..	..	..		..	..	..	..	..	6 29	..	..	..	6 32	..	6 40		..	..	..	..	..	..	..	..	6 40	..	..
64	..	..	..		..	..	Via Worcester Park	..	..	..	..	..	..	..	6 25	..		6 24	..	6 28	..	..	..	..	..	..	..	..
65	..	..	6 18		..	..		..	..	..	6 21	..	..	..	6 28	..		6 27	..	6 31	..	..	..	..	..	..	..	..
66	..	..	6 21		..	..		..	..	..	6 24	..	..	..	..	..		..	..	..	..	..	..	..	..	..	..	..
67	..	..	6 23		..	..		..	..	..	6 26	..	..	..	..	..	S O	6 32	..	..	..	..	..	..	..	..	..	..
68	..	..	6 26		..	..		..	..	..	6 28	..	..	..	..	..	6 37	6 35	..	..	..	..	..	..	..	..	..	..
69	..	..	6 28		..	..		..	..	..	6 30	..	..	..	..	..	6 39	..	..	..	..	..	..	..	..	..	..	..
70	..	..	6 31		..	..		..	..	..	6 33	..	..	..	..	..	6 42	..	..	..	..	..	..	..	..	..	..	..
71	..	..	..	6 23	..	..		6 22	..	..	..	..	6 26	..	..	..	..	..	..	..	..	6 37	6 37	6 39	6 43	..	..	..
72	..	..	..	..	..	..		..	..	..	..	..	6 28	..	..	..	..	..	..	..	..	6 39	..	6 41	..	..	..	..
73	..	..	..	6 27	..	..		6 27	..	..	..	..	6 31	..	..	..	..	..	..	..	..	6 42	6 41	6 44	6 47	..	..	..
74	..	..	..	..	..	..		..	..	..	..	..	6 34	..	..	..	..	..	..	..	..	..	..	6 47	..	..	..	..
75	6 31	6 30	6 35	..	..	6 33	..	..	6 36	6 35	6 37	..	..	6 38	6 39	6 46	6 46	6 41	6 44	6 42	..	..	..	..	..	6 46	..	..
76	6 35	..	..	..	..	..	6 23	..	..	..	..	..	..	..	..	..	..	..	..	..	..	..	..	..	..	..	..	..
77	6 37	..	..	..	..	..	..	..	..	..	..	..	..	..	..	..	..	..	..	..	..	..	..	..	..	..	..	..
78	..	..	..	6‖34	..	..	..	6 33	..	..	..	..	6 38	..	..	..	..	..	..	..	..	6 47	6 47	6 51	6 55	..	6 40	..

HORSHAM, REIGATE, REDHILL, TATTENHAM CORNER, CATERHAM,

Up	No.	p.m							Week Days—continued									p.m					No
			3	3		3	3	3	3	3	3	3	3	3	3	3	3			3	3	3	
Horsham .... dep	1	..			..													..	..				1
Reigate .... "	2	..	..	..	..	..	..	..	..	..	..	..	..	..	..	..	..	..	..	..	..	..	2
Redhill .... "	3	6 5	..	..	..	..	..	..	..	..	..	..	..	..	..	..	..	..	..	..	..	..	3
Merstham	4	..	..	..	..	..	..	..	..	..	..	..	..	..	..	..	..	..	..	..	..	..	4
Coulsdon South	5	..	..	S X	..	..	..	..	..	..	..	..	..	..	..	..	..	..	..	..	..	..	5
Tattenham Corner . dep	6	..	..	6 4	..	..	..	..	..	..	..	..	..	..	..	..	..	..	..	..	..	..	6
Tadworth **N**	7	..	..	6 7	..	..	..	..	..	..	..	..	..	..	..	..	..	..	..	..	..	..	7
Kingswood **M**	8	..	..	6 10	..	..	..	..	..	..	..	..	..	..	..	..	..	..	..	..	..	..	8
Chipstead	9	..	..	6 15	..	..	..	..	..	..	..	..	..	..	..	..	..	..	..	..	..	..	9
Woodmansterne	10	..	..	6 17	..	..	..	..	..	..	..	..	..	..	..	..	..	..	..	..	..	..	10
Smitham	11	..	..	6 20	..	..	..	..	..	..	..	..	..	..	..	..	..	..	..	..	..	..	11
Reedham	12	..	..	6 22	..	..	..	..	..	..	..	..	..	..	..	..	..	..	..	..	..	..	12
Purley 252 .... arr	13	..	..	6 25	..	..	..	..	..	..	..	..	..	..	..	..	..	..	..	..	..	..	13
Caterham .... dep	14	..	..	6 15	..	..	..	..	..	..	..	..	..	..	..	..	..	..	..	..	..	..	14
Warlingham	15	..	..	6 18	..	..	..	..	..	..	..	..	..	..	..	..	..	..	..	..	..	..	15
Whyteleafe	16	..	..	6 20	..	..	..	..	..	..	..	..	..	..	..	..	..	..	..	..	..	..	16
Kenley	17	..	..	6 23	..	..	..	..	..	..	..	..	..	..	..	..	..	..	..	..	..	..	17
Purley 252 .... arr	18	..	..	6 27	..	..	..	..	..	..	..	..	..	..	..	..	..	..	..	..	..	..	18
Coulsdon North ..... dep	19	..	..	..	..	..	..	..	..	..	..	..	..	..	..	..	..	..	..	..	..	..	19
Purley 252	20	6 20	..	6 29	..	..	..	..	..	..	..	..	..	..	..	..	..	..	..	..	..	..	20
Purley Oaks	21	..	..	..	..	..	..	..	..	..	..	..	..	..	..	..	..	..	..	..	..	..	21
South Croydon 234	22	..	..	..	..	S X	..	..	..	..	..	..	..	..	..	..	..	..	..	..	..	..	22
Effingham Junction dep	23	..	..	..	..	5 51	..	..	..	..	..	..	..	..	..	..	..	..	..	..	..	..	23
Bookham	24	..	..	..	..	5 54	S X	..	..	..	..	..	..	..	..	..	..	..	..	..	..	..	24
Dorking North ..... dep	25	..	..	..	..	..	5 55	..	..	..	..	..	..	..	..	..	..	..	..	..	..	..	25
Boxhill and Burford	26	..	..	..	..	..	5 57	..	..	..	..	..	..	..	..	..	..	..	..	..	..	..	26
Leatherhead ... [Bridge **J**	27	..	..	..	..	5 59	6 2	..	..	..	..	..	..	..	..	..	..	..	..	..	..	..	27
Ashtead	28	..	..	..	..	..	6 6	..	..	..	..	..	..	..	..	..	..	..	..	..	..	..	28
Epsom 427	29	..	..	..	..	..	6 14	6 17	..	..	..	..	..	..	..	..	..	..	..	..	..	..	29
Ewell East **H**	30	..	..	..	..	..		6 20	..	..	..	..	..	..	..	..	..	..	..	..	..	..	30
Cheam	31	..	..	..	..	..		6 23	..	..	..	..	..	..	..	..	..	..	..	S O	..	..	31
Epsom Downs ...... dep	32	..	..	..	..	..		..	..	..	..	..	..	..	..	..	..	..	..	6 19	..	..	32
Banstead	33	..	..	..	..	..	Arr. Epsom 6 10 p.m	..	..			..	..	..	..	..	..	..	..	6 22	..	..	33
Belmont	34	..	..	..	..	..		..	..			..	..		..	..	..	..	..	6 25	S O	..	34
Sutton 322	35	..	..	..	..	..		6 26	..			..	..		..	..	..	..	..	6 28	6 32	..	35
Carshalton Beeches	36	..	..	..	..	..		..	..			..	..		..	..	..	..	..	6 30	6 34	..	36
Wallington	37	..	..	..	..	..		..	..			..	..		..	..	..	..	..	6 33	6 37	..	37
Waddon **G**	38	..	..	..	..	..	..	..	..	From London Bridge, via Streatham	From London Bridge, via Forest Hill		..		..	..	..	..	..	6 36	..		38
West Croydon 319 arr	39	..	..	..	..	..	..	..	..				..	From London Bridge, via Forest Hill	..	S O	..	..	..	6 39	..		39
West Croydon 319 dep	40	..	..	..	..	..	..	..	..				..		..	6 25	..	..	..	6 39	..		40
Carshalton	41	..	..	..	..	..	..	6 29	..				..		..	..	..	..	..	..	..		41
Hackbridge	42	..	..	..	..	..	..	6 31	..				..		..	..	..	..	..	..	..		42
Mitcham Junction	43	..	..	..	..	..	..	6 34	..				..		..	..	..	..	..	..	..		43
East Croydon .... arr	44	6 28	..	6 35	..	..	..	..	..			From Victoria via Wandsworth Common	..		..	..	..	..	S O	..	..	From London Bridge via Tulse Hill	44
East Croydon .... dep	45	6 28	..	6 35	..	..	..	..	..	S X	S O		..	S X	..	..	..	..	6 42	..	..		45
Norwood Junction F ..	46	6 33	..	..	..	..	..	..	..	6 33	6 29		S X	6 32	S O	6 29	..	..	..	..	..		46
Beckenham Jn. dep	47	..	..	..	..	..	..	..	..	..	..		6 29	..	6 20	..	..	..	..	..	..		47
Birkbeck	48	..	S X	..	..	..	..	..	..	..	..		6 32	..	6 23	..	..	..	..	..	..		48
Crystal Palace D	49	..	6 25	..	..	..	..	..	..	..	..		6 36	..	6 27	6 33	6 39	..	..	..	..		49
Gipsy Hill (for Upper	50	..	6 28	..	..	..	..	..	..	..	..		6 38	..	..	6 36	..	..	..	..	..		50
West Norwood. [N'wood)	51	..	6 30	..	..	..	..	..	..	..	..	S X	6 41	..	..	6 38	..	..	..	..	..	S X	51
Streatham Hill	52	..	..	..	..	..	..	..	..	..	..	6 38	6 44	..	..	6 41	..	..	..	..	..	6 49	52
Selhurst	53	..	..	..	..	..	..	..	..	..	6 32	..	..	6 35	..	..	..	..	..	6 42	..	..	53
Thornton Heath	54	..	..	..	..	..	..	..	..	..	6 34	..	..	6 37	..	..	..	..	..	6 44	..	..	54
Norbury	55	..	..	..	..	..	..	..	..	..	6 37	..	..	6 40	..	..	..	..	..	6 47	..	..	55
Streatham Common	56	..	..	..	..	..	..	..	..	..	6 39	..	..	6 43	..	..	..	..	..	6 49	..	..	56
Anerley	57	..	..	..	..	..	..	..		6 36	..	..	..	..	..	..	..	..	..	..	..	..	57
Penge West **C**	58	..	..	..	..	..	..	..		6 37	..	..	..	..	..	..	..	..	..	..	..	..	58
Sydenham .... [Lane	59	..	..	..	..	..	..	..		6 39	..	..	..	..	..	..	6 42	..	..	..	..	..	59
Forest Hill, for Lordship	60	..	..	..	..	..	..	..		6 42	..	..	..	..	..	..	6 45	..	..	..	..	..	60
Honor Oak Park	61	..	..	..	..	..	..	..	From Victoria, dep. 6 27 p.m	6 44	..	..	..	..	..	..	6 47	..	..	..	..	..	61
Brockley **B** .... [Line)	62	..	..	..	..	..	..	..		6 47	..	..	..	..	..	..	6 50	..	..	..	..	..	62
New Cross Gate (for E.L.	63	..	..	..	..	..	..	..		6 49	..	..	..	..	..	..	6 52	..	..	..	..	..	63
Streatham	64	..	..	..	..	..		..		..	6 41	..	..	6 45	..	..	..	..	..	..	..	..	64
Tulse Hill	65	..	6 33	..	..	..		..		..	6 45	6 41	..	6 48	..	..	..	..	..	..	..	..	65
North Dulwich	66	..	6 36	..	..	..		..		..	6 48	6 44	..	..	..	..	..	..	..	..	..	..	66
East Dulwich	67	..	6 38	..	..	..		..	S X	..	6 50	6 46	..	..	..	..	..	..	..	..	..	..	67
Peckham Rye	68	..	6 41	..	..	..		..	6 44	..	6 52	6 48	..	..	..	..	..	..	..	..	..	..	68
Queen's Road, Peckham	69	..	6 43	..	..	..	Via Worcester Park	..	6 46	..	6 54	6 50	..	..	..	..	..	..	..	..	..	..	69
South Bermondsey	70	..	6 46	..	..	..		..	6 49	..	6 57	6 53	..	..	..	..	..	..	..	..	..	..	70
Balham & Upper Tooting	71	..	..	..	..	..		6 41	..	..	..	..	6 46	..	..	6 44	..	..	..	6 53	..	6 52	71
Wandsworth Common **A**	72	..	..	..	..	..		..	..	..	..	..	6 48	..	..	6 46	..	..	..	..	..	6 54	72
Clapham Junction	73	..	..	..	..	..		6 45	..	..	..	..	6 51	..	..	6 49	..	..	..	6 57	..	6 57	73
Battersea Park	74	..	..	..	..	..		..	..	..	..	..	6 54	..	..	6 52	..	..	..	..	..	7 0	74
London Bridge ..... arr	75	6 47	6 50	6 50	..	..	..	..	6 53	6 55	7 1	6 57	..	6 59	..	..	6 58	..	..	..	..	..	75
Waterloo * .... "	76	..	..	..	..	..	6 43	..	..	..	..	..	..	..	..	..	..	..	..	..	..	..	76
Charing Cross * .. "	77	..	..	..	..	..	..	..	..	..	..	..	..	..	..	..	..	..	..	..	..	..	77
Victoria .... "	78	..	..	..	..	..	..	6 50	..	..	..	..	6 58	..	..	6 56	..	..	6 58	7 3	..	7 4	78

For Notes, see page 317a

DORKING NORTH, SUTTON, CROYDON, CRYSTAL PALACE, and LONDON

Week Days—continued — p.m

No.	3	3	3		3		3		3	3	3	3	3		3	3	3		3	3	3	3	3	3	3	3		3
1				..		5§B37		..						..				5 52									..	
2	..	..	..	6 11	..	6SO23	..	..	..	..	..	..	..	..	..	..	..	3	..	..	..	..	..	..	..	..	..	..
3	..	..	..	6a16	..	6 30	..	..	..	..	..	..	..	..	..	..	..		..	..	..	..	..	..	..	..	..	..
4	..	..	..		..	6 34	..	..	..	..	..	..	..	..	..	..	..	..	..	..	..	..	..	..	..	..	..	..
5	..	..	..		..	6 41	..	..	..	..	..	..	..	..	..	..	..	..	..	..	..	..	..	SO	SX	..	..	..
6	..	..	..	a Arrival time	..	B Dep. 5 48 p.m on Sats. § Via Three Bridges	..	..	..	..	..	..	..	..	..	..	..	..	..	..	..	..	..	6 23	6 24	..	..	..
7	..	..	..		..		..	..	..	..	..	..	..	..	..	..	..	..	..	..	..	..	..	6 26	6 27	..	..	..
8	..	..	..		..		..	..	..	..	..	..	..	..	..	..	..	..	..	..	..	..	..	6 29	6 30	..	..	..
9	..	..	..		..		..	..	..	..	..	..	..	..	..	..	..	..	..	..	..	..	..	6 33	6 34	..	..	..
10	..	..	..		..		..	..	..	..	..	..	..	..	..	..	..	..	..	..	..	..	..	6 36	6 37	..	..	..
11	..	..	..		..		..	..	..	..	..	..	..	..	..	..	..	..	..	..	..	..	..	6 38	6 39	..	..	..
12	..	..	..		..		..	..	..	..	..	..	..	..	..	..	..	..	..	..	..	..	..	6 41	6 42	..	..	..
13	..	..	..		..		..	..	..	..	..	..	..	..	..	..	..	..	..	..	..	..	..	6 43	6 44	..	..	..
14	..	..	..	Stop	..		..	..	..	..	..	..	..	..	..	..	..	..	..	..	..	..	..	6 33	6 34	..	..	..
15	..	..	..		..		..	..	..	..	..	..	..	..	..	..	..	..	..	..	..	..	..	6 37	6 38	..	..	..
16	..	..	..	..	..		..	..	..	..	..	..	..	..	..	..	..	..	..	..	..	..	..	6 39	6 40	..	..	..
17	..	..	..	..	..		..	..	..	..	..	..	..	..	..	..	..	..	..	..	..	..	..	6 42	6 43	..	..	..
18	SX	..	..	..	SX		..	..	..	..	..	..	..	..	..	..	..	..	..	SO	..	..	..	6 45	6 46	..	..	..
19	6 31	..	..	..	6 36		..	..	..	..	..	..	..	..	..	..	..	..	..	6 42	..	..	..	..	..	..	..	..
20	6 34	..	..	..	6 39	6 45	..	..	..	..	..	..	..	..	..	..	..	..	..	6 45	..	..	..	6 47	6 49	..	..	..
21	6 36	..	..	..	6 42	..	..	..	..	..	..	..	..	..	..	..	..	..	..	6 47	..	..	..	6 50	..	..	..	..
22	6 39	..	..	..	6 44	..	SO	..	..	..	..	..	..	..	..	..	..	..	..	6 50	..	..	..	6 52	..	..	..	..
23	..	..	..	..	..	..	6 12	..	..	..	..	..	..	..	..	..	..	..	..	..	..	..	..	..	..	..	..	..
24	..	..	..	..	..	..	6 15	..	..	..	..	..	..	..	..	..	..	..	..	..	..	..	..	..	..	..	..	..
25	..	..	..	..	..	..	..	..	..	..	..	..	..	..	..	..	..	6 18	..	..	..	..	..	..	..	..	..	..
26	..	..	..	..	..	..	..	..	..	..	..	..	..	..	..	..	..	6 21	..	..	..	..	..	..	..	..	..	..
27	..	..	..	..	..	..	6 19	..	..	..	..	..	..	..	..	..	..	6 26	..	..	..	..	..	..	..	..	..	..
28	..	..	SX	..	..	..	6 23	..	..	..	..	..	..	..	..	..	SX	6 30	SO	..	..	..	..	..	..	..	..	..
29	..	..	6 25	..	..	..	6 28	..	..	..	..	..	..	..	..	..	6 37	6 34	6 40	..	..	..	..	..	..	..	..	..
30	..	..	6 28	..	..	..	6 31	..	..	..	..	..	..	..	..	..	6 40	..	6 43	..	..	..	..	..	..	..	..	..
31	..	SX	6 31	..	..	..	6 34	..	..	..	SX	..	..	..	..	SO	6 43	..	6 46	..	..	..	..	..	..	..	..	..
32	..	6 24	..	..	..	..	..	..	..	..	6 29	..	..	..	From London Bridge, via Tulse Hill	6 30	..	..	..	..	..	..	From London Bridge, via Forest Hill	..	..	..	..	..
33	..	6 27	..	..	..	..	..	..	..	..	6 32	..	..	..		6 33	..	..	..	..	..	..		..	..	..	..	..
34	..	6 30	..	..	..	..	..	..	..	..	6 35	SX	..	..		6 36	..	..	..	..	..	..		..	..	..	..	..
35	..	6 33	6 35	..	..	..	6 37	..	..	..	6 38	6 43	..	..		6 39	6 46	..	6 49	..	..	..		..	..	..	..	..
36	..	6 35	..	..	..	..	..	..	..	..	6 40	6 46	..	..		6 41	..	..	..	..	..	..		..	..	..	..	..
37	..	6 38	..	..	..	..	..	..	..	..	6 43	6 49	..	..		6 44	..	..	..	..	..	..		..	..	..	..	..
38	..	6 41	..	..	..	..	..	..	..	..	6 46	6 52	..	..		6 47	..	..	..	..	..	..		..	..	..	..	..
39	..	6 44	..	..	..	..	..	..	..	SX	6 49	6 55	..	..		6 50	..	..	..	..	..	..		..	..	..	..	SO
40	..	6 44	..	..	..	..	..	..	..	6 40	6 49	..	..	..		6 50	..	..	..	..	..	..		..	..	..	..	6 55
41	..	..	6 38	..	..	..	6 40	..	..	..	..	..	..	..		..	6 49	..	6 52	..	..	..		..	..	..	..	..
42	..	..	6 40	..	..	..	6 43	..	..	..	..	..	..	..		..	6 52	..	6 55	..	..	..		..	..	..	..	..
43	..	..	6 43	..	..	..	6 46	..	..	..	..	..	..	..		..	6 54	..	6 57	..	..	..		..	..	..	..	..
44	6 42	..	..	p.m	6 47	6 50	..	..	..	..	..	..	..	..	..	..	..	..	..	6 52	..	..	..	6 55	6 54	..	SO	..
45	6 42	..	..	6 47	6 47	6 51	..	..	..	..	..	..	..	..	SX	..	..	..	..	6 52	..	..	SX	6 55	6 54	..	7 0	..
46	..	6 48	..	..	6 51	..	..	..	..	6 44	..	..	..	..	6 53	6 54	..	..	..	..	SX	..	6 52	6 58	6 58	SO	..	6 59
47	..	..	..	..	..	..	..	..	..	..	..	..	..	..	..	..	..	..	..	..	6 49	..	..	..	..	6 50	..	..
48	..	..	..	..	..	..	..	..	SX	..	..	..	..	..	..	..	..	..	..	..	6 52	SX	..	..	..	6 53	..	..
49	..	..	..	..	..	..	..	..	6 45	6 49	..	..	..	..	..	..	..	..	..	..	6 56	6 59	..	..	..	6 57	..	7 3
50	..	..	..	..	..	..	..	..	6 48	6 51	..	..	..	..	..	..	..	..	..	..	6 58	..	..	..	..	..	..	7 6
51	..	..	..	..	..	..	..	..	6 50	6 54	..	..	..	..	..	..	..	..	..	..	7 1	..	..	..	..	..	..	7 8
52	..	..	..	..	..	..	..	..	..	6 57	..	..	..	..	..	..	..	..	..	..	7 4	..	..	..	..	..	..	7 11
53	6 45	..	..	..	..	..	..	..	..	..	6 52	..	..	..	..	..	..	..	..	6 55	..	..	6 55	..	..	..	..	..
54	6 47	..	..	..	..	..	..	..	..	..	6 54	..	..	..	..	..	..	..	..	6 57	..	..	6 57	..	..	..	..	..
55	6 50	..	..	..	..	..	..	..	..	..	6 57	..	..	..	..	..	..	..	..	7 0	..	..	7 0	..	..	..	..	..
56	6 52	..	..	..	..	..	..	..	..	..	6 59	..	..	..	..	..	..	..	..	7 2	..	..	7 3	..	..	..	..	..
57	..	..	..	..	..	..	..	..	..	..	..	..	..	..	6 56	6 57	..	..	..	..	..	..	..	..	..	..	..	..
58	..	..	..	..	..	..	..	..	..	..	..	..	From Victoria dep. 6 47 p.m	..	6 57	6 58	..	..	..	..	..	..	..	..	..	..	..	..
59	..	..	..	..	..	..	..	..	..	..	..	..		..	6 59	7 0	..	..	..	..	..	7 2	..	..	..	..	..	..
60	..	..	..	..	..	..	..	..	..	..	..	..		..	7 2	7 3	..	..	..	..	..	7 5	..	..	..	..	..	..
61	..	..	..	..	..	..	..	..	..	..	..	..		..	7 4	7 5	..	..	..	..	..	7 7	..	..	..	..	..	..
62	..	..	..	..	..	..	..	..	..	..	..	..		..	7 7	7 8	..	..	..	..	..	7 10	..	..	..	..	..	..
63	..	..	..	..	6 59	..	..	..	..	..	..	..		..	7 9	7 10	..	..	..	..	..	7 12	..	..	..	..	..	..
64	..	..	6 48	..	..	..	6 51	..	..	..	..	..		..	..	..	..	Via Worcester Park	..	..	..	..	7 5	..	..	..	..	..
65	..	..	6 51	..	..	..	6 55	..	6 53	..	..	..		..	..	..	..		..	..	..	..	7 8	..	..	..	..	..
66	..	..	..	..	..	..	..	..	6 56	..	..	..		..	..	..	..		..	..	..	..	..	..	..	..	..	..
67	..	..	..	..	..	..	..	..	6 58	..	..	..		..	..	..	..		..	..	..	..	..	..	..	..	..	..
68	..	..	6 56	..	..	..	7 0	..	7 1	..	..	..	7 4	..	..	..	..		..	..	..	..	..	..	..	..	..	..
69	..	..	..	..	..	..	..	..	7 3	..	..	..	7 6	..	..	..	..		..	..	..	..	..	..	..	..	..	..
70	..	..	..	..	..	..	..	..	7 6	..	..	..	7 9	..	..	..	..		..	..	..	..	..	..	..	..	..	..
71	6 56	..	..	..	..	..	..	..	..	6 59	7 3	..	..	..	..	..	7 1		7 4	7 6	7 6	..	..	..	..	..	..	7 14
72	..	..	..	..	..	..	..	..	..	7 1	..	..	..	..	..	..	..		..	..	7 8	..	..	..	..	..	..	7 16
73	7 0	..	..	..	..	7 2	..	..	..	7 4	7 7	..	..	..	..	..	7 6		7 8	7 10	7 11	..	..	..	..	..	7 12	7 19
74	..	..	..	..	..	..	..	..	..	7 7	..	..	..	..	..	..	..		..	..	7 14	..	..	..	..	..	..	7 22
75	..	7 2	7 2	..	7 5	..	7 7	..	7 10	..	..	..	7 13	..	7 15	7 16	..	..	..	..	..	7 18	7 19	7 11	7 10	..	..	..
76	..	..	..	..	..	..	..	..	..	..	..	..	..	..	..	..	..	7 3	..	..	..	..	..	7 14	7 14	..	..	..
77	..	..	..	..	..	..	..	..	..	..	..	..	..	..	..	..	..	..	..	..	..	..	..	7 17	7 17	..	..	..
78	7 7	..	..	7 2	..	7 8	..	..	..	7 11	7 14	..	..	..	..	..	7 11	..	7 13	7 16	7 18	..	..	..	..	..	7 19	7 26

HORSHAM, REIGATE, REDHILL, TATTENHAM CORNER, CATERHAM,

For Notes, see page 317a

Up.	No.	Week Days—continued p.m.																					No.
		3			3	3	3		3	3	3	3		3	3	3	3	3	3	3	3		
Horsham............dep	1		6§SXO																			..	1
Reigate............ "	2	..	6SX30	..	..	..	..	..	..	..	..	..	..	..	..	..	..	..	..	..	..	653	2
Redhill.............. "	3	..	6 50	..	..	..	..	..	..	..	..	..	..	..	..	..	..	..	..	..	..	659	3
Merstham..............	4	..		..	..	..	..	..	..	..	..	..	..	..	..	..	..	..	..	..	..	7 3	4
Coulsdon South..........	5	..		..	..	..	..	..	..	..	..	..	..	..	..	..	..	..	..	..	..	7 9	5
Tattenham Corner dep	6	..		..	..	..	..	..	..	..	..	..	..	..	..	..	..	..	..	..	6 43	..	6
Tadworth **N**..........	7	..		..	..	..	..	..	..	..	..	..	..	..	..	..	..	..	..	..	6 46	..	7
Kingswood **M**..........	8	..	§ Via Three Bridges	..	..	..	..	..	..	..	..	..	..	..	..	..	..	..	..	..	6 49	..	8
Chipstead..............	9	..		..	..	..	..	..	..	..	..	..	..	..	..	..	..	..	..	..	6 53	..	9
Woodmansterne..........	10	..		..	..	..	..	..	..	..	..	..	..	..	..	..	..	..	..	..	6 55	..	10
Smitham..............	11	..		..	..	..	..	..	..	..	..	..	..	..	..	..	..	..	..	..	6 58	..	11
Reedham..............	12	..		..	..	..	..	..	..	..	..	..	..	..	..	..	..	..	..	..	7 1	..	12
Purley 252.......... arr	13	..		..	..	..	..	..	..	..	..	..	..	..	..	..	..	..	..	..	7 3	..	13
Caterham.......... dep	14	..	..	..	..	..	..	..	..	..	..	..	..	..	..	..	..	..	..	..	6 53	..	14
Warlingham..............	15	..	..	..	..	..	..	..	..	..	..	..	..	..	..	..	..	..	..	..	6 57	..	15
Whyteleafe..............	16	..	..	..	..	..	..	..	..	..	..	..	..	..	..	..	..	..	..	..	6 59	..	16
Kenley..............	17	..	..	..	..	..	..	..	..	..	..	..	..	..	..	..	..	..	..	..	7 2	..	17
Purley 252.......... arr	18	S X	..	..	..	..	..	..	..	..	..	S X	..	..	..	..	..	..	..	..	7 5	..	18
Coulsdon North...... dep	19	6 51	..	..	..	..	..	..	..	..	..	6 56	..	..	..	..	..	..	..	..	..	..	19
Purley 252..............	20	6 54	..	..	..	..	..	..	..	..	..	6 59	..	..	..	..	..	..	..	..	7 7	713	20
Purley Oaks..............	21	6 56	..	..	..	..	..	..	..	..	..	7 2	..	..	..	..	..	..	..	..	..	..	21
South Croydon 234......	22	6 59	..	..	..	..	..	..	S X	..	..	7 4	..	..	..	..	..	..	..	..	..	..	22
Effingham Junction dep	23	..	..	..	..	..	..	..	6 22	..	..	..	..	..	..	..	..	..	..	..	..	..	23
Bookham..............	24	..	..	..	..	..	..	..	6 26	S X	..	..	..	..	..	..	..	..	..	..	..	..	24
Dorking North...... dep	25	..	..	..	..	..	..	..	..	6 29	..	..	..	..	..	..	..	..	..	..	..	..	25
Boxhill and Burford	26	..	..	..	..	..	..	..	..	6 32	..	..	..	..	..	..	..	..	..	..	..	..	26
Leatherhead...[BridgeJ	27	..	..	..	..	..	..	..	6 30	6 37	..	..	..	..	..	..	..	..	..	..	..	..	27
Ashtead..............	28	..	..	..	..	..	..	..	6 34	6 41	..	..	..	..	..	..	..	..	..	..	..	..	28
Epsom 427..............	29	..	..	..	..	..	..	..	6 39	6 45	..	..	..	..	..	..	..	..	..	..	..	..	29
Ewell East **H**..........	30	..	..	..	..	..	..	..	..	6 48	..	..	..	..	..	..	..	..	..	..	..	..	30
Cheam..............	31	..	..	..	..	..	S X	..	..	6 51	..	..	..	..	..	..	..	..	..	..	..	..	31
Epsom Downs...... dep	32	..	..	..	..	..	6 44	..	..	..	..	..	..	6 49	..	..	..	..	..	..	..	..	32
Banstead..............	33	..	..	..	..	..	6 47	..	..	..	..	..	..	6 52	..	..	..	..	..	..	..	..	33
Belmont..............	34	..	..	..	..	..	6 50	..	..	..	..	..	..	6 55	..	S O	S X	..	..		..	..	34
Sutton 322..............	35	..	..	..	..	..	6 53	..	..	6 55		..	..	6 58	..	7 1	7 2	..	..		..	..	35
Carshalton Beeches......	36	..	..	..	..	..	6 55	..	..	..		..	..	7 0	..	7 4	7 4	..	..		..	..	36
Wallington..............	37	..	..	..	..	..	6 58	..	..	..		..	..	7 3	..	7 7	7 7	..	..		..	..	37
Waddon **G**..............	38	..	..	..	..	..	7 1	..	..	..	From London Bridge, via Streatham	..	..	7 6	..	7 10	7 12		..	From London Bridge, via Forest Hill	..	..	38
West Croydon 319 arr	39	..	..	..	S X	..	7 4	..	..	..		..	..	7 9	..	7 13	7 15		..		..	..	39
West Croydon 319 dep	40	..	..	..	7 0	..	7 4	..	..	..		..	..	7 9	..	..	..		..		..	..	40
Carshalton..............	41	..	..	..	..	..	..	..	..	6 58		..	..	..	..	..	..		..		..	..	41
Hackbridge..............	42	..	..	..	..	..	..	..	..	7 0		..	..	..	..	..	..		..		..	..	42
Mitcham Junction......	43	..	..	..	..	..	..	..	..	7 3		..	..	..	..	..	..		..		..	..	43
East Croydon.... arr	44	7 2	7 4	..	..	..	..	..	..	..	..	7 7	..	..	..	..	..		..	..	7 13	720	44
East Croydon.... dep	45	7 2	7 5	..	..	..	..	..	..	..	S O	7 7	..	..	..	..	..	From Victoria, via Wandsworth Common	..	S X	7 13	720	45
Norwood Junction **F**..	46	..	..	..	7 4	..	7 8	..	..	..	7 9	7 11	..	..	..	..	..		S X	7 12	7 16	724	46
Beckenham Jn. dep	47	..	..	..	..	..	..	..	..	..	..	..	..	..	..	..	..		7 9	..	..	..	47
Birkbeck..............	48	..	..	..	..	S O	..	..	..	..	..	..	..	..	..	..	..		7 12	..	..	..	48
Crystal Palace **D**......	49	..	..	..	7 9	7 11	..	..	..	..	..	..	..	..	..	..	..		7 16	..	..	..	49
Gipsy Hill (for Upper	50	..	..	..	7 11	7 13	..	..	..	..	..	..	..	..	..	..	..		7 18	..	..	..	50
West Norwood.[N'wood)	51	..	..	..	7 14	7 16	..	..	..	..	..	..	..	..	..	..	..	S X	7 21	..	..	..	51
Streatham Hill..........	52	..	..	..	7 17	..	..	..	..	..	..	..	..	..	..	..	..	7 18	7 24	..	..	..	52
Selhurst..............	53	7 5	..	..	..	..	..	..	..	..	..	..	..	7 12		..	..	..	..	7 15	..	..	53
Thornton Heath........	54	7 7	..	..	..	..	..	..	..	..	..	..	..	7 14		..	..	..	..	7 17	..	..	54
Norbury..............	55	7 10	..	..	..	..	..	..	..	..	..	..	..	7 17		..	..	..	..	7 20	..	..	55
Streatham Common....	56	7 12	..	..	..	..	..	..	..	..	..	..	..	7 19		..	..	..	..	7 23	..	..	56
Anerley..............	57	..	..	..	..	..	..	..	..	..	7 12	..	..			..	..	..	..	..	..	..	57
Penge West **C**..........	58	..	..	..	..	..	..	..	..	..	7 13	..	..		From Victoria, dep. 7 7 p.m	..	..	..	..	..	..	..	58
Sydenham........[Lane	59	..	..	..	..	..	..	..	..	..	7 15	..	..			..	..	..	..	..	..	..	59
Forest Hill, for Lordship	60	..	..	..	..	..	..	..	..	..	7 18	..	..			..	..	..	..	..	..	..	60
Honor Oak Park........	61	..	..	..	..	..	..	..	..	..	7 20	..	..			..	..	..	..	..	..	..	61
Brockley **B**.......[Line)	62	..	..	..	..	..	..	..	..	..	7 23	..	..	L 3 mins. *earlier* on Sats. N 2 mins. *earlier* on Sats.		..	..	..	..	..	..	..	62
New Cross Gate (for E.L.	63	..	..	..	..	..	..	..	..	..	7 25	7 20	..			..	..	..	..	..	..	733	63
Streatham..............	64	..	..	..	..	..	..	..	..	7 8	..	..	..			..	..	..	..	7 25	..	..	64
Tulse Hill..............	65	..	..	..	..	7 18	..	..	..	7 11	..	..	..			..	..	7 21	..	7 28		..	65
North Dulwich..........	66	..	..	..	..	7 21	..	..	..	..	..	..	..			..	..	7 24	..	..		..	66
East Dulwich..........	67	..	..	..	..	7 23	..	..	..	..	..	..	..		SX	..	..	7 26	..	..		..	67
Peckham Rye..........	68	..	..	..	..	7 26	..	..	..	7 16	..	..	..		7 24	..	..	7 29	..	7 33		..	68
Queen's Road, Peckham	69	..	..	..	..	7 28	..	..	..	..	..	..	..		7 26	..	..	7 31	..	..		..	69
South Bermondsey......	70	..	..	..	..	7 31	..	..	..	..	..	..	..		7 29	..	..	7 34	..	..	H 1 minute *earlier* on Saturdays	..	70
Balham & Upper Tooting	71	7 16	..	..	7 19	..	..	..	..	..	..	..	..	7 23	..	..	..	..	7 26	..		..	71
Wandsworth Common **A**	72	..	..	..	7 21	..	..	..	..	..	..	..	..	..	..	..	..	..	7 28	..		..	72
Clapham Junction......	73	7 20	7 16	..	7 24	..	..	..	..	..	..	..	..	7N29	..	..	..	..	7 31	..		..	73
Battersea Park..........	74	..	..	..	7 27	..	..	..	..	..	..	..	..	..	..	..	..	..	7 34	..		..	74
London Bridge...... arr	75	..	..	..	..	7 35	7 22	..	..	7 22	7 31	7 26	..	..	7 33	..	..	7 38	..	7 40	7 31	738	75
Waterloo*........ "	76	..	..	..	..	..	..	..	..	..	..	..	..	..	..	..	..	..	..	..	7 35	..	76
Charing Cross * .. "	77	..	..	..	..	..	..	..	..	..	..	..	..	..	..	..	..	..	..	..	7H38	..	77
Victoria............ "	78	7 27	7 22	..	7 31	..	..	..	..	..	..	..	..	7L36	..	..	..	..	7 38	..	..	..	78

DORKING NORTH, SUTTON, CROYDON, CRYSTAL PALACE, and LONDON

Week Days—continued (p.m)

No.	3	3	SO	3	SX	3	3	3	3		3	3	3	3	3		3	3	3	3	3		3	3	3			3
1			6 20		6 20											..											6§48	
2	..	..	3	..	3	..	..	..	..	..	..	..	..	..	..	..	..	..	..	..	..	..	..	..	..	..	7 23	..
3	..	..		..		..	..	..	..	..	..	..	..	..	..	..	..	..	..	..	..	..	..	..	..	..	7 30	..
4	..	..	..	..	..	..	..	..	..	..	..	..	..	..	..	..	..	..	..	..	..	..	..	..	..	..	7 34	..
5	..	..	..	..	..	..	..	..	..	..	..	..	..	..	..	..	..	..	..	..	..	..	..	..	..	..	7 41	..
6	..	..	..	..	..	..	..	..	..	..	V 2 minutes *earlier* on Saturdays	..	..	..	..	..	7 0	..	..	..	..	..	..	..	..	..	§ Via Three Bridges	..
7	..	..	..	..	..	..	..	..	..	..		..	..	..	..	..	7 3	..	..	..	..	..	..	..	..	..		..
8	..	..	..	..	..	..	..	..	..	..		..	..	..	..	..	7 6	..	..	..	..	..	..	..	..	..		..
9	..	..	..	..	..	..	..	..	..	..		..	..	..	..	..	7 10	..	..	..	..	..	..	..	..	..		..
10	..	..	..	..	..	..	..	..	..	..		..	..	..	..	..	7 13	..	..	..	..	..	..	..	..	..		..
11	..	..	..	..	..	..	..	..	..	..		..	..	..	..	..	7 15	..	..	..	..	..	..	..	..	..		..
12	..	..	..	..	..	..	..	..	..	..		..	..	..	..	..	7 18	..	..	..	..	..	..	..	..	..		..
13	..	..	..	..	..	..	..	..	..	..		..	..	..	..	..	7 20	..	..	..	..	..	..	..	..	..		..
14	..	..	..	..	..	..	..	..	..	..		..	..	..	..	..	7 11	..	..	..	..	..	..	..	..	..	..	..
15	..	..	..	..	..	..	..	..	..	..		..	..	..	..	..	7 14	..	..	..	..	..	..	..	..	..	..	..
16	..	..	..	..	..	..	..	..	..	..		..	..	..	..	..	7 16	..	..	..	..	..	..	..	..	..	..	..
17	..	..	..	..	..	..	..	..	..	..		..	..	..	..	..	7 19	..	..	..	..	..	..	..	..	..	..	..
18	..	..	..	..	..	..	..	..	..	..		..	..	..	..	..	7 23	..	..	..	..	..	..	..	..	..	..	..
19	..	..	..	..	..	..	..	..	..	..	7V13	..	..	..	..	..	..	..	..	..	..	..	..	..	..	..	..	..
20	..	..	..	..	..	..	..	..	..	..	7V16	..	..	..	..	..	7 25	..	..	..	..	..	..	..	..	..	7 44	..
21	..	..	..	..	..	..	..	..	..	..	7V18	..	..	..	..	..	7 27	..	..	..	..	..	..	..	..	..	..	..
22	..	..	..	..	..	..	..	..	..	..	7V21	..	..	..	..	..	7 30	..	..	..	..	..	..	..	..	..	..	..
23	..	6 38	..	..	..	..	..	..	..	..	..	..	..	..	..	..	..	..	..	..	..	..	..	..	..	..	..	..
24	..	6 41	..	..	..	..	..	..	SX	..	..	..	..	..	..	..	..	..	..	..	..	..	..	..	..	..	..	..
25	..	..	6 46	..	6 48	..	..	..	6 58	..	..	..	..	..	..	..	..	..	..	..	..	..	..	..	..	..	..	..
26	..	..	6 48	..	6 51	..	..	..	7 1	..	..	..	..	..	..	..	..	..	..	..	..	..	..	..	..	..	..	..
27	..	6 46	6 53	..	6 56	..	..	..	7 6	..	..	..	..	..	..	..	..	..	..	..	..	..	..	..	..	..	..	..
28	..	6 50	6 57	..	7 0	SX	SO	..	7 10	..	..	..	..	..	..	..	..	..	..	..	..	..	..	..	..	..	..	..
29	..	6 54	7 1	..	7 5	7 11	7 12	..	7 14	..	..	..	..	..	..	..	..	..	..	..	..	..	..	..	..	..	..	..
30	..	..	7 4	..	7 8	7 14	7 15	..	..	..	..	..	..	..	..	..	..	..	..	..	..	..	..	..	..	..	..	..
31	..	..	7 7	..	7 11	7 17	7 18	..	..	..	..	..	..	..	..	..	..	..	..	..	..	..	..	..	..	..	..	..
32	7 0	..	..	..	..	..	..	..	..	..	J 1 minute *earlier* on Saturdays	..	..	..	..	..	..	..	From London Bridge, via Streatham	From London Bridge, via Forest Hill	From London Bridge, via Forest Hill	..	7 19	..	..	..	..	..
33	7 3	..	..	..	..	..	..	..	..	..		..	..	..	..	..	..	..				..	7 22	..	..	..	..	..
34	7 6	..	..	..	..	..	..	SX	..	..		..	..	..	..	..	..	..				..	7 25	SO	..	..	..	..
35	7 9	..	7 11	..	7 14	7 20	7 21	7 23	..	..		..	..	..	..	..	..	..				..	7 28	7 33	..	..	..	..
36	7 11	..	..	..	..	..	..	7 25	..	..		..	..	..	..	..	..	..				..	7 30	7 37	..	..	..	..
37	7 14	..	..	..	..	..	..	7 28	..	..		..	..	..	..	..	..	..				..	7 33	7 40	..	..	..	..
38	7 17	..	..	..	..	..	..	..	..	..		..	..	..	..	..	..	..				..	7 36	..	..	..	..	..
39	7 20	..	..	..	..	..	..	..	..	..		..	..	SO	SX	..	..	..				..	7 39	..	..	..	..	..
40	7 20	..	..	..	..	..	..	..	..	..		..	..	7 23	7 25	..	..	..				..	7 39	..	..	..	..	..
41	..	..	7 14	..	7 17	7 23	7 24	..	..	..		..	..	..	..	..	..	..				..	..	..	..	..	..	..
42	..	..	7 16	..	7 20	7 25	7 26	..	..	..		..	..	..	..	..	..	..				..	..	..	..	..	..	..
43	..	..	7 19	..	7 22	7 28	7 29	..	..	..		..	..	..	..	..	..	..				..	..	..	..	..	..	..
44	..	..	..	..	..	..	..	..	..	..	7 23	..	..	..	..	..	7 32	..	..	..	..	..	..	..	..	..	7 50	..
45	..	..	..	..	..	..	..	..	..	..	7 23	..	..	..	..	..	7 32	..	SX	SO	SX	..	..	..	..	..	7 51	..
46	7 24	..	..	..	..	..	..	..	..	..	..	..	SO	7 28	7 29	..	7 36	..	7 33	7 29	7 32	..	..	..	..	..	..	SX
47	..	..	..	..	..	..	..	..	..	..	..	..	7 20	..	..	..	..	..	..	..	..	..	..	..	..	..	..	7 38
48	..	..	..	..	..	..	..	..	..	..	..	SX	7 23	..	..	..	..	..	..	..	..	..	..	..	SO	..	..	7 41
49	..	..	..	..	..	..	..	..	..	..	..	7 27	7 27	7 33	7 33	..	..	..	..	..	..	..	..	..	7 39	..	..	7 47
50	..	..	..	..	..	..	..	..	..	..	..	7 29	..	7 36	7 36	..	..	..	..	..	..	..	..	..	..	..	..	7 49
51	..	..	..	..	..	..	..	..	..	..	..	7 31	..	7 38	7 38	..	..	..	..	..	..	..	..	..	..	..	..	7 52
52	..	..	..	..	..	..	..	..	..	..	..	..	..	7 41	7 41	..	..	..	..	..	..	..	..	..	..	..	..	7 55
53	..	..	..	..	..	..	..	..	..	..	7 26	..	..	..	..	..	..	..	..	7 32	7 35	..	7 42	..	..	..	..	..
54	..	..	..	..	..	..	..	..	..	..	7 28	..	..	..	..	..	..	..	..	7 34	7 37	..	7 44	..	..	..	..	..
55	..	..	..	..	..	..	..	..	..	..	7 31	..	..	..	..	..	..	..	..	7 37	7 40	..	7 47	..	..	..	..	..
56	..	..	..	..	..	..	..	..	..	..	7J34	..	..	..	..	..	..	..	..	7 39	7 43	..	7 49	..	..	..	..	..
57	7 27	..	..	From Victoria, dep. 7 18 p.m	..	..	..	..	Via Worcester Park. Change at Wimbledon	..	..	..	..	..	..	..	..	From Victoria, dep. 7 27 p.m	7 36	..	..	..	..	..	..	..	..	..
58	7H29	..	..		..	..	..	..		..	..	..	..	..	..	..	..		7 37	..	..	..	..	..	..	..	..	..
59	7H31	..	..		..	..	..	..		..	..	..	..	..	..	..	..		7 39	..	..	..	..	..	7 42	..	..	..
60	7 33	..	..		..	..	..	..		..	..	..	..	..	..	..	..		7 42	..	..	..	..	..	7 45	..	..	..
61	7H36	..	..		..	..	..	..		..	..	..	..	..	..	..	..		7 44	..	..	..	..	..	7 47	..	..	..
62	7 38	..	..		..	..	..	..		..	..	..	..	..	..	..	..		7 47	..	..	..	..	..	7 50	..	..	..
63	7 40	..	..		..	..	..	..		..	..	..	..	..	..	..	..		7 49	..	..	..	..	..	7 52	..	..	..
64	H 1 minute *earlier* on Saturdays	Via Worcester Park	7 24		7 29	..	..	..		..	..	..	..	..	..	..	..		..	7 41	7 45	..	..	..	..	..	..	..
65			7 27		7 32	..	..	..		..	..	7 35	..	..	..	..	..		..	7 45	7 48	..	..	..	..	..	..	..
66			..		..	..	..	..		..	..	7 38	..	..	..	..	..		..	7 48	..	..	..	..	..	..	..	..
67			..	SO	..	..	..	..		..	..	7 40	..	..	..	..	..	SX	..	7 50	..	..	..	..	..	..	..	..
68			7 32	7 35	7 37	..	..	..		..	..	7 42	..	..	..	..	..	7 45	..	7 52	7 53	..	..	..	..	..	..	..
69			..	7 37	..	..	..	..		..	..	7 44	..	..	..	..	..	7 47	..	7 54	..	..	..	..	..	..	..	..
70			..	7 40	..	..	..	..		..	..	7 47	..	..	..	..	..	7 50	..	7 57	..	..	..	..	..	..	..	..
71			..	..	..	7 35	7 36	..	..	..	7J38	..	..	7 44	7 44	..	..	..	..	..	..	..	7 53	..	..	..	..	7 57
72			..	..	..	..	..	..	..	..	7SO39	..	..	7 46	7 46	..	..	..	..	..	..	..	..	..	..	..	..	7 59
73			..	..	..	7 39	7 40	..	..	..	7 42	..	..	7 49	7 49	..	..	..	..	..	..	..	7 57	..	..	..	8 2	8 2
74			..	..	..	..	..	..	..	..	..	..	..	7 52	7 52	..	..	..	..	..	..	..	..	..	..	..	..	8 5
75	7 46	..	7 38	7 44	7 44	..	..	..	..	..	..	7 51	..	..	..	..	7 52	7 54	7 55	8 1	7 59	..	..	..	7 58	..	..	..
76	..	7SO22	..	..	..	..	..	..	7 43	..	..	..	..	..	..	..	..	..	..	..	..	..	..	..	..	..	..	..
77	..	..	..	..	..	..	..	..	..	..	..	..	..	..	..	..	..	..	..	..	..	..	..	..	..	..	..	..
78	..	..	..	..	..	7 44	7 45	..	..	..	7J49	..	..	7 56	7 56	..	..	..	..	..	..	..	8 3	..	..	..	8 8	8 9

HORSHAM, REIGATE, REDHILL, TATTENHAM CORNER, CATERHAM,

For Notes, see page 317a

Week Days—*continued* (p.m)

Up	No.	3	3	3		3		3		3	3	3			3	3		3	3	3	3	3	No.
Horsham .... dep	1	..	..	..	..	..	6 52	..	..	..	..	..	..	..	..	..	..	..	..	..	..	..	1
Reigate .... "	2	..	..	..	..	..	..	..	..	..	..	..	..	..	..	..	7 29	..	..	..	..	..	2
Redhill .... "	3	..	..	..	..	..	3	..	..	..	..	..	..	..	..	..	7 50	..	..	..	..	..	3
Merstham	4	..	..	..	..	..	..	..	..	..	..	..	..	..	..	..	..	..	..	..	..	..	4
Coulsdon South	5	..	..	..	..	..	..	..	..	..	..	..	..	..	..	..	..	..	..	..	..	..	5
Tattenham Corner. dep	6	..	..	..	..	..	..	..	..	..	..	7 23	..	..	..	..	..	..	..	..	..	..	6
Tadworth **N**	7	..	..	..	..	..	..	..	..	..	..	7 26	..	..	..	..	..	..	..	..	..	..	7
Kingswood **M**	8	..	..	..	..	..	..	..	..	..	..	7 29	..	..	..	..	..	..	..	..	..	..	8
Chipstead	9	..	..	..	..	..	..	..	..	..	..	7 33	..	..	..	..	..	..	..	..	..	..	9
Woodmansterne	10	..	..	..	..	..	..	..	..	..	..	7 36	..	..	..	..	..	..	..	..	..	..	10
Smitham	11	..	..	..	..	..	..	..	..	..	..	7 38	..	..	..	..	..	..	..	..	..	..	11
Reedham	12	..	..	..	..	..	..	..	..	..	..	7 41	..	..	..	..	..	..	..	..	..	..	12
Purley 252 .... arr	13	..	..	..	..	..	..	..	..	..	..	7 43	..	..	..	..	..	..	..	..	..	..	13
Caterham .... dep	14	..	..	..	..	..	..	..	..	..	..	7 33	..	..	..	..	..	..	..	..	..	..	14
Warlingham	15	..	..	..	..	..	..	..	..	..	..	7 37	..	..	..	..	..	..	..	..	..	..	15
Whyteleafe	16	..	..	..	..	..	..	..	..	..	..	7 39	..	..	..	..	..	..	..	..	..	..	16
Kenley	17	..	..	..	..	..	..	..	..	..	..	7 42	..	..	..	..	..	..	..	..	..	..	17
Purley 252 .... arr	18	..	..	..	..	..	..	..	..	..	..	7 45	..	..	..	..	..	..	..	..	..	..	18
Coulsdon North ..... dep	19	7 36	..	..	..	..	..	..	..	..	..	..	..	..	..	..	..	..	..	..	..	..	19
Purley 252	20	7 39	..	..	..	..	..	..	..	..	..	7 47	..	..	..	..	..	..	..	..	..	..	20
Purley Oaks	21	7 41	..	..	..	..	..	..	..	..	..	7 50	..	..	..	..	..	..	..	..	..	..	21
South Croydon 234	22	7 44	..	..	..	..	..	..	..	..	..	7 52	7 54	..	..	..	..	..	..	..	..	..	22
Effingham Junction dep	23	..	7 12	..	..	..	..	..	..	..	..	..	..	..	..	..	..	..	..	..	..	..	23
Bookham	24	..	7 15	..	..	..	..	..	..	..	..	..	..	..	..	..	..	..	..	..	SO	SX	24
Dorking North ..... dep	25	..	..	..	..	..	7 18	..	..	..	..	..	..	..	..	..	..	..	..	..	7 28	7 28	25
Boxhill and Burford	26	..	..	..	..	..	7 21	..	..	..	..	..	..	..	..	..	..	..	..	..	7 30	7 30	26
Leatherhead...[Bridge **J**	27	..	7 19	..	..	..	7 26	..	..	..	..	..	..	..	..	..	..	..	..	..	7 35	7 35	27
Ashtead	28	..	7 23	..	..	..	7 30	..	..	SO	SX	..	..	..	..	..	..	..	..	..	7 39	7 39	28
Epsom 427	29	..	7 28	..	..	..	7 34	..	..	7 36	7 38	..	..	..	..	..	..	..	..	..	7 44	7 44	29
Ewell East **H**	30	..	7 31	..	..	..	..	..	..	7 39	7 41	..	..	..	..	..	..	..	..	..	7 47	7 47	30
Cheam	31	..	7 34	..	..	..	..	..	..	7 42	7 44	..	..	..	..	..	..	..	..	..	7 50	7 50	31
Epsom Downs ...... dep	32	..	..	..	..	7 30	..	..	..	..	..	..	..	..	..	..	..	..	..	..	..	..	32
Banstead	33	..	..	..	..	7 33	..	..	..	..	..	..	..	..	..	..	..	..	..	..	..	..	33
Belmont	34	..	..	..	..	7 36	..	SX	..	..	..	..	..	..	..	..	..	..	..	..	..	..	34
Sutton 322	35	..	7 37	..	..	7 39	..	7 44	..	7 45	7 47	..	..	..	..	..	..	..	..	..	7 54	7 55	35
Carshalton Beeches	36	..	..	..	..	7 41	..	7 46	..	..	..	..	..	..	..	..	..	..	..	..	..	..	36
Wallington	37	..	..	..	..	7 44	..	7 51	..	..	..	..	..	..	..	..	..	..	..	..	..	..	37
Waddon **G**	38	..	..	..	..	7 47	..	7 55	..	..	..	..	..	..	..	..	..	..	..	..	..	..	38
West Croydon 319 arr	39	..	..	..	..	7 50	..	7 58	..	..	..	..	..	..	..	..	..	..	..	..	..	..	39
West Croydon 319 dep	40	..	..	..	..	7 50	..	..	..	..	..	..	..	..	..	7 55	..	..	..	..	..	..	40
Carshalton	41	..	7 40	..	..	..	..	..	..	7 48	7 50	..	..	..	..	..	..	..	..	..	7 57	7 58	41
Hackbridge	42	..	7 43	..	..	..	..	..	..	7 50	7 53	..	..	..	..	..	..	..	..	..	8 0	8 1	42
Mitcham Junction	43	..	7 45	..	..	..	..	..	..	7 53	7 55	..	..	..	..	..	..	..	..	..	8 3	8 4	43
East Croydon .... arr	44	7 47	..	..	..	..	..	..	..	..	..	7 55	7 58	..	..	..	8 4	..	..	..	..	..	44
East Croydon .... dep	45	7 47	..	..	..	..	..	..	..	..	..	7 55	7 58	..	..	..	8 5	..	..	..	..	..	45
Norwood Junction **F**	46	..	..	..	..	7 54	..	..	..	..	..	7 58	..	..	..	7 59	..	..	..	..	..	..	46
Beckenham Jn. dep	47	..	..	..	..	..	..	..	..	..	..	..	..	..	7 50	..	..	..	..	..	..	..	47
Birkbeck	48	..	..	..	..	..	..	..	..	..	..	..	..	..	7 53	..	..	SX	SO	SX	..	..	48
Crystal Palace **D**	49	..	..	..	..	..	..	..	..	..	..	..	..	..	7 57	8 3	..	8 8	8 11	8 9	..	..	49
Gipsy Hill (for Upper	50	..	..	..	..	..	..	..	..	..	..	..	..	..	..	8 6	..	8 11	8 13	..	..	..	50
West Norwood.[N'wood)	51	..	..	..	..	..	..	..	..	..	..	..	..	..	..	8 8	..	8 13	8 16	..	..	..	51
Streatham Hill	52	..	..	..	..	..	..	..	..	..	..	..	..	..	..	8 11	..	..	..	..	..	..	52
Selhurst	53	7 50	..	..	..	..	..	..	..	..	..	..	..	..	..	..	..	..	..	..	..	..	53
Thornton Heath	54	7 52	..	..	..	..	..	..	..	..	..	..	..	..	..	..	..	..	..	..	..	..	54
Norbury	55	7 55	..	..	..	..	..	..	..	..	..	..	..	..	..	..	..	..	..	..	..	..	55
Streatham Common	56	7 57	..	..	..	..	..	..	..	..	..	..	..	..	..	..	..	..	..	..	..	..	56
Anerley	57	..	..	..	..	7 57	..	..	..	..	..	..	..	..	..	..	..	..	..	..	..	..	57
Penge West **C**	58	..	J 1 minute later on Saturdays.	From Victoria, dep. 7 47 p.m J 1 minute later on Saturdays.	..	7 58	..	..	..	..	..	..	..	..	..	..	..	..	..	..	..	..	58
Sydenham .... [Lane	59	..	..	..	..	8 0	..	..	..	..	..	..	..	..	..	..	..	..	..	8 12	..	..	59
Forest Hill, for Lordship	60	..	..	..	..	8 3	..	..	..	..	..	..	..	..	..	..	..	..	..	8 14	..	..	60
Honor Oak Park	61	..	..	..	..	8 5	..	..	..	..	..	..	..	..	..	..	..	..	..	8 17	..	..	61
Brockley **E** .... [Line)	62	..	..	..	..	8 8	..	..	..	..	..	..	..	..	..	..	..	..	..	8 19	..	..	62
New Cross Gate (for E.L.	63	..	..	..	..	8V10	..	..	..	..	..	..	..	..	..	..	..	..	..	8 22	..	..	63
Streatham	64	..	7 51	..	..	..	..	..	..	..	..	..	..	..	..	..	..	..	..	..	8 8	8 10	64
Tulse Hill	65	..	7 55	..	..	..	..	..	..	..	..	..	..	..	..	..	..	8 16	8 18	..	8 11	8 14	65
North Dulwich	66	..	..	..	..	..	..	..	..	..	..	..	..	..	..	..	..	8 19	8 21	..	8 14	..	66
East Dulwich	67	..	..	..	..	..	..	..	..	..	..	..	..	..	..	..	..	8 21	8 23	..	8 16	..	67
Peckham Rye	68	..	8 0	8J 3	..	..	..	..	..	..	..	..	..	..	..	..	..	8 23	8 26	..	8 19	8 19	68
Queen's Road Peckham	69	..	..	8J 5	..	V 2 minutes later on Saturdays.	Via Worcester Park	..	..	..	..	..	..	..	..	..	..	8 25	8 28	..	8 21	..	69
South Bermondsey	70	..	..	8J 8	..	..	..	..	..	..	..	..	..	..	..	..	..	8 28	8 31	..	8 24	..	70
Balham & Upper Tooting	71	8 1	..	..	..	..	..	..	..	8 2	8 2	..	..	..	..	8 14	..	..	..	..	..	..	71
Wandsworth Common **A**	72	..	..	..	..	..	..	..	..	..	..	..	..	..	..	8 16	..	..	..	..	..	..	72
Clapham Junction	73	8 6	..	..	..	..	..	..	..	8 6	8 6	..	..	..	..	8 19	8 16	..	..	..	..	..	73
Battersea Park	74	..	..	..	..	..	..	..	..	..	..	..	..	..	..	8 22	..	..	..	..	..	..	74
London Bridge ..... arr	75	..	8J 6	8J12	..	8 16	..	..	..	..	..	8 11	..	..	..	..	..	8 32	8 35	8 27	8 28	8 25	75
Waterloo * .... "	76	..	..	..	..	..	8 3	..	..	..	..	8 15	..	..	..	..	..	..	..	..	..	..	76
Charing Cross * .. "	77	..	..	..	..	..	..	..	..	..	..	8 17	..	..	..	..	..	..	..	..	..	..	77
Victoria .... "	78	8 12	..	..	..	..	..	..	..	8 12	8 11	..	8 15	..	..	8 26	8 22	..	..	..	..	..	78

DORKING NORTH, SUTTON, CROYDON, CRYSTAL PALACE, and LONDON

p.m — Week Days—*continued* — p.m

No.																												
1	3	3	3	3	3	3	..	3	3	7 21	..	3	7 43	3	3	3	3	3	3	3	..	..	..	3	3	..	7§46	3
2	..	..	..	..	..	..	7Z48	..	..	3	..	..	..	..	..	..	..	..	..	..	..	..	..	..	..	..	8 21	..
3	..	..	..	..	..	..	7 59	..	..		..	..	..	..	..	..	..	..	..	..	..	..	..	..	..	..	8 29	..
4	..	..	..	..	..	..	8 3	..	..	..	..	..	..	..	..	..	..	..	..	..	..	..	..	..	..	..	8 33	..
5	..	..	..	..	..	..	8 9	..	..	..	..	..	..	..	..	..	..	..	..	..	..	..	..	..	..	..	8 39	..
6	..	..	..	..	..	7 43	..	..	..	..	..	..	..	..	..	..	..	..	..	..	..	..	..	..	..	..	§ Via Three Bridges	..
7	..	..	..	..	..	7 46	Z 4 minutes later on Saturdays	..	..	..	..	..	..	..	..	..	..	..	..	..	..	..	..	..	..	..		..
8	..	..	..	..	..	7 49		..	..	..	..	..	..	..	..	..	..	..	..	..	..	..	..	..	..	..		..
9	..	..	..	..	..	7 53		..	..	..	..	..	..	..	..	..	..	..	..	..	..	..	..	..	..	..		..
10	..	..	..	..	..	7 56		..	..	..	..	..	..	..	..	..	..	..	..	..	..	..	..	..	..	..		..
11	..	..	..	..	..	7 58		..	..	..	..	..	..	..	..	..	..	..	..	..	..	..	..	..	..	..		..
12	..	..	..	..	..	8 1		..	..	..	..	..	..	..	..	..	..	..	..	..	..	..	..	..	..	..		..
13	..	..	..	..	..	8 3		..	..	..	..	..	..	..	..	..	..	..	..	..	..	..	..	..	..	..		..
14	..	..	..	..	..	7 53		..	..	..	..	..	..	..	..	..	..	..	..	..	..	..	..	..	..	..	..	..
15	..	..	..	..	..	7 57		..	..	..	..	..	..	..	..	..	..	..	..	..	..	..	..	..	..	..	..	..
16	..	..	..	..	..	7 59		..	..	..	..	..	..	..	..	..	..	..	..	..	..	..	..	..	..	..	..	..
17	..	..	..	..	..	8 2		..	..	..	..	..	..	..	..	..	..	..	..	..	..	..	..	..	..	..	..	..
18	..	..	..	..	..	8 5	..	..	..	..	..	..	..	..	..	..	..	..	..	..	..	..	..	..	..	..	..	..
19	..	..	..	..	..	..	..	..	..	..	..	..	..	..	..	8 11	..	..	..	..	..	..	..	..	..	..	..	..
20	..	..	..	..	..	8 7	8 13	..	..	..	..	..	..	..	..	8 14	..	..	..	..	..	..	..	..	..	..	..	..
21	..	..	..	..	..	8 10	..	..	..	..	..	..	..	..	..	8 17	..	..	..	..	..	..	..	..	..	..	8 43	..
22	..	..	..	..	..	8 12	..	..	..	..	..	..	..	..	..	8 19	..	..	..	..	..	..	..	..	..	..	..	..
23	..	..	..	..	..	..	..	..	7 38	..	..	..	..	..	..	..	..	..	..	..	..	..	..	..	..	..	..	8 12
24	..	..	..	..	..	..	..	..	7 41	..	..	..	..	S X	..	..	..	..	..	..	..	..	..	..	..	..	..	8 15
25	..	..	..	..	..	..	..	..	..	7 46	..	..	8 2	7 55	..	..	..	..	..	..	..	..	..	..	..	..	..	..
26	..	..	..	..	..	..	..	..	..	7 48	..	..	..	7 57	..	..	..	..	..	..	..	..	..	..	..	..	..	..
27	..	..	..	..	..	..	..	..	7 46	7 53	..	..	..	8 2	..	..	..	..	..	..	..	..	..	..	..	..	..	8 19
28	..	..	..	..	..	..	..	..	7 50	7 57	..	..	..	8 6	..	..	..	..	..	..	..	..	..	..	..	..	..	8 23
29	..	..	..	..	..	..	..	..	7 54	8 2	..	..	..	8 14	8 17	..	..	..	..	..	..	..	..	..	..	..	..	8 28
30	..	..	..	..	..	..	..	..	..	8 5	..	..	..	..	8 20	..	..	..	..	..	..	..	..	..	..	..	..	8 31
31	..	..	..	..	..	..	..	..	..	8 8	..	..	..	..	8 23	..	..	..	..	..	..	..	..	..	..	..	..	8 34
32	From London Bridge, via Streatham	From London Bridge, via Streatham	7 49	..	..	..	..	8 0	..	..	..	..	..	Arrives Epsom 8 10 p.m	..	..	..	..	..	..	..	..	..	8 19	..	..	..	..
33			7 52	..	..	..	..	8 3	..	..	..	..	..		..	..	..	..	..	..	..	..	..	8 22	..	..	..	..
34			7 55	S O	S X	..	..	8 6	..	..	..	..	..		..	..	..	..	..	..	..	..	..	8 25	..	..	..	..
35			7 58	8 2	8 3	..	..	8 9	..	8 11	..	..	8 20		8 26	..	..	..	..	From London Bridge, via Forest Hill	..	..	..	8 28	8 34	..	..	8 37
36			8 0	8 4	8 6	..	..	8 11	..	..	..	..	..		..	..	..	..	..		..	..	..	8 30	8 36	..	..	..
37			8 3	8 7	8 9	..	..	8 14	..	..	..	..	..		..	..	..	..	..		..	..	..	8 33	8 39	..	..	..
38			8 6	..	8 13	..	..	8 17	..	..	..	..	..		..	..	..	..	..		..	..	..	8 36	..	..	..	..
39			8 9	..	8 16	..	..	8 20	..	..	..	..	..		..	..	..	..	..		..	..	..	8 39	..	..	..	..
40			8 9	..	..	..	..	8 20	..	..	..	..	..		..	..	..	8 25	..		..	..	..	8 39	..	..	..	..
41			..	..	..	..	..	..	..	8 14	..	..	..	..	8 29	..	..	..	..		..	..	..	..	..	..	..	8 40
42			..	..	..	..	..	..	..	8 16	..	..	..	..	8 31	..	..	..	..		..	..	..	..	..	..	..	8 43
43			..	..	..	..	..	..	..	8 19	..	..	..	..	8 34	..	..	..	..		..	..	..	..	..	..	..	8 45
44			..	..	..	8 15	8 18	..	..	..	..	..	..	..	..	8 22	..	..	..		..	..	..	..	..	..	..	..
45	S O	S X	..	..	..	8 15	8 20	..	..	..	..	..	..	..	..	8 22	..	..	..		..	..	..	..	..	..	8 50	..
46	8 9	8 10	..	..	..	8 18	8 24	8 24	..	..	..	..	..	..	..	..	..	8 29	..	8 29	..	8 42	8 47	..	..	..	8 50	..
47	..	..	..	..	..	..	..	..	..	..	..	..	..	..	..	..	8 20	..	..	..	..	..	..	..	..	..	..	..
48	..	..	..	..	..	..	..	..	..	..	..	..	..	..	..	..	8 23	..	..	..	..	..	..	..	..	..	..	..
49	..	..	..	..	..	..	..	..	..	..	..	..	..	..	..	..	8 27	8 33	8 39	..	..	..	..	..	..	..	..	..
50	..	..	..	..	..	..	..	..	..	..	..	..	..	..	..	..	..	8 36	..	..	..	..	..	..	..	..	..	..
51	..	..	..	..	..	..	..	..	..	..	..	..	..	..	..	..	..	8 38	..	..	..	..	..	..	..	..	..	..
52	..	..	..	..	..	..	..	..	..	..	..	..	..	..	..	..	..	8 41	..	..	..	..	..	..	..	..	..	..
53	..	..	8 12	..	..	..	..	..	..	..	..	..	..	..	..	8 25	..	..	..	8 32	..	..	..	8 42	..	..	..	..
54	..	..	8 14	..	..	..	..	..	..	..	..	..	..	..	..	8 27	..	..	..	8 34	..	..	..	8 44	..	..	..	..
55	..	..	8 17	..	..	..	..	..	..	..	..	..	..	..	..	8 30	..	..	..	8 37	..	..	..	8 47	..	..	..	..
56	..	..	8 19	..	..	..	..	..	..	..	..	..	..	..	..	8 32	..	..	..	8 39	..	..	..	8 49	..	..	..	..
57	8 12	8 12	..	..	..	..	..	8 27	..	..	..	..	..	Via Worcester Park Change at Wimbledon	..	..	..	..	..	..	..	..	..	..	..	..	..	..
58	8 13	8 14	..	..	..	..	..	8 28	..	..	..	From Victoria, dep. 8 18 p.m	..		..	..	..	..	..	..	..	..	..	..	..	..	..	..
59	8 15	8 16	..	..	..	..	..	8 30	..	..	..		..		..	..	..	..	8 42	..	..	..	..	..	..	..	..	..
60	8 18	8 18	..	..	..	..	..	8 33	..	..	..		..		..	..	..	..	8 45	..	..	..	..	..	..	..	..	..
61	8 20	8 21	..	..	..	..	..	8 35	..	..	..		..		..	..	..	..	8 47	..	..	..	..	..	..	..	..	..
62	8 23	8 23	..	..	..	..	..	8 38	..	..	..		..		..	..	..	..	8 50	..	..	..	..	..	..	..	..	..
63	8 25	8 26	..	..	..	..	..	8 40	..	..	..		..		..	..	..	..	8 52	..	..	..	..	..	..	..	..	..
64	..	..	..	..	..	..	..	..	..	8 24	..		..		..	..	..	..	..	8 41	..	..	..	..	..	..	..	8 51
65	..	..	..	..	..	..	..	..	..	8 27	..		..		..	..	..	..	..	8 45	..	..	..	..	..	..	..	8 55
66	..	..	..	..	..	..	..	..	Via Worcester Park	..	..		..		..	..	..	..	..	8 48	..	..	..	..	..	..	..	..
67	..	..	..	..	..	..	..	..		..	..		..		..	..	..	..	..	8 50	..	..	..	..	..	..	..	..
68	..	..	..	..	..	..	..	..		8 32	..	8 35	..		..	..	..	..	..	8 52	..	..	..	..	..	..	..	9 0
69	..	..	..	..	..	..	..	..		..	..	8 37	..		..	..	..	..	..	8 54	..	..	..	..	..	..	..	..
70	..	..	..	..	..	..	..	..		..	..	8 40	..		..	..	..	..	..	8 57	..	..	..	..	..	..	..	..
71	..	..	8 23	..	..	..	..	..		..	..	..	..	..	8 41	8 36	..	8 44	..	..	..	..	..	8 53	..	..	..	..
72	..	..	..	..	..	..	..	..		..	..	..	..	..	..	8 38	..	8 46	..	..	..	..	..	..	..	..	..	..
73	..	..	8 27	..	..	..	..	..		..	..	..	..	8 41	8 45	8 41	..	8 49	..	..	..	..	..	8 57	..	..	9 1	..
74	..	..	8SO30	..	..	..	..	..		..	..	..	..	..	8 48	..	..	8 52	..	..	..	..	..	..	..	..	..	..
75	8 31	8 31	..	..	..	8 31	8 36	8 46	..	8 38	..	8 44	..	..	..	..	..	..	8 58	9 1	..	..	..	..	..	..	..	9 7
76	..	..	..	..	..	8 35	..	..	8 22	..	..	..	..	8 50	..	..	..	..	..	..	..	..	..	..	..	..	..	..
77	..	..	..	..	..	8 37	..	..	..	..	..	..	..	..	..	..	..	..	..	..	..	..	..	..	..	..	..	..
78	..	..	8 34	..	..	..	..	..	..	..	..	..	8 40	..	8 52	8 47	..	8 56	..	..	..	8 57	9 3	9 3	..	..	9 7	..

For Notes, see page 317a

HORSHAM, REIGATE, REDHILL, TATTENHAM CORNER, CATERHAM,

Up	No.	p.m								Week Days—*continued*								p.m					No.
Horsham ... dep	1	3	3	7 52	3	3	3	3	..	3	3	3	3	..	3	..	..	3	3	..	3	3	1
Reigate ... "	2	..	..	3	..	..	..	..	..	..	..	..	..	..	..	..	..	..	..	8 52	..	..	2
Redhill ... "	3	..	..		..	..	..	..	..	..	..	..	..	..	..	..	8 50	..	..	8 59	..	..	3
Merstham	4	..	..	..	..	..	..	..	..	..	..	..	..	..	..	..	..	..	..	9 3	..	..	4
Coulsdon South	5	..	..	..	..	..	..	..	..	..	..	..	..	..	..	..	..	..	..	9 9	..	..	5
Tattenham Corner . dep	6	..	..	..	..	..	..	8 21	..	..	..	..	..	..	..	..	..	..	8 43	..	..	..	6
Tadworth **N**	7	..	..	..	..	..	..	8 24	..	..	..	..	..	..	..	..	..	..	8 46	..	..	..	7
Kingswood **M**	8	..	..	..	..	..	..	8 27	..	..	..	..	..	..	..	..	..	..	8 49	..	..	..	8
Chipstead	9	..	..	..	..	..	..	8 32	..	..	..	..	..	..	..	..	..	..	8 53	..	..	..	9
Woodmansterne	10	..	..	..	..	..	..	8 34	..	..	..	..	..	..	..	..	..	..	8 56	..	..	..	10
Smitham	11	..	..	..	..	..	..	8 37	..	..	..	..	..	..	..	..	..	..	8 58	..	..	..	11
Reedham	12	..	..	..	..	..	..	8 39	..	..	..	..	..	..	..	..	..	..	9 1	..	..	..	12
Purley 252 ... arr	13	..	..	..	..	..	..	8 42	..	..	..	..	..	..	..	..	..	..	9 3	..	..	..	13
Caterham ... dep	14	..	..	..	..	..	..	8 32	..	..	..	..	..	..	..	..	..	..	8 53	..	..	..	14
Warlingham	15	..	..	..	..	..	..	8 35	..	..	..	..	..	..	..	..	..	..	8 57	..	..	..	15
Whyteleafe	16	..	..	..	..	..	..	8 37	..	..	..	..	..	..	..	..	..	..	8 59	..	..	..	16
Kenley	17	..	..	..	..	..	..	8 40	..	..	..	..	..	..	..	..	..	..	9 2	..	..	..	17
Purley 252 ... arr	18	..	..	..	..	..	..	8 44	..	..	..	..	..	..	..	..	..	..	9 5	..	..	..	18
Coulsdon North ... dep	19	..	..	..	..	..	8 42	..	..	..	..	..	..	..	..	..	..	..	..	..	9 11	..	19
Purley 252	20	..	..	..	..	..	8 45	8 46	..	..	..	..	..	..	..	..	..	..	9 7	9 13	9 14	..	20
Purley Oaks	21	..	..	..	..	..	8 48	8 49	..	..	..	..	..	..	..	S X	..	..	9 10	..	9 16	..	21
South Croydon 234	22	..	..	..	..	S X	8 50	8 51	..	..	..	..	..	..	..	8 54	..	..	9 12	..	9 19	..	22
Effingham Junction dep	23	..	..	..	..	8 19	..	..	..	..	..	..	..	..	..	..	..	..	..	..	..	..	23
Bookham	24	..	..	..	..	8 24	..	..	..	..	..	..	..	..	..	..	..	..	..	..	..	..	24
Dorking North ... dep	25	..	..	8 18	..	..	..	..	..	..	..	..	..	..	..	..	..	..	..	..	..	..	25
Boxhill and Burford	26	..	..	8 21	..	..	..	..	..	..	..	..	..	..	..	..	..	..	..	..	..	..	26
Leatherhead ... [Bridge J	27	..	..	8 26	..	8 28	..	..	..	..	..	..	..	..	..	..	..	..	..	..	..	..	27
Ashtead	28	..	..	8 30	..	..	..	..	..	..	..	..	..	..	..	..	..	..	..	..	..	..	28
Epsom 427	29	..	..	8 34	8 40	..	..	..	..	..	..	..	..	..	..	..	..	..	..	..	..	..	29
Ewell East **H**	30	..	..	..	8 43	..	..	..	..	..	..	..	..	..	..	..	..	..	..	..	..	..	30
Cheam	31	..	..	..	8 46	..	..	..	..	..	..	..	..	..	..	..	..	..	..	..	..	..	31
Epsom Downs ... dep	32	..	8 30	..	..	..	..	..	..	..	..	8 49	..	..	..	..	..	From London Bridge, via Streatham	..	..	..	9 0	32
Banstead	33	..	8 33	..	..	..	..	..	..	..	..	8 52	..	..	..	..	..		..	..	..	9 3	33
Belmont	34	..	8 36	..	..	..	..	..	..	..	..	8 55	..	..	..	..	..		..	..	..	9 6	34
Sutton 322	35	..	8 39	..	8 49	..	..	..	..	..	..	8 58	9 2	..	..	..	..		..	..	..	9 9	35
Carshalton Beeches	36	..	8 41	..	..	..	..	..	..	..	..	9 0	9 4	..	..	..	..		..	..	..	9 11	36
Wallington	37	..	8 44	..	..	..	..	..	..	..	..	9 3	9 7	..	..	..	..		..	..	..	9 14	37
Waddon **G**	38	..	8 47	..	..	..	..	..	..	..	..	9 6	9 10	..	..	..	..		..	..	..	9 17	38
West Croydon 319 arr	39	..	8 50	..	..	..	..	..	..	..	..	9 9	9 13	..	..	..	..		..	..	..	9 20	39
dep	40	..	8 50	..	..	..	..	..	..	..	8 55	9 9	..	..	..	..	..		..	..	..	9 20	40
Carshalton	41	..	..	..	8 52	..	..	..	..	..	..	..	..	..	..	..	..		..	..	..	..	41
Hackbridge	42	..	..	..	8 55	..	..	..	..	..	..	..	..	..	..	..	..		..	..	..	..	42
Mitcham Junction	43	..	..	..	8 57	..	..	..	..	..	..	..	..	..	..	..	..		..	..	..	..	43
East Croydon ... arr	44	..	..	..	..	..	8 53	8 54	..	..	..	..	..	..	..	8 58	9 4		9 15	9 20	9 22	..	44
dep	45	..	..	..	..	..	8 53	8 54	..	..	..	..	..	..	..	8 58	9 5		9 15	9 20	9 22	..	45
Norwood Junction F	46	..	8 54	..	..	..	..	8 58	..	..	8 59	..	..	..	..	9 3	..	9 9	9 18	9 24	..	9 25	46
Beckenham Jn. dep	47	..	..	..	..	..	..	..	..	8 50	..	..	..	..	..	..	..	..	..	..	..	..	47
Birkbeck	48	..	..	..	..	..	..	..	..	8 53	..	..	..	..	..	..	..	..	..	..	..	..	48
Crystal Palace D	49	..	..	..	..	..	..	..	..	8 57	9 3	..	..	..	9 11	..	..	..	..	..	..	..	49
Gipsy Hill (for Upper	50	..	..	..	..	..	..	..	..	..	9 6	..	..	..	9 13	..	..	..	..	..	..	..	50
West Norwood. [N'wood)	51	..	..	..	..	..	..	..	..	..	9 8	..	..	..	9 16	..	..	..	..	..	..	..	51
Streatham Hill	52	..	..	..	..	..	..	..	..	..	9 11	..	..	..	..	..	..	..	..	..	..	..	52
Selhurst	53	..	..	..	..	..	8 56	..	..	..	..	9 12	..	..	..	..	..	..	..	..	9 25	..	53
Thornton Heath	54	..	..	..	..	..	8 58	..	..	..	..	9 14	..	..	..	..	..	..	..	..	9 27	..	54
Norbury	55	..	..	..	..	..	9 1	..	..	..	..	9 17	..	..	..	..	..	..	..	..	9 30	..	55
Streatham Common	56	..	..	..	..	..	9 4	..	..	..	..	9 19	..	..	..	..	..	..	..	..	9 33	..	56
Anerley	57	From Victoria, dep. 8 48 p.m	8 57	..	..	..	H 1 minute *earlier* on Sats L 3 mins *earlier* on Sats	..	..	..	..	..	..	..	..	..	..	9 12	..	..	J 1 minute later on Saturdays	9H28	57
Penge West **C**	58		8 58	..	..	..		..	..	..	..	..	..	..	..	..	..	9 13	..	..		9 29	58
Sydenham ... [Lane	59		9 0	..	..	..		..	..	..	..	..	..	..	..	..	..	9 15	..	..		9 31	59
Forest Hill, for Lordship	60		9 3	..	..	..		..	..	..	..	..	..	..	..	..	..	9 18	..	..		9 34	60
Honor Oak Park	61		9 5	..	..	..		..	..	..	..	..	..	..	..	..	..	9 20	..	..		9 36	61
Brockley **B** ... [Line)	62		9 8	..	..	..		..	..	..	..	..	..	..	..	..	..	9 23	..	..		9 39	62
New Cross Gate (for E.L.	63		9 10	..	..	..		..	..	..	..	..	..	..	..	..	..	9 25	..	..		9 41	63
Streatham	64		..	Via Worcester Park	..	..		..	..	..	..	..	..	..	..	..	..	..	..	..		H 1 minute *earlier* on Saturdays	64
Tulse Hill	65		..		..	..		..	..	..	..	..	..	..	9 18	..	..	..	..	..			65
North Dulwich	66		..		..	..		..	..	..	..	..	..	..	9 21	..	..	..	..	..			66
East Dulwich	67		..		..	..		..	..	..	..	..	..	..	9 23	..	..	..	..	..			67
Peckham Rye	68	9 4	..		..	..		..	..	..	..	..	..	..	9 26	..	..	..	..	..			68
Queen's Road, Peckham	69	9 6	..		..	..		..	..	..	..	..	..	..	9 28	..	..	..	..	..			69
South Bermondsey	70	9 9	..		..	..		..	..	..	..	..	..	..	9 31	..	..	..	..	..			70
Balham & Upper Tooting	71	..	..		9 4	..	9 8	..	..	..	9 14	9 23	..	..	..	..	..	..	..	..	9 37		71
Wandsworth Common **A**	72	..	..		..	..	9SX10	..	..	..	9 16	..	..	..	..	..	..	..	..	..	9J38		72
Clapham Junction	73	..	..		9 8	..	9H13	..	..	..	9 19	9 27	..	..	..	..	9 16	..	..	..	9 42		73
Battersea Park	74	..	..		..	..	..	..	..	..	9 22	9 31	..	..	..	..	..	..	..	..	9 45		74
London Bridge ... arr	75	9 13	9 16		..	..	..	9 11	..	..	..	..	..	..	9 34	9 18	..	9 31	9 31	9 36	..	9 47	75
Waterloo * ... "	76	..	..	9 3	..	..	..	9 15	..	..	..	..	..	..	..	..	..	..	9 35	..	..	..	76
Charing Cross * ... "	77	..	..	..	..	..	..	9 17	..	..	..	..	..	..	..	..	..	..	9 37	..	..	..	77
Victoria ... "	78	..	..	..	9 13	..	9L20	..	..	..	9 26	9 34	..	..	..	..	9 22	..	..	..	9 48	..	78

DORKING NORTH, SUTTON, CROYDON, CRYSTAL PALACE, and LONDON

p.m — **Week Days**—*continued* — p.m

No.																												
1	③	8 20	③	③	SO 8 43	③	③	③	③	..	..	③	③	③	..	8§48	③	③	③	8 52	③	③	③	③	③	..	..	③
2	..	③	..	..	..	..	..	..	..	..	..	..	..	..	..	9 22	..	..	..	..	..	..	..	..	..	..	9 41	..
3	..		..	..	..	..	..	..	..	..	..	..	..	..	..	9 29	..	..	..	③	..	..	..	..	..	..	9 50	..
4	..	..	..	..	..	..	..	..	..	..	..	..	..	..	..	9 33	..	..	..		..	..	..	..	..	..	..	..
5	..	..	..	..	..	..	..	..	..	..	..	..	..	..	..	9 39	..	..	..	..	..	..	..	..	..	..	..	..
6	..	..	..	..	..	..	..	..	..	..	..	..	..	..	..	§ Via Three Bridges	..	..	..	..	..	..	..	..	9 23	..	..	..
7	..	..	..	..	..	..	..	..	..	..	..	..	..	..	..		..	..	..	..	..	..	..	..	9 26	..	..	..
8	..	..	..	..	..	..	..	..	..	..	..	..	..	..	..		..	..	..	..	..	..	..	..	9 29	..	..	..
9	..	..	..	..	..	..	..	..	..	..	..	..	..	..	..		..	..	..	..	..	..	..	..	9 33	..	..	..
10	..	..	..	..	..	..	..	..	..	..	..	..	..	..	..		..	..	..	..	..	..	..	..	9 36	..	..	..
11	..	..	..	..	..	..	..	..	..	..	..	..	..	..	..		..	..	..	..	..	..	..	..	9 38	..	..	..
12	..	..	..	..	..	..	..	..	..	..	..	..	..	..	..		..	..	..	..	..	..	..	..	9 41	..	..	..
13	..	..	..	..	..	..	..	..	..	..	..	..	..	..	..		..	..	..	..	..	..	..	..	9 43	..	..	..
14	..	..	..	..	..	..	..	..	..	..	..	..	..	..	..	..	..	..	..	..	..	..	..	..	9 33	..	..	..
15	..	..	..	..	..	..	..	..	..	..	..	..	..	..	..	..	..	..	..	..	..	..	..	..	9 37	..	..	..
16	..	..	..	..	..	..	..	..	..	..	..	..	..	..	..	..	..	..	..	..	..	..	..	..	9 39	..	..	..
17	..	..	..	..	..	..	..	..	..	..	..	..	..	..	..	..	..	..	..	..	..	..	..	..	9 42	..	..	..
18	..	..	..	..	..	..	..	..	..	..	..	..	..	..	..	..	..	..	..	..	..	..	..	..	9 45	..	..	..
19	..	..	..	..	..	..	..	..	..	..	..	..	..	..	..	..	..	..	..	..	..	..	9 42	..	..	..	..	..
20	..	..	..	..	..	..	..	..	..	..	..	..	..	..	..	9 43	..	..	..	..	..	..	9 45	..	9 47	..	..	..
21	..	..	..	..	..	..	..	..	..	..	..	..	..	..	..	..	..	..	..	..	..	..	9 47	..	9 50	..	..	..
22	..	..	..	..	..	..	..	..	..	..	..	..	..	..	..	..	..	..	..	..	..	..	9 50	..	9 52	..	..	..
23	8 38	..	..	..	..	..	..	..	..	..	..	..	..	..	..	..	9 12	..	..	..	..	..	..	..	..	..	..	..
24	8 41	..	..	SX	..	..	..	..	..	..	..	..	..	..	..	..	9 15	..	..	..	..	..	..	..	..	..	..	..
25	..	8 46	..	8 55	9 2	..	..	..	..	..	..	..	..	..	..	..	..	..	..	9 18	..	..	..	..	..	..	..	..
26	..	8 48	..	8 57	..	..	..	..	..	..	..	..	..	..	..	..	..	..	..	9 21	..	..	..	..	..	..	..	..
27	8 46	8 53	..	9 2	..	..	..	..	..	..	..	..	..	..	..	..	9 19	..	..	9 26	..	..	..	..	..	..	..	..
28	8 50	8 57	..	9 6	..	..	..	..	..	..	..	..	..	..	..	..	9 23	..	..	9 30	..	..	..	..	..	..	..	..
29	8 54	9 2	..	9 10	..	9 17	..	..	..	..	..	..	..	..	..	..	9 28	..	..	9 34	9 40	..	..	..	..	..	..	..
30	..	9 5	..	..	..	9 20	..	..	..	..	..	..	..	..	..	..	9 31	..	..	..	9 43	..	..	..	..	..	..	..
31	..	9 8	..	..	..	9 23	..	..	..	..	..	..	..	..	..	..	9 34	..	..	..	9 46	..	..	..	..	..	..	..
32	..	..	..	..	..	..	..	..	..	..	..	..	9 19	..	..	..	..	9 30	..	..	..	..	..	..	..	..	..	..
33	..	..	..	..	..	..	..	..	..	..	..	..	9 22	..	..	..	..	9 33	..	..	..	..	..	..	..	..	..	..
34	..	..	..	..	..	..	..	..	..	..	..	..	9 25	..	..	..	..	9 36	..	..	..	..	..	..	..	..	..	..
35	..	9 11	..	..	9 20	9 26	From London Bridge, via Forest Hill	..	..	..	..	..	9 28	9 32	..	..	9 37	9 39	..	..	9 49	..	..	..	..	..	..	..
36	..	..	..	..	..	..		..	..	..	..	..	9 30	9 34	..	..	..	9 41	..	..	..	..	..	..	..	..	..	..
37	..	..	..	..	..	..		..	..	..	..	..	9 33	9 37	..	..	..	9 44	..	..	..	..	..	..	..	..	..	..
38	..	..	..	..	..	..		..	..	..	..	..	9 36	..	..	..	..	9 47	..	..	..	..	..	..	..	..	..	..
39	..	..	..	..	..	..		..	..	..	..	..	9 39	..	..	..	..	9 50	..	..	..	..	..	..	..	..	..	..
40	..	..	..	..	..	..		..	9 25	..	..	..	9 39	..	..	..	..	9 50	..	..	..	..	..	9 55	..	..	..	..
41	..	9 14	..	..	..	9 29		..	..	..	..	..	..	..	..	..	9 40	..	..	..	9 52	..	..	..	..	..	..	..
42	..	9 16	..	..	..	9 31		..	..	..	..	..	..	..	..	..	9 43	..	..	..	9 54	..	..	..	..	..	..	..
43	..	9 19	..	..	..	9 34		..	..	..	..	..	..	..	..	..	9 45	..	..	..	9 57	..	..	..	..	..	..	..
44	..	..	..	..	..	..		..	..	..	..	..	..	..	..	9 48	..	..	..	..	..	..	9 52	..	9 55	..	10 4	..
45	..	..	..	..	..	..		..	..	..	9 42	..	..	..	..	9 50	..	..	..	..	..	..	9 52	..	9 55	10 0	10 5	..
46	..	..	..	..	..	..	9 29	..	9 29	..	..	..	..	..	..	..	..	9 54	..	..	..	..	..	9 59	9 58	10 6	..	..
47	..	..	..	..	..	..	..	9 20	..	..	..	..	..	..	..	..	..	..	..	..	..	9 50	..	..	..	..	..	..
48	..	..	..	..	..	..	..	9 23	..	..	..	..	..	..	..	..	..	..	..	..	..	9 53	..	..	..	..	..	..
49	..	..	..	..	..	..	..	9 27	9 33	..	..	9 39	..	..	..	..	..	..	..	..	..	9 57	..	10 4	..	..	..	..
50	..	..	..	..	..	..	..	..	9 36	..	..	..	..	..	..	..	..	..	..	..	..	..	..	10 6	..	..	..	..
51	..	..	..	..	..	..	..	..	9 38	..	..	..	..	..	..	..	..	..	..	..	..	..	..	10 9	..	..	..	..
52	..	..	..	..	..	..	..	..	9 41	..	..	..	..	..	..	..	..	..	..	..	..	..	..	1012	..	..	..	SX
53	..	..	..	..	..	..	9 32	..	..	..	..	..	9 42	..	..	..	..	..	..	..	..	..	9 55	..	..	..	..	10 2
54	..	..	..	..	..	..	9 34	..	..	..	..	..	9 44	..	..	..	..	..	..	..	..	..	9 57	..	..	..	..	10 4
55	..	..	..	..	..	..	9 37	..	..	..	..	..	9 47	..	..	..	..	..	..	..	..	..	10 0	..	..	..	..	10 7
56	..	..	..	..	..	..	9 39	..	..	..	..	..	9 49	..	..	..	..	..	..	..	..	..	10 3	..	..	..	..	10 9
57	..	..	From Victoria, dep 9 18 p.m	Via Worcester Park Change at Wimbledon	..	..	..	..	..	..	..	..	..	..	..	..	..	9 57	From Victoria, dep. 9 48 p.m	..	..	..	..	..	..	..	..	..
58	..	..			..	..	..	..	..	..	..	..	..	..	..	..	..	9 58		..	..	..	..	..	..	..	..	..
59	..	..			..	..	..	..	..	..	..	9 42	..	..	..	..	..	10 0		..	..	..	..	..	..	..	..	..
60	..	..			..	..	..	..	..	..	..	9 45	..	..	..	..	..	10 3		..	..	..	..	..	..	..	..	..
61	..	..			..	..	..	..	..	..	..	9 47	..	..	..	..	..	10 5		..	..	..	..	..	..	..	..	..
62	..	..			..	..	..	..	..	..	..	9 50	..	..	..	..	..	10 8		..	..	..	..	..	..	..	..	..
63	..	..			..	..	..	..	..	..	..	9 52	..	..	..	..	..	1010		..	..	..	..	..	..	..	..	..
64	Via Worcester Park	9 24			..	..	9 41	..	..	..	..	..	..	..	..	..	9 51	..		..	..	..	..	..	..	..	..	1011
65		9 27			..	..	9 45	..	..	..	..	..	..	..	..	..	9 55	..		..	..	..	..	..	..	..	..	1015
66		..			..	..	9 48	..	..	..	..	..	..	..	..	..	..	..		..	..	..	..	..	..	..	..	..
67		..			..	..	9 50	..	..	..	..	..	..	..	..	..	..	..		..	..	..	..	..	..	..	..	..
68		9 32	9 35		..	..	9 52	..	..	..	..	..	..	..	..	..	10 0	..	10 4	..	..	..	..	..	..	..	..	1020
69		..	9 37		..	..	9 54	..	..	..	..	..	..	..	..	..	..	..	10 6	..	..	..	..	..	..	..	..	..
70		..	9 40		..	..	9 57	..	..	..	..	..	..	..	..	..	..	..	10 9	Via Worcester Park	..	..	..	..	..	..	..	..
71		..	..		..	9 41	..	..	9 44	..	..	..	9 53	..	..	..	..	..	..		10 4	..	10 7	1014	..	..	..	..
72		..	..		..	..	..	..	9 46	..	..	..	..	..	..	..	..	..	..		..	..	..	1016	..	..	..	..
73		..	..	9 40	..	9 45	..	..	9 49	..	..	..	9 58	..	..	10 1	..	..	..		10 8	..	1012	1019	..	..	1016	..
74		..	..	..	..	..	..	..	9 52	..	..	..	..	..	..	..	..	..	..		..	..	..	1022	..	..	..	..
75	..	9 38	9 44	..	..	..	10 1	..	..	..	..	9 58	..	..	..	..	10 7	1016	1013	..	..	..	..	..	1011	1020	..	1026
76	9 23	..	..	9 48	..	..	..	..	..	..	..	..	..	..	..	..	..	..	..	10 3	..	..	..	..	1015	..	..	..
77	..	..	..	..	..	..	..	..	..	..	..	..	..	..	..	..	..	..	..	..	..	..	..	..	1017	..	..	..
78	..	..	..	..	9 40	9 50	..	..	9 56	..	9 57	..	10 3	..	..	10 7	..	..	..	..	1013	..	1017	1026	..	..	1022	..

For Notes, see page 317a

HORSHAM, REIGATE, REDHILL, TATTENHAM CORNER, CATERHAM,

Up	No.	p.m					Week Days—continued										p.m					No.
		3	3	3			3	3	3	3	3			3	3	3		3	3	3	3	
Horsham .... dep	1	..	..	..	..	..	..	..	9 22	..	..	..	9§17	..	..	..	..	..	..	..	..	1
Reigate .... "	2	..	..	..	..	..	..	..		..	..	..	9 52	..	..	..	..	..	..	..	..	2
Redhill .... "	3	..	..	..	..	..	..	..		..	..	..	9 59	..	..	..	..	..	..	..	..	3
Merstham	4	..	..	..	..	..	..	..	..	..	..	..	10 3	..	..	..	..	..	..	..	..	4
Coulsdon South	5	..	..	..	..	..	..	..	..	..	..	..	10 9	..	..	..	..	..	..	..	..	5
Tattenham Corner . dep	6	..	..	..	..	..	..	..	..	..	..	..	§ Via Three Bridges	..	..	..	..	10 3	..	..	..	6
Tadworth **N**	7	..	..	..	..	..	..	..	..	..	..	..		..	..	..	..	10 6	..	..	..	7
Kingswood M	8	..	..	..	..	..	..	..	..	..	..	..		..	..	..	..	10 9	..	..	..	8
Chipstead	9	..	..	..	..	..	..	..	..	..	..	..		..	..	..	..	1013	..	..	..	9
Woodmansterne	10	..	..	..	..	..	..	..	..	..	..	..		..	..	..	..	1016	..	..	..	10
Smitham	11	..	..	..	..	..	..	..	..	..	..	..		..	..	..	..	1018	..	..	..	11
Reedham	12	..	..	..	..	..	..	..	..	..	..	..		..	..	..	..	1021	..	..	..	12
Purley 252 .... arr	13	..	..	..	..	..	..	..	..	..	..	..		..	..	..	..	1023	..	..	..	13
Caterham .... dep	14	..	..	..	..	..	..	..	..	..	..	..	..	..	..	..	..	1013	..	..	..	14
Warlingham	15	..	..	..	..	..	..	..	..	..	..	..	..	..	..	..	..	1017	..	..	..	15
Whyteleafe	16	..	..	..	..	..	..	..	..	..	..	..	..	..	..	..	..	1019	..	..	..	16
Kenley	17	..	..	..	..	..	..	..	..	..	..	..	..	..	..	..	..	1022	..	..	..	17
Purley 252 .... arr	18	..	..	..	..	..	..	..	..	..	..	..	..	..	..	..	..	1025	..	..	..	18
Coulsdon North ..... dep	19	..	..	..	..	..	..	..	..	..	..	..	..	1011	..	..	..	..	..	..	..	19
Purley 252	20	..	..	..	..	..	..	..	..	..	..	..	1013	1014	..	..	..	1027	..	..	..	20
Purley Oaks	21	..	..	..	..	..	..	..	..	..	..	..	..	1016	..	..	..	1030	..	..	..	21
South Croydon 234	22	..	..	..	..	10 9	..	..	..	..	..	..	..	1019	..	..	..	1032	..	..	..	22
Effingham Junction dep	23	..	..	..	..	..	..	9 38	..	..	..	..	..	..	..	..	..	..	..	..	..	23
Bookham	24	..	..	..	..	..	..	9 41	..	..	..	..	..	..	..	..	..	..	..	..	..	24
Dorking North ..... dep	25	..	..	..	..	..	..	..	9 46	..	..	..	..	..	..	..	..	..	..	..	..	25
Boxhill and Burford	26	..	..	..	..	..	..	..	9 48	..	..	..	..	..	..	..	..	..	..	..	..	26
Leatherhead ... [Bridge **J**	27	..	..	..	..	..	..	9 46	9 53	..	..	..	..	..	..	..	..	..	..	..	..	27
Ashtead	28	..	..	..	..	..	..	9 50	9 57	..	..	..	..	..	..	..	..	..	..	..	..	28
Epsom 427	29	..	..	..	..	..	..	9 54	10 2	..	1010	..	..	..	..	..	..	..	..	..	..	29
Ewell East **H**	30	..	..	..	..	..	..	..	10 5	..	1013	..	..	..	..	..	..	..	..	..	..	30
Cheam	31	..	..	..	..	..	..	..	10 8	..	1016	..	..	..	..	..	..	..	..	..	..	31
Epsom Downs ...... dep	32	From London Bridge, via Streatham	9 49	..	..	..	10 0	..	..	..	..	..	..	..	..	..	..	..	..	From London Bridge, via Forest Hill	1019	32
Banstead	33		9 52	..	..	..	10 3	..	..	..	..	..	..	..	..	..	..	..	..		1022	33
Belmont	34		9 55	..	..	..	10 6	..	..	..	..	..	..	..	..	..	..	..	..		1025	34
Sutton 322	35		9 58	10 2	..	..	10 9	..	1011	..	1019	..	..	..	..	..	..	..	..		1028	35
Carshalton Beeches	36		10 0	10 4	..	..	1011	..	..	..	..	..	..	..	..	..	..	..	..		1030	36
Wallington	37		10 3	10 7	..	..	1014	..	..	..	..	..	..	..	..	10S019	..	..	..		1033	37
Waddon **G**	38		10 6	10SX10	..	..	1017	..	..	..	..	..	..	..	..	10S022	..	..	..		1036	38
West Croydon 319 arr	39		10 9	10SX13	..	..	1020	..	..	..	..	..	..	..	..	10S025	..	..	..		1039	39
West Croydon 319 dep	40		10 9	—	..	..	1020	..	..	..	..	..	..	..	..	10 25	..	..	..		1039	40
Carshalton	41		..	Stop	..	..	..	..	1014	..	1023	..	..	..	..	..	..	..	..		..	41
Hackbridge	42		..	..	..	..	..	..	1016	..	1025	..	..	..	..	..	..	..	..		..	42
Mitcham Junction	43		..	..	..	..	..	..	1019	..	1028	..	..	..	..	..	..	..	..		..	43
East Croydon .... arr	44		..	..	..	1015	..	..	..	..	..	..	1020	1022	..	..	..	1035	..		..	44
East Croydon .... dep	45		..	..	..	1015	..	..	..	..	..	..	1020	1022	..	..	..	1035	..		..	45
Norwood Junction F ..	46	1010	..	p.m	..	..	1024	..	..	..	..	..	1024	..	..	10 29	..	1038	..	1029	..	46
Beckenham Jn. dep	47	..	..	3	..	..	..	..	..	..	..	..	..	..	1020	..	..	..	..	..	..	47
Birkbeck	48	..	..		..	..	..	..	..	..	..	..	..	..	1023	..	..	..	..	..	..	48
Crystal Palace D	49	..	..	10 11	..	..	..	..	..	..	..	..	..	..	1027	10 33	..	..	1039	..	..	49
Gipsy Hill (for Upper	50	..	..	10 13	..	..	..	..	..	..	..	..	..	..	..	10 36	..	..	..	..	..	50
West Norwood. [N'wood)	51	..	..	10 16	..	..	..	..	..	..	..	..	..	..	..	10 38	..	..	..	..	..	51
Streatham Hill	52	..	..	..	..	..	..	..	..	..	..	..	..	..	..	10 41	..	..	..	..	..	52
Selhurst	53	..	1012	..	..	..	..	..	..	..	..	..	..	1025	..	..	..	..	..	1032	1042	53
Thornton Heath	54	..	1014	..	..	..	..	..	..	..	..	..	..	1027	..	..	..	..	..	1034	1044	54
Norbury	55	..	1017	..	..	..	..	..	..	From Victoria, dep. 10 18 p.m	..	..	..	1030	..	..	..	..	..	1037	1047	55
Streatham Common	56	..	1019	..	..	..	..	..	..		..	..	..	1033	..	..	..	..	..	1039	1049	56
Anerley	57	1012	..	..	..	..	1027	..	..		..	..	..	..	..	..	..	..	..	..	..	57
Penge West **C**	58	1014	..	..	..	..	1028	..	..		..	..	..	..	..	..	..	..	..	..	..	58
Sydenham .... [Lane	59	1016	..	..	..	..	1030	..	..		..	..	..	..	..	..	..	..	1042	..	..	59
Forest Hill, for Lordship	60	1018	..	..	..	..	1033	..	..		..	..	..	..	..	..	..	..	1045	..	..	60
Honor Oak Park	61	1021	..	..	..	..	1035	..	..		..	..	..	..	..	..	..	..	1047	..	..	61
Brockley **B** .... [Line)	62	1023	..	..	..	..	1038	..	..		..	..	..	..	..	..	..	..	1050	..	..	62
New Cross Gate (for E.L.	63	1026	..	..	..	..	1040	..	..		..	..	1033	..	..	..	..	..	1052	..	..	63
Streatham	64	..	..	..	..	..	..	..	1024	..	..	..	..	..	..	..	..	..	..	1041	..	64
Tulse Hill	65	..	..	10 18	..	..	..	..	1027	..	..	..	..	..	..	..	..	..	..	1045	..	65
North Dulwich	66	..	..	10 21	..	..	..	Via Worcester Park	..	..	..	..	..	..	..	..	..	..	..	1048	..	66
East Dulwich	67	..	..	10 23	..	..	..		..	..	..	..	..	..	..	..	..	..	..	1050	..	67
Peckham Rye	68	..	..	10 26	..	..	..		1032	1035	..	..	..	..	..	..	..	..	..	1052	..	68
Queen's Road, Peckham	69	..	..	10 28	..	..	..		..	1037	..	..	..	..	..	..	..	..	..	1054	..	69
South Bermondsey	70	..	..	10 31	..	..	..		..	1040	..	..	..	..	..	..	..	..	..	1057	..	70
Balham & Upper Tooting	71	..	1023	..	..	..	..		..	..	1035	..	..	1037	..	10 44	..	..	..	..	1053	71
Wandsworth Common A	72	..	..	..	..	..	..		..	..	..	..	..	1039	..	10 46	..	..	..	..	..	72
Clapham Junction	73	..	1027	..	..	1029	..		..	..	1039	..	..	1042	..	10 49	..	..	..	..	1057	73
Battersea Park	74	..	..	..	..	..	..		..	..	..	..	..	1045	..	10 52	..	..	..	..	..	74
London Bridge ..... arr	75	1031	..	10 35	..	..	1045	..	1040	1044	..	..	1039	..	..	..	..	1051	1058	11 1	..	75
Waterloo ✻ .... "	76	..	..	..	..	..	..	1023	..	..	..	..	..	..	..	..	..	1055	..	..	..	76
Charing Cross ✻ .. "	77	..	..	..	..	..	..	..	..	..	..	..	..	..	..	..	..	1057	..	..	..	77
Victoria .... "	78	..	1033	..	..	1036	..	..	..	..	1044	..	..	1048	..	10 56	..	..	..	..	11 3	78

DORKING NORTH, SUTTON, CROYDON, CRYSTAL PALACE, and LONDON

Week Days—*continued* (p.m.)

No.	3	3		3	3		3	3	3	3	3	3	3		3	3	3	3			3	3			3			
1			9§48			9 52								..					..	1020			..	1052		..	..	..
2	..	..	1022	..	..	3	..	..	..	..	..	..	..	1042	..	..	..	..	..	3	..	..	1117	3	1122	..	..	..
3	..	..	1030	..	..		..	..	..	..	..	..	..	1050	..	..	..	..	..		..	..	1129		1244	..	..	..
4	..	..	1034	..	..	..	..	..	..	..	..	..	..	..	..	..	..	..	..	..	..	..	1133	..	..	..	..	..
5	..	..	1040	..	..	..	..	..	..	..	..	..	..	..	..	..	..	..	..	..	..	..	1139	..	..	..	..	..
6	..	..	§ Via Three Bridges	..	..	..	..	..	1023	..	..	..	..	..	..	..	..	..	..	..	..	..	..	..	..	..	..	..
7	..	..		..	..	..	..	..	1026	..	..	..	..	..	..	..	..	..	..	..	..	..	..	..	..	..	..	..
8	..	..		..	..	..	..	..	1029	..	..	..	..	..	..	..	..	..	..	..	..	..	..	..	..	..	..	..
9	..	..		..	..	..	..	..	1033	..	..	..	..	..	..	..	..	..	..	..	..	..	..	..	..	..	..	..
10	..	..		..	..	..	..	..	1036	..	..	..	..	..	..	..	..	..	..	..	..	..	..	..	..	..	..	..
11	..	..		..	..	..	..	..	1038	..	..	..	..	..	..	..	..	..	..	..	..	..	..	..	..	..	..	..
12	..	..		..	..	..	..	..	1041	..	..	..	..	..	..	..	..	..	..	..	..	..	..	..	..	..	..	..
13	..	..		..	..	..	..	..	1043	..	..	..	..	..	..	..	..	..	..	..	..	..	..	..	..	..	..	..
14	..	..	..	..	..	..	..	..	1033	..	..	..	..	..	..	..	..	..	..	..	..	..	..	..	..	..	..	..
15	..	..	..	..	..	..	..	..	1037	..	..	..	..	..	..	..	..	..	..	..	..	..	..	..	..	..	..	..
16	..	..	..	..	..	..	..	..	1039	..	..	..	..	..	..	..	..	..	..	..	..	..	..	..	..	..	..	..
17	..	..	..	..	..	..	..	..	1042	..	..	..	..	..	..	..	..	..	..	..	..	..	..	..	..	..	..	..
18	..	..	..	..	..	..	..	..	1045	..	..	..	..	..	..	..	..	..	..	..	..	..	..	..	..	..	..	..
19	..	..	..	..	..	..	..	1043	..	..	..	..	..	..	..	..	..	..	..	..	..	..	..	..	..	..	..	..
20	..	..	1044	..	..	..	..	1046	1047	..	..	..	..	..	..	..	..	..	..	..	1120	..	1143	..	..	..	..	..
21	..	..	..	..	..	..	..	1048	1050	..	..	..	..	..	..	..	..	..	..	..	1122	..	..	..	..	..	..	..
22	..	..	..	..	..	..	..	1051	1052	..	..	..	..	..	..	..	..	..	..	..	1125	..	..	..	..	..	..	..
23	..	..	..	1012	..	..	..	..	..	..	..	..	..	..	..	..	..	1038	..	..	..	..	..	..	..	..	..	..
24	..	..	..	1015	..	..	..	..	..	..	..	..	..	..	..	..	..	1041	..	..	..	..	..	..	..	..	..	..
25	..	..	..	..	..	1018	..	..	..	..	..	..	..	..	..	..	..	..	..	1046	..	..	..	1118	..	..	..	..
26	..	..	..	..	..	1021	..	..	..	..	..	..	..	..	..	..	..	..	..	1048	..	..	..	1121	..	..	..	..
27	..	..	..	1019	..	1026	..	..	..	..	..	..	..	..	..	..	..	1046	..	1053	..	..	..	1126	..	..	..	..
28	..	..	..	1023	..	1030	..	..	..	..	..	..	..	..	..	..	..	..	..	1057	..	..	..	1130	..	..	..	..
29	..	..	..	1028	..	1034	1040	..	..	..	..	..	..	..	..	..	..	..	..	11 2	..	..	..	1134	..	..	..	..
30	..	..	..	1031	..	..	1043	..	..	..	..	..	..	..	..	..	..	..	..	11 5	..	..	..	..	..	..	..	..
31	..	..	..	1034	..	..	1046	..	..	..	..	..	..	..	S X	S O	..	..	..	11 8	..	..	..	..	..	..	..	..
32	..	..	..	..	1030	..	..	..	..	..	From London Bridge, via Forest Hill	..	From London Bridge, via Streatham	..	1049	1049	..	..	..	..	..	..	..	..	..	..	..	..
33	..	..	..	..	1033	..	..	..	..	..		..		..	1052	1052	..	..	..	..	..	..	..	..	..	..	..	..
34	..	..	..	..	1036	..	..	..	..	..		..		..	1055	1055	..	..	..	..	..	..	..	..	..	..	..	..
35	1032	..	..	1037	1039	..	1049	..	..	..		..		..	1058	1058	11 2	..	..	1112	..	1131	..	..	..	..	..	..
36	1034	..	..	..	1041	..	..	..	..	..		..		..	11 0	11 0	11 4	..	..	..	..	1133	..	..	..	..	..	..
37	1037	..	..	..	1044	..	..	..	..	..		..		..	11 3	11 3	11 7	..	..	..	..	1136	..	..	..	..	..	..
38	..	..	..	..	1047	..	..	..	..	..		..		..	11 6	11 6	—	..	..	..	..	1139	..	..	..	..	..	..
39	..	..	..	..	1050	..	..	..	..	..		..		..	11 9	11 9	Stop	..	..	..	..	1142	..	..	..	..	..	..
40	..	..	..	..	1050	..	..	..	..	1055		..		..	11 9	11 9	..	..	..	..	..	..	..	..	..	..	..	..
41	..	..	..	1040	..	..	1052	..	..	..		..		..	..	..	..	..	..	1115	..	..	..	..	..	..	..	..
42	..	..	..	1043	..	..	1054	..	..	..		..		..	..	..	..	..	..	1117	..	..	..	..	..	..	..	..
43	..	..	..	1045	..	..	1056	..	..	..		..		..	..	..	..	..	..	1120	..	..	..	..	..	..	..	..
44	..	..	1050	..	..	..	..	1054	1055	..		..		11 4	..	..	..	..	..	..	1128	..	1150	..	1259	..	..	..
45	..	..	1051	..	..	..	..	1054	1055	..		..		11 5	..	..	..	..	..	..	1128	..	1150	..	..	..	..	..
46	..	..	..	..	1054	..	..	..	1058	1059	1059	..	11 9	..	..	..	p.m	..	..	..	1131	..	..	..	..	..	..	..
47	..	1050	..	..	..	..	..	..	..	..	..	..	..	..	..	..	3	..	..	..	..	..	..	..	..	..	..	..
48	..	1053	..	..	..	..	..	..	..	..	..	S O	..	..	..	..	1114	..	..	..	..	..	..	..	..	..	..	..
49	..	1057	..	..	..	..	..	..	..	11 3	..	11 9	..	..	..	..	1117	..	..	..	..	..	..	..	..	..	..	..
50	..	..	..	..	..	..	..	..	..	11 6	..	..	..	..	..	..	1119	..	..	..	..	..	..	..	..	..	..	..
51	..	..	..	..	..	..	..	..	..	11 8	..	..	..	..	..	..	..	..	..	..	..	..	..	..	..	..	..	..
52	..	..	..	..	..	..	..	..	..	1111	..	..	..	..	..	..	..	..	..	..	..	..	..	..	..	..	..	..
53	..	..	..	..	..	..	..	1057	..	..	11 2	..	..	..	1112	1112	..	..	..	..	..	..	..	..	..	..	..	..
54	..	..	..	..	..	..	..	1059	..	..	11 4	..	..	..	..	1114	..	..	..	..	..	..	..	..	..	..	..	..
55	..	..	..	..	..	..	..	11 2	..	..	11 7	..	..	..	..	1117	..	..	..	..	..	..	..	..	..	..	..	..
56	..	..	..	..	..	..	..	11 4	..	..	11 9	..	..	..	..	1119	..	..	..	..	..	..	..	..	..	..	..	..
57	..	..	..	..	1057	..	..	..	..	..	..	..	1112	..	..	..	..	..	..	..	..	..	..	Via Worcester Park. Change at Wimbledon.	..	..	..	..
58	..	..	..	..	1058	..	..	..	..	..	..	..	1113	..	..	..	..	..	..	..	..	..	..		..	..	..	..
59	..	..	..	..	11 0	..	..	..	..	..	..	1112	1115	..	..	..	..	..	..	..	..	..	..		..	..	..	..
60	..	..	..	..	11 3	..	..	..	..	..	..	1114	1118	..	..	..	..	..	..	..	..	..	..		..	..	..	..
61	..	..	..	..	11 5	..	..	..	..	..	..	1117	1120	..	..	..	..	..	..	..	..	..	..		..	..	..	..
62	..	..	..	..	11 8	..	..	..	..	..	..	1119	1123	..	..	..	..	..	..	..	..	..	..		..	..	..	..
63	..	..	..	..	1110	..	..	..	..	..	..	1122	1125	..	..	..	..	..	..	..	..	..	..		..	..	..	..
64	..	..	..	1051	..	Via Worcester Park	..	..	..	..	1111	..	..	..	..	..	..	..	..	1125	..	..	..		..	..	..	..
65	..	..	..	1055	..		..	..	..	..	1115	..	..	..	..	..	1122	..	..	1128	..	..	..		..	..	..	..
66	..	..	..	..	..		..	..	..	..	..	..	..	..	..	..	1125	..	..	1131	..	..	..		..	..	..	..
67	..	..	..	..	..		..	..	..	..	..	..	..	..	..	..	1127	..	..	1134	..	..	..		..	..	..	..
68	..	..	..	11 0	..		..	..	..	..	1120	..	..	..	..	..	1129	..	..	1136	..	..	..		..	..	..	..
69	..	..	..	..	..		..	..	..	..	..	..	..	..	..	..	1131	..	..	1138	..	..	..		..	..	..	..
70	..	..	..	..	..		..	..	..	..	..	..	..	..	..	..	1134	..	..	1141	..	..	..		..	..	..	..
71	..	..	..	..	..		11 3	11 8	..	1114	..	..	..	..	..	1123	..	..	..	..	..	..	..	..	..	..	..	..
72	..	..	..	..	..		..	..	..	1116	..	..	..	..	..	..	..	..	..	..	..	..	..	..	..	..	..	..
73	..	..	11 2	..	..		11 7	1113	..	1119	..	..	..	1116	..	1127	..	..	..	..	..	..	12 1	12 3	..	..	..	..
74	..	..	..	..	..		..	..	..	1122	..	..	..	..	..	..	..	..	..	..	..	..	..	..	..	..	..	..
75	..	..	..	11 7	1116	..	..	..	1111	..	1126	1127	1131	..	..	..	1138	..	..	1145	1144	..	..	..	1 19	..	..	..
76	..	..	..	..	..	11 3	..	..	1115	..	..	..	..	..	..	..	..	..	..	..	..	..	..	1211	..	..	..	..
77	..	..	..	..	..	..	..	..	1117	..	..	..	..	..	..	..	..	..	..	..	..	..	..	..	..	..	..	..
78	..	..	11 7	..	..	..	1113	1118	..	1125	..	..	..	1121	..	1133	..	..	..	..	..	..	12 7	..	..	..	..	..

HORSHAM, REIGATE, REDHILL, TATTENHAM CORNER, CATERHAM,

For Notes, see page 317a

Up	No.	a.m									Sundays							a.m					No.
		3	3	3	3	3	3	3	3	3	3	3	3	3			3	3	3	3	3	3	
Horsham .... dep	1														..								1
Reigate .... "	2	..	..	..	..	..	..	..	..	..	..	..	..	..	7 20	..	..	..	..	..	..	..	2
Redhill .... "	3	..	..	..	..	..	..	..	..	..	..	..	..	..	7 27	..	..	..	..	..	..	..	3
Merstham	4	..	..	..	..	..	..	..	..	..	..	..	..	..	7 31	..	..	..	..	..	..	..	4
Coulsdon South	5	..	..	..	..	..	..	..	..	..	..	..	..	..	7 37	..	..	..	..	..	..	..	5
Tattenham Corner dep	6	..	..	..	..	..	..	..	..	..	..	..	..	..	..	..	7 18	..	..	..	..	..	6
Tadworth N	7	..	..	..	..	..	..	..	..	..	..	..	..	..	..	..	7 21	..	..	..	..	..	7
Kingswood M	8	..	..	..	..	..	..	..	..	..	..	..	..	..	..	..	7 24	..	..	..	..	..	8
Chipstead	9	..	..	..	..	..	..	..	..	..	..	..	..	..	..	..	7 29	..	..	..	..	..	9
Woodmansterne	10	..	..	..	..	..	..	..	..	..	..	..	..	..	..	..	7 31	..	..	..	..	..	10
Smitham	11	..	..	..	..	..	..	..	..	..	..	..	..	..	..	..	7 34	..	..	..	..	..	11
Reedham	12	..	..	..	..	..	..	..	..	..	..	..	..	..	..	..	7 36	..	..	..	..	..	12
Purley 252 .... arr	13	..	..	..	..	..	..	..	..	..	..	..	..	..	..	..	7 39	..	..	..	..	..	13
Caterham .... dep	14	..	..	..	..	..	..	..	..	..	..	..	..	..	..	..	7 29	..	..	..	..	..	14
Warlingham	15	..	..	..	..	..	..	..	..	..	..	..	..	..	..	..	7 32	..	..	..	..	..	15
Whyteleafe	16	..	..	..	..	..	..	..	..	..	..	..	..	..	..	..	7 34	..	..	..	..	..	16
Kenley	17	..	..	..	..	..	..	..	..	..	..	..	..	..	..	..	7 37	..	..	..	..	..	17
Purley 252 .... arr	18	..	..	..	..	..	..	..	..	..	..	..	..	..	..	..	7 41	..	..	..	..	..	18
Coulsdon North ..... dep	19	..	..	..	..	..	..	..	..	..	..	7 20	..	..	..	..	..	..	..	..	..	..	19
Purley 252	20	..	..	..	..	..	..	..	..	..	..	7 23	..	..	7 41	..	7 43	..	..	..	..	..	20
Purley Oaks	21	..	..	..	..	..	..	..	..	..	..	7 25	..	..	..	..	7 46	..	..	..	..	..	21
South Croydon 234	22	..	..	..	..	..	..	..	..	..	..	7 28	..	..	..	..	7 48	..	..	..	..	..	22
Effingham Junction dep	23	..	..	..	..	..	..	..	..	..	..	..	..	..	..	..	..	..	..	..	..	..	23
Bookham	24	..	..	..	..	..	..	..	..	..	..	..	..	..	..	..	..	..	..	..	..	..	24
Dorking North ...... dep	25	..	..	..	..	6 45	..	..	..	..	..	..	7 0	..	..	..	..	..	..	..	..	..	25
Boxhill and Burford	26	..	..	..	..	6 47	..	..	..	..	..	..	7 2	..	..	..	..	..	..	..	..	..	26
Leatherhead ...[Bridge J	27	..	..	..	..	6 52	..	..	..	..	..	..	7 7	..	..	..	..	..	..	..	..	..	27
Ashtead	28	..	..	..	..	6 57	..	..	..	..	..	..	7 11	..	..	..	..	..	..	..	..	..	28
Epsom 427	29	..	..	..	..	7 9	7 3	..	..	..	..	..	7 16	..	..	..	..	..	..	..	..	..	29
Ewell East H	30	..	..	..	..		7 6	..	..	..	..	..	7 19	..	..	..	..	..	..	..	..	..	30
Cheam	31	..	..	..	..		7 9	..	..	..	..	..	7 22	..	..	..	..	..	..	..	..	..	31
Epsom Downs ...... dep	32	..	..	..	6 52	Arr. Epsom 7 1 a.m	..	..	..	..	..	..	..	7 25	..	..	..	..	..	..	..	..	32
Banstead	33	..	..	..	6 55		..	..	..	..	..	..	..	7 28	..	..	..	..	..	..	..	..	33
Belmont	34	..	..	..	6 58		..	..	..	..	..	..	..	7 31	..	..	..	..	..	..	..	..	34
Sutton 322	35	..	..	..	7 1		7 12	..	..	..	..	..	7 25	7 34	..	..	..	..	..	..	..	7 39	35
Carshalton Beeches	36	..	..	..	7 3		..	..	..	..	..	..	..	7 36	..	..	..	..	..	..	..	7 42	36
Wallington	37	..	..	..	7 6		..	7 10	..	..	..	..	..	7 39	..	..	..	..	..	..	..	7 46	37
Waddon G	38	..	..	..	7 9		..	7 13	..	..	..	..	..	7 42	..	..	..	..	..	..	..	7 49	38
West Croydon 319 arr	39	..	..	..	7 12		..	7 16	..	..	..	..	..	7 45	..	..	..	..	..	..	..	7 52	39
West Croydon 319 dep	40	..	..	6 53	7 12		..	7 16	7 23	..	..	..	..	7 45	..	..	..	..	..	..	..	7 53	40
Carshalton	41	..	..	..	..	..	7 15	..	..	..	..	..	7 28	..	..	..	..	..	..	..	..	..	41
Hackbridge	42	..	..	..	..	..	7 18	..	..	..	..	..	7 31	..	..	..	..	..	..	..	..	..	42
Mitcham Junction	43	..	..	..	..	..	7 20	..	..	..	..	..	7 33	..	..	..	..	..	..	..	..	..	43
East Croydon .... arr	44	..	..	..	..	..	..	..	..	..	..	7 31	..	..	7 46	..	7 51	..	..	..	..	..	44
East Croydon .... dep	45	..	..	..	..	..	..	..	..	..	..	7 31	..	..	7 47	..	7 51	..	..	..	..	..	45
Norwood Junction F ..	46	..	..	6 57	7 17	..	..	..	7 27	..	..	..	..	..	7 51	..	7 55	..	..	..	..	7 57	46
Beckenham Jn. dep	47	..	..	..	..	..	..	..	..	..	..	..	..	..	..	..	..	..	7 45	..	..	..	47
Birkbeck	48	..	..	..	..	..	..	..	..	..	..	..	..	..	..	..	..	..	7 48	..	..	..	48
Crystal Palace D	49	6 41	..	7 1	..	..	..	..	7 31	..	7 34	..	..	..	..	..	..	..	7 52	7 55	7 58	8 1	49
Gipsy Hill (for Upper	50	6 44	..	7 3	..	..	..	..	7 33	..	..	..	..	..	..	..	..	..	..	7 58	..	8 3	50
West Norwood.[N'wood)	51	6 46	..	7 6	..	..	..	..	7 36	..	..	..	..	..	..	..	..	..	..	8 0	..	8 6	51
Streatham Hill	52	6 49	..	7 9	..	..	..	..	7 39	..	..	..	..	..	..	..	..	..	..	..	..	8 9	52
Selhurst	53	..	..	..	..	..	..	7 19	..	..	..	7 34	..	7 48	..	..	..	..	..	..	..	..	53
Thornton Heath	54	..	..	..	..	..	..	7 21	..	..	..	7 36	..	7 50	..	..	..	..	..	..	..	..	54
Norbury	55	..	..	..	..	..	..	7 24	..	..	..	7 39	..	7 53	..	..	..	..	..	..	..	..	55
Streatham Common	56	..	..	..	..	..	..	7 26	..	..	..	7 41	..	7 56	..	..	..	..	..	..	..	..	56
Anerley	57	..	..	..	7 20	..	..	..	..	..	..	..	..	..	..	..	..	..	..	..	..	..	57
Penge West C	58	..	..	..	7 21	..	..	..	..	..	..	..	..	..	..	..	..	..	..	..	..	..	58
Sydenham ....[Lane	59	..	From Victoria, dep. 6 50 a.m	..	7 23	..	..	..	..	From Victoria, dep 7 20 a.m	7 37	..	..	..	..	..	..	From Victoria, dep 7 50 a.m	..	..	8 1	..	59
Forest Hill, for Lordship	60	..		..	7 26	..	..	..	..		7 39	..	..	..	..	..	7 59		..	..	8 3	..	60
Honor Oak Park	61	..		..	7 28	..	..	..	..		7 42	..	..	..	..	..	..		..	..	8 6	..	61
Brockley B ....[Line)	62	..		..	7 31	..	..	..	..		7 44	..	..	..	..	..	..		..	..	8 8	..	62
New Cross Gate (for E.L.	63	..		..	7 33	..	..	..	..		7 47	..	..	..	8 0	..	8 4		..	..	8 11	..	63
Streatham	64	..		..	..	Via Worcester Park	..	..	..		..	..	7 38	..	..	..	..		..	..	..	..	64
Tulse Hill	65	..		..	..		..	..	..		..	..	7 42	..	..	..	..		..	8 3	..	..	65
North Dulwich	66	..		..	..		..	..	..		..	..	7 45	..	..	..	..		..	8 6	..	..	66
East Dulwich	67	..		..	..		..	..	..		..	..	7 47	..	..	..	..		..	8 8	..	..	67
Peckham Rye	68	..	7 4	..	..		..	..	..	7 34	..	..	7 49	..	..	..	..	8 4	..	8 10	..	..	68
Queen's Road, Peckham	69	..	7 6	..	..		..	..	..	7 36	..	..	7 51	..	..	..	..	8 6	..	8 12	..	..	69
South Bermondsey	70	..	7 9	..	..		..	..	..	7 39	..	..	7 54	..	..	..	..	8 9	..	8 15	..	..	70
Balham & Upper Tooting	71	6 52	..	7 11	..		7 27	7 30	7 41	..	..	7 45	..	8 0	..	..	..	..	..	..	..	8 11	71
Wandsworth Common A	72	6 54	..	7 13	..		7 29	7 32	7 43	..	..	7 47	..	8 2	..	..	..	..	..	..	..	8 13	72
Clapham Junction	73	6 57	..	7 16	..	7 34	7 32	7 35	7 46	..	..	7 50	..	8 5	..	..	..	..	..	..	..	8 16	73
Battersea Park	74	7 0	..	7 19	..	..	..	..	7 49	..	..	..	..	..	..	..	..	..	..	..	..	8 19	74
LONDON BRIDGE ..... arr	75	..	7 13	..	7 39	..	..	..	..	7 43	7 52	..	7 58	..	8 5	..	8 10	8 13	..	8 19	8 16	..	75
WATERLOO* .... "	76	..	..	..	..	7 43	..	..	..	..	..	..	..	..	..	..	8 13	..	..	..	..	..	76
CHARING CROSS * .. "	77	..	..	..	..	..	..	..	..	..	..	..	..	..	..	..	8 16	..	..	..	..	..	77
VICTORIA .... "	78	7 3	..	7 23	..	..	7 38	7 42	7 53	..	..	7 56	..	8 11	..	..	..	..	..	..	..	8 23	78

DORKING NORTH, SUTTON, CROYDON, CRYSTAL PALACE, and LONDON

Sundays — a.m

No.	3	3	3	..	..	3		3	3	3		3	3	3	3	3		..	..	3		3		3	3	..	3	3
1																	7 34				7§46							
2					7 40												3	7 55	8 12		8 20							
3					7 57													7a59	8a16		8 27							
4					8 1																8 31							
5					8 7																8 37							
6									7 48																8 18			
7									7 51																8 21			
8									7 54									a Arrival time	a Arrival time		§ Via Three Bridges				8 24			
9									7 59																8 29			
10									8 1																8 31			
11									8 4																8 34			
12									8 6									Stop							8 36			
13									8 9																8 38			
14									7 59																8 29			
15									8 2																8 32			
16									8 4																8 34			
17									8 7																8 37			
18									8 11																8 40			
19																				8 20								
20					8 11				8 13									a.m		8 23	8 41				8 43			
21									8 16									3		8 25					8 46			
22									8 18											8 28					8 48			
23																		8 6										
24																		8 9										
25		7 25															8 0											
26		7 27															8 2											
27		7 32															8 7	8 13										
28		7 36															8 11	8 17										
29	7 33	7 40													8 3		8 15	8 21										
30	7 36														8 6		8 18											
31	7 39														8 9		8 21											
32			7 38					7 55								8 8								8 25				
33			7 41					7 58								8 11								8 28				
34			7 44					8 1								8 14								8 31				
35	7 42		7 47					8 4						8 9	8 12	8 17	8 24							8 34				
36			7 49					8 6						8 12		8 19								8 36				
37			7 52					8 9						8 14		8 22								8 39				
38			7 55					8 12						8 18		8 25						From London Bridge, via Forest Hill		8 42				
39			7 58					8 15						8 23		8 28								8 45				
40			7 58					8 15						8 23		8 28								8 45				
41	7 45														8 15		8 27											
42	7 48														8 18		8 30											
43	7 50														8 20		8 32											
44					8 16				8 21											8 31	8 46				8 51			
45				8 11	8 17				8 21											8 31	8 47				8 51	8 54		
46			8 2		8 21				8 25					8 27		8 32						8 34			8 55		8 45	
47												8 15															8 48	
48												8 18															8 52	8 55
49												8 22	8 27	8 31														8 58
50														8 33													Stop	9 0
51														8 36														
52														8 39														
53						8 7		8 18												8 34		8 37		8 48				
54						8 10		8 20												8 36		8 40		8 50				
55						8 13		8 23												8 39		8 43		8 53				
56						8 16		8 26												8 41		8 46		8 56				
57			8 5													8 35											From Victoria, dep. 8 50 a.m	
58			8 6													8 36												
59			8 8										8 30			8 38												
60			8 11						8 29	From Victoria dep. 8 20 a.m,			8 32			8 41									8 59			
61			8 13										8 35			8 43												
62			8 16										8 37			8 46												
63			8 18						8 34				8 40			8 48									9 4			
64						8 18											8 37					8 48					a.m	9 3
65						8 21											8 41					8 51					3	9 6
66						8 24											8 44					8 54						9 8
67		Via Worcester Park				8 26											8 46	Via Worcester Park				8 56					9 4	9 10
68						8 29				8 34							8 48					8 59					9 6	9 12
69						8 31				8 36							8 50					9 1					9 9	9 15
70						8 34				8 39							8 53					9 4						
71	7 57							8 30						8 41	8 27					8 45				9 0				
72	7 59							8 32						8 43	8 29					8 47				9 2				
73	8 2	8 4		8 22				8 35						8 46	8 32			8 45		8 50	8 59			9 5		9 6		
74														8 49														
75			8 24		8 34	8 38			8 40	8 43			8 45			8 54	8 57					9 8			9 10		9 13	9 19
76		8 13							8 43									8 54							9 13			
77									8 46																9 15			
78	8 8			8 27				8 41						8 53	8 38					8 56	9 5			9 11		9 12		

HORSHAM, REIGATE, REDHILL, TATTENHAM CORNER, CATERHAM,

For Notes, see page 317a

Up	No.	a.m.									Sundays—continued								a.m.				No.
Horsham .... dep	1	3	3	3	3	3	3	8§43	..	..	3	3	3	..	3	..	3	3	3	3	8 34	3	1
Reigate .... "	2	..	..	..	..	..	..	..	..	8 50	..	..	..	..	..	..	..	..	..	..	3	..	2
Redhill .... "	3	..	..	..	..	..	..	..	..	8 57	..	..	..	..	..	..	..	..	..	..		..	3
Merstham	4	..	..	..	..	..	..	..	..	9 1	..	..	..	..	..	..	..	..	..	..	..	..	4
Coulsdon South	5	..	..	..	..	..	..	..	..	9 7	..	..	..	..	..	..	..	..	..	..	..	..	5
Tattenham Corner. dep	6	..	..	..	..	..	..	..	..	..	..	8 48	..	..	..	..	..	..	..	..	..	..	6
Tadworth N	7	..	..	..	..	..	..		..	..	..	8 51	..	..	..	..	..	..	..	..	..	..	7
Kingswood M	8	..	..	..	..	..	..		..	..	..	8 54	..	..	..	..	..	..	..	..	..	..	8
Chipstead	9	..	..	..	..	..	..	§ Via Three Bridges	..	..	..	8 59	..	..	..	..	..	..	..	..	..	..	9
Woodmansterne	10	..	..	..	..	..	..		..	..	..	9 1	..	..	..	..	..	..	..	..	..	..	10
Smitham	11	..	..	..	..	..	..		..	..	..	9 4	..	..	..	..	..	..	..	..	..	..	11
Reedham	12	..	..	..	..	..	..		..	..	..	9 6	..	..	..	..	..	..	..	..	..	..	12
Purley 252 .... arr	13	..	..	..	..	..	..		..	..	..	9 9	..	..	..	..	..	..	..	..	..	..	13
Caterham .... dep	14	..	..	..	..	..	..	..	..	..	..	8 59	..	..	..	..	..	..	..	..	..	..	14
Warlingham	15	..	..	..	..	..	..	..	..	..	..	9 2	..	..	..	..	..	..	..	..	..	..	15
Whyteleafe	16	..	..	..	..	..	..	..	..	..	..	9 4	..	..	..	..	..	..	..	..	..	..	16
Kenley	17	..	..	..	..	..	..	..	..	..	..	9 7	..	..	..	..	..	..	..	..	..	..	17
Purley 252 .... arr	18	..	..	..	..	..	..	..	..	..	..	9 11	..	..	..	..	..	..	..	..	..	..	18
Coulsdon North ..... dep	19	..	..	..	..	..	8 50	..	..	..	..	..	..	..	..	..	..	..	..	..	..	..	19
Purley 252	20	..	..	..	..	..	8 53	..	..	9 11	..	9 13	..	..	..	..	..	..	..	..	..	..	20
Purley Oaks	21	..	..	..	..	..	8 55	..	..	..	..	9 16	..	..	..	..	..	..	..	..	..	..	21
South Croydon 234	22	..	..	..	..	..	8 58	..	..	..	..	9 18	..	..	..	..	..	..	..	..	..	..	22
Effingham Junction dep	23	..	..	..	8 30	..	..	..	..	..	..	..	..	..	..	..	..	..	..	..	..	9 4	23
Bookham	24	..	..	..	8 33	..	..	..	..	..	..	..	..	..	..	..	..	..	..	..	..	9 7	24
Dorking North ..... dep	25	..	..	..	..	8 35	..	..	..	..	..	..	..	..	..	..	..	..	..	..	9 0	..	25
Boxhill and Burford	26	..	..	..	..	8 37	..	..	..	..	..	..	..	..	..	..	..	..	..	..	9 2	..	26
Leatherhead ...[Bridge J	27	..	..	..	8 37	8 42	..	..	..	..	..	..	..	..	..	..	..	..	..	..	9 7	9 11	27
Ashtead	28	..	..	..	8 41	8 46	..	..	..	..	..	..	..	..	..	..	..	..	..	..	9 11	9 15	28
Epsom 427	29	..	8 33	..	8 45	8 50	..	..	..	..	..	..	..	..	..	..	..	..	9 3	..	9 15	9 19	29
Ewell East H	30	..	8 36	..	8 48	..	..	..	..	..	..	..	..	..	..	..	..	..	9 6	..	9 18	..	30
Cheam	31	..	8 39	..	8 51	..	..	..	..	..	..	..	..	..	..	..	..	..	9 9	..	9 21	..	31
Epsom Downs ...... dep	32	..	..	8 38	..	..	..	..	..	..	..	..	8 55	..	..	..	..	..	..	9 8	..	..	32
Banstead	33	..	..	8 41	..	..	..	..	..	..	..	..	8 58	..	..	..	..	..	..	9 11	..	..	33
Belmont	34	..	..	8 44	..	..	..	..	..	..	..	..	9 1	..	..	..	..	..	..	9 14	..	..	34
Sutton 322	35	8 39	8 42	8 47	8 54	..	..	..	..	..		..	9 4	..	..	..	..	9 9	9 12	9 17	9 24	..	35
Carshalton Beeches	36	8 42	..	8 49	..	..	..	..	..	..		..	9 6	..	..	..	..	9 12	..	9 19	..	..	36
Wallington	37	8 44	..	8 52	..	..	..	..	..	..		..	9 9	..	..	..	..	9 14	..	9 22	..	..	37
Waddon G	38	8 48	..	8 55	..	..	..	..	..	..		..	9 12	..	..	..	..	9 18	..	9 25	..	..	38
West Croydon 319 arr	39	8 51	..	8 58	..	..	..	..	..	..	From London Bridge, via Streatham	..	9 15	..	..	..	..	9 23	..	9 28	..	..	39
West Croydon 319 dep	40	8 53	..	8 58	..	..	..	..	..	..		..	9 15	..	..	..	..	9 23	..	9 28	..	..	40
Carshalton	41	..	8 45	..	8 57	..	..	..	..	..		..	..	..	..	..	..	..	9 15	..	9 27	..	41
Hackbridge	42	..	8 48	..	9 0	..	..	..	..	..		..	..	..	..	..	..	..	9 18	..	9 30	..	42
Mitcham Junction	43	..	8 50	..	9 2	..	..	..	..	..		..	..	..	..	..	..	..	9 20	..	9 32	..	43
East Croydon .... arr	44	..	..	..	..	..	9 1	9 16	..	9 17		9 21	..	..	..	..	..	..	..	..	..	..	44
East Croydon .... dep	45	..	..	..	..	..	9 1	9 16	..	9 17		9 21	..	9 24	..	..	..	..	..	..	..	..	45
Norwood Junction F ..	46	8 57	..	9 2	..	..	..	..	..	9 21	9 17	9 25	..	..	..	..	..	9 27	..	9 32	..	..	46
Beckenham Jn. dep	47	..	..	..	..	..	..	..	..	..	..	..	..	..	9 15	..	..	..	..	..	..	..	47
Birkbeck	48	..	..	..	..	..	..	..	..	..	..	..	..	..	9 18	..	..	..	..	..	..	..	48
Crystal Palace D	49	9 1	..	..	..	..	..	..	..	..	..	..	..	..	9 22	..	9 27	9 31	..	..	..	..	49
Gipsy Hill (for Upper	50	9 3	..	..	..	..	..	..	..	..	..	..	..	..	Stop	..	..	9 33	..	..	..	..	50
West Norwood.[N'wood)	51	9 6	..	..	..	..	..	..	..	..	..	..	..	..		..	..	9 36	..	..	..	..	51
Streatham Hill	52	9 9	..	..	..	..	..	..	..	..	..	..	..	..		..	..	9 39	..	..	..	..	52
Selhurst	53	..	..	..	..	..	9 4	..	..	..	..	..	9 18	..		..	..	..	..	..	..	..	53
Thornton Heath	54	..	..	..	..	..	9 6	..	..	..	..	..	9 20	..		..	..	..	..	..	..	..	54
Norbury	55	..	..	..	..	..	9 9	..	..	..	..	..	9 23	..		..	..	..	..	..	..	..	55
Streatham Common	56	..	..	..	..	..	9 11	..	..	..	..	..	9 26	..		..	..	..	..	..	..	..	56
Anerley	57	..	..	9 5	..	..	..	..	..	..	9 20	..	..	..	From Victoria, dep. 9 20 a.m. ☞	..	..	..	..	9 35	..	..	57
Penge West C	58	..	..	9 6	..	..	..	..	..	..	9 21	..	..	..		..	..	..	..	9 36	..	..	58
Sydenham ....[Lane	59	..	..	9 8	..	..	..	..	..	..	9 23	..	..	..		..	9 30	..	..	9 38	..	..	59
Forest Hill, for Lordship	60	..	..	9 11	..	..	..	..	..	..	9 26	9 29	..	..		..	9 32	..	..	9 41	..	..	60
Honor Oak Park	61	..	..	9 13	..	..	..	..	..	..	9 28	..	..	..		..	9 35	..	..	9 43	..	..	61
Brockley B ....[Line)	62	..	..	9 16	..	..	..	..	..	..	9 31	..	..	..		..	9 37	..	..	9 46	..	..	62
New Cross Gate (for E.L.	63	..	..	9 18	..	..	..	..	..	9 30	9 33	9 34	..	..		..	9 40	..	..	9 48	..	..	63
Streatham	64	..	..	..	9 7		..	..	..	..	..	..	..	..		..	..	..	..	..	9 37		64
Tulse Hill	65	..	..	..	9 11		..	..	..	..	..	..	..	..	a.m.	..	..	..	..	..	9 41		65
North Dulwich	66	..	..	..	9 14		..	..	..	..	..	..	..	..	3	..	..	..	..	..	9 44		66
East Dulwich	67	..	..	..	9 16	Via Worcester Park	..	..	..	..	..	..	..	..		..	..	..	..	..	9 46	Via Worcester Park	67
Peckham Rye	68	..	..	..	9 18		..	..	..	..	..	..	..	..	9 34	..	..	..	..	..	9 48		68
Queen's Road, Peckham	69	..	..	..	9 20		..	..	..	..	..	..	..	..	9 36	..	..	..	..	..	9 50		69
South Bermondsey	70	..	..	..	9 23		..	..	..	..	..	..	..	..	9 39	..	..	..	..	..	9 53		70
Balham & Upper Tooting	71	9 11	8 57	..	..		9 15	..	..	..	..	..	9 30	..	..	..	..	9 41	9 27	..	..		71
Wandsworth Common A	72	9 13	8 59	..	..		9 17	..	..	..	..	..	9 32	..	..	..	..	9 43	9 29	..	..		72
Clapham Junction	73	9 16	9 2	..	..	9 14	9 20	..	..	..	..	..	9 35	9 36	..	..	..	9 46	9 32	..	..	9 43	73
Battersea Park	74	9 19	..	..	..	..	..	..	..	..	..	..	..	..	..	..	..	9 49	..	..	..	..	74
London Bridge ..... arr	75	..	..	9 24	9 27	..	..	..	..	9 35	9 39	9 40	..	..	9 43	..	9 45	..	..	9 54	9 57	..	75
Waterloo * .... "	76	..	..	..	..	9 23	..	..	..	..	..	9 43	..	..	..	..	..	..	..	..	..	9 54	76
Charing Cross * .. "	77	..	..	..	..	..	..	..	..	..	..	9 46	..	..	..	..	..	..	..	..	..	..	77
Victoria .... "	78	9 24	9 8	..	..	..	9 26	9 31	..	..	..	..	9 42	9 42	..	..	..	9 53	9 38	..	..	..	78

DORKING NORTH, SUTTON, CROYDON, CRYSTAL PALACE, and LONDON

a.m. — **Sundays**—*continued* — a.m.

No.	3			3			3	3	3		3		3	3	3		3	3		3	3	3	3		3	3	3	3
1	..	..	8§48	..	..	..	..	..	..	..	..	..	..	..	..	..	..	..	..	..	..	..	..	..	..	..	..	..
2	..	..	9 22	..	..	..	..	..	..	..	..	..	..	..	..	9 29	..	..	..	..	..	..	..	..	..	..	..	..
3	..	..	9 29	..	..	..	..	..	..	..	..	..	..	..	..	9 49	..	..	..	..	..	..	..	..	..	..	..	..
4	..	..	9 33	..	..	..	..	..	..	..	..	..	..	..	..	..	..	..	..	..	..	..	..	..	..	..	..	..
5	..	..	9 39	..	..	..	..	..	..	..	..	..	..	..	..	..	..	..	..	..	..	..	..	..	..	..	..	..
6	..	..	§ Via Three Bridges	9 14	..	..	..	..	..	..	..	..	..	..	..	..	..	..	..	..	..	9 48	..	..	..	..	..	..
7	..	..		9 17	..	..	..	..	..	..	..	..	..	..	..	..	..	..	..	..	..	9 51	..	..	..	..	..	..
8	..	..		9 20	..	..	..	..	..	..	..	..	..	..	..	..	..	..	..	..	..	9 54	..	..	..	..	..	..
9	..	..		9 25	..	..	..	..	..	..	..	..	..	..	..	..	..	..	..	..	..	9 59	..	..	..	..	..	..
10	..	..		9 27	..	..	..	..	..	..	..	..	..	..	..	..	..	..	..	..	..	10 1	..	..	..	..	..	..
11	..	..		9 30	..	..	..	..	..	..	..	..	..	..	..	..	..	..	..	..	..	10 4	..	..	..	..	..	..
12	..	..		9 32	..	..	..	..	..	..	..	..	..	..	..	..	..	..	..	..	..	10 6	..	..	..	..	..	..
13	..	..		9 34	..	..	..	..	..	..	..	..	..	..	..	..	..	..	..	..	..	10 9	..	..	..	..	..	..
14	..	..	..	9 25	..	..	..	..	..	..	..	..	..	..	..	..	..	..	..	..	..	9 59	..	..	..	..	..	..
15	..	..	..	9 28	..	..	..	..	..	..	..	..	..	..	..	..	..	..	..	..	..	10 2	..	..	..	..	..	..
16	..	..	..	9 30	..	..	..	..	..	..	..	..	..	..	..	..	..	..	..	..	..	10 4	..	..	..	..	..	..
17	..	..	..	9 33	..	..	..	..	..	..	..	..	..	..	..	..	..	..	..	..	..	10 7	..	..	..	..	..	..
18	..	..	..	9 36	..	..	..	..	..	..	..	..	..	..	..	..	..	..	..	..	..	1011	..	..	..	..	..	..
19	..	..	..	..	..	..	..	..	..	..	..	..	..	..	9 50	..	..	..	..	..	..	..	..	..	..	..	..	..
20	..	..	9 43	9 39	..	..	..	..	..	..	..	..	..	..	9 53	..	..	..	..	..	..	1013	..	..	..	..	..	..
21	..	..	..	9 42	..	..	..	..	..	..	..	..	..	..	9 55	..	..	..	..	..	..	1016	..	..	..	..	..	..
22	..	..	..	9 44	9 47	..	..	..	..	..	..	..	..	..	9 58	..	..	..	..	..	..	1018	..	..	..	..	..	..
23	..	..	..	..	..	..	..	..	..	..	..	..	..	..	..	..	9 30	..	..	..	..	..	..	..	..	..	..	..
24	..	..	..	..	..	..	..	..	..	..	..	..	..	..	..	..	9 33	..	..	..	..	..	..	..	..	..	..	..
25	..	..	..	..	..	..	..	..	..	..	..	..	..	..	..	..	..	9 35	..	..	..	..	..	..	..	..	..	..
26	..	..	..	..	..	..	..	..	..	..	..	..	..	..	..	..	..	9 37	..	..	..	..	..	..	..	..	..	..
27	..	..	..	..	..	..	..	..	..	..	..	..	..	..	..	..	9 37	9 42	..	..	..	..	..	..	..	..	..	..
28	..	..	..	..	..	..	..	..	..	..	..	..	..	..	..	..	9 41	9 46	..	..	..	..	..	..	..	..	..	..
29	..	..	..	..	..	..	..	..	..	..	..	..	9 37	..	..	..	9 45	9 50	..	..	..	..	..	..	..	..	10 3	..
30	..	..	..	..	..	..	..	..	..	..	..	..	9 40	..	..	..	9 48	..	..	..	..	..	..	..	..	..	10 6	..
31	..	..	..	..	..	..	..	..	..	..	..	..	9 43	..	..	..	9 51	..	..	..	..	..	..	..	..	..	10 9	..
32	..	..	..	..	..	..	9 25	..	..	..	..	..	..	9 38	..	..	..	..	..	9 55	..	..	..	..	..	..	..	10 8
33	..	..	..	..	..	..	9 28	..	..	..	..	..	..	9 41	..	..	..	..	..	9 58	..	..	..	..	..	..	..	1011
34	..	..	..	..	..	..	9 31	..	..	..	..	..	..	9 44	..	..	..	..	..	10 1	..	..	..	..	..	..	..	1014
35	From London Bridge, via Forest Hill	..	..	..	..	..	9 34	..	..	..	9 39	..	9 48	9 47	..	..	9 54	..	..	10 4	From London Bridge, via Streatham	..	..	..	..	10 9	1012	1017
36		..	..	..	..	..	9 36	..	..	..	9 42	..	..	9 49	..	..	..	..	..	10 6		..	..	..	..	1012	..	1019
37		..	..	..	..	..	9 39	..	..	..	9 44	..	..	9 52	..	..	..	..	..	10 9		..	..	..	..	1014	..	1022
38		..	..	..	..	..	9 42	..	..	..	9 48	..	..	9 55	..	..	..	..	..	1012		..	..	..	..	1018	..	1025
39		..	..	..	..	..	9 45	..	..	..	9 51	..	..	9 58	..	..	..	..	..	1015		..	..	..	..	1023	..	1028
40		..	..	..	..	..	9 45	..	..	..	9 53	..	..	9 58	..	..	..	..	..	1015		..	..	..	..	1023	..	1028
41		..	..	..	..	..	..	..	..	..	..	..	9 51	..	..	..	9 57	..	..	..		..	..	..	..	..	1015	..
42		..	..	..	..	..	..	..	..	..	..	..	9 53	..	..	..	10 0	..	..	..		..	..	..	..	..	1018	..
43		..	..	..	..	..	..	..	..	..	..	..	9 56	..	..	..	10 2	..	..	..		..	..	..	..	..	1020	..
44		..	9 49	9 51	9 52	..	..	..	..	..	..	..	..	..	10 1	10 4	..	..	..	..		1021	..	..	..	..	..	..
45		..	9 49	9 51	9 52	..	..	..	..	..	..	..	..	..	10 1	10 4	..	..	..	..		1021	..	..	..	..	..	..
46	9 34	..	..	9 55	..	..	..	..	..	..	9 57	..	Arr. Sutton 9 46 a.m	10 2	..	..	..	..	..	..	1017	1025	..	..	..	1027	..	1032
47	..	..	..	..	..	..	..	9 45	..	..	..	..		..	..	..	..	..	..	..	..	..	1015	..	..	..	..	..
48	..	..	..	..	..	..	..	9 48	..	..	..	..		..	..	..	..	..	..	..	..	..	1018	..	..	..	..	..
49	..	..	..	..	..	..	..	9 52	9 55	..	10 1	..		..	..	..	..	..	..	..	..	..	1022	..	1027	1031	..	..
50	..	..	..	..	..	..	..		9 58	..	10 3	..		..	..	..	..	..	..	..	..	..		..	..	1033	..	..
51	..	..	..	..	..	..	..	Stop	10 0	..	10 6	..		..	..	..	..	..	..	..	..	..	Stop	..	..	1036	..	..
52	..	..	..	..	..	..	..		..	..	10 9	..	..	..	..	..	..	..	..	..	..	..		..	..	1039	..	..
53	9 37	..	..	..	..	..	9 48	From Victoria, dep. 9 50 a.m.	..	..	..	..	..	..	10 4	..	..	..	..	1018	..	..	From Victoria, dep. 10 20 a.m	..	..	..	..	..
54	9 40	..	..	..	..	..	9 50		..	..	..	..	..	..	10 6	..	..	..	..	1020	..	..		..	..	..	..	..
55	9 43	..	..	..	..	..	9 53		..	..	..	..	..	..	10 9	..	..	..	..	1023	..	..		..	..	..	..	..
56	9 46	..	..	..	..	..	9 56		..	..	..	..	..	..	1011	..	..	..	..	1026	..	..		..	..	..	..	..
57	..	..	..	..	..	..	..		..	..	..	..	..	10 5	..	..	..	..	..	..	1020	..		..	..	..	..	1035
58	..	..	..	..	..	..	..		..	..	..	..	..	10 6	..	..	..	..	..	..	1021	..		..	..	..	..	1036
59	..	..	..	..	..	..	..		..	..	..	..	..	10 8	..	..	..	..	..	..	1023	..		..	1030	..	..	1038
60	..	..	..	9 59	..	..	..		..	..	..	..	..	1011	..	..	..	..	..	..	1026	1029		..	1032	..	..	1041
61	..	..	..	..	..	..	..		..	..	..	..	..	1013	..	..	..	..	..	..	1028	..		..	1035	..	..	1043
62	..	..	..	..	..	..	..		..	..	..	..	..	1016	..	..	..	..	..	..	1031	..		..	1037	..	..	1046
63	..	..	..	10 4	..	..	..		..	..	..	..	..	1018	..	..	..	..	..	..	1033	1034		..	1040	..	..	1048
64	9 48	..	..	..	..	..	..		..	..	..	..	..	..	..	..	10 7	Via Worcester Park	..	..	..	..		..	..	..	..	..
65	9 51	..	..	..	..	..	..	a.m	10 3	..	..	..	..	..	..	..	1011		..	..	..	..	a.m	..	..	..	..	..
66	9 54	..	..	..	..	..	..	3	10 6	..	..	..	..	..	..	..	1014		..	..	..	..	3	..	..	..	..	..
67	9 56	..	..	..	..	..	..		10 8	..	..	..	..	..	..	..	1016		..	..	..	..		..	..	..	..	..
68	9 59	..	..	..	..	..	..	10 4	1010	..	..	..	..	..	..	..	1018		..	..	..	..	1034	..	..	..	..	..
69	10 1	..	..	..	..	..	..	10 6	1012	..	..	..	..	..	..	..	1020		..	..	..	..	1036	..	..	..	..	..
70	10 4	..	..	..	..	..	..	10 9	1015	..	..	..	..	..	..	..	1023		..	..	..	..	1039	..	..	..	..	..
71	..	..	..	..	..	..	10 0	..	..	..	1011	..	10 3	..	1015	..	..		..	1030	..	..	..	..	..	1041	1027	..
72	..	..	..	..	..	..	10 2	..	..	..	1013	..	10 5	..	1017	..	..		..	1032	..	..	..	..	..	1043	1029	..
73	..	..	10 0	..	10 4	..	10 5	..	..	..	1016	..	1010	..	1020	1014	..	1014	..	1035	..	..	..	..	..	1046	1032	..
74	..	..	..	..	..	..	..	..	..	..	1019	..	..	..	..	..	..	..	..	..	..	..	..	..	..	1049	..	..
75	10 8	..	..	1010	..	..	..	1013	1019	..	..	..	..	1024	..	..	1027	..	..	..	1039	1040	1043	..	1045	..	..	1054
76	..	..	..	1013	..	..	..	..	..	..	..	..	..	..	..	..	..	1021	..	..	..	1042	..	..	..	..	..	..
77	..	..	..	1015	..	..	..	..	..	..	..	..	..	..	..	..	..	..	..	..	..	1045	..	..	..	..	..	..
78	..	..	10 6	..	1011	..	1011	..	..	..	1023	..	1016	..	1026	1020	..	..	..	1041	..	..	..	..	..	1053	1038	..

HORSHAM, REIGATE, REDHILL, TATTENHAM CORNER, CATERHAM,

For Notes, see page 317a

Up	No.	a.m									Sundays—continued								a.m				No.
		3	3	3	..	..		..	3	..	3	3	3	..	3		3	..	3	3		3	
Horsham .... dep	1				..	..	9§48	..		..				..		9 49		..			..		1
Reigate .... "	2	..	..	..	..	..	1022	..	..	..	..	..	..	..	..	3	..	..	..	..	1042	..	2
Redhill .... "	3	..	..	..	..	..	1029	..	..	..	..	..	..	..	..		..	..	..	..	1049	..	3
Merstham	4	..	..	..	..	..	1033	..	..	..	..	..	..	..	..	..	..	..	..	..	..	..	4
Coulsdon South	5	..	..	..	..	..	1039	..	..	..	..	..	..	..	..	..	..	..	..	..	..	..	5
Tattenham Corner dep	6	..	..	..	..	..	§ Via Three Bridges	..	1014	..	..	..	..	..	..	..	..	..	..	..	..	..	6
Tadworth **N**	7	..	..	..	..	..		..	1017	..	..	..	..	..	..	..	..	..	..	..	..	..	7
Kingswood **M**	8	..	..	..	..	..		..	1020	..	..	..	..	..	..	..	..	..	..	..	..	..	8
Chipstead	9	..	..	..	..	..		..	1025	..	..	..	..	..	..	..	..	..	..	..	..	..	9
Woodmansterne	10	..	..	..	..	..		..	1027	..	..	..	..	..	..	..	..	..	..	..	..	..	10
Smitham	11	..	..	..	..	..		..	1030	..	..	..	..	..	..	..	..	..	..	..	..	..	11
Reedham	12	..	..	..	..	..		..	1032	..	..	..	..	..	..	..	..	..	..	..	..	..	12
Purley 252 .... arr	13	..	..	..	..	..		..	1034	..	..	..	..	..	..	..	..	..	..	..	..	..	13
Caterham .... dep	14	..	..	..	..	..	..	..	1025	..	..	..	..	..	..	..	..	..	..	..	..	..	14
Warlingham	15	..	..	..	..	..	..	..	1028	..	..	..	..	..	..	..	..	..	..	..	..	..	15
Whyteleafe	16	..	..	..	..	..	..	..	1030	..	..	..	..	..	..	..	..	..	..	..	..	..	16
Kenley	17	..	..	..	..	..	..	..	1033	..	..	..	..	..	..	..	..	..	..	..	..	..	17
Purley 252 .... arr	18	..	..	..	..	..	..	..	1036	..	..	..	..	..	..	..	..	..	..	..	..	..	18
Coulsdon North ..... dep	19	..	..	..	..	..	..	..	..	..	..	..	..	..	..	..	..	..	..	1050	..	..	19
Purley 252	20	..	..	..	..	..	1043	..	1039	..	..	..	..	..	..	..	..	..	..	1053	..	..	20
Purley Oaks	21	..	..	..	..	..	..	..	1042	..	..	..	..	..	..	..	..	..	..	1055	..	..	21
South Croydon 234	22	..	..	..	..	..	..	..	1044	1047	..	..	..	..	..	..	..	..	..	1058	..	..	22
Effingham Junction dep	23	9 54	..	..	..	..	..	..	..	..	..	..	..	..	..	..	..	..	..	..	..	1030	23
Bookham	24	9 58	..	..	..	..	..	..	..	..	..	..	..	..	..	..	..	..	..	..	..	1033	24
Dorking North ...... dep	25	..	10 6	..	..	..	..	..	..	..	..	..	..	..	..	1015	..	..	..	..	..	..	25
Boxhill and Burford.	26	..	10 8	..	..	..	..	..	..	..	..	..	..	..	..	1017	..	..	..	..	..	..	26
Leatherhead ... [Bridge **J**	27	10 2	1013	..	..	..	..	..	..	..	..	..	..	..	..	1022	..	..	..	..	..	1037	27
Ashtead	28	10 6	1017	..	..	..	..	..	..	..	..	..	..	..	..	1026	..	..	..	..	..	1041	28
Epsom 427	29	1010	1021	..	..	..	..	..	..	..	..	..	..	..	..	1030	1037	..	..	..	..	1045	29
Ewell East **H**	30	..	1024	..	..	..	..	..	..	..	..	..	..	..	..	..	1040	..	..	..	..	1048	30
Cheam	31	..	1027	..	..	..	..	..	..	..	..	..	..	..	..	..	1043	..	..	..	..	1051	31
Epsom Downs ...... dep	32	..	..	From London Bridge, via Forest Hill	..	..	..	..	..	..	1025	..	..	..	..	..	..	..	1038	..	..	..	32
Banstead	33	..	..		..	..	..	..	..	..	1028	..	..	..	..	..	..	..	1041	..	..	..	33
Belmont	34	..	..		..	..	..	..	..	..	1031	..	..	..	..	..	..	..	1044	..	..	..	34
Sutton 322	35	..	1030		..	..	..	..	..	..	1034	..	..	..	1039	..	1048	..	1047	..	..	1054	35
Carshalton Beeches	36	..	..		..	..	..	..	..	..	1036	..	..	..	1042	..	..	..	1049	..	..	..	36
Wallington	37	..	..		..	..	..	..	..	..	1039	..	..	..	1044	..	..	..	1052	..	..	..	37
Waddon **G**	38	..	..		..	..	..	..	..	..	1042	..	..	..	1048	..	..	..	1055	..	..	..	38
West Croydon 319 arr	39	..	..		..	..	..	..	..	..	1045	..	..	..	1051	..	..	..	1058	..	..	..	39
West Croydon 319 dep	40	..	..		..	..	..	..	..	..	1045	..	..	..	1053	..	..	..	1058	..	..	..	40
Carshalton	41	..	1034		..	..	..	..	..	..	..	..	..	..	..	..	1051	..	..	..	..	1057	41
Hackbridge	42	..	1036		..	..	..	..	..	..	..	..	..	..	..	..	1053	..	..	..	..	11 0	42
Mitcham Junction	43	..	1038		..	..	..	..	..	..	..	..	..	..	..	..	1056	..	..	..	..	11 2	43
East Croydon .... arr	44	..	..		..	..	1049	..	1051	1052	..	..	..	..	..	..	..	..	..	11 1	11 3	..	44
East Croydon .... dep	45	..	..		..	1047	1049	..	1051	1052	..	..	..	..	..	..	Arr. Sutton 10 46 a.m	..	..	11 1	11 4	..	45
Norwood Junction F ..	46	..	..	1034	..	..	..	..	1055	..	..	..	..	..	1057	..		..	11 2	..	..	..	46
— **Beckenham Jn.** dep	47	..	..	..	..	..	..	..	..	..	..	1045	..	..	..	..		..	..	..	..	..	47
Birkbeck	48	..	..	..	..	..	..	..	..	..	..	1048	..	..	..	..		..	..	..	..	..	48
Crystal Palace D	49	..	..	..	..	..	..	..	..	..	..	1052	1055	..	11 1	..		..	..	..	..	..	49
Gipsy Hill (for Upper	50	..	..	..	..	..	..	..	..	..	..	—	1058	..	11 3	..		..	..	..	..	..	50
West Norwood. [N'wood)	51	..	..	..	..	..	..	..	..	..	..	Stop	11 0	..	11 6	..	..	..	..	..	..	..	51
Streatham Hill	52	..	..	..	..	..	..	..	..	..	..	..	..	..	11 9	..	..	..	..	..	..	..	52
Selhurst	53	..	..	1037	..	..	..	..	..	..	1048	From Victoria, dep. 10 50 a.m ☞	..	..	..	..	..	..	..	11 4	..	..	53
Thornton Heath	54	..	..	1040	..	..	..	..	..	..	1050		..	..	..	..	..	..	..	11 6	..	..	54
Norbury	55	..	..	1043	..	..	..	..	..	..	1053		..	..	..	..	..	..	..	11 9	..	..	55
Streatham Common	56	..	..	1046	..	..	..	..	..	..	1056		..	..	..	..	..	..	..	1111	..	..	56
Anerley	57	..	..	..	..	..	..	..	..	..	..		..	..	..	..	..	..	11 5	..	..	..	57
Penge West **C**	58	..	..	..	..	..	..	..	..	..	..		..	..	..	..	..	..	11 6	..	..	..	58
Sydenham .... [Lane	59	..	..	..	..	..	..	..	..	..	..		..	..	..	..	..	..	11 8	..	..	..	59
Forest Hill, for Lordship	60	..	..	..	..	..	..	..	1059	..	..		..	..	..	..	..	..	1111	..	..	..	60
Honor Oak Park	61	..	..	..	..	..	..	..	..	..	..		..	..	..	..	..	..	1113	..	..	..	61
Brockley B .... [Line)	62	..	..	..	..	..	..	..	..	..	..		..	..	..	..	..	..	1116	..	..	..	62
New Cross Gate (for E.L.	63	..	..	..	..	..	..	..	11 4	..	..		..	..	..	..	..	..	1118	..	..	..	63
Streatham	64	Via Worcester Park	1043	1048	..	..	..	..	..	..	..		..	..	..	Via Worcester Park	..	..	..	..	..	11 7	64
Tulse Hill	65		1047	1051	..	..	..	..	..	..	..	a.m	11 3	..	..		..	..	..	..	..	1111	65
North Dulwich	66		1050	1054	..	..	..	..	..	..	..	3	11 6	..	..		..	..	..	..	..	1114	66
East Dulwich	67		1052	1056	..	..	..	..	..	..	..		11 8	..	..		..	..	..	..	..	1116	67
Peckham Rye	68		1054	1059	..	..	..	..	..	..	..	11 4	1110	..	..		..	..	..	..	..	1118	68
Queen's Road, Peckham	69		1056	11 1	..	..	..	..	..	..	..	11 6	1112	..	..		..	..	..	..	..	1120	69
South Bermondsey	70		1059	11 4	..	..	..	..	..	..	..	11 9	1115	..	..		..	..	..	..	..	1123	70
Balham & Upper Tooting	71		..	..	..	..	..	..	..	..	11 0	..	..	..	1111		11 3	..	..	1115	..	..	71
Wandsworth Common **A**	72		..	..	..	..	..	..	..	..	11 2	..	..	..	1113		11 5	..	..	1117	..	..	72
Clapham Junction	73	1032	..	..	..	..	11 0	..	..	11 5	11 5	..	..	..	1116	1052	1110	..	..	1120	1114	..	73
Battersea Park	74	..	..	..	..	..	..	..	..	..	..	..	..	..	1119	..	..	..	..	..	..	..	74
London Bridge ..... arr	75	..	11 3	11 8	..	..	..	..	1110	..	..	1113	1119	..	..	..	..	..	1124	..	..	1127	75
Waterloo ✻ .... "	76	1039	..	..	..	..	..	..	1113	..	..	..	..	..	..	1059	..	..	..	..	..	..	76
Charing Cross ✻ .. "	77	..	..	..	..	..	..	..	1115	..	..	..	..	..	..	..	..	..	..	..	..	..	77
Victoria .... "	78	..	..	..	..	11 3	11 6	..	..	1112	1111	..	..	..	1123	..	1116	..	..	1126	1120	..	78

DORKING NORTH, SUTTON, CROYDON, CRYSTAL PALACE, and LONDON

Sundays—*continued* (a.m)

No.	3	3	3	3	..	3	3	3	3		..	3	3	3		3	..	3	3	3	..	3		3	..	3	3	..
1	..	..	..	..	..	..	..	..	..	1043	..	..	..	..	10§48	..	..	..	..	..	..	..	1051	..	..	..	..	..
2	..	..	..	..	..	..	..	..	..	..	..	..	..	..	11 22	..	..	..	..	..	..	..	..	..	..	..	..	..
3	..	..	..	..	..	..	..	..	..	..	..	..	..	..	11 29	..	..	..	..	..	..	..	3	..	..	..	..	1149
4	..	..	..	..	..	..	..	..	..	..	..	..	..	..	11 33	..	..	..	..	..	..	..	..	..	..	..	..	..
5	..	..	..	..	..	..	..	..	..	..	..	..	..	..	11 39	..	..	..	..	..	..	..	..	..	..	..	..	..
6	..	..	1048	..	..	..	..	..	..	..	..	..	..	..	§ Via Three Bridges	..	..	1114	..	..	..	..	..	..	..	..	..	..
7	..	..	1051	..	..	..	..	..	..	..	..	..	..	..		..	..	1117	..	..	..	..	..	..	..	..	..	..
8	..	..	1054	..	..	..	..	..	..	..	..	..	..	..		..	..	1120	..	..	..	..	..	..	..	..	..	..
9	..	..	1059	..	..	..	..	..	..	..	..	..	..	..		..	..	1125	..	..	..	..	..	..	..	..	..	..
10	..	..	11 1	..	..	..	..	..	..	..	..	..	..	..		..	..	1127	..	..	..	..	..	..	..	..	..	..
11	..	..	11 4	..	..	..	..	..	..	..	..	..	..	..		..	..	1130	..	..	..	..	..	..	..	..	..	..
12	..	..	11 6	..	..	..	..	..	..	..	..	..	..	..		..	..	1132	..	..	..	..	..	..	..	..	..	..
13	..	..	11 9	..	..	..	..	..	..	..	..	..	..	..		..	..	1134	..	..	..	..	..	..	..	..	..	..
14	..	..	1059	..	..	..	..	..	..	..	..	..	..	..	..	..	..	1125	..	..	..	..	..	..	..	..	..	..
15	..	..	11 2	..	..	..	..	..	..	..	..	..	..	..	..	..	..	1128	..	..	..	..	..	..	..	..	..	..
16	..	..	11 4	..	..	..	..	..	..	..	..	..	..	..	..	..	..	1130	..	..	..	..	..	..	..	..	..	..
17	..	..	11 7	..	..	..	..	..	..	..	..	..	..	..	..	..	..	1133	..	..	..	..	..	..	..	..	..	..
18	..	..	1111	..	..	..	..	..	..	..	..	..	..	..	..	..	..	1136	..	..	..	..	..	..	..	..	..	..
19	..	..	..	..	..	..	..	..	..	..	..	..	..	..	..	..	..	..	..	..	..	..	..	..	..	..	1150	..
20	..	..	1113	..	..	..	..	..	..	..	..	..	..	..	11 43	..	..	1139	..	..	..	..	..	..	..	..	1153	..
21	..	..	1116	..	..	..	..	..	..	..	..	..	..	..	..	..	..	1142	..	..	..	..	..	..	..	..	1155	..
22	..	..	1118	..	..	..	..	..	..	..	..	..	..	..	..	..	..	1144	..	..	..	..	..	..	..	..	1158	..
23	..	..	..	..	..	..	..	..	..	..	..	10 54	..	..	..	..	..	..	..	..	..	..	..	..	..	..	..	..
24	..	..	..	..	..	..	..	..	..	..	..	10 58	..	..	..	..	..	..	..	..	..	..	..	..	..	..	..	..
25	..	..	..	..	..	..	..	..	..	11 2	..	..	11 6	..	..	..	..	..	..	..	..	..	1115	..	..	..	..	..
26	..	..	..	..	..	..	..	..	..	..	..	..	11 8	..	..	..	..	..	..	..	..	..	1117	..	..	..	..	..
27	..	..	..	..	..	..	..	..	..	..	..	11 2	1113	..	..	..	..	..	..	..	..	..	1122	..	..	..	..	..
28	..	..	..	..	..	..	..	..	..	..	..	11 6	1117	..	..	..	..	..	..	..	..	..	1126	..	..	..	..	..
29	..	..	..	..	..	..	..	11 3	..	..	..	11 10	1121	..	..	..	..	..	..	..	..	..	1130	1137	..	..	..	..
30	..	..	..	..	..	..	..	11 6	..	..	..	..	1124	..	..	..	..	..	..	..	..	..	..	1140	..	..	..	..
31	..	..	..	..	..	..	..	11 9	..	..	..	..	1127	..	..	..	..	..	..	..	..	..	..	1143	..	..	..	..
32	From London Bridge, via Streatham	1055	..	..	..	..	..	..	11 8	..	..	..	..	..	..	1125	..	..	..	..	..	..	..	..	..	1138	..	..
33		1058	..	..	..	..	..	..	1111	..	..	..	..	..	..	1128	..	..	..	..	..	..	..	..	..	1141	..	..
34		11 1	..	..	..	..	..	..	1114	..	..	..	..	..	..	1131	..	..	..	..	..	..	..	..	..	1144	..	..
35		11 4	..	..	..	..	11 9	1112	1117	1122	..	..	1130	From London Bridge, via Forest Hill	..	1134	..	..	..	..	..	1139	..	1148	..	1147	..	..
36		11 6	..	..	..	..	1112	..	1119	Arr. Sutton 11 29 a.m	..	..	..		..	1136	..	..	..	..	..	1142	..	..	..	1149	..	..
37		11 9	..	..	..	..	1114	..	1122		..	..	..		..	1139	..	..	..	..	..	1144	..	..	..	1152	..	..
38		1112	..	..	..	..	1118	..	1125		..	..	..		..	1142	..	..	..	..	..	1148	..	..	..	1155	..	..
39		1115	..	..	..	..	1123	..	1128		..	..	..		..	1145	..	..	..	..	..	1151	..	..	..	1158	..	..
40		1115	..	..	..	..	1123	..	1128		..	..	..		..	1145	..	..	..	..	..	1153	..	..	..	1158	..	..
41		..	..	..	..	..	..	1115	..		..	..	1133		..	..	..	..	..	..	..	..	..	1151	..	..	..	..
42		..	..	..	..	..	..	1118	..		..	..	1136		..	..	..	..	..	..	..	..	..	1153	..	..	..	..
43		..	..	..	..	..	..	1120	..		..	..	1138		..	..	..	..	..	..	..	..	..	1156	..	..	..	..
44		..	1121	..	..	..	..	..	..	..	..	..	..		11 49	..	..	1151	..	..	..	..	..	Arr Sutton 11 46 a.m	..	..	12 1	12 4
45		..	1121	..	..	..	..	..	..	..	..	..	..		11 50	..	..	1151	..	..	..	..	..		..	..	12 1	12 4
46	1117	..	1125	..	..	..	1127	..	1132	..	..	..	..	1134	..	..	..	1155	..	..	..	1157	..		..	12 2	..	..
47	..	..	..	1115	..	..	..	..	..	..	..	..	..	..	..	..	..	..	1145	..	..	..	..		..	..	..	..
48	..	..	..	1118	..	..	..	..	..	..	..	..	..	..	..	..	..	..	1148	..	..	..	..		..	..	..	..
49	..	..	..	1122	..	1127	1131	..	..	..	..	..	..	..	..	..	..	..	1152	1155	..	12 1	..		..	..	..	..
50	..	..	..		..	..	1133	..	..	..	..	..	..	..	..	..	..	..		1158	..	12 3	..		..	..	..	..
51	..	..	..	Stop	..	..	1136	..	..	..	..	..	..	..	..	..	..	..	Stop	12 0	..	12 6	..		..	..	..	..
52	..	..	..	..	..	..	1139	..	..	..	..	..	..	..	..	..	..	..	..	..	..	12 9	..		..	..	..	..
53	..	1118	..	From Victoria, dep 11 29 a.m ☞	..	..	..	..	..	..	..	..	..	1137	..	1148	..	..	From Victoria, dep. 11 50 a.m ☞	..	..	..	..	..	..	..	12 4	..
54	..	1120	..		..	..	..	..	..	..	..	..	..	1140	..	1150	..	..		..	..	..	..	..	..	..	12 6	..
55	..	1123	..		..	..	..	..	..	..	..	..	..	1143	..	1153	..	..		..	..	..	..	..	..	..	12 9	..
56	..	1126	..		..	..	..	..	..	..	..	..	..	1146	..	1156	..	..		..	..	..	..	..	..	..	1211	..
57	1120	..	..		..	..	..	..	1135	..	..	..	..	..	..	..	..	..		..	..	..	..	..	..	12 5	..	..
58	1121	..	..		..	..	..	..	1136	..	..	..	..	..	..	..	..	..		..	..	..	..	..	..	12 6	..	..
59	1123	..	..		..	1130	..	..	1138	..	..	..	..	..	..	..	..	..		..	..	..	..	..	..	12 8	..	..
60	1126	..	1129		..	1132	..	..	1141	..	..	..	..	..	..	..	..	1159		..	..	..	..	..	..	1211	..	..
61	1128	..	..		..	1135	..	..	1143	..	..	..	..	..	..	..	..	..		..	..	..	..	..	..	1212	..	..
62	1131	..	..		..	1137	..	..	1146	..	..	..	..	..	..	..	..	..		..	..	..	..	..	..	1216	..	..
63	1133	..	1134		..	1140	..	..	1148	..	..	..	..	..	..	..	..	12 4		..	..	..	..	..	..	1218	..	..
64	..	..	..		..	..	..	..	..	..	..	Via Worcester Park	1143	1148	..	..	..	..		..	..	..	Via Worcester Park	..	..	..	..	..
65	..	..	..	a.m	..	..	..	..	..	..	..		1147	1151	..	..	..	..	p.m	12 3	..	..		..	..	..	..	..
66	..	..	..	3	..	..	..	..	..	..	..		1150	1154	..	..	..	..	3	12 6	..	..		..	..	..	..	..
67	..	..	..		..	..	..	..	..	..	..		1152	1156	..	..	..	..		12 8	..	..		..	..	..	..	..
68	..	..	..	1134	..	..	..	..	..	..	..		1154	1159	..	..	..	..	12 4	1210	..	..		..	..	..	..	..
69	..	..	..	1136	..	..	..	..	..	..	..		1156	12 1	..	..	..	..	12 6	1212	..	..		..	..	..	..	..
70	..	..	..	1139	..	..	..	..	..	..	..		1159	12 4	..	..	..	..	12 9	1215	..	..		..	..	..	..	..
71	..	1130	..	..	..	..	1141	1127	..	..	..		..	..	..	12 0	..	..	..	..	..	1211		12 3	..	..	1215	..
72	..	1132	..	..	..	..	1143	1129	..	..	..		..	..	..	12 2	..	..	..	..	..	1213		12 5	..	..	1217	..
73	..	1135	..	..	..	..	1146	1132	..	..	..	11 32	..	..	12 2	12 5	..	..	..	..	..	1216	1152	1210	..	..	1220	1214
74	..	..	..	..	..	..	1149	..	..	..	..	..	..	..	..	..	..	..	..	..	..	1219	..	..	..	..	..	..
75	1139	..	1140	1143	..	1145	..	..	1154	..	..	..	12 3	12 8	..	..	..	1210	1213	1219	..	..	..	..	..	1224	..	..
76	..	..	1142	..	..	..	..	..	..	..	..	11 39	..	..	..	..	..	1213	..	..	..	..	1159	..	..	..	..	..
77	..	..	1145	..	..	..	..	..	..	..	..	..	..	..	..	..	..	1215	..	..	..	..	..	..	..	..	..	..
78	..	1141	..	..	..	..	1153	1138	..	1143	..	..	..	..	12 7	1211	..	..	..	..	..	1223	..	1216	..	..	1226	1220

For Notes, see page 317a

HORSHAM, REIGATE, REDHILL, TATTENHAM CORNER, CATERHAM,

Up	No.	p.m							Sundays	—continued—							p.m						No.
Horsham .... dep	1	3	..	3	3	3	3	..	3	3	..	3	3	3	3	3	..	a.m 11§48	3	3	..	3	1
Reigate .... "	2	..	..	..	..	..	..	..	..	..	..	..	..	..	..	..	..	12 22	..	..	..	..	2
Redhill .... "	3	..	..	..	..	..	..	..	..	..	..	..	..	..	..	..	..	12 29	..	..	..	..	3
Merstham	4	..	..	..	..	..	..	..	..	..	..	..	..	..	..	..	..	12 33	..	..	..	..	4
Coulsdon South	5	..	..	..	a.m	..	..	..	..	..	..	..	..	..	..	..	..	12 39	..	..	..	..	5
Tattenham Corner . dep	6	..	..	..	1148	..	..	..	..	..	..	..	..	..	..	..	..	§ Via Three Bridges	..	1214	..	..	6
Tadworth **N**	7	..	..	..	1151	..	..	..	..	..	..	..	..	..	..	..	..		..	1217	..	..	7
Kingswood **M**	8	..	..	..	1154	..	..	..	..	..	..	..	..	..	..	..	..		..	1220	..	..	8
Chipstead	9	..	..	..	1159	..	..	..	..	..	..	..	..	..	..	..	..		..	1225	..	..	9
Woodmansterne	10	..	..	..	12 1	..	..	..	..	..	..	..	..	..	..	..	..		..	1227	..	..	10
Smitham	11	..	..	..	12 4	..	..	..	..	..	..	..	..	..	..	..	..		..	1230	..	..	11
Reedham	12	..	..	..	12 6	..	..	..	..	..	..	..	..	..	..	..	..		..	1232	..	..	12
Purley 252 .... arr	13	..	..	..	12 9	..	..	..	..	..	..	..	..	..	..	..	..		..	1234	..	..	13
Caterham .... dep	14	..	..	..	1159	..	..	..	..	..	..	..	..	..	..	..	..	..	..	1225	..	..	14
Warlingham	15	..	..	..	12 2	..	..	..	..	..	..	..	..	..	..	..	..	..	..	1228	..	..	15
Whyteleafe	16	..	..	..	12 4	..	..	..	..	..	..	..	..	..	..	..	..	..	..	1230	..	..	16
Kenley	17	..	..	..	12 7	..	..	..	..	..	..	..	..	..	..	..	..	..	..	1233	..	..	17
Purley 252 .... arr	18	..	..	..	1211	..	..	..	..	..	..	..	..	..	..	..	..	..	..	1236	..	..	18
Coulsdon North ..... dep	19	..	..	..	..	..	..	..	..	..	..	..	..	..	..	..	..	..	..	..	..	..	19
Purley 252	20	..	..	..	1213	..	..	..	..	..	..	..	..	..	..	..	..	12 43	..	1239	..	..	20
Purley Oaks	21	..	..	..	1216	..	..	..	..	..	..	..	..	..	..	..	..	..	..	1242	..	..	21
South Croydon 234	22	a.m	..	..	1218	..	..	..	..	..	..	..	..	a.m	..	..	..	..	..	1244	1254	..	22
Effingham Junction dep	23	1130	..	..	..	..	..	..	..	..	..	..	..	1154	..	..	..	..	..	..	..	..	23
Bookham	24	1133	..	..	..	..	..	..	..	..	..	..	..	1158	..	..	..	..	..	..	..	..	24
Dorking North ..... dep	25	..	..	..	..	..	..	..	..	..	..	..	..	..	12 6	..	..	..	..	..	..	..	25
Boxhill and Burford	26	..	..	..	..	..	..	..	..	..	..	..	..	..	12 8	..	..	..	..	..	..	..	26
Leatherhead ... [Bridge **J**	27	1137	..	..	..	..	..	..	..	..	..	..	..	12 2	1213	..	..	..	..	..	..	..	27
Ashtead	28	1141	..	..	..	..	..	..	..	..	..	..	..	12 6	1217	..	..	..	..	..	..	..	28
Epsom 427	29	1145	..	..	..	..	..	..	..	..	..	12 3	..	1210	1221	..	..	..	..	..	..	..	29
Ewell East **H**	30	1148	..	..	..	..	..	..	..	..	..	12 6	..	..	1224	..	..	..	..	..	..	..	30
Cheam	31	1151	..	..	..	a.m	..	..	..	..	..	12 9	..	..	1227	..	..	..	..	..	..	..	31
Epsom Downs ...... dep	32	..	..	..	..	1155	..	..	..	..	..	..	12 8	..	..	..	..	..	1225	..	..	..	32
Banstead	33	..	..	..	..	1158	..	..	..	..	..	..	1211	..	..	..	..	..	1228	..	..	..	33
Belmont	34	..	..	From London Bridge, via Streatham	..	12 1	..	..	..	..	..	..	1214	..	..	From London Bridge, via Forest Hill	..	..	1231	..	..	..	34
Sutton 322	35	1154	..		..	12 4	..	..	..	12 9	..	1212	1217	..	1230		..	..	1234	..	..	..	35
Carshalton Beeches	36	..	..		..	12 6	..	..	..	1212	..	..	1219	..	..		..	..	1236	..	..	..	36
Wallington	37	..	..		..	12 9	..	..	..	1214	..	..	1222	..	..		..	..	1239	..	..	..	37
Waddon **G**	38	..	..		..	1212	..	..	..	1218	..	..	1225	..	..		..	..	1242	..	..	..	38
West Croydon 319 arr	39	..	..		..	1215	..	..	..	1223	..	..	1228	..	..		..	..	1245	..	..	..	39
West Croydon 319 dep	40	..	..		..	1215	..	..	..	1223	..	..	1228	..	..		..	..	1245	..	..	..	40
Carshalton	41	1157	..		..	..	..	..	..	..	..	1215	..	..	1233		..	..	..	..	..	..	41
Hackbridge	42	12 0	..		..	..	..	..	..	..	..	1218	..	..	1236		..	..	..	..	..	..	42
Mitcham Junction	43	12 2	..		..	..	..	..	..	..	..	1220	..	..	1238		..	..	..	..	..	..	43
East Croydon .. arr	44	..	..		1221	..	..	..	..	..	..	..	..	..	..		..	12 49	..	1251	1257	..	44
East Croydon .. dep	45	..	..	..	1221	..	..	..	..	..	..	..	..	..	..		..	12 49	..	1251	1257	..	45
Norwood Junction F ..	46	..	..	1217	1225	..	..	..	..	1227	..	..	1232	..	..	1234	..	..	..	1255	..	..	46
Beckenham Jn. dep	47	..	..	..	..	..	1215	..	..	..	..	..	..	..	..	..	..	..	..	..	..	1245	47
Birkbeck	48	..	..	..	..	..	1218	..	..	..	..	..	..	..	..	..	..	..	..	..	..	1248	48
Crystal Palace D	49	..	..	..	..	..	1222	..	1227	1231	..	..	..	..	..	..	..	..	..	..	..	1252	49
Gipsy Hill (for Upper	50	..	..	..	..	..	—	..	..	1233	..	..	..	..	..	..	..	..	..	..	..	—	50
West Norwood. [N'wood)	51	..	..	..	..	..	Stop	..	..	1236	..	..	..	..	..	..	..	..	..	..	..	Stop	51
Streatham Hill	52	..	..	..	..	..		..	..	1239	..	..	..	..	..	..	..	..	..	..	..		52
Selhurst	53	..	..	..	..	1218	From Victoria, dep. 12 20 p.m ☞	..	..	..	..	..	..	..	..	1237	..	..	1248	..	..	From Victoria, dep. 12 50 p.m ☞	53
Thornton Heath	54	..	..	..	..	1220		..	..	..	..	..	..	..	..	1240	..	..	1250	..	..		54
Norbury	55	..	..	..	..	1223		..	..	..	..	..	..	..	..	1243	..	..	1253	..	..		55
Streatham Common	56	..	..	..	..	1226		..	..	..	..	..	..	..	..	1246	..	..	1256	..	..		56
Anerley	57	..	..	1220	..	..		..	..	..	..	..	1235	..	..	..	..	..	..	..	..		57
Penge West **C**	58	..	..	1221	..	..		..	..	..	..	..	1236	..	..	..	..	..	..	..	..		58
Sydenham .... [Lane	59	..	..	1223	..	..		..	1230	..	..	..	1238	..	..	..	..	..	..	..	..		59
Forest Hill, for Lordship	60	..	..	1226	1229	..		..	1232	..	..	..	1241	..	..	..	..	..	..	1259	..		60
Honor Oak Park	61	..	..	1228	..	..		..	1235	..	..	..	1243	..	..	..	..	..	..	..	..		61
Brockley **B** .... Line)	62	..	..	1231	..	..		..	1237	..	..	..	1246	..	..	..	..	..	..	..	..		62
New Cross Gate (for E.L.	63	..	..	1233	1234	..		..	1240	..	..	..	1248	..	..	..	..	..	..	1 4	..		63
Streatham	64	12 7	..	..	..	..		..	..	..	..	..	..	Via Worcester Park	1243	1248	..	..	..	..	..		64
Tulse Hill	65	1211	..	..	..	..	p.m	..	..	..	..	..	..		1247	1251	..	..	..	..	..	p.m	65
North Dulwich	66	1214	..	..	..	..	3	..	..	..	..	..	..		1250	1254	..	..	..	..	..	3	66
East Dulwich	67	1216	..	..	..	..		..	..	..	..	..	..		1252	1256	..	..	..	..	..		67
Peckham Rye	68	1218	..	..	..	..	1234	..	..	..	..	..	..		1254	1259	..	..	..	..	..	1 4	68
Queen's Road, Peckham	69	1220	..	..	..	..	1236	..	..	..	..	..	..		1256	1 1	..	..	..	..	..	1 6	69
South Bermondsey	70	1223	..	..	..	..	1239	..	..	..	..	..	..		1259	1 4	..	..	..	..	..	1 9	70
Balham & Upper Tooting	71	..	..	..	..	1230	..	..	..	1241	..	1227	..		..	..	..	..	1 0	..	..	..	71
Wandsworth Common **A**	72	..	..	..	..	1232	..	..	..	1243	..	1229	..		..	..	..	..	1 2	..	..	..	72
Clapham Junction	73	..	..	..	..	1235	..	..	..	1246	..	1232	..	1232	..	..	..	1 0	1 5	..	1 10	..	73
Battersea Park	74	..	..	..	..	..	..	..	..	1249	..	..	..	..	..	..	..	..	..	..	..	..	74
LONDON BRIDGE ..... arr	75	1227	..	1239	1240	..	1243	..	1245	..	..	..	1254	..	1 3	1 8	..	..	..	1 10	..	1 13	75
WATERLOO * .... "	76	..	..	..	1242	..	..	..	..	..	..	..	..	1239	..	..	..	..	..	1 13	..	..	76
CHARING CROSS * .. "	77	..	..	..	1245	..	..	..	..	..	..	..	..	..	..	..	..	..	..	1 15	..	..	77
VICTORIA .... "	78	..	..	..	..	1241	..	..	..	1253	..	1238	..	..	..	..	..	1 6	1 11	..	1 17	..	78

DORKING NORTH, SUTTON, CROYDON, CRYSTAL PALACE, and LONDON

Sundays—*continued* (p.m)

No.	3		3		3	3	3		3		3	3		3	3		3		3	3	3	3	3	3			3	3
1		..		a.m 1149				..		..			..			..		..							..	12§48		
2	..	..	..	..	..	..	..	..	..	..	..	..	..	..	..	..	..	..	..	..	..	..	..	..	..	1 22	..	..
3	..	..	..	3	..	..	..	1249	..	..	..	..	..	..	..	..	..	..	..	..	..	..	..	..	..	1 29	..	..
4	..	..	..	..	..	..	..	..	..	..	..	..	..	..	..	..	..	..	..	..	..	..	..	..	..	1 33	..	..
5	..	..	..	..	..	..	..	..	..	..	..	..	..	..	..	..	..	..	..	..	..	..	..	..	..	1 39	..	..
6	..	..	..	..	..	..	..	..	..	..	..	..	..	1248	..	..	..	..	..	..	..	..	..	..	..		..	1 14
7	..	..	..	..	..	..	..	..	..	..	..	..	..	1251	..	..	..	..	..	..	..	..	..	..	..		..	1 17
8	..	..	..	..	..	..	..	..	..	..	..	..	..	1254	..	..	..	..	..	..	..	..	..	..	..		..	1 20
9	..	..	..	..	..	..	..	..	..	..	..	..	..	1259	..	..	..	..	..	..	..	..	..	..	..	§ Via Three Bridges	..	1 25
10	..	..	..	..	..	..	..	..	..	..	..	..	..	1 1	..	..	..	..	..	..	..	..	..	..	..		..	1 27
11	..	..	..	..	..	..	..	..	..	..	..	..	..	1 4	..	..	..	..	..	..	..	..	..	..	..		..	1 30
12	..	..	▼	..	..	..	..	..	..	..	..	..	..	1 6	..	..	..	..	..	..	..	..	..	..	..		..	1 32
13	..	..	..	..	..	..	..	..	..	..	..	..	..	1 9	..	..	..	..	..	..	..	..	..	..	..		..	1 34
14	..	..	..	..	..	..	..	..	..	..	..	..	..	1259	..	..	..	..	..	..	..	..	..	..	..	..	..	1 25
15	..	..	..	..	..	..	..	..	..	..	..	..	..	1 2	..	..	..	..	..	..	..	..	..	..	..	..	..	1 28
16	..	..	..	..	..	..	..	..	..	..	..	..	..	1 4	..	..	..	..	..	..	..	..	..	..	..	..	..	1 30
17	..	..	..	..	..	..	..	..	..	..	..	..	..	1 7	..	..	..	..	..	..	..	..	..	..	..	..	..	1 33
18	..	..	..	..	..	..	..	..	..	..	..	..	..	1 11	..	..	..	..	..	..	..	..	..	..	..	..	..	1 36
19	..	..	..	..	..	..	1250	..	..	..	..	..	..	..	..	..	..	..	..	..	..	..	..	..	..	..	..	..
20	..	..	..	..	..	..	1253	..	..	..	..	..	..	1 13	..	..	..	..	..	..	..	..	..	..	..	1 43	..	1 39
21	..	..	..	..	..	..	1255	..	..	..	..	..	..	1 16	..	..	..	..	..	..	..	..	..	..	..	..	..	1 42
22	..	..	..	..	..	..	1258	..	..	..	..	..	..	1 18	..	..	..	..	..	..	..	..	..	..	..	..	..	1 44
23	..	..	..	..	..	..	..	..	1230	..	..	..	..	..	..	..	..	..	..	..	..	1254	..	..	..	..	..	..
24	..	..	..	..	..	..	..	..	1233	..	..	..	..	..	..	..	..	..	..	..	..	1258	..	..	..	..	..	..
25	..	..	..	1215	..	..	..	..	..	..	..	..	..	..	..	..	..	..	..	..	..	..	1 0	..	..	..	..	..
26	..	..	..	1217	..	..	..	..	..	..	..	..	..	..	..	..	..	..	..	..	..	..	1 2	..	..	..	..	..
27	..	..	..	1222	..	..	..	..	1237	..	..	..	..	..	..	..	..	..	..	..	..	1 2	1 7	..	..	..	..	..
28	..	..	..	1226	..	..	..	..	1241	..	..	..	..	..	..	..	..	..	..	..	..	1 6	1 11	..	..	..	..	..
29	..	..	..	1230	1237	..	..	..	1245	..	..	..	..	..	..	..	..	..	..	1 3	..	1 10	1 15	..	..	..	..	..
30	..	..	..	..	1240	..	..	..	1248	..	..	..	..	..	..	..	..	..	..	1 6	..	..	1 18	..	..	..	..	..
31	..	..	..	..	1243	..	..	..	1251	..	..	..	..	..	..	..	..	..	..	1 9	..	..	1 21	..	..	..	..	..
32	..	..	..	..	..	1238	..	..	..	..	..	1255	..	..	..	..	..	..	..	..	1 8	..	..	..	..	..	1 25	..
33	..	..	..	..	..	1241	..	..	..	..	..	1258	..	..	..	..	..	..	..	..	1 11	..	..	..	..	..	1 28	..
34	..	..	..	..	..	1244	..	..	..	..	..	1 1	..	..	..	..	..	..	..	..	1 14	..	..	..	..	..	1 31	..
35	..	..	1239	..	1248	1247	..	..	1254	..	From London Bridge, via Streatham	1 4	..	..	..	..	..	..	1 9	1 12	1 17	..	1 24	From London Bridge, via Forest Hill	..	..	1 34	..
36	..	..	1242	..	..	1249	..	..	..	..		1 6	..	..	..	..	..	..	1 12	..	1 19	..	..		..	..	1 36	..
37	..	..	1244	..	..	1252	..	..	..	..		1 9	..	..	..	..	..	..	1 14	..	1 22	..	..		..	..	1 39	..
38	..	..	1248	..	..	1255	..	..	..	..		1 12	..	..	..	..	..	..	1 18	..	1 25	..	..		..	..	1 42	..
39	..	..	1251	..	..	1258	..	..	..	..		1 15	..	..	..	..	..	..	1 23	..	1 28	..	..		..	..	1 45	..
40	..	..	1253	..	..	1258	..	..	..	..		1 15	..	..	..	..	..	..	1 23	..	1 28	..	..		..	..	1 45	..
41	..	..	..	..	1251	..	..	..	1257	..		..	..	..	..	..	..	..	..	1 15	..	..	1 27		..	..	..	..
42	..	..	..	..	1253	..	..	..	1 0	..		..	..	..	..	..	..	..	..	1 18	..	..	1 30		..	..	..	..
43	..	..	..	..	1256	..	..	..	1 2	..		..	..	..	..	..	..	..	..	1 20	..	..	1 32		..	..	..	..
44	..	..	..	..	..	..	1 1	1 4	..	..		..	..	1 21	..	..	..	..	..	..	..	..	..		—	1 49	..	1 51
45	..	..	..	..	Arr. Sutton 12 46 p.m	..	1 1	1 4	..	..		..	..	1 21	..	..	..	..	..	..	..	..	..		..	1 50	..	1 51
46	..	..	1257	..		1 2	..	..	..	..	1 17	..	..	1 25	..	..	..	..	1 27	..	1 32	..	..	1 34	..	..	..	1 55
47	..	..	..	..		..	..	..	..	..	..	..	..	..	1 15	..	..	..	..	..	..	..	..	..	..	..	..	..
48	..	..	..	..		..	..	..	..	..	..	..	..	..	1 18	..	..	..	..	..	..	..	..	..	..	..	..	..
49	1255	..	1 1	..		..	..	..	..	..	..	..	..	..	1 22	..	1 27	..	1 31	..	..	..	..	..	..	..	..	..
50	1258	..	1 3	..		..	..	..	..	..	..	..	..	..	—	..	..	..	1 33	..	..	..	..	..	..	..	..	..
51	1 0	..	1 6	..		..	..	..	..	..	..	..	..	..	Stop	..	..	..	1 36	..	..	..	..	..	..	..	..	..
52	..	..	1 9	..	..	..	..	..	..	..	..	..	..	..	..	..	..	..	1 39	..	..	..	..	..	..	..	..	..
53	..	..	..	..	..	..	1 4	..	..	..	..	1 18	..	..	From Victoria, dep. 1 20 p.m	..	..	..	..	..	..	..	..	1 37	..	..	1 48	..
54	..	..	..	..	..	..	1 6	..	..	..	..	1 20	..	..		..	..	..	..	..	..	..	..	1 40	..	..	1 50	..
55	..	..	..	..	..	..	1 9	..	..	..	..	1 23	..	..		..	..	..	..	..	..	..	..	1 43	..	..	1 53	..
56	..	..	..	..	..	..	1 11	..	..	..	..	1 26	..	..		..	..	..	..	..	..	..	..	1 46	..	..	1 56	..
57	..	..	..	..	..	1 5	..	..	..	..	1 20	..	..	..		..	..	..	..	..	1 35	..	..	..	..	..	..	..
58	..	..	..	..	..	1 6	..	..	..	..	1 21	..	..	..		..	..	..	..	..	1 36	..	..	..	..	..	..	..
59	..	..	..	..	..	1 8	..	..	..	..	1 23	..	..	..		..	1 30	..	..	..	1 38	..	..	..	..	..	..	..
60	..	..	..	..	..	1 11	..	..	..	..	1 26	..	..	1 29		..	1 32	..	..	..	1 41	..	..	..	..	..	..	1 59
61	..	..	..	..	..	1 13	..	..	..	..	1 28	..	..	..		..	1 35	..	..	..	1 43	..	..	..	..	..	..	..
62	..	..	..	..	..	1 16	..	..	..	..	1 31	..	..	..		..	1 37	..	..	..	1 46	..	..	..	..	..	..	..
63	..	..	..	..	..	1 18	..	..	..	..	1 33	..	..	1 34		..	1 40	..	..	..	1 48	..	..	..	..	..	..	2 4
64	..	..	..	Via Worcester Park	..	..	..	..	1 7	..	..	..	..	..		..	..	..	..	..	..	Via Worcester Park	1 37	1 48	..	..	..	..
65	1 3	..	..		..	..	..	..	1 11	..	..	..	..	..	p.m	..	..	..	..	..	..		1 41	1 51	..	..	..	..
66	1 6	..	..		..	..	..	..	1 14	..	..	..	..	..	3	..	..	..	..	..	..		1 44	1 54	..	..	..	..
67	1 8	..	..		..	..	..	..	1 16	..	..	..	..	..		..	..	..	..	..	..		1 46	1 56	..	..	..	..
68	1 10	..	..		..	..	..	..	1 18	..	..	..	..	..	1 34	..	..	..	..	..	..		1 48	1 59	..	..	..	..
69	1 12	..	..		..	..	..	..	1 20	..	..	..	..	..	1 36	..	..	..	..	..	..		1 50	2 1	..	..	..	..
70	1 15	..	..		..	..	..	..	1 23	..	..	..	..	..	1 39	..	..	..	..	..	..		1 53	2 4	..	..	..	..
71	..	..	1 11		1 3	..	1 15	..	..	..	..	1 30	..	..	..	..	..	..	1 41	1 27	..		..	..	..	..	2 0	..
72	..	..	1 13		1 5	..	1 17	..	..	..	..	1 32	..	..	..	..	..	..	1 45	1 29	..		..	..	..	..	2 2	..
73	..	..	1 16	1252	1 10	..	1 20	1 14	..	..	..	1 35	..	..	..	..	..	..	1 46	1 32	..	1 32	..	..	..	2 2	2 5	..
74	..	..	1 19	..	..	..	..	..	..	..	..	1 38	..	..	..	..	..	..	1 49	..	..	..	..	..	..	..	..	..
75	1 19	..	..	..	..	1 24	..	..	1 27	..	1 39	..	..	1 40	1 43	..	1 45	..	..	..	1 54	..	1 57	2 8	..	..	..	2 10
76	..	..	..	1259	..	..	..	..	..	..	..	..	..	1 42	..	..	..	..	..	..	..	1 39	..	..	..	..	..	2 13
77	..	..	..	..	..	..	..	..	..	..	..	..	..	1 45	..	..	..	..	..	..	..	..	..	..	..	..	..	2 15
78	..	..	1 23	..	1 16	..	1 26	1 20	..	..	..	1 41	..	..	..	..	..	..	1 53	1 38	..	..	..	..	..	2 7	2 11	..

HORSHAM, REIGATE, REDHILL, TATTENHAM CORNER, CATERHAM,

Up	No.	p.m — Sundays—*continued* — p.m																					No.
		3	3	..	3	1249	3	..	3	3	3	..	..	3	3	3	3	..	3	3	3	3	
Horsham .... dep	1																						1
Reigate .... "	2	..	..	..	..	3	..	..	..	..	..	1 40	..	..	..	..	..	..	..	..	..	..	2
Redhill .... "	3	..	..	..	..		..	..	..	..	..	1 49	..	..	..	..	..	..	..	..	..	..	3
Merstham	4	..	..	..	..	..	..	..	..	..	..	..	..	..	..	..	..	..	..	..	..	..	4
Coulsdon South	5	..	..	..	..	..	..	..	..	..	..	..	..	..	..	..	..	..	..	..	..	..	5
Tattenham Corner dep	6	..	..	..	..	..	..	..	..	..	..	..	..	..	..	1 48	..	..	..	..	..	..	6
Tadworth **N**	7	..	..	..	..	..	..	..	..	..	..	..	..	..	..	1 51	..	..	..	..	..	..	7
Kingswood **M**	8	..	..	..	..	..	..	..	..	..	..	..	..	..	..	1 54	..	..	..	..	..	..	8
Chipstead	9	..	..	..	..	..	..	..	..	..	..	..	..	..	..	1 59	..	..	..	..	..	..	9
Woodmansterne	10	..	..	..	..	..	..	..	..	..	..	..	..	..	..	2 1	..	..	..	..	..	..	10
Smitham	11	..	..	..	..	..	..	..	..	..	..	..	..	..	..	2 4	..	..	..	..	..	..	11
Reedham	12	..	..	..	..	..	..	..	..	..	..	..	..	..	..	2 6	..	..	..	..	..	..	12
Purley 252 .... arr	13	..	..	..	..	..	..	..	..	..	..	..	..	..	..	2 9	..	..	..	..	..	..	13
Caterham .... dep	14	..	..	..	..	..	..	..	..	..	..	..	..	..	..	1 59	..	..	..	..	..	..	14
Warlingham	15	..	..	..	..	..	..	..	..	..	..	..	..	..	..	2 2	..	..	..	..	..	..	15
Whyteleafe	16	..	..	..	..	..	..	..	..	..	..	..	..	..	..	2 4	..	..	..	..	..	..	16
Kenley	17	..	..	..	..	..	..	..	..	..	..	..	..	..	..	2 7	..	..	..	..	..	..	17
Purley 252 .... arr	18	..	..	..	..	..	..	..	..	..	..	..	..	..	..	2 11	..	..	..	..	..	..	18
Coulsdon North ..... dep	19	..	..	..	..	..	..	..	..	..	1 50	..	..	..	..	..	..	..	..	..	..	..	19
Purley 252	20	..	..	..	..	..	..	..	..	..	1 53	..	..	..	..	2 13	..	..	..	..	..	..	20
Purley Oaks	21	..	..	..	..	..	..	..	..	..	1 55	..	..	..	..	2 16	..	..	..	..	..	..	21
South Croydon 234	22	..	..	..	..	..	..	..	..	..	1 58	..	..	..	..	2 18	..	..	..	..	..	..	22
Effingham Junction dep	23	..	..	..	..	..	..	..	..	1 30	..	..	..	..	..	..	..	..	..	..	..	..	23
Bookham	24	..	..	..	..	..	..	..	..	1 33	..	..	..	..	..	..	..	..	..	..	..	..	24
Dorking North ..... dep	25	..	..	..	..	1 15	..	..	..	..	..	..	..	..	..	..	..	..	..	..	..	..	25
Boxhill and Burford	26	..	..	..	..	1 17	..	..	..	..	..	..	..	..	..	..	..	..	..	..	..	..	26
Leatherhead ...[Bridge **J**	27	..	..	..	..	1 22	..	..	..	1 37	..	..	..	..	..	..	..	..	..	..	..	..	27
Ashtead	28	..	..	..	..	1 26	..	..	..	1 41	..	..	..	..	..	..	..	..	..	..	..	..	28
Epsom 427	29	..	..	..	..	1 30	1 37	..	..	1 45	..	..	..	..	..	..	..	..	..	..	2 3	..	29
Ewell East **H**	30	..	..	..	..	..	1 40	..	..	1 48	..	..	..	..	..	..	..	..	..	..	2 6	..	30
Cheam	31	..	..	..	..	..	1 43	..	..	1 51	..	..	..	..	..	..	..	..	..	..	2 9	..	31
Epsom Downs ..... dep	32	..	..	..	..	..	..	..	1 38	..	..	..	..	..	1 55	..	..	..	..	..	..	2 8	32
Banstead	33	..	..	..	..	..	..	..	1 41	..	..	..	..	..	1 58	..	..	..	..	..	..	2 11	33
Belmont	34	..	..	..	..	..	..	..	1 44	..	..	..	..	From London Bridge, via Streatham	2 1	..	..	..	..	..	..	2 14	34
Sutton 322	35	..	..	..	1 39	..	1 48	..	1 47	1 54	..	..	..		2 4	..	..	..	..	2 9	2 12	2 17	35
Carshalton Beeches	36	..	..	..	1 42	..	..	..	1 49	..	..	..	..		2 6	..	..	..	..	2 12	..	2 19	36
Wallington	37	..	..	..	1 44	..	..	..	1 52	..	..	..	..		2 9	..	..	..	..	2 14	..	2 22	37
Waddon **G**	38	..	..	..	1 48	..	..	..	1 55	..	..	..	..		2 12	..	..	..	..	2 18	..	2 25	38
West Croydon 319 arr	39	..	..	..	1 51	..	..	..	1 58	..	..	..	..		2 15	..	..	..	..	2 23	..	2 28	39
West Croydon 319 dep	40	..	..	..	1 53	..	..	..	1 58	..	..	..	..		2 15	..	..	..	..	2 23	..	2 28	40
Carshalton	41	..	..	..	..	..	1 51	..	..	1 57	..	..	..		..	..	..	..	..	..	2 15	..	41
Hackbridge	42	..	..	..	..	..	1 53	..	..	2 0	..	..	..		..	..	..	..	..	..	2 18	..	42
Mitcham Junction	43	..	..	..	..	..	1 56	..	..	2 2	..	..	..		..	..	..	..	..	..	2 20	..	43
East Croydon .. arr	44	..	..	..	..	..	Arr. Sutton 1 46 p.m	..	..	..	2 1	2 4	..		..	2 21	..	..	..	..	..	..	44
East Croydon .. dep	45	..	..	..	..	..		..	..	..	2 1	2 4	..		..	2 21	..	..	..	..	..	..	45
Norwood Junction F ..	46	..	..	..	1 57	..		..	2 2	..	..	..	..	2 17	..	2 25	..	..	..	2 27	..	2 32	46
Beckenham Jn. dep	47	1 45	..	..	..	..		..	..	..	..	..	..	..	..	..	2 15	..	..	..	..	..	47
Birkbeck	48	1 48	..	..	..	..		..	..	..	..	..	..	..	..	..	2 18	..	..	..	..	..	48
Crystal Palace D	49	1 52	1 55	..	2 1	..		..	..	..	..	..	..	..	..	..	2 22	..	2 27	2 31	..	..	49
Gipsy Hill (for Upper	50	—	1 58	..	2 3	..		..	..	..	..	..	..	..	..	..	—	..	..	2 33	..	..	50
West Norwood. [N'wood)	51	Stop	2 0	..	2 6	..	..	..	..	..	..	..	..	..	..	..	Stop	..	..	2 36	..	..	51
Streatham Hill	52	From Victoria, dep. 1 50 p.m	..	..	2 9	..	..	..	..	..	..	..	..	..	..	..	From Victoria, dep. 2 20 p.m	..	..	2 39	..	..	52
Selhurst	53		..	..	..	..	..	..	..	..	2 4	..	..	..	2 18	..		..	..	..	..	..	53
Thornton Heath	54		..	..	..	..	..	..	..	..	2 6	..	..	..	2 20	..		..	..	..	..	..	54
Norbury	55		..	..	..	..	..	..	..	..	2 9	..	..	..	2 23	..		..	..	..	..	..	55
Streatham Common	56		..	..	..	..	..	..	..	..	2 11	..	..	..	2 26	..		..	..	..	..	..	56
Anerley	57		..	..	..	..	..	..	2 5	..	..	..	..	2 20	..	..		..	..	..	..	2 35	57
Penge West **C**	58		..	..	..	..	..	..	2 6	..	..	..	..	2 21	..	..		..	..	..	..	2 36	58
Sydenham ....[Lane	59		..	..	..	..	..	..	2 8	..	..	..	..	2 23	..	..		..	2 30	..	..	2 38	59
Forest Hill, for Lordship	60		..	..	..	..	..	..	2 11	..	..	..	..	2 26	..	2 29		..	2 32	..	..	2 41	60
Honor Oak Park	61		..	..	..	..	..	..	2 13	..	..	..	..	2 28	..	..		..	2 35	..	..	2 43	61
Brockley **B** ....[Line	62		..	..	..	..	..	..	2 16	..	..	..	..	2 31	..	..		..	2 37	..	..	2 46	62
New Cross Gate (for E.L.)	63		..	..	..	..	..	..	2 18	..	..	..	..	2 33	..	2 34		..	2 40	..	..	2 48	63
Streatham	64		..	..	..	Via Worcester Park	..	..	..	2 7	..	..	..	..	..	..		..	..	..	..	..	64
Tulse Hill	65	p.m	2 3	..	..		..	..	..	2 11	..	..	..	..	..	..	p.m	..	..	..	..	..	65
North Dulwich	66	3	2 6	..	..		..	..	..	2 14	..	..	..	..	..	..		..	..	..	..	..	66
East Dulwich	67		2 8	..	..		..	..	..	2 16	..	..	..	..	..	..	3	..	..	..	..	..	67
Peckham Rye	68	2 4	2 10	..	..		..	..	..	2 18	..	..	..	..	..	..	2 34	..	..	..	..	..	68
Queen's Road Peckham	69	2 6	2 12	..	..		..	..	..	2 20	..	..	..	..	..	..	2 36	..	..	..	..	..	69
South Bermondsey	70	2 9	2 15	..	..		..	..	..	2 23	..	..	..	..	..	..	2 39	..	..	..	..	..	70
Balham & Upper Tooting	71	..	..	..	2 11		2 3	..	..	..	2 14	..	..	..	2 30	..	..	..	..	2 41	2 27	..	71
Wandsworth Common **A**	72	..	..	..	2 13		2 5	..	..	..	2 17	..	..	..	2 32	..	..	..	..	2 43	2 29	..	72
Clapham Junction	73	..	..	..	2 16	1 52	2 10	..	..	..	2 20	2 14	..	..	2 35	..	..	..	..	2 46	2 32	..	73
Battersea Park	74	..	..	..	2 19	..	..	..	..	..	..	..	..	..	..	..	..	..	..	2 49	..	..	74
LONDON BRIDGE ..... arr	75	2 13	2 19	..	..	..	..	..	2 24	2 27	..	..	..	2 39	..	2 40	2 43	..	2 45	..	..	2 54	75
WATERLOO* .... "	76	..	..	..	..	1 59	..	..	..	..	..	..	..	..	..	2 42	..	..	..	..	..	..	76
CHARING CROSS * .. "	77	..	..	..	..	..	..	..	..	..	..	..	..	..	..	2 45	..	..	..	..	..	..	77
VICTORIA .... "	78	..	..	..	2 23	..	2 16	..	..	..	2 26	2 20	..	..	2 40	..	..	..	..	2 53	2 38	..	78

For Notes, see page 317a

DORKING NORTH, SUTTON, CROYDON, CRYSTAL PALACE, and LONDON

No.	p.m													**Sundays**—*continued*								p.m						
1	3	3	3	..	1§48	3	3	3	3	..	3	1 49	3	3	..	3	..	3	..	3	3	3	3	..	3	3	3	3
2	..	..	..	..	2 22	..	..	..	..	..	..	..	..	..	..	..	..	..	..	..	..	..	..	..	..	..	..	..
3	..	..	..	..	2 29	..	..	..	..	..	..	3	..	..	..	..	2 49	..	..	..	..	..	..	..	..	..	..	..
4	..	..	..	..	2 33	..	..	..	..	..	..	..	..	..	..	..	..	..	..	..	..	..	..	..	..	..	..	..
5	..	..	..	..	2 39	..	..	..	..	..	..	..	..	..	..	..	..	..	..	..	..	..	..	..	..	..	..	..
6	..	..	..	..	§ Via Three Bridges	..	2 14	..	..	..	..	..	..	..	..	..	..	..	..	..	..	2 48	..	..	..	..	..	..
7	..	..	..	..		..	2 17	..	..	..	..	..	..	..	..	..	..	..	..	..	..	2 51	..	..	..	..	..	..
8	..	..	..	..		..	2 20	..	..	..	..	..	..	..	..	..	..	..	..	..	..	2 54	..	..	..	..	..	..
9	..	..	..	..		..	2 25	..	..	..	..	..	..	..	..	..	..	..	..	..	..	2 59	..	..	..	..	..	..
10	..	..	..	..		..	2 27	..	..	..	..	..	..	..	..	..	..	..	..	..	..	3 1	..	..	..	..	..	..
11	..	..	..	..		..	2 30	..	..	..	..	..	..	..	..	..	..	..	..	..	..	3 4	..	..	..	..	..	..
12	..	..	..	..		..	2 32	..	..	..	..	..	..	..	..	..	..	..	..	..	..	3 6	..	..	..	..	..	..
13	..	..	..	..		..	2 34	..	..	..	..	..	..	..	..	..	..	..	..	..	..	3 9	..	..	..	..	..	..
14	..	..	..	..	..	..	2 25	..	..	..	..	..	..	..	..	..	..	..	..	..	..	2 59	..	..	..	..	..	..
15	..	..	..	..	..	..	2 28	..	..	..	..	..	..	..	..	..	..	..	..	..	..	3 2	..	..	..	..	..	..
16	..	..	..	..	..	..	2 30	..	..	..	..	..	..	..	..	..	..	..	..	..	..	3 4	..	..	..	..	..	..
17	..	..	..	..	..	..	2 33	..	..	..	..	..	..	..	..	..	..	..	..	..	..	3 7	..	..	..	..	..	..
18	..	..	..	..	..	..	2 36	..	..	..	..	..	..	..	..	..	..	..	..	..	..	3 11	..	..	..	..	..	..
19	..	..	..	..	..	..	..	..	..	..	..	..	..	..	..	2 50	..	..	..	..	..	..	..	..	..	..	..	..
20	..	..	..	..	2 43	..	2 39	..	..	..	..	..	..	..	..	2 53	..	..	..	..	..	3 13	..	..	..	..	..	..
21	..	..	..	..	..	..	2 42	..	..	..	..	..	..	..	..	2 55	..	..	..	..	..	3 16	..	..	..	..	..	..
22	..	..	..	..	..	..	2 44	..	..	..	..	..	..	..	..	2 58	..	..	..	..	..	3 18	..	..	..	..	..	..
23	1 54	..	..	..	..	..	..	..	..	..	..	..	..	..	..	..	..	2 30	..	..	..	..	..	..	..	..	..	..
24	1 58	..	..	..	..	..	..	..	..	..	..	..	..	..	..	..	..	2 33	..	..	..	..	..	..	..	..	..	..
25	..	2 0	..	..	..	..	..	..	..	..	..	2 15	..	..	..	..	..	..	..	..	..	..	..	..	..	..	..	..
26	..	2 2	..	..	..	..	..	..	..	..	..	2 17	..	..	..	..	..	..	..	..	..	..	..	..	..	..	..	..
27	2 2	2 7	..	..	..	..	..	..	..	..	..	2 22	..	..	..	..	..	2 37	..	..	..	..	..	..	..	..	..	..
28	2 6	2 11	..	..	..	..	..	..	..	..	..	2 26	..	..	..	..	..	2 41	..	..	..	..	..	..	..	..	..	..
29	2 10	2 15	..	..	..	..	..	..	..	..	..	2 30	2 37	..	..	..	..	2 45	..	..	..	..	..	..	..	..	3 3	..
30	..	2 18	..	..	..	..	..	..	..	..	..	..	2 40	..	..	..	..	2 48	..	..	..	..	..	..	..	..	3 6	..
31	..	2 21	..	..	..	..	..	..	..	..	..	..	2 43	..	..	..	..	2 51	..	..	..	..	..	..	..	..	3 9	..
32	..	..	..	..	..	2 25	..	..	..	..	..	..	..	2 38	..	..	..	..	..	..	2 55	..	..	..	..	..	..	3 8
33	..	..	..	..	..	2 28	..	..	..	..	..	..	..	2 41	..	..	..	..	..	..	2 58	..	..	..	..	..	..	3 11
34	..	..	..	..	..	2 31	..	..	..	..	..	..	..	2 44	..	..	..	..	..	..	3 1	..	..	..	..	..	..	3 14
35	..	2 25	From London Bridge, via Forest Hill	..	..	2 34	..	..	..	..	2 39	..	2 48	2 47	..	..	..	2 54	..	From London Bridge, via Streatham	3 4	..	..	..	..	3 9	3 12	3 17
36	..	..		..	..	2 36	..	..	..	..	2 42	..	..	2 49	..	..	..	..	..		3 6	..	..	..	..	3 12	..	3 19
37	..	..		..	..	2 39	..	..	..	..	2 44	..	..	2 52	..	..	..	..	..		3 9	..	..	..	..	3 14	..	3 22
38	..	..		..	..	2 42	..	..	..	..	2 48	..	..	2 55	..	..	..	..	..		3 12	..	..	..	..	3 18	..	3 25
39	..	..		..	..	2 45	..	..	..	..	2 51	..	..	2 58	..	..	..	..	..		3 15	..	..	..	..	3 23	..	3 28
40	..	..		..	..	2 45	..	..	..	..	2 53	..	..	2 58	..	..	..	..	..		3 15	..	..	..	..	3 23	..	3 28
41	..	2 28		..	..	..	..	..	..	..	..	..	2 51	..	..	..	..	2 57	..		..	..	..	..	..	..	3 15	..
42	..	2 31		..	..	..	..	..	..	..	..	..	2 53	..	..	..	..	3 0	..		..	..	..	..	..	..	3 18	..
43	..	2 33		..	..	..	..	..	..	..	..	..	2 56	..	..	..	..	3 2	..		..	..	..	..	..	..	3 20	..
44	..	..		..	2 49	..	2 51	..	..	..	..	..	..	..	..	3 1	3 4	..	..		..	3 21	..	..	..	..	..	..
45	..	..		..	2 49	..	2 51	..	..	..	..	..	Arr. Sutton 2 46 p.m	..	..	3 1	3 4	..	..		..	3 21	..	..	..	..	..	..
46	..	..	2 34	..	..	..	2 55	..	..	..	2 57	..		3 2	..	..	..	..	—	3 17	..	3 25	..	..	..	3 27	..	3 32
47	..	..	..	..	..	..	..	2 45	..	..	..	..		..	..	..	..	..	..	..	..	..	3 15	..	..	..	..	..
48	..	..	..	..	..	..	..	2 48	..	..	..	..		..	..	..	..	..	..	..	..	..	3 18	..	..	..	..	..
49	..	..	..	..	..	..	..	2 52	2 55	..	3 1	..		..	..	..	..	..	..	..	..	..	3 22	..	3 27	3 31	..	..
50	..	..	..	..	..	..	..	Stop	2 58	..	3 3	..		..	..	..	..	..	..	..	..	..	Stop	..	..	3 33	..	..
51	..	..	..	..	..	..	..		3 0	..	3 6	..	..	..	..	..	..	..	..	..	..	..		..	..	3 36	..	..
52	..	..	..	..	..	..	..	..	..	..	3 9	..	..	..	..	..	..	..	..	..	..	..	..	..	..	3 39	..	..
53	..	..	2 37	..	..	2 48	..	From Victoria, dep. 2 50 p.m	..	..	..	..	..	..	..	3 4	..	..	..	..	3 18	..	From Victoria, dep. 3 20 p.m	..	..	..	..	..
54	..	..	2 40	..	..	2 50	..		..	..	..	..	..	..	..	3 6	..	..	..	..	3 20	..		..	..	..	..	..
55	..	..	2 43	..	..	2 53	..		..	..	..	..	..	..	..	3 9	..	..	..	..	3 23	..		..	..	..	..	..
56	..	..	2 46	..	..	2 56	..		..	..	..	..	..	..	..	3 11	..	..	..	..	3 26	..		..	..	..	..	..
57	..	..	..	..	..	..	..		..	..	..	..	..	3 5	..	..	..	..	..	3 20	..	..		..	..	..	..	3 35
58	..	..	..	..	..	..	..		..	..	..	..	..	3 6	..	..	..	..	..	3 21	..	..		..	..	..	..	3 36
59	..	..	..	..	..	..	..		..	..	..	..	..	3 8	..	..	..	..	..	3 23	..	..		..	3 30	..	..	3 38
60	..	..	..	..	..	..	2 59		..	..	..	..	..	3 11	..	..	..	..	..	3 26	..	3 29		..	3 32	..	..	3 41
61	..	..	..	..	..	..	..		..	..	..	..	..	3 13	..	..	..	..	..	3 28	..	..		..	3 35	..	..	3 43
62	..	..	..	..	..	..	..		..	..	..	..	..	3 16	..	..	..	..	..	3 31	..	..		..	3 37	..	..	3 46
63	..	..	..	..	..	..	3 4		..	..	..	..	..	3 18	..	..	..	..	..	3 33	..	3 34		..	3 40	..	..	3 48
64	Via Worcester Park	2 38	2 48	..	..	..	..		..	..	..	Via Worcester Park	..	..	..	..	..	3 7	..	..	..	..		..	..	..	..	..
65		2 42	2 51	..	..	..	..	p.m	3 3	..	..		..	..	..	..	..	3 11	..	..	..	..	p.m	..	..	..	..	..
66		2 45	2 54	..	..	..	..	3	3 6	..	..		..	..	..	..	..	3 14	..	..	..	..	3	..	..	..	..	..
67		2 47	2 56	..	..	..	..		3 8	..	..		..	..	..	..	..	3 16	..	..	..	..		..	..	..	..	..
68		2 49	2 59	..	..	..	..	3 4	3 10	..	..		..	..	..	..	..	3 18	..	..	..	..	3 34	..	..	..	..	..
69		2 51	3 1	..	..	..	..	3 6	3 12	..	..		..	..	..	..	..	3 20	..	..	..	..	3 36	..	..	..	..	..
70		2 54	3 4	..	..	..	..	3 9	3 15	..	..		..	..	..	..	..	3 23	..	..	..	..	3 39	..	..	..	..	..
71		..	..	..	..	3 0	..	..	..	..	3 11		3 3	..	..	3 15	..	..	..	..	3 30	..	..	..	..	3 41	3 27	..
72		..	..	..	..	3 2	..	..	..	..	3 13		3 5	..	..	3 17	..	..	..	..	3 32	..	..	..	..	3 43	3 29	..
73	2 32	..	..	..	3 0	3 5	..	..	..	..	3 16	2 52	3 10	..	..	3 20	3 14	..	..	..	3 35	..	..	..	..	3 46	3 32	..
74	..	..	..	..	..	..	..	..	..	..	3 19	..	..	..	..	..	..	..	..	..	..	..	..	..	..	3 49	..	..
75	..	2 58	3 8	..	..	..	3 10	3 13	3 19	..	..	..	..	3 24	..	..	..	3 27	..	3 39	..	3 40	3 43	..	3 45	..	..	3 54
76	2 39	..	..	..	..	..	3 13	..	..	..	..	2 59	..	..	..	..	..	..	..	..	..	3 42	..	..	..	..	..	..
77	..	..	..	..	..	..	3 15	..	..	..	..	..	..	..	..	..	..	..	..	..	..	3 45	..	..	..	..	..	..
78	..	..	..	..	3 6	3 11	..	..	..	..	3 23	..	3 16	..	..	3 26	3 20	..	..	..	3 41	..	..	..	..	3 53	3 38	..

HORSHAM, REIGATE, REDHILL, TATTENHAM CORNER, CATERHAM,

For Notes, see page 317a

Up	No.	p.m							Sundays—continued									p.m					No.
Horsham .... dep	1	3	3	3	..	2§48	3	3	2 49	3	3	..	3	3	3	..	3	3	..	..	3	3	1
Reigate .... "	2	..	..	..	..	3 22	..	..	3	..	..	..	..	..	..	..	..	..	3 40	..	..	..	2
Redhill	3	..	..	..	..	3 29	..	..		..	..	..	..	..	..	..	..	..	3 49	..	..	..	3
Merstham	4	..	..	..	..	3 33	..	..	..	..	..	..	..	..	..	..	..	..	..	..	..	..	4
Coulsdon South	5	..	..	..	..	3 39	..	..	..	..	..	..	..	..	..	..	..	..	..	..	..	..	5
Tattenham Corner. dep	6	..	..	..	..	§ Via Three Bridges	..	3 14	..	..	..	..	..	..	..	..	..	..	..	..	..	..	6
Tadworth N	7	..	..	..	..		..	3 17	..	..	..	..	..	..	..	..	..	..	..	..	..	..	7
Kingswood M	8	..	..	..	..		..	3 20	..	..	..	..	..	..	..	..	..	..	..	..	..	..	8
Chipstead	9	..	..	..	..		..	3 25	..	..	..	..	..	..	..	..	..	..	..	..	..	..	9
Woodmansterne	10	..	..	..	..		..	3 27	..	..	..	..	..	..	..	..	..	..	..	..	..	..	10
Smitham	11	..	..	..	..		..	3 30	..	..	..	..	..	..	..	..	..	..	..	..	..	..	11
Reedham	12	..	..	..	..		..	3 32	..	..	..	..	..	..	..	..	..	..	..	..	..	..	12
Purley 252 .... arr	13	..	..	..	..		..	3 34	..	..	..	..	..	..	..	..	..	..	..	..	..	..	13
Caterham .... dep	14	..	..	..	..	..	..	3 25	..	..	..	..	..	..	..	..	..	..	..	..	..	..	14
Warlingham	15	..	..	..	..	..	..	2 28	..	..	..	..	..	..	..	..	..	..	..	..	..	..	15
Whyteleafe	16	..	..	..	..	..	..	3 30	..	..	..	..	..	..	..	..	..	..	..	..	..	..	16
Kenley	17	..	..	..	..	..	..	3 33	..	..	..	..	..	..	..	..	..	..	..	..	..	..	17
Purley 252 .... arr	18	..	..	..	..	..	..	3 36	..	..	..	..	..	..	..	..	..	..	..	..	..	..	18
Coulsdon North ..... dep	19	..	..	..	..	..	..	..	..	..	..	..	..	..	..	..	..	3 50	..	..	..	..	19
Purley 252	20	..	..	..	..	3 43	..	3 39	..	..	..	..	..	..	..	..	..	3 53	..	..	..	..	20
Purley Oaks	21	..	..	..	..	..	..	3 42	..	..	..	..	..	..	..	..	..	3 55	..	..	..	..	21
South Croydon 234	22	..	..	..	..	..	..	3 44	..	..	..	..	..	..	..	..	..	3 58	..	..	..	..	22
Effingham Junction dep	23	2 54	..	..	..	..	..	..	..	..	..	..	..	..	..	..	3 30	..	..	..	..	..	23
Bookham	24	2 58	..	..	..	..	..	..	..	..	..	..	..	..	..	..	3 33	..	..	..	..	..	24
Dorking North ..... dep	25	..	3 0	..	..	..	..	..	3 15	..	..	..	..	..	..	..	..	..	..	..	..	..	25
Boxhill and Burford	26	..	3 2	..	..	..	..	..	3 17	..	..	..	..	..	..	..	..	..	..	..	..	..	26
Leatherhead ...[Bridge J	27	3 2	3 7	..	..	..	..	..	3 22	..	..	..	..	..	..	..	3 37	..	..	..	..	..	27
Ashtead	28	3 6	3 11	..	..	..	..	..	3 26	..	..	..	..	..	..	..	3 41	..	..	..	..	..	28
Epsom 427	29	3 10	3 15	..	..	..	..	..	3 30	..	..	..	..	3 37	..	..	3 45	..	..	..	..	..	29
Ewell East H	30	..	3 18	..	..	..	..	..	..	..	..	..	..	3 40	..	..	3 48	..	..	..	..	..	30
Cheam	31	..	3 21	..	..	..	..	..	..	..	..	..	..	3 43	..	..	3 51	..	..	..	..	..	31
Epsom Downs .... dep	32	..	..	..	..	..	3 25	..	..	..	..	..	..	..	3 38	..	..	..	..	..	..	3 55	32
Banstead	33	..	..	..	..	..	3 28	..	..	..	..	..	..	..	3 41	..	..	..	..	..	..	3 58	33
Belmont	34	..	..	From London Bridge, via Forest Hill	..	..	3 31	..	..	..	..	..	..	..	3 44	..	..	..	..	..	From London Bridge, via Streatham	4 1	34
Sutton 322	35	..	3 24		..	..	3 34	..	..	..	..	..	3 39	3 48	3 47	..	3 54	..	..	..		4 4	35
Carshalton Beeches	36	..	..		..	..	3 36	..	..	..	..	..	3 42	..	3 49	..	..	..	..	..		4 6	36
Wallington	37	..	..		..	..	3 39	..	..	..	..	..	3 44	..	3 52	..	..	..	..	..		4 9	37
Waddon G	38	..	..		..	..	3 42	..	..	..	..	..	3 48	..	3 55	..	..	..	..	..		4 12	38
West Croydon 319 arr	39	..	..		..	..	3 45	..	..	..	..	..	3 51	..	3 58	..	..	..	..	..		4 15	39
West Croydon 319 dep	40	..	..		..	..	3 45	..	..	..	..	..	3 53	..	3 58	..	..	..	..	..		4 15	40
Carshalton	41	..	3 27		..	..	..	..	..	..	..	..	..	3 51	..	..	3 57	..	..	..		..	41
Hackbridge	42	..	3 30		..	..	..	..	..	..	..	..	..	3 53	..	..	4 0	..	..	..		..	42
Mitcham Junction	43	..	3 32		..	..	..	..	..	..	..	..	..	3 56	..	..	4 2	..	..	..		..	43
East Croydon .... arr	44	..	..		..	3 49	..	3 51	..	..	..	..	..	Arr. Sutton 3 46 p.m	..	..	..	4 1	4 3	..		..	44
East Croydon .... dep	45	..	..		..	3 50	..	3 51	..	..	..	..	..		..	..	..	4 1	4 4	..		..	45
Norwood Junction F ..	46	..	..	3 34	..	..	..	3 55	..	..	..	..	3 57		4 2	..	..	..	..	..	4 17	..	46
Beckenham Jn. dep	47	..	..	..	..	..	..	..	..	3 45	..	..	..		..	..	..	..	..	..	..	..	47
Birkbeck	48	..	..	..	..	..	..	..	..	3 48	..	..	..		..	..	..	..	..	..	..	..	48
Crystal Palace D	49	..	..	..	..	..	..	..	..	3 52	3 55	..	4 1		..	..	..	..	..	..	..	..	49
Gipsy Hill (for Upper	50	..	..	..	..	..	..	..	..	—	3 58	..	4 3		..	..	..	..	..	..	..	..	50
West Norwood.[N'wood)	51	..	..	..	..	..	..	..	..	Stop	4 0	..	4 6	..	..	..	..	..	..	..	..	..	51
Streatham Hill	52	..	..	..	..	..	..	..	..	..	..	..	4 9	..	..	..	..	..	..	..	..	..	52
Selhurst	53	..	..	3 37	..	..	3 48	..	..	From Victoria, dep. 3 50 p.m ☞	..	..	..	..	..	..	..	4 4	..	..	..	4 18	53
Thornton Heath	54	..	..	3 40	..	..	3 50	..	..		..	..	..	..	..	..	..	4 6	..	..	..	4 20	54
Norbury	55	..	..	3 43	..	..	3 53	..	..		..	..	..	..	..	..	..	4 9	..	..	..	4 23	55
Streatham Common	56	..	..	3 46	..	..	3 56	..	..		..	..	..	..	..	..	..	4 11	..	..	..	4 26	56
Anerley	57	..	..	..	..	..	..	..	..		..	..	..	..	4 5	..	..	..	..	..	4 20	..	57
Penge West C	58	..	..	..	..	..	..	..	..		..	..	..	..	4 6	..	..	..	..	..	4 21	..	58
Sydenham ....[Lane	59	..	..	..	..	..	..	..	..		..	..	..	..	4 8	..	..	..	..	..	4 23	..	59
Forest Hill, for Lordship	60	..	..	..	..	..	..	3 59	..		..	..	..	..	4 11	..	..	..	..	..	4 26	..	60
Honor Oak Park	61	..	..	..	..	..	..	..	..		..	..	..	..	4 13	..	..	..	..	..	4 28	..	61
Brockley B ....[Line)	62	..	..	..	..	..	..	..	..		..	..	..	..	4 16	..	..	..	..	..	4 31	..	62
New Cross Gate (for E.L.	63	..	..	..	..	..	..	4 4	..		..	..	..	..	4 18	..	..	..	..	..	4 33	..	63
Streatham	64	Via Worcester Park	3 37	3 48	..	..	..	..	Via Worcester Park	..	..	..	..	..	..	..	4 7	..	..	..	..	..	64
Tulse Hill	65		3 41	3 51	..	..	..	..		p.m	4 3	..	..	..	..	..	4 11	..	..	..	..	..	65
North Dulwich	66		3 44	3 54	..	..	..	..		3	4 6	..	..	..	..	..	4 14	..	..	..	..	..	66
East Dulwich	67		3 46	3 56	..	..	..	..			4 8	..	..	..	..	..	4 16	..	..	..	..	..	67
Peckham Rye	68		3 48	3 59	..	..	..	..		4 4	4 10	..	..	..	..	..	4 18	..	..	..	..	..	68
Queen's Road, Peckham	69		3 50	4 1	..	..	..	..		4 6	4 12	..	..	..	..	..	4 20	..	..	..	..	..	69
South Bermondsey	70		3 53	4 4	..	..	..	..		4 9	4 15	..	..	..	..	..	4 23	..	..	..	..	..	70
Balham & Upper Tooting	71		..	..	..	..	4 0	..		..	..	..	4 11	4 3	..	..	..	4 15	..	..	..	4 30	71
Wandsworth Common A	72		..	..	..	..	4 2	..		..	..	..	4 13	4 5	..	..	..	4 17	..	..	..	4 32	72
Clapham Junction	73	3 32	..	..	..	4 1	4 5	..	3 52	..	..	..	4 16	4 10	..	..	..	4 20	4 14	..	..	4 35	73
Battersea Park	74	..	..	..	..	..	..	..	..	..	..	..	4 19	..	..	..	..	..	..	..	..	..	74
London Bridge ..... arr	75	..	3 57	4 8	..	..	..	4 10	..	4 13	4 19	..	..	..	4 24	..	4 27	..	..	..	4 39	..	75
Waterloo * .... "	76	3 39	..	..	..	..	..	4 13	3 59	..	..	..	..	..	..	..	..	..	..	..	..	..	76
Charing Cross * .. "	77	..	..	..	..	..	..	4 15	..	..	..	..	..	..	..	..	..	..	..	..	..	..	77
Victoria .... "	78	..	..	..	..	4 7	4 11	..	..	..	..	..	4 23	4 16	..	..	..	4 26	4 20	..	..	4 41	78

DORKING NORTH, SUTTON, CROYDON, CRYSTAL PALACE, and LONDON

No.	p.m												Sundays—continued									p.m						
1	3	3	..	3	3	3	3	..	3	3	3	..	3§48	3	..	3	3	3	..	3	3 49	3	3	3	3	..	..	3
2	..	..	..	..	..	..	..	..	..	..	..	..	4 22	..	..	..	..	..	..	..	3	..	..	..	..	..	..	..
3	..	..	..	..	..	..	..	..	..	..	..	..	4 29	..	..	..	..	..	..	..		..	..	..	..	4 49	..	..
4	..	..	..	..	..	..	..	..	..	..	..	..	4 33	..	..	..	..	..	..	..	..	..	..	..	..	..	..	..
5	..	..	..	..	..	..	..	..	..	..	..	..	4 39	..	..	..	..	..	..	..	..	..	..	..	..	..	..	..
6	3 48	..	..	..	..	..	..	..	..	..	..	..	§ Via Three Bridges	..	..	4 14	..	..	..	..	..	..	..	..	..	..	..	..
7	3 51	..	..	..	..	..	..	..	..	..	..	..		..	..	4 17	..	..	..	..	..	..	..	..	..	..	..	..
8	3 54	..	..	..	..	..	..	..	..	..	..	..		..	..	4 20	..	..	..	..	..	..	..	..	..	..	..	..
9	3 59	..	..	..	..	..	..	..	..	..	..	..		..	..	4 25	..	..	..	..	..	..	..	..	..	..	..	..
10	4 1	..	..	..	..	..	..	..	..	..	..	..		..	..	4 27	..	..	..	..	..	..	..	..	..	..	..	..
11	4 4	..	..	..	..	..	..	..	..	..	..	..		..	..	4 30	..	..	..	..	..	..	..	..	..	..	..	..
12	4 6	..	..	..	..	..	..	..	..	..	..	..		..	..	4 32	..	..	..	..	..	..	..	..	..	..	..	..
13	4 9	..	..	..	..	..	..	..	..	..	..	..		..	..	4 34	..	..	..	..	..	..	..	..	..	..	..	..
14	3 59	..	..	..	..	..	..	..	..	..	..	..	..	..	..	4 25	..	..	..	..	..	..	..	..	..	..	..	..
15	4 2	..	..	..	..	..	..	..	..	..	..	..	..	..	..	4 28	..	..	..	..	..	..	..	..	..	..	..	..
16	4 4	..	..	..	..	..	..	..	..	..	..	..	..	..	..	4 30	..	..	..	..	..	..	..	..	..	..	..	..
17	4 7	..	..	..	..	..	..	..	..	..	..	..	..	..	..	4 33	..	..	..	..	..	..	..	..	..	..	..	..
18	4 11	..	..	..	..	..	..	..	..	..	..	..	..	..	..	4 36	..	..	..	..	..	..	..	..	..	..	..	..
19	..	..	..	..	..	..	..	..	..	..	..	..	..	..	..	..	..	..	..	..	..	..	..	..	4 50	..	..	..
20	4 13	..	..	..	..	..	..	..	..	..	..	..	4 43	..	..	4 39	..	..	..	..	..	..	..	..	4 53	..	..	..
21	4 16	..	..	..	..	..	..	..	..	..	..	..	..	..	..	4 42	..	..	..	..	..	..	..	..	4 55	..	..	..
22	4 18	..	..	..	..	..	..	..	..	..	..	..	..	..	..	4 44	..	..	..	..	..	..	..	..	4 58	..	..	..
23	..	..	..	..	..	..	..	..	3 54	..	..	..	..	..	..	..	..	..	..	..	..	..	..	4 30	..	..	..	..
24	..	..	..	..	..	..	..	..	3 58	..	..	..	..	..	..	..	..	..	..	..	..	..	..	4 33	..	..	..	..
25	..	..	..	..	..	..	..	..	..	4 6	..	..	..	..	..	..	..	..	..	..	4 15	..	..	..	..	..	..	..
26	..	..	..	..	..	..	..	..	..	4 8	..	..	..	..	..	..	..	..	..	..	4 17	..	..	..	..	..	..	..
27	..	..	..	..	..	..	..	..	4 2	4 13	..	..	..	..	..	..	..	..	..	..	4 22	..	..	4 37	..	..	..	..
28	..	..	..	..	..	..	..	..	4 6	4 17	..	..	..	..	..	..	..	..	..	..	4 26	..	..	4 41	..	..	..	..
29	..	..	..	..	..	4 3	..	..	4 10	4 21	..	..	..	..	..	..	..	..	..	..	4 30	4 37	..	4 45	..	..	..	..
30	..	..	..	..	..	4 6	..	..	..	4 24	..	..	..	..	..	..	..	..	..	..	..	4 40	..	4 48	..	..	..	..
31	..	..	..	..	..	4 9	..	..	..	4 27	..	..	..	..	..	..	..	..	..	..	..	4 43	..	4 51	..	..	..	..
32	..	..	..	..	..	..	4 8	..	..	..	From London Bridge, via Forest Hill	..	..	4 25	..	..	..	..	..	..	..	..	4 38	..	..	..	..	..
33	..	..	..	..	..	..	4 11	..	..	..		..	..	4 28	..	..	..	..	..	..	..	..	4 41	..	..	..	..	..
34	..	..	..	..	..	..	4 14	..	..	..		..	..	4 31	..	..	..	..	..	..	..	..	4 44	..	..	..	..	..
35	..	..	..	..	4 9	4 12	4 17	..	..	4 30		..	..	4 34	..	..	..	..	..	4 39	..	4 48	4 47	4 54	..	..	..	From London Bridge, via Streatham
36	..	..	..	..	4 12	..	4 19	..	..	..		..	..	4 36	..	..	..	..	..	4 42	..	..	4 49	..	..	..	..	
37	..	..	..	..	4 14	..	4 22	..	..	..		..	..	4 39	..	..	..	..	..	4 44	..	..	4 52	..	..	..	..	
38	..	..	..	..	4 18	..	4 25	..	..	..		..	..	4 42	..	..	..	..	..	4 48	..	..	4 55	..	..	..	..	
39	..	..	..	..	4 23	..	4 28	..	..	..		..	..	4 45	..	..	..	..	..	4 51	..	..	4 58	..	..	..	..	
40	..	..	..	..	4 23	..	4 28	..	..	..		..	..	4 45	..	..	..	..	..	4 53	..	..	4 58	..	..	..	..	
41	..	..	..	..	..	4 15	..	..	..	4 33		..	..	..	..	..	..	..	..	..	..	4 51	..	4 57	..	..	..	
42	..	..	..	..	..	4 18	..	..	..	4 36		..	..	..	..	..	..	..	..	..	..	4 53	..	5 0	..	..	..	
43	..	..	..	..	..	4 20	..	..	..	4 38		..	..	..	..	..	..	..	..	..	..	4 56	..	5 2	..	..	..	
44	4 21	..	..	..	..	..	..	..	..	..		..	4 49	..	..	4 51	..	..	..	..	..	..	..	..	5 1	5 3	..	
45	4 21	..	..	..	..	..	..	..	..	..		4 42	4 50	..	..	4 51	..	..	..	..	..	Arr. Sutton 4 46 p.m	..	..	5 1	5 4	..	
46	4 25	..	..	..	4 27	..	4 32	..	..	..	4 34	..	..	..	..	4 55	..	..	..	4 57	..		5 2	..	..	..	..	5 17
47	..	4 15	..	..	..	..	..	..	..	..	..	..	..	..	..	..	4 45	..	..	..	..		..	..	..	..	..	..
48	..	4 18	..	..	..	..	..	..	..	..	..	..	..	..	..	..	4 48	..	..	..	..		..	..	..	..	..	..
49	..	4 22	..	4 27	4 31	..	..	..	..	..	..	..	..	..	..	..	4 52	4 55	..	5 1	..		..	..	..	..	..	..
50	..	—	..	..	4 33	..	..	..	..	..	..	..	..	..	..	..	—	4 58	..	5 3	..		..	..	..	..	..	..
51	..	Stop	..	..	4 36	..	..	..	..	..	..	..	..	..	..	..	Stop	5 0	..	5 6	..		..	..	..	..	..	..
52	..	From Victoria, dep. 4 20 p.m	..	..	4 39	..	..	..	..	..	..	..	..	..	..	..	From Victoria, dep. 4 50 p.m	..	..	5 9	..	..	..	..	..	..	..	..
53	..		..	..	..	..	..	..	..	..	4 37	..	..	4 48	..	..		..	..	..	..	..	..	..	5 4	..	..	..
54	..		..	..	..	..	..	..	..	..	4 40	..	..	4 50	..	..		..	..	..	..	..	..	..	5 6	..	..	..
55	..		..	..	..	..	..	..	..	..	4 43	..	..	4 53	..	..		..	..	..	..	..	..	..	5 9	..	..	..
56	..		..	..	..	..	..	..	..	..	4 46	..	..	4 56	..	..		..	..	..	..	..	..	..	5 11	..	..	..
57	..		..	..	..	..	4 35	..	..	..	..	..	..	..	..	..		..	..	..	..	..	5 5	..	..	..	..	5 20
58	..		..	..	..	..	4 36	..	..	..	..	..	..	..	..	..		..	..	..	..	..	5 6	..	..	..	..	5 21
59	..		..	4 30	..	..	4 38	..	..	..	..	..	..	..	..	..		..	..	..	..	..	5 8	..	..	..	..	5 23
60	4 29		..	4 32	..	..	4 41	..	..	..	..	..	..	..	..	4 59		..	..	..	..	..	5 11	..	..	..	..	5 26
61	..		..	4 35	..	..	4 43	..	..	..	..	..	..	..	..	..		..	..	..	..	..	5 13	..	..	..	..	5 28
62	..		..	4 37	..	..	4 46	..	..	..	..	..	..	..	..	..		..	..	..	..	..	5 16	..	..	..	..	5 31
63	4 34		..	4 40	..	..	4 48	..	..	..	..	..	..	..	..	5 4		..	..	..	..	..	5 18	..	..	..	..	5 33
64	..		..	..	..	..	..	..	Via Worcester Park	4 42	4 48	..	..	..	..	..		..	..	..	Via Worcester Park	..	..	5 7	..	..	..	..
65	..	p.m	..	..	..	..	..	..		4 47	4 51	..	..	..	..	..	p.m	5 3	..	..		..	..	5 11	..	..	..	..
66	..	3	..	..	..	..	..	..		4 50	4 54	..	..	..	..	..	3	5 6	..	..		..	..	5 14	..	..	..	..
67	..		..	..	..	..	..	..		4 52	4 56	..	..	..	..	..		5 8	..	..		..	..	5 16	..	..	..	..
68	..	4 34	..	..	..	..	..	..		4 54	4 59	..	..	..	..	..	5 4	5 10	..	..		..	..	5 18	..	..	..	..
69	..	4 36	..	..	..	..	..	..		4 56	5 1	..	..	..	..	..	5 6	5 12	..	..		..	..	5 20	..	..	..	..
70	..	4 39	..	..	..	..	..	..		4 59	5 4	..	..	..	..	..	5 9	5 15	..	..		..	..	5 23	..	..	..	..
71	..	..	..	..	4 41	4 27	..	..		..	..	..	..	5 0	..	..	..	..	..	5 11		5 3	..	..	5 15	..	..	..
72	..	..	..	..	4 43	4 29	..	..		..	..	..	..	5 2	..	..	..	..	..	5 13		5 5	..	..	5 17	..	..	..
73	..	..	..	..	4 46	4 32	..	..	4 32	..	..	..	5 1	5 5	..	..	..	..	..	5 16	4 52	5 10	..	..	5 20	5 14	..	..
74	..	..	..	..	4 49	..	..	..	..	..	..	..	..	..	..	..	..	..	..	5 19	..	..	..	..	..	..	..	..
75	4 40	4 43	..	4 45	..	..	4 54	..	..	5 3	5 8	..	..	..	..	5 10	5 13	5 19	..	..	..	..	5 24	5 27	..	..	..	5 39
76	4 42	..	..	..	..	..	..	..	4 39	..	..	..	..	..	..	5 13	..	..	..	..	5 9	..	..	..	..	..	..	..
77	4 45	..	..	..	..	..	..	..	..	..	..	..	..	..	..	5 15	..	..	..	..	..	..	..	..	..	..	..	..
78	..	..	..	..	4 53	4 38	..	..	..	..	..	4 57	5 7	5 11	..	..	..	..	..	5 23	..	5 16	..	..	5 26	5 20	..	..

For Notes, see page 317a

HORSHAM, REIGATE, REDHILL, TATTENHAM CORNER, CATERHAM,

Up	No.	p.m	Sundays	— continued														p.m					No.
			3	3	3		3	3	3	3			3	3	3				3	3	3	3	
Horsham .... dep	1	..									4 43	..					..	4§48					1
Reigate .... "	2	..	..	..	..	..	..	..	..	..	..	..	..	..	..	..	..	5 22	..	..	..	..	2
Redhill .... "	3	..	..	..	..	..	..	..	..	..	..	..	..	..	..	..	..	5 29	..	..	..	..	3
Merstham	4	..	..	..	..	..	..	..	..	..	..	..	..	..	..	..	..	5 33	..	..	..	..	4
Coulsdon South	5	..	..	..	..	..	..	..	..	..	..	..	..	..	..	..	..	5 39	..	..	..	..	5
Tattenham Corner. dep	6	..	..	4 48	..	..	..	..	..	..	..	..	..	..	..	..	..	§ Via Three Bridges	..	5 14	..	..	6
Tadworth N	7	..	..	4 51	..	..	..	..	..	..	..	..	..	..	..	..	..		..	5 17	..	..	7
Kingswood M	8	..	..	4 54	..	..	..	..	..	..	..	..	..	..	..	..	..		..	5 20	..	..	8
Chipstead	9	..	..	4 59	..	..	..	..	..	..	..	..	..	..	..	..	..		..	5 25	..	..	9
Woodmansterne	10	..	..	5 1	..	..	..	..	..	..	..	..	..	..	..	..	..		..	5 27	..	..	10
Smitham	11	..	..	5 4	..	..	..	..	..	..	..	..	..	..	..	..	..		..	5 30	..	..	11
Reedham	12	..	..	5 6	..	..	..	..	..	..	..	..	..	..	..	..	..		..	5 32	..	..	12
Purley 252 .... arr	13	..	..	5 9	..	..	..	..	..	..	..	..	..	..	..	..	..		..	5 34	..	..	13
Caterham .... dep	14	..	..	4 59	..	..	..	..	..	..	..	..	..	..	..	..	..	..	..	5 25	..	..	14
Warlingham	15	..	..	5 2	..	..	..	..	..	..	..	..	..	..	..	..	..	..	..	5 28	..	..	15
Whyteleafe	16	..	..	5 4	..	..	..	..	..	..	..	..	..	..	..	..	..	..	..	5 30	..	..	16
Kenley	17	..	..	5 7	..	..	..	..	..	..	..	..	..	..	..	..	..	..	..	5 33	..	..	17
Purley 252 .... arr	18	..	..	5 11	..	..	..	..	..	..	..	..	..	..	..	..	..	..	..	5 36	..	..	18
Coulsdon North ..... dep	19	..	..	..	..	..	..	..	..	..	..	..	..	..	..	..	..	..	..	..	..	..	19
Purley 252	20	..	..	5 13	..	..	..	..	..	..	..	..	..	..	..	..	..	5 43	..	5 39	..	..	20
Purley Oaks	21	..	..	5 16	..	..	..	..	..	..	..	..	..	..	..	..	..	..	..	5 42	..	..	21
South Croydon 234	22	5 13	..	5 18	..	..	..	..	..	..	..	..	..	..	..	..	..	..	..	5 44	..	..	22
Effingham Junction dep	23	..	..	..	..	..	..	..	..	..	..	..	4 54	..	..	..	..	..	..	..	..	..	23
Bookham	24	..	..	..	..	..	..	..	..	..	..	..	4 58	..	..	..	..	..	..	..	..	..	24
Dorking North ..... dep	25	..	..	..	..	..	..	..	..	..	5 2	..	..	5 6	..	..	..	..	..	..	..	..	25
Boxhill and Burford	26	..	..	..	..	..	..	..	..	..	..	..	..	5 8	..	..	..	..	..	..	..	..	26
Leatherhead...[Bridge J	27	..	..	..	..	..	..	..	..	..	..	..	5 2	5 13	..	..	..	..	..	..	..	..	27
Ashtead	28	..	..	..	..	..	..	..	..	..	..	..	5 6	5 17	..	..	..	..	..	..	..	..	28
Epsom 427	29	..	..	..	..	..	..	..	5 3	..	..	..	5 10	5 21	..	..	..	..	..	..	..	..	29
Ewell East H	30	..	..	..	..	..	..	..	5 6	..	..	..	..	5 24	..	..	..	..	..	..	..	..	30
Cheam	31	..	..	..	..	..	..	..	5 9	..	..	..	..	5 27	..	..	..	..	..	..	..	..	31
Epsom Downs ...... dep	32	..	4 55	..	..	..	..	..	..	5 8	..	..	..	..	..	..	..	..	5 25	..	..	..	32
Banstead	33	..	4 58	..	..	..	..	..	..	5 11	..	..	..	..	..	..	..	..	5 28	..	..	..	33
Belmont	34	..	5 1	..	..	..	..	..	..	5 14	..	..	..	..	..	..	..	..	5 31	..	..	..	34
Sutton 322	35	..	5 4	..	..	..	..	5 9	5 12	5 17	5 23	..	..	5 30	From London Bridge, via Forest Hill	..	..	..	5 34	..	..	..	35
Carshalton Beeches	36	..	5 6	..	..	..	..	5 12	..	5 19	Arr. Sutton 5 20 p.m	..	..	..		..	..	..	5 36	..	..	..	36
Wallington	37	..	5 9	..	..	..	..	5 14	..	5 22		..	..	..		..	..	..	5 39	..	..	..	37
Waddon G	38	..	5 12	..	..	..	..	5 18	..	5 25		..	..	..		..	..	..	5 42	..	..	..	38
West Croydon 319 arr	39	..	5 15	..	..	..	..	5 23	..	5 28		..	..	..		..	..	..	5 45	..	..	..	39
West Croydon 319 dep	40	..	5 15	..	..	..	..	5 23	..	5 28		..	..	..		..	..	..	5 45	..	..	..	40
Carshalton	41	..	..	..	..	..	..	..	5 15	..		..	..	5 33		..	..	..	..	..	..	..	41
Hackbridge	42	..	..	..	..	..	..	..	5 18	..		..	..	5 36		..	..	..	..	..	..	..	42
Mitcham Junction	43	..	..	..	..	..	..	..	5 20	..	..	..	..	5 38		..	..	..	..	..	..	..	43
East Croydon .... arr	44	5 19	..	5 21	..	..	..	..	..	..	..	..	..	..		..	..	5 49	..	5 51	..	..	44
East Croydon .... dep	45	5 19	..	5 21	..	..	..	..	..	..	..	..	..	..		..	5 47	5 50	..	5 51	..	..	45
Norwood Junction F ..	46	..	..	5 25	..	..	..	5 27	..	5 32	..	..	..	..	5 34	..	..	..	..	5 55	..	..	46
Beckenham Jn. dep	47	..	..	..	5 15	..	..	..	..	..	..	..	..	..	..	..	..	..	..	..	5 45	..	47
Birkbeck	48	..	..	..	5 18	..	..	..	..	..	..	..	..	..	..	..	..	..	..	..	5 48	..	48
Crystal Palace D	49	..	..	..	5 22	..	5 27	5 31	..	..	..	..	..	..	..	..	..	..	..	..	5 52	5 55	49
Gipsy Hill (for Upper	50	..	..	..		..	..	5 33	..	..	..	..	..	..	..	..	..	..	..	..		5 58	50
West Norwood. [N'wood)	51	..	..	..	Stop	..	..	5 36	..	..	..	..	..	..	..	..	..	..	..	..	Stop	6 0	51
Streatham Hill	52	..	..	..		..	..	5 39	..	..	..	..	..	..	..	..	..	..	..	..		..	52
Selhurst	53	..	5 18	..	From Victoria, dep. 5 20 p.m	..	..	..	..	..	..	..	..	..	5 37	..	..	..	5 48	..	From Victoria, dep. 5 50 p.m	..	53
Thornton Heath	54	..	5 20	..		..	..	..	..	..	..	..	..	..	5 40	..	..	..	5 50	..		..	54
Norbury	55	..	5 23	..		..	..	..	..	..	..	..	..	..	5 43	..	..	..	5 53	..		..	55
Streatham Common	56	..	5 26	..		..	..	..	..	..	..	..	..	..	5 46	..	..	..	5 56	..		..	56
Anerley	57	..	..	..		..	..	..	..	5 35	..	..	..	..	..	..	..	..	..	..		..	57
Penge West C	58	..	..	..		..	..	..	..	5 36	..	..	..	..	..	..	..	..	..	..		..	58
Sydenham .... [Lane	59	..	..	..		..	5 30	..	..	5 38	..	..	..	..	..	..	..	..	..	..		..	59
Forest Hill, for Lordship	60	..	..	5 29		..	5 32	..	..	5 41	..	..	..	..	..	..	..	..	..	5 59		..	60
Honor Oak Park	61	..	..	..		..	5 35	..	..	5 43	..	..	..	..	..	..	..	..	..	..		..	61
Brockley B .... [Line)	62	..	..	..		..	5 37	..	..	5 46	..	..	..	..	..	..	..	..	..	..		..	62
New Cross Gate (for E.L.	63	..	..	5 34		..	5 40	..	..	5 48	..	..	..	..	..	..	..	..	..	6 4		..	63
Streatham	64	..	..	..		..	..	..	..	..	..	..	Via Worcester Park	5 43	5 48	..	..	..	..	..		..	64
Tulse Hill	65	..	..	..	p.m	..	..	..	..	..	..	..		5 47	5 51	..	..	..	..	..	p.m	6 3	65
North Dulwich	66	..	..	..	3	..	..	..	..	..	..	..		5 50	5 54	..	..	..	..	..	3	6 6	66
East Dulwich	67	..	..	..		..	..	..	..	..	..	..		5 52	5 56	..	..	..	..	..		6 8	67
Peckham Rye.	68	..	..	..	5 34	..	..	..	..	..	..	..		5 54	5 59	..	..	..	..	..	6 4	6 10	68
Queen's Road, Peckham	69	..	..	..	5 36	..	..	..	..	..	..	..		5 56	6 1	..	..	..	..	..	6 6	6 12	69
South Bermondsey	70	..	..	..	5 39	..	..	..	..	..	..	..		5 59	6 4	..	..	..	..	..	6 9	6 15	70
Balham & Upper Tooting	71	..	5 30	..	..	..	..	5 41	5 27	..	..	..		..	..	..	..	..	6 0	..	..	..	71
Wandsworth Common A	72	..	5 32	..	..	..	..	5 43	5 29	..	..	..		..	..	..	..	..	6 2	..	..	..	72
Clapham Junction	73	5 31	5 35	..	..	..	..	5 46	5 32	..	..	..	5 32	..	..	..	..	6 1	6 5	..	..	..	73
Battersea Park	74	..	..	..	..	..	..	5 49	..	..	..	..	..	..	..	..	..	..	..	..	..	..	74
LONDON BRIDGE ..... arr	75	..	..	5 40	5 43	..	5 45	..	..	5 54	..	..	..	6 3	6 8	..	..	..	..	6 10	6 13	6 19	75
WATERLOO * .... "	76	..	..	5 42	..	..	..	..	..	..	..	..	5 39	..	..	..	..	..	..	6 13	..	..	76
CHARING CROSS * .. "	77	..	..	5 45	..	..	..	..	..	..	..	..	..	..	..	..	..	..	..	6 15	..	..	77
VICTORIA .... "	78	5 38	5 41	..	..	..	..	5 53	5 38	..	5 44	..	..	..	..	..	6 2	6 7	6 11	..	..	..	78

DORKING NORTH, SUTTON, CROYDON, CRYSTAL PALACE, and LONDON

Sundays—continued (p.m.)

No.	3		3	3		3	3			3		3	3	3		3	3	3	3	3	3	3					3	3
1		4 49																								5§48		
2		3																						6 3		6 22		
3								5 49																6a8		6 29		
4																								a Arrival time		6 33		
5																										6 39		
6													5 48													§ Via Three Bridges		6 14
7													5 51															6 17
8													5 54															6 20
9													5 59															6 25
10													6 1											Stop				6 27
11													6 4															6 30
12													6 6															6 32
13													6 9															6 34
14													5 59															6 25
15													6 2															6 28
16													6 4															6 30
17													6 7															6 33
18													6 11															6 36
19							5 50																					
20							5 53						6 14													6 43		6 39
21							5 55						6 16															6 42
22							5 58						6 19															6 44
23						5 30														5 54								
24						5 33														5 58								
25		5 15																			6 0							
26		5 17																			6 2							
27		5 22				5 37														6 2	6 7							
28		5 26				5 41														6 6	6 11							
29		5 30	5 37			5 45												6 3		6 10	6 15							
30			5 40			5 48												6 6			6 18							
31			5 43			5 51												6 9			6 21							
32				5 38								5 55							6 8								6 25	
33				5 41								5 58							6 11								6 28	
34				5 44								6 1							6 14								6 31	
35	5 39		5 48	5 47		5 54				From London Bridge, via Streatham		6 4					6 9	6 12	6 17		6 24	From London Bridge, via Forest Hill					6 34	
36	5 42			5 49								6 6					6 12		6 19								6 36	
37	5 44			5 52								6 9					6 14		6 22								6 39	
38	5 48			5 55								6 12					6 18		6 25								6 42	
39	5 51			5 58								6 15					6 23		6 28								6 45	
40	5 53			5 58								6 15					6 23		6 28								6 45	
41			5 51			5 57												6 15			6 27							
42			5 53			6 0												6 18			6 30							
43			5 56			6 2												6 20			6 32							
44			Arr. Sutton 5 46 p.m				6 1	6 5					6 22											p.m		6 49		6 51
45							6 1	6 5					6 22											6 42	6 47	6 50		6 51
46	5 57			6 2						6 17			6 25				6 27		6 32			6 34						6 55
47														6 15														
48														6 18														
49	6 1													6 22		6 27	6 31											
50	6 3													Stop			6 33											
51	6 6																6 36											
52	6 9													From Victoria, dep. 6 20 p.m			6 39											
53							6 4					6 18										6 37					6 48	
54							6 6					6 20										6 40					6 50	
55							6 9					6 23										6 43					6 53	
56							6 11					6 26										6 46					6 56	
57				6 5						6 20									6 35									
58				6 6						6 21									6 36									
59				6 8						6 23						6 30			6 38									
60				6 11						6 26			6 29			6 32			6 41									6 59
61				6 13						6 28						6 35			6 43									
62				6 16						6 31						6 37			6 46									
63				6 18						6 33			6 34			6 40			6 48									7 4
64		Via Worcester Park				6 7														Via Worcester Park	6 37	6 48						
65						6 11								p.m							6 41	6 51						
66						6 14								3							6 44	6 54						
67						6 16															6 46	6 56						
68						6 18								6 34							6 48	6 59						
69						6 20								6 36							6 50	7 1						
70						6 23								6 39							6 53	7 4						
71	6 11		6 3				6 15					6 30					6 41	6 27									7 0	
72	6 13		6 5				6 17					6 32					6 43	6 29									7 2	
73	6 16	5 52	6 10				6 20	6 16				6 35					6 46	6 32		6 32						7 1	7 5	
74	6 19																6 49											
75				6 24		6 27				6 39			6 40	6 43		6 45			6 54		6 57	7 8						7 10
76		5 59											6 42							6 39								7 13
77													6 46															7 15
78	6 23		6 16				6 26	6 21				6 41					6 53	6 38						6 57	7 3	7 7	7 11	

For Notes, see page 317a

HORSHAM, REIGATE, REDHILL, TATTENHAM CORNER, CATERHAM,

Up	No.	p.m.						Sundays—*continued*									p.m.						No.
		③	③	..	③	..		③	③	③	③	..	..	③	③	..	③	③	③	..	③	③	
Horsham .... dep	1	..	..	..	..	..	5 49	..	..	..	..	..	..	..	..	..	..	..	..	..	..	..	1
Reigate .... "	2	..	..	..	..	..	③	..	..	..	..	..	..	..	..	6 50	..	..	..	..	..	..	2
Redhill .... "	3	..	..	..	..	..		..	..	..	..	..	6 50	..	..	6 57	..	..	..	..	..	..	3
Merstham	4	..	..	..	..	..	..	..	..	..	..	..	..	..	..	7 1	..	..	..	..	..	..	4
Coulsdon South	5	..	..	..	..	..	..	..	..	..	..	..	..	..	..	7 7	..	..	..	..	..	..	5
Tattenham Corner dep	6	..	..	..	..	..	..	..	..	..	..	..	..	..	..	..	6 48	..	..	..	..	..	6
Tadworth **N**	7	..	..	..	..	..	..	..	..	..	..	..	..	..	..	..	6 51	..	..	..	..	..	7
Kingswood **M**	8	..	..	..	..	..	..	..	..	..	..	..	..	..	..	..	6 54	..	..	..	..	..	8
Chipstead	9	..	..	..	..	..	..	..	..	..	..	..	..	..	..	..	6 59	..	..	..	..	..	9
Woodmansterne	10	..	..	..	..	..	..	..	..	..	..	..	..	..	..	..	7 1	..	..	..	..	..	10
Smitham	11	..	..	..	..	..	..	..	..	..	..	..	..	..	..	..	7 4	..	..	..	..	..	11
Reedham	12	..	..	..	..	..	..	..	..	..	..	..	..	..	..	..	7 6	..	..	..	..	..	12
Purley 252 .... arr	13	..	..	..	..	..	..	..	..	..	..	..	..	..	..	..	7 9	..	..	..	..	..	13
Caterham .... dep	14	..	..	..	..	..	..	..	..	..	..	..	..	..	..	..	6 59	..	..	..	..	..	14
Warlingham	15	..	..	..	..	..	..	..	..	..	..	..	..	..	..	..	7 2	..	..	..	..	..	15
Whyteleafe	16	..	..	..	..	..	..	..	..	..	..	..	..	..	..	..	7 4	..	..	..	..	..	16
Kenley	17	..	..	..	..	..	..	..	..	..	..	..	..	..	..	..	7 7	..	..	..	..	..	17
Purley 252 .... arr	18	..	..	..	..	..	..	..	..	..	..	..	..	..	..	..	7 11	..	..	..	..	..	18
Coulsdon North ..... dep	19	..	..	..	..	..	..	..	..	..	6 50	..	..	..	..	..	..	..	..	..	..	..	19
Purley 252	20	..	..	..	..	..	..	..	..	..	6 53	..	..	..	..	7 11	7 13	..	..	..	..	..	20
Purley Oaks	21	..	..	..	..	..	..	..	..	..	6 55	..	..	..	..	..	7 16	..	..	..	..	..	21
South Croydon 234	22	..	..	..	..	..	..	..	..	..	6 58	..	..	..	..	..	7 18	..	..	..	..	..	22
Effingham Junction dep	23	..	..	..	..	..	..	..	..	6 30	..	..	..	..	..	..	..	..	..	..	..	..	23
Bookham	24	..	..	..	..	..	..	..	..	6 33	..	..	..	..	..	..	..	..	..	..	..	..	24
Dorking North ...... dep	25	..	..	..	..	..	6 15	..	..	..	..	..	..	..	..	..	..	..	..	..	..	..	25
Boxhill and Burford	26	..	..	..	..	..	6 17	..	..	..	..	..	..	..	..	..	..	..	..	..	..	..	26
Leatherhead ... [Bridge **J**	27	..	..	..	..	..	6 22	..	..	6 37	..	..	..	..	..	..	..	..	..	..	..	..	27
Ashtead	28	..	..	..	..	..	6 26	..	..	6 41	..	..	..	..	..	..	..	..	..	..	..	..	28
Epsom 427	29	..	..	..	..	..	6 30	6 37	..	6 45	..	..	..	..	..	..	..	..	..	..	..	7 3	29
Ewell East **H**	30	..	..	..	..	..	..	6 40	..	6 48	..	..	..	..	..	..	..	..	..	..	..	7 6	30
Cheam	31	..	..	..	..	..	..	6 43	..	6 51	..	..	..	..	..	..	..	..	..	..	..	7 9	31
Epsom Downs ...... dep	32	..	..	..	..	..	..	..	6 38	..	..	..	..	6 55	..	..	..	..	..	..	..	..	32
Banstead	33	..	..	..	..	..	..	..	6 41	..	..	..	..	6 58	..	..	..	..	..	..	..	..	33
Belmont	34	..	..	..	..	..	..	..	6 44	..	..	..	..	7 1	..	..	..	..	..	..	..	..	34
Sutton 322	35	..	..	..	6 39	..	..	6 48	6 47	6 54	..	..	..	7 4	From London Bridge, via Streatham	..	..	..	..	..	7 9	7 12	35
Carshalton Beeches	36	..	..	..	6 42	..	..	..	6 49	..	..	..	..	7 6		..	..	..	..	..	7 12	..	36
Wallington	37	..	..	..	6 44	..	..	..	6 52	..	..	..	..	7 9		..	..	..	..	..	7 14	..	37
Waddon **G**	38	..	..	..	6 48	..	..	..	6 55	..	..	..	..	7 12		..	..	..	..	..	7 18	..	38
West Croydon 319 arr	39	..	..	..	6 51	..	..	..	6 58	..	..	..	..	7 15		..	..	..	..	..	7 23	..	39
West Croydon 319 dep	40	..	..	..	6 53	..	..	..	6 58	..	..	..	..	7 15		..	..	..	..	..	7 23	..	40
Carshalton	41	..	..	..	..	..	..	6 51	..	6 57	..	..	..	..		..	..	..	..	..	..	7 15	41
Hackbridge	42	..	..	..	..	..	..	6 53	..	7 0	..	..	..	..		..	..	..	..	..	..	7 18	42
Mitcham Junction	43	..	..	..	..	..	..	6 56	..	7 2	..	..	..	..		..	..	..	..	..	..	7 20	43
East Croydon .. arr	44	..	..	..	..	..	..	Arr. Sutton 6 46 p.m	..	..	7 1	..	7 5	..		7 16	7 21	..	..	..	..	..	44
East Croydon .. dep	45	..	..	..	..	..	..		..	..	7 1	..	7 5	..	..	7 17	7 21	..	..	..	..	..	45
Norwood Junction F ..	46	..	..	..	6 57	..	..		7 2	..	..	..	..	..	7 17	7 21	7 25	..	..	..	7 27	..	46
Beckenham Jn. dep	47	6 45	..	..	..	..	..		..	..	..	..	..	..	..	..	..	7 15	..	..	..	..	47
Birkbeck	48	6 48	..	..	..	..	..		..	..	..	..	..	..	..	..	..	7 18	..	..	..	..	48
Crystal Palace D	49	6 52	6 55	..	7 1	..	..		..	..	..	..	..	..	..	..	..	7 22	7 27	..	7 31	..	49
Gipsy Hill (for Upper	50	—	6 58	..	7 3	..	..		..	..	..	..	..	..	..	..	..	—	..	..	7 33	..	50
West Norwood. [N'wood)	51	Stop	7 0	..	7 6	..	..	..	..	..	..	..	..	..	..	..	..	Stop	..	..	7 36	..	51
Streatham Hill	52	From Victoria, dep. 6 50 p.m	..	..	7 9	..	..	..	..	..	..	..	..	..	..	..	..	From Victoria, dep. 7 20 p.m	..	..	7 41	..	52
Selhurst	53		..	..	..	..	..	..	..	..	7 4	..	..	7 18	..	..	..		..	..	..	..	53
Thornton Heath	54		..	..	..	..	..	..	..	..	7 6	..	..	7 20	..	..	..		..	..	..	..	54
Norbury	55		..	..	..	..	..	..	..	..	7 9	..	..	7 23	..	..	..		..	..	..	..	55
Streatham Common	56		..	..	..	..	..	..	..	..	7 11	..	..	7 26	..	..	..		..	..	..	..	56
Anerley	57		..	..	..	..	..	..	7 5	..	..	..	..	..	7 20	..	..		..	..	..	..	57
Penge West **C**	58		..	..	..	..	..	..	7 6	..	..	..	..	..	7 21	..	..		..	..	..	..	58
Sydenham .... [Lane	59		..	..	..	..	..	..	7 8	..	..	..	..	..	7 23	..	..		7 30	..	..	..	59
Forest Hill, for Lordship	60		..	..	..	..	..	..	7 11	..	..	..	..	..	7 26	..	7 29		7 32	..	..	..	60
Honor Oak Park	61		..	..	..	..	..	..	7 13	..	..	..	..	..	7 28	..	..		7 35	..	..	..	61
Brockley **B** .... [Line)	62		..	..	..	..	..	..	7 16	..	..	..	..	..	7 31	..	..		7 37	..	..	..	62
New Cross Gate (for E.L.	63		..	..	..	..	..	..	7 18	..	..	..	..	..	7 33	7 30	7 34		7 40	..	..	..	63
Streatham	64		..	..	..	..	..	..	..	7 7	..	..	..	..	..	..	..		..	..	..	..	64
Tulse Hill	65	p.m	7 3	..	..	..	Via Worcester Park	..	..	7 11	..	..	..	..	..	..	..	p.m	..	..	..	..	65
North Dulwich	66	③	7 6	..	..	..		..	..	7 14	..	..	..	..	..	..	..	③	..	..	..	..	66
East Dulwich	67		7 8	..	..	..		..	..	7 16	..	..	..	..	..	..	..		..	..	..	..	67
Peckham Rye	68	7 4	7 10	..	..	..		..	..	7 18	..	..	..	..	..	..	..	7 34	..	..	..	..	68
Queen's Road, Peckham	69	7 6	7 12	..	..	..		..	..	7 20	..	..	..	..	..	..	..	7 36	..	..	..	..	69
South Bermondsey	70	7 9	7 15	..	..	..		..	..	7 23	..	..	..	..	..	..	..	7 39	..	..	..	..	70
Balham & Upper Tooting	71	..	..	..	7 11	..		7 3	..	..	7 15	..	..	7 30	..	..	..	..	..	..	7 43	7 27	71
Wandsworth Common **A**	72	..	..	..	7 13	..		7 5	..	..	7 17	..	..	7 32	..	..	..	..	..	..	7 45	7 29	72
Clapham Junction	73	..	..	..	7 16	..	6 52	7 10	..	..	7 20	..	7 15	7 35	..	..	..	..	..	..	7 48	7 32	73
Battersea Park	74	..	..	..	7 19	..	..	..	..	..	..	..	..	..	..	..	..	..	..	..	7 51	..	74
LONDON BRIDGE* ..... arr	75	7 13	7 19	..	..	..	..	..	7 24	7 27	..	..	..	..	7 39	7 35	7 40	7 43	7 45	..	..	..	75
WATERLOO✻ .... "	76	..	..	..	..	..	6 59	..	..	..	..	..	..	..	..	..	7 43	..	..	..	..	..	76
CHARING CROSS ✻ .. "	77	..	..	..	..	..	..	..	..	..	..	..	..	..	..	..	7 45	..	..	..	..	..	77
VICTORIA .... "	78	..	..	..	7 23	..	..	7 16	..	..	7 26	..	7 21	7 41	..	..	..	..	..	..	7 55	7 38	78

DORKING NORTH, SUTTON, CROYDON, CRYSTAL PALACE, and LONDON

No.						p.m.							Sundays—continued										p.m.					
1	3	6 43		3	3	3					6§46	3	3	3	3		3	6 49	3	3		3	3			3	3	3
2											7 22													7 32				
3											7 29							3						7 50				
4											7 33																	
5											7 39																	
6											§ Via Three Bridges	7 14																7 48
7												7 17																7 51
8												7 20																7 54
9												7 25																7 59
10												7 27																8 1
11												7 30																8 4
12												7 32																8 6
13												7 34																8 9
14												7 25																7 59
15												7 28																8 2
16												7 30																8 4
17												7 33																8 7
18												7 36																8 11
19																							7 50					
20											7 43	7 39											7 53					8 13
21												7 42											7 55					8 16
22												7 44											7 58					8 18
23				6 54																		7 30						
24				6 58																		7 33						
25		7 2			7 6													7 15										
26					7 8													7 17										
27				7 2	7 13													7 22				7 37						
28				7 6	7 17													7 26				7 41						
29				7 10	7 21													7 30	7 37			7 45						
30					7 24														7 40			7 48						
31					7 27														7 43			7 51						
32	7 8												7 25							7 38							7 55	
33	7 11												7 28							7 41							7 58	
34	7 14												7 31							7 44							8 1	
35	7 17	7 23			7 30	From London Bridge, via Forest Hill							7 34				7 39		7 48	7 47		7 54				From London Bridge, via Streatham	8 4	
36	7 19	Arr. Sutton 7 20 p.m.											7 36				7 42			7 49							8 6	
37	7 22												7 39				7 44			7 52							8 9	
38	7 25												7 42				7 48			7 55							8 12	
39	7 28												7 45				7 51			7 58							8 15	
40	7 28												7 45				7 53			7 58							8 15	
41					7 33														7 51			7 57						
42					7 36														7 53			8 0						
43					7 38														7 56			8 2						
44											7 49	7 51							Arr. Sutton 7 46 p.m.				8 1	8 4				8 21
45							7 39			7 48	7 50	7 51									8 0		8 1	8 5				8 21
46	7 32					7 34						7 55					7 57			8 2						8 17		8 25
47														7 45														
48														7 48														
49														7 52	7 55		8 1											
50														—	7 58		8 3											
51														Stop	8 0		8 6											
52																	8 9											
53						7 37							7 48	From Victoria, dep. 7 50 p.m.									8 4				8 18	
54						7 40							7 50										8 6				8 20	
55						7 43							7 53										8 9				8 23	
56						7 46							7 56										8 11				8 26	
57	7 35																			8 5						8 20		
58	7 36																			8 6						8 21		
59	7 38																			8 8						8 23		
60	7 41											7 59								8 11						8 26		8 29
61	7 43																			8 13						8 29		
62	7 46																			8 16						8 31		
63	7 48											8 4								8 18						8 33		8 34
64				Via Worcester Park	7 43	7 48												Via Worcester Park				8 7						
65					7 47	7 51								p.m	8 3							8 11						
66					7 50	7 54								3	8 6							8 14						
67					7 52	7 56									8 8							8 16						
68					7 54	7 59								8 4	8 10							8 18						
69					7 56	8 1								8 6	8 12							8 20						
70					7 59	8 4								8 9	8 15							8 23						
71													8 0				8 11		8 3				8 15				8 30	
72													8 2				8 13		8 5				8 17				8 32	
73				7 32							8 1		8 5				8 16	7 52	8 10		8 13		8 20	8 16			8 35	
74																	8 19											
75	7 54				8 3	8 8						8 10		8 13	8 19					8 24		8 27				8 39		8 40
76				7 39								8 13						7 59										8 43
77												8 15																8 45
78		7 44					7 55			8 3	8 7		8 11				8 23		8 16		8 19		8 26	8 22			8 41	

HORSHAM, REIGATE, REDHILL, TATTENHAM CORNER, CATERHAM,

For Notes, see page 317a

Up	No.	p.m								Sundays—*continued*						p.m							No.
Horsham .... dep	1	..	③	③	..	③	③	③	③	7 43	..	③	③	..	..	③	③	7§48	③	③	..	③	1
Reigate .... "	2	7 57	..	..	..	..	..	..	..	..	..	..	..	..	..	..	..	8 24	..	..	..	..	2
Redhill .... "	3	8 4	..	..	..	..	..	..	..	..	..	..	..	..	..	..	..	8 31	..	..	..	..	3
Merstham	4	8 8	..	..	..	..	..	..	..	..	..	..	..	..	..	..	..	8 36	..	..	..	..	4
Coulsdon South	5	8 14	..	..	..	..	..	..	..	..	..	..	..	..	..	..	..	8 42	..	..	..	..	5
Tattenham Corner. dep	6	..	..	..	..	..	..	..	..	..	..	..	..	..	..	..	8 14	..	..	..	..	..	6
Tadworth **N**	7	..	..	..	..	..	..	..	..	..	..	..	..	..	..	..	8 17	..	..	..	..	..	7
Kingswood **M**	8	..	..	..	..	..	..	..	..	..	..	..	..	..	..	..	8 20	§ Via Three Bridges	..	..	..	..	8
Chipstead	9	..	..	..	..	..	..	..	..	..	..	..	..	..	..	..	8 25		..	..	..	..	9
Woodmansterne	10	..	..	..	..	..	..	..	..	..	..	..	..	..	..	..	8 27		..	..	..	..	10
Smitham	11	..	..	..	..	..	..	..	..	..	..	..	..	..	..	..	8 30		..	..	..	..	11
Reedham	12	..	..	..	..	..	..	..	..	..	..	..	..	..	..	..	8 32		..	..	..	..	12
Purley 252 .... arr	13	..	..	..	..	..	..	..	..	..	..	..	..	..	..	..	8 34		..	..	..	..	13
Caterham .... dep	14	..	..	..	..	..	..	..	..	..	..	..	..	..	..	..	8 25	..	..	..	..	..	14
Warlingham	15	..	..	..	..	..	..	..	..	..	..	..	..	..	..	..	8 28	..	..	..	..	..	15
Whyteleafe	16	..	..	..	..	..	..	..	..	..	..	..	..	..	..	..	8 30	..	..	..	..	..	16
Kenley	17	..	..	..	..	..	..	..	..	..	..	..	..	..	..	..	8 33	..	..	..	..	..	17
Purley 252 .... arr	18	..	..	..	..	..	..	..	..	..	..	..	..	..	..	..	8 36	..	..	..	..	..	18
Coulsdon North ..... dep	19	..	..	..	..	..	..	..	..	..	..	..	..	..	..	..	..	..	..	..	..	..	19
Purley 252	20	8 18	..	..	..	..	..	..	..	..	..	..	..	..	..	..	8 39	8 47	..	..	..	..	20
Purley Oaks	21	..	..	..	..	..	..	..	..	..	..	..	..	..	..	..	8 42	..	..	..	..	..	21
South Croydon 234	22	..	..	..	..	..	..	..	..	..	..	..	..	..	..	..	8 44	..	..	..	..	..	22
Effingham Junction dep	23	..	..	..	..	..	..	..	7 54	..	..	..	..	..	..	..	..	..	..	..	..	..	23
Bookham	24	..	..	..	..	..	..	..	7 58	..	..	..	..	..	..	..	..	..	..	..	..	..	24
Dorking North ..... dep	25	..	..	..	..	..	..	..	..	8 2	..	8 7	..	..	..	..	..	..	..	..	..	..	25
Boxhill and Burford	26	..	..	..	..	..	..	..	..	..	..	8 9	..	..	..	..	..	..	..	..	..	..	26
Leatherhead ... [Bridge **J**	27	..	..	..	..	..	..	..	8 2	..	..	8 14	..	..	..	..	..	..	..	..	..	..	27
Ashtead	28	..	..	..	..	..	..	..	8 6	..	..	8 18	..	..	..	..	..	..	..	..	..	..	28
Epsom 427	29	..	..	..	..	..	8 3	..	8 10	..	..	8 22	..	..	..	..	..	..	..	..	..	..	29
Ewell East **H**	30	..	..	..	..	..	8 6	..	..	..	..	8 25	..	..	..	..	..	..	..	..	..	..	30
Cheam	31	..	..	..	..	..	8 9	..	..	..	..	8 28	..	..	..	..	..	..	..	..	..	..	31
Epsom Downs ...... dep	32	..	..	..	..	..	..	8 8	..	..	..	..	..	..	..	8 25	..	..	..	..	..	..	32
Banstead	33	..	..	..	..	..	..	8 11	..	..	..	..	..	..	..	8 28	..	..	..	..	..	..	33
Belmont	34	..	..	..	..	..	..	8 14	..	..	..	..	..	..	..	8 31	..	..	..	..	..	..	34
Sutton 322	35	..	..	..	..	8 9	8 12	8 17	..	8 23	..	8 31	From London Bridge, via Forest Hill	..	..	8 34	..	..	..	..	..	8 39	35
Carshalton Beeches	36	..	..	..	..	8 12	..	8 19	..	Arr Sutton 8 20 p.m	..	..		..	..	8 36	..	..	..	..	..	8 42	36
Wallington	37	..	..	..	..	8 14	..	8 22	..		..	..		..	..	8 39	..	..	..	..	..	8 44	37
Waddon **G**	38	..	..	..	..	8 18	..	8 25	..		..	..		..	..	8 42	..	..	..	..	..	8 48	38
West Croydon 319 arr	39	..	..	..	..	8 23	..	8 28	..		..	..		..	..	8 45	..	..	..	..	..	8 51	39
West Croydon 319 dep	40	..	..	..	..	8 23	..	8 28	..		..	..		..	..	8 45	..	..	..	..	..	8 53	40
Carshalton	41	..	..	..	..	..	8 15	..	..		..	8 34		..	..	..	..	..	..	..	..	..	41
Hackbridge	42	..	..	..	..	..	8 18	..	..		..	8 37		..	..	..	..	..	..	..	..	..	42
Mitcham Junction	43	..	..	..	..	..	8 20	..	..	..	..	8 39		..	..	..	..	..	..	..	..	..	43
East Croydon .... arr	44	8 24	..	..	..	..	..	..	..	..	..	..		..	..	..	8 51	8 53	..	..	..	..	44
East Croydon .... dep	45	8 25	..	..	..	..	..	..	..	..	..	..		8 47	8 48	..	8 51	8 54	..	..	..	..	45
Norwood Junction F ..	46	8 30	..	..	..	8 27	..	8 32	..	..	..	..	8 35	..	..	..	8 55	..	..	..	..	8 57	46
Beckenham Jn. dep	47	..	8 15	..	..	..	..	..	..	..	..	..	..	..	..	..	..	..	8 45	..	..	..	47
Birkbeck	48	..	8 18	..	..	..	..	..	..	..	..	..	..	..	..	..	..	..	8 48	..	..	..	48
Crystal Palace D	49	..	8 22	8 27	..	8 31	..	..	..	..	..	..	..	..	..	..	..	..	8 52	8 55	..	9 1	49
Gipsy Hill (for Upper	50	..	—	..	..	8 33	..	..	..	..	..	..	..	..	..	..	..	..	—	8 58	..	9 3	50
West Norwood. [N'wood)	51	..	Stop	..	..	8 36	..	..	..	..	..	..	..	..	..	..	..	..	Stop	9 0	..	9 6	51
Streatham Hill	52	..	From Victoria, dep. 8 20 p.m ☞	..	..	8 39	..	..	..	..	..	..	..	..	..	..	..	..	From Victoria, dep. 8 50 p.m ☞	..	..	9 9	52
Selhurst	53	..		..	..	..	..	..	..	..	..	..	8 37	..	..	8 48	..	..		..	..	..	53
Thornton Heath	54	..		..	..	..	..	..	..	..	..	..	8 40	..	..	8 50	..	..		..	..	..	54
Norbury	55	..		..	..	..	..	..	..	..	..	..	8 43	..	..	8 53	..	..		..	..	..	55
Streatham Common	56	..		..	..	..	..	..	..	..	..	..	8 46	..	..	8 56	..	..		..	..	..	56
Anerley	57	..		..	..	..	..	8 35	..	..	..	..	..	..	..	..	..	..		..	..	..	57
Penge West **C**	58	..		..	..	..	..	8 36	..	..	..	..	..	..	..	..	..	..		..	..	..	58
Sydenham .... [Lane	59	..		8 30	..	..	..	8 38	..	..	..	..	..	..	..	..	..	..		..	..	..	59
Forest Hill, for Lordship	60	..		8 32	..	..	..	8 41	..	..	..	..	..	..	..	..	8 59	..		..	..	..	60
Honor Oak Park	61	..		8 35	..	..	..	8 43	..	..	..	..	..	..	..	..	..	..		..	..	..	61
Brockley **B** .... [Line)	62	..		8 37	..	..	..	8 46	..	..	..	..	..	..	..	..	..	..		..	..	..	62
New Cross Gate (for E.L.	63	8 39		8 40	..	..	..	8 48	..	..	..	..	..	..	..	..	9 4	..		..	..	..	63
Streatham	64	..		..	..	..	..	..	..	..	..	8 44	8 48	..	..	..	..	..		..	..	..	64
Tulse Hill	65	..	p.m	..	..	..	..	..	Via Worcester Park	..	..	8 48	8 51	..	..	..	..	..	p.m	9 3	..	..	65
North Dulwich	66	..	③	..	..	..	..	..		..	..	8 51	8 54	..	..	..	..	..	③	9 6	..	..	66
East Dulwich	67	..		..	..	..	..	..		..	..	8 53	8 56	..	..	..	..	..		9 8	..	..	67
Peckham Rye	68	..	8 34	..	..	..	..	..		..	..	8 55	8 59	..	..	..	..	..	9 4	9 10	..	..	68
Queen's Road, Peckham	69	..	8 36	..	..	..	..	..		..	..	8 57	9 1	..	..	..	..	..	9 6	9 12	..	..	69
South Bermondsey	70	..	8 39	..	..	..	..	..		..	..	9 0	9 4	..	..	..	..	..	9 9	9 15	..	..	70
Balham & Upper Tooting	71	..	..	..	..	8 41	8 27	..		..	..	..	..	..	..	9 0	..	..	..	..	..	9 11	71
Wandsworth Common **A**	72	..	..	..	..	8 43	8 29	..		..	..	..	..	..	..	9 2	..	..	..	..	..	9 13	72
Clapham Junction	73	..	..	..	..	8 46	8 32	..	8 32	..	..	..	..	..	9 1	9 5	..	9 7	..	..	..	9 16	73
Battersea Park	74	..	..	..	..	8 49	..	..	..	..	..	..	..	..	..	..	..	..	..	..	..	9 19	74
LONDON BRIDGE ..... arr	75	8 44	8 43	8 45	..	..	..	8 54	..	..	..	9 4	9 8	..	..	..	9 10	..	9 13	9 19	..	..	75
WATERLOO ✻ .... "	76	..	..	..	..	..	..	..	8 39	..	..	..	..	..	..	..	9 13	..	..	..	..	..	76
CHARING CROSS ✻ ... "	77	..	..	..	..	..	..	..	..	..	..	..	..	..	..	..	9 15	..	..	..	..	..	77
VICTORIA .... "	78	..	..	..	..	8 53	8 38	..	..	8 43	..	..	..	9 4	9 8	9 11	..	9 13	..	..	..	9 23	78

DORKING NORTH, SUTTON, CROYDON, CRYSTAL PALACE, and LONDON

p.m — **Sundays**—*continued* — p.m

No.																												
1	7 49	3	3	3	3	..	..	..	3	8§43	3	3	3	..	3	3	3	3	3	3	..	3	3	8§48	3	..	3	3
2	3	..	..	..	..	..	..	..	..	..	..	..	..	..	..	..	..	..	..	..	9 8	..	..	9 22	..	..	..	..
3		..	..	..	..	8 49	..	..	..	..	..	..	..	..	..	..	..	..	..	..	9a13	..	..	9 29	..	..	..	..
4	..	..	..	..	..	..	..	..	..	..	..	..	..	..	..	..	..	..	..	..		..	..	9 33	..	..	..	..
5	..	..	..	..	..	..	..	..	..	..	..	..	..	..	..	..	..	..	..	..		..	..	9 39	..	..	..	..
6	..	..	..	..	..	..	..	..	..	§ Via Three Bridges	..	8 48	..	..	..	..	..	..	..	..	a Arrival time	..	..	§ Via Three Bridges	9 14	..	..	..
7	..	..	..	..	..	..	..	..	..		..	8 51	..	..	..	..	..	..	..	..		..	..		9 17	..	..	..
8	..	..	..	..	..	..	..	..	..		..	8 54	..	..	..	..	..	..	..	..		..	..		9 20	..	..	..
9	..	..	..	..	..	..	..	..	..		..	8 59	..	..	..	..	..	..	..	..		..	..		9 25	..	..	..
10	..	..	..	..	..	..	..	..	..		..	9 1	..	..	..	..	..	..	..	..		..	..		9 27	..	..	..
11	..	..	..	..	..	..	..	..	..		..	9 4	..	..	..	..	..	..	..	..		..	..		9 30	..	..	..
12	..	..	..	..	..	..	..	..	..		..	9 6	..	..	..	..	..	..	..	..	Stop	..	..		9 32	..	..	..
13	..	..	..	..	..	..	..	..	..		..	9 9	..	..	..	..	..	..	..	..	..	..	..		9 34	..	..	..
14	..	..	..	..	..	..	..	..	..	..	..	8 59	..	..	..	..	..	..	..	..	..	..	..	..	9 25	..	..	..
15	..	..	..	..	..	..	..	..	..	..	..	9 2	..	..	..	..	..	..	..	..	..	..	..	..	9 28	..	..	..
16	..	..	..	..	..	..	..	..	..	..	..	9 4	..	..	..	..	..	..	..	..	..	..	..	..	9 30	..	..	..
17	..	..	..	..	..	..	..	..	..	..	..	9 7	..	..	..	..	..	..	..	..	..	..	..	..	9 33	..	..	..
18	..	..	..	..	..	..	..	..	..	..	..	9 11	..	..	..	..	..	..	..	..	..	..	..	..	9 36	..	..	..
19	..	..	..	..	8 50	..	..	..	..	..	..	..	..	..	..	..	..	..	..	..	..	..	..	..	..	..	..	..
20	..	..	..	..	8 53	..	..	..	..	..	..	9 13	..	..	..	..	..	..	..	..	..	..	..	9 42	9 39	..	..	..
21	..	..	..	..	8 55	..	..	..	..	..	..	9 16	..	..	..	..	..	..	..	..	..	..	..	..	9 42	..	..	..
22	..	..	..	..	8 58	..	..	..	..	..	..	9 18	..	..	..	..	..	..	..	..	..	..	..	..	9 44	..	..	..
23	..	..	..	8 30	..	..	..	..	..	..	..	..	..	..	..	..	..	..	8 54	..	..	..	..	..	..	..	..	..
24	..	..	..	8 33	..	..	..	..	..	..	..	..	..	..	..	..	..	..	8 58	..	..	..	..	..	..	..	..	..
25	8 15	..	..	..	..	..	..	..	..	..	..	..	..	..	..	..	..	..	..	9 6	..	..	..	..	..	..	..	..
26	8 17	..	..	..	..	..	..	..	..	..	..	..	..	..	..	..	..	..	..	9 8	..	..	..	..	..	..	..	..
27	8 22	..	..	8 37	..	..	..	..	..	..	..	..	..	..	..	..	..	..	9 2	9 13	..	..	..	..	..	..	..	..
28	8 26	..	..	8 41	..	..	..	..	..	..	..	..	..	..	..	..	..	..	9 6	9 17	..	..	..	..	..	..	..	..
29	8 30	8 37	..	8 45	..	..	..	..	..	..	..	..	..	..	..	..	9 3	..	9 10	9 21	..	..	..	..	..	..	..	..
30	..	8 40	..	8 48	..	..	..	..	..	..	..	..	..	..	..	..	9 6	..	..	9 24	..	..	..	..	..	..	..	..
31	..	8 43	..	8 51	..	..	..	..	..	..	..	..	..	..	..	..	9 9	..	..	9 27	..	..	..	..	..	..	..	..
32	..	..	8 38	..	..	..	..	..	..	..	8 55	..	..	..	..	..	..	9 8	..	..	..	..	9 25	..	..	..	..	..
33	..	..	8 41	..	..	..	..	..	..	..	8 58	..	..	..	..	..	..	9 11	..	..	..	..	9 28	..	..	..	..	..
34	..	..	8 44	..	..	..	..	..	..	..	9 1	..	..	..	..	..	..	9 14	..	..	..	..	9 31	..	..	..	..	..
35	..	8 48	8 47	8 54	..	..	..	..	From London Bridge, via Streatham	..	9 4	..	..	..	..	9 9	9 12	9 17	..	9 30	..	From London Bridge, via Forest Hill	9 34	..	..	..	..	..
36	..	..	8 49	..	..	..	..	..		..	9 6	..	..	..	..	9 12	..	9 19	..	..	..		9 36	..	..	..	..	..
37	..	..	8 52	..	..	..	..	..		..	9 9	..	..	..	..	9 14	..	9 22	..	..	..		9 39	..	..	..	..	..
38	..	..	8 55	..	..	..	..	..		..	9 12	..	..	..	..	9 18	..	9 25	..	..	..		9 42	..	..	..	..	..
39	..	..	8 58	..	..	..	..	..		..	9 15	..	..	..	..	9 23	..	9 28	..	..	..		9 45	..	..	..	..	..
40	..	..	8 58	..	..	..	..	..		..	9 15	..	..	..	..	9 23	..	9 28	..	..	..		9 45	..	..	..	..	..
41	..	8 51	..	8 57	..	..	..	..		..	..	..	..	..	..	..	9 15	..	..	9 33	..		..	..	..	..	..	..
42	..	8 53	..	9 0	..	..	..	..		..	..	..	..	..	..	..	9 18	..	..	9 36	..		..	..	..	..	..	..
43	..	8 56	..	9 2	..	..	..	..		..	..	..	..	..	..	..	9 20	..	..	9 38	..		..	..	..	..	..	..
44	..	Arr. Sutton 8 46 p.m	..	..	9 1	9 4	..	..		9 20	..	9 21	..	..	..	..	..	..	..	..	p.m		..	9 48	9 51	..	..	..
45	..		..	..	9 1	9 4	..	9 5	..	9 23	..	9 21	..	..	..	..	..	..	..	..	9 44	..	..	9 49	9 51	..	..	..
46	..		9 2	..	..	..	..	9 11	9 17	..	..	9 25	..	..	..	9 27	..	9 32	..	..	..	9 34	..	9 52	9 55	..	..	..
47	..		..	..	..	..	..	..	..	..	..	..	9 15	..	..	..	..	..	..	..	..	..	..	..	..	..	..	9 45
48	..		..	..	..	..	..	..	..	..	..	..	9 18	..	..	..	..	..	..	..	..	..	..	..	..	..	..	9 48
49	..		..	..	..	..	..	..	..	..	..	..	9 22	..	9 27	9 31	..	..	..	..	..	..	..	..	..	..	..	9 52
50	..		..	..	..	..	..	..	..	..	..	..		..	..	9 33	..	..	..	..	..	..	..	..	..	..	..	..
51	..		..	..	..	..	..	..	..	..	..	..	Stop	..	..	9 36	..	..	..	..	..	..	..	..	..	..	..	..
52	..	..	..	..	..	..	..	..	..	..	..	..		..	..	9 39	..	..	..	..	..	..	..	..	..	..	..	..
53	..	..	..	..	9 4	..	..	..	..	..	9 18	..	From Victoria, dep. 9 20 p.m	..	..	..	..	..	..	..	..	9 37	9 48	..	..	..	..	..
54	..	..	..	..	9 6	..	..	..	..	..	9 20	..		..	..	..	..	..	..	..	..	9 40	9 50	..	..	..	..	..
55	..	..	..	..	9 9	..	..	..	..	..	9 23	..		..	..	..	..	..	..	..	..	9 43	9 53	..	..	..	..	..
56	..	..	..	..	9 11	..	..	..	..	..	9 26	..		..	..	..	..	..	..	..	..	9 46	9 56	..	..	..	..	..
57	..	..	9 5	..	..	..	..	..	9 20	..	..	..		..	..	..	..	9 35	..	..	..	..	..	..	..	..	..	..
58	..	..	9 6	..	..	..	..	..	9 21	..	..	..		..	..	..	..	9 36	..	..	..	..	..	..	..	..	..	..
59	..	..	9 8	..	..	..	..	..	9 23	..	..	..		..	9 30	..	..	9 38	..	..	..	..	..	..	..	..	From Victoria, dep. 9 50 p.m	..
60	..	..	9 11	..	..	..	..	..	9 26	..	..	9 29		..	9 32	..	..	9 41	..	..	..	..	..	..	9 59	..		..
61	..	..	9 13	..	..	..	..	..	9 29	..	..	..		..	9 35	..	..	9 43	..	..	..	..	..	..	..	..		..
62	..	..	9 16	..	..	..	..	..	9 31	..	..	..		..	9 37	..	..	9 46	..	..	..	..	..	..	..	..		..
63	..	..	9 18	..	..	..	..	9 21	9 33	..	..	9 34		..	9 40	..	..	9 48	..	..	..	..	..	10 2	10 4	..		..
64	Via Worcester Park	..	..	9 7	..	..	..	..	..	..	..	..		..	..	..	..	..	Via Worcester Park	9 43	..	9 48	..	..	..	..		..
65		..	..	9 11	..	..	..	..	..	..	..	..	p.m	..	..	..	..	..		9 47	..	9 51	..	..	..	..		..
66		..	..	9 14	..	..	..	..	..	..	..	..	3	..	..	..	..	..		9 50	..	9 54	..	..	..	..		..
67		..	..	9 16	..	..	..	..	..	..	..	..		..	..	..	..	..		9 52	..	9 56	..	..	..	..		..
68		..	..	9 18	..	..	..	..	..	..	..	..	9 34	..	..	..	..	..		9 54	..	9 59	..	..	..	..	10 4	..
69		..	..	9 20	..	..	..	..	..	..	..	..	9 36	..	..	..	..	..		9 56	..	10 1	..	..	..	..	10 6	..
70		..	..	9 23	..	..	..	..	..	..	..	..	9 39	..	..	..	..	..		9 59	..	10 4	..	..	..	..	10 9	..
71		9 3	..	..	9 15	..	..	..	..	..	9 30	..	..	..	..	9 41	9 27	..		..	..	..	10 0	..	..	..	..	..
72		9 5	..	..	9 17	..	..	..	..	..	9 32	..	..	..	..	9 43	9 29	..		..	..	..	10 2	..	..	..	..	..
73	8 52	9 10	..	..	9 20	9 16	..	..	..	..	9 35	..	..	..	..	9 46	9 32	..	9 32	..	..	..	10 5	..	..	..	..	..
74	..	..	..	..	..	..	..	..	..	..	9 38	..	..	..	..	9 49	..	..	..	..	..	..	..	..	..	..	..	..
75	..	..	9 24	9 27	..	..	..	9 28	9 39	..	..	9 40	9 43	..	9 45	..	..	9 54	..	10 3	..	10 8	..	10 7	1010	..	1013	..
76	8 59	..	..	..	..	..	..	..	..	..	..	9 42	..	..	..	..	..	..	9 39	..	..	..	..	..	1013	..	..	..
77	..	..	..	..	..	..	..	..	..	..	..	9 45	..	..	..	..	..	..	..	..	..	..	..	..	1015	..	..	..
78	..	9 16	..	..	9 26	9 22	..	..	..	9 40	9 42	..	..	..	..	9 53	9 38	..	..	..	9 59	..	1011	..	..	..	..	..

For Notes, see page 317a

HORSHAM, REIGATE, REDHILL, TATTENHAM CORNER, CATERHAM,

Sundays—continued (p.m.)

Up	No.	3	3			3	3	3	3			3	3		3	3		3	3	3	3	3	No.
Horsham dep	1			8 49	..					..	..			..			..						1
Reigate "	2	..	..	3	..	..	..	..	..	..	..	..	..	9 50	..	..	..	..	..	..	..	..	2
Redhill "	3	..	..		..	..	..	..	..	9 50	..	..	..	9 57	..	..	..	..	..	..	..	..	3
Merstham	4	..	..	..	..	..	..	..	..	..	..	..	..	10 1	..	..	..	..	..	..	..	..	4
Coulsdon South	5	..	..	..	..	..	..	..	..	..	..	..	..	10 7	..	..	..	..	..	..	..	..	5
Tattenham Corner dep	6	..	..	..	..	..	..	..	..	..	..	..	..	..	9 48	..	..	..	..	..	..	..	6
Tadworth N	7	..	..	..	..	..	..	..	..	..	..	..	..	..	9 51	..	..	..	..	..	..	..	7
Kingswood M	8	..	..	..	..	..	..	..	..	..	..	..	..	..	9 54	..	..	..	..	..	..	..	8
Chipstead	9	..	..	..	..	..	..	..	..	..	..	..	..	..	9 59	..	..	..	..	..	..	..	9
Woodmansterne	10	..	..	..	..	..	..	..	..	..	..	..	..	..	10 1	..	..	..	..	..	..	..	10
Smitham	11	..	..	..	..	..	..	..	..	..	..	..	..	..	10 4	..	..	..	..	..	..	..	11
Reedham	12	..	..	..	..	..	..	..	..	..	..	..	..	..	10 6	..	..	..	..	..	..	..	12
Purley 252 arr	13	..	..	..	..	..	..	..	..	..	..	..	..	..	10 8	..	..	..	..	..	..	..	13
Caterham dep	14	..	..	..	..	..	..	..	..	..	..	..	..	..	9 59	..	..	..	..	..	..	..	14
Warlingham	15	..	..	..	..	..	..	..	..	..	..	..	..	..	10 2	..	..	..	..	..	..	..	15
Whyteleafe	16	..	..	..	..	..	..	..	..	..	..	..	..	..	10 4	..	..	..	..	..	..	..	16
Kenley	17	..	..	..	..	..	..	..	..	..	..	..	..	..	10 7	..	..	..	..	..	..	..	17
Purley 252 arr	18	..	..	..	..	..	..	..	..	..	..	..	..	..	1011	..	..	..	..	..	..	..	18
Coulsdon North dep	19	..	..	..	..	..	..	..	9 50	..	..	..	..	..	..	..	..	..	..	..	..	..	19
Purley 252	20	..	..	..	..	..	..	..	9 53	..	..	..	..	1011	1013	..	..	..	..	..	..	..	20
Purley Oaks	21	..	..	..	..	..	..	..	9 55	..	..	..	..	..	1016	..	..	..	..	..	..	..	21
South Croydon 234	22	..	..	..	..	..	..	..	9 58	..	..	..	..	..	1018	..	..	..	..	..	..	..	22
Effingham Junction dep	23	..	..	..	..	..	..	9 30	..	..	..	..	..	..	..	..	..	..	..	..	..	..	23
Bookham	24	..	..	..	..	..	..	9 33	..	..	..	..	..	..	..	..	..	..	..	..	..	..	24
Dorking North dep	25	..	..	9 15	..	..	..	..	..	..	..	..	..	..	..	..	..	..	..	9 43	..	..	25
Boxhill and Burford	26	..	..	9 17	..	..	..	..	..	..	..	..	..	..	..	..	..	..	..	9 45	..	..	26
Leatherhead ... [Bridge J	27	..	..	9 22	..	..	..	9 37	..	..	..	..	..	..	..	..	..	..	..	9 50	..	..	27
Ashtead	28	..	..	9 26	..	..	..	9 41	..	..	..	..	..	..	..	..	..	..	..	9 54	..	..	28
Epsom 427	29	..	..	9 30	..	9 37	..	9 45	..	..	..	..	..	..	..	..	..	..	..	9 58	10 3	..	29
Ewell East H	30	..	..	..	..	9 40	..	9 48	..	..	..	..	..	..	..	..	..	..	..	..	10 6	..	30
Cheam	31	..	..	..	..	9 43	..	9 51	..	..	..	..	..	..	..	..	..	..	..	..	10 9	..	31
Epsom Downs dep	32	..	..	..	..	..	9 38	..	..	..	..		9 55	..	..	..	..	..	..	..	..	10 8	32
Banstead	33	..	..	..	..	..	9 41	..	..	..	..		9 58	..	..	..	..	..	..	..	..	1011	33
Belmont	34	..	..	..	..	..	9 44	..	..	..	..		10 1	..	..	..	..	..	..	..	..	1014	34
Sutton 322	35	..	9 39	..	..	9 48	9 47	9 54	..	..	..		10 4	..	..	..	..	..	10 9	..	1012	1017	35
Carshalton Beeches	36	..	9 42	..	..	..	9 49	..	..	..	..		10 6	..	..	..	..	..	1012	..	..	1019	36
Wallington	37	..	9 44	..	..	..	9 52	..	..	..	..		10 9	..	..	..	..	..	1014	..	..	1022	37
Waddon G	38	..	9 48	..	..	..	9 55	..	..	..	..	From London Bridge, via Streatham	1012	..	..	..	..	..	1018	..	..	1025	38
West Croydon 319 arr	39	..	9 51	..	..	..	9 58	..	..	..	..		1015	..	..	..	..	..	1023	..	..	1028	39
West Croydon 319 dep	40	..	9 52	..	..	..	9 58	..	..	..	..		1015	..	..	..	..	..	1023	..	..	1028	40
Carshalton	41	..	..	..	..	9 51	..	9 57	..	..	..		..	..	..	..	..	..	..	..	1015	..	41
Hackbridge	42	..	..	..	..	9 53	..	10 0	..	..	..		..	..	..	..	..	..	..	..	1018	..	42
Mitcham Junction	43	..	..	..	..	9 56	..	10 2	..	..	..		..	..	..	..	..	..	..	..	1020	..	43
East Croydon arr	44	..	..	..	..		..	..	10 1	10 4	..		..	1016	1021	..	..	..	..	..	..	..	44
East Croydon dep	45	..	..	..	..		..	..	10 1	10 4	..		..	1017	1021	..	..	..	..	..	..	..	45
Norwood Junction F	46	..	9 57	..	..		10 2	..	..	..	..	1017	..	1020	1025	..	..	..	1027	..	..	1032	46
Beckenham Jn. dep	47	..	..	..	..		..	..	..	..	..	..	..	..	..	1015	..	..	..	..	..	..	47
Birkbeck	48	..	..	..	..		..	..	..	..	..	..	..	..	..	1018	..	..	..	..	..	..	48
Crystal Palace D	49	9 55	10 2	..	..	Arr. Sutton 9 46 p.m.	..	..	..	..	..	..	..	..	..	1022	..	1027	1031	..	..	..	49
Gipsy Hill (for Upper	50	9 58	10 4	..	..		..	..	..	..	..	..	..	..	..	..	..	..	1033	..	..	..	50
West Norwood [N'wood)	51	10 0	10 7	..	..		..	..	..	..	..	..	..	..	..	..	..	..	1036	..	..	..	51
Streatham Hill	52	..	1010	..	..		..	..	..	..	..	..	..	..	..	..	..	..	1039	..	..	..	52
Selhurst	53	..	..	..	..	..	..	..	10 4	..	..	..	1018	..	..	..	..	..	..	..	..	..	53
Thornton Heath	54	..	..	..	..	..	..	..	10 6	..	..	..	1020	..	..	..	..	..	..	..	..	..	54
Norbury	55	..	..	..	..	..	..	..	10 9	..	..	..	1023	..	..	..	..	..	..	..	..	..	55
Streatham Common	56	..	..	..	..	..	..	..	1011	..	..	..	1026	..	..	..	..	..	..	..	..	..	56
Anerley	57	..	..	..	..	..	10 5	..	..	..	..	1020	..	..	..	..	..	..	..	..	..	1035	57
Penge West C	58	..	..	..	..	..	10 6	..	..	..	..	1021	..	..	..	..	..	..	..	..	..	1036	58
Sydenham [Lane	59	..	..	..	..	..	10 8	..	..	..	..	1023	..	..	..	..	..	1030	..	..	..	1038	59
Forest Hill, for Lordship	60	..	..	..	..	..	1011	..	..	..	..	1026	..	..	1029	..	..	1032	..	..	..	1041	60
Honor Oak Park	61	..	..	..	..	..	1013	..	..	..	..	1028	..	..	..	..	..	1035	..	..	..	1043	61
Brockley B [Line)	62	..	..	..	..	..	1016	..	..	..	..	1031	..	..	..	..	..	1037	..	..	..	1046	62
New Cross Gate (for E.L.	63	..	..	..	..	..	1018	..	..	..	..	1033	..	1030	1034	..	..	1040	..	..	..	1048	63
Streatham	64	..	..		..	..	..	10 7	..	..	..	..	..	..	..	..	..	..	..		..	..	64
Tulse Hill	65	10 3	..		..	..	..	1011	..	..	..	..	..	..	..	..	..	..	..		..	..	65
North Dulwich	66	10 6	..		..	..	..	1014	..	..	..	..	..	..	..	..	..	..	..		..	..	66
East Dulwich	67	10 8	..		..	..	..	1016	..	..	..	..	..	..	..	..	..	..	..		..	..	67
Peckham Rye	68	1010	..	Via Worcester Park	..	..	..	1018	..	..	..	..	..	..	..	..	..	..	..	Via Worcester Park	..	..	68
Queen's Road, Peckham	69	1012	..		..	..	..	1020	..	..	..	..	..	..	..	..	..	..	..		..	..	69
South Bermondsey	70	1015	..		..	..	..	1023	..	..	..	..	..	..	..	..	..	..	..		..	..	70
Balham & Upper Tooting	71	..	1012		..	10 3	..	..	1015	..	..	..	1030	..	..	..	..	..	1041		1027	..	71
Wandsworth Common A	72	..	1014		..	10 5	..	..	1017	..	..	..	1032	..	..	..	..	..	1043		1029	..	72
Clapham Junction	73	..	1017	9 52	..	1010	..	..	1020	1015	..	..	1035	..	..	..	..	..	1046	1023	1032	..	73
Battersea Park	74	..	1020	..	..	..	..	..	..	..	..	..	..	..	..	..	..	..	1049	..	..	..	74
London Bridge arr	75	1019	..	..	..	..	1024	1027	..	..	..	1039	..	1035	1040	..	..	1045	..	..	..	1054	75
Waterloo * "	76	..	..	9 59	..	..	..	..	..	..	..	..	..	..	1043	..	..	..	..	1032	..	..	76
Charing Cross * "	77	..	..	..	..	..	..	..	..	..	..	..	..	..	1045	..	..	..	..	..	..	..	77
Victoria "	78	..	1024	..	..	1016	..	..	1026	1020	..	..	1041	..	..	..	..	..	1053	..	1038	..	78

DORKING NORTH, SUTTON, CROYDON, CRYSTAL PALACE, and LONDON

No.	p.m.									**Sundays**—*continued*								p.m.			
1	3	3	9§48	3	3	3	3	..	3	9 52	3	3	3	3	3	..	3	3	..	1052	3
2	..	..	1021	..	..	..	..	..	..	3	..	..	..	..	..	..	..	..	10 47	3	1054
3	..	..	1028	..	..	..	..	..	..		..	..	..	..	..	1049	..	..	10a52		1242
4	..	..	1032	..	..	..	..	..	..	..	..	..	..	..	..	..	..	..		..	..
5	..	..	1038	..	..	..	..	..	..	..	..	..	..	..	..	..	..	..		..	..
6	..	..	§ Via Three Bridges	..	1018	..	..	..	..	..	..	..	..	..	..	..	..	..	*a* Arrival time	..	..
7	..	..		..	1021	..	..	..	..	..	..	..	..	..	..	..	..	..		..	..
8	..	..		..	1024	..	..	..	..	..	..	..	..	..	..	..	..	..		..	..
9	..	..		..	1029	..	..	..	..	..	..	..	..	..	..	..	..	..		..	..
10	..	..		..	1031	..	..	..	..	..	..	..	..	..	..	..	..	..		..	..
11	..	..		..	1034	..	..	..	..	..	..	..	..	..	..	..	..	..	Stop	..	..
12	..	..		..	1036	..	..	..	..	..	..	..	..	..	..	..	..	..		..	..
13	..	..		..	1039	..	..	..	..	..	..	..	..	..	..	..	..	..	..	..	..
14	..	..	..	..	1029	11 4	..	..	..	..	..	..	..	..	..	..	..	..	..	..	..
15	..	..	..	..	1032	11 7	..	..	..	..	..	..	..	..	..	..	..	..	..	..	..
16	..	..	..	..	1034	11 9	..	..	..	..	..	..	..	..	..	..	..	..	..	..	..
17	..	..	..	..	1037	1112	..	..	..	..	..	..	..	..	..	..	..	..	..	..	..
18	..	..	..	..	1041	1115	..	..	..	..	..	..	..	..	..	..	..	..	..	..	..
19	1020	..	..	..	..	Stop	..	..	..	..	..	..	..	..	..	..	..	..	..	..	..
20	1022	..	1042	..	1043		..	..	..	..	..	..	..	..	..	..	..	..	..	..	..
21	1025	..	..	..	1046	..	..	..	..	..	..	..	..	..	..	..	..	..	..	..	..
22	1028	..	..	..	1048	..	..	..	..	..	..	..	..	..	..	..	..	..	p.m	..	..
23	..	..	..	..	..	..	10 3	..	..	..	..	..	1030	..	..	..	..	1057	3	..	..
24	..	..	..	..	..	..	10 6	..	..	..	..	..	1033	..	..	..	..	11 0		..	..
25	..	..	..	..	..	..	..	..	..	1018	..	..	..	..	..	..	..	..	11 2	1118	..
26	..	..	..	..	..	..	..	..	..	1021	..	..	..	..	..	..	..	..	11 4	1121	..
27	..	..	..	..	..	..	1011	..	..	1026	..	..	1037	..	..	..	..	11 4	11 9	1126	..
28	..	..	..	..	..	..	1015	..	..	1030	..	..	1041	..	..	..	..	11 8	11 13	1130	..
29	..	..	..	..	..	..	1021	..	..	1034	1037	..	1045	..	..	..	11 3	1114	11 17	1134	..
30	..	..	..	..	..	..	..	..	..	..	1040	..	1048	..	..	..	11 6	..	11 20	..	..
31	..	..	..	..	..	..	..	..	..	..	1043	..	1051	..	..	..	11 9	..	11 23	..	..
32	..		..	1025	..	..	..	..	..	..	..	1040	..	..	..	..	..	..	..	..	..
33	..		..	1028	..	..	..	..	..	..	..	1043	..	..	..	..	..	..	..	..	..
34	..		..	1031	..	..	..	..	..	..	..	1046	..	..	..	..	..	..	..	..	..
35	..	From London Bridge, via Forest Hill	..	1034	..	..	..	..	1039	..	1048	1049	1054	11 3	From London Bridge, via Forest Hill	..	1112	..	11 26	..	..
36	..		..	1037	..	..	..	..	1042	..	..	1051	..	11 5		..	..	..	..	..	..
37	..		..	1039	..	..	..	..	1044	..	..	1054	..	11 8		..	..	..	..	..	..
38	..		..	1043	..	..	..	..	1048	..	..	..	..	1112		..	..	..	..	..	..
39	..		..	1045	..	..	..	..	1051	..	..	..	..	1115		..	..	..	..	..	..
40	..		..	1045	..	..	..	..	1053	..	..	..	..	..		..	..	..	..	..	..
41	..		..	..	..	..	..	..	..	..	1051	..	1057	..		..	1115	..	11 29	..	..
42	..		..	..	..	..	..	..	..	..	1053	..	11 0	..		..	1117	..	11 32	..	..
43	..		..	..	..	..	..	..	..	..	1056	..	11 2	..		..	1120	..	11 34	..	..
44	1031		1047	..	1051	p.m	..	..	..	..		..	..	..		11 4	..	..	..	..	1 2
45	1031		1048	..	1051	3	..	..	..	..		..	..	..		11 4	..	..	..	..	..
46	..	1034	..	..	1055		..	..	1057	..	Arr. Sutton 10 46 p.m.	..	..	..	11 4	..	..	..	..	..	..
47	..	..	..	..	..	1045	..	..	..	..		..	..	..	..	..	..	..	..	..	..
48	..	..	..	..	..	1048	..	..	..	..		..	..	..	..	..	..	..	..	..	..
49	..	..	..	..	..	1052	..	..	11 1	..		..	..	..	..	..	..	..	..	..	..
50	..	..	..	..	..	..	..	..	11 3	..		..	..	..	..	..	..	..	..	..	..
51	..	..	..	..	..	..	..	..	11 6	..		..	..	..	..	..	..	..	..	..	..
52	..	..	..	..	..	..	..	..	11 9	..		..	..	..	..	..	..	..	..	..	..
53	1034	1037	..	1048	..	..	..	..	..	..	..	..	..	..	11 8	..	..	..	..	..	..
54	1036	1040	..	1050	..	..	..	..	..	..	..	..	..	..	..	..	..	..	..	..	..
55	1039	1043	..	1053	..	..	..	..	..	..	..	..	..	..	..	..	..	..	..	..	..
56	1041	1046	..	1056	..	..	..	..	..	..	..	..	..	..	..	..	..	..	..	..	..
57	..	..	..	..	..	..	Via Worcester Park Change at Wimbledon	..	..	..	..	..	..	..	..	..	..	..	..	..	..
58	..	..	..	..	..	..		..	..	..	..	..	..	..	..	..	..	..	..	..	..
59	..	..	..	..	..	..		..	..	..	..	..	..	..	..	..	..	..	..	..	..
60	..	..	..	..	1059	..		..	..	..	..	..	..	..	..	..	..	..	..	..	..
61	..	..	..	..	..	..		..	..	..	..	..	..	..	..	..	..	..	..	..	..
62	..	..	..	..	..	..		..	..	..	..	..	..	..	..	..	..	..	..	..	..
63	..	..	..	..	11 4	..		..	..	..	..	..	..	..	..	..	..	..	..	..	..
64	..	1048	..	..	..	..		..	..	Via Worcester Park	..	..	11 7	..	..	..	..	Via Worcester Park	11 39	Via Worcester Park	..
6	..	1051	..	..	..	..		..	..		..	..	1111	..	..	..	..		11 43		..
66	..	1054	..	..	..	..		..	..		..	..	1114	..	..	..	..		11 46		..
67	..	1056	..	..	..	..		..	..		..	..	1116	..	..	..	..		11 48		..
68	..	1059	..	..	..	..		..	..		..	..	1118	..	..	..	..		11 51		..
69	..	11 1	..	..	..	..		..	..		..	..	1120	..	..	..	..		11 53		..
70	..	11 4	..	..	..	..		..	..		..	..	1123	..	..	..	..		11 56		..
71	1045	..	..	11 0	..	..	..	..	1111		11 3	..	..	..	..	..	1126		..		..
72	1047	..	..	11 2	..	..	..	..	1113		11 5	..	..	..	..	..	1128		..		..
73	1050	..	1059	11 5	..	..	1049	..	1116	1058	1110	..	..	..	..	1115	1132	1138	..	1158	..
74	..	..	..	..	..	..	..	..	1119	..	..	..	..	..	..	..	..	..	..	..	..
75	..	11 8	..	..	1110	..	..	..	..	..	..	..	1127	..	..	..	..	..	12 0	..	1 19
76	..	..	..	..	1113	..	1057	..	..	11 6	..	..	..	..	..	..	..	1146	..	12 6	..
77		..	..	..	1116	..	..	..	..	..	..	..	..	..	..	..	..	..	..	..	..
78	1056	..	11 4	1111	..	..	..	..	1123	..	1116	..	..	..	..	1120	1138	..	..	..	..

3 Third class only
* Trains run between London Bridge, Waterloo and Charing Cross at frequent intervals
§ Via Three Bridges.

A Station for Clapham (Nightingale Lane)
a Arrival time.
B Station for Upper New Cross and Nunhead
C Under ½ mile to Penge East Station
D Low Level, nearly ¾ mile to High Level Station
F Norwood Junction and South Norwood for Woodside
G Station for Beddington (¾ mile), Bandon Hill (½ mile), and Beddington Lane, (1½ miles) from Beddington
H 1 mile to Ewell West Station
H 1 minute *earlier* on Saturdays
J Station for Mickleham (1¼ miles)
, 1 minute later on Saturdays
L 3 minutes *earlier* on Saturdays
M Kingswood and Burgh Heath
N Tadworth and Walton-on-the-Hill
N 2 minutes *earlier* on Saturdays
P 3 minutes later on Saturdays
SO or SO Saturdays only.
SX or SX Saturdays excepted.
V 2 minutes later on Saturdays
Z 4 minutes later on Saturdays

For LOCAL TRAINS and intermediate Stations

BETWEEN	PAGE
Horsham and Dorking North	427

For OTHER TRAINS

BETWEEN	PAGE
Effingham Junction and London	427
Epsom and London	427
Sutton and London	322
Beckenham Junction and London	147
Streatham, Tulse Hill, and London	322
Battersea Park and Victoria	318

LONDON BRIDGE, PECKHAM RYE, EAST BRIXTON, and VICTORIA

3 All Trains on this page are Third class only

Miles	Down	a.m	a.m	a.m	a.m	am	a.m	a.m	a.m	am	a.m	am	am	a.m	a.m	a.m	a.m SO	a.m SX	a.m SO	a.m SO	a.m SX	a.m SO	a.m SX	a.m SO
	Week Days																							
	London Bridge ..... dep.	..	5 35	5 57	6 17	637	6 57	7 17	7 37	757	8 17	837	857	9 17	9 37	10 17	1037	1047	1057	1117	1119	1137	1148	1157
1¼	South Bermondsey	..	5 38	6 0	6 21	641	7 1	7 21	7 41	8 1	8 21	841	9 1	9 21	9 41	10 21	1041	1051	11 1	1121	1122	1141	1151	12 1
2¼	Queen's Road, Peckham..	..	5 41	6 3	6 24	644	7 4	7 24	7 44	8 4	8 24	844	9 4	9 24	9 44	10 24	1044	1054	11 4	1124	1125	1144	1154	12 4
3¼	**Peckham Rye**	5 21	5 43	6 5	6 26	646	7 6	7 26	7 46	8 6	8 26	846	9 6	9 26	9 46	10 26	1046	1056	11 6	1126	1127	1146	1156	12 6
4¼	Denmark Hill	5 23	5 46	6 8	6 28	648	7 8	7 28	7 48	8 8	8 28	848	9 8	9 28	9 48	10 28	1048	1058	11 8	1128	1130	1148	1159	12 8
5	East Brixton...........	5 26	5 48	6 10	6 31	651	7 11	7 31	7 51	811	8 31	851	911	9 31	9 51	10 31	1051	11 1	1111	1131	1132	1151	12 1	1211
6¼	Clapham...............	5 29	5 51	6 13	6 34	654	7 14	7 34	7 54	814	8 34	854	914	9 34	9 54	10 34	1054	11 4	1114	1134	1135	1154	12 4	1214
6¾	Wandsworth Road	5 30	5 53	6 15	6 35	655	7 15	7 35	7 55	815	8 35	855	915	9 35	9 55	10 35	1055	11 5	1115	1135	1137	1155	12 6	1215
7¼	Battersea Park..........	5 32	5 55	6 18	6 39	659	7 19	7 38	7 58	818	8 38	858	918	9 38	9 58	10 38	1058	11 7	1118	1138	1139	1158	12 9	1218
8½	**Victoria** .... arr.	5 36	5 58	6 22	6 43	7 3	7 23	7 42	8 1	821	8 42	9 1	922	9 41	10 1	10 43	11 2	1111	1123	1143	1143	12 3	1213	1222

Down	p.m SO	p.m SX	p.m SO	p.m SX	p.m SO	p.m SO	p.m SX	p.m SO	p.m SX	p.m SO	p.m SO	p.m SX	p.m	p.m SO	p.m	p.m	p.m	p.m SX	p.m SO	p.m SX	p.m	p.m SX	p.m SO
Week Days—continued																							
London Bridge ..... dep.	1217	1219	1237	1248	1257	1 17	1 19	1 36	1 48	1 57	2 17	2 19	2 48	3 3	3 18	3 48	4J17	4 37	4 48	4 57	5J17	5 37	5 48
South Bermondsey	1221	1222	1241	1251	1 1	1 21	1 22	1 39	1 51	2 1	2 21	2 22	2 51	..	3 21	3 51	4 21	4 41	4 51	5 1	5 21	5 41	5 51
Queen's Road, Peckham..	1224	1225	1244	1254	1 4	1 24	1 25	1 42	1 54	2 4	2 24	2 25	2 54	3 9	3 24	3 54	4 24	4 44	4 54	5 4	5 24	5 44	5 54
Peckham Rye	1226	1227	1246	1256	1 6	1 26	1 27	1 44	1 56	2 6	2 26	2 27	2 56	3 11	3 26	3C57	4 26	4 46	4 56	5 6	5 26	5 46	5 56
Denmark Hill	1228	1230	1248	1259	1 8	1 28	1 30	1 47	1 59	2 8	2 28	2 30	2 59	..	3 29	3 59	4J28	4 48	4 59	5 8	5J28	5 48	5 59
East Brixton...........	1231	1232	1251	1 1	1 11	1 31	1 32	1 49	2 1	2 11	2 31	2 32	3 1	..	3 31	4C 2	4 31	4 51	5 1	5 11	5 31	5 51	6 1
Clapham...............	1234	1235	1254	1 4	1 14	1 34	1 35	1 52	2 4	2 14	2 34	2 35	3 4	..	3 34	4C 5	4 34	4 54	5 4	5 14	5 34	5 54	6 4
Wandsworth Road	1235	1237	1255	1 6	1 15	1 35	1 37	1 54	2 6	2 15	2 35	2 37	3 6	..	3 36	4 6	4J35	4 55	5 6	5 15	5J35	5 55	6 6
Battersea Park..........	1238	1239	1258	1 9	1 19	1 38	1 39	1 58	2 9	2 19	2 38	2 39	3C 9	..	3C39	4 8	4 38	4 58	5 8	5 18	5 38	5 58	6 8
Victoria .... arr.	1241	1243	1 2	1 13	1 23	1 41	1 43	2 1	2 13	2 22	2 43	2 43	3 13	..	3 43	4 13	4J41	5 2	5 11	5 21	5J42	6 1	6 13

Down	p.m SX	p.m	p.m SX	p.m SO	p.m SX	p.m	p.m	p.m SX	p.m	p.m	p.m	p.m	p.m	p.m	Sundays a.m	a.m	a.m	EVERY HALF-HOUR to 9 21 p.m	a.m		And at	p.m	p.m Last Train.
Week Days—continued																							
London Bridge ..... dep.	5 57	6J17	6 37	6 48	6 57	7J17	7 48	8 3	8 18	8 48	9 18	9 48	1018	1048	..	..	..		7 21	..		9 51	1021
South Bermondsey	6 1	6 21	6 41	6 51	7 1	7 21	7 51	8 6	8 21	8 51	9 21	9 51	1021	1051	..	..	..		7 24	..		9 54	1024
Queen's Road, Peckham..	6 4	6 24	6 44	6 54	7 4	7 24	7 54	8 9	8 24	8 54	9 24	9 54	1024	1054	..	..	..		7 27	..		9 57	1027
Peckham Rye	6 6	6 26	6 46	6 56	7 6	7 26	7 56	8 12	8 26	8 56	9 26	9 56	1026	1056	5 52	6 29	6 59		7 29	..		10 0	1029
Denmark Hill	6 8	6J28	6 48	6 59	7 8	7J28	7 59	..	8 29	8 59	9 29	9 59	1029	1059	..	6 32	7 2		7 32	..		..	
East Brixton...........	6 11	6 31	6 51	7 1	7 11	7 31	8 1	..	8 31	9 1	9 31	10 1	1031	11 1	5 56	6 34	7 4		7 34	..		..	
Clapham...............	6 14	6 34	6 54	7 4	7 14	7 34	8 4	..	8 34	9 4	9 34	10 4	1034	11 4	5 59	6 37	7 7		7 37	..		..	
Wandsworth Road	6 15	6J35	6 55	7 6	7 15	7J35	8 6	..	8 36	9 6	9 36	10 6	1036	11 6	6 0	6 39	7 9		7 39	..		..	
Battersea Park..........	6 18	6 38	6 58	7 8	7 18	7 38	8 10	..	8 38	9 8	9 38	10 8	1038	11 8	6 2	6 41	7 11		7 41	..		..	
Victoria .... arr.	6 22	6J42	7 1	7 13	7 21	7 43	8 15	..	8 43	9 13	9 43	1013	1043	1113	6 6	6 44	7 14		7 44	..		..	

Miles	Up	am	am	am	a.m	a.m	a.m	a.m	am	a.m	a.m	a.m	a.m	a.m	a.m	a.m	a.m	a.m	a.m SO	a.m SX	a.m SO	a.m SX	a.m SO	p.m SO
	Week Days																							
	Victoria .... dep.	..	..	548	6 7	6 28	6 48	7 8	728	7 48	8 7	8 28	8 48	9 10	9 28	9 46	10 8	10 47	11 8	1118	1128	1147	1150	12 7
1½	Battersea Park..........	..	..	551	6 10	6 31	6 51	7 11	731	7 51	8 10	8 31	8 51	9 13	9 31	9 49	1011	10 50	1111	1121	1131	1150	1153	1210
2	Wandsworth Road	..	..	553	6 12	6 33	6 53	7 13	733	7 53	8 12	8 33	8 53	9 15	9 33	9 51	1013	10 52	1113	1123	1133	1152	1155	1212
2¼	Clapham...............	..	..	554	6 13	6 34	6 54	7 14	734	7 54	8 13	8 34	8 54	9 16	9 34	9 52	1014	10 53	1114	1124	1134	1153	1156	1213
3¼	East Brixton...........	..	..	557	6 16	6 37	6 57	7 17	737	7 57	8 16	8 37	8 57	9 19	9 37	9 55	1017	10 56	1117	1127	1137	1156	1159	1216
4¼	Denmark Hill	..	..	6 0	6 20	6 40	7 0	7 20	740	8 0	8 20	8 40	9 0	9 22	9 40	9 59	1020	10 59	1121	1132	1141	12 0	12 2	1220
5¼	**Peckham Rye**	523	544	6 4	6 24	6 44	7 4	7 24	744	8 4	8 24	8 44	9 4	9 24	9 44	10 1	1024	11J 1	1124	1135	1144	12 4	12 4	1224
6	Queen's Road, Peckham..	525	546	6 6	6 26	6 46	7 6	7 26	746	8 6	8 26	8 46	9 6	9 26	9 46	10 3	1026	11J 3	1126	1137	1146	12 6	12 6	1226
7¼	South Bermondsey	528	549	6 9	6 29	6 49	7 9	7 29	749	8 9	8 29	8 49	9 9	9 29	9 49	10 6	1029	11J 6	1129	1140	1149	12 9	12 9	1229
8¼	**London Bridge** ..... arr.	532	553	613	6 33	6 53	7 13	7 33	753	8 13	8 33	8 53	9 13	9 33	9 53	1010	1033	11J10	1133	1144	1153	1213	1213	1233

Up	p.m SX	p.m SO	p.m	p.m SO	p.m SX	p.m SO	p.m	p.m SO	p.m SX	pm SO	pm SO	p.m SX	p.m	p.m SO	p.m SX	p.m SO	p.m SX	p.m SO	p.m SX	p.m SX	p.m SO	p.m SX	pm	pm Sx
Week Days—continued																								
Victoria .... dep.	1218	1227	1247	1 7	1 18	1 27	1 47	2 7	2 18	228	246	2 47	3 18	3 47	3 56	4 18	4 28	4 47	4 48	5 7	5 18	5 27	547	6 7
Battersea Park..........	1221	1230	1250	1 10	1 21	1 30	1 50	2 10	2 21	231	249	2 50	3 21	3 50	3 59	4 21	4 31	4 50	4 51	5 10	5 21	5 30	550	610
Wandsworth Road	1223	1232	1252	1 12	1 23	1 32	1 52	2 12	2 23	233	251	2 52	3 23	3 52	4 1	4 23	4 33	4 52	4 53	5 12	5 23	5 32	552	612
Clapham...............	1224	1233	1253	1 13	1 24	1 33	1 53	2 13	2 24	234	252	2 53	3 24	3 53	4 2	4 24	4 34	4 53	4 54	5 13	5 24	5 33	553	613
East Brixton...........	1227	1236	1256	1 16	1 27	1 36	1 56	2 16	2 27	237	255	2 56	3 27	3 56	4 5	4 27	4 37	4 56	4 57	5 16	5 27	5 36	556	616
Denmark Hill	1232	1240	1 0	1 19	1 32	1 40	2 0	2 20	2 32	240	258	3 0	3 32	4 0	4 8	4 32	4 40	5 0	5 0	5 20	5 32	5 40	6 0	620
Peckham Rye	1235	1244	1 4	1 22	1 35	1 44	2 4	2 24	2 35	244	3 1	3 4	3 35	4 3	4 11	4 35	4 44	5 4	5 4	5 24	5 35	5 44	6 4	624
Queen's Road, Peckham..	1237	1246	1 6	1 24	1 37	1 46	2 6	2 26	2 37	246	3 3	3 6	3 37	4 5	4 13	4 37	4 46	5 6	5 6	5 26	5 37	5 46	6 6	626
South Bermondsey	1240	1249	1 9	1 27	1 40	1 49	2 9	2 29	2 40	249	3 6	3 9	3 40	4 8	4 16	4 40	4 49	5 9	5 9	5 29	5 40	5 49	6 9	629
London Bridge ..... arr.	1244	1253	1 13	1 32	1 44	1 53	2 13	2 33	2 44	253	310	3 13	3 44	4 12	4 20	4 44	4 53	5 13	5 13	5 33	5 44	5 53	613	633

Up	pm SO	pm Sx	pm	pm Sx	pm SO	pm Sx	p.m SX	p.m SO	pm	pm Sx	pm SO	pm Sx	p.m SO	p.m SX	p.m SO	p.m SX	p.m SO	p.m	p.m		Sundays a.m		EVERY HALF-HOUR to 9 50 p.m	a.m	
Week Days—continued																									
Victoria .... dep.	618	627	647	7 7	718	727	7 47	7 47	818	848	848	918	9 18	9 48	9 48	1018	1018	1048	1116	..	6 10	..		6 50	..
Battersea Park..........	621	630	650	710	721	730	7 50	7 50	821	851	851	921	9 21	9 51	9 51	1021	1021	1051	1119	..	6 13	..		6 53	..
Wandsworth Road	623	632	652	712	723	732	7 52	7 52	823	853	853	923	9 23	9 53	9 53	1023	1023	1053	1121	..	6 15	..		6 55	..
Clapham...............	624	633	653	713	724	733	7 53	7 53	824	855	854	925	9 24	9 55	9 54	1025	1024	1054	1122	..	6 16	..		6 56	..
East Brixton...........	627	636	656	716	727	736	7 56	7 56	827	858	857	928	9 27	9 58	9 57	1028	1027	1057	1125	..	6 19	..		6 59	..
Denmark Hill	635	640	7 0	720	732	742	7 59	8 0	832	9 0	9 1	931	9 32	10 0	10 1	1032	1032	11 0	1128	..	..	..		7 2	..
Peckham Rye	637	644	7 4	724	735	745	8 3	8 4	835	9 4	9 4	935	9 35	10 4	10 4	1035	1035	11 3	1131	..	6 24	..		7 4	..
Queen's Road, Peckham..	639	646	7 6	726	737	747	8 5	8 6	837	9 6	9 6	937	9 37	10 6	10 6	1037	1037	..	..	..	..	..		7 6	..
South Bermondsey	642	649	7 9	729	740	750	8 8	8 9	840	9 9	9 9	940	9 40	10 9	10 9	1040	1040	..	..	..	..	..		7 9	..
London Bridge ..... arr.	646	653	713	733	744	754	8 12	8 13	844	913	913	944	9 44	1013	1013	1044	1044	..	..	..	..	..		7 13	..

3 Third class only C 1 min. *earlier* Sats. J 1 min. later Sats. S O Sats. only. S X or SX Sats. excepted.

For **OTHER TRAINS** between London Bridge and Peckham Rye, see page 252

WEST CROYDON, MITCHAM, and WIMBLEDON

Down — Mondays to Fridays

Miles	Down	am	am	am	am	am	am	am	am	a.m	a.m	a.m	a.m	a.m	a.m	a.m
	West Croydon .....dep.	631	651	711	731	751	811	831	851	9 11	9 31	9 51	1011	1044	1114	1144
1¼	Waddon Marsh Halt...	634	654	714	734	754	814	834	854	9 14	9 34	9 54	1014	1047	1117	1147
2½	Beddington Lane Halt.	637	657	717	737	757	817	837	857	9 17	9 37	9 57	1017	1050	1120	1150
3	Mitcham Junc. ..252,	639	659	719	739	759	819	839	859	9 19	9 39	9 59	1019	1052	1122	1152
3¾	Mitcham ....[285	641	7 1	721	741	8 1	821	841	9 1	9 21	9 41	10 1	1021	1054	1124	1154
5	Morden Halt..........	644	7 4	724	744	8 4	824	844	9 4	9 24	9 44	10 4	1024	1057	1127	1157
5½	Merton Park	646	7 6	726	746	8 6	826	846	9 6	9 26	9 46	10 6	1026	1059	1129	1159
6¼	Wimbledon 394 ....arr	649	7 9	729	749	8 9	828	848	9 9	9 28	9 48	10 9	1029	11 1	1131	12 1

Down		p.m	p.m	p.m	p.m	p.m	pm	p.m	pm	p.m	pm	pm	pm	p.m	pm	p.m	p.m	pm	p.m	p.m
West Croydon dep.	..	1214	1244	1 14	1 44	2 14	244	3 14	345	4 9	429	452	512	5 31	551	6 11	6 31	651	7 11	7 31
Waddon Marsh Halt	..	1217	1247	1 17	1 47	2 17	247	3 17	348	4 12	432	455	515	5 34	554	6 14	6 34	654	7 14	7 34
Beddington Lane Halt	..	1220	1250	1 20	1 50	2 20	250	3 20	351	4 15	435	458	518	5 37	557	6 17	6 37	657	7 17	7 37
Mitcham Junc.	..	1222	1252	1 22	1 52	2 22	252	3 22	353	4 17	437	5 0	520	5 39	559	6 19	6 39	659	7 19	7 39
Mitcham	..	1224	1254	1 24	1 54	2 24	254	3 24	358	4 19	441	5 2	522	5 41	6 1	6 21	6 41	7 1	7 21	7 41
Morden Halt	..	1227	1257	1 27	1 57	2 27	257	3 27	4 1	4 21	444	5 5	525	5 44	6 4	6 24	6 44	7 4	7 24	7 44
Merton Park	..	1229	1259	1 29	1 59	2 29	259	3 29	4 3	4 24	445	5 7	526	5 46	6 6	6 26	6 46	7 6	7 26	7 46
Wimbledon 394 arr	..	1231	1 1	1 31	2 1	2 31	3 1	3 31	4 6	4 29	448	5 9	529	5 49	6 9	6 29	6 49	7 9	7 29	7 49

Down — Mondays to Fridays—*continued*

Down	p.m	p.m	pm	p.m	pm	p.m	p.m			
West Croydon..........dep.	7 51	8 14	844	9 14	944	1014	1044	..	..	..
Waddon Marsh Halt........	7 54	8 17	847	9 17	947	1017	1047	..	..	..
Beddington Lane Halt	7 57	8 20	850	9 20	950	1020	1050	..	..	..
Mitcham Junc. 252, 285..	7 59	8 22	852	9 22	952	1022	1052	..	..	..
Mitcham....................	8 1	8 24	854	9 24	954	1024	1054	..	..	..
Morden Halt	8 4	8 28	857	9 27	957	1027	1057	..	..	..
Merton Park	8 6	8 30	859	9 29	959	1029	1059	..	..	..
Wimbledon 394.......arr.	8 8	8 33	9 1	9 31	10 1	1031	11 1	..	..	..

Down — Saturdays

Down	am	am	am	am	am	am	a.m	a.m	am	am	a.m	a.m	a.m	a.m	a.m	a.m		p.m	p.m	p.m	p.m	p.m	p.m	p.m
West Croydon dep.	631	651	711	731	751	811	8 31	8 51	911	9 31	9 51	1011	1046	1111	1131	1151	..	1211	1231	1251	1 11	1 31	1 51	2 11
Waddon Marsh Halt	634	654	714	734	754	814	8 34	8 54	914	9 34	9 54	1014	1049	1114	1134	1154	..	1214	1234	1254	1 14	1 34	1 54	2 14
Beddington Lane Halt	637	657	717	737	757	817	8 37	8 57	917	9 37	9 57	1017	1052	1117	1137	1157	..	1217	1237	1257	1 17	1 37	1 57	2 17
Mitcham Junc. 252, 285	639	659	719	739	759	819	8 29	8 59	919	9 39	9 59	1019	1054	1119	1139	1159	..	1219	1239	1259	1 19	1 39	1 59	2 19
Mitcham	641	7 1	721	741	8 1	821	8 41	9 1	921	9 41	10 1	1021	1056	1121	1141	12 1	..	1221	1241	1 1	1 21	1 41	2 1	2 21
Morden Halt	644	7 4	724	744	8 4	824	8 44	9 4	924	9 44	10 4	1024	1059	1124	1144	12 4	..	1224	1244	1 4	1 24	1 44	2 4	2 24
Merton Park	646	7 6	726	746	8 6	826	8 46	9 6	926	9 46	10 6	1026	11 1	1126	1146	12 6	..	1226	1246	1 6	1 26	1 46	2 6	2 26
Wimbledon 394 arr.	649	7 9	729	749	8 9	828	8 48	9 9	928	9 48	10 9	1029	11 3	1129	1149	12 9	..	1229	1249	1 9	1 29	1 49	2 9	2 29

Down — Saturdays—*continued*

Down	p.m	p.m	p.m	p.m		p.m	p.m	p.m	p.m	p.m	p.m		p.m	p.m	p.m	p.m	p.m	p.m	p.m	p.m			
West Croydon ....dep.	2 31	2 51	3 14	3 44	..	4 13	4 42	5 14	5 41	6 14	6 44	..	7 13	7 48	8 14	8 44	9 14	9 44	1014	1044	..	..	..
Waddon Marsh Halt........	2 34	2 54	3 17	3 47	..	4 16	4 45	5 17	5 44	6 17	6 47	..	7 16	7 51	8 17	8 47	9 17	9 47	1017	1047	..	..	..
Beddington Lane Halt......	2 37	2 57	3 20	3 50	..	4 19	4 48	5 20	5 47	6 20	6 50	..	7 19	7 54	8 20	8 50	9 20	9 50	1020	1050	..	..	..
Mitcham Junc. 252, 285 ..	2 39	2 59	3 22	3 52	..	4 21	4 50	5 22	5 49	6 22	6 52	..	7 21	7 56	8 22	8 52	9 22	9 52	1022	1052	..	..	..
Mitcham	2 41	3 1	3 24	3 54	..	4 23	4 52	5 24	5 51	6 24	6 54	..	7 23	7 58	8 24	8 54	9 24	9 54	1024	1054	..	..	..
Morden Halt	2 44	3 4	3 27	3 57	..	4 26	4 54	5 27	5 54	6 27	6 57	..	7 26	8 0	8 28	8 57	9 27	9 57	1027	1057	..	..	..
Merton Park..............	2 46	3 6	3 29	3 59	..	4 28	4 56	5 29	5 56	6 29	6 59	..	7 28	8 2	8 30	8 59	9 29	9 59	1029	1059	..	..	..
Wimbledon 394 ....arr.	2 49	3 8	3 31	4 1	..	4 30	4 59	5 31	5 58	6 31	7 1	..	7 30	8 5	8 33	9 1	9 31	10 1	1031	11 1	..	..	..

Down — Sundays

Down	a.m	a.m	a.m		a.m	a.m		
West Croydon dep.	7 8	7 47	8 18	Every Half Hour until 9 44 p.m.	8 44	9 14	..	..
Waddon Marsh Halt	7 11	7 50	8 21		8 47	9 17	..	..
Beddington Lane Halt	7 14	7 53	8 24		8 50	9 20	..	..
Mitcham Junc. 252, 285	7 15	7 55	8 26		8 52	9 22	..	..
Mitcham	7 18	7 57	8 28		8 54	9 24	..	..
Morden Halt	7 20	8 0	8 31		8 57	9 27	.	..
Merton Park	7 23	8 2	8 33		8 59	9 29	..	..
Wimbledon 394 arr.	7 25	8 5	8 36		9 2	9 32	..	..

Up — Mondays to Fridays

Miles	Up	am	am	am	a.m	a.m	am	a.m	a.m	a.m	am	am	a.m	a.m	a.m	a.m
	Wimbledon........dep.	631	652	712	7 32	7 52	812	8 32	8 52	9 12	932	952	1012	1046	1117	1145
¾	Merton Park	633	654	714	7 34	7 54	814	8 34	8 54	9 14	934	954	1014	1048	1119	1147
1¼	Morden Halt	635	655	715	7 35	7 55	815	8 35	8 55	9 15	935	956	1015	1049	1120	1148
2½	Mitcham ....[285	638	658	718	7 38	7 58	818	8 38	8 58	9 18	938	958	1018	1052	1123	1151
3¼	Mitcham Junction 252,	640	7 0	720	7 40	8 0	820	8 40	9 0	9 20	940	100	1020	1054	1125	1153
3¾	Beddington Lane Halt..	642	7 2	722	7 42	8 2	822	8 42	9 2	9 22	942	102	1022	1056	1127	1155
5	Waddon Marsh Halt....	645	7 5	725	7 45	8 5	825	8 45	9 5	9 25	945	105	1025	1059	1130	1158
6¼	W.Croydon 252, 285.arr	649	7 9	729	7 49	8 9	829	8 49	9 9	9 29	949	109	1029	11 3	1134	12 2

Up		p.m	p.m	p.m	p.m	pm	p.m	pm	pm	pm	p.m	pm	pm	p.m	p.m	p.m	pm	p.m	pm	p.m
Wimbledon dep.	..	1217	1246	1 15	1 46	215	2 45	315	348	410	4 32	453	512	5 32	5 52	6 12	632	6 52	712	7 32
Merton Park	..	1219	1248	1 17	1 48	217	2 47	317	350	412	4 34	455	514	5 34	5 54	6 14	634	6 54	714	7 34
Morden Halt	..	1220	1249	1 19	1 49	219	2 48	319	351	414	4 35	457	516	5 35	5 55	6 15	635	6 55	715	7 35
Mitcham	..	1226	1252	1 21	1 52	221	2 51	321	354	416	4 38	459	519	5 38	5 58	6 18	638	6 58	718	7 38
Mitcham Junction	..	1228	1254	1 23	1 54	223	2 53	323	356	418	4 40	5 1	521	5 40	6 0	6 20	640	7 0	720	7 40
Beddington Lane Halt	..	1230	1256	1 25	1 56	225	2 55	325	358	420	4 42	5 3	523	5 42	6 2	6 22	642	7 2	722	7 42
Waddon Marsh Halt	..	1233	1259	1 28	1 59	228	2 58	328	4 1	423	4 45	5 6	526	5 45	6 5	6 25	645	7 5	725	7 45
W.Croydon arr	..	1237	1 3	1 31	2 3	231	3 2	331	4 5	427	4 49	510	529	5 49	6 9	6 29	649	7 9	729	7 49

Up — Mondays to Fridays—*continued*

Up	p.m	pm	p.m	pm	p.m	p.m	p.m			
Wimbledon ....dep.	7 52	818	8 43	915	9 45	1015	1045	..	..	..
Merton Park	7 54	820	8 45	917	9 47	1017	1047	..	..	..
Morden Halt	7 55	822	8 47	919	9 48	1019	1049	..	..	..
Mitcham	7 58	825	8 50	921	9 51	1021	1051	..	..	..
Mitcham Junction 252, 285	8 0	827	8 52	923	9 53	1023	1053	..	..	..
Beddington Lane Halt......	8 2	829	8 55	925	9 55	1025	1055	..	..	..
Waddon Marsh Halt........	8 5	832	8 58	928	9 58	1028	1058	..	..	..
W.Croydon 252, 285....arr.	8 9	836	9 2	932	10 2	1032	11 2	..	..	..

Up — Saturdays

Up	a.m	a.m	am	am	a.m	am	a.m	a.m	a.m	a.m	a.m	a.m	a.m	a.m	a.m	a.m		p.m	p.m	p.m	p.m	p.m	p.m
Wimbledon dep.	6 31	6 52	712	732	7 52	812	8 32	8 52	9 12	9 32	9 52	1012	1047	1112	1132	1152	..	1212	1232	1252	1 12	1 32	1 52
Merton Park	6 33	6 54	714	734	7 54	814	8 34	8 54	9 14	9 34	9 54	1014	1049	1114	1134	1154	..	1214	1234	1254	1 14	1 34	1 54
Morden Halt	6 35	6 55	715	735	7 55	815	8 35	8 55	9 15	9 35	9 56	1015	1050	1115	1135	1155	..	1215	1235	1255	1 15	1 35	1 55
Mitcham	6 38	6 58	718	738	7 58	818	8 38	8 58	9 18	9 38	9 58	1018	1053	1118	1138	1158	..	1218	1238	1258	1 18	1 38	1 58
Mitcham Junction 252, 285	6 40	7 0	720	740	8 0	820	8 40	9 0	9 20	9 40	10 0	1020	1055	1120	1140	12 0	..	1220	1240	1 0	1 20	1 40	2 0
Beddington Lane Halt	6 42	7 2	722	742	8 2	822	8 42	9 2	9 22	9 42	10 2	1022	1057	1122	1142	12 2	..	1222	1242	1 2	1 22	1 42	2 2
Waddon Marsh Halt	6 45	7 5	725	745	8 5	825	8 45	9 5	9 25	9 45	10 5	1025	11 0	1125	1145	12 5	..	1225	1245	1 5	1 25	1 45	2 5
W.Croydon 252, 285 arr.	6 49	7 9	729	749	8 9	829	8 49	9 9	9 29	9 49	10 9	1029	11 4	1129	1149	12 9	..	1229	1249	1 9	1 29	1 49	2 9

Up — Saturdays—*continued*

Up	p.m	p.m	p.m	p.m	p.m	p.m	p.m	p.m	p.m	p.m	p.m	p.m	p.m	p.m	p.m	p.m	p.m	p.m	p.m				
Wimbledon ....dep.	2 12	2 32	2 52	3 15	3 45	4 15	4 42	5 15	5 42	6 15	6 45	7 14	7 48	8 18	8 43	9 15	9 45	1015	1045	..	..	..	..
Merton Park..............	2 14	2 34	2 54	3 17	3 47	4 17	4 44	5 17	5 44	6 17	6 47	7 16	7 50	8 20	8 45	9 17	9 47	1017	1047	..	..	..	..
Morden Halt	2 15	2 35	2 56	3 18	3 49	4 18	4 46	5 18	5 46	6 18	6 49	7 17	7 52	8 22	8 47	9 19	9 48	1019	1049	..	..	..	..
Mitcham	2 18	2 38	2 58	3 21	3 51	4 21	4 48	5 21	5 48	6 21	6 51	7 20	7 55	8 25	8 50	9 21	9 51	1021	1051	..	..	..	..
Mitcham Junc. 252, 285...	2 20	2 40	3 0	3 23	3 53	4 23	4 51	5 23	5 50	6 23	6 53	7 22	7 57	8 27	8 52	9 23	9 53	1023	1053	..	..	..	..
Beddington Lane Halt	2 22	2 42	3 2	3 25	3 55	4 25	4 53	5 25	5 52	6 25	6 55	7 24	7 59	8 29	8 55	9 25	9 55	1025	1055	..	..	..	..
Waddon Marsh Halt........	2 25	2 45	3 5	3 28	3 58	4 28	4 56	5 28	5 55	6 28	6 58	7 27	8 2	8 32	8 58	9 28	9 58	1028	1058	..	..	..	..
W. Croydon 252, 285....arr	2 29	2 49	3 9	3 32	4 2	4 32	4 59	5 32	5 59	6 32	7 2	7 31	8 5	8 36	9 2	9 32	10 2	1032	11 2	..	..	..	..

Up — Sundays

Up	a.m	a.m	a.m		a.m	a.m		
Wimbledon dep.	7 28	7 45	8 7	Every Half Hour until 9 45 p.m.	8 45	9 15	..	..
Merton Park	7 30	7 47	8 9		8 47	9 17	..	..
Morden Halt	7 32	7 48	8 10		8 48	9 18	..	..
Mitcham	7 35	7 51	8 13		8 51	9 21	..	..
Mitcham Junc. 252, 285	7 37	7 53	8 15		8 53	9 23	..	..
Beddington Lane Halt	7 39	7 55	8 17		8 55	9 25	..	..
Waddon Marsh Halt	7 42	7 58	8 20		8 58	9 28	..	..
W. Croydon 252, 285 arr	7 45	8 2	8 24		9 2	9 32	..	..

3 Third class only

For TRAINS between West Croydon and Wimbledon, via Sutton, see page 322

HOLBORN VIADUCT, HERNE HILL, WIMBLEDON, SOUTH MERTON, SUTTON, and WEST CROYDON

3—All Trains on this page are Third class only

Miles	Down	a.m	am	am	am	am	am	am	am	am	am	a.m	am	a.m SX	a.m SO	a.m SX	a.m SO	a.m SX	a.m	a.m	a.m SX	a.m SO	a.m SX	a.m SO	a.m	a.m SO	a.m SX	a.m SX	a.m SO	a.m SO	a.m SX	a.m SO	a.m SX	a.m SO
	Week Days																																	
	Holborn Viaduct ....dep.	1A20	.	.	.	534	554	614	634	654	714	..	734	..	7 53	7 57	8 1	8 0	8 14	8 34	8 54	8 54	9 11	9 14	9 34	9 54	9 54	1014	1014	1034	1043	1054	1114	1114
½	Blackfriars	1A22	...	...	...	535	555	615	635	655	715	....	735	7 55	7 55	7 58	8 3	8 1	8 15	8 35	8 55	8 55	9 13	9 15	9 35	9 55	9 55	1015	1015	1035	1044	1055	1115	1115
1½	Elephant and Castle	1A25	.	.	.	538	558	618	638	658	718	..	738	..	7 58	..	8 6	8 4	8 18	8 38	8 58	8 58	9 16	9 18	9 38	9 58	9 58	1018	1018	1038	1047	1058	..	1118
3¼	Loughborough Junction	1A29	...	...	...	543	6 3	623	643	7 3	723	....	743	..	8 3	....	8 11	8 9	8 23	8 43	9 2	9 3	9 20	9 23	9 43	10 3	10 3	1023	1023	1043	1052	11 3	1123	1123
4½	Herne Hill	1 36	.	.	.	545	6 5	625	645	7 5	725	..	745	8 3	8 6	8 6	8 14	8 14	8 25	8 45	9 5	9 5	9 25	9 25	9 45	10 5	10 5	1025	1026	1045	1055	11 5	1126	1125
5½	Tulse Hill	1 39	...	...	...	549	6 9	629	649	7 9	729	....	749	8 6	8 9	8 9	8 21	8 21	8 29	8 49	9 10	9 10	9 29	9 29	9 49	10 9	10 9	1029	1029	1049	1059	11 9	1129	1129
7	Streatham	1 43	.	.	.	552	612	632	652	712	732	..	752	8 9	8 12	8 12	8 26	8 26	8 32	8 52	9 14	9 14	9 32	9 32	9 52	1012	1012	1032	1032	1052	11 3	1112	1132	1132
8½	Tooting	1 46	...	...	...	556	616	637	655	715	735	....	755	8 12	8 18	8 18	8 29	8 29	8 35	8 55	9 17	9 17	9 35	9 35	9 55	1015	1015	1035	1035	1055	11 6	1116	1135	1135
10	Haydons Road	..	.	.	.	559	619	640	658	718	738	..	758	8 15	8 21	8 21	8 32	8 32	8d39	8 58	9 20	9 20	9 38	9 38	9 58	1018	1018	1038	1038	1058	11 9	1120	1138	1138
10¾	**Wimbledon** arr.	1 51	...	...	...	6 2	622	643	7 1	721	741	....	8 1	8 18	8 24	8 24	8 35	8 35	8d42	9 1	9 23	9 22	9 41	9 41	10 1	1021	1021	1041	1041	11 1	1112	1123	1141	1141
	Wimbledon dep.	1 52	5 0	523	545	6 3	623	644	7 3	725	746	7 54	8 4	8 21	8 25	..	..	..	8 43	9 3	9 28	9 28	9 43	9 43	10 5	1023	1025	1043	1042	11 3	1115	1124	1142	1144
11½	Wimbledon Chase	1 54	5 2	525	547	6 5	625	646	7 5	727	748	....	8 6	8 23	8 27	....	....	....	8 46	9 5	9 30	9 30	9 45	9 45	10 7	1025	1027	1045	1044	11 5	1117	1126	1144	1146
12¼	South Merton	1 56	5 5	528	550	6 8	628	649	7 8	730	750	..	8 9	8 26	8 30	..	..	..	8 48	9 8	9 33	9 33	9 48	9 48	10 10	1028	1030	1048	1047	11 8	1120	1129	1147	1149
13	Morden South	1 58	5 7	530	552	610	630	651	710	732	752	....	811	8 28	8 32	....	....	....	8 50	9 10	9 35	9 35	9 50	9 50	10 12	1030	1032	1050	1049	1110	1122	1131	1149	1151
13¾	St. Helier	2 0	5 9	532	554	612	632	653	712	734	754	8 0	813	8a34	8 34	..	..	..	8 52	9 12	9 37	9 37	9 52	9 52	10 16	1032	1034	1052	1051	1114	1124	1133	1152	1153
14¼	Sutton Common	2 3	512	535	557	615	635	656	715	737	756	....	816	8 38	8 38	....	....	....	8 55	9 15	9 40	9 40	9 55	9 55	10 20	1035	1037	1055	....	1117	1127	1136	1155	1156
15	West Sutton	2 6	514	537	559	617	637	658	717	739	8 0	..	818	8 40	8 40	..	..	..	8 58	9 17	9 42	9 42	9 57	9 57	10 22	1037	1039	1057	..	1120	1129	1138	1157	1158
16	**Sutton 252, 285** arr.	2 9	517	540	6 2	620	640	7 1	720	742	8 3	....	821	8 43	8 43	....	....	....	9 1	9 20	9 46	9 46	10 0	10 0	10d26	1040	1042	11 0	....	1123	1132	1141	12 0	12 1
	Sutton 252, 285 dep.	..	517	542	6 2	622	642	7 2	722	743	8 3	..	822	8 43	8 43	..	..	..	9 2	9 22	9 46	9 46	10 1	10 1	10 26	1041	1042	11 2	..	1123	1132	1144	12 2	12 3
17	Carshalton Beeches	....	520	544	6 4	624	644	7 4	725	745	8 7	....	826	8 48	8 48	....	....	....	9 5	9 24	9 48	9 48	10 4	10 4	10 29	1043	1045	11 4	....	1125	1134	1146	12 5	12 5
18	Wallington	..	523	549	6 9	629	649	7 7	728	749	811	..	830	8 51	8 51	..	..	..	9g11	9 27	9 51	9 51	10 7	10 7	10 32	1046	1047	11 7	..	1128	1137	1150	12 8	12 8
19¼	Waddon **A**	....	526	552	612	632	652	710	732	752	814	....	833	8 54	8 54	....	....	....	9g14	....	....	....	....	....	10 35	....	....	1110	....	....	....	1153	....	1211
20¼	**West Croydon 285** ..arr.	..	529	555	615	635	655	713	735	755	817	..	836	8 57	8 57	..	..	..	9g17	..	..	..	..	..	10 38	..	..	1113	..	..	..	1156	..	1214

Down	a.m SO	a.m SX	a.m SO	p.m SX	p.m SO	p.m SO	p.m SX	p.m SO	p.m SO	p.m SX	p.m SO	p.m SO	p.m SX	p.m SO	p.m SX	p.m SO	p.m SO	p.m SX	pm SO	p.m SX	p.m SO	p.m SX	p.m SO	p.m SX	p.m SX	p.m SO	p.m SX	p.m SO	p.m SX	p.m SX	p.m SO	p.m SX
Week Days—*continued*																																
Holborn Viaduct ....dep.	1134	1143	1154	1214	1214	12 34	1243	1254	1 7	1 14	1 14	1 34	1 43	1 54	2 14	2 14	2 43	2 43	314	3 14	3 43	3 43	4 14	4 14	4 34	4 43	4 54	5 14	5 14	5 34	5 43	5 54
Blackfriars	1135	1144	1155	1215	1215	12 35	1244	1255	1 8	1 15	1 15	1 35	1 44	1 55	2 15	2 15	2 44	2 44	315	3 15	3 44	3 44	4 15	4 15	4 35	4 44	4 55	5 15	5 15	5 35	5 44	5 55
Elephant and Castle	1138	1147	1158	1218	1218	12 38	1247	1258	1 11	1 18	1 18	1 38	1 47	1 58	2 18	2 18	2 47	2 47	318	3 18	3 47	3 47	4 18	4 18	4 38	4 47	4 58	5 18	5 18	5 38	5 47	5 58
Loughborough Junction	1143	1152	12 3	1223	1223	12 43	1252	....	1 16	1 23	1 23	1 43	1 52	2 3	2 23	2 23	2 52	2 52	323	3 23	3 52	3 52	4 23	4 23	4 43	4 52	5 3	5 23	5 23	5 43	5 52	6 3
Herne Hill	1145	1155	12 5	1226	1225	12 45	1255	1 5	1 19	1 26	1 25	1 45	1 55	2 5	2 26	2 25	2 54	2 55	326	3 26	3 55	3 55	4 25	4 25	4 45	4 54	5 5	5 26	5 25	5 45	5 55	6 5
Tulse Hill	1149	1159	12 9	1229	1229	12K52	1259	1K12	1 23	1 29	1 29	1 49	1 59	2 9	2 29	2 29	2 59	2 59	329	3 29	3 59	3 59	4 29	4 29	4 49	4 59	5 8	5 29	5 29	5 49	5 59	6 9
Streatham	1152	12 3	1212	1233	1232	12 55	1 3	1 15	1 28	1 32	1 33	1 52	2 3	2 12	2 32	2 32	3 2	3 3	332	3 32	4 3	4 3	4 32	4 32	4 52	5 2	5 11	5 33	5 32	5 52	6 2	6 12
Tooting	1155	12 6	1215	1236	1235	12 58	1 6	1 18	1 31	1 35	1 36	1 55	2 6	2 15	2 35	2 35	3 5	3 6	335	3 35	4 6	4 6	4 35	4 35	4 55	5 5	5 15	5 36	5 35	5 56	6 5	6 15
Haydons Road	1158	12 9	1218	1239	1238	1 1	1 9	1 21	1 34	1 38	1 40	1 58	2 9	2 18	2 38	2 38	3 8	3 9	338	3 38	4 9	4 9	4 38	4 38	4 58	5 8	5 18	5 39	5 38	5 59	6 8	6 18
Wimbledon arr.	12 1	1212	1221	1242	1241	1 4	1 12	1 24	1 37	1 41	1 43	2 1	2 12	2 21	2 41	2 41	3 11	3 11	341	3 41	4 11	4 12	4 41	4 41	5 1	5 11	5 20	5 42	5 41	6 1	6 11	6 21
Wimbledon dep.	12 4	1215	1225	1242	1245	1 5	1 12	1 25	..	1 41	1 45	2 5	2 12	2 25	2 42	2 45	3 13	3 12	342	3 45	4 11	4 17	4 44	4 45	5 5	5 12	5 25	5 44	5 45	6 5	6 13	6 25
Wimbledon Chase	12 6	1217	1227	1244	1248	1 8	1 14	1 28	....	1 43	1 48	2 8	2 14	2 28	2 44	2 48	3 15	3 14	344	3 47	4 14	4 19	4 46	4 48	5 8	5 14	5 28	5 46	5 48	6 8	6 15	6 28
South Merton	12 9	1220	1229	1247	1250	1 10	1 17	1 30	..	1 46	1 50	2 10	2 17	2 30	2 47	2 50	3 18	3 17	347	3 50	4 16	4 22	4 49	4 50	5 10	5 17	5 30	5 49	5 50	6 10	6 18	6 30
Morden South	1211	1222	1231	1249	1252	1 12	1 19	1 32	....	1 48	1 52	2 12	2 19	2 32	2 49	2 52	3 20	3 19	349	3 52	4 18	4 24	4 51	4 52	5 12	5 19	5 32	5 51	5 52	6 12	6 20	6 32
St. Helier	1213	1224	1233	1252	1253	1 13	1 22	1 33	..	1 52	1 53	2 13	2 22	2 33	2 52	2 53	3 22	3 22	353	3 54	4 23	4 26	4 53	4 53	5 13	5 22	5 33	5 53	5 53	6 13	6 22	6 33
Sutton Common	1216	1227	1235	1255	1256	1 16	1 25	1 36	....	1 55	1 56	2 16	2 25	2 36	2 55	2 56	3 26	3 25	356	3 57	4 26	4 29	4 56	4 56	5 16	5 25	5 36	5 56	5 56	6 16	6 25	6 36
West Sutton	1219	1229	1238	1257	1258	1 18	1 27	1 38	..	1 57	1 58	2 20	2 27	2 38	2 57	2 58	3 29	3 27	358	3 59	4 28	4b38	4 58	4 59	5 19	5 27	5 38	5 58	5 58	6 19	6 27	6 38
Sutton 252, 285 arr.	1222	1232	1240	1 0	1 1	1 21	1 30	1 41	....	2 0	2 1	2 23	2 30	2 41	3 0	3 1	3 32	3 30	4 1	4 2	4 32	4 41	5 1	5 2	5 22	5 30	5 41	6 1	6 1	6 23	6 31	6 41
Sutton 252, 285 dep.	1222	1232	1240	1 2	1 3	1 22	1 32	1 43	..	2 2	2 2	2 23	2 32	2 44	3 2	3 2	3 32	3 32	4 2	4 2	4 32	4 41	5 2	5 2	5 22	5 32	5 42	6 2	6 1	6 23	6 32	6 43
Carshalton Beeches	1225	1234	1244	1 4	1 5	1 25	1 34	1 46	....	2 4	2 4	2 25	2 34	2 46	3 5	3 4	3 34	3 34	4 4	4 4	4 34	4 43	5 4	5 5	5 25	5 34	5 44	6 4	6 4	6 25	6 34	6 46
Wallington	1227	1237	1247	1 7	1 8	1 27	1 37	1 48	..	2 7	2 7	2 28	2 37	2 49	3 8	3 7	3 37	3 37	4 7	4 7	4 37	4 46	5 7	5 7	5 27	5 37	5 47	6 7	6 9	6 28	6 37	6 49
Waddon **A**	....	....	1251	....	1 11	1 31	....	1 52	....	....	2 10	2 31	....	2 52	....	....	....	....	..	....	....	....	....	5 11	....	....	5 50	..	6 12	6 31	....	6 52
West Croydon 285 ..arr.	1233	..	1254	..	1 14	1 34	..	1 55	..	..	2 13	2 34	..	2 55	..	..	..	..	..	..	..	..	..	5 14	5 33	..	5 53	..	6 15	6 34	..	6 55

For Notes and Continuation of Trains, see page 321

For TRAINS between Wimbledon and West Croydon, via Mitcham Junc., see page 319

HOLBORN VIADUCT, HERNE HILL, WIMBLEDON, SOUTH MERTON, SUTTON, and WEST CROYDON

3—All Trains on this page are Third class only

Down — Week Days—*continued*

Down	p.m SX	p.m SO	p.m SX	p.m SX	p.m SO	p.m SX	p.m SO	p.m SX	p.m	p.m	p.m	p.m	p.m	p.m	p.m	p.m	ngt.	
Holborn Viaduct dep.	6 7	6 14	6 14	6 34	6 43	6 54	7 14	7 14	7 43	8 14	8 43	9 14	9 43	1014	1043	1114	1220	..
Blackfriars	6 8	6 15	6 15	6 35	6 44	6 55	7 15	7 15	7 44	8 15	8 44	9 15	9 44	1015	1044	1115	1222	..
Elephant and Castle	6 12	6 18	6 18	6 38	6 47	6 58	7 18	7 18	7 47	8 18	8 47	9 18	9 47	1018	1047	1118	1225	..
Loughborough Junction	6 16	6 23	6 23	..	6 52	7 3	7 23	7 23	7 52	8 23	8 52	9 23	9 52	1023	1052	1123	1230	..
Herne Hill	6 19	6 26	6 25	6 45	6 54	7 5	7 25	7 25	7 ℓ54	8 26	8 54	9 26	9 55	1026	1055	1126	1233	..
Tulse Hill	6 22	6 29	6 29	6 49	6 59	7 9	7 29	7 29	7 ℓ58	8 30	8 59	9 29	9 59	1029	1059	1129	1236	..
Streatham	6 26	6 32	6 32	6 52	7 3	7 12	7 33	7 33	8 3	8 33	9 3	9 32	10 3	1032	11 3	1132	1240	..
Tooting	6 29	6 35	6 35	6 55	7 6	7 15	7 36	7 36	8 6	8 36	9 6	9 35	10 6	1035	11 6	1135	1243	..
Haydons Road	6 32	6 38	6 38	6 58	7 9	7 18	7 39	7 39	8 9	8 39	9 9	9 38	10 9	1038	11 9	1138	1246	..
Wimbledon arr.	6 34	6 41	6 41	7 1	7 12	7 21	7 42	7 42	8 12	8 ℓ42	9 12	9 41	1012	1041	1112	1141	1248	..
Wimbledon dep.	6 35	6 42	6 45	7 5	7 16	7 25	7 42	7 46	8 16	8 45	9 12	9 42	1012	1042	1112	1145	1248	..
Wimbledon Chase	6 38	6 44	6 48	7 8	7 18	7 28	7 45	7 48	8 18	8 47	9 14	9 44	1014	1044	1114	1147	1251	..
South Merton	6 40	6 47	6 50	7 10	7 21	7 30	7 48	7 51	8 21	8 50	9 17	9 47	1017	1047	1117	1150	1254	..
Morden South	6 42	6 49	6 52	7 12	7 23	7 32	7 50	7 53	8 23	8 52	9 19	9 49	1019	1049	1119	1152	1256	..
St. Helier	6 44	6 52	6 53	7 15	7 25	7 33	7 52	7 55	8 25	8 54	9 22	9 52	1022	1052	1121	1154	1258	..
Sutton Common	....	6 55	6 56	7 18	7 28	7 36	7 55	7 58	8 28	8 57	9 25	9 55	1025	1055	1124	....	....	..
West Sutton	..	6 57	6 58	7 20	7 30	7 38	7 57	8 0	8 30	8 59	9 28	9 57	1027	1057	1126	..	..	..
Sutton 252, 285 arr.	....	7 0	7 1	7 23	7 33	7 41	8 0	8 3	8 33	9 2	9 31	10 0	1030	11 0	1129	....	....	..
Sutton 252, 285 dep.	..	7 1	7 2	7 23	7 33	7 44	8 2	8 3	8 34	9 2	9 32	10 2	1032	11 2	1131	..	..	..
Carshalton Beeches	....	7 4	7 4	7 25	7 37	7 46	8 4	8 6	8 36	9 4	9 34	10 4	1034	11 4	1133	....	....	..
Wallington	..	7 7	7 7	7 28	7 40	7 51	8 7	8 9	8 39	9 7	9 37	10 7	1037	11 7	1136	..	..	..
Waddon A	....	7 10	7 12	....	....	7 55	....	8 13	..	9 10	....	10SX10	....	...	1139	....	....	..
West Croydon 285 arr.	..	7 13	7 15	..	..	7 58	..	8 16	..	9 13	..	10SX13	..	..	1142	..	..	..

Down — Sundays

Down	a.m	a.m	a.m	a.m	a.m	a.m	a.m	a.m	a.m	a.m	a.m	p.m	p.m
Holborn Viaduct dep.	6 48	7 17	7 47	8 17	8 47	9 17	9 47	1017	1047	1117	11 47	1217	1247
Blackfriars	6 49	7 18	7 48	8 18	8 48	9 18	9 48	1018	1048	1118	11 48	1218	1248
Elephant and Castle	6 52	7 21	7 51	8 21	8 51	9 21	9 51	1021	1051	1121	11 51	1221	1251
Loughborough Junction	6 57	7 26	7 56	8 26	8 56	9 27	9 56	1026	1056	1126	11 56	1226	1256
Herne Hill	7 3	7 28	7 58	8 28	8 58	9 30	9 59	1028	1058	1128	11 58	1228	1258
Tulse Hill	7 6	7 34	8 4	8 34	9 4	9 34	10 4	1034	11 4	1134	12 4	1234	1 4
Streatham	7 10	7 37	8 7	8 37	9 7	9 37	10 7	1037	11 7	1137	12 7	1237	1 7
Tooting	7 13	7 40	8 10	8 40	9 10	9 40	10 10	1040	1110	1140	12 10	1240	1 10
Haydons Road	7 16	7 43	8 13	8 43	9 13	9 43	10 13	1043	1113	1143	12 13	1243	1 13
Wimbledon arr.	7 19	7 46	8 16	8 46	9 16	9 46	10 16	1046	1116	1146	12 16	1246	1 16
Wimbledon dep.	7 21	7 47	8 17	8 47	9 17	9 47	10 17	1047	1120	1147	12 17	1247	1 17
Wimbledon Chase	7 23	7 49	8 19	8 49	9 19	9 49	10 19	1049	1122	1149	12 19	1249	1 19
South Merton	7 26	7 52	8 22	8 52	9 22	9 52	10 22	1052	1125	1152	12 22	1252	1 22
Morden South	7 28	7 54	8 24	8 54	9 24	9 54	10 24	1054	1127	1154	12 24	1254	1 24
St. Helier	7 30	8 *a* 0	8*a*30	9 *a* 0	9*a*30	10*a*0	10*a*30	11*a*0	1130	12*a*0	12*a*30	1 *a*0	1*a*30
Sutton Common	7 33	8 3	8 33	9 3	9 33	10 3	10 33	11	1133	12 3	12 33	1 3	1 33
West Sutton	7 35	8 5	8 35	9 5	9 35	10 5	10 35	11 5	1135	12 5	12 35	1 5	1 35
Sutton 252, 285 arr.	7 38	8 8	8 38	9 8	9 38	10 8	10 38	11 8	1138	12 8	12 38	1 8	1 38
Sutton 252, 285 dep.	7 39	8 9	8 39	9 9	9 39	10 9	10 39	11 9	1139	12 9	12 39	1 9	1 39
Carshalton Beeches	7 42	8 12	8 42	9 12	9 42	1012	10 42	1112	1142	1212	12 42	1 12	1 42
Wallington	7 46	8 14	8 44	9 14	9 44	1014	10 44	1114	1144	1214	12 44	1 14	1 44
Waddon A	7 49	8 18	8 48	9 18	9 48	1018	10 48	1118	1148	1218	12 48	1 18	1 48
West Croydon 285 arr.	7 52	8 21	8 51	9 21	9 51	1021	10 51	1121	1151	1221	12 51	1 21	1 51

Down — Sundays—*continued*

Down	p.m	p.m	p.m	p.m	p.m	p.m	p.m		p.m	p.m	p.m	p.m	p.m	p.m	p.m	p.m	p.m	p.m	p.m	p.m	p.m		
Holborn Viaduct dep.	1 17	1 47	2 17	2 47	3 17	3 47	4 17	..	4 47	5 17	5 47	6 17	6 47	7 17	7 47	8 17	8 47	9 17	9 47	1017	1047	..	..
Blackfriars	1 18	1 48	2 18	2 48	3 18	3 48	4 18	....	4 48	5 18	5 48	6 18	6 48	7 18	7 48	8 18	8 48	9 18	9 48	1018	1048	..	..
Elephant and Castle	1 21	1 51	2 21	2 51	3 21	3 51	4 21	..	4 51	5 21	5 51	6 21	6 51	7 21	7 51	8 21	8 51	9 21	9 51	1021	1051	..	..
Loughborough Junction	1 26	1 56	2 26	2 56	3 26	3 56	4 26	....	4 56	5 26	5 56	6 26	6 56	7 26	7 56	8 26	8 56	9 26	9 56	1026	1056	..	..
Herne Hill	1 28	1 58	2 28	2 58	3 28	3 58	4 29	..	4 58	5 28	5 58	6 28	6 58	7 28	7 59	8 28	8 58	9 28	9 58	1028	1058	..	..
Tulse Hill	1 34	2 4	2 34	3 4	3 34	4 4	4 34	....	5 4	5 34	6 4	6 34	7 4	7 34	8 4	8 34	9 4	9 34	10 4	1034	11 4	..	..
Streatham	1 37	2 7	2 37	3 7	3 37	4 7	4 37	..	5 7	5 37	6 7	6 37	7 7	7 37	8 7	8 37	9 7	9 37	10 7	1037	11 7	..	..
Tooting	1 40	2 10	2 40	3 10	3 40	4 10	4 40	....	5 10	5 40	6 10	6 40	7 10	7 40	8 10	8 40	9 10	9 40	10 10	1040	1110	..	..
Haydons Road	1 43	2 13	2 43	3 13	3 43	4 13	4 43	..	5 13	5 43	6 13	6 43	7 13	7 43	8 13	8 43	9 13	9 43	10 13	1043	1113	..	..
Wimbledon arr.	1 46	2 16	2 46	3 16	3 46	4 16	4 46	....	5 16	5 46	6 16	6 46	7 16	7 46	8 16	8 46	9 16	9 46	10 16	1046	1116	..	..
Wimbledon dep.	1 47	2 17	2 47	3 17	3 47	4 17	4 47	..	5 17	5 47	6 17	6 47	7 17	7 47	8 17	8 47	9 17	9 47	10 17	1046	1117	..	..
Wimbledon Chase	1 49	2 19	2 49	3 19	3 49	4 19	4 49	...	5 19	5 49	6 19	6 49	7 19	7 49	8 19	8 49	9 19	9 49	10 19	1048	1119	..	..
South Merton	1 52	2 22	2 52	3 22	3 52	4 22	4 52	..	5 22	5 52	6 22	6 52	7 22	7 52	8 22	8 52	9 22	9 52	10 22	1051	1122	..	..
Morden South	1 54	2 24	2 54	3 24	3 54	4 24	4 54	....	5 24	5 54	6 24	6 54	7 24	7 54	8 24	8 54	9 24	9 54	10 24	1053	1124	..	..
St. Helier	2 *a* 0	2*a*30	3 *a* 0	3*a*30	4 *a* 0	4*a*30	5 *a* 0	..	5*a*30	6*a* 0	6*a*30	7 *a* 0	7*a*30	8 *a* 0	8*a*30	9 *a* 0	9*a*30	10*a*0	10*a*30	1055	1126	..	..
Sutton Common	2 3	2 33	3 3	3 33	4 3	4 33	5 3	....	5 33	6 3	6 33	7 3	7 33	8 3	8 33	9 3	9 33	10 3	10 33	1058	..	..	..
West Sutton	2 5	2 35	3 5	3 35	4 5	4 35	5 5	..	5 35	6 5	6 35	7 5	7 35	8 5	8 35	9 5	9 35	10 5	10 35	11 0	....	..	..
Sutton 252, 285 arr.	2 8	2 38	3 8	3 38	4 8	4 38	5 8	....	5 38	6 8	6 38	7 8	7 38	8 8	8 38	9 8	9 38	10 8	10 38	11 3	....	..	..
Sutton 252, 285 dep.	2 9	2 39	3 9	3 39	4 9	4 39	5 9	..	5 39	6 9	6 39	7 9	7 39	8 9	8 39	9 9	9 39	10 9	10 39	11 3	..	..	..
Carshalton Beeches	2 12	2 42	3 12	3 42	4 12	4 42	5 12	....	5 42	6 12	6 42	7 12	7 42	8 12	8 42	9 12	9 42	1012	10 42	11 5	....	..	..
Wallington	2 14	2 44	3 14	3 44	4 14	4 44	5 14	..	5 44	6 14	6 44	7 14	7 44	8 14	8 44	9 14	9 44	1014	10 44	11 8	....	..	..
Waddon A	2 18	2 48	3 18	3 48	4 18	4 48	5 18	....	5 48	6 18	6 48	7 18	7 48	8 18	8 48	9 18	9 48	1018	10 48	1112	..	..	..
West Croydon 285 arr.	2 21	2 51	3 21	3 51	4 21	4 51	5 21	..	5 51	6 21	6 51	7 21	7 51	8 21	8 51	9 21	9 51	1021	10 51	1115	..	..	..

3 Third class only

A Station for Beddington (¼ mile), Bandon Hill (½ mile), and Beddington Lane, 1¼ miles from Beddington.

ℓ Change at Herne Hill.

a Arr. St. Helier 4 mins. *earlier*

b Arr. 4 32 p.m

C Arr 1 min. later on Sats.

d 1 min. *earlier* on Sats.

g 3 mins *earlier* Sats.

K Arr. 3 mins. *earlier*

S O or SO Saturdays only.

S X or SX Saturdays excepted.

For **TRAINS** between Wimbledon and West Croydon, via Mitcham Junc., see page 319

For **OTHER TRAINS** between London and Herne Hill, see page 136—London and Tulse Hill 252—London and Streatham 252—London and Wimbledon 394—London and Sutton via West Croydon 252—Sutton and West Croydon 285

WEST CROYDON, SUTTON, SOUTH MERTON, WIMBLEDON, HERNE HILL, and HOLBORN VIADUCT

3—All Trains on this page are Third class only

Miles	Up	am	a.m	a.m	a.m	a.m	a.m	a.m	a.m	a.m	a.m	a.m	a.m	a.m	a.m SX	a.m	a.m	a.m	am	a.m SX	a.m SO	a.m SO	a.m SX	a.m	a.m SO	a.m SO	a.m SX	a.m SO	a.m SX	a.m SO	a.m SO	a.m SX
—	**West Croydon** dep.	..	..	..	5 16	5 37	5 55	6 15	6 33	6 54	7 14	7 34	..	7 54	..	..	8 14	8 34	854	9 14	9 14	..	..	..	..	..	..	1052	1113	..	..	..
1	**Waddon A**	....	..	....	5 18	5 39	5 57	6 17	6 35	6 56	7 16	7 36	..	7 56	..	..	8 16	8 36	856	9 16	9 16	....	....	....	..	..	....	1054	1115	....	....	....
2¼	Wallington	..	..	..	5 22	5 43	6 1	6 21	6 39	7 0	7 20	7 40	..	8 0	..	..	8 20	8 40	9 0	9 20	9 20	9 40	9 40	10 1	1020	..	1040	1058	1119	1121	1141	1148
3½	**Carshalton** Beeches	....	..	....	5 24	5 45	6 4	6 23	6 42	7 2	7 22	7 42	..	8 2	..	..	8 22	8 42	9 2	9 22	9 22	9 42	9 42	10 3	1022	..	1042	11 0	1121	1123	1143	1151
4½	**Sutton** arr.	..	..	..	5 27	5 48	6 7	6 26	6 45	7 5	7 25	7 45	..	8 5	..	..	8 25	8 45	9 5	9 25	9 25	9 45	9 45	10 6	1025	..	1045	11 3	1124	1126	1147	1153
	Sutton dep.	3 40	..	5 7	5 27	5 48	6 8	6 27	6 47	7 7	7 27	7 47	..	8 7	..	..	8 27	8 47	9 7	9 26	9 26	9 45	9 45	10 6	1025	..	1045	11 3	1126	1127	1147	1153
5½	West Sutton	3 43	..	5 10	5 30	5 51	6 11	6 30	6 50	7 10	7 30	7 50	..	8 10	..	..	8 30	8 50	910	9 29	9 29	9 48	9 48	10 9	1028	..	1048	11 7	1129	1130	1150	1156
6½	Sutton Common	3 45	..	5 12	5 33	5 53	6 13	6 33	6 53	7 13	7 32	7 52	..	8 12	..	..	8 32	8 52	912	9 32	9 32	9 50	9 50	10 11	1031	..	1051	1110	1132	1133	1152	1159
7½	St. Helier	3 48	4 55	5 15	5 36	5 56	6 16	6 36	6 56	7 16	7 35	7 55	8 7	8 15	..	..	8 35	8 55	915	9 34	9 34	9 53	9 53	10 16	1034	1057	1057	1113	1135	1136	1155	12 2
7¾	Morden South	3 50	4 57	5 17	5 38	5 58	6 18	6 38	6 58	7 18	7 36	7 56	8 9	8 16	..	..	8 36	8 56	916	9 36	9 36	9 55	9 55	10 18	1036	1059	1059	1115	1137	1138	1157	12 4
8¼	South Merton	3 52	4 59	5 19	5 40	6 0	6 20	6 40	7 0	7 20	7 38	7 58	8 11	8 18	–	..	8 38	8 58	918	9 38	9 38	9 57	9 57	10 20	1038	11 1	11 1	1117	1139	1140	1159	12 6
9	Wimbledon Chase	3 55	5 2	5 22	5 42	6 3	6 23	6 42	7 2	7 22	7 40	8 0	8 13	8 20	..	..	8 40	9 0	920	9 40	9 40	10 0	10 0	10 22	1040	11 4	11 4	1119	1141	1142	12 3	12 8
10	**Wimbledon** arr.	3 57	5 4	5 24	5 45	6 5	6 25	6 45	7 5	7 25	7 42	8 2	8 16	8 22	..	..	8 42	9 2	922	9 42	9 42	10 2	10 2	10 25	1043	11 6	11 6	1121	1144	1145	12 5	1211
	Wimbledon dep.	4 15	5 5	5 26	5 46	6 6	6 26	6 46	7 6	7 26	7 46	8 6	8 20	8 26	8 32	8 40	8 46	9 6	926	..	9 46	10 6	10 6	10 26	1046	11 6	1112	1123	1146	1146	12 6	1212
10¾	Haydons Road	4 17	5 7	5 28	5 48	6 8	6 28	6 48	7 8	7 28	7 48	8 8	8 23	8 28	8 34	8 43	8 48	9 8	928	..	9 48	10 8	10 8	10 28	1048	11 8	1114	1125	1148	1149	12 8	1214
12	Tooting	4 20	5 10	5 31	5 51	6 11	6 31	6 51	7 11	7 31	7 51	8 11	8 28	8 31	8 37	8 48	8 51	9 11	931	..	9 51	1011	10 11	10 31	1051	1111	1117	1128	1151	1152	1211	1217
13½	Streatham	4 23	5 13	5 34	5 54	6 14	6 34	6 54	7 14	7 34	7 54	8 14	8 32	8 34	8 40	8 52	8 54	9 14	934	..	9 54	1014	10 14	10 34	1054	1114	1120	1131	1154	1154	1214	1220
15	Tulse Hill	4 28	5 17	5 38	5 58	6 18	6 38	6 58	7 18	7 38	7 58	8 18	8 35	8 38	8 41	8 55	9 0	9 18	938	..	9 58	1018	10 18	10 38	1058	1118	1124	1136	1158	1158	1218	1224
16	Herne Hill	4 35	5 20	5 43	6 1	6 21	6 41	7 1	7 21	7 41	8 1	8 25	8 39	8 43	8 48	9 0	9 5	9 21	941	..	10 1	1021	10 21	10P43	11 1	1121	1128	1140	12 3	12 4	1221	1228
17	Loughborough Junction	4A37	5 22	5 45	6 3	6 23	6 43	7 3	7 23	7 43	8 3	8 27	8 41	..	8 51	..	9 7	..	943	..	10 3	1023	10 23	10P45	11 3	1124	1131	1143	12 5	12 6	1223	1230
19	Elephant and Castle	4A42	5 27	5 50	6 8	6 28	6 48	7 8	7 28	7 48	8 8	8 32	8 46	8 49	8 56	9 8	9 12	9 27	948	..	10 8	1028	10 28	10P50	11 8	1128	1136	1147	1210	1211	1228	1235
20¼	Blackfriars	4A45	5 30	5 53	6 11	6 31	6 51	7 11	7 31	7 51	8 11	8 35	8 49	8 52	8 59	9 11	9 15	9 30	951	..	1011	1031	10 31	10P53	1111	1131	1139	1151	1213	1214	1231	1238
20¾	**Holborn Viaduct** arr.	4A47	5 32	5 56	6 13	6 33	6 53	7 13	7 33	7 53	8 13	8 37	..	8 54	9 2	9 14	9 17	9 33	953	..	1014	1033	10 33	10P55	1113	1133	1141	1153	1215	1216	1233	1240

Week Days—*continued*

Up	a.m SO	p.m SX	p.m SO	p.m SO	p.m SX	p.m SO	p.m SX	p.m SO	p.m SO	p.m SX	p.m SO	p.m SX	p.m SO	p.m SO	p.m SX	p.m SX	p.m SO	p.m SX	p.m SO	p.m SX	p.m SX	p.m SO	p.m SX	p.m SO	p.m SX	p.m SX	p.m SO	p.m SX	p.m SO	p.m SX	p.m SX	p.m SO
West Croydon dep.	1151	..	1214	1234	..	1254	..	1 9	1 34	..	1 54	..	2 14	2 34	..	..	..	..	..	..	..	..	..	.	..	5 11	..	5 34	..	5 55	6 14	..
Waddon A	1153	....	1216	1236	....	1256	....	1 11	1 36	....	1 56	....	2 16	2 36	....	....	....	....	....	....	....	....	..	....	....	5 14	..	5 36	....	5 57	6 16	....
Wallington	1158	1219	1220	1240	1249	1 0	1 19	1 19	1 40	1 49	2 0	2 19	2 20	2 40	2 49	3 18	3 21	..	3 50	3 51	4 21	4 21	4 35	4 48	5 1	5 17	5 21	5 40	5 47	6 1	6 20	6 21
Carshalton Beeches	12 0	1221	1222	1243	1251	1 3	1 21	1 21	1 43	1 51	2 2	2 21	2 22	2 43	2 51	3 20	3 23	....	3 52	3 53	4 23	4 23	4 38	4 50	5 3	5 20	5 23	5 42	5 49	6 3	6 22	6 23
Sutton arr.	12 3	1224	1225	1246	1254	1 6	1 24	1 24	1 46	1 54	2 5	2 24	2 25	2 46	2 54	3 23	3 26	..	3 55	3 56	4 26	4 26	4 41	4 54	5 6	5 22	5 26	5 46	5 52	6 6	6 25	6 26
Sutton dep	12 3	1226	1227	1246	1254	1 7	1 24	1 27	1 47	1 54	2 6	2 26	2 26	2 47	2 54	3 23	3 27	....	3 55	4 0	4 26	4 27	4 41	4 54	5 7	5 22	5 27	5 46	5 52	6 8	6 27	6 28
West Sutton	1210	1229	1230	1250	1257	1 10	1 27	1 30	1 50	1 57	2 9	2 29	2 29	2 50	2 57	3 26	3 30	..	3 58	4 3	4 29	4 30	4 45	4 57	5 10	5 25	5 30	5 49	5 55	6 11	6 30	6 31
Sutton Common	1212	1232	1233	1253	1 0	1 13	1 30	1 33	1 53	2 0	2 12	2 32	2 32	2 53	3 0	3 29	3 33	....	4 0	4 5	4 31	4 32	4 47	4 59	5 13	5 28	5 32	5 51	5 57	6 13	6 33	6 33
St. Helier	1215	1235	1236	1256	1 3	1 16	1 33	1 36	1 56	2 3	2 15	2 35	2 35	3 1	3 3	3 33	3 36	..	4 3	4 12	4 34	4 35	4 50	5 2	5 16	5 31	5 35	5 56	6 0	6 16	6 36	6 36
Morden South	1217	1237	1238	1258	1 5	1 18	1 35	1 38	1 58	2 5	2 17	2 37	2 37	3 3	3 5	3 35	3 38	....	4 5	4 14	4 36	4 37	4 52	5 4	5 18	5 33	5 37	5 58	6 2	6 18	6 38	6 38
South Merton	1219	1239	1240	1 0	1 7	1 20	1 37	1 40	2 0	2 7	2 19	2 39	2 39	3 5	3 7	3 37	3 40	..	4 7	4 16	4 38	4 39	4 54	5 6	5 20	5 35	5 39	6 0	6 4	6 20	6 40	6 40
Wimbledon Chase	1222	1241	1242	1 2	1 9	1 22	1 39	1 42	2 3	2 9	2 21	2 41	2 41	3 8	3 9	3 40	3 42	....	4 10	4 19	4 41	4 42	4 57	5 9	5 23	5 37	5 42	6 2	6 7	6 23	6 42	6 43
Wimbledon arr.	1224	1244	1245	1 5	1 12	1 25	1 42	1 45	2 5	2 12	2 24	2 44	2 44	3 11	3 12	3 42	3 44	..	4 12	4 21	4 43	4 44	4 59	5 11	5 25	5 40	5 44	6 5	6 9	6 25	6 45	6 45
Wimbledon dep.	1226	1246	1246	1 6	1 12	1 26	1 46	1 46	2 6	2 12	2 26	2 46	2 47	3 12	3 12	3 46	3 47	4 4	4 12	4 26	4 44	4 45	5 2	5 12	5 26	5 46	5 45	6 6	6 12	6 26	6 46	6 46
Haydons Road	1228	1248	1248	1 8	1 14	1 28	1 48	1 48	2 8	2 14	2 28	2 48	2 49	3 14	3 14	3 48	3 49	4 7	4 14	4 28	4 47	4 47	5 5	5 14	5 28	5 48	5 47	6 8	6 14	6 28	6 48	6 49
Tooting	1231	1251	1251	1 11	1 17	1 31	1 51	1 51	2 11	2 17	2 31	2 51	2 52	3 17	3 17	3 51	3 52	4 10	4 17	4 31	4 50	4 51	5 8	5 17	5 31	5 51	5 51	6 11	6 17	6 31	6 51	6 52
Streatham	1234	1254	1254	1 14	1 20	1 34	1 54	1 54	2 14	2 20	2 34	2 54	2 55	3 20	3 21	3 54	3 55	4 13	4 20	4 34	4 54	4 55	5 11	5 20	5 34	5 54	5 55	6 14	6 20	6 34	6 54	6 55
Tulse Hill	1238	1258	1258	1 18	1 24	1 38	1 59	1 58	2 18	2 24	2 39	2 58	2 59	3 24	3 24	3 58	3 59	4 17	4 24	4 38	4 58	4 59	5 16	5 24	5 38	6 0	6 0	6 18	6 24	6 39	6 58	6 59
Herne Hill	1242	1 3	1 1	1 21	1 28	1 41	2 3	2 1	2 21	2 28	2 44	3 3	3 3	3 29	3 28	4 2	4 3	4 24	4 28	4 42	5 1	5 3	5 19	5 29	5 41	6 3	6 3	6 20	6 29	6 42	7 1	7 4
Loughborough Junction	1245	1 5	1 3	1 23	1 30	1 43	2 5	2 3	2 23	2 30	2 47	3 5	3 5	3 21	3 31	4 5	4 5	4 27	4 31	..	..	5 6	5 21	5 31	5 43	6 5	6 5	6 23	6 31	6 44	7 3	7 7
Elephant and Castle	1249	1 10	1 8	1 28	1 35	1 48	2 10	2 8	2 28	2 35	2 51	3 10	3 10	3 36	3 35	4 9	4 10	4 32	4 35	4 47	5 7	5 10	5 26	5 36	5 47	6 10	6 10	6 28	6 36	6 48	7 8	7 11
Blackfriars	1252	1 13	1 11	1 31	1 38	1 51	2 13	2 11	2 31	2 38	2 54	3 13	3 13	3 39	3 38	4 13	4 13	4 35	4 38	4 50	5 10	5 13	5 30	5 39	5 50	6 12	6 13	6 31	6 39	6 51	7 1	7 14
Holborn Viaduct arr.	1255	1 15	1 13	1 33	1 40	1 53	2 15	2 13	2 33	2 40	2 56	3 15	3 15	3 41	3 40	4 16	4 15	4 37	4 40	4 53	5 12	5 16	5 33	5 41	5 53	6 16	6 15	6 33	6 41	6 54	7 13	7 17

For Notes and Continuation of Trains, see page 323

For TRAINS between West Croydon and Wimbledon, via Mitcham Junction, see page 319

WEST CROYDON, SUTTON, SOUTH MERTON, WIMBLEDON, HERNE HILL, and HOLBORN VIADUCT

3—All Trains on this page are Third class only

Up	Week Days—*continued*																
	p.m SX	p.m SX	p.m SO	p.m SX	p.m SX	p.m SO	p.m	p.m SO	p.m SX	p.m	p.m	p.m	p.m	p.m	p.m SX	p.m	p.m SO
West Croydon.......dep.	..	6 34	..	6 54	7 14	7 15	..	..	8 14	..	9 16	..	1015	..	11 7	..	1111
Waddon A	..	6 36	....	6 56	7 16	7 17	....	....	8 16	....	9 18	....	1017	....	1110	....	1113
Wallington	..	6 40	6 47	7 0	7 20	7 21	7 49	8 20	8 20	8 49	9 22	9 50	1021	1050	1113	..	1117
Carshalton Beeches	..	6 42	6 49	7 2	7 22	7 23	7 51	8 22	8 22	8 51	9 24	9 52	1023	1052	1116	....	1119
Sutton arr.	..	6 45	6 52	7 5	7 25	7 26	7 54	8 25	8 25	8 54	9 27	9 55	1026	1055	1118	..	1122
Sutton dep.	..	6 46	6 52	7 7	7 26	7 27	7 54	8 26	8 26	8 54	9 27	9 55	1027	1055	1118	....	1123
West Sutton	..	6 49	6 55	7 10	7 29	7 30	7 57	8 29	8 29	8 57	9 30	9 58	1030	1058	1121	..	1126
Sutton Common	..	6 52	6 57	7 13	7 31	7 33	7 59	8 32	8 32	9 0	9 33	10 0	1033	11 0	1124	....	1128
St. Helier	6 49	6 55	7 0	7 16	7 34	7 36	8 2	8 36	8 36	9 3	9 36	10 3	1036	11 3	1127	..	1131
Morden South	6 51	6 57	7 2	7 18	7 36	7 38	8 4	8 38	8 38	9 5	9 38	10 5	1038	11 5	1129	....	1133
South Merton	6 53	6 59	7 4	7 20	7 38	7 40	8 6	8 40	8 40	9 7	9 40	10 7	1040	11 7	1131	..	1135
Wimbledon Chase	6 55	7 1	7 7	7 22	7 41	7 42	8 9	8 43	8 43	9 9	9 43	1010	1042	1110	1134	....	1138
Wimbledon arr.	6 58	7 4	7 9	7 25	7 43	7 45	8 11	8 45	8 45	9 12	9 45	1012	1045	1112	1136	..	1140
Wimbledon dep.	..	7 7	7 10	..	7 46	7 46	8 13	8 47	8 47	9 12	9 47	1013	1047	1112	↲	1136	..
Haydons Road	..	7 9	7 12	..	7 48	7 49	8 15	8 49	8 49	9 14	9 49	1015	1049	1114	..	1138	..
Tooting	..	7 13	7 15	..	7 52	7 52	8 18	8 52	8 52	9 17	9 52	1018	1052	1117	....	1141	..
Streatham	..	7 16	7 19	..	7 56	7 56	8 21	8 55	8 55	9 20	9 55	1021	1055	1120	..	1144	..
Tulse Hill	..	7 23	7 23	..	8 0	8 0	8 25	8 59	8 59	9 24	9 59	1025	1059	1125	....	1149	..
Herne Hill	..	7 28	7 29	..	8 3	8 3	8 28	9 3	9 3	9 28	10 3	1028	11 3	1129	..	1152	..
Loughborough Junction	..	7 30	7 33	..	8 5	8 5	8 30	9 5	9 5	9 30	10 5	1030	11 5	1131	....	1154	..
Elephant and Castle	..	7 35	7 38	..	8 10	8 10	8 35	9 10	9 10	9 35	1010	1035	1110	1136	..	1159	..
Blackfriars	..	7 38	7 41	..	8 13	8 13	8 38	9 13	9 13	9 38	1013	1038	1113	1139	....	12 2	..
Holborn Viaduct.....arr.	..	7 40	7 43	..	8 15	8 15	8 40	9 15	9 15	9 40	1015	1040	1115	1141	..	12 4	..

Up	Sundays												
	a.m	a.m	a.m	a.m	a.m	a.m	a.m	a.m	a.m	a.m	a.m	a.m	p.m
West Croydon.......dep.	..	..	7 19	7 49	8 19	8 49	9 19	9 49	10 19	10 49	11 19	11 49	12 19
Waddon A	....	....	7 21	7 51	8 21	8 51	9 21	9 51	10 21	10 51	11 21	11 51	12 21
Wallington	..	..	7 25	7 55	8 25	8 55	9 25	9 55	10 25	10 55	11 25	11 55	12 25
Carshalton Beeches	....	....	7 27	7 57	8 27	8 57	9 27	9 57	10 27	10 57	11 27	11 57	12 27
Sutton arr.	..	..	7 30	8 0	8 30	9 0	9 30	10 0	10 30	11 0	11 30	12 0	12 30
Sutton dep.	....	....	7 30	8 0	8 30	9 0	9 30	10 0	10 30	11 0	11 30	12 0	12 30
West Sutton	..	..	7 33	8 3	8 33	9 3	9 33	10 3	10 33	11 3	11 33	12 3	12 33
Sutton Common	....	....	7 36	8 6	8 36	9 6	9 36	10 6	10 36	11 6	11 36	12 6	12 36
St. Helier	..	..	7 39	8a13	8 39	9a13	9 39	10a13	10 39	11a14	11 39	12a13	12 39
Morden South	....	....	7 41	8 15	8 41	9 15	9 41	10 15	10 41	11 16	11 41	12 15	12 41
South Merton	..	..	7 43	8 17	8 43	9 17	9 43	10 17	10 43	11 18	11 43	12 17	12 43
Wimbledon Chase	....	....	7 45	8 20	8 45	9 20	9 45	10 20	10 45	11 21	11 45	12 20	12 45
Wimbledon arr.	..	..	7 48	8 22	8 48	9 22	9 48	10 22	10 48	11 23	11 48	12 22	12 48
Wimbledon dep.	7 9	7 24	7 54	8 24	8 54	9 24	9 54	10 24	10 54	11 26	11 54	12 24	12 54
Haydons Road	7 11	7 26	7 56	8 26	8 56	9 26	9 56	10 26	10 56	11 28	11 56	12 26	12 56
Tooting	7 14	7 29	7 59	8 29	8 59	9 29	9 59	10 29	10 59	11 31	11 59	12 29	12 59
Streatham	7 17	7 32	8 2	8 32	9 2	9 32	10 2	10 32	11 2	11 34	12 2	12 32	1 2
Tulse Hill	7 21	7 36	8 8	8 37	9 8	9 37	10 8	10 39	11 8	11 39	12 8	12 37	1 8
Herne Hill	7 25	7 39	8 11	8J50	9 11	9J50	10 11	10J50	11 11	11Z50	12 11	12J50	1 11
Loughborough Junction	7 27	7 42	8 14	8 53	9 14	9 53	10 14	10 53	11 14	11 53	12 14	12 53	1 14
Elephant and Castle	7 32	7 47	8 17	8 58	9 18	9 58	10 18	10 58	11 18	11 58	12 18	12 58	1 18
Blackfriars	7 35	7 50	8 21	9 1	9 21	10 1	10 21	11 1	11 21	12 1	12 21	1 1	1 21
Holborn Viaduct.....arr.	7 37	7 52	8 24	9 3	9 24	10 3	10 24	11 3	11 24	12 3	12 24	1 3	1 24

Up	Sundays—*continued*																						
	p.m	p.m	p.m	p.m	p.m	p.m	p.m	p.m	p.m	p.m	p.m	p.m	p.m	p.m	p.m	p.m	p.m	p.m	p.m	p.m	p.m	p.m	
West Croydon.......dep.	1249	1 19	1 49	2 19	2 49	3 19	3 49	4 19	4 49	5 19	5 49	6 19	6 49	7 19	7 49	8 19	8 49	9 19	9 49	10 19	1042	..	..
Waddon A	1251	1 21	1 51	2 21	2 51	3 21	3 51	4 21	4 51	5 21	5 51	6 21	6 51	7 21	7 51	8 21	8 51	9 21	9 51	10 21	1044	....	..
Wallington	1255	1 25	1 55	2 25	2 55	3 25	3 55	4 25	4 55	5 25	5 55	6 25	6 55	7 25	7 55	8 25	8 55	9 25	9 55	10 25	1048	..	..
Carshalton Beeches	1257	1 27	1 57	2 27	2 57	3 27	3 57	4 27	4 57	5 27	5 57	6 27	6 57	7 27	7 57	8 27	8 57	9 27	9 57	10 27	1050	....	..
Sutton arr.	1 0	1 30	2 0	2 30	3 0	3 30	4 0	4 30	5 0	5 30	6 0	6 30	7 0	7 30	8 0	8 30	9 0	9 30	10 0	10 30	1053	..	..
Sutton dep.	1 0	1 30	2 0	2 30	3 0	3 30	4 0	4 30	5 0	5 30	6 0	6 30	7 0	7 30	8 0	8 30	9 0	9 30	10 0	10 30	1055	....	..
West Sutton	1 3	1 33	2 3	2 33	3 3	3 33	4 3	4 33	5 3	5 33	6 3	6 33	7 3	7 33	8 3	8 33	9 3	9 33	10 3	10 33	1058	..	..
Sutton Common	1 6	1 36	2 6	2 36	3 6	3 36	4 6	4 36	5 6	5 36	6 6	6 36	7 6	7 36	8 6	8 36	9 6	9 36	10 6	10 36	11 0	....	..
St. Helier	1a13	1 39	2a13	2 39	3a13	3 39	4a13	4 39	5a13	5 39	6a13	6 39	7a13	7 39	8a13	8 39	9a13	9 39	10a13	10 39	11 3	1132	..
Morden South	1 15	1 41	2 15	2 41	3 15	3 41	4 15	4 41	5 15	5 41	6 15	6 41	7 15	7 41	8 15	8 41	9 15	9 41	10 15	10 41	11 5	1134	..
South Merton	1 17	1 43	2 17	2 43	3 17	3 43	4 17	4 43	5 17	5 43	6 17	6 43	7 17	7 43	8 17	8 43	9 17	9 43	10 17	10 43	11 7	1136	..
Wimbledon Chase	1 20	1 45	2 20	2 45	3 20	3 45	4 20	4 45	5 20	5 45	6 20	6 45	7 20	7 45	8 20	8 45	9 20	9 45	10 20	10 45	1110	1138	..
Wimbledon arr.	1 22	1 48	2 22	2 48	3 22	3 48	4 22	4 48	5 22	5 48	6 22	6 48	7 22	7 48	8 22	8 48	9 22	9 48	10 22	10 48	1112	1140	..
Wimbledon dep.	1 24	1 54	2 24	2 54	3 24	3 54	4 24	4 54	5 24	5 54	6 24	6 54	7 24	7 54	8 24	8 54	9 24	9 54	10 24	..	....	1141	..
Haydons Road	1 26	1 56	2 26	2 56	3 26	3 56	4 26	4 56	5 26	5 56	6 26	6 56	7 26	7 56	8 26	8 56	9 26	9 56	10 26	..	..	1143	..
Tooting	1 29	1 59	2 29	2 59	3 29	3 59	4 29	4 59	5 29	5 59	6 29	6 59	7 29	7 59	8 29	8 59	9 29	9 59	10 29	..	....	1146	..
Streatham	1 32	2 2	2 32	3 2	3 32	4 2	4 32	5 2	5 32	6 2	6 32	7 2	7 32	8 2	8 32	9 2	9 32	10 2	10 32	..	..	1149	..
Tulse Hill	1 37	2 8	2 37	3 8	3 37	4 8	4 37	5 8	5 37	6 8	6 37	7 8	7 37	8 8	8 37	9 8	9 37	10 8	10 37	..	....	1153	..
Herne Hill	1J50	2 11	2J50	3 14	3J50	4 11	4J50	5 11	5J50	6 11	6Z50	7 11	7Z50	8 11	8J50	9 11	9J50	10 11	10L53	..	..	1156	..
Loughborough Junction	1 53	2 14	2 53	3 17	3 53	4 14	4 53	5 14	5 53	6 14	6 53	7 14	7 53	8 14	8 53	9 14	9 53	10 14	10 56	..	....	....	..
Elephant and Castle	1 58	2 18	2 58	3 21	3 58	4 18	4 58	5 18	5 58	6 18	6 58	7 18	7 58	8 18	8 58	9 18	9 58	10 18	11 1	..	..	..	..
Blackfriars	2 1	2 21	3 1	3 24	4 1	4 21	5 1	5 21	6 1	6 21	7 1	7 21	8 1	8 21	9 1	9 21	10 0	10 21	11 4	..	....	....	..
Holborn Viaduct.....arr.	2 3	2 24	3 3	3 27	4 3	4 24	5 3	5 24	6 3	6 24	7 3	7 24	8 3	8 24	9 3	9 24	10 3	10 24	11 6	..	..	..	..

3 Third class only

A Station for Beddington (¼ mile), Bandon Hill (½ mile), and Beddington Lane, 1½ miles from Beddington.

↲ Change at Herne Hill.

a Arr. St Helier 4 mins *earlier*

B Arr. St. Helier at 256 p.m

J Arr. Herne Hill 10 mins. *earlier*

L Arr. Herne Hill 13 mins. *earlier*

p 2 mins. *earlier* Sats.

SO or **S0** Saturdays only.

SX Saturdays excepted.

Z Arr. Herne Hill 8 mins. *earlier*.

For TRAINS between West Croydon and Wimbledon, via Mitcham Junction, see page 319

OTHER TRAINS between West Croydon and Sutton, page 252—Sutton and London, via West Croydon 285—Wimbledon and London, 427—Streatham and London 285—Tulse Hill and London, [illegible]—Herne Hill and London 147.

LONDON, BASINGSTOKE, SOUTHAMPTON, BOURNEMOUTH, WAREHAM, SWANAGE, and WEYMOUTH

Down — Week Days

Miles	Down	a.m	a.m	a.m	a.m	a.m	a.m	a.m	a.m	a.m	a.m
	WATERLOO 394 dep.	3	2 40			3		Arr. St. Denys 5 26 a.m			
12	Surbiton 394 "		3								
24¼	Woking 394 "										
28	Brookwood Z										
33½	Farnborough A		3 33								
36½	Fleet										
40	Winchfield B										
42¼	Hook C										
48	Basingstoke 340 arr.		3 56								
	Basingstoke dep.		4 0								
58½	Micheldever										
66½	Winchester D		4 30								
69½	Shawford, for Twyford										
73½	Eastleigh F 376, 380 arr.		4 44								
	Eastleigh dep.		4 50			5 5		5 17		6 5	6 20
76	Swaythling		To Portsmouth Harbour page 376					5 22			6 25
77½	St Denys 376							5 31			6 29
78½	Northam							5 35			6 33
79½	Southampton G 500 arr.							5 39			6 37
	Southampton dep.							5 56			Stop
79½	Southampton Cen. H arr.					5 18		6 1		6 15	
	Southampton Cen. dep.					5 22		6 5		6 18	
80½	Millbrook									6 23	
82	Redbridge 380									6 28	
82¾	Totton, for Eling 375							6 12		6 32	
85¼	Lyndhurst Road							Stop		6 39	
88½	Beaulieu Road									6 45	
93	Brockenhurst 338 arr.					5 43				6 53	
97¾	338 Lymington Town arr									7 15	
—	338 Yarmouth Slipway "									7 55	
—	Brockenhurst dep.	Dep. Salisbury 3 50 a.m page 339							Dep. Wimborne at 8 0 and Broadstone 8 6 a.m	6 56	
95¼	Sway									7 5	
98¾	New Milton J									7 13	
101½	Hinton Admiral W		Stop		Calls Upwey Wishing Well Halt at 6 53 a.m			a.m		7 21	
104¼	Christchurch L					6 5		6 30		7 29	
106½	Pokesdown O							6 37		7 37	
107	Boscombe							6 43		7 41	
108	Bournemouth Central arr.					6 15		6 48		7 45	
	Bournemouth Central dep.			5 47		6 32	6 25	7 10		7 50	
111½	Bournemouth West arr.		Saturdays only			6 42				8 0	a.m
	Bournemouth West dep.										8 10
110¾	Branksome			5 53			6 32	7 17			8 14
112	Parkstone for Sandbanks			5 57			6 37	7 24			8 18
114	Poole 339			6 3			6 44	7 34			8 26
116	Hamworthy Junction			6 9				7 43	8 13		
119	Holton Heath	5 17		6 15				7 49	8 18		
121	Wareham arr.	5 23		6 21				7 55	8 24		
—	Wareham dep.			6 24				8 18	8 30		
127	Corfe Castle			6 38				8 30	8 42		
132	Swanage arr.			6 48				8 40	8 52		
—	Wareham dep.	5 27						7 59	8 25		
126	Wool, for Lulworth Cove K	5 36						8 9	8 33		
130¼	Moreton	5 45	a.m					8 21	8 41		
136	Dorchester P	5 55	6 0		6 45			8 33	8 51		
140¼	Upwey Junction				6 56			8 48			
143	Weymouth 339 arr.		6 13		7 2			8 54			

Miles	Down	a.m	a.m	a.m	a.m	a.m	a.m	a.m	a.m	a.m	a.m
	WATERLOO 394 dep.			Dep Portsmouth and Southsea 6 0 a.m, page 380			5 40				
12	Surbiton 394 "						5 59				
24¼	Woking 394 "						6 21		6 30		
28	Brookwood Z								6 39		
33½	Farnborough A								6 51		
36½	Fleet								6 59		
40	Winchfield B								7 7		
42¼	Hook C								7 15		
48	Basingstoke 340 arr.						6 54		7 26	7 26	
	Basingstoke dep.						6 55		7 31	7 34	
58½	Micheldever						7 12		To Templecombe, page 340	7 52	
66½	Winchester D		6 36			6 58	7 27			8 6	
69½	Shawford, for Twyford		6 41			7 3				8 13	
73½	Eastleigh F 376, 380 arr.		6 49			7 11	7 39			8 21	
	Eastleigh dep.	6 38	6 54			7 12	7 41	7 46		8 25	8 38
76	Swaythling	6 43	6 59			7 18		7 51		8 32	8 43
77½	St Denys 376	6 49	7 3	7 6		7 22		7 56		8 37	8 47
78½	Northam		7 7	7 10		7 26				8 41	
79½	Southampton G 500 arr.		7 11	7 14		7 30				8 45	
	Southampton dep.		Stop	7 25						Through Train from Reading (G.W.R.) page 495	
79½	Southampton Cen. H arr.	6 55		7 30			7 52	8 2			8 53
	Southampton Cen. dep.	6 57		7 32			7 56	8 4			8 55
80½	Millbrook	7 2		7 36				8 9			8 59
82	Redbridge 380	7 7		7 41				8 14			9 4
82¾	Totton, for Eling 375	7 10						8 17			9 6
85¼	Lyndhurst Road	To Fawley arr 7 43 a.m page 375						8 24			9 13
88½	Beaulieu Road							8 31			9 19
93	Brockenhurst 338 arr.						8 18	8 39			9 27
97¾	338 Lymington Town arr						8 44				9 49
—	338 Yarmouth Slipway "						9 45				
—	Brockenhurst dep.				7 57		8 20	8 41			9 28
95¼	Sway				8 3			8 49			9 36
98¾	New Milton J				8 10			8 57			9 44
101½	Hinton Admiral W				8 15			9 4			9 51
104¼	Christchurch L				8 21		8 39	9 11			9 59
106½	Pokesdown O				8 27		8 45	9 17			10 5
107	Boscombe				8 29		8 49	9 20			10 8
108	Bournemouth Central arr.				8 33		8 53	9 24			10 12
	Bournemouth Central dep.				8 34		8 57				10 18
111½	Bournemouth West arr.		a.m		8 43						
	Bournemouth West dep.		8 45								
110¾	Branksome		8 48				9 5				10 26
112	Parkstone for Sandbanks		8 51				9 9				10 30
114	Poole 339		8 56				9 16				10 38
116	Hamworthy Junction		9 1								10 44
119	Holton Heath		9 6								10 50
121	Wareham arr.		9 12				9 28				10 56
—	Wareham dep.						9 45				11 5
127	Corfe Castle						9 57				11 17
132	Swanage arr.						10 7				11 27
—	Wareham dep.						9 30				10 58
126	Wool, for Lulworth Cove K						9 39				11 8
130¼	Moreton										11 18
136	Dorchester P						9 53				11 28
140¼	Upwey Junction										11 39
143	Weymouth 339 arr.						10 7				11 45

Miles	Down		a.m	a.m	a.m	a.m	a.m	a.m	a.m	a.m
	WATERLOO 394 dep.		6 25			7 20		7 25	7 55	Dep. Portsmouth and Southsea 8 55 a.m page 380
12	Surbiton 394 "		6 43			7 38		7 43	8 13	
24¼	Woking 394 "		7 8		7 25	7 57		8 8	8 45	
28	Brookwood Z		7 15	Dep Portsmouth and Southsea 8 8 a.m page 380	7 32	8 4		8 15	8 51	
33½	Farnborough A		Via Alresford, page 375		7 43	8 15		Via Alresford page 375	9 0	
36½	Fleet				7 50	8 21			9 7	
40	Winchfield B				7 57	8 28			9 13	
42¼	Hook C				8 3	8 34			9 19	
48	Basingstoke 340 arr.				8 13	8 44			9 28	
	Basingstoke dep.				8 17	8 48				
58½	Micheldever				8 34	To Salisbury, page 340				
66½	Winchester D		8 35		8 47			9 41		
69½	Shawford, for Twyford		8 42		8 53		9 13	9 47		
73½	Eastleigh F 376, 380 arr.		8 50		9 0		9 21	9 55		
	Eastleigh dep.				9 2		9 22			
76	Swaythling				9 9					
77½	St Denys 376			9 7	9 13		9 29			9 50
78½	Northam			9 11	9 17					
79½	Southampton G 500 arr.			9 15	9 20		9 35			
	Southampton dep.									
79½	Southampton Cen. H arr.									9 56
	Southampton Cen. dep.									
80½	Millbrook									
82	Redbridge 380									
82¾	Totton, for Eling 375									
85¼	Lyndhurst Road									
88½	Beaulieu Road									
93	Brockenhurst 338 arr.									
97¾	338 Lymington Town arr									
—	338 Yarmouth Slipway "									
—	Brockenhurst dep.									
95¼	Sway									
98¾	New Milton J									
101½	Hinton Admiral W									
104¼	Christchurch L									
106½	Pokesdown O									
107	Boscombe									
108	Bournemouth Central arr.									
	Bournemouth Central dep.									
111½	Bournemouth West arr.									
	Bournemouth West dep.									
110¾	Branksome									
112	Parkstone for Sandbanks									
114	Poole 339									
116	Hamworthy Junction									
119	Holton Heath									
121	Wareham arr.									
—	Wareham dep.									
127	Corfe Castle									
132	Swanage arr.									
—	Wareham dep.									
126	Wool, for Lulworth Cove K									
130¼	Moreton									
136	Dorchester P									
140¼	Upwey Junction									
143	Weymouth 339 arr.									

For Notes, see page 329

LONDON, BASINGSTOKE, SOUTHAMPTON, BOURNEMOUTH, WAREHAM, SWANAGE, and WEYMOUTH

Down — **Week Days**—*continued*

Down	a.m	a.m			a.m	a.m		a.m	a.m	a.m	a.m	p.m	a.m	p.m
		Refreshment Car, Waterloo to Bournemouth				Through Train Reading (G.W.R.) to Portsmouth and Southsea (arr 11 36 a.m.), pages 495 and 376		To Plymouth, see page 340; Refreshment Car, Waterloo to Exeter			Dep. Portsmouth and Southsea 10 34 a.m., page 380			
WATERLOO 394 dep.	..	8 30		..	..	..	..	9 0	..	..		..	9 30	..
Surbiton 394 "	..	8‖48		..	..	..	..	9‖17	..	..		..	9‖48	..
Woking 394 "	..	9 6		..	..	..	..	9 35	..	..		..	10 6	..
Brookwood Z	..	..		..	..	..	..	..	..	..		..	..	..
Farnborough A	..	..		..	..	..	..	..	..	..		..	..	..
Fleet	..	..		..	..	..	..	..	..	..		..	..	..
Winchfield B	..	..		..	..	..	..	..	..	..		..	..	..
Hook C	..	..		..	..	..	..	..	..	..		..	..	..
Basingstoke 340 arr.	..	9 38		..	..	9 45	..	10 6	..	..		..	1039	..
Basingstoke 340 dep.	..	9 40		..	..	9 55	..	10 8	..	..		..	1040	..
Micheldever	..	..		..	..	1011	..	..	..	..		..	..	..
Winchester D	..	10 7		..	..	1026	..	..	1045	..		..	11 7	..
Shawford, for Twyford	..	..		..	1021	1033	..	..	..	..		..	..	..
Eastleigh F 376, 380 arr.	..	..		..	1028	1041	..	..	1055	..		..	1119	..
Eastleigh F 376, 380 dep.	..	..		..	1029	1047	..	..	11 0	..		..	1121	..
Swaythling	..	..		..	1035		..		11 7	..		..	..	..
St. Denys 376	..	..		..	1039		..		1111	..	1122	..	..	..
Northam	..	..		..	1043		..		1115	..	..	..	..	..
Southampton G 500 arr.	..	..		..	1047		..		1119	..	..	..	..	..
Southampton G 500 dep.	1010	..		..	..		..		..	..	..	..	..	..
Southampton Cen. H arr.	1015	10 26		..	..		..		..	..	1128	..	11[illegible]1	..
Southampton Cen. H dep.	..	10 29		..	..		..		..	..	..	..	1134	..
Millbrook	..	..		..	..		..		..	..	..	..	..	..
Redbridge 380	..	..		..	..		..		..	..	..	..	..	..
Totton, for Eling 375	..	..		..	..		..		..	..	..	..	..	..
Lyndhurst Road	..	..		..	..		..		..	..	..	..	..	..
Beaulieu Road	..	..		..	..		..		..	..	..	..	..	..
Brockenhurst 338 arr.	..	10 51		..	..		..		..	..	..	..	1155	..
338 Lymington Town arr.	..	11 8		..	..		..		..	..	..	..	121[illegible]	..
338 Yarm'th via St'nway "	..	..		..	..		..		..	..	..	..	1 10	..
Brockenhurst dep.	..	10 53		..	..		..		..	1113	..	..	1156	..
Sway	..	..		..	..		..		..	1120	..	..	..	..
New Milton J	..	..		..	..		..		..	1127	..	..	12 8	..
Hinton Admiral W	..	..		..	..		..		..	1134	..	..	..	..
Christchurch L	..	..		..	..		..		..	1142	..	..	1218	..
Pokesdown O	..	..		..	..		..		..	1148	..	..	1225	..
Boscombe	..	..		..	..		..		..	1152	..	..	..	..
Bournemouth Central arr.	..	11 15		..	..		..		..	1156	..	..	1230	..
Bournemouth Central dep.	..	11 18	11 24	..	..		..	..	..	..	..	..	1233	..
Bournemouth West arr.	..	..	11 34	..	..		..	..	..	..	..	..	1243	..
Bournemouth West dep.	..	..	..	..	..		..	..	..	..	..	1235	..	1255
Branksome	..	..	..	..	..		..	..	..	..	..	1238	..	1259
Parkstone, for Sandbanks	..	..	..	..	..		..	..	..	..	..	1242	..	1 3
Poole 338	..	11 33	..	..	..		..	..	..	..	..	1247	..	1 8
Hamworthy Junction	..	..	..	..	..		..	..	..	..	..	..	..	..
Holton Heath	..	..	..	..	..		..	..	..	..	..	..	..	..
Wareham arr.	..	11 44	..	..	..		..	..	..	..	..	..	..	..
Wareham dep.	..	12 15	..	..	..	..	..	..	..	..	..	..	..	..
Corfe Castle	..	12 27	..	..	..	..	..	..	..	..	..	..	..	..
Swanage arr.	..	12 37	..	..	..	..	..	..	..	..	..	..	..	..
Wareham dep.	..	11 46	..	..	..	..	..	..	..	..	..	..	..	..
Wool, for Lulworth Cove	..	11 56	..	..	..	..	..	..	..	..	..	..	..	..
Moreton	..	..	..	..	..	..	..	..	..	..	..	..	..	..
Dorchester P	..	12 11	..	..	..	..	..	..	..	..	..	..	..	..
Upwey Junction	..	..	..	..	..	..	..	..	..	..	..	..	..	..
Weymouth 339 arr.	..	12 25	..	..	..	..	..	..	..	..	..	..	..	..

Down	a.m	p.m	p.m	p.m	a.m	a.m		p.m	p.m	p.m		p.m		p.m
	Via Alresford page 375		Dep. Portsmouth and Southsea 11 26 a.m., page 380.		To Salisbury, page 342	Refreshment Car Train		Through Train Reading (G.W.R.) to Portsmouth and Southsea (arr 2 38 p.m), pages 495 and 376	1st & 3rd class Pullman Cars only Supplementary Fees charged; Bournemouth Belle	Calls Radipole Halt 4 13 p.m; Saturdays excepted		Saturdays only; Saturdays only ☞	Saturdays only	Saturdays only ☞
WATERLOO 394 dep.	10 27	..		..	1054	1130	..	..	1230	..	..	1235		1239
Surbiton 394 "	10 43	..		..	1043	..	..	..		..	..	..		1213
Woking 394 "	11 8	..		..	1126	..	..	..		..	..	..		1 11
Brookwood Z	11 15	..		..	1134	..	..	..		..	..			..
Farnborough A		..		..	1144	..	..	..		..	..			1 25
Fleet		..		..	1150	..	..	..		..	..			1 32
Winchfield B		..		..	1157	..	..	..		..	..			1 39
Hook C		..		..	12 3	..	..	..		..	..			1 45
Basingstoke 340 arr.		..		..	1213	1227	..	1245		..	..			1 55
Basingstoke 340 dep.		..		..	1215	1229	..	1251		..	..			
Micheldever		..		..		1246	..	1 8		..	..			
Winchester D	12 40	..		..		1259	..	1 21		..	..			
Shawford, for Twyford	12 46	..		..		..	..	1 27		..	..			
Eastleigh F 376, 380 arr.	12 54	..		..		..	..	1 35		..	..			
Eastleigh F 376, 380 dep.	..	..		..		..	..	1 46		..	..			
Swaythling	..	..		1 23		..	..			..	..	..		
St. Denys 376	..	..	12 28	1 28		..	..			..	..	..		
Northam	..	..	..	1 32		..	..			..	..	..		
Southampton G 500 arr.	..	..	..	1 36		..	..			..	..	..		
Southampton G 500 dep.	..	..	..	1 40		..	..			..	..	..		
Southampton Cen. H arr.	..	..	12 34	..	..	1 19	..		1 55	..	..	2 8		..
Southampton Cen. H dep.	..	..	..	..	..	1 23	..		1 57	..	..	2 11		Stop
Millbrook	..	..	..	..	..	..	..				..	..		
Redbridge 380	..	..	..	..	..	..	..				..	..		
Totton, for Eling 375	..	..	..	..	..	..	..				..	..		
Lyndhurst Road	..	..	..	..	..	..	..				..	..		
Beaulieu Road	..	..	..	..	..	..	..				..	..		
Brockenhurst 338 arr.	..	..	..	..	..	1 44	..				..	2 32		
338 Lymington Town arr.	..	..	..	..	..	2 5	..				..	3 10		
338 Yarm'th via St'nway "	..	..	..	..	..	2 45	..				..	..		
Brockenhurst dep.	..	..	..	..	..	1 46	..				..	2 33		
Sway	..	..	..	..	..	..	..				..	..		
New Milton J	..	..	..	..	..	1 58	..		..		..	..		
Hinton Admiral W	..	..	..	..	..	..	..		..		..	..		
Christchurch L	..	..	..	..	..	2 7	..		..		..	..		
Pokesdown O	..	..	..	..	..	2 14	..		..		..	..		
Boscombe	..	..	..	..	..	2 18	..		..		..	..		
Bournemouth Central arr.	..	..	..	..	..	2 22	..		2 35		..	2 55		p.m
Bournemouth Central dep.	..	1 1	..	..	..	2 24	..		2 37	2 57	..	2 59	3 4	3 12
Bournemouth West arr.	..	..	..	..	..	2 34	..		2 47	..	..	..	3 14	..
Bournemouth West dep.	..	..	..	..	..		..		..	..	..	..		..
Branksome	..	1 7	..	..	..		..		..	3 3	..	..		3 18
Parkstone, for Sandbanks	..	1 11	..	..	..		..		..	3 7	..	..		3 22
Poole 338	..	1 18	..	..	..		..		..	3 13	..	3 13		3 27
Hamworthy Junction	..	1 24	..	..	..		..		..	3 18	..	..		3 33
Holton Heath	..	1 29	..	..	..		..		..	3 23	..	..		3 39
Wareham arr.	..	1 35	..	..	..		..		..	3 29	..	3 24		3 45
Wareham dep.	..	2 16	..	..	..		..	..	..	3 37	..	3 37		..
Corfe Castle	..	2 28	..	..	..		..	..	..	3 49	..	3 49		..
Swanage arr.	..	2 38	..	..	..		..	..	..	3 59	..	3 59		..
Wareham dep.	..	1 36	..	..	..		..	..	..	3 30	..	3 26	..	3 46
Wool, for Lulworth Cove	..	1 45	..	..	..		..	..	..	3 39	..	..	..	3 55
Moreton	..	1 54	..	..	..		..	..	..	3 48	..	..	..	4 5
Dorchester P	..	2 4	..	..	..		..	..	..	3 58	..	3 46	..	4 16
Upwey Junction	..	2 15	..	..	..		..	..	..	4 9	..	..	..	4 30
Weymouth 339 arr.	..	2 21	..	..	..		..	..	..	4 18	..	4 2	..	4 36

For Notes, see page 329: for Continuation of Trains, see pages 326 to 329

LONDON, BASINGSTOKE, SOUTHAMPTON, BOURNEMOUTH, WAREHAM, SWANAGE, and WEYMOUTH

Down — **Week Days**—*continued*

Station	p.m	p.m	p.m	p.m	p.m	p.m	p.m	p.m	p.m	p.m	p.m
	Dep Fareham 1 28 p.m page 381	Through Train from Bristol (G.W.R.) pages 494 and 377			Saturdays excepted	Dep. Portsmouth and Southsea 2 3 p.m, page 381	Refreshment Car, Waterloo to Bournemouth		Through Train Reading (G.W.R.) to Portsmouth and Southsea (arr. 4 19 p.m). pages 495 and 377.	Via Alresford page 375	
WATERLOO 394 dep.					12 54			1 30		12 57	
Surbiton 394 "					12 43					1 13	
Woking 394 "					1 26					1 38	
Brookwood Z					1 34					1 45	
Farnborough A					1 44						
Fleet					1 50						
Winchfield B					1 57						
Hook C					2 3						
Basingstoke 340 arr.					2 13			2 32	2 22		
Basingstoke dep.								2 34	2 40		
Micheldever									2 56		
Winchester D				2 10				3 2	3 9	3 16	
Shawford, for Twyford				2 15						3 22	
Eastleigh F 376, 380 arr.				2 23					3 20	3 30	
Eastleigh dep.		2 5		2 40					3 25		
Swaythling		2 10		2 45							
St. Denys 376	2 3	2 15		2 49		3 0					
Northam		2 19									
Southampton G 500 arr.		2 23									
Southampton G dep.											
Southampton Cen. H arr.	2 10			2 55		3 6		3 20			
Southampton Cen. dep.	2 19							3 22			
Millbrook	2 24										
Redbridge 380	2 29										
Totton, for Eling 375	2 32										
Lyndhurst Road	2 39										
Beaulieu Road	2 45										
Brockenhurst 338 arr.	2 53							3 43			
338 Lymington Town arr.	3 10							4 11			
338 Yarmouth Slipway "								4 50			
Brockenhurst dep.	2 54							3 45			
Sway	3 1										
New Milton J	3 9							3 57			
Hinton Admiral W	3 15										
Christchurch L	3 21							4 7			
Pokesdown O	3 27							4 13			
Boscombe	3 30							4 16			
Bournemouth Central arr.	3 34							4 20			
Bournemouth Central dep.	3 36						4 22	4 28			
Bournemouth West arr.	3 46							4 38			
Bournemouth West dep.			4 30								4 47
Branksome			4 33								4 51
Parkstone, for Sandbanks			4 37								4 55
Poole 339			4 42				4 35				5 1
Hamworthy Junction											
Holton Heath											
Wareham arr.							4 46				
Wareham dep							4 57				
Corfe Castle							5 9				
Swanage arr.							5 21				
Wareham dep							4 47				
Wool, for Lulworth Cove K							4 56				
Moreton							5 5				
Dorchester P							5 15				
Upwey Junction							5 26				
Weymouth 339 arr.							5 32				

Station	p.m	p.m	p.m	p.m	p.m	p.m	p.m	p.m	p.m
	Saturdays only	Saturdays excepted			Saturdays only. To Fawley, arr. 4 51 p.m page 375		To Plymouth, page 342. Refreshment Car, Waterloo to Exeter		
WATERLOO 394 dep.	1 24	1 54					2 50		
Surbiton 394 "	1 13	1 43							
Woking 394 "	1 56	2 26							
Brookwood Z	2 3	2 34							
Farnborough A	2 13	2 44							
Fleet	2 20	2 50							
Winchfield B	2 27	2 57							
Hook C	2 34	3 3							
Basingstoke 340 arr.	2 46	3 13					3 51		
Basingstoke dep.							3 52		
Micheldever									
Winchester D									
Shawford, for Twyford						3 29			
Eastleigh F 376, 380 arr.						3 37			
Eastleigh dep.						3 38			4 9
Swaythling						3 44			4 14
St. Denys 376						3 48			4 18
Northam						3 52			4 22
Southampton G 500 arr.						3 56			4 26
Southampton G dep.					3 55			4 30	
Southampton Cen. H arr.					4 0			4 35	
Southampton Cen. dep.				3 40	4 5			4 37	
Millbrook				3 44	4 10				
Redbridge 380				3 49	4 15			4 43	
Totton, for Eling 375				3 52	4 20				
Lyndhurst Road				4 0					
Beaulieu Road				4 7					
Brockenhurst 338 arr.				4 15					
338 Lymington Town arr.				5 22					
338 Yarmouth Slipway "				6 10					
Brockenhurst dep.				4 17					
Sway				4 26					
New Milton J				4 33					
Hinton Admiral W				4 40					
Christchurch L				4 48					
Pokesdown O				4 55					
Boscombe				4 58					
Bournemouth Central arr.				5 2					
Bournemouth Central dep.			5 0						
Bournemouth West arr.									
Bournemouth West dep.									
Branksome			5 6						
Parkstone, for Sandbanks			5 11						
Poole 339			5 18						
Hamworthy Junction			5 24						
Holton Heath			5 31						
Wareham arr.			5 37						
Wareham dep			5 38						
Corfe Castle			5 50						
Swanage arr.			6 0						
Wareham dep									
Wool, for Lulworth Cove K									
Moreton									
Dorchester P									
Upwey Junction									
Weymouth 339 arr.									

Station	p.m	p.m	p.m		p.m	p.m	p.m	p.m	p.m	p.m	p.m
			To Fawley, arr. 6 15 p.m page 375		Via Alresford, page 375					Dep. Portsmouth and Southsea, 4 35 p.m., page 381	
WATERLOO 394 dep.		3 20			2 27	3 30					3 54
Surbiton 394 "					2 43	3 13					3 43
Woking 394 "					3 8	4 12					4 26
Brookwood Z					3 15						4 34
Farnborough A											4 44
Fleet											4 50
Winchfield B											4 57
Hook C											5 4
Basingstoke 340 arr.						4 32					5 14
Basingstoke dep.						4 34					
Micheldever						4 52					
Winchester D		4 42			4 54	5 5					
Shawford, for Twyford					5 0						
Eastleigh F 376, 380 arr.					5 8	5 16					
Eastleigh dep.						5 17	5 21		5 34		
Swaythling							5 26				
St. Denys 376							5 30		5 41	5 48	
Northam							5 33				
Southampton G 500 arr.							5 37				
Southampton G dep.			5 15								
Southampton Cen. H arr.		5 0	5 21			5 28			5 48	5 54	
Southampton Cen. dep.		5 3	5 26			5 31			5 50	5 56	
Millbrook			5 35						5 54		
Redbridge 380			5 41						5 59	6 3	
Totton, for Eling 375			5 45						6 2		
Lyndhurst Road									6 9		
Beaulieu Road									6 15		
Brockenhurst 338 arr.		5 22				5 52			6 23		
338 Lymington Town arr.						6 26					
338 Yarmouth Slipway "											
Brockenhurst dep.		5 23				5 54					
Sway											
New Milton J						6 6					
Hinton Admiral W											
Christchurch L						6 15					
Pokesdown O						6 21					
Boscombe											
Bournemouth Central arr.		5 45				6 26					
Bournemouth Central dep.	5 48	5 54				6 30					
Bournemouth West arr.		6 4				6 40					
Bournemouth West dep.								6 50			
Branksome	5 56							6 54			
Parkstone, for Sandbanks	6 0							6 58			
Poole 339	6 7							7 3			
Hamworthy Junction	6 13										
Holton Heath	6 19										
Wareham arr.	6 25										
Wareham dep											
Corfe Castle											
Swanage arr.											
Wareham dep	6 27										
Wool, for Lulworth Cove K	6 36										
Moreton	6 47										
Dorchester P	6 58										
Upwey Junction	7 12										
Weymouth 339 arr.	7 18										

For Notes, see page 329

LONDON, BASINGSTOKE, SOUTHAMPTON, BOURNEMOUTH, WAREHAM, SWANAGE, and WEYMOUTH.

Week Days—*continued.*

Down	p.m		p.m	p.m	p.m	p.m	p.m	p.m	p.m	p.m	p.m	p.m	p.m	p.m	p.m	p.m
WATERLOO 394 ......dep.	4 35	Refreshment Car Waterloo to Bournemouth	..	..	..	4 27	5 0	5 9	..	5 30	..	5 39	6 0	Dep. Portsmouth and Southsea 6 45 p.m., page 381	5 54	6 9
Surbiton 394 ......"	..		..	..	..	4 43	4 43	4 43	..	..	..	5 13	..		5 43	6 13
Woking 394 ......"	..		..	..	..	5 8	5 33	5 41	..	..	..	6 11	..		6 26	6 43
Brookwood Z	..		..	..	..	5 15	..	..	Dep. Portsmouth and Southsea 6 3 p.m., page 381	..	..	6 19	..		6 35	..
Farnborough A	..		..	..	..	Via Alresford page 375	..	5 55		..	..	6 28	..		6 45	6 59
Fleet	..		..	..	..		..	6 2		..	..	6 35	..		6 51	7 6
Winchfield B	..		..	..	..		..	6 9		..	..	6 42	..		6 58	7 13
Hook C	..		..	..	..		..	6 15		..	..	6 48	..		7 4	7 19
Basingstoke 340 ...... arr.	..		..	..	5 35		6 5	6 25		6 30	..	7 1	6 58		7 14	7 29
Basingstoke 340 ...... dep.	..		..	..	5 40		6 7	Saturdays excepted		6 32	..	7 4	6 59		Saturdays only	Saturdays excepted
Micheldever	..		..	..	5 56		To Yeovil page 342			6 50	..	Saturdays excepted To Salisbury, page 342	Refreshment Car Waterloo to Exeter, page 342			
Winchester D	5 58		..	..	6 8	6 39				7 4	7 9					
Shawford, for Twyford	..		..	..	6 14	..				..	7 14					
Eastleigh F 376, 380 arr.	..		..	..	6 22	..				7 15	7 22					
Eastleigh F 376, 380 dep.	..		..	..	6 25	..				7 17	7 23					
Swaythling	..		..	..	6 32	..				..	7 29					
St. Denys 376	..		..	..	6 36	..			7 12	..	7 33			7 53		
Northam	..		..	..	6 40	..			..	..	7 37			..		
Southampton G 500 arr.	..		..	..	6 44	..			..	..	7 41			..	..	..
Southampton G 500 dep.	..		..	6 5	Through Train from Reading (G.W.R.) see page 495	..		..	..	..	..			..	..	..
Southampton Cen. H arr.	6 16		..	6 10		..		..	7 18	7 28	..			7 59	..	..
Southampton Cen. H dep.	6 18		..	6 22		..	..	..	..	7 31	..			..	..	..
Millbrook	..		..	6 26		..	..	..	..	..	..			..	..	..
Redbridge 380	..		..	6 31		..	..	..	..	..	..			..	..	..
Totton, for Eling 375	..		..	6 34		..	..	..	..	..	..			..	..	..
Lyndhurst Road	..		..	6 41		..	..	..	..	..	..			..	..	..
Beaulieu Road	..		..	6 47		..	..	..	..	..	..			..	..	..
Brockenhurst 338 ....arr.	6 38		..	6 55		..	..	..	..	7 52	..			..	..	..
338 Lymington Town ..arr.	7 6		..	..		..	..	..	..	8 20	..	..		..	..	..
338 Yarmouth Slipway "	7A45		..	..		..	..	..	..	..	..	..		..	..	..
Brockenhurst ......dep.	6 40		..	6 58		..	..	..	..	7 54	..	..	..	..	..	..
Sway	..		..	7 6		..	..	..	..	..	..	..	..	..	..	..
New Milton J	..		..	7 13		..	..	..	..	8 6	..	..	..	..	..	..
Hinton Admiral W	..		..	7 20		..	..	..	..	..	..	..	..	..	..	..
Christchurch L	..		..	7 27		..	..	..	..	8 16	..	..	..	..	..	..
Pokesdown O	..		..	7 33		..	..	..	..	8 23	..	..	..	..	..	..
Boscombe	..		..	7 36		..	..	..	..	8 27	..	..	..	..	..	..
Bournemouth Central arr.	7 2		..	7 40		..	..	..	..	8 31	..	..	..	..	..	..
Bournemouth Central dep.	7 4	7 10	7 20	..		..	..	..	..	8 34	..	..	..	..	..	..
Bournemouth West. arr.	..	7 20	..	..		..	..	..	..	8 44	..	..	..	..	..	..
Bournemouth West. dep.	..	..	..	..		..	..	..	..	..	..	..	..	..	..	..
Branksome	..	..	7 26	..	..	..	..	..	..	..	..	..	..	..	..	..
Parkstone, for Sandbanks	..	..	7 30	..	..	..	..	..	..	..	..	..	..	..	..	..
Poole 339	7 17	..	7 36	..	..	..	..	..	..	..	..	..	..	..	..	..
Hamworthy Junction	..	..	7 42	..	..	..	..	..	..	..	..	..	..	..	..	..
Holton Heath	..	..	7 47	..	..	..	..	..	..	..	..	..	..	..	..	..
Wareham ......arr.	7 28	..	7 53	..	..	..	..	..	..	..	..	..	..	..	..	..
Wareham ......dep.	7 35	..	..	..	..	..	..	..	..	..	..	..	..	..	..	..
Corfe Castle	7 49	..	..	..	..	..	..	..	..	..	..	..	..	..	..	..
Swanage ......arr.	7 59	..	..	..	..	..	..	..	..	..	..	..	..	..	..	..
Wareham ......dep.	7 30	..	7 54	..	..	..	..	..	..	..	..	..	..	..	..	..
Wool, for Lulworth Cove K	..	..	8 3	..	..	..	..	..	..	..	..	..	..	..	..	..
Moreton	..	..	8 12	..	..	..	..	..	..	..	..	..	..	..	..	..
Dorchester P	7 49	..	8 22	..	..	..	..	..	..	..	..	..	..	..	..	..
Upwey Junction	..	..	..	..	..	..	..	..	..	..	..	..	..	..	..	..
Weymouth 339 ......arr.	8 3	..	8 38	..	..	..	..	..	..	..	..	..	..	..	..	..

Down	p.m	p.m		p.m	p.m	p.m	p.m	p.m	p.m	p.m	p.m	p.m	p.m	p.m	p.m
WATERLOO 394 ......dep.	..	6 30	Refreshment Car, Waterloo to Bournemouth	..	6 54	Dep. Portsmouth and Southsea 7 45 p.m., page 381	..	7 30	..	6 57	7 54	9 0	8 54	..	1030
Surbiton 394 ......"	..	..		..	6§53		..	..	..	7 13	7 43	..	8 43	..	1013
Woking 394 ......"	..	..		..	7 26		..	..	..	7 38	8 26	..	9 26	..	11 6
Brookwood Z	..	Saturdays excepted		..	7 34		..	..	..	7 45	8 34	..	9 34	..	..
Farnborough A	..			..	7 44		..	..	..	Via Alresford page 375	8 44	..	9 44	..	1124
Fleet	..			..	7 50		..	..	..		8 51	..	9 50	..	..
Winchfield B	..			..	7 57		..	..	..		8 58	..	9 57	..	..
Hook C	..			..	8 3		..	..	..		9 4	..	10 3	..	..
Basingstoke 340 ...... arr.	..			7 30	8 13		..	8 30	..		9 14	9 56	1013	..	1144
Basingstoke 340 ...... dep.	..			7 35	..		..	8 32	..		Stop	9 58	1015	..	1151
Micheldever	..			7 50	..		..	8 49	..		..	..	To Salisbury, page 342	..	..
Winchester D	..			8 2	..		..	9 2	..	9n19	..	10 26		1033	1221
Shawford, for Twyford	..			8 9	..		8 32	..	..	9 27	..	..		1038	..
Eastleigh F 376, 380 arr.	..	..		8 17	..		8 39	9 14	..	9 35	p.m	..		1046	1233
Eastleigh F 376, 380 dep.	..	..		8 20	..		8 41	9 15	..	..	9 45	..		1047	1241
Swaythling	..	..		8 27	..		8 47	..	..	..	9 50	..		1053	..
St. Denys 376	..	..		8 31	..	8 49	8 51	9 25	..	..	9 54	..		1057	..
Northam	..	..		8 35	..	..	8 55	..	..	..	9 58	..		..	..
Southampton G 500 arr.	..	..		8 39	..	..	8 59	..	..	..	10 2	10V47		..	1253
Southampton G 500 dep.	..	..		Through Train from Reading (G.W.R.), see page 495	..	..	..	..	..	..	..	Refreshment Car provided on Mondays, Wednesdays and Fridays		..	1 18
Southampton Cen. H arr.	..	8 6			..	8 55	..	9 31	..	..	..			11 4	..
Southampton Cen. H dep.	..	8 10			..	8 59	..	9 34	..	..	..		..	..	..
Millbrook	..	..			..	9 4	..	..	..	..	..		..	..	..
Redbridge 380	..	..			..	9 9	..	..	..	..	..		..	..	..
Totton, for Eling 375	..	..			..	..	..	9 44	..	..	..		..	..	..
Lyndhurst Road	..	..			..	..	..	9 51	..	..	..		..	..	..
Beaulieu Road	..	..			..	..	..	9 57	..	..	..		..	..	..
Brockenhurst 338 ....arr.	..	..			..	..	..	10 5	..	..	..		..	..	1 40
338 Lymington Town ..arr.	..	..			..	..	..	..	..	..	..		..	..	..
338 Yarmouth Slipway "	..	..			..	..	..	..	..	..	..		..	..	..
Brockenhurst ......dep.	Saturdays only	Saturdays excepted ☞			..	..	..	10 6	..	..	..		..	..	1 45
Sway					..	..	..	10 14	..	..	..		..	..	..
New Milton J					..	..	..	10 22	..	..	..		..	..	..
Hinton Admiral W					..	..	..	10 29	..	..	..		..	..	..
Christchurch L					..	..	..	10 37	..	..	..		..	..	2 4
Pokesdown O					..	..	..	10 43	..	..	..		..	..	..
Boscombe					..	..	..	10 47	..	..	..		..	..	..
Bournemouth Central arr.		8 51			..	..	..	10 51	..	..	..		..	..	2 14
Bournemouth Central dep.	8 55	8 55	9 1		..	..	..	10 54	..	..	..	..	..	..	2 24
Bournemouth West. arr.	..	..	9 11		..	..	..	11 4	..	..	..	..	..	..	..
Bournemouth West. dep.	..	..	Saturdays excepted		..	..	..	..	..	..	..	..	..	..	..
Branksome	9 3	9 3		..	..	..	..	..	11 20	..	..	..	..	..	..
Parkstone, for Sandbanks	9 7	9 7		..	..	..	..	..	11 24	..	..	..	..	..	..
Poole 339	9 13	9 13		..	..	..	..	..	11 28	..	..	..	..	..	2 37
Hamworthy Junction	9 19	9 19		..	..	..	..	..	11 34	..	..	..	..	..	..
Holton Heath	9 25	9 25		..	..	..	..	..	..	..	..	..	..	..	..
Wareham ......arr.	9 31	9 31		..	..	..	..	..	..	..	..	..	..	..	2 50
Wareham ......dep.	9 40	9 40	..	..	..	..	..	..	..	..	..	..	..	..	..
Corfe Castle	9 52	9 52	..	..	..	..	..	..	..	..	..	..	..	..	..
Swanage ......arr.	10 2	10 2	..	..	..	..	..	..	..	..	..	..	..	..	..
Wareham ......dep.	9 32	9 32	..	..	..	..	..	..	..	..	..	..	..	..	2 53
Wool, for Lulworth Cove K	9 41	9 41	..	..	..	..	..	..	..	..	..	..	..	..	3Y1
Moreton	9 51	9 51	..	..	..	..	..	..	..	..	..	..	..	..	..
Dorchester P	10 2	10 2	..	..	..	..	..	..	..	..	..	..	..	..	3 18
Upwey Junction	1015	1015	..	..	..	..	..	..	..	..	..	..	..	..	..
Weymouth 339 ......arr.	1021	1021	..	..	..	..	..	..	..	..	..	..	..	..	..

For Notes, see page 329; for SUNDAY TRAINS, see pages 328 and 329.

LONDON, BASINGSTOKE, SOUTHAMPTON, BOURNEMOUTH, WAREHAM, SWANAGE, and WEYMOUTH

Down — **Sundays**

Station	a.m	a.m	a.m	a.m	a.m	a.m	a.m		a.m	a.m	p.m	a.m	a.m	p.m	a.m	a.m
				Via Alresford, page 375	Through Train from Reading (G.W.R.), page 495	Dep Portsmouth and Southsea 10 15 a.m., page 382						Via Alresford page 375	To Plymouth, page 344; Refreshment Car, Waterloo to Exeter	Dep Portsmouth and Southsea 11 40 a.m., page 382		Refreshment Car Train
WATERLOO 394 dep.	3 25			7 25			8 54		9 30			1027	11 0		1054	1130
Surbiton 394 "	3			7 43			8 43		9U48			1043	10 43		1143	
Woking 394 "				8 8			9 26		10U6			11 8	11U32		1126	
Brookwood Z				8 15			9 34					1115			1124	
Farnborough A	4 16						9 44								1144	
Fleet							9 50								1150	
Winchfield B							9 57								1157	
Hook C		3					10 3								12 3	
Basingstoke 340 arr	4 36				9 37		1013		1036				12 4		1213	1227
Basingstoke 340 dep.	4 38	4 52			9 43		1016		1038				12 5		Stop	1229
Micheldever					10 1		1033									
Winchester D		5 22	8 8	9 41	1015		1045		11 6			1248				1256
Shawford, for Twyford			8 13	9 47	1021							1254				
Eastleigh F 376, 380 arr.	5 11	5 34	8 21	9 55	1029		1056					1 2				1 7
Eastleigh dep.	5 12	5 55	8 22		1032		11 0				12 8					1 9
Swaythling			8 28		1039						1213					
St. Denys 376		6 4	8 33		1043	11 7	11 9				1217			1223		
Northam																
Southampton G 500 arr.		6 11					1115				1223				p.m	
Southampton G dep.		Stop													1253	
Southampton Cen. H arr.	5 23		8 39		1050	1113			1125					1230	1258	1 20
Southampton Cen. dep.	5 30		8 42		1054				1128					1232	1 0	1 22
Millbrook			8 47		1059										1 4	
Redbridge 380			8 51													
Totten, for Eling			8 53		11 4										1 9	
Lyndhurst Road			9 0		1111									1243	1 16	
Beaulieu Road			9 7		1117										1 23	
Brockenhurst 338 arr.	5Z51		9 14		1124				1149					1254	1 31	1 43
338 Lymington Town arr									1210							2 15
338 Yarmouth Slipway "									1250							3 5
Brockenhurst dep.			9 15		1125				1150					1255		1 45
Sway			9 22		1132									1 2		
New Milton J	6 7		9 29		1139				12 0					1 9		1 57
Hinton Admiral W			9 36		1145									1 15		
Christchurch L	6 17		9 43		1152				1210					1 21		2 6
Pokesdown O	6 25		9 49		1158				1216					1 27		2 13
Boscombe	6 29		9 52		12 1				1219					1 30		2 16
Bournemouth Central arr.	6 33	a.m	9 56		12 5				1223					1 34		2 20
Bournemouth Central dep.		8 5	10 7						1225	1220				1 36		2 22
Bournemouth West arr.									1234					1 46		2 32
Bournemouth West dep																
Branksome		8 13	10 16							1238						
Parkstone, for Sandbanks		8 18	10 21							1242						
Poole 339		8 25	10 29							1249						
Hamworthy Junction			10 36							1255						
Holton Heath		Stop	10 42							1 1						
Wareham arr.			10 48							1 7						
Wareham dep.			11 0													
Corfe Castle			11 12													
Swanage arr.			11 23													
Wareham dep.			10 51							1 8						
Wool, for Lulworth Cove K			11 1							1 17						
Moreton		a.m	11 11							1 27						
Dorchester P		9 20	11 21							1 37						
Upwey Junction			11 34							1 48						
Weymouth 339 arr.		9 32	11 40							1 54						

Station		p.m	p.m	p.m	p.m	p.m	p.m	p.m		pm	p.m	p.m	p.m
				Bournemouth Belle; 1st and 3rd class Pullman Cars only; Supplementary fees charged	Continuation of 11 30 a.m from Waterloo	Dep Portsmouth & Southsea 1 25 p.m., page 382		Refreshment Car, Waterloo to Bournemouth			To Andover Junction, see page 382		
WATERLOO 394 dep.			1224	1230				1 30					2 54
Surbiton 394 "			1213										2 43
Woking 394 "			1256										3 28
Brookwood Z			1 4										3 37
Farnborough A			1 14										3 47
Fleet			1 20										3 53
Winchfield B			1 27										4 0
Hook C			1 33										4 6
Basingstoke 340 arr			1 43					2 27					4 16
Basingstoke 340 dep.		1237	Stop					2 28					4 22
Micheldever		1252											4 39
Winchester D		1 5						2 56		3 4	4 20		4 52
Shawford, for Twyford		1 11								3 9	4 25		4 58
Eastleigh F 376, 380 arr.		1 19	p.m							317	4 33		5 6
Eastleigh dep.		1 21	2 16				2 28			323	4 38		5 8
Swaythling		1 28	2 21				2 33			330	4 43		5 15
St. Denys 376		1 32	2 25			2 30	2 37			334	4 47		5 19
Northam													
Southampton G 500 arr.			2 31							340			
Southampton G dep.													
Southampton Cen. H arr.		1 38		1 55		2 36	2 43	3 15			4 53		5 25
Southampton Cen. dep.		1 40		1 57		Stop	Stop	3 18			4 55		
Millbrook		1 44									4 59		
Redbridge 380		1 48									5 4		
Totten, for Eling		1 50											
Lyndhurst Road		1 57											
Beaulieu Road													
Brockenhurst 338 arr.		2 8						3 39					
338 Lymington Town arr								3 55					
338 Yarmouth Slipway "						p.m		4 40					
Brockenhurst dep.						2 20		3 40					
Sway						2 27							
New Milton J						2 34		3 52					
Hinton Admiral W						2 41							
Christchurch L						2 48		4 1					
Pokesdown O						2 54		4 8					
Boscombe						2 57		4 11					
Bournemouth Central arr.				2 35		3 1	p.m	4 15					
Bournemouth Central dep.				2 37	2 42		3 10	4 17	4 22				
Bournemouth West arr.				2 47				4 27					
Bournemouth West dep													
Branksome					2 50		3 16		4 30				
Parkstone, for Sandbanks					2 54		3 19		4 34				
Poole 339					3 1		3 24		4 39				
Hamworthy Junction					3 7				4 44				
Holton Heath					3 13				4 50				
Wareham arr.					3 19				4 56				
Wareham dep.					3 30				5 6			6 32	
Corfe Castle					3 42				5 18			6 44	
Swanage arr.					3 52				5 28			6 54	
Wareham dep.					3 21				4 57				
Wool, for Lulworth Cove K					3 30				5 6				
Moreton					3 40				5 15				
Dorchester P					3 50				5 25				
Upwey Junction					4 1				5 36				
Weymouth 339 arr.					4 8				5 42				

For Notes, see page 329

LONDON, BASINGSTOKE, SOUTHAMPTON, BOURNEMOUTH, WAREHAM, SWANAGE, and WEYMOUTH

Sundays - *continued*

Down	p.m	p.m	p.m	p.m	p.m	p.m	p.m	p.m		pm	p.m	p.m	p.m	p.m	p.m	p.m	p.m	p.m	
	Dep Portsmouth and Southsea 5 5 p.m, page 382		Via Alresford page 375	To Plymouth, page 344 Refreshment Car, Waterloo to Exeter			Dep. Portsmouth and Southsea 6 33 p.m, page 382				Via Alresford, page 375		To Yeovil page 344				To Salisbury page 344		
WATERLOO 394 .....dep			3 27	4 0		4 54		6 30			6 27	6 54	7 30			8 54	9 30	9 54	
Surbiton 394 .... "			3 43			4 43		6 13			6 43	6 43				8 43	9 51	9 51	
Woking 394 .... "			4 8			5 26		7 U2			7 8	7 26				9 26	1010	1029	
Brookwood Z			4 15			5 34					7 15	7 34				9 34			
Farnborough A						5 44						7 44				9 44	1025	1046	
Fleet						5 50						7 50				9 50	1032	1053	
Winchfield B						5 57						7 57				9 57		11 0	
Hook C						6 3						8 3				10 3		11 6	
Basingstoke 340 arr.				5 2		6 15		7 32				8 13	8 31			1013	1049	1116	
Basingstoke 340 dep				5 3		6 16		7 34		744			8 33	9 0		1016	1050	1120	
Micheldever										759						1033			
Winchester D			5 39			6 44		8 1		812	8 58			9 26	9 50	1047		1150	
Shawford, for Twyford			5 45							818	9 4				9 55	1053			
Eastleigh F 376, 380 arr.			5 53			6 55		8 15		826	9 12			9 37	10 3	11 1		12 2	
Eastleigh F 376, 380 dep			5 54		6 20	6 58		8 19		828	9 13			9 38	10 4	11 3		12 8	
Swaythling			5 59		6 25	7 5				835	9 19			9 44	1010	11 9			
St. Denys 376	5 49		6 3		6 29	7 9	7 38			839	9 23			9 48	1014	1113			
Northam																			
Southampton G 500 arr.			6 9							845	9 29				1020	1119		1220	
Southampton G 500 dep.											Stop							1 18	
Southampton Cen. H arr.	5 55				6 35	7 15	7 44	8 31						9 55					
Southampton Cen. H dep.		6 5						8 33						9 57					
Millbrook																			
Redbridge 380																			
Totton, for Eling		6 11												10 7					
Lyndhurst Road		6 18												1014					
Beaulieu Road		6 24												1021					
Brockenhurst 338 arr.		6 32						8 54						1029				1 40	
338 Lymington Town arr.		6‡50																	
338 Yarmouth slipway "																			
Brockenhurst dep.		6 33						8§56						1030				1 43	
Sway		6 40												1038					
New Milton J		6 47						9 8						1046					
Hinton Admiral W		6 54												1053					
Christchurch L		7 1						9 17						11 1				2 4	
Pokesdown O		7 7						9 23						11 7					
Boscombe		7 10						9 27						1110					
Bournemouth Central arr.		7 14						9 31			p.m			1114				2 14	
Bournemouth Central dep.								9 35	9 40		10 0							2 24	
Bournemouth West arr.									9 50										
Bournemouth West dep.																			
Branksome								9 43			10 6								
Parkstone, for Sandbanks								9 47			10 9								
Poole 339								9 53			1014							2 37	
Hamworthy Junction								9 59											
Holton Heath								10 5											
Wareham arr.								1011										2 50	
Wareham dep.																			
Corfe Castle																			
Swanage arr.																			
Wareham dep.								1012										2 53	
Wool, for Lulworth Cove K								1021										3 1	
Moreton								1030											
Dorchester P								1040										3 18	
Upwey Junction																			
Weymouth 339 arr.								1055										3 36	

3 Third class only
A Nearly 1 mile from Farnborough North Sta
A Every weekday to 1st November, 1947, Fridays and Saturdays, 7th November, 1947, to 27th March, 1948, and every week day commencing 29th March, 1948
B Station for Odiham (3 miles) and Hartley Wintney (2 miles)
C Station for Odiham (2 miles)
D 1 mile from Cheesehill Station
F Station for Bishopstoke
G Southampton Terminus for Docks
H About 1 mile from the Docks and Pier
J Sta. for Barton-on-Sea (1½ miles) and Milford-on-Sea (3¾ miles). Omnibus service available by Hants & Dorset Motor Services Ltd.
K Omnibus service available between Wool, Bovington Camp, and Lulworth Cove, by Southern National Omnibus Co. Ltd.
L Sta. for Southbourne-on-Sea
n Arr 9 15 p.m.
O For Eastern Bournemouth
P Over ½ mile to G.W. Station
S O or **S0** Saturdays only
SX Saturdays excepted
U Calls to take up only
V Passengers for Terminus alight at Southampton Dockson Mons., Weds., and Fris. arriving 10 51 p.m.
W Station for Highcliffe-on-Sea (1¼ miles)
Y Stops on Sunday morns only to set down
Z For Bisley Camp
Z Stops to set down only
‡ Commences 4th April 1948
§ 10 mins. *earlier* on Sats.

LOCAL TRAINS between Woking and Brookwood, page 390—Basingstoke and Southampton, 384—Southampton and Redbridge, 384—Christchurch and Bournemouth, 336—Bournemouth and Poole, 336

OTHER TRAINS between London and Southampton, page 375—Southampton and Totton, 375

WEYMOUTH, SWANAGE, WAREHAM, BOURNEMOUTH, SOUTHAMPTON, BASINGSTOKE, and LONDON

Week Days

Miles	Up	a.m	a.m	a.m	a.m	a.m	a.m	a.m	a.m	a.m	a.m	a.m	a.m	a.m	a.m	a.m	a.m	a.m	a.m	a.m	a.m	a.m	a.m	a.m	a.m	a.m	a.m	a.m	a.m	a.m	a.m	a.m
—	Weymouth dep.																										7 38					
2¼	Upwey Junction																															
7	Dorchester M																							7 0			7 53					
12½	Moreton																							7 9								
17	Wool, for Lulworth Cove K																							7 17			8 5					
22	Wareham 324 arr.																							7 25			8 13					
—	Mls Swanage dep.																								7 15		7 47					
—	5 Corfe Castle																								7 25		7 57					
—	11 Wareham 324 arr.																								7 37		8 9					
—	Wareham dep.																							7 26	7 39		8 14					
24	Holton Heath																							7 31	7 45							
27	Hamworthy Junction																							7 37	7 51							
29	Poole 339																	6 58						Arr Broadstone 7 45 and Wimborne 7 51 a.m	7 56		8 25					
31	Parkstone, for Sandbanks																	7 3							8 2							
32½	Branksome																	7 7							8 8							
33½	Bournemouth West arr.																	7 12							8 12							
	Bournemouth West dep.																	7 20				From Fawley (dep 8 6 a.m) page 375	7 30		Stop	8 20						8 35
35	Bournemouth Central arr.																	7 28					7 38			8 28	8 35					8 43
	Bournemouth Central dep.												6 30	7 0				7 30					7 40				8 40			From Portsmouth and Southsea (dep. 9 0 a.m), page 380		8 45
36	Boscombe												6 33	7 3				7 33					7 44									8 49
36½	Pokesdown O												6 36	7 6				7 36					7 47									8 52
38½	Christchurch L												6 43	7 11				7 41					7 52									8 58
41½	Hinton Admiral W												6 50	7 18									7 59									9 5
44½	New Milton J												6 58	7 25				7 52					8 6									9 13
47½	Sway												7 5	7 32									8 14									9 20
50	Brockenhurst 338 arr.												7 11	7 38				8 2					8 20									9 26
—	338 Yarmouth Slipway dep.																															8 20
—	338 Lymington Town "												6 20	Stop				7 30					8 7									9 10
—	Brockenhurst dep.												7 12					8 3					8 21									9 28
54½	Beaulieu Road												7 20										8 29									
57½	Lyndhurst Road												7 26										8 35									9 40
60½	Totton, for Eling 375							6 35					7 32									8 37	8 41		a.m	Bournemouth to Waterloo						
61	Redbridge 380							6 37					7 35		7 43						8 35	8 40	8 44		9 4							
62½	Millbrook							6 42					7 40		7 48						8 39	8 44	8 49									
63½	Southampton Cen. H 500 arr.							6 46					7 44	Saturdays excepted	7 52			8 23			8 43	8 48	8 53		9 11		9 15					9 52
	Southampton Cen. dep.			5 22				6 47					7 46		7 53			8 25			8 44	8 59	8 55				9 16		9 25			9 54
65½	Southampton Ter., for Docks arr.							6 53							7 58							9 6										
	Southampton Ter. dep.	1 10			6 0			6 57			7 32	7 38			8 2					8 33								9 19			9 36	
64½	Northam				6 3			7 0			7 35	7 41			8 5					8 36							Refreshment Car	9 22			9 39	
66	St. Denys 376			5 30	6 7			7 7			7 39	7 45	7 55		8 9					8 40	8 51		9 4					9 26	9 32		9 43	10 2
67	Swaythling			5 35	6 11			7 11			7 43	To Portsmouth and Southsea (arr. 8 51 a.m), page 376	7 59	☞ { a.m	To Portsmouth and Southsea (arr 9 9 a.m), page 376					8 44	To Portsmouth and Southsea (arr. 9 42 a.m), page 376		9 8					9 30	To Portsmouth and Southsea (arr. 1035 a.m.) page 376		9 47	
69½	Eastleigh F 376, 380 arr.	1 20		5 41	6 17			7 17			7 49		8 5							8 50			9 14					9 36		9 50	9 53	10 10
	Eastleigh dep.	1 29		6 4	6 18	6 35		7 18		7 40	7 50		8 7			8 20														9 52	9 56	10 11
73½	Shawford, for Twyford			6 12	6 27	6 42		7 27		7 47	8†0		8 16			8 27														10 0	10†5	
76½	Winchester D	1 46		6 21	6 35	6 50		7 35		7 56			8 24			8†35		8 47	8 57								9 38			10†8	Stop	10 25
84½	Micheldever				6 52	Via Alresford, page 375		7 51		Via Alresford page 375			8 40						9 12													10 41
95	Basingstoke 340 arr.	2 15			7 9			8 8					8 55						9 28												a.m	10 57
	Basingstoke dep.	2 13	6 35		7 12		8 1	8 9	8 25					9 2			9 7														9 56	10 59
100½	Hook C		6 44		7 22		8 10		8 33					9 10																	10 6	
103	Winchfield B		6 50		7 28		8 16		8 39					9 16																	1012	
106½	Fleet		6 57		7 35		8 23		8 46					9 23																	1019	
109½	Farnborough A	2 38	7 6		7 42		8 31		8 53					9 30																	1026	
115	Brookwood G 389, 390		7 15		7 52	8 16				9N18				9 39																		
118½	Woking N 389, 427 arr.	2 54	7 22		7 59	8 22	8 46		9 Z7	9N24				9 46																	1041	11Z33
131	Surbiton 427 "	3 30	7 46		8 23	9 0	9N20		9 23	9K39				1030																	1130	12 30
143	WATERLOO 427 "	3 55	8 8		8 36	8 57	9 20	9 2	9 42	9K55				1021			10 3	1013									10 59				1113	12 7

For Notes, see page 335

WEYMOUTH. SWANAGE, WAREHAM, BOURNEMOUTH, SOUTHAMPTON, BASINGSTOKE, and LONDON

Week Days—*continued*

Up	a.m	a.m		a.m	a.m	p.m	a.m	a.m		a.m	p.m	a.m	a.m		p.m	a.m	p.m	p.m	p.m		p.m	p.m		p.m	p.m	a.m	p.m		a.m	a.m
Weymouth dep.					8 30			9 20																						
Upwey Junction					8 37																									
Dorchester M	8 4				8 54			9 37																						
Moreton	8 12				9 6																									
Wool, for Lulworth Cove K	8 19				9 16																									
Wareham 324 arr.	8 27				9 24			9 59																						
Swanage dep.					8 58			9 26					11 6																	
Corfe Castle					9 8			9 36					1116																	
Wareham 324 arr.					9 20			9 48					1130																	
Wareham dep.	8 28				9 25			10 2																						
Holton Heath	8 33				9 31																									
Hamworthy Junction	8 38				9 37																									
Poole 339	8 44				9 43			10 15																		1123				1156
Parkstone, for Sandbanks	8 49				9 49																					1128				12 1
Branksome	8 53				9 54																					1133				12 6
Bournemouth West arr.																										1138				
Bournemouth West dep.							10 12									11 2													1148	
Bournemouth Central arr.	8 59				10 0		10 20	10 27								11 10													1157	1212
Bournemouth Central dep.							1030									11 12													12 2	
Boscombe	Saturdays excepted				Calls at Radipole Halt at 8 33 a.m											11 17					From Fawley, (dep. 12 12 p.m.) page 375								12 8	
Pokesdown O																11 21													1212	
Christchurch L																11 27													1218	
Hinton Admiral W																													1225	
New Milton J																11 40													1233	
Sway																													1240	
Brockenhurst 338 arr.							1054									11 50													1246	
338 Yarmouth (I. of W.) dep.																10 40														
338 Lymington Town "							1037									11 27														
Brockenhurst dep.							1056									11 55														
Beaulieu Road																														
Lyndhurst Road																			Saturdays excepted			Saturdays only								
Totton, for Eling 375																					1242									
Redbridge 380												1119									1245									
Millbrook												1124									1250									
Southampton Cen. H 500 arr.							1116					1128				12 16					1254									
Southampton Cen. dep.				1049			1120					1130				12 20		1225			1255									
Southampton Ter. for Docks arr.																														
Southampton Ter. dep.										11 26					12 8		1220		1245			1253			1 25					
Northam										11 29					12S011		1224		1248			1256			1 28					
St. Denys 376				1057						11 33	Saturdays only	1138			12 13		1228	1231	1254		1 2	1d 4			1 32					
Swaythling				To Portsmouth and Southsea (arr. 12 7 p.m), page 376		Saturdays excepted				11 37		To Portsmouth and Southsea (arr. 12 31 p.m.), page 376			12 17		1232	To Portsmouth and Southsea (arr. 1 33 p.m) page 376.			1 6	To Portsmouth and Southsea. (arr. 2 7 p.m.) page 376			1 36					
Eastleigh F 376 380 arr.										11 43					12 25	12 31	1238				1 12				1 42					
Eastleigh dep.		1029								11 45						12 32	1239							1 15	1 43					
Shawford, for Twyford		1036								11†53							1247		To Portsmouth & Southsea, (arr. 2 4 p.m.) page 376		Saturdays only			1 22	1 51					
Winchester D		1044														12 46	1255							1 29	1†58					
Micheldever																	1 11													
Basingstoke 340 arr.																1 13	1 27													
Basingstoke dep.						12 2					1212					1 15	1 35										2 22			
Hook C		Via Alresford, page 375				1210					1220						To Reading (G.W.R.), p. 496							Via Alresford page 375			2 32			
Winchfield B						1216					1226																2 38			
Fleet						1223					1233																2 46			
Farnborough A						1230					1240																2 55			
Brookwood G 389, 390		1226				1239					1250													2 56			3 4			
Woking N 389, 427 arr.		1232				1246					1257					1 45								3 2			3 11			
Surbiton 427 "		1 0				1 30					1 30					2 30								3 30			4 0			
WATERLOO 427 "		1 16				1 19	1259				1 30					2 19								3 46			3 49			

For Notes, see page 335; for Continuation of Trains, see pages 332 to 335

WEYMOUTH, SWANAGE, WAREHAM, BOURNEMOUTH, SOUTHAMPTON, BASINGSTOKE, and LONDON

Week Days—*continued*

Up	p.m	a.m	p.m	p.m	p.m	p.m	p.m		p.m		p.m	p.m	p.m		p.m	p.m	p.m	p.m	p.m	p.m		p.m	p.m	p.m	p.m	p.m	p.m		p.m	p.m	p.m
Weymouth ......dep.		1130											1225			1 25								2 20							
Upwey Junction													1231											2 26							
Dorchester M		1147											1246			1 43								2 42							
Moreton													1256											2 54							
Wool, for Lulworth Cove **K**		12 2											1 5			1 59								3 3							
Wareham 324 ......arr.		1211											1 13			2 8								3 11							
Swanage ......dep.		1136														1 35								2 42							
Corfe Castle		1146														1 45								2 53							
Wareham 324 ......arr.		12 2														1 58								3 8							
Wareham ......dep.		1212											1 14			2 10								3 13	Bournemouth Belle						
Holton Heath													1 20											3 19							
Hamworthy Junction													1 25											3 25							
Poole 339		1224											1 32			2 24								3 34							
Parkstone, for Sandbanks													1 37											3 39							
Branksome													1 42											3 43							
Bournemouth West arr.																															
Bournemouth West dep.	12 20								1 5						2 20							3 5			4 34						
Bournemouth Central arr.	12 28	1235							1 13				1 48		2 28	2 35						3 14		3 50	4 42						
Bournemouth Central dep.	12 [illegible]0								1 15						2 38							3 17		3 54	4 45						
Boscombe									1 20													3 22		3 59							
Pokesdown **O**									1 24													3 26		4 2							
Christchurch **L**									1 29													3 32		4 7							
Hinton Admiral **W**																								4 14	1st and 3rd Class Pullman Cars only						
New Milton **J**									1 41													3 44		4 21							
Sway									1 48															4 28							
Brockenhurst 338 ......arr.									1 54													3 54		4 34							
338 Yarmouth Slipway dep.																						2 55									
338 Lymington Town "									1 24													3 36		4 20							
Brockenhurst ......dep.			1 4						1 56									From Portsmouth & Southsea (dep. 2 45 p.m) see page 381				3 56		4 35							
Beaulieu Road			1 12																					4 43							
Lyndhurst Road			1 18																					4 49							
Totton, for Eling 375			1 25																					4 55							
Redbridge 380			1 28	1 38																				4 57						5 3[illegible]	
Millbrook			1 33	1 43																				5 2						5 3[illegible]	
Southampton Cen. H 500 arr.	1 16		1 37	1 47					2 16						3 15							4 16		5 6	5 16					5 42	
Southampton Cen. dep.	1 20		1 39	1 49			2 13		2 20			2 58			3 20					4 5		4 20		5 7	5 20					5 44	
Southampton Ter. for Docks arr.	Refreshment Car Bournemouth to Waterloo						2 20								Refreshment Car Bournemouth to Waterloo					4 10					Supplementary Fees charged					5 50	
Southampton Ter. dep.					1 55						2 54									4 18			4 55				5 18		5 25		
Northam					1 58						2 57									4 20			4 58				5 21		5 28		
St. Denys 376			1 47	1 58	2 2						3 1	3 4								4‖32		4 29	5 2	5 14			5 28		5 32		
Swaythling				To Portsmouth and Southsea (arr. 3 3 p.m), page 377	2 6						3 5	To Portsmouth and Southsea (arr. 4 7 p.m), page 377								To Portsmouth and Southsea (arr 5 36 p.m) page 377			5 5				5 32		To Portsmouth and Southsea (arr. 6 37 p.m) page 377		
Eastleigh F 376, 380 arr.			1 55		2 12				2 32		3 11							3 34				4 3[illegible]	5 11	5 22			5 38				
Eastleigh dep.			1 58			2 15			2 34									3 35	3 59			4 39	5 12	To Andover Junction page 381			5 39				
Shawford, for Twyford			2 8			2 22												3 43	4 6				5†19				5 47				
Winchester **D**			2 18			2 29			2 49									3 52	4†14			4 53					5†55				
Micheldever			2 35			Via Alresford page 375												4 8				5 9									
Basingstoke 340 arr.			2 52						3 17									4 25				5 26									
Basingstoke dep.			2 59						3 19								4 15	4 45				5 28				5 37					6 35
Hook **C**			3 9														4 23	To Reading (G W R.) p.496								5 45					6 45
Winchfield **B**			3 15														4 29									5 51					6 51
Fleet			3 22														4 35									5 57					6 58
Farnborough **A**			3 30														4 42									6 6					7 5
Brookwood **G** 389, 390			3 39			3 56											4 50									6 15					7 14
Woking N 389, 427 ....arr.			3 48			4 2											4 57									6 22					7 21
Surbiton 427 ...... "			4 30			4 30											5 15					6 17				6 47					8 0
WATERLOO 427 ...... "	2 56		4 46			4 46			4 25						4 58		5 35					6 36			6 45	7 7					8 0

For Notes, see page 335

WEYMOUTH, SWANAGE, WAREHAM, BOURNEMOUTH, SOUTHAMPTON, BASINGSTOKE, and LONDON.

Week Days—*continued*

Up	p.m	p.m	p.m	p.m		p.m	p.m	p.m		p.m
Weymouth ....dep	..	..	..	..	..	..	..	..	..	..
Upwey Junction	..	..	..	..	..	..	..	..	..	..
Dorchester M	..	..	..	..	..	..	..	..	..	..
Moreton	..	..	..	..	..	..	..	..	..	..
Wool, for Lulworth Cove K	..	..	..	..	..		..	..	..	..
Wareham 324 ......arr.	..	..	..	..	..		..	..	..	..
Swanage ....dep.	..	..	..	..	..		..	..	..	..
Corfe Castle	..	..	..	..	..		..	..	..	..
Wareham 324 ......arr.	..	..	..	..	..		..	..	..	..
Wareham ....dep.		..	..	..	..		..	..	..	..
Holton Heath		..		..	..		..	..	..	..
Hamworthy Junction		..		..	..		..	..	..	..
Poole 339		..		..	..		..	..	..	..
Parkstone, for Sandbanks		..		..	..		..	..	..	..
Branksome		..		..	..		..	..	..	..
Bournemouth West arr.		..			..		..	..	..	..
Bournemouth West dep.		..			..	5 5	..	..	..	..
Bournemouth Central arr.		..			..	5 13	..	..	..	..
Bournemouth Central dep.	4 38	..			..	5 15	5 38	..	..	..
Boscombe	4 41	..			..	5 20	5 41	..	..	..
Pokesdown O	4 52	..			..	5 23	5 44	..	..	..
Christchurch L	4 56	..			..	5 29	5 49	..	..	..
Hinton Admiral W	5 2	..			..	..	5 56	..	..	..
New Milton J	5 9	..			..	5 41	6 3	..	..	..
Sway	5 15	..			..	5 48	6 9	..	..	..
Brockenhurst 338 ....arr.	5 21	..			..	5 54	6 15	..	..	..
338 Yarmouth Slipway dep.	..	..			..	5 0	..	..	..	..
338 Lymington Town ... "	..	..			..	5 40	..	..	..	..
Brockenhurst ......dep.	5 22	..			..	5 56	6 17	..	..	..
Beaulieu Road	5 29	..			..	..	6 26	..	..	..
Lyndhurst Road	5 34	..			..	..	6 31	..	..	..
Totton, for Eling 375	5 40	..		5 47	..	..	6 37	..	..	..
Redbridge 380	..	..		5 50	..	..	6 39	..	..	..
Millbrook	5 45	..		5 55	..	..	6 43	..	..	..
Southampton Cen. H 500 arr.	5 49	..		5 59	..	6 16	6 47	..	..	..
Southampton Cen. dep.	5 50	5 55		6 4	..	6 20	6 48	..	..	..
Southampton Ter., for Docks arr.	..	..		..	..	..	..	..	..	..
Southampton Ter. dep.	..	..		..	..	..	..	..	..	6 58
Northam	..	..		..	..	..	..	..	..	7 1
St. Denys 376	5 57	6 6		6 12	..	..	6 55	..	..	7 5
Swaythling	6 2			6 16	..	..	6 58	..	..	7 8
Eastleigh F 376, 380 arr.	6 8		6 10	6 22	..	6 31	7 4	..	..	7 14
Eastleigh dep.	..		6 16		..	6 33	..	..	..	7 15
Shawford, for Twyford	..		6 23		..	..	..	..	..	7 22
Winchester D	..		6 32		..	6 48	..	..	..	7 31
Micheldever	..		6 49		..	..	..	..	..	
Basingstoke 340 arr.	..		7 8		..	7 17	..	..	..	
Basingstoke dep.	..		7 35		..	7 20	..	7 32	..	
Hook C	..		..		..	..	..	7 43	..	
Winchfield B	..		..		..	..	..	7 50	..	
Fleet	..		..		..	..	..	7 57	..	
Farnborough A	..		..		..	..	..	8 5	..	
Brookwood G 389, 390	..		..		..	..	..	8 14	..	8 56
Woking V 389, 427 ....arr.	..		..		..	7 51	..	8 21	..	9 2
Surbiton 427 .... "	..		..		..	8 12	..	8 48	..	9 30
WATERLOO 427 ...... "	..		..	..	..	8 32	..	9 14	..	9 46
Notes	Arr. Pokesdown 4 44 p.m.	To Portsmouth & Southsea (arr 7 1p.m.) page 377	Through Train. Portsmouth and Southsea (dep 5 15 p.m) to Reading (G W R.). pages 381 and 496	From Fawley (dep 5 15 p.m) page 375; To Andover Junction page 381		Refreshment Car Train				Via Alresford page 375

Up	p.m	p.m	p.m	p.m	p.m	p.m	p.m	p.m	p.m	p.m	p.m
Weymouth ....dep	4 40	5 20	..	..	..	..	..	..	..	..	5 30
Upwey Junction	4 46	..	..	..	..	..	..	..	..	..	5 36
Dorchester M	5 1	5 36	..	..	..		..	..	..	..	5 51
Moreton	5 10	..	..	..	..		..	..	..	..	6 0
Wool, for Lulworth Cove K	5 18	..	..	..	..		..	..	..	..	6 8
Wareham 324 ......arr.	5 26	5 53	..	..	..		..	..	..	..	6 17
Swanage ....dep.	4 25	..	..	..	..		..	..	..	5 38	..
Corfe Castle	4 35	..	..	..	..		..	..	..	5 48	..
Wareham 324 ......arr.	4 47	..	..	..	..		..	..	..	6 3	..
Wareham ....dep.	5 27	5 54	..	..	..		..	..	..	..	6 19
Holton Heath	5 33	..	..	..	..		..	..	..	..	6 27
Hamworthy Junction	5 39	..	..	..	..		..	..	..	..	6 33
Poole 339	5 46	6 6	..	..	..		..	6 24	..	..	6 40
Parkstone, for Sandbanks	5 52	..	..	..	..		..	..	..	..	6 46
Branksome	5 57	..	..	..	..		..	..	..	..	6 51
Bournemouth West arr.	..	..	..	..	..		..	6 35	..	..	..
Bournemouth West dep.	..	..	6 20	..	..		..	..	6 44	..	..
Bournemouth Central arr.	6 3	6 17	6 29	..	..		..	..	6 52	..	6 59
Bournemouth Central dep.	..		6 35		..		..	..	6 54	..	
Boscombe	..		..		..		..	..	6 58	..	
Pokesdown O	..		..		..		..	..	7 1	..	
Christchurch L	..		..		..		..	..	7 6	..	
Hinton Admiral W	..		..		..		..	..	7 13	..	
New Milton J	..		..		..		..	..	7 [illegible]	..	
Sway	..		..		..		..	..	7 27	..	
Brockenhurst 338 ....arr.	..		..		..		..	..	7 33	..	
338 Yarmouth Slipway dep.	..		..		..		..	..	..	..	
338 Lymington Town ... "	..		..		..		..	..	6 30	..	..
Brockenhurst ......dep.	..		..		..		..	..	7 34	..	..
Beaulieu Road	..		..		..		..	..	7 42	..	..
Lyndhurst Road	..		..		..		..	..	7 48	..	..
Totton, for Eling 375	..		..	7 13	..		..	..	7 54	..	..
Redbridge 380	..		..	7 16	..		..	..	7 57	..	..
Millbrook	..		..	7 20	..		..	..	8 2	..	..
Southampton Cen. H 500 arr.	..		7 14	7 24	..		..	..	8 6	..	..
Southampton Cen. dep.	..		7 20	7 25	..	7 45	..	..	8 9	..	..
Southampton Ter., for Docks arr.	..		..	..	..	..	..	..	..	..	..
Southampton Ter. dep.	..		..	..	7 35	..	..	..	..	..	..
Northam	..		..	..	7 38	..	..	..	..	..	..
St. Denys 376	..		..	..	7 42	7 53	..	..	8 17	..	..
Swaythling	..		..	..	7 46	..	..	..	8 21	..	..
Eastleigh F 376, 380 arr.	..		..	..	7 52	..		..	8 27	..	..
Eastleigh dep.	..		..	..	7 55	..		..	8 31	..	..
Shawford, for Twyford	..		..	..	8 †5	..		..	8 40	..	..
Winchester D	..		..	..	..	..		..	8 48	..	..
Micheldever	..		..	..	..	..		..	9 5	..	..
Basingstoke 340 arr.	..		..	..	..	..		..	9 24	..	..
Basingstoke dep.	..		..	..	..	..	9 12	..	9 30	..	..
Hook C	..		..	..	..	..	..	..		..	..
Winchfield B	..		..	..	..	..	..	..		..	..
Fleet	..		..	..	..	..	..	..		..	..
Farnborough A	..		..	..	..	..	..	..		..	..
Brookwood G 389, 390	..		..	..	..	..	..	..		..	..
Woking V 389, 427 ....arr.	..		..	..	..	..	9 42	..		..	..
Surbiton 427 .... "	..		..	..	..	..	10 3	..		..	..
WATERLOO 427 ...... "	..		8 58	..	..	..	1027	..		..	..
Notes		Bournemouth to Waterloo	Refreshment Car	From Fawley (dep 6 43 p.m) see page 375		Through Train Bristol (G.W.R.) to Portsmouth and Southsea (arr 8 59 p.m) pages 494 and 377	Refreshment Car Exeter to Waterloo, page 349		To Reading (G.W.R.) p. 496		Saturdays excepted

Up	p.m	p.m		p.m	p.m	p.m	p.m	p.m	p.m	p.m
Weymouth ....dep	6 30	..	..	..	..	..	7 48	..	9 55	11 15
Upwey Junction	..	..	..	..	..	..	7 54	..	..	11 21
Dorchester M	6 47	..	..	..	..	7 32	8 8	..	10 18	11 34
Moreton	6 56	..	..	..	..	7 41	8 17	..	10 28	..
Wool, for Lulworth Cove K	7 4	..	..	..	..	7 49	8 25	..	10 36	..
Wareham 324 ......arr.	7 13	..	..	..	..	7 58	8 33	..	10 45	..
Swanage ....dep.	6 43	..	..	..	..	..	..	..	9 0	..
Corfe Castle	6 53	..	..	..	..	..	..	..	9 10	..
Wareham 324 ......arr.	7 5	..	..	..	..	..	..	..	9 22	..
Wareham ....dep.	7 14	..	..	..	..	8 4	8 34	..	10 47	..
Holton Heath	..	..	..	..	..	8 11	8 39	..	10 53	..
Hamworthy Junction	..	..	..	..	..	8 17	8 44	..	10 58	..
Poole 339	7 29	..	..	..	..		8 50	..	11 8	..
Parkstone, for Sandbanks	7 34	..	..	..	..		8 55	..	11 14	..
Branksome	7 39	..	..	..	..		8 59	..	11 18	..
Bournemouth West arr.	..	..	..	..	..		..	..	..	..
Bournemouth West dep.	..	..	..	..	..		..	..	..	..
Bournemouth Central arr.	7 46	..	..	..	..		9 5	..	11 25	..
Bournemouth Central dep.	7 50	..	..	..	..		9 10		11 30	..
Boscombe	7 55	..	..	..	..		9 15		..	..
Pokesdown O	7 58	..	..	..	..		9 18		..	..
Christchurch L	8 3	..	..	..	..		9 24		11 39	..
Hinton Admiral W	..	..	..	..	..		9 31		..	..
New Milton J	8 14	..	..	..	..		9 39		11 51	..
Sway	..	..	..	..	..		9 46		11 57	..
Brockenhurst 338 ....arr.	8 24	..	..	..	..	9 25	9 52		12 1	..
338 Yarmouth Slipway dep.	6 25	..	..	..	..	7A55	..		..	..
338 Lymington Town ... "	7 39	..	..	..	..	8 32	..		..	..
Brockenhurst ......dep.	8 25	..	..	..	..	9 27	9 53		12 5	..
Beaulieu Road	..	..	..	..	..	..	..		..	..
Lyndhurst Road	..	..	..	..	..	9 40	10 5		..	..
Totton, for Eling 375	..	..	..	..	..	9 46	1011		..	..
Redbridge 380	..	..	..	..	..	..	..		..	..
Millbrook	..	..	..	..	..	9 53	..		..	..
Southampton Cen. H 500 arr.	8 45	..	..	..	..	9 57	1020	11 3	12 25	..
Southampton Cen. dep.	8 48	..	..	..	9SO52	10 2	1023	11 4	12 30	..
Southampton Ter., for Docks arr.	..	..	..	..	9SO57	..	..	..	12 37	..
Southampton Ter. dep.	..	..	..	9 5	10 0	..	..	..	1 10	..
Northam	..	..	..	9 8	10 3	..	..	..	..	..
St. Denys 376	8 56	..	..	9 12	10 13	1010	..	1111	..	..
Swaythling	..	..	..	9 16		1014	..	1115	..	..
Eastleigh F 376, 380 arr.	9 4	..	..	9 22		1020	1037	1121	1 20	..
Eastleigh dep.	9 7	..	..	..		..	1039	..	1 29	..
Shawford, for Twyford	9 16	..	..	..		..	1047	..	..	..
Winchester D	9 25	..	..	..		..	1056	..	1 46	..
Micheldever	..	..	..	..		..	1113	..	..	..
Basingstoke 340 arr.	9 55	..	..	..		..	1132	..	2 15	..
Basingstoke dep.	10 1	1021	..	..		..	..	..	2 18	..
Hook C	..	1031	..	..		..	..	..	..	..
Winchfield B	..	1037	..	..		..	..	..	..	..
Fleet	..	1044	..	..		..	..	..	..	..
Farnborough A	..	1052	..	..		..	..	..	2 39	..
Brookwood G 389, 390	..	11 2	..	..		..	..	..	..	..
Woking V 389, 427 ....arr.	1035	11 9	..	..		..	..	..	2 54	..
Surbiton 427 .... "	1130	..	..	..		..	..	..	3 30	..
WATERLOO 427 ...... "	1113	12SX6	..	..		..	..	..	3 55	..
Notes					To Portsmouth and Southsea (arr. 11 8 p.m), page 378	Via Wimborne page 339		From Bristol (G.W.R.) pages 494 and 378		

For Notes, see page 335; for SUNDAY TRAINS, see pages 334 and 335.

WEYMOUTH, SWANAGE, WAREHAM, BOURNEMOUTH, SOUTHAMPTON, BASINGSTOKE, and LONDON

Up — Sundays

Up	a.m	a.m	a.m	a.m	a.m	a.m	a.m	a.m	a.m	a.m	a.m	a.m	p.m	a.m	a.m	p.m
Weymouth ....dep.								7 15							10 0	
Upwey Junction															10 6	
Dorchester M								7 40							1020	
Moreton								7 48								
Wool, for Lulworth Cove K								7 56							1035	
Wareham 324 ....arr.								8 5							1044	
Swanage ....dep.															1010	
Corfe Castle															1020	
Wareham 324 ....arr.															1035	
Wareham ....dep.							To Portsmouth and Southsea arr. 11 5 a.m page 378	8 6							1045	
Holton Heath																
Hamworthy Junction								8 15								
Poole 339								8 23							1058	
Parkstone, for Sandbanks								8 29							11 4	
Branksome								8 34							11 9	
Bournemouth West arr.																
Bournemouth West dep.														11 0		
Bournemouth Central arr.								8 41						11 8	1116	
Bournemouth Central dep.					8 32	From Portsmouth and Southsea. (dep 8 8 a.m) page 382		8 50		10 5					1120	
Boscombe					8 35			8 55		10 8					1126	
Pokesdown O					8 38			8 58		1011					1129	
Christchurch L					8 43			9 3		1016					1134	
Hinton Admiral W					8 50					1023						
New Milton J					8 57			9 15		1030					1145	
Sway					9 4					1037						
Brockenhurst 338 ....arr.					9 10			9 25		1043					1155	
338 Yarmouth Slipway dep.					Stop										1040	
338 Lymington Town "															1122	
Brockenhurst ....dep.	12 5							9 28	9 40	1044					1156	
Beaulieu Road									9 47							
Lyndhurst Road									9 53	1055						
Totton, for Eling									9 59	11 1						
Redbridge 380							9 29		10 1							
Millbrook							9 34		10 6							
Southampton Cen. H 500 arr.	1225						9 37	9 49	10 9	11 8					1216	
Southampton Cen. dep.	1230						9 39	9 51	1024	Stop		1135	12 2		1220	
Southampton Ter., for Docks arr.	1237				a.m		9 46									
Southampton Ter. dep.	1 10		7 20		8 43		9 51				1125					
Northam																
St. Denys 376			7 25		8 48		10z3	10 0	1030		1130	1142	12 8			
Swaythling			7 29		8 52		Stop	10 4	1034		1134		1212			
Eastleigh F 376, 380 arr.	1 20		7 35		8 58	8 52		1010	1040	a.m	1140	To Portsmouth and Southsea arr. 12 36 p.m., page 378.	1218		1231	
Eastleigh dep.	1 29		7 36	7 45		9 1		1013	Stop	1046					1233	1248
Shawford, for Twyford				7 52		9 10				1053						1255
Winchester D	1 46		7 50	7 59		9 20		1029		11 0					1250	1 4
Micheldever				Via Alresford page 375		9 36		1045		Via Alresford page 375						1 21
Basingstoke 340 arr.	2 15					9 52	a.m	11 2	a.m							1 39
Basingstoke dep.	2 18	7 45				1010	9 59	11 4	1113							
Hook C		7 53				To Reading (G.W.R.) page 496	10 9		1121							
Winchfield B		7 59					1015		1127							
Fleet		8 5					1022		1134							
Farnborough A	2 38	8 12					1029		1141							
Brookwood G 389 390		8 20		9 26			1038		1150	1226						
Woking N 389, 427 ...arr.	2 54	8 27		9 32			1045	1136	1157	1232						
Surbiton 427 .... "	3 30	9 0		10 0			11 2	1154	1230	1 0						
WATERLOO 427 ...... "	3 55	8 59		1016			1121	1213	1230	1 16					2 12	

Up	p.m	p.m	p.m	p.m	p.m	p.m	p.m	p.m	p.m	p.m	p.m	p.m	p.m	p.m	p.m	p.m
Weymouth ....dep.									2 0							
Upwey Junction									2 6							
Dorchester M									2 20							
Moreton									2 29							
Wool, for Lulworth Cove K									2 37							
Wareham 324 ....arr.									2 46							
Swanage ....dep.									2 5		4 10					
Corfe Castle									2 15		4 20					
Wareham 324 ....arr.									2 29		4 34					
Wareham ....dep.									2 48			Bournemouth Belle				
Holton Heath									2 54		Stop					
Hamworthy Junction									3 0							
Poole 339									3 8							
Parkstone, for Sandbanks									3 14							
Branksome									3 19							
Bournemouth West arr.																
Bournemouth West dep.	1 8						2 43	3 10				4 34				
Bournemouth Central arr.	1 16						2 51	3 18	3 26		p.m	4 42				
Bournemouth Central dep.	1 20						2 52		3 30		3 55	4 45				
Boscombe	1 25						2 56				3 58					
Pokesdown O	1 28						2 59				4 1					
Christchurch L	1 33						3 4				4 6	1st and 3rd class Pullman Cars only				
Hinton Admiral W	1 40						3 11				4 13					
New Milton J	1 47						3 18				4 21					
Sway	1 53						3 25				4 28					
Brockenhurst 338 ....arr.	1 59						3 31				4 34					
338 Yarmouth Slipway dep.	1 0										3 30					
338 Lymington Town "	1 37						3 10				4 12					
Brockenhurst ....dep.	2 0						3 32				4 35					
Beaulieu Road											4 43					
Lyndhurst Road	2 11						3 43				4 49					
Totton, for Eling							3 49				4 55					
Redbridge 380							3 51									
Millbrook							3 56				5 1					
Southampton Cen. H 500 arr.	2 24						3 59		4 11		5 5	5 16				
Southampton Cen. dep.	2 26			3 20			4 1		4 15			5 20		5 24		
Southampton Ter., for Docks arr.																
Southampton Ter. dep.		3 0	Refreshment Car Exeter to Waterloo page 351							4 45					6 15	
Northam																
St. Denys 376	2 34	3 5		3 26			4 8			4 50				5 30	6 20	
Swaythling		3 9		3 30						4 54				5 34	6 24	
Eastleigh F 376, 380 arr.	To Portsmouth and Southsea, (arr. 3 34 p.m), page 378	3 15		3 36			To Portsmouth and Southsea, (arr. 5 3 p.m), page 378			5 0		Supplementary Fees Charged		5 40	6 30	
Eastleigh dep.		3 16			3 42	3 46								5 43	6 31	
Shawford, for Twyford		3 24			3 49									5 52	6 39	
Winchester D		3†32			3†56	4 1								6 1	6†46	
Micheldever						4 17								6 18		
Basingstoke 340 arr.						4 34								6 34		
Basingstoke dep.			3 10			4 37							6 17	6 36		6 54
Hook C						4 47										7 4
Winchfield B						4 53										7 10
Fleet						5 0										7 18
Farnborough A						5 7										7 26
Brookwood G 389 390						5 16										7 35
Woking N 389, 427 ...arr.			3 38			5 23							6 49	7 8		7 42
Surbiton 427 .... "			4 30			5 45							7 7	7 26		8 2
WATERLOO 427 ...... "			4 10			6 4			5 57			6 45	7 27	7 45		8 22

For Notes, see page 335

WEYMOUTH, SWANAGE, WAREHAM, BOURNEMOUTH, SOUTHAMPTON, BASINGSTOKE, and LONDON

Sundays—*continued*

Up	p.m	p.m	p.m	p.m	p.m	p.m	p.m	p.m	p.m	p.m	p.m	p.m	p.m	p.m	p.m	p.m	p.m	p.m	
Weymouth dep.				5 10	5 50										8 0			10 0	
Upwey Junction				5 16											8 6				
Dorchester M				5 30	6 6										8 20			1023	
Moreton				5 39											8 29			1033	
Wool, for Lulworth Cove K				5 47											8 37			1041	
Wareham 324 arr.				5 56	6 27										8 46			1049	
Swanage dep.			Refreshment Car Train		5 55														
Corfe Castle					6 5														
Wareham 324 arr.					6 17														
Wareham dep.				5 57	6 28										8 47			1051	
Holton Heath				6 3							Through train Bristol (G.W.R.) to Portsmouth and Southsea (arr. 10 12 p.m), pages 494 and 378				8 52				
Hamworthy Junction				6 9											8 59				
Poole 339				6 16	6 41										9 7		1051	11 7	
Parkstone, for Sandbanks				6 22											9 14		1056	1113	
Branksome				6 27											9 19		11 1		
Bournemouth West arr.																			
Bournemouth West dep.	5 20		6 5				6 55												
Bournemouth Central arr.	5 28		6 13	6 34	6 52		7 4								9 25		11 7	1123	
Bournemouth Central dep.	5 30		6 20		6 57		7 6					8 10		8 48	Stop			1130	
Boscombe	5 33		6 23				7 12					8 13		8 52					
Pokesdown O	5 36		6 27				7 15					8 16		8 55					
Christchurch L	5 41		6 33				7 20					8 21		9 0				1140	
Hinton Admiral W	5 48											8 28		9 7					
New Milton J	5 56		6 45				7 32					8 35		9 14				1151	
Sway	6 3											8 41		9 21					
Brockenhurst 338 arr.	6 9		6 55		7 20		7 42					8 47		9 27				12 1	
338 **Yarm'th Slipway** dep.	4 55				6Y20														
338 **Lymington Town** "	5 35				7Y2														
Brockenhurst dep.	6 10		6 56		7 22		7 43					8 49		9 28				12 5	
Beaulieu Road	6 17													9 36					
Lyndhurst Road	6 23	Refreshment Car Exeter to Waterloo, page 351												9 43					
Totton, for Eling	6 28													9 49					
Redbridge 380	6 30																		
Millbrook	6 35									Calls at Wimbledon 11 22 p.m				9 55					
Southampton Cen. H 500 arr.	6 38		7 16		7 42		8 3					9 12		9 59	p.m			1227	
Southampton Cen. H 500 dep.	6 40		7 20		7 45	7 55	8 5	8 15	8 22		9 0	9 14		10 1	1010			1230	
Southampton Ter., for Docks arr.				Refreshment Car, Bournemouth to Waterloo														1237	
Southampton Ter., for Docks dep.																			
Northam													9 50			1030		1 10	
St Denys 376	6 47					8 1		8 24	8 28		9 9	9 23	9 55	1010	1016	1035			
Swaythling	6 51					8 5			8 32			9 27	9 59		1020	1039			
Eastleigh F 376,380 arr.	6 57					8 11	8 18		8 38			9 34	10 5		1026	1045		1 20	
Eastleigh F 376,380 dep.	6 58					Stop	8 20	To Portsmouth and Southsea (arr 9 27 p.m page 378	8 39	9 10					1028			1 29	
Shawford, for Twyford	7 6						8 28		8 47	9 17				To Portsmouth and Southsea (arr 11 11 p.m) page 378	1036				
Winchester D	7 14		7 42				8 38		8†55	9 25					1045			1 46	
Micheldever	7 30									9 41					11 2				
Basingstoke 340 arr.	7 46		8 12			p.m	9 6			9 57					1118			2 15	
Basingstoke 340 dep.		8 12	8 14			8 30	9 8			10 0								2 18	
Hook C						8 38				1010									
Winchfield B						8 44				1016									
Fleet						8 50	9 23			1023									
Farnborough A						8 57	9 30			1030									
Brookwood G 389, 39						9 5				1039								2 38	
Woking N **389,427** arr.						9 12	9 44			1046								2 54	
Surbiton 427 "		8 54			9 9	10 0	1030			1111								3 30	
WATERLOO 427 "		9 13	9 21		9 28	9 49	1019			1136								3 55	

NOTES

A Nearly 1 mile from Farnborough North Sta.
A Every weekday to 1st November, 1947, Fridays and Saturdays 7th November, 1947 to 27th March, 1948 and every weekday commencing 29th March, 1948.
B Station for Odiham (3 miles) and Hartley Wintney (2 miles)
C Station for Odiham (2 miles)
D 1 mile from Cheesehill Station
d Arr. 1 0 p.m.
F Station for Bishopstoke
G For Bisley Camp
H About 1 mile from the Docks and Pier
J Sta. for Barton-on-Sea (1½ miles) & Milford-on-Sea (3¾ miles). Omnibus Service available by Hants & Dorset Motor Services Ltd.
K Omnibus Service available between Lulworth Cove, Bovington Camp, and Wool, by Southern National Omnibus Co. Ltd.
K Arr. Surbiton 10 0 and Waterloo 10 16 a.m on Saturdays.
k Arr. 10 8 p.m.
L Sta. for Southbourne-on-Sea
M Over ½ mile to G.W. Station
N Station for Chobham (3½ miles): for Woking Village (1½ miles)
N 10 mins later on Sats.
O For Eastern Bournemouth
P Wednesdays and Saturdays. Stops to set down only
SO or S0 Saturdays only
SX Saturdays excepted
U Arr. 4 24 p.m.
W Sta. for Highcliffe-on-Sea (1½ miles)
Y Commences 4th April 1948
Z Stops to set down only
z Arr. 9 56 a.m.
† Arrival time

LOCAL TRAINS between Poole and Bournemouth, page 337—Bournemouth and Christchurch, 337—Redbridge and Southampton 386—Southampton and Basingstoke, 386—Brookwood and Woking, 392.

OTHER TRAINS between Totton and Southampton, 375—Southampton and London 375.

CHRISTCHURCH, BOURNEMOUTH, POOLE, and WIMBORNE

Week Days

Miles		a.m	a.m	a.m	a.m	a.m	a.m	a.m	a.m	a.m		a.m	a.m		a.m	a.m	a.m	a.m	a.m	a.m		a.m	a.m		a.m		a.m		a.m		a.m		a.m
—	Christchurch ...dep.	2 4	..	..	..	..	6 5	6 30	From Dorchester (dep 7 0 a.m. p. 330)	..	..	7 29	..	..	..	..	8 21	8 39	9 11	..	..	..	..	..	9 59	..	..	..	..	..	..	..	1142
1¼	Pokesdown O	..	..	..	..	..	—	6 37		..	..	7 37	..	..	..	..	8 27	8 45	9 17	..	..	..	..	..	10 5	..	..	..	..	..	..	..	1148
2¼	Boscombe	..	..	..	..	..	..	6 43		..	..	7 41	..	..	..	..	8 29	8 49	9 20	..	..	..	..	..	10 8	..	..	..	..	..	..	..	1152
3½	Bournemouth Central arr.	2 14	..	..	..	..	6 15	6 48		..	..	7 45	..	..	..	..	8 33	8 53	9 24	..	..	..	..	..	1012	..	..	..	..	..	..	..	1156
	Bournemouth Central dep	2 24	5 47	6 25	..	..	6 32	7 10		7 42	..	7 50	..	..	..	..	8 34	8 57	..	..	..	..	..	..	1018	..	1118	..	..	..	1124	..	..
7	Bournemouth West	..	..	..	6 48	..	6 42	..		..	..	8 0	8 10	..	8 45	8 50	8 43	..	..	9 45	..	10 0	..	..	..	..	..	..	1140	..	1134	..	..
8¼	Branksome	..	5 53	6 32	.	..	(3)	7 17		7 48	..	..	8 14	..	8 48	8 54	..	9 5	..	..	..	10 4	..	..	1026	..	..	..	:	..	..	..	..
9½	Parkstone L	..	5 57	6 37	..	..		7 24		7 52	..	..	8 18	..	8 51	8 58	..	9 9	..	..	..	10 8	..	..	1030	..	..	..	..	..	..	..	..
11½	Poole	2 37	6 3	6 44	6 59	..	..	7 34		7 57	..	..	8 26	..	8 56	9 4	..	9 16	..	9 54	..	1014	1032	..	1038	..	1133	..	1149	..	..	..	..
13½	Creekmoor Halt	..	..	6 48	..	..	..	..		8 1	..	..	8 30	..	..	9 9	..	..	..	..	..	1019	1036	..	..	—	..	..	..	..	..	..	..
14¾	Broadstone Z	..	..	6 53	7 9	7 14	..	..	7 45	8 6	..	..	8 34	..	..	9 15	..	..	..	..	..	1024	1042	..	..	..	..	..	1158	..	..	..	..
17¼	Wimborne 339 ...arr.	..	..	7 0	..	7 19	..	..	7 51	8 13	..	..	8 40	..	..	..	..	..	..	..	..	1031	1048	..	..	..	..	..	..	..	..	..	..

Week Days—*continued*

	p.m		p.m		p.m		p.m	p.m		p.m	p.m		p.m SX	p.m SO	p.m SO	p.m SO	p.m		p.m	p.m		p.m	p.m	p.m		p.m	p.m		p.m	p.m	p.m	p.m	p.m
Christchurch ...dep.	..	..	1218	..	..	..	..	..	..	..	2 7	..	..	..	..	..	..	..	3 21	..	..	4 7	..	..	..	..	4 48	..	..	..	..	6 15	..
Pokesdown O	..	..	1225	..	..	..	..	..	..	..	2 14	..	..	..	..	..	..	..	3 27	..	..	4 13	..	..	..	..	4 55	..	..	..	..	6 21	..
Boscombe	..	..	..	..	..	..	..	..	..	..	2 18	..	..	..	..	..	..	..	3 30	..	..	4 16	..	..	..	..	4 58	..	..	..	..	..	..
Bournemouth Central arr.	..	..	1230	..	..	..	..	..	..	..	2 22	..	..	..	..	..	..	..	3 34	..	..	4 20	..	..	..	..	5 2	..	..	..	..	6 26	..
Bournemouth Central dep	..	..	1233	..	..	..	1 1	..	..	..	2 24	..	2 57	2 59	3 12	3 4	..	..	3 36	..	..	4 28	4 22	..	..	5 0	..	..	..	5 48	5 54	6 30	..
Bournemouth West	1235	..	1243	..	1255	..	..	1 18	..	2 35	2 34	..	..	..	..	3 14	3 30	..	3 46	4 30	..	4 38	..	4 47	..	..	..	..	5 15	..	6 4	6 40	6 50
Branksome	1238	..	..	..	1259	..	1 7	1 22	..	2 38	—	..	3 3	..	3 18	..	..	..	..	4 33	..	..	..	4 51	..	5 6	..	..	5 19	5 56	..	..	6 54
Parkstone L	1242	..	..	..	1 3	..	1 11	1 26	..	2 41	—	..	3 7	3 13	3 22	..	3 37	..	..	4 37	..	..	..	4 55	..	5 11	..	..	5 24	6 0	..	..	6 58
Poole	1247	..	.	..	1 8	..	1 18	1 33	..	2 48	—	..	3 13	..	3 27	..	3 43	..	..	4 42	..	..	4 35	5 1	..	5 18	..	..	5 33	6 7	..	..	7 3
Creekmoor Halt	1251	..	..	..	1 13	..	..	1 39	..	2 52	..	..	..	..	..	..	3 48	..	..	4 46	..	..	..	5 6	..	..	..	..	5 39	..	..	..	7 7
Broadstone Z	1255	..	..	..	1 19	.	..	1 46	..	2 57	..	..	..	..	..	..	3 52	..	..	4 50	..	..	..	5 10	..	..	..	..	5 46	..	..	..	7 11
Wimborne 339 . arr.	1 1	..	..	..	..	..	..	1 55	..	3 4	..	..	..	..	..	..	..	..	..	4 56	..	..	..	5 16	..	..	..	..	..	..	..	..	7 17

Week Days—*continued*

	p.m	p.m	p.m	p.m		p.m	p.m B	p.m	p.m		p.m	p.m SX	p.m SO	p.m	p.m				
Christchurch ...dep	..	..	..	..	..	7 27	Dep Hamworthy Junc. 8 17 p.m	..	8 16	..	..	..	..	1037	..	..	..	..	..
Pokesdown O	..	..	..	..	..	7 33		..	8 23	..	..	..	..	1043	..	..	..	..	..
Boscombe	..	..	..	..	..	7 36		..	8 27	..	..	..	..	1047	..	..	..	..	..
Bournemouth Central arr.	..	..	..	..	..	7 40		..	8 31	..	..	..	..	1051	..	..	..	..	..
Bournemouth Central dep.	7 4	7 10	7 20	..	..	..		..	8 34	..	8 55	9 1	..	1054	..	..	..	..	..
Bournemouth West	..	7 20	..	7 43	..	..		8 50	8 44	..	..	9 11	10 0	11 4	1120	..	..	..	..
Branksome	..	..	7 26	7 47	..	..		8 53	..	..	9 3	..	10 4	..	1124	..	..	..	..
Parkstone L	..	..	7 30	7 50	..	..		8 57	..	..	9 7	..	10 9	..	1128	..	..	..	..
Poole	7 17	..	7 36	7 57	..	..		9 2	..	..	9 13	..	1017	..	1134	..	..	..	..
Creekmoor Halt	..	..	..	8 3	..	..		9 6	..	..	..	..	..	..	1139	..	..	..	..
Broadstone Z	..	..	..	8 7	..	..	8 25	9 10	..	..	..	..	1027	..	1144	..	..	..	..
Wimborne 339 . arr.	..	..	..	8 13	..	..	8 31	9 16	..	..	..	..	..	..	1150	..	..	..	..

Sundays

	a.m	a.m		a.m		a.m	a.m		a.m		p.m	p.m		p.m
Christchurch ...dep	2 4	6 17	..	..	..	9 43	..	..	1152	..	1210	..	..	1 21
Pokesdown O	..	6 25	..	—	.	9 49	..	..	1158	..	1216	..	..	1 27
Boscombe	..	6 29	..	..	..	9 52	..	..	12 1	..	1219	..	..	1 30
Bournemouth Central arr.	2 14	6 33	..	..	..	9 56	..	..	12 5	..	1223	..	..	1 34
Bournemouth Central dep.	2 24	(3)	..	8 5	..	..	10 7	..	..	..	1225	1230	..	1 36
Bournemouth West	..		..	..	..	..	..	..	..		1231	..	..	1 46
Branksome	—	..	..	8 13	..	..	1016	..	..	..	..	1238	..	..
Parkstone L	..	..	—	8 18	—	..	1021	..	..	..	..	1242	..	..
Poole	2 37	..	..	8 25	..	..	1029	..	..	..	..	1249	—	..
Creekmoor Halt	..	—	..	8 29	..	—	..	..	—	..	..	..	..	..
Broadstone Z	..	—	..	8 33	..	..	..	..	..	..	..	..	..	..
Wimborne 339 . arr.	..	..	..	8 40	..	..	..	..	..	..	..	..	..	..

Sundays—*continued*

	p.m	p.m	p.m	p.m		p.m	p.m	p.m	p.m	p.m	p.m	p.m		
Christchurch ...dep.	2 6	..	2 48	..	—	4 1	..	7 1	9 17	..	..	11 1	..	..
Pokesdown O	2 13	..	2 54	..	—	4 8	..	7 7	9 23	..	..	11 7	..	..
Boscombe	2 16	..	2 57	..	—	4 11	..	7 10	9 27	..	..	1110	..	..
Bournemouth Central arr.	2 20	..	3 1	..	..	4 15	..	7 14	9 31	..	..	1114	..	..
Bournemouth Central dep.	2 22	2 42	..	3 10	..	4 17	4 22	..	9 35	9 40	10 0	..	..	..
Bournemouth West	2 32	..	..	..	..	4 27	..	..	..	9 50	..	..	..	..
Branksome	..	2 50	..	3 16	..	..	4 30	..	9 43	..	10 6	..	..	..
Parkstone L	..	2 54	..	3 19	..	..	4 34	..	9 47	..	10 9	..	..	..
Poole	..	3 1	..	3 24	..	..	4 39	..	9 53	..	1014	..	..	..
Creekmoor Halt	..	..	..	3 28	..	..	..	..	..	..	1018	..	..	..
Broadstone Z	..	..	..	3 33	..	..	..	..	..	..	1022	..	..	..
Wimborne 339 .. arr.	..	..	..	3 39	..	..	..	..	..	..	1028	..	..	..

(3) Third class only

B From Dorchester (dep. 7 32 p.m), page 333

L Station for Sandbanks
O For Eastern Bournemouth
S O Saturdays only
S X Saturdays excepted
Z Broadstone (Dorset)

WIMBORNE, POOLE, BOURNEMOUTH, and CHRISTCHURCH

Week Days

Miles		a.m B	a.m		a.m	a.m		a.m	a.m	a.m	a.m		a.m	a.m	a.m		a.m	a.m SX		a.m		a.m	a.m	a.m	a.m		a.m	a.m	a.m		a.m		a.m
	Wimborne .... dep.	4 54	..	..	..	6 45	..	.	..	..	..	..	..	..	8 0	..	8 23	..	..	..	..	9 20	..	..	..	..	..	1024	..	..	1110	..	..
2½	Broadstone Z	5 5	..	..	..	6 50	..	..	..	..	..	..	..	..	8 6	..	8 30	..	..	9 1	..	9 26	..	..	..	..	..	1030	1035	..	1115	..	..
3¼	Creekmoor Halt	③	..	..	..	6 54	..	..	..	..	..	..	..	..	To Dorchester (arr. 8 51 a.m.) p.324	..	8 34	..	..	9 5	..	9 30	..	..	..	..	..	1034	1039	..	1119	..	..
5¾	Poole	..	..	..	..	6 58	..	..	..	7 56	..	..	8 25	..		..	8 39	8 44	..	9 12	..	9 34	9 43	..	1015	..	..	1039	1046	..	1123	..	..
7¾	Parkstone L	..	..	..	..	7 3	..	..	..	8 2	..	..	..	..		..	8 44	8 49	..	9 19	..	..	9 49	..	..	..	..	1046	1052	..	1128	..	..
[illegible]	Branksome	..	..	..	..	7 7	..	..	..	8 8	..	..	..	..		..	8 48	8 53	..	9 25	..	..	9 54	..	..	..	..	1052	1058	..	1133	..	..
10½	Bournemouth West	..	..	..	..	7 12	..	7 20	7 30	8 12	8 20	..	..	8 35		..	8 53	..	..	9 30	..	..	..	1012	..	..	11 2	1057	11 3	..	1138	..	1148
13¼	Bournemouth Central arr.	..	..	..	..	..	..	7 28	7 38	..	8 28	..	8 35	8 43		..	..	8 59	..	..	..	..	10 0	1020	1027	..	1110	..	..	..	..	..	1157
	Bournemouth Central dep.	..	6 30	..	7 0	..	..	7 30	7 40	..	..	..	..	8 45		..	..	..	..	..	..	..	..	..	..	..	1112	..	..	..	..	..	12 2
14¾	Boscombe	..	6 33	..	7 3	..	..	7 33	7 44	..	..	..	..	8 49		..	..	..	..	..	..	..	..	..	..	..	1117	..	..	..	..	..	12 8
15½	Pokesdown ⊕ [330	..	6 36	..	7 6	..	..	7 36	7 47	..	..	..	..	8 52		..	..	..	..	..	..	..	..	..	..	..	1121	..	..	..	..	..	1212
17¼	Christchurch A arr.	..	6 43	..	7 11	..	..	7 41	7 52	..	..	..	..	8 58		..	..	..	..	..	..	..	..	..	..	..	1127	..	..	..	..	..	1218

Week Days—continued

	a.m		p.m	p.m		p.m		p.m		p.m	p.m		p.m	p.m		p.m		p.m	p.m		p.m	p.m		p.m	p.m	p.m		p.m	p.m SX		p.m		p.m
Wimborne .... dep.	1142	..	..	..	..	..	..	1257	..	..	..	..	..	1 56	..	..	..	..	2 46	..	..	..	..	..	..	4 52	..	..	..	..	..	..	..
Broadstone Z	1148	..	..	..	..	..	..	1 3	..	..	..	..	1 45	2 5	..	..	..	..	2 53	..	..	..	..	..	..	5 2	..	..	..	..	..	..	..
Creekmoor Halt	1152	..	..	..	..	..	..	1 8	..	..	..	..	1 50	2 9	..	..	..	..	2 57	..	..	..	..	..	..	5 7	..	..	..	..	..	..	..
Poole	1156	..	..	1224	..	..	..	1 14	..	1 32	..	..	1 57	2 15	..	2 24	..	..	3 3	..	3 34	..	..	..	5 3	5 11	..	..	..	..	5 46	..	6 6
Parkstone L	12 1	..	..	..	..	..	..	1 20	..	1 37	..	..	2 3	2 21	..	..	..	..	3 9	..	3 39	..	..	..	..	5 16	..	..	..	..	5 52	..	..
Branksome	12 6	..	..	..	..	..	..	1 25	..	1 42	..	..	2 8	2 26	..	..	..	..	3 15	..	3 43	..	..	..	..	5 21	..	..	..	..	5 57	..	..
Bournemouth West	..	..	12 20	..	..	1 5	..	1 30	..	..	2 20	..	2 13	2 31	..	..	..	3 5	3 19	..	..	..	..	5 5	5 14	5 25	..	..	..	..	..	..	..
Bournemouth Central arr.	1212	..	12 28	1235	..	1 13	..	..	..	1 48	2 28	..	..	..	..	2 35	..	3 14	..	..	3 50	..	..	5 13	..	..	..	..	..	..	6 3	..	6 17
Bournemouth Central dep.	..	..	..	..	..	1 15	..	..	..	..	..	..	..	..	..	..	..	3 17	..	..	3 54	4 38	..	5 15	..	..	..	5 38	5 56	..	..	..	..
Boscombe	..	..	..	..	..	1 20	..	..	..	..	..	..	..	..	..	..	..	3 22	..	..	3 59	4 41	..	5 20	..	..	..	5 41	6 1	..	..	..	..
Pokesdown ⊕ [330	..	..	..	..	..	1 24	..	..	..	..	..	..	..	..	..	..	..	3 26	..	..	4 2	4 52	..	5 23	..	..	..	5 44	6 4	..	..	..	..
Christchurch A arr.	..	..	..	..	..	1 29	..	..	..	..	..	..	..	..	..	..	..	3 32	..	..	4 7	4 56	..	5 29	..	..	..	5 49	6 9	..	..	..	..

Week Days—continued

	p.m	p.m	p.m	p.m	p.m SX	p.m	p.m		p.m	p.m	p.m	p.m	p.m	p.m		
Wimborne .... dep.	..	..	..	6 17	..	6 39	..	..	..	..	8 55	9 33	..	..	..	..
Broadstone Z	..	6 14	..	6 24	..	6 46	7 4	..	..	..	9 2	9 40	1017	..	..	..
Creekmoor Halt	..	6 18	..	6 27	..	6 50	..	..	..	..	9 6	9 44	1021	..	..	..
Poole	.	6 24	..	6 32	6 40	6 54	7 14	..	7 29	8 50	9 10	9 48	1027	11 8	..	..
Parkstone L	..	..	..	6 38	6 46	6 59	..	..	7 34	8 55	9 16	9 54	1033	1114	..	..
Branksome	..	..	..	6 43	6 51	7 3	..	..	7 39	8 59	9 21	10 0	1039	1118	..	..
Bournemouth West	6 20	6 35	6 44	6 48	..	7 8	7 25	..	..	..	9 26	..	1044	..	..	..
Bournemouth Central arr.	6 29	..	6 52	..	6 59	..	..	..	7 46	9 5	..	10 7	..	1125	..	..
Bournemouth Central dep.	..	..	6 54	..	..	..	..	..	7 50	9 10	..	..	..	1130	..	..
Boscombe	..	..	6 58	..	..	..	..	..	7 55	9 15	..	..	..	..	..	..
Pokesdown ⊕ [330	..	..	7 1	..	..	..	..	..	7 58	9 18	..	..	..	..	..	..
Christchurch A arr.	..	..	7 6	..	..	..	..	..	8 3	9 24	..	..	..	1139	..	..

Sundays

	a.m	a.m	a.m	a.m	a.m	a.m		p.m	p.m	p.m	p.m	p.m	p.m		p.m	p.m	p.m
Wimborne .... dep.	..	..	..	10 7	..	..	..	..	..	2 35	..	..	..	..	..	..	5 52
Broadstone Z	..	..	..	1013	..	..	..	..	..	2 42	..	..	..	..	..	..	5 59
Creekmoor Halt	..	..	..	1017	..	..	..	..	..	2 46	..	..	..	..	..	..	6 2
Poole	..	8 23	..	1022	..	1058	..	..	..	2 50	..	3 8	..	..	..	..	6 7
Parkstone L	..	8 29	..	1027	..	11 4	..	..	..	2 55	..	3 14	..	..	..	..	6 12
Branksome	..	8 34	..	1032	..	11 9	..	..	..	3 0	..	3 19	..	..	..	..	6 17
Bournemouth West	..	..	..	..	11 0	..	..	1 8	2 43	..	3 10	..	..	..	5 20	6 5	..
Bournemouth Central arr.	..	8 41	..	1039	11 8	1116	..	1 16	2 51	3 7	3 18	3 26	..	..	5 28	6 13	6 24
Bournemouth Central dep.	8 32	8 50	10 5	..	..	1120	..	1 20	2 52	..	..	..	3 55	..	5 30	6 20	..
Boscombe	8 35	8 55	10 8	..	..	1126	..	1 25	2 56	..	..	..	3 58	..	5 33	6 23	..
Pokesdown ⊕ [330	8 38	8 58	1011	..	..	1129	..	1 28	2 59	..	..	..	4 1	..	5 36	6 27	..
Christchurch A arr.	8 43	9 3	1016	..	..	1134	..	1 33	3 4	..	..	..	4 6	..	5 41	6 33	..

Sundays—continued

	p.m	p.m		p.m		p.m		p.m		p.m		p.m	p.m	
Wimborne .... dep.	..	..	..	..	..	..	..	..	..	..	..	1039	..	..
Broadstone Z	..	..	..	..	..	..	..	..	..	..	..	1045	..	..
Creekmoor Halt	..	..	..	..	..	..	..	..	..	..	..	..	..	..
Poole	6 16	6 41	..	..	..	..	..	..	..	9 7	..	1051	11 7	..
Parkstone L	6 22	.	..	..	..	..	..	..	..	9 14	..	1056	1113	..
Branksome	6 27	..	..	..	..	..	..	..	..	9 19	..	11 1	..	..
Bournemouth West	..	..	..	6 55	..	..	..	..	..	..	..	..	..	..
Bournemouth Central arr.	6 34	6 52	..	7 4	..	..	..	..	.	9 25	..	11 7	1123	..
Bournemouth Central dep.	..	..	..	7 6	..	8 10	..	8 48	..	..	..	..	1130	..
Boscombe	..	..	..	7 12	..	8 13	..	8 52	..	..	..	..	..	..
Pokesdown ⊕ [330	..	..	..	7 15	..	8 16	..	8 55	..	..	..	..	..	..
Christchurch A arr.	..	..	..	7 20	..	8 21	..	9 0	..	..	..	..	1140	..

③ Third class only

A Station for Southbourne-on-Sea

B To Dorchester (arr. 5 55 a.m.) page 324

L Station for Sandbanks

⊕ For Eastern Bournemouth

S O Saturdays only

S X Saturdays excepted

Z Broadstone (Dorset)

LONDON, SOUTHAMPTON, BROCKENHURST, LYMINGTON, and YARMOUTH (via LYMINGTON)

Miles from Brockenh'rst	Down	Week Days																		
		a.m	a.m	a.m	a.m	a.m R		a.m	a.m R		p.m	p.m.	p.m R		p.m	p.m	p.m R		p.m	p.m
	Waterloo 324 .... dep	2Ⓐ40	..	5 40	..	8 30	..	9 30	11 30	..	12P30	12SO35	1 30	..	..	3 30	4 35	..	5 30	..
	Southampton Cen. 324.. "	6 18	..	7 56	8 55	10 29	..	11 34	1 23	..	2 19		3 22	..	3 40	5 31	6 18	..	7 31	..
	Brockenhurst .... dep	7 4	7 52	8 34	9 39	10 58	..	12 2	1 55	..	3 0		4 1	..	5 12	6 16	6 56	..	8 10	9 15
4¾	Lymington Town C	7 15	8 2	8 44	9 49	11 8	..	12 12	2 5	..	3 10		4 11	..	5 22	6 26	7 6	..	8 20	9 25
5½	Lymington Pier ...... arr	7 20	..	8 48	..	11 12	..	12 15	2 8	..	3 13		4 14	..	5 26	..	7 9	..	8 23	..
	Lymington Pier ...... dep	7 25	..	9 15	..	..	..	12 40	2 15	..	..		4 20	..	5 40	..	7B15	..	..	..
—	Yarmouth Pier .... arr	..	..	..	..	..	..	..	..	..	..		..	..	..	..	..	..	..	..
—	" Slipway.... "	7 55	..	9 45	..	..	..	1 10	2 45	..	..		4 50	..	6 10	..	7B45	..	..	..

Down	Sundays																		
	a.m			a.m			a.m R			p.m R			p.m		Runs until 28th March, 1948 p.m		Commences 4th April, 1948 p.m		Commences 4th April, 1948 p.m
Waterloo 324 .... dep	..	..	..	9 30	..	..	1130	..	..	1 30	..	..	..	..	..	..	2 54	..	..
Southampton Cen. 324.. "	..	..	..	1128	..	..	1 22	..	..	3 18	..	..	..	..	..	..	6 5	..	..
Brockenhurst .... dep	..	..	..	12 0	..	..	2 2	..	..	3 45	..	..	4 55	..	5 53	..	6 40	..	7 55
Lymington Town C	..	..	..	1210	..	..	2 15	..	..	3 55	..	..	5 5	..	6† 3	..	6 50	..	8†5
Lymington Pier ...... arr	..	..	..	1213	..	..	2 20	..	..	3 58	..	..	5 8	..	..	..	6 53	..	..
Lymington Pier ...... dep	9 50	..	..	1220	..	..	2 35	..	..	4 10	..	..	5F35	..	..	..	..	..	..
Yarmouth Pier .... arr	..	..	..	..	..	..	..	..	..	..	..	..	..	..	..	..	..	..	..
" Slipway.... "	1020	..	..	1250	..	..	3 5	..	..	4 40	..	..	6F5	..	..	..	..	..	..

Miles from Lyming'n Pier	Up	Week Days																			
		a.m	a.m		a.m	a.m		a.m	a.m		p.m	p.m		p.m	p.m		p.m R	p.m		p.m	p.m
	Yarmouth Slipway.... dep	..	..	..	..	8 20	..	..	1040	..	..	1 30	..	2 55	..	..	5 0	..	..	6 25	7B55
	" Pier .... "	..	..	..	..	..	..	..	..	..	..	..	..	..	..	..	..	..	..	..	..
	Lymington Pier ...... arr	..	..	..	..	8 50	..	..	1110	..	..	2 0	..	3 25	..	..	5 30	..	..	6 55	8B25
	Lymington Pier ...... dep	..	7 28	..	..	9 5	..	..	1122	..	1 19	2 12	..	3 32	4 15	..	5 35	..	..	7 34	8 27
½	Lymington Town	6 20	7 43	..	8 7	9 10	..	1037	1127	..	1 24	2 17	..	3 36	4 20	..	5 40	6 30	..	7 39	8 32
5½	Brockenhurst 324 ...... arr	6 30	7 53	..	8 17	9 22	..	1049	1140	..	1 36	2 28	..	3 48	4 31	..	5 51	6 40	..	7 51	8 43
18¾	Southampton (Cen) 330. arr	7 44	8 23	..	8 53	9 52	..	1116	1216	..	2 16	..	..	4 16	5 6	..	6 16	8 6	..	8 45	9 57
98¾	Waterloo 330 .... "	..	1013	..	10V59	12 7	..	1259	2 19	..	4 25	..	..	6 36	6P45	..	8 32	..	..	1113	3‡55

Up	Sundays																			
	a.m			p.m			p.m			p.m			p.m			Commences 4th April, 1948 p.m R				
Yarmouth Slipway.... dep	1040	..	..	1 0	..	..	..	..	..	3 30	..	..	4 55	..	..	6 20	..	..	..	..
" Pier .... "	..	..	..	..	..	..	..	..	..	..	..	..	..	..	..	..	..	..	..	..
Lymington Pier ...... arr	1110	..	..	1 30	..	..	..	..	..	4 0	..	..	5 25	..	..	6 50	..	..	..	..
Lymington Pier ...... dep	1117	..	..	1 32	..	..	..	..	..	4 7	..	..	5 30	..	..	6 57	..	..	..	..
Lymington Town	1122	..	..	1 37	..	..	3 10	..	..	4 12	..	..	5 35	..	..	7 2	..	..	..	..
Brockenhurst 324 ...... arr	1133	..	..	1 48	..	..	3 21	..	..	4 23	..	..	5 46	..	..	7 14	..	..	..	..
Southampton (Cen) 330. arr	1216	..	..	2 24	..	..	3 59	..	..	5 5	..	..	6 38	..	..	7 42	..	..	..	..
Waterloo 330 .... "	2 12	..	..	5 57	..	..	5 57	..	6P45	7 45	..	..	9V21	..	..	9 28	..	..	..	..

Ⓐ Third class only

B Every week day to 1st Nov., 1947, Fris. and Sats. only, 7th Nov., 1947 to 27th March, 1948, and every week day commencing 29th March, 1948

C Sta. for Milford-on-Sea (3¾ miles). Omnibus Service available by Hants. and Dorset Motor Services Ltd.

F Commences 4th April, 1948

P 1st and 3rd class Pullman Car Train between Waterloo and Southampton (Central). Supplementary Fees charged.

R Refreshment Car between Waterloo and Brockenhurst

SO Saturdays only

V Refreshment Car between Southampton (Central) and Waterloo

† Arrival time

‡ Morning time

MOTOR CARS FOR THE ISLE OF WIGHT

Special arrangements are made at Lymington Station for this traffic, including slipways and ferry vessel which obviate lifting. Enquiries from Marine Agent, Lymington Tel.—No. 96.

Conveyance of Motor Cars, etc., to and from the Isle of Wight, see pages 501 and 502.

For complete Steamer Service between Lymington and Isle of Wight, see page 500.

BROCKENHURST, SALISBURY, and BOURNEMOUTH WEST

Miles	Miles		Week Days																		Sundays				
			a.m	a.m	a.m	a.m	a.m	a.m	a.m		p.m		p.m	p.m	p.m	p.m	p.m	p.m	p.m		a.m		p.m	p.m	p.m
		Brockenhurst .... dep	Ⓐ	..	..	8 37	9 32	..	11 2	..	12 15			2 5	4 5	..	5 59	8 15	..	..	9 25	..	1 51	..	5 10
4¾	—	Holmsley	a	..	..	8 47	9 41	..	11 11	..	12 25	..	..	2 14	4 15	..	6 8	8 24	..	..	9 34	..	2 2	..	5 19
10¾	—	Ringwood	..	..	..	8 59	9 53	..	11 23	..	12 36	..	..	2 25	4 28	..	6 20	8 36	..	..	9 46	..	2 15	..	5 32
13¾	—	Ashley Heath Halt	..	..	..	9 4	9 58	..	11 28	..	12 42	..	..	2 31	4 34	..	6 25	8 41	..	..	9 51	..	2 21	..	5 37
—	—	Salisbury .... dep	3 50	..	7 15	..	..	9 25	..	..	..	..	1255	..	..	5 20	..	..	8 34	..	..	..	..	2 24	..
—	9	Downton	..	..	7 32	..	..	9 42	..	..	..	..	1 12	..	..	5 37	..	..	8 51	..	..	..	..	2 44	..
—	12	Breamore	..	..	7 39	..	..	9 48	..	..	..	..	1 18	..	..	5 42	..	..	8 57	..	..	..	..	2 52	..
—	14½	Fordingbridge	4L21	..	7 45	..	..	9 54	..	..	..	..	1 24	..	..	5 48	..	..	9 4	..	..	..	..	2 59	..
—	16½	Daggons Road	..	..	7 56	..	..	9 59	..	..	..	..	1 31	..	..	5 53	..	..	9 9	..	..	..	..	3 5	..
—	19½	Verwood, for Cranborne	4L33	..	8 6	..	..	10 6	..	..	..	..	1 38	..	..	6 0	..	..	9 16	..	..	..	..	3 13	..
16	24	West Moors B	4 41	..	8 14	9 9	10 3	1014	11 33	..	12 48	..	1 46	2 36	4 41	6 7	6 30	8 46	9 24	..	9 56	..	2 26	3 25	5 43
20¼	28¼	**Wimborne**	4 54	6 45	8 23	9 20	1012	1024	11 42	..	12 57	..	1 56	2 46	4 52	6 17	6 39	8 55	9 33	..	10 7	..	2 35	3 34	5 52
22¾	30¾	Broadstone Q	5 5	6 50	8 30	9 26	..	1030	11 48	..	1 3	..	2 5	2 53	5 2	6 24	6 46	9 2	9 40	..	10 13	..	2 42	..	5 59
24	32	Creekmoor Halt	..	6 54	8 34	9 30	..	1034	11 52	..	1 8	..	2 9	2 57	5 7	6 27	6 50	9 6	9 44	..	10 17	..	2 46	..	6 2
26	34	Poole	..	6 58	8 39	9N43	..	1039	11 56	..	1 14	..	2 15	3 3	5 11	6 32	6 54	9 10	9 48	..	10 22	..	2 50	..	6 7
28	36	Parkstone, for Sandbanks	..	7 3	8 44	9 49	..	1046	12 1	..	1 20	..	2 21	3 9	5 16	6 38	6 59	9 16	9 54	..	10 27	..	2 55	..	6 12
29½	37½	Branksome	..	7 7	8 48	9 54	..	1052	12 6	..	1 25	..	2 26	3 15	5 21	6 43	7 3	9 21	10 0	..	10 32	..	3 0	..	6 17
30½	38½	**Bournemouth West 337** arr	..	7 12	8 53	10*0	..	1057	12*12	..	1 30	..	2 31	3 19	5 25	6 48	7 8	9 26	10*7	..	10*39	..	3*7	..	6*24

Mls		Week Days																		Sundays				
		a.m	a.m	a.m	a.m	a.m	a.m		p.m	p.m	p.m	p.m		p.m	p.m	p.m	pm	p.m			a.m		p.m	p.m	
—	**Bournemouth West**... dep	6*25	6 48	7*42	8 10	10 0	..	..	12 25	1 18	2 35	4 30	..	4 47	6 50	7 43	..	8 50		..	8*5	..	3*10	..	..
1¼	Branksome	6 32	..	7 48	8 14	10 4	..	..	1238	1 22	2 38	4 33	..	4 51	6 54	7 47	..	8 53	..	..	8 13	..	3 16	..	..
2½	Parkstone, for Sandbanks	6 37	c	7 52	8 18	10 8	..	..	1242	1 26	2 41	4 37	..	4 55	6 58	7 50	..	8 57	..	..	8 18	..	3 19	..	..
4½	Poole	6 44	6 59	7 57	8 26	10 14	1032	..	1247	1 33	2 48	4 42	..	5 1	7 3	7 57	..	9 2	..	..	8 25	..	3 24	..	..
6½	Creekmore Halt	6 48	..	8 1	8 30	10 19	1036	..	1251	1 39	2 52	4 46	..	5 6	7 7	8 3	d	9 6	..	..	8 29	..	3 28	..	..
7¾	Broadstone (Dorset)	6 53	7 14	8 6	8 34	10 24	1042	..	1255	1 46	2 57	4 50	..	5 10	7 11	8 7	8 25	9 10	..	..	8 33	..	3 33	..	..
10½	**Wimborne**	7 0	7 19	8 13	8 40	10 31	1048	..	1 1	1 53	3 4	4 56	..	5 16	7 17	8 13	8F41	9 16	..	..	8 40	..	3 39	4 0	..
14½	West Moors B	7 8	7 28	8 21	8 48	10 41	1056	..	1 10	1 59	3 13	5 4	..	5 25	7 25	8 21	8 51	9WSO25	..	..	8 49	..	3 47	4 8	..
19	Verwood, for Cranborne	..	7 35	8 29	..	10 49	..	..	..	2 7	..	..	..	5 32	..	8 29	..	..	..	..	..	..	..	4 17	..
22	Daggons Road	..	7 44	8 36	..	10 58	..	..	..	2 15	..	..	..	5 41	..	8 38	..	..	..	..	..	..	..	4 29	..
24	Fordingbridge	..	7 48	8 41	..	11 3	..	..	..	2 20	..	..	..	5 46	..	8 43	..	..	..	..	..	..	..	4 37	..
26½	Breamore	..	7 54	8 46	..	11 10	..	..	..	2 28	..	..	..	5 55	..	8 55	..	..	..	..	..	..	..	4 45	..
29½	Downton	..	8 0	8 52	..	11 20	..	..	..	2 35	..	..	..	6 2	..	9 5	..	..	..	..	..	..	..	4 51	..
38½	Salisbury 340, 347, 376 arr	..	8 19	9 11	..	11 29	..	..	..	2 55	..	..	..	6 22	..	9 26	..	..	..	..	..	..	..	5 16	..
16¾	Ashley Heath Halt	7 13	..	..	8 53	..	11 2	..	1 15	..	3 18	5 9	..	..	7 30	..	8 57	..	..	..	8 54	..	3 52	..	..
19¾	Ringwood	7 21	..	..	8 58	..	11 9	..	1 21	..	3 25	5 15	..	..	7 36	..	9 3	..	..	..	8 59	..	3 58	..	..
25¾	Holmsley	7 32	..	..	9 9	..	1120	..	1 32	..	3 35	5 25	..	..	7 46	..	9 14	..	..	..	9 10	..	4 9	..	..
30½	Brockenhurst 324, 330 .. arr	7 42	..	..	9 19	..	1131	..	1 42	..	3 45	5 35	..	..	7 56	..	9 25	..	..	..	9 20	..	4 19	..	..

NOTES

Ⓐ Third class only
* Bournemouth Cen.
a To Dorchester (arr 5 55 a.m.) page 324.
B West Moors for Ferndown
c Change at Broadstone
d 7 32 p.m from Dorchester. Dep Hamworthy Junc. at 8 17 p.m., page 333
F Arrive 8 31 p.m.
L Calls to set down only
N Change at Poole. Arr. 9 34 a.m.
Q Broadstone (Dorset)
WSO Weds and Sats only

LOCAL TRAINS between Wimborne and Bournemouth West, page 337

MELCOMBE REGIS (WEYMOUTH), PORTLAND, and EASTON—Southern and Great Western

Miles	Down		Week Days																				Sundays						
			a.m	a.m	a.m	a.m		a.m		p.m		p.m		p.m	p.m		pm	SO	p.m	p.m	p.m	p.m		p.m	p.m	p.m	p.m	p.m	p.m	p.m
	Melcombe Regis P	dep	6 18	7 7	7 17	8 35	..	1045	..	1 15	..	2 35	..	4 15	4 30	..	6 7	6 33	7 45	8 50	1025	1125	..	1 0	2 15	4 15	5 55	7 40	8 35	1135
¼	Westham Halt		6 20	7 9	7 19	8 37	..	1047	..	1 17	..	2 37	..	4 17	4 32	..	6 9	6 35	7 47	8 52	..	..	..	1 2	2 17	4 17	5 57	7 42	8 37	..
¾	Rodwell		6 23	7 12	7 22	8 40	..	1050	..	1 20	..	2 40	..	4 20	4 35	..	6 14	6 38	7 50	8 55	..	..	..	1 5	2 20	4 20	6 0	7 45	8 40	..
1¼	Sandsfoot Castle Halt		6 26	7 15	7 25	8 43	..	1053	..	1 23	..	2 43	..	4 2[illegible]	4 38	..	6 16	6 41	7 53	8 58	..	1133	..	1 8	2 23	4 23	6 3	7 48	8 43	1143
2¼	Wyke Regis Halt		6 28	7 17	7 27	8 45	..	1055	..	1 27	..	2 45	..	4 2[illegible]	4 40	..	6 19	6 43	7 55	9 0	..	1135	..	1 10	2 25	4 25	6 5	7 50	8 45	1145
4½	Portland	arr	6 33	7 22	7 32	8 50	..	11 0	..	1 32	..	2 50	..	4 30	4 45	..	6 24	6 48	8 0	9 5	1035	1140	..	1 15	2 30	4 30	6 10	7 55	8 50	1150
		dep	..	..	7 35	..	..	11 5	..	1 33	..	2 57	..	..	4 48	..	..	6 50	..	..	..	..	..	..	..	..	..	..	..	..
6	Easton	arr	..	..	7 47	..	..	1117	..	1 45	..	3 9	..	..	5 0	..	..	7 2	..	..	..	..	..	..	..	..	..	..	..	..

Miles	Up		Week Days																				Sundays						
			a.m	a.m	a.m		a.m		p.m		p.m		p.m	p.m	p.m	p.m	SO	p.m	p.m	p.m	p.m		p.m	p.m	p.m	p.m	p.m	p.m	ngt.
	Easton	dep	..	..	8 15	..	..	..	1212	..	1 53	..	3 20	..	5 19	..	7 10	..	..	..	..	..	..	..	..	..	..	..	..
3½	Portland	arr	..	..	8 26	..	..	..	1223	..	2 4	..	3 31	..	5 30	..	7 21	..	..	..	..	..	..	..	..	..	..	..	..
		dep	6 45	8 7	8 28	..	9 32	..	1227	..	2 5	..	3 33	4 50	5 32	7 0	7 23	8 10	9 25	1046	1150	..	1 30	2 40	4 50	6 35	8 5	9 15	12 0
5¾	Wyke Regis Halt		6 48	8 12	8 33	..	9 37	..	1232	..	2 10	..	3 38	4 55	5 37	7 5	7 28	8 15	9 30	..	1155	..	1 35	2 45	4 55	6 40	8 10	9 20	12 5
6½	Sandsfoot Castle Halt		6 53	8 15	8 36	..	9 40	..	1238	..	2 13	..	3 41	4 58	5 40	7 8	7 31	8 18	9 33	..	1158	..	1 38	2 48	4 58	6 43	8 13	9 23	12 8
7¼	Rodwell		6 55	8 17	8 41	..	9 42	..	1240	..	2 15	..	3 43	5 0	5 42	7 10	7 33	8 20	9 35	..	..	..	1 40	2 50	5 0	6 45	8 15	9 25	..
7¾	Westham Halt		6 58	8 20	8 44	..	9 45	..	1244	..	2 18	..	3 46	5 3	5 45	7 13	7 36	8 23	9 38	..	12 3	..	1 43	2 53	5 3	6 48	8 18	9 28	1212
8	Melcombe Regis P 330 ..	arr	7 0	8 21	8 45	..	9 46	..	1245	..	2 19	..	3 47	5 4	5 46	7 14	7 37	8 26	9 39	11 0	12 4	..	1 44	2 54	5 4	6 49	8 19	9 29	1214

NOTES

P Melcombe Regis (Weymouth)
SO Saturdays only

From WATERLOO to THE WEST OF ENGLAND—Weekdays

Mls. from London	Station		1	2	3	4	5	6	7	8	9	10	11	12	13	14	15	16	17	18	19	20	21	22	23	24	25	26	27	28	29	30
			p.m	a.m	a.m	a.m	a.m	a.m	a.m	a.m	a.m	a.m	a.m	a.m	a.m	a.m	a.m	a.m	a.m	p.m	a.m	p.m	p.m	a.m	a.m	a.m	a.m		p.m	noon		p.m
	324 WATERLOO	dep	10Z30		1 25													5 40	7 20		9 0					9 30	10 50			12 0		
	324 Surbiton	"	10Z13															5 59	7 38		9U17					9U48						
	324 Woking	"	11Z 6															6 30	7 57		9 35					10 6						
48	Basingstoke	dep	11Z31															7 31	8 48		10 8					1045						
52½	Oakley																	7 42	8 59							1054						
55¾	Overton																	7 48	9 5							11 0						
59½	Whitchurch A																	7 56	9 11							11 6						
61¼	Hurstbourne																	8 1	9 16							1111						
66½	Andover Junction 378				2 54													8 15	9 28		1036					1121						
72¾	Grateley																	8 27	9 40							1131						
78¼	Porton 356		a.m															8 38	9 51							1142						
83¾	SALISBURY 339, 356, 376	arr	2 36		3 18													8 48	10 2		11 1					1152	12 33					
		dep	2 48		3 24	3 35											8 0	9 30			11 5				1115		12 36					
86½	Wilton B					3 43											8 7	9 36							1121							
92	Dinton																8 17	9 46							1131							
96½	Tisbury					4 3											8 26	9 54							1139							
101¼	Semley					4 15											8 38	10 7							1149							
105½	Gillingham (Dorset)		3 23			4 24											8 48	1020							1157							
112¼	Templecombe		3 36			4 41									7 15	8 45	9 12	1032			1143			1158	1212							
114¾	Millborne Port					4 48									7 20	8 51	9 18	Stop						12 4	1220							
118¼	Sherborne		3 50			4 58									7 26	8 56	9 25	Stop			1157			1211	1229							
123	Yeovil Junction 355	arr	4 3			5 8									7 35	9 7	9 33				12 5			1219	1240							
124¾	355 Yeovil (Town)	arr	4 17			5 23									7 40	9 16	9 47				1216			1257	1257							
		dep				Stop							6 25		Stop	Stop	9 28				1155			1155								
—	Yeovil Junction	dep											6 31				9 39				12 6			1222								
128¼	Sutton Bingham																9 46							1228								
131¾	Crewkerne												6 46				9 58							1239								
139½	Chard Junction 355	arr											7 0				1012							1252								
143	355 Chard	arr											8 37				11 6							1 20								
		dep															9 34							1210								
—	Chard Junction	dep											7 1				1015							1254								
144¾	Axminster 355	arr											7 9				1024		Stop		1235			1 2								
151½	355 Lyme Regis	arr											8 56		a.m		11 4				1 18			2 14								
		dep													7J20		10 0				1134			1229					1S024			
—	Axminster	dep											7 11		7 55		1027				1236			1 4					2S02			
148	Seaton Junction 355	arr											7 18		8 1		1034				1243			1 11					2S08			
152½	355 Seaton	arr											8 17		8 17		1052				1 5			2 2								
		dep													7 46		10 5				1228			1228					1 20			
—	Seaton Junction	dep											7 20		8 2		1035				1244			1 13					2 10			
155	Honiton												7 36		8 18		1052							1 30					2 26			
159½	Sidmouth Junc. 356	arr											7 43		8 25		11 0				1 6			1 38			2 8		2 34	3 16		
167¾	356 Sidmouth	arr											8 24		8 52		1135				1 32			2 48			2 48		3 43	3 43		
171	356 Budleigh Salter'n.	"											9 23		9 23		1144				1 50			3 3			3 3					
175¾	356 Exmouth	"											9 37		9 37	a.m	1156				2 3			3 17			3 17					
—	356 Sidmouth	dep											7 20			1020	1020				1234			1234			1 35		1 35			
—	Sidmouth Junction	dep											7 45		8 26	1047	11 2				1 7			1 40			2 11		2 35	3 18		
163½	Whimple												7 52		8 32	1054				1 0			1 34	1 47					2 42			
167	Broad Clyst												7 59		8 38	11 1				1 5			1 39	1 54					2 48			
169	Pinhoe												8 4		8 43	11 6				1 10			1 44	1 59					2 53			
171½	EXETER Central 357	arr			5 13								8 12		8 50	1114	1119			1 18	1 24		1 51	2 7			2 29		3 2	3 36		
182½	357 Exmouth	arr			7 10								8 39		9 44	12 7	12 7	a.m		2 0	2 0			3 12			3 12		4L26	4L26		
		dep				a.m						6 40	7 45	8 10	Stop	Stop	1045	1045		Stop	1215	1215					1 30	1 30	Stop	2 45	2 45	
—	EXETER Central	dep			5 20	5 31						7 35	8 20	8 40			1127	1146			1 32	1 44					2 34	2 46		3 39	3 48	
172¾	Exeter (St. David's)				5 25	5 39						7 44	8 26	8 47			1135	1153			1A41	1 49					2 41	2 51		3 45	3 52	
176½	Newton St. Cyres											7 [illegible]4	8 36					12 3				1 58										
179	Crediton					5 52						8 0	8 42	9 1			1148	1211			1 54	2 4										
183	Yeoford	arr				6 0						8 8	8 50	9 9			1156	1219				2 12										

Column 1: Via Eastleigh. Tuesday to Saturday mornings.

Column 11: Calls at St. James' Park Halt at 8 10 a.m.

Column 17: Calls at Idmiston Halt at 9 48 a.m.

Column 18: Saturdays only. Calls at St. James' Park Halt at 1 15 p.m.

Column 21: Saturdays excepted.

Column 24: Calls at Idmiston Halt at 11 39 a.m.

Columns 25–26: Atlantic Coast Express. Refreshment Car, London to Exeter. Through Carriages to Seaton, Sidmouth and Exmouth.

Column 27: Calls at St. James' Park Halt at 2 59 p.m on Saturdays.

Columns 28–29: Devon Belle. Mondays, Fridays and Saturdays. Runs until 27th October, 1947.

Miles	Station	1	2	3	4	5	6	7	8	9	10	11	12	13	14	15	16	17	18	19	20	21	22	23	24	25	26	27	28	29	30
—	Yeoford .... dep				6 1						8 9		9 11				1220													1st & 3rd class Pullman Cars only to Ilfracombe. Supplementary fees charged	
187½	Bow										8 17		9 21				1230			2 10											
191	North Tawton										8 24		9 28				1237			2 16							3 21				
193¾	Sampford Courtenay										8 31		9 35				1244														
197¾	Okehampton .... arr	a.m			6 23						8 40		9 44				1253			2 29							3 34		4 25		
—	Okehampton .... dep	4 23									8 43		9 46				1256			2 31							3 36		4 27		Mondays, Fridays and Saturdays. Runs until 27th October, 1947
204	Bridestowe										9 0		10 2				1 14										3 51				
207½	Lydford										9 7		1010				1 22										3 58				
208¾	Brentor										9 11		1014				1 26		p.m								4 2	p.m.			
213¾	Tavistock C	4 55	6 0	6P55					7 58	8 44	9 21		1026				1 37		2 0	2 58							4 11	4 25			
220¼	Bere Alston 357		6 13					7 53	8 11	8 55	9 33		1043				1 52		2 11	3 10								4 36			
223	Bere Ferrers		6 21					7 59		Stop	9 39		1050				1 59		2 17									4 42			
225	Tamerton Foliot		6 26					8 4			9 44		1055				2 4		2 22									4 46			
227¼	St. Budeaux, for Saltash		6 31					8 9	8 26		9 49		11 0				2 9		2 27									4 51			
228¾	Ford (Devon)		6 35					8 13	8 32		9 53		11 4				2 16		2 31									4 58			
229½	Devonport D .... arr		6 39	7 31				8 17	8 36		9 57		11 8				2 20		2 35	3 28							4 38	5 2	5 16		
230¼	PLYMOUTH { North Rd. "		6 43	7 36				8 23	8 43		10 5		1114				2 29		2 41	3 35							4 44	5 7	5 25		
234	PLYMOUTH { Friary "		6 54	7 48				8 33	8 55		1016		1125				2 40		2 52	3 47							4 55	5 17	5 36		
—	Yeoford .... dep			Stop		6 10		Stop	Stop			8 51				1157			Saturdays only	Refreshment Car, London to Exeter	2 13							Stop	Mondays, Fridays and Saturdays. Runs until 27th October, 1947. 1st & 3rd class Pullman Cars only to Plymouth. Supplementary fees charged		
186	Copplestone					6 18						8 57				12 4					2 19										
187½	Morchard Road					6 22						9 1				12 8					2 23										
190	Lapford					6 27						9 6				1213					2 28										
193¾	Eggesford F					6 34				a.m		9 14				1221					2 35					3 14					
197¾	South Molton Road G					6 41				8 28		9 21				1229					2 42										
200¾	Portsmouth Arms					6 47				8 33		9 29				1235					2 48										
204¾	Umberleigh					6 54				8 40		9 37				1242					2 55										
207½	Chapelton									8 45		9 42				1247					3 0										
211½	Barnstaple Junc. H { arr					7 4		a.m		8 52		9 49		a.m		1254					3 7					3 44				4 49	
	Barnstaple Junc. H { dep					7 15		8 0		Stop		9 59		1113		1 0					3 9					3 49				4 50	
212½	Barnstaple Town J					7 18		8 3				10 4		1116		1 5					3 13					3 54				4 54	
216½	Wrafton					7 26		8 11				1015		1124		1 14					3 21					4 2					
217½	Braunton K					7 31		8 16				1020		1128		1 19					3 25					4 7				5 5	
223¼	Mortehoe L					7 51		8 37				1039		1146		1 38					3 43					4 27				5 24	
226½	ILFRACOMBE .... arr			a.m		8 0		8 46	a.m			1048		1155	a.m	1 47			Stop		3 52					4 36				5 33	
—	Barnstaple Junc. dep			6 55		7 25		Stop	8 14			10 5			1130	1 10					3 15					4 0				Mondays, Fridays and Saturdays. Runs until 27th October, 1947	4 56
214½	Fremington			7 0		7 30			8 19			1010			1135	1 15					3 20					4 5					5 1
218	Instow			7 8		7 40			8 26			1017			1142	1 22					3 27					4 12					5 12
220½	Bideford N			7 15		7 51			8 34			1023			1148	1 34					3 33					4 18					5 18
225¾	Torrington 358 .... arr			7 30		8 5			8 47			1037			1159	1 45		p.m			3 44					4 31		p.m			5 29
—	Okehampton .... dep						6 37						9 56					1 20										3 55			
202¾	Maddaford Moor Halt P												10 8					1 33										4 8			
206½	Ashbury, for North Lew						7 6						1016					1 39										4 17			
210½	Halwill ⊕ 358 .... arr						7 17			a.m			1024					1 46										4 27			
—	Halwill .... dep						7 25			8 53			1037					1 47										4 33			
213½	Dunsland Cross						7 31			8 59			1045					1 54										4 41			
218½	Holsworthy						7 39			9 8			1054					2 3										4 50			
223	Whitstone & Bridgerule						7 48			9 18			11 7					2 13										4 59			
228¾	Bude .... arr						7 58			9 28			1117					2 25	p.m									5 9			
—	Halwill .... dep						7 29						1028						1 53									4 29			
215½	Ashwater						7 41						1037						2 0									4 37			
219	Tower Hill						7 52	a.m					1044						2 7									4 44			
224	Launceston						8 3	8 34					1052						2 15									4 52			
228½	Egloskerry							8 42					11 3						Saturdays only									5 3			
231¾	Tresmeer							8 51					1111															5 11			
236¾	Otterham T							9 1					1121															5 21			
241¼	Camelford U							9 11					1130															5 29			
243¾	Delabole							9 19					1137															5 37			
247¾	Port Isaac Road							9 27					1144															5 46			
250¼	St. Kew Highway							9 32					1149															5 52			
254¾	Wadebridge 358 .... arr							9 40					1156															6 1			
261	358 Bodmin .... arr							10 6					1 6															6 30			
230	Padstow .... arr							10 4					1210															6 21			

For Notes, see pages 344 and 345; for Continuation of Trains, see pages 342 to 345.

From WATERLOO to THE WEST OF ENGLAND—Weekdays—*continued*

Station		1	2	3	4	5	6	7	8	9	10	11	12	13	14	15	16	17	18	19	20	21	22	23	24	25	26	27	28
		p.m	a.m	p.m	p.m	p.m		p.m	p.m	p.m	p.m	p.m	p.m		p.m	p.m	p.m	p.m	p.m	p.m	p.m	p.m	p.m	p.m	p.m	p.m	p.m	p.m	
324 WATERLOO	dep	..	1054	..	..	1250		..	..	..	..	1 30	2 50		..	..	..	3 30	5 0	6 0	..	..	..	5 39	7 30	8 54	..	10Z30	..
324 Surbiton	"	..	1043	..	..	1243		..	..	..	..	12 43	1SX43		..	..	..	3 13	4 43	4 43	..	..	..	5 13	6 43	8 43	..	10Z13	..
324 Woking	"	..	1126	..	..	1U22		..	..	..	..	1 26	2SX26		..	..	..	4 U25	5 33	5SX41	..	..	..	6 11	7 26	9 26	..	11Z 6	..
Basingstoke	dep	..	1215	..	..	..		..	..	..	..	2 45	3 52		..	..	..	4 48	6 7	6 59	..	..	..	7 4	8 50	1015	..	11Z51	..
Oakley		..	1225	..	..	..		..	..	..	..	2 54	..		..	..	..	4 57	..	..	..	..	..	7 14	8 59	1025	..	Via Eastleigh.	..
Overton		..	1231	..	..	..		..	..	..	..	3 0	..		..	..	..	5 3	6 22	..	..	..	..	7 20	9 5	1031	..		..
Whitchurch A		..	1238	..	..	..		..	..	..	..	3 7	..		..	..	..	5 10	6 29	..	..	..	..	7 27	9 13	1037	..		..
Hurstbourne		..	1242	..	..	..		..	..	..	..	3 12	..		..	..	..	5 16	..	..	..	..	..	7 32	9 18	1042	..		..
Andover Junction 376		..	1252	..	..	2 16		..	..	..	..	3 23	4 19		..	..	..	5 26	6 42	7 26	..	..	..	7 43	9 35	1052	..		..
Grateley		..	1 3	..	..	..		..	..	..	..	3 34	..		..	..	..	5 38	..	..	..	..	..	7 55	9 48	11 2	..		..
Porton 356		..	1 14	..	..	..		..	..	..	..	3 47	..		..	..	..	5 50	..	..	..	..	..	8 6	10 0	1111	..	a.m	..
SALISBURY 339, 356, 376	arr	..	1 24	..	..	2 39		..	..	..	..	3 57	4 42		..	..	..	6 0	7 8	7 49	..	..	..	8 17	1010	1121	..	2 36	..
	dep	12 45	Calls at Idmiston Halt at 1 11 p.m	..	..	2 43		..	..	..	3 5	Calls at Idmiston Halt at 3 43 p.m	4 46		..	..	5 0	Calls at Idmiston Halt at 5 47 p.m	7 13	7 52	..	..	8 5	Saturdays excepted. Calls at Idmiston Halt at 8 4 p.m	1018	..	..	2 48	..
Wilton B		..		..	..	..		..	..	..	3 11		..		..	..	5 6		..	..	..	..	8 11		1026	..	..	..	..
Dinton		12 58		..	..	..		..	..	..	3 21		..		..	..	5 16		..	..	..	..	8 21		1037	..	..	..	..
Tisbury		1 6		..	..	..		..	..	..	3 29		..		..	..	5 24		..	..	..	..	8 29		1046	..	..	..	..
Semley		1 16		..	..	..		..	..	..	3 41		..		..	..	5 36		7 41	..	..	..	8 39		1056	..	..	..	..
Gillingham (Dorset)		1 24		..	..	..		..	..	..	3 49		..		..	..	5 48		7 49	8 22	..	..	8 47		11 5	..	..	3 23	..
Templecombe		1 37		..	..	3 21		..	3 38	..	4 2		5 24		..	5 39	5 59		8 4	8 35	..	..	9 0		1117	..	..	3 36	..
Millborne Port		1 44		..	..	..		..	..	..	4 10		..		..	5 45	Stop		..	..	..	..	9 7		1124	..	..	..	..
Sherborne		1 50		..	..	3 34		..	..	..	4 17		..		..	5 52			8 19	8 46	..	..	9 17		1134	..	..	3 50	..
Yeovil Junction 355	arr	1 58		..	..	3 43		..	3 56	..	4 25		..		..	6 0	..		8 27	8 54	..	..	9 25		1142	..	..	4 3	..
355 YEOVIL (Town)	arr	2 14		..	..	3 54		..	..	..	4 39		..		Calls at St. James' Park Halt at 7 10 p.m	6 9	..		8 39	9 4	..	..	9 46		1159	..	..	4 17	..
	dep	1 50		..	..	3 30		..	3 30	..	4 19		..			5 52	..		Stop	8 45	..	8 45	..		..	..	..	Tuesday to Saturday mornings.	..
Yeovil Junction	dep	2 0	..	..	..	3 45		..	3 58	..	4 27	..	Refreshment Car London to Exeter.			6 1	..	..		8 55	..	9 3	..		Calls at Idmiston Halt at 9 56 p.m	..	..		..
Sutton Bingham		..	..	..	..	..		..	..	..	4 34	..				6 7	..	..	..	..	..	9 8	..			..	..		..
Crewkerne		2 18	..	..	..	..		..	..	..	4 46	..				6 19	..	..	..	..	..	9 20	..			..	..		..
Chard Junction 355	arr	2 32	..	..	..	..		..	4 22	..	5 0	..				6 33	..	..	..	..	..	9 34	..			..	..		..
355 CHARD	arr	3SO14	..	..	..	Refreshment Car London to Exeter		..	5 4	..	5 59	..				7 16	..	..	..	..	..	9SO58	..	..		..	..		..
	dep	1SO52	..	..	..			..	..	..	4 20	..				6 4	..	..	..	..	..	8 43	..	..		..	..		..
Chard Junction	dep	2 33	..	..	..			..	4 23	..	5 1	..				6 34	..	..	..	..	..	9 35	..	..		..	..		..
Axminster 355	arr	2 41	..	..	..			..	4 30	..	5 8	..				6 41	..	..	..	9 24	..	9 43	..	..		..	..		..
355 LYME REGIS	arr	3 11	..	..	..			..	5 1	..	5 59	..				7 11	..	..	..	10JK11	..	..	..	..		..	..		..
	dep	2 19	..	..	..			..	3 55	..	..	..				6 5	..	..	p.m	8 20	8 20	8 20	..	..		..	..		..
Axminster	dep	2 44	..	..	..			..	4 31	..	5 9	..				6 42	..	..	7 55	9 25	9 33	9 44	..	..		..	..		..
Seaton Junction 355	arr	2 51	..	..	..			..	4 38	..	5 14	..				6 49	..	..	8 1	..	9 39	9 51	..	..		..	..		..
355 SEATON	arr	3 27	..	..	..			..	4 57	..	5 51					7 10	..	..	8 59	..	9 58	..	..	..		..	..		..
	dep	2N35	..	..	..			..	3 55	..	..	..	..			6 5	..	..	..	..	..	9 3	..	..		..	..		..
Seaton Junction	dep	2V53	..	..	..			..	4 39	..	5 15	..	..			6 50	..	..	8 3	..	..	9 52	..	..		..	..	..	..
Honiton		3V10	..	..	..			..	4 57	..	5 31	..	..		6 38	7 5	..	..	8 19	..	..	10 7	..	..		..	1055	..	..
Sidmouth Junc. 356	arr	3V18	..	..	..			..	5 5	..	5 39	..	6 2		6 45	7 13	..	..	8 27	9 48	..	10 15	..	..		..	11 2	..	..
356 SIDMOUTH	arr	4 20	..	..	..			..	5 38	..	6 58	..	6 58		..	8 52	..	..	8 52	10 15	..	..	..	..	Stop	..	..	..	..
356 BUDLEIGH SALTER'N	"	4 57	..	..	..			..	..	..	7 8	..	7 8		..	9 8	..	..	9 8	10‡27	..	..	..	..		..	..	..	..
356 EXMOUTH	"	5 11	..	..	..			..	..	..	7 22	..	7 22		..	9 21	..	..	9 21	10‡40	..	..	..	..	p.m	..	..	..	..
356 SIDMOUTH	dep	..	..	..	3 24	..		..	4 36	..	..	..	5 45		5 45	..	..	..	7 45	9 25		9 25	..	..	1025	..	..	..	..
Sidmouth Junction	dep	3V19	..	..	3 55	..		..	5 7	..	5 40	..	6 29		6 46	7 14	..	..	8 29	9 49	..	10 16	..	..	1047	..	11 3	..	..
Whimple		..	..	..	4 3	..		..	5 14	..	5 46	..	..		6 51	7 20	..	..	8 36	..	..	10 22	..	..	1055	..	11 9	..	..
Broad Clyst		..	..	..	4 10	..		..	5 21	..	5 52	..	..		6 58	7 26	..	..	8 43	..	..	10 29	..	..	..	..	1118	..	..
Pinhoe		..	..	..	4 15	..		..	5 26	..	5 57	..	..		7 3	7 31	..	..	8 48	..	..	10 34	..	..	11 5	..	1124	..	..
EXETER Central 357	arr	3V36	..	..	4 23	4 46		..	5 34	..	6 5	..	6 46		7 13	7 40	..	..	8 56	10 6	..	10 42	..	..	1113	..	1133	..	..
357 EXMOUTH	arr	4†26	..	..	5 10	5 43		..	6 13	..	6 41	..	8 12		Stop	8 12	..	..	9 43	10 46	..	11 34	..	..	..	..	..	..	..
	dep	Stop	..	3 45	Stop	3 45	3H45	..	Stop	5 15		..	6 16		..		p.m 7 15	..	..		..	..	..	..	..	..	..	..	..
EXETER Central	dep	..	..	4 22	..	4 50	5 5	..	..	5 53		..	6 52	7 5	..		8 5	..	..		..	..	..	..	..	..	..	..	..
Exeter (St. David's)		..	..	4 27	..	4 57	5 10	..	..	5 58		..	6 59	7 10	..		8 11	..	..		..	..	..	..	..	..	..	..	..
Newton St. Cyres		..	..	4 36	..	..	..	..	..	6 8		..	..	..	..		8 21	..	..		..	..	..	..	..	..	..	..	..
Crediton		..	..	4 42	..	..	5 24	..	..	6 14		..	..	7 22	..		8 27	..	..		..	..	..	..	..	..	..	..	..
Yeoford	arr	..	..	4 50	..	5 14	5 32	..	..	6 22		..	7 17	7 31	..		8 35	..	..		..	..	..	..	..	..	..	..	..

Station	1	2	3	4	5	6	7	8	9	10	11	12	13	14	15	16	17	18	19	20	21	22	23	24	25	26	27	28
Yeoford .... dep					5 15				6 23	Calls at St. James' Park Halt at 6 2 p.m			7 32		Calls at St. James' Park Halt at 7 37 p.m	8 36			Refreshment Car, London to Exeter									
Bow									6 32							8 46												
North Tawton									6 39							8 53												
Sampford Courtenay									6 46							8 59												
Okehampton .... arr					5 39				6 55				7 56			9 8												
Okehampton .... dep					5 41								7 58			9 11												
Bridestowe					5 57								8 12			9 26												
Lydford					6 4											9 32												
Brentor				p.m				p.m						p.m		9 37												
Tavistock **C**				5 38	6 17			6 55					8 29	8 40		9 46												
Bere Alston 357				5 50	6 29			7 6						8 51		9 57												
Bere Ferrers				5 56				7 12						8 57		10 3												
Tamerton Foliot								7 17						9 2														
St. Budeaux, for Saltash				6 4				7 22						9 8		1010												
Ford (Devon)				6 8				7 26						9 12		1014												
Devonport **D** .... arr				6 12	6 46			7 30					8 56	9 16		1018												
PLY- { NorthRd. "				6 21	6 53			7 35					9 3	9 25		1025												
MOUTH { Friary.... "				6 34	7 5			7 45					9 14	9 35		1035												
Yeoford .... dep			4 51		Through Refreshment Car Train Brighton (dep. 11 30 a.m) and Through Carriages Portsmouth and Southsea to Plymouth see pages 163 & 380	5 33						7 18																
Copplestone			4 58			5 40						7 25																
Morchard Road			5 1			5 44						7 29																
Lapford			5 6			5 49						7 34																
Eggesford **F**			5 13			5 56						7 42																
South Molton Road **G**			5 20			6 3						7 52																
Portsmouth Arms			5 26			6 11						7 58																
Umberleigh			5 33			6 18						8 5																
Chapelton			5 38									8 10																
Barnstaple Junc. **H** { arr			5 46			6 30						8 18																
Barnstaple Junc. **H** { dep	p.m 5 15		6 5			6 33						8 23																
Barnstaple Town **J**	5 18		6 8			6 38						8 28																
Wrafton	5 26		6 17			6 46						8 38																
Braunton **K**	5 29		6 21			6 50						8 42																
Mortehoe **L**	5 47		6 39			7 9						9 2																
ILFRACOMBE .... arr	5 56		6 48			7 18						9 11																
Barnstaple Junc. dep			5 52			6 40						8 30																
Fremington			5 57			6 45						8 35																
Instow			6 4			6 52						8 42																
Bideford **N**			6 12			6 58						8 48																
Torrington 358 ...arr			6 24			7 9						8 59																
Okehampton .... dep							5 51						8 14															
Maddaford Moor Halt **P**							6 3						8 26															
Ashbury for North Lew							6 11						8 34															
Halwill **Q** 358 ...... arr							6 21						8 42															
Halwill .... dep							6 25						8 50															
Dunsland Cross							6 33						8 56															
Holsworthy							6 41						9 5															
Whitstone & Bridgerule							6 50						9 14															
Bude .... arr							7 0						9 24															
Halwill .... dep							6 22						8 44															
Ashwater							6 31						8 52															
Tower Hill							6 38						8 59															
Launceston							6 46						9 7															
Egloskerry							6 56																					
Tresmeer							7 4																					
Otterham **T**							7 14																					
Camelford **U**							7 22																					
Delabole							7 27																					
Port Isaac Road							7 34																					
St. Kew Highway							7 38																					
Wadebridge 358 .... arr							7 45																					
358 Bodmin .... arr							8 33																					
Padstow .... arr							7 56																					

For Notes and SUNDAY TRAINS, see pages 344 and 345

From WATERLOO to THE WEST OF ENGLAND—Sundays

Station		1	2	3	4	5	6	7	8	9	10	11	12	13	14	15	16	17	18	19	20	21	22	23	24	25
		p.m	a.m	a.m	a.m	a.m	a.m	a.m	a.m	p.m	p.m	noon		p.m	p.m	p.m	p.m	p.m	p.m	p.m	p.m	p.m	p.m	p.m	p.m	p.m
324 WATERLOO	dep	10 S30	..	..	1 25	..	..	9 30	11 0	..	..	12 0		..	..	..	..			..	4 0	..	..	7 30	..	9 30
324 Surbiton	"	10 S13	..	..	..	..	..	9U48	1043	..	..			..	..	..	..			..	2 43	..	..	6 43	..	9 51
324 Woking	"	11 S 6	..	..	..	..	..	10U6	11U32	..	..			..	..	..	..			..	3 28	..	..	7 28	..	1010
Basingstoke	dep	11 S51	..	..	..	..	..	1045	12 5	..	..			..	..	..	..			..	5 3	..	..	8 33	8 47	1050
Oakley		Via Eastleigh	..	..	..	..	..	1054	..	..	..	Runs until 26th October, 1947		..	..	..	..	Commences 2nd November, 1947	Runs until 26th October, 1947	..	..	..	..	..	8 56	..
Overton			..	..	..	..	..	11 0	..	..	..			..	..	..	..			..	..	..	..	..	9 1	..
Whitchurch A			..	..	2F52	..	..	11 6	..	..	..			..	..	..	..			..	..	..	..	..	9 8	..
Hurstbourne			..	..	..	..	..	1111	..	..	..			..	..	..	..			..	..	..	..	..	9 12	..
Andover Junction 376			..	..	3 7	..	..	1121	1232	..	..			..	..	..	..			..	5 30	..	..	9 2	9 22	1127
Grateley			..	..	3F20	..	..	1131	..	..	..			..	..	..	..			..	..	..	..	..	9 33	..
Porton 356		a.m	..	..	..	..	..	1141	..	..	..			..	..	..	..			..	..	..	..	..	9 43	1148
SALISBURY 339, 356, 376	arr	2 36	..	..	3 40	..	..	1151	1257	..	..			..	1 21	..	..			..	5 54	..	..	9 26	9 53	1158
	dep	2 48	..	..	3 55	..	..	Stop	1 3	..	..			..	1 26	..	..	1 40	1 54	..	6 0	..	..	9 43	..	Stop
Wilton B		..	..	..	..	..	..	..	..	..	..			..	..	..	..	1 46	2 0	..	..	..	..	9 53	..	..
Dinton		..	..	..	..	..	..	..	..	..	..			..	..	..	..	1 56	2 10	..	..	..	..	10 4	..	..
Tisbury		3 12	..	..	4 24	..	..	..	..	..	..	Devon Belle: 1st and 3rd class Pullman Cars to Plymouth and Ilfracombe. Supplementary fees charged.		..	..	..	..	2 4	2 18	..	..	..	..	1013	..	..
Semley		..	..	..	..	..	..	..	..	..	..			..	..	..	..	2 14	2 28	..	..	..	..	1024	..	..
Gillingham (Dorset)		3 31	..	..	4 51	..	..	..	..	..	..			..	..	..	..	2 22	2 36	..	..	..	..	1032	..	..
Templecombe		3 46	..	..	5 13	..	..	..	.	..	..			..	..	..	..	2 34	2 48	..	..	..	..	1045	..	..
Millborne Port		..	..	..	..	..	..	..		..	..			..	..	..	..	2 41	2 55	..	..	..	..	1052	..	..
Sherborne		4 1	..	..	5 35	..	..	..		..	..			..	2 14	..	..	2 47	3 1	..	6 48	..	..	11 1	..	..
Yeovil Junction 355	arr	4 11	..	..	5 46	..	..	..		..	..			..	2 23	..	..	2 55	3 9	..	6 56	..	..	1111	..	..
355 YEOVIL (Town)	arr	4 24	..	..	5 58	..	..	..	Refreshment Car London to Exeter	..	..			..	2 34	..	..	3 10	3 20	..	7 7	..	..	1125	..	..
	dep	..	..	..	Stop	..	10 15			..	..			..	2 20	..	..	2 45	3 0	..	6 48		7 15	..	..	..
Yeovil Junction	dep	..	..	..		..	10 21	..		..	..			..	2 30	..	..	2 58	3 12	..	6 57	..	7 21	..	..	..
Sutton Bingham		..	..	..	..	..	10 27	..		..	..			..	..	..	..	3 5	3 19	..	..	..	7 27	..	..	..
Crewkerne		..	..	..	..	..	10 40	..		..	..			..	..	..	..	3 18	3 32	..	..	..	7 39	..	..	..
Chard Junction 355	arr	..	..	..	..	..	10 54	..		..	..			..	..	..	..	3 32	3 46	..	..	..	7 53	..	..	..
355 CHARD	arr	..	..	..	..	..	..	..		..	..			..	..	..	..	..	..	..	..	..	..	..	..	..
	dep	..	..	..	..	..	..	..		..	..			..	..	..	..	..	..	..	..	..	..	..	..	..
Chard Junction	dep	..	..	..	..	..	10 55	..		..	..			..	..	..	..	3 33	3 47	..	..	..	7 54	..	..	..
Axminster 355	arr	..	..	..	..	..	11 4	..		..	..			..	3 3	..	..	3 41	3 55	..	7 28	..	8 3	..	..	..
355 LYME REGIS	arr	..	..	..	..	..	11 32	..		..	..			..	3 31	..	..	..	4 41	..	..	..	..	..	..	..
	dep	..	..	..	..	..	10 40	..		..	..			..	2 35	..	..	..	2 35	..	..	..	..	..	..	..
Axminster	dep	..	..	..	..	..	11 5	..	..	..	..			..	3 4	..	..	3 43	3 57	..	7 29	..	8 4	..	..	..
Seaton Junction 355	arr	..	..	..	..	..	11 12	..	..	..	..			..	3 10	..	..	3 50	4 4	..	7 35		8 10	..	..	..
355 SEATON	arr	..	..	..	..	..	11 30	..	..	..	..			..	3R27	..	..	4 22	4 22	..	..	..	..	..	..	..
	dep	..	..	..	..	..	11 6	..	..	..	..			..	2 45	..	..	3 35	3 45	..	..	..	..	..	..	..
Seaton Junction	dep	..	..	..	..	..	11 15	p.m	..	..	..			..	3 11	..	..	3 51	4 5	..	7 36	..	8 11	..	..	p.m
Honiton		..	..	..	..	..	11 32	1 35	..	..	..			..	..	..	..	4 7	4 21	..	7 52	..	8 28	..	..	1020
Sidmouth Junc. 356	arr	..	..	..	..	..	11 40	1 41	2 35	..	..	3 16		..	3 33	..	..	4 15	4 29	..	8 0	..	8 36	..	..	1026
356 SIDMOUTH	arr	..	..	..	..	..	12 10	3 5	3 5	..	..	3 43		..	..	..	..	..	..	..	..	..	..	..	..	..
356 BUDLEIGH SALTER'N	"	..	..	..	..	..	..	..	..	..	..	..		..	..	..	..	..	..	..	..	..	..	..	..	..
356 EXMOUTH	"	..	..	..	..	..	..	..	..	..	..	..		..	..	..	..	..	..	..	..	..	..	..	..	..
356 SIDMOUTH	dep	..	..	..	..	..	11 8	..	2 11	..	..	..		..	..	..	3 13	..	..	..	..	..	..	..	..	..
Sidmouth Junction	dep	..	..	..	..	..	11 41	1 42	2 37	..	..	3 18		..	3 34	..	3 43	4 17	4 31	..	8 1	..	8 37	..	..	1027
Whimple		..	..	..	..	..	11 48	1 47	..	..	..	..		..	..	..	3 51	4 24	4 38	..	..	..	8 44	..	..	1033
Broad Clyst		..	..	..	..	..	11 55	1 53	..	..	..	..		..	..	..	3 58	4 31	4 45	..	..	..	8 51	..	..	1040
Pinhoe		..	..	..	..	..	12 0	1 57	..	..	..	..		..	..	..	4 3	4 36	4 50	..	..	..	8 56	..	..	1045
EXETER Central 357	arr	..	..	..	..	..	12 8	2 5	2 55	..	..	3 36		..	3 51	..	4 11	4 44	4 58	..	8 18	..	9 4	..	..	1052
357 EXMOUTH	arr	..	..	..	a.m	..	1 11	2 44	3 27	..	..	4 14		..	..	..	..	5 39	5 39	..	8 51	..	9 41	..	..	1132
	dep	..	..	..	9 [illegible]	9 30	..	..	1 45	..	1 45	2 55	2 55	..	2 55	..	..	..	..	4 15	7 45	7 45	..	..	..	..
EXETER Central	dep	..	..	..	1016	1030	..	..	3 1	..	3 15	3 39	3 48	..	3 56	4 8	..	..	..	5 25	8 2[illegible]	8 35	..	..	..	..
Exeter (St. David's)		..	..	..	1023	1037	..	..	3 9	..	3 22	3 45	3 52	..	4 3	4 13	..	..	..	5 31	8 30	8 40	..	..	..	..
Newton St. Cyres		..	..	..	..	..	..	..	..	..	..	..	..	..	..	..	..	..	..	..	..	..	..	..	..	..
Crediton		..	..	..	1037	1050	..	..	..	..	..	..	..	..	4 15	4 23	..	..	..	5 44	8 43	8 53	..	..	..	..
Yeoford	arr	..	..	..	1046	1059	..	..	..	..	..	..	..	..	4 23	4 31	..	..	..	5 [illegible]	8 51	9 1	..	..	..	..

NOTES

- **A** About 1½ miles to Great Western Station
- **A** Arr. 1 37 p.m
- **B** Over ½ mile to Great Western Station
- **R** Arr. 8 58 a.m
- **C** 1 mile to Great Western Station
- **D** Nearly ½ mile to G.W. Station
- **D** Runs until 27th October, 1947
- **F** Station for Chulmleigh (3 miles)
- **F** Calls to set down only
- **G** Station for Chulmleigh (2½ miles)
- **H** About 1 mile to Great Western Station
- **H** Dep. 4 20 p.m. on Saturdays.
- **J** Over ½ mile to Barnstaple Station
- **J** By Southern National Omnibus between Axminster and Lyme Regis. Times subject to alteration
- **K** Station for Saunton Sands
- **K** Fridays and Saturdays.
- **L** Station for Lee (Devon) 3 miles and Woolacombe
- **L** Arr 4 11 p.m on Saturdays.
- **N** Station for Hartland (13 miles)
- **N** 10 minutes later until 27th October, 1947
- **P** Station for Thorndon Cross

Station	1	2	3	4	5	6	7	8	9	10	11	12	13	14	15	16	17	18	19	20	21	22	23	24	25
Yeoford dep	..	..	..	..	11 0	..	..	..	..	..	..	..	..	4 24	..	..	..	..	5 54	8 52	..	..	..	..	..
Bow	..	..	..	..	1110	..	..	..	..	..	..	..	..	..	..	..	..	..	6 4	9 1	..	..	..	..	..
North Tawton	..	..	..	..	11[illegible]	..	..	..	..	..	..	..	..	..	..	..	..	..	6 11	9 8	..	..	..	..	..
Sampford Courtenay	..	..	..	..	..	..	..	..	..	..	..	..	..	..	..	..	..	..	..	..	..	..	..	..	..
Okehampton arr	..	..	..	..	1133	..	..	3 50	..	..	4 25	..	..	4 48	..	..	..	..	6 27	9 24	..	..	..	..	..
Okehampton dep	..	..	8 30	..	1135	..	..	3 52	..	..	4 27	..	..	4 49	..	..	..	..	6 29	9 25	..	..	..	..	..
Bridestowe	..	..	8 43	..	1150	..	..	..	..	..	..	..	..	..	..	..	..	..	6 43	9 39	..	..	..	..	..
Lydford	..	..	8 49	..	1156	..	..	..	..	..	..	..	..	..	..	..	..	..	6 50	9 46	..	..	..	..	..
Brentor	..	..	8 53	..	12 0	..	..	..	..	..	..	..	..	..	..	..	..	..	6 54	9 50	..	..	..	..	..
Tavistock C	..	..	9 5	..	12 9	..	..	4 20	..	..	..	..	..	5 15	..	..	..	..	7 3	10 2	..	..	..	..	..
Bere Alston 357	..	..	9 21	..	1221	..	..	4 32	..	..	..	..	..	..	..	..	..	..	7 16	1015	..	..	..	..	..
Bere Ferrers	..	..	9 28	..	1226	..	..	..	..	..	..	..	..	..	..	..	..	..	7 23	1021	..	..	..	..	..
Tamerton Foliot	..	..	9 32	..	..	..	..	..	..	..	..	..	..	..	..	..	..	..	7 28	..	..	..	..	..	..
St. Budeaux, for Saltash	..	..	9 37	..	1233	..	..	..	..	..	..	..	..	..	..	..	..	..	7 33	1028	..	..	..	..	..
Ford (Devon)	..	..	9 41	..	1236	..	..	..	..	..	..	..	..	..	..	..	..	..	7 38	1033	..	..	..	..	..
Devonport D arr	..	..	9 45	..	1240	..	..	4 49	..	..	5 16	..	..	5 46	..	..	..	..	7 42	1037	..	..	..	..	..
PLY-MOUTH North Rd. "	..	..	9 52	..	1245	..	..	4 55	..	..	5 21	..	..	5 52	..	..	..	..	7 48	1042	..	..	..	..	..
PLY-MOUTH Friary "	..	..	10 3	..	1256	..	..	5 6	..	..	5 32	..	..	6 3	..	..	..	..	7 59	1052	..	..	..	..	..
Yeoford dep	..	..	..	1050	..	..	..	..	..	..	Runs until 26th October, 1947	Runs until 26th October, 1947	Runs until 26th October, 1947	Through Train Southampton (Central) dep 12 36 p.m to Plymouth, page 382	4 32	..	..	..	..	Refreshment Car, London to Exeter	9 2	..	..	..	..
Copplestone	..	..	..	1058	..	..	..	..	..	..					4 37	..	..	..	..		9 8	..	..	..	..
Morchard Road	..	..	..	11 2	..	..	..	..	..	..					4 41	..	..	..	..		9 11	..	..	..	..
Lapford	..	..	..	1116	..	..	..	..	..	..					4 46	..	..	..	..		9 16	..	..	..	..
Eggesford F	..	..	..	1126	..	..	..	..	..	..					4 53	..	..	..	..		9 24	..	..	..	..
South Molton Road G	..	..	..	1133	..	..	..	..	..	..					5 0	..	..	..	..		9 32	..	..	..	..
Portsmouth Arms	..	..	..	1139	..	..	..	..	..	..					5 6	..	..	..	..		9 38	..	..	..	..
Umberleigh	..	..	..	1147	..	..	..	..	..	..					5 13	..	..	..	..		9 46	..	..	..	..
Chapelton	..	..	..	1152	..	..	..	..	..	..					5 18	..	..	..	..		9 51	..	..	..	..
Barnstaple Junc. H arr	..	..	..	12 0	..	..	..	..	..	4 25	..	4 49			5 25	..	..	..	..		9 59	..	..	..	..
Barnstaple Junc. H dep	..	..	..	12 5	..	..	..	..	..	4 31	..	4 50			..	..	..	..	..		10 3	..	..	..	..
Barnstaple Town J	..	..	..	1210	..	..	..	..	..	4 36	..	4 54			..	..	..	..	..		10 8	..	..	..	..
Wrafton	..	..	..	1218	..	..	..	..	..	4 44	..	..			..	..	..	..	..		1016	..	..	..	..
Braunton K	..	..	..	1222	..	..	..	..	..	4 49	..	5 5			..	..	..	..	..		1020	..	..	..	..
Mortehoe L	..	..	..	1241	..	..	..	..	..	5 9	..	5 24			..	..	..	..	..		1039	..	..	..	..
ILFRACOMBE arr	..	..	..	1250	..	..	..	..	..	5 18	..	5 33			..	..	..	..	..		1048	..	..	..	..
Barnstaple Junc. dep	..	9 35	..	1212	..	..	..	..	..	4 40	..	..	5 0		..	..	..	..	..	..	1010	..	..	..	..
Fremington	..	9 40	..	1217	..	..	..	..	..	4 45	..	..	5 5		..	..	..	..	..	..	1015	..	..	..	..
Instow	..	9 46	..	1224	..	..	..	..	..	4 52	..	..	5 12		..	..	..	..	..	..	1022	..	..	..	..
Bideford N	..	9 52	..	1230	..	..	..	..	..	4 58	..	..	5 18		..	..	..	..	..	..	1028	..	..	..	..
Torrington arr	..	..	..	1243	..	..	..	..	..	5 10	..	..	5 29		..	..	..	..	..	..	1039	..	..	..	..
Okehampton dep	..	..	..	..	..	..	..	..	4 12	..	..	..	..	..	..	..	..	..	..	..	..	..	..	..	..
Maddaford Moor Halt P	..	..	..	..	..	..	..	..	4 24	..	..	..	..	..	..	..	..	..	..	..	..	..	..	..	..
Ashbury, for North Lew	..	..	..	..	..	..	..	..	4 32	..	..	..	..	..	..	..	..	..	..	..	..	..	..	..	..
Halwill Q arr	..	..	..	..	..	..	..	..	4 39	..	..	..	..	..	..	..	..	..	..	..	..	..	..	..	..
Halwill dep	..	..	..	..	..	..	..	..	4 41	..	..	..	..	..	..	..	..	..	..	..	..	..	..	..	..
Dunsland Cross	..	..	..	..	..	..	..	..	4 49	..	..	..	..	..	..	..	..	..	..	..	..	..	..	..	..
Holsworthy	..	..	..	..	..	..	..	..	4 58	..	..	..	..	..	..	..	..	..	..	..	..	..	..	..	..
Whitstone & Bridgerule	..	..	..	..	..	..	..	..	5 8	..	..	..	..	..	..	..	..	..	..	..	..	..	..	..	..
Bude arr	..	..	..	..	..	..	..	..	5 18	..	..	..	..	..	..	..	..	..	..	..	..	..	..	..	..
Halwill dep	..	..	..	..	..	..	..	..	4 50	..	..	..	..	..	..	..	..	..	..	..	..	..	..	..	..
Ashwater	..	..	..	..	..	..	..	..	4 59	..	..	..	..	..	..	..	..	..	..	..	..	..	..	..	..
Tower Hill	..	..	..	..	..	..	..	..	5 6	..	..	..	..	..	..	..	..	..	..	..	..	..	..	..	..
Launceston	..	..	..	..	..	..	..	..	5 14	..	..	..	..	..	..	..	..	..	..	..	..	..	..	..	..
Egloskerry	..	..	..	..	..	..	..	..	..	..	..	..	..	..	..	..	..	..	..	..	..	..	..	..	..
Tresmeer	..	..	..	..	..	..	..	..	..	..	..	..	..	..	..	..	..	..	..	..	..	..	..	..	..
Otterham T	..	..	..	..	..	..	..	..	..	..	..	..	..	..	..	..	..	..	..	..	..	..	..	..	..
Camelford U	..	..	..	..	..	..	..	..	..	..	..	..	..	..	..	..	..	..	..	..	..	..	..	..	..
Delabole	..	..	..	..	..	..	..	..	..	..	..	..	..	..	..	..	..	..	..	..	..	..	..	..	..
Port Isaac Road	..	..	..	..	..	..	..	..	..	..	..	..	..	..	..	..	..	..	..	..	..	..	..	..	..
St. Kew Highway	..	..	..	..	..	..	..	..	..	..	..	..	..	..	..	..	..	..	..	..	..	..	..	..	..
Wadebridge arr	..	..	..	..	..	..	..	..	..	..	..	..	..	..	..	..	..	..	..	..	..	..	..	..	..
Bodmin arr	..	..	..	..	..	..	..	..	..	..	..	..	..	..	..	..	..	..	..	..	..	..	..	..	..
Padstow arr	..	..	..	..	..	..	..	..	..	..	..	..	..	..	..	..	..	..	..	..	..	..	..	..	..

P Arr. 6 41 a.m.
Q Station for Beaworthy
R Arr. 5 minutes later until 26th October, 1947
S Saturday night
SO Saturdays only
SX Saturdays excepted
T Station for Wilsey Down and Davidstow (2½ miles) and Crackington Haven (5miles)
U Station for Boscastle and Tintagel
U Calls to take up only
V 15 minutes later until 27th October, 1947
Z Monday to Friday nights

† Arr. 5 10 p.m. on Saturdays until 25th October, 1947, and 4 11 p.m on Saturdays from 1st November 1947
‡ Tues., Weds., Thurs. and Fris.
** For Halts between St. Budeaux and Plymouth see page, 356

LOCAL TRAINS

OTHER TRAINS

From THE WEST OF ENGLAND to WATERLOO—Weekdays

Miles	Station	a.m	a.m	a.m	a.m	a.m	a.m	a.m	a.m	a.m	a.m	a.m	a.m	a.m	a.m	a.m	a.m	a.m	a.m	a.m	a.m	a.m	a.m	a.m	p.m	a.m	..	p.m	a.m	a.m	non
	Padstow dep																						8 25						Mondays, Fridays and Saturdays Runs until 27th October, 1947		Mondays, Fridays and Saturdays Runs until 27th October, 1947
—	358 Bodmin dep																						7 22								
5¼	Wadebridge dep																						8 40	Through Refreshment Car Train, Plymouth to Brighton, see page 377. Through Carriages, Plymouth to Portsmouth and Southsea, see page 377							
9¾	St. Kew Highway																						8 48								
12¼	Port Isaac Road																						8 55								
16½	Delabole																						9 5								
18¾	Camelford U																						9 12								
23¼	Otterham T																						9 22								
28¼	Tresmeer																						9 31								
31¾	Egloskerry																						9 39								
36	Launceston																	8 22					9 55								
41	Tower Hill																	8 29					10 5								
44¾	Ashwater																	8 36					1012								
49¾	Halwill Q 358 arr																	8 46					1022								
—	Mls Bude dep																	8 0					9 35								
—	5¾ Whitstone & Bridgerule																	8 11					9 46								
—	10½ Holsworthy																	8 21					9 56								
—	15¼ Dunsland Cross																	8 31					10 7								
—	18¾ Halwill Q 358 arr																	8 39					1015								
—	Halwill dep																	8 48					1030								
53¾	Ashbury for North Lew																	8 58					1040								
57½	Maddaford Moor Halt P																	9 6					1049								
62¼	Okehampton 341 arr																	9 17					11 0								
—	Mls Torrington dep													7 8			8 10		9 0				Atlantic Coast Express			1015			1138	Mondays, Fridays and Saturdays Runs until 27th October, 1947	
—	5¾ Bideford N													7 17			8 19		9 9							1024			1153		
—	7¾ Instow													7 24			8 27		9 16							1034			12 2		
—	11¼ Fremington													7 32			8 35		9 24							1042			1211		
—	14¼ Barnstaple Jn H arr													7 38			8 41		9 30							1048			1219		
—	Mls ILFRACOMBE dep																8 10	Through Carriages Exmouth, Sidmouth & Seaton to London	Stop			9 0				1015					12 0
—	3¼ Mortehoe L																8 23					9 13				1028					1212
—	9 Braunton K																8 35					9 25				1041					1223
—	10 Wrafton																8 38					9 28				1045					
—	14¼ Barnstaple Town J																8 46					9 36				1054					1232
—	15 Barnstaple Junc. H arr																8 51					9 40				1058					1236
—	Barnstaple Junc. H dep													7 43			8 54									11 1					1237
—	19¼ Chapelton													7 51												1110					
—	21¾ Umberleigh													7 57			9 7									1116					
—	25¾ Portsmouth Arms													8 4			9 14									1123					
—	28¾ South Molton Rd. G													8 10			9 22									1129					
—	32¾ Eggesford F													8 17			9 29									1136					
—	36¾ Lapford													8 24			9 36									1143					
—	39 Morchard Road													8 30												1149					
—	40¾ Copplestone													8 35												1154					
—	43¾ Yeoford 341 arr													8 41												12 0					
—	Mls PLYMOUTH Friary dep											5 56	6 10			7 34		8 15						10 0		Refreshment Car, Exeter to London				1130	
—	2¼ PLYMOUTH N'th Rd. "											6 5	6 19			7 42		8 25						1010						1140	
—	4¼ Devonport D											6 10	6 26			7 47		8 30						1017						1147	
—	5¼ Ford (Devon)											6 14	6 31			7 51															
—	6¾ St. Budeaux, fr Saltash											6 19	6 37			7 56															
—	9 Tamerton Foliot															8 1															
—	11 Bere Ferrers											6 27				8 7															
—	13¾ Bere Alston 357											6 37	6 58			8 18								1037							
—	20¼ Tavistock C											6 51	7 13			8 31		8 59						1051							
—	25½ Brentor																														
—	26¾ Lydford											7 8						9 13						11 5							
—	30 Bridestowe											7 17												1113							
—	36¼ Okehampton 341 arr											7 33						9 31						1126						1243	
		1	2	3	4	5	6	7	8	9	10	11	12	13	14	15	16	17	18	19	20	21	22	23	24	25	26	27	28	29	30

Miles	Station	1	2	3	4	5	6	7	8	9	10	11	12	13	14	15
—	Okehampton dep	..	..	..	..	..	Calls St. James' Park Halt at 6 41 a.m	Refreshment Car Exeter to London	Calls St. James' Park Halt at 7 35 a.m	..	Calls St. James' Park Halt at 8 1 a.m	7 35	..	..	..	..
66½	Sampford Courtenay	..	..	..	..	..				..		7 42	..	..	..	..
69	North Tawton	..	..	..	..	..				..		7 48	..	..	..	..
72½	Bow	..	..	..	..	..				..		7 55	..	..	..	..
77	Yeoford 341 arr	..	..	..	..	..				..		8 4	..	..	..	..
	Yeoford 341 dep	..	..	..	..	..				..		8 5	..	8 42	..	..
81	Crediton	..	..	..	..	..				..		8 11	..	8 50	..	..
83¼	Newton St. Cyres	..	..	..	..	..				..		8 17	..	8 56	..	..
87½	Exeter (St. David's)	..	..	..	..	..				..		8 30	..	9 7	..	..
88¼	EXETER Central 357 arr	..	..	..	..	..				..		8 35	..	9 11	..	..
98¾	357 EXMOUTH arr	..	..	..	..	..				..		9 11	..	9 44	..	..
	357 EXMOUTH dep	..	..	..	..	..		6 40	6 40	..	7 15	8 10	..	..	8 45	..
—	EXETER Central dep	6 0	..	..	..	6 30	6 40	7 30	7 34	..	8 0	8 40	..	..	9 35	..
91	Pinhoe	6 6	..	..	..	..	6 47	..	7 41	..	8 7	8 49	..	..	9 41	..
93	Broad Clyst	6 11	..	..	..	..	6 51	..	7 45	..	8 10	8 52	..	..	9 44	..
96¾	Whimple	6 19	..	..	..	..	6 59	..	7 52	..	8 17	9 0	..	..	9 52	..
100¾	Sidmouth Junc. 356 arr	6 27	..	..	..	6 48	7 7	7 47	7 59	..	8 24	9 8	..	..	10 0	..
109	356 SIDMOUTH arr	6 53	..	..	..	..	..	..	8 26	..	8 52	9 48	..	..	..	..
—	356 EXMOUTH dep	Stop	..	..	..	..	..	6 55	..	..	..	8 9	..	..	..	..
—	556 BUDLEIGH SALTER'N "	..	..	..	..	..	..	7 7	..	..	..	8 23	..	..	..	..
—	356 SIDMOUTH "	..	..	..	..	..	..	7 20	..	..	..	8 35	..	..	9 30	..
—	Sidmouth Junction dep	..	..	..	..	6 49	7 8	7 48	..	..	..	9 9	..	..	10 1	..
105	Honiton	..	..	..	..	6 59	7 16	..	..	..	..	9 17	..	..	1010	..
112	Seaton Junction 355 arr	..	..	..	..	7 11	7 28	..	..	..	..	9 29	..	..	1022	..
116½	355 SEATON arr	..	..	..	..	8 17	8 17	..	..	..	..	9 48	..	..	1052	..
	355 SEATON dep	..	..	..	..	..	..	..	..	..	..	9 5	..	..	10 5	..
—	Seaton Junction dep	..	..	..	Calls at Idmiston Halt at 8 55 a.m	7 13	7 29	..	..	..	..	9 30	..	..	1024	..
115¼	Axminster 355 arr	..	..	..		7 19	7 34	8 8	..	..	..	9 36	..	..	1031	..
122	355 LYME REGIS arr	..	..	..		..	Stop	8 56	..	..	..	11 4	..	..	11 4	..
	355 LYME REGIS dep	..	..	..		..	..	7J20	..	..	..	8 4	..	..	10 0	..
—	Axminster dep	..	..	..		7 21	..	8 9	..	..	..	9 37	..	..	1032	..
120½	Chard Junction 355 arr	..	..	..		7 30	..	..	..	..	..	9 46	..	..	1041	..
123½	355 CHARD arr	..	..	..		8 37	..	..	..	..	..	11 6	..	..	11 6	..
	355 CHARD dep	..	..	..		..	..	..	..	..	..	9 34	..	..	9 34	..
—	Chard Junction dep	..	Calls at Idmiston Halt at 6 58 a.m	..		7 32	..	..	..	..	..	9 47	..	..	1042	..
128¼	Crewkerne	..		..		7 48	..	..	..	..	..	10 2	..	..	1057	..
134¾	Sutton Bingham	..		..		7 57	..	..	..	..	..	10 12	..	..	..	..
137	Yeovil Junction 355 arr	..		..		8 3	..	8 38	..	..	..	10 18	..	..	1110	..
138¾	355 YEOVIL (Town) arr	a.m		..	..	8 11	..	8 45	..	..	..	10 34	..	..	1119	..
	355 YEOVIL (Town) dep	6 30		..	7 10	7 55	..	8 24	..	..	..	10 15	..	..	11 0	..
—	Yeovil Junction dep	6 36		..	7 20	8 5	..	8 39	..	..	..	10 24	..	..	1112	..
141¾	Sherborne	6 44		..	7 29	8 14	..	8 46	..	..	..	10 36	..	..	1122	..
145½	Milborne Port	6 52		..	7 37	8 22	..	..	..	..	..	10 45	..	..	1131	..
147¾	Templecombe	6 58		..	7 44	8 28	..	9 1	..	9 16	..	10 56	..	..	1137	..
154¼	Gillingham (Dorset)	..		..	7 54	..	a.m	9 14	..	9 26	..	11 10	..	..	..	..
158¾	Semley	..		..	8 4	..	8 48	..	..	9 36	..	11 22	..	..	..	..
163¾	Tisbury	..		..	8 12	..	8 56	..	..	9 44	..	11 30	..	..	..	..
168	Dinton	..		..	8 19	..	9 3	..	..	9 53	..	11 38	..	..	..	..
173¾	Wilton B	..		..	8 27	..	9 12	..	..	10 2	..	11 48	..	..	..	..
176¾	SALISBURY 339, 356 376 ● arr	..		..	8 33	..	9 18	9 45	..	10 8	..	11 54	..	..	..	..
	SALISBURY dep	..	6 45	8 10	8 40	..	..	9 50	..	..	..	..	..	..	..	..
181¾	Porton	..	6 55	..	8 52	..	..	..	..	..	..	..	..	..	..	..
187½	Grateley	..	7 7	..	9 4	..	..	..	..	..	..	..	..	..	..	..
193½	Andover Junction 376	..	7 18	8 35	9 15	..	..	1020	..	..	..	..	..	..	..	..
198¾	Hurstbourne	..	7 28	..	9 25	..	..	..	..	..	..	..	..	..	..	..
200¾	Whitchurch A	..	7 34	8 48	9 32	..	..	..	..	..	..	..	..	..	..	..
204¼	Overton	..	7 42	..	9 38	..	..	..	..	..	..	..	..	..	..	..
207½	Oakley	..	7 50	..	9 45	..	..	..	..	..	..	..	..	..	..	..
212	Basingstoke 324, 330 arr	..	7 59	9 6	9 54	..	..	..	..	..	..	..	..	..	..	..
235¼	330 Woking arr	..	8 46	..	1041	..	..	..	..	..	..	..	..	..	..	..
248	330 Surbiton "	..	9C20	..	1130	..	..	..	..	..	..	..	..	..	..	..
260	330 WATERLOO "	..	9 20	10 3	1113	..	..	1146	..	..	..	..	..	..	..	..

Miles	Station	16	17	18	19	20	21	22	23	24	25	26	27	28	29	30
—	Okehampton dep	..	9 33	..	..	..	..	11 3	1128	..	..	..	..	..	1245	..
66½	Sampford Courtenay	..	..	..	..	..	..	1111	..	..	..	..	..	..	..	..
69	North Tawton	..	9 45	..	..	..	..	1118	..	..	..	..	..	..	..	..
72½	Bow	..	..	..	..	..	..	1125	..	..	..	..	..	..	..	..
77	Yeoford 341 arr	..	9 56	..	Saturdays only	..	..	1134	1149	..	..	..	..	..	..	..
	Yeoford 341 dep	..	9 57	..		..	..	1135	1150	..	12 1	..	..	..	..	..
81	Crediton	..	10 3	..		..	..	1143	..	..	12 7	..	..	..	..	..
83¼	Newton St. Cyres	..	..	..		..	..	..	..	..	1213	..	..	..	..	..
87½	Exeter (St. David's)	10 6	1018	..		..	..	12 1	1212	..	1225	..	..	..	1 23	1 33
88¼	EXETER Central 357 arr	1011	1023	..		..	..	12 5	1217	..	1230	..	..	..	1 27	1 38
98¾	357 EXMOUTH arr	..	..	a.m		..	..	1 11	1 11	..	1 11	..	..	..	2 0	3 12
	357 EXMOUTH dep	..	9 50	9 50		1045	..	..	..	..	..	..	12 15	..	1215	
—	EXETER Central dep	..	1030	1038		1120	..	..	1225	1230	1240	..	12 55	..	1 40	
91	Pinhoe	..	..	1044		1126	..	..	..	1236	..	..	1 1	..	..	
93	Broad Clyst	..	..	1047		1130	..	..	..	1239	..	..	1 6	..	..	
96¾	Whimple	..	..	1055		1137	..	..	..	1246	..	..	1 13	..	..	
100¾	Sidmouth Junc. 356 arr	..	1048	11 3		1145	..	..	..	..	1 1	..	1 21	..	2 2	
109	356 SIDMOUTH arr	..	1135	1135	..	1 32	..	..	..	..	1 32	..	..	..	2 48	
—	356 EXMOUTH dep	..	9 50	Stop	..	9 50	..	..	..	..	1210	..	12 10	..	..	
—	556 BUDLEIGH SALTER'N "	..	10 4	..	..	10 4	..	..	..	..	1222	..	12 22	..	..	
—	356 SIDMOUTH "	..	1029	..	1020	1020	..	..	..	..	1234	..	12 34	..	1 35	
—	Sidmouth Junction dep	..	1053	..	1115	1146	..	..	..	..	1 4	..	1 22	..	2 3	
105	Honiton	..	..	..	1123	1156	..	..	1251	..	..	..	1 32	..	1st and 3rd class Pullman Cars from Plymouth and Ilfracombe. Devon Belle	
112	Seaton Junction 355 arr	..	..	..	..	12 8	..	..	..	..	..	..	1 44	..		
116½	355 SEATON arr	..	Refreshment Car, Exeter to London	..	..	1224	..	..	..	..	..	..	2 2	..		
	355 SEATON dep	..		..	..	1145	..	..	..	..	..	..	1 20	..		
—	Seaton Junction dep	..		..	..	12 9	..	..	..	..	..	..	1 45	..		
115¼	Axminster 355 arr	..		..	..	1215	..	..	1 7	..	1 26	..	1 51	..		
122	355 LYME REGIS arr	..		..	..	1 18	..	..	2 14	..	2 14	..	2 14	..	..	..
	355 LYME REGIS dep	..		..	..	1134	..	..	1229	..	1229	..	1 24	..	..	..
—	Axminster dep	..		..	..	1216	..	..	1 8	..	1 27	..	1 53	..	..	..
120½	Chard Junction 355 arr	..		..	..	1225	..	..	..	..	..	..	2 2	..	..	..
123½	355 CHARD arr	..		..	..	1 20	..	..	..	..	..	..	3S014	..		
	355 CHARD dep	..		..	..	1210	..	..	..	..	..	..	1S052	..		
—	Chard Junction dep	..		Calls at Idmiston Halt at 1 13 p.m	..	1226	..	..	..	..	..	..	2 6	..		
128¼	Crewkerne	..			..	1242	..	..	..	..	..	..	2 23	..		
134¾	Sutton Bingham	..			..	..	..	..	..	..	..	..	2 34	..		
137	Yeovil Junction 355 arr	..			..	1255	..	..	1 38	..	1 57	..	2 40	..		
138¾	355 YEOVIL (Town) arr	..	..		..	1 4	..	..	1 46	..	2 14	..	2 52	..		
	355 YEOVIL (Town) dep	..	..		..	1246	..	..	1 30	..	1 50	..	..	..	Mondays, Fridays and Saturdays Runs until 27th October, 1947 Supplementary fees charged.	
—	Yeovil Junction dep	..	..		..	1256	..	..	1 40	..	1 59	..	..	..		
141¾	Sherborne	..	..		..	1 5	..	..	1 50	..	2 8	..	..	..		
145½	Milborne Port	..	..		..	1 13	..	..	..	..	..	..	..	..		
147¾	Templecombe	..	1157		..	1 20	..	..	2 4	..	2 22	..	..	..		
154¼	Gillingham (Dorset)	..	..		..	1 30	..	..	2 15	..	..	..	..	..		
158¾	Semley	..	..		..	1 40	..	..	..	..	..	..	..	..		
163¾	Tisbury	..	..		..	1 48	..	..	..	..	..	..	..	..		
168	Dinton	..	..		..	1 55	..	..	..	..	..	..	..	..		
173¾	Wilton B	..	..		..	2 4	..	..	..	..	..	..	..	..		
176¾	SALISBURY 339, 356 376 ● arr	..	1236	p.m	..	2 10	..	..	2 44	..	3 0	..	..	..		
	SALISBURY dep	..	1240	1 0	..	2 20	..	..	..	..	3 4	..	..	..		
181¾	Porton	..	..	1 11	..	..	..	..	..	..	Atlantic Coast Express	..	..	..		
187½	Grateley	..	..	1 22	..	..	..	..	..	..		..	..	..		
193½	Andover Junction 376	..	1 7	1 34	..	2 47	..	..	..	..		..	..	..		
198¾	Hurstbourne	..	..	1 44	..	..	..	..	..	..		..	..	..		
200¾	Whitchurch A	..	..	1 50	..	..	..	..	..	..		..	..	..		
204¼	Overton	..	..	1 57	..	..	..	..	..	..		..	..	..		
207½	Oakley	..	..	2 4	..	..	..	..	..	..		..	..	..		
212	Basingstoke 324, 330 arr	..	..	2 13	..	..	..	..	..	..		..	..	..		
235¼	330 Woking arr	..	..	3 11	..	..	..	..	..	..		..	..	..	..	..
248	330 Surbiton "	..	..	4 0	..	..	..	..	..	..		..	..	..	..	..
260	330 WATERLOO "	..	2 29	3 49	..	4 10	..	..	..	..	4 41	..	..	..	5 20	

For Notes, see pages 350 and 351; for Continuation of Trains, see pages 348 to 351

From THE WEST OF ENGLAND to WATERLOO—Weekdays—*continued*

Station	p.m	p.m	p.m	a.m	p.m	p.m	p.m	p.m	p.m	p.m	p.m	p.m	p.m	p.m	p.m	p.m
Padstow .... dep	..	..	..	..	..	..	..	..	..	1 0	—	..	..	..	..	..
358 Bodmin .... dep	..	..	..	..	..	..	..	..	..	1128	..	..	..	..	..	..
Wadebridge .... dep	..	..	..	..	..	..	..	..	..	1 14	..	..	..	..	..	..
St. Kew Highway	..	..	..	..	..	..	..	..	..	1 22	..	..	..	..	..	..
Port Isaac Road	..	..	..	..	..	..	..	..	..	1 29	..	..	..	..	..	..
Delabole	..	..	..	..	..	..	..	..	..	1 40	..	..	..	..	..	..
Camelford **U**	..	..	..	..	..	..	..	..	..	1 47	..	..	..	..	..	..
Otterham **T**	..	..	..	..	..	..	..	..	..	1 55	..	..	..	..	..	..
Tresmeer	..	..	..	..	..	..	..	..	..	2 4	..	..	..	..	..	..
Egloskerry	..	..	..	..	..	..	..	..	..	2 11	..	..	..	..	..	..
Launceston	..	..	..	..	..	..	..	..	..	2 19	..	..	..	..	..	..
Tower Hill	..	..	..	..	..	..	..	..	..	2 32	..	..	..	..	..	..
Ashwater	..	..	..	..	..	..	..	..	..	2 39	..	..	..	..	..	..
Halwill **Q** 358 .... arr	..	..	..	..	..	..	..	..	..	2 49	..	..	..	..	..	..
Bude .... dep	..	..	..	..	..	..	..	..	..	2 3	..	..	..	..	3 13	..
Whitstone & Bridgerule	..	..	..	..	..	..	..	..	..	2 14	..	..	..	..	3 24	..
Holsworthy	..	..	..	..	..	..	..	..	..	2 24	..	..	..	..	3 33	..
Dunsland Cross	..	..	..	..	..	..	..	..	..	2 35	..	..	..	..	3 51	..
Halwill **Q** 358 .... arr	..	..	..	..	..	..	..	..	..	2 43	..	..	..	..	3 59	..
Halwill .... dep	..	..	..	..	..	..	..	..	..	2 53	..	..	..	..	4 7	..
Ashbury, for North Lew	..	..	..	..	..	..	..	..	..	3 4	..	..	..	..	4 18	..
Maddaford Moor Halt **P**	..	..	..	..	..	..	..	..	..	3 12	..	..	..	..	4 27	..
Okehampton 341 .... arr	..	..	..	..	..	..	..	..	..	3 24	..	..	..	..	4 38	..
Torrington .... dep	..	..	..	..	..	1215	..	..	..	..	2 5	..	..	2 52	Stop	..
Bideford **N**	..	..	..	..	..	1224	..	..	..	..	2 14	..	..	3 1	..	..
Instow	..	..	..	..	..	1232	..	..	..	..	2 22	..	..	3 11	..	..
Fremington	..	..	..	..	..	1240	..	..	..	..	2 30	..	..	3 19	..	..
Barnstaple Jn. **H** arr	..	..	..	..	..	1246	..	..	..	..	2 36	..	..	3 27	..	..
ILFRACOMBE .... dep	..	..	..	..	..	1215	..	..	..	..	2 5	..	..	3 0	..	..
Mortehoe **L**	..	..	..	..	..	1229	..	..	..	..	2 19	..	..	3 13	..	..
Braunton **K**	..	..	..	..	..	1242	..	..	..	..	2 32	..	..	3 25	..	..
Wrafton	..	..	..	..	..	1246	..	..	..	..	2 35	..	..	3 28	..	..
Barnstaple Town **J**	..	..	..	..	..	1254	..	..	..	..	2 43	..	..	3 36	..	..
Barnstaple Junc. **H** arr	..	..	..	..	..	1259	..	..	..	..	2 47	..	..	3 40	..	..
Barnstaple Junc. **H** dep	..	..	..	..	Saturdays only	1 3	..	..	..	..	2 50	..	..	3 45	..	..
Chapelton	..	..	..	..	..	..	..	..	..	..	2 59	..	..	3 53	..	..
Umberleigh	..	..	..	..	..	1 16	..	..	..	..	3 5	..	..	3 59	..	..
Portsmouth Arms	..	..	..	..	..	1 23	..	..	..	..	3 13	..	..	4 7	..	..
South Molton Rd. **G**	..	..	..	..	..	1 30	..	..	..	..	3 21	..	..	4 14	..	..
Eggesford **F**	..	..	..	..	..	1 38	..	..	..	..	3 30	..	..	4 22	..	..
Lapford	..	..	..	..	..	1 46	..	..	..	..	3 37	..	..	4 33	..	..
Morchard Road	..	..	..	..	..	1 51	..	..	..	..	..	..	..	4 39	..	..
Copplestone	..	..	..	..	..	1 56	..	..	..	..	..	..	..	4 44	..	..
Yeoford 341 .... arr	..	..	..	..	..	..	..	..	..	..	..	..	..	4 52	..	..
PLYMOUTH Friary .... dep	..	..	..	1138	1210	..	1 22	..	..	..	..	..	2 35	..	..	3 45
PLYMOUTH North Rd. "	..	..	..	1147	1220	..	1 30	..	..	..	..	..	2 44	..	..	3 55
Devonport **D**	..	..	..	1152	1225	..	1 37	..	..	..	..	..	2 50	..	..	4 2
Ford (Devon)	..	..	..	1156	1229	..	1 42	..	..	..	..	..	2 54	..	..	..
St. Budeaux, for Saltash	..	..	..	12 1	1234	..	1 47	..	..	..	..	..	2 59	..	..	..
Tamerton Foliot	..	..	..	12 6	1239	..	1 53	..	..	..	..	..	..	..	..	..
Bere Ferrers	..	..	..	1212	1245	..	2 1	..	..	..	..	..	3 8	..	..	..
Bere Alston 357	..	..	..	1223	1258	..	2 14	..	..	..	..	..	3 20	..	..	..
Tavistock **C**	..	..	..	1236	1 10	..	2 27	..	..	..	..	..	3 33	..	..	4 30
Brentor	..	..	..	1248	..	..	..	..	..	..	..	..	3 44	..	..	..
Lydford	..	..	..	1253	..	..	..	..	..	..	..	..	3 49	..	..	..
Bridestowe	..	..	..	1 0	..	..	..	..	..	..	..	..	3 56	..	..	..
Okehampton 341 .... arr	..	..	..	1 13	..	..	..	..	..	..	..	..	4 9	..	..	4 58
	1	2	3	4	5	6	7	8	9	10	11	12	13	14	15	16

Station	p.m	p.m	p.m	p.m	p.m	p.m	p.m	p.m	p.m	p.m	p.m	p.m	p.m	p.m	
Padstow .... dep	..	..	2 55	3 15	..	..	—	..	..	..	6 0	..	..	..	..
358 Bodmin .... dep	..	..	2 0	2 0	..	..	..	..	..	..	5 36	..	..	..	..
Wadebridge .... dep	..	..	3 20	3 30	..	..	..	..	..	..	6 11	..	..	..	..
St. Kew Highway	..	..	3 29	3 38	..	..	..	..	..	..	6 21	..	..	..	..
Port Isaac Road	..	..	3 39	3 46	..	..	..	..	..	..	6 28	..	..	..	..
Delabole	..	..	3 52	3 57	..	..	..	..	..	..	6 38	..	..	..	..
Camelford **U**	..	..	4 0	4 4	..	..	..	..	..	..	6 45	..	..	..	..
Otterham **T**	..	..	4 14	4 14	..	..	..	..	..	..	6 54	..	..	..	..
Tresmeer	..	..	4 26	4 26	..	..	..	..	..	..	7 3	..	..	..	..
Egloskerry	..	..	4 33	4 33	..	..	..	..	..	..	7 12	..	..	..	..
Launceston	..	..	4 50	4 50	..	..	..	..	..	..	7 20	..	..	..	..
Tower Hill	..	..	5 0	5 0	..	..	..	..	..	..	7 31	..	..	..	..
Ashwater	..	..	5 8	5 8	..	..	..	..	..	..	7 39	..	..	..	..
Halwill **Q** 358 .... arr	..	..	5 19	5 19	..	..	..	..	..	..	7 50	..	..	..	..
Bude .... dep	..	..	..	..	..	..	5 30	..	..	..	7 0	..	..	..	..
Whitstone & Bridgerule	..	..	..	..	..	..	5 41	..	..	..	7 13	..	..	..	..
Holsworthy	..	..	..	..	..	..	5 51	..	..	..	7 22	..	..	..	..
Dunsland Cross	..	..	..	..	..	..	6 2	..	..	..	7 34	..	..	..	..
Halwill **Q** 358 .... arr	..	..	..	..	..	..	6 10	..	..	..	7 42	..	..	..	..
Halwill .... dep	..	..	5 25	5 20	..	..	Stop	..	..	..	7 52	..	..	..	..
Ashbury, for North Lew	..	..	5 38	5 30	..	..	..	..	..	..	8 3	..	..	..	..
Maddaford Moor Halt **P**	..	..	..	..	..	..	..	..	..	..	8 12	..	..	..	..
Okehampton 341 .... arr	..	..	5 54	5 46	..	..	..	..	..	..	8 24	..	..	..	..
Torrington .... dep	..	..	Saturdays excepted	Saturdays only	4 38	5 48	..	..	..	..	..	..	7 40	..	..
Bideford **N**	..	..			4 47	5 57	..	..	..	..	..	..	7 49	..	..
Instow	..	..			4 56	6 5	..	..	..	..	..	..	7 58	..	..
Fremington	..	..			5 4	6 13	..	..	..	..	..	..	8 6	..	..
Barnstaple Jn. **H** arr	..	..			5 10	6 19	..	..	..	..	..	..	8 12	..	..
ILFRACOMBE .... dep	..	..			4 45	Stop	..	..	..	5 45	..	..	7 45	8 45	..
Mortehoe **L**	..	..			4 58	..	..	..	..	5 57	..	..	7 57	8 57	..
Braunton **K**	..	..			5 11	..	..	..	..	6 12	..	..	8 8	9 8	..
Wrafton	..	..			5 15	..	..	..	..	6 17	..	..	8 11	9 11	..
Barnstaple Town **J**	..	..			5 24	..	..	..	..	6 27	..	..	8 19	9 19	..
Barnstaple Junc. **H** arr	..	..			5 28	..	..	..	..	6 31	..	..	8 24	9 24	..
Barnstaple Junc. **H** dep	..	..	..	..	5 33	..	..	..	..	..	..	..	8 28	Stop	..
Chapelton	..	..	..	..	5 42	..	..	..	..	..	..	..	8 36	..	..
Umberleigh	..	..	..	..	5 48	..	..	..	..	..	..	..	8 41	..	..
Portsmouth Arms	..	..	..	..	5 56	..	..	..	..	..	..	..	8 49	..	..
South Molton Rd. **G**	..	..	..	..	6 4	..	..	..	..	..	..	..	8 55	..	..
Eggesford **F**	..	..	..	..	6 12	..	..	..	..	..	..	..	9 3	..	..
Lapford	..	..	..	..	6 20	..	..	..	..	..	..	..	9 12	..	..
Morchard Road	..	..	..	..	6 28	..	..	..	..	..	..	..	9 19	..	..
Copplestone	..	..	..	..	6 31	..	..	..	..	..	..	..	9 24	..	..
Yeoford 341 .... arr	..	..	..	..	6 37	..	p.m	..	..	..	..	..	9 30	p.m	..
PLYMOUTH Friary .... dep	4 5	..	..	..	..	..	4 40	5 11	6 16	..	7 10	..	..	9 15	..
PLYMOUTH North Rd. "	4 14	..	..	..	..	..	4 50	5 21	6 25	..	7 20	..	..	9 25	..
Devonport **D**	4 19	..	..	..	..	..	4 57	5 27	6 30	..	7 26	..	..	9 30	..
Ford (Devon)	4 23	..	..	..	..	..	5 1	5 31	6 35	..	7 30	..	..	9 34	..
St. Budeaux, for Saltash	4 28	..	..	..	..	..	5 6	5 36	6 41	..	7 34	..	..	9 39	..
Tamerton Foliot	4 33	..	..	..	..	..	..	5 41	6 46	..	7 39	..	..	9 44	..
Bere Ferrers	4 39	..	..	..	..	..	..	5 47	6 54	..	7 44	..	..	9 50	..
Bere Alston 357	4 52	..	..	..	..	..	5 23	5 57	7 4	..	7 55	..	..	10 0	..
Tavistock **C**	5 6	..	..	..	..	..	5 38	6 9	7 17	..	8 8	..	..	1013	..
Brentor	..	..	..	..	..	..	5 50	Stop	..	..	8 21	..	..	..	..
Lydford	..	..	..	..	..	..	5 54	..	..	..	8 25	..	..	..	..
Bridestowe	..	..	..	..	..	..	6 2	..	..	..	8 33	..	..	..	..
Okehampton 341 .... arr	..	..	..	..	..	..	6 15	..	..	..	8 46	..	..	..	..
	17	18	19	20	21	22	23	24	25	26	27	28	29	30	31

Station	1	2	3	4	5	6	7	8	9	10	11	12	13	14	15	16 (Refreshment Car, Exeter to London.)	17	18	19	20	21	22	23	24	25	26	27	28	29	30	31
Okehampton ... dep	..	..	..	1 14	..	..	..	..	..	..	..	..	4 12	..	..	5 0	..	..	5 56	..	..	..	6 18	..	..	..	8 50	..	..	..	..
Sampford Courtenay	..	..	..	1 21	..	..	..	..	..	..	..	..	4 20	..	..	..	..	..	Saturdays excepted	..	..	..	6 24	..	..	..	8 58	..	..	..	..
North Tawton	..	..	..	1 26	..	..	..	..	..	..	..	..	4 26	..	..	..	..	..		..	..	..	6 30	..	..	..	9 4	..	..	..	..
Bow	..	..	..	1 33	..	..	..	..	..	..	..	..	4 32	..	..	..	..	..		..	..	..	6 36	..	..	..	9 11	..	..	..	..
Yeoford 341 ... arr	..	..	..	1 42	..	..	..	..	..	..	..	..	4 41	..	..	5 20	..	..		..	..	..	6 45	..	..	..	9 20	..	..	..	..
Yeoford 341 ... dep	..	..	..	1 43	..	..	..	..	..	..	..	..	4 43	4 53	..	5 21	..	..		..	6 38	..	6 48	..	..	..	9 21	..	9 31	..	..
Crediton	..	..	..	1 49	..	..	..	..	..	..	..	..	..	5 0	..	..	..	..		..	..	..	6 58	..	..	..	..	..	9 38	..	..
Newton St. Cyres	..	..	..	1 55	..	..	..	..	..	..	..	..	..	5 8	..	..	..	..		..	..	..	7 4	..	..	..	..	..	9 44	..	..
Exeter (St. David's)	..	..	..	2 6	..	2 17	..	..	..	..	4 6	..	5 3	5 21	..	5 40	..	..	6 33	..	6 58	..	7 19	..	..	..	9 43	..	10T2	..	..
EXETER Central 357 ... arr	..	..	..	2 11	..	2 22	..	..	..	..	4 11	..	5 8	5 26	..	5 45	..	..	6 38	..	7 3	..	7 24	..	..	..	9 48	..	10 7	..	..
357 EXMOUTH ... arr	..	..	..	3 12	..	3 12	..	..	..	..	5 10	..	5 43	6 13	p.m	6 41	..	..	7 14	..	8 12	..	8 12	..	..	..	1046	..	1046	..	..
357 EXMOUTH ... dep	..	..	..	..	..	1 30	..	..	..	..	Stop	3 45	..	..	4Y40	5 15	..	5 45	..	..	Stop	..	7 15	..	..	..	..	8 45	..	..	..
EXETER Central ... dep	..	..	1 50	..	..	2 30	..	..	..	..		4 35	..	..	5 35	5 50	..	6 22	..	..		..	7 50	..	..	..	..	10 0	..	..	..
Pinhoe	..	..	1 56	..	..	..	..	..	..	..	..	4 41	..	..	5 41	..	..	6 28	..	..	..	..	7 56	..	..	..	..	10 7	..	..	..
Broad Clyst	..	..	1 59	..	..	..	..	..	..	..	..	4 46	..	..	5 45	..	..	6 32	..	..	..	..	8 0	..	..	..	..	1012	..	..	..
Whimple	..	..	2 6	..	..	..	..	..	..	..	..	4 54	..	..	5 52	..	..	6 39	..	..	..	..	8 8	..	..	..	..	1020	..	..	..
Sidmouth Junc. 356 ... arr	..	..	2 13	..	..	2 48	..	..	..	..	..	5 2	..	..	5 59	6 11	..	6 46	..	..	..	..	8 16	..	..	..	..	1028	..	..	..
356 SIDMOUTH ... arr	..	..	2 48	..	..	4V20	..	..	..	..	..	5 38	..	..	6 58	6 58	..	..	..	..	..	..	8 52	..	..	..	..	..	..	..	..
356 EXMOUTH ... dep	..	..	..	..	..	..	..	..	..	..	..	4 5	..	..	..	4 5	..	..	..	..	..	..	6 20	..	..	..	..	8 14	..	..	..
356 BUDLEIGH SALTER'N "	..	..	..	..	..	..	..	..	..	..	..	4 18	..	..	..	4 18	..	..	..	..	..	..	6 32	..	..	..	..	8 26	..	..	..
356 SIDMOUTH ... "	..	..	1 35	..	..	1 35	..	..	..	..	..	4 36	..	..	..	5 45	..	..	..	..	..	..	7 45	..	..	..	..	9 25	..	..	..
Sidmouth Junction ... dep	..	..	2 14	..	..	2 49	..	..	..	..	..	5 4	..	..	6 0	6 12	..	6 47	..	..	..	..	8 18	..	..	..	..	1029	..	..	..
Honiton	..	..	2 22	..	..	..	..	..	..	..	..	5 15	..	..	6 9	..	..	6 54	..	..	..	..	8 27	..	..	..	..	1037	..	..	..
Seaton Junction 355 ... arr	..	..	..	..	..	3 6	..	..	..	..	..	5 27	..	..	..	6 29	..	7 6	..	..	..	..	8 39	..	..	..	..	..	..	..	..
355 SEATON ... arr	..	..	Saturdays only	..	..	3 27	..	..	..	..	..	5 51	..	..	..	7 10	..	..	..	..	..	..	8 59	p.m	..	..	..	..	..	..	..
355 SEATON ... dep	..	..		..	..	2N35	..	..	..	..	..	5 5	..	..	..	6 5	..	..	..	..	..	..	8 15	9 3	..	..	..	..	..	..	..
Seaton Junction ... dep	..	..		..	..	3 7	..	..	..	..	..	5 29	..	..	..	6 30	..	7 7	..	..	..	..	8 40	9 21	..	..	..	..	..	..	..
Axminster 355 ... arr	..	..		..	..	3 13	..	..	..	..	..	5 36	..	..	..	6 36	..	7 12	..	..	..	..	8 46	9 27	..	..	..	..	..	..	..
355 LYME REGIS ... arr	..	..		..	..	5 1	..	..	..	..	..	5 59	..	..	..	7 11	..	Stop	..	..	..	..	9 16	10JZ11	..	..	..	..	..	..	..
355 LYME REGIS ... dep	..	..		..	..	2 19	..	..	..	..	..	5 10	..	..	..	6 5	..		..	..	..	..	8 20	..	..	..	..	..	..	..	..
Axminster ... dep	..	..		..	..	3 14	..	..	..	..	..	5 38	..	..	..	6 38	..	..	..	..	..	..	8 48	..	..	..	..	..	..	..	..
Chard Junction 355 ... arr	..	..		..	..	..	..	..	..	..	..	5 47	..	..	..	..	..	..	..	..	..	..	8 57	..	..	..	..	..	..	..	..
355 CHARD ... arr	..	..		..	..	..	..	..	..	..	..	5 59	..	..	..	..	..	..	..	..	..	..	9 19	..	..	..	..	..	..	..	..
355 CHARD ... dep	..	..		..	..	..	..	..	..	..	..	5 36	..	..	..	..	..	..	..	..	..	..	8 43	..	..	..	..	..	..	..	..
Chard Junction ... dep	Calls at Idmiston Halt at 4 14 p.m	..	..	..	..	..	..	Calls at Idmiston Halt at 5 27 p.m	..	..	..	5 53	..	..	..	..	..	..	..	..	..	..	8 59	..	..	..	..	..	..	..	..
Crewkerne		..	..	..	..	..	..		..	..	..	6 11	..	..	..	..	..	..	..	..	..	..	9 15	..	..	..	..	..	..	..	..
Sutton Bingham		..	..	..	..	..	..		..	..	..	6 22	..	..	..	..	..	..	..	..	..	..	..	..	..	..	..	..	..	..	..
Yeovil Junction 355 ... arr		..	..	..	..	3 44	..		..	..	..	6 28	..	..	..	7 8	..	..	..	..	..	..	9 30	..	..	..	..	..	..	..	..
355 YEOVIL (Town) ... arr		..	..	..	..	3 54	..		..	..	..	6 40	..	..	..	7 18	..	..	..	..	..	p.m	9 46	..	..	..	..	..	..	..	..
355 YEOVIL (Town) ... dep		2 36	..	..	..	3 30	..		4 5	..	..	6 15	..	..	..	7 0	..	..	..	..	..	8 15	9 22	..	..	..	..	..	..	..	..
Yeovil Junction ... dep		2 50	..	..	..	3 45	..		4 14	..	..	6 32	..	..	..	7 10	..	..	..	..	..	8 20	9 37	..	..	..	..	..	..	..	..
Sherborne		3 3	..	..	..	3 54	..		4 24	..	..	6 45	..	..	..	..	..	..	..	..	..	8 31	9 47	..	..	..	..	..	..	..	..
Milborne Port		3 12	..	..	..	..	..		4 33	..	..	6 55	..	..	..	..	..	..	..	..	p.m	8 40	9 56	..	..	..	..	..	..	..	..
Templecombe		3A30	..	..	..	4 8	..		4 43	..	..	7 8	..	..	..	7 30	..	..	..	..	8 10	9F20	10 4	..	..	..	..	..	..	..	..
Gillingham (Dorset)		3 41	..	..	..	..	..		4 56	..	..	7 21	..	..	..	..	..	..	..	..	8 20	9 31	1016	..	..	..	..	..	..	..	..
Semley		3 55	..	..	..	..	..		5 9	..	..	7 32	..	..	..	..	..	..	..	..	8 31	..	1026	..	..	..	..	..	..	..	..
Tisbury		4 4	..	..	..	..	..		5 18	..	..	7 40	..	..	..	..	..	..	..	..	8 40	..	1034	..	..	..	..	..	..	..	..
Dinton		4 11	..	..	..	..	..		5 26	..	..	..	..	..	..	..	..	..	..	..	8 48	..	..	..	..	..	..	..	..	..	..
Wilton B		4 20	..	..	..	..	..		5 36	..	..	..	..	..	..	..	..	..	..	..	8 57	..	..	..	..	..	..	..	..	..	..
SALISBURY 339, 356, 376 ... arr		4 26	..	..	..	4 46	..		5 42	..	p.m	8 2	..	..	..	8 9	..	p.m	..	..	9 3	..	1052	..	..	..	..	..	..	..	..
SALISBURY 339, 356, 376 ... dep	4 0	..	..	..	..	4 50	..	5 15	..	..	6 20	..	..	..	..	8 15	..	8 55	..	..	..	..	1110	..	..	..	..	..	..	..	..
Porton	4 11	..	..	..	..	..	..	5 25	..	..	..	..	..	..	..	..	..	9 6	..	..	..	..	Via Eastleigh.	..	..	..	..	..	..	..	..
Grateley	4 25	..	..	..	..	..	..	5 36	..	..	..	..	..	..	..	..	..	9 17	..	..	..	..		..	..	..	..	..	..	..	..
Andover Junction 376	4 40	..	..	..	..	5 17	..	5 48	..	..	6 47	..	..	..	..	8 44	..	9 29	..	..	..	..		..	..	..	..	..	..	..	..
Hurstbourne	4 54	..	..	..	..	..	..	6 0	..	..	..	..	..	..	..	..	..	9 40	..	..	..	..		..	..	..	..	..	..	..	..
Whitchurch A	5 1	..	..	..	..	..	..	6 7	..	..	7 4	..	..	..	..	..	..	9 46	..	..	..	..		..	..	..	..	..	..	..	..
Overton	5 9	..	..	..	..	..	..	6 15	..	..	7 11	..	..	..	..	..	..	9 54	..	..	..	..		..	..	..	..	..	..	..	..
Oakley	5 16	..	..	..	..	..	..	6 22	..	..	..	..	..	..	..	..	..	10 1	..	..	..	..		..	..	..	..	..	..	..	..
Basingstoke 324, 330 ... arr	5 25	..	..	..	..	..	..	6 31	..	..	7 26	..	..	..	..	9 10	..	1011	..	..	..	..	2 15	..	..	..	..	..	..	..	..
330 Woking ... arr	6 22	..	..	..	..	..	..	7 21	..	..	8 21	..	..	..	..	9 43	..	11 9	..	..	..	..	2 54	..	..	..	..	..	..	..	..
330 Surbiton ... "	6 47	..	..	..	..	..	..	8 0	..	..	8 48	..	..	..	..	10 3	..	..	..	..	..	..	3 30	..	..	..	..	..	..	..	..
330 WATERLOO ... "	7 7	..	..	..	..	6 40	..	8 8	..	..	9 14	..	..	..	..	1027	..	12SX6	..	..	..	..	3 55	..	..	..	..	..	..	..	..

For Notes and SUNDAY TRAINS, see pages 350 and 351

From THE WEST OF ENGLAND to WATERLOO—Sundays

	a.m	a.m	a.m		a.m	a.m	a.m	a.m	a.m	a.m	p.m	a.m	a.m	non	p.m	a.m	p.m	p.m	p.m	p.m	p.m	p.m	p.m		p.m
Padstow .... dep	..	..	..	..	..	..	..	..	..	..	..	..	..	..	..	..	..	..	..	..	..	..	..	..	..
Bodmin .... dep	..	..	..	..	..	..	..	..	..	..	..	..	..	..	..	..	..	..	..	..	..	..	..	..	..
Wadebridge .... dep	..	..	..	..	..	..	..	..	..	..	..	..	..	..	..	..	..	..	..	..	..	..	..	..	..
St. Kew Highway	..	..	..	..	..	..	..	..	..	..	..	..	..	..	..	..	..	..	..	..	..	..	..	..	..
Port Isaac Road	..	..	..	..	..	..	..	..	..	..	..	..	..	..	..	..	..	..	..	..	..	..	..	..	..
Delabole	..	..	..	..	..	..	..	..	..	..	..	..	..	..	..	..	..	..	..	..	..	..	..	..	..
Camelford U	..	..	..	..	..	..	..	..	..	..	..	..	..	..	..	..	..	..	..	..	..	..	..	..	..
Otterham T	..	..	..	..	..	..	..	..	..	..	..	..	..	..	..	..	..	..	..	..	..	..	..	..	..
Tresmeer	..	..	..	..	..	..	..	..	..	..	..	..	..	..	..	..	..	..	..	..	..	..	..	..	..
Egloskerry	..	..	..	..	..	..	..	..	..	..	..	..	..	..	..	..	..	..	..	..	..	..	..	..	..
Launceston	..	..	..	..	..	..	..	..	..	..	..	..	..	..	..	..	..	..	2 35	..	..	..	..	..	..
Tower Hill	..	..	..	..	..	..	..	..	..	..	..	..	..	..	..	..	..	..	2 42	..	..	..	..	..	..
Ashwater	..	..	..	..	..	..	..	..	..	..	..	..	..	..	..	..	..	..	2 49	..	..	..	..	..	..
Halwill G .... arr	..	..	..	..	..	..	..	..	..	..	..	..	..	..	..	..	..	..	2 59	..	..	..	..	..	..
Bude .... dep	..	..	..	..	..	..	..	..	..	..	..	Runs until 26th October, 1947.	..	..	..	..	..	..	2 35	..	..	..	..	..	..
Whitstone & Bridgerule	..	..	..	..	..	..	..	..	..	..	..	..	..	..	..	..	..	..	2 46	..	..	..	..	..	..
Holsworthy	..	..	..	..	..	..	..	..	..	..	..	..	..	..	..	..	..	..	2 56	..	..	..	..	..	..
Dunsland Cross	..	..	..	..	..	..	..	..	..	..	..	..	..	..	..	..	..	..	3 8	..	..	..	..	..	..
Halwill G .... arr	..	..	..	..	..	..	..	..	..	..	..	..	..	..	..	..	..	..	3 16	..	..	..	..	..	..
Halwill .... dep	..	..	..	..	..	..	..	..	..	Through Carriages Plymouth to Portsmouth and Southsea, see page 378	..	..	..	..	..	..	..	..	3 18	..	..	..	..	..	..
Ashbury, for North Lew	..	..	..	..	..	..	..	..	..	..	..	..	..	..	..	..	..	..	3 28	..	..	..	..	..	..
Maddaford Moor Halt P	..	..	..	..	..	..	..	..	..	..	..	..	..	..	..	..	..	..	3 36	..	..	..	..	..	..
Okehampton 341 .... arr	..	..	..	..	..	..	..	..	..	..	..	..	..	..	..	..	..	..	3 47	..	..	..	..	..	..
Torrington .... dep	..	..	..	..	..	..	..	8 55	..	..	..	1155	..	..	..	..	..	2 0	..	..	6 10	..	..	..	..
Bideford N	..	..	..	..	..	..	..	9 4	10 2	..	..	12 4	..	..	..	..	..	2 9	..	..	6 19	..	..	..	..
Instow	..	..	..	..	..	..	..	9 11	10 7	..	..	1211	..	..	..	..	..	2 17	..	..	6 26	..	..	..	..
Fremington	..	..	..	..	..	..	..	9 19	1015	..	..	1219	..	..	..	..	..	2 25	..	..	6 34	..	..	..	..
Barnstaple Jn. H .... arr	..	..	..	..	..	..	..	9 25	1021	..	..	1227	..	..	..	..	..	2 31	..	..	6 40	..	..	..	..
ILFRACOMBE .... dep	..	..	..	..	..	..	..	9 5	9 50	..	..	..	..	12 0	..	..	..	2 0	..	..	6 15	..	..	..	..
Mortehoe L	..	..	..	..	..	..	..	9 17	10 3	..	..	..	..	1212	..	..	..	2 14	..	..	6 27	..	..	..	..
Braunton K	..	..	..	..	..	..	..	9 30	1015	..	..	..	..	1223	..	..	..	2 27	Refreshment Car, Exeter to London	..	6 39	..	..	..	..
Wrafton	..	..	..	..	..	..	..	9 34	1018	..	..	..	..	..	..	..	..	2 31	..	..	6 42	..	..	..	..
Barnstaple Town J	..	..	..	..	..	..	..	9 42	1026	..	..	..	..	1232	..	..	..	2 40	..	..	6 50	..	..	..	..
Barnstaple Junc. H .... arr	..	..	..	..	..	..	..	9 46	1030	..	..	..	..	1236	..	..	..	2 44	..	..	6 54	..	..	..	..
Barnstaple Junc. H .... dep	..	..	..	..	..	..	..	9 48	1033	..	..	..	..	1237	..	..	..	2 49	..	..	6 58	..	..	..	..
Chapelton	..	..	..	..	..	..	..	9 56	..	..	..	..	Runs until 26th October, 1947	Runs until 26th October, 1947	..	..	..	2 57	..	..	7 6	..	..	..	..
Umberleigh	..	..	..	..	..	..	..	10 2	..	..	..	..	..	..	..	..	..	3 3	..	..	7 12	..	..	..	..
Portsmouth Arms	..	..	..	..	..	..	..	10 9	..	..	..	..	..	..	..	..	..	3 10	..	..	7 19	..	..	..	..
South Molton Rd. G	..	..	..	..	..	..	..	10 15	..	..	..	..	..	..	..	..	..	3 16	..	..	7 25	..	..	..	..
Eggesford F	..	..	..	..	..	..	..	10 22	..	..	..	..	..	..	..	..	..	3 24	..	..	7 32	..	..	..	..
Lapford	..	..	..	..	..	..	..	10 29	..	..	..	..	..	..	..	..	..	3 36	..	..	7 39	..	..	..	..
Morchard Road	..	..	..	..	..	..	..	10 37	..	..	..	..	..	..	..	..	..	3 45	..	..	7 46	..	..	..	..
Copplestone	..	..	..	..	..	..	..	10 42	..	..	..	..	..	..	..	..	..	3 51	..	..	7 50	..	..	..	..
Yeoford 341 .... arr	..	..	..	..	..	..	..	10 48	..	..	..	..	..	..	..	..	..	3 58	..	..	7 56	..	..	..	..
PLY-MOUTH Friary .... dep	..	..	..	..	..	8 20	..	..	..	10 0	..	..	1130	..	..	1140	..	..	2 50	..	..	6 30	..	..	9 15
PLY-MOUTH North Rd. "	..	..	..	..	..	8 29	..	..	..	10 9	..	..	1140	..	..	1149	..	..	3 0	..	..	6 39	..	..	9 24
Devonport D	..	..	..	..	..	8 34	..	..	..	1015	..	..	1147	..	..	1154	..	..	3 6	..	..	6 44	..	..	9 29
Ford (Devon)	..	..	..	..	..	8 38	..	..	..	..	..	..	..	..	..	1158	..	..	..	..	..	6 48	..	..	9 33
St. Budeaux, for Saltash	..	..	..	..	..	8 43	..	..	..	..	..	..	..	..	..	12 3	..	..	..	..	..	6 53	..	..	9 38
Tamerton Foliot	..	..	..	..	..	8 48	..	..	..	..	..	..	..	..	..	..	..	..	..	..	..	6 58	..	..	9 43
Bere Ferrers	..	..	..	..	..	8 53	..	..	..	..	..	..	..	..	..	1211	..	..	..	..	..	7 4	..	..	9 49
Bere Alston 357	..	..	..	..	..	9 3	..	..	..	..	..	..	..	..	..	1222	..	..	3 25	..	..	7 15	..	..	9 59
Tavistock C	..	..	..	..	..	9 16	..	..	..	1043	..	..	..	..	..	1234	..	..	3 39	..	..	7 28	..	..	1011
Brentor	..	..	..	..	..	9 27	..	..	..	..	..	..	..	..	..	1246	..	..	..	..	..	7 40	..	..	1024
Lydford	..	..	..	..	..	9 32	..	..	..	..	..	..	..	..	..	1250	..	..	..	..	..	7 45	..	..	1029
Bridestowe	..	..	..	..	..	9 39	..	..	..	..	..	..	..	..	..	1258	..	..	..	..	..	7 52	..	..	1038
Okehampton 341 .... arr	..	..	..	..	..	9 52	..	..	..	1111	..	..	1243	..	..	1 11	..	..	4 7	..	..	8 5	..	..	1051
	1	2	3	4	5	6	7	8	9	10	11	12	13	14	15	16	17	18	19	20	21	22	23	24	25

NOTES

- **A** About 1¼ miles to Great Western Sta.
- **A** Arr. 3 18 p.m.
- **B** Over ¼ mile to Great Western Station
- **C** 1 mile to Great Western Station
- **C** 10 mins. later on Saturdays
- **D** Nearly ½ mile to Great Western Sta.
- **F** Station for Chulmleigh (3 miles)
- **F** Arr. 8 46 p.m.
- **G** Station for Chulmleigh (2½ miles)
- **H** About 1 mile to Great Western Station
- **J** Over ¼ mile to Barnstaple Station
- **J** By Southern National Omnibus between Axminster and Lyme Regis. Times subject to alteration
- **K** Station for Saunton Sands
- **L** Station for Lee (Devon) 3 miles, and Woolacombe
- **L** 10 mins. later until 26th October, 1947.
- **N** Station for Hartland (13 miles)
- **N** 10 mins. later until 27th October, 1947.
- **P** Station for Thorndon Cross

Station	1	2	3	4	5	6	7	8	9	10	11	12	13	14	15	16	17	18	19	20	21	22	23	24	25
Okehampton .... dep	..	..	..	..	..	9 53	..	..	..	1112	..	..	1245	..	..	1 14	..	..	4 9	..	..	8 6	..	..	..
Sampford Courtenay	..	..	..	..	..	..	..	..	..	..	..	..	..	..	..	..	..	..	..	..	..	..	..	..	..
North Tawton	..	..	..	..	..	10 5	..	..	..	..	..	..	..	..	..	1 24	..	..	..	..	..	8 18	..	..	..
Bow	..	..	..	..	..	10 12	..	..	..	..	..	..	..	..	..	1 31	..	..	..	..	..	8 25	..	..	..
Yeoford 341 .... arr	..	..	..	..	..	10 20	..	..	..	..	..	..	..	..	..	1 40	..	..	..	..	..	8 34	..	..	..
Yeoford 341 .... dep	..	..	..	..	..	10 22	..	10 56	..	..	..	..	..	..	..	1 41	..	3 59	..	..	7 57	8 35	..	..	..
Crediton	..	..	..	..	..	10 29	..	10 58	..	..	..	..	..	..	..	1 48	..	4 6	..	..	8 3	8 42	..	..	..
Newton St. Cyres	..	..	..	..	..	..	..	..	..	..	..	..	..	..	..	..	..	..	..	..	..	..	..	..	..
Exeter (St. David's)	..	..	..	..	..	10 47	..	11 12	1139	1149	..	..	1 23	1 33	..	2 4	..	4 25	4 44	..	8 19	8 56	..	..	..
EXETER Central 357 ... arr	..	..	..	..	..	10 52	..	11 17	1144	1154	..	..	1 27	1 38	..	2 9	..	4 30	4 49	..	8 24	9 1	..	..	..
357 EXMOUTH .... arr	..	..	..	..	..	1 11	..	1 11	1 11	1 11	..	..	2 44		..	2 44	..	5 39	5 39	..	9 41	9 41	..	..	..
357 EXMOUTH .... dep	..	..	9 30	..	..	..	9 30	..	11 0	11 0	1215	..	1215		..	Stop	1 45	2 55	4 15	6 15	..	..	9 0	..	..
EXETER Central .... dep	..	..	10 0	..	..	..	11 5	..	1148	12 0	1250	..	1 40		..	..	3 15	4 38	4 55	7 20	..	..	9 30	..	..
Pinhoe	..	..	10 6	..	..	..	11 11	..	..		1256	..	..		..	..	3 21	..	..	7 26	..	..	9 36	..	..
Broad Clyst	..	..	10 9	..	..	..	11 16	..	..		1259	..	..		..	..	3 26	..	..	7 30	..	..	9 42	..	..
Whimple	..	..	1016	..	..	..	11 24	..	..	Refreshment Car, Exeter to London.	1 6	..	..		..	..	3 34	..	..	7 38	..	..	9 50	..	..
Sidmouth Junc. 356 ... arr	..	..	1023	..	..	..	11 32	..	..		1 13	..	2 2		..	..	3 42	..	5 14	7 46	..	..	9 58	..	..
356 SIDMOUTH .... arr	..	..	1050	..	..	..	12 10	..	..		..	..	3 5		..	..	..	..	..	..	..	..	..	..	..
356 EXMOUTH .... dep	..	..	..	..	..	..	..	..	..		..	..	..		..	..	..	..	..	..	..	..	..	..	..
356 BUDLEIGH SALTER'N "	..	..	..	..	..	..	..	..	..		..	..	..		..	..	..	..	..	..	..	..	..	..	..
356 SIDMOUTH .... "	..	..	..	..	..	..	11 8	..	..		..	..	1 35		..	..	3 13	..	..	..	..	..	..	..	..
Sidmouth Junction .... dep	..	..	..	..	..	..	11 34	..	..		1 14	..	2 3		..	..	3 43	..	5 16	7 47	..	..	9 59	..	..
Honiton	..	..	..	..	..	..	11 43	..	..		1 21	..			..	..	3 52	..	..	7 56	..	..	10 7	..	..
Seaton Junction 355 .... arr	..	..	..	..	..	..	11 55	..	..		..	..	Runs until 26th October, 1947		..	..	4 4	..	..	8 8	..	..	..	..	..
355 SEATON .... arr	..	..	..	..	..	..	12 17	..	..		..	..			..	..	4 22	..	..	..	..	..	..	..	..
355 SEATON .... dep	..	..	..	..	..	..	11 38	..	..		..	..			..	..	3L35	..	..	..	..	..	..	..	..
Seaton Junction .... dep	Calls at Idmiston Halt at 8 46 a.m.	..	..	..	..	..	11 57	..	..	..	..	..			..	..	4 6	..	..	8 11	..	..	..	..	..
Axminster 355 .... arr		..	..	..	..	..	12 3	..	..	1236	..	..			..	..	4 13	..	5 38	8 17	..	..	..	..	..
355 LYME REGIS .... arr		..	..	..	..	..	1 1	..	..	1 1	..	..			..	..	4 41	..	..	..	..	..	..	..	..
355 LYME REGIS .... dep		..	..	..	..	..	11 37	..	..	1137	..	..			..	..	3 50	..	..	..	..	..	..	..	..
Axminster .... dep		..	..	..	..	..	12 4	..	..	1238	..	..			..	..	4 15	..	5 39	8 19	..	..	..	..	..
Chard Junction 355 ..... arr		..	..	..	..	..	12 12	..	..	..	..	..			..	..	4 24	..	..	8 28	..	..	..	..	..
355 CHARD .... arr		..	..	..	..	..	..	..	..	..	..	..	Devon Belle 1st and 3rd Class Pullman Cars only from Plymouth and Ilfracombe. Supplementary fees charged		..	..	..	..	..	..	..	..	..	..	..
355 CHARD .... dep		..	..	..	..	..	..	..	..	..	..	..			..	..	..	..	..	..	..	..	..	..	..
Chard Junction .... dep		..	..	..	..	..	12 13	..	..	..	..	..			..	..	4 26	..	..	8 29	..	..	..	..	..
Crewkerne		..	..	..	..	..	12 27	..	..	..	..	..			..	..	4 41	..	..	8 43	..	..	..	..	..
Sutton Bingham		..	..	..	..	..	12 37	..	..	..	..	..			..	..	4 52	..	..	8 53	..	..	..	..	..
Yeovil Junction 355 .... arr		..	..	..	..	..	12 43	..	1255	1 7	..	..			..	..	4 58	5 45	6 8	8 59	..	..	..	..	..
355 YEOVIL (Town) ... arr	..	..	..	..	..	..	12 50	..	1 14	1 14	..	..			..	..	5 9	6 20	6 20	9 8	..	..	..	..	..
355 YEOVIL (Town) ... dep	7 0	..	..	..	1140	..	..	..	..	1253	..	..			3 25	..	4 55	4 55	6 0	..	..	..	..	..	..
Yeovil Junction .... dep	7 9		..	..	1149	..	..	..	1256	1 9	..	..			3 35	..	5 4	5 48	6 10	..	..	..	..	..	..
Sherborne	7 19	..	..	..	12 1	..	..	..	..	..	..	..			3 47	..	5 15	6 0	6 21	..	..	..	..	..	..
Milborne Port	..	..	..	..	1211	..	..	..	..	..	..	..			3 57	..	5 24	..	..	..	..	..	..	..	..
Templecombe	7 31	..	..	..	1219	..	..	..	..	..	..	..			4 5	..	5 35	..	..	..	..	..	..	..	..
Gillingham (Dorset)	7 42	..	..	..	1231	..	..	..	..	..	..	..			4 19	..	5 47	..	6 43	..	..	..	..	..	..
Semley	7 53	..	..	..	1241	..	..	..	..	..	..	..			4 33	..	5 57	..	..	..	..	..	..	..	..
Tisbury	8 1	..	..	..	1250	..	..	..	..	..	..	..			4 42	..	6 5	..	..	..	..	..	..	..	..
Dinton	8 9	..	..	..	1258	..	..	..	..	..	..	..			4 51	..	6 13	..	..	..	..	..	..	..	..
Wilton B	8 19	..	..	..	1 8	..	..	..	..	..	..	..			5 1	..	6 23	..	..	..	..	..	..	..	..
SALISBURY 339, 356, 376 arr	8 25	..	..	..	1 14	..	..	..	1 48	2 1	..	..			5 7	p.m.	6 29	6 47	7 11	..	..	..	..	..	..
SALISBURY 339, 356, 376 dep	8 32	9 55	..	..	..	..	..	..	1 52	2 18	..	..			5 25	5 40	..	6 52	7 17	..	..	..	..	..	..
Porton	8 44	..	..	..	..	..	..	..	..	..	..	..			..	5 50	..	..	..	..	..	..	..	..	..
Grateley	8 55	..	..	..	..	..	..	..	..	..	..	..			..	6 0	..	..	..	..	..	..	..	..	..
Andover Junction 376	9 8	1020	..	..	..	..	..	..	2 19	2 43	..	..			5 50	6 10	..	..	7 44	..	..	..	..	..	..
Hurstbourne	9 20	..	..	..	..	..	..	..	..	..	..	..			..	6 21	..	..	..	..	..	..	..	..	..
Whitchurch A	9 26	1033	..	..	..	..	..	..	..	..	..	..			..	6 26	..	..	..	..	..	..	..	..	..
Overton	9 34	..	..	..	..	..	..	..	..	..	..	..			..	6 33	..	..	..	..	..	..	..	..	..
Oakley	9 41	..	..	..	..	..	..	..	..	..	..	..			..	6 39	..	..	..	..	..	..	..	..	..
Basingstoke 324, 330 .. arr	9 50	1053	..	..	..	..	..	..	..	3 9	..	..			6 16	6 48	..	..	8 10	..	..	..	..	..	..
330 Woking .... arr	1045	1157	..	..	..	..	..	..	3 11	3 38	..	..	..		6 49	7 42	..	..	..	..	..	..	..	..	..
330 Surbiton .... "	11 2	1230	..	..	..	..	..	..	..	4 30	..	..	..		7 7	8 2	..	..	8 54	..	..	..	..	..	..
330 WATERLOO .... "	1121	1230	..	..	..	..	..	..	3 44	4 10	..	..	5 20		7 27	8 22	..	8 39	9 13	..	..	..	..	..	..

@ Station for Beaworthy
SO Saturdays only
SX Saturdays excepted
T Station for Wilsey Down and Davidstow (2½ miles) and Crackington Haven (5 mls.)
I Arr. 9 53 p m.
U Station for Boscastle and Tintagel
V Arr. 3 43 p.m. until 27th October, 1947.
Y Dep. 4 20 p.m on Saturdays
Z Fridays and Saturdays

** * For Halts between Plymouth and St. Budeaux, see page 356

Local Trains

BETWEEN	PAGE
Padstow and Wadebridge	358

Other Trains

Exeter and St. James' Park Halt	357
Salisbury and Porton	356

Omnibus Times subject to alteration.

For TRAIN SERVICE between WATERLOO and WEST OF ENGLAND, see pages 340 to 345

ROAD MOTOR SERVICES IN THE WEST OF ENGLAND

Miles frm London.	Down.		Week Days														Sundays.				
			a.m	a.m	a.m	a.m	a.m	a.m	p.m	p.m	p.m	p.m	p.m	p.m	p.m	p.m		a.m		p.m	p.m	
	London (Waterloo)	dep	1 25	..	5 40	9R 0	..	10R50	..	12R50	..	2R50	..	5 0	6R 0	..		11R0	..	..	..	..
	Salisbury	"	3 24	8 0	9 30	11 5	1115	12 36	1245	2 43	3 5	4 46	5 0	7 13	7 52	8 5		1 3	..	1 26		..
101½	Semley	arr.	..	8 38	10 7	..	1149	..	1 16	..	3 41	..	5 36	7 41	..	8 39		..	..	..		..
—	Semley ‡	dep.	..	8 40	1015	..	12 0	..	1 40	..	4 0	..	5 40	7 45	..	8 45		..	..	..		..
103¾	Shaftesbury ‡	arr.	..	8 55	1030	..	1215	..	1 55	..	4 15	..	5 55	8 0	..	9 0		..	..	..		..
105¼	Gillingham (Dorset)	arr.	..	8 48	1020	..	1157	..	1 24	..	3 49	..	5 48	..	8 22	8 47		..	..	..		..
—	Gillingham (D.)	dep.	..	9 10	1146	..	1226	..	..	..	4 0	..	7 26	..	8 35	10SO 6		..	..	..		..
109¼	Mere	arr.	..	9 25	12 1	..	1244	..	..	..	4 15	..	7 44	..	8 50	10SO21		..	..	..		..
112¼	Zeals *	"	..	..	1211	..	1238	..	..	..	4 25	..	7 38	..	9 0	10SO31		..	..	..		..
—	Gillingham (D.)	dep	..	10 0	1129	..	..	..	1 48	..	5 14	..	6 15	..	..	10V 5	11SO11	..		..		..
109¼	Shaftesbury	arr.	..	1020	1145	..	..	..	2 8	..	5 30	..	6 35	..	..	10V25	11SO31	..		..		..
131¾	Crewkerne	arr.	..	9 58	..	1239	..	..	..	..	..	6 19	..	..	..	..	..	..	..	..		..
—	Crewkerne *	dep	..	10 5	..	1 5	..	..	..	..	..	6 45	..	..	..	..	..	..	..	..	..	..
137¾	Beaminster	arr.	..	1030	..	1 30	..	..	..	..	..	7 10	..	..	..	..	..	..	..	..	..	..
144¾	Axminster	arr.	7 9	1024	..	1235	..	..	2 41	4 30	5 8	6 41	..	..	9 24	..	..	..	..	3 3		..
151¼	Lyme Regis	"	8 56	11 4	..	1 18	..	..	3 11	5 1	5 59	7 11	..	..	10H11	..	..	..	..	3 31		..
—	Lyme Regis *	dep	9 3	1142	..	2 3	..	..	4 3	5 3	6 3	7 13	..	..	..	..	..	..	..	4 3		..
153¼	Charmouth	arr.	9 22	12 0	..	2 22	..	..	4 22	5 22	6 22	7 32	..	..	..	..	..	..	..	4 22		..
171¾	Exeter (Central)	arr.	5 13	1119	..	1 24	..	2 29	3 51	4 46	6 5	6 46	..	..	..	..	..	2 55	..	3 51		..
—	Exeter (Paul St) ¶	dep	8 55	1235	..	2 0	..	2FO45	4 5	6 20	6 20	8 0	..	..	..	..	..	4 45	..	4 45		..
187¾	Chagford	arr	1020	2 0	..	3 25	..	4FO0	5 20	7 45	7 45	9 20	..	..	..	..	..	6 25	..	6 25		..

Miles frm London.	Down.		Week Days														Sundays.				
			a.m	a.m		a.m	a.m	a.m		p.m	p.m		p.m				a.m		a.m		p.m
—	London (Waterloo)	dep.	1 25	..	..	..	9R 0	10R50	..	..	12R50	..	2R50	..	..	..	..	..	11R0	..	4R 0
—	Salisbury	"	3 24	3 35	..	8 0	11 5	12 36	..	..	2 43	..	4 46	..	..	..	..	..	1 3	..	6 0
—	Exeter (Central)	"	5 31	8 20	..	1127	1 42	2 34	..	4 22	5 5	..	6 52	..	..	..	1016	..	3 15	..	8 35
210¼	Barnstaple Junc. A	arr.	7 4	..	..	1254	..	3 44	..	5 46	6 30	..	..	..	..	..	..	..	4 25	..	..
—	Barnstaple J. *	dep.	7 40	..	..	2 15	..	4 35	..	6 40	6 40	..	..	..	..	..	..	..	5 10	..	..
231¾	Lynton B	arr.	9 4	..	..	3 39	..	5 59	..	8 4	8 4	..	..	..	..	..	..	..	6 34	..	..
217¼	Braunton C	arr.	7 31	10 20	..	1 19	3 25	4 7	..	6 21	6 50	..	8 42	..	..	..	1222	..	4 49	..	1020
—	Braunton	dep.	7 53	10 53	..	2 53	3 53	4 53	..	6 53	6 53	..	8 53	..	..	..	1253	..	5 53	..	1053
220¼	Saunton *	arr.	8 3	11 3	..	3 3	4 3	5 3	..	7 3	7 3	..	9 3	..	..	..	1 3	..	6 3	..	11 3
222	Croyde	"	8 10	11 10	..	3 10	4 10	5 10	..	7 10	7 10	..	9 10	..	..	..	1 10	..	6 10	..	1010
223¼	Mortehoe D	arr.	7 51	10 39	..	1 38	3 43	4 27	..	6 39	7 9	..	9 2	..	..	..	1241	..	5 9	..	..
—	Mortehoe *	dep.	8 10	10 50	..	1 40	3 50	4 40	..	7 15	7 15	..	9 20	..	..	..	2 35	..	6 35	..	..
225¼	Woolacombe	arr.	8 18	10 58	..	1 48	3 58	4 48	..	7 23	7 23	..	9 28	..	..	..	2 43	..	6 43	..	..
226¼	Ilfracombe	arr.	8 0	10 48	..	1 47	3 52	4 36	..	6 48	7 18	..	9 11	..	..	..	1250	..	5 18	..	..
—	Ilfracombe *	dep.	8 30	11 0	..	2 30	4 0	5 0	..	7 0	7 25	..	9 15	..	..	..	2 0	..	5 55	..	..
232¼	Combe Martin	arr.	9 4	11 34	..	3 4	4 39	5 39	..	7 34	7 59	..	9 49	..	..	..	2 39	..	6 34	..	..
220¼	Bideford F	arr.	7 51	10 23	..	1 34	3 33	4 18	..	6 12	6 58	..	8 48	..	..	..	1230	..	4 58	..	1028
—	Bideford	dep.	8 6	10 36	..	2 6	4 6	4 36	..	6 36	7 6	..	9 6	..	..	..	1236	..	5 36	..	1036
222	Northam	arr.	8 25	10 47	..	2 17	4 17	4 47	..	6 47	7 17	..	9 17	..	..	..	1247	..	5 47	..	1047
223¼	Westward Ho!	"	8 32	10 54	..	2 24	4 24	4 54	..	6 54	7 24	..	9 24	..	..	..	1254	..	5 54	..	1054
—	Bideford *	dep	8d10	10d50	..	1d50	3d50	4d30	..	6d30	7 5	..	..	..	..	..	1d10	..	5d10	..	..
223¼	Appledore	arr	8 26	11 6	..	2 6	4 6	4 46	..	6 46	7 26	..	..	..	..	..	1 26	..	5 26	..	..
—	Bideford	dep	..	..	..	2d45	4 10	5 10	..	..	7 10	..	..	..	..	..	..	..	5d15	..	..
231¼	Clovelly	arr.	..	..	..	3 30	5 0	6 0	..	..	8 0	..	..	..	..	..	..	..	6 0	..	..

Miles frm London.	Down.		Week Days																Sundays.				
			a.m	a.m		a.m		a.m		a.m		p.m	p.m						a.m				
—	London (Waterloo)	dep.	1 25	..	..	..	..	..	..	10R50	..	12R50	..	..	..	..	..	..	11R0	..	..	..	..
—	Salisbury	"	3 24	..	..	3 35	..	8 0	..	12 36	..	2 43	..	..	..	..	..	..	1 3	..	..	..	..
—	Exeter (Central)	"	5 31	..	..	8 40	..	11 46	..	2 46	..	4 50	..	..	..	..	..	..	3 2	..	..	..	..
228¼	Bude	arr.	7 58		..	11 17	..	2 25	..	5 9	..	7 0		..	..	..	..	..	5 18	..	..	..	..
—	Bude	dep.	..	8 21	..	12 55	..	2 31	..	5 16	..	9 1	8SO31	..	..	..	..	..	6d15	..	..	..	..
231½	Marhamchurch	arr.	..	8 30	..	..	..	2 44	..	5 29	..	..	8SO40	..	..	..	..	..	..	..	..	..	..
230	Stratton *	"	..	..	..	1 0	..	2 36	..	5 21	..	9 6	..	..	..	..	..	..	6 20	..	..	..	..
—	Bude	dep.	8 30	..	..	12 0	..	3 30	..	..	..	8G 0	..	..	..	..	..	..	..	..	..	..	..
233½	Widemouth Bay	arr.	8 45	..	..	12 15	..	3 45	..	..	..	8G15	..	..	..	..	..	..	..	..	..	..	..
241½	Camelford	arr.	9 11	..	..	11 31	..	..	..	5 29	..	..	..	..	..	..	..	..	NO SERVICE				
—	Camelford	dep.	9SX25	..	..	11 35	..	..	..	5 50	..	..	..	..	..	..	..	..					
246½	Tintagel *	arr.	9SX41	..	..	11 51	..	..	..	6 6	..	..	..	..	..	..	..	..					
245¾	Boscastle	"	9SX56	..	..	12 6	..	..	..	6 21	..	..	..	..	..	..	..	..					
254¼	Wadebridge	arr.	..	..	..	11 57	..	..	..	6 1	..	..	..	..	..	..	..	..					
—	Wadebridge *	dep.	..	..	..	3 10	..	..	..	7SO20	..	..	..	..	..	..	..	..					
270	Newquay	arr.	..	..	..	4 0	..	..	..	8SO20	..	..	..	..	..	..	..	..					
260	Padstow	arr.	10 4	..	..	12 10	..	..	..	6 21	..	7 56	..	..	..	..	..	..					
—	Padstow	dep.	10 10	..	..	12 30	..	..	..	6 55	..	8 20	..	..	..	..	..	..					
266	Bedruthan *	arr.	..	..	..	..	..	..	..	..	..	..	..	..	..	..	..	..					
262	Trevone Bay	"	10 21	..	..	12 41	..	..	..	7 6	..	8 31	..	..	..	..	..	..					

A About 1 mile to G. W. Sta. B Lynton, for Lynmouth. C Sta. for Saunton Sands. G Tuesdays and Fridays only. D Sta. for Lee (Devon) 3 miles, & Woolacombe. d To and from Southern Nat. Omnibus Office. F Sta. for Hartland (13 miles) FO Fridays only H Fridays and Saturdays. By Southern National Omnibus from Axminster. R Refreshment Car Waterloo to Exeter SO Saturdays only SX Except Saturdays V Except Wednesdays and Saturdays
* By Southern National Omnibus. ‡ By Grosvenor Garage Omnibus.
¶ By Devon General Omnibus from Exeter (Paul St.) 5 minutes from Central Sta. (Queen St. exit).

ROAD MOTOR SERVICES IN THE WEST OF ENGLAND

Up. — Week Days (Sundays: NO SERVICE)

Up.		a.m	a.m			p.m	p.m	p.m (Mondays to Fridays)	p.m (Saturdays only)	p.m	p.m	
Trevone Bay … *	dep	..		..	..	11 26	..	1 53	1 53	..	5 33	..
Bedruthan … *	"	..		..	..	10 48	..	..	..	..	..	..
Padstow … *	arr.	..		..	..	11 37	..	2 4	2 4	..	5 44	..
Padstow	dep.	..		..	..	1 0	..	2 55	3 15	..	6 0	..
Newquay … *	dep.	..		..	..	9 5	..	..	..	..	4 10	..
Wadebridge … *	arr.	..		..	..	10 35	..	..	..	..	5 5	..
Wadebridge	dep.	..		..	..	1 12	..	..	..	..	6 11	..
Boscastle … *	dep.	8 3		..	..	1 5	..	3 28	3 28	..	5 18	..
Tintagel … *	"	8 18		..	..	1 20	..	3 41	3 41	..	5 33	..
Camelford … *	arr.	8 34		..	..	1 36	..	3 55	3 55	..	5 49	..
Camelford	dep.	9 12		..	..	1 47	..	4 0	4 4	..	6 45	..
WidemouthBay … *	dep.	9 10		..	..	12 15	2 15	..	..	..	..	..
Bude … *	ar	9 25		..	..	12 30	2 30	..	..	..	..	..
Stratton … *	dp	8 39	8 53	..	..	1 0	2 55	..	..	5 40	..	..
Marhamchurch … *	"	8 30	..	..	..	..	2 45	..	..	5 30	6 9	..
Bude … *	arr.	8 44	8 58	..	..	1 5	3 0	..	..	5 45	6 15	..
Bude	dep.	9 35		..	..	2 8	3 13	..	..		7 0	..
Exeter (Central)	arr.	12 5		..	..	5 8	5 45	6 38	7 24	..	9 48	..
Salisbury	"	2 44		..	..	8 9	8 9	1052	1052	..	..	..
London (Waterloo)	"	4R41		..	..	10R26	10R26	3B55	3B55	..	..	..

Week Days

Up.		a.m	a.m		a.m		p.m	p.m		p.m	p.m	p.m		
Clovelly … *	dep.	..	9 20	..	10 50	..	..	1 50	..	..	5 40	6T30	..	..
Bideford … *	arr.	..	10 5	..	11d35	..	..	2 35	..	..	6d25	7d24	..	..
Appledore … *	dep.	7 35	9 50	..	11 50	..	1 50	2 30	..	4 10	7 10		..	..
Bideford … *	arr.	7d51	10d6	..	12 20	..	2d6	2d46	..	4d26	7d26		..	..
Westward Ho! … *	dep.	7 30	10 0	..	12 0	..	1 30	2 30	..	4 0	7 0		..	..
Northam … *	"	7 37	10 7	..	12 7	..	1 37	2 37	..	4 7	7 7		..	..
Bideford … *	arr.	7d46	10 18	..	12 18	..	1 48	2 48	..	4 18	7 18		..	..
Bideford	dep.	8 19	10 24	..	12 24	..	2 14	3 1	..	4 47	7 49		..	..
Combe Martin … *	dep.	7 20	9 10	..	11 15	..	1 15	2 10	..	3 40	6 45		..	..
Ilfracombe … *	arr.	7 54	9 44	..	11 49	..	1 49	2 49	..	4 14	7 19		..	..
Ilfracombe	dep.	8 10	10 15	..	12 15	..	2 5	3 0	..	4 45	7 45		..	..
Woolacombe … *	dep.	7 55	10 0	..	12 0	..	1 50	2 50	..	4 35	7 25		..	..
Mortehoe … *	arr.	8 6	10 11	..	12 11	..	2 1	3 1	..	4 46	7 36		..	..
Mortehoe	dep.	8 23	10 28	..	12 29	..	2 19	3 13	..	4 58	7 57		..	..
Croyde … *	dep.	7 54	9 29	..	11 29	..	1 45	1 45	..	4 29	7 45		..	..
Saunton … *	"	8 1	9 36	..	11 36	..	1 52	1 52	..	4 36	7 52		..	..
Braunton … *	arr.	8 11	9 46	..	11 46	..	2 2	2 2	..	4 46	8 2		..	..
Braunton	dep.	8 35	10 41	..	12 42	..	2 32	3 25	..	5 11	8 8		..	..
Lynton … *	dep.	7 20	9 15	..	..	..	12 45	2 15	..	3 45	6 10		..	..
Barnstaple J. … *	arr.	8 44	10 39	..	..	..	2 9	3 39	..	5 9	7 34		..	..
Barnstaple Junction	dep.	8 54	11 0	..	1 3	.	2 50	3 45	..	5 33	8 28		..	..
Exeter (Central)	arr.	10 11	12 30	..	2 22	..	4 11	5 26	..	7 3	10 7		..	..
Salisbury	"	12 36	3 0	..	4 46	..	..	8 9	..	10 52	..		..	..
London (Waterloo)	"	2R29	4R41	..	6 40	..	..	10R26	..	3B55	..		..	..

Sundays

Up.		a.m	a.m	p.m		p.m		
Clovelly … *	dep.	..	..	..	..	1 50	..	..
Bideford … *	arr.	..	..	..	..	2d35	..	..
Appledore … *	dep.	8 35	9 30	1 30	..	5 30	..	..
Bideford … *	arr.	8d51	9d46	1d46	..	5d46	..	..
Westward Ho! … *	dep.	..	9 0	1 0	..	5 0	..	..
Northam … *	"	..	9 7	1 7	..	5 7	..	..
Bideford … *	arr.	..	9 18	1 18	..	5 18	..	..
Bideford	dep.	9 4	10 2	2 9	..	6 19	..	..
Combe Martin … *	dep.	..	8 50	1 15	..	5 10	..	..
Ilfracombe … *	arr.	..	9 29	1 54	..	5 49	..	..
Ilfracombe	dep.	..	9 50	2 0	..	6 15	..	..
Woolacombe … *	dep.	..	9 45	1230	..	4 45	..	..
Mortehoe … *	arr.	..	9 56	1241	..	4 56	..	..
Mortehoe	dep.	..	10 3	2 14	..	6 27	..	..
Croyde … *	dep.	..	..	1 45	..	5 45	..	..
Saunton … *	"	..	..	1 52	..	5 52	..	..
Braunton … *	arr.	..	..	2 2	..	6 2	..	..
Braunton	dep.	..	..	2 27	..	6 40	..	..
Lynton … *	dep.	..	8 50	1 10	..	..	..	..
Barnstaple J. … *	arr.	..	1014	2 34	..	..	..	..
Barnstaple Junction	dep.	..	1033	2 49	..	..	..	..
Exeter (Central)	arr.	1117	1144	4 30	..	8 24	..	..
Salisbury	"	..	1 48	6 47	..	..	..	..
London (Waterloo)	"	..	3 44	8 39	..	..	..	..

Week Days

Up.		a.m	am	a.m	am	a.m	a.m	p.m	a.m	a.m	p.m	p.m	pm	pm	p.m	pm	p.m
Chagford … ¶	dep.	..	..	..	..	..	8 40	..	1040	1040	..	1235	..	2 0	3 30	..	6 30
Exeter (Paul St) ¶	arr.	..	..	..	..	..	10 0	..	1155	1155	..	1 50	..	315	4 45	..	7 45
Exeter (Central)	dep.	..	..	..	..	..	1030	..	1225	1240	..	2 30	..	435	5 50	..	7 50
Charmouth … *	dep.	..	..	7‖5	..	7 5	9 32	..	1130	..	..	1 36	..	436	5 38	..	7 41
Lyme Regis … *	arr	..	..	..	..	7 27	9 55	..	1159	..	..	1 59	..	459	6 1	..	8 4
Lyme Regis	dep.	..	..	7‖22	..	8 4	10 0	..	12 9	..	..	2 19	..	510	6 5	..	8 20
Axminster	"	..	..	8 9	..	9 37	1032	..	1 8	..	..	3 14	..	538	6 38	..	8 48
Beaminster … *	dep.	..	..	..	..	9 28	..	..	..	..	1228	..	..	538	..	..	..
Crewkerne … *	arr.	..	..	..	..	9 53	..	..	..	..	1253	..	..	6 3	..	..	..
Crewkerne	dep.	..	..	..	..	10 2	..	..	..	..	2 31	..	..	611	..	..	..
Shaftesbury … *	dep.	..	..	..	..	..	..	1210	..	..	..	..	335	..	..	755	9SO45
Gillingham (D.) *	ar	..	..	..	..	..	..	1226	..	..	..	..	355	..	..	815	10SO5
Zeals … *	dp	..	..	8 15	..	..	..	1117	1 23	..	..	..	..	550	..	..	9V40
Mere … *	"	..	..	8 25	..	9 45	..	1111	1 33	..	..	..	..	6 0	..	..	9V50
Gillingham (D.) *	arr.	..	..	8 40	..	10 0	..	1129	1 48	..	..	..	..	615	..	..	10V5
Gillingham (Dorset)	dep.	..	..	9 14	..	1110	..	1 30	2 15	..	..	..	456	721	..	820	10 16
Shaftesbury … ‡	dep.	7 45	820	..	915	11 0	..	1 0	..	..	3 15	..	445	..	..	8 0	..
Semley … ‡	arr.	8 0	835	..	930	1115	..	1 15	..	..	3 30	..	5 0	..	..	815	..
Semley	dep.	8 4	848	..	936	1122	..	1 40	..	..	3 55	..	5 9	732	..	831	10 26
Salisbury	arr.	8 33	918	9 45	108	1154	1236	2 10	2 44	3 0	4 26	4 46	542	758	8 9	9 3	10 52
London (Waterloo)	"	11 3	..	11R46		..	2R29	4 10	..	4R41	..	6 40	..	..	10R26		3B55

Sundays

Up.		a.m	p.m	a.m	p.m	p.m	p.m
Chagford … ¶	dep.	..	..	..	..	1235	3 30
Exeter (Paul St) ¶	arr.	..	..	..	..	1 50	4 45
Exeter (Central)	dep.	..	..	..	..	3 15	4 55
Charmouth … *	dep.	..	..	11 0	..	2 46	..
Lyme Regis … *	arr	..	..	11 19	..	3 9	..
Lyme Regis	dep.	..	..	11 37	..	3 50	..
Axminster	"	..	..	12 38	..	4 15	..
Beaminster … *	dep.	..	..	..	..	..	..
Crewkerne … *	arr.	..	..	..	..	..	..
Crewkerne	dep.	..	..	..	..	..	..
Shaftesbury … *	dep.	..	12 10	..	2 30	5 6	..
Gillingham (D.) *	ar	..	12 26	..	2 50	5 20	..
Zeals … *	dp	..	11 17	..	..	5 2	..
Mere … *	"	..	11 11	..	..	4 56	..
Gillingham (D.) *	arr.	..	11 29	..	..	5 14	..
Gillingham (Dorset)	dep.	..	12 41	..	4 19	5 47	..
Shaftesbury … ‡	dep.		12 20	..	4 10		..
Semley … ‡	arr.		12 35	..	4 25		..
Semley	dep.		12 41	..	4 33	5 57	..
Salisbury	arr.		1 14	2 1	5 7	6 29	7 11
London (Waterloo)	"		..	4 10	7 27	..	9 13

B Via Eastleigh. d To Southern National Omnibus Office
‖ By Southern National Omnibus to Axminster R Refreshment Car, Exeter to Waterloo. SO Saturdays only
T Tuesdays and Saturdays only V Except Wednesdays and Saturdays
¶ By Devon General Omnibus to Exeter (Paul St) 5 mins from Cen. Sta. (Queen St. exit).
* By Southern National Omnibus ‡ By Grosvenor Garage Omnibus

For TRAIN SERVICE between WEST OF ENGLAND and WATERLOO, see pages 346 to 351

Motor Omnibus Services

(Times Subject to Alteration)

BIDEFORD, NORTHAM, WESTWARD HO! and APPLEDORE—Southern National Omnibus Co., Ltd., The Quay, Bideford. Tel.—193.

Week Days	a.m	a.m	a.m	a.m	a.m	a.m	a.m	a.m		p.m	p.m	p.m	p.m	p.m
Bideford (Omnibus Sta.) ..dep.	7 10	7 38	8 16	8 38	9 8	9 38	10 8	1038	Then every 30 minutes until	8 38	9 8	9 38	1015	1038
Northam Square	7 19	7 47	8 25	8 47	9 17	9 47	1017	1047		8 47	9 17	9 47	1024	1047
Westward Ho! ..arr.	7 26	7 54	8 32	8 54	9 24	9 54	1024	1054		8 54	9 24	9 54	1031	1054

Sundays	a.m	a.m		p.m	p.m	p.m
Bideford (Omnibus Sta.) ..dep.	8 38	9 38	Then every hour until	8 38	9 38	1038
Northam Square	8 47	9 47		8 47	9 47	1047
Westward Ho! ..arr.	8 54	9 54		8 54	9 54	1054

Week Days	a.m	a.m	a.m	a.m		p.m	p.m	p.m	p.m	p.m
Westward Ho! ..dep	7 30	8 0	8 35	9 0	Then every 30 minutes until	9 0	9 30	9 56	1035	11 0
Northam Square	7 37	8 7	8 42	9 7		9 7	9 37	10 3	1042	11 7
Bideford (Omnibus Sta.) ..arr.	7 46	8 16	8 51	9 16		9 16	9 46	1012	1051	1116

Sundays	a.m	a.m		p.m	p.m	p.m
Westward Ho! ..dep.	9 0	10 0	Then every hour until	9 0	9 56	11 0
Northam Square	9 7	10 7		9 7	10 3	11 7
Bideford (Omnibus Sta.) ..arr.	9 16	1016		9 16	1012	1116

Week Days	a.m	a.m	a.m		p.m	p.m	p.m
Bideford (Omnibus Sta.) ..dep.	7 15	8 10	8 50	Then every 20 minutes until	9 30	10 5	1030
Northam	7 24	8 19	8 59		9 39	1014	1039
Appledore ..arr.	7 31	8 26	9 6		9 46	1021	1046

Sundays	a.m	a.m		p.m	p.m	p.m
Bideford (Omnibus Sta.) ..dep.	8 15	9 10	Then every 40 minutes until	9 10	10 5	1030
Northam	8 24	9 19		9 19	1014	1039
Appledore ..arr.	8 31	9 26		9 26	1021	1046

Week Days	a.m	a.m	a.m		p.m	p.m	p.m	p.m
Appledore ..dep.	7 35	8 30	9 10	Then every 20 minutes until	9 30	9 48	1023	1047
Northam	7 42	8 37	9 17		9 37	9 55	1030	1054
Bideford (Omnibus Sta.) ..arr.	7 51	8 46	9 26		9 46	10 4	1039	11 3

Sundays	a.m	a.m		p.m	p.m	p.m
Appledore ..dep.	8 35	9 30	Then every 40 minutes until	9 30	1023	1047
Northam	8 42	9 37		9 37	1030	1054
Bideford (Omnibus Sta.) ..arr.	8 51	9 46		9 46	1039	11 3

BARNSTAPLE and LYNTON (for LYNMOUTH).—Southern National Omnibus Co., Ltd.

	Week Days.							Sundays.	
	a.m	a.m	a.m	p.m	p.m	p.m	S O	a.m	p.m
Junction Station Barnstaple ..dep.	5 50	7 40	1110	2 15	4 35	6 40	7 40	1025	5 10
" ¶ .. "	5 54	7 44	1114	2 19	4 39	6 44	7 44	1029	5 14
Chelfham Cross	6 10	8 0	1130	2 35	4 55	7 0	8 0	1045	5 30
Bratton Fleming	6 20	8 10	1140	2 45	5 5	7 10	8 10	1055	5 40
Blackmoor Gate	6 40	8 30	12 0	3 5	5 25	7 30	8 30	1115	6 0
Parracombe Village	6 48	8 38	12 8	3 13	5 33	7 38	8 38	1123	6 8
Woody Bay	6 55	8 45	1215	3 20	5 40	7 45	8 45	1130	6 15
Lynton ¶ (fr Lynmth) ar	7 14	9 4	1234	3 39	5 59	8 4	9 4	1149	6 34

	Week Days.							Sundays.		
	a.m	a.m	p.m	p.m	p.m	p.m	p.m	a.m	p.m	p.m
Lynton ¶ ..dep.	7 20	9 15	1245	2 15	3 45	6 10	8 10	8 50	1 10	6 40
Woody Bay	7 39	9 34	1 4	2 34	4 4	6 29	8 29	9 9	1 29	6 59
Parracombe Village	7 46	9 41	1 11	2 41	4 11	6 36	8 36	9 16	1 36	7 6
Blackmoor Gate	7 54	9 49	1 19	2 49	4 19	6 44	8 44	9 24	1 44	7 14
Bratton Fleming	8 14	10 9	1 39	3 9	4 39	7 4	9 4	9 44	2 4	7 34
Chelfham Cross	8 24	1019	1 49	3 19	4 49	7 14	9 14	9 54	2 14	7 44
Barnstaple ¶ ..arr.	8 40	1035	2 5	3 35	5 5	7 30	9 30	1010	2 30	8 0
" Junc. Sta. "	8 44	1039	2 9	3 39	5 9	7 34	9 34	1014	2 34	8 4

S O Saturdays only. ¶ Omnibus Station.

YEOVIL JUNCTION and YEOVIL

Miles	Down	Week Days																						
		MX	a.m	a.m	a.m		a.m	a.m	a.m	a.m	a.m		p.m	p.m	p.m		p.m	p.m	p.m		p.m	p.m	p.m
	Yeovil Junction....dep	4 12	5 18	7 36	8 7	..	8 41	9 12	9 43	1030	1115	..	1212	1252	1 0	..	1 42	2 10	2 48	..	3 50	4 35	5 12
1¾	Yeovil (Town).......arr	4 17	5 23	7 40	8 11	..	8 45	9 16	9 47	1034	1119	..	1216	1257	1 4	..	1 46	2 14	2 52	..	3 54	4 39	5 16

Down	Week Days—continued									Sundays												
	p.m	p.m	p.m	p.m	p.m	p.m	p.m	p.m		a.m	a.m		p.m	p.m	p.m	p.m	p.m	p.m	p.m	p.m	p.m	
Yeovil Junction........ dep	6 5	6 36	7 14	7 53	8 35	9 0	9 42	1154	..	4 19	5 53	..	1245	1 10	2 30	3A6	5 5	6 16	7 3	9 3	1120	..
Yeovil (Town)........... arr	6 9	6 40	7 18	7 57	8 39	9 4	9 46	1159	..	4 24	5 58	..	1250	1 14	2 34	3A10	5 9	6 20	7 7	9 8	1125	..

Miles	Up	Week Days																						
		a.m	a.m	a.m		a.m	a.m	a.m	a.m		a.m	a.m	a.m		p.m	p.m	p.m	p.m		p.m	p.m	p.m	p.m
	Yeovil (Town)....... dep	6 25	6 30	7 10	..	7 55	8 24	8 55	9 28	..	1015	11 0	1155	..	1246	1 30	1 50	2 36	..	3 30	4 5	4 19	4 55
1¾	Yeovil Junction.... arr	6 30	6 35	7 15	..	7 59	8 28	8 59	9 32	..	1019	11 4	1159	..	1250	1 34	1 54	2 40	..	3 34	4 10	4 23	4 59

Up	Week Days—continued									Sundays												
	p.m	p.m	p.m		p.m	p.m	p.m	p.m		a.m	a.m	a.m		p.m	p.m	p.m	p.m	p.m	p.m	p.m	p.m	
Yeovil (Town).......... dep	5 52	6 15	7 0	..	7 40	8 15	8 45	9 22	..	7 0	1015	1140	..	1253	2 20	2B45	3 25	4 55	6 0	6 48	7 15	..
Yeovil Junction........ arr	5 56	6 19	7 4	..	7 44	8 19	8 49	9 26	..	7 5	1020	1145	..	1257	2 24	2B49	3 30	4 59	6 4	6 52	7 20	..

A 10 mins. later until 26th October, 1947   B 15 mins. later until 26th October, 1947   MX Mondays excepted

CHARD JUNCTION and CHARD

Miles	Down	Week Days only														
		a.m	a.m		p.m		SO		p.m		p.m		p.m	p.m	SO
	Chard Junction ..dep	8 28	1056	..	1 10	..	3 5	..	4 55	..	5 50	..	7 7	9 10	9 50
3¼	Chard............arr	8 37	11 6	..	1 20	..	3 14	..	5 4	..	5 59	..	7 16	9 19	9 58

Miles	Up	Week Days only														
		a.m	a.m		p.m		SO		p.m		p.m	p.m		p.m	SO
	Chard............dep	8 10	9 34	..	1210	..	1 52	..	4 20	..	5 36	6 4	..	8 43	9 32
3¼	Chard Junction .. arr	8 18	9 42	..	1218	..	2 0	..	4 28	..	5 44	6 12	..	8 51	9 40

SO Saturdays only

AXMINSTER and LYME REGIS

Miles	Down	Week Days															Sundays						
		a.m	a.m		p.m	p.m	p.m	p.m		p.m	p.m	p.m		p.m	K		a.m		p.m		p.m		p.m
	Axminster......... dep	8 35	1043	..	12 2	1257	1 53	2 50	..	4 40	5 38	6 50	..	8 55	9J45	..	1111	..	1240	..	3 10	..	4 20
4¼	Combpyne..............	8 47	1055	..	1214	1 9	2 5	3 3	..	4 52	5 50	7 2	..	9 7	..	..	1123	..	1252	..	3 22	..	4 32
6¾	Lyme Regis .... arr	8 56	11 4	..	1223	1 18	2 14	3 11	..	5 1	5 59	7 11	..	9 16	10J11	..	1132	..	1 1	..	3 31	..	4 41

Miles	Up	Week Days																Sundays						
		a.m	a.m	a.m	a.m		p.m		p.m	p.m	p.m		p.m	p.m	p.m		a.m		a.m		p.m		p.m
	Lyme Regis.........dep	7J20	8 4	10 0	1134	..	1229	..	1 24	2 19	3 55	..	5 10	6 5	8 20	..	1040	..	1137	..	2 35	..	3 50
2½	Combpyne..............	..	8 12	10 8	1142	..	1237	..	1 32	2 27	4 3	..	5 18	6 13	8 28	..	1048	..	1145	..	2 43	..	3 58
6¾	Axminster 340, 347..arr	7J49	8 25	10 21	1155	..	1250	..	1 45	2 41	4 16	..	5 31	6 26	8 41	..	11 1	..	1158	..	2 56	..	4 11

J By Southern National Omnibus. Times subject to alteration.   K Fridays and Saturdays

SEATON JUNCTION and SEATON

Miles	Down	Week Days																							
		a.m	a.m		a.m	a.m		p.m		p.m		p.m		p.m		p.m	p.m		p.m		p.m	p.m	
	Seaton Junction....dep	8 5	8 45	..	9 36	1040	..	12 12	..	1250	..	1 50	..	3 15	..	4 45	5 36	..	6 55	..	8 44	9 43	..
1¼	Colyton.................	8 9	8 49	..	9 40	1044	..	12 16	..	1254	..	1 54	..	3 19	..	4 49	5 40	..	6 59	..	8 48	9 47	..
2½	Colyford................	8 12	8 52	..	9 43	1047	..	12 19	..	1258	..	1 57	..	3 22	..	4 52	5 43	..	7 2	..	8 51	9 50	..
4¼	Seaton ....arr	8 17	8 57	..	9 48	1052	..	12 24	..	1 5	..	2 2	..	3 27	..	4 57	5 51	..	7 10	..	8 59	9 58	..

Miles	Up	Week Days																								
		a.m	a.m		a.m		a.m		a.m		p.m		p.m	p.m		p.m		p.m	p.m		p.m	p.m	
	Seaton.............. dep	7 46	8 23	..	9 5	..	10 5	..	1145	..	1228	..	1 20	2F35	..	3 55	..	5 5	6 5	..	8 15	9 3	..
1¾	Colyford.................	7 50	8 27	..	9 9	..	10 9	..	1149	..	1232	..	1 25	2F39	..	3 59	..	5 9	6 10	..	8 20	9 8	..
2¾	Colyton........ .... [347	7 54	8 31	..	9 13	..	10 13	..	1153	..	1236	..	1 30	2F43	..	4 3	..	5 14	6 16	..	8 26	9 14	..
4¼	Seaton Junct. 340,.. arr	7 59	8 36	..	9 18	..	10 18	..	1158	..	1241	..	1 35	2F48	..	4 8	..	5 21	6 21	..	8 31	9 19	..

Down	Sundays								Up	Sundays						
	a.m		p.m		p.m		p.m			a.m		a.m		p.m		p.m
Seaton Junction........dep	1118	..	12 5	..	3H15	..	4 10	..	Seaton.................. dep	11 0	..	1138	..	2 45	..	3A35
Colyton....................	1122	..	12 9	..	3H19	..	4 14	..	Colyford..................	11 4	..	1142	..	2 49	..	3A39
Colyford..................	1125	..	1212	..	3H22	..	4 17	..	Colyton....................	11 8	..	1146	..	2 53	..	3A43
Seaton................. arr	1130	..	1217	..	3H27	..	4 22	..	Seaton Junction 340, 347 arr	1113	..	1151	..	2 58	..	3A48

A 10 mins. later until 26th October, 1947   F 10 mins. later until 27th October, 1947
H 5 mins. later until 26th October, 1947

SIDMOUTH JUNCTION, SIDMOUTH, and EXMOUTH

Miles	Down — Week Days	a.m	a.m		a.m	a.m		a.m	a.m	a.m	a.m		p.m	T	V	p.m		p.m	p.m		p.m		p.m		p.m U	
	Sidmouth Junction .dep	6 36	..	..	8 4	8 30	..	..	9 25	..	1112	..	1 12	2 25	3 22	4 0	..	5 18	6 35	..	8 30	..	9 55	..	..	..
2¼	Ottery St. Mary	6 37	..	..	8 11	8 36	..	..	9 30	..	1118	..	1 17	2 30	3 27	4 5	..	5 23	6 40	..	8 35	..	10 0	..	..	..
5	Tipton St. John's ... arr	6 42	..	..	8 16	8 41	..	..	9 36	..	1123	..	1 22	2 35	3 32	4 10	..	5 28	6 45	..	8 40	..	10 5	..	..	..
—	Tipton St. John's .. dep	6 43	..	..	8 17	8 43	..	..	9 40	1036	1125	..	1 23	2 37	3 34	4 11	..	5 29	6 47	..	8 44	..	10 6	..	..	..
8¼	Sidmouth .... arr	6 53	..	..	8 26	8 52	..	..	9 48	1044	1135	..	1 32	2 48	3 43	4 20	..	5 38	6 58	..	8 52	..	1015	..	..	..
—	Tipton St. John's .... dep	..	7 40	..	..	..	..	9 10	9 42	..	1130	..	1 36	2 50	..	4 45	..	..	6 55	..	8 53	..	..	..	1012	..
6½	Newton Poppleford	..	7 43	..	..	..	..	9 13	9 46	..	1134	..	1 38	2 52	..	4 48	..	..	6 58	..	8 56	..	..	..	1015	..
9¼	East Budleigh	..	7 48	..	..	..	..	9 18	9 52	..	1139	..	1 44	2 58	..	4 52	..	..	7 3	..	9 2	..	..	..	1021	..
11½	Budleigh Salterton arr	..	7 53	..	..	..	..	9 23	9 58	..	1144	..	1 50	3 3	..	4 57	..	..	7 8	..	9 8	..	..	..	1027	..
	Budleigh Salterton dep	..	7 54	..	..	..	..	9 24	10 3	..	1145	..	1 51	3 4	..	4 58	..	..	7 9	..	9 9	..	..	..	1028	..
14½	Littleham	..	8 2	..	..	..	..	9 32	10 14	..	1151	..	1 58	3 12	..	5 6	..	..	7 17	..	9 16	..	..	..	1035	..
16½	Exmouth 357 .... arr	..	8 7	..	..	..	..	9 37	10 19	..	1156	..	2 3	3 17	..	5 11	..	..	7 22	..	9 21	..	..	..	1040	..

Miles	Up — Week Days	a.m	a.m	a.m		T		a.m		p.m		p.m	p.m	p.m	p.m	p.m		p.m	p.m		p.m	p.m		U	p.m	
	Exmouth .... dep	6 55	8 9	..	..	9 50	..	..	..	1210	..	..	..	2 5	..	4 5	..	..	6 20	..	..	8 14	..	9 35	..	..
1½	Littleham	6 59	8 14	..	..	9 54	..	..	..	1214	..	..	..	2 9	..	4 10	..	..	6 24	..	..	8 18	..	9 39	..	..
4½	Budleigh Salterton arr	7 6	8 22	..	..	10 3	..	..	..	1221	..	..	..	2 16	..	4 17	..	..	6 31	..	..	8 25	..	9 46	..	..
	Budleigh Salterton dep	7 7	8 23	..	..	10 4	..	..	..	1222	..	..	..	2 17	..	4 18	..	..	6 32	..	..	8 26	..	9 47	..	..
7	East Budleigh	7 12	8 27	..	..	10 8	..	..	..	1226	..	..	..	2 20	..	4 23	..	..	6 35	..	..	8 31	..	9 50	..	..
10	Newton Poppleford	7 18	8 33	..	..	1014	..	..	..	1233	..	..	..	2 26	..	4 29	..	..	6 41	..	..	8 37	..	9 56	..	..
11½	Tipton St. John's ... arr	7 22	8 37	..	..	1019	..	..	..	1237	..	..	..	2 30	..	4 34	..	..	6 45	..	..	8 42	..	10 0	..	..
—	Mls — Sidmouth ...... dep	7 20	8 35	9 30	..	1020	..	1114	..	1234	..	1 16	1 35	..	3 24	4 36	..	5 45	..	..	7 45	9 25	..	..	1025	..
—	3½ Tipton St. John's arr	7 27	8 42	9 37	..	1028	..	1121	..	1242	..	1 23	1 42	..	3 31	4 43	..	5 52	..	..	7 52	9 32	..	..	1032	..
—	Tipton St. John's .... dep	7 28	8 43	9 39	..	1030	..	..	..	1244	..	..	1 43	..	3 32	4 45	..	5 53	..	..	7 53	9 33	..	..	1033	..
13½	Ottery St. Mary	7 33	8 49	9 44	..	1036	..	..	..	1250	..	..	1 48	..	3 37	4 50	..	5 58	..	..	7 58	9 38	..	..	1038	..
16½	Sidmouth Jn 340, 347 arr	7 41	8 57	9 52	..	1045	..	..	..	1258	..	..	1 56	.	3 45	4 58	..	6 6	..	..	8 6	9 46	..	..	1046	..

Down — Sundays	a.m			a.m			p.m			Z			
Sidmouth Junction .dep	1028	..	..	1150	..	..	2 43	..	..	3 22	..	..	..
Ottery St. Mary	1035	..	..	1155	..	..	2 48	..	..	3 27	..	..	..
Tipton St. John's ... arr	1040	..	..	12 0	..	..	2 53	..	..	3 32	..	..	..
Tipton St. John's .. dep	1041	..	..	12 1	..	..	2 55	..	..	3 33	..	..	..
Sidmouth .... arr	1050	..	..	1210	..	..	3 5	..	..	3 43	..	..	..
Tipton St. John's .... dep	..	..	..	..	..	..	..	..	..	..	..	..	..
Newton Poppleford	..	..	..	..	..	..	..	..	..	..	..	..	..
East Budleigh	..	..	..	..	..	..	..	..	..	..	..	..	..
Budleigh Salterton arr	..	..	..	..	..	..	..	..	..	..	..	..	..
Budleigh Salterton dep	..	..	..	..	..	..	..	..	..	..	..	..	..
Littleham	..	..	..	..	..	..	..	..	..	..	..	..	..
Exmouth 357 .... arr	..	..	..	..	..	..	..	..	..	..	..	..	..

Up — Sundays	a.m			p.m Z			p.m			p.m				
Exmouth .... dep	..	..	..	..	..	..	..	..	..	..	..	..	..	..
Littleham	..	..	..	..	..	..	..	..	..	..	..	..	..	..
Budleigh Salterton arr	..	..	..	..	..	..	..	..	..	..	..	..	..	..
Budleigh Salterton dep	..	..	..	..	..	..	..	..	..	..	..	..	..	..
East Budleigh	..	..	..	..	..	..	..	..	..	..	..	..	..	..
Newton Poppleford	..	..	..	..	..	..	..	..	..	..	..	..	..	..
Tipton St. John's ... arr	..	..	..	..	..	..	..	..	..	..	..	..	..	..
Sidmouth .... dep	11 8	..	..	1 35	..	..	2 11	..	..	3 13	..	..	..	..
Tipton St. John's .. arr	1115	..	..	1 42	..	..	2 18	..	..	3 20	..	..	..	..
Tipton St. John's ... dep	1116	..	..	1 43	..	..	2 19	..	..	3 21	..	..	..	..
Ottery St. Mary	1121	..	..	1 47	..	..	2 24	..	..	3 26	..	..	..	..
Sidmouth Jn 340, 347 arr	1129	..	..	1 55	..	..	2 32	..	..	3 36	..	..	..	..

T Through Carriages to or from Waterloo, see pages 340 and 347

U Tues., Weds., Thurs. and Fris.

V Runs until 27th October, 1947

Z Runs until 26th October, 1947

LONDON, SALISBURY, AMESBURY, and BULFORD

Miles	Down — Week Days only	a.m		a.m	a.m		p.m	p.m		p.m	p.m	
	340 London (W.) ..... dep	5L40	..	9 0	10 50	..	1250	3L30	..	6 0	7L30	..
	Salisbury .... dep	8 55	..	11 10	1 8	..	2 56	5 43	..	7 55	9 55	..
5½	Porton	9 4	..	11 20	1 17	..	3 5	5 54	..	8 5	10 4	..
6	Idmiston Halt	9 6	..	11 22	1 19	..	3 7	5 56	..	8 7	10 6	..
9½	Newton Tony	9 14	..	11 30	1 27	..	3 15	6 4	..	8 15	10 14	..
12¾	Amesbury	9 23	..	11 39	1 36	..	3 24	6 13	..	8 24	10 23	..
14	Bulford .... arr	9 28	..	11 45	1 43	..	3 30	6 19	..	8 30	10 29	..

Miles	Up — Week Days only	a.m	a.m		a.m		p.m		p.m	p.m		p.m	
	Bulford .... dep	7 50	9 40	..	11 52	..	1 51	..	3 55	6 26	..	8 38	..
1¼	Amesbury	7 55	9 44	..	11 56	..	1 56	..	4 0	6 30	..	8 42	..
4½	Newton Tony	8 4	9 53	..	12 5	..	2 5	..	4 9	6 39	..	8 51	..
8	Idmiston Halt	8 13	10 1	..	12 13	..	2 13	..	4 17	6 47	..	8 59	..
8½	Porton 347	8 15	10 4	..	12 16	..	2 16	..	4 20	6 49	..	9 2	..
14	Salisbury 340, 347 ... arr	8 26	1013	..	12 25	..	2 25	..	4 29	6 58	..	9 13	..
81½	347 London (W.) .... arr	11L13	..	..	2 29	..	4 41	..	6 40	1026	..	12B36	..

B Except Sat. night. Via Porton. L Via Porton.

OTHER TRAINS between Porton and Salisbury, see page 340

EXETER, TOPSHAM, and EXMOUTH

Down — Week Days

Miles	Down	am	am	am	am	am	a.m	a.m	p.m	pm	pm	S O	S X	pm	pm	pm	pm	pm	p.m	p.m	p.m	p.m
	Exeter (Central) ...... dep	645	715	815	845	915	9 50	1140	12 45	135	245	3 45	4 0	445	515	545	615	645	7 45	9 15	1915	11 0
½	St. James' Park Halt.....	..	717	..	..	..	9 54	1142	..	..	..	3 47	4 2	..	..	547	..	..	7 47	..	..	..
1½	Polsloe Bridge Halt	..	721	819	851	922	9 58	1146	12 49	140	250	3 51	4 6	449	520	551	620	650	7 51	9 20	1020	11 5
3½	Clyst St. Mary & Digby Halt	..	..	..	..	..	10 2	..	12SO53	..	254	..	..	..	524	..	..	..	..	..	1025	1112
5½	Topsham	656	728	826	858	930	10 7	1154	12 58	147	259	3 58	4 13	457	529	559	630	7 0	7 58	9 28	1030	1117
7	Woodbury Road............	7 0	732	830	9 2	935	1011	1158	1 2	151	3 3	4 2	4 17	5 1	533	6 3	..	7 4	8 2	9 32	1034	1121
8½	Lympstone..............	7 5	737	834	9 6	939	1015	12 2	1 6	155	3 7	4 6	4 21	5 5	538	6 8	..	7 9	8 7	9 37	1040	1123
10½	Exmouth 356 .... arr	710	742	839	911	944	1020	12 7	1 11	2 0	312	4 11	4 26	510	543	613	641	714	8 12	9 43	1046	1134

Down — Sundays

Down	a.m	p.m	p.m	p.m	p.m	p.m	p.m	p.m	p.m	p.m	p.m
Exeter (Central) ...... dep	1010	1245	2 15	3 0	3 45	5 15	6 15	8 25	9 15	9 35	11 0
St. James' Park Halt.....	1012	1247	2 17	3 2	3 47	..	6 20	..	..	..	..
Polsloe Bridge Halt	1016	1251	2 22	3 6	3 51	5 19	6 24	8 30	9 20	9 39	11 4
Clyst St. Mary & Digby Halt	..	..	..	3 10	3 55	..	6 28	..	..	9 44	1110
Topsham	1023	1258	2 30	3 15	4 0	5 26	6 33	8 37	9 27	9 49	1115
Woodbury Road............	1027	1 2	2 34	3 18	4 4	5 29	6 36	8 42	9 31	9 54	1121
Lympstone..............	1031	1 6	2 39	3 22	4 8	5 34	6 40	8 46	9 35	9 58	1126
Exmouth 356.......... arr	1036	1 11	2 44	3 27	4 14	5 39	6 45	8 51	9 41	10 3	1132

Up — Week Days

Miles	Up	am	am	am	am	am	am	a.m	a.m	p.m	p.m	pm	pm	S O	S X	pm	pm	pm	pm	pm	pm	p.m	p.m
	Exmouth .... dep	640	715	745	810	845	918	9 50	1045	1215	1 30	245	345	4 20	4 40	515	545	615	645	715	845	9 45	1055
2	Lympstone..............	645	719	752	815	849	922	9 56	1049	1219	1 35	249	349	4 24	4 44	519	549	619	651	721	849	9 51	11 0
3½	Woodbury Road............	649	723	756	819	853	926	10 0	1053	1223	1 39	253	353	4 28	4 49	523	553	623	655	725	853	9 55	11 4
5	Topsham	655	727	8 0	823	857	930	10 5	1057	1228	1 45	257	357	4 36	4 54	527	558	628	659	730	858	10 0	1110
7½	Clyst St. Mary & Digby Halt	..	733	8 6	..	..	..	..	..	..	..	3 3	..	..	..	..	..	634	..	..	..	..	1118
9	Polsloe Bridge Halt	7 3	738	811	833	9 5	940	1015	11 5	1236	1 54	3 8	4 7	4 46	5 3	536	6 8	642	710	740	9 9	1010	1124
10	St. James' Park Halt.....	..	742	..	..	..	..	..	..	..	..	312	..	4 50	5 7	..	..	..	715	..	..	1014	..
10½	Exeter D 340. 347...... arr	7 8	744	816	838	910	945	1020	1110	1241	1 59	314	412	4 52	5 9	541	613	648	718	745	914	1016	1130

Up — Sundays

Up	a.m	a.m	p.m	p.m	p.m	p.m	p.m	p.m	p.m	p.m	p.m
Exmouth .... dep	9 30	11 0	1215	1 45	2 55	4 15	5 45	6 15	7 45	9 0	1010
Lympstone..............	9 24	11 4	1219	1 49	2 59	4 19	5 49	6 19	7 49	9 4	1014
Woodbury Road............	9 38	11 7	1223	1 52	3 3	4 23	5 52	6 23	7 52	9 8	1018
Topsham	9 42	1111	1227	1 56	3 7	4 31	5 56	6 28	7 56	9 12	1022
Clyst St. Mary & Digby Halt	..	..	..	2 1	..	4 37	..	6 34	..	..	1028
Polsloe Bridge Halt	9 51	1121	1235	2 6	3 15	4 43	6 4	6 40	8 5	9 21	1033
St. James' Park Halt.....	9 54	1124	..	2 9	..	4 46	6 7	..	..	..	..
Exeter D 340, 347...... arr	9 57	1127	1240	2 12	3 20	4 49	6 10	6 45	8 10	9 26	1039

D Central
SO or **S0** Saturdays only
SX Saturdays excepted

OTHER TRAINS between Exeter and St. James' Park Halt, see page 347.

BERE ALSTON and CALLINGTON

Down

Miles	Down	Week Days a.m	a.m	p.m SO	p.m Z	a.m	a.m	p.m	p.m SO	Sundays a.m	p.m	a.m	p.m
	340 London (W.)... dep	1 25	..	..	..	9 0	1050	1250	2 50	..	..	11V0	4 0
—	Bere Alston........dep	8 24	1050	1 0	2 16	3 22	5 22	7 10	10 5	9 26	1224	7 21	1020
1¾	Calstock	8 30	1056	1 6	2 22	3 28	5 28	7 16	1011	9 32	1230	7 27	1026
4¼	Gunnislake	8 45	1111	1 19	2 36	3 42	5 42	7 30	1025	9 46	1244	7 41	1040
5¾	Chilsworthy............	8 52	1118	1 27	..	3 47	5 48	7 37	1032	9 51	1249	7 46	1045
6¾	Latchley	8 56	1122	1 32	..	3 52	5 53	7 43	1037	9 56	1254	7 50	1050
7¾	Luckett	9 1	1127	1 37	..	3 57	5 58	7 49	1042	10 1	1259	7 55	1055
9½	Callington G...... arr	9 8	1134	1 44	..	4 4	6 5	7 57	1049	10 8	1 6	8 2	11 2

Up

Miles	Up	Week Days a.m	a.m	p.m	p.m Z	p.m	p.m	p.m SO	Sundays a.m	a.m	p.m	p.m
	Callington G....... dep	7 18	9 47	1 0	..	4 23	6 22	9 5	8 15	1130	6 30	9 10
1¾	Luckett	7 24	9 53	1 6	..	4 29	6 28	9 11	8 21	1136	6 36	9 16
3	Latchley	7 29	9 58	1 11	..	4 33	6 33	9 16	8 26	1141	6 41	9 21
4	Chilsworthy............	7 34	10 3	1 16	..	4 38	6 38	9 21	8 31	1145	6 45	9 26
5	Gunnislake	7 38	10 7	1 20	2 42	4 42	6 42	9 25	8 35	1149	6 49	9 30
7¾	Calstock	7 52	1021	1 34	2 54	4 55	6 55	9 40	8 48	12 2	7 2	9 43
9½	Bere Alston 341.....arr	8 1	1030	1 42	3 6	5 6	7 3	9 48	8 57	1211	7 10	9 51
229¾	347 London (W.)....arr	2 29	4 41	10 27	1027	3U55	..	..	3 44	8 39	..	..

G Station for Stoke Climsland (1 mile) Omnibus services, operated by the Western National Omnibus Company, run between Callington Station and Callington Village, also Callington Station and Stoke Climsland **SO** Sats. only **U** Morning time **V** Passengers can dep. 12 0 noon by Pullman Car Train until 26th October, 1947. Supplementary fees charged. **Z** Wednesdays, Thursdays, and Saturdays

HALWILL, HATHERLEIGH, and TORRINGTON

Week Days only

Miles		a.m	a.m		p.m	p.m	p.m		
	Halwill .... dep	..	1040	..	SO	SX	6 40	..	..
2¾	Hole	..	1049	..	..	..	6 49	..	..
7¾	Hatherleigh	..	11 7	..	..	..	7 7	..	..
9¾	Meeth Halt	..	1120	..	..	..	7 18	..	..
12½	Petrockstow	8 8	1130	..	1 5	5 6	7 28	..	..
14¾	Dunsbear Halt	8 17	1139	..	1 14	5 9	7 38	..	..
16	Yarde Halt	8 23	1145	..	1 21	5 15	7 44	..	..
18¾	Watergate Halt	8 37	1158	..	1 35	5 29	7 58	..	..
20½	Torrington 346 ..... arr	8 45	12 6	..	1 43	5 37	8 6	..	..

Week Days only

Miles		a.m		a.m		p.m		
	Torrington .... dep	6 25	..	9 0	..	4 22	..	..
1¾	Watergate Halt	6 32	..	9 7	..	4 29	..	..
4½	Yarde Halt	6 46	..	9 21	..	4 43	..	..
5¾	Dunsbear Halt	6 52	..	9 26	..	4 48	..	..
8	Petrockstow	7 4	..	9 36	..	4 58	..	..
10¾	Meeth Halt	..	..	9 46	..	5 8	..	..
12¾	Hatherleigh	..	..	9 56	..	5 18	..	..
17¾	Hole	..	..	1016	..	5 38	..	..
20½	Halwill C 341, 346 ... arr	..	..	1026	..	5 48	..	..

C Station or Beaworthy. SO Saturdays only. SX Saturdays excepted.

BODMIN, WADEBRIDGE, and PADSTOW

Week Days only

Miles		a.m		a.m		a.m		a.m		p.m		p.m		p.m		p.m		p.m		p.m		p.m	
	Bodmin .... dep	7 22	..	..	..	9 0	..	11 28	..	..	..	2 0	..	4 23	..	5 36	..	6 43	..	..	..	8 50	..
1½	Dunmere Halt	7 25	..	..	..	9 3		11 31	..	..	..	2 4	..	4 26	..	5 39	..	6 46	..	..	..	8 53	..
2¼	Nanstallon Halt	7 28	..	..	..	9 6	..	11 34	..	..	..	2 8	..	4 29	..	5 42	..	6 49	..	..	..	8 56	..
3¾	Grogley Halt	7 33	..	..	..	9 11	..	11 39	..	..	..	2 13	..	4 34	..	5 47	..	6 54	..	..	..	9 1	..
6¾	Wadebridge 346 .. arr	7 41	..	..	..	9 19	..	11 47	..	..	..	2 23	..	4 42	..	5 55	..	7 2	..	..	..	9 9	..
	Wadebridge 346 .. dep	7 43	..	8 50	..	9 50	..	12 0	..	1 45	..	2 30	..	4 43	..	6 11	..	7 4	..	7 46	..	9 10	..
12¼	Padstow .... arr	7 52	..	8 59	..	10 4	..	12 10	..	1 59	..	2 40	..	4 53	..	6 21	..	7 19	..	7 56	..	9 20	..

Week Days only

Miles		a.m	a.m		a.m	a.m	a.m		p.m	p.m	p.m		SO		p.m		p.m		p.m		p.m	p.m	
	Padstow .... dep	..	7 57	..	8 25	9 10	1135	..	..	1 0	2 55	..	3 15	..	4 58	..	6 0	..	8 2	..	8 40	9 30	..
5½	Wadebridge ...... arr	..	8 6	..	8 34	9 19	1149	..	..	1 9	3 4	..	3 24	..	5 7	..	6 9	..	8 11	..	8 54	9 39	..
	Wadebridge ...... dep	6 55	8 11	..	..	9 46	..	..	1242	..	3 14	..	..	..	5 10	..	6 10	..	8 13	..	..	..	..
8½	Grogley Halt	7 2	8 18	..	..	9 53	..	..	1252	..	3 21	..	..	..	5 17	..	6 17	..	8 20	..	..	..	..
10	Nanstallon Halt	7 7	8 23	..	..	9 58	..	..	1258	..	3 26	..	..	..	5 22	..	6 22	..	8 25	..	..	..	..
10¾	Dunmere Halt	7 10	8 28	..	..	10 1	..	..	1 2	..	3 31	..	..	..	5 25	..	6 25	..	8 28	..	..	..	..
12¼	Bodmin D .... arr	7 15	8 34	..	..	10 6	..	..	1 6	..	3 37	..	..	..	5 30	..	6 30	..	8 33	..	..	..	..

D 1 mile to Great Western Station. SO Saturdays only

PLYMOUTH, PLYMSTOCK, and TURNCHAPEL

3–All Trains are Third class only

Week Days only

Miles		a.m	a.m		a.m		a.m		a.m	a.m		a.m	a.m		a.m		a.m		p.m		p.m		p.m
	Plymouth (Friary) .. dep	5 35	6 18	..	6 48	..	7 0	..	7 28	8 17	..	8 48	8 53	..	1033	..	1040	..	1215	..	1248	..	1 14
½	Lucas Terrace Halt	5 37	6 19	..	6 49	..	7 2	..	7 29	8 18	..	8 49	8 55	..	1035	..	1041	..	1216	..	1249	..	1 16
1½	Plymstock	5 42	6 23	..	6 53	..	7 6	..	7 33	8 22	..	8 53	8 59	..	1039	..	1045	..	1220	..	1253	..	1 20
2	Oreston	5 44	6 25	..	6 55	..	..	..	7 35	8 24	..	8 55	..	..	..	..	1047	..	1222	..	1255	..	..
2½	Turnchapel .... arr	5 47	6 28	..	6 58	..	..	..	7 38	8 27	..	8 58	..	..	..	..	1050	..	1225	..	1258	..	..

Week Days only—*continued*

	p.m	p.m		p.m	p.m		p.m	p.m		p.m	p.m		p.m		p.m		p.m	p.m	SO	p.m		
Plymouth (Friary) ...... dep	1 26	2 5	..	2 50	4 22	..	4 57	5 20	..	5 39	6 30	..	6 40	..	7 30	..	8 30	9 9	9 45	1015	..	..
Lucas Terrace Halt	1 27	2 6	..	2 52	4 23	..	4 58	5 22	..	5 40	6 31	..	6 42	..	7 31	..	8 31	9 10	9 47	1016	..	..
Plymstock	1 31	2 10	..	2 56	4 27	..	5 2	5 26	..	5 44	6 35	..	6 46	..	7 35	..	8 35	9 14	9 51	1020	..	..
Oreston	1 33	2 12	..	..	4 29	..	5 4	..	..	5 46	6 37	..	..	..	7 37	..	8 37	9 16	..	1022	..	..
Turnchapel .... arr	1 36	2 15	..	..	4 32	..	5 7	..	..	5 49	6 40	..	..	..	7 40	..	8 40	9 19	..	1025	..	..

Week Days only

Miles		a.m	a.m		a.m	a.m		a.m	a.m		a.m		a.m		a.m	a.m		p.m	p.m		p.m		p.m
	Turnchapel .... dep	5 55	6 33	..	7 3	7 42	..	..	8 29	..	9 3	..	..	..	11 3	..	..	1228	1 3	..	1 39	..	..
½	Oreston	5 56	6 34	..	7 4	7 43	..	..	8 30	..	9 4	..	..	..	11 4	..	..	1229	1 4	..	1 40	..	..
1	Plymstock	5 59	6 37	..	7 7	7 46	..	8 2	8 33	..	9 7	..	9 50	..	11 7	1139	..	1232	1 7	..	1 43	..	2 17
2	Lucas Terrace Halt	6 2	6 40	..	7 10	7 49	..	8 5	8 36	..	9 10	..	9 53	..	1110	1142	..	1235	1 10	..	1 46	..	2 20
2½	Plymouth (Fr'ry 346 arr	6 5	6 43	..	7 13	7 52	..	8 7	8 39	..	9 13	..	9 55	..	1113	1144	..	1238	1 13	..	1 49	..	2 22

Week Days only—*continued*

	p.m		p.m	p.m		p.m	p.m		p.m		p.m		p.m	p.m		p.m	p.m		p.m		p.m	
Turnchapel .... dep	2 20	..	..	4 35	..	5 9	5 52	..	..	..	6 45	..	..	7 50	..	8 50	9 22	..	1030	..	SO	..
Oreston	2 21	..	..	4 36	..	5 10	5 53	..	..	..	6 46	..	..	7 51	..	8 51	9 23	..	1031	..	..	..
Plymstock	2 24	..	3 52	4 39	..	5 13	5 56	..	6 17	..	6 49	..	7 37	7 54	..	8 54	9 26	..	1034	..	1055	..
Lucas Terrace Halt	2 27	..	3 55	4 42	..	5 16	5 59	..	6 20	..	6 52	..	7 40	7 57	..	8 57	9 29	..	1037	..	1058	..
Plymouth (Friary) 346 ... arr	2 30	..	3 57	4 45	..	5 19	6 2	..	6 22	..	6 55	..	7 42	8 0	..	9 0	9 32	..	1040	..	11 0	..

3 Third class only SO Saturdays only.

Printed and Published by—Henry Blacklock & Co. Ltd., London, and Albert Square, Manchester, 2.

COMPLETE SERVICE between WATERLOO and GUILDFORD, see pages 394 to 426

LONDON, GODALMING, HASLEMERE, PETERSFIELD, PORTSMOUTH, and THE ISLE OF WIGHT

Miles	Miles	Down — Week Days	a.m	a.m	a.m		a.m	a.m		a.m	a.m	a.m		a.m	a.m	a.m		a.m		am	a.m	a.m	a.m	a.m	a.m R		a.m	a.m	a.m	a.m	a.m R	
		WATERLOO dep	..	..	..	..	..	..		..	..	..		..	..	..	..	5 25		..	5 55	6 25	6 55	7 25	7 45		..	7 55	..	8 25	8 45	
12		Surbiton	..	..	..	..	..	..		..	..	..		..	..	..	..	5 43		..	6 13	6 43	7 13	7 43	..		..	8 13	..	8 43	..	
14½		Esher, for Sandown Park	..	..	..	..	..	..		..	..	..		..	..	..	..	5 47		..	6 17	6 47	7 17	7 47	..		..	8 17	..	8 47	..	
16		Hersham	..	..	..	..	..	..		..	..	..		..	..	..	..	5 50		..	6 20	6 50	7 20	7 50	..		..	8 20	..	8 50	..	
17½		Walton-on-Thames	..	..	..	..	..	..		..	..	..		..	..	..	..	5 53		..	6 23	6 53	7 23	7 53	..		..	8 23	..	8 53	..	
19½		Weybridge **A**	..	..	..	..	..	..		..	..	..		..	..	..	..	5 57		..	6 27	6 57	7 27	7 57	..		..	8 27	..	8 57	..	
20½		West Weybridge	..	..	..	..	..	..		..	..	..		..	..	..	..	6 0		..	6 30	7 0	7 30	8 0	..		..	8 30	..	9 0	..	
21½		Byfleet **B**	..	..	..	..	..	..		..	..	..		..	..	..	..	6 3		..	6 33	7 3	7 33	8 3	..		..	8 33	..	9 3	..	
24½		Woking **C**	..	..	..	..	..	..		..	..	..		..	..	..	..	6 9		..	6 39	7 9	7 39	8 9	8 16		..	8 39	..	9 9	9 16	
26½		Worplesdon	..	..	..	..	..	..		..	..	..		..	..	..	..	6 15		..	6 45	7 15	7 45	8 15	..		..	8 45	..	9 15	..	
30½		Guildford 246, 390 arr	..	..	..	..	..	..		..	..	..		..	..	..	..	6 21		..	6 51	7 21	7 51	8 21	8 25		..	8 51	..	9 21	9 25	
		Guildford dep	..	..	..	..	..	..		..	..	..		..	..	..	..	6 31		..	7 1	7 31	8 1	..	8 26		8 31	9 1	..	Stop	9 26	
33½		Farncombe	..	..	..	..	..	..		..	..	..		..	..	..	..	6 36		..	7 6	7 36	8 6	..	..		8 36	9 6	..	..	..	
34½		Godalming	..	..	..	..	..	..		..	..	..		..	..	..	..	6 39		.	7 9	7 39	8 9	..	..		9 39	9 9	..	..	..	
36½		Milford	..	..	..	..	..	..		..	..	..		..	..	..	..	6 43		..	7 13	7 43	8 13	..	..		8 43	9 13	..	..	..	
38½		Witley, for Chiddingfold	..	..	..	..	..	..		..	..	..		..	..	..	..	6 48		..	7 18	7 48	8 18	..	..		8 48	9 18	..	..	..	
43		Haslemere, for Hindhead	..	..	..	..	..	..		..	..	..		..	..	..	..	6 56		..	7 26	7 56	8 26	..	8 45		8 56	9 26	..	..	9 45	
47		Liphook	..	..	..	..	..	..		..	..	..		..	..	..	..	7 2		..	7 32	8 2	8 32	..	..		9 2	9 32	..	..	..	
51½		Liss	..	..	..	..	..	..		..	..	..		..	..	..	..	7 9		..	7 39	8 9	8 39	..	..		9 9	9 39	..	..	..	
55		Petersfield 374	..	..	..	..	..	..		..	..	..		..	..	..	..	7 14		..	7 44	8 14	8 44	..	..		9 14	9 44	..	..	..	
63½		Rowlands Castle	..	..	..	..	..	..		..	..	..		..	..	..	..	7 26		..	7 56	8 26	8 56	..	..		9 26	9 56	..	..	..	
66½		Havant 196, 244	..	..	..	..	..	..		..	..	..		..	..	..	..	7 31		..	8 1	8 31	9 1	..	..		9 31	10 1	..	..	..	
71		244 Hayling Island arr	..	..	..	..	..	..		..	..	..		..	..	..	..	..		..	8 29	..	9 22	..	..		..	1032	..	..	..	
67½		Bedhampton Halt	..	..	..	..	..	..		..	..	..		Through Train from Sandown (dep. 8 23 a.m.) see page 373	..	..	..	7 33		..	8 3	8 33	9 3	..	..		9 33	10 3	..	..	..	
70½		Hilsea Halt	..	..	..	..	..	..		..	..	..			..	..	..	7 38		..	8 8	8 38	..	..	..		..	..	..	..	..	
73		Fratton 196	..	..	..	..	..	..		..	..	..			..	..	..	7 42		..	8 12	8 42	9 11	..	..		9 41	1011	..	..	..	
73½		Portsmouth & Southsea	..	..	..	..	..	..		..	..	..			..	..	..	7 45		..	8 15	8 45	9 14	..	9 20		9 44	1014	..	..	1020	
74½		Portsmouth Harbour arr	..	..	..	..	..	..		..	..	..			..	..	..	7 50		..	..	..	..	..	9 26		..	..	..	..	1026	
—	—	¶Portsmouth Harbour dp	2 50	..	..	..	..	6 0		..	..	7 40			..	..	..	8 35		..	..	..	..	..	9 40		..	..	..	..	1035	
—	—	‖Ryde Pier Head arr	3 20	..	..	..	..	6 30		..	..	8 10			..	..	..	9 5		..	..	..	..	..	1010		..	..	..	..	11 5	
—	—	Ryde, Pier Head § dep	4 5	..	..	..	..	6 58	7 5	..	7 45	8 25	8 35		..		..	9 25	9 35	..	..	..	..	..	1028	1035	..	..	..	..	1128	1135
79½	79½	" Esplanade §	4 9	..	..	..	..	7 3	7 8	..	7 49	8 27	8 38		..		..	9 28	9 38	..	..	..	..	..	1031	1038	..	..	..	..	1131	1138
80½	80½	" St. John's Road	4 13	..	6 46	..	..	7 7	7 12	..	7 53	8 31	8 42		..		..	9 32	9 42	..	..	..	..	..	1035	1042	..	..	..	..	1135	1142
—	83	Ashey	..	..	..	..	..	..	7 18	..	..	8 38	..		..	Through Train from Cowes (dep. 8 43 a.m., see page 373)	..	..	9 48	..	..	..	..	..	..	1048	..	..	..	..	..	1148
—	84½	Haven Street	..	..	..	..	..	..	7 22	..	..	8 42	..		..		..	..	9 53	..	..	..	..	..	..	1053	..	..	..	..	..	1153
—	86	Wootton	..	..	..	..	..	..	7 26	..	..	8 46	..		..		..	..	9 57	..	..	..	..	..	..	1057	..	..	..	..	..	1157
—	86¾	Whippingham	..	..	..	..	..	..	7 29	..	..	8 50	..		..		..	..	10 0	..	..	..	..	..	..	11 0	..	..	..	..	..	12 0
—	89	Newport **F** 373 arr	..	..	..	..	..	..	7 35	..	..	8 56	..		..		..	..	10 6	..	..	..	..	..	..	11 6	..	..	..	..	..	12 6
—	—	Newport dep	..	..	..	..	..	..	..	..	..	..	..	9 6	..		..	..	..	..	..	..	..	..	..	..	..	..	1110	..	..	..
—	90½	Carisbrooke Halt **G**	..	..	..	..	..	..	..	..	..	..	..	9 7	..		..	..	..	..	..	..	..	..	..	..	..	..	1114	..	..	..
—	94½	Calbourne and Shalfleet	..	..	..	..	..	..	..	..	..	..	..	9 20	..		..	..	..	..	..	..	..	..	..	..	..	..	1127	..	..	..
—	96	Ningwood	..	..	..	..	..	..	..	..	..	..	..	9 25	..		..	..	..	..	..	..	..	..	..	..	..	..	1132	..	..	..
—	99	Yarmouth 338	..	..	..	..	..	..	..	..	..	..	..	9 33	..		..	..	..	..	..	..	..	..	..	..	..	..	1140	..	..	..
—	101	Freshwater **J** arr	..	..	..	..	..	..	..	..	..	..	..	9 39	..		..	..	..	..	..	..	..	..	..	..	..	..	1146	..	..	..
—	—	Newport dep	..	6 37	..	..	7 15	..	7 38	8 12	..	8 58	..	..	9 39		..	..	1018	..	..	..	..	..	..	11 8	..	..	..	..	..	12 8
—	92¾	Mill Hill	..	6 47	..	..	7 26	..	7 46	8 21	..	9 8	..	..	9 47		..	..	1027	..	..	..	..	..	..	1117	..	..	..	..	..	1217
—	93¼	Cowes **K** arr	..	6 50	..	..	7 29	..	7 49	8 24	..	9 11	..	..	9 50		..	..	1030	..	..	..	..	..	..	1120	..	..	..	..	..	1220
83¾	—	Brading **N**	4 22	..	6 54	..	..	7 17	..	..	8 2	..	8 51	..	..		..	9 41	..	..	..	..	..	..	1043	..	..	..	..	a.m	1143	..
—	—	Brading dep	..	..	..	..	..	7 25	..	..	8 10	..	9 10	..	..		..	9 45	..	1010	..	..	..	..	1045	..	..	..	..	1110	1210	..
85½	—	St. Helens	..	..	..	..	..	7 30	..	..	8 14	..	9 14	..	..		..	9 49	..	1014	..	..	..	..	1049	..	..	..	..	1114	1214	..
86½	—	Bembridge arr	..	..	..	..	..	7 35	..	..	8 18	..	9 18	..	..		..	9 53	..	1018	..	..	..	..	1053	..	..	..	..	1118	1218	..
85½	—	Sandown 373	4 28	..	6 59	..	..	7 23	..	..	8 7	..	8 57	..	..	9 25	..	9 46	..	..	..	..	..	..	1048	..	..	..	..	..	1148	..
87½	—	Shanklin	4 36	..	7 5	.	..	7 31	..	..	8 15	..	9 5	..	..	‡34	..	9 55	..	..	..	..	..	..	1055	..	..	..	..	..	1155	..
90	—	Wroxall **O**	4 47	..	7 14	..	..	7 44	..	..	8 26	..	9 15	..	..	..	..	10 6	..	..	..	..	..	..	11 5	..	..	..	..	..	12 5	..
91½	—	Ventnor **Q** 373 arr	4 53	..	7 20	..	..	7 52	..	..	8 32	..	9 21	..	..	..	..	1012	..	..	..	..	..	..	1111	..	..	..	..	..	1211	..

Conveyance of Motor Cars, etc., to and from the Isle of Wight, see pages 501 and 502.

For Notes, see page 365; for Continuation of Trains, see pages 360 to 365

For LOCAL TRAINS and INTERMEDIATE STATIONS between WATERLOO and SURBITON and COMPLETE SERVICE between WATERLOO and GUILDFORD, see pages 394 to 426.

LONDON, GODALMING, HASLEMERE, PETERSFIELD, PORTSMOUTH, and THE ISLE OF WIGHT

Weekdays—continued

Down	a.m	a.m	a.m	p.m		a.m R	p.m	a.m	a.m	a.m			a.m R	a.m.	a.m.	a.m			a.m R	p.m	p.m.	a.m	p.m		p.m R	p.m	p.m.	p.m SX	p.m SO	p.m SO	p.m SX
WATERLOO dep	..	8 57	9 27	..		9 45	..	..	9 57	1027	..		10S045	..	10 57	1127	..		1145	..	..	11 57	1227		12 45	..	..	1257	1257	1 15	..
Surbiton	..	9 13	9 43	..		..	..	..	1013	1043	..		..	..	11 13	1143	..		..	..	..	12 13	1243		..	..	..	1 13	1 13	R	
Esher, for Sandown Park	..	9 17	9 47	..		..	..	..	1017	1047	..		..	..	11 17	1147	..		..	..	..	12 17	1247		..	..	..	1 17	1 17	..	
Hersham	..	9 20	9 50	..		..	..	..	1020	1050	..		..	..	11 20	1150	..		..	..	..	12 20	1250		..	..	..	1 20	1 20	..	Saturdays excepted
Walton-on-Thames	..	9 23	9 53	..		..	..	..	1023	1053	..		..	..	11 23	1153	..		..	..	..	12 23	1253		..	..	..	1 23	1 23	..	
Weybridge A	..	9 27	9 57	..		..	..	..	1027	1057	..		..	..	11 27	1157	..		..	..	..	12 27	1257		..	..	..	1 27	1 27	..	
West Weybridge	..	9 30	10 0	..		..	..	..	1030	11 0	..		..	..	11 30	12 0	..		..	..	..	12 30	1 0		..	..	..	1 30	1 30	..	
Byfleet B	..	9 33	10 3	..		..	..	..	1033	11 3	..		..	..	11 33	12 3	..		..	..	..	12 33	1 3		..	..	..	1 33	1 33	..	
Woking C	..	9 39	10 9	..		1016	..	..	1039	11 9	..		11S016	..	11 39	12 9	..		1216	..	..	12 39	1 9		1 16	..	..	1 39	1 39	1 46	
Worplesdon	..	9 45	1015	..		..	..	..	1045	1115	..		..	..	11 45	1215	..		..	..	..	12 45	1 15		..	..	..	1 45	1 45	..	
Guildford 246, 390 arr	..	9 51	1021	..		1025	..	..	1051	1121	..		11S025	..	11 51	1221	..		1225	..	..	12 51	1 21		1 25	..	..	1 51	1 51	1 55	
Guildford 246, 390 dep	9 31	10 1	Stop	..		1026	..	1031	11 1	..	..		11S026	11 31	12 1	Stop	..		1226	..	12 31	1 1	Stop		1 26	..	1 31	Saturdays excepted	1 52	1 56	2 1
Farncombe	9 36	10 6		..		..	..	1036	11 6	..	..		..	11 36	12 6		..		..	..	12 36	1 6			..	..	1 36		..	2 1	2 6
Godalming	9 39	10 9	..	..		..	..	1039	11 9	..	..		..	11 39	12 9	..	..		..	..	12 39	1 9	..		..	..	1 39		1 59	2 4	2 9
Milford	9 43	1013	..	..		..	..	1043	1113	..	..		..	11 43	12 13	..	..		..	..	12 43	1 13	..		..	..	1 43		..	2 8	2 13
Witley, for Chiddingfold	9 48	1018	..	..		..	..	1048	1118	..	..		..	11 48	12 18	..	..		..	..	12 48	1 18	..		..	..	1 48		..	2 13	2 18
Haslemere, for Hindhead	9 56	1026	..	..		1045	..	1056	1126	..	..		11S045	11 56	12 26	..	..		1245	..	12 56	1 26	..		1 45	..	1 56		2 11	2 21	2 26
Liphook	10 2	1032	..	..		..	..	11 2	1132	..	..		..	12 2	12 32	..	..		..	..	1 2	1 32	..		..	..	2 2		Saturdays only	..	2 32
Liss	10 9	1039	..	..		..	..	11 9	1139	..	..		..	12 9	12 39	..	..		..	..	1 9	1 39	..		..	..	2 9			..	2 39
Petersfield 374	1014	1044	..	..		..	..	1114	1144	..	..		..	12 14	12 44	..	..		..	..	1 14	1 44	..		..	..	2 14			2 35	2 44
Rowlands Castle	1026	1056	..	..		..	..	1126	1158	..	..		..	12 28	12 56	..	..		..	..	1 26	1 56	..		..	..	2 26			..	2 56
Havant 196, 244	1031	11 1	..	..		..	..	1131	12 4	..	..		..	12 34	1 1	..	..		..	..	1 31	2 1	..		2S011	..	2 31			2 50	3 1
244 Hayling Island arr	..	..	..	..		..	..	..	..	..	..		..	1 3	..	..	..		..	..	1 47	2S033	..		2S033	..	..	..		..	..
Bedhampton Halt	1033	11 3	..	..		..	..	1133	12 7	..	..		..	12 36	1 3	..	..		..	..	1 33	2 3	..		..	..	2 33	..		..	3 3
Hilsea Halt	..	..	..	..		..	..	..	..	..	..		..	12S041	1S08	..	..		..	..	1S038	2S08	..		..	..	2S038	..		..	..
Fratton 196	1041	1111	..	..		..	..	1141	1214	..	..		..	12 44	1 11	..	..		..	..	1 41	2 11	..		2S020	..	2 41	..		2 59	3 11
Portsmouth & Southsea	1044	1114	..	..		1120	..	1144	1217	..	..		12S020	12 47	1 14	..	..		1 20	..	1 44	2 14	..		2 22	..	2 44	..		3 1	3 14
Portsmouth Harbour arr	..	..	..	..		1126	..	..	..	..	..		12S02 6	..	Stop	..	..		1 26	..	..	..	..		2 28	..	Stop	..		..	..
¶Portsmouth Harbour dp	..	..	..	..		1135		..	..	..	..		12S035	..		..	..		1 35		..	..	..		2 35	..		..	..		..
¶Ryde Pier Head arr	..	..	..	..		12 5		..	..	..	..		1 S0 5	..	..	..	..		2 5		..	..	..		3 5	..	..	..	..		..
Ryde, Pier Head § dep	..	..	..	..	1228	1235	Wednesdays, Thursdays, and Saturdays	..	..	..	..	1 28	1V35	..	..	..	..	2 28	2 35	Through Train from Freshwater (dep. 1 55 p.m.) see pages 368 and 373	..	..	..	3 28	3 35	..	..	..	..	Saturdays only	..
" Esplanade §	..	..	..	..	1231	1238		..	..	..	..	1 31	1V38	..	..	..	..	2 31	3 38		..	..	..	3 31	3 38	..	..	..	..		..
" St. John's Road	..	..	..	..	1235	1242		..	..	..	..	1 35	1V42	..	..	..	..	2 35	2 42		..	..	..	3 35	3 42	..	..	..	..		..
Ashey	..	..	..	..	..	1248		..	..	..	..	Weds., Thurs., and Sats.	1V48	..	..	..	..	..	2 48		..	..	..	..	3 48	..	..	..	..		..
Haven Street	..	..	..	..	..	1253		..	..	..	..		1V53	..	..	..	..	..	2 53		..	..	..	..	3 53	..	..	..	..		..
Wootten	..	..	..	..	..	1257		..	..	..	..		1V57	..	..	..	..	..	2 57		..	..	..	..	3 57	..	..	..	..		..
Whippingham	..	..	..	..	..	1 0		..	..	..	..		2V 0	..	..	..	..	..	3 0		..	..	..	..	4 0	..	..	..	..		..
Newport F 373 arr	..	..	..	..	..	1 6		..	..	..	..		2V 6	..	..	p.m	..	..	3 6		..	..	..	..	4 6	..	..	..	..		..
Newport dep	..	..	..	1240	..	..		..	..	..	..		..	..	..	2 40	..	..	..		..	..	..	..	..	4 10	..	..	..	..	..
Carisbrooke Halt G	..	..	..	1244	..	..		..	..	..	..		..	..	..	2 44	..	..	..		..	..	..	..	..	4 14	..	..	..	..	..
Calbourne and Shalfleet	..	..	..	1257	..	..		..	..	..	..		..	..	..	2 57	..	..	..		..	..	..	..	..	4 27	..	..	..	..	..
Ningwood	..	..	..	1 2	..	..		..	..	..	..		..	..	..	3 2	..	..	..		..	..	..	..	..	4 32	..	..	..	..	..
Yarmouth 338	..	..	..	1 10	..	..		..	..	..	..		..	..	..	3 10	..	..	..		..	..	..	..	..	4 40	..	..	..	..	..
Freshwater J arr	..	..	p.m	1 16	..	..		..	..	..	..		..	..	p.m.	3 16	..	..	..		..	..	..	..	..	4 46	..	..	..	..	..
Newport dep	..	..	1238	..	..	1 8		..	..	..	..		2 8	..	2 38	..	..	..	3 8		..	..	..	..	4 8	..	..	..	..	..	..
Mill Hill	..	..	1247	..	..	1 17		..	..	..	..		2 17	..	2 47	..	..	..	3 17		..	..	..	..	4 17	..	..	..	..	..	..
Cowes K arr	..	..	1250	..	..	1 20		..	..	..	..		20	..	2 50	..	..	..	3 20		..	..	..	..	4 20	..	..	..	..	..	..
Brading N	..	..	..	..	1243	..	..	..	..	..	..	1 43	..	..	..	..	..	2 43	..		..	..	p.m	3 43	..	..	p.m.	..	..	..	..
Brading dep	..	..	..	..	1245	..	1 10	..	..	..	..	1 45	..	..	..	..	..	2 45	..	..	..	..	3 10	3 45	..	..	4 10	..	..	..	..
St. Helens	..	..	..	..	1249	..	1 14	..	..	..	..	1 49	..	..	..	..	..	2 49	..	..	..	..	3 14	3 49	..	..	4 14	..	..	..	..
Bembridge arr	..	..	..	..	1253	..	1 18	..	..	..	..	1 53	..	..	..	..	..	2 53	..	..	..	..	3 18	3 53	..	..	4 18	..	..	..	..
Sandown 373	..	..	..	..	1248	..	..	..	..	..	..	1 48	..	..	..	..	..	2 48	..	3 6	..	..	..	3 48	..	..	..	..	..	..	..
Shanklin	..	..	..	..	1255	..	..	..	..	..	..	1 55	..	..	..	..	..	2 55	..	3 14	..	..	..	3 55	..	..	..	..	..	..	..
Wroxall O	..	..	..	..	1 5	..	..	..	..	..	..	2 5	..	..	..	..	..	3 5	..	..	..	..	..	4 5	..	..	..	..	..	..	..
Ventnor Q 373 arr	..	..	..	..	1 11	..	..	..	..	..	..	2 11	..	..	..	..	..	3 11	..	..	..	..	..	4 11	..	..	..	..	..	..	..

Conveyance of Motor Cars, etc., to and from the Isle of Wight, see pages 501 and 502

For Notes, see page 365.

For LOCAL TRAINS and INTERMEDIATE STATIONS between WATERLOO and SURBITON and COMPLETE SERVICE between WATERLOO and GUILDFORD, see pages 394 to 426.

LONDON, GODALMING, HASLEMERE, PETERSFIELD, PORTSMOUTH, and THE ISLE OF WIGHT

Week Days—*continued*

Down	p.m SX	p.m. SO	p.m	p.m R	p.m.		p.m	p.m	p.m	p.m	p.m R		p.m.	p.m.	p.m
WATERLOO ... dep	..	..	1 27	1 45		..	..	1 57	..	2 27		2 45	..	2 57	3 27
Surbiton	..	..	1 43			..	..	2 13	..	2 43		..	..	3 13	3 43
Esher, for Sandown Park	..	..	1 47			..	..	2 17	..	2 47		..	..	3 17	3 47
Hersham	..	..	1 50	Sats. only.		..	..	2 20	..	2 50		..	..	3 20	3 50
Walton-on-Thames	..	..	1 53			..	..	2 23	..	2 53		..	..	3 23	3 53
Weybridge A	..	..	1 57			..	..	2 27	..	2 57		..	..	3 27	3 57
West Weybridge	..	..	2 0			..	..	2 30	..	3 0		..	..	3 30	4 0
Byfleet B	..		2 3			..	..	2 33	..	3 3		..	..	3 33	4 3
Woking C	..	Saturdays only	2 9	2 16		..	..	2 39	..	3 9		3 16	..	3 39	4 9
Worplesdon	..		2 15	..		..	..	2 45	..	3 15		..	..	3 45	4 15
Guildford 246, 390 ... arr	..		2 21	2 25		..	..	2 51	..	3 21		3 25	..	3 51	4 21
Guildford ... dep	..		Stop	2 26		..	2 31	3 1	..	Stop		3 26	3 31	4 1	Stop
Farncombe	..			..		..	2 36	3 6	..			..	3 36	4 6	
Godalming	..		..	..		..	2 39	3 9	..	..		..	3 39	4 9	..
Milford	..		..	..		..	2 43	3 13	..	..		..	3 43	4 13	..
Witley, for Chiddingfold	..		..	..		..	2 48	3 18	..	..		..	3 48	4 18	..
Haslemere, for Hindhead	..	2 26	..	2 45		..	2 56	3 26	..	..		3 45	3 56	4 26	..
Liphook	..	2 32	..	..		..	3 2	3 32	..	..		..	4 2	4 32	..
Liss	..	2 39	..	..		..	3 9	3 39	..	..		..	4 9	4 39	..
Petersfield 374	..	2 44	..	..		..	3 14	3 44	..	..		..	4 14	4 44	..
Rowlands Castle	..	2 56	..	..		..	3 26	3 56	..	..		..	4 26	4 56	..
Havant 196, 244	..	3 1	..	3 11		..	3 31	4 1	..	..		4SO11	4 31	5 1	..
244 Hayling Island ... arr	..	..	..	..		..	..	..	..	..		4SO55	4 55	..	..
Bedhampton Halt	..	3 3	..	..		..	3 33	4 3	..	..		..	4 33	5 3	..
Hilsea Halt	..	..	..	..		..	..	..	..	..		..	4SX38	5SX8	..
Fratton 196	..	3 11	..	3 19		..	3 41	4 11	..	..		..	4 41	5 11	..
Portsmouth & Southsea	..	3 14	..	3 21		..	3 44	4 14	..	..		4 21	4 44	5 14	..
Portsmouth Harbour .. arr	..	..	..	3 27		..	Stop	..	..	..		4 27	Stop	Stop	..
¶Portsmouth Harbour dp	..	..	..	..		3 35		..	..	..		4 35			..
Ryde Pier Head ... arr	..	..	..	..		4 5	..	..	..	..		5 5	..	..	..
Ryde, Pier Head § .. dep	..	..	..	..	4 28	4 35	..	..	..	..	5 28	5 35	..	..	..
" Esplanade §	..	..	..	..	4 31	4 38	..	..	..	..	5 31	5 38	..	..	..
" St. John's Road	4 16	..	..	..	4 35	4 42	..	..	..	..	5 35	5 42	..	..	..
Ashey	..	..	..	..	..	4 48	..	..	..	..	..	5 48	..	..	..
Haven Street		..	..	..	..	4 53	..	..	..	..	..	5 53	..	..	..
Wootton		..	..	..	..	4 57	..	..	..	..	..	5 57	..	..	..
Whippingham		..	..	..	..	5 0	..	..	..	..	..	6 0	..	..	..
Newport F 373 ... arr	Saturdays excepted	..	..	..	..	5 6	..	..	..	..	..	6 6	..	p.m.	..
Newport ... dep		..	..	..	..	..	..	..	5 15	..	..	..	..	6 10	..
Carisbrooke Halt G		..	..	..	..	..	..	..	5 19	..	..	..	..	6 14	..
Calbourne and Shalfleet		..	..	..	..	..	..	..	5 32	..	..	..	..	6 27	..
Ningwood		..	..	..	..	..	..	..	5 37	..	..	..	..	6 32	..
Yarmouth 338		..	..	..	..	..	..	..	5 45	..	..	..	..	6 40	..
Freshwater J ... arr		..	p.m	..	..	..	..	..	5 51	p.m	..	..	..	6 46	p.m
Newport ... dep	..	..	4 38	..	..	5 8	..	..	..	5 38	..	6 8	..	..	6 38
Mill Hill	..	..	4 47	..	..	5 17	..	..	..	5 47	..	6 17	..	..	6 47
Cowes K ... arr	..	..	4 50	..	..	5 20	..	..	..	5 50	..	6 20	..	..	6 50
Brading N	4 23	..	..	..	4 43	..	p.m	..	..	..	5 43	..	p.m.	..	..
Brading ... dep	..	..	..	..	4 45	..	5 10	..	..	..	5 45	..	6 10	..	..
St. Helens	..	..	..	..	4 49	..	5 14	..	..	..	5 49	..	6 14	..	..
Bembridge ... arr	..	..	..	..	4 53	..	5 18	..	..	..	5 53	..	6 18	..	..
Sandown 373	4 28	..	..	..	4 48	..	..	..	..	..	5 48	..	..	..	..
Shanklin	4 35	..	..	..	4 55	..	..	..	..	..	5 55	..	..	..	..
Wroxall O	4 45	..	..	..	5 5	..	..	..	..	..	6 5	..	..	..	..
Ventnor Q 373 ... arr	4 54	..	..	..	5 11	..	..	..	..	..	6 11	..	..	..	..

Down	p.m R		p.m.	p.m SO	p.m SX	p.m SX	p.m SO	p.m SX	p.m.	p.m. R		p.m.	p.m SO	p.m SX	p.m SX
WATERLOO ... dep		3 45	..	3 57	3 57	4 20	..	..	4 27		4 45	..	4 57	4 57	5 20
Surbiton		..	..	4 13	4 13	..		..	4 43		..	..	5 13	5 13	R
Esher, for Sandown Park		..	..	4 17	4 17	R	Saturdays only	..	4 47		..	..	5 17	5 17	..
Hersham		..	..	4 20	4 20	..		..	4 50		..	..	5 20	5 20	..
Walton-on-Thames		..	..	4 23	4 23	..		..	4 53		..	..	5 23	5 23	..
Weybridge A		..	..	4 27	4 27	..		..	4 57		..	..	5 27	5 27	..
West Weybridge		..	..	4 30	4 30	..			5 0		..	..	5 30	5 30	..
Byfleet B		..	..	4 33	4 33	..			5 3		..	..	5 33	5 33	..
Woking C		4 16	..	4 39	4 39	..		Saturdays excepted	5 9		..	..	5 39	5 39	..
Worplesdon		..	..	4 45	4 45	..			5 15		..	..	5 45	5 45	..
Guildford 246, 390 ... arr		4 25	..	4 51	4 51	4 55			5 21		5 25	..	5 51	5 51	5 57
Guildford ... dep		4 26	4 31		4 51	4 56	5 1		Stop		5 26	5 31		5 52	5 58
Farncombe		..	4 36		..	5 1	5 6				..	5 36		..	6 3
Godalming		..	4 39		4 58	5 4	5 9		..		..	5 39	Saturdays only	5 59	6 6
Milford		..	4 43	Saturdays only	..	5 8	5 13		..		..	5 43		..	6 10
Witley, for Chiddingfold		..	4 48		..	5 13	5 18		..		..	5 48		..	6 15
Haslemere, for Hindhead		4 45	4 56		5 11	5 21	5 26	5 26	..		5 45	5 56		6 11	6 23
Liphook		..	5 2			..	5 32	5 32	..		..	6 2		..	..
Liss		..	5 9			..	5 39	5 39	..		..	6 9			..
Petersfield 374		..	5 14		Saturdays excepted	5 35	5 44	5 44	..		..	6 14			6 37
Rowlands Castle		..	5 26			..	5 56	5 56	..		..	6 26			..
Havant 196, 244		..	5 31			5 50	6 1	6 1	..		6SX11	6 31		Saturdays excepted	6 52
244 Hayling Island ... arr		..	5 46	..		..	..	6 33	..		6SX33	6SO47	..		..
Bedhampton Halt		..	5 33	..		..	6 3	6 3	..		..	6 33	..		..
Hilsea Halt		..	5SX38	..		..	..	6 8	..		..	6SX38	..		..
Fratton 196		..	5 41	..		5 59	6 11	6 13	..		..	6 41	..		7 1
Portsmouth & Southsea		5 20	5 44	..		6 1	6 14	6 15			6 21	6 44	..		7 3
Portsmouth Harbour .. arr		5 26	Stop	..		6 5	..	..	..		6 26	Stop	..		7 7
¶Portsmouth Harbour dp		5 35		..	..		..	..	..		6 35		..	..	..
Ryde Pier Head ... arr		6 5	..	..	..		..	..	..		7 5	..	..	..	..
Ryde, Pier Head § .. dep	6 28	6 35	..	..	..		..	..	..	7 28	7 35	..	..	..	
" Esplanade §	6 31	6 38	..	..	..		..	..	..	7 31	7 38	..	..	..	
" St. John's Road	6 35	6 42	..	..	..		..	..	..	7 35	7 42	..	..	..	
Ashey	..	6 48	..	..	..	Saturdays excepted	..	..	..	..	7 48	..	..	..	Saturdays excepted
Haven Street	..	6 53	..	..	..		..	..	..	..	7 53	..	..	..	
Wootton	..	6 57	..	..	..		..	..	..	..	7 57	..	..	..	
Whippingham	..	7 0	..	..	..		..	..	..	..	8 0	..	..	..	
Newport F 373 ... arr	..	7 6	..	..	..		..	..	..	..	8 6	..	..	..	
Newport ... dep	..	7 10	..	..	..	..	..	..	..	..	..	..	..	..	..
Carisbrooke Halt G	..	7 14	..	..	..	..	..	..	..	..	..	..	..	..	..
Calbourne and Shalfleet	..	7 27	..	..	..	..	..	..	..	..	..	..	..	..	..
Ningwood	..	7 32	..	..	..	..	..	..	..	..	..	..	..	..	..
Yarmouth 338	..	7 40	..	..	..	..	..	..	..	..	..	..	..	..	..
Freshwater J ... arr	..	7 46	..	..	..	..	..	..	p.m	..	..	..	..	..	..
Newport ... dep	..	Through Train from Ryde	..	..	..	..	..	..	7 38	..	8 8	..	..	..	..
Mill Hill	..		..	..	..	..	..	..	7 47	..	8 17	..	..	..	..
Cowes K ... arr	..		..	..	..	..	..	..	7 50	..	8 20	..	..	..	..
Brading N	6 43		p.m	..	..	..	..	..	..	7 43	..	p.m	..	..	..
Brading ... dep	6 45		7 10	..	..	..	..	..	..	7 45	..	8 10	..	..	..
St. Helens	6 49		7 14	..	..	..	..	..	..	7 49	..	8 14	..	..	..
Bembridge ... arr	6 53		7 18	..	..	..	..	..	..	7 53	..	8 18	..	..	..
Sandown 373	6 48		..	..	..	..	..	..	..	7 48	..	..	..	..	..
Shanklin	6 55	..	..	..	..	..	..	..	..	7 55	..	..	..	..	..
Wroxall O	7 5	..	..	..	..	..	..	..	..	8 5	..	..	..	..	..
Ventnor Q 373 ... arr	7 11	..	..	..	..	..	..	..	..	8 11	..	..	..	..	..

Conveyance of Motor Cars, etc., to and from the Isle of Wight, see pages 501 and 502

For Notes, see page 365; for Continuation of Trains, see pages 362 to 365

☞ For LOCAL TRAINS and INTERMEDIATE STATIONS between WATERLOO and SURBITON and COMPLETE SERVICE between WATERLOO and GUILDFORD, see pages 394 to 426.

LONDON, GODALMING, HASLEMERE, PETERSFIELD, PORTSMOUTH, and THE ISLE OF WIGHT

Week Days—*continued*

Down	p.m SO	p.m SX	p.m	p.m R		p.m.	p.m SX	p.m SO	p.m SX	p.m ..	p.m	p.m SX	p.m R		pm.	p.m	p.m	p.m R	p.m	p.m	p.m	p.m R	p.m	p.m	p.m	p.m R	p.m	p.m	p.m	p.m	p.m
WATERLOO ... dep	..	..	5 27	5 45		..	5 57	5 57	6 29		6 27	..	6 45		..	6 57	7 27	7 45	..	7 57	8 27	8 45	..	8 57	9 27	9 45	..	9 57	1025	1057	1155
Surbiton	..	..	5 43	..		..	6 13	6 13	R	Saturdays only	6 43	..	..		..	7 13	7 43	Saturdays only	..	8 13	8 43	..	..	9 13	9 43	..	..	1013	1043	1113	1213
Esher, for Sandown Park	..	..	5 47	..		..	6 17	6 17	..		6 47	..	..		..	7 17	7 47		..	8 17	8 47	..	..	9 17	9 47	..	..	1017	1047	1117	1217
Hersham	..	..	5 50	..		..	6 20	6 20	..		6 50	..	..		..	7 20	7 50		..	8 20	8 50	..	..	9 20	9 50	..	..	1020	1050	1120	1220
Walton-on-Thames	..		5 53	..		..	6 23	6 23	..		6 53	..	..		..	7 23	7 53		..	8 23	8 53	..	..	9 23	9 53	..	..	1023	1053	1123	1223
Weybridge A	..		5 57	..		..	6 27	6 27	..		6 57	..	..		..	7 27	7 57		..	8 27	8 57	..	..	9 27	9 57	..	..	1027	1057	1127	1227
West Weybridge	..		6 0	..		..	6 30	6 30	..		7 0	..	..		..	7 30	8 0		..	8 30	9 0	..	..	9 30	10 0	..	..	1030	11 0	1130	1230
Byfleet B	..	Saturdays excepted	6 3	..		..	6 33	6 33	..		7 3	..	..		..	7 33	8 3		..	8 33	9 3	..	..	9 33	10 3	..	..	1033	11 3	1133	1233
Woking C	..		6 9	..		..	6 39	6 39	..		7 9	..	7 16		..	7 39	8 9		..	8 39	9 9	9 16	..	9 39	10 9	1016	..	1039	11 9	1139	1239
Worplesdon	..		6 15	..		..	6 45	6 45	..		7 15	..	..		..	7 45	8 15		..	8 45	9 15	..	..	9 45	1015	..	..	1045	1116	1145	1244
Guildford 246, 390 ... arr	..		6 21	6 25		..	6 51	6 51	6 56		7 21	..	7 25		..	7 51	8 21	8 25	..	8 51	9 21	9 25	..	9 51	1021	1025	..	1051	1122	1151	1250
Guildford 246, 390 ... dep	6 1		..	6 26		6 31	6 52		6 57	7 1	Stop	..	7 26		7 31	8 1	..	8 26	8 31	9 1	..	9 26	9 31	10 1	..	1026	1031	..	..	..	..
Farncombe	6 6		..	..		6 36	..	Saturdays only	7 2	7 6		..	..		7 36	8 6	..	..	8 36	9 6	..	..	9 36	10 6	..	..	1036	..	..	..	..
Godalming	6 9		..	..		6 39	6 59		7 5	7 9	..	..	..		7 39	8 9	..	..	8 39	9 9	..	..	9 39	10 9	..	..	1039	..	..	..	..
Milford	6 13		..	..		6 43	..		7 9	7 13	..	..	..		7 43	8 13	..	..	8 43	9 13	..	..	9 43	1013	..	..	1043	..	..	..	..
Witley, for Chiddingfold	6 18		..	..		6 48	..		7 14	7 18	..	..	..		7 48	8 18	..	..	8 48	9 18	..	..	9 48	1018	..	..	1048	..	..	..	..
Haslemere, for Hindhead	6 26	6 28	..	6 45		6 56	7 11		7 22	7 26	..	7 26	7 45		7 56	8 26	..	8 45	8 56	9 26	..	9 45	9 56	1026	..	1045	1056	..	..	..	..
Liphook	6 32	6 34	..	..		7 2	Saturdays excepted		..	7 32	..	7 32	..		8 2	8 32	..	..	9 2	9 32	..	..	10 2	1032	..	..	11 2	..	..	..	..
Liss	6 39	6 41	..	..		7 9			..	7 39	..	7 39	..		8 9	8 39	..	..	9 9	9 39	..	..	10 9	1039	..	..	11 9	..	..	..	..
Petersfield 374	6 44	6 46	..	..		7 14			7 36	7 44	..	7 44	..		8 14	8 44	..	..	9 14	9 44	..	..	1014	1044	..	..	1114	..	..	..	..
Rowlands Castle	6 56	6 58	..	..		7 26			..	7 56	..	7 56	..		8 26	8 56	..	..	9 26	9 56	..	..	1026	1056	..	..	1126	..	..	..	..
Havant 196, 244	7 1	7 3	..	7SX11		7 31		..	7 51	8 1	..	8 1	8SX11		8 31	9 1	..	..	9 31	10 1	..	..	1031	11 1	..	..	1131	..	..	..	..
244 Hayling Island ... arr	..	7 33	..	7SX33		7SO47		..	..	..	..	8 33	8SX33		8SO47	..	..	..	..	..	..	..	..	..	..	..	..	..	..	..	..
Bedhampton Halt	7 3	7 5	..	..		7 33		..	..	8 3	..	8 3	..		8 33	9 3	..	..	9 33	10 3	..	..	1033	11 3	..	..	1133	..	..	..	..
Hilsea Halt	..	..	..	..		..		..	..	..	..	..	..		..	..	..	..	..	..	..	..	..	..	..	..	..	..	..	..	..
Fratton 196	7 11	7 13	..	7SX20		7 41		—	8 0	8 11	..	8 11	8SX20		8 41	9 11	..	..	9 41	1011	..	1018	1041	1111	..	1118	1141	..	..	..	..
Portsmouth & Southsea	7 14	7 16	..	7 22		7 44		..	8 2	8 14	..	8 14	8 22		8 44	9 14	..	9 29	9 44	1014	..	1021	1044	1114	..	1121	1144	..	..	..	..
Portsmouth Harbour ... arr	..	..	..	7 27		..		..	8 6	Stop	..	..	8 27		Stop	..	..	..	..	..	..	..	..	..	..	..	..	..	..	..	..
¶ Portsmouth Harbour dp		..	..	7 35		..	..	..			..		8 40			..	..	..	..	..	..	..	..	..	..	..	..	..	..	..	..
¶ Ryde Pier Head ... arr		..	..	8 5		..	..	..			..		9 10		..	..	..	..	..	..	..	..	..	..	..	..	..	..	..	..	..
Ryde, Pier Head § dep	Saturdays only	..	..	8 28	8 35	..	..	..	Saturdays excepted	Saturdays only	..	Saturdays excepted	9 28	9 35	..	..	..	..	..	..	..	..	..	..	..	..	..	..	..	..	..
" Esplanade §		..	..	8 31	8 38	..	..	..			..		9 31	9 38	..	..	..	..	..	..	..	..	..	..	..	..	..	..	..	..	..
" St. John's Road		..	..	8 35	8 42	..	..	..			..		9 35	9 42	..	..	..	..	..	..	..	..	..	..	..	..	..	..	..	..	..
Ashey		..	..	..	8 48	..	..	..			..		..	9 48	..	..	..	..	..	..	..	..	..	..	..	..	..	..	..	..	..
Haven Street		..	..	..	8 53	..	..	..			..		..	9 53	..	..	..	..	..	..	..	..	..	..	..	..	..	..	..	..	..
Wootton		..	..	..	8 57	..	..	..			..		..	9 57	..	..	..	..	..	..	..	..	..	..	..	..	..	..	..	..	..
Whippingham		..	..	..	9 0	..	..	..			..		..	10 0	..	..	..	..	..	..	..	..	..	..	..	..	..	..	..	..	..
Newport F 373 ... arr		..	..	..	9 6	..	..	..			..		..	10 6	..	..	..	..	..	..	..	..	..	..	..	..	..	..	..	..	..
Newport ... dep	..	..	..	..	..	..	..	..	..	☞	..	..	..	..	..	..	..	..	..	..	..	..	..	..	..	..	..	..	..	..	..
Carisbrooke Halt G	..	..	..	..	..	..	..	..	..		..	..	..	..	..	..	..	..	..	..	..	..	..	..	..	..	..	..	..	..	..
Calbourne and Shalfleet	..	..	..	..	..	..	..	..	..		..	..	..	..	..	..	..	..	..	..	..	..	..	..	..	..	..	..	..	..	..
Ningwood	..	..	..	..	..	..	..	..	..		..	..	..	..	..	..	..	..	..	..	..	..	..	..	..	..	..	..	..	..	..
Yarmouth 338	..	..	..	..	..	..	..	..	..		..	..	..	..	..	..	..	..	..	..	..	..	..	..	..	..	..	..	..	..	..
Freshwater J ... arr	..	..	..	..	..	..	..	..	..	p.m	..	..	..	..	..	..	..	..	..	..	..	..	..	..	..	..	..	..	..	..	..
Newport ... dep	..	..	..	..	9 8	..	..	..	..	9 38	..	..	..	10 8	..	..	..	..	..	..	..	..	..	..	..	..	..	..	..	..	..
Mill Hill	..	..	..	..	9 17	..	..	..	..	9 47	..	..	..	1017	..	..	..	..	..	..	..	..	..	..	..	..	..	..	..	..	..
Cowes K ... arr	..	..	..	..	9 20	..	..	..	..	9 50	..	..	..	1020	..	..	..	..	..	..	..	..	..	..	..	..	..	..	..	..	..
Brading N	..	..	..	8 43	..	..	..	..	..	..	p.m	..	9 43	..	p.m.	..	..	..	..	..	..	..	..	..	..	..	..	..	..	..	..
Brading ... dep	..	..	..	8 47	..	..	..	..	..	..	9 12	..	9 45	..	10 10	..	..	..	..	..	..	..	..	..	..	..	..	..	..	..	..
St. Helens	..	..	..	8 51	..	..	..	..	..	..	9 16	..	9 49	..	10 14	..	..	..	..	..	..	..	..	..	..	..	..	..	..	..	..
Bembridge ... arr	..	..	..	8 55	..	..	..	..	..	..	9 20	..	9 53	..	10 18	..	..	..	..	..	..	..	..	..	..	..	..	..	..	..	..
Sandown 373	..	..	..	8 48	..	..	..	..	..	..	..	..	9 48	..	..	..	..	..	..	..	..	..	..	..	..	..	..	..	..	..	..
Shanklin	..	..	..	8 55	..	..	..	..	..	..	..	..	9 55	..	..	..	..	..	..	..	..	..	..	..	..	..	..	..	..	..	..
Wroxall O	..	..	..	9 5	..	..	..	..	..	..	..	..	10 5	..	..	..	..	..	..	..	..	..	..	..	..	..	..	..	..	..	..
Ventnor Q 373 ... arr	..	..	..	9 11	..	..	..	..	..	..	..	..	1011	..	..	..	..	..	..	..	..	..	..	..	..	..	..	..	..	..	..

Conveyance of Motor Cars, etc., to and from the Isle of Wight, see pages 501 and 502

For Notes, see page 365

… STATIONS between WATERLOO and SURBITON and COMPLETE SERVICE between WATERLOO and GUILDFORD, see pages 394 to 426.

LONDON, GODALMING, HASLEMERE, PETERSFIELD, PORTSMOUTH, and THE ISLE OF WIGHT

Down	Sundays																															
	3		a.m 3	a.m	a.m		a.m			a.m	a.m	a.m	a.m	a.m	a.m	a.m	a.m R			a.m	a.m		p.m	a.m	p.m	a.m R	p.m	a.m	a.m	a.m	a.m R	
WATERLOO dep	3 35			..	..	..	..		..	..	..	..	..	7 25	7 57	8 27	9 45		..	..	8 57	..	..	9 27	..	9 45	..	..	9 57	1027	1045	
Surbiton	..		..	..	..	..	..		..	..	..	..	..	7 43	8 13	8 43	..		..	..	9 13	..	..	9 43	..	..	..	..	1013	1043	..	
Esher, for Sandown Park	..		..	..	..	..	..		..	..	..	..	..	7 47	8 17	8 47	..		..	..	9 17	..	..	9 47	..	..	..	..	1017	1047	..	
Hersham	..		..	..	..	..	..		..	..	..	..	..	7 50	8 20	8 50	..		..	..	9 20	..	..	9 50	..	..	..	..	1020	1050	..	
Walton-on-Thames	..		..	..	..	..	..		..	..	..	..	..	7 53	8 23	8 53	..		..	..	9 23	..	..	9 53	..	..	..	..	1023	1053	..	
Weybridge **A**	4 13		..	..	..	..	..		..	..	..	..	..	7 57	8 27	8 57	..		..	..	9 27	..	..	9 57	..	..	..	..	1027	1057	..	
West Weybridge	..		..	..	..	..	..		..	..	..	..	..	8 0	8 30	9 0	..		..	..	9 30	..	..	10 0	..	..	..	..	1030	11 0	..	
Byfleet **B**	..		..	..	..	..	..		..	..	..	..	..	8 3	8 33	9 3	..		..	..	9 33	..	..	10 3	..	..	..	..	1033	11 3	..	
Woking C	4 26		..	..	..	..	..		..	7 15	..	..	..	8 9	8 39	9 9	9 16		..	..	9 39	..	..	10 9	..	1016	..	..	1039	11 9	1116	
Worplesdon	..		..	..	..	..	..		..	..	..	..	..	8 15	8 45	9 15	..		..	..	9 45	..	..	1015	..	..	..	..	1045	1115	..	
Guildford 246, 390 arr	4 37		..	..	..	..	..		..	7 24	..	..	..	8 21	8 51	9 21	9 25		..	..	9 51	..	..	1021	..	1025	..	..	1051	1121	1125	
Guildford dep	4 38		4 50	..	..	..	..		..	7 27	..	..	..	8 31	9 1	..	9 26		..	9 31	10 1	..	..	..	..	1026	..	1031	11 1	..	1126	
Farncombe	..		..	..	..	..	..		..	7 32	..	..	..	8 36	9 6	..	..		..	9 36	10 6	..	..	..	..	..	..	1036	11 6	..	..	
Godalming	..		..	..	..	..	..		..	7 35	..	..	..	8 39	9 9	..	..		..	9 39	10 9	..	..	..	..	..	..	1039	11 9	..	..	
Milford	..		..	..	..	..	..		..	7 40	..	..	..	8 43	9 13	..	..		..	9 43	1013	..	..	..	..	..	..	1043	1113	..	..	
Witley, for Chiddingfold	..		..	..	..	..	..		..	7 44	..	..	..	8 48	9 18	..	..		..	9 48	1018	..	..	..	..	..	..	1048	1118	..	..	
Haslemere, for Hindhead	..		5 18	..	..	..	..		..	7 54	..	..	..	8 56	9 26	..	9 45		..	9 56	1026	..	..	..	..	1045	..	1056	1126	..	1145	
Liphook	..		..	..	..	..	..		..	8 0	..	..	..	9 2	9 32	..	..		..	10 2	1032	..	..	..	..	..	..	11 2	1132	..	..	
Liss	..		..	..	..	..	..		..	8 7	..	..	..	9 9	9 39	..	..		..	10 9	1039	..	..	..	..	..	..	11 9	1139	..	..	
Petersfield 374	..		5 40	..	..	..	..		..	8 14	..	..	..	9 14	9 44	..	..		..	1014	1044	..	..	..	..	..	..	1114	1144	..	..	
Rowlands Castle	..		..	..	..	..	..		..	8 25	..	..	..	9 26	9 56	..	..		..	1026	1056	..	..	..	..	..	..	1126	1156	..	..	
Havant **196**, 244	5 33		..	..	..	..	..		..	8 31	..	..	..	9 31	10 1	..	..		..	1031	11 1	..	..	..	..	..	..	1131	12 1	..	..	
244 Hayling Island arr	..		..	..	..	..	..		..	..	..	..	..	..	..	..	..		..	..	..	..	..	..	..	..	..	..	..	..	..	
Bedhampton Halt	..		..	..	..	..	..		..	8 33	..	..	..	9 33	10 3	..	..		..	1033	11 3	..	Through Train from Ventnor (dep. 11 30 a.m), see page 373	..	..	..	..	1133	12 3	..	..	
Hilsea Halt	..		..	..	..	..	..		..	..	..	..	..	..	..	..	..		..	..	..	..		..	..	..	..	..	..	..	..	
Fratton 196	5 45		..	..	..	..	..		..	8 41	..	..	..	9 41	1011	..	..		..	1041	1111	..		..	..	..	..	1141	1211	..	..	
Portsmouth & Southsea	5 58		..	..	..	..	..		..	8 44	..	..	..	9 44	1014	..	1020		..	1044	1114	..		..	..	1120	..	1144	1214	..	1220	
Portsmouth Harbour arr	6 5		..	..	..	..	..		..	..	..	..	..	..	..	..	1026		..	..	..	..		..	..	1126	..	Stop	..	..	1226	
¶Portsmouth Harbour dp	6 25		..	..	..	..	8 25		..	..	Through Train from Ventnor (dep 9 50 a.m.), see page 373	..	..	..	..	..	1035		..	..	..	..		..	..	..	..	..	..	..	1235	
¶Ryde Pier Head arr	6 55		..	..	..	..	8 55		..	..		..	..	..	..	..	11 5		..	..	..	..		..	..	..	..	..	..	..	1 5	
Ryde, Pier Head § dep	7 15	7 20	..	..	..	..	9 20	9 28	..	..		Through Train from Cowes (dep. 9 56 a.m.), see page 373	..	..	..	..	1128	1135	..	..	..	..		..	Through Train from Freshwater (dep. 11 35 a.m.) see pages 371 and 373	..	..	..	..	..	1 28	1 35
" Esplanade §	7 18	7 24	..	..	..	..	9 23	9 31	..	..			..	..	..	..	1131	1138	..	..	..	..		..		..	..	..	..	..	1 31	1 38
" St. John's Road	7 22	7 28	..	9 5	..	..	9 27	9 35	..	..			..	..	..	..	1135	1142	..	..	..	..		..		..	..	..	..	..	1 35	1 42
Ashey	7 29	..	..	..	..	..	9 34	..	..	..			..	..	..	..	..	1148	..	..	..	..		..		..	..	..	..	..	..	1 48
Haven Street	7 35	..	..	..	..	..	9 38	..	..	..			..	..	..	..	..	1153	..	..	..	..		..		..	..	..	..	..	..	1 53
Wootton	7 39	..	..	..	..	..	9 42	..	..	..			..	..	..	..	..	1157	..	..	..	..		..		..	..	..	..	..	..	1 57
Whippingham	7 42	..	..	..	..	..	9 46	..	..	..			..	..	..	..	..	12 0	..	..	..	..		..		..	..	..	..	..	..	2 0
Newport F 373 arr	7 48	..	..	..	..	..	9 52	..	..	..			..	..	..	..	..	12 6	..	..	..	..		..		..	..	..	..	..	..	2 6
Newport dep	..	..	..	..	..	..	..	..	..	..			1040	..	..	..	..	..	..	..	..	..	1218	..		..	..	..	..	..	..	..
Carisbrooke Halt **G**	..	..	..	..	..	..	..	..	..	..			1044	..	..	..	..	..	..	..	..	..	..	..		..	..	..	..	..	..	..
Calbourne and Shalfleet	..	..	..	..	..	..	..	..	..	..			1057	..	..	..	..	..	..	..	..	..	..	..		..	..	..	..	..	..	..
Ningwood	..	..	..	..	..	..	..	..	..	..			11 2	..	..	..	..	..	..	..	..	..	..	..		..	..	..	..	..	..	..
Yarmouth 338	..	..	..	..	..	..	..	..	..	..			1110	..	..	..	..	..	..	..	..	..	1246	..		..	..	..	..	..	..	..
Freshwater J arr	..	..	..	..	..	..	..	..	..	..			1116	..	..	..	..	..	..	..	..	..	1252	..		..	..	..	..	..	..	..
Newport dep	7 50	..	..	..	9 38	..	10 8	..	..	..	1038		..	..	..	..	..	12 8	..	..	..	..	..	..		..	..	p.m 1 48	..	..	..	..
Mill Hill	8 0	..	..	..	9 47	..	1017	..	..	..	1047		..	..	..	..	..	1217	..	..	..	..	..	..		..	..	1 57	..	..	..	..
Cowes K arr	8 3	..	..	..	9 50	..	1020	..	..	..	1050		..	..	..	..	..	1220	..	..	..	..	..	..		..	..	2 0	..	..	..	..
Brading N	..	7 37	..	9 13	..	..	..	9 43	..	..	..		..	..	..	..	1143	..	..	..	..	..	..	..		..	..	..	..	..	1 43	..
Brading dep	..	..	..	..	..	..	..	..	..	..	..	..	..	..	..	..	1145	..	..	..	..	..	..	..		..	1255	..	..	..	1 45	..
St. Helens	..	..	..	..	..	..	..	..	..	..	..	..	..	..	..	..	1149	..	..	..	..	..	..	..		..	1259	..	..	..	1 49	..
Bembridge arr	..	..	..	..	..	..	..	..	..	..	..	..	..	..	..	..	1153	..	..	..	..	..	..	..		..	1 3	..	..	..	1 53	..
Sandown 373	..	7 42	..	9 18	..	..	..	9 48	..	..	..	1048	..	..	..	..	1148	..	..	..	..	..	..	..	1248	..	..	..	..	..	1 48	..
Shanklin	..	7 49	..	9 24	..	..	..	9 57	..	..	..	1054	..	..	..	..	1155	..	..	..	..	..	..	..	1255	..	..	..	..	..	1 55	..
Wroxall **O**	..	7 59	..	9 34	..	..	..	1010	..	..	..	11 3	..	..	..	..	12 5	..	..	..	..	..	..	..	1 5	..	..	..	..	..	2 5	..
Ventnor Q 373 arr	..	8 5	..	9 40	..	..	..	1016	..	..	..	11 9	..	..	..	..	1211	..	..	..	..	..	..	..	1 11	..	..	..	..	..	2 11	..

Conveyance of Motor Cars, etc., to and from the Isle of Wight, see pages 501 and 502

For Notes and Continuation of SUNDAY TRAINS, see pages 364 and 365

For LOCAL TRAINS and INTERMEDIATE STATIONS between WATERLOO and SURBITON and COMPLETE SERVICE between WATERLOO and GUILDFORD, see pages 394 to 436.

LONDON, GODALMING, HASLEMERE, PETERSFIELD, PORTSMOUTH, and THE ISLE OF WIGHT

Sundays—*continued*

Down	p.m	a.m	p.m	a.m	p.m	p.m	a.m	a.m	p.m	p.m		p.m R	p.m	p.m	p.m	p.m	p.m	p.m	p.m	p.m	p.m		p.m R	p.m	p.m	p.m	p.m	p.m	pm.	pm		p.m R
WATERLOO dep	..	..	..	1057	..	..	1127	1157	1227	..		1245	..	..	..	1257	..	..	1 27	1 57	2 27		2 45	..	2 57	..	3 27	..	3 57	427		4 45
Surbiton	..	..	..	1113	..	..	1143	1213	1243	..		..	..	..	..	1 13	..	..	1 43	2 13	2 43		..	..	3 13	..	3 43	..	4 13	443		..
Esher, for Sandown Park	..	..	..	1117	..	..	1147	1217	1247	..		..	..	..	..	1 17	..	..	1 47	2 17	2 47		..	..	3 17	..	3 47	..	4 17	447		..
Hersham	..	..	..	1120	..	..	1150	1220	1250	..		..	..	..	..	1 20	..	..	1 50	2 20	2 50		..	..	3 20	..	3 50	..	4 20	450		..
Walton-on-Thames	..	..	..	1123	..	..	1153	1223	1253	..		..	..	..	..	1 23	..	..	1 53	2 23	2 53		..	..	3 23	..	3 53	..	4 23	453		..
Weybridge A	..	..	..	1127	..	..	1157	1227	1257	..		..	..	..	..	1 27	..	..	1 57	2 27	2 57		..	..	3 27	..	3 57	..	4 27	457		..
West Weybridge	..	..	..	1130	..	..	12 0	1230	1 0	..		..	..	..	..	1 30	..	..	2 0	2 30	3 0		..	..	3 30	..	4 0	..	4 30	5 0		..
Byfleet B	..	..	..	1133	..	..	12 3	1233	1 3	..		..	..	..	..	1 33	..	..	2 3	2 33	3 3		..	..	3 33	..	4 3	..	4 33	5 3		..
Woking C	..	..	..	1139	..	..	12 9	1239	1 9	..		1 16	..	..	..	1 39	..	..	2 9	2 39	3 9		3 16	..	3 39	..	4 9	..	4 39	5 9		5 16
Worplesdon	..	..	..	1145	..	..	1215	1245	1 15	..		..	..	..	..	1 45	..	..	2 15	2 45	3 15		..	..	3 45	..	4 15	..	4 45	515		..
Guildford 246, 390 arr	..	..	..	1151	..	..	1221	1251	1 21	..		1 25	..	..	..	1 51	..	..	2 21	2 51	3 21		3 25	..	3 51	..	4 21	..	4 51	521		5 25
Guildford 246, 390 dep	..	1131	..	12 1	..	..	1231	1 1	..	..		1 26	1 31	..	..	2 1	..	..	2 31	3 1	..		3 26	3 31	4 1	..	4 31	..	5 1	..		5 26
Farncombe	..	1136	..	12 6	..	..	1236	1 6	..	..		..	1 36	..	..	2 6	..	..	2 36	3 6	..		..	3 36	4 6	..	4 36	..	5 6	..		..
Godalming	..	1139	..	12 9	..	..	1239	1 9	..	..		..	1 39	..	..	2 9	..	..	2 39	3 9	..		..	3 39	4 9	..	4 39	..	5 9	..		..
Milford	..	1143	..	1213	..	..	1243	1 13	..	..		1 35	1 43	..	..	2 13	..	..	2 43	3 13	..		..	3 43	4 13	..	4 43	..	5 13	..		..
Witley, for Chiddingfold	..	1148	..	1218	..	..	1248	1 18	..	..		..	1 48	..	..	2 18	..	..	2 48	3 18	..		..	3 48	4 18	..	4 48	..	5 18	..		..
Haslemere, for Hindhead	..	1153	..	1226	..	..	1256	1 26	..	..		1 47	1 56	..	..	2 26	..	..	2 56	3 26	..		3 45	3 56	4 26	..	4 56	..	5 26	..		5 45
Liphook	..	12 2	..	1232	..	..	1 2	1 32	..	..		..	2 2	..	..	2 32	..	..	3 2	2 32	..		..	4 2	4 32	..	5 2	..	5 32	..		..
Liss	..	12 9	..	1239	..	..	1 9	1 39	..	..		..	2 9	..	..	2 39	..	..	3 9	3 39	..		..	4 9	4 39	..	5 9	..	5 39	..		..
Petersfield 374	..	1214	..	1244	..	..	1 14	1 44	..	..		..	2 14	..	..	2 44	..	..	3 14	3 44	..		..	4 14	4 44	..	5 14	..	5 44	..		..
Rowlands Castle	..	1226	..	1256	..	..	1 26	1 56	..	..		..	2 26	..	..	2 56	..	..	3 26	3 56	..		..	4 26	4 56	..	5 26	..	5 56	..		..
Havant 196, 244	..	1231	..	1 1	..	..	1 31	2 1	..	..		..	2 31	..	..	3 1	..	..	3 31	4 1	..		..	4 31	5 1	..	5 31	..	6 1	..		..
244 Hayling Island arr	..	..	..	..	..	..	..	..	..	..		..	..	..	..	..	..	..	..	..	..		..	..	..	..	..	..	..	..		..
Bedhampton Halt	..	1233	..	1 3	..	..	1 33	2 3	..	..		..	2 33	..	..	3 3	..	..	3 33	4 3	..		..	4 33	5 3	..	5 33	..	6 3	..		..
Hilsea Halt	..	..	..	..	..	..	..	..	..	..		..	..	..	..	..	..	..	..	..	..		..	..	..	..	..	..	..	..		..
Fratton 196	..	1241	..	1 11	..	..	1 41	2 11	..	..		..	2 41	..	..	3 11	..	..	3 41	4 11	..		..	4 41	5 11	..	5 41	..	6 11	..		..
Portsmouth & Southsea	..	1244	..	1 14	..	..	1 44	2 14	..	..		2 21	2 44	..	..	3 14	..	..	3 44	4 14	..		4 20	4 44	5 14	..	5 44	..	6 14	..		6 20
Portsmouth Harbour arr	..	..	..	..	..	..	..	..	..	..		2 26	..	..	..	..	..	..	..	..	..		4 26	..	..	..	..	..		..		6 26
¶ Portsmouth Harbour dp	Through Train from Ventnor (dep. 1 30 p.m.) see page 373	..	..	..	..	..	..	..	..	..		2 35	..	Through Train from Ventnor (dep. 3 17 p.m.) see page 373	..	..	..	..	..	..	..		4 35	..	..	..	..	..	Stop	..		6 35
Ryde Pier Head arr		..	..	..	..	..	..	..	..	..		3 5	..		..	..	..	..	..	..	..		5 5	..	..	..	..	..	..	..		7 5
Ryde, Pier Head § dep		..	..	..	..	..	..	..	..	..	3 28	3 35	..		..	..	..	..	..	..	..	5 28	5 35	..	..	6 28	..	6 35	..	..	7 28	7 35
" Esplanade §		..	..	..	..	..	..	..	..	..	3 31	3 38	..		..	..	..	..	..	..	..	5 31	5 38	..	..	6 31	..	6 38	..	..	7 31	7 38
" St. John's Road		..	..	..	2 30	..	..	..	..	..	3 35	3 42	..		..	..	..	..	..	..	..	5 35	5 42	..	..	6 35	..	6 42	..	..	7 35	7 42
Ashey		..	..	..	..	..	..	..	..	..	..	3 48	..		..	..	..	..	..	..	..	..	5 48	..	..	..	..	6 48	..	..	..	7 48
Haven Street		..	..	..	..	..	..	..	..	..	..	3 53	..		..	..	..	..	..	..	..	..	5 53	..	..	..	..	6 53	..	..	..	7 53
Wootton		..	..	..	..	..	..	..	..	..	..	3 57	..		..	..	..	..	..	..	..	..	5 57	..	..	..	..	6 57	..	..	..	7 57
Whippingham		..	..	..	..	..	..	..	..	..	..	4 0	..		..	..	..	..	..	..	..	..	6 0	..	..	..	..	7 0	..	..	..	8 0
Newport F 373 arr		..	..	..	..	..	..	..	..	..	..	4 6	..		..	..	..	..	..	..	..	..	6 6	..	..	..	..	7 6	..	..	..	8 6
Newport dep		..	2 20	..	..	Through Train from Cowes (dep. 2 6 p.m.) see page 373	..	..	..	..	..	4 10	..		Through Train from Cowes (dep. 3 56 p.m.) see page 373	..	..	..	..	..	..	..	..	..	..	..	..	7 18	..	..	..	..
Carisbrooke Halt G		..	2 24	..	..		..	..	..	..	..	4 14	..			..	..	..	..	..	..	..	..	..	..	..	..	7 24	..	..	..	..
Calbourne and Shalfleet		..	2 37	..	..		..	..	..	..	..	4 27	..			..	..	..	..	..	..	..	..	..	..	..	..	7 37	..	..	..	..
Ningwood		..	2 42	..	..		..	..	..	..	..	4 32	..			..	..	..	..	..	..	..	..	..	..	..	..	7 42	..	..	..	..
Yarmouth 338		..	2 50	..	..		..	..	..	..	..	4 41	..			..	..	..	..	..	..	..	..	..	..	..	..	7 51	..	..	..	..
Freshwater J arr		..	2 56	..	..		..	..	..	..	..	4 47	..			..	..	..	..	..	..	..	..	..	..	..	..	7 57	p.m	..	..	..
Newport dep	2 18	..	..	..	..		..	..	..	3 38	..	Through Train from Ryde	..	4 8		..	..	5 38	..	..	..	..	6 8	..	..	..	..	Through Train from Ryde	7 18	..	..	..
Mill Hill	2 27	..	..	..	..		..	..	..	3 47	..		..	4 17		..	..	5 47	..	..	..	..	6 17	..	..	..	..		7 27	..	..	..
Cowes K arr	2 30	..	..	..	..		..	..	..	3 50	..		..	4 20		..	..	5 50	..	..	..	..	6 20	..	..	..	..		7 30	..	..	..
Brading N	..	..	..	..	2 37		..	..	..	..	3 43		..	..		..	..	..	..	..	..	5 43	..	..	..	6 43	..		..	..	7 43	..
Brading dep	..	..	..	..	3 3		..	..	..	..	3 45		..	..		..	4 55	..	..	..	..	5 55	..	..	..	6 55	..		..	..	7 45	..
St. Helens	..	..	..	..	3 7		..	..	..	..	3 49		..	..		..	4 59	..	..	..	..	5 59	..	..	..	6 59	..		..	..	7 49	..
Bembridge arr	..	..	..	..	3 11		..	..	..	..	3 53		..	..		..	5 3	..	..	..	..	6 3	..	..	..	7 3	..		..	..	7 53	..
Sandown 373	..	..	..	..	2 42	2 48	..	..	..	..	3 48		..	..	4 48	..	..	..	..	..	..	5 48	..	..	..	6 48	..		..	..	7 48	..
Shanklin	..	..	..	..	..	2 54	..	..	..	..	3 55		..	..	4 55	..	..	..	..	..	..	5 55	..	..	..	6 55	..		..	..	7 55	..
Wroxall H	..	..	..	..	..	3 2	..	..	..	..	4 5		..	..	5 5	..	..	..	..	..	..	6 5	..	..	..	7 5	..		..	..	8 5	..
Ventnor G 373 arr	..	..	..	..	..	3 8	..	..	..	..	4 11		..	..	5 11	..	..	..	..	..	..	6 11	..	..	..	7 11	..		..	..	8 11	..

Conveyance of Motor Cars, etc., to and from the Isle of Wight, see pages 501 and 502

For Notes, see page 365

For LOCAL TRAINS and INTERMEDIATE STATIONS between WATERLOO and SURBITON and COMPLETE SERVICE between WATERLOO and GUILDFORD, see pages 394 to 426.

LONDON, GODALMING, HASLEMERE, PETERSFIELD, PORTSMOUTH, and THE ISLE OF WIGHT

Sundays —*continued*

Down	p.m	p.m	p.m	p.m	p.m	p.m	p.m	p.m R		p.m	p.m	p.m	p.m R	pm	p.m	p.m	p.m R	p.m	p.m	p.m	p.m R	p.m	p.m	p.m	p.m
WATERLOO .... dep	..	4 57	..	..	5 27	5 57	6 27	6 45		..	6 57	7 27	7 45	..	7 57	8 27	8 45	..	8 57	9 27	9 45	..	9 57	1027	1127
Surbiton	..	5 13	..	..	5 43	6 13	6 43	..		..	7 13	7 43	..	..	8 13	8 43	..	..	9 13	9 42	..	..	1013	1043	1143
Esher, for Sandown Park	..	5 17	..	..	5 47	6 17	6 47	..		..	7 17	7 47	..	..	8 17	8 47	..	..	9 17	9 47	..	..	1017	1047	1147
Hersham	..	5 20	..	..	5 50	6 20	6 50	..		..	7 20	7 50	..	..	8 20	8 50	..	..	9 20	9 50	..	..	1020	1050	1150
Walton-on-Thames	..	5 22	..	..	5 53	6 23	6 53	..		..	7 23	7 53	..	..	8 23	8 53	..	..	9 23	9 53	..	..	1023	1053	1153
Weybridge **A**	..	5 27	..	..	5 57	6 27	6 57	..		..	7 27	7 57	..	..	8 27	8 57	..	..	9 27	9 57	..	..	1027	1057	1157
West Weybridge	..	5 30	..	..	6 0	6 30	7 0	..		..	7 30	8 0	..	..	8 30	9 0	..	..	9 30	10 0	..	..	1030	11 0	12 0
Byfleet **B**	..	5 33	..	..	6 3	6 33	7 3	..		..	7 33	8 3	..	..	8 33	9 3	..	..	9 33	10 3	...	..	1033	11 3	12 3
Woking C	..	5 39	..	..	6 9	6 39	7 9	7 16		..	7 39	8 9	..	..	8 39	9 9	..	..	9 39	10 9	1016	..	1039	11 9	12 9
Worplesdon	..	5 45	..	..	6 15	6 45	7 15	..		..	7 45	8 15	..	..	8 45	9 15	..	..	9 45	1015	..	..	1045	1115	1215
Guildford 246, 390 arr	..	5 51	..	..	6 21	6 51	7 21	7 25		..	7 51	8 21	8 25	..	8 51	9 21	9 25	..	9 51	1021	1025	..	1051	1121	1221
Guildford 246, 390 dep	5 31	6 1	..	..	6 31	7 1	Stop	7 26		7 31	8 1	..	8 26	831	9 1	..	9 26	9 31	10 1	..	1026	1031	..	..	..
Farncombe	5 36	6 6	..	..	6 36	7 6		..		7 36	8 6	..	..	836	9 6	..	..	9 36	10 6	..	..	1036	..	..	..
Godalming	5 39	6 9	..	..	6 39	7 9	..	..		7 39	8 9	..	..	839	9 9	..	..	9 39	10 9	..	..	1039	..	..	..
Milford	5 43	6 13	..	..	6 43	7 13	..	..		7 43	8 13	..	..	843	9 13	..	..	9 43	1013	..	..	1043	..	..	..
Witley, for Chiddingfold	5 48	6 18	..	..	6 48	7 18	..	..		7 48	8 18	..	..	848	9 18	..	..	9 48	1018	..	..	1048	..	..	..
Haslemere, for Hindhead	5 56	6 26	..	..	6 56	7 26	..	7 45		7 56	8 26	..	8 45	856	9 26	..	9 45	9 56	1026	..	1045	1056	..	..	..
Liphook	6 2	6 32	..	..	7 2	7 32	..	..		8 2	8 32	..	..	9 2	9 32	..	..	10 2	1032	..	..	11 2	..	..	..
Liss	6 9	6 39	..	..	7 9	7 39	..	..		8 9	8 39	..	..	9 9	9 39	..	..	10 9	1039	..	..	11 9	..	..	..
Petersfield 374	6 14	6 44	..	..	7 14	7 44	..	..		8 14	8 44	..	..	914	9 44	..	..	1014	1044	..	..	1114	..	..	..
Rowlands Castle	6 26	6 56	..	..	7 26	7 56	..	..		8 26	8 56	..	..	927	9 56	..	..	1026	1056	..	..	1126	..	..	..
Havant **196**, 244	6 31	7 1	..	..	7 31	8 1	..	..		8 31	9 1	..	..	933	10 1	..	..	1031	11 1	..	..	1131	..	..	..
244 Hayling Island .... arr	..	..	..	..	..	..	..	..		..	..	..	..	..	..	..	..	..	..	..	..	..	..	..	..
Bedhampton Halt	6 33	7 3		..	7 33	8 3	..	..		8 33	9 3	..	..	935	10 3	..	..	1033	11 3	..	..	..	..	..	..
Hilsea Halt	..	..		..	..	..	..	..		..	..	..	..	..	..	..	..	..	..	..	..	..	..	..	..
Fratton 196	6 41	7 11	Through Train from Ventnor (dep. 7.30 p.m.) see page 373	..	7 41	8 11	..	..		8 41	9 11	..	9 18	943	1011	..	1018	1041	1111	..	1118	1141	..	..	..
Portsmouth & Southsea	6 44	7 14		..	7 44	8 14	..	8 20		8 44	9 14	..	9 21	946	1014	..	1021	1044	1114	..	1121	1143	..	..	..
Portsmouth Harbour.. arr	..	..		..	..	..	..	8 26		..	..	..	9 26	..	..	..	..	..	..	..	..	..	..	..	..
¶ **Portsmouth Harbour** dp	..	..		..	..	..	..	8 40		..	..	..	..	..	..	..	..	..	..	..	..	..	..	..	..
Ryde Pier Head .... arr	..	..		..	..	..	..	9 10		..	..	..	..	..	..	..	..	..	..	..	..	..	..	..	..
Ryde, Pier Head § dep	..	..		..	..	..	..	9 25	9 35	..	..	..	..	..	..	..	..	..	..	..	..	..	..	..	..
" **Esplanade** §	..	..		Through train from Cowes (dep. 7 36 p.m) see page 372	..	..	..	9 31	9 38	..	..	..	..	..	..	..	..	..	..	..	..	..	..	..	..
" **St. John's Road**	..	..			..	..	..	9 35	9 42	..	..	..	..	..	..	..	..	..	..	..	..	..	..	..	..
Ashey	..	..			..	..	..	..	9 48	..	..	..	..	..	..	..	..	..	..	..	..	..	..	..	..
Haven Street	..	..			..	..	..	..	9 53	..	..	..	..	..	..	..	..	..	..	..	..	..	..	..	..
Wootton	..	..			..	..	..	..	9 57	..	..	..	..	..	..	..	..	..	..	..	..	..	..	..	..
Whippingham	..	..			..	..	..	..	10 0	..	..	..	..	..	..	..	..	..	..	..	..	..	..	..	..
Newport F 373 ...... arr	..	..			..	..	..	..	10 6	..	..	..	..	..	..	..	..	..	..	..	..	..	..	..	..
Newport .... dep	..	..			..	..	..	..	..	..	..	..	..	..	..	..	..	..	..	..	..	..	..	..	..
Carisbrooke Halt **G**	..	..			..	..	..	..	..	..	..	..	..	..	..	..	..	..	..	..	..	..	..	..	..
Calbourne and Shalfleet	..	..			..	..	..	..	..	..	..	..	..	..	..	..	..	..	..	..	..	..	..	..	..
Ningwood	..	..			..	..	..	..	..	..	..	..	..	..	..	..	..	..	..	..	..	..	..	..	..
Yarmouth 338	..	..			..	..	..	..	..	..	..	..	..	..	..	..	..	..	..	..	..	..	..	..	..
Freshwater J ...... arr	..	..			..	..	..	..	..	..	..	..	..	..	..	..	..	..	..	..	..	..	..	..	..
Newport .... dep	..	..	8 18		..	..	..	..	10 8	..	..	..	..	..	..	..	..	..	..	..	..	..	..	..	..
Mill Hill	..	..	8 27		..	..	..	..	1017	..	..	..	..	..	..	..	..	..	..	..	..	..	..	..	..
Cowes K .... arr	..	..	8 30		..	..	..	..	1020	..	..	..	..	..	..	..	..	..	..	..	..	..	..	..	..
Brading N	..	..	..		..	..	p.m	9 43	..	..	..	..	..	..	..	..	..	..	..	..	..	..	..	..	..
Brading .... dep	..	..	..	..	..	..	8 57	9 55	..	..	..	..	..	..	..	..	..	..	..	..	..	..	..	..	..
St. Helens	..	..	..	..	..	..	9 1	9 59	..	..	..	..	..	..	..	..	..	..	..	..	..	..	..	..	..
Bembridge .... arr	..	..	..	..	..	..	9 5	10 3	..	..	..	..	..	..	..	..	..	..	..	..	..	..	..	..	..
Sandown 373	..	..	..	8 20	..	..	..	9 48	..	..	..	..	..	..	..	..	..	..	..	..	..	..	..	..	..
Shanklin	..	..	..	8 26	..	..	..	9 55	..	..	..	..	..	..	..	..	..	..	..	..	..	..	..	..	..
Wroxall **O**	..	..	..	8 36	..	..	..	10 5	..	..	..	..	..	..	..	..	..	..	..	..	..	..	..	..	..
Ventnor Q 373 ...... arr	..	..	..	8 42	..	..	..	1011	..	..	..	..	..	..	..	..	..	..	..	..	..	..	..	..	..

Conveyance of Motor Cars, etc., to and from the Isle of Wight, see pages 501 and 502

3 Third class only.
A Station for Brooklands, St. George's Hill, and Oatlands Park
B Sta for Woodham & Pyrford.
C Sta. for Chobham (3¼ miles) to Woking Village (1¼ miles)
F Station for Brighstone.
G Station for Castle
J Sta for Totland Bay (1 mile), Alum Bay (3¼ miles) and The Needles (3¾ miles)
K Nearest Station to Osborne House (by Ferry to East Cowes) thence Southern Vectis Bus)
N Sta for Yaverland (1½ miles), The Roman Villa (1 mile), and Nunwell (1½ miles)
O Station for Appuldurcombe (¾ mile)
Q Sta for Bonchurch (1 mile), and The Landslip (1½ miles).
R Refreshment Car between Waterloo and Portsmouth
SO or **S0** Saturdays only.
SX or **SX** Saturdays excepted
V Wednesdays, Thursdays, and Saturdays

§ A frequent service of trams operates between Ryde Pier Head & Esplanade, Railway Tickets being available

¶ By Boat

OTHER TRAINS

BETWEEN	PAGE
London and Guildford....	246
London and Portsmouth..	158
Havant and Portsmouth..	159
Fratton and Portsmouth Harbour	378

For COMPLETE SERVICE between GUILDFORD and WATERLOO and LOCAL TRAINS and INTERMEDIATE STATIONS between SURBITON and WATERLOO, see pages 427 to 459.

THE ISLE OF WIGHT, PORTSMOUTH, PETERSFIELD, HASLEMERE, GODALMING, and LONDON

Up — Week Days

Miles	Miles from Cowes	Up	a.m	a.m	a.m	a.m	a.m	a.m SX	a.m	a.m	a.m SX	a.m	a.m	a.m	a.m	a.m SX	a.m
		Ventnor ... dep	..	..	..	..	..	..	..	..	..	..	..	..	..	..	6 30
1½		Wroxall O	..	..	..	..	..	..	..	..	..	..	..	..	..	..	6 35
4		Shanklin	..	..	..	..	..	..	..	..	..	..	..	..	..	..	6 42
6		Sandown 373	..	..	..	..	..	..	..	..	..	..	..	..	..	..	6 47
—		Mls Bembridge ... dep	..	..	..	..	..	..	..	..	..	..	..	..	..	..	Through Train to Cowes (arr. 7 29 a.m.) see page 373
—		1 St. Helens	..	..	..	..	..	..	..	..	..	..	..	..	..	..	
—		2¾ Brading N 359 ... arr	..	..	..	..	..	..	..	..	..	..	..	..	..	..	
7¾		Brading 359	..	..	..	..	..	..	..	..	..	..	..	..	..	..	
—	—	Cowes ... dep	..	..	..	..	..	..	..	..	..	..	..	..	..	..	
—	½	Mill Hill	..	..	..	..	..	..	..	..	..	..	..	..	..	..	
—	4½	Newport F 359, 373 ... arr	..	..	..	..	..	..	..	..	..	..	..	..	..	..	
—	—	Mls Freshwater ... dep	..	..	..	..	..	..	..	..	..	..	..	..	..	..	
—	—	2 Yarmouth	..	..	..	..	..	..	..	..	..	..	..	..	..	..	
—	—	5 Ningwood	..	..	..	..	..	..	..	..	..	..	..	..	..	..	
—	—	6½ Calbourne & Shalfleet	..	..	..	..	..	..	..	..	..	..	..	..	..	..	
—	—	10¾ Carisbrooke Halt G	..	..	..	..	..	..	..	..	..	..	..	..	..	..	
—	—	12 Newport F 373 ... arr	..	..	..	..	..	..	..	..	..	..	..	..	..	..	
—	—	Newport ... dep	..	..	..	..	..	Saturdays excepted	..	..	..	..	..	..	..	..	
—	6½	Whippingham	..	..	..	..	..		..	..	..	..	..	..	..	..	
—	7¼	Wootton	..	..	..	..	..		..	..	..	..	..	..	..	..	
—	8¾	Haven Street	..	..	..	..	..		..	..	..	..	..	..	..	..	
—	10½	Ashey	..	..	..	..	..		..	..	..	..	..	..	..	..	
11¼	13	Ryde, St. John's Road	..	..	..	..	..		..	..	..	..	..	..	..	..	
12	13¾	„ Esplanade } §	..	..	..	..	..		..	..	..	..	..	..	..	..	
12½	14¼	„ Pier Head } § ... arr	..	..	..	..	..		..	..	..	..	..	..	..	..	Stop
—	—	¶ Ryde, Pier Head ... dep	..	..	..	..	..		..	..	..	..	..	..	..	..	
17	18¾	Portsmouth Harb. ... arr	..	..	..	..	..		..	..	..	..	..	..	..	..	..
—	—	Portsmouth Harbour ... dep	..	..	..	..	..	..	..	..	..	..	..	7 35	..	..	a.m
17¾	19½	Portsmouth & Southsea	..	..	..	..	..	6 10	6 33	..	..	7 8	7 27	7 39	..		8 0
18½	20¼	Fratton	..	..	..	..	..	6 12	6 37	..	..	7 10	7 29	7 42	..		8 2
20¾	22½	Hilsea Halt	..	..	..	..	..	6 16	..	..	..	..	..	..	..		8 6
24¼	26	Bedhampton Halt	..	..	..	..	..	6 21	6 45	..	..	7 18	R	R	..		8 11
—	—	245 Hayling Island ... dep	..	..	..	..	..	..	..	..	..	6 58	6 58	..	..		7 46
25	26¾	Havant 244	..	..	..	..	..	6 24	6 47	..	..	7 21	7 38	7 51	..	Saturdays excepted	8 14
28½	30	Rowlands Castle	..	..	..	..	..	6 29	6 52	..		7 26	..	7 57	..		8 19
36¼	38¼	Petersfield 374	..	..	..	..	..	6 42	7 5	..		7 40	7 54	8 9	..		8 31
40	41¾	Liss	..	..	..	..	..	6 48	7 10	..	Saturdays excepted	7 46	..	8 14	..		8 37
44½	46¼	Liphook	..	..	..	..	..	6 55	7 17	..		7 53	..	8 21	..		8 44
48½	50¼	Haslemere, for Hindhead	..	..	..	6 29	..	7 1	7 24	..		7 59	8 9	8 27	..	8 45	8 50
53	54¾	Witley, for Chiddingfold	..	..	..	6 35	..	7 8	7 30	..		8 5	8 15	8 33	..	8 51	8 56
55	56¾	Milford	..	..	..	6 39	..	7 12	7 34	..		8 9	8 19	8 37	..	8 55	9 0
57	58¾	Godalming	..	..	..	6 43	..	7 16	7 38	..		8 13	8 23	8 41	..	8 59	9 4
58	59¾	Farncombe	..	..	..	6 45	..	7 18	7 41	..		8 15	8 25	8 44	..	9 2	9 6
61	62¾	Guildford 245, 246, 390 ... arr	..	..	..	6 51	..	7 24	7 47	..		8 21	8 31	8 49	..	9 8	9 12
		dep	5 22	5 52	6 22	6 52	7 22	7 34	7 48	..	8 9	8 25	8 32	8 50	8 52	9 9	..
64¾	66½	Worplesdon	5 29	5 59	6 29	6 59	7 28	..	7 55	..	8 15	8 31	8 38	..	8 59	..	..
67	68¾	Woking C 324, 389, 390	5 34	6 4	6 34	7 4	7 32	7 43	7 59	8 6	8 19	8 36	..	..	9 4	9 18	..
69¾	71½	Byfleet B	5 40	6 10	6 40	7 10	7 40	7 48	..	8 10	..	8 40	..	..	9 10	..	..
71	72¾	West Weybridge	5 43	6 13	6 43	7 13	7 43	..	..	8 13	..	8 43	..	..	9 13	..	..
72½	74¼	Weybridge A	5 46	6 16	6 46	7 16	7 46	7 53	..	8 16	..	8 46	..	..	9 16	..	..
74¼	76	Walton-on-Thames	5 50	6 20	6 50	7 20	7 50	7 57	..	8 20	..	8 50	..	..	9 20	..	..
75½	77¼	Hersham	5 52	6 22	6 52	7 22	7 52	..	..	8 22	..	8 52	..	..	9 22	..	..
77	78¾	Esher, for Sandown Park	5 55	6 25	6 55	7 25	7 55	8 1	..	8 25	..	8 55	..	..	9 25	..	..
79½	81¼	Surbiton	6 0	6 30	7 0	7 30	8 0	8 5	..	8 30	8 35	9 0	..	9 14	9 30	..	..
91½	93¼	WATERLOO ... arr	6 20	6 46	7 16	7 46	8 17	8 22	8 29	8 47	8 52	9 16	9 13	9 30	9 47	9 49	..

Up	a.m	a.m	a.m SX	a.m	a.m	a.m	a.m SX	a.m	a.m	a.m	a.m	a.m SO	a.m	a.m	a.m
Ventnor ... dep	..	..	..	..	..	..	..	..	..	..	7 40	..	..	..	..
Wroxall O	..	..	..	..	..	..	..	..	..	..	7 45	..	..	..	..
Shanklin	..	..	..	..	..	..	..	..	..	..	7 52	..	..	..	..
Sandown 373	..	6 50	..	..	..	..	..	..	..	..	7 58	..	..	..	..
Mls Bembridge ... dep	..	6 45	..	..	..	..	..	..	..	..	7 53	..	..	..	..
1 St. Helens	..	6 47	..	..	..	..	..	..	..	..	7 55	..	..	..	..
2¾ Brading N 359 ... arr	..	6 53	..	..	..	..	..	..	..	..	8 1	..	..	..	..
Brading 359	..	6 57	..	..	..	..	..	..	..	..	8 7	..	..	..	..
Cowes ... dep	6 20	..	..	..	..	6 56	..	..	..	..	..	..	..	7 56	..
Mill Hill	6 22	..	..	..	..	6 57	..	..	..	..	..	..	..	7 57	..
Newport F 359, 373 ... arr	6 33	..	..	..	..	7 7	..	..	..	..	..	..	..	8 7	..
Mls Freshwater ... dep	..	..	..	..	..	Stop	..	..	..	..	..	..	..	Stop	..
2 Yarmouth	..	..	..	..	..	..	..	..	..	..	..	..	..	..	..
5 Ningwood	..	..	..	..	..	..	..	..	..	..	..	..	..	..	..
6½ Calbourne & Shalfleet	..	..	..	..	..	..	..	..	..	..	..	..	..	..	..
10¾ Carisbrooke Halt G	..	..	..	..	..	..	..	..	..	..	..	..	..	..	..
12 Newport F 373 ... arr	..	..	..	..	..	..	..	..	..	..	..	..	..	..	..
Newport ... dep	6 35	..	Saturdays excepted	..	..	..	Saturdays excepted	..	..	7 38	..	Saturdays only	..	..	..
Whippingham	6 41	..		..	..	..		..	..	7 44	..		..	..	..
Wootton	6 44	..		..	..	..		..	..	7 47	..		..	..	..
Haven Street	6 48	..		..	..	..		..	..	7 52	..		..	..	..
Ashey	6 53	..		..	..	..		..	..	7 58	..		..	..	..
Ryde, St. John's Road	6 59	7 4		..	..	..		..	..	8 4	8 14		..	..	..
„ Esplanade } §	7 3	7 9		..	..	..		..	..	8 8	8 19		..	..	..
„ Pier Head } § ... arr	7 6	7 12		..	..	..		..	..	8 11	8 22		..	..	..
¶ Ryde, Pier Head ... dep	7 30			..	..	..		..	..	8 35			..	..	..
Portsmouth Harb. ... arr	8 0			..	..	..		..	..	9 5			..	..	..
Portsmouth Harbour ... dep	..		8 15	..	8 20	a.m	8 42	..	..	..		9 20	..	a.m	..
Portsmouth & Southsea	..		8 19	..	8 24	8 30	8 46	..	9 0	..		9 24	..	9 30	10 0
Fratton	..		8 21	..	8 27	8 32	..	..	9 2	..		..	..	9 32	10 2
Hilsea Halt	..		..	..	..	8 36	..	..	..	..		..	..	..	..
Bedhampton Halt	..		R	..	R	8 41	R	..	9 10	..		R	..	9 40	1010
245 Hayling Island ... dep	..		..	..	..	..	8 40	..	8 40	..		8 40	..	..	9 45
Havant 244	..		8 30		8SO36	8 44	8 56	..	9 13	..		9 33	..	9 43	1013
Rowlands Castle	..		..	..	..	8 49	..	..	9 18	..		..	..	9 48	1018
Petersfield 374	..		8 46		8SO52	9 1	9 12	..	9 30	..		..	..	10 0	1030
Liss	..		..	..	..	9 7	..	..	9 36	..		..	..	10 6	1036
Liphook	..		..	..	..	9 14	..	..	9 43	..		..	..	1013	1043
Haslemere, for Hindhead	..		9 1	..	9 7	9 20	9 27	..	9 49	..		10 2	..	1019	1049
Witley, for Chiddingfold	..		..	..	9 13	9 26	9 33	..	9 55	..		..	..	1025	1055
Milford	..		..	..	9 17	9 30	9 37	..	9 59	..		..	..	1029	1059
Godalming	..		..	..	9 21	9 34	9 41	..	10 3	..		..	..	1033	11 3
Farncombe	..		..	..	..	9 36	..	..	10 5	..		..	..	1035	11 5
Guildford 245, 246, 390 ... arr	..		..	..	9 28	9 42	9 48	..	1011	..		1019	..	1041	1112
dep	..		..	9 22	9 30	..	9 49	9 52	..	..		1020	1022	1052	..
Worplesdon	..		..	9 28	..	..	..	9 59	..	..		..	1029	1059	..
Woking C 324, 389, 390	..		..	9 33	..	..	..	10 4	..	..		1031	1034	11 4	..
Byfleet B	..		..	9 40	..	..	..	1010	..	..		..	1040	1110	..
West Weybridge	..		..	9 43	..	..	..	1013	..	..		..	1043	1113	..
Weybridge A	..		..	9 46	..	..	..	1016	..	..		..	1046	1116	..
Walton-on-Thames	..		..	9 50	..	..	..	1020	..	..		..	1050	1120	..
Hersham	..		..	9 52	..	..	..	1022	..	..		..	1052	1122	..
Esher, for Sandown Park	..		..	9 55	..	..	..	1025	..	..		..	1055	1125	..
Surbiton	..		..	10 0	..	..	..	1030	..	..		..	11 0	1130	..
WATERLOO ... arr	..		9 52	1016	10 5	..	1028	1046	..	..		11 2	1116	1148	..

Conveyance of Motor Cars, etc., to and from the Isle of Wight, see pages 501 and 502

For Notes, see page 372

For COMPLETE SERVICE between GUILDFORD and WATERLOO and LOCAL TRAINS and INTERMEDIATE STATIONS between SURBITON and WATERLOO, see pages 427 to 459.

THE ISLE OF WIGHT, PORTSMOUTH, PETERSFIELD, HASLEMERE, GODALMING, and LONDON

Week Days—*continued*

Up	a.m	a.m	a.m	a.m	a.m	a.m.	a.m	a.m	a.m	a.m	a.m	p.m	a.m.	a.m	a.m.	a.m	a.m	p.m	a.m.	a.m.	a.m	a.m	p.m	p.m.	p.m	a.m	p.m	p.m	p.m	p.m S O
Ventnor dep	8 5	Thro Train Freshwater to Ryde	8 40								9 42					Through Train from Freshwater	1042					1142						Wednesdays, Thursdays, and Saturdays	1242	
Wroxall O	8 9		8 45								9 47						1047					1147							1247	
Shanklin	8 16		8 52						9 43		9 54						1054					1154							1254	
Sandown 373	8 21		8 58						9 47		10 1						11 1					12 1							1 1	
Bembridge dep			8 42					9 32			9 57			1032			1057			11 32					1232				1257	
St. Helens			8 44					9 34			9 59			1034			1059			11 34					1234				1259	
Brading N 359 arr			8 50					9 40			10 5			1040			11 5			11 40					1240				1 5	
Brading 359	8 27		9 7								10 7						11 7			Stop		12 7			Stop				1 7	
Cowes dep		8 29					8 43		Through Train to Cowes (arr. 10 30 a.m.) see page 373	9 26					10 3				10 56		1126						1226			
Mill Hill		8 30					8 44			9 27					10 4				10 57		1127						1227			
Newport F 359, 373 arr		8 40					8 54			9 37					10 14				11 7		1137						1237			
Freshwater dep		7 50					Through Train to Shanklin (arr. 9 34 a.m.) see page 373								Stop	9 55			Stop							1155			Weds., Thurs., and Sats.	
Yarmouth		7 55														10 0										12 0				
Ningwood		8 4														10 9										12 9				
Calbourne & Shalfleet		8 13														1013										1213				
Carisbrooke Halt G		8 28														1025										1225				
Newport F 373 arr		8 35														1033										1232				
Newport dep		8 42								9 38						1038					1138							1238		Saturdays only
Whippingham		8 49								9 44						1044					1144							1244		
Wootton		8 54								9 47						1047					1147							1247		
Haven Street		9 0								9 52						1052					1152							1252		
Ashey		9 5								9 59						1059					1159							1259		
Ryde, St. John's Road	8 34	9 11	9 14							10 5	1014					11 5	1114				12 5	1214						1 5	1 14	
" Esplanade } §		9 15	9 19							10 9	1019					11 9	1119				12 9	1219						1 9	1 19	
" Pier Head } arr		9 18	9 23							1012	1022					1112	1122				1212	1222						1 12	1 22	
¶ Ryde, Pier Head dep		9 35								1035						1135					1235							1S035		
¶ Portsmouth Harb. arr		10 5								11 5						12 5					1 5							2S05		
Portsmouth Harbour dep		1020								1120					noon	1220			p.m.	p.m.	1 20				p.m					2 20
Portsmouth & Southsea		1024			1030	11 0				1124			11 30		12 0	1224			12 30	1 0	1 24			1 30	2 0					2 24
Fratton					1032	11 2							11 32		12 2				12 32	1 2				1 32	2 2					
Hilsea Halt						11S06							11S036		12S06				12S036	1S06				1S036						
Bedhampton Halt		R			1040	11 10				R			11 40		12 10	R			12 40	1 10	R			1 40	2 10					R
245 Hayling Island dep		9 45																	12 27					1 12	1S057					
Havant 244		1033			1043	11 13							11 43		12 13				12 43	1 13				1 43	2 13					
Rowlands Castle					1048	11 18							11 48		12 18				12 48	1 18				1 48	2 18					
Petersfield 374					11 0	11 30							12 0		12 30				1 0	1 30				2 0	2 30					
Liss					11 6	11 36							12 6		12 36				1 6	1 36				2 6	2 36					
Liphook					1113	11 43							12 13		12 43				1 13	1 43				2 13	2 43					
Haslemere, for Hindhead		11 2			1119	11 49				12 2			12 19		12 49	1 2			1 19	1 49	2 2			2 19	2 49					3 2
Witley, for Chiddingfold					1125	11 55							12 25		12 55				1 25	1 55				2 25	2 55					
Milford					1129	11 59							12 29		12 59				1 29	1 59				2 29	2 59					
Godalming					1133	12 3							12 33		1 3				1 33	2 3				2 33	3 3					
Farncombe					1135	12 5							12 35		1 5				1 35	2 5				2 35	3 5					
Guildford 245, 246, 390 arr		1119			1141	12 11				1219			12 41		1 11	1 19			1 41	2 11	2 19			2 41	3 11					3 19
Guildford dep		1120		1122	1152					1220		1222	12 52			1 20		1 22	1 52		2 20		2 22	2 52						3 20
Worplesdon 390				1129	1159							1229	12 59					1 29	1 59				2 29	2 59						
Woking C 324, 389		1129		1134	12 4					1230		1234	1 4			1 29		1 34	2 4		2 29		2 34	3 4						3 29
Byfleet B				1140	1210							1240	1 10					1 40	2 10				2 40	3 10						
West Weybridge				1143	1213							1243	1 13					1 43	2 13				2 43	3 13						
Weybridge A				1146	1216							1246	1 16					1 46	2 16				2 46	3 16						
Walton-on-Thames				1150	1220							1250	1 20					1 50	2 20				2 50	3 20						
Hersham				1152	1222							1252	1 22					1 52	2 22				2 52	3 22						
Esher, for Sandown Park				1155	1225							1255	1 25					1 55	2 25				2 55	3 25						
Surbiton				12 0	1230							1 0	1 30					2 0	2 30				3 0	3 30						
WATERLOO arr		12 1		1216	1246					1 1		1 16	1 46			2 1		2 16	2 46		3 1		3 16	3 46						4 1

Conveyance of Motor Cars, etc., to and from the Isle of Wight, see pages 501 and 502

For Notes, see page 372; for Continuation of Trains, see pages 368 to 372

For COMPLETE SERVICE between GUILDFORD and WATERLOO and LOCAL TRAINS and INTERMEDIATE STATIONS between SURBITON and WATERLOO, see pages 427 to 459.

THE ISLE OF WIGHT, PORTSMOUTH, PETERSFIELD, HASLEMERE, GODALMING, and LONDON

Week Days—*continued*

Up	p.m	p.m	p.m	pm.	p.m	p.m	p.m	p.m	p.m	p.m	p.m	p.m	p.m	p.m.	p.m	p.m
Ventnor dep						1 42						2 42				
Wroxall O						1 47						2 47				
Shanklin						1 54						2 54				3 27
Sandown 373						2 1						3 1				3 31
Bembridge dep	1 32					1 57						2 57				
St. Helens	1 34					1 59						2 59				
Brading N 359 arr	1 40					2 5						3 5				
Brading 359	Wednesdays, Thursdays, and Saturdays					2 7						3 7				
Cowes dep			12 56		1 26						2 26					
Mill Hill			12 57		1 27						2 27					
Newport F 359, 373 arr			1 7		1 37						2 37					
Freshwater dep			Stop							1 55						Through Train to Newport (arr. 4 1 p.m.) see page 373
Yarmouth										2 0						
Ningwood										2 9						
Calbourne & Shalfleet										2 13						
Carisbrooke Halt G										2 25						
Newport F 373 arr										2 32						
Newport dep					1 38					Through Train to Shanklin (arr. 3 14 p.m.) see page 373	2 38					
Whippingham					1 44						2 44					
Wootton					1 47						2 47					
Haven Street					1 52						2 52					
Ashey					1 59						2 59					
Ryde, St. John's Road					2 5	2 14					3 5	3 14				
" Esplanade §					2 9	2 19					3 9	3 19				
" Pier Head § arr					2 12	2 22					3 12	3 22				
¶ Ryde, Pier Head dep					2 35						3 35					
¶ Portsmouth Harb. arr					3 5						4 5					
Portsmouth Harbour dep			p.m		3 20						4 20					
Portsmouth & Southsea			2 30	3 0	3 24			3 30	4 0		4 24			4 30	5 0	
Fratton			2 32	3 2				3 32	4 2					4 32	5 2	
Hilsea Halt														4SX36	5SX6	
Bedhampton Halt			2 40	3 10	R			3 40	4 10		R			4 40	5 10	
245 Hayling Island dep								3d18								
Havant 244			2 43	3 13				3 43	4 13					4 43	5 13	
Rowlands Castle			2 48	3 18				3 48	4 18					4 48	5 18	
Petersfield 374			3 0	3 30				4 0	4 30					5 0	5 30	
Liss			3 6	3 36				4 6	4 36					5 6	5 36	
Liphook			3 13	3 43				4 13	4 43					5 13	5 43	
Haslemere, for Hindhead			3 19	3 49	4 2			4 19	4 49		5 2			5 19	5 49	
Witley, for Chiddingfold			3 25	3 55				4 25	4 55					5 25	5 55	
Milford			3 29	3 59				4 29	4 59					5 29	5 59	
Godalming			3 33	4 3				4 33	5 3					5 33	6 3	
Farncombe			3 35	4 5				4 35	5 5					5 35	6 5	
Guildford 245, 246, 390 arr			3 41	4 11	4 19			4 41	5 11		5 19			5 41	6 11	
Guildford dep		3 22	3 52		4 20		4 22	4 52			5 20		5 22	5 52		
Worplesdon		3 29	3 59				4 29	4 59					5 29	5 59		
Woking C 324, 389, 390		3 34	4 4		4 30		4 34	5 4			5 29		5 34	6 4		
Byfleet B		3 40	4 10				4 40	5 10					5 40	6 10		
West Weybridge		3 43	4 13				4 43	5 13					5 43	6 13		
Weybridge A		3 46	4 16				4 46	5 16					5 46	6 16		
Walton-on-Thames		3 50	4 20				4 50	5 20					5 50	6 20		
Hersham		3 52	4 22				4 52	5 22					5 52	6 22		
Esher, for Sandown Park		3 55	4 25				4 55	5 25					5 55	6 25		
Surbiton		4 0	4 30				5 0	5 30					6 0	6 30		
WATERLOO arr		4 16	4 46		5 3		5 16	5 48			6 1		6 48	6 48		

Up	p.m	p.m	p.m	p.m	p.m.	p.m		p.m	p.m	p.m.	p.m	p.m	p.m	p.m	p.m
Ventnor dep			3 42						4 42				5 20		5 42
Wroxall O			3 47						4 47				5 25		5 47
Shanklin			3 54						4 54				5 32		5 54
Sandown 373			4 1						5 1				5 38		6 1
Bembridge dep	3 32		3 57		4 32				4 57			5 32			5 57
St. Helens	3 34		3 59		4 34				4 59			5 34			5 59
Brading N 359 arr	3 40		4 5		4 40				5 5			5 40			6 5
Brading 359			4 7		Stop				5 7			Stop	5 44		6 7
Cowes dep		3 26		3 56				4 26		4 56				5 26	
Mill Hill		3 27		3 57				4 27		4 57				5 27	
Newport F 359, 373 arr		3 37		4 7				4 37		5 7				5 37	
Freshwater dep				Stop				3 25		Stop			Saturdays excepted		
Yarmouth								3 30							
Ningwood								3 39							
Calbourne & Shalfleet								3 43							
Carisbrooke Halt G								3 55							
Newport F 373 arr								4 2							
Newport dep		3 38						4 38			5 10			5 38	
Whippingham		3 44						4 44			5 15			5 44	
Wootton		3 47						4 47			5 18			5 47	
Haven Street		3 52						4 52			5 22			5 52	
Ashey		3 59						4 59			5 27			159	
Ryde, St. John's Road		4 5	4 14					5 5	5 14		5 33		5 51	6 5	6 14
" Esplanade §		4 9	4 19					5 9	5 19		5 37			6 9	6 19
" Pier Head § arr		4 12	4 22					5 12	5 22					6 12	6 22
¶ Ryde, Pier Head dep		4 35						5 35						6 35	
¶ Portsmouth Harb. arr		5 5						6 5						7 5	
Portsmouth Harbour dep		5 20			p.m.					p.m.		p.m		7 20	
Portsmouth & Southsea		5 24			5 30	6 0				6 30		7 0		7 24	
Fratton					5 32	6 2				6 32		7 2			
Hilsea Halt					5SX36	6SX6				6SX36					
Bedhampton Halt		R			5 40	6 10				6 40		7 10		R	
245 Hayling Island dep					5 6	5 57						6 52			
Havant 244					5 43	6 13				6 43		7 13			
Rowlands Castle					5 48	6 18				6 48		7 18			
Petersfield 374					6 0	6 30				7 0		7 30			
Liss					6 6	6 36				7 6		7 36			
Liphook					6 13	6 43				7 13		7 43			
Haslemere, for Hindhead		6 2			6 19	6 49				7 19		7 49		8 2	
Witley, for Chiddingfold					6 25	6 55				7 25		7 55			
Milford					6 29	6 59				7 29		7 59			
Godalming					6 33	7 3				7 33		8 3			
Farncombe					6 35	7 5				7 35		8 5			
Guildford 245, 246, 390 arr		6 19		p.m	6 41	7 11				7 41		8 11		8 19	
Guildford dep		6 20		6 22	6 52	7 22				7 52				8 20	
Worplesdon				6 29	6 59	7 29				7 59					
Woking C 324, 389, 390		6 29		6 34	7 4	7 34				8 4				8 29	
Byfleet B				6 40	7 10	7 40				8 10					
West Weybridge				6 43	7 13	7 43				8 13					
Weybridge A				6 46	7 16	7 46				8 16					
Walton-on-Thames				6 50	7 20	7 59				8 20					
Hersham				6 52	7 22	7 52				8 22					
Esher, for Sandown Park				6 55	7 25	7 55				8 25					
Surbiton				7 0	7 30	8 0				8 30					
WATERLOO arr		7 3		7 16	7 46	8 16				8 46				9 1	

Conveyance of Motor Cars, etc., to and from the Isle of Wight, see pages 501 and 502

For Notes, see page 372

For COMPLETE SERVICE between GUILDFORD and WATERLOO and LOCAL TRAINS and INTERMEDIATE STATIONS between SURBITON and WATERLOO, see pages 427 to 459

THE ISLE OF WIGHT, PORTSMOUTH, PETERSFIELD, HASLEMERE, GODALMING, and LONDON

Weekdays—*continued*

Up	p.m	p.m	p.m	p.m	p.m		p.m	p.m	p.m	p.m	p.m	p.m		p.m	p.m	p.m	p.m	p.m	p.m	p.m	p.m	p.m	p.m		p.m	p.m	p.m		p.m SO	p.m		
Ventnor ... dep	..	..	..	..	..	..	..	..	6 42	..	..	..	..	..	..	7 42	..	..	..	..	..	..	8 42	..	..	..	9 42	..	..	..	..	..
Wroxall ⓘ	..	..	..	..	..	..	..	..	6 47	..	..	..	..	..	..	7 47	..	..	..	..	..	..	8 47	..	..	..	9 47	..	..	..	..	..
Shanklin	..	..	..	..	..	..	..	..	6 54	..	..	..	..	..	..	7 54	..	..	..	..	..	..	8 54	..	..	..	9 54	..	..	..	..	..
Sandown 373	..	..	..	..	..	..	..	..	7 1	..	..	..	..	..	..	8 1	..	..	..	..	..	..	9 1	..	..	..	10 1	..	..	..	..	..
Bembridge ... dep	..	..	..	..	..	..	6 32	..	6 57	..	..	..	..	7 32	..	7 57	..	8 32	..	..	..	..	8 59	..	9 32	..	9 57	..	..	..	..	..
St. Helens	..	..	..	..	..	..	6 34	..	6 59	..	..	..	..	7 34	..	7 59	..	8 34	..	..	..	..	9 1	..	9 34	..	9 59	..	..	..	..	..
Brading N 359 ... arr	..	..	..	..	..	..	6 40	..	7 5	..	..	..	..	7 40	..	8 5	..	8 40	..	..	..	..	9 7	..	9 40	..	10 5	..	..	..	..	..
Brading 359	..	..	..	..	..	..	..	..	7 7	..	..	..	..	..	..	8 7	..	..	..	..	..	..	9 8	..	..	..	10 7	..	..	..	..	..
Cowes ... dep	..	..	..	..	5 56	..	..	6 26	..	..	..	..	..	..	7 26	..	..	..	..	7 56	..	8 26	..	..	..	9 26	..	..	9 56	1026	..	..
Mill Hill	..	..	..	..	5 57	..	..	6 27	..	..	..	..	..	..	7 27	..	..	..	..	7 57	..	8 27	..	..	..	9 27	..	..	9 57	1027	..	..
Newport F 353, 373 ... arr	..	..	..	..	6 7	..	..	6 37	..	..	..	..	..	..	7 37	..	..	..	..	8 7	..	8 37	..	..	..	9 37	..	..	10 7	1037	..	..
Freshwater ... dep	..	5 22	..	..	..	..	..	..	..	..	..	..	..	..	..	..	7 17	..	..	..	7 55	..	..	..	..	..	..	..	..	..	..	..
Yarmouth	..	5 27	..	..	..	..	..	..	..	..	..	..	..	..	..	..	7 22	..	..	..	8 0	..	..	..	..	..	..	..	..	..	..	..
Ningwood	..	5 38	..	..	..	..	..	..	..	..	..	..	..	..	..	..	7 30	..	..	..	8 9	..	..	..	..	..	..	..	..	..	..	..
Calbourne & Shalfleet	..	5 43	..	..	..	..	..	..	..	..	..	..	..	..	..	..	7 38	..	..	..	8 13	..	..	..	..	..	..	..	..	..	..	..
Carisbrooke Halt G	..	5 55	..	..	..	..	..	..	..	..	..	..	..	..	..	..	7 50	..	..	..	8 25	..	..	..	..	..	..	..	..	..	..	..
Newport F 373 ... arr	..	6 2	..	..	..	..	..	..	..	..	..	..	..	..	..	..	7 57	..	..	..	8 33	..	..	..	..	..	..	..	..	..	..	..
Newport ... dep	..	..	..	..	..	..	..	6 38	..	..	..	..	..	..	7 38	..	..	..	..	..	..	8 38	..	..	..	..	..	..	Saturdays only	..	..	..
Whippingham	..	..	..	..	..	..	..	6 44	..	..	..	..	..	..	7 44	..	..	..	..	..	..	8 44	..	..	..	..	..	..		..	..	..
Wootton	..	..	..	..	..	..	..	6 47	..	..	..	..	..	..	7 47	..	..	..	..	..	..	8 47	..	..	..	..	..	..		..	..	..
Haven Street	..	..	..	..	..	..	..	6 52	..	..	..	..	..	..	7 52	..	..	..	..	..	..	8 52	..	..	..	..	..	..		..	..	..
Ashey	..	..	..	..	..	..	..	6 59	..	..	..	..	..	..	7 59	..	..	..	..	..	..	8 59	..	..	..	..	..	..		..	..	..
Ryde, St. John's Road	..	..	..	..	..	..	..	7 5	7 14	..	..	..	..	..	8 5	8 14	..	..	..	..	..	9 5	9 15	..	..	..	1014	..		..	..	..
" Esplanade } §	..	..	..	..	..	..	..	7 9	7 19	..	..	..	..	..	8 9	8 19	..	..	..	..	..	9 9	9 19	..	..	..	..	..		..	..	..
" Pier Head } ... arr	..	..	..	..	..	..	..	7 12	7 22	..	..	..	..	..	8 12	8 22	..	..	..	..	..	9 12	9 22	..	..	..	..	..		..	..	..
¶ Ryde, Pier Head ... dep	..	..	..	..	..	..	..	7 35	..	..	..	..	..	..	8 35	..	..	..	..	..	..	9 35	..	..	..	..	..	..	..	..	..	..
¶ Portsmouth Harb. ... arr	..	..	..	..	..	..	..	8 5	..	..	..	..	..	..	9 5	..	..	..	..	..	..	10 5	..	..	..	..	..	..	..	..	..	..
Portsmouth Harbour ... dep	..	..	..	..	..	..	..	8 20	..	..	..	..	..	..	9 20	..	..	..	..	..	..	..	..	..	..	..	..	..	..	..	..	..
Portsmouth & Southsea	..	..	7 30	8 0	..	..	..	8 24	..	..	8 30	9 0	..	..	9 30	..	..	..	10 0	..	..	..	..	..	..	..	..	..	..	..	..	..
Fratton	..	..	7 32	8 2	..	..	..	..	..	..	8 32	9 2	..	..	9 32	..	..	..	10 2	..	..	..	..	..	..	..	..	..	..	..	..	..
Hilsea Halt	..	..	..	..	..	..	..	..	..	..	..	..	..	..	..	..	..	..	..	..	..	..	..	..	..	..	..	..	..	..	..	..
Bedhampton Halt	..	..	7 40	8 10	..	..	..	R	..	..	8 40	9 10	..	..	9 40	..	..	..	10 10	..	..	..	..	..	..	..	..	..	..	..	..	..
245 Hayling Island ... dep	..	..	..	7 52	..	..	..	..	..	..	..	8 52	..	..	..	..	..	..	..	..	..	..	..	..	..	..	..	..	..	..	..	..
Havant 244	..	..	7 43	8 13	..	..	..	..	..	..	8 43	9 13	..	..	9 43	..	..	..	10 13	..	..	..	..	..	..	..	..	..	..	..	..	..
Rowlands Castle	..	..	7 48	8 18	..	..	..	..	..	..	8 48	9 18	..	..	9 48	..	..	..	10 18	..	..	..	..	..	..	..	..	..	..	..	..	..
Petersfield 374	..	..	8 0	8 30	..	..	..	..	..	..	9 0	9 30	..	..	10 0	..	..	..	10 30	..	..	..	..	..	..	..	..	..	..	..	..	..
Liss	..	..	8 6	8 36	..	..	..	..	..	..	9 6	9 36	..	..	10 6	..	..	..	10 36	..	..	..	..	..	..	..	..	..	..	..	..	..
Liphook	..	..	8 13	8 43	..	..	..	..	..	..	9 13	9 43	..	..	1013	..	..	..	10 43	..	..	..	..	..	..	..	..	..	..	..	..	..
Haslemere, for Hindhead	..	..	8 19	8 49	..	..	..	9 2	..	..	9 19	9 49	..	..	1019	..	..	..	10 49	..	..	..	..	..	..	..	..	..	..	..	..	..
Witley, for Chiddingfold	..	..	8 25	8 55	..	..	..	..	..	..	9 25	9 55	..	..	1025	..	..	..	10 55	..	..	..	..	..	..	..	..	..	..	..	..	..
Milford	..	..	8 29	8 59	..	..	..	..	..	..	9 29	9 59	..	..	1029	..	..	..	10 59	..	..	..	..	..	..	..	..	..	..	..	..	..
Godalming	..	..	8 33	9 3	..	..	..	..	..	..	9 33	10 3	..	..	1033	..	..	..	11 3	..	..	..	..	..	..	..	..	..	..	..	..	..
Farncombe	..	..	8 35	9 5	..	..	..	..	..	..	9 35	10 5	..	..	1035	..	..	..	11 5	..	..	..	..	..	..	..	..	..	..	..	..	..
Guildford 245, 246, 390 ... arr	..	..	8 41	9 11	..	..	..	9 19	..	..	9 41	1011	..	..	1041	..	..	..	11 11	..	..	..	..	..	..	..	..	..	..	..	..	..
Guildford ... dep	8 22	..	8 52	..	..	..	..	9 20	..	9 22	9 52	1022	..	..	1052	..	..	..	11 22	..	..	..	..	..	..	..	..	..	..	..	..	..
Worplesdon	8 29	..	8 59	..	..	..	..	..	..	9 29	9 59	1029	..	..	1059	..	..	..	11 29	..	..	..	..	..	..	..	..	..	..	..	..	..
Woking C 324, 89, 390	8 34	..	9 4	..	..	..	..	9 29	..	9 34	10 4	1034	..	..	11 4	..	..	..	11 34	..	..	..	..	..	..	..	..	..	..	..	..	..
Byfleet B	8 40	..	9 10	..	..	..	..	..	..	9 40	1010	1040	..	..	1110	..	..	..	..	..	..	..	..	..	..	..	..	..	..	..	..	..
West Weybridge	8 43	..	9 13	..	..	..	..	..	..	9 43	1013	1043	..	..	1113	..	..	..	..	..	..	..	..	..	..	..	..	..	..	..	..	..
Weybridge A	8 46	..	9 16	..	..	..	..	..	..	9 46	1016	1046	..	..	1116	..	..	..	..	..	..	..	..	..	..	..	..	..	..	..	..	..
Walton-on-Thames	8 50	..	9 20	..	..	..	..	..	..	9 50	1020	1050	..	..	1120	..	..	..	..	..	..	..	..	..	..	..	..	..	..	..	..	..
Hersham	8 52	..	9 22	..	..	..	..	..	..	9 52	1022	1052	..	..	1122	..	..	..	..	..	..	..	..	..	..	..	..	..	..	..	..	..
Esher for Sandown Park	8 55	..	9 25	..	..	..	..	..	..	9 55	1025	1055	..	..	1125	..	..	..	..	..	..	..	..	..	..	..	..	..	..	..	..	..
Surbiton	9 0	..	9 30	..	..	..	..	..	..	10 0	1030	11 0	..	..	1130	..	..	..	..	..	..	..	..	..	..	..	..	..	..	..	..	..
WATERLOO ... arr	9 16	..	9 46	..	..	..	..	10 1	..	1016	1046	1116	..	..	1146	..	..	..	12SX6	..	..	..	..	..	..	..	..	..	..	..	..	..

Conveyance of Motor Cars, etc., to and from the Isle of Wight, see pages 501 and 502

For Notes, see page 372; for SUNDAY TRAINS, see pages 370 to 372

For COMPLETE SERVICE between GUILDFORD and WATERLOO and LOCAL TRAINS and INTERMEDIATE STATIONS between SURBITON and WATERLOO, see pages 427 to 459

THE ISLE OF WIGHT, PORTSMOUTH, PETERSFIELD, HASLEMERE, GODALMING, and LONDON

Sundays

Up	a.m	a.m	a.m	a.m	a.m	a.m	a.m	a.m	a.m	a.m	a.m		a.m	a.m	a.m	a.m
Ventnor .... dep													Through Train from Freshwater	8 30		9 50
Wroxall ❶														8 35		9 54
Shanklin														8 42		10 1
Sandown 373														8 48		10 7
Bembridge .... dep																Through Train to Cowes (arr. 10 50 a.m.), see page 373
St. Helens																
Brading N 359 .... arr																
Brading 359														8 53		
Cowes .... dep											8 8					
Mill Hill											8 10					
Newport F 359, 373 .. arr											8 21					
Freshwater .... dep													7 30			
Yarmouth													7 35			
Ningwood													7 44			
Calbourne & Shalfleet													7 52			
Carisbrooke Halt G													8 6			
Newport F 373 .... arr													8 14			
Newport .... dep					6 20								8 23			
Whippingham					6 25								8 30			
Wootton					6 29								8 34			
Haven Street					6 34								8 39			
Ashey					6 41								8 45			
Ryde, St. John's Road					6 47								8 51	9 0		
" Esplanade §					6 52								8 56	9 5		
" Pier Head § .. arr					6 55								8 59	9 8		
Ryde, Pier Head .... dep					7 30								9 35			
Portsmouth Harb. .. arr					8 0								10 5			
Portsmouth Harbour .. dep					8 20								1020			
Portsmouth & Southsea			7 30	8 0	8 24		8 30	9 0	9 30	10 0			1024			
Fratton			7 32	8 2			8 32	9 2	9 32	10 2						
Hilsea Halt																
Bedhampton Halt			7 40	8 10	R		8 40	9 10	9 40	1010			R			
245 Hayling Island .... dep																
Havant 244			7 43	8 13			8 43	9 13	9 43	1013						
Rowlands Castle			7 48	8 18			8 48	9 18	9 48	1018						
Petersfield 374			8 0	8 30			9 0	9 30	10 0	1030						
Liss			8 6	8 36			9 6	9 36	10 6	1036						
Liphook			8 13	8 43			9 13	9 43	1013	1043						
Haslemere, for Hindhead			8 19	8 49	9 2		9 19	9 49	1019	1049			11 2			
Witley, for Chiddingfold			8 25	8 55			9 25	9 55	1025	1055						
Milford			8 29	8 59			9 29	9 59	1029	1059						
Godalming			8 33	9 3			9 33	10 3	1033	11 3						
Farncombe			8 35	9 5			9 35	10 5	1035	11 5						
Guildford 245, 246, 390 arr			8 41	9 11	9 19		9 41	1011	1041	1111			1119			
Guildford dep	7 22	8 22	8 52		9 20	9 22	9 52	1022	1052				1120		1122	
Worplesdon	7 29	8 29	8 59			9 29	9 59	1029	1059						1129	
Woking C 324, 389, 390	7 34	8 34	9 4		9 29	9 34	10 4	1034	11 4				1129		1134	
Byfleet B	7 40	8 40	9 10			9 40	1010	1040	1110						1140	
West Weybridge	7 43	8 43	9 13			9 43	1013	1043	1113						1143	
Weybridge A	7 46	8 46	9 16			9 46	1016	1046	1116						1146	
Walton-on-Thames	7 50	8 50	9 20			9 50	1020	1050	1120						1150	
Hersham	7 52	8 52	9 22			9 52	1022	1052	1122						1152	
Esher, for Sandown Park	7 55	8 55	9 25			9 55	1025	1055	1125						1155	
Surbiton	8 0	9 0	9 30			10 0	1030	11 0	1130						12 0	
WATERLOO .... arr	8 16	9 16	9 46		10 1	1016	1046	1116	1146				12 1		1216	

Up	a.m	a.m	a.m	a.m		non		a.m	a.m	a.m		p.m	a.m	p.m	p.m	p.m
Ventnor .... dep								1030					1130			
Wroxall ❶								1035					1135			
Shanklin								1042					1142			
Sandown 373								1048					1148			
Bembridge .... dep													Through Train to Freshwater (arr. 12 52 p.m.), see pages 373 and 363			
St. Helens																
Brading N 359 .... arr																
Brading 359								1053								
Cowes .... dep		9 56							1026	1056						
Mill Hill		9 57							1027	1057						
Newport F 359, 373 .. arr		10 7							1037	11 7						
Freshwater .... dep		Through Train to Ventnor (arr. 11 9 a.m.), see page 373														
Yarmouth																
Ningwood																
Calbourne & Shalfleet																
Carisbrooke Halt G																
Newport F 373 .... arr																
Newport .... dep									1038							
Whippingham									1044							
Wootton									1047							
Haven Street									1052							
Ashey									1059							
Ryde, St. John's Road								11 0	11 6							
" Esplanade §								11 4	1110							
" Pier Head § .. arr								11 7	1113							
Ryde, Pier Head .... dep								1135								
Portsmouth Harb. .. arr								12 5								
Portsmouth Harbour .. dep								1220								
Portsmouth & Southsea	1030		11 0	1130		12 0		1224						1230	1 0	1 30
Fratton	1032		11 2	1132		12 2								1232	1 2	1 32
Hilsea Halt																
Bedhampton Halt	1040		1110	1140		1210		R						1240	1 10	1 40
245 Hayling Island .... dep																
Havant 244	1043		1113	1143		1213								1243	1 13	1 43
Rowlands Castle	1048		1118	1148		1218								1248	1 18	1 48
Petersfield 374	11 0		1130	12 0		1230								1 0	1 30	2 0
Liss	11 6		1136	12 6		1236								1 6	1 36	2 6
Liphook	1113		1143	1213		1243								1 13	1 43	2 13
Haslemere, for Hindhead	1119		1149	1219		1249		1 2						1 19	1 49	2 19
Witley, for Chiddingfold	1125		1155	1225		1255								1 25	1 55	2 25
Milford	1129		1159	1229		1259								1 29	1 59	2 29
Godalming	1133		12 3	1233		1 3								1 33	2 3	2 33
Farncombe	1135		12 5	1235		1 5								1 35	2 5	2 35
Guildford 245, 246, 390 arr	1141		1211	1241		1 11		1 19						1 41	2 11	2 41
Guildford dep	1152		1222	1252				1 20				1 22		1 52	2 22	2 52
Worplesdon	1159		1229	1259								1 29		1 59	2 29	2 59
Woking C 324, 389, 390	12 4		1234	1 4				1 29				1 34		2 4	2 34	3 4
Byfleet B	1210		1240	1 10								1 40		2 10	2 40	3 10
West Weybridge	1213		1243	1 13								1 43		2 13	2 43	3 13
Weybridge A	1216		1246	1 16								1 46		2 16	2 46	3 16
Walton-on-Thames	1220		1250	1 20								1 50		2 20	2 50	3 20
Hersham	1222		1252	1 22								1 52		2 22	2 52	3 22
Esher, for Sandown Park	1225		1255	1 25								1 55		2 25	2 55	3 25
Surbiton	1230		1 0	1 30								2 0		2 30	3 0	3 30
WATERLOO .... arr	1246		1 16	1 46				2 1				2 16		2 46	3 16	3 46

Conveyance of Motor Cars, etc., to and from the Isle of Wight, see pages 501 and 502

For Notes, see page 372

[illegible] SERVICE between GUILDFORD and WATERLOO and LOCAL TRAINS and INTERMEDIATE STATIONS between SURBITON and WATERLOO, see pages 427 to 459

THE ISLE OF WIGHT, PORTSMOUTH, PETERSFIELD, HASLEMERE, GODALMING, and LONDON

Up — **Sundays**—*continued*

Station	a.m	p.m	p.m	p.m	p.m	p.m		p.m	p.m		p.m	p.m	p.m	p.m	p.m	p.m	p.m	p.m	p.m	p.m	p.m	p.m	p.m	p.m	p.m	p.m	p.m	p.m	p.m	p.m	p.m
Ventnor dep			1230								1 30			2 30			3 17										4 30				
Wroxall ◐			1235								1 35			2 35			3 22										4 35				
Shanklin			1242								1 42			2 42			3 29										4 42				
Sandown 373			1248								1 48			2 48			3 34										4 48				
Bembridge dep			1242		1 32						Through Train to Cowes (arr. 2 30 p.m.), see page 373	1 57					☞		3 32								4 42				
St. Helens			1244		1 34							1 59							3 34								4 44				
Brading **N** 359 arr			1250		1 40							2 5							3 40								4 50				
Brading 359			1253		Stop									2 53													4 53				
Cowes dep				1226									2 6			2 56									3 56			4 26			
Mill Hill				1227									2 7			2 57	Through Train to Cowes (arr. 4 20 p.m.), see page 373								3 57			4 27			
Newport F 359, 373 arr				1237									2 17			3 7									4 7			4 37			
Freshwater dep	1135												Stop		1 35										Through Train to Ventnor (arr. 5 11 p.m.), see page 373	3 25					
Yarmouth	1140														1 40											3 30					
Ningwood	1149														1 49											3 39					
Calbourne & Shalfleet	1153														1 54											3 44					
Carisbrooke Halt **G**	12 5														2 6											3 55					
Newport **F** 373 arr	1212														2 13											4 2					
Newport dep	Through Train to Ventnor (arr. 1 11 p.m.), see page 373			1238											2 42													4 38			
Whippingham				1244											2 47													4 44			
Wootton				1247											2 50													4 47			
Haven Street				1252											2 54													4 52			
Ashey				1259											2 59													4 59			
Ryde, St. John's Road			1 0	1 6										3 0	3 6												5 0	5 6			
,, Esplanade } §			1 4	1 10										3 4	3 10												5 4	5 10			
,, Pier Head } § arr			1 7	1 13										3 7	3 13												5 7	5 13			
¶ **Ryde, Pier Head** dep			1 35											3 35			Stop										5 35				
¶ **Portsmouth Harb.** arr			2 5											4 5													6 5				
Portsmouth Harbour dep			2 20										p.m	4 20							5 20						6 20				6 50
Portsmouth & Southsea		2 0	2 24			2 30		3 0	3 30				4 0	4 24				4 30		5 0	5 24		5 30	6 0			6 24			6 30	6 54
Fratton		2 2				2 32		3 2	3 32				4 2					4 32		5 2			5 32	6 2						6 32	
Hilsea Halt																															
Bedhampton Halt		2 10	**R**			2 40		3 10	3 40				4 10	**R**				4 40		5 10	**R**		5 40	6 10			**R**			6 40	**R**
245 Hayling Island dep																															
Havant 244		2 13				2 43		3 13	3 43				4 13					4 43		5 13			5 43	6 13						6 43	
Rowlands Castle		2 18				2 48		3 18	3 48				4 18					4 48		5 18			5 48	6 18						6 48	
Petersfield 374		2 30				3 0		3 30	4 0				4 30					5 0		5 30			6 0	6 30						7 0	
Liss		2 36				3 6		3 36	4 6				4 36					5 6		5 36			6 6	6 36						7 6	
Liphook		2 43				3 13		3 43	4 13				4 43					5 13		5 43			6 13	6 43						7 13	
Haslemere, for Hindhead		2 49	3 2			3 19		3 49	4 19				4 49	5 2				5 19		5 49	6 2		6 19	6 49			7 2			7 19	7 31
Witley, for Chiddingfold		2 55				3 25		3 55	4 25				4 55					5 25		5 55			6 25	6 55						7 25	
Milford		2 59				3 29		3 59	4 29				4 59					5 29		5 59			6 29	6 59						7 29	
Godalming		3 3				3 33		4 3	4 33				5 3					5 33		6 3			6 33	7 3						7 33	
Farncombe		3 5				3 35		4 5	4 35				5 5					5 35		6 5			6 35	7 5						7 35	
Guildford 245, 246, 390 arr		3 11	3 19		p.m	3 41		4 11	4 41				5 11	5 19			p.m	5 41		6 11	6 19		6 41	7 11			7 19			7 41	7 47
Guildford dep			3 20		3 22	3 52		4 22	4 52					5 20			5 22	5 52			6 20	6 22	6 52				7 20		7 22		7 48
Worplesdon					3 29	3 59		4 29	4 59								5 29	5 59				6 29	6 59						7 29		
Woking C 324, 389, 390			3 29		3 34	4 4		4 34	5 4					5 29			5 34	6 4			6 29	6 34	7 4				7 29		7 34		7 57
Byfleet **B**					3 40	4 10		4 40	5 10								5 40	6 10				6 40	7 10						7 40		
West Weybridge					3 43	4 13		4 43	5 13								5 43	6 13				6 43	7 13						7 43		
Weybridge **A**					3 46	4 16		4 46	5 16								5 46	6 16				6 46	7 16						7 46		
Walton-on-Thames					3 50	4 20		4 50	5 20								5 50	6 20				6 50	7 20						7 50		
Hersham					3 52	4 22		4 52	5 22								5 52	6 22				6 52	7 22						7 52		
Esher, for Sandown Park					3 55	4 25		4 55	5 25								5 55	6 25				6 55	7 25						7 55		
Surbiton					4 0	4 30		5 0	5 30								6 0	6 30				7 0	7 30						8 0		8 13
WATERLOO arr			4 1		4 16	4 46		5 16	5 46					6 1			6 16	6 48			7 1	7 16	7 47				8 1		8 16		8 30

Conveyance of Motor Cars, etc., to and from the Isle of Wight, see pages 501 and 502

For Notes and Continuation of SUNDAY TRAINS, see page 372

For COMPLETE SERVICE between GUILDFORD and WATERLOO and LOCAL TRAINS and INTERMEDIATE STATIONS between SURBITON and WATERLOO, see pages 427 to 459.

THE ISLE OF WIGHT, PORTSMOUTH, PETERSFIELD, HASLEMERE, GODALMING, and LONDON

Sundays—*continued*

Up	p.m	p.m	p.m	p.m	p.m	p.m		p.m	p.m	p.m	p.m	p.m	p.m	p.m	p.m	p.m	p.m	p.m	p.m	p.m	p.m	p.m	p.m	p.m
Ventnor dep	5 30	..	Through Train from Freshwater	..	..	..	..	..	6 30	..	..	..	7 30	..	..	..	..	..	..	8 30	..	9 30	1030	..
Wroxall O	5 35	..		..	..	..	..	..	6 35	..	..	..	7 35	..	..	..	..	..	..	8 35	..	9 35	1035	..
Shanklin	5 42	..		..	..	..	..	..	6 42	..	..	..	7 42	..	..	..	..	..	..	8 44	..	9 42	1042	..
Sandown 373	5 48	..		..	..	..	..	..	6 48	..	..	..	7 48	..	..	..	..	..	..	8 49	..	9 48	1048	..
Bembridge dep	5 32	..		..	..	..	..	..	6 32	..	..	7 32		..	..	..	..	..	..	8 42	..	9 32	..	..
St. Helens	5 34	..		..	..	..	..	..	6 34	..	..	7 34		..	..	..	..	..	..	8 44	..	9 34	..	..
Brading N 359 arr	5 40	..		..	..	..	..	..	6 40	..	..	7 40		..	..	..	..	..	..	8 50	..	9 40	..	..
Brading 359	5 53	..		..	..	..	..	..	6 53	..	..	Stop	Through Train to Cowes (arr. 8 30 p.m.), see page 373	..	..	..	..	..	..	8 54	..	9 52	1053	..
Cowes dep	..	..		..	5 56	..	..	..	..	6 26	7 36	..		..	..	..	..	..	..	..	8 36	..	..	1026
Mill Hill	..	..		..	5 57	..	..	..	..	6 27	7 37	..		..	..	..	..	..	..	..	8 37	..	..	1027
Newport F 359, 373 arr	..	..		..	6 7	..	..	..	..	6 37	7 47	..		..	..	..	..	..	..	..	8 47	..	..	1037
Freshwater dep	..	..	4 55	..	Stop	..	..	..	..	..		..		..	..	..	..	8 5	..	..	..	..	..	..
Yarmouth	..	..	5 0	..		..	..	..	..	..		..		..	..	..	..	8 10	..	..	..	..	..	..
Ningwood	..	..	5 9	..	..	..	..	..	..	..		..		..	..	..	..	8 19	..	..	..	..	..	..
Calbourne & Shalfleet	..	..	5 13	..	..	..	..	..	..	..		..		..	..	..	..	8 24	..	..	..	..	..	..
Carisbrooke Halt G	..	..	5 25	..	..	..	..	..	..	..		..		..	..	..	..	8 36	..	..	..	..	..	..
Newport F 373 arr	..	..	5 32	..	..	..	..	..	..	..		..		..	..	..	..	8 44	..	..	..	..	..	..
Newport dep	..	..	5 38	..	..	..	..	..	..	6 38	Through Train to Ventnor (arr. 8 42 p.m.), see page 373	..		..	..	..	..	..	..	..	8 48	..	..	..
Whippingham	..	..	5 44	..	..	..	..	..	..	6 44		..		..	..	..	..	..	..	..	8 54	..	..	..
Wootton	..	..	5 47	..	..	..	..	..	..	6 47		..		..	..	..	..	..	..	..	8 57	..	..	..
Haven Street	..	..	5 52	..	..	..	..	..	..	6 52		..		..	..	..	..	..	..	..	9 1	..	..	..
Ashey	..	..	5 59	..	..	..	..	..	..	6 59		..		..	..	..	..	..	..	..	9 6	..	..	..
Ryde, St. John's Road	6 0	..	6 6	..	..	..	..	..	7 0	7 6		..		..	..	..	..	..	..	9 1	9 13	10 0	11 0	..
„ Esplanade } §	6 4	..	6 10	..	..	..	..	..	7 4	7 10		..		..	..	..	..	..	..	9 5	9 17	..	..	..
„ Pier Head } § arr	6 7	..	6 13	..	..	..	..	..	7 7	7 13		..		..	..	..	..	..	..	9 8	9 20	..	..	..
¶ Ryde, Pier Head dep	Stop	..	..	..	..	..	..	..	7 35			..	..	..	..	..	..	..	..	9 35		..	..	..
¶ Portsmouth Harb. arr		..	..	..	..	..	..	..	8 5			..	..	..	..	..	..	..	..	10 5		..	..	..
Portsmouth Harbour dep	..	..	..	7 20	..	..	..	..	8 20			p.m	..	..	9 20	..	..	..	..	1020		..	..	..
Portsmouth & Southsea	..	7 0	..	7 24	..	7 30	..	8 0	8 24			8 30	..	9 0	9 24	..	9 30	..	10 0	1024		..	..	..
Fratton	..	7 2	..	..	..	7 32	..	8 2	..			8 32	..	9 2	..	..	9 32	..	10 2	..		..	..	..
Hilsea Halt	..	..	..	..	..	..	..	..	..			..	..	..	..	..	..	..	..	..		..	..	..
Bedhampton Halt	..	7 10	..	R	..	7 40	..	8 10	R			8 40	..	9 10	R	..	9 40	..	1010	R		..	..	..
245 Hayling Island dep	..	..	..	..	..	..	..	..	..			..	..	..	..	..	..	..	..	..		..	..	..
Havant 744	..	7 13	..	..	..	7 43	..	8 13	..		..	8 43	..	9 13	..	..	9 43	..	1013	..		..	..	..
Rowlands Castle	..	7 18	..	..	..	7 48	..	8 18	..		..	8 48	..	9 18	..	..	9 48	..	1018	..		..	..	..
Petersfield 374	..	7 30	..	..	..	8 0	..	8 30	..		..	9 0	..	9 30	..	..	10 0	..	1030	..		..	..	..
Liss	..	7 36	..	..	..	8 6	..	8 36	..		..	9 6	..	9 36	..	..	10 6	..	1036	..		..	..	..
Liphook	..	7 43	..	..	..	8 13	..	8 43	..		..	9 13	..	9 43	..	..	1013	..	1043	..		..	..	..
Haslemere, for Hindhead	..	7 49	..	8 2	..	8 19	..	8 49	9 2		..	9 19	..	9 49	10 2	..	1019	..	1049	11 2		..	..	..
Witley, for Chiddingfold	..	7 55	..	..	..	8 25	..	8 55	..		..	9 25	..	9 55	..	..	1025	..	1055	..		..	..	..
Milford	..	7 59	..	..	..	8 29	..	8 59	..		..	9 29	..	9 59	..	..	1029	..	1059	..		..	..	..
Godalming	..	8 3	..	..	..	8 33	..	9 3	..		..	9 33	..	10 3	..	..	1033	..	11 3	..		..	..	..
Farncombe	..	8 5	..	..	..	8 35	..	9 5	..		..	9 35	..	10 5	..	..	1035	..	11 5	..		..	..	..
Guildford 245, 246, 390 arr	p.m	8 11	..	8 19	p.m	8 41	..	9 11	9 19		p.m	9 41	..	1011	1019	..	1041	..	1111	1119		..	..	..
Guildford dep	7 52	..	..	8 20	8 22	8 52	..	..	9 20		9 22	9 52	..	..	1020	1022	1052	..	..	1120		..	..	..
Worplesdon	7 59	..	..	..	8 29	8 59	..	..	..		9 29	9 59	..	..	..	1029	1059	..	..	..		..	..	..
Woking C 324, 389, 390	8 4	..	..	8 29	8 34	9 4	..	..	9 29		9 34	10 4	..	..	1029	1034	11 4	..	..	1129		..	..	..
Byfleet B	8 10	..	..	..	8 40	9 10	..	..	..		9 40	1010	..	..	..	1040	1110	..	..	..		..	..	..
West Weybridge	8 13	..	..	..	8 43	9 13	..	..	..		9 43	1013	..	..	..	1043	1113	..	..	..		..	..	..
Weybridge A	8 16	..	..	..	8 46	9 16	..	..	..		9 46	1016	..	..	..	1046	1116	..	..	..		..	..	..
Walton-on-Thames	8 20	..	..	..	8 50	9 20	..	..	..		9 50	1020	..	..	..	1050	1120	..	..	..		..	..	..
Hersham	8 22	..	..	..	8 52	9 22	..	..	..		9 52	1022	..	..	..	1052	1122	..	..	..		..	..	..
Esher, for Sandown Park	8 25	..	..	..	8 55	9 25	..	..	..		9 55	1025	..	..	..	1055	1125	..	..	..		..	..	..
Surbiton	8 30	..	..	..	9 0	9 30	..	..	..		10 0	1030	..	..	..	11 0	1130	..	..	..		..	..	..
WATERLOO arr	8 46	..	..	9 1	9 21	9 46	..	..	10 1		1016	1046	..	..	11 1	1116	1146	..	..	12 1		..	..	..

Conveyance of Motor Cars, etc., to and from the Isle of Wight, see pages 501 and 502

NOTES

- **A** Station for Brooklands, St. George's Hill, and Oatlands Park
- **B** Station for Woodham and Pyrford.
- **C** Station for Chobham (3¼ miles) to Woking Village (1½ miles).
- *d* 4 minutes later on Saturdays.
- **F** Station for Brighstone.
- **G** Station for Castle
- **N** Station for Yaverland (1¼ miles), The Roman Villa (1 mile), and Nunwell (1¼ miles)
- **O** Station for Appuldurcombe (½ mile).
- **R** Refreshment Car between Portsmouth and Waterloo
- **SO** or **S0** Saturdays only
- **SX** Saturdays excepted.
- **§** A frequent Service of Trams operates between Ryde Esplanade and Pier Head. Railway Tickets being available.
- **¶** By Boat.

OTHER TRAINS

Between	Page
Portsmouth Harbour and Fratton	380
Portsmouth and Havant	196
Portsmouth and London	19
Guildford and London	249

COWES, NEWPORT, MERSTONE, VENTNOR WEST, SANDOWN, and VENTNOR

Miles	Up	Week Days																				Sundays						
		a.m	a.m		a.m	a.m		p.m	p.m	p.m		p.m	p.m		p.m	p.m	p.m					a.m	p.m	p.m	p.m	p.m	p.m	
			Through Train to Shanklin						Through Train Freshwater (dep. 1 55 p.m.) to Shanklin, see page 368													Through Train to Ventnor	Through Train Freshwater (dep. 11 35 a.m.) to Ventnor, see page 371	Through Train to Ventnor	Through Train to Ventnor		Through Train to Ventnor	
	Cowes D 366 ... dep	6 56	8 43	..	10 3	1056	..	1256	2 26	3 56	..	4 56	5 56	..	6 26	7 56	..	..	..	..	..	9 56	..	2 6	3 56	5 56	7 36	..
4¼	Newport F 366 ... arr	7 7	8 54	..	1014	11 7	..	1 7	2 37	4 7	..	5 7	6 7	..	6 37	8 7	..	..	..	..	..	10 7	..	2 17	4 7	6 7	7 47	..
—	Newport ... dep	7 13	8 58	..	1018	11 8	..	1 8	2 40	4 8	..	5 8	6 8	..	7 8	8 8	..	..	..	..	..	10 8	1218	2 18	4 8	6 10	7 48	..
5¼	Shide	7 18	9 2	..	1021	1112	..	1 12	2 43	4 12	..	5 12	6 12	..	7 12	8 12	..	..	..	..	..	1012	1223	2 23	4 13	6 15	7 53	..
6½	Blackwater (Isle of Wight)	7 22	9 5	..	1024	1115	..	1 15	2 46	4 16	..	5 15	6 15	..	7 15	8 15	..	..	..	..	..	1015	1226	2 26	4 17	6 18	7 56	..
8¼	Merstone ... arr	7 28	9 10	..	1030	1121	..	1 20	2 51	4 21	..	5 21	6 21	..	7 21	8 21	..	..	..	..	..	1021	1231	2 31	4 22	6 23	8 2	..
—	Merstone ... dep	7 35	9 12	..	..	1127	..	1 25	..	4 25	..	5 27	6 27	..	7 27	..	8 27	..	..	..	..	..	..	..	..	..	..	..
9¾	Godshill Halt A	7 39	9 16	..	..	1131	..	1 29	..	4 29	..	5 31	6 31	..	7 31	..	8 31	..	..	..	..	..	..	..	..	..	..	..
12¼	Whitwell Halt B	7 46	9 23	..	..	1138	..	1 36	..	4 36	..	5 38	6 38	..	7 38	..	8 38	..	..	..	..	..	..	..	..	..	..	..
13¾	St. Lawrence Halt C	7 52	9 29	..	..	1144	..	1 42	..	4 42	..	5 44	6 44	..	7 44	..	8 44	..	..	..	..	..	..	..	..	..	..	..
15	Ventnor West ... arr	7 57	9 34	..	..	1149	..	1 47	..	4 47	..	5 49	6 49	..	7 49	..	8 49	..	..	..	..	..	..	..	..	..	..	..
—	Merstone ... dep	7 31	9 11	..	1031	1123	..	1 21	2 52	4 23	..	5 23	6 23	..	7 23	8 23	Sats. only.	..	..	..	..	1023	1232	2 32	4 23	6 23	8 4	..
9¾	Horringford	7 35	9 14	..	1034	1127	..	1 25	2 55	4 28	..	5 27	6 27	..	7 27	8 27		..	..	..	..	1027	1235	2 35	4 28	6 27	8 9	..
10¾	Newchurch	7 39	9 17	..	1037	1130	..	1 28	2 58	4 31	..	5 30	6 30	..	7 30	8 30		..	..	..	..	1030	1238	2 38	4 32	6 30	8 12	..
12	Alverstone	7 43	9 20	..	1040	1133	..	1 31	3 1	4 35	..	5 33	6 33	..	7 33	8 33		..	..	..	..	1033	1241	2 41	4 36	6 33	8 15	..
13½	Sandown 366 ... arr	7 49	9 25	..	1045	1138	..	1 36	3 6	4 40	..	5 38	6 38	..	7 38	8 38		..	..	..	..	1038	1246	2 46	4 41	6 38	8 20	..
15½	Shanklin ... "	8 15	9 34	..	1055	1155	..	1H55	3 14	4 55	..	5 55	6 55	..	7 55	8 55		..	..	..	..	1054	1255	2 54	4 55	6 55	8 26	..
19½	Ventnor ... "	8 32	1012	..	1111	1211	..	2H11	4 11	5 11	..	6 11	7 11	..	8 11	9 11		..	..	..	..	11 9	1 11	3 8	5 11	7 11	8 42	..

Miles	Down	Week Days																			Sundays.						
		a.m	a.m	a.m		a.m	a.m		p.m	p.m	p.m		p.m	p.m	p.m	p.m	p.m				a.m	a.m	p.m	p.m	p.m	p.m	
			Through Train Sandown to Freshwater, see page 359	Through Train Shanklin to Cowes						Thro' Train Shanklin to Newport											Through Train from Ventnor	Through Train Ventnor to Freshwater, see page 363	Through Train from Ventnor	Through Train from Ventnor		Through Train from Ventnor	
	Ventnor ... dep	6 30	8 5	8 40	..	1042	1142	..	1 42	2 42	4 42	..	5 42	6 42	7 42	..	8 42	..	..	..	9 50	1130	1 30	3 17	6 30	7 30	..
4	Shanklin ... "	6 42	8 16	9 43	..	1054	1154	..	1 54	3 27	4 54	..	5 54	6 54	7 54	..	8 54	..	..	..	10 1	1142	1 42	3 29	6 42	7 42	..
6	Sandown ... "	6 48	8 23	9 48	..	11 8	12 8	..	2 8	3 35	5 8	..	6 8	7 8	8 8	..	9 8	..	..	..	10 8	1150	1 50	3 35	6 50	7 50	..
7¼	Alverstone	6 52	8 26	9 52	..	1111	1211	..	2 11	3 38	5 11	..	6 11	7 11	8 11	..	9 11	..	..	..	1011	1153	1 53	3 38	6 53	7 53	..
8¾	Newchurch	6 55	8 29	9 55	..	1114	1214	..	2 14	3 41	5 14	..	6 14	7 14	8 14	..	9 14	..	..	..	1014	1156	1 56	3 41	6 56	7 56	..
9¾	Horringford	6 58	8 32	9 58	..	1117	1217	..	2 17	3 44	5 17	..	6 17	7 17	8 17	..	9 17	..	..	..	1017	1159	1 59	3 44	6 59	7 59	..
11¼	Merstone ... arr	7 3	8 37	10 3	..	1122	1222	..	2 22	3 49	5 22	..	6 22	7 22	8 22	..	9 22	..	..	..	1022	12 4	2 4	3 49	7 4	8 4	..
—	Mls Ventnor West ... dep	..	8 12	9 40	..	..	12 0	..	2 0	..	4 57	..	5 57	6 57	7 57	8 57	..	..	..	..	..	..	..	..	..	..	..
—	1¼ St. Lawrence Halt C	..	8 16	9 44	..	..	12 4	..	2 4	..	5 1	..	6 1	7 1	8 1	9 1	..	..	..	..	..	..	..	..	..	..	..
—	2¾ Whitwell Halt B	..	8 22	9 49	..	..	12 9	..	2 9	..	5 6	..	6 6	7 6	8 6	9 6	..	..	..	..	..	..	..	..	..	..	..
—	5¼ Godshill Halt A	..	8 29	9 56	..	..	1216	..	2 16	..	5 13	..	6 13	7 13	8 13	9 13	..	..	..	..	..	..	..	..	..	..	..
—	6¾ Merstone ... arr	..	8 35	10 1	..	..	1221	..	2 21	..	5 19	..	6 19	7 19	8 19	9 19	..	..	..	..	..	..	..	..	..	..	..
—	Merstone ... dep	7 3	8 38	10 3	..	1123	1223	..	2 23	3 49	5 23	..	6 23	7 23	8 23	Sats. only	9 23	..	..	..	1023	12 4	2 4	3 49	7 4	8 4	..
13	Blackwater (Isle of Wight)	..	8 43	10 7	..	1127	1227	..	2 27	3 53	5 27	..	6 27	7 27	8 27		9 27	..	..	..	1027	12 8	2 8	3 53	7 8	8 8	..
14¼	Shide	7 9	8 47	1011	..	1131	1231	..	2 31	3 57	5 31	..	6 31	7 31	8 31		9 31	..	..	..	1031	1212	2 12	3 57	7 12	8 12	..
15¼	Newport F 359, 366 ... arr	7 13	8 51	1016	..	1135	1235	..	2 35	4 1	5 35	..	6 35	7 35	8 35		9 35	..	..	..	1035	1216	2 16	4 1	7 16	8 16	..
—	Newport 359 ... dep	7 15	8 58	1018	..	12 8	1238	..	2 38	4 8	5 38	..	6 38	7 38	9 8		10B8	..	..	..	1038	1 48	2 18	4 8	7 18	8 18	..
19¼	Cowes D 359 ... arr.	7 29	9 11	1030	..	1220	1250	..	2 50	4 20	5 50	..	6 50	7 50	9 20		10B20	..	..	..	1050	2 0	2 30	4 20	7 30	8 30	..

A Godshill Halt for Sandford (1½ miles)

B Whitwell Halt for Niton (1¾ miles) and Chale (4½ miles)

B 30 minutes *earlier* on Saturdays

C St. Lawrence Halt for Blackgang (3½ miles)

D Nearest Sta. to Osborne House (by Ferry to East Cowes, thence Southern Vectis Bus).

F Sta. for Brighstone

H Wednesdays, Thursdays, and Saturdays

LOCAL TRAINS between Cowes and Newport, page 363—Sandown and Ventnor, 359

Conveyance of Motor Cars, etc., to and from the Isle of Wight, see pages 501 and 502

LONDON, PETERSFIELD, MIDHURST, PULBOROUGH, and LONDON
Third class only between Petersfield and Pulborough

Miles	Down		Week Days a.m	a.m	a.m	a.m		a.m	p.m	SX	SO	p.m	p.m	p.m	p.m		Sundays a.m	a.m	a.m	p.m	p.m
	Waterloo 359	dep	..	5 25	6 55	8 45	..	10A27	..	1245	1R15	2 45	..	5RF20	6Rn20	..	..	..	9 45	1 27	5 27
—	Petersfield	dep	6 33	7 37	8 50	10 35	..	12 35	..	2 40	2 40	4 18	..	6 41	7 41	..	6 33	8 15	11 22	3 19	7 19
4½	Rogate, for Harting		6 43	7 47	9 0	10 45	..	12 45	..	2 50	2 50	4 28	..	6 51	7 51	..	6 43	8 25	11 32	3 29	7 29
6½	Elsted		6 49	7 53	9 6	10 51	..	12 51	..	2 56	2 56	4 34	..	6 57	7 57	..	6 49	8 31	11 38	3 35	7 35
9½	Midhurst	arr	6 58	8 2	9 15	11 0	..	1 0	..	3 5	3 5	4 43	..	7 6	8 6	..	6 58	8 40	11 47	3 44	7 44
	Midhurst	dep	7 27	8 51	9 43	11 5	..	1 11	2 45	..	..	4 44	6 45	..	8 45	..	..	8 45	11 48	3 45	7 45
13	Selham		7 35	8 59	9 51	11 13	..	1 19	2 53	..	..	4 52	6 53	..	8 53	..	..	8 53	11 56	3 53	7 53
15¼	Petworth		7 43	9 6	9 59	11 19	..	1 25	2 59	..	..	4 59	6 59	..	8 59	..	..	9 0	12 3	4 0	8 0
17¾	Fittleworth		7 50	9 13	10 6	11 27	..	1 33	3 7	..	..	5 6	7 7	..	9 7	..	..	9 7	12 10	4 7	8 7
20¼	Pulborough A 159, 196	arr	7 58	9 21	1014	11 35	..	1 41	3 15	..	..	5 14	7 15	..	9 15	..	..	9 15	12 17	4 15	8 15
70½	London Bridge 197	arr	9 28	10*40	..	1 36	..	3 35	5SX3	..	..	..	..	..	11③11	..	..	11③10	2③10	6③3	10 7
70½	Victoria 197	"	9 34	10 31	1132	1 21	..	3 40	5S07	..	..	6 40	8 40	..	11 7	..	..	11 6	2 7	5 44	9 40

LONDON, PULBOROUGH, MIDHURST, PETERSFIELD, and LONDON
Third class only between Pulborough and Petersfield

Miles	Up		Week Days a.m	a.m	a.m	a.m	a.m	a.m	SX	SO	SO	SX	SO	SX	p.m	Sundays a.m	a.m	a.m	p.m	p.m
	Victoria 153	dep	..	..	5*20	6③15	9 18	11 18	12*3	12 18	2 18	..	4 18	4 18	6N18	..	7 46	10 48	3 48	7 18
	London Bridge 153	"	..	..	5 25	6③28	9③15	..	12 18	12*15	2③8	2 18	..	4③7	5X48	..	7 43	10③30	3③30	6③55
—	Pulborough	dep	..	..	7 56	8 15	10 33	12 33	1 56	1 56	3 35	4 5	5 41	5 41	7 35	..	9 33	12 33	6 0	8 35
2¾	Fittleworth		..	..	8 3	8 22	10 40	12 40	2 3	2 3	3 42	4 12	5 48	5 48	7 42	..	9 40	12 40	6 7	8 42
5¼	Petworth		..	..	8 9	8 28	10 46	12 46	2 10	2 10	3 48	4 18	5 55	5 55	7 48	..	9 46	12 46	6 13	8 48
7¾	Selham		..	..	8 16	8 35	10 53	12 53	2 16	2 16	3 55	4 25	6 1	6 1	7 55	..	9 53	12 53	6 20	8 55
11	Midhurst	arr	..	..	8 25	8 44	11 2	1 2	2 25	2 25	4 4	4 34	6 10	6 10	8 4	..	10 1	1 1	6 29	9 3
	Midhurst	dep	7 8	8 11	..	9 33	11 2	1 2	3 46	3 46	5 2	5 2	7 10	7 10	8 11	7 28	10 2	1 2	6 42	9 4
14¼	Elsted		7 16	8 19	..	9 41	11 11	1 11	3 54	3 54	5 10	5 10	7 18	7 18	8 19	7 36	1011	1 11	6 50	9 13
16½	Rogate, for Harting		7 22	8 25	..	9 47	11 16	1 16	4 0	4 0	5 16	5 16	7 24	7 24	8 25	7 42	1016	1 16	6 56	9 18
20¾	Petersfield 359, 366	arr	7 33	8 36	..	9 58	11 28	1 28	4 11	4 11	5 27	5 27	7 35	7 35	8 36	7 53	1027	1 28	7 7	9 30
75¾	Waterloo 366	arr	9R13	9RH52	..	11 48	1 1	3 1	6 1	6 1	7 3	7 3	9 46	9 46	10 46	9 46	12 1	3 16	9 1	11 46

NOTES

③ Third class only.
* Change at East Croydon.
A Station for Storrington (5 miles).
A Dep. 10 45 a.m on Sats.
F Dep. 4 45 p.m on Sats.
H Arr. 10R5 a.m on Saturdays
N Dep. 5 48 p.m on Sats.
n Dep. 5 45 p.m on Sats.
R Refreshment Car facilities available
S O or SO Saturdays only.
S X or SX Saturdays excepted.
X Dep. 5③31 p.m on Sats.

LONDON, GUILDFORD, SHALFORD, and CHILWORTH & ALBURY

Miles	Down		Week Days a.m	a.m	a.m	a.m	a.m	a.m		p.m	p.m	p.m	p.m		p.m	p.m		p.m	p.m		Sundays a.m	a.m	a.m		p.m	p.m	p.m	p.m	p.m
	Waterloo 394	dep	6d12	6 25	7d37	8d12	8 57	9d52	..	12d12	1d32	2d52	3 45	..	4K20	5 45	..	7dL42	9 45	..	7 25	8 57	11d38	..	1d38	4d2	5d38	7d2	8 57
30	Guildford 394	arr	7d3	7 21	8d33	9d6	9 51	10d46	..	1d5	2d45	3d45	4 25	..	4K55	6 25	.	8dL36	1025	..	8 21	9 51	12d33	..	2d33	5d6	6d33	8d6	9 51
—	Guildford	dep	7 8	7 45	8 22	9 20	10 2	10 51	..	1 15	2 50	3 50	4 34	..	5 20	6 40	..	8 53	1039	..	8 43	10 4	12 51	..	2 50	5 20	6 45	8 20	10 0
31¼	Shalford		7 14	7 52	8 30	9 27	10 9	11 1	..	1 20	2 59	3 58	4 39	..	5 29	6 47	..	9 1	1044	..	8 50	10 9	1 0	..	3 0	5 25	6 51	8 28	10 5
33¼	Chilworth & Albury 249	arr	7 19	7 57	8 35	9 32	1014	11 6	..	1 25	3 5	4 3	4 44	..	5 35	6 52	..	9 7	1049	..	8 55	1013	1 6	..	3 6	5 30	6 56	8 33	10 10

CHILWORTH & ALBURY, SHALFORD, GUILDFORD, and LONDON

Miles	Up		Week Days a.m	am	a.m	a.m	p.m SO	p.m SX	p.m SO	p.m SX	pm SO	p.m SX	p.m	p.m	p.m	p.m SX	p.m SO	pm	p.m	p.m	Sundays a.m	a.m	p.m	pm	p.m	p.m	pm	p.m	p.m
	Chilw'th & Albury	dep	6 44	823	9 20	10 53	12 10	12 10	1 8	1 8	155	2 8	3 41	4 55	6 11	6 43	6 45	740	9 10	10 17	8 10	1040	12 8	240	3 39	5 40	741	9 12	10 17
1¾	Shalford		6 51	828	9 25	10 58	12 15	12 15	1 15	1 15	2 2	2 14	3 45	5 2	6 15	6 48	6 50	745	9 14	10 22	8 15	1045	12 14	244	3 44	5 44	746	9 17	10 22
3¼	Guildford 427	arr	6 58	834	9 32	11 4	12 22	12 22	1 22	1 22	2 8	2 22	3 51	5 9	6 21	6 54	6 56	751	9 21	10 28	8 21	1051	12 20	250	3 50	5 50	752	9 23	10 28
—	Guildford 427	dep	7d10	850	9N48	11d10	12d30	12d50	1d30	1d50	220	2d50	4 20	5 20	6dJ30	7d10	7d10	820	9d40	10d40	8d37	1120	12 52	320	4d10	6 20	820	9d37	10d37
33½	Waterloo 427	arr	8d5	930	10N28	12d4	1d21	1d43	2d21	2d43	3 1	3d43	5 3	6 1	7dJ26	8d4	8d4	9 1	10d33	11d34	9d32	12 1	1 46	4 1	5d5	7 1	9 1	10d31	11d31

C Change at Wimbledon.
d Third class only between Waterloo and Guildford.
J Dep. Guildford 6 50 and arr. Waterloo 7 43 p.m on Sats.
K Dep. Waterloo 4 12 and arr. Guildford 5 5 p.m on Saturdays. Third class only.
L Dep. Waterloo 7 45 and arr. Guildford 8 25 p.m on Saturdays.
N Dep. Guildford 9 50 and arr. Waterloo 10 43 a.m on Saturdays. Third class only.
S O Saturdays only.
SX Saturdays excepted.

OTHER TRAINS between Guildford and Chilworth & Albury, see page 249.

LONDON, ALTON, DROXFORD, FAREHAM, EASTLEIGH, and SOUTHAMPTON

Mls fr'm London	Down	Week Days a.m	a.m	a.m	a.m	a.m	a.m		p.m	p.m	p.m	p.m	p.m	p.m			Sundays a.m	a.m.	a.m		p.m	p.m	p.m
	London (Waterloo) 390 dep	5 55	6 25	7 25	7 25	10 27	11 57	..	1257	2 27	2 57	4 27	6 57	6 57	..	..	..	7 25	1027	..	3 27	6 27	6 57
	Alton .... dep.	7 36	..	..	9 5	..	1 30	..	..	..	4 35	..	8 30	..	..	..	8 23	..	..	..	..	..	8 28
48½	Farringdon	7 43	..	..	9 12	..	1 37	..	..	..	4 42	..	8 37	..	..	..	8 30	..	..	..	..	..	8 35
52½	Tisted	7 48	..	..	9 16	..	1 41	..	..	..	4 46	..	8 41	..	..	..	8 35	..	..	..	..	..	8 41
55½	Privett	7 55	..	..	9 23	..	1 48	..	..	..	4 53	..	8 48	..	..	..	8 43	..	..	..	..	..	8 48
59½	West Meon	8 3	..	..	9 31	..	1 56	..	..	..	5 1	..	8 56	..	..	..	8 51	..	..	..	..	..	8 56
63½	Droxford **B**	8 11	..	..	9 38	..	2 3	..	..	..	5 9	..	9 3	..	..	..	9 0	..	..	..	..	..	9 4
68½	Wickham	8 22	..	..	9 48	..	2 13	..	..	..	5 18	..	9 14	..	..	..	9 9	..	..	..	..	..	9 13
70½	Knowle Halt	8 28	..	..	9 53	..	2 18	..	..	..	5 23	..	9 20	..	..	..	9 15	..	..	..	..	..	9 19
72½	Fareham 376, 380. arr.	8 33	..	..	9 59	..	2 24	..	..	..	5 29	..	9 25	..	..	..	9 21	..	..	..	..	..	9 25
76½	Fort Brockhurst	9 37	..	..	1023	..	3 51	..	..	..	6 19	..	9 37	..	..	..	..	..	..	..	..	..	..
77	Gosport .... arr.	9 41	..	..	1027	..	3 55	..	..	..	6 23	..	9 41	..	..	..	h	..	..	..	..	..	h
—	**Alton**	..	7 53	9 0	..	12 0	..	..	2 30	4 10	..	6 0	..	8 35	..	..	..	9 0	12 5	..	5 0	8 15	..
51½	Medstead & Four Marks.	..	8 5	9 12	..	12 12	..	..	2 42	4 22	..	6 12	..	8 47	..	..	..	9 12	1217	..	5 12	8 27	..
54½	Ropley	..	8 11	9 18	..	12 18	..	..	2 48	4 28	..	6 18	..	8 53	..	..	..	9 17	1223	..	5 17	8 33	..
57	Alresford	..	8 16	9 22	..	12 22	..	..	2 53	4 32	..	6 22	..	8 58	..	..	..	9 22	1228	..	5 22	8 38	..
60½	Itchen Abbas	..	8 24	9 29	..	12 28	..	..	3 2	4 41	..	6 28	..	9 4	..	..	..	9 30	1235	..	5 28	8 46	..
66	**Winchester C** ...... arr.	..	8 35	9 40	..	12 40	..	..	3 15	4 54	..	6 39	..	9 15	..	..	..	9 41	1248	..	5 39	8 57	..
69	Shawford **D** ...... "	..	8 42	9 47	..	12 46	..	..	3 22	5 0	..	7 14	..	9 27	..	..	..	9 47	1254	..	5 45	9 4	..
73	**Eastleigh F** 376, 380 "	..	8 50	9 55	..	12 54	..	..	3 30	5 8	..	7 15	..	9 35	..	..	..	9 55	1 2	..	5 53	9 12	..
75½	Swaythling ...... "	..	9 9	1035	..	1 28	..	..	3 44	5 26	..	7 29	..	9 50	..	..	..	10 39	1 28	..	5 59	9 19	..
76½	St. Denys 376 ...... "	..	9 13	1039	..	1 32	..	..	3 48	5 30	..	7 33	..	9 54	..	..	..	10 43	1 32	.	6 3	9 23	..
77½	Northam ...... "	..	9 17	1043	..	1 36	..	..	3 52	5 33	..	7 37	..	9 58	..	..	..	..	.	..	..	..	..
78½	**Southampton G** .. "	..	9 20	1047	..	1 40	..	..	3 56	5 37	..	7 41	..	10 2	..	..	..	11 15	..	..	6 9	9 29	..
78½	**Southampton Cen.** . "	..	9 56	1026	..	1 19	..	..	4 35	5 28	..	7 28	..	..	..	..	..	10 50	1 20	..	6 35	9 55	..

¶ Miles	Up	Week Days a.m	a.m	a.m	a.m	a.m	p.m.	p.m	p.m	p.m	p.m	p.m	p.m	p.m		Sundays a.m	a.m	a.m	p.m	p.m	p.m
	Southampton Cen. dep.	..	6 47	..	9 54	..	12SX20	12SO55	1 49	..	..	..	6 48	..	..	Thro' Train Portsmouth & S. to Woking, pages 382 and 393	..	10 24	3 20	..	6 40
	Southampton Ter. . "	6 0	6 57	..	9 36	..	12SX20	12SO53	1 55	..	2 54	..	6 58	..	..		7 20	9 51	3 0	..	6 15
½	Northam ...... "	6 3	7 0	..	9 39	..	12SX24	12SO56	1 58	..	2 57	..	7 1	..	..		..	..	..	..	..
2	St. Denys ...... "	6 7	7 7	..	10 2	..	12SX28	1SO 2	2 2	..	3 1	..	7 5	..	..		7 25	10 30	3 26	..	6 47
3	Swaythling ...... "	6 11	7 11	..	9 47	..	12SX32	1SO 6	2 5	..	3 5	..	7 8	..	..		7 29	10 34	3 30	..	6 51
5½	**Eastleigh F** ...... "	6 35	7 40	..	1029	..	1 15		2 15	..	3 59	..	7 15	..	..		7 45	10 46	3 42	..	6 58
9½	Shawford **D** ...... "	6 42	7 47	..	1036	..	1 22		2 22	..	4 6	..	7 22	..	..		7 52	10 53	3 49	..	7 6
12½	Winchester **C** ...... "	6 50	7 56	..	1044	..	1 29		2 29	..	4 14	..	7 31	..	..		7 59	11 0	3 56	..	7 21
17½	Itchen Abbas	7 2	8 8	..	1056	..	1 41		2 41	..	4 26	..	7 44	..	..		8 11	11 12	4 8	..	7 32
21½	Alresford	7 9	8 15	..	11 3	..	1 48		2 50	..	4 34	..	7 51	..	..		8 18	11 19	4 15	..	7 39
24	Ropley	7 15	8 22	..	1110	..	1 54		2 59	..	4 41	..	7 59	..	..		8 26	11 25	4 21	..	7 45
27½	Medstead & Four Marks.	7 25	8 32	..	1120	..	2 4		3 9	..	4 51	..	8 9	..	..		8 36	11 35	4 31	..	7 33
31½	**Alton A** 392 ...... arr.	7 34	8 41	..	1129	..	2 13		3 18	..	5 0	..	8 18	..	..		8 45	11 44	4 41	..	8 4
—	Mls **Gosport** ...... dep.	..	..	7 40	..	11 3	..		..	..	..	5 30	..	7 54	..		..	..	..	..	..
—	½ Fort Brockhurst ..	..	..	7 43	..	11 6	..		..	..	..	5 33	..	7 58	..		..	..	..	h	..
—	Mls **Fareham** ...... dep.	..	..	7 53	..	1147	..		..	2 48	..	6 50	..	8 45	..	8 21	..	..	..	6 36	..
—	2 Knowle Halt	..	..	7 58	..	1151	..		..	2 52	..	6 54	..	8 49	..	8 27	..	..	..	6 42	..
—	4½ Wickham	..	..	8 3	..	1157	..		..	2 58	..	7 0	..	8 55	..	8 33	..	..	..	6 48	..
—	9½ Droxford **B**	..	..	8 12	..	12 7	..		..	3 8	..	7 10	..	9 4	..	8 43	..	..	..	6 58	..
—	13½ West Meon	..	..	8 21	..	1219	..		..	3 17	..	7 19	..	9 14	..	8 52	..	..	..	7 7	..
—	17½ Privett	..	..	8 30	..	1232	..		..	3 29	..	7 29	..	9 23	..	9 5	..	..	..	7 18	..
—	20½ Tisted	..	..	8 36	..	1238	..		..	3 36	..	7 36	..	9 29	..	9 13	..	..	..	7 25	..
—	22½ Farringdon	..	..	8 41	..	1242	..		..	3 40	..	7 40	..	9 33	..	9 19	..	..	..	7 30	..
—	25½ **Alton A** 392 ... arr.	..	..	8 49	..	1249	..		..	3 47	..	7 48	..	9 41	..	9 27	..	..	..	7 38	..
78½	**London** (Waterloo) 392 arr	8 57	9B55	1016	1 16	2 16	3 46		4 46	5 16	6 48	9 16	9 46	1116	..	1116	1016	1 16	6 16	9 21	9 46

¶ Miles from Southampton Terminus **A** Station for Selborne (4½ miles) **B** Station for Hambledon (3½ miles).
B Arr. 1016 a.m on Sats. **C** 1 mile from Cheesehill Station. **D** Sta. for Twyford. **F** Sta. for Bishopstoke.
G Southampton Terminus (for Docks). **h** Thro Train to or from Portsmouth and Southsea, see pages 378 and 382.
SO Saturdays only SX Saturdays excepted

LOCAL TRAINS between Winchester and Southampton, page 384—Knowle Halt and Fareham, 376—Fareham and Gosport, 376

OTHER TRAINS between London & Southampton, 324

SOUTHAMPTON, TOTTON, and FAWLEY

Miles		Week Days only a.m		SO		p.m		
	London (Waterloo) **K** 324 dep.	2③40	..	1 30	..	1 30	..	..
—	**Southampton Terminus** dep.	..	..	3 55	..	5 15	..	..
1½	**Southampton Central** ... "	6 57	..	4 5	..	5 26	..	..
2½	Millbrook	7 2	..	4 10	..	5 35	..	..
4½	Redbridge	7 7	..	4 15	..	5 41	..	..
5	**Totton L**	7 10	..	4 20	..	5 45	..	..
8½	Marchwood	7 22	..	4 31	..	5 55	..	..
11½	Hythe (Hants)	7 32	..	4 41	..	6 5	..	..
14½	Fawley (Hants) .... arr.	7 43	..	4 51	..	6 15	..	..

Miles		Week Days only a.m		SO	p.m	p.m	
	Fawley (Hants) .... dep	8 6	..	1212	5 15	6 43	..
3	Hythe (Hants)	8 14	..	1220	5 23	6 51	..
6	Marchwood	8 24	..	1229	5 34	7 1	..
9½	**Totton L** 324	8 37	..	1242	5 47	7 13	..
10½	Redbridge 380	8 40	..	1245	5 50	7 16	..
12	Millbrook	8 44	..	1250	5 55	7 20	..
12½	**Southampton Cen.** 330 .. arr.	8 48	..	1254	5 59	7 24	..
14½	**Southampton G** 494 .... "	9 6	..	..	..	7 31	..
94	London (Waterloo) **K** 330 . arr	10 59	..	2 56	8 32	1113	..

③ Third class only **G** Southampton Terminus (for Docks). **K** Via Southampton Central. **L** Station for Eling
SO Saturdays only.

LOCAL TRAINS between Southampton and Redbridge, page 384—Southampton and Totton, 324

SALISBURY, ANDOVER, SOUTHAMPTON, FAREHAM GOSPORT, and PORTSMOUTH

Week Days

Miles from Salisbury			a.m	a.m	a.m	a.m	a.m	a.m	a.m	a.m	a.m	a.m	a.m	a.m	a.m	a.m	a.m	a.m	a.m	a.m	a.m	a.m	a.m	a.m	a.m	p.m	p.m	p.m SX	p.m SO	p.m
											From Alton (dep. 7 36 a.m), see page 375						From Alton (dep. 9 5 a.m) see page 375					Through Train, Reading (G.W.R.) to Portsmouth and Southsea, see pages 495 and 325		Through Train, Bristol (G.W.R.) to Portsmouth and Southsea, see page 494				Saturdays excepted	Saturdays only	Through Train, Reading (G.W.R.) to Portsmouth and Southsea, see pages 495 and 325
		346 PLYMOUTH (N R.) ...dep.	..	③	③	..	..	..	..	..	..	..	..	..	..	..	..	..	..	..	..	..	..	..	..	..	..	..	..	..
		346 ILFRACOMBE .... "	..			..	..	..	..	..	..	..	..	..	..	..	..	..	..	..	..	..	..	..	..	..	..	..	..	..
		347 EXETER (Cen.) ..... "	..	..	..	..	..	..	..	..	..	..	..	..	..	..	..	..	..	..	..	..	7 30	..	..	..	..	..	..	..
		Salisbury ....dep.	..	..	..	..	..	..	..	..	..	..	..	..	7 52	..	..	..	..	..	..	..	10 0	1032	..	..	..	..	..	..
9		Dean	..	..	..	..	..	..	..	..	..	..	..	..	8 8	..	..	..	..	..	..	..	1016	1050	..	..	..	..	..	..
12¼		Dunbridge	..	..	..	..	..	..	..	..	..	..	..	..	8 16	..	..	..	..	..	..	..	1024	1058	..	..	..	..	..	..
—		Mls Andover Junction.dep.	..	..	..	..	..	..	..	..	..	6 45	..	7 30	..	..	..	..	..	9 20	..		..	..	1127	..	..	..	..	
—		¾ Andover Town	..	..	..	..	..	..	..	..	..	6 48	..	7 33	..	..	..	..	..	9 23	..		..	..	1130	..	..	..	..	
—		2¾ Clatford	..	..	..	..	..	..	..	..	..	6 54	..	7 38	..	..	..	..	..	9 27	..		..	..	1134	..	..	..	..	
—		5⅛ Fullerton	..	..	..	..	..	..	..	..	..	7 1	..	7 44	..	..	..	..	..	9 33	..		..	..	1140	..	..	..	..	
—		8½ Stockbridge	..	..	..	..	..	..	..	..	..	7 8	..	7 50	..	..	..	..	..	9 39	..		..	..	1146	..	..	..	..	
—		11¾ Horsebridge	..	..	..	..	..	..	..	..	..	7 16	..	7 57	..	..	..	..	..	9 45	..		..	..	1152	..	..	..	..	
—		14½ Mottisfont	..	..	..	..	..	..	..	..	..	7 23	..	8 3	..	..	..	..	..	9 51	..		..	..	1158	..	..	..	..	
16½		Romsey	..	..	..	..	..	..	6 50	..	..	7 31	8 0	8 11	8 24	8 32		8 54	9 27	9 58	10 6		1032	11 6	12 5	..	..			
21¾	—	Chandlers Ford	..	..	..	..	..	..	6 59	..	..	..	8 9	..	..	8 41		..	9 36	..	1017		..	..	1214	..	..			
23¾	—	Eastleigh A 330, 375 arr.	..	..	..	..	..	..	7 5	..	..	..	8 15	..	..	8 47		..	9 42	..	1023		..	..	1220	..	..			
—	20¼	Nursling	..	..	..	..	..	..	..	..		7 38	..	..	8 30	..		8 59	..	..	..		..	1113	..	..	..			
—	22	Redbridge	..	..	..	..	..	..	..	..		7 43	..	..	8 35	..		9 4	..	..	..		..	1119	..	..	..			
—	23¾	Millbrook	..	..	..	..	..	..	..	..		7 48	..	..	8 39	..		..	..	..	..		..	1124	..	..	..			
—	24¾	Southampton Central B ... arr.	..	..	..	..	..	..	..	..		7 52	..	..	8 43	..		9 11	..	..	..		1047	1128	..	..	..			
		dep.	..	..	..	..	6 30	..	..	..		7 53	..	..	8 44	..		9 25	..	..	..		1049	1130	..	1225	..			
—	26½	Southampton Ter. (for Docks) arr.	..	..	..	..	..	..	..	..		7 58	..	..	..	..		..	..	..	..		..	..	..	..	..	..	..	
		dep.	..	..	..	5 15	..	..	..	7 38		8 2	..	..	..	..		..	..	..	..		..	..	..	..	..	1245	1253	
—	27	Northam	..	..	..	..	..	..	..	7 41		8 5	..	..	..	..		..	..	..	..		..	..	..	..	..	1248	1256	
—	26½	St. Denys	..	..	..	5L32	6 36	..	..	7 45		8 9	..	..	8 51	..		9 32	..	..	..		1057	1138	..	1231	..	1254	1 4	
—	27½	Bitterne	..	..	..	5 35	6 40	..	..	7 48		8 13	..	..	..	..		9 35	..	..	..		11 2	..	..	..	..	1258	1 8	
—	29	Woolston	..	..	..	5 40	6 45	..	..	7 55		8 17	..	..	8 57	..		9 39	..	..	..		11 7	1144	..	1237	..	1 5	1 13	
—	29½	Sholing	..	..	..	..	6 48	..	..	7 58		8 20	..	..	..	..		9 42	..	..	..		1110	..	..	..	..	1 8	1 16	
—	31½	Netley	..	..	..	5 46	6 54	..	..	8 3		8 25	..	..	9 3	..		9 47	..	..	..		1116	1150	..	1243	..	1 13	1 21	
—	32¼	Hamble Halt	..	..	..	..	6 58	..	..	8 7		8 28	..	..	..	..		9 50	..	..	..		1119	..	..	1247	..	1 17	1 24	
—	33½	Bursledon	..	..	..	5 51	7 2	..	..	8 11		8 31	..	..	..	..		9 53	..	..	..		1123	..	..	..	..	1 21	1 28	
—	35½	Swanwick	..	..	..	5 57	7 8	..	..	8 17		8 37	..	..	9 11	..		9 59	..	..	..		1129	..	..	1256	..	1 27	1 33	
—	—	Eastleigh A ....dep.	1 44	4 50	..	..	..	6 56	7 52	..	..	..	..	..	..	9 3	..	..	..	..	..	10 47	..	..	..	..	1 5	..	..	1 46
29½	—	Botley	..	..	..	..	..	7 7	8 2	..	..	..	..	..	..	9 13	..	..	..	..	..	10 59	..	..	..	..	1 15	..	..	1 58
32½	—	Knowle Halt 375	..	..	..	..	..	..	..	..	8 28	..	..	..	..	..	9 53	..	..	..	..	11THO5	..	..	..	..	1THO22	..	..	..
35¼	39¼	Fareham ☾ ....arr.	2 3	5 9	..	6 7	7 15	7 18	8 13	8 24	8 33	8 44	..	..	9 17	9 23	9 59	10 6	..	..	..	11 10	1137	12 3	..	1 4	1 25	1 34	1 41	2 9
—	—	Fareham ☾ ....dep.	..	..	..	..	..	7 23	8 15	..	..	..	..	..	..	9 30	..	10 16	..	..	..	..	..	..	..	..	..	..	..	..
38¾	—	Fort Brockhurst	..	..	..	..	..	7 30	8 24	..	..	..	..	..	..	9 37	..	10 23	..	..	..	..	..	..	..	..	..	..	..	..
40½	—	Gosport ....arr.	..	..	..	..	..	7 35	8 29	..	..	..	..	..	..	9 41	..	10 27	..	..	..	..	..	..	..	..	..	..	..	..
—	—	Fareham ☾ ....dep.	2 7	5 11	5 21	6 9	7 23	..	..	8 25	..	8 45	..	..	9 18	9 25	..	10 8	..	..	..	11 12	1139	12 5	..	1 5	1SO26	1 36	1 42	2 11
38¼	42½	Portchester	..	..	..	6 15	7 31	..	..	8 32	..	8 50	..	..	..	9 32	..	10 15	..	..	..	..	1145	..	..	1 12	..	1 44	1 49	2 18
41	45	Cosham	..	..	5 33	6 21	7 39	..	..	8 38	..	8 56	..	..	9 29	9 37	..	10 22	..	..	..	11 23	1153	1217	..	1 19	1SO36	1 50	1 54	2 24
42½	46¼	Hilsea Halt	..	..	..	..	7 45	..	..	8 42	..	..	..	..	..	..	..	..	..	..	..	..	..	..	..	..	..	..	..	..
44¼	48¾	Fratton 196, 366	..	..	5 42	6 31	7 50	..	..	8 48	..	9 5	..	..	9 38	9 47	..	10 31	..	..	..	11 31	12 2	1226	..	1 28	1SO45	1 59	2 3	2 33
45½	49½	Portsmouth & Southsea arr.	2 28	..	5 53	6 36	7 55	..	..	8 51	..	9 9	..	..	9 42	9 53	..	10 35	..	..	..	11 36	12 7	1231	..	1 33	1SO49	2 4	2 7	2 38
46¼	50½	Portsmouth Harbour .. "	..	5 33	..	..	..	..	..	..	..	..	..	..	..	..	..	..	..	..	..	..	..	..	..	..	..	..	..	..
88¾	92¾	196 BRIGHTON ....arr.	7 35	..	7a35	8 29	9 36	..		10SXa6	..	10a36	..	..	..	11a7	..	12V36	..	..	..	1SO10	1a36	2 36	..	..	3SOa6	3 36	3a36	4SO6

③ Third class only
A Sta. for Bishopstoke
a Change at Fratton
B About 1 mile from the Docks & Pier
☾ Frequent service by Hants & Dorset Motor Omnibus between Fareham and Lee-on-the-Solent

L Arr. 5 21 a.m
SO or SO Saturdays only
SX or SX Saturdays excepted
THO Thursdays only
V Arr. 12 6 p.m on Saturdays.

LOCAL TRAINS

BETWEEN	PAGE
Eastleigh and Southampton	384
Redbridge and St. Denys	386

OTHER TRAINS

BETWEEN	PAGE
Fratton and Portsmouth Harbour	158 and 359

For Continuation of Trains, see pages 377 and 378

SALISBURY, ANDOVER, SOUTHAMPTON, FAREHAM, GOSPORT, and PORTSMOUTH

Week Days—*continued*

Station	p.m	p.m	a.m		p.m	p.m		p.m	p.m	p.m	a.m		p.m	p.m	a.m SO	
Notes	From Alton (dep 1 30 p.m), see page 375		Through Train, Bristol (G.W.R.) to Southampton Terminus (arr 2 23 p.m) see pages 494 and 326		Through Train from Cheltenham (G.W.R.) (dep 10 5 a.m), see page 496	Through Train, Cardiff (G.W.R.) to Portsmouth and Southsea, see page 494				Through Train from Reading (G.W.R.) to Portsmouth and Southsea, see pages 495 and 326	Through Refreshment Car Train, Plymouth (Friary) (dep. 10 0 a.m) to Brighton	Through Carriages, Plymouth to Portsmouth and Southsea			Saturdays only. Through Train Cardiff (G.W.R.) to Brighton see page 494	Through Carrs. Cardiff (G.W.R.) to Portsmouth and Southsea, see page 494. Sats. only
346 Plymouth (N R) ... dep			8 25								10 10				S O	
346 Ilfracombe ... "			8 10												1015	
347 Exeter (Cen.) ... "			1030								12 25				1240	
Salisbury ... dep			1 2			1 38					2 48				4 8	
Dean			1 20													
Dunbridge			1 27													
Andover Junction ... dep					1 10											
Andover Town					1 14											
Clatford																
Fullerton					1 22											
Stockbridge					1 30											
Horsebridge					1 36											
Mottisfont					1 42											
Romsey		1 28	1 35		1 51	2 7			3 5							
Chandlers Ford			1 45						3 14							
Eastleigh A 330, 375 arr			1 51						3 20							
Nursling		1 34														
Redbridge		1 38														
Millbrook		1 43														
Southampton Central B arr		1 47			2 9	2 23					3 26				4 47	
Southampton Central B dep		1 49			2 13	2 27		2 58			3 28			4 5	4 49	
Southampton Ter. (for Docks) arr					2 20									4 10		
Southampton Ter. (for Docks) dep														4 18		
Northam														4 20		
St. Denys		1 58						3 4						4F32		
Bitterne		2 2						3 8						4 35		
Woolston		2 6						3 12						4 39		
Sholing		2 9						3 15						4 42		
Netley		2 14						3 20						4 47		
Hamble Halt		2 17												4 51		
Bursledon		2 20						3 24						4 55		
Swanwick		2 25						3 30						5 1		
Eastleigh A dep										3 25						
Botley										3 38						
Knowle Halt 375	2 18															
Fareham C arr	2 24	2 32				2 52		3 39		3 49	3 55			5 8	5 17	
Fareham C dep								3 44					4 30			
Fort Brockhurst								3 51					4 37			
Gosport arr								3 55					4 42			
Fareham C dep		2 33				2 54		3 40		3 50	3 58	4 6		5 9	5 19	5SO26
Portchester		2 40						3 47						5 16		
Cosham		2 46				3 6		3 53		4 3		4 19		5 22		5SO37
Hilsea Halt																
Fratton 196, 368		2 57				3 15		4 2		4 15		4 29		5 32		5SO46
Portsmouth & Southsea arr		3 3				3 20		4 7		4 19		4 34		5 36		5SO51
Portsmouth Harbour "																
196 Brighton arr		4a36						5a38			5 22			7Y17	6 54	

Station	p.m	p.m SX	p.m	p.m	p.m	a.m	p.m		p.m	p.m	p.m	p.m	p.m	p.m
Notes	From Alton (dep. 4 35 p.m) see page 375	Saturdays excepted			Through Train from Marlborough (G.W.R.) (dep 3 50 p.m) see page 496						Through Train, Bristol (G.W.R.) to Portsmouth and Southsea, see page 494		From Alton (dep 8 30 p.m) see page 375	
346 Plymouth (N R) ... dep						11 47								
346 Ilfracombe ... "						12 15								
347 Exeter (Cen.) ... "						2 30								
Salisbury ... dep						5 5					6 53			
Dean						5 22					7 10			
Dunbridge						5 30					7 18			
Andover Junction ... dep		4 5			4 41							6 55		7 35
Andover Town		4 10			4 46							6 58		7 40
Clatford					4 51							7 2		7 45
Fullerton		4 23			4 56							7 8		7 51
Stockbridge		4 30			5 3							7 14		7 58
Horsebridge		4 37			5 9							7 21		8 5
Mottisfont		4 43			5 15							7 27		8 11
Romsey		4 50	5 5		5 22	5 38	5 55				7 26	7 34		8 20
Chandlers Ford			5 15				6 4					7 44		8 30
Eastleigh A 330, 375 arr			5 23				6 10					7 50		8 36
Nursling					5 28									
Redbridge					5 33									
Millbrook					5 38									
Southampton Central B arr					5 42	5 53					7 41			
Southampton Central B dep					5 44	5 55					7 45			
Southampton Ter. (for Docks) arr					5 50									
Southampton Ter. (for Docks) dep				5 25					6 15					
Northam				5 28					6 18					
St. Denys				5 32		6 6			6 22		7 53			
Bitterne				5 36					6 25		7 57			
Woolston				5 40		6 13			6 30		8 1			
Sholing				5 43					6 33		8 4			
Netley				5 48		6 19			6 38		8 10			
Hamble Halt				5 52										
Bursledon				5 56		6 27			6 42		8 15			
Swanwick				6 1					6 48		8 21			
Eastleigh A dep			5 30							7 40				
Botley			5 42							7 50				
Knowle Halt 375	5 23												9 20	
Fareham C arr	5 29		5 53	6 9		6 37			6 55	8 1	8 29		9 25	
Fareham C dep				6 12									9 28	
Fort Brockhurst				6 19									9 37	
Gosport arr				6 23									9 41	
Fareham C dep			5 54	6 10		6 38			6 56	8 3	8 31			
Portchester				6 16					7 2	8 10	8 38			
Cosham			6 6	6 23		6 48			7 7	8 16	8 45			
Hilsea Halt														
Fratton 196, 368			6 15	6 32		6 56			7 16	8 27	8 54			
Portsmouth & Southsea arr			6 19	6 37		7 1			7 20	8 31	8 59			
Portsmouth Harbour "														
196 Brighton arr				8 8		8 36			9 37		1036			

A Station for Bishopstoke
a Change at Fratton
B About 1 mile from the Docks and Pier

C Frequent service by Hants and Dorset Motor Omnibus between Fareham and Lee-on-the-Solent

F Arr. 4 24 p.m.
S O or **SO** Saturdays only
S X Saturdays excepted

Y Arr. 7 10 p.m. on Saturdays

For Continuation of Trains, see page 378

SALISBURY, ANDOVER, SOUTHAMPTON, FAREHAM, GOSPORT, and PORTSMOUTH

	Week Days—continued					Sundays																				
	p.m	p.m	p.m	p.m		a.m	a.m	a.m	a.m	a.m		p.m	p.m	p.m	p.m		a.m	p.m	p.m	p.m	p.m	p.m	p.m	p.m	p.m	p.m
		Arr St. Denys at 10 8 p.m	To Eastleigh, arr 11 21 p.m page 387	Through Train from Exeter (Central)			Through Train Alton (dep. 8 23 a.m) to Portsmouth and Southsea see page 375						Through Train, Bristol (G.W.R.) to Portsmouth and Southsea, see page 494		From Bournemouth West (dep. 1 8 p.m) to Portsmouth and Southsea, see page 334		From Plymouth (Friary) dep 10 0 a.m to Portsmouth and Southsea	From Bournemouth West (dep. 2 43 p.m) to Portsmouth and Southsea, see page 334				Through Train Alton (dep. 8 28 p.m) to Portsmouth and Southsea, see page 375	Through Train, Bristol (G.W.R) to Portsmouth and Southsea, see page 494		From Bournemouth Cen. (dep. 8 48 p.m) to Portsmouth and Southsea, see page 335	
346 Plymouth (N.R.) ....dep.	3 55	..	..	4 50	..	..	..	..	..	..	..	..	..	..	..	..	10 9	..	..	..	3 0	..	..	..	..	..
346 Ilfracombe .... "	3 0	..	..	4 45	..	..	..	..	..	..	..	..	..	..	..	..	9 50	..	..	..	2 0	..	..	..	..	..
347 Exeter (Cen.) .... "	5 50	..	..	7 50	..	..	..	..	..	..	..	..	..	..	..	..	12 0	..	..	..	4 55	..	..	..	..	..
Salisbury ....dep.	8 28	..	1015	11 10	..	..	..	8 50	..	..	..	..	1 26	..	..	..	2 7	..	..	..	7 25	..	8 10	..	..	..
Dean	8 43	..	1032	..	..	..	..	9 6	..	..	..	..	..	..	..	..	..	..	..	..	7 40	..	8 25	..	..	..
Dunbridge	8 51	..	1039	..	..	..	..	9 13	..	..	..	..	..	..	..	..	..	..	..	..	7 48	..	8 33	..	..	..
Andover Junction ...dep.	..	..	..	..	..	..		..	..	..	..	..	..	..	..	..	..	..	5 35	6 38	..		..	..	..	..
Andover Town	..		..	..	..	..		..	..	..	..	..	..	..	..	..	..	..	5 38	6 41	..		..	..	..	..
Clatford	..		..	..	..	..		..	..	..	..	..	..	..	..	..	..	..	5 42	6 45	..		..	..	..	..
Fullerton	..		..	..	..	..		..	..	..	..	..	..	..	..	..	..	..	5 48	6 51	..		..	..	..	..
Stockbridge	..		..	..	..	..		..	..	..	..	..	..	..	..	..	..	..	5 54	6 57	..		..	..	..	..
Horsebridge	..		..	..	..	..		..	..	..	..	..	..	..	..	..	..	..	6 1	7 3	..		..	..	..	..
Mottisfont	..		..	..	..	..		..	..	..	..	..	..	..	..	..	..	..	6 6	7 9	..		..	..	..	..
Romsey	8 59		1048	11WSO35	..	..		9 20	9 36	1135	..	..	1 53	2 0	..	..	..	..	6 14	7 16	7 56		8 40	8 50	..	..
Chandlers Ford	9 9		..	..	..	..		..	9 45	1144	..	..	..	2 9	..	..	..	..	6 23	7 25	..		..	8 59	..	..
Eastleigh A 330, 375 arr.	9 20		..	11 48	..	..		..	9 51	1150	..	..	..	2 15	..	..	..	..	6 29	7 32	..		..	9 5	..	..
Nursling	..		..		..	..		..	Stop	Stop	..	..	..	..	..	..	..	..	..	..	..		..	..	..	..
Redbridge	..		..		..	..		9 29			..	..	..	..	..	..	..	3 51	..	..	..		..	..	..	..
Millbrook	..		..		..	..		9 34	..	..	..	..	..	..	..	..	..	3 56	..	..	..		..	..	9 55	..
Southampton Central **B** .... arr.	..		11 3		..	..		9 37	..	a.m	..	..	2 8	..	2 24	..	2 47	3 59	..	..	8 12		8 55	..	9 59	..
Southampton Central **B** .... dep.	..	9S052	11 4		..	..		9 39	..	1135	..	..	2 11	..	2 26	..	2 53	4 1	..	..	8 15		9 0	..	10 1	..
Southampton Ter. (for Docks) arr.	..	9S057	..		..	..		9 46	..	..	..	..	..	..	..	..	..	..	..	..	..		..	..	..	..
Southampton Ter. (for Docks) dep.	..	10 0	..		..	..		9 51	..	..	..	..	..	..	..	..	..	..	..	..	..		..	..	..	..
Northam	..	10 3	..		..	..		..	..	..	..	..	..	..	..	..	..	..	..	..	..		..	..	..	..
St. Denys	..	10 13	1111		..	..		10H3	..	1142	..	..	..	..	2 34	..	..	4 8	..	..	8 24		9 9	..	1010	..
Bitterne	..	10 16	..		..	..		10 6	..	..	..	..	..	..	2 37	..	..	..	..	..	8 28		9 13	..	1014	..
Woolston	..	10 21	..		..	..		10 12	..	1148	..	..	..	..	2 42	..	..	4 14	..	..	8 34		9 18	..	1019	..
Sholing	..	..			..	..		..	..	..	..	..	..	..	..	..	..	..	..	..	..		..	..	..	..
Netley	..	10 27			..	..		10 19	..	1154	..	..	..	..	2 48	..	..	4 22	..	..	8 41		9 25	..	1025	..
Hamble Halt	..	..			..	..		10 22	..	..	..	..	..	..	2 51	..	..	..	..	..	..		..	..	..	..
Bursledon	..	10 31			..	..		10 26	..	..	..	..	..	..	2 54	..	..	..	..	..	8 46		9 30	..	1030	..
Swanwick	..	10 36			..	..		10 32	a.m	..	..	..	..	..	3 0	..	..	4 30	..	..	8 53		9 36	..	1036	..
Eastleigh A ....dep.	9 26	..			..	1 44	..	..	11 3	..	..	1 30	..	..	..	..	..	..	6 34		..	..	..	9 45	..	11 5
Botley	9 38	..			..	..	..	..	1113	..	..	1 40	..	..	..	..	..	..	6 46	..	..	..	..	9 55	..	1115
Knowle Halt 375	..	..			..	..	9 15	..	..	..	..	1 47	..	..	..	..	..	..	..	..	..	9 19	..	..	..	..
Fareham C ....arr.	9 48	10 43			..	2 3	9 21	10 40	1123	12 9	..	1 53	2 39	..	3 7	..	3 21	4 38	6 56	..	9 1	9 25	9 44	10 6	1044	1125
Fareham C ....dep.	..	..		..	..	..	..	..	..	..	..	..	..	..	..	..	..	..	..	..	..	..	..	..	..	..
Fort Brockhurst	..	..		..	..	..	..	..	..	..	..	..	..	..	..	..	..	..	..	..	..	..	..	..	..	..
Gosport ....arr	..	..		..	..	..	..	..	..	..	..	..	..	..	..	..	..	..	..	..	..	..	..	..	..	..
Fareham C ....dep.	9 50	10 44		..	..	2 7	9 22	10 41	1126	1210	..	1 54	2 41	..	3 9	..	3 23	4 39	6 58	..	9 2	9 26	9 46	10 7	1045	1126
Portchester	9 58	10 50		..	..	..	9 29	..	1134	..	..	2 1	..	..	3 15	..	..	..	7 6	..	..	9 33	..	10 14	1052	..
Cosham	10 6	10 55		..	..	..	9 35	10 51	1140	1221	..	2 6	2 51	..	3 20	..	3 36	4 49	7 13	..	9 13	9 39	9 58	10 21	1058	1136
Hilsea Halt	..	..		..	..	..	..	..	..	..	..	..	..	..	..	..	..	..	..	..	..	..	..	..	..	..
Fratton 196, 366	10 14	11 4	..	..	..	..	9 45	11 0	1149	1231	..	2 15	3 0	..	3 29	..	3 45	4 58	7 22	..	9 22	9 48	10 7	10 30	11 7	1145
Portsmouth&Southsea arr.	10 19	11 8	..	..	..	2 28	9 50	11 5	1154	1236	..	2 19	3 4	..	3 34	..	3 50	5 3	7 27	..	9 27	9 53	1012	10 35	1111	1150
Portsmouth Harbour .. "	..	..	..	..	..	..	..	..	..	..	..	..	..	..	..	..	..	..	..	..	..	..	..	..	..	..
196 Brighton ....arr.	..	..	..	..	..	7 50	11 6	12 36	1 36	2 36	..	4 6	4 36	..	..	..	5 36	6 36	9 6	..	--	11a8	..	..	..	..

A Station for Bishopstoke
a Change at Fratton
B About 1 mile from the Docks and Pier

C Frequent service by Hants and Dorset Motor Omnibus between Fareham and Lee-on-the-Solent
H Arr. 9 56 a.m.
SO Saturdays only
WSO Wednesdays and Saturdays only

LOCAL TRAINS

BETWEEN	PAGE
Eastleigh and Southampton	384
Redbridge and St. Denys	386

OTHER TRAINS

BETWEEN	PAGE
Fratton and Portsmouth Harbour	159 and 359

PORTSMOUTH, GOSPORT, FAREHAM, SOUTHAMPTON, ANDOVER, and SALISBURY

Week Days

Miles	Station	a.m	a.m	a.m	a.m	a.m	a.m		a.m	a.m	a.m (Through Train, Portsmouth and Southsea to Bristol (G.W.R.), see page 493)	a.m	a.m	a.m	a.m (Through Train, Portsmouth and Southsea to Cardiff (G.W.R.), see page 493)	a.m	a.m		a.m (Through Train, Portsmouth and Southsea to Bristol (G.W.R.), see page 493)	a.m	a.m	p.m	a.m	a.m	a.m SO	SO		p.m	a.m
	159 Brighton ....dep	..	..	..	..	..	..	..	4 55	..	..	..	..	6 17	7 7	..	..	..	8 47	9 17	..	..	9S047	..		11 0	..	..	1130
—	Portsmouth Harbour ..dep	..	..	..	..	..	..	..	..	..	..	..	..	..	..	..	..	..	..	..	..	..	..	..	..	..	..	..	..
¼	Portsmouth & Southsea "	..	..	..	6 0	..	..	..	6 55	..	7 29	..	..	8 8	8 55	9 0	..	..	10 34	10 48	..	..	11 26	..	1145	..	..	1215	..
1½	Fratton	..	..	..	6 3	..	..	..	6 58	..	7 32	..	..	8 10	8 58	9 5	..	..	10 37	10 51	..	..	11 29	..	..	..	..	..	..
3¼	Hilsea Halt	..	..	..	..	..	..	..	..	..	..	..	..	..	..	..	..	..	..	..	..	..	..	..	..	..	..	..	..
4¾	Cosham	..	..	..	6 12	..	..	..	7 7	..	7 40	..	..	8 19	9 9	9 15	..	..	10 46	11 1	..	..	11 37	..	..	..	..	1225	..
8	Portchester	..	..	..	6 18	..	..	..	7 14	..	7 46	..	..	8 25	..	9 21	..	..	..	11 8	..	..	11 44	..	..	..	..	..	..
11¼	**Fareham** C 375, 376 ...arr	..	..	..	6 26	..	..	..	7 21	..	7 53	..	..	8 32	9 19	9 28	..	..	10 56	11 14	..	..	11 51	..	12 5	12 17	..	1235	1246
—	Mls Gosport ....dep	..	..	..	6 10	..	..	..	..	7 40	..	..	..	..	8 47	..		..	..	11 3	..	..	..	1148	..	..	..	..	..
¾	Fort Brockhurst	..	..	..	6 13	..	..	..	..	7 43	..	..	..	..	8 50	..		..	..	11 6	..	..	..	1151	..	..	..	..	..
4¾	Fareham C 375 ....arr	..	..	..	6 21	..	..	..	..	7 51	..	..	..	..	9 0	..		..	..	11 14	..	..	..	1159	..	..	..	..	..
—	Fareham C ....dep	..	..	..	6 27	6 44	..	..	7 22	7 53	7 55	8 2	..	8 32	9 22	9 29		..	10 57	11 16	1147	..	11 52	..		12 22	..		12 51
13½	Knowle Halt	..	..	..	..	..	..	..	..	7 58	..	..	..	..	..	..		..	..	..	1151	..	..	..			..		
17	Botley	..	..	..	..	6 54	..	..	..	..	8 6	..	..	..	..	9 40		..	..	11 28		..	..	..			..		
22¼	**Eastleigh** A 330, 375 arr	..	..	..	..	7 4	..	..	..	..	8 16	..	..	..	..	9 50		..	..	11 39		..	..	..			..		
15	Swanwick	To Yeovil, see page 340	..	..	6 36	..	..	..	7 31	To Alton (arr. 8 49 a.m.), see page 375	..	8 10	..	8 42	..	To Winchester (arr 10 8 a.m) see page 330	Through Train to Cheltenham Spa arr. 1 30 p.m. see page 495	..	..	..	To Alton (arr. 12 49 p.m) see page 375	..	12 1	..	Saturdays only. Through Train Brighton to Cardiff, and Through Carriages Portsmouth and Southsea to Cardiff (G.W.R.) see page 493		..	Through Refreshment Car Train, Brighton to Plymouth (Friary), & Through Carriages, Portsmouth and Southsea to Plymouth (Friary) arr 7 [illegible]5 p.m.	
17	Bursledon		..	..	6 41	..	..	..	7 36		..	8 15	..	8 47	..			..	..	..		..	12 6	..			..		
18¼	Hamble Halt		..	..	6 45	..	..	..	7 40		..	8 18	..	8 50	..			..	..	..		..	12 10	..			..		
19	Netley		..	..	6 49	..	..	..	7 44		..	8 22	..	8 53	9 36			..	11 10	..		..	12 13	..			..		
20¼	Sholing		..	..	6 54	..	..	..	7 49		..	8 26	..	8 58	..			..	..	..		..	12 18	..			..		
21½	Woolston		..	..	6 57	..	..	..	7 52		..	8 29	..	9 0	9 43			..	11 16	..		..	12 20	..			..		
23¼	Bitterne		..	..	7 1	..	..	..	7 57		..	8 33	..	9 4	..			..	..	..		..	12 24	..			..		
24	St. Denys 330, 375		..	..	7 6	..	..	..	8 0		..	8 36	..	9 7	9 50			..	11 22	..		..	12 28	..			..		
24¾	Northam		..	..	7 10	..	..	..	..		..	..	..	9 11	..			..	..	..		..	..	..			..		
25½	Southampton Ter. (for Docks) arr		..	..	7 14	..	..	..	..		..	..	..	9 15	..			..	..	..		..	..	..			..		
	dep		..	..	7 25	..	..	..	..		..	..	..	..	..		1010	..	..	..		..	..	..			..		
25¾	Southampton Central B arr		..	..	7 30	..	..	..	8 6		..	8 42	..	..	9 56		1015	..	11 28	..	..	..	12 34	..		12 47	..		1 16
	dep		..	..	7 32	..	..	..	8 11		..	8 45	..	..	10 0		1017	..	11 30	..	..	..	12 35	..		12 52	..		1 19
26¾	Millbrook		..	..	7 36	..	..	..	8 16		..	8 50	..	..	..		..	..	..	..	..	..	..	..			..		
28½	Redbridge		..	..	7 41	..	..	..	..		..	8 56	..	..	..		..	..	..	..	..	..	12 41	..			..		
30¾	Nursling		..	..	7 46	..	..	..	8 25		..	9 0	..	..	..		..	..	..	..	..	..	12 46	..			..		
—	Eastleigh A ....dep	1 55	6 7	7 34	..	..	7 54	..	..	..	8 25	..	9 0	..	..	..	..	..	..	..	..	1228	..	..			..		
24½	Chandlers Ford	..	6 13	7 38	..	..	7 59	..	..	..	8 32	..	9 5	..	..	..	..	..	..	..	..	1233	..	..			..		
29¾	Romsey	..	6 23	7 48	7 56	..	8 10	..	8 32	..	8 44	9 8	9 16	..	1017	..	1031	..	11 47	..	..	1245	12 56	..			..		
33½	Mottisfont	Tues. to Sats. only.	..	..	..	..	8 18	..	..	..	..	..	9 24	..	..	..	..	..	..	..	..	..	1 4	..			..		
36	Horsebridge		..	..	..	..	8 23	..	..	..	..	..	9 30	..	..	..	..	..	..	..	..	..	1 9	..			..		
39½	Stockbridge		..	..	..	..	8 30	..	..	..	..	..	9 36	..	..	..	..	..	..	..	..	..	1 16	..			..		
42¼	Fullerton		..	..	..	..	8 36	..	..	..	..	..	9 43	..	..	..	..	..	..	..	..	..	1 22	..			..		
45	Clatford		..	..	..	..	8 41	..	..	..	..	..	9 49	..	..	..	..	..	..	..	..	..	1 27	..			..		
47	Andover Town		..	..	..	..	8 48	..	..	..	..	..	9 56	..	..	..	1059	..	..	..	..	..	1 33	..			..		
47¾	**Andover** Junction 340 arr		..	..	..	..	8 52	..	..	..	..	..	10 1	..	..	..	11 5	..	..	..	..	..	1 38	..			..		
33½	Dunbridge		..	..	8 4	..	..	..	..	..	8 53	..	..	..	..	..	..	..	11 55	..	..	..	..	..		..	..		..
37½	Dean 337, 357		..	..	8 13	..	..	..	..	..	9 2	..	..	..	..	..	..	..	12 3	..	..	..	..	..		..	..		..
46½	**Salisbury** 339, 340, arr	2 36	..	..	8 30	..	..	..	..	..	9 19	..	..	..	1041	..	..	..	12 20	..	..	..	..	..		1 31	..		1 58
134½	340 Exeter Cen. ....arr	5 13	..	..	..	..	..	..	..	..	..	..	..	..	1 [illegible]	..	..	..	2 29	..	..	..	..	..		..	..		4 46
189	341 Ilfracombe .... "	8 0	..	..	..	..	..	..	..	..	..	..	..	..	3 52	..	..	..	4 36	..	..	..	..	..		..	..		7 18
193½	341 Plymouth (N.R.) ... "	7 36	..	..	..	..	..	..	..	..	..	..	..	..	3 35	..	..	..	4 44	..	..	..	..	..		..	..		6 53

A Station for Bishopstoke
B About 1 mile from the Docks and Pier

C Frequent service by Hants and Dorset Motor Omnibus between Fareham and Lee-on-the-Solent

S O or SO Saturdays only

LOCAL TRAINS
BETWEEN

	PAGE
Southampton and Eastleigh	336
St. Denys and Redbridge	384

OTHER TRAINS
BETWEEN

	PAGE
Portsmouth Harbour and Fratton	196 and 366

For Continuation of Trains, see pages 381 and 382

PORTSMOUTH, GOSPORT, FAREHAM, SOUTHAMPTON, ANDOVER, and SALISBURY

Week Days—*continued*

	p.m	SO	a.m	p.m	p.m	p.m	p.m	p.m	p.m	p.m	p.m	p.m	p.m	p.m	p.m	p.m	p.m	p.m	p.m	p.m	p.m	p.m	p.m	p.m	p.m	p.m	p.m
15° Brighton ....dep.	S O	11a 0	11V17		12Y17		..	1a16	..	..	..	S X	..	2 47	3H17	..	..	4 16	..	5a17		6aSO17	6aSO47	..	..	8 17	9 17
Portsmouth Harbour ..dep.	..	..	..	..	..	..	..	..	..	..	..	..	..	..	..	..	..	..	..	..	..	..	..	..	..	..	..
Portsmouth & Southsea "	..	12p33	1256	..	2 3	..	2 33	2 45	..	..	3 35	..	..	4 35	5 15	..	5 35	6 3	..	6 45	7 17	7 45	8 3	..	..	9 46	1116
Fratton	..	12 36	1258	..	2 6	..	2 36	2 47	..	..	3 38	..	..	4 39	5 19	..	5 39	6 6	..	6 48	7 20	7 49	8 6	..	..	9 51	1120
Hilsea Halt	..	..	..	..	..	..	..	..	..	Through Train to Cheltenham Spa, arr. 8 10 p.m. see page 495	..	..	..	..	5SX25	..	..	6SX11		..	..	..	..	..	..	..	..
Cosham	..	12 44	1 8	..	2 14	..	..	2 57	..		3 46	..	..	4 51	5 31	..	5 49	6 16	..	6 58	7 29	7 59	8 15	..	..	10 0	1129
Portchester	..	12 50	1 15	..	2 20	..	..	3 3	..		3 53	..	..	4 58	5 38	..	..	6 23	..	7 5	7 36	8 5	..	..	..	10 7	1136
Fareham C 375, 376 ... arr.	..	12 58	1 23	..	2 27	..	..	3 10	..		4 0	..	..	5 6	5 45	..	5 59	6 31	..	7 11	7 44	8 13	8 25	..	..	1013	1144
Gosport ....dep.	1245	..	..	..	..	..	..	..	..		..	4 15	..	..	5 30	..	5 30	..	..	..	..	7 54	..	..	..	..	..
Fort Brockhurst	1248	..	..	..	..	..	..	..	..		..	4 18	..	..	5 33	..	5 33	..	..	..	..	7 58	..	..	..	..	..
Fareham C 375 ..... arr.	1256	..	..	..	..	..	..	..	..		..	4 26	..	..	5 41	..	5 41	..	..	..	..	8 8	..	..	..	..	..
Fareham C ....dep.	1258	1 1	1 24	1 28	2 28	2 48	..	3 11	..		4 2	4 27	..	5 8	5 47	..	6 1	6 32	6 50	7 13	7 46	8 14	8 28	8 45	..	1014	1146
Knowle Halt	..	..	..	..	..	2 52	..	..	..		4THO8	..	..	..	..	..	..	..	6 54	..	..	..	..	8 49	..	..	..
Botley	1 10	..	1 34	..	..		..	3 22	..		4 17	..	..	..	5 59	..	..	..		..	7 57	..	8 42		..	..	1157
Eastleigh A 330, 375 .. arr.	1 22	..	1 45	..	..		..	3 34	..		4 28	..	..	..	6 10	..	..	..		..	8 7	..	8 52		..	..	12 7
Swanwick	Saturdays only	1 10	..	1 36	2 35	To Alton (arr. 3 47 p.m). see page 375.	..	Through Train Portsmouth and Southsea to Reading (G.W.R.), see pages 332 and 496.	..		..	4 35	..	5 18	Through Train. Portsmouth and Southsea to Reading (G W.R.), see pages 333 and 496	..	..	6 41	To Alton (arr 7 48p.m) see page 375	7 23	..	8 22	..	To Alton (arr 9 41 p.m) see page 375	..	1022	..
Bursledon		1 15	..	1 41	2 40		..		..		..	4 39	..	5 23		..	..	6 47		7 29	..	8 27	..		..	1027	..
Hamble Halt		..	..	1 45	..		..		..		..	4 43	..	..		..	..	6 52		7 35	..	..	..		..	..	..
Netley		1 22	..	1 48	2 46		..		..		..	4 46	..	5 30		..	6 16	6 56		7 39	..	8 33	..		..	1034	..
Sholing		1 27	..	1 53	2 50		..		..		..		..	5 35		..	..	7 1		7 43	..	8 38	..		..	..	..
Woolston		1 29	..	1 56	2 53		..		..		..		..	5 39		..	6 23	7 4		7 46	..	8 41	..		..	1040	..
Bitterne		1 33	..	2 0	2 57		..		..		..		..	5 44		..	..	7 9		7 50	..	8 46	..		..	1044	..
St. Denys 330, 375		1 36	..	2 3	3 0		..		..		..		..	5 48		..	6 30	7 12		7 53	..	8 49	..		..	1048	..
Northam		1 40	..	..	..		..		..		..		..	..		..	..	..		..	..	..	..		..	..	..
Southampton Ter. arr.		1 44	..	..	..		..		..		..		..	..		..	..	..		..	..	..	..		..	1054	..
(for Docks) dep.	..	..	..	..	..		..		..	4 30	..	Saturdays excepted.	..	..		..	..	..		..	..	..	..		..	..	..
Southampton Central B arr.	..	..	..	2 10	3 6		3 16		..	4 35	..		..	5 54		..	6 36	7 18	..	7 59	..	8 55	..		..	..	..
Southampton Central B dep.	..	Saturdays only	..	2 19	..		3 18		..	4 37	..		..	5 56		..	6 38	Stop	..	..	..	8 59	..		..	..	..
Millbrook	..		..	2 24	..		..		..	..	..		..	..		..	..		..	..	..	9 4	..		..	..	..
Redbridge	..		..	2 29	..		..		..	4 43	..		..	6 3		..	..	..	..	..	..	9 9	..		..	..	..
Nursling	..		..	..	..		..		..	..	..		..	6 8		..	..	..	..	..	..	9Z15	..		..	..	..
Eastleigh A ....dep.	..		2 5	To Bournemouth West arr. 3 46 p.m see page 326	..	..	..		4 22	..	5 13	..	5 40	..		6 28	..	..	..	..	8 15	..	..		9 39	..	..
Chandlers Ford	..		2 10		..	..	..		4 27	..	5 18	..	5 45	..		6 35	..	p.m	..	..	8 21	..	..		9 44	..	..
Romsey	..		2 20		..	..	3 36		4 37	4 54	5 28	..	5 57	6 18		6 45	6 55	7 5	..	..	8 32	9 23	..		9 56	..	..
Mottisfont	..		..		..	..	..		..	5 1	..	..	6 5	..		..	..	7 12	..	..	..	9 31	..	..	..	..	..
Horsebridge	..		..		..	..	..		..	5 7	..	..	6 11	..		..	..	7 18	..	..	..	9 36	..	..	..	..	..
Stockbridge	..		..		..	..	..		..	5 14	..	..	6 18	..		..	..	7 26	..	..	..	9 42	..	..	..	..	..
Fullerton	..		..		..	..	..		..	5 21	..	..	6 25	..		..	..	7 33	..	..	..	9 48	..	..	..	..	..
Clatford	..	..	..		..	..	..		..	..	..	..	6 32	..		..	..	7 39	..	..	..	9 54	..	..	..	..	..
Andover Town	..	..	..		..	..	..		..	5 30	..	..	6 38	..		..	..	7 45	..	..	..	9 59	..	..	..	..	..
Andover Junction 340 arr	..	..	..		..	..	..		..	5 34	..	..	6 43	..		..	..	7 50	..	..	..	10 4	..	..	..	..	..
Dunbridge	..	..	..		..	..	3 44		..	..	..	..	..	6 26		..	..	..	..	..	8 40	..	..	..	10 5	..	..
Dean 347, 357	..	..	..		..	..	3 54		..	..	..	..	..	6 34		..	..	..	..	..	8 49	..	..	..	1013	..	..
Salisbury 339, 340 arr.	..	..	..		..	..	4 12		..	..	..	..	..	6 51		..	7 21	..	..	..	9 6	..	..	..	1031	..	..
340 Exeter (Cen.) ....arr.	..	..	..	..	..	..	6 46		..	..	..	..	..	..		..	10 6	..	..	..	..	..	..	..	..	..	..
341 Ilfracombe .... "	..	..	..	..	..	..	9 11		..	..	..	..	..	..		..	..	..	..	..	..	..	..	..	..	..	..
341 Plymouth (N.R.) .. "	..	..	..	..	..	..	9 3		..	..	..	..	..	..		..	..	..	..	..	..	..	..	..	..	..	..

Through Train, Portsmouth and Southsea to Bristol (G.W.R.) see page 493 (7th column).

Through Train, Portsmouth and Southsea to Cardiff (G.W.R.), see page 493 (17th column).

A Station for Bishopstoke
a Change at Fratton
B About 1 mile from the Docks and Pier

C Frequent service by Hants and Dorset Motor Omnibus between Fareham and Lee-on-the-Solent

H Dep. 3 47 p.m. on Saturdays
p p.m.
S O or **SO** Saturday only
S X or **SX** Saturdays excepted

THO Thursdays only
V Dep. 11 47 a.m. on Sats. Change at Fratton

Y Dep. 12 47 p.m. on Sats. Change at Fratton
Z Stops to set down only

For SUNDAY TRAINS, see page 382

PORTSMOUTH, GOSPORT, FAREHAM, SOUTHAMPTON, ANDOVER, and SALISBURY

Sundays

Station	a.m	a.m	a.m	a.m	a.m	a.m	a.m (Through Train, Portsmouth and Southsea to Bristol (G.W.R.) see page 493)	a.m	a.m	a.m (To Plymouth (Friary) arr 6 3 p.m)			p.m	a.m	p.m (Through Train, Portsmouth and Southsea to Bristol (G.W.R.), see page 493)
159 Brighton ... dep.	..	..	..	..	..	..	8 17	..	9a47	10a17		..	..	1117	1215
Portsmouth Harbour ... dep.	..	..	..	..	..	..	..	..	..	..		..	..	..	..
Portsmouth & Southsea "	..	7 56	8 8	..	8 35	..	1015	..	1055	1140		..	..	1 25	1 55
Fratton	..	7 59	8 11	..	8 39	..	1019	..	1058	1143		..	..	1 28	1 58
Hilsea Halt	..	..	..	..	..	..	..	..	..	..		..	..	..	..
Cosham	..	8 8	8 20	..	8 49	..	1020	..	11 8	1151		..	..	1 37	2 8
Portchester	..	8 13	..	..	8 55	..	..	..	1114	..		..	..	1 44	..
Fareham C 375, 376 ... arr.	..	8 20	8 30	..	9 2	..	1039	..	1122	12 1		..	..	1 52	2 18
Gosport ... dep.	..	..	..	..	..	..	..	..	..	..		..	..	..	..
Fort Brockhurst	..	..	..	..	..	..	..	..	..	..		..	..	..	..
Fareham C 375 ... arr.	..	..	..	..	..	..	..	..	..	..		..	..	..	..
Fareham C ... dep.	..	8 21	8 31	..	9 3	..	1040	..	1124	12 2		..	..	1 53	2 20
Knowle Halt	..	8 27	..	..	..	..	..	..	..	..		..	..	..	..
Botley	..	..	8 41	..	..	..	..	..	1134	..		..	..	..	..
Eastleigh A 330, 375 arr	..	..	8 52	..	..	..	..	..	1145	..		..	..	..	..
Swanwick	To Yeovil, see page 344	Through Train, Portsmouth and Southsea to Woking (arr. 10 21 a.m) see pages 375 and 393	Through Train Portsmouth and Southsea to Reading (G.W.R.), see pages 334 and 496	..	9 12	..	..	..	..	..		..	..	2 2	..
Bursledon				..	9 17	..	..	..	..	..		..	..	2 7	..
Hamble Halt				..	9 21	..	..	..	..	..		..	..	2 11	..
Netley				..	9 24	..	1053	..	..	..		..	..	2 15	..
Sholing				..	..	..	..	..	..	..		..	..	..	..
Woolston				..	9 30	..	1059	..	..	..		..	..	2 22	..
Bitterne				..	9 35	..	11 4	..	..	..		..	..	2 27	..
St. Denys 330, 375				..	9 38	..	11 7	..	..	1223		..	..	2 30	..
Northam				..	..	..	..	..	..	..		..	..	..	..
Southampton Ter. (for Docks) arr.				..	..	..	..	..	..	..		..	..	..	..
Southampton Ter. dep.				..	..	..	..	..	..	..		..	..	..	..
Southampton Central B arr.				..	9 44	..	1113	..	..	1230		..	..	2 36	2 48
Southampton Central B dep.				..	..	..	1116	..	..	1232	1236	..	..	..	2 51
Millbrook				..	..	..	..	..	..	To Bournemouth West (arr 1 46 p.m) see page 328	..	..	..	..	..
Redbridge				..	..	..	..	..	..		..	..	..	..	..
Nursling				..	..	..	..	..	..		..	..	..	..	..
Eastleigh A ... dep.	1 55			9 13	..	11 2	..	..	1153		..	..	1 27	..	..
Chandlers Ford	..			9 18	..	11 7	..	..	12 0		..	..	1 32	..	..
Romsey	..			9 28	..	1117	1134	1142	1211		1253	..	1 42	..	3 8
Mottisfont	..			..	..	..	..	1149	..		..	..	..	..	..
Horsebridge	..			..	..	..	..	1154	..		..	..	..	..	..
Stockbridge	..			..	..	..	..	12 1	..		..	..	..	..	..
Fullerton	..			..	..	..	..	12 8	..		..	..	..	..	..
Clatford	..			..	..	..	..	1214	..		..	..	..	..	..
Andover Town	..			..	..	..	..	1219	..		..	..	..	..	..
Andover Junction 340 arr	..			..	..	..	..	1224	..		..	..	..	..	..
Dunbridge	..	..	..	..	..	..	1143	..	1219		..	..	..	..	..
Dean ... 347, 357	..	..	..	..	..	..	1152	..	1227		..	..	..	..	..
Salisbury 339, 340, arr.	2 36	..	..	..	..	..	1210	..	1245		1 21	..	..	..	3 36
340 Exeter (Cen.) ... arr.	12p8	..	..	..	..	..	..	..	2 55	..	3 51	..	..	..	..
341 Ilfracombe ... "	..	..	..	..	..	..	..	..	5 18	..	..	..	..	..	..
341 Plymouth (N.R.) "	..	..	..	..	..	..	..	..	4 55	..	5 52	..	..	..	..

Station	p.m	p.m	p.m	p.m	p.m	p.m	p.m (Through Train, Portsmouth and Southsea to Bristol (G.W.R.), see page 493)	p.m	p.m	p.m	p.m	p.m	p.m	p.m	p.m
159 Brighton ... dep.	1 15	..	2 47	3 17	..	4 17	..	5 17	..	6 17	..	..	8 47	9 17	..
Portsmouth Harbour ... dep.	..	..	..	..	..	..	..	..	..	..	..	..	..	..	..
Portsmouth & Southsea "	3 17	Through Train from Winchester (dep 4 20 p.m) see page 328	4 35	4 48	5 5	6 7	6 33	6 48	..	8 3	..	8 15	1015	1055	1125
Fratton	3 20		4 37	4 51	5 8	6 10	6 36	6 51	..	8 6	..	8 19	1018	1059	1128
Hilsea Halt	..		..	..	..	..	..	..	..	..	..	..	..	..	..
Cosham	3 29		4 47	5 1	5 17	6 20	6 45	7 1	..	8 15	..	8 28	1027	11 8	1136
Portchester	3 36		4 53	5 7	..	6 27	6 52	7 7	..	8 22	..	..	1033	1114	..
Fareham C 375, 376 ... arr.	3 43		5 0	5 14	5 27	6 35	6 58	7 15	..	8 29	..	8 38	1040	1121	1146
Gosport ... dep.	..		..	..	..	..	..	..	Continuation of 6 33 p.m Portsmouth and Southsea to Bristol	..	..	..	..	..	..
Fort Brockhurst	..		..	..	..	..	..	..		..	..	..	..	..	..
Fareham C 375 ... arr.	..		..	..	..	..	..	..		..	..	..	..	..	..
Fareham C ... dep.	3 44		5 1	5 15	5 28	6 36	6 59	7 16		8 31	..	8 39	1041	1122	1147
Knowle Halt	..		..	5 21	..	6 42	..	..		..	..	..	..	..	..
Botley	..		..	5 28	..	..	..	7 27		8 45	..	..	..	1132	..
Eastleigh A 330, 375 arr	..		..	5 39	..	..	..	7 37		8 56	..	..	..	1142	12 5
Swanwick	..		5 9	..	..	Through Train Portsmouth and Southsea to Alton (arr 7 38 p.m), see page 375	7 8	..		..	..	8 48	1050	..	..
Bursledon	..		5 14	..	..		7 13	..		..	..	8 53	1054	..	..
Hamble Halt	..		5 18	..	..		7 17	..		..	..	..	..	..	..
Netley	3 56		5 21	..	..		7 22	..		..	..	8 59	11 0	..	..
Sholing	..		..	..	..		..	..		..	..	..	..	..	..
Woolston	4 2		5 29	..	..		7 29	..		..	..	9 6	11 6	..	..
Bitterne	..		5 33	..	..		7 34	..		..	..	9 10	1110	..	..
St. Denys 330, 375	4 8	4 47	5 36	..	5 49		7 38	..		..	..	9 13	1115	..	..
Northam	..	..	..	..	..		..	..		..	..	..	..	..	..
Southampton Ter. (for Docks) arr.	..	..	..	..	..		..	..		..	..	..	..	..	..
Southampton Ter. dep.	..	..	..	..	..		..	..		..	..	..	..	..	..
Southampton Central B arr.	4 14	4 53	5 42	..	5 55		7 44	..	..	..	..	9 19	1122	..	..
Southampton Central B dep.	4 20	4 55	..	..	..		Dep. Southampton (Central) 7 57 p.m	..	7 57	..	..	..	..	..	..
Millbrook	..	4 59	..	..	..			..	..	..	..	..	..	..	..
Redbridge	..	5 4	..	..	..			..	..	..	..	..	..	..	..
Nursling	..	..	..	..	..			..	..	..	..	..	..	..	..
Eastleigh A ... dep.	..	..	..	..	..	..	..	7 39	..	..	9 45	..	..	..	..
Chandlers Ford	..	..	..	..	..	..	..	7 45	..	..	9 50	..	..	..	..
Romsey	4 35	5 14	..	..	..	..	..	7 55	8 12	..	10 1	..	..	..	..
Mottisfont	..	5 22	..	..	..	..	..	..	..	..	..	..	..	..	..
Horsebridge	..	5 27	..	..	..	..	..	..	..	..	..	..	..	..	..
Stockbridge	..	5 33	..	..	..	..	..	..	..	..	..	..	..	..	..
Fullerton	..	5 39	..	..	..	..	..	..	..	..	..	..	..	..	..
Clatford	..	5 45	..	..	..	..	..	..	..	..	..	..	..	..	..
Andover Town	..	5 51	..	..	..	..	..	..	..	..	..	..	..	..	..
Andover Junction 340 arr	..	5 55	..	..	..	..	..	..	..	..	..	..	..	..	..
Dunbridge	4 43	..	..	..	..	..	..	..	..	..	10 9	..	..	..	..
Dean ... 347, 357	4 51	..	..	..	..	..	..	..	..	..	1017	..	..	..	..
Salisbury 339, 340, arr.	5 8	..	..	..	..	..	..	..	8 37	..	1034	..	..	..	..
340 Exeter (Cen.) ... arr.	8 18	..	..	..	..	..	..	..	..	..	5 13	..	..	..	..
341 Ilfracombe ... "	1048	..	..	..	..	..	..	..	..	..	8 0	..	..	..	..
341 Plymouth (N.R.) "	1042	..	..	..	..	..	..	..	..	..	7 36	..	..	..	..

A Sta. for Bishopstoke
a Change at Fratton
B About 1 mile from the Docks and Pier.

C Frequent service by Hants and Dorset Motor Omnibus between Fareham and Lee-on-the-Solent.
p p.m.

LOCAL TRAINS

BETWEEN	PAGE
Southampton and Eastleigh	386
St. Denys and Redbridge	384

OTHER TRAINS

BETWEEN	PAGE
Portsmouth Harbour and Fratton	196 and 366

BASINGSTOKE, WINCHESTER, EASTLEIGH, SOUTHAMPTON, and REDBRIDGE

Week Days

Miles		Tuesdays to Saturdays a.m	3	3	a.m		a.m	a.m	a.m	a.m	a.m	a.m	a.m	a.m	a.m		a.m	a.m	a.m	a.m	a.m	a.m
	Basingstoke ....dep.	..	4 0	..	..	..	..	..	..	..	..	Dep Portsmouth 6 0 a.m	..	6 55	..	..	Dep. Portsmouth 6 55 a.m	Dep. Fareham 8 2 a.m	7 34	..	..	Dep Portsmouth 8 8 a.m
10¼	Micheldever	..	..	..	..	..	..	..	..	..	..		..	7 12	..	..			7 52	..	..	
18¼	Winchester 375	1221	4 30	..	..	..	..	..	..	..	6 36		6 58	7 27	..	..			8 6	..	8 35	
—	Winchester (Cheesehill)	..	..	..	..	..	..	..	..	..	..		..	..	..	..			..	..	..	
21¼	Shawford, for Twyford.,	..	..	..	..	..	..	..	..	..	6 41		7 3	..	..	..			8 13	..	8 42	
25¼	Eastleigh A 376, 380 arr.	1233	4 44	..	..	..	..	..	..	..	6 49		7 11	7 39	..	..			8 21	..	8 50	
	Eastleigh A 376, 380 dep.	1241	4 50	5 5	5 17	..	..	6 5	6 20	6 38	6 54		7 12	7 41	7 46	..			8 25	8 38	..	
28	Swaythling	..	To Portsmouth	..	5 22	..	..	..	6 25	6 43	6 59		7 18	..	7 51	..			8 32	8 43	..	
29¼	St. Denys.............	..		..	5H31	..	..	..	6 29	6 49	7 3	7 6	7 22	..	7 56	..	8 0	8 36	8 37	8 47	..	9 7
30¼	Northam	..		..	5 25	..	..	..	6 33	..	7 7	7 10	7 26	..	..	..	..	..	8 41	..	..	9 11
31½	Southampton Ter. (for Docks) arr.	1253		..	5 39	..	..	..	6 37	..	7 11	7 14	7 30	..	..	..	..	..	8 45	..	..	9 15
	Southampton Ter. (for Docks) dep.	..		..	..	..	5 56	..	..	..	..	7 25	..	..	..	..	..	..	..	..	..	..
31½	Southampton Central D 494 arr.	..		5 18	..	..	6 1	6 15	..	6 55	..	7 30	..	7 52	8 2	..	8 6	8 42	..	8 53	..	..
	Southampton Central D 494 dep	..		..	..	..	..	6 18	..	6 57	..	7 32	..	..	8 4	..	8 11	8 45	..	8 55	..	..
32½	Millbrook	..		..	..	..	..	6 23	..	7 2	..	7 36	..	..	8 9	..	8 16	8 50	..	8 59	..	..
34	Redbridge ....arr.	..		..	..	..	..	6 28	..	7 7	..	7 41	..	..	8 14	..	..	8 56	..	9 4	..	..

Week Days—*continued*

	a.m		a.m	a.m		a.m	a.m		a.m	a.m	a.m	a.m	a.m	a.m		p.m	p.m	p.m	p.m	p.m S O	p.m		p.m
Basingstoke ....dep.	8 17	..	..	Dep Portsmouth 8 55 a.m	..	..	..	..	9 40	..	9 55	..	Dep Portsmouth 10 34 a.m	1040	..	Dep Portsmouth 11 26 a.m	..	1229	..	..	1251	..	..
Micheldever............	8 34	..	..		..	..	..	..	..	..	1011	..		..	..		..	1246	..	..	1 8	..	..
Winchester 375	8 47	..	..		..	..	9 41	..	10 7	..	1026	1045		11 7	..		1240	1259	..	..	1 21	..	..
Winchester (Cheesehill)	..	..	9 6		..	..	..	..	..	1014	..	..		..	..		..	..	..	..	..	..	1 26
Shawford, for Twyford..	8 53	..	9 13		..	..	9 47	..	..	1021	1033	..		..	..		1246	..	..	..	1 27	..	1 34
Eastleigh A 376, 380 arr.	9 0	..	9 21		..	..	9 55	..	..	1028	1041	1055		1119	..		1254	..	..	..	1 35	..	1 41
Eastleigh A 376, 380 dep.	9 2	..	9 22		..	..	..	..	..	1029	1047	11 0		1121	..		..	..	1 23	..	1 46	..	..
Swaythling	9 9	..	..		..	..	..	..	..	1035	To Portsmouth	11 7		..	..		..	..	1 28	..	To Portsmouth	..	..
St. Denys..............	9 13	..	9 29	9 50	..	..	..	..	..	1039		1111	1122	..	..	1228	..	..	1 32	1 36		..	..
Northam	9 17	..	..	..	..	..	..	..	..	1043		1115	..	..	..	..	..	..	1 36	1 40		..	..
Southampton Ter. (for Docks) arr.	9 20	..	9 35	..	..	..	..	..	..	1047		1119	..	..	..	..	..	..	1 40	1 44		..	..
Southampton Ter. (for Docks) dep.	..	..	..	..	..	1010	..	..	..	..		..	..	..	..	..	..	..	..	..		..	..
Southampton Central D 494 arr.	..	..	..	9 56	..	1015	..	..	1026	..		..	1128	1131	..	1234	..	1 19	..	..		..	..
Southampton Central D 494 dep.	..	..	..	..	..	..	..	..	..	..		..	..	..	..	1235	..	..	..	..		..	..
Millbrook..............	..	..	..	..	..	..	..	..	..	..		..	..	..	..	..	..	..	..	..		..	..
Redbridge.........arr.	..	..	..	..	..	..	..	..	..	..	..	..	..	..	..	1241	..	..	..	..	..	..	..

	p.m	p.m	p.m	p.m	p.m	p.m	p.m	p.m	p.m S O	p.m	p.m	p.m	p.m	p.m	p.m	p.m	p.m	p.m	p.m		p.m	p.m	p.m
Basingstoke ....dep.	Dep Fareham 1 28 p.m	..	..	Dep Portsmouth 2 3 p.m	2 34	..	2 40	..	..	..	..	..	..	..	..	..	..	4 34	..	..	..	Dep. Portsmouth 4 35 p.m	..
Micheldever.....		..	..		..	..	2 56	..	..	..	..	..	..	..	..	..	..	4 52	..	..	..		..
Winchester 375		..	2 10		3 2	..	3 9	3 16	..	..	..	..	4 25	4 42	..	..	4 54	5 5	..	..	..		..
Winchester (Cheesehill)		..	..		..	..	..	..	..	3 22	..	..	..	..	..	..	..	..	..	..	..		..
Shawford, for Twyford..		..	2 15		..	..	..	3 22	..	3 29	..	..	..	..	..	..	5 0	..	..	..	..		..
Eastleigh A 376, 380 arr.		..	2 23		..	..	3 20	3 30	..	3 37	..	..	4 36	..	..	..	5 8	5 16	..	..	..		..
Eastleigh A 376, 380 dep.		2 5	2 40		..	..	3 25	..	..	3 38	..	4 9	..	..	..	5 9	..	5 17	5 21	..	5 34		..
Swaythling		2 10	2 45		..	..	To Portsmouth	..	..	3 44	..	4 14	..	..	..	5 14	..	..	5 26	..	..		..
St. Denys	2 3	2 15	2 49	3 0	..	..		..	..	3 48	..	4 18	..	..	..	5 18	..	..	5 30	..	5 41	5 48	..
Northam...............	..	2 19	..	..	..	..		..	..	3 52	..	4 22	..	..	..	5 21	..	..	5 33	..	..	..	..
Southampton Ter. (for Docks) arr.	..	2 23	..	..	..	..		..	..	3 56	..	4 26	..	..	..	5 25	..	..	5 37	..	..	..	..
Southampton Ter. (for Docks) dep.	..	..	..	..	..	..		..	3 55	..	4 30	..	..	..	5 15	..	..	..	..	..	..	..	6 5
Southampton Central D 494 arr.	2 10	..	2 55	3 6	3 20	..		..	4 0	..	4 35	..	..	5 0	5 21	..	..	5 28	..	..	5 48	5 54	6 10
Southampton Central D 494 dep.	2 19	..	..	..	..	3 40		..	4 5	..	4 37	..	..	..	5 26	..	..	..	..	..	5 50	5 56	..
Millbrook..............	2 24	..	..	..	..	3 44		..	4 10	..	..	..	..	..	5 35	..	..	..	..	..	5 54	..	..
Redbridge.........arr.	2 29	..	..	..	..	3 49		..	4 15	..	4 43	..	..	..	5 41	..	..	..	..	..	5 59	6 3	..

Week Days—*continued*

	p.m	p.m	p.m	p.m	p.m	p.m	p.m	p.m	p.m		p.m		p.m	p.m	p.m	p.m	p.m		p.m	p.m	p.m	p.m	
Basingstoke ....dep.	..	..	..	Dep. Portsmouth 5 35 p.m	5 40	Dep Portsmouth 6 3 p.m	6 32	..	Dep. Portsmouth 6 45 p.m	..	7 35	..	Dep. Portsmouth 7 45 p.m	..	8 32	..	..	..	9 58	Dep. Portsmouth 9 46 p.m	..	1151	..
Micheldever	..	..	..		5 50		6 50	..		..	7 50	..		..	8 49	..	..	..	..		..	..	..
Winchester 375........	..	5 58	..		6 8		7 4	7 9		..	8 2	..		..	9 2	9 19	..	..	10 26		1033	1221	..
Winchester (Cheesehill)	5 40	..	..		..		..	..		..	..	..		8 23	..	..	..	..	..		..	..	..
Shawford, for Twyford..	5 47	..	..		6 14		..	7 14		..	8 9	..		8 32	..	9 27	..	..	..		1038	..	..
Eastleigh A 376, 380 arr.	5 54	..	..		6 22		7 15	7 22		..	8 17	..		8 39	9 14	9 35	..	..	..		1046	1233	..
Eastleigh A 376, 380 dep.	5 55	..	..		6 25		7 17	7 23		..	8 20	..		8 41	9 15	..	9 45	..	..		1047	1241	..
Swaythling	6 1	..	..		6 32		..	7 29		..	8 27	..		8 47	..	..	9 50	..	..		1053	..	..
St. Denys..............	6 5	..	..	6 30	6 36	7 12	..	7 33	7 53	..	8 31	..	8 49	8 51	9 25	..	9 54	..	..	1048	1057	..	..
Northam................	6 9	..	..	..	6 40	..	..	7 37	..	..	8 35	..	..	8 55	..	..	9 58	..	..	..	..	..	..
Southampton Ter. (for Docks) arr.	6 13	..	..	..	6 44	..	..	7 41	..	..	8 39	..	..	8 59	..	..	10 2	..	10v47	1054	..	1253	..
Southampton Ter. (for Docks) dep.	..	..	..	..	..	..	..	..	..	..	..	..	..	..	..	..	..	..	..	..	..	..	..
Southampton Central D 494 arr.	..	6 16	..	6 36	..	7 18	7 28	..	7 59	..	..	..	8 55	..	9 31	..	..	..	..	..	11 4	..	..
Southampton Central D 494 dep	..	..	6 22	..	..	..	..	..	..	..	..	..	8 59	..	..	..	..	..	..	..	..	..	..
Millbrook	..	..	6 26	..	..	..	..	..	..	..	..	..	9 4	..	..	..	..	..	..	..	..	..	..
Redbridge ....arr.	..	..	6 31	..	..	..	..	..	..	..	..	..	9 9	..	..	..	..	..	..	..	..	..	..

3 Third class only. S O Saturdays only   **A** Station for Bishopstoke   **D** About 1 mile from Docks and Pier   H Arr. 5 26 a.m

v Passengers for Southampton Terminus alight at Southampton Docks Station on Mondays, Wednesdays and Fridays, arr. 10 51 p.m

For SUNDAY TRAINS, see page 386

BASINGSTOKE, WINCHESTER, EASTLEIGH, SOUTHAMPTON, and REDBRIDGE

Sundays

	a.m		3	3		a.m	a.m Dep. Portsmouth 8 35 a.m	a.m	a.m		a.m Dep Portsmouth 10 15 a.m	a.m	a.m		p.m	p.m Dep Portsmouth 11 40 a.m	p.m	p.m	p.m	p.m	p.m	p.m Dep. Portsmouth 1 25 pm	p.m
Basingstoke........dep.	..	..	4 38	4 52	..	..		..	9 43	..		1016	1038	..	..		..	..	1229	1237	..		..
Micheldever	..	..	..	..	..	..		..	10 1	..		1033	..	..	..		..	..	..	1252	..		..
Winchester 375	1221	..	..	5 22	..	8 8		9 41	1015	..		1045	11 6	..	..		..	1248	1256	1 5	..		..
Winchester(Cheesehill)	..	..	..	..	..	..		..	..	..		..	..	..	..		..	..	..	..	..		..
Shawford, for Twyford..	..	..	..	..	..	8 13		9 47	1021	..		..	..	..	..		..	1254	..	1 11	..		..
Eastleigh A 376, 380 arr.	1233	..	5 11	5 34	..	8 21		9 55	1029	..		1056	..	..	..		..	1 2	1 7	1 19	..		..
Eastleigh A 376, 380 dep.	1241	..	5 12	5 55	..	8 22		..	1032	..		11 0	..	..	12 8		..	..	1 9	1 21	2 16		2 28
Swaythling	..	..	..	..	..	8 28		..	1039	..		..	..	..	1213		..	..	..	1 28	2 21		2 33
St. Denys	..	..	..	6 4	..	8 33	9 38	..	1043	..	11 7	11 9	..	..	1217	1223	..	..	..	1 32	2 25	2 30	2 37
Northam	..	..	..	..	..	..	..	..	..	..	..	..	..	..	..	..	..	..	..	..	..	..	..
Southampton Ter. (for Docks) arr.	1253	..	..	6 11	..	..	..	..	..	..	..	1115	..	..	1223	..	..	..	..	..	2 31	..	..
Southampton Ter. (for Docks) dep	..	..	..	..	..	..	..	..	..	..	..	..	..	..	..	..	1253	..	..	..	..	..	..
Southampton Central D 494 arr.	..	..	5 23	..	..	8 39	9 44	..	1050	..	1113	..	1125	..	..	1230	1258	..	1 20	1 38	..	2 36	2 43
Southampton Central D 494 dep.	..	..	..	..	..	8 42	..	..	1054	..	..	..	..	..	..	..	1 0	..	..	1 40	..	..	..
Millbrook	..	..	..	..	..	8 47	..	..	1059	..	..	..	..	..	..	..	1 4	..	..	1 44	..	..	..
Redbridge.........arr.	..	..	..	..	..	8 51	..	..	..	..	..	..	..	..	..	..	..	..	..	1 48	..	..	..

Sundays—continued

	p.m	p.m	p.m Dep. Portsmouth 3 17 pm	p.m	p.m	p.m Dep. Portsmouth 4 35 pm	p.m Dep. Portsmouth 5 5 pm	p.m	p.m	p.m	p.m Dep. Portsmouth 6 33 pm		p.m	p.m	p.m Dep. Portsmouth 8 15 pm	p.m	p.m	p.m		p.m	p.m Dep. Portsmouth 10 15 pm	p.m	
Basingstoke........dep.	2 28	..		..	4 22			..	..	6 16		..	7 34	7 44		..	9 0	..	..	1016		1120	..
Micheldever	..	..		..	4 39			..	..	..		..	..	7 59		..	..	..	..	1033		..	..
Winchester 375	2 56	3 4		4 20	4 52			5 39	..	6 44		..	8 1	8 12		8 58	9 26	9 50	..	1047		1150	..
Winchester(Cheesehill)	..	..		..	..			..	..	..		..	..	..		..	..	..	..	..		..	..
Shawford, for Twyford..	..	3 9		4 25	4 58			5 45	..	..		..	..	8 18		9 4	..	9 55	..	1053		..	..
Eastleigh A 376, 380 arr.	..	3 17		4 33	5 6			5 53	..	6 55		..	8 15	8 26		9 12	9 37	10 3	..	11 1		12 2	..
Eastleigh A 376, 380 dep.	..	3 23		4 36	5 8			5 54	6 20	6 58		..	8 19	8 28		9 13	9 38	10 4	..	11 3		12 8	..
Swaythling	..	3 30		4 43	5 15			5 59	6 25	7 5		..	..	8 35		9 19	9 44	1010	..	11 9		..	..
St. Denys	..	3 34	4 8	4 47	5 19	5 36	5 49	6 3	6 29	7 9	7 38	..	..	8 39	9 13	9 23	9 48	1014	..	1113	1115	..	..
Northam	..	..	..	..	..	..	..	..	..	..	..	..	..	..	..	..	..	..	..	..	..	..	..
Southampton Ter. (for Docks) arr.	..	3 40	..	..	..	..	..	6 9	..	..	..	..	..	8 45	..	9 29	..	1020	..	1119	..	1220	..
Southampton Ter. (for Docks) dep.	..	..	..	..	..	..	..	..	..	..	..	..	..	..	..	..	..	..	..	..	..	..	..
Southampton Central D 494 arr.	3 15	..	4 14	4 53	5 25	5 42	5 55	..	6 35	7 15	7 44	..	8 31	..	9 19	..	9 55	..	..	..	1122	..	..
Southampton Central D 494 dep.	..	..	..	4 55	..	..	..	..	..	..	..	..	..	..	..	..	..	..	..	..	..	..	..
Millbrook	..	..	..	4 59	..	..	..	..	..	..	..	..	..	..	..	..	..	..	..	..	..	..	..
Redbridge.........arr.	..	..	..	5 4	..	..	..	..	..	..	..	..	..	..	..	..	..	..	..	..	..	..	..

REDBRIDGE, SOUTHAMPTON, EASTLEIGH, WINCHESTER, and BASINGSTOKE

Week Days

	a.m	a.m	a.m	a.m To Portsmouth		a.m	a.m	a.m To Portsmouth	a.m		a.m	a.m	a.m To Portsmouth		a.m	a.m To Portsmouth	a.m	a.m		a.m	a.m	a.m To Portsmouth	a.m
Redbridge.........dep.	..	..	..	..	..	..	..	..	6 37	..	..	..	..	..	7 35	7 43	..	..	..	..	..	8 35	8 40
Millbrook	..	..	..	..	..	..	..	..	6 42	..	..	..	..	..	7 40	7 48	..	..	..	..	..	8 39	8 44
Southampton Central D 494 arr.	..	..	..	..	..	..	..	..	6 46	..	..	..	..	..	7 44	7 52	..	..	..	..	..	8 43	8 48
Southampton Central D 494 dep.	1230	..	5 22	..	..	..	..	6 30	6 47	..	..	..	..	..	7 46	7 53	..	8 25	..	..	..	8 44	8 59
Southampton Ter. (for Docks) arr.	1237	..	..	..	..	..	..	..	6 53	..	..	..	..	..	..	7 58	..	..	..	..	..	..	9 6
Southampton Ter. (for Docks) dep.	..	1 10	..	5 15	..	6 0	..	..	6 57	..	..	7 32	7 38	..	..	8 2	..	..	..	..	8 33	..	..
Northam	..	..	..	..	..	6 3	..	..	7 0	..	..	7 35	7 41	..	..	8 5	..	..	..	..	8 36	..	..
St. Denys	..	..	5 30	5b32	..	6 7	..	6 36	7 7	..	..	7 39	7 45	..	7 55	8 9	..	..	..	..	8 40	8 51	..
Swaythling	..	..	5 35		..	6 11	..		7 11	..	..	7 43		..	7 59		..	..	..	..	8 44		..
Eastleigh A 376, 380 arr.	..	1 20	5 41		..	6 17	..		7 17	..	..	7 49		..	8 5		..	..	..	..	8 50		..
Eastleigh A 376, 380 dep.	..	1 29	6 4		..	6 18	6 35		7 18	..	7 40	7 50		..	8 7		8 20	..	..	..	..		..
Shawford, for Twyford..	..	..	6 12		..	6 27	6 42		7 27	..	7 47	8 0		..	8 16		8 27	..	..	..	..		..
Winchester(Cheesehill)	..	..	..		..	..	..		..	..	..	8 8		..	..		..	..	..	..	..		..
Winchester	..	1 46	6 21		..	6 35	6 50		7 35	..	7 56	..		..	8 24		8 35	8 47	..	8 57	..		..
Micheldever	..	..	..		..	6 52	..		7 51	..	..	..		..	8 40		..	..	..	9 12	..		..
Basingstoke 340....arr	..	2 15	..		..	7 9	..		8 8	..	..	..		..	8 55		..	..	..	9 28	..		..

Week Days—continued

	a.m	a.m	a.m	a.m	a.m To Portsmouth	a.m From Portsmouth	a.m	a.m	a.m	a.m To Portsmouth	a.m	a.m To Portsmouth		p.m	p.m		p.m	p.m To Portsmouth		p.m SX To Portsmouth	p.m SO	p.m
Redbridge.........dep.	8 44	9 4	..	..	..		..	..	..	..	..	1119	..	..	..	..	..	..	..	..	1245	..
Millbrook	8 49	..	..	..	..		..	..	..	..	..	1124	..	..	..	..	..	..	..	..	1250	..
Southampton Central D 494 arr.	8 53	9 11	..	..	..		..	..	..	..	..	1128	..	..	..	..	..	..	..	..	1254	..
Southampton Central D 494 dep.	8 55	..	9 16	..	9 25		..	9 54	..	1049	..	1130	..	..	1220	..	..	12 25	..	..	1255	..
Southampton Ter. (for Docks) arr.	..	..	..	..	..		..	..	..	..	..	..	..	..	..	..	..	..	..	..	..	..
Southampton Ter. (for Docks) dep.	..	..	..	9 19	..		9 36	..	..	..	1126	..	..	12 8	..	..	1220	..	..	12 45	..	..
Northam	..	..	..	9 22	..		9 39	..	..	..	1129	..	..	12S011	..	..	1224	..	..	12 48	..	..
St. Denys	9 4	..	..	9 26	9 32		9 43	10 2	..	1057	1133	1138	..	12 13	..	..	1228	12 31	..	12 54	1 2	..
Swaythling	9 8	..	..	9 30			9 47	..	..		1137		..	12 17	..	..	1232		..		1 6	..
Eastleigh A 376, 380 arr.	9 14	..	..	9 36			9 53	1010	..		1143		..	12 25	1231	..	1238		..		1 12	..
Eastleigh A 376, 380 dep.	..	..	..	..		9 52	9 56	1011	1029		1145		..	..	1232	..	1239		..		..	1 15
Shawford, for Twyford..	..	..	..	..		10 0	10 5	..	1036		1153		..	..	..	..	1247		..		..	1 22
Winchester(Cheesehill)	..	..	..	..		..	1013	..	..		12 1		..	..	..	..	..		..		..	..
Winchester	..	..	9 38	..		10 8	..	1025	1044		..		..	..	1246	..	1255		..		..	1 29
Micheldever	..	..	..	..		..	..	1041	..		..		..	..	..	..	1 11		..		..	..
Basingstoke 340...arr.	..	..	..	..		..	..	1057	..		..		..	..	1 13	..	1 27		..		..	..

For Notes, see page 387

REDBRIDGE, SOUTHAMPTON, EASTLEIGH, WINCHESTER, and BASINGSTOKE

Week Days—*continued*

	p.m SO	p.m	p.m		p.m	p.m	p.m	p.m		p.m		p.m	p.m		p.m	p.m	p.m	p.m	p.m	p.m	p.m	p.m	p.m
Redbridge dep.	..	..	1 28	..	1 38		..	..	..	..	..	..	..	..	Dep. Portsmouth 2 45 pm	..	..	..	..	4 57	..	..	5 33
Millbrook	..	..	1 33	..	1 43		..	..	..	..	..	..	..	..		..	..	..	..	5 2	..	..	5 38
Southampton Central D 494 arr.	..	..	1 37	..	1 47		..	..	..	..	..	..	..	..		..	..	..	..	5 6	..	..	5 42
dep.	..	..	1 39	..	1 49		..	2 13	..	2 20	..	..	2 58	..		..	4 5	4 20	..	5 7	..	..	5 44
Southampton Ter. (for Docks) arr.	..	..	..	..	..		..	2 20	..	..	..	..	..	..		..	4 10	..	..	..	..	..	5 50
dep.	1253	1 25	..	..	..		1 55	..	..	..	..	2 54	..	..		..	4 18	..	4 55	..	5 18	5 25	..
Northam	1256	1 28	..	..	..		1 58	..	..	..	..	2 57	..	..		..	4 20	..	4 58	..	5 21	5 28	..
St. Denys	1v4	1 32	1 47	..	1 58		2 2	..	..	..	..	3 1	3 4	..		..	4c32	4 29	5 2	5 14	5 28	5 32	..
Swaythling		1 36	..	..			2 6	..	..	..	..	3 5		..		..		..	5 5	..	5 32		..
Eastleigh A 376, 380 arr.		1 42	1 55	..			2 12	..	..	2 32	..	3 11		..		..		4 37	5 11	5 22	5 38		..
dep.	To Portsmouth	1 43	1 58	..	To Portsmouth	2 15	2 20	..	..	2 34	..	..	To Portsmouth	..	3 35	3 59	To Portsmouth	4 39	5 12	..	5 39	To Portsmouth	..
Shawford, for Twyford		1 51	2 8	..		2 22	2 29	..	..	..	..	..		..	3 43	4 6		..	5 19	..	5 47		..
Winchester (Cheesehill)		..	..	..		..	2 37	..	..	..	..	..		..	..	..		..	5 27	..	..		..
Winchester		1 58	2 18	..		2 29	..	..	..	2 49	..	..		..	3 52	4 14		4 53	..	..	5 55		..
Micheldever		..	2 35	..		..	..	..	..	..	..	..		..	4 8	..		5 9	..	..	..		..
Basingstoke 340 arr.		..	2 52	..		..	..	..	..	3 17	..	..		..	4 25	..		5 26	..	..	..		..

Week Days—*continued*

	p.m	p.m	p.m	p.m	p.m		p.m	p.m	p.m	p.m	p.m		p.m	p.m	p.m		p.m		p.m	p.m		p.m	p.m
Redbridge dep.	..	..	Dep Portsmouth 5 15 pm	5 50	..	..	..	6 39	..	7 16	..	..	..	7 57	..	..	..	..	..	..	..	..	..
Millbrook	5 45	..		5 55	..	..	..	6 43	..	7 20	..	..	..	8 2	..	..	..	..	..	9 53	..	..	..
Southampton Central D 494 arr.	5 49	..		5 59	..	..	..	6 47	..	7 24	..	..	..	8 6	..	..	..	..	..	9 57	..	..	..
dep.	5 50	5 55		6 4	..	..	6 20	6 48	..	7 25	..	..	7 45	8 9	8 48	..	..	..	9SO52	10 2	..	1023	11 4
Southampton Ter. (for Docks) arr.	..	..		..	..	..	..	..	..	7 31	..	..	..	..	..	..	..	..	9SO57	..	..	..	..
dep.	..	..		..	6 15	..	..	..	6 58	..	7 35	..	..	..	..	..	9 5	..	10 0	..	..	..	..
Northam	..	..		..	6 18	..	..	..	7 1	..	7 38	..	..	..	..	..	9 8	..	10 3	..	..	..	..
St. Denys	5 57	6 6		6 12	6 22	..	..	6 55	7 5	..	7 42	..	7 53	8 17	8 56	..	9 12	..	10ß13	1010	..	..	1111
Swaythling	6 2			6 16		..	..	6 58	7 8	..	7 46	..		8 21	..	..	9 16	..		1014	..	..	1115
Eastleigh A 376, 380 arr.	6 8			6 22		..	6 31	7 4	7 14	..	7 52	..		8 27	9 4	..	9 22	..		1020	..	1037	1121
dep.	..	To Portsmouth	6 16	..	To Portsmouth	..	6 33	..	7 15	..	7 55	..	To Portsmouth	8 31	9 7	..	..	..	To Portsmouth	..	..	1039	..
Shawford, for Twyford	..		6 23	..		..	..	..	7 22	..	8 5	..		8 40	9 16	..	..	..		..	..	1047	..
Winchester (Cheesehill)	..		..	..		..	..	..	..	.	8 13	..		..	..	..	..	..		..	..	..	..
Winchester	..		6 32	..		.	6 48	..	7 31	..	..	..		8 48	9 25	..	..	..		..	..	1056	..
Micheldever	..		6 49	..		..	..	..	..	..	..	..		9 5	..	..	..	..		..	..	1113	..
Basingstoke 340 arr.	..		7 8	..		..	7 17	..	..	..	..	..		9 24	9 55	..	..	..		..	..	1132	..

Sundays

	a.m	a.m		a.m	a.m	a.m	a.m	a.m		a.m	a.m	a.m		a.m	a.m		p.m	p.m	p.m		p.m	p.m	p.m
Redbridge dep.	..	..	..	..	..	..	Dep. Portsmouth 8 8 a.m	9 29	..	..	10 1	..	..	..	..	..	..	..	..	..	..	..	..
Millbrook	..	..	..	..	..	..		9 34	..	..	10 6	..	..	..	..	..	..	..	..	..	..	..	..
Southampton Central D 494 arr.	..	..	..	..	..	..		9 37	..	..	10 9	..	..	..	..	..	..	..	..	..	..	..	..
dep.	1230	..	..	..	..	..		9 39	..	9 51	..	1024	..	..	1135	..	12 2	1220	..	..	..	..	2 26
Southampton Ter. (for Docks) arr.	1237	..	..	..	..	..		9 46	..	..	..	..	..	..	..	..	..	..	..	..	..	..	..
dep.	..	1 10	..	7 20	..	8 43		9 51	..	..	..	..	..	1125	..	..	..	..	..	..	1 8	1 42	..
Northam	..	..	..	..	..	..		..	..	..	..	..	..	..	..	..	..	..	..	..	..	..	..
St. Denys	..	..	..	7 25	..	8 48		10ǂ3	..	10 0	..	1030	..	1130	1142	..	12 8	..	..	..	1 13	1 47	2 34
Swaythling	..	..	..	7 29	..	8 52		..	..	10 4	..	1034	..	1134		..	1212	..	..	..	1 17	1 51	
Eastleigh A 376, 380 arr.	..	1 20	..	7 35	..	8 58		..	..	1010	..	1040	..	1140		..	1218	1231	..	..	1 23	1 57	
dep.	..	1 29	..	7 36	7 45	..	9 1	To Portsmouth	..	1013	..	1046	..	..	To Portsmouth	..	..	1233	1248	..	..	1 58	To Portsmouth
Shawford, for Twyford	..	..	..	..	7 52	..	9 10		..	..	..	1053	..	..		..	..	..	1255	..	..	2 5	
Winchester (Cheesehill)	..	..	..	..	..	..	..		..	..	..	..	..	..		..	..	..	..	..	..	..	
Winchester	..	1 46	..	7 50	7 59	..	9 20		..	1029	..	11 0	..	..		..	..	1250	1 4	..	..	2 13	
Micheldever	..	..	..	..	..	..	9 36		..	1045	..	..	..	..		..	..	..	1 21	..	..	..	
Basingstoke 340 arr.	..	2 15	..	..	..	..	9 52		..	11 2	..	..	..	..		..	..	..	1 39	..	..	..	

Sundays—*continued*

	p.m	p.m	p.m	p.m	p.m	p.m	p.m	p.m		p.m	p.m	p.m	p.m	p.m	p.m	p.m	p.m	p.m	p.m	p.m	p.m	p.m	
Redbridge dep.	..	..	..	..	3 51	..	..	..	..	6 30	..	..	..	..	..	..	..	..	..	..	..	..	..
Millbrook	..	..	..	..	3 56	..	5 1	..	..	6 35	..	..	..	..	..	..	..	..	..	9 55	..	..	..
Southampton Central D 494 arr.	..	..	..	..	3 59	..	5 5	..	..	6 38	..	..	..	..	..	..	..	..	..	9 59	..	..	..
dep.	..	3 20	..	..	4 1	..	5 24	..	..	6 40	7 20	7 55	8 5	8 15	8 22	..	9 0	9 14	..	10 1	1010	..	..
Southampton Ter. (for Docks) arr.	..	..	..	..	..	..	..	..	..	..	..	..	..	..	..	..	..	..	..	..	..	..	..
dep.	3 0	..	..	..	..	4 45	..	6 15	.	..	..	..	..	..	..	..	..	..	9 50	..	..	1030	..
Northam	..	..	..	..	..	..	..	..	..	..	..	..	..	..	..	..	..	..	..	..	..	..	..
St. Denys	3 5	3 26	..	..	4 8	4 50	5 30	6 20	..	6 47	..	8 1	..	8 24	8 28	..	9 9	9 23	9 55	1010	1016	1035	..
Swaythling	3 9	3 30	..	..		4 54	5 34	6 24	..	6 51	..	8 5	..		8 32	..		9 27	9 59		1020	1039	..
Eastleigh A 376, 380 arr.	3 15	3 36	..	..		5 0	5 40	6 30	..	6 57	..	8 11	8 18		8 38	..		9 34	10 5		1026	1045	..
dep.	3 16	..	3 42	3 46	To Portsmouth	..	5 43	6 31	..	6 58	..	..	8 20	To Portsmouth	8 39	9 10	To Portsmouth	..	..	To Portsmouth	1028	..	..
Shawford, for Twyford	3 24	..	3 49	..		..	5 52	6 39	..	7 6	..	..	8 28		8 47	9 17		..	..		1036	..	..
Winchester (Cheesehill)	..	..	..	..		..	..	..	..	..	..	.	..		..	..		..	..		..	..	..
Winchester	3 32	..	3 56	4 1		..	6 1	6 46	..	7 14	7 42	..	8 38		8 55	9 25		..	..		1045	..	..
Micheldever	..	..	..	4 17		..	6 18	..	..	7 30	..	..	..		..	9 41		..	..		11 2	..	..
Basingstoke 340 arr.	..	..	..	4 34		..	6 34	..	..	7 46	8 12	..	9 6		..	9 57		..	..		1118	..	..

3 Third class only from Docks and Pier **A** Sta. for Bishopstoke ß Arr 10 8 p.m b Arr. 5 21 a.m c Arr 4 24 p.m **D** About 1 mile ǂ Arr. 9 56 a.m **S O** or **SO** Saturdays only **S X** Saturdays excepted v Arr 1 0 p.m

ASCOT, ASH VALE, FARNHAM, and WOKING

Week Days

Miles		a.m		a.m	a.m		a.m	a.m SX	a.m SO		a.m	a.m	a.m		a.m	a.m		p.m SO	p.m		p.m SO	p.m SO
	460 Waterloo ....dep.	5 24	..	6 52	..	..	7 24	7 48	7 48	..	8 24	8 48	9 54	..	1054	1154	..	1234	1254	..	1 14	1 34
—	**Ascot**..................dep.	6 32	..	7 51	8 10	..	8 18	8 43	8 43	..	9 16	9 44	1046	..	1146	1246	..	1 26	1 46	..	2 6	2 25
3½	Bagshot.........................	6 37	..	7 56	8 15	..	8 23	8 48	8 48	..	9 21	9 49	1051	..	1151	1251	..	1 31	1 51	..	2 11	2 30
6¾	Camberley **A**..................	6 46	..	8 2	8 22	..	8 29	8 55	8 55	..	9 29	9 56	1059	..	1159	1259	..	1 37	1 59	..	2 17	2 36
8¾	Frimley **B**......................	6 51	..	8 6	8 27	..	8 33	8 59	8 59	..	9 33	10 0	11 3	..	12 3	1 3	..	1 41	2 3	..	2 21	2 40
11¾	Ash Vale **C**.....................	6 58	..	8 12	..	..	8 39	9 5	9 5	..	9 39	10 6	11 9	..	12 9	1 9	..	1 47	2 9	..	2 27	..
14½	Aldershot **D** 390 ....arr	7 3	..	8 17	..	..	8 44	9 10	9 10	..	9 44	10 11	1114	..	1214	1 14	..	1 52	2 14	..	2 32	..
17½	390 Farnham .... "	7 33	..	8 33	..	..	9 3	9 33	9 33	..	10 3	10 33	1123	..	1233	1 33	..	2 3	2 33	..	3 3	..
—	Mls **Aldershot**.........dep.	7 8	..	8 20	..	..	8 50	9 20	9 20	..	9 55	10 20	1121	..	1220	1 18	..	1 58	2 20	..	2 50	..
—	3 Ash **K**..............arr.	7 14	..	8 26	..	..	8 56	9 26	9 26	..	10 1	10 26	1127	..	1226	1 24	..	2 4	2 26	..	2 56	..
—	5 Wanborough **J**.... "	7 19	..	8 35	..	..	9 1	9 35	9 35	..	10 6	10 31	1132	..	1231	1 29	..	2 9	2 31	..	3 1	..
—	9 **Guildford** .... "	7 25	..	8 41	..	..	9 7	9 41	9 41	..	1012	10 37	1138	..	1237	1 35	..	2 15	2 37	..	3 7	..
—	Ash Vale...............dep.	7 3	..	8 19	..	..	8 49	9 11	9 21	..	9 49	10 19	1119	..	1219	1 19	..	..	2 19	..	2 49	..
16½	Brookwood **F** 324	7 10	..	8 26	8 36	..	8 56	9 18	9 28	..	9 56	10 25	1126	..	1226	1 26	..	..	2 26	..	2 56	..
19¾	**Woking H** 324, 427....arr.	7 15	..	8 32	8 4[illegible]	..	9 2	9 24	9 34	..	10 2	10 32	1132	..	1232	1 32	..	..	2 32	..	3 2	2 53
44½	427 Waterloo ....arr.	7 56	..	9Y10	9 20	..	9 47	9 55	1016	..	1046	11 16	1216	..	1 16	2 16	..	..	3 16	..	3 46	3 46

Week Days—*continued*

	p.m	p.m SO	p.m SO	p.m		p.m	p.m SX	p.m	p.m SX		p.m SX	p.m	p.m SX	p.m SX	p.m		p.m	p.m		p.m	p.m
460 Waterloo ....dep.	1 54	2 14	2 34	2 54	..	3 54	4 24	4 54	5 14	..	5 34	5 54	6 14	6 34	6 54	..	7 54	8 54	..	9 54	1054
Ascot..................dep.	2 46	3 6	3 25	3 46	..	4 46	5 16	5 47	6 6	..	6 26	6 47	7 6	7 26	7 46	..	8 46	9 46	..	10 46	1146
Bagshot..........................	2 51	3 11	3 30	3 51	..	4 51	5 21	5 52	6 11	..	6 31	6 52	7 11	7 31	7 51	..	8 51	9 51	..	10 51	1151
Camberley A..................	2 59	3 17	3 36	3 59	..	4 59	5 29	5 59	6 17	..	6 37	6 58	7 17	7 37	7 59	..	8 59	9 59	..	10 59	1157
Frimley B......................	3 3	3 21	3 40	4 3	..	5 3	5 33	6 3	6 21	..	6 41	7 3	7 21	7 41	8 3	..	9 3	10 3	..	11 3	12 1
Ash Vale C.....................	3 9	3 27	..	4 9	..	5 9	5 39	6 9	6 27	..	..	7 10	7 27	.	8 9	..	9 9	10 9	..	11 9	12 7
Aldershot **D** 390....arr.	3 14	3 32	..	4 14	..	5 14	5 44	6 14	6 32	..	..	7 15	7 32	..	8 14	..	9 14	1014	..	11 14	1212
390 **Farnham** .... "	3 33	4 3	..	4 33	..	5 33	6 3	6 33	6 47	..	..	7 33	8 3	..	8 33	..	9 33	1033	..	11 33	..
Aldershot............dep.	3 20	3 50	..	4 20	..	5 20	5 50	6 20	6 50	..	..	7 20	7 50	..	8 20	..	9 20	1020	..	11 20	..
Ash K................arr.	3 26	3 56	..	4 26	..	5 26	5 56	6 26	6 56	..	..	7 26	7 56	..	8 26	..	9 26	1026	..	11 26	..
Wanborough **J**...... "	3 31	4 1	..	4 31	..	5 31	6 1	6 32	7 1	..	..	7 31	8 1	..	8 31	..	9 31	1031	..	11 31	..
Guildford .... "	3 37	4 7	..	4 37	..	5 37	6 7	6 38	7 7	..	..	7 37	8 7	..	8 37	..	9 37	1037	..	11 37	..
Ash Vale..............dep.	3 19	3 49	..	4 19	..	5 19	5 49	6 19	6 49	..	..	7 19	7 49	..	8 19	..	9 19	1019	..	11 19	..
Brookwood **F** 324	3 26	3 56	..	4 26	..	5 26	5 56	6 26	6 56	..	6 50	7 26	7 56	..	8 26	..	9 26	1026	..	11 26	..
Woking H 324, 427 ..arr.	3 32	4 2	3 54	4 32	..	5 32	6 2	6 32	7 2	..	6 56	7 32	8 2	7 54	8 32	..	9 32	1032	..	11 32	..
427 **Waterloo** ....arr.	4 16	4 46	4 46	5 16	..	6 18	6 48	7 16	7 46	..	7 46	8 16	8 46	8 46	9 16	..	1016	1116	..	12SX 6	..

Sundays

	a.m		a.m		a.m		a.m		a.m		p.m		p.m		p.m		p.m			p.m		p.m
460 Waterloo ....dep	7 54	..	8 54	..	9 54	..	1054	..	1154	..	1254	..	1 54	..	2 54	..	3 54	..	..	4 54	..	5 54
Ascot..................dep.	8 46	..	9 46	..	1046	..	1146	..	1246	..	1 46	..	2 46	..	3 46	..	4 46	..	..	5 46	..	6 46
Bagshot..........................	8 51	..	9 51	..	1051	..	1151	..	1251	..	1 51	..	2 51	..	3 51	..	4 51	..	..	5 51	..	6 51
Camberley A..................	8 59	..	9 59	..	1059	..	1159	..	1259	..	1 59	..	2 59	..	3 59	..	4 59	..	..	5 59	..	6 59
Frimley B......................	9 3	..	10 3	..	11 3	..	12 3	..	1 3	..	2 3	..	3 3	..	4 3	..	5 3	..	..	6 3	..	7 3
Ash Vale C.....................	9 9	..	10 9	..	11 9	..	12 9	..	1 9	..	2 9	..	3 9	..	4 9	..	5 9	..	..	6 9	..	7 9
Aldershot **D** 390....arr.	9 14	..	1014	..	1114	..	1214	..	1 14	..	2 14	..	3 14	..	4 14	..	5 14	..	..	6 14	..	7 14
390 **Farnham** .... "	9 33	..	1033	..	1133	..	1233	..	1 33	..	2 33	..	3 33	..	4 33	..	5 33	..	..	6 33	..	7 33
Aldershot............dep.	9 20	..	1020	..	1120	..	1220	..	1 20	..	2 20	..	3 20	..	4 20	..	5 20	..	..	6 20	..	7 20
Ash K................arr.	9 26	..	1026	..	1126	..	1226	..	1 26	..	2 26	..	3 26	..	4 26	..	5 26	..	..	6 26	..	7 26
Wanborough **J**...... "	9 31	..	1031	..	1131	..	1231	..	1 31	..	2 31	..	3 21	..	4 31	..	5 31	..	..	6 31	..	7 31
Guildford .... "	9 37	..	1037	..	1137	..	1237	..	1 37	..	2 37	..	3 37	..	4 37	..	5 37	..	..	6 37	..	7 37
Ash Vale..............dep.	9 19	..	1019	..	1119	..	1219	..	1 19	..	2 19	..	3 19	..	4 19	..	5 19	..	..	6 19	..	7 19
Brookwood **F** 324	9 26	..	1026	..	1126	..	1226	..	1 26	..	2 26	..	3 26	..	4 26	..	5 26	..	..	6 26	..	7 26
Woking H 324, 427....arr.	9 32	..	1032	..	1132	..	1232	..	1 32	..	2 32	..	3 32	..	4 32	..	5 32	..	..	6 32	..	7 32
427 **Waterloo** ....arr.	1016	..	1116	..	1216	..	1 16	..	2 16	..	3 16	..	4 16	..	5 16	..	6 16	..	..	7 16	..	8 16

Sundays—*continued*

	p.m		p.m		p.m		p.m		p.m					
460 Waterloo ....dep.	6 54	..	7 54	..	8 54	..	9 24	..	1024	..	..	..	..	..
Ascot..................dep.	7 46	..	8 46	..	9 46	..	1016	..	1116	..	..	..	..	..
Bagshot..........................	7 51	..	8 51	..	9 51	..	1021	..	1121	..	..	..	..	..
Camberley A..................	7 59	..	8 59	..	9 59	..	1029	..	1129	..	..	..	..	..
Frimley B......................	8 3	..	9 3	..	10 3	..	1033	..	1133	..	..	..	..	..
Ash Vale C.....................	8 9	..	9 9	..	10 9	..	1039	..	1139	..	..	..	..	..
Aldershot **D** 390....arr.	8 14	..	9 14	..	1014	..	1044	..	1144	..	..	..	..	..
390 **Farnham** .... "	8 33	..	9 33	..	1025	..	11 3	..	12 3	..	..	..	..	..
Aldershot............dep.	8 21	..	9 20	..	1020	..	1050	..	..	..	..	..	..	..
Ash K................arr.	8 27	..	9 26	..	1026	..	1056	..	..	..	..	..	..	..
Wanborough **J**...... "	8 32	..	9 31	..	1031	..	11 1	..	..	..	..	..	..	..
Guildford .... "	8 38	..	9 37	..	1037	..	11 7	..	..	..	..	..	..	..
Ash Vale..............dep.	8 19	..	9 19	..	1019	..	1049	..	..	..	..	..	..	..
Brookwood **F** 324.......	8 26	..	9 26	..	1026	..	1056	..	..	..	..	..	..	..
Woking H 324, 427....arr.	8 32	..	9 32	..	1032	..	11 2	..	..	..	..	..	..	..
427 **Waterloo**.........arr.	9 21	..	1016	..	1116	..	1146	..	..	..	..	..	..	..

A Sta for Sandhurst (1½ miles) and nearly 1½ miles to Blackwater (Hants.) Station
B About 1 mile to Farnborough North Station
C For North Camp and South Farnborough
D For South Camp
F For Bisley Camp
H For Chobham (3½ miles) to Woking Village (1½ miles).
J Station for Normandy
K For Ash Green
S O or SO Sats only
S X or SX Sats excepted
Y 6 mins. later on Sats.

LOCAL TRAINS between Brookwood & Woking, page 392

OTHER TRAINS between London and Aldershot, page 246

WOKING, FARNHAM, ASH VALE, and ASCOT

Week Days

Miles		a.m	a.m		a.m	a.m	a.m		a.m	a.m	a.m		a.m			a.m		a.m	a.m SO		p.m	p.m SO
	394 Waterloo ....dep.	..	5 25	..	5 55	6 25	6 55	..	7 25	..	8 25	..	9 27	..	..	10 27	..	1127	1157	..	1227	1257
—	Woking ....dep.	..	6 20	..	6 38	7 20	7 38	..	8 8	..	9 8	..	10 8	..	..	11 8	..	12 8	1238	..	1 8	1 38
3½	Brookwood F	..	..	..	6 45	7 26	7 45	..	8 15	..	9 15	..	1015	..	..	11 15	..	1215	1245	..	1 15	1 45
8	Ash Vale C ....arr.	..	..	..	6 52	..	7 52	..	8 22	..	9 22	..	1022	..	..	11 22	..	1222	1252	..	1 22	1 52
—	Mls Guildford ....dep.	..	..	..	6 54	..	7 30	..	8 3	8 3	8 55	..	10 0	..	..	11 2	..	12 0	1230	..	1 0	1 30
—	4 Wanborough ...... "	..	..	..	7 1	..	7 37	..	8 10	8 10	9 2	..	10 7	..	..	11 9	..	12 7	1237	..	1 7	1 37
—	6 Ash .... "	..	..	..	7 5	..	7 41	..	8 14	8 31	9 6	..	1011	..	..	11 13	..	1211	1241	..	1 11	1 41
—	9 Aldershot D 392 .arr.	..	..	..	7 12	..	7 48	..	8 21	8 38	9 13	..	1018	..	..	11 20	..	1218	1248	..	1 18	1 48
—	392 Farnham ......dep.	6 5	..	..	7 7	..	7 39	..	8 7	8SX25	9 9	..	10 7	..	..	11 7	..	12 7	1237	..	1 7	1 37
—	Aldershot D ...... "	6 15	..	..	7 17	..	7 52	..	8 24	8 41	9 24	..	1024	..	..	11 24	..	1224	1252	..	1 24	1 54
—	Ash Vale C	6 19	..	..	7 22	..	7 58	..	8 29	8 46	9 29	..	1029	..	..	11 29	..	1229	1257	..	1 29	1 59
11	Frimley B	6 25	6 35	..	7 28	7 38	8 6	..	8 35	8 52	9 35	..	1035	..	..	11 35	..	1235	1 3	..	1 35	2 5
13½	Camberley A	6 29	6P54	..	7 32	7 46	8 11	..	8 40	9 0	9 40	..	1040	..	..	11 40	..	1240	1 10	..	1 40	2 10
16½	Bagshot	6 35	7 1	..	7 38	7 54	8 17	..	8 46	9 6	9 46	..	1046	..	..	11 46	..	1246	1 16	..	1 46	2 16
19½	Ascot 476 ....arr.	6 41	7 7	..	7 43	7 59	8 22	..	8 51	9 11	9 52	..	1051	..	..	11 51	..	1251	1 21	..	1 51	2 21
48¾	476 Waterloo ....arr.	7 35	8 2	..	8 39	8 54	9 14	..	9 40	10 3	1042	..	1142	..	..	12U42	..	1U42	2 12	..	2 43	3 12

Week Days—*continued*

	p.m	p.m SO	p.m SO	p.m		p.m		p.m SX	p.m	p.m SX	p.m	p.m SX	p.m SX	p.m		p.m		p.m		p.m	p.m	
394 Waterloo ....dep.	1 27	1 37	1 57	2 27	..	3 27	..	3 57	4 27	4 57	5 27	5 37	5 57	6 27	..	7 27	..	8 27	..	9 27	9 57	..
Woking ....dep.	2 8	2 18	2 38	3 8	..	4 8	..	4 38	5 8	5 38	6 8	6 18	6 38	7 8	..	8 8	..	9 8	..	10 8	1038	..
Brookwood F	2 15	..	2 45	3 15	..	4 15	..	4 45	5 15	5 45	6 15	6 27	6 45	7 15	..	8 15	..	9 15	..	1015	1045	..
Ash Vale C ....arr.	2 22	..	2 52	3 22	..	4 22	..	4 52	5 22	5 52	6 22	..	6 52	7 22	..	8 22	..	9 22	..	1022	1052	..
Guildford ....dep.	2 0	..	2 30	3 0	..	4 0	..	4 30	5 0	5 30	6 0	..	6 30	7 0	..	8 3	..	9 2	..	10 0	1030	..
Wanborough ...... "	2 7	..	2 37	3 7	..	4 7	..	4 37	5 7	5 37	6 7	..	6 37	7 7	..	8 10	..	9 9	..	10 7	1037	..
Ash .... "	2 11	..	2 41	3 11	..	4 11	..	4 41	5 11	5 41	6 11	..	6 41	7 11	..	8 15	..	9 13	..	1011	1041	..
Aldershot D 392 ....arr.	2 18	..	2 48	3 18	..	4 18	..	4 48	5 18	5 48	6 18	..	6 48	7 18	..	8 22	..	9 20	..	1018	1048	..
392 Farnham ....dep.	2 7	..	2 37	3 7	..	4 7	..	4 37	5 7	5 37	6 7	..	6 37	7 7	..	8 7	..	9 7	..	10 7	1037	..
Aldershot D ...... "	2 24	..	2 54	3 24	..	4 24	..	4 54	5 24	5 54	6 24	..	6 54	7 24	..	8 24	..	9 24	..	1024	1054	..
Ash Vale C	2 29	..	2 59	3 29	..	4 29	..	4 59	5 29	5 59	6 29	..	6 59	7 29	..	8 29	..	9 29	..	1029	1059	..
Frimley B	2 35	2 31	3 5	3 35	..	4 35	..	5 5	5 35	6 5	6 35	6 39	7 5	7 35	..	8 35	..	9 35	..	1035	11 5	..
Camberley A	2 40	2 35	3 10	3 40	..	4 40	..	5 10	5 40	6 10	6 40	6 46	7 10	7 40	..	8 40	..	9 40	..	1040	1110	..
Bagshot	2 46	..	3 16	3 46	..	4 46	..	5 16	5 46	6 16	6 46	6 52	7 16	7 46	..	8 46	..	9 46	..	1046	1116	..
Ascot 476 ....arr.	2 51	2 45	3 21	3 51	..	4 51	..	5 21	5 51	6 21	6 51	6 59	7 21	7 51	..	8 51	..	9 51	..	1051	1121	..
476 Waterloo ....arr	3 42	..	4 12	4 42	..	5 42	..	6 17	6 44	7 12	7 42	..	8 12	8 42	..	9 42	..	1042	..	1145	1217	..

Sundays.

	a.m	a.m		a.m			a.m		a.m		a.m			p.m		p.m		p.m			p.m	
394 Waterloo ....dep.	..	7 25	..	8 27	..	..	9 27	..	1027	..	1127	..	..	1227	..	1 27	..	2 27	..	..	3 27	..
Woking ....dep.	7 38	8 8	..	9 8	..	..	10 8	..	11 8	..	12 8	..	..	1 8	..	2 8	..	3 8	..	..	4 8	..
Brookwood F	7 45	8 15	..	9 15	..	..	1015	..	1115	..	1215	..	..	1 15	..	2 15	..	3 15	..	..	4 15	..
Ash Vale C ....arr.	7 52	8 22	..	9 22	..	..	1022	..	1122	..	1222	..	..	1 22	..	2 22	..	3 22	..	..	4 22	..
Guildford ....dep.	7 30	..	..	9 0	..	..	10 0	..	11 0		12 0	..	..	1 0	..	2 0	..	3 0	..	..	4 0	..
Wanborough ...... "	7 37	..	..	9 7	..	..	10 7	..	11 7	..	12 7	..	..	1 7	..	2 7	..	3 7	..	..	4 7	..
Ash .... "	7 41	..	..	9 11	..	..	1011	..	1111	..	1211	..	..	1 11	..	2 11	..	3 11	..	..	4 11	..
Aldershot D 392 ....arr.	7 48	..	..	9 18	..	..	1018	..	1118	..	1218	..	..	1 18	..	2 18	..	3 18	..	..	4 18	..
392 Farnham ....dep.	7 9	8 7	..	9 7	..	..	10 7	..	11 7	..	12 7	..	..	1 7	..	2 7	..	3 7	..	..	4 7	..
Aldershot D ...... "	7 54	8 24	..	9 24	..	..	1024	..	1124	..	1224	..	..	1 24	..	2 24	..	3 24	..	..	4 24	..
Ash Vale C	7 59	8 29	..	9 29	..	..	1029	..	1129	..	1229	..	..	1 29	..	2 29	..	3 29	..	..	4 29	..
Frimley B	8 5	8 35	..	9 35	..	..	1035	..	1135	..	1235	..	..	1 35	..	2 35	..	3 35	..	..	4 35	..
Camberley A	8 10	8 40	..	9 40	..	..	1040	..	1140	..	1240	..	..	1 40	..	2 40	..	3 40	..	..	4 40	..
Bagshot	8 16	8 46	..	9 46	..	..	1046	..	1146	..	1246	..	..	1 46	..	2 46	..	3 46	..	..	4 46	..
Ascot 476 ....arr.	8 22	8 51	..	9 51	..	..	1051	..	1151	..	1251	..	..	1 51	..	2 51	..	3 51	.	..	4 51	..
476 Waterloo ....arr.	9 12	9 42	..	1042	..	..	1142	..	1242	..	1 42	..	..	2 42	..	3 42	..	4 42	..	..	5 42	..

Sundays—*continued*

	p.m		p.m			p.m		p.m		p.m	p.m			
394 Waterloo ....dep.	4 27	..	5 27	..	..	6 27	..	7 27	..	8 27	8 57	..	..	..
Woking ....dep.	5 8	..	6 8	..	..	7 8	..	8 8	..	9 8	9 38	..	..	..
Brookwood F	5 15	..	6 15	..	..	7 15	..	8 15	..	9 15	9 45	..	..	..
Ash Vale C ....arr.	5 22	..	6 22	..	..	7 22	..	8 22	..	9 22	9 52	..	..	..
Guildford ....dep.	5 0	..	6 0	..	..	7 0	..	8 2	..	9 0	9 30	..	..	..
Wanborough ...... "	5 7	..	6 7	..	..	7 7	..	8 9	..	9 7	9 37	..	..	..
Ash .... "	5 11	..	6 11	..	..	7 11	..	8 13	..	9 11	9 41	..	..	..
Aldershot D 392 ....arr.	5 18	..	6 18	..	..	7 18	..	8 20	..	9 18	9 48	..	..	..
392 Farnham ....dep.	5 7	..	6 7	..	..	7 7	..	8 7	..	9 7	9 37	..	..	..
Aldershot D ...... "	5 24	..	6 24	..	..	7 24	..	8 24	..	9 24	9 54	..	..	..
Ash Vale C	5 29	..	6 29	..	..	7 29	..	8 29	..	9 29	9 59	..	..	..
Frimley B	5 35	..	6 35	..	..	7 35	..	8 35	..	9 35	10 5	..	..	..
Camberley A	5 40	..	6 40	..	..	7 40	..	8 40	..	9 40	1010	..	..	..
Bagshot	5 46	..	6 46	..	..	7 46	..	8 46	..	9 46	1016	..	..	..
Ascot 476 ....arr.	5 51	..	6 51	..	..	7 51	..	8 51	..	9 51	1021	..	..	..
476 Waterloo ....arr.	6 42	..	7 42	..	..	8 42	..	9 42	..	1042	1112	..	..	..

A Station for Sandhurst (1½ miles) and nearly 1½ miles to Blackwater (Hants.) Station
B About [illegible] mile to Farnborough North Station
C For North Camp and South Farnborough
D For South Camp
F For Bisley Camp
P Arr. 6 54 a.m
S O or SO Sats. only
S X or SX Sats. excepted
U Arr. 6 mins. later on Sats.

LOCAL TRAINS between Woking and Brookwood, 390

OTHER TRAINS between Aldershot and London, 249

LONDON, WOKING, GUILDFORD, ALDERSHOT, FARNHAM, BORDON, and ALTON

Week Days

Miles	Miles	Down	a.m	a.m	a.m	a.m	a.m	a.m	a.m	a.m		a.m	a.m	a.m	a.m	a.m	a.m	a.m	a.m	a.m	a.m	a.m	a.m	a.m	a.m SX		a.m	a.m	a.m	a.m		a.m
		Waterloo 394 ......dep.	5 25	5 25	..	5 55	..	6d12	6 25	..	..	6 25	..	..	6 55	..	6 55	..	7 20	7 25	7 55	7d52	..	8 25	8 37	..	8 57	8 57	9 27	9 45	..	9 57
12	12	Surbiton 394 ...... "	5 43	5 43	..	6 13	..	6B28	6 43	..	..	6 43	..	..	7 13	..	7 13	..	7 38	7 43	8 13	8B8	..	8 43	8 55	..	9 13	9 13	9 43	9B50	..	10 13
24½	24½	Woking .... "	6 8	6 9	6 30	6 38	..	6 39	7 8	..	..	7 9	7 20	7 25	7 38	..	7 39	..	7 57	8 8	8 38	8 16	8 45	9 8	9 19	..	9 38	9 39	10 8	1016	..	10 38
28	—	Brookwood A	6 15	..	6 39	6 45	..	..	7 15	..	..	..	7 26	7 32	7 45	..	..	..	8 4	8 15	8 45	..	8 51	9 15	9 25	..	9 45	..	10 15	..	..	10 45
32½	—	Ash Vale B	6 22	..	..	6 52	..	..	7 22	..	..	..	..	..	7 52	..	..	..	..	8 22	8 52	..	..	9 22	9 33	..	9 52	..	10 22	..	..	10 52
—	30½	Guildford ......dep.	..	6 35	..	..	6 54	7 7	..	..	..	7 30	..	..	..	..	8 8	..	..	..	..	8 55	..	..	..	..	..	10 0	..	1032	..	..
—	34½	Wanborough C	..	..	..	..	7 1	..	..	..	..	7 37	..	..	..	..	8 10	..	..	..	..	9 2	..	..	..	..	..	10 7	..	1039	..	..
—	36½	Ash G ....[389	..	7U0	..	..	7 5	7 18	..	7 34	..	7 41	..	..	..	8 0	8 14	8 31	..	..	..	9 6	..	..	..	..	..	1011	..	1043	..	..
—	39½	Aldershot D arr.	..	7 7	..	..	7 12	..	..	7 41	..	7 48	..	..	..	8 6	8 21	8 38	..	..	..	9 13	..	..	..	..	..	1018	..	1050	..	..
35½	—	Aldershot	6 27	Arr. Ash 6 47 a.m	..	6 57	..	..	7 27	..	..	..	..	..	7 57	..	..	..	..	8 27	8 57	..	..	9 27	9 37	..	9 57	..	10 27	..	..	10 57
38½	40½	Farnham	6 33		..	7 3	..	..	7 33	..	..	..	..	..	8 3	..	..	..	..	8 33	9 3	..	..	9 33	9 44	..	10 3	..	10 33	..	..	11 3
42	44½	Bentley	6Z47		..	7 10	..	..	7 40	..	..	..	..	..	8 10	..	..	..	..	8 40	9 10	..	..	9 40	..	..	10 10	..	10 40	..	..	11 10
—	—	Bentley ....dep.	..		..	..	..	..	..	..	..	..	..	..	8 15	..	..	..	..	..	9 15	..	..	..	..	..	10 15	..	..	..	..	..
44½	47½	Kingsley Halt	..		..	..	..	..	..	..	..	..	..	..	8 23	..	..	..	..	..	9 23	..	..	..	..	..	10 23	..	..	..	..	..
46½	49½	Bordon ....arr.	..		..	..	..	..	..	..	..	..	..	..	8 30	..	..	..	..	..	9 30	..	..	..	..	..	10 30	..	..	..	..	..
47	49½	Alton F 375 ......arr.	6 56		..	7 17	..	..	7 47	..	..	..	..	..	8 17	..	..	..	..	8 47	9 17	..	..	9 47	..	..	10 17	..	10 47	..	..	11 17

Week Days—*continued*

Down	a.m	a.m	a.m	a.m	a.m	a.m	a.m SO	a.m	a.m	p.m SO	p.m	p.m	p.m SO	p.m SX	p.m	p.m SO	p.m SO	p.m	p.m SX	p.m	p.m SO	p.m SX	p.m	p.m	p.m	p.m SO	p.m SX	p.m	p.m	p.m	p.m SX
Waterloo 394 ......dep.	9 57	10 27	1054	1057	10 57	11 27	11 45	1157	11 57	1217	1227	12 45	1247	1254	12 57	1 17	1 24	12J57	1d12	1 27	1 45	1 54	1 57	1 57	2 27	45	..	2 57	2 57	3 27	..
Surbiton 394 ...... "	10 13	10 43	..	1113	11 13	11 43	11 43	1213	12 13	..	1243	12K43	1 3	..	1 13	..	..	1 13	1B28	1 43	1B49	..	2 13	2 13	2 43	2B49	..	3 13	3 13	3 43	..
Woking .... "	10 39	11 8	1126	1138	11 39	12 8	12 16	1238	12 39	1251	1 8	1 16	1 26	1 26	1 38	1 51	1 56	1J39	..	2 8	2 16	2 26	2 38	2 39	3 8	16	..	3 38	3 39	4 [illegible]	..
Brookwood A	..	11 15	1134	1145	..	12 15	..	1245	..	1257	1 15	..	1 32	1 34	1 45	1 57	2 3	..	..	2 15	..	2 34	2 45	..	3 15	..	..	3 45	..	4 15	..
Ash Vale B	..	11 22	..	1152	..	12 22	..	1252	..	1 5	1 22	..	1 40	..	1 52	2 5	..	..	..	2 22	..	..	2 52	..	3 22	..	..	3 52	..	4 22	..
Guildford ....dep.	11 2	..	..	..	12 0	..	12 30	..	1 0	..	..	1 30	..	..	..	..	..	2 0	2 23	..	2 30	..	..	3 0	..	3 30	..	..	4 0	..	..
Wanborough C	11 9	..	..	..	12 7	..	12 37	..	1 7	..	..	1 37	..	..	..	..	..	2 7	2 32	..	2 37	..	..	3 7	..	3 37	..	..	4 7	..	..
Ash G ....[389	11 13	..	..	..	12 11	..	12 41	..	1 11	..	..	1 41	..	..	..	..	..	2 11	2U41	..	2 41	..	..	3 11	..	3 41	3 41	..	4 11	..	4 33
Aldershot D arr.	11 20	..	..	..	12 18	..	12 48	..	1 18	..	..	1 48	..	..	..	..	..	2 18	2 48	..	2 48	..	..	3 18	..	3 48	3 48	..	4 18	..	4 40
Aldershot	..	11 27	..	1157	..	12 27	..	1257	..	1 9	1 27	..	1 44	..	1 57	2 9	..	..	Arr Ash 2 37 p.m	2 27	..	..	2 57	..	3 27	..	..	3 57	..	4 27	..
Farnham	..	11 33	..	12 3	..	12 33	..	1 3	..	1 15	1 33	..	1 50	..	2 3	2 15	..	..		2 33	..	..	3 3	..	3 33	..	..	4 3	..	4 33	..
Bentley	..	11 40	..	1210	..	12 40	..	1 10	..	..	1 40	..	..	..	2 10	..	..	..		2 40	..	..	3 10	..	3 40	..	..	4 10	..	4 40	..
Bentley ....dep.	..	12SO5	..	..	..	12L45	..	..	..	..	..	..	..	..	..	..	..	..		2 45	..	..	..	..	..	..	..	..	..	4 45	..
Kingsley Halt	..	12SO13	..	..	..	12L53	..	..	..	..	..	..	..	..	..	..	..	..		2 53	..	..	..	..	..	..	..	..	..	4 53	..
Bordon ....arr.	..	12SO20	..	..	..	1 L0	..	..	..	..	..	..	..	..	..	..	..	..		3 0	..	..	..	..	..	..	..	..	..	5 0	..
Alton F 375 ......arr.	..	11 47	..	1217	..	12 47	..	1 17	..	..	1 47	..	..	..	2 17	..	..	..		2 47	..	..	3 17	..	3 47	..	..	4 17	..	4 47	..

Week Days—*continued*

Down	p.m SX	p.m	p.m	p.m	p.m SX	p.m	p.m SO	p.m SX	p.m SX	p.m	p.m	p.m SX	p.m	p.m SX	p.m SX	p.m SO	p.m SX	p.m SX	p.m SO	p.m	p.m	p.m SX	p.m SX	p.m SO	p.m	p.m SX	p.m	p.m	p.m	p.m SX	p.m	p.m
Waterloo 394 ......dep.	3 45	3 54	3 57	4B20	4 17	4 27	4d12	4 45	4 47	4 57	4 57	5 17	5 27	5 37	5 39	..	5 45	5 47	5 54	5 57	6V20	6 14	6 17	..	6 27	6 45	6 54	6 57	6 57	7 17	7 27	..
Surbiton 394 ...... "	3 43	..	4 13	4 13	..	4 43	4B30	4B50	..	5 13	5 13	..	5 43	5 53	..	..	5B49	..	..	6 13	6 13	..	6 34	..	6 43	6B48	..	7 13	7 13	7 35	7 43	..
Woking .... "	4 16	4 26	4 38	4 39	4 51	5 8	..	5 9	5 21	5 38	5 39	5 52	6 8	6 19	6 11	..	6 9	6 22	6 27	6 38	6 39	6 48	6 56	..	7 8	7 16	7 26	7 38	7 39	8 0	8 8	..
Brookwood A	..	4 34	4 45	..	4 57	5 15	..	..	5 27	5 45	..	5 58	6 15	6 27	6 19	..	..	6 29	6 35	6 45	..	6 54	7 2	..	7 15	..	7 34	7 45	..	8 7	8 15	..
Ash Vale B	..	..	4 52	..	5 5	5 22	..	..	5 35	5 52	..	6 5	6 22	..	..	..	..	6 36	..	6 52	..	..	7 9	..	7 22	..	..	7 52	..	8 15	8 22	..
Guildford ....dep.	4 30	..	..	5 0	..	..	5 24	5 30	..	..	6 0	..	..	..	..	..	6 30	..	..	..	7 0	..	..	7 3	..	7 30	..	..	8 3	..	..	..
Wanborough C	4 37	..	..	5 7	..	..	5 32	5 37	..	..	6 7	..	..	..	..	..	6 37	..	..	..	7 7	..	..	7 13	..	7 37	..	..	8 10	..	..	..
Ash G ....[389	4 41	..	..	5 11	..	..	5U41	5 41	..	..	6 11	..	..	..	..	6 41	6 41	..	..	..	7 11	..	..	7U41	..	7 41	..	..	8 15	..	..	8 41
Aldershot D arr.	4 48	..	..	5 18	..	..	5 48	5 48	..	..	6 18	..	..	..	..	6 48	6 48	..	..	..	7 18	..	..	7 48	..	7 48	..	..	8 22	..	..	8 48
Aldershot	..	..	4 57	..	5 9	5 27	Arr Ash 5 37 p.m	..	5 39	5 57	..	6 10	6 27	..	..	..	..	6 40	..	6 57	..	7 5	7 13	Arr. Ash 7 18 p.m.	7 27	..	..	7 57	..	8 19	8 27	..
Farnham	..	..	5 3	..	5 15	5 33		..	5 45	6 3	..	6 16	6 33	..	..	..	..	6 47	..	7 3	..	7 10	7 19		7 33	..	..	8 3	..	8 26	8 33	..
Bentley	..	..	5 10	..	..	5 40		..	..	6 10	..	6 23	6 40	..	..	..	..	6 55	..	7 10	..	..	..		7 40	..	..	8 10	..	..	8 40	..
Bentley ....dep.	..	..	..	..	..	..		..	..	..	..	..	6 45	..	..	..	..	..	..	..	..	..	..		8 15	..	..	..	..	..	..	..
Kingsley Halt	..	..	..	..	..	..		..	..	..	..	..	6 53	..	..	..	..	..	..	..	..	..	..		8 23	..	..	..	..	..	..	..
Bordon ....arr.	..	..	..	..	..	..		..	..	..	..	..	7 0	..	..	..	..	..	..	..	..	..	..		8 30	..	..	..	..	..	..	..
Alton F 375 ......arr.	..	..	5 17	..	..	5 47		..	5 57	6 17	..	6 31	6 47	..	..	..	..	7 3	..	7 17	..	..	..		7 47	..	..	8 17	..	..	8 47	..

For Notes and Continuation of Trains, see page 391

Printed and Published by— Henry Blacklock & Co. Ltd., London, and Albert Square, Manchester, 2.

LONDON, WOKING, GUILDFORD, ALDERSHOT, FARNHAM, BORDON, and ALTON

Down	Week Days—continued																
	p.m	p.m	p.m	p.m	p.m	p.m	p.m	p.m	p.m	p.m	p.m	p.m	p.m	p.m	ngt. SX	a.m SO	
Waterloo 394 ....dep.	7 54	7 57	7 57	8d12	8 27	8 54	8 57	8 57	9 27	9 45	9 57	9 57	1025	1057	..	..	..
Surbiton 394 ...... "	..	8 13	8 13	8B30	8 43	..	9 13	9 13	9 43	9 43	1013	1013	1043	1113	..	..	..
Woking .... "	8 27	8 39	8 38	..	9 8	9 26	9 38	9 39	10 8	10 16	1038	1039	11 8	1138	..	..	..
Brookwood A........	8 35	..	8 45	..	9 15	9 34	9 45	..	10 15	..	1045	..	1115	1145	..	..	..
Ash Vale B..........	..	..	8 52	..	9 22	..	9 52	..	10 22	..	1052	..	1122	1152	..	..	..
Guildford ......dep.	..	9 2	..	9 23	..	..	..	10 0	..	10 30	..	11 0	..	..	..	..	..
Wanborough C......	..	9 9	..	..	..	..	..	10 7	..	10 37	..	11 7	..	..	..	..	..
Ash G .... [389	..	9 13	..	9U41	..	..	..	1011	..	10 41	..	1111	..	..	12 0	1218	..
Aldershot D arr.	..	9 20	..	9 48	..	..	..	1018	..	10 48	..	1118	..	..	12 7	1225	..
Aldershot............	..	..	8 57	Arr. Ash 9 36 p.m.	9 27	..	9 57	..	10 27	..	1057	..	1127	1157	..	..	..
Farnham	..	..	9 3		9 33	..	10 3	..	10 33	..	11 3	..	1133	12 4	..	..	..
Bentley...............	..	..	9 10		9 40	..	1010	..	10 40	..	1110	..	1140	..	..	..	..
Bentley.........dep.	..	..	..		1015	..	..	..	11 15	..	..	..	..	..	..	..	..
Kingsley Halt.......	..	..	..		1023	..	..	..	11 23	..	..	..	..	..	..	..	..
Bordon..........arr.	..	..	..		1030	..	..	..	11 30	..	..	..	..	..	..	..	..
Alton F 375.......arr.	..	..	9 17		9 47	..	1017	..	10 47	..	1117	..	1147	..	..	..	..

Down	Sundays														
	a.m	a.m	a.m	a.m	a.m	a.m	a.m	a.m	a.m	a.m	a.m	a.m	a.m	a.m	a.m
Waterloo 394 ....dep.	..	..	..	7 25	7 25	7 57	7 57	8 27	8 54	8 57	8 57	9 27	9 57	9 57	1027
Surbiton 394 ...... "	..	..	..	7 43	7 43	8 13	8 13	8 43	..	9 13	9 13	9 43	1013	1013	1043
Woking .... "	7 15	7 38	..	8 8	8 9	8 38	8 39	9 8	9 26	9 38	9 39	10 8	1038	1039	11 8
Brookwood A........	..	7 45	..	8 15	..	8 45	..	9 15	9 34	9 45	..	1015	1045	..	1115
Ash Vale B..........	..	7 52	..	8 22	..	8 52	..	9 22	..	9 52	..	1022	1052	..	1122
Guildford ......dep.	7 30	..	7 58	..	8 25	..	9 0	..	..	..	10 0	..	..	11 0	..
Wanborough C......	7 37	..	8 6	..	8 34	..	9 7	..	..	..	10 7	..	..	11 7	..
Ash G .... [389	7 41	..	8 11	..	8U43	..	9 11	..	..	..	1011	..	..	1111	..
Aldershot D arr.	7 48	..	8 17	..	8 50	..	9 18	..	..	..	1018	..	..	1118	..
Aldershot............	..	7 57	8 17	8 27	Arr. Ash 8 39 a.m	8 57	..	9 27	..	9 57	..	1027	1057	..	1127
Farnham	..	8 4	8 24	8 33		9 3	..	9 33	..	10 3	..	1033	11 3	..	1133
Bentley...............	..	8 12	8 32	8 40		9 10	..	9 40	..	1010	..	1040	1110	..	1140
Bentley.........dep.	..	..	..	8 45		..	..	9 45	..	..	..	1045	..	..	1145
Kingsley Halt.......	..	..	..	8 53		..	..	9 53	..	..	..	1053	..	..	1153
Bordon..........arr.	..	..	..	9 0		..	..	10 0	..	..	..	11 0	..	..	12 0
Alton F 375.......arr.	..	8 20	..	8 47		9 17	..	9 47	..	1017	..	1047	1117	..	1147

Down	Sundays—continued																																
	a.m	a.m	a.m	a.m	a.m	a.m	a.m	p.m	p.m	p.m	p.m	p.m	p.m	pm	p.m	p.m	p.m	p.m	p.m	p.m	p.m	p.m	p.m	p.m	p.m	p.m	p.m	p.m	p.m	p.m	p.m	p.m	p.m
Waterloo 394 ....dep.	1054	1057	1057	11d 2	1127	1157	1157	1224	1227	1245	1257	1257	1 27	..	1 57	1 57	2 27	..	2 54	2 57	2 57	3 27	3 57	3 57	4 27	..	4 54	4 57	4 57	5 27	..	5 57	5 57
Surbiton 394 ...... "	..	1113	1113	..	1143	1213	1213	..	1243	1243	1 13	1 13	1 43	..	2 13	2 13	2 43	..	..	3 13	3 13	3 43	4 13	4 13	4 43	..	..	5 13	5 13	5 43	..	6 13	6 13
Woking .... "	1126	1138	1139	..	12 8	1238	1239	1256	1 8	1 16	1 38	1 39	2 8	..	2 38	2 39	3 8	..	3 28	3 38	3 39	4 8	4 38	4 39	5 8	..	5 26	5 38	5 39	6 8	..	6 38	6 39
Brookwood A........	1134	1145	..	..	1215	1245	..	1 4	1 15	..	1 45	..	2 15	..	2 45	..	3 15	..	3 37	3 45	..	4 15	4 45	..	5 15	..	5 34	5 45	..	6 15	..	6 45	..
Ash Vale B..........	..	1152	..	..	1222	1252	..	..	1 22	..	1 52	..	2 22	..	2 52	..	3 22	..	..	3 52	..	4 22	4 52	..	5 22	..	..	5 52	..	6 22	..	6 52	..
Guildford ......dep.	..	..	12 0	12 21	..	..	1 0	..	..	1 30	..	2 0	..	..	..	3 0	..	..	..	..	4 0	..	..	5 0	..	..	..	..	6 0	..	..	..	7 0
Wanborough C......	..	..	12 7	12 30	..	..	1 7	..	..	1 37	..	2 7	..	..	..	3 7	..	..	..	..	4 7	..	..	5 7	..	..	..	..	6 7	..	..	..	7 7
Ash G .... [389	..	..	1211	12U41	..	..	1 11	..	..	1 41	..	2 11	..	241	..	3 11	..	3 41	..	..	4 11	..	..	5 11	..	5 24	..	..	6 11	..	6 41	..	7 11
Aldershot D arr.	..	..	1218	12 48	..	..	1 18	..	..	1 48	..	2 18	..	248	..	3 18	..	3 48	..	..	4 18	..	..	5 18	..	5 31	..	..	6 18	..	6 48	..	7 18
Aldershot............	..	1157	..	Arr. Ash 12 35 p.m.	1227	1257	..	..	1 27	..	1 57	..	2 27	..	2 57	..	3 27	..	..	3 57	..	4 27	4 57	..	5 27	..	..	5 57	..	6 27	..	6 57	..
Farnham	..	12 3	..		1232	1 3	..	..	1 33	..	2 3	..	2 33	..	3 3	..	3 33	..	..	4 3	..	4 33	5 3	..	5 33	..	..	6 3	..	6 33	..	7 3	..
Bentley...............	..	1210	..		1240	1 10	..	..	1 40	..	2 10	..	2 40	..	3 10	..	3 40	..	..	4 10	..	4 40	5 10	..	5 40	..	..	6 10	..	6 40	..	7 10	..
Bentley.........dep.	..	..	..		..	..	..	..	..	..	..	..	..	..	..	..	3 45	..	..	..	..	4 55	..	..	5 55	..	..	..	..	..	..	..	..
Kingsley Halt.......	..	..	..		..	..	..	..	..	..	..	..	..	..	..	..	3 53	..	..	..	..	5 3	..	..	6 3	..	..	..	..	..	..	..	..
Bordon..........arr.	..	..	..		..	..	..	..	..	..	..	..	..	..	..	..	4 0	..	..	..	..	5 10	..	..	6 10	..	..	..	..	..	..	..	..
Alton F 375.......arr.	..	1217	..		1247	1 17	..	..	1 47	..	2 17	..	2 47	..	3 17	..	3 47	..	..	4 17	..	4 47	5 17	..	5 47	..	..	6 17	..	6 47	..	7 17	..

Down	Sundays—continued																			
	p.m	p.m	p.m	p.m	p.m	p.m	p.m	p.m	p.m	p.m	p.m	p.m.	p.m	p.m.	p.m	p.m	p.m	p.m	p.m	
Waterloo 394 ....dep.	6 27	6 54	6 57	6 57	7 27	..	7 57	7 57	8 27	8 45	8 54	8 57	8 57	9 27	9 57	1027	10 27	1057	1127	..
Surbiton 394 ...... "	6 43	..	7 13	7 13	7 43	..	8 13	8 13	8 43	8 43	..	9 13	9 13	9 43	1013	1043	10 43	1113	1143	..
Woking .... "	7 8	7 26	7 38	7 39	8 8	..	8 38	8 39	9 8	9 9	9 26	9 38	9 39	10 8	1038	11 8	11 9	1138	12 8	..
Brookwood A........	7 15	7 34	7 45	..	8 15	..	8 45	..	9 15	..	9 34	9 45	..	10 15	1045	1115	..	1145	1215	..
Ash Vale B..........	7 22	..	7 52	..	8 22	..	8 52	..	9 22	..	..	9 52	..	10 22	1052	1122	..	1152	1222	..
Guildford ......dep.	..	..	..	8 2	..	..	..	9 0	..	9 22	..	..	10 0	..	..	..	11 30	..	..	..
Wanborough C......	..	..	..	8 9	..	..	..	9 7	..	9 39	..	..	10 7	..	..	..	11 37	..	..	..
Ash G .... [389	..	..	..	8 13	..	8 41	..	9 11	..	9 43	..	..	1011	..	..	..	11U47	..	..	..
Aldershot D arr.	..	..	..	8 20	..	8 48	..	9 18	..	9 50	..	..	1018	..	..	..	11 54	..	..	..
Aldershot............	7 27	..	7 57	..	8 27	..	8 57	..	9 27	..	..	9 57	1018	10 27	1057	1127	Arr. Ash 11 41 p.m	1157	1227	..
Farnham	7 33	..	8 3	..	8 33	..	9 3	..	9 33	..	..	10 3	1025	10 33	11 3	1148		12 3	1233	..
Bentley...............	7 40	..	8 10	..	8 40	..	9 10	..	9Y49	..	..	10Y19	..	10Y49	1110	..		1210	..	..
Bentley.........dep.	8 5	..	..	..	..	..	9 35	..	..	..	..	10 20	..	11 8	..	..		1215	..	..
Kingsley Halt.......	8 13	..	..	..	..	..	9 43	..	..	..	..	10 28	..	11 18	..	..		1223	..	..
Bordon..........arr.	8 20	..	..	..	..	..	9 50	..	..	..	..	10 35	..	11 25	..	..		1230	..	..
Alton F 375.......arr	7 47	..	8 17	..	8 47	..	9 17	..	9 56	..	..	10 26	..	10 56	1117	..		..	..	..

A For Bisley Camp
B Sta. for North Camp & South Farnborough
B Third class only between Surbiton and Guildford
C Sta. for Normandy
D Sta. for South Camp
d Third class only between Waterloo and Guildford
F Station for Selborne (4½ miles)
G Sta. for Ash Green
H Dep. 3 57 p.m. on Sats.
J Dep. Waterloo 1 15 and Woking 1 46 p.m. on Sats.
K 6 mins. later and Third class only to Guildford on Sats.
L 5 mins. later on Sats.
SO or SO Saturdays only.
SX or SX Sats. excepted
U Change at Ash
V Dep. 5 57 p.m. on Sats.
Y Arr. 9 mins. *earlier*.
Z Arr. 6 40 a.m.
z Third class only except on Saturdays between Waterloo and Guildford. Dep. Waterloo 6 25 and Surbiton 6 43 a.m. on Saturdays (1st and 3rd class)

OTHER TRAINS between Guildford and Ash, 246—London and Aldershot, 246.

ALTON, BORDON, FARNHAM, ALDERSHOT, GUILDFORD, WOKING, and LONDON

Up — Week Days

Miles	Up	a.m	a.m	a.m	a.m	a.m	a.m	a.m	a.m	a.m	a.m	a.m	a.m	a.m	a.m	a.m	a.m	a.m	a.m	a.m	a.m	a.m	a.m	a.m	a.m	a.m	a.m	a.m	a.m	a.m	a.m
									SX							SX	SO			SX			SX			SX					
	Alton ....dep.	..	..	..	..		6 54	..	..	..	..	7 24	..	7 44	..	7 54	7 54	..	..	8 10	..	8 24	8 46	..	8 56	..	9 24	..	..	9 54	..
—	Mls Bordon ......dep.	..	..	..	..	Arr. Ash 6 47 a.m.	..	..	..	..	Arr. Ash 7 26 a.m.	..	..	..	Arr. Ash 7 55 a.m.	7 40	7 40	..	..	..	Arr. Ash 8 26 a.m.	..	..	..	8 40	..	..	Arr. Ash 9 26 a.m.	..	9 40	..
—	2 Kingsley Halt	..	..	..	..		..	..	..	..		..	..	..		7 46	7 46	..	..	..		..	..	..	8 46	..	..		..	9 46	..
—	4¾ Bentley ......arr.	..	..	..	..		..	..	..	..		..	..	..		7 55	7 55	..	..	..		..	..	..	8 55	..	..		..	9 55	..
5	Bentley	..	..	..	..		7 0	..	..	..		7 30	..	7 50		8 0	8 0	..	..	8 16		8 30	8 52	..	9 2	..	9 30		..	10 0	..
8¾	Farnham	6 5	6 39	6 53	..		7 7	..	7 27	..		7 39	..	7 59		8 7	8 7	..	..	8 25		8 37	9 1	..	9 9	..	9 37		..	10 7	..
11¾	Aldershot D 389....	6 11	6 44	6 58	..		7 13	..	7 32	..		7 45	..	8 4		8 13	8 13	..	..	8 30		8 43	9 6	..	9 16	..	9 44		..	10 14	..
—	Aldershot ....dep.	..	..	..	..	6 41	..	7 8	..	..	7 20	..	7 40	..	7 49	..	..	..	8 12	..	8 20	..	..	8 50	..	..	..	9 20	9 55	..	10 20
14¾	Ash	..	..	..	..	[illegible]U 1	..	7 14	..	..	7U32	..	7 46	..	8U 9	..	..	..	8 18	..	8U28	..	..	8 56	..	..	..	9U28	10 1	..	10 26
14¾	Wanborough C	..	..	..	..	6 57	..	7 19	..	..	7 36	..	7 51	..	8 13	..	..	..	..	..	8 35	..	..	9 1	..	..	..	9 35	10 6	..	10 31
19	Guildford 427..arr.	..	..	..	..	7 4	..	7 25	..	..	7 44	..	7 58	..	8 20	..	..	..	..	..	8 41	..	..	9 7	..	..	..	9 41	10 12	..	10 37
14½	Ash Vale B	6 16	6 49	7 3	..	..	7 18	..	7 37	..	..	7 51	..	8 9	..	8 19	8 19	..	..	8 35	..	8 49	9 11	..	9 21	..	9 49	..	..	10 19	..
19	Brookwood A	6 24	6 56	7 10	7 15	..	7 26	..	7 44	7 52	..	7 58	..	8 16	..	8 26	8 26	8 36	..	8 43	..	8 56	9 18	..	9 28	9 39	9 56	..	..	10 26	..
22½	Woking H 359..arr	6 30	7 2	7 15	7 22	7 32	7 34	7‡43	7 49	7 59	7 59	8 4	8‡19	8 22	8 35	8 32	8 32	8 42	..	8 49	9 4	9 2	9 24	9 33	9 34	9 46	10 2	10 4	10z34	10 32	11 4
35	Surbiton 427....... "	7 0	7 30	7 40	7 46	7B45	8 0	8† 5	8 15	..	8 23	8 23	8Y35	..	9 0	..	9 0	9SX8	..	9 8	9 14	9 30	9 39	10 0	10 0	..	10 30	10B25	11 0	11 0	11B25
47	Waterloo427 ...... "	7 16	7 46	7 56	8 8	8d 5	8 17	8D22	8 31	8 36	8 29	8 40	8L52	8 57	9 13	9 10	9 16	9 20	..	9 25	9 30	9 47	9 55	10 5	10 16	10 21	10 46	10N28	11P16	11 16	11d43

Up — Week Days—*continued*

Up	a.m	a.m	a.m	a.m	a.m	a.m		p.m	p.m	p.m	p.m	p.m	p.m	p.m	p.m	p.m	p.m	p.m	p.m	p.m	p.m	p.m	p.m	p.m	p.m	p.m	p.m	p.m	p.m	p.m
								SX	SO			SO				SX	SO					SO	SX					SO	SX	
Alton ....dep.	1024	..	1054	..	1124	1154	..	..	..	..	1224	..	1254	..	1 24	..	..	1 54	2 24	..	..	..	..	2 54	..	..	3 24	..		3 54
Bordon ....dep.	..	..	..	..	1110	..	..	..	..	..	..	12 30	..	..	..	..	..	1 40	..	..	..	..	..	..	..	..	3 10	..	Arr. Ash 3 56 p.m	..
Kingsley Halt	..	..	..	..	1116	..	..	..	..	..	..	12 36	..	..	..	..	..	1 46	..	..	..	..	..	..	..	..	3 16	..		..
Bentley.........arr.	..	..	..	..	1125	..	..	..	..	..	..	12 45	..	..	..	..	..	1 55	..	..	..	..	..	..	..	..	3 25	..		..
Bentley..............	1030	..	11 0	..	1130	12 0	..	..	..	..	1230	..	1 0	..	1 30	..	..	2 0	2 30	..	..	..	..	3 0	..	..	3 30	..		4 0
Farnham	1037	..	11 7	..	1137	12 7	..	..	..	..	1237	..	1 7	..	1 37	..	..	2 7	2 37	..	..	..	..	3 7	..	..	3 37	..		4 7
Aldershot D 389 ...	1044	..	1114	..	1144	1214	..	..	..	..	1244	..	1 14	..	1 44	..	..	2 14	2 44	..	..	..	..	3 14	..	..	3 44	..		4 14
Aldershot ....dep.	..	10 54	..	11 21	..	..	..	..	..	12 20	..	..	..	1 18	..	1 51	1 58	..	..	..	2 20	2 50	2 50	..	..	3 20	..	3 50	3 50	..
Ash	..	11 0	..	11 27	..	..	..	..	..	12 26	..	..	..	1 24	..	1 57	2 4	..	..	..	2 26	2 56	2 56	..	..	3 26	..	3 56	4U6	..
Wanborough C	..	11 6	..	11 32	..	..	..	..	..	12 31	..	..	..	1 29	..	..	2 9	..	..	..	2 31	3 1	..	..	..	3 31	..	4 1	4 10	..
Guildford 427....arr.	..	11 12	..	11 38	..	..	..	..	..	12 37	..	..	..	1 35	..	..	2 15	..	..	..	2 37	3 7	..	..	..	3 37	..	4 7	4 17	..
Ash Vale B..........	1049	..	1119	..	1149	1219	..	..	..	..	1249	..	1 19	..	1 49	..	..	2 19	2 49	..	..	..	..	3 19	..	..	3 49	..	..	4 19
Brookwood A	1056	..	1126	..	1156	1226	..	1239	1250	..	1256	..	1 26	..	1 56	..	..	2 26	2 56	3 4	..	..	..	3 26	3 39	..	3 56	..	..	4 26
Woking H 359...arr	11 2	11 29	1132	12 4	12 2	1232	..	1246	1257	1 4	1 2	..	1 32	2 4	2 2	..	2 29	2 32	3 2	3 11	3 4	3 29	..	3 32	3 48	4 4	4 2	4 29	4 34	4 32
Surbiton 427....... "	1130	12 0	12 0	12B25	1230	1 0	..	..	..	1B25	1 30	..	2 0	2B25	2 30	..	3 0	3 0	3 30	..	3B25	4 0	..	4 0	..	4B26	4 30	5 0	5 0	5 0
Waterloo 427...... "	1148	12 1	1216	12d43	1246	1 16	..	1 19	1 30	1d43	1 46	..	2 16	2d43	2 46	..	3 13	3 16	3 46	3 49	3d43	4 1	..	4 16	..	4d44	4 46	5 3	5 16	5 16

Up — Week Days—*continued*

Up	p.m	p.m	p.m	p.m	p.m	p.m	p.m	p.m	p.m	p.m	p.m	p.m	p.m	p.m	p.m	p.m	p.m	p.m	p.m	p.m	p.m	p.m	p.m	p.m	p.m	p.m	p.m	p.m	p.m	p.m
				SX	SO					SX	SO		SX									SX								
Alton ....dep.	..	..	4 24	..		4 54	..	5 24	..	..		5 54	..	6 24	..	..	..	6 54	..	7 24	..	..	..	7 54	..	8 24	..	..	8 54	..
Bordon ....dep.	..	..	..	..	Arr Ash 4 56 p.m	..	..	5 10	..	..	Arr Ash 5 57 p.m	..	..	..	..	..	..	..	..	..	..	..	..	7 40	..	..	..	..	8 40	..
Kingsley Halt.......	..	..	..	..		..	..	5 16	..	..		..	..	..	..	..	..	..	..	..	..	..	..	7 46	..	..	..	..	8 46	..
Bentley ....arr.	..	..	..	..		..	..	5 25	..	..		..	..	..	..	..	..	..	..	..	..	..	..	7 55	..	..	..	..	8 55	..
Bentley..............	..	..	4 30	..		5 0	..	5 30	..	..		6 0	..	6 30	..	..	..	7 0	..	7 30	..	..	..	8 0	..	8 30	..	..	9 0	..
Farnham	..	..	4 37	..		5 7	..	5 37	..	..		6 7	..	6 37	..	..	..	7 7	..	7 37	..	..	..	8 7	..	8 37	..	..	9 7	..
Aldershot D 389.....	..	..	4 44	..		5 14	..	5 44	..	..		6 14	..	6 44	..	..	..	7 14	..	7 44	..	..	..	8 14	..	8 44	..	..	9 11	..
Aldershot.....dep.	..	4 20	..	4 50	4 50	..	5 20	..	..	5 50	5 51	..	..	..	6 20	..	6 50	..	7 20	..	7 50	8 10	..	..	8 20	..	8 51	9 20	..	9 51
Ash	..	4 26	..	4 56	5U6	..	5 26	..	..	5 56	6U22	..	..	..	6 27	..	6 56	..	7 26	..	7 56	8 16	..	..	8 26	..	8 57	9 26	..	9 57
Wanborough C ...	..	4 31	..	5 1	5 10	..	5 31	..	..	6 1	..	..	..	..	6 32	..	7SX 1	..	7 31	..	8SX1	..	..	..	8 31	..	..	9 31	..	10 2
Guildford 427...arr.	..	4 37	..	5 7	5 17	..	5 37	..	..	6 7	6 33	..	..	..	6 38	..	7SX 7	..	7 37	..	8SX7	..	..	..	8 37	..	..	9 37	..	10 8
Ash Vale B..........	..	..	4 49	..	..	5 19	..	5 49	..	..	..	6 19	..	6 49	..	..	..	7 19	..	7 49	..	..	..	8 19	..	8 49	..	..	9 19	..
Brookwood A	4 50	..	4 56	..	..	5 26	..	5 56	6 15	..	..	6 26	6 50	6 56	..	7 14	..	7 26	..	7 56	..	..	8 14	8 26	..	8 56	..	..	9 26	..
Woking H 359...arr	4 57	5 4	5 2	5 29	5 34	5 22	6 4	6 2	6 22	6 29	7 4	6 32	6 56	7 2	7 4	7 21	7SX34	7 32	8 4	8 2	8SX29	..	8 21	8 32	9 4	9 2	..	10 4	9 32	10 34
Surbiton 427 ...... "	5 15	5B25	5 30	6 0	6 0	6 0	6B25	6 30	6 47	7 0	7B25	7 0	..	7 30	7B25	..	8SX 0	8 0	8 30	8 30	9SX0	..	8 48	9 0	9 30	9 30	..	10 30	10 0	11 0
Waterloo 427 .... "	5 35	5d44	5 48	6 1	6 18	6 18	6d43	6 48	7 7	7 3	7d43	7 16	..	7 46	7d43	8 0	8SX16	8 16	8 46	8 46	9SX1	..	9 14	9 16	9 46	9 46	..	10 46	1016	11 16

For Notes and Continuation of Trains, see page 393

ALTON, BORDON, FARNHAM, ALDERSHOT, GUILDFORD, WOKING, and LONDON

Up — Week Days—*continued*

Up	p.m	p.m	p.m	p.m	p.m	p.m	p.m	p.m. SX	p.m. SO	
Alton ....dep.	9 24	9 54	..	1024	..	1054	..	..	..	..
Bordon ....dep.	..	..	..	..	..	1040	..	Arr. Ash 11 46 p.m	Arr. Ash 11 46 p.m	..
Kingsley Halt	..	..	..	..	..	1046	..			..
Bentley ....arr.	..	..	..	..	..	1055	..			..
Bentley	9 30	10 0	..	1030	..	11 0	..			..
Farnham	9 37	10 7	..	1037	..	11 7	..			..
Aldershot D 389	9 44	1014	..	1044	..	1114	..			..
Aldershot ....dep.	..	..	1020	..	..	..	1120	11 40	11 40	..
Ash	..	..	1026	..	..	..	1126	11U57	12U12	..
Wanborough C	..	..	1031	..	..	..	1131	..	..	..
Guildford 427 ....arr	..	..	1037	..	..	..	1137	12 8	12 23	..
Ash Vale B	9 49	1019	..	1049	..	1119	..	..	..	..
Brookwood A	9 56	1026	..	1056	11 2	1126	..	..	..	..
Woking H 359 ....arr	10 2	1032	11 4	11 2	11 9	1132	..	..	..	..
Surbiton 427 .... "	1030	11 0	1130	1130	..	..	..	..	..	..
Waterloo 427 .... "	1046	1116	1146	1146	..	12SX6	..	..	..	..

Up — Sundays

Up	a.m	a.m	a.m	a.m	a.m	a.m	a.m	a.m	a.m	a.m Z	a.m	a.m	a.m	a.m	a.m	a.m	a.m	a.m	a.m	a.m		p.m	p.m
Alton ....dep.	..	..	..	..	7 54	8 24	8 54	..	9 24	9 31	9 54	..	..	1024	..	1054	..	1124	..	1154	..	..	1224
Bordon ....dep.	..	Arr. Ash 826 a.m	..	..	..	..	..	..	9 10	..	..	..	..	1010	..	..	..	1110	..	..	..	..	..
Kingsley Halt	..		..	..	..	..	..	..	9 16	..	..	..	..	1016	..	..	..	1116	..	..	..	..	..
Bentley ....arr.	..		..	..	..	..	..	..	9 25	..	..	..	..	1025	..	..	..	1125	..	..	..	..	..
Bentley	..		..	..	8 0	8 30	9 0	..	9 30	9 40	10 0	..	..	1030	..	11 0	..	1130	..	12 0	..	..	1230
Farnham	7 9		..	..	8 7	8 37	9 7	..	9 37	9 50	10 7	..	..	1037	..	11 7	..	1137	..	12 7	..	..	1237
Aldershot D 389	7 14		..	..	8 14	8 44	9 13	..	9 43	9 59	1014	..	..	1044	..	1114	..	1144	..	1214	..	..	1244
Aldershot ....dep.	..	8 20	..	8 50	..	..	..	9 20	..	..	..	..	1020	..	1050	..	..	..	1120	..	..	1220	.
Ash	..	8U29	..	8 56	..	..	..	9 26	..	..	..	..	1026	..	1056	..	..	..	1126	..	..	1226	..
Wanborough C	..	8 34	..	9 1	..	..	..	9 31	..	..	..	..	1031	..	..	..	..	..	1131	..	..	1231	..
Guildford 427 ....arr	..	8 41	..	9 7	..	..	..	9 37	..	..	..	..	1037	..	..	..	..	..	1137	..	..	1237	..
Ash Vale B	7 19	..	..	..	8 19	8 49	9 19	..	9 49	10 4	1019	..	..	1049	..	1119	..	1149	..	1219	..	..	1249
Brookwood A	7 26	..	8 20	..	8 26	8 56	9 26	..	9 56	1014	1026	1038	..	1056	..	1126	1150	1156	..	1226	..	..	1256
Woking H 359 ....arr	7 32	9 4	8 27	9 29	8 32	9 2	9 32	10 4	10 2	1021	1032	1045	11 4	11 2	..	1132	1157	12 2	12 4	1232	..	1 4	1 2
Surbiton 427 .... "	8 0	9 30	..	10 0	9 0	9 30	10 0	1030	1030	..	11 0	11 2	1130	1130	..	12 0	..	1230	1230	1 0	..	1 30	1 30
Waterloo 427 .... "	8 16	9 46	8 59	10 0	9 16	9 46	1016	1046	1046	..	1116	1121	1146	1146	..	1216	1230	1246	1246	1 16	..	1 46	1 46

Up — Sundays—*continued*

Up	p.m	p.m	p.m	p.m	p.m	p.m	p.m	p.m	p.m	p.m	p.m	p.m		p.m	p.m	p.m
Alton ....dep.	..	1254	..	1 24	..	1 54	..	2 24	..	2 54	..	3 24	..	3 54	..	4 24
Bordon ....dep.	..	..	..	..	..	..	..	..	..	..	..	3 10	..	..	..	4 10
Kingsley Halt	..	..	..	..	..	..	..	..	..	..	..	3 16	..	..	..	4 16
Bentley ....arr.	..	..	..	..	..	..	..	..	..	..	..	3 25	..	..	..	4 25
Bentley	..	1 0	..	1 30	..	2 0	..	2 30	..	3 0	..	3 30	..	4 0	..	4 30
Farnham	..	1 7	..	1 37	..	2 7	..	2 37	..	3 7	..	3 37	..	4 7	..	4 37
Aldershot D 389	..	1 14	..	1 44	..	2 14	..	2 44	..	3 14	..	3 44	..	4 14		4 44
Aldershot ....dep.	1251	..	1 20	..	1 54	..	2 20	..	2 51	..	3 20	..	..	..	4 20	..
Ash	1257	..	1 26	..	2 1	..	2 26	..	2 58	..	3 26	..	..	..	4 26	..
Wanborough C	1 2	..	1 31	..	..	..	2 31	..	..	..	3 31	..	..	..	4 31	..
Guildford 427 ....arr	1 8	..	1 37	..	..	..	2 37	..	..	..	3 37	..	..	..	4 37	..
Ash Vale B	..	1 19	..	1 49	..	2 19	..	2 49	..	3 19	..	3 49	..	4 19	..	4 49
Brookwood A	..	1 26	..	1 56	..	2 26	..	2 56	..	3 26	..	3 56	..	4 26	..	4 56
Woking H 359 ....arr	1 29	1 32	2 4	2 2	..	2 32	3 4	3 2	..	3 22	4 4	4 2	..	4 32	5 4	5 2
Surbiton 427 .... "	2 0	2 0	2 30	2 30	..	3 0	3 30	3 30	..	4 0	4 30	4 30	..	5 0	5 30	5 30
Waterloo 427 .... "	2 1	2 16	2 46	2 46	..	3 16	3 46	3 46	..	4 16	4 46	4 46	..	5 16	5 46	5 46

Up	p.m	p.m	p.m	p.m	p.m	p.m	p.m	p.m	p.m	p.m	p.m	p.m	p.m	p.m	p.m	p.m	p.m
Alton ....dep.	..		4 54	..	5 24	..	5 54	..	6 24	6 54	..	..	7 24		7 54	..	8 24
Bordon ....dep.	..	Arr. Ash 4 57 p.m.	..	..	..	..	5 35	..	..	..	..	..	7 10	Arr. Ash 7 57 p.m.	..	..	..
Kingsley Halt	..		..	..	..	..	5 41	..	..	..	..	..	7 16		..	..	..
Bentley ....arr.	..		..	..	..	..	5 50	..	..	..	..	..	7 25		..	..	..
Bentley	..		5 0	..	5 30	..	6 0	..	6 30	7 0	..	..	7 30		8 0	..	8 30
Farnham	..		5 7	..	5 37	..	6 7	..	6 37	7 7	..	..	7 37		8 7	..	8 37
Aldershot D 389	..		5 14	..	5 44	..	6 14	..	6 44	7 14	..	..	7 44		8 14	..	8 44
Aldershot ....dep.	..	4 50	..	5 20	..	5 50	..	6 20	..	..	..	7 20	..	7 50	..	8 21	..
Ash	..	5U5	..	5 26	..	5 57	..	6 26	..	..	..	7 26	..	8U5	..	8 27	..
Wanborough C	..	5 10	..	5 31	..	..	..	6 31	..	..	..	7 31	..	8 10	..	8 32	..
Guildford 427 ....arr	..	5 17	..	5 37	..	..	..	6 37	..	..	..	7 37	..	8 17	..	8 38	..
Ash Vale B	..	..	5 19	..	5 49	..	6 19	..	6 49	7 19	..	..	7 49	..	8 19	..	8 49
Brookwood A	5 16	..	5 26	..	5 56	..	6 26	..	6 56	7 26	7 35	..	7 56	..	8 26	..	8 56
Woking H 359 ....arr	5 23	5 34	5 32	6 4	6 2	..	6 32	7 4	7 2	7 32	7 42	7 57	8 2	8 34	8 32	9 4	9 2
Surbiton 427 .... "	5 45	6 0	6 0	6 30	6 30	..	7 0	7 30	7 30	8 0	8 2	8 13	8 30	9 0	9 0	9 30	9 30
Waterloo 427 .... "	6 4	6 16	6 16	6 48	6 48	..	7 16	7 47	7 47	8 16	8 22	8 30	8 46	9 21	9 21	9 46	9 46

Up — Sundays—*continued*

Up	p.m	p.m	p.m	p.m	p.m	p.m	p.m	p.m	p.m	p.m	p.m	p.m	p.m	
Alton ....dep.	..	8 54	..	9 24	..	9 54	..	..	1024	..	1054	..	..	..
Bordon ....dep.	..	..	..	9 10	..	..	..	..	10 0	..	..	1048	1130	..
Kingsley Halt	..	..	..	9 16	..	..	..	..	10 6	..	..	1053	1136	..
Bentley ....arr.	..	..	..	9 25	..	..	..	..	1015	..	..	11 3	1145	..
Bentley	..	9 0	..	9 30	..	10 0	..	..	1030	..	11 1	..	..	..
Farnham	..	9 7	..	9 37	..	10 7	..	..	1037	..	11 8	..	..	..
Aldershot D 389	..	9 14	..	9 44	..	1014	..	..	1044	..	..	..	..	..
Aldershot ....dep.	..	..	9 20	..	9 50	..	..	1020	..	1050	..	..	..	..
Ash	..	..	9 26	..	9 56	..	..	1026	..	1056	..	..	..	..
Wanborough C	..	..	9 31	..	10 1	..	..	1031	..	11 1	..	..	..	..
Guildford 427 ....arr	..	..	9 37	..	10 7	..	..	1037	..	11 7	..	..	..	..
Ash Vale B	..	9 19	..	9 49	..	1019	..	..	1049	..	..	..	..	..
Brookwood A	9 5	9 26	..	9 56	..	1026	1039	..	1056	..	..	..	..	..
Woking H 359 ....arr	9 12	9 32	10 4	10 2	1029	1032	1046	11 4	11 2	1129	..	..	..	..
Surbiton 427 .... "	..	10 0	1030	1030	11 0	11 0	1111	1130	1130	..	..	..	..	..
Waterloo 427 .... "	9 49	1016	1046	1046	11 1	1116	1136	1146	1146	12 1	..	..	..	..

A For Bisley Camp
B Sta. for North Camp & South Farnborough
B Third class only between Guildford and Surbiton
C Sta. for Normandy
D Sta. for South Camp
D Arr. 8d27 a.m. on Sats.
d Third class only between Guildford and Waterloo

H Station for Chobham (3¼ miles), to Woking Village (1½ miles)
L Arr. 9d8 a.m. on Sats.
N Arr. 10d43 a.m. on Sats.
P Arr. 11 2 a.m on Sats.
SO or SO Saturdays only
SX or SX Sats. excepted
U Change at Ash
Y Arr. 8†50 a.m. on Sats.

Z From Portsmouth and Southsea, depart 7 56 a.m., pages 382 and 375
z Arr. 10 30 a.m. on Sats.
† Third class only between Guildford and Surbiton on Sats.
‡ 16 minutes later on Sats.

OTHER TRAINS between Aldershot and London, page 249—Ash and Guildford, 249

LONDON, DORKING NORTH, HORSHAM, KINGSTON, SHEPPERTON, HAMPTON COURT, CHERTSEY, WOKING, & GUILDFORD

Mls	Down	Week Days a.m																														
—	Waterloo ... dep.	1 30	2 15	3 48	3	4 45	3	5 1	3	3	3	5 25	3	5 25	3	5 36	..	..	5 40	5 49	5 55	5 56	5 59	6 4	3	6 12	3	3	6 16	..	6 19	6 21
1½	Vauxhall	1 34	2 18	3 52		..		5 4				..		5 29		5 39	..	..	..	5 52	..	5 59	6 2	6 7		3			6 19	..	6 22	6 24
4	Clapham Junction A	1 42	2 22	3 57	..	..	..	5 8	..	..	..	5 32	..	5 34	..	5 44	..	..	..	5 56	..	6 4	6 6	6 12	..		..	..	6 24	..	6 26	6 29
5½	Earlsfield B	1 45	2 26	4 1	..	..	..	5 12	..	..	..	..	..	5 38	..	5 47	..	Via Three Bridges, see page 158	..	6 0	..	6 7	6 10	6 15	..	..	..	..	6 27	..	6 30	6 32
7½	Wimbledon	1 49	2 29	4 4	4 51	4 58	..	5 17	5 21	5 29	5 32	..	5 38	5 43	..	5 51	..		..	6 3	6 6	6 11	6 13	6 19	6 23	..	..	..	6 31	Via Three Bridges, see page 158	6 33	6 36
8½	Raynes Park	1 52	2 32	4 7	4 54	..	..	5 21	5 24	5 32	5 35	..	5 41	5 47	..	5 54	..		..	6 6	..	6 14	6 16	6 22	6 26	..	..	..	6 34		6 36	6 39
9¾	Motspur Park				4 56	..	..		5 26	..	5 37	..	..		..	5 56	..		..		..	6 16		6 24	..	..	..	..	6 36			
11	Malden Manor	3	3	3	5 0	..	..	3	5 30	..	..	..	..	3	..	6 0	..		..	3	..	6 20	3	3	..	..	..	..	6 40		3	3
12	Tolworth				5 2	..	..		5 32	..	..	..	..		..	6 2	..		..		..	6 22			..	..	..	..	6 42			
13½	Chessington North		..	..	5 5	..	..	..	5 35	..	..	..	..	..	..	6 5	..		..	..	..	6 25	..	..	..	..	..	..	6 45		..	..
14	Chessington South ¶ ar		..	..	5 7	..	..	..	5 37	..	..	..	..	..	..	6 7	..		..	..	..	6 27	..	..	..	..	..	..	6 47		..	..
10¾	Worcester Park	Calls at Queen's Road 1 38 a.m	..	..	Stop	..	..	..	..	..	5 43	..	..	..	..	3	..		..	..	..	3	..	6 27	..	..	..	..	3		..	..
12	Stoneleigh		..	..		..	..	..	..	..	5 46	..	..	..	..		..		..	..	..		..	6 30	..	..	..	..			..	..
13	Ewell West C		..	..	..	..	..	..	..	..	5 49	..	..	..	..		..		..	..	..		..	6 32	..	..	..	..			..	..
—	London Bridge ... dep.		..	..	..	..	..	..	..	..	..	..	..	..	..	Stop	5 10	5 25	..	..	..	Stop	..	5‡34	..	..	..	6 8	Stop	6 16	..	..
—	Victoria ... "		..	..	..	..	..	..	..	..	..	..	..	..	..	..	5F14	5 20	..	..	..	..	..	..	..	..	..	6*0	..	..	..	..
—	Sutton ... "		..	..	..	..	..	..	..	..	..	..	..	..	..	..	5 54	..	..	..	..	..	..	6‡19	..	..	..	6 35	..	..	..	..
14¼	Epsom 285		..	..	..	..	..	..	..	..	5 54	..	..	..	..	..	6 11	..	..	..	..	..	..	6 36	..	..	..	6 46	..	..	..	..
16¼	Ashtead		..	..	..	..	..	..	..	..	5 58	..	..	..	..	a.m	6 18	..	..	..	..	..	..	6 40	..	..	..	6 50	..	..	..	..
18	Leatherhead		..	..	..	..	..	..	..	..	6 2	..	..	..	6 17	3	6 25	..	..	..	..	..	..	6 44	..	..	6 50	6 55	..	..	..	..
21½	Boxhill & Burford Bdg D		..	..	..	..	Dep. Strawberry Hill 5 20 a.m	..	..	..	..	..	..	..	..		6 31	..	..	..	..	..	..	6 49	..	..	..	..	..	..	..	..
22	Dorking North F		..	..	..	..		..	..	..	..	..	..	..	..	6 26	6 35	..	..	..	..	..	..	6 52	..	..	..	..	..	..	..	..
27	Holmwood G		..	..	..	..		..	..	..	..	..	..	..	..	6 35	6 48	..	..	..	..	..	..	7 9	..	..	..	..	..	..	..	..
29½	Ockley, for Capel		..	..	..	..		..	..	..	..	..	..	..	..	6 39	6 53	..	..	..	..	..	..	7 13	..	..	..	..	..	..	..	..
33½	Warnham [196, 245		..	..	..	..		..	..	..	..	..	..	..	..	6 45	7 2	..	..	..	..	..	..	7 19	..	..	..	..	..	..	..	..
35½	Horsham 159, arr.		..	..	..	..		..	..	..	..	..	..	..	..	6 49	7 7	7 4	..	..	..	..	..	7 24	..	..	..	..	..	7 49	..	..
20½	Bookham	..	..	..	..	..		..	..	..	..	..	..	..	6 21	..	..	..	..	..	..	..	..		..	..	6 54	6 59	..	..	..	..
9¾	Malden, for Coombe	1 55	2 35	4 12	..	5 5		5 24	..	5 35	..	..	5 44	5 50	..	..	..	..	..	6 9	..	..	6 19	Dep Dorking North 7 1 a.m	6 29	..	..	..	..	..	6 39	6 42
11½	Norbiton H	1 58	2 39	4 16	..	..		5 28	..	5 38	..	..	..	5 53	..	..	..	..	..	6 13	..	..	..		6 33	..	..	..	..	..	..	6 45
12½	Kingston	2 1	2 41	4 19	..	..		5 30	..	5 41	..	..	..	5 58	..	..	..	..	..	6 15	..	..	..		6 35	..	..	..	a.m	..	..	6 48
12¾	Hampton Wick	..	..	4 21	a.m	..		5 32	..	5 43	..	..	..	6 0	..	..	..	..	..	6 17	..	..	..		6 37	..	..	..	3	..	..	6 50
13¾	Teddington J	2 6	2 47	4 25	3	..		5 36	..	5 46	..	..	..	6 3	..	..	..	..	..	6 21	..	..	..		6 41	..	..	..		..	..	6 53
15	Fulwell K	V	To Strawberry Hill, arr. 2 50 a.m	V		..	5 23	5 41	..	V	..	..	..	V	..	..	..	..	..	6 25	..	..	..		V	..	..	..	6 57	..	..	V
16½	Hampton	To Waterloo via Richmond Arr. Twickenham 2 12 a.m		To Waterloo via Richmond Arr. Twickenham 4 37 a.m	5 6	..	5 27	5 46	..	To Waterloo via Richmond Arr. Twickenham 5 54 a.m	..	..	..	To Waterloo via Richmond Arr. Twickenham 6 14 a.m	..	..	..	..	..	6 29	..	..	..		To Waterloo via Richmond Arr. Twickenham 6 47 a.m	..	..	..	7 1	..	..	To Waterloo, via Richmond Arr. Twickenham 6 59 a.m
18¾	Sunbury L				5 10	..	5 31	5 53	..		..	..	..		..	..	..	..	..	6 33	..	..	..			..	..	..	7 5	..	..	
19½	Upper Halliford Halt				..	..	..	..	..		..	..	..		..	..	..	..	..	6 35	..	..	..			..	..	..	7 7	..	..	
21	Shepperton M ... arr.				5 14	..	5 35	5 57	..		..	..	..		..	..	..	..	..	6 37	..	..	..			..	..	..	7 10	..	..	
11	Berrylands N				Dep. Strawberry Hill 5 0 a.m	..	..	..	..		..	..	5 47		..	..	..	..	..	..	..	..	6 22			..	..	..	Dep. Strawberry Hill 6 55 a.m	..	6 42	
12	Surbiton					5 13	..	..	..		..	5 43	5 49		..	..	..	..	5 59	..	6 13	..	6 25			6 28	..	..		..	6 45	
14	Thames Ditton					..	..	..	..		..	..	5 53		..	..	..	..	..	..	..	..	6 29			..	..	..		..	6 49	
15	Hampton Court P arr.					..	..	..	..		..	..	5 57		..	..	..	..	..	..	..	..	6 32			..	..	..		..	6 52	
14	Hinchley Wood					..	..	..	..		..	..	Stop		..	..	..	..	..	..	..	..	Stop	..		6 31	..	..		..	..	
15½	Claygate, for Claremont					..	..	..	..		..	..	..		..	..	..	..	..	..	..	..	..	..		6 34	..	..		..	..	
17	Oxshott, for Fairmile					..	..	..	..		..	..	..		..	..	..	..	..	..	..	..	..	..		6 38	..	..		..	..	
18¾	Cobham Q					..	..	..	..		..	..	..		..	..	..	..	..	..	..	..	..	..		6 41	..	..		..	..	
21	Effingham Junction					..	..	..	..		..	..	..		6 25	..	..	..	..	..	..	..	..	..		6 46	6 58	7 3		..	..	
22	Horsley R		Stop			..	..	..	..		..	..	..		6 27	..	..	..	..	..	..	..	..	..		6 48	7 4	..		..	..	
25¼	Clandon T					..	..	..	..		..	..	..		6 32	..	..	..	..	..	..	..	..	..		6 53	7 9	..		..	..	
28½	London Road (Guildford)		..			..	..	..	..		..	..	..		6 38	..	..	..	..	..	..	..	..	..		6 59	7 14	..		..	..	
14½	Esher, for Sandown Park		..			5 20	..	..	..		..	5 47	a.m		..	..	..	..	..	..	6 17	a.m	a.m	..		..	..	..		..	..	
16	Hersham		..			..	..	..	..		..	5 50	3		..	..	..	..	..	..	6 20	3	3	..		..	..	..		..	..	
17½	Walton-on-Thames	..	a.m	..	..	5 28	..	..	..		..	5 53			..	..	..	..	..	..	6 23			..		..	..	..		..	..	..
19½	Weybridge U	..	3	..	..	5 34	..	..	..		..	5 57	6 3	..	..	..	..	..	..	..	6 27	6 32	6 49	..	..	..	..	..	..	..	..	..
21	Addlestone	..		..	..	..	..	..	..	..	..	..	6 7	..	..	..	..	..	..	..	..	6 36	6 53	..	..	..	..	..	..	..	..	..
22½	Chertsey	..	5 39	..	..	..	..	..	..	..	..	..	6 10	..	..	..	..	..	..	..	..	6 41	7 0	..	..	..	..	..	..	..	..	..
25	Virginia Water Z 460 arr	..	5 43	..	..	..	..	..	..	..	..	..	6 14	..	..	..	..	..	..	..	..	6 46	7 4	..	..	..	..	..	..	..	..	..
20½	West Weybridge	..	..	..	..	..	..	..	..	..	..	6 0	..	..	..	..	..	..	..	..	6 30	..	..	..	..	..	..	..	..	..	..	..
21¾	Byfleet W	..	..	..	..	..	..	..	..	..	..	6 3	..	..	..	..	..	..	..	..	6 33	..	..	..	..	..	..	..	..	..	..	..
24½	Woking X 324, 389, 390	..	..	..	..	5 47	..	..	..	..	..	6 7	..	..	..	..	..	..	6 16	..	6 37	..	..	..	..	..	..	..	..	..	..	..
26¾	Worplesdon	..	..	..	..	..	..	..	..	..	..	6 15	..	..	..	..	..	..	..	..	6 45	..	..	..	..	..	..	..	..	..	..	..
30¼	Guildford 246, 359 ... arr.	..	..	..	..	..	..	..	..	..	..	6 21	..	..	6 42	..	..	..	..	..	6 51	..	..	..	..	7 3	7 18	..	..	..	..	..

FOR NOTES, SEE PAGE 426

FOR NOTES, SEE PAGE 426

LONDON, DORKING NORTH, HORSHAM, KINGSTON, SHEPPERTON, HAMPTON COURT, CHERTSEY, WOKING, & GUILDFORD

Down	Week Days—continued (a.m)																				8 X											
Waterloo dep.	6 25	6 27	3	3	6 36	6 39	6 41	..	6 47	3	..	6 49	6 52	6 55	3	3	6 59	7 1	7 7	3	7 9	3	3	..	..	7 16	..	7 19	7 20	7 21	7 25	7 27
Vauxhall	..	3	..	..	6 39	6 42	6 44	..	3	..	..	6 52	3	..	..	..	7 2	7 4	3	..	7 12	..	..	..	..	7 19	..	7 22	..	7 24	..	3
Clapham Junction A	..	..	..	..	6 44	6 46	6 49	..	..	..	..	6 56	..	..	..	..	7 6	7 9	..	..	7 16	..	..	..	..	7 24	..	7 26	..	7 28	..	..
Earlsfield B	..	..	..	..	6 47	6 50	6 52	..	..	..	..	7 0	..	..	..	..	7 10	7 12	..	..	7 20	..	..	..	..	7 27	..	7 30	..	7 32	..	..
Wimbledon	6 36	6 38	6 46	..	6 51	6 53	6 56	6 57	6 58	..	..	7 3	..	7 6	7 7	7 11	7 13	7 16	7 18	7 19	7 23	7 23	..	..	7 27	7 31	..	7 33	..	7 35	7 36	7 38
Raynes Park	..	..	6 49	..	6 54	6 56	6 59	..	..	..	..	7 6	..	..	7 10	7 14	7 16	7 19	..	..	7 26	7 27	..	..	..	7 34	..	7 36	..	7 38	..	..
Motspur Park	..	6 44	6 52	..	6 56	..	..	..	7 4	..	Via Three Bridges, see page 160	..	..	..	7 13	7 16	..	..	7 24	..	..	7 29	..	..	..	7 36	Via Three Bridges, see page 160	..	..	..	..	7 44
Malden Manor	..	..	..	..	7 0	3	3	..	..	..	..	3	..	..	..	7 20	3	3	..	..	3	..	..	..	..	7 40	..	3	..	3	..	..
Tolworth	..	..	..	..	7 2	..	..	..	..	..	..	..	..	..	..	7 22	..	..	..	..	..	..	..	..	..	7 42	..	..	..	..	..	..
Chessington North	..	..	..	..	7 5	..	..	..	..	..	..	..	..	..	..	7 25	..	..	..	..	..	..	..	..	..	7 45	..	..	..	..	..	..
Chessington South¶ar.	..	..	..	..	7 7	..	..	..	..	..	..	..	..	..	..	7 27	..	..	..	..	..	..	..	..	..	7 47	..	..	..	..	..	..
Worcester Park	..	6 46	6 54	..	3	..	..	..	7 6	..	..	..	..	..	7 18	..	..	..	7 26	..	..	7 32	..	..	..	3	..	..	..	..	..	7 46
Stoneleigh	..	6 49	6 57	..	..	..	..	..	7 9	..	..	..	..	..	7 21	..	..	..	7 29	..	..	7 35	..	..	..	..	..	..	..	..	..	7 49
Ewell West C	..	6 52	7 0	..	Stop	..	..	..	7 12	..	..	..	..	..	7 24	..	..	..	7 32	..	..	7 39	..	..	..	Stop	..	..	..	..	..	7 52
London Bridge dep.	..	..	..	6 28	..	..	..	..	..	6 48	..	..	..	..	..	..	..	..	..	..	..	..	7 8	..	..	..	7 20	..	..	..	..	..
Victoria "	..	6‡15	..	6*18	..	..	..	..	6‡38	..	6 40	..	..	..	..	..	..	..	6‡58	..	..	..	6‡58	..	..	..	..	..	..	..	..	7‡17
Sutton "	..	6‡42	..	6 57	..	..	..	..	7‡1	7 15	..	..	..	..	..	..	..	..	7‡21	..	..	..	7 35	..	..	..	..	..	..	..	..	7‡41
Epsom 285	..	6 55	7 3	7 7	a.m	..	..	..	7 15	7 24	..	..	..	..	7 28	..	..	..	7 35	..	..	7 43	7 45	..	..	..	..	..	..	..	..	7 55
Ashtead	..	6 59	7 7	7 11	3	..	..	..	7 19	7 28	..	..	..	..	7 32	..	..	..	7 39	..	..	..	7 49	..	..	..	..	..	..	..	..	7 59
Leatherhead	..	7 3	7 11	7 15	..	..	..	..	7 23	7 32	..	..	..	..	7 38	..	..	..	7 43	..	..	..	7 53	..	..	..	..	..	..	..	..	8 3
Boxhill & Burford Bdg D	..	7 8	..	7 20	..	..	..	..	..	7 37	..	..	..	..	..	..	..	..	7 48	..	..	..	..	..	..	..	..	..	..	..	..	8 8
Dorking North F	..	7 11	..	7 23	7 40	..	..	..	..	7 41	..	..	..	..	..	..	..	..	7 51	..	..	..	..	..	..	..	..	..	..	..	..	8 11
Holmwood G	..	7 23	..	7 34	7 49	..	..	..	..	..	..	..	..	..	..	..	..	..	8 2	..	..	..	..	..	..	..	..	..	..	..	..	Stop
Ockley, for Capel	..	..	..	7 38	7 53	..	..	..	..	..	..	..	..	..	..	..	..	..	8 6	..	..	..	..	..	..	..	..	..	..	..	..	..
Warnham [196, 245	..	..	..	7 44	7 59	..	..	..	..	..	..	..	..	..	..	..	..	..	8 11	..	..	..	..	..	..	..	..	..	..	..	..	..
Horsham 159, arr.	..	..	..	7 49	8 3	..	..	..	..	..	8 5	..	..	..	..	..	..	..	8 16	..	..	..	..	..	..	..	8 49	..	..	..	..	..
Bookham	..	..	7 16	..	..	..	..	..	7 28	..	..	..	..	..	7‖46	..	..	..	..	..	..	..	7 58	..	..	..	..	..	..	..	..	..
Malden, for Coombe	..	Dep Dorking North 7 14 a.m	..	..	..	6 59	7 2	..	..	..	..	7 9	..	..	..	..	7 19	7 22	..	..	7 29	..	..	..	..	..	..	7 39	..	7 41	..	..
Norbiton H	..	..	..	..	..	..	7 5	..	..	..	..	7 13	..	..	..	..	..	7 25	..	..	7 33	..	..	..	..	..	..	..	..	7 45	..	..
Kingston	..	..	..	..	..	..	7 8	..	..	..	..	7 15	..	..	..	..	..	7 28	..	..	7 35	..	..	..	..	..	..	..	..	7 47	..	..
Hampton Wick	..	..	..	..	v	..	7 10	..	..	..	..	7 17	..	..	..	..	..	7 30	..	..	7 37	..	..	..	..	..	..	..	..	7 49	..	..
Teddington J	..	..	..	..	..	..	7 13	..	..	..	..	7 21	..	..	..	..	..	7 33	..	..	7 41	..	..	..	..	..	..	..	..	7 53	..	..
Fulwell K	..	..	..	..	..	..	7 17	..	..	..	..	V	..	..	..	..	..	7 37	..	..	V	..	..	..	..	..	..	..	..	V	..	..
Hampton	..	..	..	..	..	..	7 21	..	..	..	..	To Waterloo via Richmond Arr. Twickenham 7 27 a.m	..	..	..	..	..	7 41	..	..	To Waterloo via Richmond Arr. Twickenham 7 47 a.m	..	..	..	..	..	..	..	..	To Waterloo via Richmond Arr. Twickenham 7 59 a.m	..	..
Sunbury L	..	..	..	..	..	..	7 28	..	..	..	..	..	..	..	..	..	..	7 46	..	..	..	..	..	..	..	..	..	..	..	..	..	..
Upper Halliford Halt	..	..	..	..	..	..	7 30	..	..	..	..	..	..	..	..	..	..	7 48	..	..	..	..	..	..	..	..	..	..	..	..	..	..
Shepperton M arr.	..	..	..	..	..	..	7 33	..	..	..	..	..	..	..	..	..	..	7 51	..	..	..	..	..	..	..	..	..	..	..	..	..	..
Berrylands N	..	..	..	..	..	7 2	..	..	..	..	..	..	..	..	..	..	7 22	..	..	..	..	..	..	..	..	..	..	7 42	..	..	..	..
Surbiton	6 43	..	..	..	..	7 5	..	7 4	..	..	..	..	7 8	7 13	..	..	7 25	..	..	7 28	..	..	..	..	7 34	..	..	7 45	7 38	..	7 43	..
Thames Ditton	..	..	..	..	..	7 9	..	..	..	..	..	..	..	..	..	..	7 29	..	..	..	..	..	..	..	..	..	..	7 49	..	..	..	..
Hampton Court P arr.	..	..	..	..	..	7 12	..	..	..	..	..	..	..	..	..	..	7 32	..	..	..	..	..	..	..	..	..	..	7 52	..	..	..	..
Hinchley Wood	..	..	..	..	..	..	..	..	..	..	..	..	7 11	..	..	..	Stop	..	..	7 31	..	..	..	..	..	..	..	..	..	..	..	..
Claygate, for Claremont	..	..	..	..	..	..	..	..	..	..	..	..	7 14	..	..	..	..	..	..	7 34	..	..	..	..	..	..	..	..	..	..	..	..
Oxshott, for Fairmile	..	..	..	..	..	..	..	..	..	..	..	..	7 18	..	..	..	..	..	..	7 38	..	..	..	..	..	..	..	..	..	..	..	..
Cobham Q	..	..	..	..	..	..	..	..	..	..	..	..	7 21	..	..	..	..	..	..	7 41	..	..	..	..	..	..	..	..	..	..	..	..
Effingham Junction	..	..	7 19	..	..	..	..	..	7 22	..	..	..	7 26	..	7 50	..	..	..	..	7 46	..	..	..	..	..	..	..	..	..	..	..	..
Horsley R	..	..	Stop	..	..	..	..	..	..	..	..	..	7 28	..	..	..	..	..	..	7 48	..	..	..	..	..	..	..	..	..	..	..	..
Clandon T	..	..	..	..	..	..	..	..	..	..	..	..	7 33	..	..	..	..	..	..	7 53	..	..	..	..	..	..	..	..	..	..	..	..
London Road (Guildford)	..	..	..	..	..	..	..	..	..	..	..	..	7 39	..	..	..	..	..	..	7 59	..	..	..	..	..	..	..	..	..	..	..	..
Esher, for Sandown Park	6 47	..	a.m	..	..	..	..	..	..	..	..	..	..	7 17	..	..	a.m	..	..	..	..	..	..	..	..	a.m	..	..	..	..	7 47	a.m
Hersham	6 50	..	3	..	..	..	..	..	..	..	..	..	..	7 20	..	..	3	..	..	..	..	..	..	..	..	3	..	..	..	..	7 50	3
Walton-on-Thames	6 53	..	..	..	..	..	..	7 11	..	..	..	..	..	7 23	..	..	..	..	..	..	..	..	..	..	7 41	..	..	..	..	..	7 53	..
Weybridge U	6 57	..	7 11	..	..	..	..	7 14	..	..	..	..	..	7 27	..	..	7 35	..	..	..	..	..	..	..	7 45	7 50	..	..	..	..	7 57	8 13
Addlestone	..	..	7 15	..	..	..	..	..	..	..	..	..	..	..	..	..	7 39	..	..	..	..	..	..	..	..	7 54	..	..	..	..	..	8 17
Chertsey	..	..	7 22	..	..	..	..	..	..	..	..	..	..	..	..	..	7 42	..	..	..	..	..	..	..	..	7 57	..	..	..	..	..	8 20
Virginia Water Z 460 arr	..	..	7 26	..	..	..	..	..	..	..	..	..	..	..	..	..	7 46	..	..	..	..	..	..	..	..	8 1	..	..	..	..	..	8 24
West Weybridge	7 0	..	..	..	..	..	..	7 17	..	..	..	..	..	7 30	..	..	..	..	..	..	..	..	..	..	7 49	..	..	..	..	..	8 0	..
Byfleet W	7 3	..	..	..	..	..	..	7 20	..	..	..	..	..	7 33	..	..	..	..	..	..	..	..	..	..	7 53	..	..	..	..	..	8 3	..
Woking X 324, 389, 390	7 7	..	..	..	..	..	..	7 26	..	..	..	..	..	7 37	..	..	..	..	..	..	..	..	..	..	7 59	..	..	..	7 55	..	8 7	..
Worplesdon	7 15	..	..	..	..	..	..	..	..	..	..	..	..	7 45	..	..	..	..	..	..	..	..	..	..	..	..	..	..	..	..	8 15	..
Guildford 246, 359 arr	7 21	..	..	..	..	..	..	..	..	..	..	..	7 43	7 51	..	..	..	..	..	8 3	..	..	..	..	..	..	..	..	..	..	8 21	..

LONDON, DORKING NORTH, HORSHAM, KINGSTON, SHEPPERTON, HAMPTON COURT, CHERTSEY, WOKING, & GUILDFORD

Down	a.m															Week Days—continued														a.m		
Waterloo dep.	7 29	7 32	7 34	3	7 36	7 39	7 41	7 45	7 47		7 52	..	7 52	3	7 55	7 56	7 59	8 1	8 7	3	3	3	8 9	8 12	SX 8 13	..	8 16	8 19	..	8 23	8 25	..
Vauxhall	7 32	3	3	..	7 39	7 42	7 44	..	..		3	..	7 55	..	..	7 59	8 2	8 4	..	..	..	..	8 12	3	3	..	8 19	8 22	..	..	..	..
Clapham Junction **A**	7 36			..	7 44	7 46	7 49	..	..			..	7 59	..	..	8 4	8 6	8 9	..	..	..	..	8 16			..	8 24	8 26	..	8 30	..	..
Earlsfield **B**	7 40	..	..	..	7 47	7 50	7 52	..	..		..	..	8 3	..	..	8 7	8 10	8 12	..	..	..	..	8 20	..	..	..	8 27	8 30	..	..	..	..
Wimbledon	7 43	..	7 46	..	7 51	7 53	7 56	..	7 58	Via Three Bridges, see page 160	..	8 4	8 6	..	8 6	8 11	8 13	8 16	8 18	..	..	..	8 23	..	..	..	8 31	8 33	..	8 36	8 36	Via Three Bridges see page 160
Raynes Park	7 46	..	7 49	..	7 54	7 56	7 59	..	..		..	..	8 9	..	..	8 14	8 16	8 19	8 21	..	..	..	8 26	..	..	..	8 34	8 36	..	8 39	..	
Motspur Park	3	..	7 51	..	7 56	..	..	..	8 4		..	Mondays only	8 12	..	..	8 16	..	..	8 24	..	..	..	..	..	..	..	8 36	..	..	..	..	
Malden Manor		..	..	..	8 0	3	3	..	3		..		3	..	..	8 20	3	3	3	..	..	..	3	..	..	..	8 40	3	..	3	..	
Tolworth		..	..	..	8 2			..			..			..	..	8 22				..	..	..		..	..	..	8 42		..		..	
Chessington North	..	..	..	..	8 5	..	..	..	..		..		..	..	..	8 25	..	..	..	..	..	..	..	..	..	..	8 45	..	..	..	..	
Chessington South ¶ ar	..	..	..	..	8 7	..	..	..	..		..		..	..	..	8 27	..	..	..	..	..	..	..	..	..	..	8 47	..	..	..	..	
Worcester Park	..	..	..	..	3	..	..	..	8 6		..		8 14	..	..	3	..	..	8 26	..	..	..	..	..	8 32	..	3	..	..	..	..	
Stoneleigh	..	..	..	..		..	..	..	8 9		..		8 17	..	..		..	..	8 29	..	..	..	..	..	..	..		..	..	..	..	
Ewell West **C**	..	..	..	..	..	..	..	..	8 12		..		8 20	..	..	Stop	..	..	8 32	..	..	..	..	..	..	..	..	..	..	..	..	
London Bridge dep.	..	..	..	7 28	..	..	..	..	..	..	..	..	..	7 48	..		..	..	..	8 10	..	8 8	..	..	..	..	..	..	..	..	..	8 18
Victoria "	..	..	..	..	..	..	..	..	7‡38	7 47	..	..	..	..	..		..	..	7‡56	8* 7	..	8‡7	..	..	..	..	..	..	..	..	..	8 28
Sutton "	..	..	..	7 55	..	..	..	..	8‡1	..	..	..	..	8 15	..	..	..	..	8‡21	8 38	..	8 35	..	..	..	..	..	..	..	..	..	..
Epsom 285	..	..	8 0	8 4	..	..	..	..	8 15	..	..	..	8 23	8 26	..	..	..	..	8 35	8 44	..	8 49	..	..	..	..	..	..	..	..	..	..
Ashtead	..	..	8 4	8 8	..	..	..	..	8 19	..	..	..	8 27	8 30	..	..	..	..	8 39	8 48	..	8 53	..	..	..	..	..	..	..	..	..	..
Leatherhead	..	..	8 8	8 12	..	..	..	..	8 23	..	..	..	8 31	8 34	..	..	..	..	8 43	8 52	..	8 58	..	..	..	..	..	..	..	..	..	..
Boxhill & Burford Bdg **D**	..	..	..	8 17	..	..	..	..	8 28	..	..	..	..	8 39	..	..	..	..	8 48	..	..	..	..	..	..	..	..	..	..	..	..	..
Dorking North F	..	..	..	8 20	..	..	..	..	8 31	..	..	..	..	8 42	..	..	..	..	8 51	8 58	9 1	..	..	..	..	..	..	..	..	..	..	..
Holmwood **G**	..	..	..	8 30	..	..	..	..	..	..	..	..	..	..	..	..	..	..	..	..	9 9	..	..	..	..	..	..	..	..	..	..	..
Ockley, for Capel	..	..	..	8 34	..	..	..	..	..	..	..	..	..	..	..	..	..	..	..	..	9 13	..	..	..	..	..	..	..	..	..	..	..
Warnham ... 198, 245	..	..	..	8 40	..	..	..	..	..	..	..	..	..	..	..	..	..	..	..	..	9 19	..	..	..	..	..	..	..	..	..	..	..
Horsham 159. arr.	..	..	..	8 44	..	..	..	..	..	9 5	..	..	..	..	..	..	..	..	..	..	9 24	..	..	..	..	..	..	..	..	..	..	9 35
Bookham	..	..	8 12	..	..	..	..	..	..	..	..	..	8 36	..	..	..	..	..	..	..	..	9 3	..	..	..	..	..	..	..	..	..	Stop
Malden, for Coombe	7 49	..	..	..	..	7 59	8 2	..	..	..	..	..	..	..	..	..	8 19	8 22	..	..	..	..	8 29	..	..	..	..	8 39	..	8 42	..	..
Norbiton **H**	7 53	..	..	..	..	..	8 5	..	..	..	..	..	..	..	..	..	..	8 25	..	..	..	..	8 33	..	..	..	..	..	..	8 45	..	..
Kingston	7 55	..	..	..	..	..	8 8	..	..	..	..	..	..	..	..	..	..	8 28	..	..	..	..	8 35	..	..	..	..	..	..	8 48	..	..
Hampton Wick	7 57	..	..	..	..	..	8 10	..	..	..	..	..	..	..	..	..	..	8 30	..	..	..	..	8 37	..	..	..	..	..	..	8 50	..	..
Teddington J	8 1	..	..	..	..	..	8 13	..	..	..	..	..	..	..	..	..	..	8b33	..	..	..	..	8 41	..	..	..	..	..	..	8 53	..	..
Fulwell **K**	8 5	..	..	..	..	..	V	..	..	..	..	..	..	..	..	..	..	8b37	..	..	..	..	V	..	..	..	..	..	..	V	..	..
Hampton	8 9	..	..	..	..	..	To Waterloo via Richmond Arr. **Twickenham** 8 19 a.m	..	..	..	..	..	..	..	..	..	..	8b41	..	..	..	..	To Waterloo via Richmond Arr. **Twickenham** 8 47 a.m	..	..	..	..	..	..	To Waterloo via Richmond Arr. **Twickenham** 8 59 a.m	..	..
Sunbury **L**	8 14	..	..	..	..	..		..	..	..	..	..	..	..	..	..	..	8b45	..	..	..	..		..	..	..	..	..	..		..	..
Upper Halliford Halt	8 16	..	..	..	..	..		..	..	..	..	..	..	..	..	..	..	8b47	..	..	..	..		..	..	..	..	..	..		..	..
Shepperton M arr.	8 19	..	..	..	..	..		..	..	..	..	..	..	..	..	..	..	8b50	..	..	..	..		..	..	..	..	..	..		..	..
Berrylands **N**	..	..	..	..	..	8 2		..	..	..	..	..	..	..	..	..	8 22	..	..	..	..	..		..	..	..	..	8 42	..		..	..
Surbiton	..	7 49	..	..	..	8 5		..	..	..	8 8	8 11	..	..	8 13	..	8 25	..	..	..	..	..		8 28	..	..	..	8 45	..		8 43	..
Thames Ditton	..	..	..	..	..	8 9		..	..	..	..	..	..	..	..	..	8 29	..	..	..	..	..		..	..	..	..	8 49	..		..	..
Hampton Court P arr.	..	..	..	..	..	8 12		..	..	..	..	..	..	..	..	..	8 32	..	..	..	..	..		..	..	..	..	8 52	..		..	..
Hinchley Wood	..	7 52	..	..	..	..		..	..	..	8 11	..	..	..	..	..	..	..	..	..	..	..		8 31	..	..	..	..	..		..	..
Claygate, for Claremont	..	7 55	..	..	..	..		..	..	..	8 14	..	..	..	..	..	..	..	..	..	..	..		8 34	..	..	..	..	..		..	..
Oxshott, for Fairmile	..	7 59	..	..	..	..		..	..	..	8 18	..	..	..	..	..	..	..	..	..	..	..		8 38	..	..	..	..	..		..	..
Cobham **Q**	..	8 2	..	..	..	..		..	..	..	8 21	..	..	..	..	..	..	..	..	..	..	..		8 44	..	..	..	..	..		..	..
Effingham Junction	..	8 7	8 16	..	..	..		..	..	..	8 27	..	8 40	..	..	..	..	..	..	..	..	..		8 49	..	..	..	..	..		..	..
Horsley **R**	..	8 9	..	..	..	..		..	..	..	8 30	..	8 43	..	..	..	..	..	..	..	..	..		8 52	..	..	..	..	..		..	..
Clandon **T**	..	8 14	..	..	..	..		..	..	..	8 35	..	8 48	..	..	..	..	..	..	..	..	..		8 57	..	..	..	..	..		..	..
London Road (Guildford)	..	8 20	..	..	..	..		..	..	..	8 40	..	8 53	..	..	..	..	..	..	..	..	..		9 2	..	..	..	..	..		..	..
Esher, for Sandown Park	..	..	..	..	..	..	..	..	..	..	..	..	..	..	8 17	a.m	..	..	..	..	..	..	..	..	..	..	..	..	..	..	8 47	a.m
Hersham	..	..	..	..	..	..	..	..	..	..	..	..	..	..	8 20	3	..	..	..	..	..	..	..	..	..	..	..	..	..	..	8 50	3
Walton-on-Thames	..	..	..	..	..	..	..	..	..	..	..	8 19	..	..	8 23		..	..	..	..	..	..	..	..	..	..	..	..	..	..	8 53	
Weybridge U	..	..	..	..	..	..	..	..	..	..	..	8 23	..	..	8 27	8 35	..	..	..	..	..	..	..	..	..	..	..	..	..	..	8 57	9 1
Addlestone	..	..	..	..	..	..	..	..	..	..	..	..	..	..	..	8 39	..	..	..	..	..	..	..	..	..	..	..	..	..	..	..	9 5
Chertsey	..	..	..	..	..	..	..	..	..	..	..	..	..	..	..	8 42	..	..	..	..	..	..	..	..	..	..	..	..	..	..	..	9 8
Virginia Water Z 460 arr	..	..	..	..	..	..	..	..	..	..	..	..	..	..	..	8 46	..	..	..	..	..	..	..	..	..	..	..	..	..	..	..	9 12
West Weybridge	..	..	..	..	..	..	..	..	..	..	..	8 26	..	..	8 30	..	..	..	..	..	..	..	..	..	..	..	..	..	..	..	9 0	..
Byfleet **W**	..	..	..	..	..	..	..	..	..	..	..	8 29	..	..	8 33	..	..	..	..	..	..	..	..	..	..	..	..	..	..	..	9 3	..
Woking X 324, 389, 390	..	..	..	..	..	..	..	8 15	..	..	..	8 33	..	..	8 37	..	..	..	..	..	..	..	..	..	..	..	..	..	..	..	9 7	..
Worplesdon	..	..	..	..	..	..	..	..	..	..	..	..	..	..	8 45	..	..	..	..	..	..	..	..	..	..	..	..	..	..	..	9 15	..
Guildford 246, 359 ... arr.	..	8 24	..	..	..	..	..	8 25	..	..	8 44	..	8 57	..	8 51	..	..	..	..	..	..	..	..	9 6	..	..	..	..	..	..	9 21	..

FOR NOTES, SEE PAGE 426

FOR NOTES, SEE PAGE 426

LONDON, DORKING NORTH, HORSHAM, KINGSTON, SHEPPERTON, HAMPTON COURT, CHERTSEY, WOKING, & GUILDFORD

Week Days—*continued*

Down (a.m)							SX		SX		SX	SX		SO		
Waterloo ....dep.	8 27	8 29	8 30	8 32	(3)	(3)	8 34	8 36	8 37	8 39	8 40	8 41	8 45	8 47	8 47	..
Vauxhall	..	8 32	..	(3)	..	..	8 37	8 39	..	8 42	..	8 44	..	..	(3)	..
Clapham Junction A	..	8 36	..	..	..	..	8 41	8 44	..	8 46	..	8 49	..	..	..	..
Earlsfield **B**	..	8 40	..	..	..	..	8 45	8 47	..	8 50	..	8 52	..	..	..	..
Wimbledon	8 38	8 43	..	..	..	..	8 48	8 51	..	8 53	..	8 56	..	..	8 58	..
Raynes Park	..	8 46	..	..	..	..	8 51	8 54	..	8 56	..	8 59	..	..	..	..
Motspur Park	8 44	..	..	..	..	..	..	8 56	..	..	..	..	..	..	9 4	..
Malden Manor	(3)	(3)	..	..	..	..	(3)	9 0	..	(3)	..	(3)	..	..	..	..
Tolworth	..	..	..	..	..	..	..	9 2	..	..	..	..	..	..	..	..
Chessington North	..	..	..	..	..	..	..	9 5	..	..	..	..	..	..	..	..
Chessington South ¶arr.	..	..	..	..	..	..	..	9 7	..	..	..	..	..	..	..	..
Worcester Park	8 46	..	..	..	..	..	..	(3)	..	..	..	..	..	..	9 6	..
Stoneleigh	8 49	..	..	..	..	..	..	..	..	..	..	..	..	..	9 9	..
Ewell West **C**	8 52	..	..	..	..	..	..	..	..	..	..	..	..	..	9 12	..
London Bridge ....dep.	..	..	..	..	..	8 28	..	..	..	..	..	..	..	..	..	..
Victoria "	..	..	..	..	..	..	..	..	..	..	..	..	..	..	8‡36	..
Sutton "	..	..	..	..	..	8 55	..	..	..	..	..	..	..	..	9‡1	..
Epsom 285	8 55	..	..	..	..	9 5	..	..	..	..	..	..	..	..	9 15	..
Ashtead	8 59	..	..	..	..	9 9	..	..	..	..	..	..	..	..	9 19	..
Leatherhead	9 3	..	..	..	9 9	9 13	..	..	..	..	..	..	..	..	9 23	..
Boxhill & Burford Bdg **D**	9 8	..	..	..	..	9 18	..	..	..	..	..	..	..	..	..	..
Dorking North F	9 11	..	..	..	..	9 21	..	..	..	..	..	..	..	..	..	..
Holmwood **G**	..	..	..	..	..	9 32	..	..	..	..	..	..	..	..	..	..
Ockley, for Capel	..	..	..	..	..	9 36	..	..	..	..	..	..	..	..	..	..
Warnham...[**196**, 245	..	..	..	..	..	9 42	..	..	..	..	..	..	..	..	..	..
Horsham 159, arr.	..	..	..	..	..	9 46	..	..	..	..	..	..	..	..	..	..
Bookham	..	..	..	..	9 14	..	..	..	..	..	..	..	..	..	9 29	..
Malden, for Coombe	..	8 49	..	..	..	..	8 54	..	..	8 59	..	9 2	..	..	..	..
Norbiton **H**	..	8 53	..	..	..	..	8 58	..	..	..	..	9 5	..	..	..	..
Kingston	..	8 55	..	..	..	..	9 0	..	..	..	..	9 8	..	..	..	..
Hampton Wick	..	8 57	..	..	..	..	9 2	..	..	..	..	9 10	..	..	..	..
Teddington J	..	9 1	..	..	..	..	9 6	..	..	..	..	9 13	..	..	..	..
Fulwell **K**	..	9 5	..	..	..	..	To Strawberry Hill (arr. 9 9 a.m)	..	..	..	..	V To Waterloo via Richmond Arr. Twickenham 9 24 a.m	..	..	..	..
Hampton	..	9 9	..	..	..	..		..	..	..	..		..	..	..	..
Sunbury **L**	..	9 13	..	..	..	..		..	..	..	..		..	..	..	..
Upper Halliford Halt	..	9 15	..	..	..	..		..	..	..	..		..	..	..	..
Shepperton M ......arr.	..	9 18	..	..	..	..		..	..	..	..		..	..	..	..
Berrylands **N**	..	..	..	..	..	..		..	..	9 2	..		..	..	..	..
Surbiton	..	..	8 48	8 50	..	..		..	8 55	9 5	..		..	9 5	..	..
Thames Ditton	..	..	..	..	..	..		..	..	9 9	..		..	..	..	..
Hampton Court P arr.	..	..	..	..	..	..		..	..	9 12	..		..	..	..	..
Hinchley Wood	..	..	..	8 53	..	..	..	..	..	..	..	..	..	..	..	..
Claygate, for Claremont	..	..	..	8 56	..	..	..	..	..	..	..	..	..	..	..	..
Oxshott, for Fairmile	..	..	..	9 0	..	..	..	..	..	..	..	..	..	..	..	..
Cobham **Q**	..	..	..	9 3	..	..	..	..	..	..	..	..	..	..	..	..
Effingham Junction	..	..	..	9 9	9 18	..	..	..	..	..	..	..	..	..	9 32	..
Horsley **R**	..	..	..	9 11	..	..	..	..	..	..	..	..	..	..	..	..
Clandon **T**	..	..	..	9 16	..	..	..	..	..	..	..	..	..	..	..	..
London Road (Guildford)	..	..	..	9 22	..	..	..	..	..	..	..	..	..	..	..	..
Esher, for Sandown Park	..	..	..	..	..	..	..	..	8 59	..	..	..	..	..	..	..
Hersham	..	..	..	..	..	..	..	..	9 2	..	..	..	..	..	..	..
Walton-on-Thames	..	..	..	..	..	..	..	..	9 5	..	..	..	..	..	..	..
Weybridge U	..	..	..	..	..	..	..	..	9 9	..	..	..	..	9 14	..	..
Addlestone	..	..	..	..	..	..	..	..	..	..	..	..	..	..	..	..
Chertsey	..	..	..	..	..	..	..	..	..	..	..	..	..	..	..	..
Virginia Water Z 460 arr	..	..	..	..	..	..	..	..	..	..	..	..	..	..	..	..
West Weybridge	..	..	..	..	..	..	..	..	9 12	..	..	..	..	..	..	..
Byfleet **W**	..	..	..	..	..	..	..	..	9 15	..	..	..	..	..	..	..
Woking X 324, 389, 390	..	..	9 5	..	..	..	..	..	9 19	..	9 13	..	9 15	9 21	..	..
Worplesdon	..	..	..	..	..	..	..	..	..	..	..	..	..	..	..	..
Guildford 246, 359 ..arr.	..	..	..	9 26	..	..	..	..	..	..	..	..	9 25	..	..	..

Down (a.m)															SX
Waterloo ....dep.	(3)	8 49	8 52	8 56	8 57	8 59	9 0	9 1	9 7	9 9	9 12	(3)	9 14	..	9 16
Vauxhall	..	8 52	(3)	8 59	..	9 2	..	9 4	(3)	9 12	(3)	..	9 17	..	9 19
Clapham Junction A	..	8 56	..	9 4	..	9 6	..	9 9	..	9 16	..	..	9 21	..	9 24
Earlsfield **B**	..	9 0	..	9 7	..	9 10	..	9 12	..	9 20	..	..	9 25	..	9 27
Wimbledon	..	9 3	..	9 11	..	9 13	..	9 16	9 18	9 23	..	..	9 28	..	9 31
Raynes Park	..	9 6	..	9 14	..	9 16	..	9 19	..	9 26	..	..	9 31	..	9 34
Motspur Park	..	..	..	9 16	..	..	..	..	9 23	..	..	..	..	..	9 36
Malden Manor	..	(3)	..	9 20	..	(3)	..	(3)	..	(3)	..	..	(3)	..	9 40
Tolworth	..	..	..	9 22	..	..	..	..	..	..	..	..	..	..	9 42
Chessington North	..	..	..	9 25	..	..	..	..	..	..	..	..	..	..	9 45
Chessington South ¶arr.	..	..	..	9 27	..	..	..	..	..	..	..	..	..	..	9 47
Worcester Park	..	..	..	(3)	..	..	..	..	9 26	..	..	..	..	..	(3)
Stoneleigh	..	..	..	..	..	..	..	..	9 29	..	..	..	..	..	..
Ewell West **C**	..	..	..	..	..	..	..	..	9 31	..	..	..	..	..	..
London Bridge ....dep.	8 48	..	..	..	..	..	..	..	..	..	..	9 8	..	..	..
Victoria "	..	..	..	..	..	..	..	..	8‡55	..	..	9‡8	..	..	..
Sutton "	9 15	..	..	..	..	..	..	..	9‡21	..	..	9 35	..	..	..
Epsom 285	9 25	..	..	..	..	..	..	..	9 35	..	..	9 45	..	..	..
Ashtead	9 29	..	..	..	..	..	..	..	9 39	..	..	9 49	..	..	..
Leatherhead	9 33	..	..	..	..	..	..	..	9 43	..	..	9 53	..	..	..
Boxhill & Burford Bdg **D**	9 38	..	..	..	..	..	..	..	9 48	..	..	..	..	..	..
Dorking North F	9 41	..	..	..	..	..	..	..	9 51	..	..	..	..	..	..
Holmwood **G**	Stop	..	..	..	..	..	..	..	10 2	..	..	..	..	..	..
Ockley, for Capel	..	..	..	..	..	..	..	..	10 7	..	..	..	..	..	..
Warnham...[**196**, 245	..	..	..	..	..	..	..	..	1016	..	..	..	..	..	..
Horsham 159, arr.	..	..	..	..	..	..	..	..	1020	..	..	..	..	..	..
Bookham	..	..	..	..	..	..	..	..	..	..	..	9 57	..	..	..
Malden, for Coombe	..	9 9	..	..	..	9 19	..	9 22	..	9 29	..	..	9 34	..	..
Norbiton **H**	..	9 13	..	..	..	..	..	9 25	..	9 33	..	..	9 38	..	..
Kingston	..	9 15	..	..	..	..	..	9 28	..	9 35	..	..	9 40	..	..
Hampton Wick	..	9 17	..	..	..	..	..	9 30	..	9 37	..	..	9 42	..	..
Teddington J	..	9 21	..	..	..	..	..	9 33	..	9 41	..	..	9 46	..	..
Fulwell **K**	..	V To Waterloo via Richmond Arr. Twickenham 9 28 a.m	..	..	..	..	..	9 37	..	V To Waterloo via Richmond Arr. Twickenham 9 47 a.m	..	..	To Strawberry Hill (arr. 9 49 a.m)	..	..
Hampton	..		..	..	..	..	..	9 41	..		..	..		..	..
Sunbury **L**	..		..	..	..	..	..	9 45	..		..	..		..	..
Upper Halliford Halt	..		..	..	..	..	..	9 47	..		..	..		..	..
Shepperton M ......arr.	..		..	..	..	..	..	9 50	..		..	..		..	..
Berrylands **N**	..		..	..	..	9 22	..	..	..		..	..		..	..
Surbiton	..		9 8	..	9 13	9 25	9U17	..	..		9 29	..		..	..
Thames Ditton	..		..	..	..	9 29	..	..	..		..	..		..	..
Hampton Court P arr.	..		..	..	..	9 32	..	..	..		..	..		..	..
Hinchley Wood	..	..	9 11	..	..	Stop	..	..	..	..	9 32	..	..	..	..
Claygate, for Claremont	..	..	9 14	..	..	..	..	..	..	..	9 35	..	..	..	..
Oxshott, for Fairmile	..	..	9 18	..	..	..	..	..	..	..	9 39	..	..	..	..
Cobham **Q**	..	..	9 21	..	..	..	..	..	..	..	9 42	..	..	..	..
Effingham Junction	..	..	9 27	..	..	..	..	..	..	..	9 48	10 1	..	..	..
Horsley **R**	..	..	9 29	..	..	..	..	..	..	..	9 50	..	..	..	..
Clandon **T**	..	..	9 34	..	..	..	..	..	..	..	9 55	..	..	..	..
London Road (Guildford)	..	..	9 40	..	..	..	..	..	..	..	10 1	..	..	..	..
Esher, for Sandown Park	a.m	..	..	..	9 17	a.m	..	..	..	..	..	..	..	..	..
Hersham	(3)	..	..	..	9 20	(3)	..	..	..	..	..	..	..	..	..
Walton-on-Thames	..	..	..	..	9 23	..	..	..	..	..	..	..	..	..	..
Weybridge U	9 20	..	..	..	9 27	9 35	..	..	..	..	..	..	..	..	..
Addlestone	9 24	..	..	..	..	9 39	..	..	..	..	..	..	..	..	..
Chertsey	9 27	..	..	..	..	9 42	..	..	..	..	..	..	..	..	..
Virginia Water Z 460 arr	9 31	..	..	..	..	9 46	..	..	..	..	..	..	..	..	..
West Weybridge	..	..	..	..	9 30	..	..	..	..	..	..	..	..	..	..
Byfleet **W**	..	..	..	..	9 33	..	..	..	..	..	..	..	..	..	..
Woking X 324, 389, 390	..	..	..	..	9 37	..	9 34	..	..	..	..	..	..	..	..
Worplesdon	..	..	..	..	9 45	..	..	..	..	..	..	..	..	..	..
Guildford 246, 359 ..arr.	..	..	9 44	..	9 51	..	..	..	..	..	10 5	..	..	..	..

LONDON, DORKING NORTH, HORSHAM, KINGSTON, SHEPPERTON, HAMPTON COURT, CHERTSEY, WOKING, & GUILDFORD

Week Days—*continued* — a.m

Down					SX							SO			
Waterloo dep.	..	9 19	9 21	9 27	9 27	3	9 29	9 30	9 32	9 36	9 39	9 41	9 45	9 47	..
Vauxhall	..	9 22	9 24	..	3	..	9 32	..	3	9 39	9 42	9 44	..	3	..
Clapham Junction A	..	9 26	9 29	..	..	..	9 36	..	..	9 44	9 46	9 49	..	..	..
Earlsfield **B**	..	9 30	9 32	..	..	..	9 40	..	..	9 47	9 50	9 52	..	..	..
Wimbledon	..	9 33	9 36	..	9 38	..	9 43	..	..	9 51	9 53	9 56	..	9 58	..
Raynes Park	..	9 36	9 39	..	..	..	9 46	..	..	9 54	9 56	9 59	..	..	..
Motspur Park	Via Three Bridges, see page 162			..	9 44	..		..	..	9 56			..	10 3	..
Malden Manor		3	3	..	..	..	3	..	..	10 0	3	3	..	..	..
Tolworth		..	..	..	..	..	..	..	..	10 2	..	..	..	..	..
Chessington North		..	..	..	..	..	..	..	..	10 5	..	..	..	..	..
Chessington South ¶ ar		..	..	..	..	..	..	..	..	10 7	..	..	..	..	..
Worcester Park		..	..	..	9 46	..	..	..	..	3	..	..	..	10 6	..
Stoneleigh		..	..	..	9 49	..	..	..	..	..	..	..	..	10 9	..
Ewell West **C**		..	..	..	9 52	..	..	..	..	..	..	..	..	10 11	..
London Bridge dep.	9 0	..	..	..	..	9 28	..	..	..	..	..	..	..	..	..
Victoria "	9 18	..	..	..	..	..	..	..	..	..	..	..	..	9‡37	..
Sutton "	..	..	..	..	..	9 55	..	..	..	..	..	..	..	10‡ 1	..
Epsom **285**	..	..	..	..	9 55	10 5	..	..	..	..	..	..	..	10 15	..
Ashtead	..	..	..	..	9 59	10 9	..	..	..	..	..	..	..	10 19	..
Leatherhead	..	..	..	..	10 3	1013	..	..	..	..	..	..	..	10 23	..
Boxhill & Burford Bdg **D**	..	..	..	..	10 8	1018	..	..	..	..	..	..	..	..	..
Dorking North F	..	..	..	..	1011	1021	..	..	..	..	..	..	..	..	..
Holmwood **G**	..	..	..	..	..	1032	..	..	..	..	..	..	..	..	..
Ockley, for Capel	..	..	..	..	..	1036	..	..	..	..	..	..	..	..	..
Warnham [**196, 245**	..	..	..	..	..	1042	..	..	..	..	..	..	..	..	..
Horsham 159, arr.	1013	..	..	..	..	1046	..	..	..	..	..	..	..	..	..
Bookham	..	..	..	..	..	Stop	..	..	..	..	..	..	..	10 29	..
Malden, for Coombe	..	9 39	9 42	..	..	..	9 49	..	..	..	9 59	10 2	..	..	..
Norbiton **H**	..	..	9 45	..	..	..	9 53	..	..	..	..	10 5	..	..	..
Kingston	..	..	9 48	..	..	..	9 55	..	..	..	..	10 8	..	..	..
Hampton Wick	..	..	9 50	..	..	..	9 57	..	..	..	..	1010	..	..	..
Teddington J	..	..	9 53	..	..	..	10 1	..	..	..	..	1013	..	..	..
Fulwell **K**	..	..	V	..	..	..	10 5	..	..	..	..	V	..	..	..
Hampton	..	..	To Waterloo via Richmond Arr. **Twickenham** 9 59 a.m.	..	..	..	10 9	..	..	..	..	To Waterloo via Richmond Arr. **Twickenham** 10 19 a.m.	..	..	..
Sunbury **L**	..	..		..	..	..	1013	..	..	..	..		..	..	..
Upper Halliford Halt	..	..		..	..	..	1015	..	..	..	..		..	..	..
Shepperton M arr.	..	..		..	..	..	1018	..	..	..	..		..	..	..
Berrylands **N**	..	9 42		..	..	..	..	..	..	..	10 2		..	..	..
Surbiton	..	9 45		9 43	..	..	..	9U48	9 50	..	10 5		..	..	..
Thames Ditton	..	9 49		..	..	..	..	..	..	..	10 9		..	..	..
Hampton Court P arr.	..	9 52		..	..	..	..	..	..	..	1012		..	..	..
Hinchley Wood	..	..		..	..	..	..	..	9 53	..	..		..	..	..
Claygate, for Claremont	..	..		..	..	..	..	..	9 56	..	..		..	..	..
Oxshott, for Fairmile	..	..		..	..	..	..	..	10 0	..	..		..	..	..
Cobham **Q**	..	..		..	..	..	..	..	10 3	..	..		..	..	..
Effingham Junction	..	..		..	..	..	..	..	10 9	..	..		..	10 32	..
Horsley **R**	..	..		..	..	..	..	..	1011	..	..		..	..	..
Clandon **T**	..	..		..	..	..	..	..	1016	..	..		..	..	..
London Road (Guildford)	..	..		..	..	..	..	..	1022	..	..		..	..	..
Esher, for Sandown Park	..	..		9 47	..	a.m	..	..	..	..	..		..	..	..
Hersham	..	..	..	9 50	..	3	..	..	..	..	..	..	..	..	..
Walton-on-Thames	..	..	..	9 53	..	..	..	..	..	..	..	..	..	..	..
Weybridge U	..	..	..	9 57	..	10 5	..	..	..	..	..	..	..	..	..
Addlestone	..	..	..	..	..	10 9	..	..	..	..	..	..	..	..	..
Chertsey	..	..	..	..	..	1012	..	..	..	..	..	..	..	..	..
Virginia Water Z 460 arr.	..	..	..	..	..	1016	..	..	..	..	..	..	..	..	..
West Weybridge	..	..	..	10 0	..	..	..	..	..	..	..	..	..	..	..
Byfleet **W**	..	..	..	10 3	..	..	..	..	..	..	..	..	..	..	..
Woking X 324, 389, 390	..	..	..	10 7	..	..	..	10 5	..	..	..	..	1015	..	..
Worplesdon	..	..	..	1015	..	..	..	..	..	..	..	..	..	..	..
Guildford 246, 359 arr.	..	..	..	1021	..	..	..	..	1026	..	..	..	1025	..	..

Down														SO	
Waterloo dep.	3	9 49	9 52	..	9 56	9 57	9 59	10 1	10 7	10 9	10 12	3	1016	1019	1021
Vauxhall	..	9 52	3	..	9 59	..	10 2	10 4	..	1012	..	..	1019	1022	1024
Clapham Junction A	..	9 56	..	..	10 4	..	10 6	10 9	..	1016	..	..	1024	1026	1029
Earlsfield **B**	..	10 0	..	..	10 7	..	1010	1012	..	1020	..	..	1027	1030	1032
Wimbledon	..	10 3	10SX3	..	1011	..	1013	1016	10 18	1023	10SX23	..	1031	1033	1036
Raynes Park	..	10 6	..	..	1014	..	1016	1019	..	1026	..	..	1034	1036	1039
Motspur Park	..		..	..	1016	..			10 24			..	1036		
Malden Manor	..	3	..	..	1020	..	3	3	3	3	3	..	1040	3	3
Tolworth	..	..	..	..	1022	..	..	..	..	..	..	..	1042	..	..
Chessington North	..	..	..	..	1025	..	..	..	..	..	..	..	1045	..	..
Chessington South ¶ ar	..	..	..	..	1027	..	..	..	..	..	..	..	1047	..	..
Worcester Park	..	..	..	..	3	..	..	..	10 26	..	..	..	3	..	..
Stoneleigh	..	..	..	..	..	..	..	..	10 29	..	..	..	..	..	..
Ewell West **C**	..	..	..	..	..	..	..	..	10 32	..	..	..	..	..	..
London Bridge dep.	9 48	..	..	..	..	..	..	..	..	..	..	10 8	..	..	..
Victoria "	..	..	..	1018	..	..	..	..	9‡55	..	..	..	..	..	..
Sutton "	1015	..	..	1039	..	..	..	..	10‡21	..	..	1035	..	..	..
Epsom **285**	1025	..	..	..	..	..	..	..	10 35	..	..	1049	..	..	..
Ashtead	1029	..	..	..	..	..	..	..	10 39	..	..	1053	..	..	..
Leatherhead	1033	..	..	..	..	..	..	..	10 43	..	..	1057	..	..	..
Boxhill & Burford Bdg **D**	1038	..	..	..	..	..	..	..	10 48	..	..	..	..	..	..
Dorking North F	1041	..	..	1055	..	..	..	..	10 51	..	..	..	..	..	..
Holmwood **G**	..	..	..	..	..	..	..	..	11 9	..	..	..	..	..	..
Ockley, for Capel	..	..	..	..	..	..	..	..	11 13	..	..	..	..	..	..
Warnham [**196, 245**	..	..	..	..	..	..	..	..	11 19	..	..	..	..	..	..
Horsham 159, arr.	..	..	..	1113	..	..	..	..	11 24	..	..	..	..	..	..
Bookham	..	..	..	..	..	..	..	..	Dep Dorking North 11 1 a.m	..	..	11 1	..	..	..
Malden, for Coombe	..	10 9	..	..	..	..	1019	1022		1029	..	..	..	1039	1042
Norbiton **H**	..	1013	..	..	..	..	..	1025		1033	..	..	..	..	1045
Kingston	..	1015	..	..	..	..	..	1028		1035	..	..	..	..	1048
Hampton Wick	..	1017	..	..	..	..	..	1030		1037	..	..	..	..	1050
Teddington J	..	1021	..	..	..	..	..	1033		1041	..	..	..	..	1053
Fulwell **K**	..	V	..	..	..	..	..	1037		V	..	..	..	..	V
Hampton	..	To Waterloo via Richmond Arr. **Twickenham** 10v29 a.m.	..	..	..	..	..	1041		To Waterloo via Richmond Arr. **Twickenham** 10 47 a.m.	..	..	..	..	To Waterloo via Richmond Arr. **Twickenham** 11 0 a.m
Sunbury **L**	..		..	..	..	..	..	1045			..	..	..	..	
Upper Halliford Halt	..		..	..	..	..	..	1047			..	..	..	..	
Shepperton M arr.	..		..	..	..	..	..	1050			..	..	..	..	
Berrylands **N**	..		..	..	..	..	1022	..	..		..	..	..	1042	
Surbiton	..		10 8	..	..	1013	1025	..	..		10 28	..	..	1045	
Thames Ditton	..		..	..	..	..	1029	..	..		..	..	..	1049	
Hampton Court P arr.	..		..	..	..	..	1032	..	..		..	..	..	1052	
Hinchley Wood	..		10 11	..	..	..	Stop	..	..		10 31	..	..	..	
Claygate, for Claremont	..		10 14	..	..	..	..	..	..		10 34	..	..	..	
Oxshott, for Fairmile	..		10 18	..	..	..	..	..	..		10 38	..	..	..	
Cobham **Q**	..		10 21	..	..	..	..	..	..		10 41	..	..	..	
Effingham Junction	..		10 27	..	..	..	..	..	..		10 47	11 5	..	..	
Horsley **R**	..		10 29	..	..	..	..	..	..		10 49	..	..	..	
Clandon **T**	..		10 34	..	..	..	..	..	..		10 54	..	..	..	
London Road (Guildford)	..		10 40	..	..	..	..	..	..		11 0	..	..	..	
Esher, for Sandown Park	..		..	..	..	1017	a.m	..	..		..	..	..	..	
Hersham	..	..	..	..	..	1020	3	..	..	..	..	..	..	..	..
Walton-on-Thames	..	..	..	..	..	1023	..	..	..	..	..	..	..	..	..
Weybridge U	..	..	..	..	..	1027	1035	..	..	..	..	..	..	..	..
Addlestone	..	..	..	..	..	..	1039	..	..	..	..	..	..	..	..
Chertsey	..	..	..	..	..	..	1042	..	..	..	..	..	..	..	..
Virginia Water Z 460 arr.	..	..	..	..	..	..	1046	..	..	..	..	..	..	..	..
West Weybridge	..	..	..	..	..	1030	..	..	..	..	..	..	..	..	..
Byfleet **W**	..	..	..	..	..	1033	..	..	..	..	..	..	..	..	..
Woking X 324, 389, 390	..	..	..	..	..	1037	..	..	..	..	..	..	..	..	..
Worplesdon	..	..	..	..	..	1045	..	..	..	..	..	..	..	..	..
Guildford 246, 359 arr.	..	..	10 46	..	..	1051	..	..	..	..	11 5	..	..	..	..

FOR NOTES, SEE PAGE 426

FOR NOTES, SEE PAGE 426

LONDON, DORKING NORTH, HORSHAM, KINGSTON, SHEPPERTON, HAMPTON COURT, CHERTSEY, WOKING, & GUILDFORD

Week Days—*continued*

Down	a.m					S O	S X			S X	S O													a.m			S O			
Waterloo dep	1027	..	3	3	1029	1032	1032	1036	1039	1041	1045	1047	3	1049	10 52	3	1054	1056	1057	1059	11 1	11 7	11 9	11 12	..	3	1116	1121	..	1127
Vauxhall	..	..	..	..	1032	3	3	1039	1042	1044	..	..	..	1052	..	..	..	1059	..	11 2	11 4	..	1112	..	..	..	1119	1124	..	..
Clapham Junction **A**	..	..	..	..	1036	..	..	1044	1046	1049	..	3	..	1056	3	..	..	11 4	..	11 6	11 9	..	1116	..	..	..	1124	1129	..	..
Earlsfield **B**	..	..	..	..	1040	..	..	1047	1050	1052	..	..	..	11 0	..	..	..	11 7	..	1110	1112	..	1120	..	..	..	1127	1132	..	..
Wimbledon	..	Via Three Bridges, see page 169	..	..	1043	..	1043	1051	1053	1056	..	1058	..	11 3	11SX3	..	..	1111	..	1113	1116	1118	1123	11SX23	..	..	1131	1136	..	..
Raynes Park	..		..	..	1046	..	..	1054	1056	1059	..	..	..	11 6	..	..	..	1114	..	1116	1119	..	1126	..	..	..	1134	1139	..	..
Motspur Park	..		..	..	..	..	..	1056	..	..	..	11 4	..	..	..	..	..	1116	..	..	..	1124	..	..	..	..	1136	..	..	..
Malden Manor	..		..	..	3	..	..	11 0	3	3	..	..	..	3	..	..	..	1120	..	3	3	3	3	3	..	..	1140	3	..	..
Tolworth	..		..	..	..	..	..	11 2	..	..	..	..	..	..	..	..	..	1122	..	..	..	..	..	..	..	..	1142	..	..	..
Chessington North	..		..	..	..	..	..	11 5	..	..	..	..	..	..	..	..	..	1125	..	..	..	..	..	..	..	..	1145	..	..	..
Chessington South¶ar	..		..	..	..	..	..	11 7	..	..	..	..	..	..	..	..	..	1127	..	..	..	..	..	..	..	..	1147	..	..	..
Worcester Park	..		..	..	..	..	..	3	..	..	..	11 6	..	..	..	..	..	3	..	..	..	1126	..	..	..	..	3	..	..	..
Stoneleigh	..		..	..	..	..	..	..	..	..	..	11 9	..	..	..	..	..	..	..	..	..	1129	..	..	..	..	..	..	..	..
Ewell West **C**	..		S X	S O	..	..	..	..	..	..	..	1112	S O	..	..	S X	..	..	..	..	..	1132	..	..	..	S O	..	..	..	..
London Bridge dep.	..	1016	10 27	10 28	..	..	..	..	..	..	..	..	1048	..	..	10 53	..	..	..	..	..	..	..	..	..	11 8	..	..	..	..
Victoria "	..	..	10‡24	10‡23	..	..	..	..	..	..	..	..	..	..	..	10‡51	..	..	..	..	..	10SO‡55	..	..	..	..	..	..	1118	..
Sutton "	..	..	10 55	10 55	..	..	..	..	..	..	..	..	1115	..	..	11 21	..	..	..	..	..	11SO‡21	..	..	..	1135	..	..	1139	..
Epsom 285	..	..	11 5	11 5	..	..	..	..	..	..	..	1115	1125	..	..	11 30	..	..	..	..	..	1135	..	..	..	1149	..	..	..	..
Ashtead	..	..	11 9	11 9	..	..	..	..	..	..	..	1119	1129	..	..	11 34	..	..	..	..	..	1139	..	..	..	1153	..	..	..	..
Leatherhead	..	..	11 13	11 13	..	..	..	..	..	..	..	1123	1133	..	..	11 38	..	..	..	..	..	1143	..	..	..	1157	..	..	..	..
Boxhill & Burford Bdg **D**	..	..	11 18	11 18	..	..	..	..	..	..	..	..	1138	..	..	..	..	..	..	..	..	1148	..	..	..	..	..	..	..	..
Dorking North F	..	..	11 21	11 21	..	..	..	..	..	..	..	..	1141	..	..	..	..	..	..	..	..	1151	..	..	..	..	..	..	1155	..
Holmwood **G**	..	..	11 32	11 32	..	..	..	..	..	..	..	..	..	..	..	..	..	..	..	..	..	12 9	..	..	..	..	..	..	..	..
Ockley, for Capel	..	..	11 36	11 36	..	..	..	..	..	..	..	..	..	..	..	..	..	..	..	..	..	1213	..	..	..	..	..	..	..	..
Warnham. [**196**, 245.	..	..	11 42	11 42	..	..	..	..	..	..	..	..	..	..	..	..	..	..	..	..	..	1220	..	..	..	..	..	..	..	..
Horsham 159, ... arr.	..	1125	11 46	11 46	..	..	..	..	..	..	..	..	..	..	..	..	..	..	..	..	..	1225	..	..	..	..	..	..	1213	..
Bookham	..	Stop	..	..	..	..	..	..	..	..	..	1128	..	..	..	11 43	..	..	..	..	..	..	..	..	..	12 2	..	..	..	..
Malden, for Coombe	..	..	..	..	1049	..	..	..	1059	11 2	..	..	..	11 9	..	..	..	..	..	1119	1122	Dep Dorking North 121 p.m	1129	..	..	..	..	1142	..	..
Norbiton **H**	..	..	..	..	1053	..	..	..	..	11 5	..	..	..	1113	..	..	..	..	..	..	1125		1133	..	..	..	..	1145	..	..
Kingston	..	..	..	..	1055	..	..	..	..	11 8	..	..	..	1115	..	..	..	..	..	..	1128		1135	..	..	..	..	1148	..	..
Hampton Wick	..	..	..	..	1057	..	..	..	..	1110	..	..	..	1117	..	..	..	..	..	..	1130		1137	..	..	..	..	1150	..	..
Teddington J	..	..	..	..	11 1	..	..	..	..	1113	..	..	..	1121	..	..	..	..	..	..	1133		1141	..	..	..	..	1153	..	..
Fulwell **K**	..	..	..	..	11 5	..	..	..	..	To Strawberry Hill (arr. 11 16 a.m)	..	..	..	V To Waterloo via Richmond Arr **Twickenham** 11 27 a.m	..	..	..	..	..	..	1137		V To Waterloo via Richmond Arr **Twickenham** 11 47 a.m	..	..	..	..	V To Waterloo via Richmond Arr **Twickenham** 12 0 noon	..	..
Hampton	..	..	..	..	11 9	..	..	..	..		..	..	..		..	..	..	..	..	..	1141			..	..	..	..		..	..
Sunbury **L**	..	..	..	..	1113	..	..	..	..		..	..	..		..	..	..	..	..	..	1145			..	..	..	..		..	..
Upper Halliford Halt	..	..	..	..	1115	..	..	..	..		..	..	..		..	..	..	..	..	..	1147			..	..	..	..		..	..
Shepperton M arr.	..	..	..	..	1118	..	..	..	..		..	..	..		..	..	..	..	..	..	1150			..	..	..	..		..	..
Berrylands N	..	..	..	..	..	..	..	..	11 2		..	..	..		..	..	..	..	..	1122	Stop			..	..	..	..		..	..
Surbiton	1043	..	..	..	..	1049	1050	..	11 5		..	..	..		11 8	..	..	..	1113	1125	..			11 28	..	..	..		..	1143
Thames Ditton	..	..	..	..	..	..	..	..	11 9		..	..	..		..	..	..	..	..	1129	..			..	..	..	..		..	..
Hampton Court P arr.	..	..	..	..	..	..	..	..	1112		..	..	..		..	..	..	..	..	1132	..			..	..	..	..		..	..
Hinchley Wood	..	..	..	..	..	1052	1054	..	..	..	..	..	..		11 11	..	..	..	..	Stop	..	..		11 31	..	..	..		..	..
Claygate, for Claremont	..	..	..	..	..	1055	1057	..	..	..	..	..	..		11 14	..	..	..	..	..	..	..		11 34	..	..	..		..	..
Oxshott, for Fairmile	..	..	..	..	..	1059	11 0	..	..	..	..	..	..		11 18	..	..	..	..	..	..	..		11 38	..	..	..		..	..
Cobham **Q**	..	..	..	..	..	11 2	11 4	..	..	..	..	..	..		11 21	..	..	..	..	..	..	..		11 41	..	..	..		..	..
Effingham Junction	..	..	..	..	..	11 8	11 8	..	..	..	..	1132	..		11 26	11 46	..	..	..	..	..	..		11 46	..	..	..		..	..
Horsley **R**	..	..	..	..	..	1110	..	..	..	..	..	..	..		11 28	..	..	..	..	..	..	..		11 48	..	..	..		..	..
Clandon **T**	..	..	..	..	..	1115	..	..	..	..	..	..	..		11 33	..	..	..	..	..	..	..		11 53	..	..	..		..	..
London Road (Guildford)	..	..	..	..	..	1121	..	..	..	..	..	..	..		11 39	..	..	..	..	..	a.m	..		11 59	..	..	..		..	..
Esher, for Sandown Park	1047	a.m	..	..	..	..	..	..	..	..	..	..	..	..	..	..	..	..	1117	a.m	3	..	..	..	..	..	..	..	..	114[illegible]
Hersham	1050	3	..	..	..	..	..	..	..	..	..	..	..	..	..	..	..	..	1120	3	..	..	..	..	..	..	..	..	..	1150
Walton-on-Thames	1053		..	..	..	..	..	..	..	..	..	..	..	..	..	..	..	..	1123		S O	..	..	..	..	..	..	..	..	1153
Weybridge U	1057	11 5	..	..	..	..	..	..	..	..	..	..	..	..	..	..	..	..	1127	1135	1155	..	..	..	..	..	..	..	..	1157
Addlestone	..	11 9	..	..	..	..	..	..	..	..	..	..	..	..	..	..	..	..	..	1139	1159	..	..	..	..	..	..	..	..	..
Chertsey	..	1112	..	..	..	..	..	..	..	..	..	..	..	..	..	..	..	..	..	1142	12 5	..	..	..	..	..	..	..	..	..
Virginia Water Z 460 arr	..	1116	..	..	..	..	..	..	..	..	..	..	..	..	..	..	..	..	..	1146	1210	..	..	..	..	..	..	..	..	..
West Weybridge	11 0	..	..	..	..	..	..	..	..	..	..	..	..	..	..	..	..	..	1130	..	..	..	..	..	..	..	..	..	..	12 0
Byfleet **W**	11 3	..	..	..	..	..	..	..	..	..	..	..	..	..	..	..	..	..	1133	..	..	..	..	..	..	..	..	..	..	12 3
Woking X 324, 389, 390	11 7	..	..	..	..	..	..	..	..	..	1115	..	..	..	..	..	1125	..	1137	..	..	..	..	..	..	..	..	..	..	12 7
Worplesdon	1115	..	..	..	..	..	..	..	..	..	..	..	..	..	..	..	..	..	1145	..	..	..	..	..	..	..	..	..	..	1215
Guildford 246, 359 ... arr.	1121	..	..	..	..	1125	..	..	..	..	1125	..	..	..	11 46	..	..	..	1151	..	..	..	..	12 5	..	..	..	..	..	1221

LONDON, DORKING NORTH, HORSHAM, KINGSTON, SHEPPERTON, HAMPTON COURT, CHERTSEY, WOKING & GUILDFORD

Down	a.m. SO								SO			Week Days—continued									p.m.					SO	SO		SO
Waterloo ....dep.	1127	..	3	3	3	1129	1136	1139	1141	1145	11 47	..	3	1149	11 52	3	1156	1157	1159	12 1	12 7	12 9	12 12	3	..	1216	1217	..	1219
Vauxhall	3	Via Three Bridges see page 164	..	..	..	1132	1139	1142	1144	..	3	..	..	1152	..	..	1159	..	12 2	12 4	3	1212	..	..	..	1219	..	..	1222
Clapham Junction A	..		..	..	..	1136	1144	1146	1149	..	..	..	..	1156	..	..	12 4	..	12 6	12 9	..	1216	..	..	Via Three Bridges see page 164	1224	..	..	1226
Earlsfield B	..		..	..	..	1140	1147	1150	1152	..	..	..	..	12 0	..	..	12 7	..	1210	1212	..	1220	..	..		1227	..	Via Three Bridges see page 166	1230
Wimbledon	1138		..	..	..	1143	1151	1153	1156	..	11 58	Via Three Bridges see page 164	..	12 3	12SX3	..	1211	..	1213	1216	12 18	1223	12SX23	..		1231	..		1233
Raynes Park	..		..	..	..	1146	1154	1156	1159	..	..		..	12 6	..	..	1214	..	1216	1219	..	1226	..	..		1234	..		1236
Motspur Park	1144		..	..	..	..	1156	..	..	..	12 4		..	..	..	..	1216	..	..	..	12 24	..	..	..		1236	..		..
Malden Manor	..		..	..	..	3	12 0	3	3	..	..		..	3	3	..	1220	..	3	3	..	3	3	..		1240	..		3
Tolworth	..		..	..	..	..	12 2	..	..	..	..		..	..	..	..	1222	..	..	..	..	..	..	..		1242	..		..
Chessington North	..		..	..	..	..	12 5	..	..	..	..		..	..	..	..	1225	..	..	..	..	..	..	..		1245	..		..
Chessington South ¶ar	..		..	..	..	..	12 7	..	..	..	..		..	..	..	..	1227	..	..	..	..	..	..	..		1247	..		..
Worcester Park	1146		..	..	..	..	3	..	..	..	12 6		..	..	..	..	3	..	..	..	12 26	..	..	..		3	..		..
Stoneleigh	1149		..	..	..	..	..	..	..	..	12 9		..	..	..	..	..	..	..	..	12 29	..	..	..		..	..		..
Ewell West C	1152	..	..	SX	SO	..	..	..	..	..	12 12		SO	..	..	SX	..	..	..	..	12 32	..	..	SO	SO	..	..		..
London Bridge ....dep.	..	1118	..	11 25	1128	..	..	..	..	..	..	..	11 48	..	..	11 53	..	..	..	..	..	..	..	12 8	..	..	..	12J18	..
Victoria "	..	..	..	11‡24	..	..	..	..	..	..	11SO‡36	1148	..	..	..	11‡51	..	..	..	..	11b‡51	..	..	11‡55	1218	..	..	..	..
Sutton "	..	..	..	11 56	1155	..	..	..	..	..	12SO10	..	12 15	..	..	12 20	..	..	..	..	12z‡20	..	..	12 35	..	..	..	..	..
Epsom 285	1155	..	p.m	12 5	12 5	..	..	..	..	..	12 15	..	12 25	..	..	12 29	..	..	..	..	12 35	..	..	12 45	..	..	..	..	..
Ashtead	1159	..	SO	12 9	12 9	..	..	..	..	..	12 19	..	12 29	..	..	12 33	..	..	..	..	12 39	..	..	12 49	..	..	..	..	..
Leatherhead	12 3	..	12 9	12 13	1213	..	..	..	..	..	12 23	..	12 33	..	..	12 37	..	..	..	..	12 43	..	..	12 53	..	..	..	..	..
Boxhill & Burford Bdg D	12 8	..	..	12 18	1218	..	..	..	..	..	..	..	12 38	..	..	..	..	..	..	..	12 48	..	..	..	..	..	..	..	..
Dorking North F	1211	..	..	12 21	1221	..	..	..	..	..	..	..	12 41	..	..	..	..	..	..	..	12 51	..	..	..	..	..	..	..	..
Holmwood G	1221	..	..	12 32	1232	..	..	..	..	..	..	..	12 51	..	..	..	..	..	..	..	1 9	..	..	..	..	..	..	..	..
Ockley, for Capel	Stop	..	..	12 36	1236	..	..	..	..	..	..	..	12 55	..	..	..	..	..	..	..	1 13	..	..	..	..	..	..	..	..
Warnham 245	..	..	..	12 42	1242	..	..	..	..	..	..	..	1 3	..	..	..	..	..	..	..	1 19	..	..	..	..	..	..	..	..
Horsham 159, 196, ar.	..	1235	..	12 46	1246	..	..	..	..	..	..	1 5	1 7	..	..	..	..	..	..	..	1 24	..	..	..	1 13	..	..	1 35	..
Bookham	..	..	1213	Stop	Stop	..	..	..	..	..	12 27	..	..	..	..	12 42	..	..	..	..	..	..	..	12 57	..	..	..	..	..
Malden, for Coombe	..	..	..			1149	..	1159	12 2	..	..	..	..	12 9	..	..	..	..	1219	1222	Dep. Dorking North 1 1 p.m	1229	..	..	..	..	..	..	1239
Norbiton H	..	..	..	..	..	1153	..	..	12 6	..	..	..	..	1213	..	..	..	..	..	1225		1233	..	..	..	..	..	..	..
Kingston	..	..	..	..	..	1155	..	..	12 8	..	..	..	..	1215	..	..	..	..	..	1228		1235	..	..	..	..	..	..	..
Hampton Wick	..	..	..	..	..	1157	..	..	1210	..	..	..	..	1217	..	..	..	..	..	1230		1237	..	..	..	..	..	..	..
Teddington J	..	..	..	..	..	12 1	..	..	1213	..	..	..	..	1221	..	..	..	..	..	1233		1241	..	..	..	..	..	..	..
Fulwell K	..	..	..	..	..	12 5	..	..	V	..	..	..	..	V	..	..	..	..	..	1237		V	..	..	..	..	..	..	..
Hampton	..	..	..	..	..	12 9	..	..	To Waterloo via Richmond Arr. Twickenham 12 19 p.m	..	..	..	..	⊖ To Waterloo via Richmond Arr. Twickenham 12 27 p.m	..	..	..	..	..	1241		To Waterloo via Richmond Arr. Twickenham 12 47 p.m	..	..	..	..	..	..	..
Sunbury L	..	..	..	..	..	1213	..	..		..	..	..	..		..	..	..	..	..	1245			..	..	..	..	..	..	..
Upper Halliford Halt	..	..	..	..	..	1215	..	..		..	..	..	..		..	..	..	..	..	1247			..	..	..	..	..	..	..
Shepperton M ......arr.	..	..	..	..	..	1218	..	..		..	..	..	..		..	..	..	..	..	1250			..	..	..	..	..	..	..
Berrylands N	..	..	..	..	..	..	..	12 2		..	..	..	..		..	..	..	..	1222	..	..		..	..	..	..	..	..	1242
Surbiton	..	..	..	..	..	..	..	12 5		..	..	..	..		12 8	..	..	1213	1225	..	..		12 28	..	..	..	..	..	1245
Thames Ditton	..	..	..	..	..	..	..	12 9		..	..	..	..		..	..	..	..	1229	..	..		..	..	..	..	..	..	1249
Hampton Court P arr.	..	..	..	..	..	..	..	1212		..	..	..	..		..	..	..	..	1232	..	..		..	..	..	..	..	..	1252
Hinchley Wood	p.m	..	..	..	..	..	..	..		..	..	..	..		12 11	..	..	..	Stop	..	..		12 31	..	..	..	..	..	Stop
Claygate, for Claremont	3	..	..	..	..	..	..	..		..	..	..	..		12 14	..	..	..	..	..	..		12 34	..	..	..	..	..	..
Oxshott, for Fairmile	..	..	..	..	..	..	..	..		..	..	..	..		12 18	..	..	..	..	..	..		12 38	..	..	..	..	..	..
Cobham Q	SO	..	..	..	..	..	..	..		..	..	..	..		12 21	..	..	..	..	..	..		12 41	..	..	..	..	..	..
Effingham Junction	12 6	..	1217	..	..	..	..	..		..	12 32	..	..		12 26	12 45	..	..	..	..	..		12 46	1 1	..	..	..	..	..
Horsley R	12 8	..	..	..	..	..	..	..		..	..	..	..		12 28	..	..	..	..	..	..		12 48	..	..	..	..	..	..
Clandon T	1213	..	..	..	..	..	..	..		..	..	..	..		12 33	..	..	..	..	..	..		12 53	..	..	..	..	..	..
London Road (Guildford)	1219	..	..	p.m.	p.m	..	..	..		..	..	..	..		12 39	..	..	..	p.m	..	..		12 59	..	..	..	..	..	p.m
Esher, for Sandown Park	..	..	..	..	..	..	..	..	..	..	..	..	..	..	..	..	..	1217	..	..	..	..	..	..	..	..	..	..	..
Hersham	..	..	..	3	3	..	..	..	..	..	..	..	..	..	..	..	..	1220	3	..	..	..	..	..	..	..	..	..	3
Walton-on-Thames	..	..	..	SX	SO	..	..	..	..	..	..	..	..	..	..	..	..	1223	SX	..	..	..	..	..	..	..	1238	..	SO
Weybridge U	..	..	..	12 5	1215	..	..	..	..	..	..	..	..	..	..	..	..	1227	1235	..	..	..	..	..	..	..	1242	..	1245
Addlestone	..	..	..	12 9	1219	..	..	..	..	..	..	..	..	..	..	..	..	..	1239	..	..	..	..	..	..	..	..	..	1249
Chertsey	..	..	..	12 12	1222	..	..	..	..	..	..	..	..	..	..	..	..	..	1242	..	..	..	..	..	..	..	..	..	1252
Virginia Water Z 460 arr.	..	..	..	12 16	1226	..	..	..	..	..	..	..	..	..	..	..	..	..	1246	..	..	..	..	..	..	..	..	..	1256
West Weybridge	..	..	..	..	..	..	..	..	..	..	..	..	..	..	..	..	..	1230	..	..	..	..	..	..	..	..	..	..	..
Byfleet W	..	..	..	..	..	..	..	..	..	..	..	..	..	..	..	..	..	1233	..	..	..	..	..	..	..	..	1246	..	..
Woking X 324, 389, 390	..	..	..	..	..	..	..	..	..	1215	..	..	..	..	..	..	..	1237	..	..	..	..	..	..	..	..	1251	..	..
Worplesdon	..	..	..	..	..	..	..	..	..	..	..	..	..	..	..	..	..	1245	..	..	..	..	..	..	..	..	..	..	..
Guildford 246, 359 ...arr.	1223	..	..	..	..	..	..	..	..	1225	..	..	..	..	12 45	..	..	1251	..	..	..	..	1 5	..	..	..	..	..	..

FOR NOTES, SEE PAGE 426

FOR NOTES, SEE PAGE 426

LONDON, DORKING NORTH, HORSHAM, KINGSTON, SHEPPERTON, HAMPTON COURT, CHERTSEY, WOKING, & GUILDFORD

Week Days—*continued* (p.m)

Down		SO						SO		SO		SO		SO		
Waterloo ....dep	1221	12 27	(3)	(3)	1227	1229	(3)	1232	1236	1239	1239	1243	1245	1247	12 47	1249
Vauxhall	1224					1232			1239		1242	(3)				1252
Clapham Junction **A**	1229	(3)				1236		(3)	1244		1246				(3)	1256
Earlsfield **B**	1232					1240			1247		1250					1 0
Wimbledon	1236					1243			1251		1253	Via Richmond see page 464			12SX58	1 3
Raynes Park	1239					1246			1254		1256					1 6
Motspur Park		12 44							1256						1 4	
Malden Manor	(3)					(3)			1 0		(3)					(3)
Tolworth									1 2							
Chessington North									1 5							
Chessington South ¶ ar									1 7							
Worcester Park		12 46							(3)						1 6	
Stoneleigh		12 49													1 9	
Ewell West **C**		12 52		SX			SO								1 12	
London Bridge ....dep.				12 25			1228									
Victoria ...... "		12‡20		12‡20			12‡20								12SO‡27	
Sutton ...... "		12‡43		12 52			1255								1SO‡1	
Epsom 285		12 55		1 3			1 5								1 15	
Ashtead		12 59	SO	1 7			1 9								1 19	
Leatherhead		1 3	1 [illegible]	1 11			1 13								1 23	
Boxhill & Burford Bdg **D**		1 8		1 17			1 18									
Dorking North **F**		1 11		1 20			1 21									
Holmwood **G**		1 2[illegible]		1 31			1 31									
Ockley, for Capel				1 35			1 35									
Warnham 196, 245				1 41			1 41									
Horsham 159, arr.				1 46			1 46									
Bookham			1 14												1 28	
Malden, for Coombe	1242					1249					1259					1 9
Norbiton **H**	1245			Dep Dorking North 1 23 p.m		1253										1 13
Kingston	1248					1255										1 15
Hampton Wick	1250					1257										1 17
Teddington **J**	1253					1 1										1 20
Fulwell **K**	V					1 5						1 11				V
Hampton	To Waterloo via Richmond Arr Twickenham 1 0 p.m					1 9						1 15				To Waterloo via Richmond Arr Twickenham 1 27 p.m
Sunbury **L**						1 13						1 19				
Upper Halliford Halt						1 15						1 21				
Shepperton **M** ......arr.						1 18						1 24				
Berrylands **N**						Stop					1 2					
Surbiton					1243			1249			1 5			1 3		
Thames Ditton											1 9					
Hampton Court **P** arr.											1 12					
Hinchley Wood								1252								
Claygate, for Claremont								1255								
Oxshott for Fairmile								1259								
Cobham **Q**								1 2								
Effingham Junction			1 18					1 7							1 31	
Horsley **R**								1 9							Stop	
Clandon **T**								1 14								
London Road (Guildford)								1 20							p.m	
Esher, for Sandown Park					1247	p.m								1 7	(3)	
Hersham					1250	(3)										
Walton-on-Thames					1253									1 13	SO	
Weybridge **U**					1257	1 5								1 17	1 25	
Addlestone						1 9									1 29	
Chertsey						1 12									1 35	
Virginia Water **Z** 460 arr						1 16									1 40	
West Weybridge					1 0											
Byfleet **W**					1 3									1 21		
Woking **X** 324, 389, 390					1 7					1 10			1 15	1 26		
Worplesdon					1 15											
Guildford 246, 359 ....arr.					1 21			1 24					1 25			

Down				SX							SO				SO
Waterloo ....dep	1252	(3)		1254	(3)	1256	1257	1259		1 1		1 7	1 9	1 12	1 15
Vauxhall						1259		1 2		1 4			1 12	(3)	
Clapham Junction **A**	(3)					1 4		1 6		1 9			1 16		
Earlsfield **B**						1 7		1 10		1 12			1 20		
Wimbledon	1SX3		Via Three Bridges, see page 166			1 11		1 13	Via Three Bridges, see page 166	1 16		1SX18	1 23	1SX23	
Raynes Park						1 14		1 16		1 19			1 26		
Motspur Park						1 16						1 24			
Malden Manor						1 20		(3)		(3)		(3)	(3)		
Tolworth						1 22									
Chessington North						1 25									
Chessington South ¶ ar						1 27									
Worcester Park						(3)						1 26			
Stoneleigh												1 29			
Ewell West **C**		SO			SX				SO			1 32			
London Bridge ....dep.		1248			1253				1 5						
Victoria ...... "		12‡37	1248		12‡51						1 18	12b‡51			
Sutton ...... "		1 15			1 20						1 39	1z‡20			
Epsom 285		1 25			1 29							1 35			
Ashtead		1 29			1 33							1 39			
Leatherhead		1 33			1 37							1 43			
Boxhill & Burford Bdg **D**		1 38										1 48			
Dorking North **F**		1 41									1 55	1 51			
Holmwood **G**		1 51										2 9			
Ockley, for Capel		1 55										2 13			
Warnham 196, 245		2 3										2 19			
Horsham 159, arr.		2 7	2 5						2 5		2 13	2 24			
Bookham					1 42										
Malden, for Coombe								1 19		1 22			1 29		
Norbiton **H**										1 25		Dep. Dorking North 2 1 p.m	1 33		
Kingston										1 28			1 35		
Hampton Wick										1 30			1 37		
Teddington **J**										1 33			1 40		
Fulwell **K**										1 37			V		
Hampton										1 41			To Waterloo via Richmond Arr Twickenham 1 47 p.m		
Sunbury **L**										1 45					
Upper Halliford Halt										1 47					
Shepperton **M** ......arr.										1 50					
Berrylands **N**								1 22							
Surbiton	1 8						1 13	1 25						1 28	
Thames Ditton								1 29							
Hampton Court **P** arr.								1 32							
Hinchley Wood	1 11							Stop						1 31	
Claygate, for Claremont	1 14													1 34	
Oxshott for Fairmile	1 18													1 38	
Cobham **Q**	1 21													1 41	
Effingham Junction	1 26				1 44									1 46	
Horsley **R**	1 28													1 48	
Clandon **T**	1 33													1 53	
London Road (Guildford)	1 39							p.m						1 59	
Esher, for Sandown Park							1 17	(3)							
Hersham							1 20								
Walton-on-Thames							1 23	SX							
Weybridge **U**							1 27	1 35							
Addlestone								1 39							
Chertsey								1 42							
Virginia Water **Z** 460 arr								1 46							
West Weybridge							1 30								
Byfleet **W**							1 33								
Woking **X** 324, 389, 390				1 25			1 37								1 45
Worplesdon							1 45								
Guildford 246, 359 ....arr.	1 45						1 51							2 5	1 55

LONDON, DORKING NORTH, HORSHAM, KINGSTON, SHEPPERTON, HAMPTON COURT, CHERTSEY, WOKING, & GUILDFORD

Week Days—continued (p.m.)

Down	SO	SO		SO	SO			SO	SO	
Waterloo dep.	1 16	1 16		1 17	1 19		1 21	1 24	1 27	
Vauxhall		1 19	3		1 22	Via Three Bridges, see page 168	1 24			
Clapham Junction A	3	1 24			1 26		1 29		3	
Earlsfield B		1 27			1 30		1 32			
Wimbledon		1 31			1 33		1 36			
Raynes Park		1 34			1 36		1 39			
Motspur Park	Via Richmond, see page 464	1 36							1 44	
Malden Manor		1 40			3		3			
Tolworth		1 42								
Chessington North		1 45								
Chessington South ¶ arr.		1 47								
Worcester Park									1 46	
Stoneleigh		3							1 49	
Ewell West C			SO			SX			1 52	
London Bridge dep.			1 8			1 18				
Victoria "			12‡55						1‡20	
Sutton "			1 35						1‡43	
Epsom 285			1 49						1 55	
Ashtead			1 53						1 59	
Leatherhead			1 57						2 3	
Boxhill & Burford Bdg D									2 8	
Dorking North F									2 11	
Holmwood G									2 21	
Ockley, for Capel										
Warnham [196, 245										
Horsham 159, arr.						2 35				
Bookham			2 1							
Malden, for Coombe					1 39		1 42			
Norbiton H							1 45			
Kingston							1 48			
Hampton Wick							1 50			
Teddington J							1 53			
Fulwell K	1 42						V			
Hampton	1 46						To Waterloo via Richmond Arr. Twickenham 2 0 p.m			
Sunbury L	1 50									
Upper Halliford Halt	1 52									
Shepperton M arr.	1 55									
Berrylands N					1 42					
Surbiton					1 45					
Thames Ditton					1 49					
Hampton Court P arr.					1 52					
Hinchley Wood					Stop					
Claygate, for Claremont										
Oxshott, for Fairmile										
Cobham Q										
Effingham Junction			2 4							
Horsley R										
Clandon T										
London Road (Guildford)					p.m					
Esher, for Sandown Park										
Hersham					3					
Walton-on-Thames				1 38	SO					
Weybridge U				1 42	1 45					
Addlestone					1 49					
Chertsey					1 52					
Virginia Water Z 460 arr.					1 56					
West Weybridge										
Byfleet W				1 46						
Woking X 324, 389, 390				1 51				1 55		
Worplesdon										
Guildford 246, 359 arr.										

Down					SO		SO			SO
Waterloo dep.		1 27	1 29		1 32	1 36	1 37		1 39	1 43
Vauxhall	3		1 32	3		1 39		Via Three Bridges, see page 168	1 42	
Clapham Junction A			1 36		3	1 44			1 46	3
Earlsfield B			1 40			1 47			1 50	Via Richmond, see page 465
Wimbledon			1 43			1 51			1 53	
Raynes Park			1 46			1 54			1 56	
Motspur Park						1 56				
Malden Manor			3			2 0			3	
Tolworth						2 2				
Chessington North						2 5				
Chessington South ¶ arr.						2 7				
Worcester Park										
Stoneleigh						3				
Ewell West C	SX			SO				SO		
London Bridge dep.	1 25			1 28				1 40		
Victoria "	1‡20									
Sutton "	1 52			1 55						
Epsom 285	2 3			2 5						
Ashtead	2 7			2 9						
Leatherhead	2 11			2 13						
Boxhill & Burford Bdg D	2 17			2 18						
Dorking North F	2 20			2 21						
Holmwood G	2 32			2 32						
Ockley, for Capel	2 36			2 36						
Warnham [196, 245	2 42			2 42						
Horsham 159, arr.	2 46			2 46				2 32		
Bookham										
Malden, for Coombe			1 49						1 59	
Norbiton H	Dep. Dorking North 2 23 p.m		1 53							
Kingston			1 55							
Hampton Wick			1 57							
Teddington J			2 1							
Fulwell K			2 5							2 11
Hampton			2 9							2 15
Sunbury L			2 13							2 19
Upper Halliford Halt			2 15							2 21
Shepperton M arr.			2 18							2 24
Berrylands N									2 2	
Surbiton		1 43	Stop		1 49		1 53		2 5	
Thames Ditton									2 9	
Hampton Court P arr.									2 12	
Hinchley Wood					1 52					
Claygate, for Claremont					1 55					
Oxshott, for Fairmile					1 59					
Cobham Q					2 2					
Effingham Junction					2 8					
Horsley R					2 10					
Clandon T					2 15					
London Road (Guildford)					2 21					
Esher, for Sandown Park		1 47	p.m				1 57			
Hersham		1 50	3				2 0			
Walton-on-Thames		1 53					2 3			
Weybridge U		1 57	2 5				2 7			
Addlestone			2 9							
Chertsey			2 12							
Virginia Water Z 460 arr.			2 16							
West Weybridge		2 0					2 10			
Byfleet W		2 3					2 13			
Woking X 324, 389, 390		2 7					2 18			
Worplesdon		2 15								
Guildford 246, 359 arr.		2 21			2 25					

Down	SO					SX					
Waterloo dep.	1 45	1 47		1 49	1 52	1 54			1 56	1 57	1 59
Vauxhall			3	1 52	3		3	3	1 59		2 2
Clapham Junction A		3		1 56					2 4		2 6
Earlsfield B				2 0					2 7		2 10
Wimbledon				2 3					2 11		2 13
Raynes Park		1SX58		2 6	2SX3				2 14		2 16
Motspur Park		2 4							2 16		
Malden Manor				3					2 20		3
Tolworth									2 22		
Chessington North									2 25		
Chessington South ¶ arr.									2 27		
Worcester Park		2 6									
Stoneleigh		2 9							3		
Ewell West C		2 12	SO					SX			
London Bridge dep.			1 48					1 53			
Victoria "		1SO‡37	1‡37					1‡51			
Sutton "		2SO‡1	2 15					2 20			
Epsom 285		2 15	2 25					2 29			
Ashtead		2 19	2 29				SO	2 33			
Leatherhead		2 23	2 33				2 36	2 37			
Boxhill & Burford Bdg D			2 38								
Dorking North F			2 41								
Holmwood G											
Ockley, for Capel											
Warnham [196, 245											
Horsham 159, arr.											
Bookham		2 28					2 40	2 42			
Malden, for Coombe				2 9							2 19
Norbiton H				2 13							
Kingston				2 15							
Hampton Wick				2 17							
Teddington J				2 21							
Fulwell K				V							
Hampton				To Waterloo via Richmond Arr. Twickenham 2 27 p.m							
Sunbury L											
Upper Halliford Halt											
Shepperton M arr.											
Berrylands N											2 22
Surbiton					2 8					2 13	2 25
Thames Ditton											2 29
Hampton Court P arr.											2 32
Hinchley Wood					2 11						Stop
Claygate, for Claremont					2 14						
Oxshott, for Fairmile					2 18						
Cobham Q					2 21						
Effingham Junction		2 31			2 27		2 44	2 45			
Horsley R					2 29						
Clandon T					2 34						
London Road (Guildford)					2 40						
Esher, for Sandown Park										2 17	p.m
Hersham										2 20	3
Walton-on-Thames										2 23	
Weybridge U										2 27	2 35
Addlestone											2 39
Chertsey											2 42
Virginia Water Z 460 arr.											2 46
West Weybridge										2 30	
Byfleet W										2 33	
Woking X 324, 389, 390	2 15					2 25				2 37	
Worplesdon										2 45	
Guildford 246, 359 arr.	2 25				2 45					2 51	

FOR NOTES, SEE PAGE 426

FOR NOTES, SEE PAGE 426

LONDON, DORKING NORTH, HORSHAM, KINGSTON, SHEPPERTON, HAMPTON COURT, CHERTSEY, WOKING, & GUILDFORD

Week Days—continued (p.m.)

Down							SO			SO				SO				SO												
Waterloo dep.	..	2 1	2 7	2 9	2 12	..	2 16	3	..	2 19	2 21	2 27		2 27	3	3	2 29	2 32	2 36	2 39	2 45	2 47	2 49	2 52	3	2 56	2 57	2 59	3 1	3 7
Vauxhall	..	2 4	3	2 12	3	..	2 19	..	..	2 22	2 24	..		3	..	..	2 32	3	2 39	2 42	..	..	2 52	..	..	2 59	..	3 2	3 4	..
Clapham Junction A	Via Three Bridges see page 168	2 9	..	2 16	..	..	2 24	..	..	2 26	2 29	..	Via Three Bridges, see page 168	..	..	..	2 36	..	2 44	2 46	..	..	2 56	..	..	3 4	..	3 6	3 9	..
Earlsfield B		2 12	..	2 20	..	..	2 27	..	..	2 30	2 32	..		..	..	..	2 40	..	2 47	2 50	..	..	3 0	..	..	3 7	..	3 10	3 12	..
Wimbledon		2 16	2SX18	2 23	2SX23	..	2 31	..	..	2 33	2 36	..		2 38	..	..	2 43	..	2 51	2 53	..	2 58	3 3	3 3	..	3 11	..	3 13	3 16	3 18
Raynes Park		2 19	..	2 26	..	..	2 34	..	..	2 36	2 39	..		..	..	..	2 46	..	2 54	2 56	..	..	3 6	..	..	3 14	..	3 16	3 19	..
Motspur Park		..	2 24	..	..	..	2 36	..	..	..	..	..		2 44	..	..	..	..	2 56	..	..	3 4	..	..	..	3 16	..	..	..	3 24
Malden Manor		3	..	3	..	..	2 40	..	..	3	3	..		..	..	..	3	..	3 0	3	..	3	3	3	..	3 20	..	3	3	3
Tolworth		..	..	..	..	..	2 42	..	..	..	..	..		..	..	..	..	..	3 2	..	..	..	..	..	..	3 22	..	..	..	..
Chessington North		..	..	..	..	..	2 45	..	..	..	..	..		..	..	..	..	..	3 5	..	..	..	..	..	..	3 25	..	..	..	..
Chessington South ¶ar		..	..	..	..	..	2 47	..	..	..	..	..		..	..	..	..	..	3 7	..	..	..	..	..	..	3 27	..	..	..	..
Worcester Park		..	2 26	..	..	..	3	..	..	..	..	..		2 46	..	..	..	..	3	..	..	3 6	..	..	..	3	..	..	..	3 26
Stoneleigh		..	2 29	..	..	..	..	..	..	..	..	..		2 49	..	..	..	..	..	..	..	3 9	..	..	..	..	..	..	..	3 29
Ewell West C		..	2 32	..	..	..	..	SO	SO	..	..	..		2 52	SX	SO	..	..	..	..	..	3 12	..	..	SX	..	..	..	..	3 32
London Bridge dep.	..	..	..	..	..	..	..	2 8	..	..	..	..	2 18	..	2 25	2 28	..	..	..	..	..	2x‡25	..	..	2 53	..	..	..	..	..
Victoria "	1 48	..	1SO‡55	..	..	..	..	1*55	2 18	..	..	..	..	2‡20	2‡20	2‡20	..	..	..	..	..	2‡SO37	..	..	2‡51	..	..	..	..	2‡b51
Sutton "	..	..	2‡SO21	..	..	..	..	2 35	2 39	..	..	..	..	2‡44	2 52	2 55	..	..	..	..	..	3‡SO1	..	..	3 20	..	..	..	..	3‡v20
Epsom 285	..	..	2 35	..	..	..	..	2 49	..	..	..	..	..	2 55	3 2	3 5	..	..	..	..	..	3 15	..	..	3 29	..	..	..	..	3 35
Ashtead	..	..	2 39	..	..	..	..	2 53	..	..	..	..	..	2 59	3 6	3 9	..	..	..	..	..	3 19	..	..	3 33	..	..	..	..	3 39
Leatherhead	..	..	2 43	..	..	..	..	2 57	..	..	..	..	..	3 3	3 11	3 13	..	..	..	..	..	3 23	..	..	3 37	..	..	..	..	3 43
Boxhill & Burford Bdg D	..	..	2 48	..	..	..	..	..	..	..	..	..	..	3 8	3 17	3 18	..	..	..	..	..	..	..	..	..	..	..	..	..	3 48
Dorking North F	..	..	2 51	..	..	..	..	..	2 55	..	..	..	..	3 11	3 20	3 21	..	..	..	..	..	..	..	..	..	..	..	..	..	3 51
Holmwood G	..	..	3 9	..	..	..	..	..	..	..	..	..	..	3 21	3 32	3 32	..	..	..	..	..	..	..	..	..	..	..	..	..	4 9
Ockley, for Capel	..	..	3 13	..	..	..	..	..	..	..	..	..	..	..	3 36	3 36	..	..	..	..	..	..	..	..	..	..	..	..	..	4 13
Warnham [196, 245	..	..	3 20	..	..	..	..	..	..	..	..	..	..	..	3 42	3 42	..	..	..	..	..	..	..	..	..	..	..	..	..	4 19
Horsham 159, arr.	3 5	..	3 25	..	..	..	..	..	3 13	..	..	..	3 35	..	3 46	3 46	..	..	..	..	..	..	..	..	..	..	..	..	..	4 24
Bookham	Stop	..	..	..	..	..	..	3 1	..	..	..	..	Stop	..	..	..	..	..	..	..	..	3 28	..	..	3 42	..	..	..	..	..
Malden, for Coombe	..	2 22		2 29	..	..	..	..	..	2 39	2 42	..	..	..	..	..	2 49	..	..	2 59	..	..	3 9	..	..	..	..	3 19	3 22	
Norbiton H	..	2 25	Dep Dorking North 3 1 p.m	2 33	..	..	..	..	..	..	2 45	..	..	..	Dep. Dorking North 3 23 p.m	..	2 53	..	..	..	..	..	3 13	..	..	..	..	..	3 25	Dep. Dorking North 4 1 p.m
Kingston	..	2 28		2 35	..	..	..	..	..	..	2 48	..	..	..		..	2 55	..	..	..	..	..	3 15	..	..	..	..	..	3 28	
Hampton Wick	..	2 30		2 37	..	..	..	..	..	..	2 50	..	..	..		..	2 57	..	..	..	..	..	3 17	..	..	..	..	..	3 30	
Teddington J	..	2 33		2 41	..	..	..	..	..	..	2 53	..	..	..		..	3 1	..	..	..	..	..	3 21	..	..	..	..	..	3 33	
Fulwell K	..	2 37		V	..	..	..	..	..	..	V	..	..	..		..	3 5	..	..	..	..	..	V	..	..	..	..	..	3 37	
Hampton	..	2 41		To Waterloo via Richmond Arr. Twickenham 2 47 p.m.	..	..	..	..	..	..	To Waterloo via Richmond Arr. Twickenham 3 0 p.m.	..	..	..		..	3 9	..	..	..	..	..	To Waterloo via Richmond Arr. Twickenham 3 29 p.m.	..	..	..	..	..	3 41	
Sunbury L	..	2 45			..	..	..	..	..	..		..	..	..		..	3 13	..	..	..	..	..		..	..	..	..	..	3 45	
Upper Halliford Halt	..	2 47			..	..	..	..	..	..		..	..	..		..	3 15	..	..	..	..	..		..	..	..	..	..	3 47	
Shepperton M arr.	..	2 50			..	..	..	..	..	..		..	..	..		..	3 18	..	..	..	..	..		..	..	..	..	..	3 50	
Berrylands N	..	..			..	..	..	..	..	2 42		..	..	..		..	..	..	..	3 2	..	..		..	..	..	..	3 22	Stop	..
Surbiton	..	..			2 28	..	..	..	..	2 45		2 43	..	..		..	..	2 49	..	3 5	..	..		3 10	..	..	3 13	3 25	..	..
Thames Ditton	..	..			..	..	..	..	..	2 49		..	..	..		..	..	..	..	3 9	..	..		..	..	..	..	3 29	..	..
Hampton Court P arr.	..	..			..	..	..	..	..	2 52		..	..	..		..	..	..	..	3 12	..	..		..	..	..	..	3 32	..	..
Hinchley Wood	..	..	..		2 31	..	..	..	..	..		..	..	..	..	..	..	2 52	..	..	..	..		3 14	..	..	..	..	..	..
Claygate, for Claremont	..	..	..		2 34	..	..	..	..	..		..	..	..	..	..	..	2 55	..	..	..	..		3 17	..	..	..	..	..	..
Oxshott, for Fairmile	..	..	..		2 38	..	..	..	..	..		..	..	..	..	..	..	2 59	..	..	..	..		3 20	..	..	..	..	..	..
Cobham Q	..	..	..		2 42	..	..	..	..	..		..	..	..	..	..	..	3 2	..	..	..	..		3 24	..	..	..	..	..	..
Effingham Junction	..	..	..		2 48	..	..	3 4	..	..		..	..	..	..	..	..	3 8	..	..	..	3 32		3 28	3 44	..	..	..	..	..
Horsley R	..	..	..		2 50	..	..	..	..	..		..	..	..	..	..	..	3 10	..	..	..	..		3 31	..	..	..	..	..	..
Clandon T	..	..	..		2 55	..	..	..	..	..		..	..	..	..	..	..	3 15	..	..	..	..		3 36	..	..	..	..	..	..
London Road (Guildford)	p.m	..	..		3 1	..	..	..	..	..		..	..	..	..	..	..	3 21	..	..	..	..		3 41	..	..	..	..	..	..
Esher, for Sandown Park	3	..	..	..	..	..	..	..	..	..	..	2 47	p.m	..	..	..	..	..	..	..	..	..	..	..	..	..	3 17	..	p.m	..
Hersham		..	..	..	..	..	..	..	..	..	..	2 50	3	..	..	..	..	..	..	..	..	..	..	..	..	..	3 20	..	3	..
Walton-on-Thames	SO	..	..	..	..	..	..	..	..	..	..	2 53		..	..	..	..	..	..	..	..	..	..	..	..	..	3 23	..		..
Weybridge U	2 50	..	..	..	..	..	..	..	..	..	..	2 57	3 5	..	..	..	..	..	..	..	..	..	..	..	..	..	3 27	..	3 35	..
Addlestone	2 54	..	..	..	..	..	..	..	..	..	..	..	3 9	..	..	..	..	..	..	..	..	..	..	..	..	..	..	..	3 39	..
Chertsey	2 57	..	..	..	..	..	..	..	..	..	..	..	3 12	..	..	..	..	..	..	..	..	..	..	..	..	..	..	..	3 42	..
Virginia Water Z 460 arr	..	..	..	..	..	..	..	..	..	..	..	..	3 16	..	..	..	..	..	..	..	..	..	..	..	..	..	..	..	3 46	..
West Weybridge	..	..	..	..	..	..	..	..	..	..	..	3 0	..	..	..	..	..	..	..	..	..	..	..	..	..	..	3 30	..	..	..
Byfleet W	..	..	..	..	..	..	..	..	..	..	..	3 3	..	..	..	..	..	..	..	..	..	..	..	..	..	..	3 33	..	..	..
Woking X 324, 389, 390	..	..	..	..	..	..	..	..	..	..	..	3 7	..	..	..	..	..	..	..	..	3 15	..	..	..	..	..	3 37	..	..	..
Worplesdon	..	..	..	..	..	..	..	..	..	..	..	3 15	..	..	..	..	..	..	..	..	..	..	..	..	..	..	3 45	..	..	..
Guildford 246, 359 arr.	..	..	..	..	3 5	..	..	..	..	..	..	3 21	..	..	..	..	..	3 25	..	..	3 25	..	..	3 45	..	..	3 51	..	..	..

…, KINGSTON, SHEPPERTON, HAMPTON COURT, CHERTSEY, WOKING, & GUILDFORD

Week Days—continued (p.m.)

Down										
Waterloo dep.	3 9	..	3 12	..	(3)	3 21	3 27	(3)	..	(3)
Vauxhall	3 12	..	..	..	..	3 24	..	..	..	..
Clapham Junction A	3 16	..	..	..	..	3 29	..	..	..	..
Earlsfield B	3 20		..	..	SX	3 32	..	..		..
Wimbledon	3 23		3 23	..	3 31	3 36	..	..		..
Raynes Park	3 26		..	..	3 34	3 39	..	..		..
Motspur Park	..	Via Three Bridges, see page 170	..	..	3 36	..	..	..	Via Three Bridges see page 170	..
Malden Manor	..		..	..	3 40	..	..	..		..
Tolworth	(3)		(3)	..	3 42	(3)	..	..		..
Chessington North	..		..	..	3 45	..	..	..		..
Chessington South ¶ ar	..		..	..	3 47	..	..	..		..
Worcester Park	..		..	..	..	..	..	..		..
Stoneleigh	..		..	..	..	..	..	..		..
Ewell West C	..		..	..	..	..	..	SO		..
London Bridge dep.	..	..	..	..	..	..	..	3 8	3 18	3 25
Victoria "	..	3 18	..	..	..	..	..	2‡55	..	3‡24
Sutton "	..	..	..	..	..	..	..	3 35	..	3a53
Epsom 285	..	..	..	..	..	..	..	3 45	..	4 4
Ashtead	..	..	..	..	..	..	..	3 49	..	4 8
Leatherhead	..	..	..	..	..	..	..	3 54	..	4 13
Boxhill & Burford Bdg D	..	..	..	..	..	..	..	..	..	4 18
Dorking North F	..	..	..	..	..	..	..	..	..	4 21
Holmwood G	..	..	..	..	..	..	..	..	..	4 32
Ockley, for Capel	..	..	..	..	..	..	..	..	..	4 36
Warnham 245	..	..	..	..	..	..	..	..	..	4 42
Horsham 159, 196 ar	..	4 13	..	..	..	..	..	..	4 35	4 46
Bookham	..	..	..	..	..	..	..	3 58	..	Stop
Malden, for Coombe	3 29	..	..	..	..	3 42	..	..	..	..
Norbiton H	3 33	..	..	..	..	3 45	..	..	..	..
Kingston	3 35	..	..	..	..	3 48	..	..	..	..
Hampton Wick	3 37	..	..	..	..	3 50	..	..	..	..
Teddington J	3 41	..	..	..	..	3 53	..	..	..	..
Fulwell K	V	..	..	..	..	V	..	..	..	..
Hampton	To Waterloo via Richmond Arr. Twickenham 3 47 p.m	..	..	..	..	To Waterloo via Richmond Arr. Twickenham 4 1 p.m	..	..	..	..
Sunbury L		..	..	..	..		..	..	..	..
Upper Halliford Halt		..	..	..	..		..	..	..	..
Shepperton M arr.		..	..	..	..		..	..	..	..
Berrylands N		..	..	..	..		..	..	..	..
Surbiton		..	3 30	..	..		3 43	..	..	..
Thames Ditton		..	..	..	..		..	..	..	..
Hampton Court P arr.		..	..	..	..		..	..	..	..
Hinchley Wood		..	3 34	..	..		..	..	..	..
Claygate, for Claremont		..	3 37	..	..		..	..	..	..
Oxshott, for Fairmile		..	3 40	..	..		..	..	..	..
Cobham Q		..	3 44	..	..		..	..	..	..
Effingham Junction		..	3 48	..	..		..	4 2	..	..
Horsley R		..	3 51	..	..		..	..	..	..
Clandon T		..	3 56	..	..		..	..	..	..
London Road (Guildford)		..	4 1	..	..		..	..	..	..
Esher, for Sandown Park	..	..	..	..	..	..	3 47	..	..	..
Hersham	..	..	..	..	..	..	3 50	..	..	p.m
Walton-on-Thames	..	..	..	..	..	..	3 53	..	..	(3)
Weybridge U	..	..	..	..	..	..	3 57	..	..	4 5
Addlestone	..	..	..	..	..	..	..	..	..	4 9
Chertsey	..	..	..	..	..	..	..	..	..	4 12
Virginia Water Z 460 ar.	..	..	..	..	..	..	..	..	..	4 16
West Weybridge	..	..	..	..	..	..	4 0	..	..	..
Byfleet W	..	..	..	..	..	..	4 3	..	..	..
Woking X 324, 389, 390	..	..	..	..	..	..	4 7	..	..	..
Worplesdon	..	..	..	..	..	..	4 15	..	..	..
Guildford 246, 359 arr.	..	..	4 5	..	..	..	4 21	..	..	..

Down				SX						
Waterloo dep.	3 29	3 36	3 39	3 41	3 45	3 47	(3)	3 49	3 52	(3)
Vauxhall	3 32	3 39	3 42	3 44	..	..	..	3 52	..	..
Clapham Junction A	3 36	3 44	3 46	3 49	..	..	..	3 56	(3)	..
Earlsfield B	3 40	3 47	3 50	3 52	..	..	..	4 0	..	..
Wimbledon	3 43	3 51	3 53	3 56	..	3 58	..	4 3	4 3	..
Raynes Park	3 46	3 54	3 56	3 59	..	..	..	4 6	..	..
Motspur Park	..	3 56	..	..	..	4 4	..	..	..	..
Malden Manor	..	4 0	..	..	..	..	..	..	..	..
Tolworth	(3)	4 2	(3)	(3)	..	(3)	..	(3)	..	..
Chessington North	..	4 5	..	..	..	..	..	..	..	..
Chessington South ¶ ar	..	4 7	..	..	..	..	..	..	..	..
Worcester Park	..		..	..	..	4 6	..	..	..	..
Stoneleigh	..	(3)	..	..	..	4 9	..	..	..	..
Ewell West C	..		..	..	..	4 12	..	..	..	SO
London Bridge dep.	..	Stop	..	..	..	3‡25	..	..	..	3 53
Victoria "	..	..	..	..	..	3‡24	..	..	..	3‡51
Sutton "	..	..	..	..	..	3a‡53	..	..	..	4 20
Epsom 285	..	..	..	..	..	4 15	..	..	..	4 29
Ashtead	..	..	..	..	..	4 19	SX	..	..	4 33
Leatherhead	..	..	..	..	..	4 23	4 31	..	..	4 37
Boxhill & Burford Bdg D	..	..	..	..	..	..	4 36	..	..	..
Dorking North F	..	..	..	..	..	..	4 39	..	..	..
Holmwood G	..	..	..	..	..	..	..	..	..	..
Ockley, for Capel	..	..	..	..	..	..	..	..	..	..
Warnham 245	..	..	..	..	..	..	..	..	..	..
Horsham 159, 196 ar	..	..	..	..	..	..	..	..	..	..
Bookham	..	..	..	..	..	4 28	..	..	..	4 41
Malden, for Coombe	3 49	..	3 59	4 2	..	..	..	4 9	..	..
Norbiton H	3 53	..	..	4 5	..	..	..	4 13	..	..
Kingston	3 55	..	..	4 8	..	..	..	4 15	..	..
Hampton Wick	3 57	..	..	4 10	..	..	..	4 17	..	..
Teddington J	4 1	..	..	4 13	..	..	..	4 21	..	..
Fulwell K	4 5	..	..	V	..	..	..	V	..	..
Hampton	4 9	..	..	To Waterloo via Richmond Arr. Twickenham 4 19 p.m	..	..	..	To Waterloo via Richmond Arr. Twickenham 4 29 p.m	..	..
Sunbury L	4 13	..	..		..	..	..		..	..
Upper Halliford Halt	4 15	..	..		..	..	..		..	..
Shepperton M arr.	4 18	..	..		..	..	..		..	..
Berrylands N	..	..	4 2		..	..	..		..	..
Surbiton	..	..	4 5		..	..	..		4 10	..
Thames Ditton	..	..	4 9		..	..	..		..	..
Hampton Court P arr.	..	..	4 12		..	..	..		..	..
Hinchley Wood	..	p.m	..		..	..	..		4 14	..
Claygate, for Claremont	..	(3)	..		..	..	..		4 17	..
Oxshott, for Fairmile	..		..		..	..	..		4 20	..
Cobham Q	..	SX	..		..	..	..		4 24	..
Effingham Junction	..	4 8	..		..	4 31	..		4 28	4 44
Horsley R	..	4 11	..		..	..	..		4 31	..
Clandon T	..	4 16	..		..	..	..		4 36	..
London Road (Guildford)	..	4 21	..		..	..	..		4 41	..
Esher, for Sandown Park	..	..	..	..	..	..	..	..	..	..
Hersham	..	..	..	..	..	..	..	..	..	..
Walton-on-Thames	..	..	..	..	..	..	..	..	..	..
Weybridge U	..	..	..	..	..	..	..	..	..	..
Addlestone	..	..	..	..	..	..	..	..	..	..
Chertsey	..	..	..	..	..	..	..	..	..	..
Virginia Water Z 460 ar.	..	..	..	..	..	..	..	..	..	..
West Weybridge	..	..	..	..	..	..	..	..	..	..
Byfleet W	..	..	..	..	..	..	..	..	..	..
Woking X 324, 389, 390	..	..	..	..	4 15	..	..	..	..	..
Worplesdon	..	..	..	..	..	..	..	..	..	..
Guildford 246, 359 arr.	..	4 25	..	..	4 25	..	..	..	4 45	..

Down											
Waterloo dep.	3 54	3 56	3 57	3 59	..	4 1	..	4 7	4 9	4 12	(3)
Vauxhall	..	3 59	..	4 2	..	4 4	..	..	4 12	..	..
Clapham Junction A	..	4 4	..	4 6		4 9	..	(3)	4 16	(3)	..
Earlsfield B	..	4 7	..	4 10		4 12	..	..	4 20	..	..
Wimbledon	..	4 11	..	4 13		4 16	..	4 18	4 23	4 23	..
Raynes Park	..	4 14	..	4 16		4 19	..	..	4 26	..	..
Motspur Park	..	4 16	..	..	Via Three Bridges see page 170	..	..	4 24	..	..	..
Malden Manor	..	4 20	..	..		..	..	..	..	..	..
Tolworth	..	4 22	..	(3)		(3)	..	..	(3)	..	..
Chessington North	..	4 25	..	..		..	..	..	..	..	..
Chessington South ¶ ar	..	4 27	..	..		..	..	..	..	..	..
Worcester Park	..	..	..	..		..	..	4 26	..	..	..
Stoneleigh	..	(3)	..	..		..	..	4 29	..	..	..
Ewell West C	..	..	..	..	SX	..	..	4 32	..	..	SX
London Bridge dep.	..	..	..	..	4 0	..	..	3‡SO53	..	..	4 7
Victoria "	..	..	..	..	..	..	4 18	3‡51	..	..	..
Sutton "	..	..	..	..	..	..	4 39	4y‡14	..	..	4 35
Epsom 285	..	..	..	..	..	..	..	4 35	..	..	4 49
Ashtead	..	..	..	..	..	..	..	4 39	..	..	4 53
Leatherhead	..	..	..	..	..	..	..	4 43	..	..	4 57
Boxhill & Burford Bdg D	..	..	..	..	..	..	..	4 48	..	..	..
Dorking North F	..	..	..	..	..	..	4 55	4 51	..	..	..
Holmwood G	..	..	..	..	..	..	..	5 9	..	..	..
Ockley, for Capel	..	..	..	..	..	..	..	5 13	..	..	..
Warnham 245	..	..	..	..	..	..	..	5 19	..	..	..
Horsham 159, 196 ar	..	..	..	..	5 5	..	5 14	5 24	..	..	..
Bookham	..	..	..	..	..	..	..		..	..	5 1
Malden, for Coombe	..	..	..	4 19	..	4 22	..	Dep. Dorking North 5 1 p.m	4 29	..	..
Norbiton H	..	..	..	..	..	4 25	..		4 33	..	..
Kingston	..	..	..	..	..	4 28	..		4 35	..	..
Hampton Wick	..	..	..	..	..	4 30	..		4 37	..	..
Teddington J	..	..	..	..	..	4 33	..		4 41	..	..
Fulwell K	..	..	..	..	..	4 37	..		V	..	..
Hampton	..	..	..	..	..	4 41	..		To Waterloo via Richmond Arr. Twickenham 4 47 p.m	..	..
Sunbury L	..	..	..	..	..	4 45	..			..	..
Upper Halliford Halt	..	..	..	..	..	4 47	..			..	..
Shepperton M arr.	..	..	..	..	..	4 50	..			..	..
Berrylands N	..	..	..	4 22	..	..	..	..		..	..
Surbiton	..	..	4 13	4 25	..	..	..	..		4 30	..
Thames Ditton	..	..	..	4 29	..	..	..	..		..	..
Hampton Court P arr.	..	..	..	4 32	..	..	..	..		..	..
Hinchley Wood	..	..	..	Stop	..	..	..	..		4 34	..
Claygate, for Claremont	..	..	..	..	..	..	..	..		4 37	..
Oxshott, for Fairmile	..	..	..	..	..	..	..	..		4 40	..
Cobham Q	..	..	..	..	..	..	..	..		4 44	..
Effingham Junction	..	..	..	..	..	..	..	..		4 48	5 4
Horsley R	..	..	..	..	..	..	..	..		4 51	..
Clandon T	..	..	..	..	..	..	..	..		4 56	..
London Road (Guildford)	..	..	..	..	..	..	..	..		5 1	..
Esher, for Sandown Park	..	..	4 17	..	..	..	..	..	..	..	..
Hersham	..	..	4 20	p.m	..	..	..	..	..	..	..
Walton-on-Thames	..	..	4 23	(3)	..	..	..	..	..	..	..
Weybridge U	..	..	4 27	4 32	..	..	..	..	..	..	..
Addlestone	..	..	..	4 36	..	..	..	..	..	..	..
Chertsey	..	..	..	4 41	..	..	..	..	..	..	..
Virginia Water Z 460 ar.	..	..	..	4 46	..	..	..	..	..	..	..
West Weybridge	..	..	4 30	..	..	..	..	..	..	..	..
Byfleet W	..	..	4 33	..	..	..	..	..	..	..	..
Woking X 324, 389, 390	4 25	..	4 37	..	..	..	..	..	..	..	..
Worplesdon	..	..	4 45	..	..	..	..	..	..	..	..
Guildford 246, 359 arr.	..	..	4 51	..	..	..	..	..	..	5 5	..

FOR NOTES, SEE PAGE 426

FOR NOTES, SEE PAGE 426

LONDON, DORKING NORTH, HORSHAM, KINGSTON, SHEPPERTON, HAMPTON COURT, CHERTSEY, WOKING, & GUILDFORD

Week Days—*continued* (p.m)

Down	SX	SX	SX	SX			SX			SX					SX			SX	SX	SO			SX								
Waterloo dep.	4 16	4 17	4 19	4 20	4 21	4 27	4 27	Via Three Bridges, see page 172.	4 29	4 32	4 36	3	3	4 39	4 41	Via Three Bridges, see page 172.	4 45	4 47	4 47	4 47	4 49	4 52	4 52	3	3	..	4 56	4 57	4 59	5 0	..
Vauxhall	4 19	..	4 22	..	4 24	..	3		4 32	3	4 39	..	..	4 42	4 44		..	..	3	..	4 52	3	4 55	..	..	..	4 59	..	5 2	..	..
Clapham Junction A	4 24	..	4 26	..	4 29	..	..		4 36	..	4 44	..	..	4 46	4 49		..	..	..	..	4 56	..	4 59	..	..	..	5 4	..	5 6	..	..
Earlsfield B	4 27	..	4 30	..	4 32	..	..		4 40	..	4 47	..	..	4 50	4 52		..	..	..	..	5 0	..	5 3	..	..	..	5 7	..	5 10	..	..
Wimbledon	4 31	..	4 33	..	4 36	..	4 38		4 43	4 43	4 51	..	..	4 53	4 56		..	..	4 58	4 58	5 3	5 3	5 6	..	..	..	5 11	..	5 13	..	..
Raynes Park	4 34	..	4 36	..	4 39	..	..		4 46	..	4 54	..	..	4 56	4 59		..	..	..	..	5 6	..	5 9	..	..	..	5 14	..	5 16	..	..
Motspur Park	4 36	..	..	..	..	..	4 44		..	..	4 56	..	..	..	..		..	..	5 4	5 4	..	..	5 12	..	..	..	5 16	..	..	..	..
Malden Manor	4 40	..	3	..	3	..	..		3	..	5 0	..	..	3	3		..	..	..	3	3	..	3	..	..	..	5 20	..	3	..	..
Tolworth	4 42	..	..	..	..	..	..		..	..	5 2	..	..	..	..		..	..	..	..	..	..	..	..	..	..	5 22	..	..	..	..
Chessington North	4 45	..	..	..	..	..	..		..	..	5 5	..	..	..	..		..	..	..	..	..	..	..	..	..	..	5 25	..	..	..	..
Chessington South ¶ arr	4 47	..	..	..	..	..	..		..	..	5 7	..	..	..	..		..	..	..	..	..	..	..	..	..	..	5 27	..	..	..	..
Worcester Park	3	..	..	..	..	..	4 46		..	..	3	..	..	..	..		..	..	5 6	5 6	..	..	5 14	..	..	..	3	..	..	..	..
Stoneleigh	..	..	..	..	..	..	4 49		..	..	..	..	..	..	..		..	..	5 9	5 9	..	..	5 17	..	..	..	..	..	..	..	..
Ewell West C	..	..	..	..	..	..	4 52	SX	..	..	..	..	..	..	..	SX	..	..	5 12	5 12	..	..	5 20	SX	SO	..	..	..	..	..	SX
London Bridge dep.	..	..	..	..	..	..	..	4 20	..	..	..	..	4 28	..	..	4 47	..	..	..	..	..	..	..	4 48	4 55	..	..	..	..	..	5 4
Victoria "	..	..	..	..	..	..	4‡19	4 25	..	..	..	..	4SO*26	..	..	4 45	..	..	4‡38	..	..	..	..	..	4‡54	..	..	..	..	..	5 27
Sutton "	..	..	..	..	..	..	4‡43	..	..	..	..	..	4z55	..	..	..	..	..	5‡1	..	..	..	..	5 15	5 22	..	..	..	..	..	..
Epsom 285	..	..	..	..	..	..	4 55	..	..	..	..	..	5 5	..	..	..	..	..	5 15	5 15	..	..	5 23	5 24	5 32	..	..	..	..	..	..
Ashtead	..	..	..	..	..	..	4 59	..	..	..	..	SX	5 9	..	..	..	..	..	5 19	5 19	..	..	..	5 28	5 36	..	..	..	..	..	..
Leatherhead	..	..	..	..	..	..	5 3	..	..	..	..	5 9	5 13	..	..	..	..	..	5‖28	5 23	..	..	..	5 32	5 40	..	..	..	..	..	..
Boxhill & Burford Bdg D	..	..	..	..	..	..	5 8	..	..	..	..	..	5 18	..	..	..	..	..	..	..	..	..	..	5 37	..	..	..	..	..	..	5 43
Dorking North F	..	..	..	..	..	..	5 11	..	..	..	..	..	5 22	..	..	..	..	..	..	..	..	..	..	5 40	..	..	..	..	..	..	5 46
Holmwood G	..	..	..	..	..	..	5 21	..	..	..	..	..	5Y41	..	..	..	..	..	..	..	..	..	..	..	..	..	..	..	..	..	5 55
Ockley, for Capel	..	..	..	..	..	..	..	..	..	..	..	..	5Y45	..	..	..	..	..	..	..	..	..	..	..	..	..	..	..	..	..	5 59
Warnham [196, 245	..	..	..	..	..	..	..	..	..	..	..	..	5Y51	..	..	..	..	..	..	..	..	..	..	..	..	..	..	..	..	..	6 6
Horsham 159, arr.	..	..	..	..	..	..	..	5 32	..	..	..	..	5Y56	..	..	5 58	..	..	..	..	..	..	..	..	..	..	..	..	..	..	6 10
Bookham	..	..	..	..	..	..	..	..	..	..	..	5 15		..	..	Stop	..	..	5 32	5 28	..	..	..	..	5 47	..	..	..	..	..	..
Malden, for Coombe	..	..	4 39	..	4 42	..	..	..	4 49	..	..			4 59	5 2	..	..	..	..	..	5 9	..	..	..	..	..	..	..	5 19	..	..
Norbiton H	..	..	..	..	4 45	..	..	..	4 53	..	..	Dep Bookham 5 22 p.m	Dep Dorking North 5Y33 p.m	..	5 5	..	..	..	..	..	5 13	..	..	..	..	..	..	..	..	..	..
Kingston	..	..	..	..	4 48	..	..	..	4 55	..	..			..	5 8	..	..	..	..	..	5 15	..	..	..	..	..	..	..	..	..	..
Hampton Wick	..	..	..	..	4 50	..	..	..	4 57	..	..			..	5 10	..	..	..	..	..	5 17	..	..	..	..	..	..	..	..	..	..
Teddington J	..	..	..	..	4 53	..	..	..	5 1	..	..			..	5 13	..	..	..	..	..	5 21	..	..	..	..	..	..	..	..	..	..
Fulwell K	..	..	..	..	V	..	..	..	5 5	..	..			..	V	..	..	..	..	..	V	..	..	..	..	..	..	..	..	..	..
Hampton	..	..	..	..	To Waterloo via Richmond Arr Twickenham 4 59 p.m	..	..	..	5 9	..	..			..	To Waterloo via Richmond Arr Twickenham 5 19 p.m	..	..	..	..	..	To Waterloo via Richmond Arr Twickenham 5 27 p.m	..	..	..	..	..	..	..	..	..	..
Sunbury L	..	..	..	..		..	..	..	5 13	..	..			..		..	..	..	..	..		..	..	..	..	..	..	..	..	..	..
Upper Halliford Halt	..	..	..	..		..	..	..	5 15	..	..			..		..	..	..	..	..		..	..	..	..	..	..	..	..	..	..
Shepperton M arr.	..	..	..	..		..	..	..	5 18	..	..			..		..	..	..	..	..		..	..	..	..	..	..	..	..	..	..
Berrylands N	..	..	4 42	..		..	..	..	Stop	..	..	..		5 2		..	..	..	..	..		..	..	..	..	..	..	..	5 22	..	..
Surbiton	..	..	4 45	..		4 43	..	..	..	4 50	..	..		5 5		..	..	..	..	..		5 10	..	..	..	..	..	5 13	5 25	..	..
Thames Ditton	..	..	4 49	..		..	..	..	..	..	..	..		5 9		..	..	..	..	..		..	..	..	..	..	..	..	5 29	..	..
Hampton Court P arr.	..	..	4 52	..		..	..	..	..	..	..	..		5 12		..	..	..	..	..		..	..	..	..	..	..	..	5 32	..	..
Hinchley Wood	..	..	Stop	..		..	..	..	..	4 54	..	..	..	..		..	..	..	..	..		5 14	..	..	..	..	..	..	Stop	..	..
Claygate, for Claremont	..	..	..	..		..	..	..	..	4 57	..	..	..	..		..	..	..	..	..		5 17	..	..	..	..	..	..	..	..	..
Oxshott, for Fairmile	..	..	..	..		..	..	..	..	5 0	..	..	..	..		..	..	..	..	..		5 20	..	..	..	..	..	..	..	..	..
Cobham Q	..	..	..	..		..	..	..	..	5 4	..	..	..	..		..	..	..	..	..		5 24	..	..	..	..	..	..	..	..	..
Effingham Junction	..	..	..	..		..	..	..	..	5 8	..	5 25	..	..		..	..	..	5 36	5 31		5 28	..	..	5 51	..	..	..	..	..	..
Horsley R	..	..	..	..		..	..	..	..	5 11	..	..	..	..		..	..	..	5 38	..		5 31	..	..	..	..	..	..	..	..	..
Clandon T	..	..	..	..		..	..	..	..	5 16	..	..	..	..		..	..	..	5 43	..		5 36	..	..	..	..	..	..	..	..	..
London Road (Guildford)	..	..	p.m	..		..	..	..	p.m	5 21	..	..	..	..		p.m	..	..	5 49	..		5 41	..	..	..	..	..	..	p.m	..	..
Esher, for Sandown Park	..	..	3	..	..	4 47	..	..	3	..	..	..	..	..	..	3	..	..	..	..	..	..	..	..	..	..	..	5 17	3	..	..
Hersham	..	..	..	..	..	4 50	..	..	..	..	..	..	..	..	..	..	..	..	..	..	..	..	..	..	..	..	..	5 20	..	..	..
Walton-on-Thames	..	4 38	SX	..	..	4 53	..	..	SO	..	..	..	..	..	..	SX	..	5 8	..	..	..	..	..	..	..	..	..	5 23	SO	..	..
Weybridge U	..	4 42	4 55	..	..	4 57	..	..	5 5	..	..	..	..	..	..	5 15	..	5 12	..	..	..	..	..	..	..	..	..	5 27	5 35	..	..
Addlestone	..	..	4 59	..	..	..	..	..	5 9	..	..	..	..	..	..	5 19	..	..	..	..	..	..	..	..	..	..	..	..	5 39	..	..
Chertsey	..	..	5 5	..	..	..	..	..	5 12	..	..	..	..	..	..	5 22	..	..	..	..	..	..	..	..	..	..	..	..	5 42	..	..
Virginia Water Z 460 arr	..	..	5 10	..	..	..	..	..	5 16	..	..	..	..	..	..	5 26	..	..	..	..	..	..	..	..	..	..	..	..	5 46	..	..
West Weybridge	..	..	..	..	..	5 0	..	..	..	..	..	..	..	..	..	..	..	..	..	..	..	..	..	..	..	..	..	5 30	..	..	..
Byfleet W	..	4 46	..	..	..	5 3	..	..	..	..	..	..	..	..	..	..	..	5 16	..	..	..	..	..	..	..	..	..	5 33	..	..	..
Woking X 324, 389, 390	..	4 51	..	..	..	5 7	..	..	..	..	..	..	..	..	..	..	..	5 21	..	..	..	..	..	..	..	..	..	5 37	..	5 31	..
Worplesdon	..	..	..	..	..	5 15	..	..	..	..	..	..	..	..	..	..	..	..	..	..	..	..	..	..	..	..	..	5 45	..	..	..
Guildford [illegible]	..	..	..	4 55	..	5 21	..	..	..	5 25	..	..	..	..	..	..	5 25	..	5 53	..	..	5 45	..	..	..	..	..	5 51	..	..	..

[illegible]RTH, HORSHAM, KINGSTON, SHEPPERTON, HAMPTON COURT, CHERTSEY, WOKING, & GUILDFORD

Week Days—*continued* (p.m)

Down		SX		SX				SX		SX	SX		SX		SX	SX	SX					SX		SX	SX					SX	SX
Waterloo dep.	5 1	5 7	5 7	5 9	..	5 9	5 12	5 15	..	5 12	5 16	..	5 16	..	5 17	5 18	5 20	5 21	5 27	..	..	5 27	5 29	5 32	5 32	..	..	..	5 36	5 37	5 39
Vauxhall	5 4	..	..	..	(3)	5 12	..	..	(3)	5 15	..	Via Three Bridges see page 172	5 19	..	..	5 21	..	5 24	..	..	..	..	5 32	5 35	..	(3)	(3)	(3)	5 39	..	..
Clapham Junction A	5 9	(3)	(3)	..	..	5 16	(3)	(3)	..	5 20	(3)	..	5 24	..	..	5 26	..	5 29	..	..	..	(3)	5 36	5 39	(3)	..	..	..	5 44	..	..
Earlsfield B	5 12	..	..	..	..	5 20	..	..	..	5 24	..	..	5 27	..	..	5 29	..	5 32	..	..	..	..	5 40	5 43	..	..	..	..	5 47	..	..
Wimbledon	5 16	..	5 18	..	..	5 23	5SO23	..	..	5 28	..	..	5 31	..	..	5 33	..	5 36	..	..	..	..	5 43	5 46	..	..	..	..	5 51	..	..
Raynes Park	5 19	..	..	..	..	5 26	..	..	..	5 31	..	..	5 34	..	..	5 36	..	5 39	..	..	..	..	5 46	5 49	..	..	..	..	5 54	..	..
Motspur Park	..	..	5 23	..	..	..	..	..	..	5 33	Via Richmond see page 467	..	5 36	..	..	..	..	..	..	..	..	5 44	..	5 52	..	..	..	..	5 56	..	..
Malden Manor	..	..	..	..	..	..	..	..	..	..	..	..	5 40	..	..	..	..	..	..	..	..	..	..	..	..	..	..	..	6 0	..	..
Tolworth	(3)	..	..	..	..	(3)	..	..	..	(3)	..	..	5 42	..	..	(3)	..	(3)	..	..	..	..	(3)	(3)	..	..	..	..	6 2	..	..
Chessington North	..	..	..	..	..	..	..	..	..	..	..	..	5 45	..	..	..	..	..	..	..	..	..	..	..	..	..	..	..	6 5	..	..
Chessington South ¶ arr	..	..	..	..	..	..	..	..	..	..	..	..	5 47	..	..	..	..	..	..	..	..	..	..	..	..	..	..	..	6 7	..	..
Worcester Park	..	..	5 26	..	..	..	..	5 32	..	5 37	..	..	..	..	..	..	..	..	..	..	..	5 46	..	5 54	..	..	..	..	..	..	..
Stoneleigh	..	..	5 29	..	..	..	..	5 35	..	5 40	..	..	(3)	..	..	..	..	..	..	..	..	5 49	..	5 57	..	..	..	..	(3)	..	..
Ewell West C	..	..	5 31	..	..	..	..	..	SX	5 43	..	SX	..	SO	..	..	..	..	..	..	..	5 52	..	6 0	..	..	SO	SX	..	..	..
London Bridge dep.	..	..	..	..	..	..	..	..	5 8	..	..	5 15	Stop	4*55	..	..	..	..	..	..	SX	..	..	..	..	..	5 25	5 28	..	..	..
Victoria "	..	..	4SX‡55	..	..	..	..	..	5 B 4	..	..	..	..	5 18	..	..	..	..	..	..	5 30	5‡15	..	..	..	..	5‡20	..	..	..	..
Sutton "	..	..	5SX‡19	..	..	..	..	..	5 35	..	..	..	..	5 39	..	..	..	..	..	..	..	5‡40	..	..	..	..	5 55	5 57	..	..	..
Epsom 285	..	..	5 35	..	..	..	..	5 40	5 45	5 47	..	..	..	..	..	..	..	..	..	..	..	5 56	..	6 3	..	..	6 5	6 7	..	..	..
Ashtead	..	..	5 39	..	..	..	..	5 44	5 49	..	..	..	..	..	..	..	..	..	..	..	..	6 0	..	..	..	SX	6 9	6 11	..	..	..
Leatherhead	..	..	5 43	..	..	..	..	5 48	5 54	..	..	..	..	..	..	..	..	..	..	..	..	6 4	..	..	..	6 9	6 13	6 15	..	..	..
Boxhill & Burford Bdg D	..	..	5 48	..	SO	..	..	..	..	..	..	..	..	..	..	..	..	..	..	..	..	6 9	..	..	..	..	6 18	6 20	..	..	..
Dorking North F	..	..	5 51	..	6 5	..	..	..	..	..	..	..	..	5 55	..	..	..	..	..	..	6 3	6 12	..	..	..	..	6 21	6 25	..	..	..
Holmwood G	..	..	..	..	6 13	..	..	..	..	..	..	..	..	..	..	..	..	..	..	..	..	6 21	..	..	..	..	6 31	6 33	..	..	..
Ockley, for Capel	..	..	..	..	6 17	..	..	..	..	..	..	..	..	..	..	..	..	..	..	..	..	6 25	..	..	..	..	6 35	6 37	..	..	..
Warnham [196, 245	..	..	..	..	6 23	..	..	..	..	..	..	..	..	..	..	..	..	..	..	..	..	6 31	..	..	..	..	6 42	6 44	..	..	..
Horsham 159, arr.	..	..	..	..	6 28	..	..	..	..	..	..	6 8	..	6 13	..	..	..	..	..	..	6 21	6 36	..	..	..	..	6 46	6 49	..	..	..
Bookham	..	..	..	..	..	..	..	5 52	5 58	..	..	..	..	..	..	..	..	..	..	..	..	..	..	..	..	6 13	..	..	..	..	..
Malden, for Coombe	5 22	..	..	..	..	5 29	..	..	..	..	..	..	..	..	..	5 39	..	5 42	..	..	..	..	5 49	..	..	..	..	..	..	..	..
Norbiton H	5 25	..	..	..	..	5 33	..	..	..	..	..	..	..	..	..	..	..	5 45	..	..	..	..	5 53	..	..	..	..	..	..	..	..
Kingston	5 28	..	..	..	..	5 35	..	..	..	..	..	..	..	..	..	..	..	5 48	..	..	..	..	5 55	..	..	..	..	..	..	..	..
Hampton Wick	5 30	..	..	..	..	5 37	..	..	..	..	..	..	..	..	..	..	..	5 50	..	..	..	..	5 57	..	..	..	..	..	..	..	..
Teddington J	5 33	..	..	..	..	5 41	..	..	..	..	..	..	..	..	..	..	..	5 53	..	..	..	..	6 1	..	..	..	..	..	..	..	..
Fulwell K	5 37	..	..	..	..	V	..	..	..	..	5 42	..	..	..	..	..	..	V	..	..	..	..	6 5	..	..	..	..	..	..	..	..
Hampton	5 41	..	..	..	..	To Waterloo via Richmond Arr. Twickenham 5 47 p.m	..	..	..	..	5 46	..	..	..	..	..	..	To Waterloo via Richmond Arr. Twickenham 6 0 p.m	..	..	..	..	6 9	..	..	..	..	..	..	..	..
Sunbury L	5 45	..	..	..	..		..	..	..	..	5 51	..	..	..	..	..	..		..	..	..	..	6 13	..	..	..	..	..	..	..	..
Upper Halliford Halt	5 47	..	..	..	..		..	..	..	..	5 53	..	..	..	..	..	..		..	..	..	..	6 15	..	..	..	..	..	..	..	..
Shepperton M arr.	5 50	..	..	..	..		..	..	..	..	5 57	..	..	..	..	..	..		..	..	..	..	6 18	..	..	..	..	..	..	..	..
Berrylands N	..	..	..	..	..		..	..	..	..	..	..	..	..	..	5 42	..		..	..	..	..	..	..	..	..	..	..	..	..	..
Surbiton	..	5 23	..	..	..		5 28	..	..	..	..	..	..	..	..	5 44	..		5 43	..	..	..	..	..	5 49	..	..	..	..	5 53	..
Thames Ditton	..	..	..	..	..		..	..	..	..	..	..	..	..	..	5 48	..		..	..	..	..	..	..	..	..	..	..	..	..	..
Hampton Court P arr.	..	..	..	..	..		..	..	..	..	..	..	..	..	..	5 52	..		..	..	..	..	..	..	..	..	..	..	..	..	..
Hinchley Wood	..	..	..	..	..		5 31	..	..	..	..	..	..	..	..	..	..		..	..	..	..	..	..	5 52	..	..	..	..	..	..
Claygate, for Claremont	..	..	..	..	..		5 34	..	..	..	..	..	..	..	..	..	..		..	..	..	..	..	..	5 55	..	..	..	..	..	..
Oxshott, for Fairmile	..	..	..	..	..		5 38	..	..	..	..	..	..	..	..	..	..		..	..	..	..	..	..	5 59	..	..	..	..	..	..
Cobham Q	..	..	..	..	..		5 41	..	..	..	..	..	..	..	..	..	..		..	..	..	..	..	..	6 2	..	..	..	..	..	..
Effingham Junction	..	..	..	..	..		5 47	5 55	6 2	..	..	..	..	..	..	..	..		..	..	..	..	..	..	6 8	6 16	..	..	..	..	..
Horsley R	..	..	..	..	..		5 49	..	..	..	..	..	..	..	..	..	..		..	..	..	..	..	..	6 10	..	..	..	..	..	..
Clandon T	..	..	..	..	..		5 54	..	..	..	..	..	..	..	..	..	..		..	..	..	..	..	..	6 15	..	..	..	..	..	..
London Road (Guildford)	..	..	..	..	..		6 0	..	..	..	..	..	..	..	..	..	..		..	..	..	..	..	..	6 21	..	..	..	..	..	..
Esher, for Sandown Park	..	5 27	..	..	..	..	..	..	..	..	..	..	p.m	..	..	..	..	..	5 47	..	..	..	..	..	..	..	..	..	..	5 57	..
Hersham	..	5 30	..	..	..	..	..	..	..	..	..	..	(3)	..	..	..	..	..	5 50	..	..	..	..	..	..	..	..	..	..	6 0	..
Walton-on-Thames	..	5 33	..	..	..	..	..	..	..	..	..	..	SX	..	5 39	..	..	..	5 53	(3)	..	..	..	..	..	..	..	..	..	6 3	..
Weybridge U	..	5 37	..	..	..	..	..	..	..	..	..	..	5 45	..	5 43	..	..	..	5 57	6 5	..	..	..	..	..	..	..	..	..	6 7	..
Addlestone	..	5 41	..	..	..	..	..	..	..	..	..	..	5 49	..	..	..	..	..	..	6 9	..	..	..	..	..	..	..	..	..	..	..
Chertsey	..	5 44	..	..	..	..	..	..	..	..	..	..	5 52	..	..	..	..	..	..	6 12	..	..	..	..	..	..	..	..	..	..	..
Virginia Water Z 460 arr	..	..	..	..	..	..	..	..	..	..	..	..	5 56	..	..	..	..	..	..	6 16	..	..	..	..	..	..	..	..	..	..	..
West Weybridge	..	..	..	..	..	..	..	..	..	..	..	..	..	..	..	..	..	..	6 0	..	..	..	..	..	..	..	..	..	..	6 10	..
Byfleet W	..	..	..	..	..	..	..	..	..	..	..	..	..	..	5 47	..	..	..	6 3	..	..	..	..	..	..	..	..	..	..	6 13	..
Woking X 324, 389, 390	..	..	..	5 40	..	..	..	..	..	..	..	..	..	..	5 51	..	..	..	6 7	..	..	..	..	..	..	..	..	..	..	6 17	6 10
Worplesdon	..	..	..	..	..	..	..	..	..	..	..	..	..	..	..	..	..	..	6 15	..	..	..	..	..	..	..	..	..	..	..	..
Guildford 246, 359 arr.	..	..	..	..	..	..	6 5	..	..	..	..	..	..	..	..	..	5 57	..	6 21	..	..	..	..	..	6 25	..	..	..	..	..	..

FOR NOTES, SEE PAGE 426

FOR NOTES, SEE PAGE 426

LONDON, DORKING NORTH, HORSHAM, KINGSTON, SHEPPERTON, HAMPTON COURT, CHERTSEY, WOKING, & GUILDFORD

Week Days—continued (p.m.)

Down		SX		SX			SX					SX	SX	SO								SX	SX				SX	SX	SX	SX	SX
Waterloo ....dep.	5 39	5 41	5 45	5 47	5 47	..	5 48	③	5 49	5 52		5 54	5 52	554	③	5 56	557	③	5 59	6 1	6 7	6 7	6 9	6 9	6 12	③	6 12	6 14	6 16	6 16	6 17
Vauxhall	5 42	5 44	..	..	③	..	③	..	5 52	③	Via Three Bridges, see page 174	③	5 55	..	..	5 59	..	..	6 2	6 4	③	③	..	6 12	③	..	6 15	..	③	6 19	..
Clapham Junction A	5 46	5 49	..	..		Via Three Bridges, see page 174	..	..	5 56				6 0	..	..	6 4	..	..	6 6	6 9			..	6 16		..	6 19	..		6 23	..
Earlsfield B	5 50	5 52	..	..	..		..	..	6 0	..		..	6 4	..	..	6 7	..	..	6 10	6 12	..	..	..	6 20	..	..	6 23	..	Via Richmond, see page 467	6 27	..
Wimbledon	5 53	5 56	..	..	5S058		..	..	6 3	6S03		..	6 8	..	..	6 11	..	..	6 13	6 16	6S018	..	..	6 23	6S023	..	6 26	..		6 30	..
Raynes Park	5 56	5 59	..	..	..		..	..	6 6	..		..	6 11	..	..	6 14	..	..	6 16	6 19	..	..	..	6 26	..	..	6 29	..		6 33	..
Motspur Park	..	..	..	..	6 4		Via Richmond, see page 467	..	..	..		..	6 14	..	..	6 16	..	..	..	..	6 24	..	..	..	..	..	6 32	..		6 36	..
Malden Manor	③	③	..	..	..			..	③	..		..	③	..	..	6 20	..	..	③	③	..	..	..	③	..	..	③	..		6 40	..
Tolworth	..	..	..	..	..			..	..	..		..	..	..	..	6 22	..	..	..	..	..	..	..	..	..	..	..	..		6 42	..
Chessington North	..	..	..	..	..			..	..	..		..	..	..	..	6 25	..	..	..	..	..	..	..	..	..	..	..	..		6 45	..
Chessington South ¶ar	..	..	..	..	..			..	..	..		..	..	..	..	6 27	..	..	..	..	..	..	..	..	..	..	..	..		6 47	..
Worcester Park	..	..	..	..	6 6			..	..	..		6 12	6 17	..	..	③	..	..	..	..	6 26	..	..	..	..	..	6 34	..	..	③	..
Stoneleigh	..	..	..	..	6 9			..	..	..		6 15	6 20	..	..	..	..	..	..	..	6 29	..	..	..	..	..	6 37	..	..	..	..
Ewell West C	..	..	..	..	6 12	SX		SX	..	..	SO	..	6 23	..	SO	..	..	..	..	..	6 32	..	..	..	..	SX	6 40	..	..	..	..
London Bridge ....dep.	..	..	..	..	..	5 48		5 48	..	..	..	..	..	..	5 55	..	..	..	..	..	..	..	..	..	..	6 8	..	..	..	..	..
Victoria ...."	..	..	..	..	5‡SX40	5 38		..	..	..	5 48	..	..	..	5‡54	..	..	..	..	..	5SX‡55	..	..	..	..	5‡55	..	..	..	..	..
Sutton ...."	..	..	..	..	6SX‡4	..		6 15	..	..	..	..	..	..	6 22	..	..	..	..	..	6SX‡22	..	..	..	..	6 35	..	..	..	..	..
Epsom 285	..	..	..	..	6 15	..		6 25	..	..	..	6 20	6 30	..	6 31	..	..	..	..	..	6 35	..	..	..	..	6 45	6 44	..	..	..	..
Ashtead	..	..	..	..	6 19	..		6 29	..	..	..	6 24	6 34	..	6 35	..	..	..	..	..	6 39	..	..	..	..	6 49	..	..	..	..	..
Leatherhead	..	..	..	..	6 23	..		6 33	..	..	..	6 28	6 38	..	6 39	..	..	..	..	..	6 43	..	..	..	..	6 53	..	..	..	..	..
Boxhill & Burford Bdg D	..	..	..	..	..	..	..	6 38	..	..	..	6 33	Arr. Epsom 6 26 p.m	..	..	..	..	..	..	..	6 48	..	..	..	..	..	..	..	..	..	..
Dorking North F	..	..	..	..	..	..	..	6 41	..	..	..	6 36		..	..	..	..	..	..	..	6 51	..	..	..	..	..	..	..	..	..	..
Holmwood G	..	..	..	..	..	..	..	..	..	..	..	..		..	..	..	..	..	..	..	7g1	..	..	..	..	..	..	..	..	..	..
Ockley, for Capel	..	..	..	..	..	..	..	..	..	..	..	..		..	..	..	..	..	..	..	7g5	..	..	..	..	..	..	..	..	..	..
Warnham ....[245, ..	..	..	..	..	..	..	..	..	..	..	..	..		..	..	..	..	..	..	..	7g11	..	..	..	..	..	..	..	..	..	..
Horsham 159, 196, ar	..	..	..	..	..	6 44	..	..	..	..	7 5	..		..	..	..	..	..	..	..	7g16	..	..	..	..	..	..	..	..	..	..
Bookham	..	..	..	..	6 28	Stop	..	..	..	..	..	..	6 45	..	6 44	..	..	..	..	..	Dep Dorking North 6 53 p.m (7 1 p.m. on Saturdays)	..	..	..	..	6 57	..	..	..	..	..
Malden, for Coombe	5 59	6 2	..	..	..	..	..	..	6 9	..	..	..	..	..	..	..	..	..	6 19	6 22		..	..	6 29	..	..	..	..	..	..	..
Norbiton H	..	6 5	..	..	..	..	..	..	6 13	..	..	..	..	..	..	..	..	..	..	6 25		..	..	6 33	..	..	..	..	..	..	..
Kingston	..	6 8	..	..	..	..	..	..	6 15	..	..	..	..	..	..	..	..	..	..	6 28		..	..	6 35	..	..	..	..	..	..	..
Hampton Wick	..	6 10	..	..	..	..	..	..	6 17	..	..	..	..	..	..	..	..	..	..	6 30		..	..	6 37	..	..	..	..	..	..	..
Teddington J	..	6 13	..	..	..	..	..	..	6 21	..	..	..	..	..	..	..	..	..	..	6 33		..	..	6 41	..	..	..	..	6 42	..	..
Fulwell K	..	V	..	..	..	..	6 14	..	V	..	..	..	..	..	..	..	..	..	..	6 37		..	..	V	..	..	..	..	6 46	..	..
Hampton	..	To Waterloo via Richmond Arr. Twickenham 6 19 p.m	..	..	..	..	6 18	..	To Waterloo via Richmond Arr. Twickenham 6 27 p.m	..	..	..	..	..	..	..	..	..	..	6 41		..	..	To Waterloo via Richmond Arr. Twickenham 6 47 p.m	..	..	..	..	6 51	..	..
Sunbury L	..		..	..	..	..	6 22	..		..	..	..	..	..	..	..	..	..	..	6 45		..	..		..	..	..	..	6 53	..	..
Upper Halliford Halt	..		..	..	..	..	6 24	..		..	..	..	..	..	..	..	..	..	..	6 47		..	..		..	..	..	..	6 57	..	..
Shepperton M ....arr.	..		..	..	..	..	6 27	..		..	..	..	..	..	..	..	..	..	..	6 50		..	..		..	..	..	..	..	..	..
Berrylands N	6 2		..	..	..	..	..	..		..	..	..	..	..	..	..	..	..	6 22	..		6 23	..		6 28	..	..	..	..	..	6 34
Surbiton	6 5		..	..	..	..	..	..		6 8	..	..	..	..	..	..	613	..	6 25	..		..	..		..	..	..	..	..	..	..
Thames Ditton	6 9		..	..	..	..	..	..		..	..	..	..	..	..	..	..	..	6 29	..		..	..		..	..	..	..	..	..	..
Hampton Court P arr.	6 12		..	..	..	..	..	..		..	..	..	..	..	..	..	..	..	6 32	..		..	..		..	..	..	..	..	..	..
Hinchley Wood	..		..	..	..	..	..	..		6 11	..	..	..	..	..	..	..	..	..	..	..	..	..		6 31	..	..	..	..	..	..
Claygate, for Claremont	..		..	..	..	..	..	..		6 14	..	..	..	..	..	..	..	..	..	..	..	..	..		6 34	..	..	..	..	..	..
Oxshott, for Fairmile	..		..	..	..	..	..	..		6 18	..	..	..	..	..	..	..	..	..	..	..	..	..		6 38	..	..	..	..	..	..
Cobham Q	..		..	..	..	..	..	..		6 21	..	..	..	..	..	..	..	..	..	..	..	..	..		6 41	..	..	..	..	..	..
Effingham Junction	..		..	..	6 32	..	..	..		6 27	..	..	6 49	..	6 46	..	..	..	..	..	..	..	..		6 47	7 1	..	..	..	..	..
Horsley R	..		..	..	..	..	..	..		6 29	..	..	..	..	..	..	..	..	..	..	..	..	..		6 49	..	..	..	..	..	..
Clandon T	..		..	..	..	..	..	..		6 34	..	..	..	..	..	..	..	..	..	..	..	..	..		6 54	..	..	..	..	..	..
London Road (Guildford)	..		..	..	..	p.m	..	..		6 40	..	..	..	..	..	..	..	..	..	..	..	..	..		7 0	..	..	..	..	..	..
Esher, for Sandown Park	..	..	..	..	..	③	..	..	..	..	..	..	..	..	..	..	617	③	..	..	..	6 27	..	..	..	..	..	6 33	..	..	..
Hersham	..	..	..	..	..		..	..	..	..	..	..	..	..	..	..	620		..	..	..	6 30	..	..	..	..	..	..	..	..	6 41
Walton-on-Thames	..	..	..	6 8	..	SX	..	..	..	..	..	..	..	..	..	..	623	SO	..	..	..	6 33	..	..	..	..	..	6 40	..	..	6 45
Weybridge U	..	..	..	6 12	..	6 25	..	..	..	..	..	..	..	..	..	..	627	6 35	..	..	..	6 37	..	..	..	..	..	..	..	..	..
Addlestone	..	..	..	..	..	6 29	..	..	..	..	..	..	..	..	..	..	..	6 39	..	..	..	6 41	..	..	..	..	..	..	..	..	..
Chertsey	..	..	..	..	..	6 32	..	..	..	..	..	..	..	..	..	..	..	6 42	..	..	..	6 44	..	..	..	..	..	..	..	..	..
Virginia Water Z 460 arr.	..	..	..	..	..	6 36	..	..	..	..	..	..	..	..	..	..	..	6 46	..	..	..	..	..	..	..	..	..	..	..	..	..
West Weybridge	..	..	..	..	..	..	..	..	..	..	..	..	..	..	..	..	630	..	..	..	..	..	..	..	..	..	..	..	..	..	6 48
Byfleet W	..	..	..	6 16	..	..	..	..	..	..	..	..	..	..	..	..	633	..	..	..	..	..	..	..	..	..	..	6 47	..	..	6 51
Woking X 324, 389, 390	..	..	..	6 21	..	..	..	..	..	..	..	..	..	625	..	..	637	..	..	..	..	..	6 42	..	..	..	..	..	..	..	6 55
Worplesdon	..	..	..	..	..	..	..	..	..	..	..	..	..	..	..	..	645	..	..	..	..	..	..	..	..	..	..	..	..	..	..
Guildford [illegible]	..	..	6 25	..	..	..	..	..	..	6 45	..	..	..	..	..	..	651	..	..	..	..	..	..	..	7 5	..	..	..	..	..	..

[...]DORKING NORTH, HORSHAM, KINGSTON, SHEPPERTON, HAMPTON COURT, CHERTSEY, WOKING, & GUILDFORD

Week Days—*continued* (p.m.)

Down	SX Vir Three Bridges, see page 174	SX Via Three Bridges, see page 176	SX 3	SX	3	SX Via Three Bridges see page 176		SX 3	3	SX 3	SX 3	3 SO	3 SX	3	SX	3
Waterloo dep.			6 18	6 20	6 21		6 27	6 27	6 29	6 32	6 32			6 36	6 37	6 39
Vauxhall			6 21		6 24				6 32		6 35			6 39		6 42
Clapham Junction A			6 26		6 29				6 36		6 39			6 44		6 46
Earlsfield B			6 29		6 32				6 40		6 43			6 47		6 50
Wimbledon			6 33		6 36				6 43		6 46			6 51		6 53
Raynes Park			6 36		6 39				6 46		6 49			6 54		6 56
Motspur Park								6 44			6 52			6 56		
Malden Manor														7 0		
Tolworth														7 2		
Chessington North														7 5		
Chessington South ¶ arr.														7 7		
Worcester Park								6 47			6 54					
Stoneleigh								6 50			6 57					
Ewell West C								6 52			7 0					
London Bridge dep.		6 9				6 20						6 25	6 28			
Victoria "	6 18							6‡20				6‡20				
Sutton "								6‡43				6 55	6 55			
Epsom 285								6 56			7 3	7 5	7 7			
Ashtead								7 0			7 7	7 9	7 11			
Leatherhead								7 4			7 11	7 13	7 15			
Boxhill & Burford Bdg								7 9				7 18	7 20			
Dorking North F								7 11				7 21	7 23			
Holmwood G								7 21				7 31	7 31			
Ockley, for Capel												7 35	7 35			
Warnham [245												7 41	7 41			
Horsham 159, 196 arr.	7 5	7 23				7 34						7 46	7 46			
Bookham	Stop										7 16					
Malden, for Coombe			6 39		6 42				6 49							6 59
Norbiton H					6 45				6 53							
Kingston					6 48				6 55							
Hampton Wick					6 50				6 57							
Teddington J					6 53				7 1							
Fulwell K					V				7 5							
Hampton					To Waterloo via Richmond Arr. Twickenham 7 1 p.m.				7 9							
Sunbury L									7 13							
Upper Halliford Halt									7 15							
Shepperton M arr.									7 18							
Berrylands N			6 42						Stop							7 2
Surbiton			6 44				6 43			6 48					6 53	7 5
Thames Ditton			6 48													7 9
Hampton Court P arr.			6 52													7 12
Hinchley Wood										6 51						
Claygate, for Claremont										6 54						
Oxshott, for Fairmile										6 58						
Cobham Q										7 1						
Effingham Junction										7 6	7 19					
Horsley R										7 9						
Clandon T										7 14						
London Road (Guildford)	p.m.									7 20						
Esher, for Sandown Park	3						6 47								6 57	
Hersham							6 50		p.m.						7 0	
Walton-on-Thames	SX						6 53		3						7 3	
Weybridge U	6 50						6 57		7 5						7 7	
Addlestone	6 54								7 9							
Chertsey	6 57								7 12							
Virginia Water Z 460 arr.	7 2								7 16							
West Weybridge							7 0								7 10	
Byfleet W							7 3								7 13	
Woking X 324, 389, 390							7 7								7 17	
Worplesdon							7 15									
Guildford 246, 359 arr.				6 56			7 21			7 24						

Down	SO	SX Via Three Bridges see page 176		3	3	SX 3		3	3 SX	3 SX	3 SO		3	3	
Waterloo dep.	6 42		6 45	6 47	6 49	6 52	6 54	6 56				6 57	6 59	7 1	
Vauxhall					6 52			6 59					7 2	7 4	
Clapham Junction A					6 56			7 4					7 6	7 9	
Earlsfield B					7 0			7 7					7 10	7 12	
Wimbledon					7 3			7 11					7 13	7 16	
Raynes Park	6 53			6S058	7 6			7 14					7 16	7 19	
Motspur Park				7 4				7 16							
Malden Manor								7 20							
Tolworth								7 22							
Chessington North								7 25							
Chessington South ¶ arr.								7 27							
Worcester Park				7 6											
Stoneleigh				7 9											
Ewell West C				7 12											
London Bridge dep.		6 35							6 48		6 53				
Victoria "		6 38		6SX‡38							6‡50				7 18
Sutton "				7SX‡2					7 15		7 20				7 39
Epsom 285				7 15					7 25		7 29				
Ashtead				7 19					7 29		7 33				
Leatherhead				7 23					7 33	7 36	7 37				
Boxhill & Burford Bdg									7 38						
Dorking North F									7 41						7 55
Holmwood G									7 51						
Ockley, for Capel									7 55						
Warnham [245									8 2						
Horsham 159, 196 arr.		7 55							8 6						8 13
Bookham				7 28						7 40	7 42				
Malden, for Coombe					7 9								7 19	7 22	
Norbiton H					7 13									7 25	
Kingston					7 15									7 28	
Hampton Wick					7 17									7 30	
Teddington J					7 21									7 33	
Fulwell K					V									7 37	
Hampton					To Waterloo via Richmond Arr. Twickenham 7 29 p.m.									7 41	
Sunbury L														7 45	
Upper Halliford Halt														7 47	
Shepperton M arr.														7 50	
Berrylands N													7 22		
Surbiton	7 0					7 8						7 13	7 25		
Thames Ditton													7 29		
Hampton Court P arr.													7 32		
Hinchley Wood	7 3					7 11							Stop		
Claygate, for Claremont	7 6					7 14									
Oxshott, for Fairmile	7 10					7 18									
Cobham Q	7 13					7 21									
Effingham Junction	7 18			7 31		7 27				7 43	7 45				
Horsley R	7 20					7 29									
Clandon T	7 25					7 34									
London Road (Guildford)	7 31					7 40									
Esher, for Sandown Park												7 17	p.m.		
Hersham												7 20	3		
Walton-on-Thames												7 23			
Weybridge U												7 27	7 35		
Addlestone													7 39		
Chertsey													7 42		
Virginia Water Z 460 arr.													7 46		
West Weybridge												7 30			
Byfleet W												7 33			
Woking X 324, 389, 390			7 15				7 25					7 37			
Worplesdon												7 45			
Guildford 246, 359 arr.	7 35		7 25			7 44						7 31			

FOR NOTES, SEE PAGE 426

FOR NOTES, SEE PAGE 426

LONDON, DORKING NORTH, HORSHAM, KINGSTON, SHEPPERTON, HAMPTON COURT, CHERTSEY, WOKING, & GUILDFORD

Week Days—continued (p.m)

Down				SX	SX			SX						SO													SX			
Waterloo dep.	7 7	7 9	7 12	7 17	7 19	7 21	7 27	7 27	(3)	7 29	7 36	7 39	7 42	7 45	7 47	7 49	7 54	7 56	7 57	7 59	8 1		(3)	8 7	8 9	8 12	8 19	8 21	8 27	(3)
Vauxhall		7 12	(3)		7 22	7 24		(3)		7 32	7 39	7 42	(3)		(3)	7 52		7 59		8 2	8 4				8 12		8 22	8 24		
Clapham Junction A		7 16			7 26	7 29				7 36	7 44	7 46				7 56		8 4		8 6	8 9				8 16		8 26	8 29		
Earlsfield B		7 20			7 30	7 32				7 40	7 47	7 50				8 0		8 7		8 10	8 12	Via Three Bridges, see page 178			8 20		8 30	8 32		
Wimbledon	7 18	7 23	7SO23	7U28	7 33	7 36		7 38		7 43	7 51	7 53	7 53		7 58	8 3		8 11		8 13	8 16			8 18	8 23	8 23	8 33	8 36		
Raynes Park		7 26			7 36	7 39				7 46	7 54	7 56				8 6		8 14		8 16	8 19				8 26		8 36	8 39		
Motspur Park	7 24							7 44			7 56				8 4			8 16						8 24						
Malden Manor	(3)	(3)			(3)	(3)				(3)	8 0	(3)				(3)		8 20		(3)	(3)			(3)	(3)	(3)	(3)	(3)		
Tolworth											8 2							8 22												
Chessington North											8 5							8 25												
Chessington South ¶ arr											8 7							8 27												
Worcester Park	7 26							7 46			(3)				8 6			(3)						8 26						
Stoneleigh	7 29							7 49							8 9									8 29						
Ewell West C	7 32							7 52							8 12									8 32						
London Bridge dep.									7 28														7 53	7‡53						8 25
Victoria "	6SX‡55								7‡§20													7 48	7‡51							8‡24
Sutton "	7SX‡21								7 56														8a21	8‡a21						8 52
Epsom 285	7 35							7 55	8 5						8 15								8 30	8 35						9 3
Ashtead	7 39							7 59	8 9						8 19								8 34	8 39						9 7
Leatherhead	7 43							8 3	8 13						8 23								8 38	8 43						9 12
Boxhill & Burford Bdg D	7 48							8 8	8 18															8 48						9 17
Dorking North F	7 51							8 11	8 21															8 51						9 20
Holmwood G	8 9								8 31															9 9						9 32
Ockley, for Capel	8 13								8 35															9 13						9 36
Warnham 196, 245	8 19								8 41															9 19						9 42
Horsham 159, arr.	8 24								8 46													9 5		9 24						9 46
Bookham	Dep. Dorking North 8 1 p.m								Stop						8 28								8 42	Dep. Dorking North 9 1 p.m						Dep. Dorking North 9 23 p.m
Malden, for Coombe		7 29			7 39	7 42				7 49		7 59				8 9				8 19	8 22				8 29		8 39	8 42		
Norbiton H		7 33				7 45				7 53						8 13					8 25				8 33			8 45		
Kingston		7 35				7 48				7 55						8 15					8 28				8 35			8 48		
Hampton Wick		7 37				7 50				7 57						8 17					8 30				8 37			8 50		
Teddington J		7 41				7 53				8 1						8 21					8 33				8 41			8 53		
Fulwell K		V				V				8 5						V					8 37				V			V		
Hampton		To Waterloo via Richmond Arr. Twickenham 7 47 p.m				To Waterloo via Richmond Arr. Twickenham 8 1 p.m				8 9						To Waterloo via Richmond Arr. Twickenham 8 28 p.m					8 41				To Waterloo via Richmond Arr. Twickenham 8 47 p.m			To Waterloo via Richmond Arr. Twickenham 9 0 p.m		
Sunbury L										8 13											8 45									
Upper Halliford Halt										8 15											8 47									
Shepperton M arr.										8 18											8 50									
Berrylands N					7 42							8 2								8 22							8 42			
Surbiton			7 28	7 35	7 45		7 43					8 5	8 0						8 13	8 25						8 30	8 45		8 43	
Thames Ditton					7 49							8 9								8 29							8 49			
Hampton Court P arr.					7 52							8 12								8 32							8 52			
Hinchley Wood			7 31										8 3							Stop						8 33				Stop
Claygate, for Claremont			7 34										8 6													8 36				
Oxshott, for Fairmile			7 38										8 10													8 40				
Cobham Q			7 41										8 13													8 43				
Effingham Junction			7 47										8 19		8 32								8 45			8 49				
Horsley R			7 49										8 21													8 51				
Clandon T			7 54										8 26													8 56				
London Road (Guildford)			8 0										8 32													9 2				
Esher, for Sandown Park				7 39			7 47		p.m										8 17	p.m									8 47	p.m
Hersham				7 42			7 50		(3)										8 20	(3)									8 50	(3)
Walton-on-Thames				7 45			7 53												8 23										8 53	
Weybridge U				7 49			7 57		8 5										8 27	8 35									8 57	9 5
Addlestone									8 9											8 39										9 9
Chertsey									8 12											8 42										9 12
Virginia Water Z 460 arr									8 16											8 46										9 16
West Weybridge				7 52			8 0												8 30										9 0	
Byfleet W				7 55			8 3												8 33										9 2	
Woking X 324, 389, 390				8 0			8 7										8 25		8 37										9 7	
Worplesdon							8 15												8 45										9 15	
[illegible]							[illegible]						8 36	8 25					8 51							9 6			9 21	

WATERLOO, WIMBLEDON, EPSOM, DORKING, HORSHAM, KINGSTON, SHEPPERTON, HAMPTON COURT, CHERTSEY, WOKING, & GUILDFORD

Week Days—*continued*

Down	p.m							
Waterloo dep.	8 29	8 36	8 39	8 42	8 45	8 47	8 49	3
Vauxhall	8 32	8 39	8 42	3	..	3	8 52	..
Clapham Junction A	8 36	8 44	8 46		..		8 56	..
Earlsfield B	8 40	8 47	8 50	..	..	..	9 0	..
Wimbledon	8 43	8 51	8 53	8 53	..	8 58	9 3	..
Raynes Park	8 46	8 54	8 56	..	..	..	9 6	..
Motspur Park		8 56		..	..	9 4		..
Malden Manor	3	9 0	3	..	..	..	3	..
Tolworth		9 2		..	..	..		..
Chessington North	..	9 5	..	..	..	..	..	..
Chessington South ¶ ar	..	9 7	..	..	..	..	..	..
Worcester Park	..	3	..	..	..	9 6	..	..
Stoneleigh	..		..	..	..	9 9	..	..
Ewell West C	..	..	..	..	..	9 12	..	..
London Bridge dep.	..	..	..	..	..	8‡25	..	8 53
Victoria "	..	..	..	..	..	8‡24	..	8‡51
Sutton "	..	..	..	..	..	8‡52	..	9 20
Epsom 285	..	..	..	..	..	9 15	..	9 29
Ashtead	..	..	..	..	..	9 19	..	9 33
Leatherhead	..	..	..	..	..	9 23	..	9 37
Boxhill & Burford Bdg D	..	..	..	..	..	..	..	..
Dorking North F	..	..	..	..	..	..	..	..
Holmwood G	..	..	..	..	..	..	..	..
Ockley, for Capel	..	..	..	..	..	..	..	..
Warnham 196, 245	..	..	..	..	..	..	..	..
Horsham 159, arr.	..	..	..	..	..	..	..	..
Bookham	..	..	..	..	..	9 28	..	9 42
Malden, for Coombe	8 49	..	8 59	..	..	..	9 9	..
Norbiton H	8 53	..	..	..	..	..	9 13	..
Kingston	8 55	..	..	..	..	..	9 15	..
Hampton Wick	8 57	..	..	..	..	..	9 17	..
Teddington J	9 1	..	..	..	..	..	9 21	..
Fulwell K	9 5	..	..	..	..	..	V	..
Hampton	9 9	..	..	..	..	..	To Waterloo via Richmond Arr. Twickenham 9 28 p.m	..
Sunbury L	9 13	..	..	..	..	..		..
Upper Halliford Halt	9 15	..	..	..	..	..		..
Shepperton M arr.	9 18	..	..	..	..	..		..
Berrylands N	..	..	9 2	..	..	..		..
Surbiton	..	..	9 5	9 0	..	..		..
Thames Ditton	..	..	9 9	..	..	..		..
Hampton Court P arr.	..	..	9 12	..	..	..		..
Hinchley Wood	..	..	..	9 3	..	..		..
Claygate, for Claremont	..	..	..	9 6	..	..		..
Oxshott, for Fairmile	..	..	..	9 10	..	..		..
Cobham Q	..	..	..	9 13	..	..		..
Effingham Junction	..	..	..	9 18	..	9 32		9 46
Horsley R	..	..	..	9 20	..	..		..
Clandon T	..	..	..	9 25	..	..		..
London Road (Guildford)	..	..	..	9 31	..	..		..
Esher, for Sandown Park	..	..	..	..	..	..		..
Hersham	..	..	..	..	..	..		..
Walton-on-Thames	..	..	..	..	..	..	..	..
Weybridge U	..	..	..	..	..	..	..	..
Addlestone	..	..	..	..	..	..	..	..
Chertsey	..	..	..	..	..	..	..	..
Virginia Water Z 460 arr	..	..	..	..	..	..	..	..
West Weybridge	..	..	..	..	..	..	..	..
Byfleet W	..	..	..	..	..	..	..	..
Woking X 324, 389, 390	..	..	..	..	9 15	..	..	..
Worplesdon	..	..	..	..	..	..	..	..
Guildford 246, 359 arr.	..	..	..	9 35	9 25	..	..	..

Down	p.m							
Waterloo dep.	8 54	8 56	8 57	8 59	9 1	..	9 7	9 9
Vauxhall	..	8 59	..	9 2	9 4	..	..	9 12
Clapham Junction A	..	9 4	..	9 6	9 9	..	..	9 16
Earlsfield B	..	9 7	..	9 10	9 12	..	..	9 20
Wimbledon	..	9 11	..	9 13	9 16	..	9 18	9 23
Raynes Park	..	9 14	..	9 16	9 19	..	..	9 26
Motspur Park	..	9 16	..			..	9 24	
Malden Manor	..	9 20	..	3	3	..	3	3
Tolworth	..	9 22	..			..		
Chessington North	..	9 25	..	..	..	..	..	..
Chessington South ¶ ar	..	9 27	..	..	..	..	..	..
Worcester Park	..	3	..	..	..	..	9 26	..
Stoneleigh	..		..	..	..	..	9 29	..
Ewell West C	..	..	..	..	..	..	9 31	..
London Bridge dep.	..	..	..	..	..	8*53	8‡53	..
Victoria "	..	..	..	..	..	9 18	8‡51	..
Sutton "	..	..	..	..	..	9 39	9‡20	..
Epsom 285	..	..	..	..	..	..	9 35	..
Ashtead	..	..	..	..	..	..	9 39	..
Leatherhead	..	..	..	..	..	..	9 43	..
Boxhill & Burford Bdg D	..	..	..	..	..	..	9 48	..
Dorking North F	..	..	..	..	..	9 55	9 51	..
Holmwood G	..	..	..	..	..	..	10 9	..
Ockley, for Capel	..	..	..	..	..	..	1013	..
Warnham 196, 245	..	..	..	..	..	..	1019	..
Horsham 159, arr.	..	..	..	..	..	1013	1024	..
Bookham	..	..	..	..	..	..		..
Malden, for Coombe	..	..	..	9 19	9 22	..		9 29
Norbiton H	..	..	..	..	9 25	..	Dep Dorking North 10 1 p.m	9 33
Kingston	..	..	..	..	9 28	..		9 35
Hampton Wick	..	..	..	..	9 30	..		9 37
Teddington J	..	..	..	..	9 33	..		9 41
Fulwell K	..	..	..	..	9 37	..		V
Hampton	..	..	..	..	9 41	..		To Waterloo via Richmond Arr. Twickenham 9 47 p.m
Sunbury L	..	..	..	..	9 45	..		
Upper Halliford Halt	..	..	..	..	9 47	..		
Shepperton M arr.	..	..	..	..	9 50	..		
Berrylands N	..	..	..	9 22	..	..		
Surbiton	..	..	9 13	9 25	..	..		
Thames Ditton	..	..	..	9 29	..	..		
Hampton Court P arr.	..	..	..	9 32	..	..		
Hinchley Wood	..	..	..	Stop	..	..	..	
Claygate, for Claremont	..	..	..		..	..	..	
Oxshott, for Fairmile	..	..	..	..	..	..	..	
Cobham Q	..	..	..	..	..	..	..	
Effingham Junction	..	..	..	..	..	..	..	
Horsley R	..	..	..	..	..	..	..	
Clandon T	..	..	..	..	..	..	..	
London Road (Guildford)	..	..	..	..	..	..	..	
Esher, for Sandown Park	..	..	9 17	p.m	..	..	..	..
Hersham	..	..	9 20	3	..	..	..	..
Walton-on-Thames	..	..	9 23		..	..	..	..
Weybridge U	..	..	9 27	9 35	..	..	..	..
Addlestone	..	..	..	9 39	..	..	..	..
Chertsey	..	..	..	9 42	..	..	..	..
Virginia Water Z 460 arr	..	..	..	9 46	..	..	..	..
West Weybridge	..	..	9 30	..	..	..	..	..
Byfleet W	..	..	9 33	..	..	..	..	..
Woking X 324, 389, 390	9 25	..	9 37	..	..	..	..	..
Worplesdon	..	..	9 45	..	..	..	..	..
Guildford 246, 359 arr.	..	..	9 51	..	..	..	..	..

Down	p.m							
Waterloo dep.	9 12	9 21	9 27	9 29	Via Three Bridges see page 178	3	9 36	9 39
Vauxhall	..	9 24	..	9 32			9 39	9 42
Clapham Junction A	..	9 29	..	9 36		..	9 44	9 46
Earlsfield B	..	9 32	..	9 40		..	9 47	9 50
Wimbledon	9 23	9 36	..	9 43		..	9 51	9 53
Raynes Park	..	9 39	..	9 46		..	9 54	9 56
Motspur Park			..			..	9 56	
Malden Manor	3	3	..	3		..	10 0	3
Tolworth			..			..	10 2	
Chessington North	..	..	..	..		..	10 5	..
Chessington South ¶ ar	..	..	..	..		..	10 7	..
Worcester Park	..	..	..	..		..	3	..
Stoneleigh	..	..	..	..		..		..
Ewell West C	..	..	..	..	..	..	..	..
London Bridge dep.	..	..	..	..	9 16	9 24	..	..
Victoria "	..	..	..	..	9 28	9‡20	..	..
Sutton "	..	..	..	..	..	9 52	..	..
Epsom 285	..	..	..	..	..	10 3	..	..
Ashtead	..	..	..	..	..	10 7	..	..
Leatherhead	..	..	..	..	..	1011	..	..
Boxhill & Burford Bdg D	..	..	..	..	..	1017	..	..
Dorking North F	..	..	..	..	..	1020	..	..
Holmwood G	..	..	..	..	..	1031	..	..
Ockley, for Capel	..	..	..	..	..	1035	..	..
Warnham 196, 245	..	..	..	..	..	1041	..	..
Horsham 159, arr.	..	..	..	..	1035	1046	..	..
Bookham	..	..	..	..	..		..	..
Malden, for Coombe	..	9 42	..	9 49	..		..	9 59
Norbiton H	..	9 45	..	9 53	..	Dep Dorking North 10 23 p.m	..	..
Kingston	..	9 48	..	9 55	..		..	..
Hampton Wick	..	9 50	..	9 57	..		..	..
Teddington J	..	9 53	..	10 1	..		..	..
Fulwell K	..	V	..	10 5	..		..	..
Hampton	..	To Waterloo via Richmond Arr. Twickenham 10 0 p.m	..	10 9	..		..	..
Sunbury L	..		..	1013	..		..	..
Upper Halliford Halt	..		..	1015	..		..	..
Shepperton M arr.	..		..	1018	..		..	..
Berrylands N	..		..	Stop	..		..	10 2
Surbiton	9 30		9 43		..		..	10 5
Thames Ditton	..		..	..	..		..	10 9
Hampton Court P arr.	..		..	..	..		..	1012
Hinchley Wood	9 33		..	..	..	..	..	..
Claygate, for Claremont	9 36		..	..	..	..	..	..
Oxshott, for Fairmile	9 40		..	..	..	..	..	..
Cobham Q	9 43		..	..	..	..	..	..
Effingham Junction	9 49		..	..	..	..	..	..
Horsley R	9 51		..	..	..	..	..	..
Clandon T	9 56		..	..	..	..	..	..
London Road (Guildford)	10 2		..	..	..	..	..	..
Esher, for Sandown Park	..	..	9 47	p.m	..	..	..	..
Hersham	..	..	9 50	3	..	..	..	..
Walton-on-Thames	..	..	9 53		..	..	..	..
Weybridge U	..	..	9 57	10 5	..	..	..	..
Addlestone	..	..	..	10 9	..	..	..	..
Chertsey	..	..	..	1012	..	..	..	..
Virginia Water Z 460 arr	..	..	..	1016	..	..	..	..
West Weybridge	..	..	10 0	..	..	..	..	..
Byfleet W	..	..	10 3	..	..	..	..	..
Woking X 324, 389, 390	..	..	10 7	..	..	..	..	..
Worplesdon	..	..	1015	..	..	..	..	..
Guildford 246, 359 arr.	10 6	..	1021	..	..	..	..	..

Down	p.m							
Waterloo dep.	9 42	9 45	9 47	9 49	9 57	9 56	9 59	10 1
Vauxhall	3	..	3	9 52	..	9 59	10 2	10 4
Clapham Junction A		..		9 56	..	10 4	10 6	10 9
Earlsfield B	..	..	..	10 0	..	10 7	1010	1012
Wimbledon	9 53	..	9 58	10 3	..	1011	1013	1016
Raynes Park	..	..	..	10 6	..	1014	1016	1019
Motspur Park	..	..	10 4		..	1016		
Malden Manor	..	..	..	3	..	1020	3	3
Tolworth	..	..	..		..	1022		
Chessington North	..	..	..	..	..	1025	..	..
Chessington South ¶ ar	..	..	..	..	..	1027	..	..
Worcester Park	..	..	10 6	..	..	3	..	..
Stoneleigh	..	..	10 9	..	..		..	..
Ewell West C	..	..	1012	..	..		..	..
London Bridge dep.	..	..	9‡24	..	..	Stop	..	..
Victoria "	..	..	9‡20	..	..	..	..	..
Sutton "	..	..	9‡52	..	..	..	..	..
Epsom 285	..	..	1015	..	..	..	..	..
Ashtead	..	..	1019	..	..	..	..	..
Leatherhead	..	..	1023	..	..	..	..	..
Boxhill & Burford Bdg D	..	..	..	..	..	..	..	..
Dorking North F	..	..	..	..	..	..	..	..
Holmwood G	..	..	..	..	..	..	..	..
Ockley, for Capel	..	..	..	..	..	..	..	..
Warnham 196, 245	..	..	..	..	..	..	..	..
Horsham 159, arr.	..	..	..	..	..	..	..	..
Bookham	..	..	1028	..	..	..	..	..
Malden, for Coombe	..	..	..	10 9	..	..	1019	1022
Norbiton H	..	..	..	1013	..	..	..	1025
Kingston	..	..	..	1015	..	..	..	1028
Hampton Wick	..	..	..	1017	..	..	..	1030
Teddington J	..	..	..	1021	..	..	..	1033
Fulwell K	..	..	..	V	..	..	..	1037
Hampton	..	..	..	To Waterloo via Richmond Arr. Twickenham 10 27 p.m	..	..	..	1041
Sunbury L	..	..	..		..	..	..	1045
Upper Halliford Halt	..	..	..		..	..	..	1047
Shepperton M arr.	..	..	..		..	..	..	1050
Berrylands N	..	..	..		..	..	1022	..
Surbiton	10 0	..	..		1013	..	1025	..
Thames Ditton	..	..	..		..	..	1029	..
Hampton Court P arr.	..	..	..		..	..	1032	..
Hinchley Wood	10 3	..	..		..	..	..	..
Claygate, for Claremont	10 6	..	..		..	..	..	..
Oxshott, for Fairmile	1010	..	..		..	..	..	..
Cobham Q	1013	..	..		..	..	..	..
Effingham Junction	1018	..	1032		..	..	..	..
Horsley R	1020	..	..		..	..	..	..
Clandon T	1025	..	..		..	..	..	..
London Road (Guildford)	1031	..	..		..	..	..	..
Esher, for Sandown Park	..	..	..	..	1017	p.m	..	..
Hersham	..	..	..	..	1020	3	..	..
Walton-on-Thames	..	..	..	..	1023		..	..
Weybridge U	..	..	..	..	1027	1035	..	..
Addlestone	..	..	..	..	..	1039	..	..
Chertsey	..	..	..	..	..	1042	..	..
Virginia Water Z 460 arr	..	..	..	..	..	1046	..	..
West Weybridge	..	..	..	..	1030	..	..	..
Byfleet W	..	..	..	..	1033	..	..	..
Woking X 324, 389, 390	..	1015	..	..	1037	..	..	..
Worplesdon	..	..	..	..	1045	..	..	..
Guildford 246, 359 arr.	1035	1025	..	..	1051	..	..	..

FOR NOTES, SEE PAGE 426

FOR NOTES, SEE PAGE 426

LONDON, DORKING NORTH, HORSHAM, KINGSTON, SHEPPERTON, HAMPTON COURT, CHERTSEY, WOKING, & GUILDFORD

Week Days—*continued*

Down	p.m									
Waterloo dep.	3	10 7	10 9	1012	3	1021	1025	1029	1030	1036
Vauxhall			1012			1024		1032		1039
Clapham Junction A			1016			1029		1036		1043
Earlsfield B			1020			1032		1040		1047
Wimbledon		10 18	1023	1023		1036	1036	1043		1050
Raynes Park			1026			1039		1046		1053
Motspur Park		10 24								1056
Malden Manor		3	3	3		3		3		11 0
Tolworth										11 2
Chessington North										11 5
Chessington South ¶ arr										11 7
Worcester Park		10 26								3
Stoneleigh		10 29								
Ewell West C		10 32								
London Bridge dep.	9 53	9‡53								
Victoria "	9‡51	9‡51								
Sutton "	1020	10‡20								
Epsom 285	1029	10 35								
Ashtead	1033	10 39								
Leatherhead	1037	10 43			11 0					
Boxhill & Burford Bdg D		10 48								
Dorking North F		10 52								
Holmwood G		11 9								
Ockley, for Capel		11 13								
Warnham [196, 245		11 19								
Horsham 159, arr.		11 24								
Bookham	1042				11 4					
Malden, for Coombe		Dep. Dorking North 11 1 p.m	1029			1042		1049		
Norbiton H			1033			1045		1053		
Kingston			1035			1048		1055		
Hampton Wick			1037			1050		1057		
Teddington J			1041			1053		11 1		
Fulwell K			V			V		11 5		
Hampton			To Waterloo via Richmond Arr Twickenham 10 47 p.m			To Waterloo via Richmond Arr Twickenham 10 59 p.m		11 9		
Sunbury L								1113		
Upper Halliford Halt										
Shepperton M arr.								1117		
Berrylands N								Stop		
Surbiton				1030			1043			
Thames Ditton										
Hampton Court P arr.										
Hinchley Wood				1033						
Claygate, for Claremont				1036						
Oxshott, for Fairmile				1040						
Cobham Q				1043						
Effingham Junction	1046			1048	11 8					
Horsley R				1050						
Clandon T				1055						
London Road (Guildford)				11 1						
Esher, for Sandown Park							1047	p.m		
Hersham							1050	3		
Walton-on-Thames							1053			
Weybridge U							1057	11 5		
Addlestone								11 9		
Chertsey								1112		
Virginia Water Z 460 arr										
West Weybridge							11 0			
Byfleet W							11 3			
Woking X 324, 389, 390							11 7		11 1	
Worplesdon							1115			
[illegible]							1122			

Down	p.m									
Waterloo dep.	3	1039	1042	10 47	1049	1056	1057	10 59	11 1	11 7
Vauxhall		1042	3	3	1052	1059		11 2	11 4	3
Clapham Junction A		1046			1056	11 4		11 6	11 9	
Earlsfield B		1050			11 0	11 7		11 10	1112	
Wimbledon		1053	1053	10 58	11 3	1111		11 13	1116	11 18
Raynes Park		1056			11 6	1114		11 16	1119	
Motspur Park				11 4		1116				11 24
Malden Manor		3			3	1120		3	3	
Tolworth						1122				
Chessington North						1125				
Chessington South ¶ arr						1127				
Worcester Park				11 6		3				11 26
Stoneleigh				11 9						11 29
Ewell West C				11 12						11 32
London Bridge dep.	10 24			10‡24						
Victoria "	10‡20			10‡20						10‡51
Sutton "	10 52			10‡52						11‡14
Epsom 285	11 3			11 15						11 35
Ashtead	11 8			11 19						11 39
Leatherhead	11 12			11 23						11 43
Boxhill & Burford Bdg D	11 17									11 48
Dorking North F	11 20									11 52
Holmwood G										
Ockley, for Capel										
Warnham [196, 245										
Horsham 159, arr.										
Bookham				11 28						
Malden, for Coombe		1059			11 9			11 19	1122	
Norbiton H					1113				1125	
Kingston					1115				1128	
Hampton Wick					1117				1130	
Teddington J					1121				1133	
Fulwell K					V				1137	
Hampton					To Waterloo via Richmond Arr Twickenham 11 30 p.m				1141	
Sunbury L									1145	
Upper Halliford Halt										
Shepperton M arr.									1149	
Berrylands N		11 2						11 22		
Surbiton		11 5	11 0				1113	11 25		
Thames Ditton		11 9						11 29		
Hampton Court P arr.		1112						11 32		
Hinchley Wood			11 3					Stop		
Claygate, for Claremont			11 6							
Oxshott, for Fairmile			1110							
Cobham Q			1113							
Effingham Junction			1118	11 32						
Horsley R			1120							
Clandon T			1125							
London Road (Guildford)			1131							
Esher, for Sandown Park							1117	p.m		
Hersham							1120	3		
Walton-on-Thames							1123			
Weybridge U							1127	11 35		
Addlestone								11 39		
Chertsey								11 42		
Virginia Water Z 460 arr										
West Weybridge							1130			
Byfleet W							1133			
Woking X 324, 389, 390							1137			
Worplesdon							1145			
[illegible]			1135				1151			

Down			p.m							ngt.
Waterloo dep.	11 9	1112	1126	3	1131	3	1142	11 47	1155	12 9
Vauxhall	1112	3	1129		1134		1145	11 50	3	1212
Clapham Junction A	1116		1134		1139		1149	11 54		1216
Earlsfield B	1120		1137		1142		1153	11 58		1220
Wimbledon	1123	1123	1141		1146		1156	12 1	12 6	1223
Raynes Park	1126		1144		1149		1159	12 4		1226
Motspur Park			1146					12 7		
Malden Manor	3		1150		3		3	3		3
Tolworth			1152							
Chessington North			1155							
Chessington South ¶ arr			1157							
Worcester Park			3					12 9		
Stoneleigh								12 12		
Ewell West C								12 15		
London Bridge dep.				11 23						
Victoria "				11‡29						
Sutton "				11 50						
Epsom 285				12 0				12 18		
Ashtead				12 4				12 22		
Leatherhead				12 8				12 28		
Boxhill & Burford Bdg D				12 13				12 33		
Dorking North F				12 16				12 36		
Holmwood G										
Ockley, for Capel										
Warnham [196, 245										
Horsham 159, arr.										
Bookham										
Malden, for Coombe	1129				1152		12 2			1229
Norbiton H	1133				1155	ngt.				1233
Kingston	1135				1158	12 5				1235
Hampton Wick	1137				12 0	12 7				1237
Teddington J	1141				12 3	1210				1241
Fulwell K	To Strawberry Hill (arr. 11 44 p.m)				12 7	To Strawberry Hill (arr. 12 13 ngt.)				To Strawberry Hill (arr. 12 44 ngt.)
Hampton					1211					
Sunbury L					1215					
Upper Halliford Halt										
Shepperton M arr.					1219					
Berrylands N							12 5			
Surbiton		1130					12 8		1213	
Thames Ditton							1212			
Hampton Court P arr.							1215			
Hinchley Wood		1133								
Claygate, for Claremont		1136								
Oxshott, for Fairmile		1140								
Cobham Q		1143								
Effingham Junction		1148								
Horsley R		1150								
Clandon T		1155								
London Road (Guildford)		12 1								
Esher, for Sandown Park									1217	
Hersham									1220	
Walton-on-Thames									1223	
Weybridge U									1227	
Addlestone										
Chertsey										
Virginia Water Z 460 arr										
West Weybridge									1230	
Byfleet W									1233	
Woking X 324, 389, 390									1238	
Worplesdon									1244	
[illegible]		12 5							1250	

LONDON, DORKING NORTH, HORSHAM, KINGSTON, SHEPPERTON, HAMPTON COURT, CHERTSEY, WOKING, & GUILDFORD

Down	Sundays a.m																															
Waterloo dep.	1 30	3 35	6 25	..	3	3	3	7 20	7 23	3	7 25	7 33	7 36	3	7 49	7 56	7 57	3	8 2	..	8 8	3	3	8 13	8 20	8 23	8 27	3	8 33	3	8 38	3
Vauxhall	1 34	3	6 28	..				7 23	7 26		..	7 36	7 39		7 52	7 59	..		..	..	..			8 16	8 23	8 26	..		8 36		..	
Clapham Junction A	1 42		6 32	Via Three Bridges, see page 182	..	..	..	7 27	7 31	..	..	7 40	7 43	..	7 56	8 3	..	..	8 9	Via Three Bridges, see page 182	8 15	..	..	8 20	8 27	8 31	..	..	8 40	..	8 45	..
Earlsfield B	1 45	..	6 36		..	..	..	7 31	7 34	..	..	7 44	7 47	..	8 0	8 7	..	..	..		..	..	..	8 24	8 31	8 34	..	..	8 44	..	..	..
Wimbledon	1 49	..	6 39		6 44	..	6 50	7 34	7 38	..	7 36	7 47	7 50	..	8 3	8 10	..	..	8 15		8 21	..	8 24	8 27	8 34	8 38	..	..	8 47	8 50	8 51	..
Raynes Park	1 52	..	6 42		6 47	..	6 53	7 37	7 41	..	..	7 50	7 53	..	8 6	8 13	..	..	..		..	..	8 27	8 30	8 37	8 41	..	..	8 50	8 53	..	..
Motspur Park		..			6 49	..	6 56	7 40	..	..	..	..	7 56	..	..	8 16	..	..	8 20		..	..	..	..	8 40	..	..	..	..	8 56	..	..
Malden Manor	3	..	3		..	..	6 59	3	3	..	..	3	7 59	..	3	8 19	..	..	3		3	..	..	3	3	3	..	..	3	8 59	3	..
Tolworth		..			..	..	7 2			..	..		8 2	..		8 22	..	..				..	..				..	..		9 2		..
Chessington North		..	..		..	..	7 5	..	..	..	..	..	8 5	..	..	8 25	..	..	..		..	..	..	..	..	..	..	..	..	9 5	..	..
Chessington South ¶ ar		..	..		..	..	7 7	..	..	..	..	..	8 7	..	..	8 27	..	..	..		..	..	..	..	..	..	..	..	..	9 7	..	..
Worcester Park	Calls at Queen's Road at 1 38 a.m	..	..		6 52	..	Stop	7 42	..	..	..	..	3	..	..	3	..	..	8 22		..	..	..	..	8 42	..	..	..	..	..	..	..
Stoneleigh		..	..		6 55	..		7 45	..	..	..	..		..	..		..	..	8 25		..	..	..	..	8 45	..	..	..	..	..	..	..
Ewell West C		..	..		6 57	..	..	7 48	..	..	..	..	Stop	..	..	Stop	..	..	8 28		..	..	..	..	8 48	..	..	..	..	..	..	..
London Bridge dep.		..	..	..	..	..	..	..	..	..	..	..	..	..	..	From Strawberry Hill, dep 8 32 a.m	..	..	..	7 40	..	7 55	..	..	..	..	..	..	..	..	..	8 25
Victoria "		..	..	6 40	..	..	..	7‡15	..	..	..	..	..	..	..		..	..	7‡45	7 46	..	7‡45	..	..	8‡15	..	..	..	..	..	..	8‡15
Sutton "		..	..	..	..	..	..	7‡39	..	..	..	..	..	..	..		..	..	8‡9	..	..	8 27	..	..	8‡39	..	..	..	..	..	..	8 58
Epsom 285		..	..	..	7 2	..	..	7 53	..	..	..	..	..	..	..		..	..	8 31	..	..	8 38	..	..	8 53	..	..	..	..	..	..	9 7
Ashtead		..	..	..	7 6	..	..	7 57	..	..	..	..	..	..	..		..	..	8 35	..	..	8 42	..	..	8 57	..	..	..	..	..	..	9 11
Leatherhead		..	..	..	7 10	..	..	8 1	..	..	..	..	..	..	..		..	..	8 39	..	..	8 46	..	..	9 1	..	..	..	..	..	..	9 15
Boxhill & Burford Bdg D		..	..	..	7 15	..	..	8 6	..	..	..	..	..	..	..		..	..	..	..	..	8 51	..	..	9 6	..	..	..	..	..	..	..
Dorking North F		..	..	..	7 18	..	..	8 9	..	..	..	..	..	..	..		..	..	..	..	..	8 53	..	..	9 9	..	..	..	..	..	..	..
Holmwood G		..	..	..	..	..	..	8 18	..	..	..	..	..	..	..		..	..	..	..	..	9 3	..	..	..	..	..	..	..	..	..	..
Ockley, for Capel		..	..	..	..	..	..	8 22	..	..	..	..	..	..	..		..	..	..	..	..	9 7	..	..	..	..	..	..	..	..	..	..
Warnham [196, 245	..	..	..	..	..	..	..	8 28	..	..	..	..	..	..	..		..	..	..	..	..	9 13	..	..	..	..	..	..	..	..	..	..
Horsham 159, arr.	..	..	..	8 5	..	..	..	8 33	..	..	..	..	..	..	..		..	..	..	9 5	..	9 17	..	..	..	..	..	..	..	..	..	..
Bookham	..	..	..	Stop	..	..	..	..	..	..	..	..	..	..	..		..	..	8 45	..	..	..	..	..	..	..	..	..	..	..	..	9 19
Malden, for Coombe	1 55	..	6 45		..	..	..	..	7 44	..	..	7 53	..	..	8 9		..	..	..	..	..	..	8 30	8 33	..	8 44	..	..	8 53	..	..	..
Norbiton H	1 58	..	6 49	..	..	..	..	..	7 47	..	..	..	..	..	8 13		..	..	..	..	..	..	8 33	..	..	8 47	..	..	..	..	..	..
Kingston	2 1	..	6 53	..	..	6 58	..	..	7 50	..	..	..	..	8 1	8 15	a.m 3	..	..	..	..	..	..	8 36	..	..	8 50	..	..	..	..	..	..
Hampton Wick	..	..	6 55	..	..	7 0	..	..	7 52	..	..	..	..	8 3	8 17		..	..	..	..	..	..	8 38	..	..	8 52	..	..	..	..	..	..
Teddington J	2 6	..	6 58	..	..	7 3	..	..	7 55	..	..	..	..	8 6	8 21		..	..	..	..	..	..	8 41	..	..	8 55	..	..	..	..	..	..
Fulwell K	..	..	V	..	..	7 7	..	..	V	..	..	..	..	8 10	V	8 35	..	..	..	..	..	..	V	..	..	8 59	..	..	..	..	..	..
Hampton	To Twickenham only (arr 2 12 a.m)	..	To Waterloo via Richmond Arr. Twickenham 7 7 a.m	..	..	7 11	..	..	To Waterloo via Richmond Arr. Twickenham 8 1 a.m	..	..	..	..	8 14	To Waterloo via Richmond Arr. Twickenham 8 27 a.m	8 39	..	..	..	..	..	..	To Waterloo via Richmond Arr. Twickenham 8 47 a.m	..	..	9 3	..	..	..	..	..	..
Sunbury L		..		..	..	7 15	..	..		..	..	..	..	8 18		8 43	..	..	..	..	..	..		..	..	9 7	..	..	..	..	..	..
Upper Halliford Halt		..		..	..	7 17	..	..		..	..	..	..	8 20		8 45	..	..	..	..	..	..		..	..	9 9	..	..	..	..	..	..
Shepperton M arr.		..		..	..	7 20	..	..		..	..	..	..	8 23		8 48	..	..	..	..	..	..		..	..	9 12	..	..	..	..	..	..
Berrylands N		..		..	..	..	..	..		..	..	7 57	..	..		..	..	..	..	..	..	..		8 36	..	..	..	..	8 57	..	..	..
Surbiton		..		..	..	..	..	..		..	7 43	8 0	..	..		..	8 13	..	..	..	8 28	..		8 39	..	..	8 43	..	9 0	..	8 58	..
Thames Ditton		..		..	..	..	..	..		..	..	8 4	..	..		..	..	..	..	..	..	..		8 43	..	..	..	..	9 4	..	..	..
Hampton Court P arr.		..		..	..	..	..	..		..	..	8 7	..	..		..	..	..	..	..	..	..		8 46	..	..	..	..	9 7	..	..	..
Hinchley Wood		..		..	..	..	..	..		..	..	..	..	..		..	..	..	..	..	8 31	..		..	..	..	..	..	..	..	9 1	..
Claygate, for Claremont		..		..	..	..	..	..		..	..	..	..	..		..	..	..	..	..	8 34	..		..	..	..	..	..	..	..	9 4	..
Oxshott, for Fairmile		..		..	..	..	..	..		..	..	..	..	..		..	..	..	..	..	8 38	..		..	..	..	..	..	..	..	9 8	..
Cobham Q		..		..	..	..	..	..		..	..	..	..	..		..	..	..	..	..	8 41	..		..	..	..	..	..	..	..	9 11	..
Effingham Junction	..	Arr Weybridge 4 5 a.m		..	..	..	..	..		7 56	..	..	..	..		..	..	..	8 49	..	8 46	..		..	..	..	..	..	..	..	9 15	9 23
Horsley R	..			..	..	..	..	..		7 59	..	..	..	..		..	..	..	8 51	..	..	..		..	..	..	..	..	..	..	9 18	..
Clandon T	..			..	..	..	..	..		8 4	..	..	..	..		..	..	..	8 56	..	..	..		..	..	..	..	..	..	..	9 23	..
London Road (Guildford)	..			..	..	..	..	..		8 9	..	..	..	..		..	..	..	9 2	..	..	..		..	..	..	..	..	..	..	9 28	..
Esher, for Sandown Park	..			..	..	..	..	..		..	7 47	..	a.m	..		..	8 17	..	..	..	..	..		..	..	..	8 47	..	..	..	..	..
Hersham	..		..	..	..	..	..	..	..	..	7 50	..	3	..	..	..	8 20	3	..	..	..	..	..	..	..	..	8 50	3	..	..	..	..
Walton-on-Thames	..		..	..	..	..	a.m	..	..	..	7 53	..		..	..	..	8 23		..	..	..	..	..	..	..	..	8 53		..	..	..	..
Weybridge U	..	4 13	..	..	..	..	3	..	..	..	7 57	..	8 5	..	..	..	8 27	8 35	..	..	..	..	..	..	..	..	8 57	9 5	..	..	..	..
Addlestone	..	..	..	..	..	..		..	..	..	..	..	8 9	..	..	..	..	8 39	..	..	..	..	..	..	..	..	..	9 9	..	..	..	..
Chertsey	..	..	..	..	..	..	7 42	..	..	..	..	..	8 12	..	..	..	..	8 42	..	..	..	..	..	..	..	..	..	9 12	..	..	..	..
Virginia Water Z 460 arr.	..	..	..	..	..	..	7 46	..	..	..	..	..	8 16	..	..	..	..	8 46	..	..	..	..	..	..	..	..	..	9 16	..	..	..	..
West Weybridge	..	..	..	..	..	..	..	..	..	..	8 0	..	..	..	..	..	8 30	..	..	..	..	..	..	..	..	..	9 0	..	..	..	..	..
Byfleet W	..	..	..	a.m	..	..	..	..	..	..	8 3	..	..	..	..	..	8 33	..	..	..	..	..	..	..	..	..	9 3	..	..	..	..	..
Woking X 324, 389, 390	..	4 24	..	7 15	..	..	..	..	..	..	8 7	..	..	..	..	..	8 37	..	..	..	..	..	..	..	..	..	9 7	..	..	..	..	..
Worplesdon	..	..	..	..	..	..	..	..	..	..	8 15	..	..	..	..	..	8 45	..	..	..	..	..	..	..	..	..	9 15	..	..	..	..	..
Guildford 246, 359 arr.	..	4 37	..	7 24	..	..	..	..	..	8 13	8 21	..	..	..	..	..	8 51	..	9 6	..	..	..	..	..	..	..	9 21	..	..	..	9 31	..

FOR NOTES, SEE PAGE 426

LONDON, DORKING NORTH, HORSHAM, KINGSTON, SHEPPERTON, HAMPTON COURT, CHERTSEY, WOKING, & GUILDFORD

Sundays—continued

Down	a.m.																														a.m.
Waterloo dep.	8 45	8 49		8 54	8 56	8 57	8 59	9 2	9 8	9 9	3	9 13		9 23	9 27	3	9 33		9 36	9 38	3	9 42	9 45		9 49	3	9 56	9 57	3	9 59	
Vauxhall		8 52			8 59		3			9 12		9 16		9 26			9 36		9 39						9 52		9 59			3	
Clapham Junction A		8 56			9 3			9 9	9 15	9 16		9 20		9 31			9 40		9 43	9 45		9 49			9 56		10 3				
Earlsfield B		9 0			9 7					9 20		9 24		9 34			9 44		9 47						10 0		10 7				
Wimbledon		9 3			9 10			9 15	9 21	9 23		9 27		9 38			9 47		9 50	9 51		9 55			10 3		1010				
Raynes Park		9 6			9 13					9 26		9 30		9 41			9 50		9 53						10 6		1013				Via Three Bridges, see page 184.
Motspur Park					9 16			9 20											9 56			10 0					1016				
Malden Manor		3			9 19			3	3	3		3		3			3		9 59	3		3			3		1019				
Tolworth					9 22														10 [illegible]								1022				
Chessington North					9 25														10 5								1025				
Chessington South ¶ ar.					9 27														10 7								1027				
Worcester Park					3			9 22											3			10 2					3				
Stoneleigh								9 25														10 5									
Ewell West C								9 28														10 8									
London Bridge dep.											8 55		8*55								9 25	9‡25				9 55				Via Richmond, see page 471	
Victoria "								8‡45			8‡45		9 18								9‡24					9‡45					1018
Sutton "								9‡ 9			9 27		9 39								9 57					1027					
Epsom 235								9 31			9 36										10 6	1012				1036					
Ashtead								9 35			9 40										1010	1016				1040					
Leatherhead								9 39			9 44										1014	1020				1044					
Boxhill & Burford Bdg D							Via Richmond, see page 470				9 49											1025				1049					
Dorking North F											9 52		9 55									1028				1052					
Holmwood G											Stop											1038									
Ockley, for Capel																						1042									
Warnham [245																						1048									
Horsham 159, 193 ar.													1013									1053									1113
Bookham								9 45													1019										
Malden, for Coombe		9 9								9 29		9 33		9 44			9 53								10 9						
Norbiton H		9 13								9 33				9 47											1013						
Kingston		9 15								9 35				9 50											1015						
Hampton Wick		9 17								9 37				9 52											1017						
Teddington J		9 21								9 41				9 55											1021						
Fulwell K		V					9 35			V				9 59											V					1035	
Hampton		To Waterloo via Richmond Arr. Twickenham 9 27 a.m					9 39			To Waterloo via Richmond Arr. Twickenham 9 47 a.m				10 3											To Waterloo via Richmond Arr. Twickenham 10 27 a.m					1029	
Sunbury L							9 43							10 7																1043	
Upper Halliford Halt							9 45							10 9																1045	
Shepperton M arr.							9 48							1012																1048	
Berrylands N												9 36					9 57														
Surbiton						9 13			9 28			9 39			9 43		10 0			9 58								1013			
Thames Ditton												9 43					10 4														
Hampton Court P arr.												9 46					10 7														
Hinchley Wood									9 31											10 1											
Claygate, for Claremont									9 34											10 4											
Oxshott, for Fairmile									9 38											10 8											
Cobham Q									9 41											1011											
Effingham Junction								9 49	9 46											1016	1023										
Horsley R								9 51												1018											
Clandon T								9 56												1023											
London Road (Guildford)								10 2												1029											
Esher, for Sandown Park						9 17					a.m				9 47													1017			
Hersham						9 20					3				9 50	3												1020	3		
Walton-on-Thames						9 23									9 53													1023			
Weybridge U						9 27					9 35				9 57	10 5												1027	1035		
Addlestone											9 39					10 9													1039		
Chertsey											9 42					1012													1042		
Virginia Water Z 460 arr											9 46					1016													1046		
West Weybridge						9 30									10 0													1030			
Byfleet W						9 33									10 3													1033			
Woking X 324, 389, 390	9 15			9 25		9 37									10 7								1015					1037			
Worplesdon						9 45									1015													1045			
Guildford 246, 359 arr.	9 25					9 51		10 6							1021					1033			1025					1051			

LONDON, DORKING NORTH, HORSHAM, KINGSTON, SHEPPERTON, HAMPTON COURT, CHERTSEY, WOKING, & GUILDFORD

Down	Sundays—continued, a.m.																													
Waterloo dep.	10 2	10 8	10 9	1013	1023	1027	1033	1036	1038	3	10 42	1045	1049	1054	1056	1057	3	1059	11 2	Via Three Bridges see page 184	11 8	3	11 9	1113	1123	1127	1133	1136	1138	3
Vauxhall	..	..	1012	1016	1026	..	1036	1039	..		..	..	1052	..	1059	..		3	..		..		1112	1116	1126	..	1136	1139	..	
Clapham Junction A	10 9	1015	1016	1020	1031	..	1040	1043	1045	..	10 49	..	1056	..	11 3	..	..		11 9		1115	..	1116	1120	1131	..	1140	1143	1145	..
Earlsfield **B**	..	..	1020	1024	1034	..	1044	1047	..	..	..	..	11 0	..	11 7	..	..	..	..		..	..	1120	1124	1134	..	1144	1147	..	..
Wimbledon	10 15	1021	1023	1027	1038	..	1047	1050	1051	..	10 55	..	11 3	..	1110	..	..	..	11 15		1121	..	1123	1127	1138	..	1147	1150	1151	..
Raynes Park	..	..	1026	1030	1041	..	1050	1053	..	..	..	..	11 6	..	1113	..	..	..	..		..	..	1126	1130	1141	..	1150	1153	..	..
Motspur Park	10 20					..	..	1056		..	11 0	..		..	1116	..	..	..	11 20			..				..		1156		..
Malden Manor	3	3	3	3	3	..	3	1059	3	..	3	..	3	..	1119	..	..	..	3		3	..	3	3	3	..	3	1159	3	..
Tolworth						..		11 2		..		..		..	1122	..	..	..				..				..		12 2		..
Chessington North	..	..	..	..	..	..	..	11 5	..	..	..	..	..	..	1125	..	..	..	..		..	..	..	..	..	..	..	12 5	..	..
Chessington South ¶ ar.	..	..	..	..	..	..	..	11 7	..	..	..	..	..	..	1127	..	..	..	..		..	..	..	..	..	..	..	12 7	..	..
Worcester Park	10 22	..	..	..	..	..	..	3	..	..	11 2	..	..	..	3	..	..	..	11 22		..	..	..	..	..	..	..	3	..	..
Stoneleigh	10 25	..	..	..	..	..	..		..	..	11 5	..	..	..		..	..	..	11 25		..	..	..	..	..	..	..		..	..
Ewell West **C**	10 28	..	..	..	..	..	..	Stop	..	..	11 8	..	..	..	..	..	..	..	11 28	..	..	..	..	..	..	..	..	Stop	..	..
London Bridge dep.	..	..	..	..	..	..	..		..	10 25	10‡25	..	..	..	..	..	..		..	..	..	10 54	..	..	..	..	..		.	11 25
Victoria "	9‡45	..	..	..	..	..	..	..	..	10‡15	..	..	..	..	..	..	..	Via Richmond, see page 471	10‡45	10 48	..	10*45	..	..	..	..	..	..	..	11‡24
Sutton "	10‡ 9	..	..	..	..	..	..	..	..	10 57	10‡57	..	..	..	..	..	..		11‡ 9	..	..	11 27	..	..	..	..	..	..	..	11 57
Epsom **285**	10 31	..	..	..	..	..	..	..	..	11 6	11 11	..	..	..	..	..	..		11 31	..	..	11 36	..	..	..	..	..	..	..	12 6
Ashtead	10 35	..	..	..	..	..	..	..	..	11 10	11 15	..	..	..	..	..	..		11 35	..	..	11 40	..	..	..	..	..	..	..	12 10
Leatherhead	10 39	..	..	..	..	..	..	..	..	11 14	11 19	..	..	..	..	..	..		11 39	..	..	11 44	..	..	..	..	..	..	..	12 14
Boxhill & Burford Bdg **D**	..	..	..	..	..	..	..	..	..	..	11 24	..	..	..	..	..	..		..	..	..	11 49	..	..	..	..	..	..	..	..
Dorking North F	..	..	..	..	..	..	..	..	..	..	11 28	..	..	..	..	..	..		..	..	..	11 52	..	..	..	..	..	..	..	..
Holmwood **G**	..	..	..	..	..	..	..	..	..	..	11 38	..	..	..	..	..	..		..	..	..	..	..	..	..	..	..	..	..	..
Ockley, for Capel	..	..	..	..	..	..	..	..	..	..	11 42	..	..	..	..	..	..		..	..	..	..	..	..	..	..	..	..	..	..
Warnham **196**, 245,	..	..	..	..	..	..	..	..	..	..	11 48	..	..	..	..	..	..		..	..	..	..	..	..	..	..	..	..	..	..
Horsham 159, arr.	..	..	..	..	..	..	..	..	..	..	11 53	..	..	..	..	..	..		..	12 5	..	..	..	..	..	..	..	..	..	..
Bookham	10 45	..	..	..	..	..	..	..	..	11 19	..	..	..	..	..	..	..	..	11 45	..	..	..	..	..	..	..	..	..	..	12 19
Malden, for Coombe	..	..	1029	1033	1044	..	1053	..	..	..	..	..	11 9	..	..	..	..	..	..	..	..	..	1129	1133	1144	..	1153	..	..	..
Norbiton **H**	..	..	1033	..	1047	..	..	..	..	..	..	..	1113	..	..	..	..	..	..	..	..	..	1133	..	1147	..	..	..	..	..
Kingston	..	..	1035	..	1050	..	..	..	..	..	..	..	1115	..	..	..	..	..	..	..	..	..	1135	..	1150	..	..	..	..	..
Hampton Wick	..	..	1037	..	1052	..	..	..	..	..	..	..	1117	..	..	..	..	..	..	..	..	..	1137	..	1152	..	..	..	..	..
Teddington J	..	..	1041	..	1055	..	..	..	..	..	..	..	1121	..	..	..	..	..	..	..	..	..	1141	..	1155	..	..	..	..	..
Fulwell **K**	..	..	V	..	1059	..	..	..	..	..	..	..	V	..	..	..	..	1135	..	..	..	..	V	..	1159	..	..	..	..	..
Hampton	..	..		..	11 3	..	..	..	..	..	..	..		..	..	..	..	1139	..	..	..	..		..	12 3	..	..	..	..	..
Sunbury **L**	..	..		..	11 7	..	..	..	..	..	..	..		..	..	..	..	1143	..	..	..	..		..	12 7	..	..	..	..	..
Upper Halliford Halt	..	..	To Waterloo via Richmond Arr. **Twickenham** 10 47 a.m	..	11 9	..	..	..	..	..	..	..	To Waterloo via Richmond Arr. **Twickenham** 11 27 a.m	..	..	..	..	1145	..	..	..	..	To Waterloo via Richmond Arr. **Twickenham** 11 47 a.m	..	12 9	..	..	..	..	..
Shepperton M arr.	..	..		..	1112	..	..	..	..	..	..	..		..	..	..	..	1148	..	..	..	..		..	1212	..	..	..	..	..
Berrylands **N**	..	..		1036	..	..	1057	..	..	..	..	..		..	..	..	..	..	..	..	..	..		1136	..	..	1157	..	..	..
Surbiton	..	1028		1039	..	1043	11 0	..	1058	..	..	..		..	..	1113	..	..	..	..	1128	..		1139	..	1143	12 0	..	1158	..
Thames Ditton	..	..		1043	..	..	11 4	..	..	..	..	..		..	..	..	..	..	..	..	..	..		1143	..	..	12 4	..	..	..
Hampton Court P arr.	..	..		1046	..	..	11 7	..	..	..	..	..		..	..	..	..	..	..	..	..	..		1146	..	..	12 7	..	..	..
Hinchley Wood	..	1031		..	..	..	..	..	11 1	..	..	..		..	..	..	..	..	..	..	1131	..		..	..	..	..	..	12 1	..
Claygate, for Claremont	..	1034		..	..	..	..	..	11 4	..	..	..		..	..	..	..	..	..	..	1134	..		..	..	..	..	..	12 4	..
Oxshott, for Fairmile	..	1038		..	..	..	..	..	11 8	..	..	..		..	..	..	..	..	..	..	1138	..		..	..	..	..	..	12 8	..
Cobham **Q**	..	1041		..	..	..	..	..	1111	..	..	..		..	..	..	..	..	..	..	1141	..		..	..	..	..	..	1211	..
Effingham Junction	10 49	1046		..	..	..	..	..	1116	11 23	..	..		..	..	..	..	..	11 49	..	1146	..		..	..	..	..	..	1216	12 23
Horsley R	10 51	..		..	..	..	..	..	1118	..	..	..		..	..	..	..	..	11 51	..	..	..		..	..	..	..	..	1218	..
Clandon **T**	10 56	..		..	..	..	..	..	1123	..	..	..		..	..	..	..	..	11 56	..	..	..		..	..	..	..	..	1223	..
London Road (Guildford)	11 2	..		..	..	..	..	..	1129	..	..	..		..	..	..	..	..	12 2	..	..	..		..	..	..	..	..	1229	..
Esher, for Sandown Park	..	..	..	..	..	1047	..	a.m	..	..	..	..	..	..	..	1117	..	..	..	..	..	..	..	..	..	1147	..	p.m	..	..
Hersham	..	..	..	..	..	1050	..	3	..	..	..	..	..	..	..	1120	3	..	..	..	..	..	..	..	..	1150	..	3	..	..
Walton-on-Thames	..	..	..	..	..	1053	..		..	..	..	..	..	..	..	1123		..	..	..	..	..	..	..	..	1153	..		..	..
Weybridge U	..	..	..	..	..	1057	..	11 5	..	..	..	..	..	..	..	1127	1135	..	..	..	..	..	..	..	..	1157	..	12 5	..	..
Addlestone	..	..	..	..	..	..	..	11 9	..	..	..	..	..	..	..	..	1139	..	..	..	..	..	..	..	..	..	..	12 9	..	..
Chertsey	..	..	..	..	..	..	..	1112	..	..	..	..	..	..	..	..	1142	..	..	..	..	..	..	..	..	..	..	1212	..	..
Virginia Water Z 460 arr.	..	..	..	..	..	..	..	1116	..	..	..	..	..	..	..	..	1146	..	..	..	..	..	..	..	..	..	..	1216	..	..
West Weybridge	..	..	..	..	..	11 0	..	..	..	..	..	..	..	..	..	1130	..	..	..	..	..	..	..	..	..	12 0	..	..	..	..
Byfleet **W**	..	..	..	..	..	11 3	..	..	..	..	..	..	..	..	..	1133	..	..	..	..	..	..	..	..	..	12 3	..	..	..	..
Woking X 324, 389, 390	..	..	..	..	..	11 7	..	..	..	..	..	1115	..	1125	..	1137	..	..	..	..	..	..	..	..	..	12 7	..	..	..	..
Worplesdon	..	..	..	..	..	1115	..	..	..	..	..	..	..	..	..	1145	..	..	..	..	..	..	..	..	..	1215	..	..	..	..
Guildford 246, 359 arr.	11 6	..	..	..	..	1121	..	..	1133	..	..	1127	..	..	..	1151	..	..	12 6	..	..	..	..	..	..	1221	..	..	1233	..

FOR NOTES, SEE PAGE 426

FOR NOTES, SEE PAGE 426

LONDON, DORKING NORTH, HORSHAM, KINGSTON, SHEPPERTON, HAMPTON COURT, CHERTSEY, WOKING, & GUILDFORD

Down	a.m.												Sundays—continued								p.m.									
Waterloo .... dep.	11 42	1149	..	1156	1157	1159	12 2	12 8	[3]	12 9	1213	1223	..	1224	1227	1233	1236	1238	[3]	12 42	1245	1249	1256	1257	1259	1 2	[3]	..	..	1 8
Vauxhall	..	1152	..	1159	..	[3]	..	..		12 12	1216	1226	..	..	..	1236	1239	..		..	..	1252	1259	..	[3]	..		..	..	..
Clapham Junction A	11 49	1156	..	12 3	..		12 9	1215	..	12 16	1220	1231	..	..	..	1240	1243	1245	..	12 49	..	1256	1 3	..		1 9	..	..	..	1 15
Earlsfield B	..	12 0		12 7	..	..	..	..	..	12 20	1224	1234	..	..	..	1244	1247	..	..	..	..	1 0	1 7	..	..	..	..		..	..
Wimbledon	11 55	12 3	Via Three Bridges, see page 184	1210	..	..	12 15	1221	..	12 23	1227	1238	..	..	..	1247	1250	1251	..	12 55	..	1 3	1 10	..	..	1 15	..	Via Three Bridges see page 190	..	1 21
Raynes Park	..	12 6		1213	..	..	..	..	..	12 26	1230	1241	..	..	..	1250	1253	..	..	..	..	1 6	1 13	..	..	..	..		..	..
Motspur Park	12 0			1216	..	..	12 20		..				..	..	..	[3]	1256		..	1 0	..		1 16	..	..	1 20	..		..	
Malden Manor	..	[3]		1219	..	..	[3]	[3]	..	[3]	[3]	[3]	..	..	..		1259	[3]	..	[3]	..	[3]	1 19	..	..	[3]	..		..	[3]
Tolworth	..			1222	..	..			..				..	..	..	..	1 2		..		..		1 22	..	..		..		..	
Chessington North	[3]	..		1225	..	..	..	..	..	..	..	..	..	..	..	..	1 5	..	..	..	..	..	1 25	..	..	..	..		..	..
Chessington South ¶ar		..		1227	..	..	..	..	..	..	..	..	..	..	..	..	1 7	..	..	..	..	..	1 27	..	..	..	..		..	..
Worcester Park	12 2	..		[3]	..	..	12 22	..	..	..	..	..	..	..	..	..	[3]	..	..	1 2	..	..	[3]	..	..	1 22	..		..	..
Stoneleigh	12 5	..			..	..	12 25	..	..	..	..	..	..	..	..	..		..	..	1 5	..	..		..	..	1 25	..		..	..
Ewell West C	12 8	..		..	..	..	12 28	..	..	..	..	..	..	..	..	..	Stop	..	..	1 8	..	..	..	..	..	1 28	..		..	..
London Bridge .... dep.	11‡25	..	..	..	..	..	..	..	11 55	..	..	..	..	..	..	..		..	12 25	12‡25	..	..	..	..	..	..	12 55	..	..	..
Victoria .... "	11‡24	..	1148	..	..	..	11‡45	..	11‡45	..	..	..	..	..	..	..	..	..	12‡15	..	..	..	..	..	..	12‡45	12‡45	1248	..	..
Sutton .... "	11‡57	..	..	..	..	..	12‡9	..	12 27	..	..	..	..	..	..	..	..	..	12 57	12‡57	..	..	..	..	..	1‡9	1 27	..	..	..
Epsom 285	12 11	..	..	..	..	..	12 31	..	12 36	..	..	..	..	..	..	..	..	..	1 6	1 11	..	..	..	..	..	1 31	1 36	..	..	..
Ashtead	12 15	..	..	..	..	..	12 35	..	12 40	..	..	..	..	..	..	..	..	..	1 10	1 15	..	..	..	..	..	1 35	1 40	..	..	..
Leatherhead	12 19	..	..	..	..	..	12 39	..	12 44	..	..	..	..	..	..	..	..	..	1 14	1 19	..	..	..	..	..	1 39	1 44	..	..	..
Boxhill & Burford Bdg D	12 24	..	..	..	..		..	..	12 49	..	..	..	..	..	..	..	..	..	..	1 24	..	..	..	..		..	1 49	..	..	..
Dorking North F	12 28	..	..	..	..		..	..	12 52	..	..	..	..	..	..	..	..	..	..	1 28	..	..	..	..		..	1 52	..	..	..
Holmwood G	12 38	..	..	..	..		..	..	..	..	..	..	..	..	..	..	..	..	..	1 38	..	..	..	..		..	Stop	..	..	..
Ockley, for Capel	12 42	..	..	..	..	Via Richmond, see page 471	..	..	..	..	..	..	..	..	..	..	..	..	..	1 42	..	..	..	..	Via Richmond, see page 472	..		..	..	..
Warnham [196, 245	12 48	..	..	..	..		..	..	..	..	..	..	..	..	..	..	..	..	..	1 48	..	..	..	..		..	..	..	..	..
Horsham 159, arr.	12 53	..	1 5	..	..		..	..	..	..	..	..	..	..	..	..	..	..	..	1 53	..	..	..	..		..	..	2 5	..	..
Bookham	..	..	..	..	..		12 45	..	..	..	..	..	..	..	..	..	..	..	1 19	..	..	..	..	..		1 45	..	..	..	..
Malden, for Coombe	..	12 9	..	..	..		..	..	..	12 29	1233	1244	..	..	..	1253	..	..	..	..	..	1 9	..	..		..	..	..	..	..
Norbiton H	..	1213	..	..	..		..	..	..	12 33	..	1247	..	..	..	..	..	..	..	..	..	1 13	..	..		..	..	..	..	..
Kingston	..	1215	..	..	..		..	..	..	12 35	..	1250	..	..	..	..	..	..	..	..	..	1 15	..	..		..	..	..	..	..
Hampton Wick	..	1217	..	..	..		..	..	..	12 37	..	1252	..	..	..	..	..	..	..	..	..	1 17	..	..	..	..	..	..	..	..
Teddington J	..	1221	..	..	..		..	..	..	12 41	..	1255	..	..	..	..	..	..	..	..	..	1 21	..	..	..	..	..	..	..	..
Fulwell K	..	V	..	..	..	1235	..	..	..	V	..	1259	..	..	..	..	..	..	..	..	..	V	..	..	1 35	..	..	..	..	..
Hampton	..		..	..	..	1239	..	..	..		..	1 3	..	..	..	..	..	..	..	..	..		..	..	1 39	..	..	..	..	..
Sunbury L	..		..	..	..	1243	..	..	..		..	1 7	..	..	..	..	..	..	..	..	..		..	..	1 43	..	..	..	..	..
Upper Halliford Halt	..	To Waterloo via Richmond Arr. Twickenham 12 27 p.m.	..	..	..	1245	..	..	..	To Waterloo via Richmond Arr. Twickenham 12 47 p.m.	..	1 9	..	..	..	..	..	..	..	..	..	To Waterloo via Richmond Arr. Twickenham 1 27 p.m.	..	..	1 45	..	..	..	..	..
Shepperton M ..... arr.	..		..	..	..	1248	..	..	..		..	1 12	..	..	..	..	..	..	..	..	..		..	..	1 48	..	..	..	..	..
Berrylands N	..		..	..	..		..	..	..		1236	..	..	..	..	1257	..	..	..	..	..		..	..	..	..	..	..	..	..
Surbiton	..		..	..	1213	Stop	..	1228	..		1239	..	..	..	1243	1 0	..	1258	..	..	..		..	1 13	..	..	..	..	..	1 28
Thames Ditton	..		..	..	..	..	..	..	..		1243	..	..	..	..	1 4	..	..	..	..	..		..	..	..	..	..	..	..	..
Hampton Court P arr.	..		..	..	..	..	..	..	..		1246	..	..	..	..	1 7	..	..	..	..	..		..	..	..	..	..	..	..	..
Hinchley Wood	..		..	..	..	..	..	1231	..		..	..	..	..	..	..	..	1 1	..	..	..		..	..	..	..	..	..	..	1 31
Claygate, for Claremont	..		..	..	..	..	..	1234	..		..	..	..	..	..	..	..	1 4	..	..	..		..	..	..	..	..	..	..	1 34
Oxshott, for Fairmile	..		..	..	..	..	..	1238	..		..	..	..	..	..	..	..	1 8	..	..	..		..	..	..	..	..	..	..	1 38
Cobham Q	..		..	..	..	..	..	1241	..		..	..	..	..	..	..	..	1 11	..	..	..		..	..	..	..	..	..	..	1 41
Effingham Junction	..		..	..	..	..	12 49	1246	..		..	..	..	..	..	..	..	1 16	1 23	..	..		..	..	..	1 49	..	..	..	1 46
Horsley R	..		..	..	..	..	12 51	..	..		..	..	..	..	..	..	..	1 18	..	..	..		..	..	..	1 51	..	..	..	..
Clandon T	..		..	..	..	..	12 56	..	..		..	..	..	..	..	..	..	1 23	..	..	..		..	..	..	1 56	..	..	..	..
London Road (Guildford)	..		..	..	..	..	1 2	..	..		..	..	..	..	..	..	..	1 29	..	..	..		..	..	..	2 2	..	..	..	..
Esher, for Sandown Park	..		..	..	1217	p.m.	..	..	..		..	..	..	..	1247	..	p.m.	..	..	..	..		..	1 17	..	..	p.m.	..	..	..
Hersham	..	..	..	..	1220	[3]	..	..	..	..	..	..	..	..	1250	..	[3]	..	..	..	..	..	..	1 20	..	..	[3]	..	..	..
Walton-on-Thames	..	..	..	..	1223		..	..	..	..	..	..	..	..	1253	..		..	..	..	..	..	..	1 23	..	..		..	..	..
Weybridge U	..	..	..	..	1227	1235	..	..	..	..	..	..	..	..	1257	..	1 5	..	..	..	..	..	..	1 27	..	..	1 35	..	..	..
Addlestone	..	..	..	..	..	1239	..	..	..	..	..	..	..	..	..	..	1 9	..	..	..	..	..	..	..	..	..	1 39	..	..	..
Chertsey	..	..	..	..	..	1242	..	..	..	..	..	..	..	..	..	..	1 12	..	..	..	..	..	..	..	..	..	1 42	..	..	..
Virginia Water Z 460ar.	..	..	..	..	..	1246	..	..	..	..	..	..	..	..	..	..	1 16	..	..	..	..	..	..	..	..	..	1 46	..	..	..
West Weybridge	..	..	..	..	1230	..	..	..	..	..	..	..	..	..	1 0	..	..	..	..	..	..	..	..	1 30	..	..	..	..	..	..
Byfleet W	..	..	..	..	1233	..	..	..	..	..	..	..	..	..	1 3	..	..	..	..	..	..	..	..	1 33	..	..	..	..	..	..
Woking X 324, 389, 390	..	..	..	..	1237	..	..	..	..	..	..	..	..	1255	1 7	..	..	..	..	..	1 15	..	..	1 37	..	..	..	..	..	..
Worplesdon	..	..	..	..	1245	..	..	..	..	..	..	..	..	..	1 15	..	..	..	..	..	..	..	..	1 45	..	..	..	..	..	..
Guildford 246, 359 ... arr.	..	..	..	..	1251	..	1 6	..	..	..	..	..	..	..	1 21	..	..	1 33	..	..	1 25	..	..	1 51	..	2 6	..	..	..	..

LONDON, DORKING NORTH, HORSHAM, KINGSTON, SHEPPERTON, HAMPTON COURT, CHERTSEY, WOKING, & GUILDFORD

Down	p.m												Sundays—continued											p.m								
Waterloo dep.	1 9	1 13	1 23	1 27	1 33	1 36	1 38	3	1 42	1 49	1 56	1 57	..	1 59	2 2	3	2 8	2 9	2 13	2 23	2 27	2 33	2 36	2 38	3	2 42	2 45	2 49	2 54	..	2 56	2 57
Vauxhall	1 12	1 16	1 26	..	1 36	1 39	..		..	1 52	1 59	..	..	3	..		..	2 12	2 16	2 26	..	2 36	2 39	..		..	..	2 52	..	..	2 59	..
Clapham Junction A	1 16	1 20	1 31	..	1 40	1 43	1 45	..	1 49	1 56	2 3	..	..		2 9	..	2 15	2 16	2 20	2 31	..	2 40	2 43	2 45	..	2 49	..	2 56	..	..	3 3	..
Earlsfield B	1 20	1 24	1 34	..	1 44	1 47	..	..	..	2 0	2 7	..	..	..	..	..	..	2 20	2 24	2 34	..	2 44	2 47	..	..	..	..	3 0	..	..	3 7	..
Wimbledon	1 23	1 27	1 38	..	1 47	1 50	1 51	..	1 55	2 3	2 10	..	..	..	2 15	..	2 21	2 23	2 27	2 38	..	2 47	2 50	2 51	..	2 55	..	3 3	..	..	3 10	..
Raynes Park	1 26	1 30	1 41	..	1 50	1 53	..	..	..	2 6	2 13	..	..	..	..	..	..	2 26	2 30	2 41	..	2 50	2 53	..	..	..	..	3 6	..	..	3 13	..
Motspur Park				..		1 56		..	2 0		2 16	..	Via Three Bridges, see page 190	..	2 20	..					..		2 56		..	3 0	..		..	..	3 16	..
Malden Manor	3	3	3	..	3	1 59	3	..	3	3	2 19	..		..	3	..	3	3	3	3	..	3	2 59	3	..	3	..	3	..	..	3 19	..
Tolworth				..		2 2		..			2 22	..		..		..					..		3 2		..		..		..	..	3 22	..
Chessington North	..	..	..	..	..	2 5	..	..	..	..	2 25	..		..	..	..	..	..	..	..	..	..	3 5	..	..	..	..	..	..	..	3 25	..
Chessington South ¶ arr	..	..	..	..	..	2 7	..	..	..	..	2 27	..		..	..	..	..	..	..	..	..	..	3 7	..	..	..	..	..	..	..	3 27	..
Worcester Park	..	..	..	..	..	3	..	..	2 2	..	3	..		..	2 22	..	..	..	..	..	..	..	3	..	..	3 2	..	..	..	..	3	..
Stoneleigh	..	..	..	..	..		..	..	2 5	..		..		..	2 25	..	..	..	..	..	..	..		..	..	3 5	..	..	..	..		..
Ewell West C	..	..	..	..	..	..	..	..	2 8	..	..	..		..	2 28	..	..	..	..	..	..	..	..	..	..	3 8	..	..	..	..	..	..
London Bridge dep.	..	..	..	..	..	..	..	1 25	1‡25	..	..	..	..	..	..	1 55	..	..	..	..	..	..	..	..	2 25	2‡25	..	..	..	..	..	..
Victoria "	..	..	..	..	..	..	..	1‡15	..	..	..	..	1 48	..	1‡45	1‡45	..	..	..	..	..	..	..	..	2‡15	..	..	..	..	..	..	..
Sutton "	..	..	..	..	..	..	..	1 57	1‡57	..	..	..	..	..	2‡ 9	2 27	..	..	..	..	..	..	..	..	2 57	2‡57	..	..	..	..	..	..
Epsom 285	..	..	..	..	..	..	..	2 6	2 11	..	..	..	..	..	2 31	2 36	..	..	..	..	..	..	..	..	3 6	3 11	..	..	..	..	..	..
Ashtead	..	..	..	..	..	..	..	2 10	2 15	..	..	..	..	..	2 35	2 40	..	..	..	..	..	..	..	..	3 10	3 15	..	..	..	..	..	..
Leatherhead	..	..	..	..	..	..	..	2 14	2 19	..	..	..	..	..	2 39	2 44	..	..	..	..	..	..	..	..	3 14	3 19	..	..	..	..	..	..
Boxhill & Burford Bdg D	..	..	..	..	..	..	..	..	2 24	..	..	..	..	..	..	2 49	..	..	..	..	..	..	..	..	..	3 24	..	..	..	..	..	..
Dorking North F	..	..	..	..	..	..	..	..	2 28	..	..	..	..	..	..	2 52	..	..	..	..	..	..	..	..	..	3 28	..	..	..	..	..	..
Holmwood G	..	..	..	..	..	..	..	..	2 38	..	..	..	..	..	..	..	..	..	..	..	..	..	..	..	..	3 38	..	..	..	..	..	..
Ockley, for Capel	..	..	..	..	..	..	..	..	2 42	..	..	..	..	Via Richmond, see page 472	..	..	..	..	..	..	..	..	..	..	..	3 42	..	..	..	..	..	..
Warnham 196, 245	..	..	..	..	..	..	..	..	2 48	..	..	..	..		..	..	..	..	..	..	..	..	..	..	..	3 48	..	..	..	..	..	..
Horsham 159, arr.	..	..	..	..	..	..	..	..	2 53	..	..	..	3 5		..	..	..	..	..	..	..	..	..	..	..	3 53	..	..	..	..	..	..
Bookham	..	..	..	..	..	..	..	2 19	..	..	..	..	..		2 45	..	..	..	..	..	..	..	..	..	3 19	..	..	..	..	..	..	..
Malden, for Coombe	1 29	1 33	1 44	..	1 53	..	..	..	..	2 9	..	..	..		..	..	..	2 29	2 33	2 44	..	2 53	..	..	..	..	..	3 9	..	..	..	..
Norbiton H	1 33	..	1 47	..	..	..	..	..	..	2 13	..	..	..		..	..	..	2 33	..	2 47	..	..	..	..	..	..	..	3 13	..	..	..	..
Kingston	1 35	..	1 50	..	..	..	..	..	..	2 15	..	..	..		..	..	..	2 35	..	2 50	..	..	..	..	..	..	..	3 15	..	..	..	..
Hampton Wick	1 37	..	1 52	..	..	..	..	..	..	2 17	..	..	..		..	..	..	2 37	..	2 52	..	..	..	..	..	..	..	3 17	..	..	..	..
Teddington J	1 41	..	1 55	..	..	..	..	..	..	2 21	..	..	..		..	..	..	2 41	..	2 55	..	..	..	..	..	..	..	3 21	..	..	..	..
Fulwell K	V	..	1 59	..	..	..	..	..	..	V	..	..	..	2 35	..	..	..	V	..	2 59	..	..	..	..	..	..	..	V	..	..	..	..
Hampton	To Waterloo via Richmond Arr. Twickenham 1 47 p.m	..	2 3	..	..	..	..	..	..	To Waterloo via Richmond Arr. Twickenham 2 27 p.m	..	..	..	2 39	..	..	..	To Waterloo via Richmond Arr. Twickenham 2 47 p.m	..	3 3	..	..	..	..	..	..	..	To Waterloo via Richmond Arr. Twickenham 3 27 p.m	..	..	..	..
Sunbury L		..	2 7	..	..	..	..	..	..		..	..	..	2 43	..	..	..		..	3 7	..	..	..	..	..	..	..		..	..	..	..
Upper Halliford Halt		..	2 9	..	..	..	..	..	..		..	..	..	2 45	..	..	..		..	3 9	..	..	..	..	..	..	..		..	..	..	..
Shepperton M arr.		..	2 12	..	..	..	..	..	..		..	..	..	2 48	..	..	..		..	3 12	..	..	..	..	..	..	..		..	..	..	..
Berrylands N		1 36	..	..	1 57	..	..	..	..		..	..	..	Stop	..	..	..		2 36	..	..	2 57	..	..	..	..	..		..	..	..	..
Surbiton		1 39	..	1 43	2 0	..	1 58	..	..		..	2 13	..	..	..	..	2 28		2 39	..	2 43	3 0	..	2 58	..	..	..		..	..	..	3 13
Thames Ditton		1 43	..	..	2 4	..	..	..	..		..	..	..	..	..	..	..		2 43	..	..	3 4	..	..	..	..	..		..	..	..	..
Hampton Court P arr.		1 46	..	..	2 7	..	..	..	..		..	..	..	..	..	..	..		2 46	..	..	3 7	..	..	..	..	..		..	..	..	..
Hinchley Wood		..	..	..	..	..	2 1	..	..		..	..	..	..	..	..	2 31		..	..	..	..	..	3 1	..	..	..		..	..	..	..
Claygate, for Claremont		..	..	..	..	..	2 4	..	..		..	..	..	..	..	..	2 34		..	..	..	..	..	3 4	..	..	..		..	..	..	..
Oxshott, for Fairmile		..	..	..	..	..	2 8	..	..		..	..	..	..	..	..	2 38		..	..	..	..	..	3 8	..	..	..		..	..	..	..
Cobham Q		..	..	..	..	..	2 11	..	..		..	..	..	..	..	..	2 41		..	..	..	..	..	3 11	..	..	..		..	..	..	..
Effingham Junction		..	..	..	..	..	2 16	2 23	..		..	..	..	..	2 49	..	2 46		..	..	..	..	..	3 16	3 23	..	..		..	..	..	..
Horsley R		..	..	..	..	..	2 18	Stop	..		..	..	..	..	2 51	..	..		..	..	..	..	..	3 18	Stop	..	..		..	..	..	..
Clandon T		..	..	..	..	..	2 23	..	..		..	..	..	..	2 56	..	..		..	..	..	..	..	3 23	..	..	..		..	..	..	..
London Road (Guildford)		..	..	..	..	..	2 29	..	..		..	..	..	..	3 2	..	..		..	..	..	..	..	3 29	..	..	..		..	..	..	..
Esher, for Sandown Park		..	..	1 47	..	..	..	p.m	..		..	2 17	..	p.m	..	..	..		..	..	2 47	..	..	..	p.m	..	..		..	..	..	3 17
Hersham	..	..	..	1 50	..	..	..	3	..	..	..	2 20	..	3	..	..	..	..	..	..	2 50	..	..	..	3	..	..	..	..	..	..	3 20
Walton-on-Thames	..	..	..	1 53	..	..	..		..	..	..	2 23	..		..	..	..	..	..	..	2 53	..	..	..		..	..	..	..	..	..	3 23
Weybridge U	..	..	..	1 57	..	..	..	2 5	..	..	..	2 27	..	2 35	..	..	..	..	..	..	2 57	..	..	..	3 5	..	..	..	..	..	..	3 27
Addlestone	..	..	..	..	..	..	..	2 9	..	..	..	..	..	2 39	..	..	..	..	..	..	..	..	..	..	3 9	..	..	..	..	..	..	..
Chertsey	..	..	..	..	..	..	..	2 12	..	..	..	..	..	2 42	..	..	..	..	..	..	..	..	..	..	3 12	..	..	..	..	..	..	..
Virginia Water Z 460 arr	..	..	..	..	..	..	..	2 16	..	..	..	..	..	2 46	..	..	..	..	..	..	..	..	..	..	3 16	..	..	..	..	..	..	..
West Weybridge	..	..	..	2 0	..	..	..	..	..	..	..	2 30	..	..	..	..	..	..	..	..	3 0	..	..	..	..	..	..	..	..	..	..	3 30
Byfleet W	..	..	..	2 3	..	..	..	..	..	..	..	2 33	..	..	..	..	..	..	..	..	3 3	..	..	..	..	..	..	..	..	..	..	3 33
Woking X 324, 389, 390	..	..	..	2 7	..	..	..	..	..	..	..	2 37	..	..	..	..	..	..	..	..	3 7	..	..	..	..	..	3 15	..	3 25	..	..	3 37
Worplesdon	..	..	..	2 15	..	..	..	..	..	..	..	2 45	..	..	..	..	..	..	..	..	3 15	..	..	..	..	..	..	..	..	..	..	3 45
Guildford 246, 359 arr.	..	..	..	2 21	..	..	2 33	..	..	..	..	2 51	..	..	3 6	..	..	..	..	..	3 21	..	..	3 33	..	..	3 25	..	..	..	..	3 51

FOR NOTES, SEE PAGE 426

FOR NOTES, SEE PAGE 426

DON, DORKING NORTH, HORSHAM, KINGSTON, SHEPPERTON, HAMPTON COURT, CHERTSEY, WOKING, & GUILDFORD

Sundays—*continued*

Down	p.m.															
Waterloo dep.	2 59	..	3 2	(3)	3 8	3 9	3 13	3 23	3 27	3 33	3 36	3 38	(3)	3 42	3 49	3 56
Vauxhall	(3)	..	..	..	..	3 12	3 16	3 26	..	3 36	3 39	..	..	..	3 52	3 59
Clapham Junction **A**	..	..	3 9	..	3 15	3 16	3 20	3 31	..	3 40	3 43	3 45	..	3 49	3 56	4 3
Earlsfield **B**	..	..	..	..	..	3 20	3 24	3 34	..	3 44	3 47	..	..	..	4 0	4 7
Wimbledon	..	..	3 15	..	3 21	3 23	3 27	3 38	..	3 47	3 50	3 51	..	3 55	4 3	4 10
Raynes Park	..	..	..	..	..	3 26	3 30	3 41	..	3 50	3 53	..	..	..	4 6	4 13
Motspur Park	..	..	3 20	..	..	..	..	..	..	..	3 56	..	..	4 0	..	4 16
Malden Manor	..	..	(3)	..	(3)	(3)	(3)	(3)	..	(3)	3 59	(3)	..	(3)	(3)	4 19
Tolworth	..	..	..	..	..	..	..	..	..	..	4 2	..	..	..	..	4 22
Chessington North	..	..	..	..	..	..	..	..	..	..	4 5	..	..	..	..	4 25
Chessington South ¶ ar	..	..	..	..	..	..	..	..	..	..	4 7	..	..	..	..	4 27
Worcester Park	..	..	3 22	..	..	..	..	..	..	..	(3)	..	..	4 2	..	(3)
Stoneleigh	..	..	3 25	..	..	..	..	..	..	..	..	..	..	4 5	..	..
Ewell West **C**	..	..	3 28	..	..	..	..	..	..	..	..	..	..	4 8	..	..
London Bridge dep.	..	2*55	..	2 55	..	..	..	..	..	..	..	..	3 25	3‡25	..	..
Victoria "	..	3 18	2‡45	2‡45	..	..	..	..	..	..	..	..	3‡20	..	..	..
Sutton "	..	3 29	3‡9	3 27	..	..	..	..	..	..	..	..	3 57	3‡57	..	..
Epsom **285**	..	..	3 31	3 36	..	..	..	..	..	..	..	..	4 6	4 11	..	..
Ashtead	..	..	3 35	3 40	..	..	..	..	..	..	..	..	4 10	4 15	..	..
Leatherhead	..	..	3 39	3 44	..	..	..	..	..	..	..	..	4 14	4 19	..	..
Boxhill & Burford Bdg **D**	Via Richmond, see page 472	..	..	3 49	..	..	..	..	..	..	..	..	..	4 24	..	..
Dorking North F		3 55	..	3 52	..	..	..	..	..	..	..	..	..	4 28	..	..
Holmwood **G**		..	..	..	..	..	..	..	..	..	..	..	..	4 38	..	..
Ockley, for Capel		..	..	..	..	..	..	..	..	..	..	..	..	4 42	..	..
Warnham [**196**, 245		..	..	..	..	..	..	..	..	..	..	..	..	4 48	..	..
Horsham 159, arr.		4 13	..	..	..	..	..	..	..	..	..	..	..	4 53	..	..
Bookham		..	3 45	..	..	..	..	..	..	..	..	..	4 19	..	..	..
Malden, for Coombe		..	..	..	..	3 29	3 33	3 44	..	3 53	..	..	..	..	4 9	..
Norbiton **H**		..	..	..	..	3 33	..	3 47	..	..	..	..	..	..	4 13	..
Kingston		..	..	..	..	3 35	..	3 50	..	..	..	..	..	..	4 15	..
Hampton Wick		..	..	..	..	3 37	..	3 52	..	..	..	..	..	..	4 17	..
Teddington J		..	..	..	..	3 41	..	3 55	..	..	..	..	..	..	4 21	..
Fulwell **K**	3 35	..	..	..	..	V	..	3 59	..	..	..	..	..	..	V	..
Hampton	3 39	..	..	..	..	To Waterloo via Richmond Arr. **Twickenham** 3 47 p.m.	..	4 3	..	..	..	..	..	..	To Waterloo via Richmond Arr. **Twickenham** 4 27 p.m.	..
Sunbury **L**	3 43	..	..	..	..		..	4 7	..	..	..	..	..	..		..
Upper Halliford Halt	3 45	..	..	..	..		..	4 9	..	..	..	..	..	..		..
Shepperton M arr.	3 48	..	..	..	..		..	4 12	..	..	..	..	..	..		..
Berrylands **N**	Stop	..	..	..	..		3 36	..	..	3 57	..	..	..	..		..
Surbiton	..	..	..	..	3 28		3 39	..	3 43	4 0	..	3 58	..	..		..
Thames Ditton	..	..	..	..	..		3 43	..	..	4 4	..	..	..	..		..
Hampton Court P arr.	..	..	..	..	..		3 46	..	..	4 7	..	..	..	..		..
Hinchley Wood	..	..	..	..	3 31		..	..	..	..	..	4 1	..	..		..
Claygate, for Claremont	..	..	..	..	3 34		..	..	..	..	..	4 4	..	..		..
Oxshott, for Fairmile	..	..	..	..	3 38		..	..	..	..	..	4 8	..	..		..
Cobham **Q**	..	..	..	..	3 41		..	..	..	..	..	4 11	..	..		..
Effingham Junction	..	..	3 49	..	3 46		..	..	..	..	..	4 16	4 23	..		..
Horsley **R**	..	..	3 51	..	..		..	..	..	..	..	4 18	Stop	..		..
Clandon **T**	..	..	3 56	..	..		..	..	..	..	..	4 23	..	..		..
London Road (Guildford)	..	..	4 2	..	..		..	..	..	..	..	4 29	..	..		..
Esher, for Sandown Park	p.m	..	..	..	..	..	..	..	3 47	..	..	..	p.m	..	..	..
Hersham	(3)	..	..	..	..	..	..	..	3 50	..	..	..	(3)	..	..	..
Walton-on-Thames	..	..	..	..	..	..	..	..	3 53	..	..	..	..	..	..	..
Weybridge U	3 35	..	..	..	..	..	..	..	3 57	..	..	..	4 5	..	..	..
Addlestone	3 39	..	..	..	..	..	..	..	..	..	..	..	4 9	..	..	..
Chertsey	3 42	..	..	..	..	..	..	..	..	..	..	..	4 12	..	..	..
Virginia Water Z 460 arr	3 46	..	..	..	..	..	..	..	..	..	..	..	4 16	..	..	..
West Weybridge	..	..	..	..	..	..	..	..	4 0	..	..	..	..	..	..	..
Byfleet **W**	..	..	..	..	..	..	..	..	4 3	..	..	..	..	..	..	..
Woking X 324, 389, 390	..	..	..	..	..	..	..	..	4 7	..	..	..	..	..	..	..
Worplesdon	..	..	..	..	..	..	..	..	4 15	..	..	..	..	..	..	..
Guildford 246, 359 arr.	..	..	4 6	..	..	..	..	..	4 21	..	..	4 33	..	..	..	..

Down	p.m.															
Waterloo dep.	3 57	..	3 59	4 2	(3)	4 8	4 9	4 13	4 23	4 27	4 33	4 36	4 38	(3)	4 42	4 45
Vauxhall	..	..	(3)	..	..	..	4 12	4 16	4 26	..	4 36	4 39	..	..	..	..
Clapham Junction **A**	..	..	..	4 9	..	4 15	4 16	4 20	4 31	..	4 40	4 43	4 45	..	4 49	..
Earlsfield **B**	..	..	..	..	..	..	4 20	4 24	4 34	..	4 44	4 47	..	..	..	..
Wimbledon	..	..	..	4 15	..	4 21	4 23	4 27	4 38	..	4 47	4 50	4 51	..	4 55	..
Raynes Park	..	..	..	..	..	..	4 26	4 30	4 41	..	4 50	4 53	..	..	..	..
Motspur Park	..	Via Three Bridges, see page 190	..	4 20	..	..	..	..	..	..	..	4 56	..	..	5 0	..
Malden Manor	..		..	(3)	..	(3)	(3)	(3)	(3)	..	(3)	4 59	(3)	..	(3)	..
Tolworth	..		..	..	..	..	..	..	..	..	..	5 2	..	..	..	..
Chessington North	..		..	..	..	..	..	..	..	..	..	5 5	..	..	..	..
Chessington South ¶ ar	..		..	..	..	..	..	..	..	..	..	5 7	..	..	..	..
Worcester Park	..		..	4 22	..	..	..	..	..	..	..	(3)	..	..	5 2	..
Stoneleigh	..		..	4 25	..	..	..	..	..	..	..	..	..	..	5 5	..
Ewell West **C**	..		..	4 28	..	..	..	..	..	..	..	Stop	..	..	5 8	..
London Bridge dep.	..	..	..	..	3 55	..	..	..	..	..	..	..	..	4 25	4‡25	..
Victoria "	..	3 48	..	3‡45	3‡45	..	..	..	..	..	..	..	..	4‡15	..	..
Sutton "	..	..	..	4‡9	4 27	..	..	..	..	..	..	..	..	4 57	4‡57	..
Epsom **285**	..	..	..	4 31	4 36	..	..	..	..	..	..	..	..	5 6	5 11	..
Ashtead	..	..	..	4 35	4 40	..	..	..	..	..	..	..	..	5 10	5 15	..
Leatherhead	..	..	..	4 39	4 44	..	..	..	..	..	..	..	..	5 14	5 19	..
Boxhill & Burford Bdg **D**	..	..	..	..	4 49	..	..	..	..	..	..	..	..	..	5 24	..
Dorking North F	..	..	..	..	4 52	..	..	..	..	..	..	..	..	..	5 28	..
Holmwood **G**	..	..	Via Richmond see page 473	..	..	..	..	..	..	..	..	..	..	..	5 38	..
Ockley, for Capel	..	..		..	..	..	..	..	..	..	..	..	..	..	5 42	..
Warnham [**196**, 245	..	..		..	..	..	..	..	..	..	..	..	..	..	5 48	..
Horsham 159, arr.	..	5 5		..	..	..	..	..	..	..	..	..	..	..	5 53	..
Bookham	..	..		4 45	..	..	..	..	..	..	..	..	..	5 19	..	..
Malden, for Coombe	..	..		..	..	..	4 29	4 33	4 44	..	4 53	..	..	..	..	..
Norbiton **H**	..	..		..	..	..	4 33	..	4 47	..	..	..	..	..	..	..
Kingston	..	..		..	..	..	4 35	..	4 50	..	..	..	..	..	..	..
Hampton Wick	..	..		..	..	..	4 37	..	4 52	..	..	..	..	..	..	..
Teddington J	..	..		..	..	..	4 41	..	4 55	..	..	..	..	..	..	..
Fulwell **K**	..	..	4 35	..	..	..	V	..	4 59	..	..	..	..	..	..	..
Hampton	..	..	4 39	..	..	..	To Waterloo via Richmond Arr. **Twickenham** 4 47 p.m.	..	5 3	..	..	..	..	..	..	..
Sunbury **L**	..	..	4 43	..	..	..		..	5 7	..	..	..	..	..	..	..
Upper Halliford Halt	..	..	4 45	..	..	..		..	5 9	..	..	..	..	..	..	..
Shepperton M arr.	..	..	4 48	..	..	..		..	5 12	..	..	..	..	..	..	..
Berrylands **N**	..	..	Stop	..	..	..		4 36	..	..	4 57	..	..	..	..	..
Surbiton	4 13	..	..	..	..	4 28		4 39	..	4 43	5 0	..	4 58	..	..	..
Thames Ditton	..	..	..	..	..	..		4 43	..	..	5 4	..	..	..	..	..
Hampton Court P arr.	..	..	..	..	..	..		4 46	..	..	5 7	..	..	..	..	..
Hinchley Wood	..	..	..	..	..	4 31		..	..	..	..	..	5 1	..	..	..
Claygate, for Claremont	..	..	..	..	..	4 34		..	..	..	..	..	5 4	..	..	..
Oxshott, for Fairmile	..	..	..	..	..	4 38		..	..	..	..	..	5 8	..	..	..
Cobham **Q**	..	..	..	..	..	4 41		..	..	..	..	..	5 11	..	..	..
Effingham Junction	..	..	..	4 49	..	4 46		..	..	..	..	..	5 16	5 23	..	..
Horsley **R**	..	..	..	4 51	..	..		..	..	..	..	..	5 18	..	..	..
Clandon **T**	..	..	..	4 56	..	..		..	..	..	..	..	5 23	..	..	..
London Road (Guildford)	..	..	..	5 2	..	..		..	..	..	..	..	5 29	..	..	..
Esher, for Sandown Park	4 17	..	p.m	..	..	..	..	..	..	4 47	..	p.m	..	..	..	..
Hersham	4 20	..	(3)	..	..	..	..	..	..	4 50	..	(3)	..	..	..	..
Walton-on-Thames	4 23	..	..	..	..	..	..	..	..	4 53	..	..	..	..	..	..
Weybridge U	4 27	..	4 35	..	..	..	..	..	..	4 57	..	5 5	..	..	..	..
Addlestone	..	..	4 39	..	..	..	..	..	..	..	..	5 9	..	..	..	..
Chertsey	..	..	4 42	..	..	..	..	..	..	..	..	5 12	..	..	..	..
Virginia Water Z 460 arr	..	..	4 46	..	..	..	..	..	..	..	..	5 16	..	..	..	..
West Weybridge	4 30	..	..	..	..	..	..	..	..	5 0	..	..	..	..	..	..
Byfleet **W**	4 33	..	..	..	..	..	..	..	..	5 3	..	..	..	..	..	..
Woking X 324, 389, 390	4 37	..	..	..	..	..	..	..	..	5 7	..	..	..	..	..	5 15
Worplesdon	4 45	..	..	..	..	..	..	..	..	5 15	..	..	..	..	..	..
Guildford 246, 359 arr.	4 51	..	..	5 6	..	..	..	..	..	5 21	..	..	5 33	..	..	5 25

LONDON, DORKING NORTH, HORSHAM, KINGSTON, SHEPPERTON, HAMPTON COURT, CHERTSEY, WOKING, & GUILDFORD

Sundays—*continued* (p.m)

Down																
Waterloo dep.	4 49	4 54	4 56	4 57	3	4 59	..	5 2	5 8	3	5 9	5 13	5 23	5 27	5 33	5 36
Vauxhall	4 52	..	4 59	..	..	3	..	..	..	..	5 12	5 16	5 26	..	5 36	5 39
Clapham Junction A	4 56	..	5 3	..	..	..	..	5 9	5 15	..	5 16	5 20	5 31	..	5 40	5 43
Earlsfield B	5 0	..	5 7	..	..	..	Via Three Bridges, see page 192	..	..	..	5 20	5 24	5 34	..	5 44	5 47
Wimbledon	5 3	..	5 10	..	..	..		5 15	5 21	..	5 23	5 27	5 38	..	5 47	5 50
Raynes Park	5 6	..	5 13	..	..	..		..	..	..	5 26	5 30	5 41	..	5 50	5 53
Motspur Park	..	..	5 16	..	..	..		5 20	..	..	..	..	..	..	..	5 56
Malden Manor	3	..	5 19	..	..	..		3	3	..	3	3	3	..	3	5 59
Tolworth	..	..	5 22	..	..	..		..	..	..	..	..	..	..	..	6 2
Chessington North	..	..	5 25	..	..	..		..	..	..	..	..	..	..	..	6 5
Chessington South ¶ arr	..	..	5 27	..	..	..		..	..	..	..	..	..	..	..	6 7
Worcester Park	..	..	3	..	..	..		5 22	..	..	..	..	..	..	..	3
Stoneleigh	..	..	..	..	..	..		5 25	..	..	..	..	..	..	..	..
Ewell West C	..	..	..	..	..	..		5 28	..	..	..	..	..	..	..	Stop
London Bridge dep.	..	..	..	..	..	..	..	..	..	4 55	..	..	..	..	..	..
Victoria "	..	..	..	..	..	..	4 48	4‡45	..	4‡45	..	..	..	..	..	..
Sutton "	..	..	..	..	..	..	..	5‡ 9	..	5 27	..	..	..	..	..	..
Epsom 285	..	..	..	..	..	..	..	5 31	..	5 36	..	..	..	..	..	..
Ashtead	..	..	..	..	..	..	..	5 35	..	5 40	..	..	..	..	..	..
Leatherhead	..	..	..	..	..	..	..	5 39	..	5 44	..	..	..	..	..	..
Boxhill & Burford Bdg D	..	..	..	..	..	..	..	..	..	5 49	..	..	..	..	..	..
Dorking North F	..	..	..	..	..	..	..	..	..	5 52	..	..	..	..	..	..
Holmwood G	..	..	..	..	..	..	..	..	..	..	..	..	..	..	..	..
Ockley, for Capel	..	..	..	..	..	Via Richmond, see page 473	..	..	..	..	..	..	..	..	..	..
Warnham [196, 245	..	..	..	..	..		..	..	..	..	..	..	..	..	..	..
Horsham 159, arr.	..	..	..	..	..		6 5	..	..	..	..	..	..	..	..	..
Bookham	..	..	..	..	..		..	5 45	..	..	..	..	..	..	5 53	..
Malden, for Coombe	5 9	..	..	..	..		..	..	..	..	5 29	5 33	5 44	..	..	..
Norbiton H	5 13	..	..	..	..		..	..	..	..	5 33	..	5 47	..	..	..
Kingston	5 15	..	..	..	..		..	..	..	..	5 35	..	5 50	..	..	..
Hampton Wick	5 17	..	..	..	..		..	..	..	..	5 37	..	5 52	..	..	..
Teddington J	5 21	..	..	..	..		..	..	..	..	5 41	..	5 55	..	..	..
Fulwell K	V	..	..	..	..	5 35	..	..	..	..	V	..	5 59	..	..	..
Hampton		..	..	..	..	5 39	..	..	..	..		..	6 3	..	..	..
Sunbury L		..	..	..	..	5 43	..	..	..	..		..	6 7	..	..	..
Upper Halliford Halt	To Waterloo via Richmond Arr. Twickenham 5 27 p.m	..	..	..	..	5 45	..	..	..	..	To Waterloo via Richmond Arr. Twickenham 5 47 p.m	..	6 9	..	..	..
Shepperton M arr.		..	..	..	..	5 48	..	..	..	..		..	6 12	..	..	..
Berrylands N		..	..	..	..	..	..	..	..	..		5 36	..	..	5 57	..
Surbiton		..	..	5 13	..	..	..	..	5 28	..		5 39	..	5 43	6 0	..
Thames Ditton		..	..	..	..	..	..	..	..	..		5 43	..	..	6 4	..
Hampton Court P arr.		..	..	..	..	..	..	..	..	..		5 46	..	..	6 7	..
Hinchley Wood		..	..	..	..	..	..	..	5 31	..		..	..	..	..	..
Claygate, for Claremont		..	..	..	..	..	..	..	5 34	..		..	..	..	..	..
Oxshott, for Fairmile		..	..	..	..	..	..	..	5 38	..		..	..	..	..	..
Cobham Q		..	..	..	..	..	..	..	5 41	..		..	..	..	..	..
Effingham Junction		..	..	..	..	..	..	5 49	5 46	..		..	..	..	..	..
Horsley R		..	..	..	..	..	..	5 51	..	..		..	..	..	..	..
Clandon T		..	..	..	..	..	..	5 56	..	..		..	..	..	..	..
London Road (Guildford)		..	..	..	..	..	..	6 2	..	..		..	..	..	..	..
Esher, for Sandown Park	..	..	..	5 17	..	..	..	..	..	..	..	..	..	5 47	..	p.m
Hersham	..	..	..	5 20	..	..	..	..	..	..	..	..	..	5 50	..	..
Walton-on-Thames	..	..	..	5 23	3	..	..	..	..	..	..	..	..	5 53	..	3
Weybridge U	..	..	..	5 27	5 35	..	..	..	..	..	..	..	..	5 57	..	6 5
Addlestone	..	..	..	..	5 39	..	..	..	..	..	..	..	..	..	..	6 9
Chertsey	..	..	..	..	5 42	..	..	..	..	..	..	..	..	..	..	6 12
Virginia Water Z 460 arr	..	..	..	..	5 46	..	..	..	..	..	..	..	..	..	..	6 16
West Weybridge	..	..	..	5 30	..	..	..	..	..	..	..	..	..	6 0	..	..
Byfleet W	..	..	..	5 33	..	..	..	..	..	..	..	..	..	6 3	..	..
Woking X 324, 389, 390	..	5 25	..	5 37	..	..	..	..	..	..	..	..	..	6 7	..	..
Worplesdon	..	..	..	5 45	..	..	..	..	..	..	..	..	..	6 15	..	..
Guildford 246, 359 arr.	..	..	..	5 51	..	..	..	6 6	..	..	..	..	..	6 21	..	..

Down																
Waterloo dep.	3	5 38	5 42	..	5 49	..	5 56	5 57		5 59	6 2	6 8	3	6 9	6 13	6 23
Vauxhall	..	..	..	..	5 52	..	5 59	..	..	3	..	..	..	6 12	6 16	6 26
Clapham Junction A	..	5 45	5 49	..	5 56	..	6 3	..	Via Three Bridges, see page 192	..	6 9	6 15	..	6 16	6 20	6 31
Earlsfield B	..	..	..	..	6 0	..	6 7	..		..	..	..	..	6 20	6 24	6 34
Wimbledon	..	5 51	5 55	..	6 3	..	6 10	..		..	6 15	6 21	..	6 23	6 27	6 38
Raynes Park	..	..	..	..	6 6	..	6 13	..		..	..	..	..	6 26	6 30	6 41
Motspur Park	..	..	6 0	..	..	..	6 16	..		..	6 20	..	..	..	..	..
Malden Manor	..	3	3	..	3	..	6 19	..		..	3	3	..	3	3	3
Tolworth	..	..	..	..	..	..	6 22	..		..	..	..	..	..	..	..
Chessington North	..	..	..	..	..	..	6 25	..		..	..	..	..	..	..	..
Chessington South ¶ arr	..	..	..	..	..	..	6 27	..		..	..	..	..	..	..	..
Worcester Park	..	..	6 2	..	..	..	3	..		..	6 22	..	..	..	..	..
Stoneleigh	..	..	6 5	..	..	..	..	..		..	6 25	..	..	..	..	..
Ewell West C	..	..	6 8	..	..	..	..	..		..	6 28	..	..	..	..	..
London Bridge dep.	5 25	..	5‡25	..	..	..	..	..	..	..	..	..	5 55	..	..	..
Victoria "	5‡15	..	..	..	..	..	..	..	5 48	..	5‡45	..	5‡45	..	..	..
Sutton "	5 57	..	5‡57	..	..	..	..	..	..	..	6‡ 9	..	6 27	..	..	..
Epsom 285	6 6	..	6 11	..	..	..	..	..	..	..	6 31	..	6 36	..	..	..
Ashtead	6 10	..	6 15	..	..	..	..	..	..	..	6 35	..	6 40	..	..	..
Leatherhead	6 14	..	6 19	..	..	..	..	..	..	..	6 39	..	6 44	..	..	..
Boxhill & Burford Bdg D	..	..	6 24	..	..	..	..	..	..	..	..	..	6 49	..	..	..
Dorking North F	..	..	6 28	..	..	..	..	..	..	..	..	..	6 52	..	..	..
Holmwood G	..	..	6 38	..	..	..	..	..	..	Via Richmond, see page 473	..	..	..	..	..	..
Ockley, for Capel	..	..	6 42	..	..	..	..	..	..		..	..	..	..	..	..
Warnham [196, 245	..	..	6 48	..	..	..	..	..	..		..	..	..	..	..	..
Horsham 159, arr.	..	..	6 53	..	..	..	..	..	7 5		..	..	..	..	..	..
Bookham	6 19	..	..	..	..	..	..	..	..		6 45	..	..	..	..	..
Malden, for Coombe	..	..	..	..	6 9	..	..	..	..		..	..	..	6 29	6 33	6 44
Norbiton H	..	..	..	..	6 13	..	..	..	..		..	..	..	6 33	..	6 47
Kingston	..	..	..	..	6 15	..	..	..	..		..	..	..	6 35	..	6 50
Hampton Wick	..	..	..	..	6 17	..	..	..	..		..	..	..	6 37	..	6 52
Teddington J	..	..	..	..	6 21	..	..	..	..		..	..	..	6 41	..	6 55
Fulwell K	..	..	..	..	V	..	..	..	..	6 35	..	..	..	V	..	6 59
Hampton	..	..	..	..		..	..	..	..	6 39	..	..	..		..	7 3
Sunbury L	..	..	..	..		..	..	..	..	6 43	..	..	..		..	7 7
Upper Halliford Halt	..	..	..	..	To Waterloo via Richmond Arr. Twickenham 6 27 p.m	..	..	..	..	6 45	..	..	..	To Waterloo via Richmond Arr. Twickenham 6 47 p.m	..	7 9
Shepperton M arr.	..	..	..	..		..	..	..	..	6 48	..	..	..		..	7 12
Berrylands N	..	..	..	..		..	..	..	..	Stop	..	..	..		6 36	..
Surbiton	..	5 58	..	..		..	..	6 13	..	..	..	6 28	..		6 39	..
Thames Ditton	..	..	..	..		..	..	..	..	..	..	..	..		6 43	..
Hampton Court P arr.	..	..	..	..		..	..	..	..	..	..	..	..		6 46	..
Hinchley Wood	..	6 1	..	..		..	..	..	..	..	..	6 31	..		..	..
Claygate, for Claremont	..	6 4	..	..		..	..	..	..	..	..	6 34	..		..	..
Oxshott, for Fairmile	..	6 8	..	..		..	..	..	..	..	..	6 38	..		..	..
Cobham Q	..	6 11	..	..		..	..	..	..	..	..	6 41	..		..	..
Effingham Junction	6 23	6 16	..	..		..	..	..	..	..	6 49	6 46	..		..	..
Horsley R	..	6 18	..	..		..	..	..	..	..	6 51	..	..		..	..
Clandon T	..	6 23	..	..		..	..	..	..	..	6 56	..	..		..	..
London Road (Guildford)	..	6 29	..	..		..	..	..	..	..	7 2	..	..		..	..
Esher, for Sandown Park	..	..	..	..	..	..	..	6 17	..	p.m	..	..	..	..	..	..
Hersham	..	..	..	..	..	..	..	6 20	..	..	..	..	..	..	..	..
Walton-on-Thames	..	..	..	..	..	..	..	6 23	..	3	..	..	..	..	..	..
Weybridge U	..	..	..	..	..	..	..	6 27	..	6 35	..	..	..	..	..	..
Addlestone	..	..	..	..	..	..	..	..	..	6 39	..	..	..	..	..	..
Chertsey	..	..	..	..	..	..	..	..	..	6 42	..	..	..	..	..	..
Virginia Water Z 460 arr	..	..	..	..	..	..	..	..	..	6 46	..	..	..	..	..	..
West Weybridge	..	..	..	..	..	..	..	6 30	..	..	..	..	..	..	..	..
Byfleet W	..	..	..	..	..	..	..	6 33	..	..	..	..	..	..	..	..
Woking X 324, 389, 390	..	..	..	..	..	..	..	6 37	..	..	..	..	..	..	..	..
Worplesdon	..	..	..	..	..	..	..	6 45	..	..	..	..	..	..	..	..
Guildford 246, 359 arr.	..	6 33	..	..	..	..	..	6 51	..	..	7 6	..	..	..	..	..

FOR NOTES, SEE PAGE 426

FOR NOTES, SEE PAGE 426

LONDON, DORKING NORTH, HORSHAM, KINGSTON, SHEPPERTON, HAMPTON COURT, CHERTSEY, WOKING, & GUILDFORD.

Sundays—*continued* (p.m.)

Down																
Waterloo ....dep.	6 27	③	6 33	6 36	6 38	③	6 42	6 45	6 49	6 54	..	6 56	6 57	6 59	7 2	③
Vauxhall	..	..	6 36	6 39	..	..	..	..	6 52	..	..	6 59	..	③	..	..
Clapham Junction **A**	..	..	6 40	6 43	6 45	..	6 49	..	6 56	..	..	7 3	..	..	7 9	..
Earlsfield **B**	..	..	6 44	6 47	..	..	..	..	7 0	..	..	7 7	..	..	..	..
Wimbledon	..	..	6 47	6 50	6 51	..	6 55	..	7 3	..	..	7 10	..	..	7 15	..
Raynes Park	..	..	6 50	6 53	..	..	..	..	7 6	..	..	7 13	..	..	..	..
Motspur Park	..	..	..	6 56	..	..	7 0	..	..	..	..	7 16	..	..	7 20	..
Malden Manor	..	..	③	6 59	③	..	③	..	③	..	..	7 19	..	..	③	..
Tolworth	..	..	..	7 2	..	..	..	..	..	..	..	7 22	..	..	..	..
Chessington North	..	..	..	7 5	..	..	..	..	..	..	..	7 25	..	..	..	..
Chessington South ¶ ar	..	..	..	7 7	..	..	..	..	..	..	..	7 27	..	..	..	..
Worcester Park	..	..	..	③	..	..	7 2	..	..	..	..	③	..	..	7 22	..
Stoneleigh	..	..	..	..	..	..	7 5	..	..	..	..	..	..	..	7 25	..
Ewell West **C**	..	..	..	..	..	..	7 8	..	..	..	..	..	..	..	7 28	..
London Bridge ....dep.	..	..	..	..	..	6 25	6‡25	..	..	..	..	..	..	Via Richmond, see page 474	..	6 55
Victoria .... "	..	..	..	..	..	6‡1[illegible]	..	..	..	..	..	..	..		6‡45	6‡45
Sutton .... "	..	..	..	..	..	6 57	6‡57	..	..	..	..	..	..		7 ‡9	7 27
Epsom 285	..	..	..	..	..	7 6	7 11	..	..	..	..	..	..		7 31	7 36
Ashtead	..	..	..	..	..	7 10	7 15	..	..	..	..	..	..		7 35	7 40
Leatherhead	..	..	..	..	..	7 14	7 19	..	..	..	..	..	..		7 39	7 44
Boxhill & Burford Bdg **D**	..	..	..	..	..	..	7 24	..	..	..	..	..	..		..	7 49
Dorking North **F**	..	..	..	..	..	..	7 28	..	..	..	..	..	..		..	7 52
Holmwood **G**	..	..	..	..	..	..	7 38	..	..	..	..	..	..		..	..
Ockley, for Capel	..	..	..	..	..	..	7 42	..	..	..	..	..	..		..	..
Warnham ..[**196**, 245	..	..	..	..	..	..	7 48	..	..	..	..	..	..		..	..
Horsham **159**, arr.	..	..	..	..	..	..	7 53	..	..	..	..	..	..		..	..
Bookham	..	..	..	..	..	7 19	..	..	..	..	..	..	..	..	7 45	..
Malden, for Coombe	..	..	6 53	..	..	..	..	..	7 9	..	..	..	..	..	..	..
Norbiton **H**	..	..	..	..	..	..	..	..	7 13	..	..	..	..	..	..	..
Kingston	..	..	..	..	..	..	..	..	7 15	..	..	..	..	..	..	..
Hampton Wick	..	..	..	..	..	..	..	..	7 17	..	..	..	..	..	..	..
Teddington J	..	..	..	..	..	..	..	..	7 21	..	..	..	..	7 35	..	..
Fulwell **K**	..	..	..	..	..	..	..	..	V	..	..	..	..	7 39	..	..
Hampton	..	..	..	..	..	..	..	..	To Waterloo via Richmond Arr. Twickenham 7 27 p.m.	..	..	..	..	7 43	..	..
Sunbury **L**	..	..	..	..	..	..	..	..		..	..	..	..	7 45	..	..
Upper Halliford Halt	..	..	..	..	..	..	..	..		..	..	..	..	7 48	..	..
Shepperton M ......arr.	..	..	..	..	..	..	..	..		..	..	..	..	..	..	..
Berrylands **N**	..	..	6 57	..	..	..	..	..		..	..	..	..	Stop	..	..
Surbiton	6 43	..	7 0	..	6 58	..	..	..		..	..	..	7 13	..	..	..
Thames Ditton	..	..	7 4	..	..	..	..	..		..	..	..	..	..	..	..
Hampton Court P arr.	..	..	7 7	..	..	..	..	..		..	..	..	..	..	..	..
Hinchley Wood	..	..	..	..	7 1	..	..	..		..	..	..	..	..	..	..
Claygate, for Claremont	..	..	..	..	7 4	..	..	..		..	..	..	..	..	..	..
Oxshott, for Fairmile	..	..	..	..	7 8	..	..	..		..	..	..	..	..	..	..
Cobham **Q**	..	..	..	..	7 11	..	..	..		..	..	..	..	..	..	..
Effingham Junction	..	..	..	..	7 16	7 23	..	..		..	..	..	..	..	7 49	..
Horsley **R**	..	..	..	..	7 18	..	..	..		..	..	..	..	..	7 51	..
Clandon **T**	..	..	..	..	7 23	..	..	..		..	..	..	..	..	7 56	..
London Road (Guildford)	..	..	..	..	7 29	..	..	..		..	..	..	..	..	8 2	..
Esher, for Sandown Park	6 47	..	..	..	..	..	..	..	..	..	..	..	7 17	p.m.	..	..
Hersham	6 50	③	..	..	..	..	..	..	..	..	..	..	7 20	③	..	..
Walton-on-Thames	6 53	..	..	..	..	..	..	..	..	..	..	..	7 23	..	..	..
Weybridge U	6 57	7 5	..	..	..	..	..	..	..	..	..	..	7 27	7 35	..	..
Addlestone	..	7 9	..	..	..	..	..	..	..	..	..	..	..	7 39	..	..
Chertsey	..	7 12	..	..	..	..	..	..	..	..	..	..	..	7 42	..	..
Virginia Water Z 460 arr	..	7 16	..	..	..	..	..	..	..	..	..	..	..	7 46	..	..
West Weybridge	7 0	..	..	..	..	..	..	..	..	..	..	..	7 30	..	..	..
Byfleet **W**	7 3	..	..	..	..	..	..	..	..	..	..	..	7 33	..	..	..
Woking X 324, 389, 390	7 7	..	..	..	..	..	..	7 15	..	7 25	..	..	7 37	..	..	..
Worplesdon	7 15	..	..	..	..	..	..	..	..	..	..	..	7 45	..	..	..
Guildford 246, 359 ....arr.	7 21	..	..	..	7 33	..	..	7 25	..	..	..	..	7 51	..	8 6	..

Down															
Waterloo ....dep.	..	7 8	7 9	7 13	7 23	7 27	7 33	7 36	7 38	③	7 42	7 45	7 49	7 56	Via Three Bridges, see page 194
Vauxhall	..	..	7 12	7 16	7 26	..	7 36	7 39	..	..	..	..	7 52	7 59	
Clapham Junction **A**	..	7 15	7 16	7 20	7 31	..	7 40	7 43	7 45	..	7 49	..	7 56	8 3	
Earlsfield **B**	..	..	7 20	7 24	7 34	..	7 44	7 47	..	..	..	..	8 0	8 7	
Wimbledon	..	7 21	7 23	7 27	7 38	..	7 47	7 50	7 51	..	7 55	..	8 3	8 10	
Raynes Park	..	..	7 26	7 30	7 41	..	7 50	7 53	..	..	..	..	8 6	8 13	
Motspur Park	..	..	..	..	..	..	..	7 56	..	..	8 0	..	..	8 16	
Malden Manor	..	③	③	③	③	..	③	7 59	③	..	③	..	③	8 19	
Tolworth	..	..	..	..	..	..	..	8 2	..	..	..	..	..	8 22	
Chessington North	..	..	..	..	..	..	..	8 5	..	..	..	..	..	8 25	
Chessington South ¶ ar	..	..	..	..	..	..	..	8 7	..	..	..	..	..	8 27	
Worcester Park	..	..	..	..	..	..	..	③	..	..	8 2	..	..	③	
Stoneleigh	..	..	..	..	..	..	..	..	..	..	8 5	..	..	..	
Ewell West **C**	..	..	..	..	..	..	..	..	..	..	8 8	..	..	..	
London Bridge ....dep.	6*55	..	..	..	..	..	..	Stop	..	7 25	7‡25	..	..	..	..
Victoria .... "	7 12	..	..	..	..	..	..	..	..	7‡24	7‡24	..	..	..	7 48
Sutton .... "	7 39	..	..	..	..	..	..	..	..	7 57	7‡57	..	..	..	..
Epsom 285	..	..	..	..	..	..	..	..	..	8 6	8 11	..	..	..	..
Ashtead	..	..	..	..	..	..	..	..	..	8 10	8 15	..	..	..	..
Leatherhead	..	..	..	..	..	..	..	..	..	8 14	8 19	..	..	..	..
Boxhill & Burford Bdg **D**	..	..	..	..	..	..	..	..	..	..	8 24	..	..	..	..
Dorking North **F**	7 55	..	..	..	..	..	..	..	..	..	8 28	..	..	..	..
Holmwood **G**	..	..	..	..	..	..	..	..	..	..	8 38	..	..	..	..
Ockley, for Capel	..	..	..	..	..	..	..	..	..	..	8 42	..	..	..	..
Warnham ..[**196**, 245	..	..	..	..	..	..	..	..	..	..	8 48	..	..	..	..
Horsham **159**, arr.	8 12	..	..	..	..	..	..	..	..	..	8 53	..	..	..	9 5
Bookham	..	..	..	..	..	..	..	..	..	8 19	..	..	..	..	..
Malden, for Coombe	..	..	7 29	7 33	7 44	..	7 53	..	..	..	..	..	8 9	..	..
Norbiton **H**	..	..	7 33	..	7 47	..	..	..	..	..	..	..	8 13	..	..
Kingston	..	..	7 35	..	7 50	..	..	..	..	..	..	..	8 15	..	..
Hampton Wick	..	..	7 37	..	7 52	..	..	..	..	..	..	..	8 17	..	..
Teddington J	..	..	7 41	..	7 55	..	..	..	..	..	..	..	8 21	..	..
Fulwell **K**	..	..	V	..	7 59	..	..	..	..	..	..	..	V	..	..
Hampton	..	..	To Waterloo via Richmond Arr. Twickenham 7 47 p.m.	..	8 3	..	..	..	..	..	..	..	To Waterloo via Richmond Arr. Twickenham 8 27 p.m.	..	..
Sunbury **L**	..	..		..	8 7	..	..	..	..	..	..	..		..	..
Upper Halliford Halt	..	..		..	8 9	..	..	..	..	..	..	..		..	..
Shepperton M ......arr.	..	..		..	8 12	..	..	..	..	..	..	..		..	..
Berrylands **N**	..	..		7 36	..	..	7 57	..	..	..	..	..		..	..
Surbiton	..	7 28		7 39	..	7 43	8 0	..	7 58	..	..	..		..	..
Thames Ditton	..	..		7 43	..	..	8 4	..	..	..	..	..		..	..
Hampton Court P arr.	..	..		7 46	..	..	8 7	..	..	..	..	..		..	..
Hinchley Wood	..	7 31		..	..	..	..	..	8 1	..	..	..		..	..
Claygate, for Claremont	..	7 34		..	..	..	..	..	8 4	..	..	..		..	..
Oxshott, for Fairmile	..	7 38		..	..	..	..	..	8 8	..	..	..		..	..
Cobham **Q**	..	7 41		..	..	..	..	..	8 11	..	..	..		..	..
Effingham Junction	..	7 46		..	..	..	..	..	8 16	8 23	..	..		..	..
Horsley **R**	..	..		..	..	..	..	..	8 18	..	..	..		..	..
Clandon **T**	..	..		..	..	..	..	..	8 23	..	..	..		..	..
London Road (Guildford)	..	..		..	..	..	..	..	8 29	..	..	..		..	..
Esher, for Sandown Park	..	..	..	..	..	7 47	..	p.m.	..	..	..	..	..	..	..
Hersham	..	..	..	..	..	7 50	..	③	..	..	..	..	..	..	..
Walton-on-Thames	..	..	..	..	..	7 53	..	..	..	..	..	..	..	..	..
Weybridge U	..	..	..	..	..	7 57	..	8 5	..	..	..	..	..	..	..
Addlestone	..	..	..	..	..	..	..	8 9	..	..	..	..	..	..	..
Chertsey	..	..	..	..	..	..	..	8 12	..	..	..	..	..	..	..
Virginia Water Z 460 arr	..	..	..	..	..	..	..	8 16	..	..	..	..	..	..	..
West Weybridge	..	..	..	..	..	8 0	..	..	..	..	..	..	..	..	..
Byfleet **W**	..	..	..	..	..	8 3	..	..	..	..	..	..	..	..	..
Woking X 324, 389, 390	..	..	..	..	..	8 7	..	..	..	..	..	..	..	..	..
Worplesdon	..	..	..	..	..	8 15	..	..	..	..	..	..	..	..	..
Guildford 246, 359 ....arr.	..	..	..	..	..	8 21	..	..	8 33	..	..	8 25	..	..	..

LONDON, DORKING NORTH, HORSHAM, KINGSTON, SHEPPERTON, HAMPTON COURT, CHERTSEY, WOKING, & GUILDFORD

Down — p.m. — **Sundays**—*continued* — p.m.

Down																
Waterloo ....dep.	7 57	7 59	8 2	8 8	3	8 9	8 13	8 23	8 27	3	8 33	8 36	8 38	3	..	8 42
Vauxhall	..	3	..	..	..	8 12	8 16	8 26	..	..	8 36	8 39	..	..	..	..
Clapham Junction A	..		8 9	8 15	..	8 16	8 20	8 31	..	..	8 40	8 43	8 45	..	..	8 49
Earlsfield B	..	..	..	..	..	8 20	8 24	8 34	..	..	8 44	8 47	..	..	..	..
Wimbledon	..	..	8 15	8 21	..	8 23	8 27	8 38	..	..	8 47	8 50	8 51	..	..	8 55
Raynes Park	..	..	..	..	..	8 26	8 30	8 41	..	..	8 50	8 53	..	..	..	..
Motspur Park	..	..	8 20		..				..	..		8 56		..	Via Three Bridges see page 194	9 0
Malden Manor	..	..	3	3	..	3	3	3	..	..	3	8 59	3	..		3
Tolworth	..	..			..				..	..		9 2		..		
Chessington North	..	..	..	..	..	..	..	..	..	..	..	9 5	..	..		..
Chessington South ¶ arr.	..	..	..	..	..	..	..	..	..	..	..	9 7	..	..		..
Worcester Park	..	..	8 22	..	..	..	..	..	..	..	..	3	..	..		9 2
Stoneleigh	..	..	8 25	..	..	..	..	..	..	..	..		..	..		9 5
Ewell West C	..	..	8 28	..	..	..	..	..	..	..	..	..	..	..		9 8
London Bridge ....dep.	..	Via Richmond see page 474	..	..	7 55	..	..	..	..	..	..	..	..	8 25	8 16	8‡25
Victoria ...."	..		7‡45	..	7‡45	..	..	..	..	..	..	..	..	8‡15	8 28	..
Sutton ...."	..		8‡ 9	..	8 27	..	..	..	..	..	..	..	..	8 57	..	8‡57
Epsom 235	..		8 31	..	8 36	..	..	..	..	..	..	..	..	9 6	..	9 11
Ashtead	..		8 35	..	8 40	..	..	..	..	..	..	..	..	9 10	..	9 15
Leatherhead	..		8 39	..	8 44	..	..	..	..	..	..	..	..	9 14	..	9 19
Boxhill & Burford Bdg D	..		..	..	8 49	..	..	..	..	..	..	..	..	..	..	9 24
Dorking North F	..		..	..	8 52	..	..	..	..	..	..	..	..	..	..	9 28
Holmwood G	..		..	..	..	..	..	..	..	..	..	..	..	..	..	9 38
Ockley, for Capel	..		..	..	..	..	..	..	..	..	..	..	..	..	..	9 42
Warnham.. [196, 245	..		..	..	..	..	..	..	..	..	..	..	..	..	..	9 48
Horsham 159, arr	..		..	..	..	..	..	..	..	..	..	..	..	..	9 40	9 53
Bookham	..	..	8 45	..	..	..	..	..	..	..	..	..	..	9 19	..	..
Malden, for Coombe	..	..	..	..	..	8 29	8 33	8 44	..	..	8 53	..	..	..	..	..
Norbiton H	..	..	..	..	..	8 33	..	8 47	..	..	..	..	..	..	..	..
Kingston	..	..	..	..	..	8 35	..	8 50	..	..	..	..	..	..	..	..
Hampton Wick	..	..	..	..	..	8 37	..	8 52	..	..	..	..	..	..	..	..
Teddington J	..	..	..	..	..	8 41	..	8 55	..	..	..	..	..	..	..	..
Fulwell K	..	8 35	..	..	..	V	..	8 59	..	..	..	..	..	..	..	..
Hampton	..	8 39	..	..	..	To Waterloo via Richmond Arr Twickenham 8 47 p.m	..	9 3	..	..	..	..	..	..	..	..
Sunbury L	..	8 43	..	..	..		..	9 7	..	..	..	..	..	..	..	..
Upper Halliford Halt	..	8 45	..	..	..		..	9 9	..	..	..	..	..	..	..	..
Shepperton M ....arr.	..	8 48	..	..	..		..	9 12	..	..	..	..	..	..	..	..
Berrylands N	..	Stop	..	..	..		8 36	..	..	..	8 57	..	..	..	..	..
Surbiton	8 13		..	8 28	..		8 39	..	8 43	..	9 0	..	8 58	..	..	..
Thames Ditton	..	..	..	..	..		8 43	..	..	..	9 4	..	..	..	..	..
Hampton Court P arr.	..	..	..	..	..		8 46	..	..	..	9 7	..	..	..	..	..
Hinchley Wood	..	..	..	8 31	..		..	..	..	..	..	..	9 1	..	..	..
Claygate, for Claremont	..	..	..	8 34	..		..	..	..	..	..	..	9 4	..	..	..
Oxshott, for Fairmile	..	..	..	8 38	..		..	..	..	..	..	..	9 8	..	..	..
Cobham Q	..	..	..	8 41	..		..	..	..	..	..	..	9 11	..	..	..
Effingham Junction	..	..	8 49	8 46	..		..	..	..	..	..	..	9 16	9 23	..	..
Horsley R	..	..	8 51	..	..		..	..	..	..	..	..	9 18	..	..	..
Clandon T	..	..	8 56	..	..		..	..	..	..	..	..	9 23	..	..	..
London Road (Guildford)	..	..	9 2	..	..		..	..	..	..	..	..	9 29	..	..	..
Esher, for Sandown Park	8 17	p.m	..	..	..		..	..	8 47	..	..	..	..	..	..	..
Hersham	8 20	3	..	..	..	..	..	..	8 50	3	..	..	..	..	..	..
Walton-on-Thames	8 23		..	..	..	..	..	..	8 53		..	..	..	..	..	..
Weybridge U	8 27	8 35	..	..	..	..	..	..	8 57	9 5	..	..	..	..	..	..
Addlestone	..	8 39	..	..	..	..	..	..	..	9 9	..	..	..	..	..	..
Chertsey	..	8 42	..	..	..	..	..	..	..	9 12	..	..	..	..	..	..
Virginia Water Z 460 arr	..	8 46	..	..	..	..	..	..	..	9 16	..	..	..	..	..	..
West Weybridge	8 30	..	..	..	..	..	..	..	9 0	..	..	..	..	..	..	..
Byfleet W	8 33	..	..	..	..	..	..	..	9 3	..	..	..	..	..	..	..
Woking X 324, 389, 390	8 37	..	..	..	..	..	..	..	9 7	..	..	..	..	..	..	..
Worplesdon	8 45	..	..	..	..	..	..	..	9 15	..	..	..	..	..	..	..
Guildford 246, 359 ...arr.	8 51	..	9 6	..	..	..	..	..	9 21	..	..	..	9 33	..	..	..

Down																
Waterloo ....dep.	8 45	8 49	8 54	8 56	8 57	3	8 59	9 2	3	..	9 8	9 9	9 13	9 23	9 27	3
Vauxhall	..	8 52	..	8 59	..	..	3	..	..	..	..	9 12	9 16	9 26	..	..
Clapham Junction A	..	8 56	..	9 3	..	..		9 9	..	..	9 15	9 16	9 20	9 31	..	..
Earlsfield B	..	9 0	..	9 7	..	..	..	..	..	..	..	9 20	9 24	9 34	..	..
Wimbledon	..	9 3	..	9 10	..	..	..	9 15	..	..	9 21	9 23	9 27	9 38	..	..
Raynes Park	..	9 6	..	9 13	..	..	..	..	..	..	..	9 26	9 30	9 41	..	..
Motspur Park	..		..	9 16	..	..	..	9 20	..	..					..	..
Malden Manor	..	3	..	9 19	..	..	..	3	..	..	3	3	3	3	..	..
Tolworth	..		..	9 22	..	..	..		..	..					..	..
Chessington North	..	..	..	9 25	..	..	..	..	..	..	..	..	..	..	..	..
Chessington South ¶ arr.	..	..	..	9 27	..	..		..	..	..	..	..	..	..	..	..
Worcester Park	..	..	..	3	..	..	Via Richmond, see page 475	9 22	..	..	..	..	..	..	..	..
Stoneleigh	..	..	..		..	..		9 25	..	..	..	..	..	..	..	..
Ewell West C	..	..	..	..	..	..		9 28	..	..	..	..	..	..	..	..
London Bridge ....dep.	..	..	..	..	..	..		..	8 55	8*55	..	..	..	..	..	..
Victoria ...."	..	..	..	..	..	..		8‡45	8‡45	9 18	..	..	..	..	..	..
Sutton ...."	..	..	..	..	..	..		9‡ 9	9 27	9 39	..	..	..	..	..	..
Epsom 235	..	..	..	..	..	..		9 31	9 36	..	..	..	..	..	..	..
Ashtead	..	..	..	..	..	..		9 35	9 40	..	..	..	..	..	..	..
Leatherhead	..	..	..	..	..	..		9 39	9 44	..	..	..	..	..	..	..
Boxhill & Burford Bdg D	..	..	..	..	..	..		..	9 49	..	..	..	..	..	..	..
Dorking North F	..	..	..	..	..	..		..	9 52	9 55	..	..	..	..	..	..
Holmwood G	..	..	..	..	..	..	..	..	..	..	..	..	..	..	..	..
Ockley, for Capel	..	..	..	..	..	..	..	..	..	..	..	..	..	..	..	..
Warnham.. [196, 245	..	..	..	..	..	..	..	..	..	..	..	..	..	..	..	..
Horsham 159, arr	..	..	..	..	..	..	..	..	..	1013	..	..	..	..	..	..
Bookham	..	..	..	..	..	..	..	9 45	..	..	..	..	..	..	..	..
Malden, for Coombe	..	9 9	..	..	..	..	..	..	..	..	..	9 29	9 33	9 44	..	..
Norbiton H	..	9 13	..	..	..	..	..	..	..	..	..	9 33	..	9 47	..	..
Kingston	..	9 15	..	..	..	..	..	..	..	..	..	9 35	..	9 50	..	..
Hampton Wick	..	9 17	..	..	..	..	..	..	..	..	..	9 37	..	9 52	..	..
Teddington J	..	9 21	..	..	..	..	..	..	..	..	..	9 41	..	9 55	..	..
Fulwell K	..	V	..	..	..	..	9 35	..	..	..	..	V	..	9 59	..	..
Hampton	..	To Waterloo via Richmond Arr Twickenham 9 27 p.m	..	..	..	..	9 39	..	..	..	..	To Waterloo via Richmond Arr Twickenham 9 47 p.m	..	10 3	..	..
Sunbury L	..		..	..	..	..	9 43	..	..	..	..		..	10 7	..	..
Upper Halliford Halt	..		..	..	..	..	9 45	..	..	..	..		..	10 9	..	..
Shepperton M ....arr.	..		..	..	..	..	9 48	..	..	..	..		..	1012	..	..
Berrylands N	..		..	..	..	..	..	..	..	..	..		9 36	..	..	..
Surbiton	..		..	..	9 13	..	..	..	..	..	9 28		9 39	..	9 43	..
Thames Ditton	..		..	..	..	..	..	..	..	..	..		9 43	..	..	..
Hampton Court P arr.	..		..	..	..	..	..	..	..	..	..		9 46	..	..	..
Hinchley Wood	..		..	..	..	..	..	..	..	..	9 31		..	..	..	..
Claygate, for Claremont	..		..	..	..	..	..	..	..	..	9 34		..	..	..	..
Oxshott, for Fairmile	..		..	..	..	..	..	..	..	..	9 38		..	..	..	..
Cobham Q	..		..	..	..	..	..	..	..	..	9 41		..	..	..	..
Effingham Junction	..		..	..	..	..	..	9 49	..	..	9 46		..	..	..	..
Horsley R	..		..	..	..	..	..	9 51	..	..	..		..	..	..	..
Clandon T	..		..	..	..	..	..	9 56	..	..	..		..	..	..	..
London Road (Guildford)	..		..	..	..	..	..	10 2	..	..	..		..	..	..	..
Esher, for Sandown Park	..		..	..	9 17	..	..	..	..	..	..		..	..	9 47	..
Hersham	..	..	..	..	9 20	3	..	..	..	..	..	..	..	..	9 50	3
Walton-on-Thames	..	..	..	..	9 23		..	..	..	..	..	..	..	..	9 53	
Weybridge U	..	..	..	..	9 27	9 35	..	..	..	..	..	..	..	..	9 57	10 5
Addlestone	..	..	..	..	..	9 39	..	..	..	..	..	..	..	..	..	10 9
Chertsey	..	..	..	..	..	9 42	..	..	..	..	..	..	..	..	..	1012
Virginia Water Z 460 arr	..	..	..	..	..	9 46	..	..	..	..	..	..	..	..	..	1016
West Weybridge	..	..	..	..	9 30	..	..	..	..	..	..	..	..	..	10 0	..
Byfleet W	..	..	..	..	9 33	..	..	..	..	..	..	..	..	..	10 3	..
Woking X 324, 389, 390	..	..	9 25	..	9 37	..	..	..	..	..	..	..	..	..	10 7	..
Worplesdon	..	..	..	..	9 45	..	..	..	..	..	..	..	..	..	1015	..
Guildford 246, 359 ...arr.	9 25	..	..	..	9 51	..	..	10 6	..	..	..	..	..	..	1021	..

FOR NOTES, SEE PAGE 426

FOR NOTES, SEE PAGE 426

LONDON, DORKING NORTH, HORSHAM, KINGSTON, SHEPPERTON, HAMPTON COURT, CHERTSEY, WOKING, & GUILDFORD

Down — **Sundays**—*continued* — p.m

Down	(3)	9 32	9 33	9 36	9 38	(3)	9 42	9 45	9 49	9 54
Waterloo dep.	(3)	9 32	9 33	9 36	9 38	(3)	9 42	9 45	9 49	9 54
Vauxhall			9 36	9 39					9 52	
Clapham Junction A			9 40	9 43	9 45		9 49		9 56	
Earlsfield **B**			9 44	9 47					10 0	
Wimbledon			9 47	9 50	9 51		9 55		10 3	
Raynes Park			9 50	9 53					10 6	
Motspur Park				9 56			10 0			
Malden Manor				9 59						
Tolworth			(3)	10 2	(3)		(3)		(3)	
Chessington North				10 5						
Chessington South ¶ar				10 7						
Worcester Park							10 2			
Stoneleigh				(3)			10 5			
Ewell West **C**							10 8			
London Bridge dep.						9 25	9‡25			
Victoria "	9 24					9‡24				
Sutton "	9 48					9 57	9‡57			
Epsom **285**	10 0					10 6	1011			
Ashtead	10 4					1010	1015			
Leatherhead	10 8					1014	1019			
Boxhill & Burford Bdg **D**	1013						1024			
Dorking North F	1016						1028			
Holmwood **G**	1027						1038			
Ockley, for Capel	1031						1042			
Warnham [**196**, 245	1037						1048			
Horsham 159, arr.	1042						1053			
Bookham						1019				
Malden, for Coombe			9 53						10 9	
Norbiton **H**	Dep. Dorking North at 10 19 p.m								1013	
Kingston									1015	
Hampton Wick									1017	
Teddington J									1021	
Fulwell **K**									V	
Hampton									To Waterloo via Richmond Arr. **Twickenham** 10 27 p.m	
Sunbury **L**										
Upper Halliford Halt										
Shepperton M arr.										
Berrylands **N**			9 57							
Surbiton		9 51	10 0		9 58					
Thames Ditton			10 4							
Hampton Court P arr.			10 7							
Hinchley Wood					10 1					
Claygate, for Claremont					10 4					
Oxshott, for Fairmile					10 8					
Cobham **Q**					1011					
Effingham Junction					1016	1023				
Horsley **R**					1018					
Clandon **T**					1023					
London Road (Guildford)					1029					
Esher, for Sandown Park										
Hersham										
Walton-on-Thames										
Weybridge U										
Addlestone										
Chertsey										
Virginia Water Z 460 arr.										
West Weybridge										
Byfleet **W**										
Woking X 324, 389, 390		10 9						1015		10 25
Worplesdon										
Guildford 246, 359 arr.					1033			1025		

Down	9 56	9 57	9 59	10 2	(3)	(3)	..	10 8	10 9	1013
Waterloo dep.	9 56	9 57	9 59	10 2	(3)	(3)	..	10 8	10 9	1013
Vauxhall	9 59								1012	1016
Clapham Junction A	10 3		(3)	10 9				1015	1016	1020
Earlsfield **B**	10 7								1020	1024
Wimbledon	1010			1015				1021	1023	1027
Raynes Park	1013								1026	1030
Motspur Park	1016			1020						
Malden Manor	1019									
Tolworth	1022			(3)				(3)	(3)	(3)
Chessington North	1025									
Chessington South ¶ar	1027									
Worcester Park				1022						
Stoneleigh	(3)			1025						
Ewell West **C**				1028						
London Bridge dep.						9 55				
Victoria "				9‡45		9‡45				
Sutton "				10‡19		1027				
Epsom **285**				1031		1036				
Ashtead				1035		1040				
Leatherhead				1039		1044				
Boxhill & Burford Bdg **D**						1049				
Dorking North F						1052				
Holmwood **G**										
Ockley, for Capel										
Warnham [**196**, 245										
Horsham 159, arr.										
Bookham				1045						
Malden, for Coombe									1029	1033
Norbiton **H**			Via Richmond, see page 475						1033	
Kingston									1035	
Hampton Wick									1037	
Teddington J									1041	
Fulwell **K**			1035						V	
Hampton			1039						To Waterloo via Richmond Arr. **Twickenham** 10 47 p.m	
Sunbury **L**			1043							
Upper Halliford Halt			1045							
Shepperton M arr.			1048							
Berrylands **N**										1036
Surbiton		1013						1028		1039
Thames Ditton										1043
Hampton Court P arr.										1046
Hinchley Wood								1031		
Claygate, for Claremont								1034		
Oxshott, for Fairmile								1038		
Cobham **Q**								1041		
Effingham Junction				1049				1046		
Horsley **R**				1051						
Clandon **T**				1056						
London Road (Guildford)				11 2						
Esher, for Sandown Park		1017								
Hersham		1020								
Walton-on-Thames		1023			(3)					
Weybridge U		1027			1035					
Addlestone					1039					
Chertsey					1042					
Virginia Water Z 460 arr.					1046					
West Weybridge		1030								
Byfleet **W**		1033								
Woking X 324, 389, 390		1037								
Worplesdon		1045								
Guildford 246, 359 arr.		1051		11 6						

Down	1023	(3)	(3)	1027	(3)	10 33	1036	1038	10 42	1049	1056
Waterloo dep.	1023	(3)	(3)	1027	(3)	10 33	1036	1038	10 42	1049	1056
Vauxhall	1026					10 36	1039			1052	1059
Clapham Junction A	1031					10 40	1043	1045	10 49	1056	11 4
Earlsfield **B**	1034					10 44	1047			11 0	11 7
Wimbledon	1038					10 47	1050	1051	10 55	11 3	1111
Raynes Park	1041					10 50	1053			11 6	1114
Motspur Park							1056		11 0		1116
Malden Manor							1059				1120
Tolworth	(3)					(3)	11 2	(3)	(3)	(3)	1122
Chessington North							11 5				1125
Chessington South ¶ar							11 7				1127
Worcester Park									11 2		
Stoneleigh							(3)		11 5		(3)
Ewell West **C**									11 8		
London Bridge dep.					10 25				10‡25		
Victoria "					10‡15						
Sutton "					10 59				10‡59		
Epsom **285**					11 8				11 13		
Ashtead					11 12				11 17		
Leatherhead					11 16				11 21		
Boxhill & Burford Bdg **D**									11 26		
Dorking North F									11 29		
Holmwood **G**									11 38		
Ockley, for Capel									11 42		
Warnham [**196**, 245									11 48		
Horsham 159, arr.									11 53		
Bookham					11 20						
Malden, for Coombe	1044					10 53				11 9	
Norbiton **H**	1047									1113	
Kingston	1050									1115	
Hampton Wick	1052	1056								1117	
Teddington J	1055	1058								1121	
Fulwell **K**	1059	11 1								To **Strawberry Hill** (arr. 11 24 p.m)	
Hampton	11 3	To **Strawberry Hill** (arr. 11 4 p.m)									
Sunbury **L**	11 7										
Upper Halliford Halt											
Shepperton M arr.	1112										
Berrylands **N**						10 5[illegible]					
Surbiton				1043		11 0		1058			
Thames Ditton						11 4					
Hampton Court P arr.						11 7					
Hinchley Wood								11 1			
Claygate, for Claremont								11 4			
Oxshott, for Fairmile								11 8			
Cobham **Q**								1111			
Effingham Junction					11 24			1116			
Horsley **R**											
Clandon **T**											
London Road (Guildford)											
Esher, for Sandown Park				1047							
Hersham				1050							
Walton-on-Thames			(3)	1053							
Weybridge U			1050	1057							
Addlestone			1054								
Chertsey			1057								
Virginia Water Z 460 arr.											
West Weybridge				11 0							
Byfleet **W**				11 3							
Woking X 324, 389, 390				11 7							
Worplesdon				1115							
Guildford 246, 359 arr.				1121							

LONDON, DORKING NORTH, HORSHAM, KINGSTON, SHEPPERTON, HAMPTON COURT, CHERTSEY, WOKING, & GUILDFORD

Down	p.m				Sundays—continued							p.m		
Waterloo dep.	1057	1059	11 7	(3)	11 8	11 9	1113	1123	1127	1142	11 47	..	1149	..
Vauxhall	..	(3)	..	..	..	1112	1116	1126	..	1145	11 50	..	1152	..
Clapham Junction A	..		11 14	..	11 15	1116	1120	1131	..	1149	11 54	..	1156	..
Earlsfield **B**	..	..	..	..	..	1120	1124	1134	..	1153	11 58	..	12 0	..
Wimbledon	..	..	11 20	..	11 21	1123	1127	1138	..	1156	12 1	..	12 3	..
Raynes Park	..	..	..	..	..	1126	1130	1141	..	1159	12 4	..	12 6	..
Motspur Park	..	..	11 25	..	..	..	..	..	..	..	12 7	..	..	..
Malden Manor	..	..	(3)	..	(3)	(3)	(3)	(3)	..	(3)	(3)	..	(3)	..
Tolworth	..	..		..					..			..		..
Chessington North	..	..	..	..	..	..	..	..	..	..	..	..	..	..
Chessington South ¶ arr	..	..	..	..	..	..	..	..	..	..	..	..	..	..
Worcester Park	..	..	11 27	..	..	..	..	..	..	..	12 9	..	..	..
Stoneleigh	..	..	11 30	..	..	..	..	..	..	..	12 12	..	..	..
Ewell West **C**	..	..	11 33	..	..	..	..	..	..	..	12 15	..	..	..
London Bridge dep	..	..	..	..	..	..	..	..	..	..	..	..	..	..
Victoria "	..	..	10‡45	..	..	..	..	..	..	..	11‡15	..	..	..
Sutton "	..	..	11‡ 9	..	..	..	..	..	..	..	11‡39	..	..	..
Epsom 285	..	..	11 37	..	..	..	..	..	..	..	12 20	..	..	..
Ashtead	..	..	11 41	..	..	..	..	..	..	..	12 24	..	..	..
Leatherhead	..	..	11 45	..	..	..	..	..	..	..	12 28	..	..	..
Boxhill & Burford Bdg **D**	..	Via Richmond, see page 475	..	..	..	..	..	..	..	..	12 33	..	..	..
Dorking North F	..		..	..	..	..	..	..	..	..	12 36	..	..	..
Holmwood **G**	..		..	..	..	..	..	..	..	..	..	..	..	..
Ockley for Capel	..		..	..	..	..	..	..	..	..	..	..	..	..
Warnham [245	..		..	..	..	..	..	..	..	..	..	..	..	..
Horsham 159, 196 arr	..		..	..	..	..	..	..	..	..	..	..	..	..
Bookham	..		11 49	..	..	..	..	..	..	..	..	..	..	..
Malden, for Coombe	..		..	..	..	1129	1133	1144	..	12 2	..	..	12 9	..
Norbiton **H**	..		..	..	..	1133	..	1147	..	..	..	..	1213	..
Kingston	..		..	..	..	1135	..	1150	..	..	..	..	1215	..
Hampton Wick	..		..	..	..	1137	..	1152	..	..	..	..	1217	..
Teddington J	..		..	..	..	1141	..	1155	..	..	..	..	1221	..
Fulwell **K**	..	1135	..	..	..	To Strawberry Hill (arr. 11 44 p.m)	..	To Strawberry Hill (arr. 11 58 p.m)	..	..	..	..	To Strawberry Hill (arr 12 24 a.m)	..
Hampton	..	1139	..	..	..		..		..	..	..	..		..
Sunbury **L**	..	1143	..	..	..		..		..	..	..	..		..
Upper Halliford Halt	..	..	..	..	..		..		..	..	..	..		..
Shepperton M arr.	..	1147	..	..	..		..		..	..	..	..		..
Berrylands **N**	..	..	..	..	..		1136		..	12 5	..	..		..
Surbiton	1113	..	..	..	11 28		1139		1143	12 8	..	..		..
Thames Ditton	..	..	..	..	..		1143		..	1212	..	..		..
Hampton Court P arr.	..	..	..	..	..		1146		..	1215	..	..		..
Hinchley Wood	..	..	..	..	11 31		..		..	..	..	..		..
Claygate, for Claremont	..	..	..	..	11 34		..		..	..	..	..		..
Oxshott, for Fairmile	..	..	..	..	11 38		..		..	..	..	..		..
Cobham **Q**	..	..	..	..	11 41		..		..	..	..	..		..
Effingham Junction	..	..	11 55	..	11 46	..	..	..	..	..	..	..	..	..
Horsley **R**	..	..	11 57	..	..	..	..	..	..	..	..	..	..	..
Clandon **T**	..	..	12 2	..	..	..	..	..	..	..	..	..	..	..
London Road (Guildford)	..	..	12 8	..	..	..	..	..	..	..	..	..	..	..
Esher, for Sandown Park	1117	..	..	..	..	..	..	..	1147	..	..	..	..	..
Hersham	1120	..	..	(3)	..	..	..	..	1150	..	..	..	..	..
Walton-on-Thames	1123	..	..		..	..	..	..	1153	..	..	..	..	..
Weybridge U	1127	..	..	1135	..	..	..	..	1157	..	..	..	..	..
Addlestone	..	..	..	1139	..	..	..	..	..	..	..	..	..	..
Chertsey	..	..	..	1142	..	..	..	..	..	..	..	..	..	..
Virginia Water Z 460 arr	..	..	..	..	..	..	..	..	..	..	..	..	..	..
West Weybridge	1130	..	..	..	..	..	..	..	12 0	..	..	..	..	..
Byfleet **W**	1133	..	..	..	..	..	..	..	12 2	..	..	..	..	..
Woking X 324, 389, 390	1137	..	..	..	..	..	..	..	12 7	..	..	..	..	..
Worplesdon	..	..	..	..	..	..	..	..	1215	..	..	..	..	..
Guildford, 246, 359 arr.	..	..	12 12	..	..	..	..	..	1221	..	..	..	..	..

NOTES

(3) Third class only
* Change at Sutton see pages 252 to 284a
‡ Change at Epsom, see pages 252 to 284a
§ 5 mins. later on Sats.
‖ Arr. 4 mins *earlier*
¶ Chessington South for Chessington Zoo

A Mid Battersea, 1½ miles from Clapham
a 1 min. *earlier* on Sats.
B For Summerstown
b Change at Sutton. First and third class between Victoria and Sutton.
b 4 mins later on Sats.
C 1 mile to Ewell East Station
c Arrives 8 mins *earlier*
D Station for Mickleham (1½ miles)
F Nearly 1½ miles to Dorking Town and under ½ mile to Deepdene Stations
F Change at Sutton. Third class only between Victoria and Sutton.
G Sta for Leith Hill (2¼ miles)
g 8 mins later on Sats
H For Kingston Hill.
J For Bushy Park.
j 12 mins. later on Sats
K Station for Upper Teddington (¼ mile) and Hampton Hill.
L Sunbury Common (1 mile from Sunbury).
M Station for Halliford (¼ mile).
N Station for Surbiton Hill Park

n 4 mins. *earlier* on Sats
P Station for East and West Molesey (1½ miles).
Q Cobham (1½ miles) for Stoke d'Abernon
R Station for East Horsley (1 mile), West Horsley (1¾ miles) Ockham (1¼ miles), and Ripley (3¼ miles)
S O or SO Saturdays only
S X or SX Saturdays excepted
T Station for Burnt Common, Newlands Corner, East Clandon (2 miles) and Ripley (2¾ miles)
U Station for Brooklands, St. George's Hill, & Oatlands Park.
U Calls to take up only
V For Continuation of Service from Teddington to Waterloo via Twickenham and Richmond, pp. 476 to 489
v 2 mins. *earlier* on Sats
W Station for Woodham & Pyrford
X Station for Chobham (3¾ miles) to Woking Village (1½ miles).
x 3 mins. later on Saturdays.
y 10 mins. *earlier* on Sats.
y 6 mins later on Sats.
Z Virginia Water, for Wentworth
z 1 min later on Saturdays

For **OTHER TRAINS**

Waterloo & Clapham Junc. ... 460
London & Wimbledon ... 32)
London and Dorking ... 243
London and Horsham ... 158
Waterloo & Teddington ... 460
Waterloo & Virginia Water ... 460
London and Guildford ... 246

For **LOCAL TRAINS** between London Bridge and Victoria and Epsom, see page 252

FOR NOTES, SEE PAGE 459

GUILDFORD, WOKING, CHERTSEY, HAMPTON COURT, SHEPPERTON, KINGSTON, HORSHAM, DORKING NORTH, & LONDON

Miles	Miles from Guildford	Up	Week Days a.m.																											a.m.
		Guildford dep.	3	..	3	3	4 5	3	3	3	3	3	3	3	3	3	5 22	3	3	3	3	5 37	5 52	3	3	3	3	3	3	3	3	3
3¾		Worplesdon	..	..	..	..	..	..	..	..	..	..	..	..	..	..	5 29	..	..	..	..		5 59	..	..	..	..	..	..	..	..	..
6		Woking X 324, 389, 390	..	2 58	..	..	4 15	..	..	..	..	..	..	..	..	..	5 36	..	..	..	..	3	6 6	..	..	..	..	..	..	..	..	..
8¾		Byfleet W	..	..	..	..	..	..	..	..	..	..	..	..	..	..	5 40	..	..	..	..	..	6 10	..	..	..	..	..	..	..	..	..
10		West Weybridge	..	..	..	..	..	..	..	..	..	..	..	..	..	..	5 43	..	..	..	..	..	6 13	..	..	..	..	..	..	..	..	..
—		Mls Virginia Water Z dep.	..	..	..	..	..	..	..	..	..	..	..	..	..	..	..	..	..	6 2	..	..	..	..	..	..	..	..	..	..	..	..
—		2½ Chertsey	..	..	..	..	..	..	..	..	..	..	..	..	..	5 37	..	..	..	6 7	..	..	..	..	..	..	..	..	..	..	..	..
—		4 Addlestone	..	..	..	..	..	..	..	..	..	..	..	..	..	5 40	..	..	..	6 10	..	..	..	..	..	..	..	..	..	..	..	..
11¼		Weybridge U 394		3 11			..	..	..	..	..	..	..	..	..	5 44	5 46	..	..	6 14	..	..	6 16	..	..	..	..	..	..	..	..	..
13¼		Walton-on-Thames	From Waterloo via Richmond Dep. Twickenham 1 48 a.m	3 17	From Waterloo via Richmond Dep. Twickenham 3 16 a.m	From Waterloo via Richmond Dep. Twickenham 4 3 a.m	4 26	..	..	..	..	..	..	..	..	Stop	5 50	..	..	Stop	..	..	6 20	..	..	..	..	..	..	..	..	..
14½		Hersham		..			..	..	..	..	..	..	..	..	..		5 52	..	..		..	..	6 22	..	..	..	..	..	..	..	..	..
16		Esher, for Sandown Park		3 23			4 30	..	..	..	..	..	..	..	..	..	5 55	..	..	..	..	..	6 25	..	..	..	..	From Waterloo via Richmond Dep. Twickenham 6 19 a.m	..	..	..	..
—	1½	London Road (Guildford)		..			..	..	..	..	..	..	..	..	..	..	..	..	..	..		5 40	..	..	..	..	..		..	..	..	..
—	4½	Clandon T		..			..	..	..	..	..	..	..	..	..	..	..	..	..	..		5 46	..	..	..	..	..		..	..	..	..
—	7¼	Horsley R		..			..	..	..	..	..	..	..	..	..	..	..	..	..	..	Arr Teddington 6 4 a.m	5 51	..	..	..	..	..		..	..	..	..
—	8¾	Effingham Junction		..			..	..	..	4 57	..	..	..	5 14	..	..	..	..	..	..		5 56	..	..	..	6 9	6 17		..	..	..	..
—	11	Cobham Q		..			..	..	..	..	..	..	..	..	..	..	..	..	..	..		..	..	..	..	..	6 21		..	..	..	..
—	13	Oxshott, for Fairmile		..			..	..	..	..	..	..	..	..	..	a.m	..	..	..	a.m		..	..	..	..	..	6 25		..	..	..	..
—	14¾	Claygate, for Claremont		..			..	..	..	..	..	..	..	..	..		..	..	..			..	..	..	..	..	6 28		..	..	..	..
—	16	Hinchley Wood		..			..	..	..	..	..	..	..	..	..	3	..	..	..	3		..	..	..	..	..	6 31		..	..	..	..
—	—	Hampton Court dep.		..			..	..	..	..	..	..	5 25	..	..	5 45	..	..	..	6 3		..	..	..	..	..	..		6 25	..	..	..
—	—	Thames Ditton		..			..	..	..	..	..	..	5 28	..	..	5 48	..	..	..	6 5		..	..	..	..	..	..		6 28	..	..	..
18½	18	Surbiton		3 32			4 35	..	..	..	..	..	5 33	..	..	5 53	6 0	..	..	6 10		..	6 30	..	..	..	6 35		6 33	..	..	..
19½	19	Berrylands N		..			..	..	..	..	..	..	5 35	..	..	5 55	..	..	..	6 13		..	..	..	..	..	..		6 35	..	..	..
—	—	Shepperton dep.		..			..	..	..	..	..	..	..	..	5 18	..	..	..	..	..	5 48	..	..	..	..	..	..		..	..	6 18	..
—	—	Upper Halliford Halt		..			..	..	..	..	..	..	..	..	..	..	..	..	..	..	..	..	..	..	..	..	..		..	..	6 21	..
—	—	Sunbury L		..			..	..	..	..	..	..	..	..	5 22	..	..	..	..	..	5 52	..	..	..	..	..	..		..	..	6 23	..
—	—	Hampton		..			..	..	..	..	..	..	..	..	5 26	..	..	..	..	..	5 56	..	..	..	..	..	..		..	..	6 27	..
—	—	Fulwell K	V	..	V	V	..	..	..	..	..	..	..	..	5 30	..	..	..	..	..	6 0	..	..	..	..	..	..	V	..	..	6 31	..
—	—	Teddington J	1 58	..	3 39	4 10	..	..	5 5	..	..	5 25	..	..	5 35	..	..	..	5 55	..	6 7	..	..	6 15	..	..	..	6 25	..	..	6 36	..
—	—	Hampton Wick	..	..	..	4 13	..	..	5 8	..	..	5 28	..	..	5 38	..	..	..	5 58	..	6 10	..	..	6 18	..	..	..	6 28	..	..	6 39	..
—	—	Kingston	2 6	..	3 47	4 16	..	..	5 10	..	..	5 30	..	..	5 40	..	..	..	6 0	..	6 12	..	..	6 20	..	..	..	6 30	..	..	6 41	..
—	—	Norbiton H	2 8	..	3 50	4 18	..	..	5 12	..	..	5 32	..	..	5 42	..	..	..	6 2	..	6 14	..	..	6 22	..	..	..	6 32	..	..	6 43	..
20¼	20¼	Malden, for Coombe	2 10	..	3 55	4 22	4 39	..	5 16	..	..	5 36	5 38	..	5 46	5 58	..	..	6 6	6 16	6 18	..	..	6 26	..	..	..	6 36	6 38	..	6 47	..
—	—	Bookham	..	..	..	..	..	..	..	5 0	..	..	..	5 17	..	..	..	..	..	..	..	5 59	..	..	..	6 12	..	..	..	..	..	..
—	—	Horsham dep.	..	..	..	..	..	..	..	..	..	..	..	..	..	..	..	..	..	..	..	..	..	..	..	..	..	..	..	..	..	..
—	—	Warnham	..	..	..	..	..	..	..	..	..	..	..	..	..	..	..	..	..	..	..	..	..	..	..	..	..	..	..	..	..	..
—	—	Ockley, for Capel	..	..	..	..	..	..	..	..	..	..	..	..	..	..	..	..	..	..	..	..	..	..	..	..	..	..	..	..	..	..
—	—	Holmwood G	..	..	..	..	..	..	..	..	..	..	..	..	..	..	..	..	..	..	..	..	..	..	..	..	..	..	..	..	..	..
—	—	Dorking North F	..	..	..	..	..	..	..	..	..	..	..	..	..	..	..	..	..	..	..	..	..	..	..	..	..	..	..	6 18	..	..
—	—	Boxhill & Burford Bdg D	..	..	..	..	..	..	..	..	..	..	..	..	..	..	..	..	..	..	..	..	..	..	..	..	..	..	..	6 21	..	..
—	—	Leatherhead	..	..	..	..	..	..	..	5 5	..	..	..	5 22	..	..	..	..	..	..	..	6 4	..	..	..	6 17	..	..	..	6 26	..	..
—	—	Ashtead	..	..	..	..	..	..	..	5 9	..	..	..	5 26	..	..	..	..	..	..	..	6 8	..	..	..	6 21	..	..	..	6 30	..	..
—	—	Epsom 285	..	..	..	..	..	..	..	5 13	..	..	..	5 30	..	..	..	..	..	..	..	6 12	..	..	..	6 25	..	..	..	6 34	..	..
—	—	Sutton arr.	..	..	..	..	..	..	..	5‡30	..	..	..	5‡45	..	..	..	..	..	..	..	6‡26	..	..	..	6 35	..	..	..	6‡46	..	..
—	—	Victoria "	..	..	..	..	..	..	..	..	..	..	..	6‡10	..	..	..	..	..	..	..	6‡51	..	..	..	7*10	..	..	..	7‡10	..	..
—	—	London Bridge "	..	..	..	..	..	..	..	6‡0	..	..	..	..	..	..	..	..	..	..	..	..	..	..	..	7 2	..	..	..	..	..	..
—	—	Ewell West C	..	..	..	..	..	..	..	5 16	..	..	..	5 33	..	..	..	..	..	..	..	6 15	..	..	..	..	..	..	..	6 37	..	..
—	—	Stoneleigh	..	..	..	..	..	..	..	5 18	..	..	..	5 35	..	..	..	..	..	..	..	6 17	..	..	..	..	..	..	..	6 39	..	..
—	—	Worcester Park	..	..	..	..	..	..	..	5 21	..	..	..	5 38	..	..	..	..	..	..	..	6 20	..	..	..	..	..	..	..	6 42	..	..
—	—	Chessington South ¶dp	..	..	..	..	..	..	..	..	5 19	..	..	..	..	..	..	5 49	..	..	..	..	..	..	6 19	..	..	..	..	..	..	6 39
—	—	Chessington North	..	..	..	..	..	..	..	..	5 21	..	..	..	..	..	..	5 51	..	..	..	..	..	..	6 21	..	..	..	..	..	..	6 41
—	—	Tolworth	..	..	..	..	..	..	..	..	5 24	..	..	..	..	..	..	5 54	..	..	..	..	..	..	6 24	..	..	..	..	..	..	6 44
—	—	Malden Manor	..	..	..	..	..	..	..	..	5 26	..	..	..	..	..	..	5 56	..	..	..	..	..	..	6 26	..	..	..	..	..	..	6 46
—	—	Motspur Park	..	..	..	..	..	..	..	5 24	5 30	..	..	5 41	..	..	..	6 2	..	..	..	6 24	..	..	6 32	..	..	..	..	6 45	..	6 50
21¾	21½	Raynes Park	2 14	..	3 59	4 25	4 42	..	5 19	5 27	5 33	5 39	5 41	5 44	5 49	6 1	..	6 5	6 9	6 19	6 21	..	..	6 29	6 35	..	..	6 39	6 41	..	6 50	6 53
23¼	22¾	Wimbledon 319, 320, 322	2 18	..	4 3	4 28	4 45	..	5 22	5 30	5 36	5 42	5 44	5 47	5 52	6 4	6 7	6 8	6 12	6 22	6 24	6 29	..	6 22	6 38	..	6 42	6 42	6 44	6 49	6 53	6 56
25	24½	Earlsfield B	2 23	..	4 8	4 31	4 48	5 7	5 25	5 34	5 39	5 45	5 48	5 51	5 56	6 8	..	6 11	6 16	6 25	6 28	..	..	6 36	6 41	..	..	6 45	6 48	..	6 57	6 59
26½	26	Clapham Junction A	2 28	..	4 13	4 35	4 52	5 10	5 29	5 37	5 43	5 49	5 51	5 54	5 59	6 11	6 13	6 15	6 19	6 29	6 31	..	..	6 39	6 45	..	..	6 49	6 51	..	7 0	7 3
29¼	28¾	Vauxhall	2 34	..	4 18	4 39	4 56	5 14	5 33	5 42	5 47	5 53	5 56	5 59	6 4	6 16	..	6 19	6 24	6 33	6 36	..	..	6 44	6 49	..	..	6 53	6 56	..	7 5	7 7
30½	30	Waterloo arr.	2 38	3 55	4 22	4 43	5 0	5 18	5 37	5 46	5 51	5 57	6 0	6 3	6 8	6 21	6 20	6 23	6 28	6 38	6 40	6 41	6 46	6 48	6 53	..	6 55	6 58	7 0	7 2	7 9	7 11

GUILDFORD, WOKING, CHERTSEY, HAMPTON COURT, SHEPPERTON, KINGSTON, HORSHAM, DORKING NORTH, & LONDON

Up	a.m.															Week Days—continued										a.m.					
Guildford dep.	(3)	(3)	(3)	(3)	6 22	6 27	(3)	(3)	(3)	..	(3)	(3)	(3)	(3)	6 47	(3)	6 52	(3)	(3)	(3)	(3)	..	(3)	(3)	..	(3)	7 10	(3)	(3)	..	(3)	(3)
Worplesdon	..	..	..	..	6 29	(3)	..	..	..	..	..	..	..	..	(3)	..	6 59	..	..	..	..	..	..	..	..	..	(3)	..	..	..	..	..
Woking **X 324**, 389, 390	..	..	..	..	6 36	..	..	..	..	..	..	..	..	..	..	..	7 6	..	..	..	..	..	..	..	7 16	..	..	..	..	7 23	..	..
Byfleet **W**	..	..	..	..	6 40	..	..	..	..	..	..	..	..	..	..	..	7 10	..	..	..	..	..	..	..	7 20	..	..	..	..	..	..	..
West Weybridge	..	..	..	..	6 43	..	..	..	..	..	..	..	..	..	..	..	7 13	..	..	..	..	..	..	..	7 23	..	..	..	..	..	..	..
Virginia Water **Z** dep.	..	..	..	..	..	..	..	..	6 34	..	..	..	..	..	..	7 1	..	..	..	..	..	..	..	..	..	..	..	..	..	..	..	..
Chertsey	..	..	..	6 36	..	..	..	..	6A44	..	..	..	..	..	..	7 6	..	..	..	..	..	..	..	..	..	..	..	..	7 20	..	..	..
Addlestone	..	..	..	6 39	..	..	..	..	6 47	..	..	..	..	..	..	7 9	..	..	..	..	..	..	..	..	..	..	..	..	7 23	..	..	..
Weybridge U 394	..	..	..	6 43	6 46	..	..	..	6 51	..	..	..	..	..	..	7 13	7 16	..	..	..	..	..	..	..	7 25	..	..	..	7 27	7 34	..	..
Walton-on-Thames	..	..	..	Stop	6 50	..		..	Stop	..	..		..	..	..	..	7 20	..	..	..		..	..	..	7 29	..	..	D	..	..	..	..
Hersham	..	..	..		6 52	..		..		..	..		..	..	..	..	7 22	..	..	..		..	..	..	7 32	..	..		..	..	..	..
Esher, for Sandown Park	..	..	..	..	6 55	..	From Waterloo via Richmond Dep. Twickenham 6 47 a.m	..	..	..	..	From Waterloo via Richmond Dep. Twickenham 6 57 a.m	..	..	..	..	7 25	..	..	..	From Waterloo via Richmond Dep. Twickenham 7 17 a.m	..	..	..	7 35	..	..	From Waterloo via Richmond Dep. Twickenham 7 27 a.m	..	..	..	..
London Road (Guildford)	..	..	..	..	..	6 30		..	..	..	..		..	..	6 50	..	Arr Woking 7 4 a.m.	..	..	..		..	..	..	..	..	7 13		..	..	..	..
Clandon **T**	..	..	..	..	..	6 36		..	..	..	..		..	..	6 56	..		..	..	..		..	..	..	..	..	7 19		..	..	..	..
Horsley **R**	..	..	..	..	..	6 41		..	..	..	..		..	..	7 1	..		..	..	..		..	..	..	..	..	7 24		..	..	..	..
Effingham Junction	..	..	6 38	..	..	6 47		..	..	..	..		..	..	7 7	..		..	..	..		..	7 10	..	..	..	7 27		..	..	..	..
Cobham **Q**	..	..	..	..	..	6 51		..	..	..	..		..	..	7 11	..		..	..	..		..	..	..	..	..	7 31		..	..	..	..
Oxshott, for Fairmile	..	..	..	..	..	6 55		..	a.m	..	..		..	..	7 15	..		..	..	..		..	..	..	..	..	7 35		..	..	..	..
Claygate, for Claremont	..	..	..	..	..	6 58		..	(3)	..	..		..	..	7 18	..		..	..	..		..	..	..	..	..	7 38		..	..	..	..
Hinchley Wood	..	..	..	..	..	7 1		..	..	..	..		..	..	7 21	..		..	..	..		..	..	..	..	..	7 41		..	..	..	..
Hampton Court dep.	..	6 45	..	..	..	..		..	7 3	..	..		..	..	..	..		..	..	..		..	..	7 25	..	..	..		..	..	..	7 43
Thames Ditton	..	6 48	..	a.m	..	..		..	7 5	..	..		..	..	..	..		..	..	..		..	..	7 28	..	..	..		..	..	..	7 45
Surbiton	..	6 53	..	(3)	7 0	7 5		..	7 10	..	..		..	..	7 25	..	7 30	..	..	..		..	..	7 33	7 40	..	7 45		..	7 46	..	7 50
Berrylands **N**	..	6 55	..	..	..	..		..	7 13	..	..		..	..	..	..	..	..	..	..		..	..	7 35	..	Arr Dorking North 7 15 a.m.	..		..	..	..	7 53
Shepperton dep	..	..	..	6 46	..	..		..	..	Via Three Bridges, see page 196	Arr Dorking North 6 46 a.m.		..	7 0	..	..	..	..	7 16	..		Via Three Bridges see page 196	..	..	..		..		..	..	..	..
Upper Halliford Halt	..	..	..	6 49	..	..		..	..				..	7 3	..	..	..	..	7 19	..			..	..	..		..		..	..	..	..
Sunbury L	..	..	..	6 51	..	..		..	..				..	7 5	..	..	..	..	7 21	..			..	..	..		..		..	..	..	..
Hampton	..	..	..	6 55	..	..		..	..				..	7 9	..	..	..	..	7 25	..			..	..	..		..		..	..	..	..
Fulwell **K**	..	..	..	6 59	..	..	▼	..	..			▼	..	7 13	..	..	..	..	7 29	..	▼		..	..	..		..	▼	..	..	..	..
Teddington J	..	..	..	..	..	..	6 55	..	..			7 5	..	7 16	..	..	..	..	..	..	7 25		..	..	..		..	7 35	..	..	..	..
Hampton Wick	..	..	..	..	..	..	6 58	..	..			7 8	..	7 19	..	..	..	..	..	..	7 28		..	..	..		..	7 38	..	..	..	..
Kingston	..	..	..	..	..	..	7 0	..	..			7 12	..	7 21	..	..	..	..	..	..	7 30		..	..	..		..	7 40	..	..	..	..
Norbiton **H**	..	..	..	..	..	..	7 2	..	..			7 14	..	7 23	..	..	..	..	..	..	7 32		..	..	..		..	7 42	..	..	..	..
Malden, for Coombe	..	6 58	..	..	..	..	7 6	..	7 16		..	7 18	..	7 27	7 29	..	..	..	..	..	7 36		..	7 38	..	..	..	7 46	..	7 52	..	7 56
Bookham	..	..	6 41	..	..	..	..	..	..	..	..	..	..	..	..	..	..	..	..	..	..	..	7 13	..	..	..	..	..	..	..	..	..
Horsham dep.	..	..	..	Via Richmond see page 476	..	..	..	..	..	6 17	6 23	..	..	..	..	..	..	..	Via Richmond see page 477	..	..	6 45	..	..	..	6 52	..	..	..	..	..	..
Warnham	..	..	..		..	..	..	..	..	..	6 27	..	..	..	..	..	..	..		..	..	..	..	..	..	6 56	..	..	..	..	..	..
Ockley, for Capel	..	..	..		..	..	..	..	..	..	6 34	..	..	..	..	..	..	..		..	..	..	..	..	..	7 3	..	..	..	..	..	..
Holmwood **G**	..	..	..		..	..	..	..	..	..	6 38	..	6 48	..	..	..	..	..		..	..	..	..	..	..	7 7	..	..	..	..	..	..
Dorking North F	6 29	..	..		..	..	..	..	..	..	6 49	..	6 58	..	..	..	..	..		..	..	..	..	..	..	7 18	..	..	..	..	..	..
Boxhill & Burford Bdg **D**	6 32	..	..		..	..	..	..	..	..	6 52	..	7 1	..	..	..	..	..		..	..	..	..	..	..	7 21	..	..	..	..	..	..
Leatherhead	6 37	..	6 46		..	..	..	..	..	..	6 57	..	7 6	..	..	..	..	..		..	..	..	7 18	..	..	7 26	..	..	..	..	..	..
Ashtead	6 41	..	6 50		..	..	..	..	..	..	7 1	..	7 10	..	..	..	..	..		..	..	..	7 22	..	..	7 30	..	..	..	..	..	..
Epsom **285**	6 45	..	6 54		..	..	..	..	..	..	7 5	..	7 14	..	..	..	..	..		7 22	..	..	7 26	..	..	7 34	..	..	..	..	..	..
Sutton arr.	6 55	..	7‡6		..	..	..	..	..	..	7 15	..	7‡26	..	..	..	..	..		..	..	..	7 35	..	..	7‡46	..	..	..	..	..	..
Victoria "	7*30	..	7‡30		..	..	..	..	..	7 36	7*50	..	7‡50	..	..	..	..	..		..	..	..	8*10	..	..	8‡10	..	..	..	..	..	..
London Bridge "	7 22	..	..		..	..	..	..	..	7 39	7 42	..	..	..	..	..	..	..		..	..	8 0	8 2	..	..	..	..	..	..	..	..	..
Ewell West **C**	..	..	6 57		..	..	..	..	..	..	..	..	7 17	..	..	..	..	..	..	7 25	..	..	..	..	..	7 37	..	..	..	..	..	..
Stoneleigh	..	..	6 59		..	..	..	..	..	..	..	..	7 19	..	..	..	..	..	..	7 27	..	..	..	..	..	7 39	..	..	..	..	..	..
Worcester Park	..	..	7 2		..	..	..	..	..	..	..	..	7 22	..	..	..	..	..	..	7 30	..	..	..	..	..	7 42	..	..	..	..	..	..
Chessington South ¶ dp	..	..	..		..	..	..	6 59	..	..	..	..	..	..	..	..	..	7 19	..	..	..	..	..	..	..	..	..	..	..	..	7 39	..
Chessington North	..	..	..		..	..	..	7 1	..	..	..	..	..	..	..	..	..	7 21	..	..	..	..	..	..	..	..	..	..	..	..	7 41	..
Tolworth	..	..	..		..	..	..	7 4	..	..	..	..	..	..	..	..	..	7 24	..	..	..	..	..	..	..	..	..	..	..	..	7 44	..
Malden Manor	..	..	..		..	..	..	7 6	..	..	..	..	..	..	..	..	..	7 26	..	..	..	..	..	..	..	..	..	..	..	..	7 46	..
Motspur Park	..	..	7 5		..	..	..	7 10	..	..	..	..	7 25	..	..	..	..	7 30	..	7 33	..	..	..	..	..	7 45	..	..	..	..	7 50	..
Raynes Park	..	7 1	..	..	..	..	7 9	7 13	7 19	..	..	7 21	..	7 30	..	..	..	7 33	..	7 36	7 39	..	..	7 41	..	..	..	7 49	..	..	7 53	7 59
Wimbledon 319, 320, 322	..	7 4	..	..	..	7 12	7 12	7 16	7 22	..	..	7 24	..	7 33	7 33	..	..	7 36	..	7 39	7 42	..	..	7 44	..	..	7 53	7 52	..	..	7 56	8 2
Earlsfield **B**	..	7 8	..	..	..	..	7 16	7 19	7 25	..	..	7 28	..	7 37	..	..	..	7 39	..	7 43	7 45	..	..	7 48	..	..	..	7 56	..	..	7 59	8 5
Clapham Junction A	..	7 11	..	..	..	..	7 19	7 23	7 29	..	..	7 31	..	7 40	..	..	..	7 43	..	7 46	7 49	..	..	7 51	..	..	7 58	7 59	..	..	8 3	8 9
Vauxhall	..	7 16	..	..	..	..	7 24	7 27	7 33	..	..	7 36	..	7 45	..	..	..	7 47	..	7 51	7 53	..	..	7 56	..	..	..	8 4	..	..	8 7	8 13
Waterloo arr.	..	7 20	7 23	7 24	7 16	7 23	7 28	7 31	7 37	..	..	7 40	7 43	7 49	7 44	..	7 46	7 51	7 55	7 55	7 57	..	..	8 0	7 56	8 3	8 5	8 8	..	8 8	8 11	8 17

FOR NOTES, SEE PAGE 459

FOR NOTES, SEE PAGE 459

GUILDFORD, WOKING, CHERTSEY, HAMPTON COURT, SHEPPERTON, KINGSTON, HORSHAM, DORKING NORTH, & LONDON

Week Days—*continued* (a.m.)

Up	③		③		SX	③	③	③	③	③	③	③	SX ③	③	SX	
Guildford dep.				7 22	7 34				7 30							7 49
Worplesdon				7 28												7 55
Woking X 324, 389, 390				7 36	7 44										7 50	8 0
Byfleet **W**				7 40	7 48										7 54	
West Weybridge				7 43											7 57	
Virginia Water Z dep.			7 26													
Chertsey			7 34													
Addlestone			7 37													
Weybridge U 394			7 42	7 46	7 53										8 0	
Walton-on-Thames			Stop	7 50	7 57										8 4	
Hersham				7 52											8 7	
Esher, for Sandown Park				7 55	8 1										8 10	
London Road (Guildford)				Arr Woking 7 32 a.m				From Waterloo via Richmond Dep. **Twickenham** 7 48 a.m	7 34							
Clandon **T**									7 39							
Horsley **R**									7 44							
Effingham Junction						7 38			7 47		7 42					
Cobham **Q**									7 51							
Oxshott, for **Fairmile**									7 55							
Claygate, for **Claremont**									7 58							
Hinchley Wood									8 1							
Hampton Court dep.														8 3		
Thames Ditton			a.m. ③											8 5		
Surbiton		Via Three Bridges, see page 196		8 0	8 5				8 5					8 10	8 15	
Berrylands **N**									8 7					8 13		
Shepperton dep.	Arr. Dorking North 7 26 a.m		7 30				7 44					Arr. Dorking North 7 46 a.m				
Upper Halliford Halt			7 33				7 47									
Sunbury **L**			7 35				7 49									
Hampton			7 40				7 53									
Fulwell **K**			7 44				7 57	V								
Teddington J			7 46					7 55								
Hampton Wick			7 49					7 58								
Kingston			7 52					8 0								
Norbiton **H**			7 54					8 2								
Malden, for Coombe			7 58					8 6	8 11					8 16		
Bookham						7 41					7 48					
Horsham dep.	7 3	7 7					Via Richmond see page 477					7 23				
Warnham	7 7											7 27				
Ockley, for Capel	7 14											7 34				
Holmwood **G**	7 18											7 38				
Dorking North F	7 29											7 49				
Boxhill & Burford Bdg **D**	7 32											7 52				
Leatherhead	7 37					7 45					7 52	7 57				
Ashtead	7 41					7 49					7 56	8 1				
Epsom 285	7 45					7 53					8 0	8 5	8 7			
Sutton arr.	7 55					8‡6					8‡14	8 14				
Victoria "	8*31	8 28				8‡31						8*50				
London Bridge "	8 22	8 26									8‡42	8 42				
Ewell West **C**						7 56					8 3		8 10			
Stoneleigh						7 59					8 6		8 13			
Worcester Park						8 2					8 9		8 16			
Chessington South ¶ dp										7 58						
Chessington North										8 0						
Tolworth										8 3						
Malden Manor										8 5						
Motspur Park						8 5				8 9	8 12					
Raynes Park			8 1					8 9		8 12	8 16			8 19		
Wimbledon 319, 320, 322			8 4					8 12	8 16	8 15	8 19		8 23	8 22		
Earlsfield **B**			8 8					8 15		8 18	8 23			8 25		
Clapham Junction A			8 11					8 19		8 22	8 26			8 29		
Vauxhall			8 16					8 23		8 26	8 31			8 33		
Waterloo arr.			8 20	8 17	8 22	8 22	8 24	8 27	8 27	8 30	8 36		8 34	8 38	8 31	8 29

Up		③		③		③	③		③	SX ③	③	SX	③	③	③	③
Guildford dep.						7 50						8 9				
Worplesdon												8 15				
Woking X 324, 389, 390	8 0				8 4			8 6				8 19				
Byfleet **W**								8 10								
West Weybridge								8 13								
Virginia Water Z dep.							7 56									
Chertsey							8 2									
Addlestone							8 5									
Weybridge U 394							8 9	8 16								
Walton-on-Thames					8 15			8 20								
Hersham								8 22								
Esher, for Sandown Park								8 25								
London Road (Guildford)		From Waterloo via Richmond Dep. **Twickenham** 7 59 a.m				7 54				From Waterloo via Richmond Dep. **Twickenham** 8 18 a.m						
Clandon **T**						7 59										
Horsley **R**						8 4									8 12	
Effingham Junction						8 7										
Cobham **Q**						8 11										
Oxshott, for **Fairmile**						8 15										
Claygate, for **Claremont**						8 18										
Hinchley Wood						8 21										
Hampton Court dep.																
Thames Ditton																
Surbiton					8 23	8 25		8 30				8 35				
Berrylands **N**																
Shepperton dep.			Via Three Bridges, see page 196						7 59							8 15
Upper Halliford Halt									8 1							8 18
Sunbury **L**									8 4							8 20
Hampton									8 8							8 24
Fulwell **K**		V							8 12	V						8 28
Teddington J		8 9							8 15	8 24						
Hampton Wick		8 12							8 18	8 27						
Kingston		8 14							8 20	8 29						
Norbiton **H**		8 16							8 22	8 31						
Malden, for Coombe		8 20							8 26	8 35						
Bookham														8 10	8 15	
Horsham dep.			7 46													Via Richmond see page 477
Warnham																
Ockley, for Capel																
Holmwood **G**				7 48												
Dorking North F				7 58												
Boxhill & Burford Bdg **D**				8 1												
Leatherhead				8 6										8 14	8 19	
Ashtead				8 10									8 15	8 19	8 23	
Epsom 285				8 14									8 20	8 25	8 27	
Sutton arr.				8‡26										8 35	8‡47	
Victoria "			8 37	8‡50											9‡11	
London Bridge "			8 43											9 2		
Ewell West **C**				8 17									8 23		8 30	
Stoneleigh				8 19									8 25		8 33	
Worcester Park				8 22									8 28			
Chessington South ¶ dp											8 17					
Chessington North											8 19					
Tolworth											8 22					
Malden Manor											8 25					
Motspur Park				8 25							8 28		8 31			
Raynes Park		8 23							8 29		8 31		8 34			
Wimbledon 319, 320, 322		8 26							8 32		8 34		8 37		8 41	
Earlsfield **B**		8 30							8 35		8 38		8 40			
Clapham Junction A		8 33							8 39		8 41		8 44		8 47	
Vauxhall		8 38							8 43		8 46		8 48			
Waterloo arr.	8 36	8 42		8 43	8 40	8 42		8 47	8 48	8 50	8 50	8 52	8 52		8 54	8 56

GUILDFORD, WOKING, CHERTSEY, HAMPTON COURT, SHEPPERTON, KINGSTON, HORSHAM, DORKING NORTH, & LONDON

Up — **Week Days**—*continued* — a.m.

Up	SX ③	③	SX ③		③	③	SX ③	③	SX	③		③	③	③		
Guildford dep.								8 15							8 25	8 32
Worplesdon															8 31	8 38
Woking X 324, 389, 390				8 22					8 32						8 36	
Byfleet W				8 26											8 40	
West Weybridge															8 43	
Virginia Water Z dep.												8 16				
Chertsey			8 17									8 21				
Addlestone			8 20									8 24				
Weybridge U 394			8 24	8 31								8 28			8 46	
Walton-on-Thames			8 27	8 35		From Waterloo via Richmond Dep. Twickenham 8 29 a.m.			8 43			Stop			8 50	
Hersham			8 30						8 45						8 52	
Esher, for Sandown Park			8 33						8 48						8 55	
London Road (Guildford)								8 19								
Clandon T								8 24								
Horsley R								8 29								
Effingham Junction								8 32								
Cobham Q								8 36								
Oxshott, for Fairmile								8 40								
Claygate, for Claremont								8 43								
Hinchley Wood								8 46								
Hampton Court dep.		8 25					8 36						8 43			
Thames Ditton		8 27					8 38						8 45			
Surbiton		8 33	8 37				8 43	8 50					8 52		9 0	
Berrylands N		8 36					8 46						8 54			
Shepperton dep.					Arr. Dorking North 8 15 a.m.						Via Three Bridges, see page 196			8 31		
Upper Halliford Halt														8 34		
Sunbury L														8 36		
Hampton														8 40		
Fulwell K						▼								8 44		
Teddington J						8 35								8 47		
Hampton Wick						8 38								8 50		
Kingston						8 40								8 53		
Norbiton H						8 42								8 55		
Malden, for Coombe		8 39				8 46	8 50						8 57	8 59		
Bookham																
Horsham dep.					7 52						7 59					
Warnham					7 56											
Ockley, for Capel					8 3											
Holmwood G					8 7											
Dorking North F					8 18							a.m.				
Boxhill & Burford Bdg D					8 21							SX ③				
Leatherhead					8 26											
Ashtead					8 30											
Epsom 285					8 35							8 42				
Sutton arr.					8‡47											
Victoria "					9‡11						9 15					
London Bridge "											9 6					
Ewell West C					8 38							8 45				
Stoneleigh					8 40							8 47				
Worcester Park	8 37				8 43							8 50				
Chessington South ¶dp										8 39						
Chessington North										8 41						
Tolworth										8 44						
Malden Manor										8 46						
Motspur Park					8 46					8 50		8 53				
Raynes Park		8 43				8 50				8 54		8 56	9 0	9 2		
Wimbledon 319, 320, 322	8 44	8 46				8 53	8 55			8 57		8 59	9 3	9 5		
Earlsfield B		8 50				8 57				9 0		9 3	9 7	9 9		
Clapham Junction A	8 50	8 53				9 0				9 4		9 6	9 10	9 12		
Vauxhall		8 58				9 5				9 8		9 11	9 15	9 17		
Waterloo arr.	8 57	9 2	8 54	8 57	9 4	9 9	9 6	9 8	9 10	9 12		9 15	9 19	9 21	9 16	9 13

Up		③	③	③	③	SX	SX ③		③	③	③	③	③	SX	③	
Guildford dep.				8 30				8 50								
Worplesdon																
Woking X 324, 389, 390	8 47					8 50								8 57		
Byfleet W														9 1		
West Weybridge														9 4		
Virginia Water Z dep.					8 40											
Chertsey					8 45											
Addlestone					8 48											
Weybridge U 394					8 53	8 57								9 6		
Walton-on-Thames						9 1			From Waterloo via Richmond Dep. Twickenham 8 49 a.m.					9 11	From Waterloo via Richmond Dep. Twickenham 9 0 a.m.	
Hersham																
Esher, for Sandown Park														9 15		
London Road (Guildford)				8 34												
Clandon T				8 39												
Horsley R				8 44												
Effingham Junction			8 38	8 47								8 54				
Cobham Q				8 51												
Oxshott, for Fairmile				8 55												
Claygate, for Claremont				8 58												
Hinchley Wood				9 1												
Hampton Court dep.													9 3			
Thames Ditton													9 5			
Surbiton				9 5		9 8		9 14					9 10	9 20		9 23
Berrylands N													9 13			
Shepperton dep.							8 45			Arr. Dorking North 8 46 a.m.						
Upper Halliford Halt							8 48									
Sunbury L							8 50									
Hampton							8 54									
Fulwell K		Arr. Dorking North 8 26 a.m.					8 58		▼						▼	
Teddington J									8 55						9 6	
Hampton Wick									8 58						9 9	
Kingston									9 0						9 12	
Norbiton H									9 2						9 14	
Malden, for Coombe									9 6				9 16		9 18	
Bookham			8 41									8 57				
Horsham dep.										8 22						
Warnham										8 27						
Ockley, for Capel										8 34						
Holmwood G		8 18								8 38						
Dorking North F		8 29								8 49						
Boxhill & Burford Bdg D		8 32								8 52						
Leatherhead		8 37	8 46							8 57		9 2				
Ashtead		8 41	8 50							9 1						
Epsom 285		8 45	8 54							9 5						
Sutton arr.		8 55	9‡6				Via Richmond, see page 477			9 15						
Victoria "		9*31	9‡31													
London Bridge "		9 22								9 42						
Ewell West C			8 57													
Stoneleigh			8 59													
Worcester Park			9 2													
Chessington South ¶dp											8 59					
Chessington North											9 1					
Tolworth											9 4					
Malden Manor											9 6					
Motspur Park			9 5								9 10					
Raynes Park									9 9		9 13		9 19		9 21	
Wimbledon 319, 320, 322									9 12		9 16		9 22		9 24	
Earlsfield B									9 16		9 19		9 25		9 28	
Clapham Junction A									9 19		9 23		9 29		9 31	
Vauxhall									9 24		9 27		9 33		9 36	
Waterloo arr.	9 20		9 23	9 22		9 25	9 26	9 30	9 29		9 31		9 37	9 36	9 40	9 42

FOR NOTES, SEE PAGE 459

FOR NOTES. SEE PAGE 459

GUILDFORD, WOKING, CHERTSEY, HAMPTON COURT, SHEPPERTON, KINGSTON, HORSHAM, DORKING NORTH, & LONDON

Week Days—continued (a.m.)

Up	3		3	3			SX	3	3	3
Guildford dep.			8 52		8 52		9 9			
Worplesdon					8 59					
Woking X 324, 389, 390					9 6		9 18			
Byfleet W					9 10					
West Weybridge					9 13					
Virginia Water Z dep.				8 56						
Chertsey				9 1						
Addlestone				9 4						
Weybridge U 394				9 8	9 16					
Walton-on-Thames					9 20					
Hersham					9 22					
Esher, for Sandown Park					9 25					
London Road (Guildford)			8 55							From Waterloo via Richmond Dep. Twickenham 9 19 a.m.
Clandon T			9 1							
Horsley R			9 6							
Effingham Junction			9 8							
Cobham Q			9 12							
Oxshott, for Fairmile			9 16							
Claygate, for Claremont			9 19							
Hinchley Wood			9 22							
Hampton Court dep.										
Thames Ditton										
Surbiton			9 27		9 30					
Berrylands N										
Shepperton dep.		Via Three Bridges see page 198				Via Three Bridges, see page 198		9 0		
Upper Halliford Halt								9 3		
Sunbury L								9 5		
Hampton								9 9		
Fulwell K								9 13		V
Teddington J								9 16		9 25
Hampton Wick								9 19		9 28
Kingston								9 21		9 30
Norbiton H								9 23		9 32
Malden, for Coombe								9 27		9 36
Bookham										
Horsham dep.	8 34	8 39				8 46				
Warnham	8 38									
Ockley, for Capel	8 45									
Holmwood G	8 49									
Dorking North F	8 59									
Boxhill & Burford Bdg D	9 2									
Leatherhead	9 7									
Ashtead	9 11									
Epsom 285	9 15									
Sutton arr.	9‡26									
Victoria "	9‡50	9 33				9 55				
London Bridge "		9 38								
Ewell West C	9 18									
Stoneleigh	9 20									
Worcester Park	9 23									
Chessington South ¶ dp									9 19	
Chessington North									9 21	
Tolworth									9 24	
Malden Manor									9 26	
Motspur Park	9 26								9 30	
Raynes Park								9 30	9 33	9 39
Wimbledon 319, 320, 322								9 33	9 36	9 42
Earlsfield B								9 37	9 39	9 45
Clapham Junction A								9 40	9 43	9 49
Vauxhall								9 45	9 47	9 53
Waterloo arr.	9 43		9 45		9 47		9 49	9 50	9 52	9 58

Up	SX	3	3	SX	3	3			3	3
Guildford dep.					9 10			9 30		
Worplesdon										
Woking X 324, 389, 390				9 24						
Byfleet W										
West Weybridge										
Virginia Water Z dep.										
Chertsey										
Addlestone										
Weybridge U 394										
Walton-on-Thames										
Hersham										
Esher, for Sandown Park										
London Road (Guildford)					9 14				From Waterloo via Richmond Dep. Twickenham 9 29 a.m.	
Clandon T					9 19					
Horsley R					9 24					
Effingham Junction					9 27					
Cobham Q					9 31					
Oxshott, for Fairmile					9 35					
Claygate, for Claremont					9 38					
Hinchley Wood					9 41					
Hampton Court dep.		9 25								
Thames Ditton		9 28								
Surbiton		9 33		9 39	9 45					
Berrylands N		9 35								
Shepperton dep.	Via Three Bridges, see page 198.									
Upper Halliford Halt										
Sunbury L										
Hampton										
Fulwell K									V	
Teddington J									9 37	
Hampton Wick									9 40	
Kingston									9 42	
Norbiton H									9 44	
Malden, for Coombe		9 38							9 48	
Bookham			9 12							
Horsham dep.	9 9						9 1			
Warnham							9 5			
Ockley, for Capel							9 12			
Holmwood G							9 17			
Dorking North F						9 18	9 26			
Boxhill & Burford Bdg D						9 20				
Leatherhead			9 17			9 25				
Ashtead			9 21			9 29				
Epsom 285			9 25			9 34				
Sutton arr.			9 35			9‡49	9 43			
Victoria "			10*13			10‡13	10*13			
London Bridge "	9 57		10 2				10 4			
Ewell West C						9 37				
Stoneleigh						9 39				
Worcester Park						9 42				
Chessington South ¶ dp										9 39
Chessington North										9 41
Tolworth										9 44
Malden Manor										9 46
Motspur Park						9 45				9 50
Raynes Park		9 41							9 51	9 53
Wimbledon 319, 320, 322		9 44				9 49			9 54	9 56
Earlsfield B		9 48							9 57	10 0
Clapham Junction A		9 51							10 1	10 3
Vauxhall		9 56							10 5	10 8
Waterloo arr.		10 1		9 55	10 1	10 4		10 5	10 9	1012

Up	3		3		3	3		SX	3	SX 3
Guildford dep.		9 22				9 20	9 30	9 48		
Worplesdon		9 28								
Woking X 324, 389, 390		9 36								
Byfleet W		9 40								
West Weybridge		9 43								
Virginia Water Z dep.	9 17		9 36							
Chertsey	9 22		9 43							
Addlestone	9 25		9 46							
Weybridge U 394	9 29	9 46	9 50							
Walton-on-Thames	Stop	9 50	Stop							
Hersham		9 52								
Esher, for Sandown Park		9 55								
London Road (Guildford)		Arr Woking 9 33 a.m				9 24	9 34		From Waterloo via Richmond Dep. Twickenham 9 49 a.m.	
Clandon T						9 30	9 39			
Horsley R						9 35	9 44			
Effingham Junction						9 38	9 47			
Cobham Q							9 51			
Oxshott, for Fairmile							9 55			
Claygate, for Claremont							9 58			
Hinchley Wood	a.m 3						10 1			
Hampton Court dep.	9 43									
Thames Ditton	9 45		a.m 3							
Surbiton	9 50	10 0					10 5			
Berrylands N	9 53									
Shepperton dep.			9 31	Via Three Bridges, see page 200						
Upper Halliford Halt			9 34							
Sunbury L			9 36							
Hampton			9 40							
Fulwell K			9 44						V	
Teddington J			9 47						9 57	
Hampton Wick			9 50						10 0	
Kingston			9 52						10 2	
Norbiton H			9 54						10 4	
Malden, for Coombe	9 56		9 58						10 8	
Bookham						9 41				
Horsham dep.				9 16						
Warnham										
Ockley, for Capel										
Holmwood G										
Dorking North F					9 30					
Boxhill & Burford Bdg D					9 33					
Leatherhead					9 38	9 46				
Ashtead					9 42	9 50				
Epsom 285					9 46	9 54				
Sutton arr.					9 55	10‡14				
Victoria "				10 26	10‡29					
London Bridge "				10SX21	10 23	10‡42				
Ewell West C						9 57				
Stoneleigh						9 59				
Worcester Park						10 2				
Chessington South ¶ dp										9 59
Chessington North										10 1
Tolworth										10 4
Malden Manor										10 6
Motspur Park						10 5				1010
Raynes Park	9 59		10 1						1011	1013
Wimbledon 319, 320, 322	10 2		10 4			10 9	10SX12		1014	1016
Earlsfield B	10 5		10 8						1017	1020
Clapham Junction A	10 9		1011						1021	1023
Vauxhall	1013		1016						1025	1028
Waterloo arr.	1017	1016	1020			10 23	10 23	1028	1029	1032

GUILDFORD, WOKING, CHERTSEY, HAMPTON COURT, SHEPPERTON, KINGSTON, HORSHAM, DORKING NORTH, & LONDON

Up — Week Days—*continued* — a.m

Up	③	③	③		③		③	③		③	③	③	③		SO	③	③			③	③	③	③	③		③	③	③	③
Guildford dep.				9 50		9 52			..					10 10	1020			1022	..						1035				
Worplesdon	..	..	..		..	9 59	..	..	..	..	..	..	..		..	..	..	1029	..	..	..	..	..	..		..	..	..	..
Woking X 324, 389, 390	..	..	..	③	..	10 6	..	..	..	..	..	..	..	③	1031	..	..	1036	1042	..	..	..	..	..	③	..	..	..	..
Byfleet **W**	..	..	..	..	..	1010	..	..	..	..	..	..	..	..	..	..	..	1040	..	..	..	..	..	..	..	..	..	..	..
West Weybridge	..	..	..	..	..	1013	..	..	..	..	..	..	..	..	..	..	..	1043	..	..	..	..	..	..	..	..	..	..	..
Virginia Water Z dep.	..	..	..	..	9 56	..	..	..	..	..	..	..	..	..	..	1026	..	..	..	..	..	..	..	..	..	..	..	..	..
Chertsey	..	..	..	..	10 3	..	..	..	..	..	..	..	..	..	..	1034	..	..	..	..	..	..	..	..	..	..	..	..	..
Addlestone	..	..	..	..	10 6	..	..	..	..	..	..	..	..	..	..	1037	..	..	..	..	..	..	..	..	..	..	..	..	..
Weybridge U 394	From Waterloo via Richmond Dep. **Twickenham** 9 59 a.m	..	..	..	1010	1016	..	..	..	From Waterloo via Richmond Dep. **Twickenham** 10 19 a.m	..	..	..	..	..	1041	..	1046	..	..	..	..	From Waterloo via Richmond Dep. **Twickenham** 10 49 a.m	..	..	..	..	From Waterloo via Richmond Dep. **Twickenham** 10 59 a.m	..
Walton-on-Thames		..	..	..	▬	1020	..	..	..		..	..	..	..	..	▬	..	1050	..	..	..	..		..	..	..	..		..
Hersham		..	..	..	Stop	1022	..	..	..		..	..	..	..	..	Stop	..	1052	..	..	..	..		..	..	..	..		..
Esher, for Sandown Park		..	..	..	..	1025	..	..	..		..	..	..	..	..	..	..	1055	..	..	..	..		..	..	..	..		..
London Road (Guildford)		..	..	9 54	..	..	..	..	..		..	..	..	10 14	..	..	..	..	..	..	..	..		..	1038	..	..		..
Clandon **T**		..	..	9 59	..	..	..	..	..		..	..	..	10 19	..	..	..	..	..	..	..	..		..	1044	..	..		..
Horsley **R**		..	..	10 4	..	..	..	..	..		..	..	..	10 24	..	..	..	..	..	..	..	SO		..	1049	..	..		..
Effingham Junction		..	..	10 7	..	..	..	..	..		10 13	..	..	10 27	..	..	..	..	..	..	..	10 38		..	1051	..	..		..
Cobham **Q**		..	..	10 11	..	..	..	..	..		..	..	..	10 31	..	..	..	..	..	..	..	..		..	..	..	..		..
Oxshott, for Fairmile		..	..	10 15	..	..	..	..	..		..	..	..	10 35	..	..	..	..	..	..	..	..		..	..	..	..		..
Claygate, for Claremont		..	..	10 18	..	..	..	..	..		..	..	..	10 38	..	..	..	..	..	..	..	..		..	..	..	..		..
Hinchley Wood		..	..	10 21	..	..	..	..	..		..	..	..	10 41	..	..	..	..	..	..	..	..		..	..	SO	..		..
Hampton Court dep.		Arr Dorking North 9 46 a.m	..	..	..	..	..	..	..		..	1025	..	..	..	..	1043	..	..	..	..	..		..	..	11 3	..		..
Thames Ditton			..	..	..	..	..	..	..		..	1028	..	..	..	..	1045	..	..	..	..	..		..	..	11 5	..		..
Surbiton			..	10 25	..	1030	..	..	..		..	1033	..	10 47	..	..	1050	11 0	..	..	..	..		..	..	1110	..		..
Berrylands **N**			..	..	..	..	..	..	..		..	1036	..	..	..	..	1053	..	..	..	..	..		..	..	1113	..		..
Shepperton dep.			..	..	..	..	10 0	..	Via Three Bridges, see page 200		..	..	..	..	..	..	..	..	..	1031	..	..		..	..	..	Arr. Dorking North 1043 a.m		..
Upper Halliford Halt			..	..	..	..	10 3	..			..	..	..	..	..	..	..	..	..	1034	..	..		..	..	..			..
Sunbury **L**			..	..	..	..	10 5	..			..	..	..	..	..	..	..	..	..	1036	..	..		..	..	..			..
Hampton			..	..	..	..	10 9	..			..	..	..	..	..	..	..	..	..	1040	..	..		..	..	..			..
Fulwell **K**	V		..	..	..	..	1013	..		V	..	..	..	..	..	..	..	..	..	1044	..	..	V	..	..	..		V	..
Teddington J	10 7		..	..	..	..	1016	..		1025	..	..	..	..	..	..	..	..	..	1047	..	..	1055	..	..	..		11 7	..
Hampton Wick	1010		..	..	..	..	1019	..		1028	..	..	..	..	..	..	..	..	..	1050	..	..	1058	..	..	..		1110	..
Kingston	1012		..	..	..	..	1021	..		1030	..	..	..	..	..	..	..	..	..	1052	..	..	11 0	..	..	..		1112	..
Norbiton **H**	1014		..	..	..	..	1023	..		1032	..	..	..	..	..	..	..	..	..	1054	..	..	11 2	..	..	..		1114	..
Malden, for Coombe	1018		..	..	..	..	1027	..		1036	..	1039	..	..	..	..	1056	..	..	1058	..	..	11 6	..	..	1116		1118	..
Bookham	..		..	..	a.m	..	..	..		..	10 16	..	..	..	..	..	..	..	..	..	..	10 41	..	..	..	..	SX	..	SO
Horsham dep.	..	9 23	..	..	9 37	..	..	..	9 42	..	..	..	9 52	..	..	..	..	..	..	..	..	..	..	..	..	..	1020	..	10 22
Warnham	..	9 27	..	..	9 42	..	..	..	..	..	..	..	9 56	..	..	..	..	..	..	..	..	..	..	..	..	..	1024	..	10 26
Ockley, for Capel	..	9 34	..	..	9 50	..	..	..	..	..	..	..	10 3	..	..	..	..	..	..	..	..	..	..	..	..	..	1031	..	10 33
Holmwood **G**	..	9 38	SO	..	9 54	..	..	..	..	..	..	..	10 7	..	..	..	..	..	..	..	SO	..	..	..	..	..	1035	..	10 37
Dorking North F	..	9 49	9 55	..	10 3	..	..	..	..	..	..	..	10 18	..	..	..	..	..	..	..	1029	..	..	..	..	..	1046	..	10 48
Boxhill & Burford Bdg **D**	..	9 52	9 58	..	..	..	..	..	..	..	..	..	10 21	..	..	..	..	..	..	..	1032	..	..	..	..	..	1048	..	10 51
Leatherhead	..	9 57	10 3	..	..	..	..	..	..	..	10 20	..	10 26	..	..	..	..	..	..	..	1037	10 46	..	..	..	..	1053	..	10 56
Ashtead	..	10 1	10 7	..	..	..	..	..	..	..	10 24	..	10 30	..	..	..	..	..	..	..	1041	10 50	..	..	..	..	1057	..	11 0
Epsom 285	..	10 5	10 14	..	1015	..	..	..	..	..	10 28	..	10 34	..	..	..	..	..	..	..	1045	10 54	..	..	..	..	11 2	..	11 5
Sutton arr.	..	10 14	10‡22	..	1022	..	..	..	..	..	10 37	..	10‡Z57	..	..	..	..	..	..	..	1054	11‡14	..	..	..	..	1111	..	11 14
Victoria "	..	10‡42	10‡42	..	1042	..	..	..	1031	..	..	..	11‡Z21	..	..	..	..	..	..	..	..	..	..	..	..	..	..	..	11*50
London Bridge "	..	10 42	..	..	..	..	..	..	1040	..	11 5	..	..	..	..	..	..	..	..	..	1122	11‡42	..	..	..	..	1139	..	11 42
Ewell West **C**	..	..	10 17	..	..	..	..	..	..	..	..	..	10 37	..	..	a.m	..	..	..	..	..	10 57	..	..	..	..	..	..	..
Stoneleigh	..	..	10 19	..	..	..	..	..	..	..	..	..	10 39	..	..	③	..	..	..	..	..	10 59	..	..	..	..	..	..	..
Worcester Park	..	..	10 22	..	..	..	..	..	..	..	..	..	10 42	..	..		..	..	..	..	..	11 2	..	..	..	..	..	..	..
Chessington South ¶ dp	..	..	..	..	..	..	..	1019	..	..	..	..	..	..	..	1039	..	..	..	..	..	..	..	10 59	..	..	..	..	..
Chessington North	..	..	..	..	..	..	..	1021	..	..	..	..	..	..	..	1041	..	..	..	..	..	..	..	11 1	..	..	..	..	..
Tolworth	..	..	..	..	..	..	..	1024	..	..	..	..	..	..	..	1044	..	..	..	..	..	..	..	11 4	..	..	..	..	..
Malden Manor	..	..	..	..	..	..	..	1026	..	..	..	..	..	..	..	1046	..	..	..	..	..	..	..	11 6	..	..	..	..	..
Motspur Park	..	..	10 25	..	..	..	..	1030	..	..	..	..	10 45	..	..	1050	..	..	..	..	..	11 5	..	11 10	..	..	..	..	..
Raynes Park	1021	..	..	..	..	..	1030	1033	..	1039	..	1042	..	..	..	1053	1059	..	..	11 1	..	..	11 9	11 13	..	1119	..	1121	..
Wimbledon 319, 320, 322	1024	..	10 29	10SX32	..	..	1033	1036	..	1042	..	1045	10 49	10SX54	..	1056	11 2	..	..	11 4	..	11 10	1112	11 16	..	1122	..	1124	..
Earlsfield **B**	1028	..	..	..	..	..	1037	1039	..	1045	..	1049	..	..	..	1059	11 5	..	..	11 8	..	..	1116	11SO19	..	1125	..	1128	..
Clapham Junction A	1031	..	..	..	..	..	1040	1043	..	1049	..	1052	..	..	..	11 3	11 9	..	..	1111	..	..	1119	11SO23	..	1129	..	1131	..
Vauxhall	1036	..	..	..	..	..	1045	1047	..	1053	..	1057	..	..	..	11 7	1113	..	..	1116	..	..	1124	11SO27	..	1133	..	1136	..
Waterloo arr.	1040	..	10 43	10 43	..	1046	1049	1051	..	1057	..	11 1	11 3	11 5	11 2	1111	1117	1116	1113	1120	..	11 22	1128	11SO31	..	1138		1140	..

FOR NOTES, SEE PAGE 459

FOR NOTES, SEE PAGE 459

GUILDFORD, WOKING CHERTSEY, HAMPTON COURT, SHEPPERTON, KINGSTON, HORSHAM, DORKING NORTH, & LONDON

Week Days—continued

Up	a.m	3	3		3	3		3	3			3	3	3	3	3	3	3		3	3	S O	3	3	3	3	3	3
Guildford ....dep.	..			10 50			1052			11 10	1120								1122			1130						
Worplesdon							1059												1129									
Woking X 324, 389, 390				3			11 6			3	1130								1136			3						
Byfleet W							1110												1140									
West Weybridge							1113												1143									
Virginia Water Z ..dep.						1056												1126										
Chertsey						11 3												1134										
Addlestone						11 6												1137										
Weybridge U 394						1110	1116											1141	1146									
Walton-on-Thames							1120												1150									
Hersham						Stop	1122											Stop	1152									
Esher, for Sandown Park							1125												1155									
London Road (Guildford)				10 54				From Waterloo via Richmond Dep. Twickenham 11 19 a.m		11 14					From Waterloo via Richmond Dep. Twickenham 11 29 a.m							1134	From Waterloo via Richmond Dep. Twickenham 11 49 a.m				From Waterloo via Richmond Dep. Twickenham 11 59 a.m	
Clandon T				10 59						11 19												1139						
Horsley R		S X		11 4						11 24		S O	S X								S O	1144						
Effingham Junction		10 55		11 7						11 27		11 10	11 13								11 38	1147						
Cobham Q				11 11						11 31												1151						
Oxshott, for Fairmile				11 15						11 35												1155						
Claygate, for Claremont				11 18						11 38												1158			p.m S O			
Hinchley Wood				11 21						11 41												12 1						
Hampton Court...dep.									1125								1143								12 3			
Thames Ditton									1128								1145	a.m							12 5	Arr. Dorking North 11 43 a.m		
Surbiton				11 25			1130		1133	11 45							1150	3	12 0			12 5			1210			
Berrylands N									1136								1153								1213			
Shepperton ....dep.	Via Three Bridges, see page 200	Arr. Epsom 11 10 a.m	Arr. Epsom 11 10 a.m		11 0													1131										
Upper Halliford Halt					11 3													1134										
Sunbury L					11 5													1136										
Hampton					11 9										S O			1140									p.m	
Fulwell K					1113			V							V			1144					V				V	
Teddington J					1116			1125							1135			1147					1155				12 7	
Hampton Wick					1119			1128							1138			1150					1158				1210	
Kingston					1121			1130							1140			1152					12 0				1212	
Norbiton H					1123			1132							1142			1154					12 2				1214	
Malden, for Coombe					1127			1136	1139						1146		1156	1158					12 6		1216		1218	
Bookham		10 58										11 13	11 16								11 41					S X		S O
Horsham ....dep.	1042													10 52												11 20		11 22
Warnham														10 56												11 24		11 26
Ockley, for Capel														11 3												11 31		11 33
Holmwood G			S O											11 7						S O						11 35		11 37
Dorking North F			10 55											11 18						11 29						11 46		11 48
Boxhill & Burford Bge D			10 57											11 21						11 32						11 48		11 51
Leatherhead		11 2	11 2									11 17	11 20	11 26						11 37	11 46					11 53		11 56
Ashtead		11 6	11 6									11 21	11 24	11 30						11 41	11 50					11 57		12 0
Epsom 285		11 14	11 14									11 25	11 28	11 34						11 45	11 54					12 1		12 5
Sutton ....arr.		11‡26	11‡26									11 34	11 38	11‡49						11 55	12‡ 6					12 10		12 14
Victoria .... "	1132	11‡50	11‡50									12‡14	12‡14	12‡14						12*30	12†30					12*40		12*40
London Bridge .... "												12 2	12 7							12 22	12‡42					12 38		12 42
Ewell West C		11 17	11 17			a.m								11 37							11 57							
Stoneleigh		11 19	11 19			3								11 39							11 59							
Worcester Park		11 22	11 22											11 42							12 2			S O				
Chessington South ¶dp						1119										1139								11 59				
Chessington North						1121										1141								12 1				
Tolworth						1124										1144								12 4				
Malden Manor						1126										1146								12 6				
Motspur Park		11 25	11 25			1130								11 45		1150					12 5			12 10				
Raynes Park					1130	1133		1139	1142						11 49	1153	1159	12 1					12 9	12 13	1219		1221	
Wimbledon 319, 320, 322		11 30	11 30	11SX32	1133	1136		1142	1145	11SX53				11 50	1152	1156	12 2	12 4			12 10		1212	12 16	1222		1224	
Earlsfield B					1137	1139		1145	1149						1156	1159	12 5	12 8					1216	12 19	1225		1228	
Clapham Junction A					1140	1143		1149	1152						1159	12 3	12 9	1211					1219	12 23	1229		1231	
Vauxhall					1145	1147		1153	1157						12 4	12 7	1213	1216					1224	12 27	1233		1236	
Waterloo ....arr.		11 42	11 42	11 43	1149	1151	1148	1157	12 1	12 4	12 1			12 3	12 9	1211	1218	1220	1216		12 23	1221	1228	12 31	1238		1240	

GUILDFORD, WOKING, CHERTSEY, HAMPTON COURT, SHEPPERTON, KINGSTON, HORSHAM, DORKING NORTH, & LONDON

Up — Week Days—continued (a.m. … p.m.)

Up																														
		3	3		3		3	3	3	3			3	3	3	3	3	3		SX	SO	3		3	3	3	SO	SO	3	3
Guildford dep.	..	..	..	11 50	..	1152	..	..	..	..	12 10	1220	..	..	..	..	..	..	1222	..	1230	..		..	..	..	..	..	..	..
Worplesdon	..	..	..	..	..	1159	..	..	..	..	..	..	..	..	..	..	..	..	1229	..	..	..	..	..	..	..	..	..	..	..
Woking X 324, 389, 390	..	..	..	3	..	12 6	..	..	..	..	3	1230	..	..	..	..	..	..	1236	1247	3	..	..	..	..	..	1250	1258	..	..
Byfleet **W**	..	..	..	..	..	1210	..	..	..	..	..	..	..	..	..	..	..	..	1240	..	..	..	..	..	..	..	..	..	..	..
West Weybridge	..	..	..	..	..	1213	..	..	..	..	..	..	..	..	..	..	..	..	1243	..	..	..	..	..	..	SO	..	..	..	..
Virginia Water Z ..dep.	..	..	..	..	1156	..	..	..	..	..	..	..	..	..	..	..	..	1226	..	..	..	..	..	..	..	1246	..	..	..	..
Chertsey	..	..	..	..	12 1	..	..	..	..	..	..	..	..	..	..	..	..	1231	..	..	..	..	..	..	..	1251	..	..	..	..
Addlestone	..	..	..	..	12 4	..	..	..	..	..	..	..	..	..	..	..	..	1234	..	..	..	..	..	..	..	1254	..	..	..	..
Weybridge U 394	..	..	..	..	12 8	1216	..	..	..	..	..	..	..	..	..	..	..	1238	1246	..	..	..	..	..	..	1258	1259	..	..	..
Walton-on-Thames	..	..	..	..	Stop	1220	..	..	..	..	..	..	..	..	..	..	..	Stop	1250	..	..	..	..	..	..	Stop	..	..	..	..
Hersham	..	..	..	..		1222	..	..	From Waterloo via Richmond Dep. **Twickenham** 12 19 p.m	..	..	..	..	..	..	..	..		1252	..	..	..	..	..	From Waterloo via Richmond Dep. **Twickenham** 12 49 p.m		..	..	..	..
Esher, for Sandown Park	..	..	..	..	..	1225	..	..		..	..	..	..	..	..	..	..	..	1255	..	..	..	..	..		..	..	..	..	..
London Road (Guildford)	..	..	..	11 54	..	..	..	..		..	12 14	..	..	..	..	..	..	..	..	..	1234	..	..	..		..	..	..	..	..
Clandon **T**	..	..	..	11 59	..	..	..	..		..	12 19	..	..	..	..	..	..	..	..	..	1239	..	..	..		..	..	..	..	..
Horsley **R**	..	SO	SX	12 4	..	..	..	..		..	12 24	..	..	SX	..	..	..	..	..	..	1244	..	..	SO		..	..	..	..	..
Effingham Junction	..	1151	11 55	12 7	..	..	..	..		..	12 27	..	..	1213	..	..	..	..	..	..	1247	..	..	1238		..	..	..	..	..
Cobham **Q**	..	..	..	12 11	..	..	..	..		..	12 31	..	..	..	..	..	..	..	..	..	1251	..	..	..		..	..	..	..	..
Oxshott, for Fairmile	..	..	..	12 15	..	..	..	..		..	12 35	..	..	..	..	..	..	..	..	..	1255	..	..	..		..	..	..	..	..
Claygate, for Claremont	..	..	..	12 18	..	..	..	..		..	12 38	..	..	..	..	..	..	..	..	..	1258	..	..	..		..	..	..	..	..
Hinchley Wood	..	..	..	12 21	..	..	..	..		..	12 41	..	..	..	..	..	..	..	..	..	1 1	..	..	..		..	..	..	SO	..
Hampton Court...dep.	..	..	..	..	..	..	..	..		1225	..	..	..	..	..	..	1243	..	..	..	..	..	..	..		..	..	..	1 3	..
Thames Ditton	..	..	..	..	non	..	..	..	..	1228	..	..	..	..	..	..	1245	p.m	..	..	..	..	..	..	..	..	..	..	1 5	..
Surbiton	..	..	..	12 25	3	1230	..	..	..	1234	12 45	..	..	..	..	..	1250	3	1 0	..	1 5	..	Via Three Bridges see page 204	..	..	..	1 8	..	1 10	Arr. Dorking North 12 43 p.m
Berrylands **N**	..	..	..	..	..	..	..	..	..	1236	..	..	..	..	..	..	1253	..	..	..	..	..		..	..	..	..	..	1 13	
Shepperton ....dep.	..	..	..	..	12 0	..	..	..	..	..	..	..	..	..	..	..	..	1231	..	..	..	..		..	..	..	..	..	..	
Upper Halliford Halt	..	..	Arr. Epsom 12 10 p.m	..	12 3	..	..	..	..	..	..	..	..	..	..	..	..	1234	..	..	..	..		..	..	..	..	..	..	
Sunbury **L**	..	..		..	12 5	..	..	..	..	..	..	..	..	..	..	..	..	1236	..	..	..	..		..	..	..	..	..	..	
Hampton	..	..		..	12 9	..	..	..	..	..	..	..	..	..	..	..	..	1240	..	..	..	..		..	..	..	..	..	..	
Fulwell **K**	..	..		..	1213	..	..	..	V	..	..	..	..	..	..	..	..	1244	..	..	..	..		..	V	..	..	..	..	
Teddington J	..	..		..	1216	..	..	..	1225	..	..	..	..	..	..	..	..	1247	..	..	..	..		..	1255	..	..	..	..	
Hampton Wick	..	..		..	1219	..	..	..	1228	..	..	..	..	..	..	..	..	1250	..	..	..	..		..	1258	..	..	..	..	
Kingston	..	..		..	1221	..	..	..	1230	..	..	..	..	..	..	..	..	1252	..	..	..	..		..	1 0	..	..	..	..	
Norbiton **H**	..	..		..	1223	..	..	..	1232	..	..	..	..	..	..	..	..	1254	..	..	..	..	..	..	1 2	..	..	..	..	
Malden, for Coombe	..	..	..	..	1227	..	..	..	1236	1239	..	..	SO	..	..	..	1256	1258	..	..	..	..	..	..	1 6	..	..	..	1 16	
Bookham	..	1154	11 58	..	..	..	..	..	..	..	..	..	1213	1216	a.m	..	..	..	..	..	..	..	..	1241	..	..	..	..	..	SX
Horsham ....dep.	1143	..	..	..	..	..	..	..	..	..	..	..	..	..	11 52	..	..	..	..	..	..	..	1215	..	..	..	..	..	..	1220
Warnham	..	..	..	..	..	..	..	..	..	..	..	..	..	..	11 56	..	..	..	..	..	..	..	..	..	..	..	..	..	..	1224
Ockley, for Capel	..	..	..	..	..	..	..	..	..	..	..	..	..	..	12 3	..	..	..	..	..	..	..	..	..	..	..	..	..	..	1231
Holmwood **G**	..	..	..	..	..	..	SO	..	..	..	..	..	..	..	12 7	..	..	..	..	..	..	SO	..	..	..	..	..	..	..	1235
Dorking North F	12 2	..	..	..	..	..	12 8	..	..	..	..	..	..	..	12 18	..	..	..	..	..	..	1229	..	..	..	..	..	..	..	1246
Boxhill & Burford Bdg **D**	..	..	..	..	..	..	..	..	..	..	..	..	..	..	12 21	..	..	..	..	..	..	1232	..	..	..	..	..	..	..	1248
Leatherhead	..	1159	12 2	..	..	..	1214	..	..	..	..	..	1217	1220	12 26	..	..	..	..	..	..	1237	..	1246	..	..	..	..	..	1253
Ashtead	..	..	12 6	..	..	..	..	..	..	..	..	..	1221	1224	12 30	..	..	..	..	..	..	1241	..	1250	..	..	..	..	..	1257
Epsom **285**	..	..	12 14	..	..	..	1220	..	..	..	..	..	1225	1228	12 34	..	..	..	..	..	..	1245	..	1254	..	..	..	..	..	1 2
Sutton ....arr.	1220	..	12‡26	..	..	..	1229	..	..	..	..	..	1235	1238	12‡49	..	..	..	..	..	..	1255	..	1‡6	..	..	..	..	..	1 11
Victoria .... "	1240	..	12‡50	..	..	..	..	..	..	..	..	..	1*13	..	1‡13	..	..	..	..	..	..	1*31	1 21	1‡31	..	..	..	..	..	1*45
London Bridge ... "	..	..	..	..	..	..	1 0	..	..	..	..	..	1 2	1 7	..	..	..	..	..	..	..	1 22	1 36	1‡42	..	p.m	..	..	..	1 38
Ewell West **C**	..	..	12 17	..	..	..	..	..	..	..	..	..	..	..	12 37	..	..	..	..	..	..	..	..	1257	..	3	..	..	..	..
Stoneleigh	..	..	12 19	..	..	..	..	..	..	..	..	..	..	..	12 39	..	..	..	..	..	..	..	..	1259	..		..	..	..	..
Worcester Park	..	..	12 22	..	..	..	..	..	..	..	..	..	..	..	12 42	..	..	..	..	..	..	..	..	1 2	..	SO	..	..	..	..
Chessington South ¶ dp	..	..	..	..	..	..	..	1219	..	..	..	..	..	..	..	1239	..	..	..	..	..	..	..	..	..	1259	..	..	..	..
Chessington North	..	..	..	..	..	..	..	1221	..	..	..	..	..	..	..	1241	..	..	..	..	..	..	..	..	..	1 1	..	..	..	..
Tolworth	..	..	..	..	..	..	..	1224	..	..	..	..	..	..	..	1244	..	..	..	..	..	..	..	..	..	1 4	..	..	..	..
Malden Manor	..	..	..	..	..	..	..	1226	..	..	..	..	..	..	..	1246	..	..	..	..	..	..	..	..	..	1 6	..	..	..	..
Motspur Park	..	..	12 25	..	..	..	..	1230	..	..	..	..	..	..	12 45	1250	..	..	..	..	..	..	..	1 5	..	1 10	..	..	..	..
Raynes Park	..	..	..	..	1230	..	..	1233	1239	1242	..	..	..	..	..	1253	1259	1 1	..	..	..	..	..	..	1 9	1 13	..	..	1 19	..
Wimbledon 319, 320, 322	..	..	12 30	12SX32	1233	..	..	1236	1242	1245	12SX53	..	..	..	12 50	1256	1 2	1 4	..	..	..	..	..	1 10	1 12	1 16	..	..	1 22	..
Earlsfield **B**	..	..	..	..	1237	..	..	1239	1245	1249	..	..	..	..	..	1259	1 5	1 8	..	..	..	..	..	..	1 16	1 19	..	..	1 25	..
Clapham Junction A	..	..	..	..	1240	..	..	1243	1249	1252	..	..	..	..	..	1 3	1 9	1 11	..	..	..	..	..	..	1 19	1 23	..	..	1 29	..
Vauxhall	..	..	..	..	1245	..	..	1247	1253	1257	..	..	..	..	..	1 7	1 13	1 16	..	..	..	..	..	..	1 24	1 27	..	..	1 33	..
Waterloo ....arr.	..	..	12 42	12 43	1249	1246	..	1251	1257	1 1	1 4	1 1	..	..	1 3	1 11	1 17	1 20	1 16	1 19	1 21	..	..	1 22	1 28	1 31	1 24	1 30	1 38	..

FOR NOTES, SEE PAGE 459

GUILDFORD, WOKING, CHERTSEY, HAMPTON COURT, SHEPPERTON, KINGSTON, HORSHAM, DORKING NORTH, & LONDON

Week Days—continued (p.m)

Up	3	3	3	3	3	SO	3	3		3	3	3	3	3		3	3	3	3		3	3	3	3	3		3	3	3	SO 3	
Guildford dep.					12 50				1252										1 10	1 20						1 22				1 30	
Worplesdon									1259																	1 29					
Woking X 324, 389, 390									1 6											1 30						1 36					1 46
Byfleet W									1 10																	1 40					
West Weybridge								SX	1 13			SO												SO	SX	1 43					
Virginia Water Z dep.								1256				1 6												1 26	1 26						
Chertsey								1 1				1 11												1 31	1 34						
Addlestone								1 4				1 14												1 34	1 37						
Weybridge U 394								1 8	1 16			1 18												1 38	1 41	1 46					
Walton-on-Thames									1 20																	1 50					
Hersham									1 22																	1 52					
Esher, for Sandown Park									1 25																	1 55					
London Road (Guildford)					12 54								From Waterloo via Richmond Dep. Twickenham 1 19 p.m.						1 14		From Waterloo via Richmond Dep. Twickenham 1 29 p.m.									1 34	
Clandon T		From Waterloo via Richmond Dep. Twickenham 12 59 p.m.			12 59														1 19											1 39	
Horsley R			SO	SX	1 4											SO	SX		1 24										SO	1 44	
Effingham Junction			1252	1255	1 7											1 10	1 13		1 27										1 38	1 47	
Cobham Q					1 11														1 31											1 51	
Oxshott, for Fairmile					1 15														1 35											1 55	
Claygate, for Claremont					1 18														1 38											1 58	
Hinchley Wood					1 21														1 41											2 1	
Hampton Court dep.	Arr. Dorking North 12 45 p.m													1 25									1 43								
Thames Ditton														1 28									1 45								
Surbiton					1 25				1 30					1 33					1 45				1 50			2 0				2 5	
Berrylands N														1 36									1 53								
Shepperton dep.				Arr Epsom 1 10 p.m		Via Three Bridges, see page 204				1 0					Via Three Bridges, see page 204												1 31	Arr. Dorking North 1 26 p.m.			
Upper Halliford Halt										1 3																	1 34				
Sunbury L										1 5																	1 36				
Hampton										1 9																	1 40				
Fulwell K		V								1 13			V								SO V						1 44				
Teddington J		1 5								1 16			1 25								1 35						1 47				
Hampton Wick		1 8								1 19			1 28								1 38						1 50				
Kingston		1 12								1 21			1 30								1 40						1 52				
Norbiton H		1 14								1 23			1 32								1 42						1 54				
Malden, for Coombe		1 18								1 27			1 36	1 39							1 46		1 56				1 58				
Bookham	SO		1255	1258		SO										1 13	1 16											SO	1 41		
Horsham dep.	1220					1243									1248			12 52										1 3			
Warnham	1225																	12 56										1 7			
Ockley, for Capel	1232						SO											1 3										1 14			
Holmwood G	1237						1248											1 7										1 18			
Dorking North F	1248						1258											1 18										1 29			
Boxhill & Burford Bdg D	1251						1 1											1 21										1 32			
Leatherhead	1256		1 0	1 2			1 6									1 17	1 20	1 26										1 37	1 46		
Ashtead	1 0			1 6			1 10									1 21	1 24	1 30										1 41			
Epsom 285	1 4			1 14			1 14									1 25	1 28	1 34										1 45			
Sutton arr.	1 14			1‡38			1‡26									1 35	1 38	1‡49										1 55			
Victoria "	1*50					1 40	1‡50								2 7	2*11		2‡13										2‡30			
London Bridge "	1 42			2‡7												2 2	2 7											2 22			
Ewell West C				1 17			1 17											1 37													
Stoneleigh				1 19			1 19											1 39													
Worcester Park				1 22			1 22											1 42													
Chessington South ¶ dp											1 19											1 39									
Chessington North											1 21											1 41									
Tolworth											1 24											1 44									
Malden Manor											1 26											1 46									
Motspur Park				1 25			1 25				1 30							1 45				1 50									
Raynes Park		1 21								1 30	1 33		1 39	1 42							1 49	1 53	1 59				2 1				
Wimbledon 319, 320, 322		1 24		1 30	1SX32		1 30			1 33	1 36		1 42	1 45				1 49	1SX53		1 52	1 56	2 2				2 4				
Earlsfield B		1 28								1 37	1 39		1 45	1 49							1 56	1 59	2 5				2 8				
Clapham Junction A		1 31								1 40	1 43		1 49	1 52							1 59	2 3	2 9				2 11				
Vauxhall		1 36								1 45	1 47		1 53	1 57							2 4	2 7	2 13				2 16				
Waterloo arr.		1 40		1 42	1 43		1 42		1 46	1 49	1 51		1 57	2 1				2 3	2 4	2 1	2 8	2 11	2 17			2 16	2 20			2 21	2 19

GUILDFORD, WOKING, CHERTSEY, HAMPTON COURT, SHEPPERTON, KINGSTON, HORSHAM, DORKING NORTH, & LONDON

Up — Week Days—continued — p.m

Up	SX 3	3	3	3	3	3	3	3	3	3	3	3			3	3	3		3	3	3	3		3	3	3		3	SO 3	3	3
Guildford ... dep.	..	..	..	..	..	..	..	..	..	..	1 50	..	1 52	..	..	..	..	..	..	..	..	2 10	2 20	..	..	..	2 22	..	2 30	..	..
Worplesdon	..	..	..	..	..	..	..	..	..	..	..	..	1 59	..	..	..	..	..	..	..	..	..	..	..	..	..	2 29	..	..	..	..
Woking X 324, 389, 390	..	..	..	..	..	..	..	..	..	..	..	..	2 6	..	..	..	..	..	..	..	..	..	2 30	..	..	..	2 36	..	..	..	..
Byfleet W	..	..	..	..	..	..	..	..	..	..	..	..	2 10	..	..	..	..	..	..	..	..	..	..	..	..	..	2 40	..	..	..	..
West Weybridge	..	..	..	..	SO	..	..	SX	..	..	..	..	2 13	..	..	..	..	..	SO	..	..	..	..	..	..	..	2 43	..	..	..	..
Virginia Water Z ... dep.	..	..	..	..	1 46	..	..	1 56	..	..	..	..	..	..	..	..	..	..	2 9	..	..	..	..	..	..	2 26	..	..	..	..	..
Chertsey	..	..	..	..	1 51	..	..	2 1	..	..	..	..	..	..	..	..	..	..	2 16	..	..	..	..	..	..	2‡34	..	..	..	..	..
Addlestone	..	..	..	..	1 54	..	..	2 4	..	..	..	..	..	..	..	..	..	..	2 19	..	..	..	..	..	..	2‡37	..	..	..	..	..
Weybridge U 394	From Waterloo via Richmond Dep. Twickenham 1 49 p.m	..	..	From Waterloo via Richmond Dep. Twickenham 1 59 p.m	1 58	..	..	2 8	..	..	..	..	2 16	..	..	From Waterloo via Richmond Dep. Twickenham 2 19 p.m	..	..	2 23	..	..	..	..	..	..	2‡41	2 46	..	..	..	..
Walton-on-Thames		..	..		..	..	..	..	..	..	..	..	2 20	..	..		..	..	—	..	..	..	..	..	..	—	2 50	..	..	..	..
Hersham		..	..		..	..	..	..	..	..	..	..	2 22	..	..		..	..	Stop	..	..	..	..	..	..	Stop	2 52	..	..	..	..
Esher, for Sandown Park		..	..		..	..	..	..	..	..	..	..	2 25	..	..		..	..	p.m	..	..	..	..	..	..	..	2 55	..	..	..	..
London Road (Guildford)		..	..		..	..	..	..	..	..	1 54	..	..	..	..		..	..	3	..	..	2 14	..	..	..	..	..	..	2 34	From Waterloo via Richmond Dep. Twickenham 2 49 p.m	..
Clandon T		..	..		..	..	..	..	..	..	1 59	..	..	..	..		..	..	..	..	..	2 19	..	..	..	..	..	..	2 39		..
Horsley R		..	..		..	..	..	..	..	SX	2 4	..	..	..	..		..	..	SO	SX	..	2 24	..	..	..	..	..	..	2 44		..
Effingham Junction		..	..		..	..	..	..	..	1 55	2 7	..	..	..	..		..	..	2 10	2 13	..	2 27	..	..	..	..	..	..	2 47		..
Cobham Q		..	..		..	..	..	..	..	..	2 11	..	..	..	..		..	..	..	..	..	2 31	..	..	..	..	..	..	..		..
Oxshott, for Fairmile		..	..		..	..	..	..	..	..	2 15	..	..	..	..		..	..	..	..	..	2 35	..	..	..	..	..	..	..		..
Claygate, for Claremont		..	..		..	..	..	..	..	..	2 18	..	..	..	..		..	..	..	..	..	2 38	..	..	..	..	..	..	..		..
Hinchley Wood		..	SO		..	..	..	..	..	..	2 21	..	..	..	..		..	..	..	..	..	2 41	..	..	..	..	..	..	..		..
Hampton Court ... dep.		..	2 3		..	Arr. Dorking North 1 43 p.m.	Arr Dorking North 1 43 p.m.	..	..	..	..	..	..	..	..		2 25	Via Three Bridges see page 206	..	..	..	..	..	..	2 43	..	..	..	..		Arr. Dorking North 2 43 p.m
Thames Ditton		..	2 5		..			..	..	..	..	..	..	..	..		2 28		..	..	..	..	..	..	2 45	p.m	..	..	..		
Surbiton		..	2 10		..			..	..	..	2 25	..	2 30	..	..		2 33		..	..	..	2 45	..	..	2 50	3	3 0	..	..		
Berrylands N		..	2 13		..			..	..	..	..	..	..	..	..		2 36		..	..	..	..	..	..	2 53		..	..	..		
Shepperton ... dep.		..	..		..			..	..	..	..	2 1	..	..	..		..		..	..	..	..	..	..	..	2 31	..	..	..		
Upper Halliford Halt		..	..		..			..	..	..	..	2 4	..	..	..		..		..	..	..	..	..	..	..	2 34	..	..	..		
Sunbury L		..	..		..			..	..	..	..	2 6	..	..	..		..		..	..	..	..	..	..	..	2 36	..	..	..		
Hampton		..	..		..			..	..	..	..	2 10	..	..	..		..		..	..	..	..	..	..	..	2 40	..	..	..		
Fulwell K	▼	..	..	▼	..			..	..	..	..	2 14	..	..	..	▼	..		..	..	..	..	..	..	..	2 44	..	..	..	▼	
Teddington J	1 55	..	..	2 5	..			..	..	..	..	2 17	..	..	..	2 25	..		..	..	..	..	..	..	..	2 47	..	..	..	2 55	
Hampton Wick	1 58	..	..	2 8	..			..	..	..	..	2 20	..	..	..	2 28	..		..	..	..	..	..	..	..	2 50	..	..	..	2 58	
Kingston	2 0	..	..	2 12	..			..	Arr. Epsom 2 10 p.m	..	..	2 22	..	..	..	2 30	..		..	..	..	..	..	..	..	2 52	..	..	..	3 0	
Norbiton H	2 2	..	..	2 14	..			..		..	..	2 24	..	..	..	2 32	..	..	..	..	..	..	..	..	..	2 54	..	..	..	3 2	
Malden, for Coombe	2 6	..	2 16	2 18	..			..		..	..	2 28	..	..	..	2 36	2 39	..	..	..	..	..	..	..	2 56	2 58	..	..	..	3 6	
Bookham	..	..	..	..	..	SX	SO	..		1 58	..	..	..	SO	..	..	..	..	2 13	2 16	..	..	..	..	..	..	..	..	..	..	..
Horsham ... dep.	..	..	..	..	..	1 20	1 20	..		Arr Epsom 2 10 p.m.	..	..	..	1 43	..	..	..	1 48	..	..	1 52	..	..	..	..	..	..	..	..	..	2 20
Warnham	..	..	..	..	..	1 24	1 24	..			..	..	..	..	..	..	..	..	..	..	1 56	..	..	..	..	..	..	..	..	..	2 24
Ockley, for Capel	..	..	..	..	..	1 31	1 31	..	SO		..	..	..	..	..	..	..	..	..	..	2 3	..	..	..	..	..	..	SO	..	..	2 31
Holmwood G	..	..	..	..	..	1 35	1 35	..	1 45		..	..	..	..	..	..	..	..	..	..	2 7	..	..	..	..	..	..	2 30	..	..	2 35
Dorking North F	..	..	..	..	..	1 46	1 48	..	1 55		..	..	..	2 2	..	..	..	..	..	..	2 18	..	..	..	..	..	..	2 38	..	..	2 46
Boxhill & Burford Bdg D	..	..	..	..	..	1 48	1 51	..	1 57		..	..	..	..	..	..	..	..	..	..	2 21	..	..	..	..	..	..	2 41	..	..	2 48
Leatherhead	..	..	..	..	..	1 53	1 56	..	2 2	2 2	..	..	..	..	..	..	..	..	2 17	2 20	2 26	..	..	..	..	..	..	2 46	..	..	2 53
Ashtead	..	..	..	..	..	1 57	2 0	..	2 6	2 6	..	..	..	..	..	..	..	..	2 21	2 24	2 30	..	..	..	..	..	..	2 50	..	..	2 57
Epsom 285	..	..	..	..	..	2 2	2 5	..	2 14	2 14	..	..	..	..	..	..	..	..	2 25	2 28	2 34	..	..	..	..	..	..	2 54	..	..	3 2
Sutton ... arr.	..	..	..	..	..	2 11	2 14	..	2‡26	2‡26	..	..	..	2 20	..	..	..	..	2 35	2 38	2‡49	..	..	..	..	..	..	..	..	..	3 11
Victoria ... "	..	..	..	..	..	2*50	2*40	..	2‡50	2‡50	..	..	..	2 40	..	..	..	3 8	..	..	3‡13	..	..	..	..	..	..	..	..	..	3*40
London Bridge ... "	..	..	..	..	..	2 38	2 45	..	..	..	..	..	..	..	..	..	..	..	3 5	3 7	..	..	..	..	..	..	..	..	..	..	3 38
Ewell West C	..	..	..	..	..	..	..	..	2 17	2 17	..	..	..	..	..	..	..	..	..	..	2 37	..	..	..	..	..	..	2 57	..	..	..
Stoneleigh	..	..	..	..	..	..	..	..	2 19	2 19	..	..	..	..	..	..	..	..	..	..	2 39	..	..	..	..	..	..	2 59	..	..	..
Worcester Park	..	SO	..	..	..	..	..	..	2 22	2 22	..	..	..	..	..	..	..	..	..	..	2 42	..	..	..	..	..	..	3 2	..	..	..
Chessington South ¶ dp	..	1 59	..	..	..	..	..	..	..	..	..	..	..	..	2 19	..	..	..	..	..	..	..	..	2 39	..	..	..	..	..	..	..
Chessington North	..	2 1	..	..	..	..	..	..	..	..	..	..	..	..	2 21	..	..	..	..	..	..	..	..	2 41	..	..	..	..	..	..	..
Tolworth	..	2 4	..	..	..	..	..	..	..	..	..	..	..	..	2 24	..	..	..	..	..	..	..	..	2 44	..	..	..	..	..	..	..
Malden Manor	..	2 6	..	..	..	..	..	..	..	..	..	..	..	..	2 26	..	..	..	..	..	..	..	..	2 46	..	..	..	..	..	..	..
Motspur Park	..	2 10	..	..	..	..	..	..	2 25	2 25	..	..	..	..	2 30	..	..	..	..	..	2 45	..	..	2 50	..	..	..	3 5	..	..	..
Raynes Park	2 9	2 13	2 19	2 21	..	..	..	..	..	..	..	2 31	..	..	2 33	2 39	2 42	..	..	..	..	..	..	2 53	2 59	3 1	..	..	..	3 9	..
Wimbledon 319, 320, 322	2 12	2 16	2 22	2 24	..	..	..	..	2 30	2 30	2SX32	2 34	..	..	2 36	2 42	2 45	..	..	..	2 50	2SX53	..	2 56	3 2	3 4	..	3 10	..	3 12	..
Earlsfield B	2 16	2 19	2 25	2 28	..	..	..	..	..	..	..	2 37	..	..	2 40	2 45	2 49	..	..	..	..	..	..	2SX59	3 5	3 8	..	..	..	3 16	..
Clapham Junction A	2 19	2 23	2 29	2 31	..	..	..	..	..	..	..	2 41	..	..	2 43	2 49	2 52	..	..	..	..	..	..	3SX3	3 9	3 11	..	..	..	3 19	..
Vauxhall	2 24	2 27	2 33	2 36	..	..	..	..	..	..	..	2 45	..	..	2 48	2 53	2 57	..	..	..	..	..	..	3SX7	3 13	3 16	..	..	..	3 24	..
Waterloo ... arr.	2 28	2 31	2 38	2 40	..	..	..	..	2 42	2 42	2 43	2 49	2 46	..	2 52	2 57	3 1	..	..	..	3 3	3 4	3 1	3SX11	3 17	3 20	3 16	3 23	..	3 28	..

FOR NOTES, SEE PAGE 459

FOR NOTES, SEE PAGE 459

GUILDFORD, WOKING, CHERTSEY, HAMPTON COURT, SHEPPERTON, KINGSTON, HORSHAM, DORKING NORTH, & LONDON

Week Days—*continued* — p.m.

Up	3	3	3		3	3	3	3			3		3	3	3	3
Guildford ......dep	..	..	..	2 50	..	..	..	..	2 52	..	..	..	..	..	..	..
Worplesdon	..	..	..	3	..	..	..	..	2 59	..	..	..	..	..	..	..
Woking X 324, 389, 390	..	..	..		..	..	..	..	3 6	3 12	..	..	..	..	..	..
Byfleet W	..	..	..	..	..	..	..	..	3 10	..	..	..	..	..	..	..
West Weybridge	..	..	..	..	..	..	S O	S X	3 13	..	..	..	..	..	S O	..
Virginia Water Z ..dep.	..	..	..	..	..	..	2 46	2 56	..	..	..	..	..	..	3 9	..
Chertsey	..	..	..	..	..	..	2 51	3 2	..	..	..	..	..	..	3 14	..
Addlestone	..	..	..	..	..	..	2 54	3 5	..	..	..	..	..	..	3 17	..
Weybridge U 394	..	From Waterloo via Richmond Dep. Twickenham 2 59 p.m	..	..	..	..	2 58	3 9	3 16	..	From Waterloo via Richmond Dep. Twickenham 3 19 p.m	..	..	..	3 22	..
Walton-on-Thames	..		..	..	..	..	..	..	3 20	..		..	..	..	..	..
Hersham	..		..	..	..	..	..	..	3 22	..		..	..	..	..	..
Esher, for Sandown Park	..		..	..	..	..	..	..	3 25	..		..	..	..	..	..
London Road (Guildford)	..		..	2 54	..	..	..	..	..	..		..	..	..	..	..
Clandon T	..		..	2 59	..	..	..	..	..	..		..	..	..	..	..
Horsley R	..		..	3 4	..	..	..	..	..	..		..	S X	S O	..	..
Effingham Junction	..		2 55	3 7	..	..	..	..	..	..		..	3 10	3 12	..	..
Cobham Q	..		..	3 11	..	..	..	..	..	..		..	..	..	..	..
Oxshott, for Fairmile	..		..	3 15	..	..	..	..	..	..		..	..	..	..	..
Claygate, for Claremont	..		..	3 18	..	..	..	..	..	..		..	..	..	..	..
Hinchley Wood	..		..	3 21	..	..	..	..	..	..		..	..	..	..	..
Hampton Court ...dep.	..		Arr Epsom 3 10 p.m	..	..	..	..	..	..	..		..	..	..	..	3 25
Thames Ditton	..			..	..	..	..	..	..	..		..	..	..	..	3 28
Surbiton	..			3 25	..	..	..	..	3 30	..		..	..	..	..	3 34
Berrylands N	..			..	..	..	..	..	..	..		..	..	..	..	3 36
Shepperton ......dep.	..			..	3 0	..	..	..	..	..		..	..	..	..	..
Upper Halliford Halt	..			..	3 3	..	..	..	..	..		..	..	..	..	..
Sunbury L	..			..	3 5	..	..	..	..	..		..	..	..	..	..
Hampton	..			..	3 9	..	..	..	..	..		..	..	..	..	..
Fulwell K	..	V		..	3 13	..	..	..	..	..	V	..	..	..	..	..
Teddington J	..	3 7		..	3 16	..	..	..	..	..	3 25	..	..	..	..	..
Hampton Wick	..	3 10		..	3 19	..	..	..	..	..	3 28	..	..	..	..	..
Kingston	..	3 12		..	3 21	..	..	..	..	..	3 30	..	..	..	..	..
Norbiton H	..	3 14		..	3 23	..	..	..	..	..	3 32	..	..	..	..	..
Malden, for Coombe	..	3 18	..	..	3 27	..	..	..	..	..	3 36	..	..	..	..	3 39
Bookham	..	..	2 58	..	..	..	..	..	..	..	..	..	3 13	3 15	..	..
Horsham ......dep	..	..	..	..	..	..	..	..	..	..	..	2 43	..	..	..	..
Warnham	..	..	..	..	..	..	..	..	..	..	..	..	..	..	..	..
Ockley, for Capel	..	..	..	..	..	..	..	..	..	..	..	..	..	..	..	..
Holmwood G	..	..	..	..	..	..	..	..	..	..	..	..	..	..	..	..
Dorking North F	..	..	..	..	..	..	..	..	..	..	..	3 2	..	..	..	..
Boxhill & Burford Bdg D	..	..	..	..	..	..	..	..	..	..	..	..	..	..	..	..
Leatherhead	..	..	3 2	..	..	..	..	..	..	..	..	..	3 17	3 19	..	..
Ashtead	..	..	3 6	..	..	..	..	..	..	..	..	..	3 21	3 23	..	..
Epsom 285	..	..	3 14	..	..	..	..	..	..	..	..	..	3 26	3 28	..	..
Sutton ......arr.	..	..	3‡27	..	..	..	..	..	..	..	..	3 20	3 35	3 37	..	..
Victoria ...... "	..	..	3‡51	..	..	..	..	..	..	..	..	3 40	4‡14	4‡14	..	..
London Bridge .... "	..	..	..	..	..	..	..	..	..	..	..	..	4 4	4 7	..	..
Ewell West C	..	..	3 17	..	..	..	..	..	..	..	..	..	..	..	..	..
Stoneleigh	..	..	3 19	..	..	..	..	..	..	..	..	..	..	..	..	..
Worcester Park	S O	..	3 22	..	..	..	..	..	..	..	..	..	..	..	..	..
Chessington South ¶ dp.	2 59	..	..	..	..	3 19	..	..	..	..	..	..	..	..	..	..
Chessington North	3 1	..	..	..	..	3 21	..	..	..	..	..	..	..	..	..	..
Tolworth	3 4	..	..	..	..	3 24	..	..	..	..	..	..	..	..	..	..
Malden Manor	3 6	..	..	..	..	3 26	..	..	..	..	..	..	..	..	..	..
Motspur Park	3 10	..	3 25	..	..	3 30	..	..	..	..	..	..	..	..	..	..
Raynes Park	3 13	3 21	..	..	3 30	3 33	..	..	..	..	3 39	..	..	..	..	3 42
Wimbledon 319, 320, 322	3 16	3 24	3 30	3 32	3 33	3 36	..	..	..	..	3 42	..	..	..	..	3 45
Earlsfield B	..	3 28	..	..	3 37	3 39	..	..	..	..	3 45	..	..	..	..	3 49
Clapham Junction A	..	3 31	..	..	3 40	3 43	..	..	..	..	3 49	..	..	..	..	3 52
Vauxhall	..	3 36	..	..	3 45	3 47	..	..	..	..	3 53	..	..	..	..	3 57
Waterloo ......arr.	..	3 40	3 41	3 43	3 50	3 51	..	..	3 46	3 49	3 57	..	..	..	..	4 1

Up	3	3	S O	3	3	3		3	3	3	S O	3	3	3	3
Guildford ......dep	..	3 10	3 20	..	..	..	3 22	..	..	..	3 30	..	..	..	..
Worplesdon	..	3	..	..	..	..	3 29	..	..	..	3	..	..	..	..
Woking X 324, 389, 390	..		3 30	..	..	..	3 36	..	..	..		..	..	..	..
Byfleet W	..	..	..	..	..	..	3 40	..	..	..	..	..	..	..	..
West Weybridge	..	..	..	..	..	..	3 43	..	..	..	..	..	..	..	..
Virginia Water Z ..dep.	..	..	..	..	..	3 26	..	..	..	..	..	..	..	..	..
Chertsey	..	..	..	..	..	3 32	..	..	..	..	..	..	..	..	..
Addlestone	..	..	..	..	..	3 35	..	..	..	..	..	..	..	..	..
Weybridge U 394	..	..	..	..	..	3 39 Stop	3 46	From Waterloo via Richmond Dep. Twickenham 3 49 p.m	..	..	..	..	..	From Waterloo via Richmond Dep. Twickenham 3 59 p.m	..
Walton-on-Thames	..	..	..	..	..		3 50		..	..	..	..	..		..
Hersham	..	..	..	..	..		3 52		..	..	..	..	..		..
Esher, for Sandown Park	..	..	..	..	..	..	3 55		..	..	..	..	..		..
London Road (Guildford)	..	3 14	..	..	..	..	..		..	..	3 33	..	..		Arr. Dorking North 3 43 p.m
Clandon T	..	3 19	..	..	..	..	..		..	..	3 39	..	..		
Horsley R	..	3 24	..	..	..	..	..		S X	S X	3 44	..	..		
Effingham Junction	..	3 27	..	..	..	..	..		3 38	3 46	3 47	..	..		
Cobham Q	..	3 31	..	..	..	..	..		..	3 50	3 51	..	..		
Oxshott, for Fairmile	..	3 35	..	..	..	..	..		..	3 54	3 55	..	..		
Claygate, for Claremont	..	3 38	..	..	..	..	..		..	3 57	3 58	..	..		
Hinchley Wood	..	3 41	..	..	..	..	..		..	4 0	4 1	..	S X		
Hampton Court ...dep.	..	..	..	..	3 43	..	..		..	..	..	..	4 3		
Thames Ditton	..	..	..	..	3 45	p.m.	..		..	..	..	..	4 5		
Surbiton	..	3 45	..	..	3 50	3	4 0		..	4 4	4 5	..	4 10		
Berrylands N	..	..	..	..	3 53		..		..	..	..	..	4 13		
Shepperton ......dep.	..	..	..	..	..	3 31	..		..	..	..	..	..		
Upper Halliford Halt	..	..	..	..	..	3 34	..		..	..	..	..	..		
Sunbury L	..	..	..	..	..	3 36	..		..	..	..	..	..		
Hampton	..	..	..	..	..	3 40	..		..	..	..	..	..		
Fulwell K	..	..	..	..	..	3 44	..	V	..	..	..	..	..	V	
Teddington J	..	..	..	..	..	3 47	..	3 55	..	..	..	..	..	4 7	
Hampton Wick	..	..	..	..	..	3 50	..	3 58	..	..	..	..	..	4 10	
Kingston	..	..	..	..	..	3 52	..	4 0	..	..	..	..	..	4 12	
Norbiton H	..	..	..	..	..	3 54	..	4 2	..	..	..	..	..	4 14	
Malden, for Coombe	..	..	..	..	3 56	3 58	..	4 6	..	..	..	..	4 16	4 18	..
Bookham	..	..	..	..	..	..	..	..	3 41	..	..	..	..	..	..
Horsham ......dep	2 52	..	..	..	..	..	..	..	..	..	..	..	..	..	3 20
Warnham	2 56	..	..	..	..	..	..	..	..	..	..	..	..	..	3 24
Ockley, for Capel	3 3	..	..	..	..	..	..	..	..	..	..	..	..	..	3 31
Holmwood G	3 7	..	..	..	..	..	..	..	..	..	..	..	..	..	3 35
Dorking North F	3 18	..	..	..	..	..	..	..	..	..	..	..	..	..	3 46
Boxhill & Burford Bdg D	3 21	..	..	..	..	..	..	..	..	..	..	..	..	..	3 48
Leatherhead	3 26	..	..	..	..	..	..	..	3 46	..	..	..	..	..	3 53
Ashtead	3 30	..	..	..	..	..	..	..	3 50	..	..	..	..	..	3 57
Epsom 285	3 34	..	..	..	..	..	..	..	3 54	..	..	..	..	..	4 1
Sutton ......arr.	3‡49	..	..	..	..	..	..	..	4‡5	..	..	..	..	..	4 11
Victoria ...... "	4‡14	..	..	..	..	..	..	..	4‡30	..	..	..	..	..	4‡50
London Bridge .... "	..	..	..	..	..	..	..	..	4‡39	..	..	..	..	..	4 39
Ewell West C	3 37	..	..	..	..	..	..	..	3 57	..	..	..	..	..	..
Stoneleigh	3 39	..	..	..	..	..	..	..	3 59	..	..	..	..	..	..
Worcester Park	3 42	..	..	..	..	..	..	..	4 2	..	..	S X	..	..	..
Chessington South ¶ dp.	..	..	..	3 39	..	..	..	..	..	..	..	3 59	..	..	..
Chessington North	..	..	..	3 41	..	..	..	..	..	..	..	4 1	..	..	..
Tolworth	..	..	..	3 44	..	..	..	..	..	..	..	4 4	..	..	..
Malden Manor	..	..	..	3 46	..	..	..	..	..	..	..	4 6	..	..	..
Motspur Park	3 45	..	..	3 50	..	..	..	..	4 5	..	..	4 10	..	..	..
Raynes Park	..	..	..	3 53	3 59	4 1	..	4 9	..	..	..	4 13	4 19	4 21	..
Wimbledon 319, 320, 322	3 50	3 53	..	3 56	4 2	4 4	..	4 12	4 10	4 11	4 12	4 16	4 22	4 24	..
Earlsfield B	..	..	..	3 59	4 5	4 8	..	4 16	..	..	..	4 19	4 25	4 28	..
Clapham Junction A	..	..	..	4 3	4 9	4 11	..	4 19	..	..	..	4 23	4 29	4 31	..
Vauxhall	..	..	..	4 7	4 13	4 16	..	4 24	..	..	..	4 27	4 33	4 36	..
Waterloo ......arr.	4 3	4 5	4 1	4 11	4 18	4 21	4 16	4 29	4 23	4 22	..	4 31	4 38	4 41	..

GUILDFORD, WOKING, CHERTSEY, HAMPTON COURT, SHEPPERTON, KINGSTON, HORSHAM, DORKING NORTH, & LONDON

Up — **Week Days**—*continued* — p.m

Up	(3)	(3)	(3)	(3)		(3)	(3)		(3)		(3)	(3)		(3)	(3)	
Guildford dep					3 50			3 52					4 10			420
Worplesdon								3 59								
Woking X 324, 389, 390					(3)			4 6					(3)			430
Byfleet W								4 10								
West Weybridge								4 13								
Virginia Water Z dep.						3 56										
Chertsey						4 2										
Addlestone						4 5										
Weybridge U 394						4 9		4 16								
Walton-on-Thames						Stop		4 20								
Hersham							From Waterloo via Richmond Dep. Twickenham 4 19 p.m	4 22							From Waterloo via Richmond Dep. Twickenham 4 29 p.m	
Esher, for Sandown Park								4 25								
London Road (Guildford)					3 54								4 13			
Clandon T					3 59								4 19			
Horsley R		SO			4 4						SX	SO	4 24			
Effingham Junction		3 55			4 8						4 10	4 12	4 28			
Cobham Q					4 12								4 32			
Oxshott, for Fairmile					4 16								4 36			
Claygate, for Claremont					4 19								4 39			
Hinchley Wood					4 22								4 42			
Hampton Court dep.									4 25							
Thames Ditton									4 28							
Surbiton					4 26			4 30	4 33				4 46			
Berrylands N									4 36							
Shepperton dep.				4 0												
Upper Halliford Halt		Arr. Epsom 4 10 p.m		4 3												
Sunbury L				4 5						Via Three Bridges, see page 208						
Hampton				4 9											SX	
Fulwell K				4 13			V								V	
Teddington J				4 16			4 25								4 35	
Hampton Wick				4 19			4 28								4 38	
Kingston				4 21			4 30								4 43	
Norbiton H				4 23			4 32								4 45	
Malden, for Coombe				4 27			4 36		4 39						4 49	
Bookham		3 58									4 13	4 15				
Horsham dep.										3 48				3 52		
Warnham														3 56		
Ockley, for Capel			SO											4 3		
Holmwood G	SX		3 55											4 7		
Dorking North F	3 58		4 3											4 18		
Boxhill & Burford Bdg D	4 1		4 6											4 21		
Leatherhead	4 6	4 2	4 10								4 17	4 20		4 26		
Ashtead	4 10	4 6									4 21	4 24		4 30		
Epsom 285	4 14	4 14									4 25	4 28		4 34		
Sutton arr.		4‡25									4 34	4 37		4h‡45		
Victoria "		4‡50								5SO7	5*9	5*13		5h‡9		
London Bridge "										5SX3	5 2	5 7				
Ewell West C	4 17	4 17				p.m								4 37		
Stoneleigh	4 19	4 19				(3)								4 39		
Worcester Park	4 22	4 22												4 43		
Chessington South ¶ dp						4 19										
Chessington North						4 21										
Tolworth						4 24										
Malden Manor						4 26										
Motspur Park	4 25	4 25				4 30								4 46		
Raynes Park				4 30		4 33	4 39		4 42						4 52	
Wimbledon 319, 320, 322	4 30	4 30		4 33	4 33	4 36	4 42		4 45				4SO53	4 51	4 55	
Earlsfield B				4 37		4 39	4 45		4 49						4 58	
Clapham Junction A				4 40		4 43	4 49		4 52						5 2	
Vauxhall				4 45		4 47	4 53		4 57						5 6	
Waterloo arr.	4 43	4 43		4 49	4 44	4 51	4 57	4 46	5 1				5 5	5 4	5 11	5 3

Up	(3)	(3)		(3)	(3)	(3)		(3)	(3)	(3)	(3)	(3)	(3)	(3)		(3)
Guildford dep			4 22				SX 4 30									
Worplesdon			4 29													
Woking X 324, 389, 390			4 36				(3)								4 58	
Byfleet W			4 40													
West Weybridge			4 43													
Virginia Water Z dep.	4 27															
Chertsey	4 32															
Addlestone	4 35															
Weybridge U 394	4 39		4 46													
Walton-on-Thames	Stop		4 50													
Hersham			4 52					From Waterloo via Richmond Dep. Twickenham 4 49 p.m								From Waterloo via Richmond Dep. Twickenham 4 59 p.m
Esher, for Sandown Park			4 55													
London Road (Guildford)							4 33									
Clandon T							4 39									
Horsley R						SX	4 44						SX			
Effingham Junction						4 38	4 48						4 51			
Cobham Q							4 52									
Oxshott, for Fairmile							4 56									
Claygate, for Claremont							4 59									
Hinchley Wood							5 2							SX		
Hampton Court dep.		4 43												5 1		
Thames Ditton		4 45												5 3		
Surbiton		4 50	5 0				5 6							5 10	5 15	
Berrylands N		4 53												5 13		
Shepperton dep.				4 31							Arr. Dorking North 4 43 p.m	Arr. Dorking North 4 43 p.m				
Upper Halliford Halt				4 34												
Sunbury L				4 36												
Hampton				4 40												
Fulwell K				4 44				V		SX						V
Teddington J				4 47				4 55		5 0						5 5
Hampton Wick				4 50				4 58		5 3						5 8
Kingston				4 52				5 0		5 5						5 12
Norbiton H				4 54				5 2		5 7						5 14
Malden, for Coombe		4 56		4 58				5 6		5 11				5 16		5 18
Bookham						4 41					SO	SX	4 54			
Horsham dep.											4 20	4 20				
Warnham											4 24	4 24				
Ockley, for Capel											4 31	4 31				
Holmwood G					SX						4 35	4 35				
Dorking North F					4 29						4 46	4 48				
Boxhill & Burford Bdg D					4 32						4 48	4 50				
Leatherhead					4 37	4 46					4 53	4 55	4 59			
Ashtead					4 41	4 50					4 57	5 0				
Epsom 285					4 45	4 54					5 1	5 5				
Sutton arr.					4 55	5‡7					5 11	5 15				
Victoria "					5*31	5‡31					5*43	5*43				
London Bridge "					5 22	5‡42					5 38	5 42				
Ewell West C	p.m					4 57										
Stoneleigh	(3)					4 59										
Worcester Park						5 2			SX							
Chessington South ¶ dp	4 39								4 59							
Chessington North	4 41								5 1							
Tolworth	4 44								5 4							
Malden Manor	4 46								5 6							
Motspur Park	4 50					5 5			5 10							
Raynes Park	4 54	4 59		5 1				5 9	5 13	5 15				5 19		5 21
Wimbledon 319, 320, 322	4 57	5 2		5 4		5 10		5 12	5 16	5 18				5 22		5 24
Earlsfield B	5 1	5 5		5 8				5 16	5 19	5 22				5 25		5 28
Clapham Junction A	5 4	5 9		5 11				5 19	5 23	5 25				5 29		5 31
Vauxhall	5 9	5 13		5 16				5 24	5 27	5 30				5 33		5 36
Waterloo arr.	5 14	5 18	5 16	5 20		5 23	5 22	5 28	5 31	5 34				5 38	5 35	5 40

FOR NOTES SEE PAGE 459

FOR NOTES, SEE PAGE 459

GUILDFORD, WOKING, CHERTSEY, HAMPTON COURT, SHEPPERTON, KINGSTON, HORSHAM, DORKING NORTH, & LONDON

Week Days—continued (p.m)

Up	(3)	(3)			(3)	(3)	(3)	(3)	(3)		(3)	SX		(3)	(3)	
Guildford dep.			4 50							4 52						5 10
Worplesdon										4 59						
Woking X 324, 389, 390			(3)							5 6		5 19				(3)
Byfleet W										5 10						
West Weybridge										5 13						
Virginia Water Z dep.							4 57									
Chertsey							5 2									
Addlestone							5 5									
Weybridge U 394							5 9		From Waterloo via Richmond Dep. Twickenham 5 19 p.m	5 16		5 26				
Walton-on-Thames										5 20		5 30				
Hersham							Stop			5 22						
Esher, for Sandown Park										5 25						
London Road (Guildford)			4 54												—	5 14
Clandon T			4 59													5 19
Horsley R		SO	5 4													5 24
Effingham Junction		4 55	5 7			5 12										5 27
Cobham Q			5 11													5 31
Oxshott, for Fairmile			5 15													5 35
Claygate, for Claremont			5 18													5 28
Hinchley Wood			5 21													5 41
Hampton Court dep.											5 25					
Thames Ditton											5 28					
Surbiton			5 25							5 30	5 33	5 37				5 45
Berrylands N											5 36					
Shepperton dep.	Arr. Dorking 4 52 p.m Arr. Epsom 5 10 p.m				5 0											
Upper Halliford Halt					5 3											
Sunbury L					5 5		—									
Hampton					5 9		—									
Fulwell K					5 13			SX	V							
Teddington J					5 16			5 20	5 25							
Hampton Wick					5 19			5 23	5 28							
Kingston					5 21			5 25	5 30							
Norbiton H					5 23			5 27	5 32							
Malden, for Coombe					5 27			5 31	5 36		5 39					
Bookham		4 58				5 15							SX		SX	
Horsham dep		Arr Epsom 5 10 p.m		443									4 48	4SO52	5 2	
Warnham														4SO56	5 6	
Ockley for Capel	SX													5 SO 3	5 13	
Holmwood G	4 45													5 SO 7	5 17	
Dorking North F	4 55			5 2									5 8	5 18	5 26	
Boxhill & Burford Bdg D	4 57													5 21		
Leatherhead	5 2	5 2				5 19							5 14	5 26		
Ashtead	5 6	5 6				5 23								5 30		
Epsom 285	5 14	5 14				5 27							5 20	5 34		
Sutton arr.	5‡26	5‡26		520		5 35							5 29	5‡46		
Victoria "	5‡50	5‡50		543		6‡10								6‡10		
London Bridge "						6 Y 2							6 0			
Ewell West C	5 17	5 17					p.m							5 37		
Stoneleigh	5 19	5 19					(3)							5 39		
Worcester Park	5 22	5 22												5 42		
Chessington South ¶dp							5 19									
Chessington North							5 21									
Tolworth							5 24									
Malden Manor							5 26									
Motspur Park	5 25	5 25					5 30							5 45		
Raynes Park					5 30		5 33	5 35	5 39		5 42			5SX48		
Wimbledon 319, 320, 322	5 30	5 30	5SO32		5 33		5 36	5 38	5 42		5 45	5 44		5 50		5S52
Earlsfield B					5 37		5 39	5 42	5 45		5 49					
Clapham Junction A					5 40		5 43	5 45	5 49		5 52					
Vauxhall					5 45		5 47	5 50	5 53		5 57					
Waterloo arr.	5 43	5 43	5 44		5 49		5 51	5 54	5 57	5 46	6 1	5 55		6 3		6 4

Up	(3)		(3)	(3)	(3)		(3)	(3)	(3)	SX	(3)	(3)	(3)	(3)	(3)
Guildford dep.		520				5 22				5 30					
Worplesdon						5 29				(3)					
Woking X 324, 389, 390		530				5 36									
Byfleet W						5 40									
West Weybridge						5 43									
Virginia Water Z dep.				5 27											
Chertsey				5 32											
Addlestone				5 35											
Weybridge U 394	From Waterloo via Richmond Dep. Twickenham 5 29 p.m.			5 39		5 46									
Walton-on-Thames						5 50									
Hersham				Stop		5 52									
Esher, for Sandown Park						5 55									
London Road (Guildford)										5 34	From Waterloo via Richmond Dep. Twickenham 5 49 p.m.				
Clandon T										5 39					
Horsley R										5 44					
Effingham Junction									5 38	5 47					
Cobham Q										5 51					
Oxshott, for Fairmile										5 55					
Claygate, for Claremont										5 58					
Hinchley Wood										6 1				SX	
Hampton Court dep.							5 43							6 3	
Thames Ditton							5 45							6 5	
Surbiton						6 0	5 50			6 5				6 10	
Berrylands N							5 53							6 13	
Shepperton dep.								5 31							
Upper Halliford Halt								5 34							
Sunbury L								5 36							
Hampton	SX							5 40							
Fulwell K	V							5 44			V				
Teddington J	5 35							5 47			5 55				
Hampton Wick	5 38							5 50			5 58				
Kingston	5 42							5 52			6 0				
Norbiton H	5 44							5 54			6 2				
Malden, for Coombe	5 48						5 56	5 58			6 6			6 16	
Bookham									5 41						SO
Horsham dep												—			5 20
Warnham												—			5 24
Ockley for Capel										—		—			5 31
Holmwood G					SX					—		—			5 35
Dorking North F				p.m	5 29					—					5 46
Boxhill & Burford Bdg D					5 32										5 48
Leatherhead				(3)	5 37				5 46						5 53
Ashtead				SX	5 41				5 50				SX		5 57
Epsom 285				5 42	5 45				5 54				6 2		6 2
Sutton arr.					5 55				6‡SX6						6 11
Victoria "					6‡34				6‡SX33						6*40
London Bridge "					6 22				6‡B45						6 41
Ewell West C				5 46					5 57				6 5		
Stoneleigh				5 49					5 59				6 7		
Worcester Park				5 52					6 2			SX	6 10		
Chessington South ¶dp			5 39									5 59			
Chessington North			5 41									6 1			
Tolworth			5 44									6 4			
Malden Manor			5 46									6 6			
Motspur Park			5 51	5 54					6 5			6 10	6 13		
Raynes Park	5 51		5 54	5 57			6 0	6 2			6 9	6 13	6 16	6 19	
Wimbledon 319, 320, 322	5 54		5 57	6 0			6 3	6 5	6 10		6 12	6 16	6 19	6 22	
Earlsfield B	5 57		6 0				6 6	6 9		—	6 16	6 19	6 23	6 25	
Clapham Junction A	6 1		6 4	6 6			6 10	6 12			6 19	6 23	6 26	6 29	
Vauxhall	6 5		6 8				6 14	6 17			6 24	6 27	6 31	6 33	
Waterloo arr.	6 9	6 1	6 12	6 14		6 18	6 18	6 21	6 23	6 21	6 29	6 31	6 35	6 37	

GUILDFORD, WOKING, CHERTSEY, HAMPTON COURT, SHEPPERTON, KINGSTON, HORSHAM, DORKING NORTH, & LONDON

Up — **Week Days**—*continued* — p.m.

Up	(3)	(3)	(3)	(3)		(3)		(3)	(3)		(3)	(3)	(3)	(3)	(3)	(3)
Guildford dep.	..	..	..	..	5 50	..	5 52	..	..	..	..	..	..	..	..	..
Worplesdon	..	..	..	..	(3)	..	5 59	..	..	..	..	..	..	..	..	..
Woking X 324, 389, 390	..	..	..	..		..	6 6	..	..	..	..	..	..	..	..	..
Byfleet **W**	..	..	..	..	..	..	6 10	..	..	..	..	..	..	..	..	..
West Weybridge	..	..	..	SX	..	SO	6 13	..	..	..	..	..	..	..	..	..
Virginia Water Z dep.	..	..	..	5 46	..	5 56	..	..	..	..	..	..	..	..	..	..
Chertsey	..	..	..	5 51	..	6 1	..	..	..	..	..	..	..	..	..	..
Addlestone	..	..	..	5 54	..	6 4	..	..	..	..	..	..	..	..	..	..
Weybridge U 394	..	From Waterloo via Richmond Dep. Twickenham 5 59 p.m.	..	5 58	..	6 8	6 16	..	..	..	..	From Waterloo via Richmond Dep. Twickenham 6 19 p.m.	..	..	..	..
Walton-on-Thames	..		..	—	..	..	6 20	..	..	..	..		..	..	..	..
Hersham	..		..	Stop	..	..	6 22	..	..	..	..		..	..	..	..
Esher, for Sandown Park	..		..	..	..	..	6 25	..	..	..	..		..	..	..	..
London Road (Guildford)	..		..	..	5 54	..	..	..	..	..	..		..	..	..	..
Clandon **T**	..		..	..	5 59	..	..	..	..	..	..		..	..	..	..
Horsley **R**	..		SX	..	6 4	..	..	..	..	..	..		..	..	SO	..
Effingham Junction	..		5 51	..	6 7	..	..	..	..	..	..		..	..	6 12	..
Cobham **Q**	..		..	..	6 11	..	..	..	..	..	..		..	..	..	..
Oxshott, for Fairmile	..		..	..	6 15	..	..	..	..	..	..		..	..	..	..
Claygate, for Claremont	..		..	..	6 18	..	..	..	..	..	..		..	..	..	..
Hinchley Wood	..		..	..	6 21	..	..	..	..	..	..		..	..	..	..
Hampton Court dep.	Arr. Dorking North 5 44 p.m.		..	..	..	..	..	..	..	..	..		6 25	..	..	..
Thames Ditton			..	..	..	..	..	..	..	..	..		6 28	..	..	..
Surbiton			..	..	6 25	..	6 30	..	..	..	..		6 33	..	..	..
Berrylands **N**			..	..	..	..	..	..	..	..	..		6 36	SX	..	..
Shepperton dep.			..	..	..	..	..	..	6 2	..	..		..	6 14	..	..
Upper Halliford Halt			..	..	..	..	..	..	6 5	..	..		..	6 17	..	..
Sunbury **L**			..	..	..	..	..	..	6 7	..	..		..	6 19	..	..
Hampton			..	..	..	..	..	..	6 11	..	..		..	6 23	..	..
Fulwell **K**		V	..	..	..	..	..	..	6 15	..	..	V	..	6 27	..	..
Teddington J		6 5	..	..	..	..	..	..	6 18	..	..	6 25	..	To Strawberry Hill arr. 6 30 p.m.	..	..
Hampton Wick		6 8	..	..	..	..	..	..	6 21	..	..	6 28	..		..	..
Kingston		6 12	..	..	..	..	..	..	6 23	..	..	6 30	..		..	..
Norbiton **H**		6 14	..	..	..	..	..	..	6 25	..	..	6 32	..		..	..
Malden, for Coombe		6 18	..	..	..	..	..	..	6 29	..	..	6 36	6 39		..	..
Bookham	SX	..	5 54	p.m	..	..	..	..	..	..	..	..	..		6 15	..
Horsham dep.	5 20	..	..		..	..	..	..	..	5 43	..	..	..		..	5 52
Warnham	5 24	..	..	(3)	..	..	..	..	..	..	..	..	..		..	5 56
Ockley, for Capel	5 31	..	..	SX	..	..	..	..	..	..	..	..	..		..	6 3
Holmwood **G**	5 35	..	..	5 45	..	..	..	..	..	..	..	..	..		..	6 7
Dorking North F	5 48	..	..	5 55	..	..	..	..	..	6 2	..	..	..		..	6 18
Boxhill & Burford Bdg **D**	5 51	..	..	5 57	..	..	..	..	..	..	..	..	..		..	6 21
Leatherhead	5 56	..	5 59	6 2	..	..	..	..	..	..	..	..	..		6 19	6 26
Ashtead	6 0	..	..	6 6	..	..	..	..	..	..	SX	..	..		6 23	6 30
Epsom 285	6 5	..	..	6b14	..	..	..	..	..	..	6 22	..	..		6 28	6 34
Sutton arr.	6 14	..	..	6‡26	..	..	..	..	..	6 20	..	..	..	..	6 37	6h‡46
Victoria "	6*40	..	..	6‡50	..	..	..	..	..	6 40	..	..	..	..	..	7‡11
London Bridge "	6 42	..	..	..	..	..	..	..	..	..	..	..	..	..	7 7	..
Ewell West **C**	..	..	..	6 17	..	..	..	..	..	..	6 25	..	..	..	..	6 37
Stoneleigh	..	..	..	6 19	..	..	..	..	..	..	6 27	..	..	..	..	6 39
Worcester Park	..	..	..	6 22	..	..	..	..	..	..	6 30	..	..	..	..	6 42
Chessington South ¶ dp	..	..	..	..	..	..	..	6 17	..	..	..	..	..	..	..	..
Chessington North	..	..	..	..	..	..	..	6 19	..	..	..	..	..	..	..	..
Tolworth	..	..	..	..	..	..	..	6 21	..	..	..	..	..	..	..	..
Malden Manor	..	..	..	..	..	..	..	6 24	..	..	..	..	..	..	..	..
Motspur Park	..	..	..	6 25	..	..	..	6 28	..	..	6 33	..	..	..	..	6 45
Raynes Park	..	6 21	..	..	..	..	..	6 31	6 33	..	6 36	6 39	6 42	..	..	..
Wimbledon 319, 320, 322	..	6 24	..	6 30	6SO32	..	—	6 34	6 36	..	6 39	6 42	45	..	..	6 50
Earlsfield **B**	..	6 28	..	..	..	..	..	6 37	6 40	..	..	6 45	6 49	..	..	..
Clapham Junction A	..	6 31	..	..	..	..	..	6 41	6 43	..	..	6 49	6 52	..	..	..
Vauxhall	..	6 36	..	..	..	..	..	6 45	6 48	..	..	6 53	6 57	..	..	..
Waterloo arr.	..	6 41	..	6 43	6 43	..	6 48	6 49	6 52	..	..	6 57	7 1	..	..	7 3

Up	(3)		(3)				(3)	(3)	(3)		(3)	(3)	(3)		(3)
Guildford dep.	..	SX 6 0	..	6 10	..	6 20	..	..	..	6 22	..	..	..	SX 6 30	..
Worplesdon	..	(3)	..	(3)	..	..	..	..	..	6 29	..	..	..	(3)	..
Woking X 324, 389, 390	..		..		6 23	6 30	..	..	..	6 36	..	..	..		..
Byfleet **W**	..	..	..	..	..	..	..	..	..	6 40	..	..	..	..	..
West Weybridge	SX	..	..	..	..	..	..	..	..	6 43	..	..	..	..	..
Virginia Water Z dep.	6 6	..	..	..	..	..	..	6 25	..	..	..	..	..	..	..
Chertsey	6 11	..	..	..	..	..	..	6 31	..	..	..	..	..	..	..
Addlestone	6 14	..	..	..	..	..	..	6 34	..	..	..	..	..	..	..
Weybridge U 394	6 18	..	From Waterloo via Richmond Dep. Twickenham 6 29 p.m	..	6 33	..	..	6 39	..	6 46	..	..	From Waterloo via Richmond Dep. Twickenham 6 49 p.m	..	..
Walton-on-Thames	..	..		..	..	..	..	—	..	6 50	..	..		..	..
Hersham	..	..		..	..	..	..	Stop	..	6 52	..	..		..	..
Esher, for Sandown Park	..	..		..	..	..	..	..	..	6 55	..	..		..	..
London Road (Guildford)	..	6 4		6 14	..	..	..	..	..	..	..	..		6 34	..
Clandon **T**	..	6 9		6 19	..	..	..	..	..	..	..	..		6 39	..
Horsley **R**	..	6 14		6 24	..	..	..	..	..	..	..	..		6 44	..
Effingham Junction	..	6 22		6 27	..	..	..	..	..	..	..	..		6 47	..
Cobham **Q**	..	—		6 31	..	..	..	..	..	..	..	6 38		6 52	..
Oxshott, for Fairmile	..	..		6 35	..	..	..	p.m	..	..	..	..		6 56	..
Claygate, for Claremont	..	..		6 38	..	..	..	(3)	..	..	..	..		7 0	..
Hinchley Wood	..	..		6 41	..	..	..		..	..	..	..		7 3	..
Hampton Court dep.	..	..		..	..	..	..	6 43	..	..	..	..		..	..
Thames Ditton	..	..		..	..	..	..	6 45	..	..	..	..		..	..
Surbiton	..	..		6 45	6 47	..	..	6 50	..	7 0	..	..		7 8	..
Berrylands **N**	..	..		..	..	..	..	6 53	..	..	..	..		..	..
Shepperton dep.	..	..		..	..	..	..	..	..	..	6 31	..		..	..
Upper Halliford Halt	..	..		..	..	..	..	..	..	..	6 34	..		..	..
Sunbury **L**	..	..		..	..	..	..	..	..	..	6 36	..		..	..
Hampton	..	..	SX	..	..	..	..	..	..	..	6 40	..		—	..
Fulwell **K**	..	..	V	..	..	..	..	..	..	..	6 44	..	V	..	..
Teddington J	..	..	6 35	..	..	..	..	..	..	..	6 47	..	6 55	..	..
Hampton Wick	..	..	6 38	..	..	..	..	..	..	..	6 50	..	6 58	..	..
Kingston	..	..	6 41	..	..	..	..	..	..	..	6 52	..	7 0	..	..
Norbiton **H**	..	..	..	..	..	..	..	..	..	..	6 54	..	7 2	..	..
Malden, for Coombe	..	..	..	..	..	..	..	6 56	..	..	6 58	..	7 6	..	..
Bookham	..	6 26	..	..	..	..	..	..	..	..	..	6 41	..	..	..
Horsham dep.	..	..	..	..	..	..	..	..	..	..	..	..	..	..	..
Warnham	..	..	..	..	..	..	..	..	..	..	..	..	..	..	..
Ockley, for Capel	..	..	..	..	..	..	..	..	..	..	..	..	..	..	..
Holmwood **G**	..	..	..	..	..	..	..	..	SX	..	..	..	..	..	..
Dorking North F	..	..	..	..	..	..	..	..	6 29	..	..	..	..	..	..
Boxhill & Burford Bdg **D**	..	..	—	..	..	..	..	..	6 32	..	..	..	..	..	..
Leatherhead	..	6 30	..	..	..	..	..	..	6 37	..	..	6 46	..	..	..
Ashtead	..	6 34	..	..	..	..	..	..	6 41	..	..	6 50	..	..	..
Epsom 285	..	6 39	..	..	..	..	..	..	6 45	..	..	6 54	..	..	..
Sutton arr.	..	6‡55	..	..	..	..	..	..	6 55	..	..	7‡B14	..	..	..
Victoria "	..	..	..	..	..	..	..	..	..	..	..	..	..	..	..
London Bridge "	..	7‡22	..	..	..	..	..	..	7 22	..	..	7‡d44	..	..	..
Ewell West **C**	..	6 42	..	..	..	..	..	..	..	..	..	6 57	..	..	..
Stoneleigh	..	6 44	..	..	..	..	..	..	..	..	..	6 59	..	..	..
Worcester Park	..	6 48	..	..	..	..	..	..	..	..	..	7 2	..	..	SX
Chessington South ¶ dp	..	..	..	..	..	..	6 39	..	..	..	..	..	..	..	6 59
Chessington North	..	..	..	..	..	..	6 41	..	..	..	..	..	..	..	7 1
Tolworth	..	..	..	—	..	..	6 44	..	..	..	..	..	..	..	7 4
Malden Manor	..	..	..	..	..	..	6 46	..	..	..	..	..	..	..	7 6
Motspur Park	..	6 53	..	..	..	..	6 50	..	..	..	..	7 5	..	..	7 10
Raynes Park	..	6 56	..	..	..	..	6 53	6 59	..	..	7 1	..	7 9	..	7 13
Wimbledon 319, 320, 322	..	7 0	..	6 53	..	..	6 56	7 2	..	..	7 4	7 10	7 12	7 15	7 17
Earlsfield **B**	..	..	..	..	..	..	6 59	7 5	..	..	7 8	..	7 16	..	7 20
Clapham Junction A	..	..	..	..	..	..	7 3	7 9	..	..	7 11	..	7 19	..	7 24
Vauxhall	..	..	..	..	..	..	7 7	7 13	..	..	7 16	..	7 24	..	7 28
Waterloo arr.	..	..	..	7 5	7 7	7 3	7 11	7 17	..	7 16	7 20	7SO22	7 28	7 26	7 33

FOR NOTES, SEE PAGE 459

FOR NOTES, SEE PAGE 459

GUILDFORD, WOKING, CHERTSEY, HAMPTON COURT, SHEPPERTON, KINGSTON, HORSHAM, DORKING NORTH, & LONDON

Week Days—*continued* (p.m)

Up	3	3	3	3	3		3	3		3	3	3	3	3		3	3	3	3	3	3	3	3	3	3		3	3	3		3
			From Waterloo via Richmond Dep. Twickenham 6 59 p.m	Arr. Dorking North 6 43 p.m	Arr. Dorking North 6 43 p.m	Via Three Bridges, see page 212							From Waterloo via Richmond Dep. Twickenham 7 19 p.m.								From Waterloo via Richmond Dep. Twickenham 7 29 p.m.							From Waterloo via Richmond Dep. Twickenham 7 49 p.m.			
Guildford dep.								6 50	6 52										7 10							7 22					7 40
Worplesdon									6 59																	7 29					
Woking X 324, 389, 390									7 6						7 22											7 36				7 53	
Byfleet W									7 10																	7 40					
West Weybridge							SX		7 13					SO			SX									7 43					
Virginia Water Z dep.							6 46							6 56			7 9								7 26						
Chertsey							6 52							7 2			7 14								7 31						
Addlestone							6 55							7 5			7 17								7 34						
Weybridge U 394							7 0		7 16					7 9			7 21								7 38	7 46					
Walton-on-Thames									7 20																	7 50					
Hersham							Stop		7 22																	7 52					
Esher, for Sandown Park									7 25																	7 55					
London Road (Guildford)								6 54											7 14												7 44
Clandon T								6 59											7 19												7 49
Horsley R								7 4											7 24												7 54
Effingham Junction								7 7			7 12								7 27								7 38				7 57
Cobham Q								7 11											7 31												8 1
Oxshott, for Fairmile								7 15											7 35												8 5
Claygate, for Claremont								7 18											7 38												8 8
Hinchley Wood		SX						7 21											7 41												8 11
Hampton Court dep.		7 3														7 25							7 43								
Thames Ditton		7 5														7 28							7 45								
Surbiton		7 10						7 25	7 30							7 33			7 45				7 50			8 0				8 12	8 15
Berrylands N	SX	7 13														7 37							7 53								
Shepperton dep.	6 44									7 2														7 31							
Upper Halliford Halt	6 47									7 5														7 34							
Sunbury L	6 49									7 7														7 36							
Hampton	6 53									7 11											SX			7 40							
Fulwell K	6 57		V							7 15			V								V			7 44				V			
Teddington J	7 0		7 6							7 18			7 26								7 35			7 47				7 56			
Hampton Wick	7 3		7 9							7 21			7 29								7 38			7 50				7 59			
Kingston	7 5		7 12							7 23			7 31								7 40			7 52				8 1			
Norbiton H	7 7		7 14							7 26			7 33								7 42			7 54				8 3			
Malden, for Coombe	7 11	7 16	7 18							7 30			7 37			7 40					7 46		7 56	7 58				8 7			
Bookham				SO	SX		p.m				7 15																7 41				
Horsham dep.				6 20	6 20	6 48	3											6 52											7 21		
Warnham				6 24	6 24													6 56											7 25		
Ockley, for Capel				6 31	6 31		SX											7 3											7 32		
Holmwood G				6 35	6 35		6 48											7 7											7 36		
Dorking North F				6 46	6 48		6 58											7 18		7 28									7 46		
Boxhill & Burford Bdg D				6 48	6 51		7 1											7 21		7 30									7 48		
Leatherhead				6 53	6 56		7 6				7 19							7 26		7 35							7 46		7 53		
Ashtead				6 57	7 0		7 10				7 23							7 30		7 39							7 50		7 57		
Epsom 285				7 1	7 5		7 14				7 28							7 34		7 44							7 54		8 2		
Sutton arr.				7 11	7 14						7 37							7‡47		7 55							8‡11		8 11		
Victoria "				7*45	7*44	8 8					8*11							8‡11											8*40		
London Bridge "				7 38	7 44						8 6									8 25							8‡38		8 38		
Ewell West C							7 17											7 37									7 57				
Stoneleigh							7 19											7 39									7 59				
Worcester Park							7 22											7 42									8 2				
Chessington South ¶ dp												7 17										7 39									
Chessington North												7 19										7 41									
Tolworth												7 22										7 44									
Malden Manor												7 24										7 46									
Motspur Park							7 25					7 28						7 45				7 50					8 5				
Raynes Park	7 15	7 19	7 21							7 33		7 31	7 40			7 43					7 49	7 53	7 59	8 1				8 10			
Wimbledon 319, 320, 322	7 19	7 22	7 24				7 30	7 32		7 36		7 34	7 43			7 46		7 50	7 53		7 54	7 56	8 2	8 4			8 10	8 13			8 24
Earlsfield B			7 28							7 40		7 37	7 46			7 49						7 59	8 5	8 8				8 17			
Clapham Junction A			7 31							7 43		7 41	7 50			7 53						8 3	8 9	8 11				8 20			
Vauxhall			7 36				—			7 48		7 45	7 54			7 57						8 7	8 13	8 16				8 25			
Waterloo arr.			7 40					7 43	7 46	7 52		7 49	7 58	—	8 0	8 1		8 3	8 4			8 11	8 17	8 20		8 16	8 22	8 29		8 32	8 35

GUILDFORD, WOKING, CHERTSEY, HAMPTON COURT, SHEPPERTON, KINGSTON, HORSHAM, DORKING NORTH, & LONDON

Week Days—continued (p.m.)

Up																															
Guildford dep.	3	3	3		3	7 52	3	SX 7 58	3	3	3	..	8 10	8 20	3	3	3	8 22	3	3	3	8 40	3	3	..	8 52	3	3	3	3	3
Worplesdon	..	..	..	..	..	7 59	..	3	..	..	..	..	..	..	..	..	..	8 29	..	..	..	..	..	..	..	8 59	..	..	..	..	..
Woking X 324, 389, 390	..	..	..	..	..	8 6	..		..	..	..	8 24	3	8 30	..	..	..	8 36	..	..	..	3	..	..	..	9 6	..	..	..	..	..
Byfleet W	..	..	..	..	..	8 10	..	..	..	..	..	..	..	..	..	..	..	8 40	..	..	..	..	..	..	..	9 10	..	..	..	..	..
West Weybridge	..	SX	..	..	SO	8 13	..	..	..	..	..	..	..	..	..	..	..	8 43	..	..	..	..	..	..	..	9 13	..	..	..	..	..
Virginia Water Z dep.	..	7 46	..	..	7 56	..	..	..	..	..	..	..	..	..	..	..	8 26	..	..	..	8 56	..	..	..	..	..	..	..	..	..	..
Chertsey	..	7F57	..	..	8 1	..	..	..	..	..	..	..	..	..	..	..	8 33	..	..	..	9 1	..	..	..	..	..	..	..	..	..	..
Addlestone	..	8 3	..	..	8 4	..	..	..	..	..	..	..	..	..	..	..	8 36	..	..	..	9 4	..	..	..	..	..	..	..	..	..	..
Weybridge U 394		8 7	..	..	8 8	8 16	..	..		..	..	..	..	..	..	..	8 40	8 46	..		9 8	..		..	..	9 16	..	..	..		..
Walton-on-Thames			..	..		8 20	..	..		..	..	..	..	..	..	..		8 50	..			..		..	..	9 20	..	..	..		..
Hersham		Stop	..	..	Stop	8 22	..	..		..	..	..	..	..	..	..	Stop	8 52	..		Stop	..		..	..	9 22	..	..	..		..
Esher, for Sandown Park		..	..	..	..	8 25	..	..		..	..	..	..	..	..	..	..	8 55	..		..	..		..	..	9 25	..	..	..		..
London Road (Guildford)	From Waterloo, via Richmond Dep. Twickenham 7 59 p.m.	..	..	..	..	..	..	8 1	From Waterloo, via Richmond Dep. Twickenham 8 19 p.m.	..	..	..	8 14	..	..	..	..	..	..	From Waterloo via Richmond Dep. Twickenham 8 49 p.m	Arr. Dorking North 8 43 p.m	8 44	From Waterloo via Richmond Dep. Twickenham 8 59 p.m	..	..	..	..	..	..	From Waterloo via Richmond Dep. Twickenham 9 19 p.m	..
Clandon T		..	..	..	..	..	..	8 7		..	..	..	8 19	..	..	..	..	..	..			8 49		..	..	..	..	..	..		..
Horsley R		..	..	..	..	..	..	8 12		..	..	..	8 24	..	..	..	..	..	..			8 54		..	..	..	..	..	..		..
Effingham Junction		..	..	..	..	..	8 12	8b19		..	..	..	8 27	..	..	..	..	..	8 38			8 57		..	..	..	..	..	9 12		..
Cobham Q		..	..	..	..	..	..	..		..	..	..	8 31	..	..	..	..	..	..			9 1		..	..	..	..	..	..		..
Oxshott, for Fairmile		..	..	..	..	..	..	..		..	..	..	8 35	..	..	..	..	..	..			9 5		..	..	..	..	..	..		..
Claygate, for Claremont		..	..	..	..	..	..	..		..	..	..	8 38	..	..	..	..	..	..			9 8		..	..	..	..	..	..		..
Hinchley Wood		..	..	..	..	..	..	..		..	..	..	8 41	..	..	..	..	..	..			9 11		..	..	..	..	..	..		..
Hampton Court dep.		..	..	..	..	..	..	..		8 25	..	..	..	..	..	8 43	..	..	..			..		..	..	..	..	..	..		9 25
Thames Ditton		..	..	..	..	..	..	..		8 28	..	..	..	..	..	8 45	p.m	..	..			..		..	..	..	..	..	..		9 28
Surbiton		..	..	..	..	8 30	..	..		8 33	..	8 48	8 45	..	..	8 50	3	9 0	..			9 15		..	..	9 30	..	..	..		9 33
Berrylands N		..	..	..	..	..	..	..		8 36	..	..	..	..	..	8 53		..	..			..		..	..	..	..	..	..		9 36
Shepperton dep		..	8 0	..	..	..	..	..		..	..	..	..	..	..	..	8 31	..	..			..		..	..	..	9 0	..	..		..
Upper Halliford Halt		..	8 3	..	..	..	..	..		..	..	..	..	..	..	..	8 34	..	..			..		..	..	..	9 3	..	..		..
Sunbury L		..	8 5	..	..	..	..	..		..	..	..	..	..	..	..	8 36	..	..			..		..	..	..	9 5	..	..		..
Hampton		..	8 9	..	..	..	..	..		..	..	..	..	..	..	..	8 40	..	..			..		..	..	..	9 9	..	..		..
Fulwell K	V	..	8 14	..	..	..	..	..	V	..	..	..	..	..	..	..	8 44	..	..	V		..	V	..	..	..	9 13	..	..	V	..
Teddington J	8 7	..	8 17	..	..	..	..	..	8 25	..	..	..	..	..	..	..	8 47	..	..	8 55		..	9 7	..	..	..	9 16	..	..	9 25	..
Hampton Wick	8 10	..	8 20	..	..	..	..	..	8 28	..	..	..	..	..	..	..	8 50	..	..	8 58		..	9 10	..	..	..	9 19	..	..	9 28	..
Kingston	8 12	..	8 22	..	..	..	..	..	8 30	..	..	..	..	..	..	..	8 52	..	..	9 0		..	9 12	..	..	..	9 21	..	..	9 30	..
Norbiton H	8 14	..	8 24	..	..	..	..	..	8 32	..	..	..	..	..	..	..	8 54	..	..	9 2	p.m	..	9 14	..	..	..	9 23	..	..	9 32	..
Malden, for Coombe	8 18	..	8 28	..	..	..	..	..	8 36	8 39	..	..	..	..	..	8 56	8 58	..	..	9 6	3	..	9 18	..	..	..	9 27	..	..	9 36	9 39
Bookham	..	p.m	..	..	..	..	8 15	8 24	..	..	..	..	..	..	..	..	..	..	8 41			..	..	..	SO	..	..	..	9 15	..	..
Horsham dep.	..	3	..	7 43	..	..	..	..	..	..	7 52	..	..	..	..	..	..	..	..	..	8 20	..	..	..	8 43	..	..	..	..	..	..
Warnham	..		..	..	..	..	..	..	..	..	7 56	..	..	..	..	..	..	..	..	..	8 24	..	..	..	..	..	..	..	..	..	..
Ockley, for Capel	..	SX	..	..	..	..	..	..	..	..	8 3	..	..	..	..	..	..	..	..	..	8 31	..	..	..	..	..	..	..	..	..	..
Holmwood G	..	7 46	..	..	..	..	..	..	..	..	8 7	..	..	..	..	..	..	..	..	..	8 35	..	..	SX	..	..	..	..	..	..	..
Dorking North F	..	7 55	..	8 2	..	..	..	..	..	..	8 18	..	..	..	..	..	..	..	..	..	8 46	..	..	8 55	9 2	..	..	..	..	..	..
Boxhill & Burford Bdg D	..	7 57	..	..	..	..	..	..	..	..	8 21	..	..	..	..	..	..	..	..	..	8 48	..	..	8 57	..	..	..	..	..	..	..
Leatherhead	..	8 2	..	..	..	..	8 19	8 28	..	..	8 26	..	..	..	..	..	..	..	8 46	..	8 53	..	..	9 2	..	..	..	..	9 19	..	..
Ashtead	..	8 6	..	..	..	..	8 23	..	..	..	8 30	..	..	..	..	..	..	..	8 50	..	8 57	..	..	9 6	..	..	..	..	9 23	..	..
Epsom 285	..	8b14	..	..	..	..	8 28	..	..	..	8 34	..	..	..	..	..	..	..	8 54	..	9 2	..	..	9 10	..	..	..	..	9 28	..	..
Sutton arr.	..	8‡26	..	8 20	..	..	8 37	..	..	..	8‡49	..	..	..	..	..	..	..	..	..	9 11	..	..	9‡26	9 20	..	..	..	9 37	..	..
Victoria "	..	8‡52	..	8 40	..	..	9*13	..	..	..	9‡13	..	..	..	..	..	..	..	..	..	9‡50	..	..	9‡50	9 40	..	..	..	10*13	..	..
London Bridge "	..	9‡7	..	..	..	..	9 7	..	..	..	..	..	..	..	..	..	..	..	..	..	9 38	..	..	..	..	..	..	..	10 7	..	..
Ewell West C	..	8 17	..	..	p.m	..	..	..	..	..	8 37	..	..	..	..	..	..	..	8 57	..	..	..	..	9 13	..	..	..	..	..	..	..
Stoneleigh	..	8 19	..	..	3	..	..	..	..	..	8 39	..	..	..	..	..	..	..	8 59	..	..	..	..	9 16	..	..	..	..	..	..	..
Worcester Park	..	8 22	..	..		..	..	..	..	..	8 42	..	..	..	..	..	..	..	9 2	..	..	..	..	9 19	..	..	..	..	..	..	..
Chessington South ¶dp	..	..	..	..	8 19	..	..	..	..	..	..	..	..	..	8 39	..	..	..	..	..	..	..	..	..	..	..	..	9 19	..	..	..
Chessington North	..	..	..	..	8 21	..	..	..	..	..	..	..	..	..	8 41	..	..	..	..	..	..	..	..	..	..	..	..	9 21	..	..	..
Tolworth	..	..	..	..	8 24	..	..	..	..	..	..	..	..	..	8 44	..	..	..	..	..	..	..	..	..	..	..	..	9 24	..	..	..
Malden Manor	..	..	..	..	8 26	..	..	..	..	..	..	..	..	..	8 46	..	..	..	..	..	..	..	..	..	..	..	..	9 26	..	..	..
Motspur Park	..	8 25	..	..	8 30	..	..	..	..	..	8 45	..	..	..	8 50	..	..	..	9 5	..	..	..	..	9 21	..	..	..	9 30	..	..	..
Raynes Park	8 21	8 28	8 31	..	8 34	..	..	..	8 39	8 42	..	..	..	..	8 53	8 59	9 1	..	..	9 9	..	..	9 21	9 24	..	..	9 30	9 33	..	9 39	9 42
Wimbledon 319, 320, 322	8 24	8 31	8 34	..	8 37	..	..	..	8 42	8 45	8 50	..	8 53	..	8 56	9 2	9 4	..	9 10	9 12	..	9 22	9 24	9 27	..	..	9 33	9 36	..	9 42	9 45
Earlsfield B	8 28	..	8 38	..	8 40	..	..	..	8 45	8 49	..	..	..	..	8 59	9 5	9 8	..	..	9 16	..	..	9 28	..	..	..	9 36	9 39	..	9 45	9 49
Clapham Junction A	8 31	..	8 41	..	8 44	..	..	..	8 49	8 53	..	..	..	..	9 3	9 9	9 11	..	..	9 19	..	..	9 31	..	..	..	9 40	9 43	..	9 49	9 52
Vauxhall	8 36	..	8 46	..	8 48	..	..	..	8 53	8 57	..	..	..	..	9 7	9 13	9 16	..	..	9 24	..	..	9 36	..	..	..	9 44	9 47	..	9 53	9 57
Waterloo arr.	8 40	..	8 50	..	8 52	8 46	..	..	8 57	9 1	9 3	9 14	9 4	9 1	9 11	9 17	9 20	9 16	9 23	9 28	..	9 33	9 40	..	..	9 46	9 48	9 51	..	9 57	10 1

FOR NOTES, SEE PAGE 459

FOR NOTES, SEE PAGE 459

GUILDFORD, WOKING, CHERTSEY, HAMPTON COURT, SHEPPERTON, KINGSTON, HORSHAM, DORKING NORTH, & LONDON

Week Days—continued (p.m.)

Up	3	3		3	3			3	3		3	3	3	3		3
Guildford ......dep.	..	9 10	929	..	..	9 22	..	..	..	..	..	..	9 40	..	9 52	..
Worplesdon	..	..	..	..	..	9 29	..	..	..	..	..	..	..	..	9 59	..
Woking X 324, 389, 396	..	..	930	..	..	9 36	..	..	..	9 46	..	..	..	..	10 6	..
Byfleet W	..	..	—	..	..	9 40	..	..	..	..	..	..	..	..	1010	..
West Weybridge	..	..	—	..	..	9 43	..	..	..	..	..	..	..	..	1013	..
Virginia Water Z ...dep.	..	..	—	9 26	..	..	..	..	..	..	..	9 56	..	..	..	..
Chertsey	..	..	..	9 34	..	..	..	..	..	..	..	10 1	..	..	..	..
Addlestone	..	..	..	9 37	..	..	..	..	..	..	..	10 4	..	..	..	..
Weybridge U 394	..	..	..	9 41	..	9 46	..	..	..	..		10 8	..		1016	..
Walton-on-Thames	..	..	..		..	9 50	..	..	..	..			..		1020	..
Hersham	..	..	..	Stop	..	9 52	..	..	..	..		Stop	..		1022	..
Esher, for Sandown Park	..	..	..	..	..	9 55	..	..	..	..		..	..		1025	..
London Road (Guildford)	..	9 14	..	..	..	..	..	..	..	..	From Waterloo via Richmond Dep. Twickenham 9 49 p.m	..	9 44	From Waterloo, via Richmond Dep. Twickenham 9 59 p.m	..	..
Clandon T	..	9 19	..	..	..	..	..	..	..	..		..	9 49		..	..
Horsley R	..	9 24	..	..	..	..	..	..	..	..		..	9 54		..	..
Effingham Junction	..	9 27	..	..	..	..	..	..	9 38	..		..	9 57		..	..
Cobham Q	..	9 31	..	..	..	..	..	..	..	..		..	10 1		..	..
Oxshott, for Fairmile	..	9 35	..	..	..	..	..	..	..	..		..	10 5		..	..
Claygate, for Claremont	..	9 38	..	..	..	..	..	..	..	..		..	10 8		..	..
Hinchley Wood	..	9 41	..	..	..	..	..	..	..	..		..	1011		..	..
Hampton Court ...dep.	..	..	..	..	9 43	..		..	..	..		..	..		..	..
Thames Ditton	..	..	..	..	9 45	..		..	..	..		..	..		..	..
Surbiton	..	9 45	..	..	9 50	10 0		..	..	10 3		..	1015		1039	..
Berrylands N	..	..	..	..	9 53	..		..	..	..		..	..		..	..
Shepperton ......dep.	..	..	..	..	..	..	Via Three Bridges, see page 214	9 31	..	..		..	..		..	10 0
Upper Halliford Halt	..	..	..	..	..	..		9 34	..	..		..	..		..	10 3
Sunbury L	..	..	..	..	..	..		9 36	..	..		..	..		..	10 5
Hampton	..	..	..	..	..	..		9 40	..	..		..	..		..	10 9
Fulwell K	..	..	..	..	..	..		9 44	..	..	V	..	..	V	..	1013
Teddington J	..	..	..	..	..	..		9 47	..	..	9 55	..	..	10 5	..	1016
Hampton Wick	..	..	..	..	..	..		9 50	..	..	9 58	..	..	10 8	..	1019
Kingston	..	..	..	..	..	..		9 52	..	..	10 0	..	..	1012	..	1021
Norbiton H	..	..	..	..	..	..		9 54	..	..	10 2	p.m	..	1014	..	1023
Malden, for Coombe	..	..	..	..	9 56	..	..	9 58	..	..	10 6	3	..	1018	..	1027
Bookham	..	..	..	..	..	..	..	..	9 41	..	..		..	..	..	..
Horsham ......dep.	8 52	..	..	..	..	..	9 17	..	..	..	..	9 22	..	..	..	..
Warnham	8 56	..	..	..	..	..	..	..	..	..	..	9 26	..	..	..	..
Ockley, for Capel	9 3	..	..	..	..	..	..	..	..	..	..	9 33	..	..	..	..
Holmwood G	9 7	..	..	..	..	..	..	..	..	..	..	9 37	..	..	..	..
Dorking North F	9 13	..	..	..	..	..	..	..	..	..	..	9 46	..	..	..	..
Boxhill & Burford Bdg D	9 21	..	..	..	..	..	..	..	..	..	..	9 48	..	..	..	..
Leatherhead	9 26	..	..	..	..	..	..	..	9 46	..	..	9 53	..	..	..	..
Ashtead	9 30	..	..	..	..	..	..	..	9 50	..	..	9 57	..	..	..	..
Epsom 285	9 34	..	..	..	..	..	..	..	9 54	..	..	10 2	..	..	..	..
Sutton ......arr.	9‡49	..	..	..	..	..	..	..	10‡11	..	..	1011	..	..	..	..
Victoria ...... "	10‡13	..	..	..	..	..	..	..	10‡44	..	..	10*44	..	..	..	..
London Bridge .... "	..	..	..	..	..	..	1039	..	10‡40	..	..	1040	..	..	..	..
Ewell West C	9 37	..	..	p.m	..	..	..	..	9 57	..	..	..	..	..	..	..
Stoneleigh	9 39	..	..	3	..	..	..	..	9 59	..	..	..	..	..	..	..
Worcester Park	9 42	..	..		..	..	..	..	10 2	..	..	..	..	..	..	..
Chessington South ¶ dep.	..	..	..	9 39	..	..	..	..	..	..	..	..	..	..	..	..
Chessington North	..	..	..	9 41	..	..	..	..	..	..	..	..	..	..	..	..
Tolworth	..	..	..	9 44	..	..	..	..	..	..	..	..	..	..	..	..
Malden Manor	..	..	..	9 46	..	..	..	..	..	..	..	..	..	..	..	..
Motspur Park	9 45	..	..	9 50	..	..	..	..	10 5	..	..	..	..	..	..	..
Raynes Park	..	..	..	9 53	9 59	..	..	10 1	..	..	10 9	..	..	1021	..	1030
Wimbledon 319, 320, 322	9 50	9 54	..	9 56	10 2	..	..	10 4	10 10	..	1012	..	1022	1024	..	1033
Earlsfield B	..	..	..	9 59	10 5	..	..	10 8	..	..	1016	..	..	1028	..	1036
Clapham Junction A	..	..	..	10 3	10 9	..	..	1011	..	..	1019	..	..	1031	..	1040
Vauxhall	..	..	..	10 7	1013	..	..	1016	..	..	1024	..	..	1035	..	1044
Waterloo ......arr.	10 3	10 5	101	1011	1017	1016	..	1020	10 23	1027	1028	—	1033	1040	1046	1048

Up	3		3	3	3	3	3	3	3	3			3	3	3
Guildford ......dep.	..	..	..	..	..	..	1010	..	..	..	1022	..	..	1040	..
Worplesdon	..	..	..	..	..	..	..	..	..	..	1029	..	..	..	..
Woking X 324, 389, 396	..	..	..	..	..	..	..	..	..	..	1036	1039	..	..	..
Byfleet W	..	..	..	..	..	..	..	..	..	..	1040	..	..	..	..
West Weybridge	..	..	..	..	..	..	..	..	..	..	1043	..	..	..	..
Virginia Water Z ...dep.	..	..	..	..	..	..	..	..	1030	..	..	..	..	..	1056
Chertsey	..	..	..	..	..	..	..	..	1035	..	..	..	..	..	11 1
Addlestone	..	..	..	..	..	..	..	..	1038	..	..	..	..	..	11 5
Weybridge U 394	..	..	..		..	..	..	..	1042	..	1046	..		..	11 9
Walton-on-Thames	..	..	..		..	..	..	..		..	1050	..		..	
Hersham	..	..	..		..	..	..	..	Stop	..	1052	..		..	Stop
Esher, for Sandown Park	..	..	..		..	..	..	..	..	..	1055	..		..	..
London Road (Guildford)	..	..	..	From Waterloo via Richmond Dep. Twickenham 10 19 p.m	..	..	1014	..	..	..	..	..	From Waterloo via Richmond Dep. Twickenham 10 49 p.m	1044	..
Clandon T	..	..	..		..	..	1019	..	..	..	..	..		1049	..
Horsley R	..	..	..		..	..	1024	..	..	..	..	..		1054	..
Effingham Junction	..	..	10 12		..	..	1027	1038	..	..	..	..		1057	..
Cobham Q	..	..	..		..	..	1031	..	..	..	..	..		11 1	..
Oxshott, for Fairmile	..	..	..		..	..	1035	..	p.m	..	..	..		11 5	..
Claygate, for Claremont	..	..	..		..	..	1038	..	3	..	..	..		11 8	..
Hinchley Wood	..	..	..		..	..	1041	..		..	..	..		1111	..
Hampton Court ...dep.	..	..	..		1025	..	..	..	1043	..	..	..		..	..
Thames Ditton	..	..	..		1028	..	..	..	1045	..	..	..		..	..
Surbiton	..	..	..		1033	..	1045	..	1050	..	11 0	..		1115	..
Berrylands N	..	..	..		1036	..	..	..	1053	..	..	..		..	..
Shepperton ......dep.	..	Via Three Bridges, see page 216	..		..	..	..	..	..	1031	..	..		..	..
Upper Halliford Halt	..		..		..	..	..	..	..	1034	..	..		..	..
Sunbury L	..		..		..	..	..	..	..	1036	..	..		..	..
Hampton	..		..		..	..	..	..	..	1040	..	..		..	..
Fulwell K	..		..	V	..	..	..	..	..	1044	..	..	V	..	..
Teddington J	..		..	1025	..	..	..	..	..	1047	..	..	1055	..	..
Hampton Wick	..		..	1028	..	..	..	..	..	1050	..	..	1058	..	..
Kingston	..		..	1030	..	..	..	..	..	1052	..	..	11 3	..	..
Norbiton H	..		..	1032	..	..	..	..	..	1054	..	..	11 5	..	..
Malden, for Coombe	..		..	1036	1039	..	..	..	1056	1058	..	..	11 9	..	..
Bookham	..		10 15	..	..	..	..	1041	..	..	..	..	..	..	..
Horsham ......dep.	..	9 48	..	..	..	9 52	..	..	..	..	..	..	..	..	..
Warnham	..	..	..	..	..	9 56	..	..	..	..	..	..	..	..	..
Ockley, for Capel	..	..	..	..	..	10 3	..	..	..	..	..	..	..	..	..
Holmwood G	..	..	..	..	..	10 7	..	..	..	..	..	..	..	..	..
Dorking North F	..	..	..	..	..	10 18	..	..	..	..	..	..	..	..	..
Boxhill & Burford Bdg D	..	..	..	..	..	10 21	..	..	..	..	..	..	..	..	..
Leatherhead	..	..	10 19	..	..	10 26	..	1046	..	..	..	..	..	..	..
Ashtead	..	..	10 23	..	..	10 30	..		..	..	..	..	..	..	..
Epsom 285	..	..	10 28	..	..	10 34	..	Stop	..	..	..	..	..	..	..
Sutton ......arr.	..	..	10 37	..	..	10‡49	..	..	..	..	..	..	..	..	..
Victoria ...... "	..	11 7	11*13	..	..	11‡13	..	..	..	..	..	..	..	..	..
London Bridge .... "	..	..	11 7	..	..	..	..	..	..	..	..	..	..	..	..
Ewell West C	..	..	..	..	..	10 37	..	p.m	..	..	..	..	..	..	p.m
Stoneleigh	..	..	..	..	..	10 39	..	3	..	..	..	..	..	..	3
Worcester Park	..	..	..	..	..	10 42	..		..	..	..	..	..	..	
Chessington South ¶ dep.	1019	..	..	..	..	..	..	1039	..	..	..	..	..	..	1119
Chessington North	1021	..	..	..	..	..	..	1041	..	..	..	..	..	..	1121
Tolworth	1024	..	..	..	..	..	..	1044	..	..	..	..	..	..	1124
Malden Manor	1026	..	..	..	..	..	..	1046	..	..	..	..	..	..	1126
Motspur Park	1030	..	..	..	..	10 45	..	1050	..	..	..	..	..	..	1130
Raynes Park	1033	..	..	1039	1042	..	..	1053	1059	11 1	..	..	1112	..	1133
Wimbledon 319, 320, 322	1036	..	..	1042	1045	10 50	1052	1056	11 2	11 4	..	..	1115	1122	1136
Earlsfield B	1039	..	..	1045	1049	..	..	1059	11 5	11 8	..	..	1118	..	11SX39
Clapham Junction A	1043	..	..	1049	1052	..	..	11 3	11 9	1111	..	..	1122	..	11SX43
Vauxhall	1047	..	..	1053	1057	..	..	11 7	1113	1116	..	..	1126	..	11SX47
Waterloo ......arr.	1051	..	..	1057	11 1	11 3	11 3	1111	1117	1120	1116	1113	1130	1134	11SX51

GUILDFORD, WOKING, CHERTSEY, HAMPTON COURT, SHEPPERTON, KINGSTON, HORSHAM, DORKING NORTH, & LONDON

Up	Week Days—continued p.m.	3	3	3	3	3	3		S X		Sundays a.m.	3	3	3	3	3	3	3	3	3	3	3	3		3	3	3	3		3	3	
Guildford ... dep.	1052	..	..	..	..	1118	..	1122	..	..	..	..	..	..	..	..	..	..	..	..	..	..	..	7 22	..	..	7 37	..	..	..	..	..
Worplesdon	1059	..	..	..	..	..	..	1129	..	..	..	..	..	..	..	..	..	..	..	..	..	..	..	7 29	..	..	..	..	..	..	..	..
Woking X 324, 389, 390	11 6	..	..	..	..	..	..	1134	1135	..	2 58	..	..	..	..	..	..	..	..	..	..	..	..	7 36	..	..	..	..	..	..	..	8 28
Byfleet W	1110	..	..	..	..	..	..	..	..	..	..	..	..	..	..	..	..	..	..	..	..	..	..	7 40	..	..	..	..	..	..	..	..
West Weybridge	1113	..	..	..	..	..	..	..	..	..	..	..	..	..	..	..	..	..	..	..	..	..	..	7 43	..	..	..	..	..	..	..	..
Virginia Water Z ... dep.	..	..	..	1126	..	..	..	..	..	..	..	..	..	..	..	..	..	..	..	..	..	..	..	..	..	..	..	..	..	..	..	..
Chertsey	..	..	..	1131	..	..	..	..	..	..	..	..	..	..	..	..	..	..	..	..	..	..	..	..	8 2	..	..	..	..	..	..	..
Addlestone	..	..	..	..	..	..	..	..	..	..	..	..	..	..	..	..	..	..	..	..	..	..	..	..	8 5	..	..	..	..	..	..	..
Weybridge U 394	1116	..	From Waterloo via Richmond Dep Twickenham 11 19 p.m	Stop	..	..	From Waterloo via Richmond Dep. Twickenham 11 31 p.m	..	..	..	3 11	From Twickenham (dep. 5 8 a.m) and Strawberry Hill (dep. 5 11 a.m)	..	..	..	..	..	..	..	..	..	..	..	7 46	8 9	..	..	..	..	..	..	..
Walton-on-Thames	1120	..		..	..	..		..	..	..	3 17		..	..	..	..	..	..	..	..	..	..	..	7 50	Stop	..	..	..	..	..	..	..
Hersham	1122	..		..	..	..		..	..	..	..		..	..	..	..	..	..	..	..	..	..	..	7 52	..	..	..	..	..	..	..	..
Esher, for Sandown Park	1125	..		..	..	..		..	..	..	3 23		..	..	..	..	..	..	..	..	..	..	..	7 55	..	..	..	..	..	..	..	..
London Road (Guildford)	..	..		..	..	1121		..	..	..	..		..	..	..	..	..	..	..	..	..	..	..	..	..	..	7 40	From Waterloo via Richmond Dep. Twickenham 7 59 a.m	..	..	..	..
Clandon T	..	..		..	..	1127		..	..	..	..		..	..	..	..	..	..	..	..	..	..	..	..	..	..	7 46		..	..	..	..
Horsley R	..	..		..	..	1132		..	..	..	..		..	..	..	..	..	..	..	..	..	..	..	..	..	..	7 51		..	..	..	..
Effingham Junction	..	..		..	..	1135		..	..	..	..		..	..	..	..	..	..	..	..	..	..	..	..	..	..	7 53		..	..	8 6	..
Cobham Q	..	..		..	..	Stop		..	..	..	..		..	..	..	..	..	..	..	..	..	..	..	..	..	..	7 57		..	..	..	..
Oxshott, for Fairmile	..	..		p.m 3	..	..		..	..	..	..		..	..	..	..	..	..	..	..	..	..	..	..	..	..	8 1		..	..	..	..
Claygate, for Claremont	..	..		..	..	..		..	..	..	..		..	..	..	..	..	..	..	..	..	..	..	..	..	..	8 4		..	..	..	..
Hinchley Wood	..	..		..	..	..		..	..	..	..		..	..	..	..	..	..	..	..	..	..	..	..	..	..	8 7		..	..	..	..
Hampton Court ... dep.	..	Arr Dorking North 10 43 p.m		1129	..	..		..	..	..	..		..	..	6 45	..	..	..	..	..	7 29	..	..	..	..	..	..		..	..	..	..
Thames Ditton	..			1131	..	..		..	..	..	..		..	..	6 47	..	..	..	..	..	7 31	..	..	..	..	..	..		..	..	..	..
Surbiton	1130			1136	..	..		..	..	..	3 32		..	..	6 52	..	..	..	..	..	7 36	..	..	8 0	..	..	8 11		..	..	..	..
Berrylands N	..			1139	..	..		..	..	..	..		..	..	6 55	..	..	..	..	..	7 39	..	..	..	..	..	..		..	..	..	..
Shepperton ... dep.	..			..	..	..		..	..	..	..		..	..	..	..	..	..	..	..	..	..	7 25	..	..	Arr Dorking North 7 57 a.m	..		Via Three Bridges, see page 220	..	..	..
Upper Halliford Halt	..			..	..	..		..	..	..	..		..	..	..	..	..	..	..	..	..	..	7 28	..	..		..			..	..	..
Sunbury L	..			..	..	..		..	..	..	..		..	..	..	..	..	..	..	..	..	..	7 30	..	..		..			..	..	..
Hampton	..			..	..	..		..	..	..	..		..	..	..	..	..	..	..	..	..	..	7 34	..	a.m 3		..			..	..	..
Fulwell K	..		V	..	..	..	V	..	..	..	..		..	..	..	..	..	..	..	..	..	..	7 38	..			..	V		..	..	..
Teddington J	..		1125	..	..	..	1137	..	..	..	..	5 16	..	6 20	..	6 50	..	..	7 25	..	..	..	7 41	..	7 46		..	8 5		..	..	..
Hampton Wick	..		1128	..	..	..	1140	..	..	..	..	..	..	6 23	..	6 53	..	..	7 28	..	..	..	7 44	..	7 49		..	8 8		..	..	..
Kingston	..		1130	..	..	..	1143	..	..	..	..	5 20	..	6 25	..	6 55	..	..	7 30	..	..	..	7 47	..	7 51		..	8 10		..	..	..
Norbiton H	..		1132	..	..	..	..	..	..	..	..	5 22	..	6 27	..	6 57	..	..	7 32	..	..	..	..	..	7 53		..	8 12		..	..	..
Malden, for Coombe	..		1136	1142	..	..	..	..	..	..	..	5 27	..	6 31	6 58	7 1		..	7 36	..	7 42	..	..	..	7 57		..	8 16		..	..	..
Bookham	..	..	..	..	..	..	..	..	..	..	..	..	..	..	..	..	Arr. Epsom 7 1 a.m	..	..	..	..	..	..	..	..		..	..		..	8 9	..
Horsham ... dep.	..	1020	..	..	1052	..	..	..	..	..	..	..	..	..	..	..		..	..	..	..	..	..	..	..	7 34	..	..	7 46	..	..	..
Warnham	..	1024	..	..	1056	..	..	..	..	..	..	..	..	..	..	..		..	..	..	..	..	..	..	..	7 38	..	..	..	..	..	..
Ockley, for Capel	..	1031	..	..	11 3	..	..	..	..	..	..	..	..	..	..	..		..	..	..	..	..	..	..	..	7 45	..	..	..	..	..	..
Holmwood G	..	1035	..	..	11 7	..	..	..	..	..	..	..	..	..	..	..		..	..	..	..	..	..	..	..	7 49	..	..	..	..	..	..
Dorking North F	..	1046	..	..	1118	..	..	..	..	..	..	..	..	..	..	..	6 45	..	..	7 0	..	7 25	..	..	..	8 0	..	..	..	..	..	..
Boxhill & Burford Bdg D	..	1048	..	..	1121	..	..	..	..	..	..	..	..	..	..	..	6 47	..	..	7 2	..	7 27	..	..	..	8 2	..	..	..	..	..	..
Leatherhead	..	1053	..	..	1126	..	..	..	..	..	..	..	..	..	..	..	6 52	..	..	7 7	..	7 32	..	..	..	8 7	..	..	..	..	8 13	..
Ashtead	..	1057	..	..	1130	..	..	..	..	..	..	..	..	..	..	..	6 57	..	..	7 11	..	7 36	..	..	..	8 11	..	..	..	..	8 17	..
Epsom 285	..	11 2	..	..	1134	..	..	..	..	..	..	..	..	..	..	..	7 9	..	..	7 16	..	7 40	..	..	..	8 15	..	..	..	..	8 21	..
Sutton ... arr.	..	1112	..	..	..	..	..	..	..	..	..	..	..	..	..	..	7‡12	..	..	7 25	..	..	..	..	..	8 24	..	..	..	..	8‡42	..
Victoria ... "	..	..	..	..	..	..	..	..	..	..	..	..	..	..	..	..	7‡38	..	..	8* 8	..	..	..	..	..	9* 8	..	..	9 5	..	9‡8	..
London Bridge ... "	..	1145	..	..	..	..	..	..	..	..	..	..	..	..	..	..	..	..	..	7 58	..	..	..	..	..	8 57	..	..	9 10	..	..	..
Ewell West C	..	..	..	..	1137	p.m 3	..	..	..	..	..	..	..	..	..	..	7 12	..	..	..	..	7 43	..	..	..	..	..	..	..	..	8 24	..
Stoneleigh	..	..	..	..	1139		..	..	..	..	..	..	..	..	..	..	7 15	..	..	..	..	7 46	..	..	..	..	..	..	..	..	8 27	..
Worcester Park	..	..	..	..	1142		..	..	..	..	..	..	..	..	..	..	7 18	..	..	..	..	7 49	..	..	..	..	..	..	..	..	8 30	..
Chessington South ¶ dp	..	..	..	..	..	1139	..	..	..	..	..	..	..	..	..	..	..	7 13	..	..	..	..	..	..	..	..	..	..	..	8 19	..	..
Chessington North	..	..	..	..	..	1141	..	..	..	..	..	..	..	..	..	..	..	7 15	..	..	..	..	..	..	..	..	..	..	..	8 21	..	..
Tolworth	..	..	..	..	..	1144	..	..	..	..	..	..	..	..	..	..	..	7 18	..	..	..	..	..	..	..	..	..	..	..	8 24	..	..
Malden Manor	..	..	..	..	..	1146	..	..	..	..	..	..	..	..	..	..	..	7 21	..	..	..	..	..	..	..	..	..	..	..	8 26	..	..
Motspur Park	..	..	..	..	1145	1150	..	..	..	..	..	..	..	..	..	..	7 20	7 24	..	..	..	7 51	..	..	..	..	..	..	..	8 30	8 32	..
Raynes Park	..	..	1139	1145	1148	1153	..	..	..	..	..	5 31	..	6 34	7 1	7 4	7 24	7 27	7 39	..	7 45	7 54	..	..	8 0	..	..	8 19	..	8 33	8 35	..
Wimbledon 319, 320, 322	..	..	1142	1148	1152	1156	..	..	..	..	..	5 35	..	6 37	7 4	7 7	7 27	7 30	7 42	..	7 48	7 57	..	..	8 3	..	8 18	8 22	..	8 36	8 38	..
Earlsfield B	..	..	1145	1151	..	1159	..	..	..	..	..	5 40	6 5	6 40	7 7	7 10	7 31	7 34	7 45	..	7 51	8 1	..	..	8 6	..	..	8 25	..	8 39	8 42	..
Clapham Junction A	..	..	1149	1155	..	12 3	..	..	..	..	..	5 45	6 9	6 44	7 11	7 14	7 34	7 37	7 49	..	7 55	8 4	..	..	8 10	..	8 24	8 29	..	8 43	8 45	..
Vauxhall	..	..	1153	1159	..	12 7	..	..	..	..	..	5 53	6 13	6 48	7 15	7 18	7 39	7 42	7 53	..	7 59	8 9	..	..	8 14	..	..	8 33	..	8 47	8 50	..
Waterloo ... arr.	1146	..	1157	12 3	..	1211	..	..	12 6	..	3 55	5 57	6 17	6 52	7 19	7 22	7 43	7 46	7 57	..	8 3	8 13	..	8 16	8 18	..	8 32	8 37	..	8 51	8 54	8 59

FOR NOTES, SEE PAGE 459

FOR NOTES, SEE PAGE 459

GUILDFORD, WOKING, CHERTSEY, HAMPTON COURT, SHEPPERTON, KINGSTON, HORSHAM, DORKING NORTH, & LONDON

Sundays—continued (a.m.)

Up	3	3	3		3	3	3		3	3		3	3	3	3	3	3	3				3	3		3	3		3	3	3	3
Guildford ....dep				8 22				8 37			8 52								..	9 10	9 20			9 22			9 37				
Worplesdon	..	..	..	8 29	..	..	..	3	..	..	8 59	..	..	..	..	..	..	..	..	3	..	..	..	9 29	..	..	3	..	..	..	..
Woking X 324, 389, 390	..	..	..	8 36	..	..	..	..	..	..	9 6	..	..	..	..	..	..	..	..	..	9 30	..	..	9 36	..	..	..	..	..	..	..
Byfleet W	..	..	..	8 40	..	..	..	..	..	..	9 10	..	..	..	..	..	..	..	..	..	..	..	..	9 40	..	..	..	..	..	..	..
West Weybridge	..	..	..	8 43	..	..	..	..	..	..	9 13	..	..	..	..	..	..	..	..	..	..	..	..	9 43	..	..	..	..	..	..	..
Virginia Water Z ..dep.	..	..	8 27	..	..	..	..	..	..	8 57	..	..	..	..	..	..	..	..	..	..	..	..	9 27	..	..	..	..	..	..	..	9 57
Chertsey	..	..	8 32	..	..	..	..	..	..	9 2	..	..	..	..	..	..	..	..	..	..	..	..	9 32	..	..	..	..	..	..	..	10 2
Addlestone	..	..	8 35	..	..	..	..	..	..	9 5	..	..	..	..	..	..	..	..	..	..	..	..	9 35	..	..	..	..	..	..	..	10 5
Weybridge U 394	..	..	8 39	8 46	..	..	..	..	..	9 9	9 16	..	..	..	..	..	..	..	..	..	..	..	9 39	9 46	..	..	..	..	..	..	10 9
Walton-on-Thames	..	..	Stop	8 50	From Waterloo via Richmond Dep. Twickenham 8 39 a.m	..	..	..	..	Stop	9 20	..	..	..	..	..	..	..	..	..	..	..	..	9 50	..	..	..	..	..	From Waterloo via Richmond Dep. Twickenham 9 59 a.m.	..
Hersham	..	..		8 52		..	..	..	..		9 22	..	..	..	..	From Waterloo via Richmond Dep. Twickenham 9 19 a.m.	..	..	..	..	..	..	..	9 52	..	..	..	..	..		..
Esher, for Sandown Park	..	..	..	8 55		..	..	..	..	..	9 25	..	..	..	..		..	..	..	..	..	..	..	9 55	..	..	..	..	..		..
London Road (Guildford)	..	..	..	..		..	..	8 40	..	..	..	..	..	..	..		..	..	..	9 14	..	..	..	..	..	..	9 40	..	..		..
Clandon T	..	..	..	..		..	..	8 46	..	..	..	..	..	..	..		..	..	..	9 19	..	..	..	..	..	..	9 46	..	..		..
Horsley R	..	..	..	..		..	..	8 51	..	..	..	..	..	..	..		..	..	..	9 24	..	..	..	..	..	..	9 51	..	..		..
Effingham Junction	..	..	..	..		8 30	..	8 53	..	..	..	..	..	..	9 4		..	..	..	9 27	..	9 30	..	..	..	..	9 54	..	9 57		..
Cobham Q	..	..	..	..		..	..	8 57	..	..	..	..	..	..	..		..	..	..	9 31	..	..	..	..	..	..	..	..	10 1		..
Oxshott, for Fairmile	..	..	..	..		..	..	9 1	..	..	..	..	..	..	..		..	..	..	9 35	..	..	..	..	..	..	..	..	10 5		..
Claygate, for Claremont	..	..	..	..		..	..	9 4	..	..	..	..	..	..	..		..	..	..	9 38	..	..	..	..	..	..	..	..	10 8		..
Hinchley Wood	..	..	..	..		..	..	9 7	..	..	..	..	..	..	..		..	..	..	9 41	..	..	..	..	..	..	..	..	1011		..
Hampton Court ....dep.	8 29	..	..	..		..	..	..	9 1	..	..	..	..	..	..		..	9 35	..	..	..	..	..	..	..	..	..	9 55	..		..
Thames Ditton	8 31	..	a.m	..		..	..	..	9 3	..	..	..	..	..	..		..	9 37	..	..	..	..	..	..	..	..	..	9 57	..		..
Surbiton	8 36	..	3	9 0		..	..	9 11	9 9	..	9 30	..	..	..	..		..	9 42	..	9 45	..	..	..	10 0	..	..	..	10 2	1015		..
Berrylands N	8 39	..		..		..	..	..	9 12	..	..	..	..	..	..		..	9 45	..	..	..	..	..	..	..	..	..	10 5	..		..
Shepperton ....dep.	..	..	8 26	..		..	..	..	..	..	..	8 58	..	Arr. Dorking North 8 57 a.m	..		..	..	Via Three Bridges, see page 220	..	..	..	..	..	9 31	..	..	..	..		..
Upper Halliford Halt	..	..	8 29	..		..	..	..	..	..	..	9 1	..		..		..	..		..	..	..	..	..	9 34	..	..	..	..		..
Sunbury L	..	..	8 31	..		..	..	..	..	a.m	..	9 3	..		..		..	..		..	..	..	..	..	9 36	..	..	..	..		..
Hampton	..	..	8 35	..		..	..	..	..	3	..	9 7	..		..		..	..		..	..	..	..	..	9 40	..	..	..	..		..
Fulwell K	..	..	8 39	..	V	..	..	..	..		..	9 11	..		..	V	..	..		..	..	..	..	..	9 44	..	..	..	..	V	..
Teddington J	..	..	8 42	..	8 47	..	..	..	..	9 5	..	..	..		..	9 25	..	..		..	..	..	..	..	9 47	..	..	..	..	10 5	..
Hampton Wick	..	..	8 45	..	8 50	..	..	..	..	9 8	..	..	..		..	9 28	..	..		..	..	..	..	..	9 50	..	..	..	..	10 8	..
Kingston	..	..	8 47	..	8 52	..	..	..	..	9 12	..	..	..		..	9 30	..	..		..	..	..	..	..	9 52	..	..	..	..	1010	..
Norbiton H	..	..	8 49	..	8 54	..	..	..	..	9 14	..	..	..		..	9 32	..	..		..	..	..	..	..	9 54	..	..	..	..	1012	..
Malden, for Coombe	8 42	..	8 53	..	8 58	..	..	..	9 15	9 18	..	..	..		..	9 36	..	9 48		..	..	..	..	..	9 58	..	..	10 8	..	1016	..
Bookham	..	..	..	..	..	8 33	..	..	..	..	..	..	..		9 7	..	..	..		..	..	9 33	..	..	..	..	9 58	..	..	..	..
Horsham ....dep.	..	..	..	..	..	..	..	..	..	..	..	Via Richmond, see page 484	..	8 34	..	..	..	..	8 43	..	..	..	..	..	..	..	..	..	..	..	..
Warnham	..	..	..	..	..	..	..	..	..	..	..		..	8 38	..	..	..	..	..	..	..	..	..	..	..	..	..	..	..	..	..
Ockley, for Capel	..	..	..	..	..	..	..	..	..	..	..		..	8 45	..	..	..	..	..	..	..	..	..	..	..	..	..	..	..	..	..
Holmwood G	..	..	..	..	..	..	..	..	..	..	..		..	8 49	..	..	..	..	..	..	..	..	..	..	..	..	..	..	..	..	..
Dorking North F	..	..	..	..	..	..	8 35	..	..	..	..		..	9 0	..	..	..	..	..	..	..	..	..	..	..	9 35	..	..	..	..	..
Boxhill & Burford Bdg D	..	..	..	..	..	..	8 37	..	..	..	..		..	9 2	..	..	..	..	..	..	..	..	..	..	..	9 37	..	..	..	..	..
Leatherhead	..	..	..	..	..	8 27	8 42	..	..	..	..		..	9 7	9 11	..	..	..	..	..	..	9 37	..	..	..	9 42	10 2	..	..	..	..
Ashtead	..	..	..	..	..	8 41	8 46	..	..	..	..		..	9 11	9 15	..	..	..	..	..	..	9 41	..	..	..	9 46	10 6	..	..	..	..
Epsom 285	..	..	..	..	..	8 45	8 50	..	..	..	..		..	9 15	9 19	..	..	..	..	..	..	9 45	..	..	..	9 50	10 10	..	..	..	..
Sutton ....arr.	..	..	..	..	..	8 54	9‡12	..	..	..	..		..	9 24	9‡46	..	..	..	..	..	..	9 54	..	..	..	10‡12	10‡30	..	..	..	..
Victoria ....„	..	..	..	..	..	9*38	9‡38	..	..	..	..		..	10*16	10‡16	..	..	..	9 31	..	..	10*38	..	..	..	10‡38	..	..	..	..	..
London Bridge ....„	..	..	..	..	..	9 27	..	..	..	..	..		..	9 57	..	..	..	..	9 40	..	..	1027	..	..	..	..	11‡3	..	..	..	..
Ewell West C	..	..	..	..	..	..	8 53	..	..	..	..	..	..	..	9 22	..	..	..	..	..	..	..	..	..	..	9 53	10 13	..	..	..	..
Stoneleigh	..	..	..	..	..	..	8 56	..	..	..	..	..	..	..	9 25	..	..	..	..	..	..	..	..	..	..	9 56	10 16	..	..	..	..
Worcester Park	..	..	..	..	..	..	8 59	..	..	..	..	..	..	..	9 28	..	..	..	..	..	..	..	..	..	..	9 59	10 19	..	..	..	..
Chessington South ¶ dp	..	8 39	..	..	..	..	..	..	..	..	..	..	9 13	..	..	..	9 33	..	..	..	..	..	..	..	..	..	..	..	..	..	..
Chessington North	..	8 41	..	..	..	..	..	..	..	..	..	..	9 15	..	..	..	9 35	..	..	..	..	..	..	..	..	..	..	..	..	..	..
Tolworth	..	8 44	..	..	..	..	..	..	..	..	..	..	9 18	..	..	..	9 38	..	..	..	..	..	..	..	..	..	..	..	..	..	..
Malden Manor	..	8 46	..	..	..	..	..	..	..	..	..	..	9 21	..	..	..	9 41	..	..	..	..	..	..	..	..	..	..	..	..	..	..
Motspur Park	..	8 50	..	..	..	..	9 1	..	..	..	..	..	9 24	..	9 30	..	9 44	..	..	..	..	..	..	..	..	10 2	10 21	..	..	..	..
Raynes Park	8 45	8 53	8 56	..	9 1	..	9 4	..	9 18	9 21	..	..	9 27	..	9 34	9 39	9 47	9 51	..	..	..	..	..	..	10 1	10 5	..	1011	..	1019	..
Wimbledon 319, 320 322	8 48	8 56	8 59	..	9 4	..	9 7	9 18	9 21	9 24	..	..	9 30	..	9 37	9 42	9 50	9 54	..	9 53	..	..	..	..	10 4	10 8	10 26	1014	1022	1022	..
Earlsfield B	8 51	8 59	9 3	..	9 7	..	9 11	..	9 24	9 27	..	..	9 34	..	..	9 45	9 54	9 57	..	..	..	..	..	..	10 7	..	..	1017	..	1025	..
Clapham Junction A	8 55	9 3	9 6	..	9 11	..	9 14	9 24	9 28	9 31	..	..	9 37	..	9 43	9 49	9 57	10 1	..	9 59	..	..	..	..	1011	10 14	10 32	1021	1028	1029	..
Vauxhall	8 59	9 7	9 11	..	9 15	..	9 19	..	9 32	9 35	..	..	9 42	..	..	9 53	10 2	10 5	..	..	..	..	..	..	1015	..	..	1025	..	1033	..
[illegible]	[illegible]	[illegible]	[illegible]	[illegible]	[illegible]	[illegible]	9 23	9 32	9 36	9 39	9 46	9 48	9 46	..	9 50	9 57	10 6	10 9	..	10 6	10 1	..	..	1016	1019	10 21	10 39	1029	1035	1037	..

GUILDFORD, WOKING, CHERTSEY, HAMPTON COURT, SHEPPERTON, KINGSTON, HORSHAM, DORKING NORTH, & LONDON

Sundays—*continued*

Up	a.m																				a.m										
		3	3	3	3		3	3		3		3	3			3	3		3	3		3	3	3	3	3	3			3	3
Guildford dep.	9 52					..			1010		1022			..	..			10 37			1052							1110	1120		
Worplesdon	9 59	..	..	..	..	..	..	..	3	..	1029	..	..	..	..	..	..	3	..	..	1059	..	..	..	..	..	..	3	..	..	..
Woking X 324, 389, 390	10 6	..	..	..	..	..	..	..	..	..	1036	..	..	..	1046	..	..	..	..	..	11 6	..	..	..	..	..	..	..	1130	..	..
Byfleet W	1010	..	..	..	..	..	..	..	..	..	1040	..	..	..	..	..	..	..	..	..	1110	..	..	..	..	..	..	..	..	..	..
West Weybridge	1013	..	..	..	..	..	..	..	..	..	1043	..	..	..	..	..	..	..	..	..	1113	..	..	..	..	..	..	..	..	..	..
Virginia Water Z dep.	..	..	..	..	..	..	..	..	..	10 27	..	..	..	..	..	..	..	..	..	1057	..	..	..	..	..	..	..	..	..	..	..
Chertsey	..	..	..	..	..	..	..	..	..	10 32	..	..	..	..	..	..	..	..	..	11 2	..	..	..	..	..	..	..	..	..	..	..
Addlestone	..	..	..	..	..	..	..	..	..	10 35	..	..	..	..	..	..	..	..	..	11 5	..	..	..	..	..	..	..	..	..	..	..
Weybridge U 394	1016	..	..	..	..	..	..	..	..	10 39	1046	..	..	..	..	..	..	..	..	11 9	1116	..	..	..	..	..	..	..	..	..	..
Walton-on-Thames	1020	..	..	..	From Waterloo via Richmond Dep. Twickenham 10 19 a.m.	..	..	..	..	Stop	1050	..	..	..	..	..	From Waterloo via Richmond Dep. Twickenham 10 59 a.m	..	..	..	1120	..	..	..	From Waterloo via Richmond Dep. Twickenham 11 19 a.m	..	..	..	..	..	..
Hersham	1022	..	..	..		..	..	..	..		1052	..	..	..	..	..		..	..	..	1122	..	..	..		..	..	..	..	..	..
Esher, for Sandown Park	1025	..	..	..		..	..	..	..	..	1055	..	..	..	..	..		..	..	..	1125	..	..	..		..	..	..	..	..	..
London Road (Guildford)	..	..	..	..		..	..	..	1014	..	..	..	..	..	..	..		10 40	..	..	..	..	..	..		..	..	1114	..	..	..
Clandon T	..	..	..	..		..	..	..	1019	..	..	..	..	..	..	..		10 46	..	..	..	..	..	..		..	..	1119	..	..	..
Horsley R	..	..	..	..		..	..	..	1024	..	..	..	..	..	..	..		10 51	..	..	..	..	..	..		..	..	1124	..	..	..
Effingham Junction	..	..	..	..		..	..	..	1027	..	..	10 30	..	..	..	..		10 54	1057	..	..	..	..	..		..	..	1127	..	..	11 30
Cobham Q	..	..	..	..		..	..	..	1031	..	..	..	..	..	..	..		..	11 1	..	..	..	..	..		..	..	1131	..	..	..
Oxshott, for Fairmile	..	..	..	..		..	..	..	1035	..	..	..	..	..	..	..		..	11 5	..	..	..	..	..		..	..	1135	..	..	..
Claygate, for Claremont	..	..	..	..		..	..	..	1038	..	..	..	..	..	..	..		..	11 8	..	..	..	..	..		..	..	1138	..	..	..
Hinchley Wood	..	..	..	..		..	..	..	1041	..	..	..	..	..	..	..		..	1111	..	..	..	..	..		..	..	1141	..	..	..
Hampton Court dep.	..	..		..		..	..	1035	..	..	..	..	..	..	..	1055		..	..	..	..	..	..	..		..	..	..	..	1135	..
Thames Ditton	..	..	..	..		..	..	1037	..	..	..	..	..	..	..	1057		..	..	..	..	..	..	..		..	..	..	..	1137	..
Surbiton	1030	..	..	..		..	..	1042	1045	..	11 0	..	..	..	11 2	11 2		..	1115	..	1130	..	..	..		..	..	1145	..	1142	..
Berrylands N	..	..	..	..		..	..	1045	..	..	..	..	..	..	..	11 5		..	..	..	..	..	..	..		..	..	..	..	1145	..
Shepperton dep.	..	..	9 58	..		..	..	..	..	..	..	..	1031	..	..	..		..	..	..	..	1058	..	..		..	..	..	..	..	..
Upper Halliford Halt	..	..	10 1	..		Via Three Bridges, see page 220	..	..	..	..	..	..	1034	..	..	..		..	..	..	..	11 1	..	..		..	..	..	..	..	..
Sunbury L	..	..	10 3	..			..	..	..	..	..	..	1036	..	..	..		..	..	..	..	11 3	..	..		..	..	..	..	..	..
Hampton	..	..	10 7	..			..	..	..	..	..	..	1040	..	..	..		..	..	..	..	11 7	..	..		..	..	..	..	..	..
Fulwell K	..	..	1011	..	V		..	..	..	..	..	..	1044	..	..	..	V	..	..	..	..	1111	..	..	V	..	..	..	..	..	..
Teddington J	..	..	..	..	1025		..	..	..	..	..	..	1047	..	..	..	11 5	..	..	..	..	Via Richmond, see page 485	..	..	1125	..	..	..	..	..	..
Hampton Wick	..	..	..	..	1028		..	..	..	..	..	..	1050	..	..	..	11 8	..	..	..	..		..	..	1128	..	..	..	..	..	..
Kingston	..	..	..	..	1030		..	..	..	..	..	..	1052	..	..	..	1110	..	..	..	..		..	..	1130	..	..	..	..	..	..
Norbiton H	..	..	..	..	1032		..	..	..	..	..	..	1054	..	..	..	1112	..	..	..	..		..	..	1132	..	..	..	..	..	..
Malden, for Coombe	..	..	..	..	1036		..	1048	..	a.m.	..	..	1058	..	..	11 8	1116	..	..	..	..		..	..	1136	..	..	..	..	1148	..
Bookham	..	..	..	..	..		..	..	..	3	..	10 33	..	..	..	..	..	10 58	..	..	..		..	..	..	..	..	..	..	..	11 33
Horsham dep.	..	..	Via Richmond, see page 485	..	..	9 48	..	..	..	9 49	..	..	..	1043	..	..	..	..	..	..	..		..	..	..	1051	..	..	..	..	..
Warnham	..	..		..	..	..	..	..	..	9 54	..	..	..	..	..	..	..	..	..	..	..		..	..	..	1056	..	..	..	..	..
Ockley, for Capel	..	..		..	..	..	..	..	..	10 1	..	..	..	..	..	..	..	..	..	..	..		..	..	..	11 2	..	..	..	..	..
Holmwood G	..	..		..	..	..	..	..	..	10 5	..	..	..	..	..	..	..	..	..	..	..		..	..	..	11 6	..	..	..	..	..
Dorking North F	..	10 6		..	..	..	..	..	..	10 15	..	..	..	11 2	..	..	..	..	..	..	..		11 6	..	..	1115	..	..	..	..	..
Boxhill & Burford Bdg D	..	10 8		..	..	..	..	..	..	10 17	..	..	..	..	..	..	..	..	..	..	..		11 8	..	..	1117	..	..	..	..	..
Leatherhead	..	1013		..	..	..	..	..	..	10 22	..	10 37	..	..	..	..	..	11 2	..	..	..	..	1113	..	..	1122	..	..	..	..	11 37
Ashtead	..	1017		..	..	..	..	..	..	10 26	..	10 41	..	..	..	..	..	11 6	..	..	..	..	1117	..	..	1126	..	..	..	..	11 41
Epsom 285	..	1021		..	..	..	..	..	..	10 30	..	10 45	..	..	..	..	..	11 10	..	..	..	..	1121	..	..	1130	..	..	..	..	11 45
Sutton arr.	..	1030		..	..	..	..	..	..	10‡46	..	10 54	..	1120	..	..	..	11‡30	..	..	..	..	1130	..	..	11‡46	..	..	..	..	11 54
Victoria "	..	..		..	..	11 6	..	..	..	11‡16	..	11*38	..	1143	..	..	..	..	..	..	..	..	..	..	..	12‡16	..	..	..	..	12*38
London Bridge "	..	11 3		..	..	1110	..	..	..	11‡27	..	11 27	..	12*3	..	..	..	12‡ 3	..	..	..	..	12 3	..	..	12‡27	..	..	..	..	12 27
Ewell West C	..	..	..	..	..	..	..	..	..	10 33	..	..	..	..	..	..	..	11 13	..	..	..	..	..	..	..	1133	..	..	..	..	..
Stoneleigh	..	..	..	..	..	..	..	..	..	10 36	..	..	..	..	..	..	..	11 16	..	..	..	..	..	..	..	1136	..	..	..	..	..
Worcester Park	..	..	..	..	..	..	..	..	..	10 39	..	..	..	..	..	..	..	11 19	..	..	..	..	..	..	..	1139	..	..	..	..	..
Chessington South ¶ dep.	..	..	..	1013	..	..	1033	..	..	..	..	..	..	..	..	..	..	..	..	..	..	..	..	1113	..	..	1133	..	..	..	..
Chessington North	..	..	..	1015	..	..	1035	..	..	..	..	..	..	..	..	..	..	..	..	..	..	..	..	1115	..	..	1135	..	..	..	..
Tolworth	..	..	..	1018	..	..	1038	..	..	..	..	..	..	..	..	..	..	..	..	..	..	..	..	1118	..	..	1138	..	..	..	..
Malden Manor	..	..	..	1021	..	..	1041	..	..	..	..	..	..	..	..	..	..	..	..	..	..	..	..	1121	..	..	1141	..	..	..	..
Motspur Park	..	..	..	1024	..	..	1044	..	..	10 41	..	..	..	..	..	..	..	11 21	..	..	..	..	..	1124	..	1141	1144	..	..	..	..
Raynes Park	..	..	..	1027	1039	..	1047	1051	..	..	..	..	11 1	..	..	1111	1119	..	..	..	..	..	..	1127	1139	..	1147	..	..	1151	..
Wimbledon 319, 320, 322	..	..	..	1030	1042	..	1050	1054	1053	10 46	..	..	11 4	..	..	1114	1122	11 26	1123	..	..	..	..	1130	1142	1146	1150	1153	..	1154	..
Earlsfield B	..	..	..	1034	1045	..	1054	1057	..	..	..	..	11 7	..	..	1117	1125	..	..	..	..	..	..	1134	1145	..	1154	..	..	1157	..
Clapham Junction A	..	..	..	1037	1049	..	1057	11 1	1059	10 52	..	..	1111	..	..	1121	1129	11 32	1128	..	..	..	..	1137	1149	1152	1157	1159	..	12 1	..
Vauxhall	..	..	..	1042	1053	..	11 2	11 5	..	..	..	..	1115	..	..	1125	1133	..	..	..	..	..	..	1142	1153	..	12 2	..	..	12 5	..
Waterloo arr.	1046	..	1048	1046	1057	..	11 6	11 9	11 6	10 59	1116	..	1119	..	1121	1129	1137	11 39	1135	..	1146	1148	..	1146	1157	1159	12 6	12 6	12 1	12 9	..

FOR NOTES, SEE PAGE 459

FOR NOTES SEE PAGE 459

GUILDFORD, WOKING, CHERTSEY, HAMPTON COURT, SHEPPERTON, KINGSTON, HORSHAM, DORKING NORTH, & LONDON

Sundays—*continued*

Up (a.m / p.m)		3		3	3	3	3		3	3		3		3	3	
Guildford ....dep.	..	..	1122	..	..	1137	..	..	..	..	1152	..	..	..	..	..
Worplesdon	..	..	1129	..	..	..	..	..	..	..	1159	..	..	..	..	..
Woking X 324, 339, 390	1137	..	1136	..	..	..	..	1158	..	..	12 6	..	..	..	..	..
Byfleet **W**	..	..	1140	..	..	..	..	..	..	..	1210	..	..	..	..	..
West Weybridge	..	..	1143	..	..	..	..	..	..	..	1213	..	..	..	..	..
Virginia Water Z ...dep.	..	1127	..	..	..	..	..	..	..	1157	..	..	..	..	..	..
Chertsey	..	1132	..	..	..	..	..	..	..	12 2	..	..	..	..	..	..
Addlestone	..	1135	..	..	..	..	..	..	..	12 5	..	..	..	..	..	..
Weybridge U 394	..	1139	1146	..	..	..	..	..	..	12 9	1216	..	..	..	..	..
Walton-on-Thames	..	..	1150	..	..	..	..	..	..	..	1220	..	..	..	..	..
Hersham	..	..	1152	..	..	..	..	..	..	..	1222	..	..	..	..	..
Esher, for Sandown Park	..	..	1155	..	..	..	..	..	..	..	1225	..	..	..	..	..
London Road (Guildford)	..	..	..	..	..	1140	..	..		..	..	..	..	..	..	..
Clandon **T**	..	..	..	..	..	1146	..	..		..	..	..	..	..	..	..
Horsley **R**	..	..	..	..	..	1151	..	..		..	..	..	..	..	..	..
Effingham Junction	..	..	..	..	..	1154	1157	..		..	..	..	..	..	..	..
Cobham **Q**	..	..	..	..	..	..	12 1	..	From Waterloo via Richmond Dep. **Twickenham** 11 59 a.m	..	..	..	..	..	..	..
Oxshott, for Fairmile	..	..	..	..	..	..	12 5	..		..	..	..	..	..	..	..
Claygate, for Claremont	..	..	..	..	..	..	12 8	..		..	..	..	..	..	..	..
Hinchley Wood	..	..	..	..	..	..	1211	..		..	..	..	..	..	..	..
Hampton Court ...dep.	..	..	..	..	1155	..	..	..		..	..	..	..	..	..	..
Thames Ditton	..	..	..	..	1157	..	..	..		..	..	..	..	..	..	..
Surbiton	1154	..	12 0	..	12 2	..	1216	..		..	1230	..	..	..	..	..
Berrylands **N**	..	..	..	..	12 5	..	..	..		..	..	..	..	..	..	..
Shepperton ....dep.	..	..	..	1131	..	..	..	..		..	..	1158	..	..	..	
Upper Halliford Halt	..	..	..	1134	..	..	..	..		..	..	12 1	..	..	..	
Sunbury **L**	..	..	..	1136	..	..	..	..		..	..	12 3	..	..	..	
Hampton	..	..	..	1140	..	..	..	..	p.m	..	..	12 7	..	..	..	
Fulwell **K**	..	..	..	1144	..	..	..	..	▽	..	..	1211	..	..	..	Via Three Bridges, see page 222
Teddington J	..	..	..	1147	..	..	..	..	12 5	..	..		..	..	..	
Hampton Wick	..	..	..	1150	..	..	..	..	12 8	..	..		..	..	..	
Kingston	..	..	..	1152	..	..	..	..	1210	..	..		..	..	..	
Norbiton **H**	..	..	..	1154	..	..	..	..	1212	..	..		..	..	..	
Malden, for Coombe	..	..	..	1158	12 8	..	..	..	1216	..	..		..	..	..	
Bookham	..	..	..	..	..	1158	..	..	..	..	..		..	..	..	a.m
Horsham ....dep.	..	..	..	..	..	..	..	..	..	..	..		..	..	..	1148
Warnham	..	..	..	..	..	..	..	..	..	..	..		..	..	..	..
Ockley, for Capel	..	..	..	..	..	..	..	..	..	..	..		..	..	..	..
Holmwood **G**	..	..	..	..	..	..	..	..	..	..	..	Via Richmond, see page 485	..	..	..	..
Dorking North F	..	..	..	..	..	..	..	..	..	..	..		..	12 6	..	..
Boxhill & Burford Bdg **D**	..	..	..	..	..	..	..	..	..	..	..		..	12 8	..	..
Leatherhead	..	..	..	..	..	12 2	..	..	..	..	..	..	..	1213	..	..
Ashtead	..	..	..	..	..	12 6	..	..	..	..	..	..	..	1217	..	..
Epsom 285	..	..	..	..	..	1210	..	..	..	..	..	..	..	1221	..	..
Sutton ....arr.	..	..	..	..	..	12‡30	..	..	..	..	..	..	..	1230	..	..
Victoria ...."	..	..	..	..	..	..	..	..	..	..	..	..	..	..	..	1 6
London Bridge ...."	..	..	..	..	..	1‡3	..	..	..	..	..	..	..	1 3	..	1 10
Ewell West **C**	..	..	..	..	..	1213	..	..	..	..	..	..	..	..	..	..
Stoneleigh	..	..	..	..	..	1216	..	..	..	..	..	..	..	..	..	..
Worcester Park	..	..	..	..	..	1219	..	..	..	..	..	..	..	..	..	..
Chessington South ¶dp.	..	..	..	..	..	..	..	..	..	..	..	..	..	..	1213	..
Chessington North	..	..	..	..	..	..	..	..	..	..	..	..	..	..	1215	..
Tolworth	..	..	..	..	..	..	..	..	..	..	..	..	..	..	1218	..
Malden Manor	..	..	..	..	..	..	..	..	..	..	..	..	..	..	1221	..
Motspur Park	..	..	..	..	..	1221	..	..	..	..	..	..	..	..	1224	..
Raynes Park	..	..	..	12 1	1211	..	..	..	1219	..	..	..	..	..	1227	..
Wimbledon 319, 320, 322	..	..	..	12 4	1214	1226	1222	..	1222	..	..	..	..	..	1230	..
Earlsfield **B**	..	..	..	12 7	1217	..	..	..	1225	..	..	..	..	..	1234	..
Clapham Junction **A**	..	..	..	1211	1221	1232	1228	..	1229	..	..	..	..	..	1237	..
Vauxhall	..	..	..	1215	1225	..	..	..	1233	..	..	..	..	..	1242	..
Wat[illegible]	[illegible]	..	1216	1219	1229	1239	1235	1230	1237	..	1246	1248	..	..	1246	..

Up (p.m)	3	3	3	3	3	3	3		3	3	3	3	3	3		3
Guildford ....dep.	..	..	..	..	1210	..	..	1222	..	..	1237	..	..	..	1252	..
Worplesdon	..	..	..	..	..	..	..	1229	..	..	..	..	..	..	1259	..
Woking X 324, 339, 390	..	..	..	..	..	..	..	1236	..	..	..	..	..	..	1 6	..
Byfleet **W**	..	..	..	..	..	..	..	1240	..	..	..	..	..	..	1 10	..
West Weybridge	..	..	..	..	..	..	..	1243	..	..	..	..	..	..	1 13	..
Virginia Water Z ...dep.	..	..	..	..	..	..	1227	..	..	..	..	..	..	1257	..	..
Chertsey	..	..	..	..	..	..	1232	..	..	..	..	..	..	1 2	..	..
Addlestone	..	..	..	..	..	..	1235	..	..	..	..	..	..	1 5	..	..
Weybridge U 394	..	..	..	..	..	..	1239	1246	..	..	..	..	..	1 9	1 16	..
Walton-on-Thames	..	..	..	..	..	..	..	1250	..	..	..	..	..	..	1 20	..
Hersham	..	..	..	..	..	..	..	1252	..	..	..	..	..	..	1 22	..
Esher, for Sandown Park	..	..	..	..	..	..	..	1255	..	..	..	..	..	..	1 25	..
London Road (Guildford)		..	..	..	1214	..	..	..	..	..	1240	..		..	..	..
Clandon **T**		..	..	..	1219	..	..	..	..	..	1246	..		..	..	..
Horsley **R**		..	..	..	1224	..	..	..	..	..	1251	..		..	..	..
Effingham Junction		..	..	..	1227	1230	..	..	..	..	1254	1257		..	..	..
Cobham **Q**	From Waterloo via Richmond Dep. **Twickenham** 12 19 p.m	..	..	..	1231	..	..	..	..	..	..	1 1	From Waterloo via Richmond Dep. **Twickenham** 12 59 p.m	..	..	..
Oxshott, for Fairmile		..	..	..	1235	..	..	..	..	..	..	1 5		..	..	..
Claygate, for Claremont		..	..	..	1238	..	..	..	..	..	..	1 8		..	..	..
Hinchley Wood		..	..	..	1241	..	..	..	..	..	..	1 11		..	..	..
Hampton Court ...dep.		..	..	1235	..	..	..	..	..	1255	..	..		..	..	..
Thames Ditton		..	..	1237	..	..	..	..	..	1257	..	..		..	..	..
Surbiton		..	..	1242	1245	..	..	1 0	..	1 2	..	1 15		..	1 30	..
Berrylands **N**		..	..	1245	..	..	..	..	..	1 5	..	..		..	..	..
Shepperton ....dep.		..	..	..	..	..	..	..	1231	..	..	..		..	..	1258
Upper Halliford Halt		..	..	..	..	..	..	..	1234	..	..	..		..	..	1 1
Sunbury **L**		..	..	..	..	..	..	..	1236	..	..	..		..	..	1 3
Hampton		..	..	..	..	..	..	..	1240	..	..	..		..	..	1 7
Fulwell **K**	▽	..	..	..	..	..	..	..	1244	..	..	..	▽	..	..	1 11
Teddington J	1225	..	..	..	..	..	..	..	1247	..	..	..	1 5	..	..	
Hampton Wick	1228	..	..	..	..	..	..	..	1250	..	..	..	1 8	..	..	
Kingston	1230	..	..	..	..	..	..	..	1252	..	..	..	1 10	..	..	
Norbiton **H**	1232	..	..	..	..	..	..	..	1254	..	..	..	1 12	..	..	
Malden, for Coombe	1236	..	..	1248	..	..	..	..	1258	1 8	..	..	1 16	..	..	
Bookham	..	a.m	..	..	..	1233	..	..	..	..	1258	..	..	..	..	
Horsham ....dep.	..	1149	..	..	..	..	..	..	..	..	..	..	..	..	..	
Warnham	..	1154	..	..	..	..	..	..	..	..	..	..	..	..	..	
Ockley, for Capel	..	12 1	..	..	..	..	..	..	..	..	..	..	..	..	..	
Holmwood **G**	..	12 5	..	..	..	..	..	..	..	..	..	..	..	..	..	Via Richmond, see page 486
Dorking North F	..	1215	..	..	..	..	..	..	..	..	..	..	..	..	..	
Boxhill & Burford Bdg **D**	..	1217	..	..	..	..	..	..	..	..	..	..	..	..	..	
Leatherhead	..	1222	..	..	..	1237	..	..	..	..	1 2	..	..	..	..	..
Ashtead	..	1226	..	..	..	1241	..	..	..	..	1 6	..	..	..	..	..
Epsom 285	..	1230	..	..	..	1245	..	..	..	..	1 10	..	..	..	..	..
Sutton ....arr.	..	12‡46	..	..	..	1254	..	..	..	..	1‡24	..	..	..	..	..
Victoria ...."	..	1‡16	..	..	..	1*38	..	..	..	..	..	..	..	..	..	..
London Bridge ...."	..	1‡27	..	..	..	1 27	..	..	..	..	1‡57	..	..	..	..	..
Ewell West **C**	..	1233	..	..	..	..	..	..	..	..	1 13	..	..	..	..	..
Stoneleigh	..	1236	..	..	..	..	..	..	..	..	1 16	..	..	..	..	..
Worcester Park	..	1239	..	..	..	..	..	..	..	..	1 19	..	..	..	..	..
Chessington South ¶dp.	..	..	1233	..	..	..	..	..	..	..	..	..	..	..	..	..
Chessington North	..	..	1235	..	..	..	..	..	..	..	..	..	..	..	..	..
Tolworth	..	..	1238	..	..	..	..	..	..	..	..	..	..	..	..	..
Malden Manor	..	..	1241	..	..	..	..	..	..	..	..	..	..	..	..	..
Motspur Park	..	1241	1244	..	..	..	..	..	..	..	1 21	..	..	..	..	..
Raynes Park	1239	..	1247	1251	..	..	..	..	1 1	1 11	..	..	1 19	..	..	..
Wimbledon 319, 320, 322	1242	1246	1250	1254	1252	..	..	..	1 4	1 14	1 26	1 22	1 22	..	..	..
Earlsfield **B**	1245	..	1254	1257	..	..	..	..	1 7	1 17	..	..	1 25	..	..	..
Clapham Junction **A**	1249	1252	1257	1 1	1258	..	..	..	1 11	1 21	1 32	1 28	1 29	..	..	..
Vauxhall	1253	..	1 2	1 5	..	..	..	..	1 15	1 25	..	..	1 33	..	..	..
Wat[illegible]	1257	1259	1 6	1 9	1 5	..	..	1 16	1 19	1 29	1 39	1 35	1 37	..	1 46	1 48

GUILDFORD, WOKING, CHERTSEY, HAMPTON COURT, SHEPPERTON, KINGSTON, HORSHAM, DORKING NORTH, & LONDON

Sundays—continued (p.m)

Up	3	3	3	..	3	3	3	3			3	3	3	3	3	3	3		3	3	3	3	..	3	3	3	3	3	3		3	3
Guildford ....dep.	..	..	..	..	..	..	1 10	..	1 20	1 22	..	..	..	1 37	..	..	..	1 52	..	..	..	..	..	..	..	..	2 10	..	..	2 22	..	..
Worplesdon	..	..	..	..	..	..	..	..	..	1 29	..	..	..	..	..	..	..	1 59	..	..	..	..	..	..	..	..	..	..	..	2 29	..	..
Woking X 324, 389, 390	..	..	..	..	..	..	..	..	1 30	1 36	..	..	..	..	..	..	..	2 6	..	..	..	..	..	..	..	..	..	..	..	2 36	..	..
Byfleet W	..	..	..	..	..	..	..	..	..	1 40	..	..	..	..	..	..	..	2 10	..	..	..	..	..	..	..	..	..	..	..	2 40	..	..
West Weybridge	..	..	..	..	..	..	..	..	..	1 43	..	..	..	..	..	..	..	2 13	..	..	..	..	..	..	..	..	..	..	..	2 43	..	..
Virginia Water Z ...dep.	..	..	..	..	..	..	..	1 27	..	..	..	..	..	..	..	..	1 57	..	..	..	..	..	..	..	..	..	..	2 27	..	..	..	..
Chertsey	..	..	..	..	..	..	..	1 32	..	..	..	..	..	..	..	..	2 2	..	..	..	..	..	..	..	..	..	..	2 32	..	..	..	..
Addlestone	..	..	..	..	..	..	..	1 35	..	..	..	..	..	..	..	..	2 5	..	..	..	..	..	..	..	..	..	..	2 35	..	..	..	..
Weybridge U 394	..	From Waterloo via Richmond Dep. Twickenham 1 19 p.m	..	..	..	..	..	1 39	..	1 46	..	..	..	..	..	From Waterloo, via Richmond Dep. Twickenham 1 59 p.m	2 9	2 16	..	..	From Waterloo, via Richmond Dep. Twickenham 2 19 p.m	..	..	..	..	..	..	2 39	..	2 46	..	..
Walton-on-Thames	..		..	..	..	..	..	Stop	..	1 50	..	..	..	..	..		..	2 20	..	..		..	..	..	..	..	..	..	..	2 50	..	..
Hersham	..		..	..	..	..	..		..	1 52	..	..	..	..	..		..	2 22	..	..		..	..	..	..	..	..	..	..	2 52	..	..
Esher, for Sandown Park	..		..	..	..	..	..	..	..	1 55	..	..	..	..	..		..	2 25	..	..		..	..	..	..	..	..	..	..	2 55	..	..
London Road (Guildford)	..		..	..	..	..	1 14	..	..	..	..	..	..	1 40	..		..	..	..	..		..	..	..	..	..	2 14	..	..	..	..	..
Clandon T	..		..	..	..	..	1 19	..	..	..	..	..	..	1 46	..		..	..	..	..		..	..	..	..	..	2 19	..	..	..	..	..
Horsley R	..		..	..	..	..	1 24	..	..	..	..	..	..	1 51	..		..	..	..	..		..	..	..	..	..	2 24	..	..	..	..	..
Effingham Junction	..		..	..	..	..	1 27	..	..	..	1 30	..	..	1 54	1 57		..	..	..	..		..	..	..	..	..	2 27	..	2 30	..	..	..
Cobham Q	..		..	..	..	..	1 31	..	..	..	..	..	..	..	2 1		..	..	..	..		..	..	..	..	..	2 31	..	..	..	..	..
Oxshott, for Fairmile	..		..	..	..	..	1 35	p.m	..	..	..	..	..	..	2 5		..	..	..	..		..	..	..	..	..	2 35	..	..	..	..	..
Claygate, for Claremont	..		..	..	..	..	1 38	3	..	..	..	..	..	..	2 8		..	..	..	..		..	..	..	..	..	2 38	..	..	..	..	..
Hinchley Wood	..		..	..	..	..	1 41		..	..	..	..	..	..	2 11		..	..	..	..		..	..	..	..	..	2 41	..	..	..	..	..
Hampton Court ...dep.	..		..	..	..	..	..	1 35	..	..	..	..	1 55	..	..		..	..	..	..		..	..	..	..	2 35	..	..	..	..	..	2 55
Thames Ditton	..		..	..	..	..	..	1 37	..	..	..	..	1 57	..	..		..	..	..	..		..	..	..	..	2 37	..	..	..	..	..	2 57
Surbiton	..		..	..	..	..	1 45	1 42	..	2 0	..	..	2 2	..	2 15		..	2 30	..	..		..	..	..	..	2 42	2 45	..	..	3 0	..	3 2
Berrylands N	..		..	..	..	..	..	1 45	..	..	..	..	2 5	..	..		..	..	..	..		..	..	..	..	2 45	..	..	..	..	..	3 5
Shepperton ....dep.	..		..	Via Three Bridges, see page 222.	..	..	..	..	..	..	..	1 31	..	..	..		..	..	1 58	..		..	Via Three Bridges see page 222	..	..	..	..	..	..	..	2 31	..
Upper Halliford Halt	..		..		..	..	..	..	..	..	..	1 34	..	..	..		..	..	2 1	..		..		..	..	..	..	..	..	..	2 34	..
Sunbury L	..		..		..	..	..	..	..	..	..	1 36	..	..	..		..	..	2 3	..		..		..	..	..	..	..	..	..	2 36	..
Hampton	..		..		..	..	..	..	..	..	..	1 40	..	..	..		..	..	2 7	..		..		..	..	..	..	..	..	..	2 40	..
Fulwell K	..	V	..		..	..	..	..	..	..	..	1 44	..	..	..	V	..	..	2 11	..	V	..		..	..	..	..	..	..	..	2 44	..
Teddington J	..	1 25	..		..	..	..	..	..	..	..	1 47	..	..	..	2 5	..	..	..	..	2 25	..		..	..	..	..	..	..	..	2 47	..
Hampton Wick	..	1 28	..		..	..	..	..	..	..	..	1 50	..	..	..	2 8	..	..	..	..	2 28	..		..	..	..	..	..	..	..	2 50	..
Kingston	..	1 30	..		..	..	..	..	..	..	..	1 52	..	..	..	2 10	..	..	..	..	2 30	..		..	..	..	..	..	..	..	2 52	..
Norbiton H	..	1 32	..		..	..	..	..	..	..	..	1 54	..	..	..	2 12	..	..	..	..	2 32	..		..	..	..	..	..	..	..	2 54	..
Malden, for Coombe	..	1 36	..		..	..	..	1 48	..	..	..	1 58	2 8	..	..	2 16	..	..	..	..	2 36	..		..	..	2 48	..	..	..	..	2 58	3 8
Bookham	..	..	..	..	..	..	..	..	..	..	1 33	..	..	1 58	..	..	..	..	..	..	..	..		..	..	..	..	..	2 33	..	..	..
Horsham ....dep.	..	..	..	1248	1249	..	..	..	..	..	..	..	..	..	..	..	..	..	..	..	..	..	1 48	1 49	..	..	..	..	..	..	..	..
Warnham	..	..	..	..	1254	..	..	..	..	..	..	..	..	..	..	..	..	..	..	..	..	..	..	1 54	..	..	..	..	..	..	..	..
Ockley, for Capel	..	..	..	..	1 1	..	..	..	..	..	..	..	..	..	..	..	..	..	..	..	..	..	..	2 1	..	..	..	..	..	..	..	..
Holmwood G	..	..	..	..	1 5	..	..	..	..	..	..	..	..	..	..	..	..	..	..	..	..	..	..	2 5	..	..	..	..	..	..	..	..
Dorking North F	..	..	1 0	..	1 15	..	..	..	..	..	..	..	..	..	..	..	..	..	..	..	..	2 0	..	2 15	..	..	..	..	..	..	..	..
Boxhill & Burford Bdg D	..	..	1 2	..	1 17	..	..	..	..	..	..	..	..	..	..	..	..	..	..	..	..	2 2	..	2 17	..	..	..	..	..	..	..	..
Leatherhead	..	..	1 7	..	1 22	..	..	..	..	..	1 37	..	..	2 2	..	..	..	..	..	..	..	2 7	..	2 22	..	..	..	..	2 37	..	..	..
Ashtead	..	..	1 11	..	1 26	..	..	..	..	..	1 41	..	..	2 6	..	..	..	..	..	..	..	2 11	..	2 26	..	..	..	..	2 41	..	..	..
Epsom 285	..	..	1 15	..	1 30	..	..	..	..	..	1 45	..	..	2 10	..	..	..	..	..	..	..	2 15	..	2 30	..	..	..	..	2 45	..	..	..
Sutton ....arr.	..	..	1 24	..	1‡46	..	..	..	..	..	1 54	..	..	2‡25	..	..	..	..	Via Richmond, see page 486	..	..	2 25	..	2‡46	..	..	..	..	2 54	..	..	..
Victoria .... "	..	..	..	2 7	2‡16	..	..	..	..	..	2*38	..	..	..	..	..	..	..		..	..	..	3 6	3‡16	..	..	..	..	3*38	..	..	..
London Bridge ..... "	..	..	1 57	2 10	2‡27	..	..	..	..	..	2 27	..	..	2‡58	..	..	..	..		..	..	2 58	3 10	3‡27	..	..	..	..	3 27	..	..	..
Ewell West C	..	..	..	..	1 33	..	..	..	..	..	..	..	..	2 13	..	..	..	..		..	..	..	..	2 33	..	..	..	..	..	..	..	..
Stoneleigh	..	..	..	..	1 36	..	..	..	..	..	..	..	..	2 16	..	..	..	..		..	..	..	..	2 36	..	..	..	..	..	..	..	..
Worcester Park	..	..	..	..	1 39	..	..	..	..	..	..	..	..	2 19	..	..	..	..		..	..	..	..	2 39	..	..	..	..	..	..	..	..
Chessington South ¶dp	1 13	..	..	..	..	1 33	..	..	..	..	..	..	..	..	..	..	..	..		2 13	..	..	..	..	2 33	..	..	..	..	..	..	..
Chessington North	1 15	..	..	..	..	1 35	..	..	..	..	..	..	..	..	..	..	..	..		2 15	..	..	..	..	2 35	..	..	..	..	..	..	..
Tolworth	1 18	..	..	..	..	1 38	..	..	..	..	..	..	..	..	..	..	..	..		2 18	..	..	..	..	2 38	..	..	..	..	..	..	..
Malden Manor	1 21	..	..	..	..	1 41	..	..	..	..	..	..	..	..	..	..	..	..		2 21	..	..	..	..	2 41	..	..	..	..	..	..	..
Motspur Park	1 24	..	..	..	1 41	1 44	..	..	..	..	..	..	..	2 21	..	..	..	..		2 24	..	..	..	2 41	2 44	..	..	..	..	..	..	..
Raynes Park	1 27	1 39	..	..	..	1 47	..	1 51	..	..	..	2 1	2 11	..	..	2 19	..	..	..	2 27	2 39	..	..	..	2 47	2 51	..	..	..	..	3 1	3 11
Wimbledon 319, 320, 322	1 30	1 42	..	..	1 46	1 50	1 53	1 54	..	..	..	2 4	2 14	2 26	2 22	2 22	..	..	..	2 30	2 42	..	..	2 46	2 50	2 54	2 52	..	..	..	3 4	3 14
Earlsfield B	1 34	1 45	..	..	..	1 54	..	1 57	..	..	..	2 7	2 17	..	..	2 25	..	..	..	2 34	2 45	..	..	..	2 54	2 57	..	..	..	..	3 7	3 17
Clapham Junction A	1 37	1 49	..	..	1 52	1 57	1 59	2 1	..	..	..	2 11	2 21	2 32	2 28	2 29	..	..	..	2 37	2 49	..	..	2 52	2 57	3 1	2 58	..	..	..	3 11	3 21
Vauxhall	1 42	1 53	..	..	..	2 2	..	2 5	..	..	..	2 15	2 25	..	..	2 33	..	..	..	2 42	2 53	..	..	..	3 2	3 5	..	..	..	..	3 15	3 25
Waterloo ....arr.	1 46	1 57	..	..	1 59	2 6	2 6	2 9	2 1	2 16	..	2 19	2 29	2 39	2 35	2 37	..	2 46	2 48	2 46	2 57	..	..	2 59	3 6	3 9	3 5	..	..	3 16	3 19	3 29

FOR NOTES, SEE PAGE 459

FOR NOTES, SEE PAGE 459

GUILDFORD, WOKING, CHERTSEY, HAMPTON COURT, SHEPPERTON, KINGSTON, HORSHAM, DORKING NORTH, & LONDON

Sundays—continued (p.m.)

Up		3	3	3		3	3	3	3	..	3	3			3	..		3	3	3		3	3	3		3	3	3	3	..	3	
Guildford ......dep.	2 37	..	..	..	2 52	..	..	..	..	..	..	..	3 10	3 20	..	..	3 22	..	..	..	3 37	..	..	..	3 52	..	..	..	..	..	..	4 10
Worplesdon	..	..	..	..	2 59	..	..	..	..	..	..	..	..	..	..	..	3 29	..	..	..	..	..	..	..	3 59	..	..	..	..	..	..	..
Woking X 324, 389, 390	3	..	..	..	3 6	..	..	..	..	..	..	..	3	3 30	..	3 39	3 36	..	..	..	3	..	..	..	4 6	..	..	..	..	..	..	3
Byfleet W	..	..	..	..	3 10	..	..	..	..	..	..	..	..	..	..	..	3 40	..	..	..	..	..	..	..	4 10	..	..	..	..	..	..	..
West Weybridge	..	..	..	..	3 13	..	..	..	..	..	..	..	..	..	..	..	3 43	..	..	..	..	..	..	..	4 13	..	..	..	..	..	..	..
Virginia Water Z ..dep.	..	..	..	2 57	..	..	..	..	..	..	..	..	..	..	3 27	..	..	..	..	..	..	..	..	3 57	..	..	..	..	..	..	..	..
Chertsey	..	..	..	3 2	..	..	..	..	..	..	..	..	..	..	3 32	..	..	..	..	..	..	..	..	4 2	..	..	..	..	..	..	..	..
Addlestone	..	..	..	3 5	..	..	..	..	..	..	..	..	..	..	3 35	..	..	..	..	..	..	..	..	4 5	..	..	..	..	..	..	..	..
Weybridge U 394	..	..	From Waterloo, via Richmond Dep. Twickenham 2 59 p.m	3 9	3 16	..	..	From Waterloo, via Richmond Dep. Twickenham 3 19 p.m	..	..	..	..	..	..	3 39	..	3 46	..	..	..	..	..	From Waterloo via Richmond Dep. Twickenham 3 59 p.m	4 9	4 16	..	..	..	From Waterloo, via Richmond Dep. Twickenham 4 19 p.m	..	..	..
Walton-on-Thames	..	..		..	3 20	..	..		..	..	..	..	..	..	Stop	..	3 50	..	..	..	..	..		..	4 20	..	..	..		..	..	..
Hersham	..	..		..	3 22	..	..		..	..	..	..	..	..	..	..	3 52	..	..	..	..	..		..	4 22	..	..	..		..	..	..
Esher, for Sandown Park	..	..		..	3 25	..	..		..	..	..	..	..	..	..	..	3 55	..	..	..	..	..		..	4 25	..	..	..		..	..	..
London Road (Guildford)	2 40	..		..	..	..	..		..	..	..	..	3 14	..	..	..	..	..	..	..	3 40	..		..	..	..	..	..		..	..	4 14
Clandon T	2 46	..		..	..	..	..		..	..	..	..	3 19	..	..	..	..	..	..	..	3 46	..		..	..	..	..	..		..	..	4 19
Horsley R	2 51	..		..	..	..	..		..	..	..	..	3 24	..	..	..	..	..	..	..	3 51	..		..	..	..	..	..		..	..	4 24
Effingham Junction	2 54	2 57		..	..	..	..		..	..	..	..	3 27	..	..	..	..	..	3 30	..	3 54	3 57		..	..	..	..	..		..	..	4 27
Cobham Q	..	3 1		..	..	..	..		..	..	..	..	3 31	..	..	..	..	..	..	..	..	4 1		..	..	..	..	..		..	..	4 31
Oxshott, for Fairmile	..	3 5		..	..	..	..		..	..	..	..	3 35	..	..	..	..	..	..	..	..	4 5		..	..	..	..	..		..	..	4 35
Claygate, for Claremont	..	3 8		..	..	..	..		..	..	..	..	3 38	..	..	..	..	..	..	..	..	4 8		..	..	..	..	..		..	..	4 38
Hinchley Wood	..	3 11		..	..	..	..		..	..	..	..	3 41	..	..	..	..	..	..	..	..	4 11		..	..	..	..	..		..	..	4 41
Hampton Court ...dep.	..	..		..	..	..	..		..	..	..	3 35	..	..	..	..	..	..	..	3 55	..	..		..	..	..	..	..		Via Three Bridges, see page 228	4 35	..
Thames Ditton	..	..		..	..	..	..		..	..	..	3 37	..	..	..	..	..	..	..	3 57	..	..		..	..	..	..	..			4 37	..
Surbiton	..	3 15		..	3 30	..	..		..	..	..	3 42	3 45	..	..	..	4 0	..	..	4 2	..	4 15		..	4 30	..	..	..			4 42	4 45
Berrylands N	..	..		..	..	..	..		..	..	..	3 45	..	..	..	..	..	..	..	4 5	..	..		..	..	..	..	..			4 45	..
Shepperton ......dep.	..	..		..	..	..	2 58		..	Via Three Bridges see page 228	..	..	..	..	..	..	..	3 31	..	..	..	..		..	..	..	..	3 58			..	..
Upper Halliford Halt	..	..		..	..	..	3 1		..		..	..	..	..	..	..	..	3 34	..	..	..	..		..	..	..	..	4 1			..	..
Sunbury L	..	..		..	..	..	3 3		..		..	..	..	..	..	..	..	3 36	..	..	..	..		..	..	..	..	4 3			..	..
Hampton	..	..		..	..	..	3 7		..		..	..	..	..	..	..	..	3 40	..	..	..	..		..	..	..	..	4 7			..	..
Fulwell K	..	..	V	..	..	..	3 11	V	..		..	..	..	..	..	..	..	3 44	..	..	..	..	V	..	..	..	..	4 11	V		..	..
Teddington J	..	..	3 5	..	..	..	Via Richmond see page 486	3 25	..		..	..	..	..	..	..	..	3 47	..	..	..	..	4 5	..	..	..	..	Via Richmond, see page 487	4 25		..	..
Hampton Wick	..	..	3 8	..	..	..		3 28	..		..	..	..	..	..	..	..	3 50	..	..	..	..	4 8	..	..	..	..		4 28		..	..
Kingston	..	..	3 10	..	..	..		3 30	..		..	..	..	..	..	..	..	3 52	..	..	..	..	4 10	..	..	..	..		4 30		..	..
Norbiton H	..	..	3 12	..	..	..		3 32	..		..	..	..	..	..	..	..	3 54	..	..	..	..	4 12	..	..	..	..		4 32		..	..
Malden, for Coombe	..	..	3 16	..	..	..		3 36	..		..	3 48	..	..	..	..	..	3 58	..	4 8	..	..	4 16	..	..	..	..		4 36		4 48	..
Bookham	2 58	..	..	..	..	..		..	..		..	..	..	..	..	..	..	..	3 33	..	3 58	..	..	..	..	..	..		..		..	..
Horsham ......dep.	..	..	..	..	..	..		..	..	2 48	2 49	..	..	..	..	..	..	..	..	..	..	..	..	..	..	..	..		..	3 48	..	..
Warnham	..	..	..	..	..	..		..	..	..	2 54	..	..	..	..	..	..	..	..	..	..	..	..	..	..	..	..		..	..	..	..
Ockley, for Capel	..	..	..	..	..	..		..	..	..	3 1	..	..	..	..	..	..	..	..	..	..	..	..	..	..	..	..		..	..	..	..
Holmwood G	..	..	..	..	..	..		..	..	..	3 5	..	..	..	..	..	..	..	..	..	..	..	..	..	..	..	..		..	..	..	..
Dorking North F	..	..	..	..	..	..		..	3 0	..	3 15	..	..	..	..	..	..	..	..	..	..	..	..	..	..	4 6	..		..	..	..	..
Boxhill & Burford Bdg D	..	..	..	..	..	..		..	3 2	..	3 17	..	..	..	..	..	..	..	..	..	..	..	..	..	..	4 8	..		..	..	..	..
Leatherhead	3 2	..	..	..	..	..	..	..	3 7	..	3 22	..	..	..	..	..	..	..	3 37	..	4 2	..	..	..	..	4 13	..	..	..	..	..	..
Ashtead	3 6	..	..	..	..	..	..	..	3 11	..	3 26	..	..	..	..	..	..	..	3 41	..	4 6	..	..	..	..	4 17	..	..	..	..	..	..
Epsom 285	3 10	..	..	..	..	..	..	..	3 15	..	3 30	..	..	..	..	..	..	..	3 45	..	4 10	..	..	..	..	4 21	..	..	..	..	..	..
Sutton ......arr.	3‡24	..	..	..	..	..	..	..	3 24	..	3‡46	..	..	..	..	..	..	..	3 54	..	4‡30	..	..	..	..	4 30	..	..	..	..	..	..
Victoria ...... "	..	..	..	..	..	..	..	..	..	4 7	4‡16	..	..	..	..	..	..	..	4*38	..	..	..	..	..	..	..	..	..	..	5 7	..	..
London Bridge .... "	3‡57	..	..	..	..	..	..	..	3 57	4 10	4‡27	..	..	..	..	..	..	..	4 27	..	5‡3	..	..	..	..	5 3	..	..	..	5 10	..	..
Ewell West C	3 13	..	..	..	..	..	..	..	..	..	3 33	..	..	..	p.m.	..	..	..	..	..	4 13	..	..	..	..	..	..	..	..	..	..	..
Stoneleigh	3 16	..	..	..	..	..	..	..	..	..	3 36	..	..	..	3	..	..	..	..	..	4 16	..	..	..	..	..	..	..	..	..	..	..
Worcester Park	3 19	..	..	..	..	..	..	..	..	..	3 39	..	..	..		..	..	..	..	..	4 19	..	..	..	..	..	..	..	..	..	..	..
Chessington South ¶ dp	..	..	..	..	..	3 13	..	..	..	..	..	..	..	..	3 33	..	..	..	..	..	..	..	..	..	..	..	4 13	..	..	..	..	..
Chessington North	..	..	..	..	..	3 15	..	..	..	..	..	..	..	..	3 35	..	..	..	..	..	..	..	..	..	..	..	4 15	..	..	..	..	..
Tolworth	..	..	..	..	..	3 18	..	..	..	..	..	..	..	..	3 38	..	..	..	..	..	..	..	..	..	..	..	4 18	..	..	..	..	..
Malden Manor	..	..	..	..	..	3 21	..	..	..	..	..	..	..	..	3 41	..	..	..	..	..	..	..	..	..	..	..	4 21	..	..	..	..	..
Motspur Park	3 21	..	..	..	..	3 24	..	..	..	..	3 41	..	..	..	3 44	..	..	..	..	..	4 21	..	..	..	..	..	4 24	..	..	..	..	..
Raynes Park	..	..	3 19	..	..	3 27	..	3 39	..	..	..	3 51	..	..	3 47	..	..	4 1	..	4 11	..	..	4 19	..	..	..	4 27	..	4 39	..	4 51	..
Wimbledon 319, 320, 322	3 26	3 22	3 22	..	..	3 30	..	3 42	..	..	3 46	3 54	3 53	..	3 50	..	..	4 4	..	4 14	4 26	4 22	4 22	..	..	..	4 30	..	4 42	..	4 54	4 52
Earlsfield B	..	..	3 25	..	..	3 34	..	3 45	..	..	..	3 57	..	..	3 54	..	..	4 7	..	4 17	..	..	4 25	..	..	..	4 34	..	4 45	..	4 57	..
Clapham Junction A	3 32	3 28	3 29	..	..	3 37	..	3 49	..	..	3 52	4 1	3 59	..	3 57	..	..	4 11	..	4 21	4 32	4 28	4 29	..	..	..	4 37	..	4 49	..	5 1	4 58
Vauxhall	..	..	3 33	..	..	3 42	..	3 53	..	..	..	4 5	..	..	4 2	..	..	4 15	..	4 25	..	..	4 33	..	..	..	4 42	..	4 53	..	5 5	..
Waterloo ......arr.	3 39	3 35	3 37	..	3 46	3 46	3 48	3 57	..	..	3 59	4 9	4 6	4 1	4 6	4 10	4 16	4 19	..	4 29	4 39	4 35	4 37	..	4 46	..	4 46	4 48	4 57	..	5 9	5 5

GUILDFORD, WOKING, CHERTSEY, HAMPTON COURT, SHEPPERTON, KINGSTON, HORSHAM, DORKING NORTH, & LONDON

Up	Sundays—continued (p.m.)																														
Guildford dep.	3	3	4 22	3	3	3	4 37	3	3	..	3	4 52	3	3	3	3	3	3	..	5 20	3	5 10	3	3	5 22	3	3	5 37	3	3	3	5 52
Worplesdon	..	..	4 29	..	..	..	..	..	..	..	..	4 59	..	..	..	..	..	..	..	..	..	..	..	..	5 29	..	..	..	..	..	..	5 59
Woking X 324, 339, 390	..	..	4 36	..	..	..	3	..	..	..	..	5 6	..	..	..	..	..	..	5 25	5 30	..	3	..	..	5 36	..	..	3	..	..	..	6 6
Byfleet **W**	..	..	4 40	..	..	..	..	..	..	..	..	5 10	..	..	..	..	..	..	..	..	..	..	..	..	5 40	..	..	..	..	..	..	6 10
West Weybridge	..	..	4 43	..	..	..	..	..	..	..	..	5 13	..	..	..	..	..	..	..	..	..	..	..	..	5 43	..	..	..	..	..	..	6 13
Virginia Water Z dep.	..	4 27	..	..	..	..	..	..	..	..	4 57	..	..	..	..	..	..	..	..	..	..	..	..	5 27	..	..	..	..	..	..	5 57	..
Chertsey	..	4 32	..	..	..	..	..	..	..	..	5 2	..	..	..	..	..	..	..	..	..	..	..	..	5 32	..	..	..	..	..	..	6 2	..
Addlestone	..	4 35	..	..	..	..	..	..	..	..	5 5	..	..	..	..	..	..	..	..	..	..	..	..	5 35	..	..	..	..	..	..	6 5	..
Weybridge U 394	..	4 39	4 46	..	..	..	..	..	..	..	5 9	5 16	..	..	..	..	..	..	..	..	..	..	..	5 39	5 46	..	..	..	..	..	6 9	6 16
Walton-on-Thames	..	—	4 50	..	..	..	..	..	..	..	..	5 20	..	..	..	..	..	..	..	..	..	..	..	..	5 50	..	..	..	..	..	..	6 20
Hersham	..	Stop	4 52	..	..	..	..	..	..	..	..	5 22	..	..	..	..	..	..	..	..	..	..	..	..	5 52	..	..	..	..	..	..	6 22
Esher, for Sandown Park	..	..	4 55	..	..	..	..	..	..	..	..	5 25	..	..	..	..	..	..	..	..	..	..	..	..	5 55	..	..	..	..	..	..	6 25
London Road (Guildford)	..	..	..	..	..	..	4 40	..	From Waterloo via Richmond Dep. **Twickenham** 4 59 p.m	..	..	..	..	..	From Waterloo via Richmond Dep. **Twickenham** 5 19 p.m	..	..	..	..	..	..	5 14	..	..	..	..	..	5 40	..	From Waterloo via Richmond Dep. **Twickenham** 5 59 p.m	..	..
Clandon **T**	..	..	..	..	..	..	4 46	..		..	..	..	..	..		..	..	..	..	..	..	5 19	..	..	..	..	..	5 46	..		..	..
Horsley **R**	..	..	..	..	..	..	4 51	..		..	..	..	..	..		..	..	..	..	..	..	5 24	..	..	..	..	..	5 51	..		..	..
Effingham Junction	..	..	..	4 30	..	..	4 54	4 57		..	..	..	..	..		..	..	..	..	..	..	5 27	5 30	..	..	..	..	5 54	5 57		..	..
Cobham **Q**	..	..	..	..	..	..	..	5 1		..	..	..	..	..		..	..	..	..	..	..	5 31	..	..	..	..	..	..	6 1		..	..
Oxshott, for Fairmile	..	..	..	..	..	..	..	5 5		..	..	..	..	..		..	..	..	..	..	..	5 35	..	..	..	..	..	..	6 5		..	..
Claygate, for Claremont	..	..	..	..	..	..	..	5 8		..	..	..	..	..		..	..	..	..	..	..	5 39	..	..	..	..	..	..	6 8		..	..
Hinchley Wood	..	..	..	..	..	..	..	5 11		..	..	..	..	..		..	..	..	..	..	..	5 43	..	..	..	..	..	..	6 11		..	..
Hampton Court dep.	..	..	..	..	..	4 55	..	..		..	..	..	..	..		..	..	5 35	..	..	..	..	..	..	..	..	5 55	..	..		..	..
Thames Ditton	..	..	..	..	..	4 57	..	..		..	..	..	..	..		..	..	5 37	..	..	..	..	..	..	..	..	5 57	..	..		..	..
Surbiton	..	..	5 0	..	..	5 2	..	5 15		..	..	5 30	..	..		..	..	5 42	5 45	..	..	5 49	..	..	6 0	..	6 2	..	6 15		..	6 30
Berrylands **N**	..	..	..	..	..	5 5	..	..		..	..	..	..	..		..	..	5 45	..	..	..	..	..	..	..	..	6 5	..	..		..	..
Shepperton dep.	..	..	..	..	4 31	..	..	..		..	..	..	..	4 58		..	..	..	..	..	..	..	..	..	..	5 31	..	..	..		..	..
Upper Halliford Halt	..	..	..	..	4 34	..	..	..		..	..	..	..	5 1		..	..	..	..	..	..	..	..	..	..	5 34	..	..	..		..	..
Sunbury **L**	..	..	..	..	4 36	..	..	..		..	..	..	..	5 3		..	..	..	..	..	..	..	..	..	..	5 36	..	..	..		..	..
Hampton	..	..	..	..	4 40	..	..	..		..	..	..	..	5 7		..	..	..	..	..	..	..	..	..	..	5 40	..	..	..		..	..
Fulwell **K**	..	..	..	..	4 44	..	..	..	V	..	..	..	..	5 11	V	..	..	..	..	..	..	..	..	..	..	5 44	..	..	..	V	..	..
Teddington J	..	..	..	..	4 47	..	..	..	5 5	..	..	..	..	Via Richmond, see page 487	5 25	..	..	..	..	..	..	..	..	..	..	5 47	..	..	..	6 5	..	..
Hampton Wick	..	..	..	..	4 50	..	..	..	5 8	..	..	..	..		5 28	..	..	..	..	..	..	..	..	..	..	5 50	..	..	..	6 8	..	..
Kingston	..	..	..	..	4 52	..	..	..	5 10	..	..	..	..		5 30	..	..	..	..	..	..	..	..	..	..	5 52	..	..	..	6 10	..	..
Norbiton **H**	..	..	..	..	4 54	..	..	..	5 12	..	..	..	..		5 32	..	..	..	..	..	..	..	..	..	..	5 54	..	..	..	6 12	..	..
Malden, for Coombe	..	..	..	..	4 58	5 8	..	..	5 16	..	..	..	..		5 36	..	..	5 48	..	..	..	..	..	..	..	5 58	6 8	..	..	6 16	..	..
Bookham	..	..	..	4 33	..	..	4 58	..	..	..	..	..	..		..	..	..	..	..	..	..	..	5 33	..	..	..	..	5 58	..	..	..	..
Horsham dep.	3 49	..	..	..	..	..	..	..	..	4 43	..	..	..		..	..	4 49	..	..	..	..	..	..	..	..	..	..	..	..	..	..	..
Warnham	3 54	..	..	..	..	..	..	..	..	..	..	..	..		..	..	4 54	..	..	..	..	..	..	..	..	..	..	..	..	..	..	..
Ockley, for Capel	4 1	..	..	..	..	..	..	..	..	..	..	..	..		..	..	5 1	..	..	..	..	..	..	..	..	..	..	..	..	..	..	..
Holmwood **G**	4 5	..	..	..	..	..	..	..	..	..	..	..	..		..	..	5 5	..	..	..	..	..	..	..	..	..	..	..	..	..	..	..
Dorking North F	4 15	..	..	..	..	..	..	..	..	5 2	..	..	..		..	5 6	5 15	..	..	..	..	..	..	..	..	..	..	..	..	..	..	..
Boxhill & Burford Bdg **D**	4 17	..	..	..	..	..	..	..	..	..	..	..	..		..	5 8	5 17	..	..	..	..	..	..	..	..	..	..	..	..	..	..	..
Leatherhead	4 22	..	..	4 37	..	..	5 2	..	..	..	..	..	..	..	..	5 13	5 22	..	..	..	..	..	5 37	..	..	..	..	6 2	..	..	..	..
Ashtead	4 26	..	..	4 41	..	..	5 6	..	..	..	..	..	..	..	..	5 17	5 26	..	..	..	..	..	5 41	..	..	..	..	6 6	..	..	..	..
Epsom 285	4 30	..	..	4 45	..	..	5 10	..	..	..	..	..	..	..	..	5 21	5 30	..	..	..	..	..	5 45	..	..	..	..	6 10	..	..	..	..
Sutton arr.	4‡46	..	..	4 54	..	..	5‡30	..	..	5 20	..	..	..	..	..	5 30	5‡46	..	..	..	..	..	5 54	..	..	..	..	6‡24	..	..	..	..
Victoria "	5‡16	..	..	5*38	..	..	..	..	..	5 44	..	..	..	..	..	..	6‡16	..	..	..	..	..	6*38	..	..	..	..	..	..	..	..	..
London Bridge "	5‡27	..	..	5 27	..	..	6‡3	..	..	6* 3	..	..	..	..	..	6 3	6‡27	..	..	..	..	..	6 27	..	..	..	..	6‡57	..	..	..	..
Ewell West **C**	4 33	p.m.	..	..	..	..	5 13	..	..	..	..	..	..	..	..	..	5 33	..	..	..	..	..	..	..	..	..	..	6 13	..	..	..	..
Stoneleigh	4 36	3	..	..	..	..	5 16	..	..	..	..	..	..	..	..	..	5 36	..	..	..	..	..	..	..	..	..	..	6 16	..	..	..	..
Worcester Park	4 39		..	..	..	..	5 19	..	..	..	..	..	..	..	..	..	5 39	..	..	..	..	..	..	..	..	..	..	6 19	..	..	..	..
Chessington South¶ dp	..	4 33	..	..	..	..	..	..	..	..	..	..	5 13	..	..	..	..	..	..	..	5 33	..	..	..	..	..	..	..	..	..	..	..
Chessington North	..	4 35	..	..	..	..	..	..	..	..	..	..	5 15	..	..	..	..	..	..	..	5 35	..	..	..	..	..	..	..	..	..	..	..
Tolworth	..	4 38	..	..	..	..	..	..	..	..	..	..	5 18	..	..	..	..	..	..	..	5 38	..	..	..	..	..	..	..	..	..	..	..
Malden Manor	..	4 41	..	..	..	..	..	..	..	..	..	..	5 21	..	..	..	..	..	..	..	5 41	..	..	..	..	..	..	..	..	..	..	..
Motspur Park	4 41	4 44	..	..	..	..	5 21	..	..	..	..	..	5 24	..	..	..	5 41	..	..	..	5 44	..	..	..	..	..	..	6 21	..	..	..	..
Raynes Park	..	4 47	..	..	5 1	5 11	..	..	5 19	..	..	..	5 27	..	5 39	..	..	5 51	..	..	5 47	..	..	..	..	6 1	6 11	..	..	6 19	..	..
Wimbledon 319, 320, 322	4 46	4 50	..	..	5 4	5 14	5 26	5 22	5 22	..	..	..	5 30	..	5 42	..	5 46	5 54	..	..	5 50	5 56	..	..	..	6 4	6 14	6 26	6 22	6 22	..	..
Earlsfield **B**	..	4 54	..	..	5 7	5 17	..	..	5 25	..	..	..	5 34	..	5 45	..	..	5 57	..	..	5 54	..	..	..	..	6 7	6 17	..	..	6 25	..	..
Clapham Junction A	4 52	4 57	..	..	5 11	5 21	5 32	5 28	5 29	..	..	..	5 37	..	5 49	..	5 52	6 1	..	..	5 57	6 2	..	..	..	6 11	6 21	6 32	6 28	6 29	..	..
Vauxhall	..	5 2	..	..	5 15	5 25	..	..	5 33	..	..	..	5 42	..	5 53	..	..	6 5	..	..	6 2	..	..	..	..	6 15	6 25	..	..	6 33	..	..
Waterloo arr.	5 9	5 6	5 16	..	5 19	5 29	5 39	5 35	5 37	..	..	5 46	5 46	5 48	5 57	..	5 59	6 9	6 4	6 1	6 6	6 10	..	..	6 16	6 19	6 29	6 39	6 35	6 37	..	6 48

FOR NOTES, SEE PAGE 459

FOR NOTES, SEE PAGE 459

GUILDFORD, WOKING, CHERTSEY, HAMPTON COURT, SHEPPERTON, KINGSTON, HORSHAM, DORKING NORTH, & LONDON

Sundays—continued (p.m)

Up	3	3	3		3	3	3		3		3		3	3	3			3		3		3		3	3	3	3	3	3			3
Guildford dep.	..	..	..	..	..	..	..	6 10	..	620	..	6 22	..	..	..	..	6 37	..	..	..	..	..	6 52	..	..	..	..	..	..	7 10	7 20	..
Worplesdon	..	..	..	..	..	..	..	..	..	..	..	6 29	..	..	..	..	..	..	..	..	..	..	6 59	..	..	..	..	..	..	..	..	..
Woking X 324, 389, 390	..	..	..	..	..	..	..	3	..	630	..	6 36	..	..	..	6 50	3	..	..	..	7 9	..	7 6	..	..	..	..	..	..	3	7 30	..
Byfleet W	..	..	..	..	..	..	..	..	..	..	..	6 40	..	..	..	..	..	..	..	..	..	..	7 10	..	..	..	..	..	..	..	..	..
West Weybridge	..	..	..	..	..	..	..	..	..	..	..	6 43	..	..	..	..	..	..	..	..	..	..	7 13	..	..	..	..	..	..	..	..	..
Virginia Water Z ... dep.	..	..	..	..	..	..	..	..	..	..	6 27	..	..	..	..	..	..	..	..	..	..	6 57	..	..	..	..	..	..	..	..	..	..
Chertsey	..	..	..	..	..	..	..	..	..	..	6 32	..	..	..	..	..	..	..	..	..	..	7 2	..	..	..	..	..	..	..	..	..	..
Addlestone	..	..	..	..	..	..	..	..	..	..	6 35	..	..	..	..	..	..	..	..	..	..	7 5	..	..	..	..	..	..	..	..	..	..
Weybridge U 394	..	..	..	..	From Waterloo, via Richmond Dep. Twickenham 6 19 p.m.	..	..	..	..	..	6 39	6 46	..	..	..	..	..	..	..	From Waterloo, via Richmond Dep. Twickenham 6 59 p.m.	..	7 9	7 16	..	..	..	From Waterloo, via Richmond Dep. Twickenham 7 19 p.m.	..	..	..	..	..
Walton-on-Thames	..	..	..	..		..	..	..	..	..	..	6 50	..	..	..	..	..	..	..		..	..	7 20	..	..	..		..	..	..	..	..
Hersham	..	..	..	..		..	..	..	..	..	..	6 52	..	..	..	..	..	..	..		..	..	7 22	..	..	..		..	..	..	..	..
Esher, for Sandown Park	..	..	..	..		..	..	..	..	..	..	6 55	..	..	..	..	..	..	..		..	..	7 25	..	..	..		..	..	..	..	..
London Road (Guildford)	..	..	..	..		..	..	6 14	..	..	..	..	..	..	..	..	6 40	..	..		..	..	..	..	..	..		..	..	7 14	..	..
Clandon T	..	..	..	..		..	..	6 19	..	..	..	..	..	..	..	..	6 46	..	..		..	..	..	..	..	..		..	..	7 19	..	..
Horsley R	..	..	..	..		..	..	6 24	..	..	..	..	..	..	..	..	6 51	..	..		..	..	..	..	..	..		..	..	7 24	..	..
Effingham Junction	..	..	..	..		..	..	6 27	..	..	..	..	..	6 30	..	..	6 54	6 57	..		..	..	..	..	..	..		..	..	7 27	..	..
Cobham Q	..	..	..	..		..	..	6 31	..	..	..	..	..	..	..	..	..	7 1	..		..	..	..	..	..	..		..	..	7 31	..	..
Oxshott, for Fairmile	..	..	..	..		..	..	6 35	..	..	..	..	..	..	..	..	..	7 5	..		..	..	..	..	..	..		..	..	7 35	..	..
Claygate, for Claremont	..	..	..	..		..	..	6 38	..	..	..	..	..	..	..	..	..	7 8	..		..	..	..	..	..	..		..	..	7 38	..	..
Hinchley Wood	..	..	..	..		..	..	6 41	..	..	..	..	..	..	..	..	..	7 11	..		..	..	..	..	..	..		..	..	7 41	..	..
Hampton Court ... dep.	..	..	..	..		..	6 35	..	..	..	..	..	..	..	6 55	..	..	..	..		..	..	..	..	..	..		..	7 35	..	..	..
Thames Ditton	..	..	..	..		..	6 37	..	..	..	..	..	..	..	6 57	..	..	..	..		..	..	..	..	..	..		..	7 37	..	..	..
Surbiton	..	..	..	..		..	6 42	6 45	..	..	..	7 0	..	..	7 2	7 8	..	7 15	..		7 26	..	7 30	..	..	..		..	7 42	7 45	..	..
Berrylands N	..	..	..	..		..	6 45	..	..	..	..	..	..	..	7 5	..	..	..	..		..	..	..	..	..	..		..	7 45	..	..	..
Shepperton ... dep.	..	5 58	..	Via Three Bridges, see page 228		..	..	..	..	..	..	..	6 31	..	..	..	..	..	..		..	..	..	6 58	..	..		..	..	..	..	..
Upper Halliford Halt	..	6 1	..			..	..	..	..	..	..	..	6 34	..	..	..	..	..	..		..	..	..	7 1	..	..		..	..	..	..	..
Sunbury L	..	6 3	..			..	..	..	..	..	..	..	6 36	..	..	..	..	..	..		..	..	..	7 3	..	..		..	..	..	..	..
Hampton	..	6 7	..			..	..	..	..	..	..	..	6 40	..	..	..	..	..	..		..	..	..	7 7	..	..		..	..	..	..	..
Fulwell K	..	6 11	..		V	..	..	..	..	..	..	..	6 44	..	..	..	..	..	..	V	..	..	..	7 11	..	..	V	..	..	..	..	..
Teddington J	..	Via Richmond, see page 487	..		6 25	..	..	..	..	..	..	..	6 47	..	..	..	..	..	..	7 5	..	..	..	..	..	..	7 25	..	..	..	..	..
Hampton Wick	..		..		6 28	..	..	..	..	..	..	..	6 50	..	..	..	..	..	..	7 8	..	..	..	..	..	..	7 28	..	..	..	..	..
Kingston	..		..		6 30	..	..	..	..	..	..	..	6 52	..	..	..	..	..	..	7 10	..	..	..	..	..	..	7 30	..	..	..	..	..
Norbiton H	..		..		6 32	..	..	..	..	..	..	..	6 54	..	..	..	..	..	..	7 12	..	..	..		..	..	7 32	..	..	..	..	..
Malden, for Coombe	..		..		6 36	..	6 48	..	..	..	..	..	6 58	..	7 8	..	..	..	..	7 16	..	..	..	Via Richmond, see page 488	..	..	7 36	..	7 48	..	..	..
Bookham	..		..		..	..	..	..	..	..	..	..	..	6 33	..	..	6 58	..	..	..	..	..	..		..	..	..	..	..	..	..	..
Horsham ... dep.	..		..	5 48	..	5 49	..	..	..	..	..	..	..	..	..	..	..	..	6 43	..	..	..	..		..	..	..	6 49	..	..	..	..
Warnham	..		..	..	..	5 54	..	..	..	..	..	..	..	..	..	..	..	..	..	..	..	..	..		..	..	..	6 54	..	..	..	..
Ockley, for Capel	..		..	..	..	6 1	..	..	..	..	..	..	..	..	..	..	..	..	..	..	..	..	..		..	..	..	7 1	..	..	..	..
Holmwood G	..		..	..	..	6 5	..	..	..	..	..	..	..	..	..	..	..	..	..	..	..	..	..		..	..	..	7 5	..	..	..	..
Dorking North F	6 0		..	..	..	6 15	..	..	..	..	..	..	..	..	..	..	..	..	7 2	..	..	..	..		..	7 6	..	7 15	..	..	..	..
Boxhill & Burford Bdg D	6 2		..	..	..	6 17	..	..	..	..	..	..	..	..	..	..	..	..	..	..	..	..	..		..	7 8	..	7 17	..	..	..	..
Leatherhead	6 7	..	..	..	..	6 22	..	..	..	..	..	..	..	6 37	..	..	7 2	..	..	..	..	..	..		..	7 13	..	7 22	..	..	..	..
Ashtead	6 11	..	..	..	..	6 26	..	..	..	..	..	..	..	6 41	..	..	7 6	..	..	..	..	..	..		..	7 17	..	7 26	..	..	..	..
Epsom 285	6 15	..	..	..	..	6 30	..	..	..	..	..	..	..	6 45	..	..	7 10	..	..	..	..	..	..		..	7 21	..	7 30	..	..	..	..
Sutton ... arr.	6 24	..	..	..	..	6‡46	..	..	..	..	..	..	..	6 54	..	..	7‡30	..	7 20	..	..	..	..	..	..	7 30	..	7‡46	..	..	..	..
Victoria "	..	..	..	7 7	..	7‡16	..	..	..	..	..	..	..	7*38	..	..	..	..	7 44	..	..	..	..	..	..	..	..	8‡16	..	..	..	..
London Bridge "	6 57	..	..	7 10	..	7‡27	..	..	..	..	..	..	..	7 27	..	..	8‡3	..	8* 3	..	..	..	..	..	..	8 3	..	8‡27	..	..	..	..
Ewell West C	..	..	..	..	..	6 33	..	..	..	..	..	..	..	..	..	..	7 13	..	..	..	..	..	..	..	..	..	..	7 33	..	..	..	..
Stoneleigh	..	..	..	..	..	6 36	..	..	..	..	..	..	..	..	..	..	7 16	..	..	..	..	..	..	..	..	..	..	7 36	..	..	..	..
Worcester Park	..	..	..	..	..	6 39	..	..	..	..	..	..	..	..	..	..	7 19	..	..	..	..	..	..	..	..	..	..	7 39	..	..	..	..
Chessington South ¶ dp.	..	..	6 13	..	..	..	..	..	6 33	..	..	..	..	..	..	..	..	..	..	..	..	..	..	..	7 13	..	..	..	..	..	..	7 33
Chessington North	..	..	6 15	..	..	..	..	..	6 35	..	..	..	..	..	..	..	..	..	..	..	..	..	..	..	7 15	..	..	..	..	..	..	7 35
Tolworth	..	..	6 18	..	..	..	..	..	6 38	..	..	..	..	..	..	..	..	..	..	..	..	..	..	..	7 18	..	..	..	..	..	..	7 38
Malden Manor	..	..	6 21	..	..	..	..	..	6 41	..	..	..	..	..	..	..	..	..	..	..	..	..	..	..	7 21	..	..	..	..	..	..	7 41
Motspur Park	..	..	6 24	..	..	6 41	..	..	6 44	..	..	..	..	..	..	..	7 21	..	..	..	..	..	..	..	7 24	..	..	7 41	..	..	..	7 44
Raynes Park	..	..	6 27	..	6 39	..	6 51	..	6 47	..	..	..	7 1	..	7 11	..	..	..	..	7 19	..	..	..	..	7 27	..	7 39	..	7 51	..	..	7 47
Wimbledon 319, 320, 322	..	..	6 30	..	6 42	6 46	6 54	6 53	6 50	..	..	..	7 4	..	7 14	..	7 26	7 22	..	7 22	..	..	..	..	7 30	..	7 42	7 46	7 54	7 53	..	7 50
Earlsfield B	..	..	6 34	..	6 45	..	6 57	..	6 54	..	..	..	7 7	..	7 17	..	..	..	..	7 25	..	..	..	..	7 34	..	7 45	..	7 57	..	..	7 54
Clapham Junction A	..	..	6 37	..	6 49	6 52	7 1	6 59	6 57	..	..	..	7 11	..	7 21	..	7 32	7 28	..	7 29	..	..	..	..	7 37	..	7 49	7 52	8 1	7 59	..	7 57
Vauxhall	..	..	6 42	..	6 53	..	7 5	..	7 2	..	..	..	7 15	..	7 25	..	..	..	..	7 33	..	..	..	..	7 42	..	7 53	..	8 5	..	..	8 2
Waterloo ... arr.	..	6 48	6 46	..	6 57	6 59	7 9	7 6	7 6	7 1	..	7 16	7 19	..	7 29	7 27	7 39	7 35	..	7 37	7 45	..	7 47	7 48	7 46	..	7 57	7 59	8 9	8 6	8 1	8 6

GUILDFORD, WOKING, CHERTSEY, HAMPTON COURT, SHEPPERTON, KINGSTON, HORSHAM, DORKING NORTH, & LONDON

Sundays—continued (p.m.)

Up	Ⓢ	Ⓢ		Ⓢ		Ⓢ		Ⓢ	Ⓢ		Ⓢ		Ⓢ	Ⓢ		Ⓢ	Ⓢ	Ⓢ			Ⓢ	Ⓢ	Ⓢ		Ⓢ	Ⓢ		Ⓢ	Ⓢ	Ⓢ		Ⓢ
Guildford dep.	..	..	7 22	..	..	..	7 37	..	..	7 48	..	7 52	..	..	..	..	..	..	8 10	8 20	..	..	..	8 22	..	..	8 37	..	..	..	8 52	..
Worpledon	..	..	7 29	..	..	..	..	..	..	..	..	7 59	..	..	..	..	..	..	..	..	..	..	..	8 29	..	..	..	..	..	..	8 59	..
Woking X 324, 389, 390	..	..	7 36	..	7 44	..	Ⓢ	..	..	7 58	..	8 6	..	..	..	..	..	..	Ⓢ	8 30	..	..	..	8 36	..	..	Ⓢ	..	..	..	9 6	..
Byfleet W	..	..	7 40	..	..	..	..	..	..	..	..	8 10	..	..	..	..	..	..	..	..	..	..	..	8 40	..	..	..	..	..	..	9 10	..
West Weybridge	..	..	7 43	..	..	..	..	..	..	..	..	8 13	..	..	..	..	..	..	..	..	..	..	..	8 43	..	..	..	..	..	..	9 13	..
Virginia Water Z dep.	..	7 27	..	..	..	..	..	..	..	..	7 57	..	..	..	..	..	..	..	..	..	..	8 27	..	..	..	..	..	..	..	8 57	..	..
Chertsey	..	7 32	..	..	..	..	..	..	..	..	8 2	..	..	..	..	..	..	..	..	..	..	8 32	..	..	..	..	..	..	..	9 2	..	..
Addlestone	..	7 35	..	..	..	..	..	..	..	..	8 5	..	..	..	..	..	..	..	..	..	..	8 35	..	..	..	..	..	..	..	9 5	..	..
Weybridge U 394	..	7 39	7 46	..	..	..	..	..	From Waterloo via Richmond Dep. Twickenham 7 59 p.m	..	8 9	8 16	..	..	..	..	From Waterloo via Richmond Dep. Twickenham 8 19 p.m	..	..	..	..	8 39	..	8 46	..	..	..	..	From Waterloo via Richmond Dep. Twickenham 8 59 p.m	9 9	9 16	..
Walton-on-Thames	..	..	7 50	..	..	..	..	..		..	..	8 20	..	..	..	..		..	..	..	..	—	..	8 50	..	..	..	..		..	9 20	..
Hersham	..	..	7 52	..	..	..	..	..		..	..	8 22	..	..	..	..		..	..	..	..	Stop	..	8 52	..	..	..	..		..	9 22	..
Esher, for Sandown Park	..	..	7 55	..	..	..	..	..		..	..	8 25	..	..	..	..		..	..	..	..	..	..	8 55	..	..	..	..		..	9 25	..
London Road (Guildford)	..	..	..	..	..	..	7 40	..		..	..	..	..	..	..	..		..	8 14	..	..	..	..	..	..	..	8 40	..		..	..	..
Clandon T	..	..	..	..	..	..	7 46	..		..	..	..	..	..	..	..		..	8 19	..	..	..	..	..	..	..	8 46	..		..	..	..
Horsley R	..	..	..	..	..	..	7 51	..		..	..	..	..	..	..	..		..	8 24	..	..	..	..	..	..	..	8 51	..		..	..	..
Effingham Junction	7 30	..	..	..	..	..	7 54	7 57		..	..	..	..	..	..	..		..	8 27	..	..	..	8 20	..	..	..	8 54	8 57		..	..	..
Cobham Q	..	..	..	..	..	..	..	8 1		..	..	..	..	..	..	..		..	8 31	..	..	..	..	..	..	..	..	9 1		..	..	..
Oxshott, for Fairmile	..	..	..	..	..	..	..	8 5		..	..	..	..	..	..	..		..	8 35	..	..	..	..	..	..	..	..	9 5		..	..	..
Claygate for Claremont	..	..	..	..	..	..	..	8 8		..	..	..	..	..	..	..		..	8 38	..	..	..	..	..	..	..	..	9 8		..	..	..
Hinchley Wood	..	..	..	..	..	..	..	8 11		..	..	..	..	..	..	..		..	8 41	..	..	..	..	..	..	..	..	9 11		..	..	..
Hampton Court dep.	..	..	..	..	..	7 55	..	..		..	..	..	..	..	..	..		8 35	..	..	..	..	..	..	..	8 55	..	..		..	..	..
Thames Ditton	..	..	..	..	..	7 57	..	..		..	..	..	..	..	..	..		8 37	..	..	..	..	..	..	..	8 57	..	..		..	..	..
Surbiton	..	..	8 0	..	8 2	8 2	..	8 15		8 13	..	8 30	..	..	..	..		8 42	8 45	..	..	..	..	9 0	..	9 2	..	9 15		..	9 30	..
Berrylands N	..	..	..	..	..	8 5	..	..		..	..	..	..	..	..	..		8 45	..	..	..	..	..	..	..	9 5	..	..		..	..	..
Shepperton dep.	..	..	..	7 31	..	..	..	..		..	..	..	..	7 58	..	..		..	..	..	..	..	..	..	8 31	..	..	..		..	..	8 58
Upper Halliford Halt	..	..	..	7 34	..	..	..	..		..	..	..	..	8 1	..	..		..	..	..	..	..	..	..	8 34	..	..	..		..	..	9 1
Sunbury L	..	..	..	7 36	..	..	..	..		..	..	..	..	8 3	..	..		..	..	..	..	..	..	..	8 36	..	..	..		..	..	9 3
Hampton	..	..	..	7 40	..	..	..	..		..	..	..	..	8 7	..	..		..	..	..	..	..	..	..	8 40	..	..	..		..	..	9 7
Fulwell K	..	..	..	7 44	..	..	..	..	▼	..	..	..	..	8 11	..	..	▼	..	..	..	..	..	..	..	8 44	..	..	..	▼	..	..	9 11
Teddington J	..	..	..	7 47	..	..	..	..	8 5	..	..	..	..	Via Richmond, see page 488	..	..	8 25	..	..	..	..	..	..	..	8 47	..	..	..	9 5	..	..	Via Richmond, see page 488
Hampton Wick	..	..	..	7 50	..	..	..	..	8 8	..	..	..	..		..	..	8 28	..	..	..	..	..	..	..	8 50	..	..	..	9 8	..	..	
Kingston	..	..	..	7 52	..	..	..	..	8 10	..	..	..	..		..	..	8 30	..	..	..	..	..	..	..	8 52	..	..	..	9 10	..	..	
Norbiton H	..	..	..	7 54	..	..	..	..	8 12	..	..	..	..		..	..	8 32	..	..	..	..	..	..	..	8 54	..	..	..	9 12	..	..	
Malden, for Coombe	..	..	..	7 58	..	8 8	..	..	8 16	..	..	..	..		..	..	8 36	8 48	..	..	..	..	..	..	8 58	9 8	..	..	9 16	..	..	..
Bookham	7 23	..	..	..	..	..	7 58	..	..	..	..	..	..		..	..	..	..	..	..	..	..	8 33	..	..	..	8 58	..	..	..	..	..
Horsham dep.	..	..	..	..	..	..	..	..	..	..	..	..	..		7 43	..	..	..	..	..	7 49	..	..	..	..	..	..	..	..	..	..	..
Warnham	..	..	..	..	..	..	..	..	..	..	..	..	..		..	..	..	..	..	..	7 54	..	..	..	..	..	..	..	..	..	..	..
Ockley, for Capel	..	..	..	..	..	..	..	..	..	..	..	..	..		..	..	..	..	..	..	8 1	..	..	..	..	..	..	..	..	..	..	..
Holmwood G	..	..	..	..	..	..	..	..	..	..	..	..	..		..	..	..	..	..	..	8 5	..	..	..	..	..	..	..	..	..	..	..
Dorking North F	..	..	..	..	..	..	..	..	..	..	..	..	..		8 2	8 7	..	..	..	..	8 15	..	..	..	..	..	..	..	..	..	..	..
Boxhill & Burford Bdg D	..	..	..	..	..	..	..	..	..	..	..	..	..		..	8 9	..	..	..	..	8 17	..	..	..	..	..	..	..	..	..	..	..
Leatherhead	7 37	..	..	..	..	..	8 2	..	..	..	..	..	..	..	..	8 14	..	..	..	..	8 22	..	8 37	..	..	..	9 2	..	..	..	..	..
Ashtead	7 41	..	..	..	..	..	8 6	..	..	..	..	..	..	..	..	8 18	..	..	..	..	8 26	..	8 41	..	..	..	9 6	..	..	..	..	..
Epsom 285	7 45	..	..	..	..	..	8 10	..	..	..	..	..	..	..	..	8 22	..	..	..	..	8 30	..	8 45	..	..	..	9 10	..	..	..	..	..
Sutton arr.	7 54	..	..	..	..	..	8‡31	..	..	..	..	..	..	..	8 20	8 31	..	..	..	..	8‡46	..	8 54	..	..	..	9‡30	..	..	..	..	..
Victoria "	8*38	..	..	..	..	..	..	..	..	..	..	..	..	..	8 43	..	..	..	..	..	9‡16	..	9*38	..	..	..	..	..	..	..	..	..
London Bridge "	8 27	..	..	..	..	..	9‡4	..	..	..	..	..	..	..	9*4	9 4	..	..	..	..	9‡27	..	9 2[illegible]	..	..	..	10‡3	..	..	..	..	..
Ewell West C	..	..	..	..	..	..	8 13	..	..	..	..	..	..	..	..	..	..	..	..	..	8 33	p.m	..	..	..	..	9 13	..	..	..	..	..
Stoneleigh	..	..	..	..	..	..	8 16	..	..	..	..	..	..	..	..	..	..	..	..	..	8 36	..	..	..	..	..	9 16	..	..	..	..	..
Worcester Park	..	..	..	..	..	..	8 19	..	..	..	..	..	..	..	..	..	..	..	..	..	8 39	Ⓢ	..	..	..	..	9 19	..	..	..	..	..
Chessington South ¶dp	..	..	..	..	..	..	..	..	..	..	..	..	8 13	..	..	..	..	..	..	..	..	8 33	..	..	..	..	..	..	..	..	..	..
Chessington North	..	..	..	..	..	..	..	..	..	..	..	..	8 15	..	..	..	..	..	..	..	..	8 35	..	..	..	..	..	..	..	..	..	..
Tolworth	..	..	..	..	..	..	..	..	..	..	..	..	8 18	..	..	..	..	..	..	..	..	8 38	..	..	..	..	..	..	..	..	..	..
Malden Manor	..	..	..	..	..	..	..	..	..	..	..	..	8 21	..	..	..	..	..	..	..	..	8 41	..	..	..	..	..	..	..	..	..	..
Motspur Park	..	..	..	..	..	..	8 21	..	..	..	..	..	8 24	..	..	..	..	..	..	..	8 41	8 44	..	..	..	..	9 21	..	..	..	..	..
Raynes Park	..	..	..	8 1	..	8 11	..	..	8 19	..	..	..	8 27	..	..	..	8 39	8 51	..	..	..	8 47	..	..	9 1	9 11	..	..	9 19	..	..	..
Wimbledon 319, 320, 322	..	..	..	8 4	..	8 14	8 26	8 22	8 22	..	..	..	8 30	..	..	..	8 42	8 54	8 53	..	8 46	8 50	..	..	9 4	9 14	9 26	9 22	9 22	..	..	..
Earlsfield B	..	..	..	8 7	..	8 17	..	..	8 25	..	..	..	8 34	..	..	..	8 45	8 57	..	..	..	8 54	..	..	9 7	9 17	..	..	9 25	..	..	..
Clapham Junction A	..	..	..	8 11	..	8 21	8 32	8 28	8 29	..	..	..	8 37	..	..	..	8 49	9 1	8 59	..	8 52	8 57	..	..	9 11	9 21	9 32	9 28	9 29	..	..	..
Vauxhall	..	..	..	8 15	..	8 25	..	..	8 33	..	..	..	8 42	..	..	..	8 53	9 5	..	..	..	9 2	..	..	9 15	9 25	..	..	9 33	..	..	..
Waterloo arr.	..	..	8 16	8 19	8 22	8 29	8 39	8 35	8 37	8 30	..	8 46	8 46	8 48	..	..	8 57	9 9	9 6	9 1	8 59	9 6	..	9 21	9 19	9 29	9 39	9 35	9 37	..	9 46	9 48

FOR NOTES. SEE PAGE 459

FOR NOTES, SEE PAGE 459

GUILDFORD, WOKING, CHERTSEY, HAMPTON COURT, SHEPPERTON, KINGSTON, HORSHAM, DORKING NORTH, & LONDON

Sundays—*continued* (p.m.)

Up		3	3		3	3	3			3		3	3		3
Guildford ....dep.								9 10	9 20		9 22				
Worplesdon								3			9 29				
Woking X 324, 389, 390	9 14								9 30		9 36			9 46	
Byfleet **W**											9 40				
West Weybridge											9 43				
Virginia Water Z ..dep.										9 27					
Chertsey										9 32					
Addlestone										9 35					
Weybridge U 394										9 39	9 46				
Walton-on-Thames										Stop	9 50				
Hersham											9 52				
Esher, for Sandown Park											9 55				
London Road (Guildford)					From Waterloo via Richmond Dep. **Twickenham** 9 19 p.m.			9 14							
Clandon **T**								9 19							
Horsley **R**								9 24							
Effingham Junction								9 27					9 30		
Cobham **Q**								9 31							
Oxshott, for Fairmile								9 35							
Claygate, for Claremont								9 38							
Hinchley Wood								9 41							
Hampton Court ...dep.						9 35									9 55
Thames Ditton						9 37									9 57
Surbiton						9 42		9 45			10 0				10 2
Berrylands **N**						9 45									10 5
Shepperton ....dep.				Via Three Bridges, see page 232								9 31			
Upper Halliford Halt												9 34			
Sunbury **L**												9 36			
Hampton												9 40			
Fulwell **K**					V							9 44			
Teddington J					9 25							9 47			
Hampton Wick					9 28							9 50			
Kingston					9 30							9 52			
Norbiton **H**					9 32							9 54			
Malden, for Coombe					9 36	9 48						9 58			10 8
Bookham													9 33		
Horsham ....dep.				8 43			8 49								
Warnham							8 54								
Ockley, for Capel							9 1								
Holmwood **G**							9 5								
Dorking North F			9 6				9 15								
Boxhill&BurfordBdg **D**			9 8				9 17								
Leatherhead			9 13				9 22						9 37		
Ashtead			9 17				9 26						9 41		
Epsom 285			9 21				9 30						9 45		
Sutton ....arr.			9 30				9‡46						9 54		
Victoria .... "				9 40			10‡16						10*38		
London Bridge .... "			10 3	10 7			10‡27						1027		
Ewell West **C**							9 33			p.m					
Stoneleigh							9 36			3					
Worcester Park							9 39								
Chessington South ¶dp		9 13								9 33					
Chessington North		9 15								9 35					
Tolworth		9 18								9 38					
Malden Manor		9 21								9 41					
Motspur Park		9 24					9 41			9 44					
Raynes Park		9 27			9 39	9 51				9 47		10 1			1011
Wimbledon 319, 320, 322		9 30			9 42	9 54	9 46	9 53		9 50		10 4			1014
Earlsfield **B**		9 34			9 45	9 57				9 54		10 7			1017
Clapham Junction **A**		9 37			9 49	10 1	9 52	9 59		9 57		1011			1021
Vauxhall		9 42			9 53	10 5				10 2		1015			1025
Waterloo ....arr.	9 49	9 46			9 57	10 9	9 59	10 6	10 1	10 6	1016	1019		1019	1029

Up	3		3		3	3	3		3	3	3	3			3
Guildford ....dep.		9 37						9 52					1010	1020	
Worplesdon								9 59							
Woking X 324, 389, 390		3						10 6					3	1030	
Byfleet **W**								1010							
West Weybridge								1013							
Virginia Water Z ..dep.							9 57								
Chertsey							10 2								
Addlestone							10 5								
Weybridge U 394							10 9	1016							
Walton-on-Thames								1020							
Hersham								1022							
Esher, for Sandown Park								1025							
London Road (Guildford)		9 40	From Waterloo via Richmond Dep. **Twickenham** 9 59 p.m.							From Waterloo via Richmond Dep. **Twickenham** 10 19 p.m.			1014		
Clandon **T**		9 46											1019		
Horsley **R**		9 51											1024		
Effingham Junction		9 53				10 3							1027		
Cobham **Q**		9 57											1031		
Oxshott, for Fairmile		10 1											1035		
Claygate, for Claremont		10 4											1038		
Hinchley Wood		10 7											1041		
Hampton Court ...dep.											1029				
Thames Ditton											1031				
Surbiton		1011						1030			1036		1045		Arr. Dorking North 10 15 p.m
Berrylands **N**											1039				
Shepperton ....dep.				Via Three Bridges, see page 233					9 58			1031			
Upper Halliford Halt									10 1			1034			
Sunbury **L**									10 3			1036			
Hampton									10 7			1040			
Fulwell **K**			V						1011	V		1044			
Teddington J			10 5							1025		1047			
Hampton Wick			10 8							1028		1050			
Kingston			1012							1030		1052			
Norbiton **H**			1014							1032					
Malden, for Coombe			1018							1036	1042				
Bookham						10 6									
Horsham ....dep.				9 48											9 52
Warnham															9 56
Ockley, for Capel									Via Richmond, see page 489						10 3
Holmwood **G**															10 7
Dorking North F	9 43														10 18
Boxhill&BurfordBdg **D**	9 45														10 21
Leatherhead	9 50					10 11									10 26
Ashtead	9 54					10 15									10 30
Epsom 285	9 58					10 21									10 34
Sutton ....arr.	10‡12					10‡46									10‡46
Victoria .... "	10‡38			11 4		11‡16									11‡16
London Bridge .... "				11 10											11‡27
Ewell West **C**	10 1					10 24									10 37
Stoneleigh	10 4					10 26									10 39
Worcester Park	10 7					10 29									10 42
Chessington South ¶dp					1019										
Chessington North					1021										
Tolworth					1024										
Malden Manor					1026										
Motspur Park	10 9				1030	10 32									10 45
Raynes Park	10 13		1021		1033	10 35				1039	1045				10 48
Wimbledon 319, 320, 322	10 16	1018	1024		1036	10 38				1042	1048		1053		10 51
Earlsfield **B**	10 20				1039					1045	1051				10 54
Clapham Junction **A**	10 23	1024			1043					1049	1055		1059		10 58
Vauxhall	10 28				1047					1053	1059				11 2
Waterloo ....arr.	10 32	1031			1051			1046	1048	1057	11 3		11 6	11 1	11 6

GUILDFORD, WOKING, CHERTSEY, HAMPTON COURT, SHEPPERTON, KINGSTON, HORSHAM, DORKING NORTH, & LONDON

Up	p.m	Sundays—continued											p.m			
Guildford ......dep.	3	1022	3	1037	3	..	3	1052	3	3	3	3	1110	1120	3	3
Worplesdon	..	1029	..	..	..	..	..	1059	..	..	..	..	..	..	..	..
Woking X 324, 389, 390	..	1036	..	3	..	1048	..	11 6	..	..	..	..	3	1130	..	..
Byfleet **W**	..	1040	..	..	..	..	..	1110	..	..	..	..	..	..	..	..
West Weybridge	..	1043	..	..	..	..	..	1113	..	..	..	..	..	..	..	..
Virginia Water Z ...dep.	1027	..	..	..	..	..	1057	..	..	..	..	..	..	..	..	1127
Chertsey	1032	..	..	..	..	..	11 2	..	..	..	..	..	..	..	..	1132
Addlestone	1035	..	..	..	..	..	11 5	..	..	..	..	..	..	..	..	—
Weybridge U 394	1039	1046	..	..	..	1058	11 9	1116	..	..	..	..	..	..	..	Stop
Walton-on-Thames	—	1050	..	..	..	..	—	1120	..	..	..	..	..	..	..	..
Hersham	Stop	1052	..	..	..	..	Stop	1122	..	..	..	..	..	..	..	..
Esher, for Sandown Park	..	1055	..	..	..	..	..	1125	..	..	..	..	..	..	..	..
London Road (Guildford)	..	..	..	1040	..	..	..	..	..	..	..	..	1113	..	..	..
Clandon **T**	..	..	..	1046	..	..	..	..	..	..	..	..	1119	..	..	..
Horsley **R**	..	..	..	1051	..	..	..	..	..	..	..	..	1124	..	..	..
Effingham Junction	..	..	1030	1053	..	..	..	..	1057	..	..	..	1127	..	..	..
Cobham **Q**	..	..	..	1057	..	..	..	..	..	..	..	..	—	..	..	..
Oxshott, for Fairmile	..	..	..	11 1	..	..	..	..	..	..	..	..	Stop	..	..	..
Claygate, for Claremont	..	..	..	11 4	..	..	..	..	..	..	..	..	..	..	..	..
Hinchley Wood	..	..	..	11 7	..	..	..	..	..	..	..	..	..	..	..	..
Hampton Court ...dep.	..	..	..	..	11 1	..	..	..	..	..	..	1129	..	..	Arr. Dorking North 11 15 p.m	..
Thames Ditton	..	..	..	..	11 3	..	..	..	..	..	..	1131	..	..		..
Surbiton	..	11 0	..	1111	11 9	1113	..	1130	..	..	..	1136	..	..		..
Berrylands **N**	..	..	..	..	1112	..	..	..	..	..	..	1139	..	..		..
Shepperton ...dep.	..	..	..	..	..	..	..	..	..	..	1058	..	..	..		..
Upper Halliford Halt	..	..	..	..	..	..	p.m	..	..	..	..	..	..	..		..
Sunbury **L**	..	..	..	..	..	..	3	..	..	..	11 3	..	..	..		p.m
Hampton	..	..	..	..	..	..		..	..	..	11 7	..	..	..		3
Fulwell **K**	..	..	..	..	..	..	**V**	..	..	..	1111	..	..	..		**V**
Teddington J	..	..	..	..	..	..	11 5	..	..	..	..	..	..	..		1157
Hampton Wick	..	..	..	..	..	..	11 8	..	..	..	..	..	..	..		12 0
Kingston	..	..	..	..	..	..	1111	..	..	..	..	..	..	..		12 2
Norbiton **H**	..	..	..	..	..	..	1113	..	..	..	..	..	..	..		12 5
Malden, for Coombe	..	..	..	..	1115	..	1117	..	..	..	..	1142	..	..	..	12 9
Bookham	..	..	1033	..	..	..	..	..	11 0	..	..	..	..	..	..	..
Horsham ...dep.	..	..	..	..	..	..	From Waterloo via Richmond Dep. **Twickenham** 10 59 p.m.	..	..	..	Via Richmond, see page 489	..	..	..	1052	From Waterloo, via Richmond Dep. **Twickenham** 11 49 p.m.
Warnham	..	..	..	..	..	..		..	..	..		..	p.m	..	1056	
Ockley, for Capel	..	..	..	..	..	..		..	..	..		..	3	..	11 3	
Holmwood **G**	..	..	..	..	..	..		..	..	..		..		..	11 7	
Dorking North F	..	..	..	..	..	..		..	..	..		..	11 2	..	1118	
Boxhill & Burford Bdg **D**	..	..	..	..	..	..		..	..	..		..	11 4	..	1121	
Leatherhead	..	..	1037	..	..	..		..	11 4	..		..	11 9	..	1126	
Ashtead	..	..	1041	..	..	..		..	11 8	..		..	1113	..	1130	
Epsom 285	..	..	1045	..	..	..		..	1114	..		..	1117	..	1134	
Sutton ...arr.	..	..	1054	..	..	..		11‡26		..		..	1126	..	..	
Victoria "	..	..	11*38		..	..		..	..	..		..	..	..	..	
London Bridge "	..	..	1127	..	..	..		..	12†0	..		..	12 0	..	..	
Ewell West **C**	p.m	..	..	..	..	..		..	1117	..	..	..	..	..	1137	
Stoneleigh	3	..	..	..	..	..		..	1119	..	..	..	..	..	1139	
Worcester Park		..	..	..	..	..		..	1122	..	..	..	..	..	1142	
Chessington South ¶dp	1039	..	..	..	..	..		..	..	1119	..	..	..	..	..	
Chessington North	1041	..	..	..	..	..		..	..	1121	..	..	..	..	..	
Tolworth	1044	..	..	..	..	..		..	..	1124	..	..	..	..	..	
Malden Manor	1046	..	..	..	..	..		..	..	1126	..	..	..	..	..	
Motspur Park	1050	..	..	..	..	..		..	1125	1130	..	..	..	..	1145	
Raynes Park	1053	..	..	..	1118	..	1120	..	1128	1133	..	1145	..	..	1148	1212
Wimbledon 319, 320 322	1056	..	..	1118	1121	1122	1124	..	1131	1136	..	1148	..	..	1151	1215
Earlsfield **B**	1059	..	..	..	1124	..	1127	..	1134	..	..	..	..	..	1154	..
Clapham Junction A	11 3	..	..	1124	1128	..	1131	..	1138	..	..	..	..	..	1158	..
Vauxhall	11 7	..	..	..	1132	..	1135	..	1142	..	..	..	..	..	12 2	..
Waterloo ...arr.	1111	1116		1131	1136	1136	1139	1146	1146	..	1148	..	..	12 1	12 6	..

3 Third class only

* Change at Sutton, see pages 285 to 317a.

‡ Change at Epsom, see pages 285 to 317a.

¶ Chessington South for Chessington Zoo.

A Mid Battersea, 1¼ miles from Clapham

A Arr. 5 mins. *earlier*

B Sta for Summerstown

B 3 minutes *earlier* on Sats.

b Arr. 4 mins *earlier*

C 1 mile to Ewell East Station

D Sta for Mickleham (1¼ miles)

d Arr 7 38 p.m on Saturdays

F Nearly 1¼ miles to Dorking Town and under ¼ mile to Deepdene Station

F Arr. 7 51 p.m

G Sta for Leith Hill (2¼ miles)

H Sta for Kingston Hill

h 4 minutes later on Saturdays

J Sta for Bushy Park

K Sta for Upper Teddington (½ mile) and Hampton Hill

K 10 mins. later on Saturdays

L Sunbury Common (1 mile from Sunbury)

N Sta for Surbiton Hill Park

P Change at East Croydon

Q Cobham (1½ miles) for Stoke d'Abernon

R Station for East Horsley (1 mile) West Horsley (1½ miles), Ockham (1½ miles), and Ripley (3½ miles)

S O or SO Saturdays only

S X or SX Saturdays excepted

T Station for Burnt Common, Newlands Corner; East Clandon (2 miles) & Ripley (2¾ miles)

U Sta for Brooklands, St. George's Hill, & Oatlands Park

V For Service from Waterloo to Teddington, via Richmond and Twickenham, see pages 463 to 475

W Sta for Woodham & Pyrford

X Sta for Chobham, 3½ miles to Woking Village, 1½ miles

Y 5 mins. later on Saturdays

Z Sta for Wentworth

Z 8 mins. *earlier* on Sats.

For LOCAL TRAINS

BETWEEN	PAGE
Epsom and Victoria and London Bridge	285

For OTHER TRAINS

Guildford and London	249
Virginia Water & Waterloo	476
Teddington and Waterloo	476
Horsham and London	196
Dorking and London	249
Wimbledon & London	322
Clapham and London	476

FOR NOTES, SEE PAGE 475

LONDON, HOUNSLOW, RICHMOND, TWICKENHAM, TEDDINGTON, STAINES, WINDSOR, and READING

Week Days — a.m

Miles	Down	3	3	3	3	3	3	3	3	3	3		3	3		3	3	3	3	3	3	3	3	3	3	3	3			3	3	3
	Waterloo ....dep.	1 30	1 20	2 40	..	3 35	..	..	..	..	5 0	5 24	..	5 34	..	5 50	5 55	6 14	..	..	6 19	6 23	..	6 28	6 44	..	6 48	6 52	..	6 54	6 59	7 7
1¼	Vauxhall	1 34	1 24	2 44	..	3 39	..	..	..	..	5 3	..	..	..	..	5 53	5 58	..	..	..	6 22	6 26	..	6 31	..	..	6 51	..	..	6 57	7 2	7 10
2¾	Queen's Road	1 38	1 27	..	..	..	..	..	..	..	..	..	..	..	..	..	6 1	..	..	..	..	6 29	..	..	..	..	..	..	..	7 0	..	7 13
4	Clapham Junction A	To Teddington, via Kingston, see page 394	1 30	2 51	..	3 44	..	..	..	..	5 10	..	..	5 42	..	5 58	6 4	..	..	..	6 26	6 32	..	6 36	..	..	6 56	..	..	7 3	7 6	7 17
4½	Wandsworth Town		..	..	..	..	..	..	..	..	5 12	..	..	..	..	6 0	6 6	..	..	..	6 28	6 34	..	6 38	..	..	6 58	..	..	7 5	7 8	..
6	Putney		1 34	2 57	..	..	..	..	..	..	5 15	..	..	5 46	..	6 3	6 9	..	..	..	6 31	6 37	..	6 41	..	..	7 1	..	..	7 8	7 11	7 21
7	Barnes		1 37	3 1	..	..	..	..	..	..	5 18	..	..	5 49	..	6 6	6 12	..	..	..	6 34	6 40	..	6 44	..	..	7 4	..	..	7 11	7 14	7 25
8	Barnes Bridge		..	..	..	..	..	..	..	..	..	..	..	..	..	..	6 14	..	..	..	..	6 42	..	..	..	..	..	..	..	7 13	..	..
8¼	Chiswick, for Grove Park		..	..	..	..	..	..	..	..	..	..	..	..	..	..	6 16	..	..	..	..	6 44	..	..	..	..	..	..	..	7 16	..	..
9¼	Kew Bridge		..	..	..	..	..	..	..	..	5 23	..	..	..	..	..	6 19	..	..	..	..	6 48	..	..	..	..	..	..	..	7 18	..	..
10¼	Brentford B		..	..	..	..	..	..	..	..	5 27	..	..	..	..	..	6 22	..	..	..	..	6 51	..	..	..	..	..	..	..	7 21	..	..
11½	Syon Lane		..	..	..	..	..	..	..	..	5 30	..	..	..	..	..	6 24	..	..	..	..	6 53	..	..	..	..	..	..	..	7 23	..	..
12½	Isleworth C		..	..	..	..	..	..	..	..	5 33	..	..	..	..	..	6 26	..	..	..	..	6 55	..	..	..	..	..	..	..	7 25	..	..
13¾	Hounslow D		..	..	..	..	..	..	..	..	5 36	..	..	..	..	..	6 29	..	..	6 40	..	6 59	..	..	..	..	..	..	..	7 30	..	..
15	Whitton		..	..	..	..	..	..	..	..	..	..	..	..	..	..	6 33	..	..	6 44	..	7 3	..	..	..	..	..	..	..	7 34	..	..
8½	Mortlake, for East Sheen		1 40	3 4	..	..	..	..	..	..	..	..	..	5 52	..	6 9	..	..	..	..	6 37	..	..	6 47	..	..	7 7	..	..	..	7 17	7 28
9	North Sheen		..	..	..	..	..	..	..	..	..	..	..	..	..	6 11	..	..	..	..	6 40	..	..	6 49	..	..	7 9	..	..	..	7 20	7 30
9¾	Richmond		1 43	3 10	..	3 57	..	..	..	..	..	..	..	5 57	..	6 14	..	6 29	..	..	6 42	..	..	6 52	6 58	..	7 12	7 7	..	..	7 22	7 33
10¾	St. Margaret's		1 46	..	..	..	..	..	..	..	..	..	..	..	..	6 17	..	..	..	..	6 45	..	..	6 55	..	..	7 15	..	..	..	7 25	7 36
11½	Twickenham	..	1 48	3 16	3 21	4 3	4 54	..	..	..	..	5 41	..	6 2	..	6 19	6 36	6 33	..	6 46	6 47	7 6	..	6 57	7 2	7 7	7 17	7 12	..	7 37	7 27	7 38
12½	Strawberry Hill	..	1 51	3 35	..	4 7	..	5 0	5 20	..	..	..	..	..	..	6 22	..	..	6 55	..	6 50	..	..	7 0	..	..	7 20	..	..	..	7 30	..
13½	Teddington F ....arr.	..	1 54	3 39	..	4 10	..	..	..	..	..	..	..	..	..	6 25	..	..	..	..	6 55	..	..	7 5	..	..	7 25	..	..	..	7 35	..
12½	Whitton	..	V	V	..	V	..	To Shepperton, arr. 5 14 a.m., see page 394	To Shepperton, arr. 5 35 a.m. see page 394	..	..	5 44	..	6 4	..	V	..	6 36	To Shepperton, arr. 7 10 a.m., see page 394	..	V	..	..	V	7 4	7 10	V	..	..	..	V	7 40
14	Hounslow D ....arr.	..	To Waterloo, via Kingston	To Waterloo, via Kingston	..	To Waterloo, via Kingston	..			..	..	..	..	..	..	To Waterloo, via Kingston	..	..		..	To Waterloo, via Kingston	..	..	To Waterloo, via Kingston	..	7 15	To Waterloo via Kingston	..	..	..	To Waterloo via Kingston	7 45
14½	Feltham	..			3 27		5 0			..	5 41	5 49	..	6 9	..		..	6 41		..		..	..		7 8	..		7 18	..	..		..
17½	Ashford (Middlesex)	..			..		..			..	5 47	5 56	..	6 15	..		..	6 46		..		..	..		7 13	..		..	..	..		..
19	Staines J ....arr.	..			..		..			..	5 51	6 0	..	6 18	..		..	6 49		..		..	..		7 16	..		7 25	..	..		..
—	Staines ....dep.	..			..		..			..	5 54	..	..	6 20	..		..	6 52		..		..	..		7 18	..		..	..	..		..
21½	Wraysbury	..			..		..			..	6 0	..	..	6 27	..		..	6 58		..		..	..		7 25	..		..	..	..		..
22½	Sunnymeads	..			..		..			..	6 3	..	..	6 30	..		..	7 0		..		..	..		7 28	..		..	..	..		..
24	Datchet	..			..		..			..	6 7	..	..	6 33	..		..	7 5		..		..	..		7 31	..		..	..	..		..
25½	Windsor and Eton K arr.	..			..		..			..	6 12	..	..	6 38	..		..	7 10		..		..	..		7 36	..		..	..	..		..
—	Staines ....dep.	..			..		..			..	5 53	6 1	..	6 19	..		..	6 51		..		..	..		7 17	..	..	7 26	..	..	..	..
21	Egham L	..			..		..			..	5 58	6 7	..	6 24	..		..	6 55		..		..	..		7 22	..	..	7 30	..	..	..	..
23½	Virginia Water M ....arr.	..			..		..			..	6 2	6 12	..	6 28	..		..	7 6		..		..	..		7 26	..	..	7 34	..	..	..	..
—	Virginia Water M ..dep.	..			..		..	..	..	..	6 2	..	..	6 34	..		..	7 1	..	..		..	..		7 26	..	..	..	..	..	..	..
25¼	Chertsey	..			..		..	..	..	5 37	6 7	..	6 36	6A44	..		..	7 6	..	..		..	7 20		7 34	..	..	..	..	..	..	..
27½	Addlestone	..			..		..	..	..	5 40	6 10	..	6 39	6 47	..		..	7 9	..	..		..	7 23		7 37	..	..	..	..	..	..	..
29	Weybridge N 394 ...arr.	..			..		..	..	..	5 44	6 14	..	6 43	6 51	..		..	7 13	..	..		..	7 27		7 42	..	..	..	..	..	..	..
—	Virginia Water M ....dep.	..	..	..	..	..	..	..	..	..	..	6 14	..	..	..	..	..	..	..	..	..	..	..	..	..	..	..	7 34	..	..	..	..
25¼	Longcross Halt	..	..	..	..	..	..	..	..	..	..	6 19	..	..	..	..	..	..	..	..	..	..	..	..	..	..	..	7 38	..	..	..	..
27	Sunningdale P	..	..	..	..	..	..	..	..	..	..	6 23	..	..	..	..	..	..	..	..	..	..	..	..	..	..	..	7 42	..	..	..	..
29	Ascot ....arr.	..	..	..	..	..	..	..	..	..	..	6 28	..	..	..	..	..	..	..	..	..	..	..	..	..	..	..	7 47	..	..	..	..
—	Ascot ....dep.	..	..	..	..	..	..	..	..	..	..	6 32	..	..	..	..	..	..	..	..	..	..	..	..	..	..	..	7 51	8 10	..	..	..
32½	Bagshot	..	..	..	..	..	..	..	..	..	..	6 37	..	..	..	..	..	..	..	..	..	..	..	..	..	..	..	7 56	8 15	..	..	..
35½	Camberley Q	..	..	..	..	..	..	..	..	..	..	6 46	..	..	..	..	..	..	..	..	..	..	..	..	..	..	..	8 2	8 22	..	..	..
37½	Frimley T	..	..	..	..	..	..	..	..	..	..	6 51	..	..	..	..	..	..	..	..	..	..	..	..	..	..	..	8 6	8 27	..	..	..
40¾	Ash Vale W	..	..	..	..	..	..	..	..	..	..	6 58	..	..	..	..	..	..	..	..	..	..	..	..	..	..	..	8 12	To Woking arr. 8 42 a.m page 388	..	..	..
43½	Aldershot Y ....arr.	..	..	..	..	..	..	..	..	..	..	7 3	..	..	..	..	..	..	..	..	..	..	..	..	..	..	..	8 17		..	..	..
—	Ascot ....dep.	..	..	..	..	..	..	..	..	..	..	6 30	..	..	7 27	..	..	..	..	..	..	..	..	..	..	..	..	7 50	..	..	..	..
32½	Bracknell	..	..	..	..	..	..	..	..	..	..	6 35	..	..	7 32	..	..	..	..	..	..	..	..	..	..	..	..	7 55	..	..	..	..
36½	Wokingham 249	..	..	..	..	..	..	..	..	..	..	6 43	..	..	7 38	..	..	..	..	..	..	..	..	..	..	..	..	8 1	..	..	..	..
38½	Winnersh Halt Z	..	..	..	..	..	..	..	..	..	..	6 47	..	..	7 42	..	..	..	..	..	..	..	..	..	..	..	..	8 5	..	..	..	..
40½	Earley	..	..	..	..	..	..	..	..	..	..	6 51	..	..	7 46	..	..	..	..	..	..	..	..	..	..	..	..	8 9	..	..	..	..
43½	Reading ....arr.	..	..	..	..	..	..	..	..	..	..	6 56	..	..	7 52	..	..	..	..	..	..	..	..	..	..	..	..	8 15	..	..	..	..

LONDON, HOUNSLOW, RICHMOND, TWICKENHAM, TEDDINGTON, STAINES, WINDSOR, and READING

Week Days—*continued*

Down	a.m.	SX									SX
Waterloo dep.	7 12	7 14	..	7 18	7 24	7 26	7 30	7 34	7 39	7 48	7 50
Vauxhall	..	7 17	..	7 21	--	..	7 33	..	7 42	..	7 53
Queen's Road	..	7 20	..	..	--	..	..	..	7 45	..	..
Clapham Junction **A**	7 19	7 23	..	7 27	..	7 33	7 38	..	7 48	7 56	7 58
Wandsworth Town	..	7 25	..	7 29	..	7 35	7 40	..	7 50	..	..
Putney	..	7 28	..	7 32	..	7 38	7 43	..	7 53	..	8 2
Barnes	..	7 31	..	7 35	..	7 41	7 46	..	7 56	..	8 5
Barnes Bridge	..	7 33	..	..	..	7 43	..	..	..	..	..
Chiswick, for Grove Park	..	7 36	..	..	..	7 45	..	..	..	..	..
Kew Bridge	..	7 38	..	..	..	7 48	..	..	..	..	..
Brentford **B**	..	7 41	..	..	..	7 51	..	..	..	..	..
Syon Lane	..	7 43	..	..	..	7 53	..	..	..	..	..
Isleworth **C**	..	7 45	..	..	..	7 55	..	..	..	..	..
Hounslow D	..	7 49	..	..	..	7 58	..	..	..	..	..
Whitton	..	..	..	..	..	8 1	..	..	..	..	..
Mortlake, for East Sheen	..	..	..	7 38	..	..	7 49	..	7 59	..	8 8
North Sheen	..	..	..	7 40	..	..	7 51	..	..	..	8 10
Richmond	7 27	..	..	7 43	..	..	7 54	7 48	8 2	..	8 13
St. Margaret's	..	..	..	7 46	..	..	7 57	..	8 5	..	8 16
Twickenham	7 32	..	..	7 48	7U43	8 6	7 59	7 52	8 7	..	8 18
Strawberry Hill	..	..	..	7 51	..	..	8 2	..	..	..	8 21
Teddington F arr.	..	..	..	7 55	..	..	8 5	..	..	..	8 24
Whitton	7 34	..	..	V	..	..	V	7 54	8 9	..	V
Hounslow D arr.	..	..	..		..	..		..	8 15	..	
Feltham	7 38	..	..	To Waterloo via Kingston	..	..	To Waterloo via Kingston	7 58	..	..	To Waterloo via Kingston
Ashford (Middlesex)	7 43	..	..		..	..		8 3	..	..	
Staines J arr.	7 46	..	..		7 54	..		8 6	..	8 18	
Staines dep.	7 48	..	..		..	..		8 8	..	..	
Wraysbury	7 55	..	..		..	..		8 15	..	..	
Sunnymeads	7 58	..	.		..	..		8 18	..	..	
Datchet	8 1	..	..		..	..		8 21	..	..	
Windsor and Eton K arr.	8 6	..	..		..	..		8 26	..	..	
Staines dep.	7 47	..	..	..	7 55	..	..	8 7	..	8 19	..
Egham **L**	7 52	..	..	..	7 59	..	..	8 12	..	8 24	..
Virginia Water M arr.	7 56	..	..	..	8 3	..	..	8 16	..	8 28	..
Virginia Water M dep	7 56	..	..	..	..	..	..	8 16	..	..	..
Chertsey	8 2	..	8 17	..	..	..	..	8 21	..	..	..
Addlestone	8 5	..	8 20	..	..	..	..	8 24	..	..	..
Weybridge **N** 394 arr.	8 9	..	8 24	..	..	..	..	8 28	..	..	..
Virginia Water M dep.	..	..	..	..	8 3	..	..	..	..	8 28	..
Longcross Halt	..	..	..	..	8 7	..	..	..	..	8 32	..
Sunningdale **P**	..	..	..	..	8 11	..	..	..	..	8 35	..
Ascot arr.	..	..	..	..	8 16	..	..	..	..	8 40	..
Ascot dep	..	..	..	..	8 18	..	..	..	..	8 43	..
Bagshot	..	..	..	..	8 23	..	..	..	..	8 48	..
Camberley **Q**	..	..	..	..	8 29	..	..	..	..	8 55	..
Frimley **T**	..	..	..	..	8 33	..	..	..	..	8 59	..
Ash Vale W	..	..	..	..	8 39	..	..	..	..	9 5	..
Aldershot Y arr	..	..	..	..	8 44	..	..	..	..	9 10	..
Ascot dep	..	..	..	..	8 17	..	..	..	..	8 41	..
Bracknell	..	..	..	..	8 22	..	..	..	..	8 46	..
Wokingham 249	..	..	..	..	8 28	..	..	..	..	8 53	..
Winnersh Halt **Z**	..	..	..	..	8 32	..	..	..	..	8 57	..
Earley	..	..	..	..	8 36	..	..	..	..	9 1	..
Reading arr.	..	..	..	..	8 42	..	..	..	..	9 6	..

Down	a.m.										
Waterloo dep.	7 54	..	7 56	8 1	8 9	..	8 14	8 21	8 24	8 26	8 32
Vauxhall	..	..	7 59	8 4	8 12	..	..	8 24	..	8 29	..
Queen's Road	..	..	8 2	..	8 15	..	..	..	..	8 32	..
Clapham Junction **A**	..	..	8 5	8 8	8 18	..	..	8 28	8 31	8 35	8 39
Wandsworth Town	..	..	8 7	8 10	..	..	..	8 30	..	8 37	8 41
Putney	..	..	8 10	8 13	8 22	..	..	8 33	..	8 40	8 44
Barnes	..	..	8 13	8 16	8 25	..	..	8 36	..	8 43	8 47
Barnes Bridge	..	..	8 15	..	..	..	..	..	..	8 44	..
Chiswick, for Grove Park	..	..	8 17	..	..	..	..	..	..	8 47	..
Kew Bridge	..	..	8 20	..	..	..	..	..	..	8 49	..
Brentford **B**	..	..	8 23	..	..	..	..	..	..	8 52	..
Syon Lane	..	..	8 25	..	..	..	..	..	..	8 54	..
Isleworth **C**	..	..	8 27	..	..	..	..	..	..	8 56	..
Hounslow D	..	8 21	8 30	..	..	..	..	..	..	8 59	..
Whitton	..	8 24	8 33	..	..	..	..	..	..	9 3	..
Mortlake, for East Sheen	..	..	..	8 19	8 28	..	..	8 39	..	..	8 50
North Sheen	..	..	..	8 22	..	..	..	8 42	..	..	8 52
Richmond	8 8	..	..	8 24	8 31	..	8 28	8 44	..	..	8 55
St. Margaret's	..	..	..	8 27	8 34	..	..	8 47	..	..	8 58
Twickenham	8 13	8 27	8 36	8 29	8 36	..	8 32	8 49	8 42	9 6	9 0
Strawberry Hill	..	..	..	8 32	..	..	..	8 52	..	..	9 3
Teddington F arr.	..	..	..	8 35	..	..	..	8 55	..	..	9 6
Whitton	8 15	..	..	V	8 38	..	8 34	V	..	..	V
Hounslow D arr.	..	..	..		8 45	..	..		..	..	
Feltham	8 19	..	..	To Waterloo via Kingston	..	..	8 38	To Waterloo via Kingston	..	..	To Waterloo via Kingston
Ashford (Middlesex)	8 24	..	..		..	..	8 43		..	..	
Staines J arr.	8 27	..	..		..	..	8 46		8 52	..	
Staines dep.	8 29	..	..		..	..	8 48		..	..	
Wraysbury	8 36	..	..		..	..	8 55		..	..	
Sunnymeads	8 39	..	..		..	..	8 58		..	..	
Datchet	8 42	..	..		..	..	9 1		..	..	
Windsor and Eton K arr.	8 47	..	..		..	..	9 6		..	..	
Staines dep.	8 28	..	..	..	..	..	8 47	..	8 52	..	
Egham **L**	8 33	..	..	..	..	..	8 52	..	8 57	..	
Virginia Water M arr.	8 37	..	..	..	..	..	8 56	..	9 1	..	
Virginia Water M dep	8 40	..	..	..	..	..	8 56	..	..	..	..
Chertsey	8 45	..	..	..	..	..	9 1	..	..	..	..
Addlestone	8 48	..	..	..	..	..	9 4	..	..	..	..
Weybridge **N** 394 arr.	8 53	..	..	..	..	..	9 8	..	..	..	..
Virginia Water M dep.	..	..	..	..	..	..	..	..	9 1	..	..
Longcross Halt	..	..	..	..	..	..	..	..	9 5	..	..
Sunningdale **P**	..	..	..	..	..	..	..	..	9 8	..	..
Ascot arr.	..	..	..	..	..	..	..	..	9 13	..	..
Ascot dep	..	..	..	..	..	..	..	..	9 16	..	..
Bagshot	..	..	..	..	..	..	..	..	9 21	..	..
Camberley **Q**	..	..	..	..	..	..	..	..	9 29	..	..
Frimley **T**	..	..	..	..	..	..	..	..	9 33	..	..
Ash Vale W	..	..	..	..	..	..	..	..	9 39	..	..
Aldershot Y arr	..	..	..	..	..	..	..	..	9 44	..	..
Ascot dep	..	..	..	..	..	..	..	..	9 14	..	..
Bracknell	..	..	..	..	..	..	..	..	9 19	..	..
Wokingham 249	..	..	..	..	..	..	..	..	9 26	..	..
Winnersh Halt **Z**	..	..	..	..	..	..	..	..	9 30	..	..
Earley	..	..	..	..	..	..	..	..	9 34	..	..
Reading arr.	..	..	..	..	..	..	..	..	9 39	..	..

Down	a.m.									
Waterloo dep.	8 34	8 39	8 48	8 50	8 54	8 56	9 1	9 9	9 14	9 21
Vauxhall	..	8 42	..	8 53	..	8 59	9 4	..	..	9 24
Queen's Road	..	8 45	..	..	..	9 2	..	9 13	..	..
Clapham Junction **A**	8 41	8 48	..	8 58	..	9 5	9 8	9 16	..	9 28
Wandsworth Town	..	..	..	9 0	..	..	9 10	..	..	9 30
Putney	..	8 53	..	9 3	..	9 9	9 13	9 20	.	9 33
Barnes	..	8 56	..	9 6	..	9 12	9 16	9 25	..	9 36
Barnes Bridge	..	..	..	..	..	9 13	..	..	..	..
Chiswick, for Grove Park	..	..	..	..	..	9 16	..	..	..	..
Kew Bridge	..	..	..	..	..	9 18	..	..	..	..
Brentford **B**	..	..	..	..	..	9 21	..	..	..	..
Syon Lane	..	..	..	..	..	9 23	..	..	..	..
Isleworth **C**	..	..	..	..	..	9 25	..	..	..	..
Hounslow D	..	..	..	..	..	9 29	..	..	..	..
Whitton	..	..	..	..	..	9 33	..	..	..	..
Mortlake, for East Sheen	..	8 59	..	9 9	..	..	9 19	9 29	..	9 39
North Sheen	..	..	..	9 11	..	..	9 22	..	..	9 42
Richmond	8 49	9 2	..	9 14	9 8	..	9 24	9 32	9 28	9 44
St. Margaret's	..	9 5	..	9 17	..	..	9 27	9 35	..	9 47
Twickenham	8 53	9 7	..	9 19	9 12	9 35	9 29	9 37	9 32	9 49
Strawberry Hill	..	..	..	9 22	..	..	9 34	..	..	9 54
Teddington F arr.	..	..	..	9 25	..	..	9 37	..	..	9 57
Whitton	8 55	9 9	..	V	9 14	..	V	9 39	9 34	V
Hounslow D arr.	..	9 15	..		..	..		9 44	..	
Feltham	8 59	..	..	To Waterloo via Kingston	9 18	..	To Waterloo via Kingston	..	9 38	To Waterloo via Kingston
Ashford (Middlesex)	9 4	..	..		9 23	..		..	9 43	
Staines J arr.	9 7	..	9 18		9 26	..		..	9 46	
Staines dep.	9 9	..	..		9 28	..		..	9 48	
Wraysbury	9 16	..	..		9 35	..		..	9 55	
Sunnymeads	9 19	..	..		9 38	..		..	9 58	
Datchet	9 22	..	..		9 41	..		..	10 1	
Windsor and Eton K arr.	9 27	..	..		9 46	..		..	10 6	
Staines dep.	9 8	..	9 20		9 27	..		..	9 47	
Egham **L**	9 13	..	9 25		9 32	..		..	9 52	
Virginia Water M arr.	9 17	..	9 29		9 36	..		..	9 56	
Virginia Water M dep	9 17	..	..	..	9 36	..	..	..	9 56	..
Chertsey	9 22	..	..	..	9 43	..	..	..	10 3	..
Addlestone	9 25	..	..	..	9 46	..	..	..	10 6	..
Weybridge **N** 394 arr.	9 29	..	..	..	9 50	..	..	..	10 10	..
Virginia Water M dep.	..	..	9 29	..	..	..	..	..	..	..
Longcross Halt	..	..	9 33	..	..	..	..	..	..	..
Sunningdale **P**	..	..	9 36	..	..	..	..	..	..	..
Ascot arr.	..	..	9 41	..	..	..	..	..	..	..
Ascot dep	..	..	9 44	..	..	..	..	..	..	..
Bagshot	..	..	9 49	..	..	..	..	..	..	..
Camberley **Q**	..	..	9 56	..	..	..	..	..	..	..
Frimley **T**	..	..	10 0	..	..	..	..	..	..	..
Ash Vale W	..	..	10 6	..	..	..	..	..	..	..
Aldershot Y arr	..	..	10 11	..	..	..	..	..	..	..
Ascot dep	..	..	9 42	..	..	..	..	..	..	..
Bracknell	..	..	9 47	..	..	..	..	..	..	..
Wokingham 249	..	..	9 54	..	..	..	..	..	..	..
Winnersh Halt **Z**	..	..	9 58	..	..	..	..	..	..	..
Earley	..	..	10 2	..	..	..	..	..	..	..
Reading arr.	..	..	10 7	..	..	..	..	..	..	..

FOR NOTES, SEE PAGE 478

FOR NOTES, SEE PAGE 475

LONDON, HOUNSLOW, RICHMOND, TWICKENHAM, TEDDINGTON, STAINES, WINDSOR, and READING

Week Days—continued (a.m.)

Down	3	3	3	3	3		3	3	3	3	3	3	3	3	3	3			3	3	3	3	3		3	3	3	3	3		3
								SX												SO											
Waterloo dep.	9 26	9 30	9 39	9 44	9 46	9 54	9 56	10 1	10 9	1014	1021	1026	1030	1039	1044	1050	..	1054	1056	11 1	11 9	1114	1121	..	1126	1130	1139	1144	1150	1154	1156
Vauxhall	9 29	9 33	9 42	..	9 49	..	9 59	10 4	1012	..	1024	1029	1033	1042	..	1053	..	..	1059	11 4	1112	..	1124	..	1129	1133	1142	..	1153	..	1159
Queen's Road	9 32	..	..	..	9 52	..	10 2	..	1015	..	..	1032	..	1045	..	..	..	..	11 2	..	1115	..	..	..	1132	..	1145	..	..	..	12 2
Clapham Junction A	9 35	9 37	9 46	..	9 55	..	10 5	10 8	1018	..	1028	1035	1038	1048	..	1058	..	..	11 5	11 8	1118	..	1128	..	1135	1138	1148	..	1158	..	12 5
Wandsworth Town	..	9 39	..	..	9 57	..	..	1010	1020	..	1030	1037	1040	..	..	11 0	..	..	..	1110	1120	..	1130	..	1137	1140	..	..	12 0	..	..
Putney	9 39	9 42	9 50	..	10 0	..	10 9	1013	1023	..	1033	1040	1043	1053	..	11 3	..	..	11 9	1113	1123	..	1133	..	1140	1143	1153	..	12 3	..	12 9
Barnes	9 42	9 46	9 55	..	10 5	..	1013	1016	1026	..	1036	1043	1046	1056	..	11 6	..	..	1113	1116	1126	..	1136	..	1143	1146	1156	..	12 6	..	1212
Barnes Bridge	9 44	..	..	..	..	..	1014	..	..	..	..	1045	..	..	..	..	..	..	1114	..	..	..	..	..	1145	..	..	..	..	..	1214
Chiswick, for Grove Park	9 46	..	..	..	..	..	1017	..	..	..	..	1047	..	..	..	..	..	..	1117	..	..	..	..	..	1147	..	..	..	..	..	1216
Kew Bridge	9 49	..	..	..	..	..	1019	..	..	..	..	1050	..	..	..	..	..	..	1119	..	..	..	..	..	1150	..	..	..	..	..	1219
Brentford B	9 52	..	..	..	..	..	1022	..	..	..	..	1053	..	..	..	..	..	..	1122	..	..	..	..	..	1153	..	..	..	..	..	1222
Syon Lane	9 54	..	..	..	..	..	1024	..	..	..	..	1055	..	..	..	..	..	..	1124	..	..	..	..	..	1155	..	..	..	..	..	1224
Isleworth C	9 56	..	..	..	..	..	1026	..	..	..	..	1057	..	..	..	..	..	..	1126	..	..	..	..	..	1157	..	..	..	..	..	1226
Hounslow D	9 59	..	..	..	..	..	1030	..	..	..	..	11 0	..	..	..	..	..	..	1130	..	..	..	..	..	12 0	..	..	..	..	..	1229
Whitton	10 2	..	..	..	..	..	1034	..	..	..	..	11 3	..	..	..	..	..	..	1133	..	..	..	..	..	12 3	..	..	..	..	..	1232
Mortlake, for East Sheen	..	9 49	9 59	..	10 9	..	..	1019	1029	..	1039	..	1049	1059	..	11 9	..	..	..	1119	1129	..	1139	..	..	1149	1159	..	12 9	..	..
North Sheen	..	9 51	..	..	1011	..	..	1022	..	..	1042	..	1051	..	..	1111	..	..	..	1122	..	..	1142	..	..	1151	..	..	1211	..	..
Richmond	..	9 54	10 2	9 58	1014	..	..	1024	1032	1028	1044	..	1054	11 2	1058	1114	..	..	..	1124	1132	1128	1144	..	..	1154	12 2	1158	1214	..	..
St. Margaret's	..	9 57	10 5	..	1017	..	..	1027	1035	..	1047	..	1057	11 5	..	1117	..	..	..	1127	1135	..	1147	..	..	1157	12 5	..	1217	..	..
Twickenham	10 5	9 59	10 7	10 2	1019	..	1036	1029	1037	1032	1049	11 6	1059	11 7	11 2	1119	..	..	1136	1129	1137	1132	1149	..	12 6	1159	12 7	12 2	1219	..	1235
Strawberry Hill	..	10 3	..	..	1022	..	..	1033	..	..	1052	..	11 3	..	..	1122	..	..	..	1132	..	..	1152	..	..	12 4	..	..	1222	..	..
Teddington F arr.	..	10 7	..	..	1025	..	..	..	..	..	1055	..	11 7	..	..	1125	..	..	..	1135	..	..	1155	..	..	12 7	..	..	1225	..	..
Whitton	..	V	10 9	10 4	V	..	..	..	1039	1034	V	..	V	11 9	11 4	V	..	..	..	V	1139	1134	V	..	..	V	12 9	12 4	V	..	..
Hounslow D arr.	..		1014	..		..	..	..	1044	..		..		1114	..		..	..	..		1144	..		..	..		1214	..		..	..
Feltham	..	To Waterloo via Kingston	..	10 8	To Waterloo via Kingston	..	..	..	..	1038	To Waterloo, via Kingston.	..	To Waterloo via Kingston	..	11 8	To Waterloo via Kingston	..	..	..	To Waterloo via Kingston	..	1138	To Waterloo via Kingston	..	..	To Waterloo via Kingston	..	12 8	To Waterloo via Kingston	..	..
Ashford (Middlesex)	..		..	1013		..	..	..	..	1043		..		..	1113		..	..	..		..	1143		..	..		..	1213		..	..
Staines J arr.	..		..	1016		1022	..	..	..	1046		..		..	1116		..	1122	..		..	1146		..	..		..	1216		1222	..
Staines dep.	..		..	1018		..	..	..	..	1048		..		..	1118		..	..	..		..	1148		..	..		..	1218		..	..
Wraysbury	..		..	1025		..	..	..	..	1055		..		..	1125		..	..	..		..	1155		..	..		..	1225		..	..
Sunnymeads	..		..	1028		..	..	..	..	1058		..		..	1128		..	..	..		..	1158		..	..		..	1228		..	..
Datchet	..		..	1031		..	..	..	..	11 1		..		..	1131		..	..	..		..	12 1		..	..		..	1231		..	..
Windsor and Eton K arr.	..		..	1038		..	..	..	..	11 6		..		..	1138		..	..	..		..	12 6		..	..		..	1238		..	..
Staines dep.	..		..	1017		1022	..	..	..	1047		..		..	1117		..	1122	..		..	1147		..	..		..	1217		1222	..
Egham L	..		..	1022		1027	..	..	..	1052		..		..	1122		..	1127	..		..	1152		..	..		..	1222		1227	..
Virginia Water M arr.	..		..	1026		1031	..	..	..	1056		..		..	1126		..	1131	..		..	1156		..	..		..	1226		1231	..
Virginia Water M dep.	..	..	..	1026	..	..	..	..	..	1056	..	..	..	..	1126	..	..	..	..	..	..	1156	..	..	..	..	..	1226	..	..	..
Chertsey	..	..	..	1034	..	..	..	..	..	11 3	..	..	..	..	1134	..	..	..	..	..	..	12 1	..	..	..	..	..	1231	..	..	..
Addlestone	..	..	..	1037	..	..	..	..	..	11 6	..	..	..	..	1137	..	..	..	..	..	..	12 4	..	..	..	..	..	1234	..	..	..
Weybridge N394 arr.	..	..	..	1041	..	..	..	..	..	1110	..	..	..	..	1141	..	..	..	..	..	..	12 8	..	..	..	..	..	1238	..	..	..
Virginia Water M dep.	..	..	..	..	..	1031	..	..	..	..	..	..	..	..	..	..	..	1131	..	..	..	..	..	..	..	..	..	..	..	1231	..
Longcross Halt	..	..	..	..	..	1035	..	..	..	..	..	..	..	..	..	..	..	1135	..	..	..	..	..	..	..	..	..	..	..	1235	..
Sunningdale P	..	..	..	..	..	1038	..	..	..	..	..	..	..	..	..	..	..	1138	..	..	..	..	..	..	..	..	..	..	..	1238	..
Ascot arr.	..	..	..	..	..	1043	..	..	..	..	..	..	..	..	..	..	..	1143	..	..	..	..	..	..	..	..	..	..	..	1243	..
Ascot dep.	..	..	..	..	..	1046	..	..	..	..	..	..	..	..	..	..	..	1146	..	..	..	..	..	..	..	..	..	..	..	1246	..
Bagshot	..	..	..	..	..	1051	..	..	..	..	..	..	..	..	..	..	..	1151	..	..	..	..	..	..	..	..	..	..	..	1251	..
Camberley Q	..	..	..	..	..	1059	..	..	..	..	..	..	..	..	..	..	..	1159	..	..	..	..	..	..	..	..	..	..	..	1259	..
Frimley T	..	..	..	..	..	11 3	..	..	..	..	..	..	..	..	..	..	..	12 3	..	..	..	..	..	..	..	..	..	..	..	1 3	..
Ash Vale W	..	..	..	..	..	11 9	..	..	..	..	..	..	..	..	..	..	..	12 9	..	..	..	..	..	..	..	..	..	..	..	1 9	..
Aldershot Y arr.	..	..	..	..	..	1114	..	..	..	..	..	..	..	..	..	..	..	1214	..	..	..	..	..	..	..	..	..	..	..	1 14	..
Ascot dep.	..	..	..	..	..	1044	..	..	..	..	..	..	..	..	..	..	..	1144	..	..	..	..	..	..	..	..	..	..	..	1244	..
Bracknell	..	..	..	..	..	1049	..	..	..	..	..	..	..	..	..	..	..	1149	..	..	..	..	..	..	..	..	..	..	..	1249	..
Wokingham 249	..	..	..	..	..	1056	..	..	..	..	..	..	..	..	..	..	..	1156	..	..	..	..	..	..	..	..	..	..	..	1256	..
Winnersh Halt Z	..	..	..	..	..	11 0	..	..	..	..	..	..	..	..	..	..	..	12 0	..	..	..	..	..	..	..	..	..	..	..	1 0	..
Earley	..	..	..	..	..	11 4	..	..	..	..	..	..	..	..	..	..	..	12 4	..	..	..	..	..	..	..	..	..	..	..	1 4	..
Reading arr	..	..	..	..	..	11 9	..	..	..	..	..	..	..	..	..	..	..	12 9	..	..	..	..	..	..	..	..	..	..	..	1 9	..

LONDON, HOUNSLOW, RICHMOND, TWICKENHAM, TEDDINGTON, STAINES, WINDSOR, and READING

Week Days—continued (p.m.)

Down	SO		SX		SO			SO		SO	SX	SO				SO
Waterloo dep	12 4	12 9	1214	1221	1224	1226	1230	1234	1239	1243	1244	1246	1250	1254	1256	1 1
Vauxhall	..	1212	..	1224	..	1229	1233	..	1242	..	..	..	1253	..	1259	1 4
Queen's Road	..	1215	..	..	..	1232	..	..	1245	..	..	..	..	..	1 2	..
Clapham Junction A	..	1218	..	1228	..	1235	1238	..	1248	..	..	..	1258	..	1 5	1 8
Wandsworth Town	..	1220	..	1230	..	1237	1240	..	..	..	..	..	1 0	..	..	1 10
Putney	..	1223	..	1233	..	1240	1243	..	1253	..	..	..	1 3	..	1 9	1 13
Barnes	..	1226	..	1236	..	1243	1246	..	1256	..	..	..	1 6	..	1 12	1 16
Barnes Bridge	..	..	..	..	..	1245	..	..	..	..	..	..	..	..	1 14	..
Chiswick, for Grove Park	..	..	..	..	..	1247	..	..	..	..	..	..	..	..	1 16	..
Kew Bridge	..	..	..	..	..	1250	..	..	..	..	..	..	..	..	1 19	..
Brentford **B**	..	..	..	..	..	1253	..	..	..	..	..	..	..	..	1 22	..
Syon Lane	..	..	..	..	..	1255	..	..	..	..	..	..	..	..	1 24	..
Isleworth **C**	..	..	..	..	..	1257	..	..	..	..	..	..	..	..	1 26	..
Hounslow D	..	..	..	..	..	1 0	..	..	..	..	..	1 4	..	..	1 29	..
Whitton	..	..	..	..	..	1 3	..	..	..	..	..	..	..	..	1 32	..
Mortlake, for East Sheen	..	1229	..	1239	..	..	1249	..	1259	..	..	..	1 9	..	..	1 19
North Sheen	..	..	..	1242	..	..	1251	..	..	..	..	..	1 11	..	..	1 22
Richmond	1218	1232	1228	1244	1238	..	1254	..	1 2	1258	1258	..	1 14	..	..	1 24
St. Margaret's	..	1235	..	1247	..	..	1257	..	1 5	1 1	..	..	1 17	..	..	1 27
Twickenham	1222	1237	1232	1249	1242	1 6	1259	..	1 7	1 3	1 2	..	1 19	..	1 35	1 29
Strawberry Hill	..	..	..	1252	..	..	1 2	..	..	1 7	..	..	1 22	..	..	1 32
Teddington F arr.	..		..	1255	..	..	1 5	..	..	..	..	..	1 25	..	..	1 35
Whitton	1224	1239	1234	V	1244	..	V	..	1 9	To Shepperton, arr. 1 24 p.m., see page 401	1 4	..	V	..	..	V
Hounslow D arr.	..	1244	..		..	.		..	1 14		..	..		..	..	
Feltham	1228	..	1238	To Waterloo via Kingston	1248	..	To Waterloo via Kingston	..	..		1 8	1 8	To Waterloo via Kingston	..	..	To Waterloo via Kingston
Ashford (Middlesex)	1233	..	1243		1253	..		..	..		1 13	1 13		..	..	
Staines J arr.	1236	..	1246		1256	..		1 2	..		1 16	1 16		1 22	..	
Staines dep.	1238	..	1248		1258	..		..	..		1 18	1 18		..	..	
Wraysbury	1245	..	1255		1 5	..		..	..		1 25	1 25		..	..	
Sunnymeads	1248	..	1258		1 8	..		..	..		1 28	1 28		..	..	
Datchet	1251	..	1 1		1 11	..		..	..		1 31	1 31		..	..	
Windsor and Eton K arr.	1256	..	1 6		1 16	.		..	..		1 38	1 36		..	..	
Staines dep.	1237	..	1247		1257	..		1 2	..		1 17	1 17		1 22	..	
Egham **L**	1242	..	1252		1 2	..		1 7	..		1 22	1 22		1 27	..	
Virginia Water M arr.	1246	..	1256		1 6	..		1 11	..		1 26	1 26		1 31	..	
Virginia Water M dep.	1246	..	1256		1 6	..		..	..		1 28	1 26		..	..	
Chertsey	1251	..	1 1		1 11	..		..	..		1 34	1 31		..	..	
Addlestone	1254	..	1 4		1 14	..		..	..		1 37	1 34		..	..	
Weybridge N 394 arr.	1258	..	1 8		1 18	..		..	..		1 41	1 38		..	..	
Virginia Water M dep.	..	..	..	..	..	..	..	1 11	..	..	..	..	..	1 31	..	..
Longcross Halt	..	..	..	..	..	..	..	1 15	..	..	..	..	..	1 35	..	..
Sunningdale **P**	..	..	..	..	..	..	..	1 18	..	..	..	..	..	1 38	..	..
Ascot arr.	..	..	..	..	..	..	..	1 23	..	..	..	..	..	1 43	..	..
Ascot dep.	..	..	..	..	..	..	..	1 26	..	..	..	..	..	1 46	..	..
Bagshot	..	..	..	..	..	..	..	1 31	..	..	..	..	..	1 51	..	..
Camberley **Q**	..	..	..	..	..	..	..	1 37	..	..	..	..	..	1 59	..	..
Frimley **T**	..	..	..	..	..	..	..	1 41	..	..	..	..	..	2 3	..	..
Ash Vale **W**	..	..	..	..	..	..	..	1 47	..	..	..	..	..	2 9	..	..
Aldershot Y arr.	..	..	..	..	..	..	..	1 52	..	..	..	..	..	2 14	..	..
Ascot dep.	..	..	..	..	..	..	..	1 24	..	..	..	..	..	1 44	..	..
Bracknell	..	..	..	..	..	..	..	1 29	..	..	..	..	..	1 50	..	..
Wokingham 249	..	..	..	..	..	..	..	1 36	..	..	..	..	..	1 56	..	..
Winnersh Halt **Z**	..	..	..	..	..	..	..	1 40	..	..	..	..	..	2 0	..	..
Earley	..	..	..	..	..	..	..	1 44	..	..	..	..	..	2 4	..	..
Reading arr.	..	..	..	..	..	..	..	1 49	..	..	..	..	..	2 9	..	..

Down	SO		SO	SX	SO		SO			SO	SO		SO	SX	SO	
Waterloo dep	1 4	1 9	1 14	1 14	1 16	1 21	1 24	1 26	1 30	1 34	1 34	1 39	1 42	1 44	1 46	1 50
Vauxhall	..	1 12	..	..	..	1 24	..	1 29	1 33	..	..	1 42	..	..	..	1 53
Queen's Road	..	1 15	..	..	..	..	..	1 32	..	..	..	1 45	..	..	..	..
Clapham Junction A	..	1 18	..	..	..	1 28	..	1 35	1 38	..	..	1 48	..	..	..	1 58
Wandsworth Town	..	1 20	..	..	..	1 30	..	1 37	1 40	..	..	..	..	..	..	2 0
Putney	..	1 23	..	..	..	1 33	..	1 40	1 43	..	..	1 53	..	..	..	2 3
Barnes	..	1 26	..	..	..	1 36	..	1 43	1 46	..	..	1 56	..	..	..	2 6
Barnes Bridge	..	..	..	..	..	..	..	1 45	..	..	..	..	..	..	..	..
Chiswick, for Grove Park	..	..	..	..	..	..	..	1 47	..	..	..	..	..	..	..	..
Kew Bridge	..	..	..	..	..	..	..	1 50	..	..	..	..	..	..	..	..
Brentford **B**	..	..	..	..	..	..	..	1 53	..	..	..	..	..	..	..	..
Syon Lane	..	..	..	..	..	..	..	1 55	..	..	..	..	..	..	..	..
Isleworth **C**	..	..	..	..	..	..	..	1 57	..	..	..	..	..	..	..	..
Hounslow D	..	..	..	..	..	..	..	2 0	..	..	..	..	..	..	2 4	..
Whitton	..	..	..	..	..	..	..	2 3	..	..	..	..	..	..	..	..
Mortlake, for East Sheen	..	1 29	..	..	..	1 39	..	..	1 49	..	..	1 59	..	..	..	2 9
North Sheen	..	..	..	..	..	1 42	..	..	1 51	..	..	..	..	..	..	2 11
Richmond	1 18	1 32	..	1 28	1 30	1 44	1 38	..	1 54	..	..	2 2	1 58	1 58	..	2 14
St. Margaret's	..	1 35	..	..	1 33	1 47	..	..	1 57	..	..	2 5	2 1	..	..	2 17
Twickenham	1 22	1 37	..	1 32	1 35	1 49	1 42	2 6	1 59	..	..	2 7	2 3	2 2	..	2 19
Strawberry Hill	..	..	..	..	1 38	1 52	..	..	2 2	..	..	..	2 7	..	..	2 22
Teddington F arr.	..	..	..	..	..	1SX55	..	..	2 5	..	..	..	..	..	..	2 25
Whitton	1 24	1 39	..	1 34	..	V	1 44	..	V	..	..	2 9	..	2 4	..	V
Hounslow D arr.	..	1 44	..	..	..		..	..		..	..	2 14		..	..	
Feltham	1 28	..	..	1 38	To Shepperton, arr. 1 55 p.m., see page 402	To Waterloo (Saturdays excepted) via Kingston	1 48	..	To Waterloo via Kingston	..	..	..	To Shepperton, arr 2 24 p.m see page 402	2 8	2 8	To Waterloo via Kingston
Ashford (Middlesex)	1 33	..	..	1 43			1 53	..		..	..	..		2 13	2 13	
Staines J arr.	1 36	..	1 42	1 46			1 56	..		2 2	2 2	..		2 16	2 16	
Staines dep.	1 38	..	..	1 48			1 58	..		..	..	..		2 18	2 18	
Wraysbury	1 45	..	..	1 55			2 5	..		..	..	..		2 25	2 25	
Sunnymeads	1 48	..	..	1 58			2 8	..		..	..	..		2 28	2 28	
Datchet	1 51	..	..	2 1			2 11	..		..	..	..		2 31	2 31	
Windsor and Eton K arr.	1 56	..	..	2 6			2 16	..		..	..	..		2 38	2 38	
Staines dep.	1 37	..	1 42	1 47			1 57	..		2 2	2 2	..		2 17	2 17	
Egham **L**	1 42	..	1 47	1 52			2 2	..		2 7	2 7	..		2 22	2 22	
Virginia Water M arr.	1 46	..	1 51	1 56			2 7	..		2 11	2 11	..		2 26	2 26	
Virginia Water M dep.	1 46	..	..	1 56			2 9	..		..	..	..		2 26	2 26	
Chertsey	1 51	..	..	2 1			2 16	..		..	..	..		2 34	2 31	
Addlestone	1 54	..	..	2 4			2 19	..		..	..	..		2 37	2 34	
Weybridge N 394 arr.	1 58	..	..	2 8			2 23	..		..	..	..		2 41	2 38	
Virginia Water M dep.	..	..	1 51	..	..	..	..	..	..	2 11	2 11	..	..	..	..	..
Longcross Halt	..	..	1 55	..	..	..	..	..	..	2 15	2 15	..	..	..	..	..
Sunningdale **P**	..	..	1 53	..	..	..	..	..	..	2 18	2 18	..	..	..	..	..
Ascot arr.	..	..	2 3	..	..	..	..	..	..	2 23	2 23	..	..	..	..	..
Ascot dep.	..	..	2 6	..	..	..	..	..	..	..	2 25	..	..	..	..	..
Bagshot	..	..	2 11	..	..	..	..	..	..	..	2 30	..	..	..	..	..
Camberley **Q**	..	..	2 17	..	..	..	..	..	..	..	2 36	..	..	..	..	..
Frimley **T**	..	..	2 21	..	..	..	..	..	..	..	2 40	..	..	..	..	..
Ash Vale **W**	..	..	2 27	..	..	..	..	..	..	..	To Woking, arr 2 53p.m.page388	..	..	..	..	..
Aldershot Y arr.	..	..	2 32	..	..	..	..	..	..	..		..	..	..	..	..
Ascot dep.	..	..	2 4	..	..	..	..	..	..	2 24		..	..	..	..	..
Bracknell	..	..	2 9	..	..	..	..	..	..	2 29		..	..	..	..	..
Wokingham 249	..	..	2 16	..	..	..	..	..	..	2 36		..	..	..	..	..
Winnersh Halt **Z**	..	..	2 20	..	..	..	..	..	..	2 40		..	..	..	..	..
Earley	..	..	2 24	..	..	..	..	..	..	2 44		..	..	..	..	..
Reading arr.	..	..	2 29	..	..	..	..	..	..	2 49		..	..	..	..	..

FOR NOTES, SEE PAGE 475

FOR NOTES, SEE PAGE 475

LONDON, HOUNSLOW, RICHMOND, TWICKENHAM, TEDDINGTON, STAINES, WINDSOR, and READING

Down — Week Days—*continued* — p.m.

Down		3	3 SO	3	SO	3 SX	3	3 SO	3	3	SO	SO	3	3	3	
Waterloo dep	1 54	1 56	2 4	2 9	2 14	2 14	2 21	2 24	2 26	2 30	2 34	2 34	2 39	2 44	2 50	2 54
Vauxhall	..	1 59	..	2 12	..	..	2 24	..	2 29	2 33	..	..	2 42	..	2 53	..
Queen's Road	..	2 2	..	2 15	..	..	..	..	2 32	..	..	..	2 45	..	..	..
Clapham Junction A	..	2 5	..	2 18	..	..	2 28	..	2 35	2 38	..	..	2 48	..	2 58	..
Wandsworth Town	..	..	..	2 20	..	..	2 30	..	2 37	2 40	..	..	..	..	3 0	..
Putney	..	2 9	..	2 23	..	..	2 33	..	2 40	2 43	..	..	2 53	..	3 3	..
Barnes	..	2 13	..	2 26	..	..	2 36	..	2 43	2 46	..	..	2 56	..	3 6	..
Barnes Bridge	..	2 14	..	..	..	..	..	..	2 45	..	..	..	..	..	..	..
Chiswick, for Grove Park	..	2 17	..	..	..	..	..	..	2 47	..	..	..	..	..	..	..
Kew Bridge	..	2 19	..	..	..	..	..	..	2 50	..	..	..	..	..	..	..
Brentford B	..	2 22	..	..	..	..	..	..	2 53	..	..	..	..	..	..	..
Syon Lane	..	2 24	..	..	..	..	..	..	2 55	..	..	..	..	..	..	..
Isleworth C	..	2 26	..	..	..	..	..	..	2 57	..	..	..	..	..	..	..
Hounslow D	..	2 30	..	..	..	..	..	..	3 0	..	..	..	..	..	..	..
Whitton	..	2 33	..	..	..	..	..	..	3 3	..	..	..	..	..	..	..
Mortlake, for East Sheen	..	..	..	2 29	..	..	2 39	..	..	2 49	..	..	2 59	..	3 9	..
North Sheen	..	..	..	..	..	..	2 42	..	..	2 51	..	..	..	..	3 11	..
Richmond	..	..	2 18	2 32	..	2 28	2 44	2 38	..	2 54	..	..	3 2	2 58	3 14	..
St. Margaret's	..	..	..	2 35	..	..	2 47	..	..	2 57	..	..	3 5	..	3 17	..
Twickenham	..	2 36	2 22	2 37	..	2 32	2 49	2 42	3 6	2 59	..	..	3 7	3 2	3 19	..
Strawberry Hill	..	..	..	..	..	..	2 52	..	..	3 4	..	..	..	..	3 22	..
Teddington F arr	..	..	..	..	..	..	2 55	..	..	3 7	..	..	..	..	3 25	..
Whitton	..	..	2 24	2 39	..	2 34	V	2 44	..	V	..	..	3 9	3 4	V	..
Hounslow D arr	..	..	..	2 44	..	..		..	..		..	..	3 14	..		..
Feltham	..	..	2 28	..	..	2 38	To Waterloo, via Kingston	2 48	..	To Waterloo, via Kingston	..	..	..	3 8	To Waterloo, via Kingston	..
Ashford (Middlesex)	..	..	2 33	..	..	2 43		2 53	..		..	..	..	3 13		..
Staines J arr	2 22	..	2 36	..	2 42	2 46		2 56	..		3 2	3 2	..	3 16		3 22
Staines dep	..	..	2 38	..	..	2 48		2 58	..		..	..	..	3 18		..
Wraysbury	..	..	2 45	..	..	2 55		3 5	..		..	..	..	3 25		..
Sunnymeads	..	..	2 48	..	..	2 58		3 8	..		..	..	..	3 28		..
Datchet	..	..	2 51	..	..	3 1		3 11	..		..	..	..	3 31		..
Windsor and Eton K arr	..	..	2 56	..	..	3 6		3 16	..		..	..	..	3 38		..
Staines dep	2 22	..	2 37	..	2 42	2 47		2 57	..		3 2	3 2	..	3 17		3 22
Egham L	2 27	..	2 42	..	2 47	2 52		3 2	..		3 7	3 7	..	3 22		3 27
Virginia Water M arr	2 31	..	2 46	..	2 51	2 56		3 7	..		3 11	3 11	..	3 26		3 31
Virginia Water M dep	..	..	2 46	..	..	2 56		3 9	..		..	..	..	3 26		..
Chertsey	..	..	2 51	..	..	3 2		3 14	..		..	..	..	3 32		..
Addlestone	..	..	2 54	..	..	3 5		3 17	..		..	..	..	3 35		..
Weybridge N 394 arr	..	..	2 58	..	..	3 9		3 22	..		..	..	..	3 39		..
Virginia Water M dep	2 31	..	..	..	2 51	..	..	..	..	..	3 11	3 11	..	..	..	3 31
Longcross Halt	2 35	..	..	..	2 55	..	..	..	..	..	3 15	3 15	..	..	..	3 35
Sunningdale P	2 38	..	..	..	2 58	..	..	..	..	..	3 18	3 18	..	..	..	3 38
Ascot arr.	2 43	..	..	..	3 3	..	..	..	..	..	3 23	3 23	..	..	..	3 43
Ascot dep.	2 46	..	..	..	3 6	..	..	..	..	..	..	3 25	..	..	..	3 46
Bagshot	2 51	..	..	..	3 11	..	..	..	..	..	..	3 30	..	..	..	3 51
Camberley Q	2 59	..	..	..	3 17	..	..	..	..	..	..	3 36	..	..	..	3 59
Frimley T	3 3	..	..	..	3 21	..	..	..	..	..	..	3 40	..	..	..	4 3
Ash Vale W	3 9	..	..	..	3 27	..	..	..	..	..	..	To Woking, arr 3 54 p.m. page 388	..	..	..	4 9
Aldershot Y arr.	3 14	..	..	..	3 32	..	..	..	..	..	..		..	..	..	4 14
Ascot dep.	2 44	..	..	..	3 4	..	..	..	..	..	3 24		..	..	..	3 44
Bracknell	2 49	..	..	..	3 9	..	..	..	..	..	3 29		..	..	..	3 49
Wokingham 249	2 56	..	..	..	3 16	..	..	..	..	..	3 36		..	..	..	3 56
Winnersh Halt Z	3 0	..	..	..	3 20	..	..	..	..	..	3 40		..	..	..	4 0
Earley	3 4	..	..	..	3 24	..	..	..	..	..	3 44		..	..	..	4 4
Reading arr	3 9	..	..	..	3 29	..	..	..	..	..	3 49		..	..	..	4 9

Down	3	3	3	3	3	3	3	3	3		3	3 SX	3	3	3	SX
Waterloo dep	2 56	3 9	3 14	3 21	3 26	3 30	3 39	3 44	3 50	3 54	3 56	4 1	4 9	4 14	4 21	4 24
Vauxhall	2 59	3 12	..	3 24	3 29	3 33	3 42	..	3 53	..	3 59	4 4	4 12	..	4 24	..
Queen's Road	3 2	3 15	..	..	3 32	..	3 45	..	..	..	4 2	..	4 15	..	..	..
Clapham Junction A	3 5	3 18	..	3 28	3 35	3 38	3 48	..	3 58	..	4 5	4 8	4 18	..	4 28	..
Wandsworth Town	..	3 20	..	3 30	3 37	3 40	..	..	4 0	..	..	4 10	4 20	..	4 30	..
Putney	3 9	3 23	..	3 33	3 40	3 43	3 53	..	4 3	..	4 9	4 13	4 23	..	4 33	..
Barnes	3 13	3 26	..	3 36	3 43	3 46	3 56	..	4 6	..	4 12	4 16	4 26	..	4 36	..
Barnes Bridge	3 14	..	..	..	3 44	..	..	..	..	..	4 14	..	..	..	..	..
Chiswick, for Grove Park	3 17	..	..	..	3 47	..	..	..	..	..	4 16	..	..	..	..	..
Kew Bridge	3 19	..	..	..	3 49	..	..	..	..	..	4 19	..	..	..	..	..
Brentford B	3 22	..	..	..	3 52	..	..	..	..	..	4 22	..	..	..	..	..
Syon Lane	3 24	..	..	..	3 54	..	..	..	..	..	4 24	..	..	..	..	..
Isleworth C	3 26	..	..	..	3 56	..	..	..	..	..	4 26	..	..	..	..	..
Hounslow D	3 30	..	..	..	4 0	..	..	..	..	..	4 30	..	..	..	..	..
Whitton	3 33	..	..	..	4 3	..	..	..	..	..	4 33	..	..	..	..	..
Mortlake, for East Sheen	..	3 29	..	3 39	..	3 49	3 59	..	4 9	..	..	4 19	4 29	..	4 39	..
North Sheen	..	..	..	3 41	..	3 51	..	..	4 11	..	..	4 22	..	..	4 42	..
Richmond	..	3 32	3 28	3 44	..	3 54	4 2	3 58	4 14	..	..	4 24	4 32	4 28	4 44	..
St. Margaret's	..	3 35	..	3 47	..	3 57	4 5	..	4 17	..	..	4 27	4 35	..	4 47	..
Twickenham	3 36	3 37	3 32	3 49	4 6	3 59	4 7	4 3	4 19	..	4 36	4 29	4 37	4 33	4 49	..
Strawberry Hill	..	..	..	3 52	..	4 3	..	..	4 22	..	..	4 32	..	..	4 52	..
Teddington F arr	..	..	..	3 55	..	4 7	..	..	4 25	..	..	4 35	..	..	4 55	..
Whitton	..	3 39	3 34	V	..	V	4 9	4 5	V	..	..	V	4 39	4 35	V	..
Hounslow D arr	..	3 44	..		..		4 15	..		..	..		4 45	..		..
Feltham	..	..	3 38	To Waterloo, via Kingston	..	To Waterloo, via Kingston	..	4 9	To Waterloo, via Kingston	..	..	To Waterloo, via Kingston	..	4 39	To Waterloo, via Kingston	..
Ashford (Middlesex)	..	..	3 43		..		..	4 14		..	..		..	4 44		..
Staines J arr	..	..	3 46		..		..	4 17		4 22	..		..	4 47		4 52
Staines dep	..	..	3 48		..		..	4 19		..	..		..	4 49		..
Wraysbury	..	..	3 55		..		..	4 26		..	..		..	4 56		..
Sunnymeads	..	..	3 58		..		..	4 29		..	..		..	4 59		..
Datchet	..	..	4 1		..		..	4 32		..	..		..	5 2		..
Windsor and Eton K arr	..	..	4 6		..		..	4 38		..	..		..	5 7		..
Staines dep	..	..	3 47		..		..	4 18		4 22	..		..	4 48		4 52
Egham L	..	..	3 52		..		..	4 23		4 27	..		..	4 53		4 57
Virginia Water M arr	..	..	3 56		..		..	4 27		4 31	..		..	4 57		5 1
Virginia Water M dep	..	..	3 56		..		..	4 27		..	..		..	4 57		..
Chertsey	..	..	4 2		..		..	4 32		..	..		..	5 2		..
Addlestone	..	..	4 5		..		..	4 35		..	..		..	5 5		..
Weybridge N 394 arr	..	..	4 9		..		..	4 39		..	..		..	5 9		..
Virginia Water M dep	..	..	..	..	..	..	..	..	..	4 31	..	..	..	..	..	5 1
Longcross Halt	..	..	..	..	..	..	..	..	..	4 35	..	..	..	..	..	5 5
Sunningdale P	..	..	..	..	..	..	..	..	..	4 38	..	..	..	..	..	5 9
Ascot arr.	..	..	..	..	..	..	..	..	..	4 43	..	..	..	..	..	5 13
Ascot dep.	..	..	..	..	..	..	..	..	..	4 46	..	..	..	..	..	5 16
Bagshot	..	..	..	..	..	..	..	..	..	4 51	..	..	..	..	..	5 21
Camberley Q	..	..	..	..	..	..	..	..	..	4 59	..	..	..	..	..	5 29
Frimley T	..	..	..	..	..	..	..	..	..	5 3	..	..	..	..	..	5 33
Ash Vale W	..	..	..	..	..	..	..	..	..	5 9	..	..	..	..	..	5 39
Aldershot Y arr.	..	..	..	..	..	..	..	..	..	5 14	..	..	..	..	..	5 44
Ascot dep.	..	..	..	..	..	..	..	..	..	4 44	..	..	..	..	..	5 15
Bracknell	..	..	..	..	..	..	..	..	..	4 49	..	..	..	..	..	5 20
Wokingham 249	..	..	..	..	..	..	..	..	..	4 56	..	..	..	..	..	5 26
Winnersh Halt Z	..	..	..	..	..	..	..	..	..	5 0	..	..	..	..	..	5 30
Earley	..	..	..	..	..	..	..	..	..	5 4	..	..	..	..	..	5 34
Reading arr	..	..	..	..	..	..	..	..	..	5 9	..	..	..	..	..	5 40

LONDON, HOUNSLOW, RICHMOND, TWICKENHAM, TEDDINGTON, STAINES, WINDSOR, and READING

Week Days—continued (p.m)

Down	3	3	3	3	3 SX	3		3	3 SX	3 SX	3	SX	3 SO	3 SX	3	3 SX	3	3	SX	SX	3	3 SX	3 SO	3 SX	3 SX	3			3	3 SX	3 SX	3
Waterloo dep	4 26	4 30	4 39	4 44	4 48	4 50	4 54	4 56	5 1	5 4	5 9	5 14	5 14	5 16	5 21	5 24	5 26	5 30	5 34	5 34	5 39	5 42	5 44	5 44	5 48	5 50	..	5 54	5 56	6 1	6 4	6 9
Vauxhall	4 29	4 33	4 42	..	..	4 53	..	4 59	5 4	..	5 12	..	..	..	5 24	..	5 29	5 33	..	..	5 42	..	..	..	..	5 53	..	..	5 59	6 4	..	6 12
Queen's Road	4 32	..	4 45	..	..	..	..	5 2	—	..	5 15	..	..	..	..	..	5 32	..	..	..	5 45	..	..	..	..	..	..	..	6 2	..	..	6 15
Clapham Junction A	4 35	4 38	4 48	..	..	4 58	..	5 5	5 8	..	5 18	..	..	..	5 28	..	5 35	5 38	..	..	5 48	..	..	..	..	5 58	..	..	6 5	6 8	..	6 18
Wandsworth Town	4 37	4 40	..	..	4 56	5 0	..	..	5 10	..	5 20	..	..	..	5 30	..	5 37	5 40	..	..	..	..	..	..	..	6 0	..	..	..	6 10	..	6 20
Putney	4 40	4 43	4 53	..	4 59	5 3	..	5 9	5 13	..	5 23	..	..	..	5 33	..	5 40	5 43	..	..	5 52	..	..	..	..	6 3	..	..	6 9	6 13	..	6 23
Barnes	4 43	4 46	4 56	..	5 2	5 6	..	5 12	5 16	..	5 26	..	..	..	5 36	..	5 43	5 46	..	..	5 55	..	..	..	..	6 6	..	..	6 13	6 16	..	6 26
Barnes Bridge	4 45	..	..	..	5 3	..	..	5 14	..	..	..	..	..	..	..	..	5 45	..	..	..	..	..	..	..	..	..	..	..	6 14	..	..	..
Chiswick, for Grove Park	4 47	..	..	..	5 6	..	..	5 16	..	..	..	..	..	..	..	..	5 47	..	..	..	..	..	..	..	..	..	..	..	6 17	..	..	..
Kew Bridge	4 50	..	..	..	5 8	..	..	5 19	..	..	..	..	..	..	..	..	5 50	..	..	..	..	..	..	..	..	..	..	..	6 19	..	..	..
Brentford B	4 53	..	..	..	5 11	..	..	5 22	..	..	..	..	..	..	..	..	5 53	..	..	..	..	..	..	..	..	..	..	..	6 22	..	..	..
Syon Lane	4 55	..	..	..	5 13	..	..	5 24	..	..	..	..	..	..	..	..	5 55	..	..	..	..	..	..	..	..	..	..	..	6 24	..	..	..
Isleworth C	4 57	..	..	..	5 15	..	..	5 26	..	..	..	..	..	..	..	..	5 57	..	..	..	..	..	..	..	..	..	..	..	6 26	..	..	..
Hounslow D	5 0	..	..	..	5 19	..	..	5 30	..	..	..	..	..	..	..	..	6 0	..	..	..	..	..	..	6 5	..	..	..	..	6 29	..	..	..
Whitton	5 3	..	..	..	..	..	..	5 33	..	..	..	..	..	..	..	..	6 3	..	..	..	..	..	..	..	..	..	..	..	6 33	..	..	..
Mortlake, for East Sheen	..	4 49	4 59	..	..	5 9	..	..	5 19	..	5 29	..	..	..	5 39	..	..	5 49	..	..	5 58	..	..	..	..	6 9	..	..	..	6 19	..	6 29
North Sheen	..	4 51	..	..	..	5 11	..	..	5 22	..	..	..	..	..	5 42	..	..	5 51	..	..	..	..	..	..	..	6 11	..	..	..	6 22	..	..
Richmond	..	4 54	5 2	4 58	..	5 14	..	..	5 24	5 18	5 32	..	5 28	5 30	5 44	5 38	..	5 54	..	..	6 1	5 58	5 58	..	6 4	6 14	..	..	..	6 24	6 18	6 32
St. Margaret's	..	4 57	5 5	..	..	5 17	..	..	5 27	..	5 35	..	..	5 33	5 47	..	..	5 57	..	..	6 4	..	..	..	6 7	6 17	..	..	..	6 27	..	6 35
Twickenham	5 6	4 59	5 7	5 3	..	5 19	..	5 36	5 29	5 22	5 37	..	5 32	5 35	5 49	5 42	6 6	5 59	..	..	6 6	6 2	6 2	..	6 9	6 19	..	..	6 36	6 29	6 22	6 37
Strawberry Hill	..	5 2	..	..	..	5 22	..	..	5 32	..	..	..	..	5 38	5 52	..	..	6 2	..	..	..	..	..	..	6 12	6 22	..	..	..	6 32	..	..
Teddington F arr	..	5 5	..	..	..	5 25	..	..	5 35	..	..	..	..	To Shepperton, arr 5 57 p.m see page 406	5 55	..	..	6 5	..	..	..	..	..	..	To Shepperton, arr 6 27 p.m see page 407	6 25	..	..	..	6 35	..	..
Whitton	..	V	5 9	5 5	..	V	..	..	V	5 24	5 40	..	5 34		V	5 44	..	V	..	..	6 8	6 4	6 4	..		V	..	..	..	V	6 24	6 40
Hounslow D arr	..	..	5 15	..	..		..	..		..	5 44	..	..			..	..		..	..	6 14	..	..	..			..	..	..		..	6 45
Feltham	..	To Waterloo via Kingston	..	5 9	..	To Waterloo via Kingston	..	..	To Waterloo via Kingston	5 28	..	..	5 38		To Waterloo via Kingston	5 48	..	To Waterloo via Kingston	..	..	..	6 8	6 8	6 11		To Waterloo via Kingston	..	..	..	To Kingston	6 28	..
Ashford (Middlesex)	..		..	5 14	..		..	..		5 33	..	..	5 43			5 53	..		..	..	..	6 13	6 13	6 16			..	..	..		6 33	..
Staines J arr	..		..	5 17	..		5 23	..		5 36	..	5 42	5 46			5 56	..		6 2	6 2	..	6 16	6 16	6 19			..	6 23	..		6 36	..
Staines dep	..		..	5 19	..		..	..		5 38	..	..	5 48			5 58	..		..	..	..	..	6 18	6 20			..	..	..		6 38	..
Wraysbury	..		..	5 26	..		..	..		5 45	..	..	5 55			6 5	..		..	..	..	..	6 25	6 26			..	..	..		6 45	..
Sunnymeads	..		..	5 29	..		..	..		5 48	..	..	5 58			6 8	..		..	..	..	..	6 28	6 29			..	..	..		6 48	..
Datchet	..		..	5 32	..		..	..		5 51	..	..	6 1			6 11	..		..	..	..	..	6 31	6 33			..	..	..		6 51	..
Windsor and Eton K arr	..		..	5 38	..		..	..		5 56	..	..	6 8			6 16	..		..	..	..	..	6 36	6 38			..	..	..		6 56	..
Staines dep	..		..	5 18	..		5 23	..		5 37	..	5 42	5 47	..		5 57	..		6 2	6 2	..	6 16	6 16	..			..	6 23	..		6 37	..
Egham L	..		..	5 23	..		5 28	..		5 42	..	5 47	5 52	..		6 2	..		6 7	6 7	..	6 21	6 21	..			..	6 28	..		6 42	..
Virginia Water M arr	..		..	5 27	..		5 32	..		5 46	..	5 51	5 55	..		6 6	..		6 11	6 11	..	6 25	6 25	..			..	6 32	..		6 46	..
Virginia Water M dep	..		..	5 27	..		..	..		5 46	..	..	5 56	..		6 6	..		..	..	..	6 25	6 25	..			..	..	..		6 46	..
Chertsey	..		..	5 32	..		..	..		5 51	..	..	6 1	..		6 11	..		..	..	..	6 31	6 31	..			..	..	..		6 52	..
Addlestone	..		..	5 35	..		..	..		5 54	..	..	6 4	..		6 14	..		..	..	..	6 34	6 34	..			..	..	..		6 55	..
Weybridge N 394 arr	..		..	5 39	..		..	..		5 58	..	..	6 8	..		6 18	..		..	..	..	6 39	6 39	..			..	..	..		7 0	..
Virginia Water M dep	..	..	..	..	..	..	5 32	..	..	..	..	5 51	..	..	..	..	..	..	6 11	6 11	..	..	..	..	..	..	..	6 32	..	..	..	..
Longcross Halt	..	..	..	..	..	..	5 36	..	..	..	..	5 55	..	..	..	..	..	..	6 15	6 15	..	..	..	..	..	..	..	6 36	..	..	..	..
Sunningdale P	..	..	..	..	..	..	5 39	..	..	..	..	5 58	..	..	..	..	..	..	6 18	6 18	..	..	..	..	..	..	..	6 39	..	..	..	..
Ascot arr	..	..	..	..	..	..	5 44	..	..	..	..	6 3	..	..	..	..	..	..	6 23	6 23	..	..	..	..	..	..	..	6 44	..	..	..	..
Ascot dep	..	..	..	..	..	..	5 47	..	..	..	..	6 6	..	..	..	..	..	..	..	6 26	..	..	..	..	..	..	..	6 47	..	..	..	..
Bagshot	..	..	..	..	..	..	5 52	..	..	..	..	6 11	..	..	..	..	..	..	..	6 31	..	..	..	..	..	..	..	6 52	..	..	..	..
Camberley Q	..	..	..	..	..	..	5 59	..	..	..	..	6 17	..	..	..	..	..	..	..	6 37	..	..	..	..	..	..	..	6 58	..	..	..	..
Frimley T	..	..	..	..	..	..	6 3	..	..	..	..	6 21	..	..	..	..	..	..	..	6 41	..	..	..	..	..	..	..	7 3	..	..	..	..
Ash Vale W	..	..	..	..	..	..	6 9	..	..	..	..	6 27	..	..	..	..	..	..	..	To Woking, arr. 6 56 p.m, page 388	..	..	..	..	..	..	..	7 10	..	..	..	..
Aldershot Y arr	..	..	..	..	..	..	6 14	..	..	..	..	6 32	..	..	..	..	..	..	..		..	..	..	..	..	..	..	7 15	..	..	..	..
Ascot dep	..	..	..	..	..	..	5 45	..	..	..	..	6 4	..	..	..	..	..	..	6 24	..	..	..	..	..	..	..	..	6 45	..	..	..	..
Bracknell	..	..	..	..	..	..	5 50	..	..	..	..	6 9	..	..	..	..	..	..	6 29	..	..	..	..	..	..	..	..	6 50	..	..	..	..
Wokingham 249	..	..	..	..	..	..	5 57	..	..	..	..	6 16	..	..	..	..	..	..	6 36	..	..	..	..	..	..	..	..	6 57	..	..	..	..
Winnersh Halt Z	..	..	..	..	..	..	6 1	..	..	..	..	6 20	..	..	..	..	..	..	6 40	..	..	..	..	..	..	..	..	7 1	..	..	..	..
Earley	..	..	..	..	..	..	6 5	..	..	..	..	6 24	..	..	..	..	..	..	6 44	..	..	..	..	..	..	..	..	7 5	..	..	..	..
Reading arr	..	..	..	..	..	..	6 10	..	..	..	..	6 29	..	..	..	..	..	..	6 49	..	..	..	..	..	..	..	..	7 10	..	..	..	..

FOR NOTES, SEE PAGE 475

FOR NOTES, SEE PAGE 475

LONDON, HOUNSLOW, RICHMOND, TWICKENHAM, TEDDINGTON, STAINES, WINDSOR, and READING

Week Days—continued (p.m.)

Down	SX	3 SO	3 SX	3	3 SX	3	3	SX	SX	3	3 SO	3 SX	3		3	3 SX
Waterloo ....dep	6 14	6 14	6 16	6 21	6 24	6 26	6 30	6 34	6 34	6 39	6 44	6 46	6 50	6 54	6 56	7 1
Vauxhall	..	..	..	6 24	..	6 29	6 33	..	..	6 42	..	..	6 53	..	6 59	7 4
Queen's Road	..	..	..	..	..	6 32	..	..	..	6 45	..	..	..	..	7 2	..
Clapham Junction A	..	..	..	6 28	..	6 35	6 38	..	..	6 48	..	..	6 58	..	7 5	7 8
Wandsworth Town	..	..	..	6 30	..	6 37	6 40	..	..	..	..	..	7 0	..	..	7 10
Putney	..	..	..	6 33	..	6 40	6 43	..	..	6 53	..	..	7 3	..	7 9	7 13
Barnes	..	..	..	6 36	..	6 43	6 46	..	..	6 56	..	..	7 6	..	7 12	7 16
Barnes Bridge	..	..	..	..	..	6 45	..	..	..	..	..	..	..	..	7 14	..
Chiswick, for Grove Park	..	..	..	..	..	6 47	..	..	..	..	..	..	..	..	7 16	..
Kew Bridge	..	..	..	..	..	6 50	..	..	..	..	..	..	..	..	7 19	..
Brentford **B**	..	..	..	..	..	6 53	..	..	..	..	..	..	..	..	7 22	..
Syon Lane	..	..	..	..	..	6 55	..	..	..	..	..	..	..	..	7 24	..
Isleworth **C**	..	..	..	..	..	6 57	..	..	..	..	..	..	..	..	7 26	..
Hounslow D	..	..	..	..	..	7 0	..	..	..	..	..	7 4	..	..	7 30	..
Whitton	..	..	..	..	..	7 4	..	..	..	..	..	..	..	..	7 33	..
Mortlake, for East Sheen	..	..	..	6 39	..	..	6 49	..	..	6 59	..	..	7 9	..	..	7 19
North Sheen	..	..	..	6 42	..	..	6 51	..	..	..	..	..	7 11	..	..	7 22
Richmond	..	6 28	6 30	6 44	6 38	..	6 54	..	..	7 2	6 58	..	7 14	..	..	7 24
St. Margaret's	..	..	6 33	6 47	..	..	6 57	..	..	7 5	..	..	7 17	..	..	7 27
Twickenham	..	6 32	6 35	6 49	6 42	7 7	6 59	..	..	7 7	7 2	..	7 19	..	7 36	7 29
Strawberry Hill	..	..	6 38	6 52	..	..	7 3	..	..	..	..	..	7 23	..	..	7 32
Teddington F ....arr.	..	..		6 55	..	..	7 6	..	..	..	..	..	7 26	..	..	7 35
Whitton	..	6 34	To Shepperton, arr. 6 57 p.m see page 407	V	6 44	..	V	..	..	7 9	7 4	..	V	..	..	V
Hounslow D ....arr.	..	..		To Waterloo, via Kingston	..	..	To Waterloo, via Kingston	..	..	7 14	..	..	To Waterloo, via Kingston	..	..	To Wimbledon via Kingston
Feltham	..	6 38			6 48	..		..	..	..	7 8	7 8		..	..	
Ashford (Middlesex)	..	6 43			6 53	..		..	..	..	7 13	7 13		..	..	
Staines J ....arr.	6 42	6 46			6 56	..		7 2	7 2	..	7 16	7 16		7 22	..	
Staines ....dep.	..	6 48			6 58	..		..	..	..	7 18	7 18		..	..	
Wraysbury	..	6 55			7 5	..		..	..	..	7 26	7 26		..	..	
Sunnymeads	..	6 58			7 8	..		..	..	..	7 29	7 29		..	..	
Datchet	..	7 1			7 11	..		..	..	..	7 32	7 32		..	..	
Windsor and Eton K arr.	..	7 8			7 16	..		..	..	..	7 37	7 37		..	..	
Staines ....dep.	6 42	6 47			6 57	..		7 2	7 2	..	7 17	7 17		7 22	..	
Egham **L**	6 47	6 52			7 2	..		7 7	7 7	..	7 22	7 22		7 27	..	
Virginia Water M ....arr.	6 51	6 56			7 7	..		7 11	7 11	..	7 26	7 26		7 31	..	
Virginia Water M ..dep.	..	6 56			7 9	..		..	..	..	7 26	7 26	..	..	..	..
Chertsey	..	7 2			7 14	..		..	..	..	7 31	7 31	..	..	..	..
Addlestone	..	7 5			7 17	..		..	..	..	7 34	7 34	..	..	..	..
Weybridge N 394 ...arr.	..	7 9			7 21	..		..	..	..	7 38	7 38	..	..	..	..
Virginia Water M ....dep.	6 51	..	..	..	..	..	..	7 11	7 11	..	..	..	..	7 31	..	..
Longcross Halt	6 55	..	..	..	..	..	..	7 15	7 15	..	..	..	..	7 35	..	..
Sunningdale **P**	6 58	..	..	..	..	..	..	7 18	7 18	..	..	..	..	7 38	..	..
Ascot ....arr.	7 3	..	..	..	..	..	..	7 23	7 23	..	..	..	..	7 43	..	..
Ascot ....dep.	7 6	..	..	..	..	..	..	..	7 26	..	..	..	..	7 46	..	..
Bagshot	7 11	..	..	..	..	..	..	..	7 31	..	..	..	..	7 51	..	..
Camberley **Q**	7 17	..	..	..	..	..	..	..	7 37	..	..	..	..	7 59	..	..
Frimley **T**	7 21	..	..	..	..	..	..	..	7 41	..	..	..	..	8 3	..	..
Ash Vale **W**	7 27	..	..	..	..	..	..	..	To Woking, arr. 7 54 p.m page 388	..	..	..	..	8 9	..	..
Aldershot Y ....arr.	7 32	..	..	..	..	..	..	..		..	..	..	..	8 14	..	..
Ascot ....dep.	7 4	..	..	..	..	..	..	7 24		..	..	..	..	7 44	..	..
Bracknell	7 9	..	..	..	..	..	..	7 29		..	..	..	..	7 49	..	..
Wokingham 249	7 16	..	..	..	..	..	..	7 36		..	..	..	..	7 56	..	..
Winnersh Halt **Z**	7 20	..	..	..	..	..	..	7 40		..	..	..	..	8 0	..	..
Earley	7 24	..	..	..	..	..	..	7 44		..	..	..	..	8 4	..	..
Reading ....arr.	7 29	..	..	..	..	..	..	7 49		..	..	..	..	8 9	..	..

Down	3 SX	3	3 SO	3	3	3	3	3	3		3	3	3	3	3	3
Waterloo ....dep	7 4	7 9	7 14	7 21	7 26	7 30	7 39	7 44	7 50	7 54	7 56	8 9	8 14	8 21	8 26	8 30
Vauxhall	..	7 12	..	7 24	7 29	7 33	7 42	..	7 53	..	7 59	8 12	..	8 24	8 29	8 33
Queen's Road	..	7 15	..	..	7 32	..	7 45	..	..	..	8 2	8 15	..	..	8 32	..
Clapham Junction A	..	7 18	..	7 28	7 35	7 38	7 48	..	7 58	..	8 5	8 18	..	8 28	8 35	8 38
Wandsworth Town	..	7 20	..	7 30	7 37	7 40	..	..	8 0	..	..	8 20	..	8 30	8 37	8 40
Putney	..	7 23	..	7 33	7 40	7 43	7 53	..	8 3	..	8 9	8 23	..	8 33	8 40	8 43
Barnes	..	7 26	..	7 36	7 43	7 46	7 56	..	8 6	..	8 12	8 26	..	8 36	8 43	8 46
Barnes Bridge	..	..	..	..	7 44	..	..	..	..	..	8 14	..	..	..	8 45	..
Chiswick, for Grove Park	..	..	..	..	7 47	..	..	..	..	..	8 16	..	..	..	8 47	..
Kew Bridge	..	..	..	..	7 49	..	..	..	..	..	8 19	..	..	..	8 50	..
Brentford **B**	..	..	..	..	7 52	..	..	..	..	..	8 22	..	..	..	8 53	..
Syon Lane	..	..	..	..	7 54	..	..	..	..	..	8 24	..	..	..	8 55	..
Isleworth **C**	..	..	..	..	7 56	..	..	..	..	..	8 26	..	..	..	8 57	..
Hounslow D	..	..	..	..	8 0	..	..	..	..	..	8 29	..	..	..	9 0	..
Whitton	..	..	..	..	8 3	..	..	..	..	..	8 32	..	..	..	9 3	..
Mortlake, for East Sheen	..	7 29	..	7 39	..	7 49	7 59	..	8 9	..	..	8 29	..	8 39	..	8 49
North Sheen	..	..	..	7 42	..	7 51	..	..	8 11	..	..	..	..	8 42	..	8 51
Richmond	7 18	7 32	7 28	7 44	..	7 54	8 2	7 58	8 14	..	..	8 32	8 28	8 44	..	8 54
St. Margaret's	..	7 35	..	7 47	..	7 57	8 5	..	8 17	..	..	8 35	..	8 47	..	8 57
Twickenham	7 22	7 37	7 32	7 49	8 6	7 59	8 7	8 2	8 19	..	8 35	8 37	8 32	8 49	9 6	8 59
Strawberry Hill	..	..	..	7 53	..	8 3	..	..	8 22	..	..	..	..	8 52	..	9 4
Teddington F ....arr.	..	..	..	7 56	..	8 7	..	..	8 25	..	..	..	..	8 55	..	9 7
Whitton	7 24	7 39	7 34	V	..	V	8 9	8 4	V	..	..	8 39	8 34	V	..	V
Hounslow D ....arr.	..	7 44	..	To Waterloo via Kingston	..	To Waterloo, via Kingston	8 14	..	To Waterloo, via Kingston	..	..	8 44	..	To Waterloo via Kingston	..	To Waterloo, via Kingston
Feltham	7 28	..	7 38		..		..	8 8		..	..	..	8 38		..	
Ashford (Middlesex)	7 33	..	7 43		..		..	8 13		..	..	..	8 43		..	
Staines J ....arr.	7 36	..	7 46		..		..	8 16		8 22	..	..	8 46		..	
Staines ....dep.	7 38	..	7 48		..		..	8 18		..	..	..	8 48		..	
Wraysbury	7 46	..	7 55		..		..	8 25		..	..	..	8 55		..	
Sunnymeads	7 49	..	7 58		..		..	8 28		..	..	..	8 58		..	
Datchet	7 52	..	8 1		..		..	8 31		..	..	..	9 1		..	
Windsor and Eton K arr.	7 57	..	8 8		..		..	8 36		..	..	..	9 8		..	
Staines ....dep.	7 37	..	7 47		..		..	8 17		8 22	..	..	8 47		..	
Egham **L**	7 42	..	7 52		..		..	8 22		8 27	..	..	8 52		..	
Virginia Water M ....arr.	7 46	..	7 56		..		..	8 26		8 31	..	..	8 56		..	
Virginia Water M ..dep.	7 46	..	7 56	..	..	..	..	8 26	..	..	..	..	8 56	..	..	..
Chertsey	7B57	..	8 1	..	..	..	..	8 33	..	..	..	..	9 1	..	..	..
Addlestone	8 3	..	8 4	..	..	..	..	8 36	..	..	..	..	9 4	..	..	..
Weybridge N 394 ...arr.	8 7	..	8 8	..	..	..	..	8 40	..	..	..	..	9 8	..	..	..
Virginia Water M ....dep.	..	..	..	..	..	..	..	..	..	8 31	..	..	..	..	..	..
Longcross Halt	..	..	..	..	..	..	..	..	..	8 35	..	..	..	..	..	..
Sunningdale **P**	..	..	..	..	..	..	..	..	..	8 38	..	..	..	..	..	..
Ascot ....arr.	..	..	..	..	..	..	..	..	..	8 43	..	..	..	..	..	..
Ascot ....dep.	..	..	..	..	..	..	..	..	..	8 46	..	..	..	..	..	..
Bagshot	..	..	..	..	..	..	..	..	..	8 51	..	..	..	..	..	..
Camberley **Q**	..	..	..	..	..	..	..	..	..	8 59	..	..	..	..	..	..
Frimley **T**	..	..	..	..	..	..	..	..	..	9 3	..	..	..	..	..	..
Ash Vale **W**	..	..	..	..	..	..	..	..	..	9 9	..	..	..	..	..	..
Aldershot Y ....arr.	..	..	..	..	..	..	..	..	..	9 14	..	..	..	..	..	..
Ascot ....dep.	..	..	..	..	..	..	..	..	..	8 44	..	..	..	..	..	..
Bracknell	..	..	..	..	..	..	..	..	..	8 49	..	..	..	..	..	..
Wokingham 249	..	..	..	..	..	..	..	..	..	8 56	..	..	..	..	..	..
Winnersh Halt **Z**	..	..	..	..	..	..	..	..	..	9 0	..	..	..	..	..	..
Earley	..	..	..	..	..	..	..	..	..	9 4	..	..	..	..	..	..
Reading ....arr.	..	..	..	..	..	..	..	..	..	9 9	..	..	..	..	..	..

LONDON, HOUNSLOW, RICHMOND, TWICKENHAM, TEDDINGTON, STAINES, WINDSOR, and READING

Week Days—continued (p.m)

Down	3	3	3		3	3	3	3	3	3	3	3	3		3	3
Waterloo ....dep.	8 39	8 44	8 50	8 54	8 56	9 9	9 14	9 21	9 26	9 30	9 39	9 44	9 50	9 54	9 56	10 9
Vauxhall	8 42	..	8 53	..	8 59	9 12	..	9 24	9 29	9 33	9 42	..	9 53	..	9 59	1012
Queen's Road	8 45	..	..	..	9 2	9 15	..	..	9 32	..	9 45	..	..	..	10 2	1015
Clapham Junction **A**	8 48	..	8 58	..	9 5	9 18	..	9 28	9 35	9 38	9 48	9 51	9 58	..	10 5	1018
Wandsworth Town	..	..	9 0	..	..	9 20	..	9 30	9 37	9 40	..	..	10 0	..	..	1020
Putney	8 53	..	9 3	..	9 9	9 23	..	9 33	9 40	9 43	9 53	..	10 3	..	10 9	1023
Barnes	8 56	..	9 6	..	9 12	9 26	..	9 36	9 43	9 46	9 56	..	10 6	..	1012	1026
Barnes Bridge	..	..	..	..	9 14	..	..	..	9 45	..	..	..	..	..	1014	..
Chiswick, for Grove Park	..	..	..	..	9 16	..	..	..	9 47	..	..	..	..	..	1016	..
Kew Bridge	..	..	..	..	9 19	..	..	..	9 50	..	..	..	..	..	1019	..
Brentford **B**	..	..	..	..	9 22	..	..	..	9 53	..	..	..	..	..	1022	..
Syon Lane	..	..	..	..	9 24	..	..	..	9 55	..	..	..	..	..	1024	..
Isleworth **C**	..	..	..	..	9 26	..	..	..	9 57	..	..	..	..	..	1026	..
Hounslow D	..	..	..	..	9 29	..	..	..	10 0	..	..	..	..	..	1029	..
Whitton	..	..	..	..	9 32	..	..	..	10 3	..	..	..	..	..	1032	..
Mortlake, for East Sheen	8 59	..	9 9	..	..	9 29	..	9 39	..	9 49	9 59	..	10 9	..	..	1029
North Sheen	..	..	9 11	..	..	..	..	9 42	..	9 51	..	..	1011	..	..	..
Richmond	9 2	8 58	9 14	..	..	9 32	9 28	9 44	..	9 54	10 2	9 59	1014	..	..	1032
St. Margaret's	9 5	..	9 17	..	..	9 35	..	9 47	..	9 57	10 5	..	1017	..	..	1035
Twickenham	9 7	9 2	9 19	..	9 35	9 37	9 32	9 49	10 6	9 59	10 7	10 3	1019	..	1035	1037
Strawberry Hill	..	..	9 22	..	..	..	..	9 52	..	10 2	..	..	1022	..	..	..
Teddington F ......arr.	..	..	9 25	..	..	..	..	9 55	..	10 5	..	..	1025	..	..	..
Whitton	9 9	9 4	V	..	..	9 39	9 34	V	..	V	10 9	10 5	V	..	..	1039
Hounslow D ......arr.	9 14	..		..	..	9 44	..		..		1014	..		..	..	1043
Feltham	..	9 8		..	..	..	9 38		..		..	10 9		..	..	..
Ashford (Middlesex)	..	9 13		..	..	..	9 43		..		..	1014		..	..	..
Staines J ......arr.	..	9 16		9 22	..	..	9 46		..		..	1017		1022	..	..
Staines ......dep.	..	9 18	To Waterloo, via Kingston	..	..	..	9 48	To Waterloo via Kingston	..	To Waterloo via Kingston	..	1019	To Waterloo via Kingston	..	..	..
Wraysbury	..	9 25		..	..	..	9 55		..		..	1026		..	..	..
Sunnymeads	..	9 28		..	..	..	9 58		..		..	1029		..	..	..
Datchet	..	9 31		..	..	..	10 1		..		..	1032		..	..	..
Windsor and Eton K arr.	..	9 36		..	..	..	10 8		..		..	1037		..	..	..
Staines ......dep.	..	9 17		9 22	..	..	9 47		..		..	1018		1022	..	..
Egham L	..	9 22		9 27	..	..	9 52		..		..	1023		1027	..	..
Virginia Water M ....arr.	..	9 26		9 31	..	..	9 56		..		..	1027		1031	..	..
Virginia Water M ..dep.	..	9 26	..	..	..	..	9 56		..		..	1030		..	..	..
Chertsey	..	9 34	..	..	..	..	10 1		..		..	1035		..	..	..
Addlestone	..	9 37	..	..	..	..	10 4		..		..	1038		..	..	..
Weybridge N 394 ..arr.	..	9 41	..	..	..	..	10 8		..		..	1042		..	..	..
Virginia Water M ....dep.	..	..	..	9 31	..	..	..	..	..	..	..	..	..	1031	..	..
Longcross Halt	..	..	..	9 35	..	..	..	..	..	..	..	..	..	1035	..	..
Sunningdale **P**	..	..	..	9 38	..	..	..	..	..	..	..	..	..	1038	..	..
Ascot ......arr	..	..	..	9 43	..	..	..	..	..	..	..	..	..	1043	..	..
Ascot ......dep	..	..	..	9 46	..	..	..	..	..	..	..	..	..	1046	..	..
Bagshot	..	..	..	9 51	..	..	..	..	..	..	..	..	..	1051	..	..
Camberley **Q**	..	..	..	9 59	..	..	..	..	..	..	..	..	..	1059	..	..
Frimley **T**	..	..	..	10 3	..	..	..	..	..	..	..	..	..	11 3	..	..
Ash Vale W	..	..	..	10 9	..	..	..	..	..	..	..	..	..	11 9	..	..
Aldershot Y ......arr.	..	..	..	1014	..	..	..	..	..	..	..	..	..	1114	..	..
Ascot ......dep	..	..	..	9 44	..	..	..	..	..	..	..	..	..	1044	..	..
Bracknell	..	..	..	9 49	..	..	..	..	..	..	..	..	..	1049	..	..
Wokingham 249	..	..	..	9 56	..	..	..	..	..	..	..	..	..	1056	..	..
Winnersh Halt **Z**	..	..	..	10 0	..	..	..	..	..	..	..	..	..	11 0	..	..
Earley	..	..	..	10 4	..	..	..	..	..	..	..	..	..	11 4	..	..
Reading ......arr.	..	..	..	10 9	..	..	..	..	..	..	..	..	..	11 9	..	..

Down	3	3	3	3	3	3	3		3	3	3	3	3	3	3 (Ngt.)	
Waterloo ....dep.	1014	1021	1026	1030	1039	1044	1050	1054	1056	11 3	11 9	1126	1150	1156	1230	..
Vauxhall	..	1024	1029	1033	1042	..	1053	..	1059	11 6	1112	1129	1153	1159	1233	..
Queen's Road	..	..	1032	..	1045	..	..	..	11 2	..	1115	1132	1156	12 2	1236	..
Clapham Junction **A**	..	1028	1035	1038	1048	..	1058	..	11 5	1110	1118	1135	1159	12 5	1239	..
Wandsworth Town	..	1030	1037	1040	1050	..	11 0	..	..	1112	1120	..	12 1	12 7	1241	..
Putney	..	1033	1040	1043	1053	..	11 3	..	1110	1115	1123	1139	12 4	1210	1244	..
Barnes	..	1036	1043	1046	1056	..	11 6	..	1113	1118	1126	1142	12 7	1213	1247	..
Barnes Bridge	..	..	1045	..	..	..	..	..	1115	..	..	1144	..	1215	..	..
Chiswick, for Grove Park	..	..	1047	..	..	..	..	..	1117	..	..	1146	..	1217	..	..
Kew Bridge	..	..	1050	..	..	..	..	..	1120	..	..	1149	..	1220	..	..
Brentford **B**	..	..	1053	..	..	..	..	..	1123	..	..	1152	..	1223	..	..
Syon Lane	..	..	1055	..	..	..	..	..	1125	..	..	1154	..	..	..	..
Isleworth **C**	..	..	1057	..	..	..	..	..	1127	..	..	1156	..	1227	..	..
Hounslow D	..	..	11 0	..	..	..	..	..	1130	..	..	1159	..	1230	..	..
Whitton	..	..	..	..	..	..	..	..	..	..	..	..	..	..	..	..
Mortlake, for East Sheen	..	1039	..	1049	1059	..	11 9	..	..	1121	1129	..	1210	..	1250	..
North Sheen	..	1042	..	1051	..	..	1111	..	..	1124	..	..	..	..	..	..
Richmond	1028	1044	..	1054	11 2	1058	1114	..	..	1126	1132	..	1215	..	1253	..
St. Margaret's	..	1047	..	1057	11 5	..	1117	..	..	1129	1135	..	1218	..	1256	..
Twickenham	1032	1049	..	1059	11 7	11 2	1119	..	..	1131	1137	..	1220	..	1258	..
Strawberry Hill	..	1052	..	11 2	..	..	1122	..	..	1134	..	..	1223	..	1 1	..
Teddington F ......arr.	..	1055	..	..	..	..	1125	..	..	1137	..	..	..	..	..	..
Whitton	1034	V	..	..	11 9	11 4	V	..	..	V	1139	..	..	..	..	..
Hounslow D ......arr.	..		..	..	1115	..		..	..		1144	..	..	..	..	..
Feltham	1038		..	..	..	11 8		..	..	To Kingston	..	..	..	1234	..	..
Ashford (Middlesex)	1043		..	..	..	1113		..	..		..	..	..	1238	..	..
Staines J ......arr.	1046		..	..	..	1116		1122	..		..	..	..	1242	..	..
Staines ......dep.	1048	To Waterloo, via Kingston	..	..	..	1118	To Waterloo, via Kingston	..	..		..	..	..	..	..	..
Wraysbury	1055		..	..	..	1125		..	..		..	..	..	..	..	..
Sunnymeads	1058		..	..	..	1128		..	..		..	..	..	..	..	..
Datchet	11 1		..	..	..	1131		..	..		..	..	..	..	..	..
Windsor and Eton K arr.	11 6		..	..	..	1136		..	..	..	..	..	..	..	..	..
Staines ......dep.	1047		..	..	..	1117		1122	..	..	..	..	..	..	..	..
Egham L	1052		..	..	..	1122		1127	..	..	..	..	..	..	..	..
Virginia Water M ....arr.	1056		..	..	..	1126		1131	..	..	..	..	..	..	..	..
Virginia Water M ..dep.	1056		..	..	..	1126		..	..	..	..	..	..	..	..	..
Chertsey	11 1		..	..	..	1131		..	..	..	..	..	..	..	..	..
Addlestone	11 5		..	..	..	..		..	..	..	..	..	..	..	..	..
Weybridge N 394 ..arr.	11 9		..	..	..	..		..	..	..	..	..	..	..	..	..
Virginia Water M ....dep.	..	..	..	..	..	..	..	1131	..	..	..	..	..	..	..	..
Longcross Halt	..	..	..	..	..	..	..	1135	..	..	..	..	..	..	..	..
Sunningdale **P**	..	..	..	..	..	..	..	1138	..	..	..	..	..	..	..	..
Ascot ......arr	..	..	..	..	..	..	..	1143	..	..	..	..	..	..	..	..
Ascot ......dep	..	..	..	..	..	..	..	1146	..	..	..	..	..	..	..	..
Bagshot	..	..	..	..	..	..	..	1151	..	..	..	..	..	..	..	..
Camberley **Q**	..	..	..	..	..	..	..	1157	..	..	..	..	..	..	..	..
Frimley **T**	..	..	..	..	..	..	..	12 1	..	..	..	..	..	..	..	..
Ash Vale W	..	..	..	..	..	..	..	12 7	..	..	..	..	..	..	..	..
Aldershot Y ......arr.	..	..	..	..	..	..	..	1212	..	..	..	..	..	..	..	..
Ascot ......dep	..	..	..	..	..	..	..	1144	..	..	..	..	..	..	..	..
Bracknell	..	..	..	..	..	..	..	1149	..	..	..	..	..	..	..	..
Wokingham 249	..	..	..	..	..	..	..	1156	..	..	..	..	..	..	..	..
Winnersh Halt **Z**	..	..	..	..	..	..	..	12 0	..	..	..	..	..	..	..	..
Earley	..	..	..	..	..	..	..	12 4	..	..	..	..	..	..	..	..
Reading ......arr.	..	..	..	..	..	..	..	12 9	..	..	..	..	..	..	..	..

FOR NOTES, SEE PAGE 475

FOR NOTES, SEE PAGE 475

LONDON, HOUNSLOW, RICHMOND, TWICKENHAM, TEDDINGTON, STAINES, WINDSOR, and READING

Sundays — a.m.

Down	3	3	3	3	3	3	3	3	3		3	3	3	3	3	3		3	3	3		3	3	3	3	3		3	3	3	3	3
Waterloo dep.	1 30	..	4 45	..	..	7 26	..	7 29	7 42	7 54	..	..	7 56	8 9	8 12	8 19	..	8 26	8 42	8 49	8 54	..	8 56	8 59	9 12	9 19	..	9 26	9 29	9 42	9 49	..
Vauxhall	1 34	..	4 50	..	..	7 29	..	7 32	..	..	..	..	7 59	8 12	..	8 22	..	8 29	..	8 52	..	..	8 59	9 2	..	9 22	..	9 29	9 32	..	9 52	..
Queen's Road	1 38	..	4 54	..	..	7 32	..	7 35	..	..	..	..	8 2	8 15	..	8 25	..	8 32	..	8 55	..	..	9 2	..	..	9 25	..	9 32	9 35	..	9 55	..
Clapham Junction A	..	..	4 59	..	..	7 35	..	7 38	7 49	..	..	..	8 5	8 18	8 19	8 28	..	8 35	8 49	8 58	..	..	9 5	9 8	9 19	9 28	..	9 35	9 38	9 49	9 58	..
Wandsworth Town	..	..	..	..	..	7 37	..	7 40	..	..	..	..	8 7	8 20	..	8 30	.	8 37	..	9 0	..	..	9 7	9 10	..	9 30	..	9 37	9 40	..	10 0	..
Putney	..	..	..	..	..	7 40	..	7 43	7 53	..	..	..	8 10	8 23	8 23	8 33	..	8 40	8 53	9 3	..	..	9 10	9 13	9 23	9 33	..	9 40	9 43	..	10 3	..
Barnes	..	..	..	..	..	7 43	..	7 46	..	..	..	..	8 13	8 26	..	8 36	..	8 43	..	9 6	..	..	9 13	9 16	..	9 36	..	9 43	9 46	..	10 6	..
Barnes Bridge	To Twickenham via Wimbledon, see page 412	..	..	..	..	7 44	..	..	..	..	..	..	8 14	..	..	..	..	8 44	..	..	..	..	9 14	..	..	..	..	9 44	..	..	..	..
Chiswick, for Grove Park		..	..	..	..	7 47	..	..	..	..	..	..	8 17	..	..	..	..	8 47	..	..	..	..	9 17	..	..	..	..	9 47	..	..	..	..
Kew Bridge		..	..	..	..	7 49	..	..	..	..	..	..	8 19	..	..	..	..	8 49	..	..	..	..	9 19	..	..	..	..	9 49	..	..	..	..
Brentford **B**		..	..	..	..	7 52	..	..	..	..	..	..	8 22	..	..	..	..	8 52	..	..	..	..	9 22	..	..	..	..	9 52	..	..	..	..
Syon Lane		..	..	..	..	7 54	..	..	..	..	..	..	8 24	..	..	..	..	8 54	..	..	..	..	9 24	..	..	..	..	9 54	..	..	..	..
Isleworth **C**		..	..	..	..	7 56	..	..	..	..	..	..	8 26	..	..	..	..	8 56	..	..	..	..	9 26	..	..	..	..	9 56	..	..	..	..
Hounslow D		..	..	..	7 21	7 59	..	..	..	..	..	..	8 29	..	..	..	..	8 59	..	..	..	..	9 29	..	..	..	..	9 59	..	..	..	..
Whitton		..	..	..	7 24	8 3	..	..	..	..	..	..	8 33	..	..	..	..	9 3	..	..	..	..	9 33	..	..	..	..	10 3	..	..	..	..
Mortlake, for East Sheen		..	..	..	..	..	..	7 49	..	..	..	..	..	8 29	..	8 39	..	..	..	9 9	..	..	..	9 19	..	9 39	..	..	9 49	..	10 9	..
North Sheen		..	..	..	..	..	..	7 51	..	..	..	..	..	8 31	..	8 41	..	..	..	9 11	..	..	..	9 21	..	9 41	..	..	9 51	..	1011	..
Richmond		..	..	..	..	..	..	7 54	7 59	..	..	..	..	8 34	8 29	8 44	..	..	8 59	9 14	..	..	..	9 24	9 29	9 44	..	..	9 54	9 59	1014	..
St. Margaret's		..	..	..	..	..	..	7 57	..	..	..	..	..	8 37	..	8 47	..	..	..	9 17	..	..	..	9 27	..	9 47	..	..	9 57	..	1017	..
Twickenham		2 25	..	5 8	7 27	8 5	..	7 59	8 3	..	8 26	..	8 35	8 39	8 33	8 49	..	9 5	9 3	9 19	..	9 26	9 35	9 29	9 33	9 49	..	10 5	9 59	10 3	1019	1026
Strawberry Hill		..	..	5 11	..	..	..	8 2	..	..	..	8 32	..	8 44	..	..	..	..	..	9 22	..	..	..	9 32	..	..	..	..	10 2	..	1022	..
Teddington F arr.		..	..	5 15	..	..	..	8 5	..	..	..	..	..	8 47	..	..	..	..	..	9 25	..	..	..	..	..	..	..	..	10 5	..	1025	..
Whitton	..	..	..	V	..	..	..	V	8 5	..	8 28		..	V	8 35	8 51	..	..	9 5	V	..	9 28	..		9 35	9 51	..	..	V	10 5	V	1028
Hounslow D arr.	..	..	..	To Waterloo via Kingston	..	..	..	To Waterloo via Kingston	..	..	8 33	To Shepperton, arr. 8 48 a.m., see page 412.	..	To Waterloo via Kingston	..	8 58	..	..	..	To Waterloo via Kingston	..	9 33	..	To Shepperton, arr 9 48 a.m., see page 413.	..	9 58	..	..	To Waterloo via Kingston	..	To Waterloo, via Kingston	1033
Feltham	..	2 32	..		..	..	..		8 9	..	..		..		8 39	..	..	..	9 9		..	..	..		9 39	..	..	..		10 9		..
Ashford (Middlesex)	..	..	..		..	..	..		8 14	..	..		..		8 44	..	..	..	9 14		..	..	..		9 44	..	..	..		1014		..
Staines J arr.	..	..	..		..	..	..		8 17	8 22	..		..		8 47	..	..	..	9 17		9 22	..	..		9 47	..	..	..		1017		..
Staines dep.	..	..	..		..	..	..		8 19	..	..		..		8 49	..	..	..	9 19		..	..	..		9 49	..	..	..		1019		..
Wraysbury	..	..	..		..	..	..		8 26	..	..		..		8 56	..	..	..	9 26		..	..	..		9 56	..	..	..		1026		..
Sunnymeads	..	..	..		..	..	..		8 29	..	..		..		8 59	..	..	..	9 29		..	..	..		9 59	..	..	..		1029		..
Datchet	..	..	..		..	..	..		8 32	..	..		..		9 2	..	..	..	9 32		..	..	..		10 2	..	..	..		1032		..
Windsor and Eton K arr.	..	..	..		..	..	..		8 38	..	..		..		9 8	..	..	..	9 38		..	..	..		10 8	..	..	..		1038		..
Staines dep.	..	..	..		..	..	..		8 18	8 22	..		..		8 48	..	..	..	9 18		9 22	..	..		9 48	..	..	..		1018		..
Egham **L**	..	..	..		..	..	..		8 23	8 27	..		..		8 53	..	..	..	9 23		9 27	..	..		9 53	..	..	..		1023		..
Virginia Water **M** arr.	..	..	..		..	..	..		8 27	8 31	..		..		8 57	..	..	..	9 27		9 31	..	..		9 57	..	..	..		1027		..
Virginia Water M dep.	..	..	..	..	..	..	..	..	8 27	..	..		..	..	8 57	..	..	..	9 27	..	..	..	..		9 57	..	..	..	..	1027	..	..
Chertsey	..	..	..	..	..	..	8 2	..	8 32	..	..		..	..	9 2	..	..	..	9 32	..	..	..	..		10 2	..	..	..	..	1032	..	..
Addlestone	..	..	..	..	..	..	8 5	..	8 35	..	..		..	..	9 5	..	..	..	9 35	..	..	..	..		10 5	..	..	..	..	1035	..	..
Weybridge N 394 arr.	..	..	..	..	..	..	8 9	..	8 39	..	..		..	..	9 9	..	..	..	9 39	..	..	..	..		10 9	..	..	..	..	1039	..	..
Virginia Water M dep.	..	..	..	..	..	..	..	..	..	8 31	..	..	..	..	..	..	..	..	..	..	9 31	..	..	..	..	..	..	..	..	..	..	..
Longcross Halt	..	..	..	..	..	..	..	..	..	8 35	..	..	..	..	..	..	..	..	..	..	9 35	..	..	..	..	..	..	..	..	..	..	..
Sunningdale **P**	..	..	..	..	..	..	..	..	..	8 38	..	..	..	..	..	..	..	..	..	..	9 38	..	..	..	..	..	..	..	..	..	..	..
Ascot arr.	..	..	..	..	..	..	..	..	..	8 43	..	..	..	..	..	..	..	..	..	..	9 43	..	..	..	..	..	..	..	..	..	..	..
Ascot dep.	..	..	..	..	..	..	..	..	..	8 46	..	..	..	..	..	..	..	..	..	..	9 46	..	..	..	..	..	..	..	..	..	..	..
Bagshot	..	..	..	..	..	..	..	..	..	8 51	..	..	..	..	..	..	..	..	..	..	9 51	..	..	..	..	..	..	..	..	..	..	..
Camberley **Q**	..	..	..	..	..	..	..	..	..	8 59	..	..	..	..	..	..	..	..	..	..	9 59	..	..	..	..	..	..	..	..	..	..	..
Frimley **T**	..	..	..	..	..	..	..	..	..	9 3	..	..	..	..	..	..	..	..	..	..	10 3	..	..	..	..	..	..	..	..	..	..	..
Ash Vale **W**	..	..	..	..	..	..	..	..	..	9 9	..	..	..	..	..	..	..	..	..	..	10 9	..	..	..	..	..	..	..	..	..	..	..
Aldershot Y arr.	..	..	..	..	..	..	..	..	..	9 14	..	..	..	..	..	..	..	..	..	..	1014	..	..	..	..	..	..	..	..	..	..	..
Ascot dep.	..	..	..	..	..	..	..	..	..	8 44	..	..	..	..	..	..	..	..	..	..	9 44	..	..	..	..	..	..	..	..	..	..	..
Bracknell	..	..	..	..	..	..	..	..	..	8 49	..	..	..	..	..	..	..	..	..	..	9 49	..	..	..	..	..	..	..	..	..	..	..
Wokingham 249	..	..	..	..	..	..	..	..	..	8 56	..	..	..	..	..	..	..	..	..	..	9 56	..	..	..	..	..	..	..	..	..	..	..
Winnersh Halt **Z**	..	..	..	..	..	..	..	..	..	9 0	..	..	..	..	..	..	..	..	..	..	10 0	..	..	..	..	..	..	..	..	..	..	..
Earley	..	..	..	..	..	..	..	..	..	9 4	..	..	..	..	..	..	..	..	..	..	10 4	..	..	..	..	..	..	..	..	..	..	..
Reading arr.	..	..	..	..	..	..	..	..	..	9 9	..	..	..	..	..	..	..	..	..	..	10 9	..	..	..	..	..	..	..	..	..	..	..

LONDON, HOUNSLOW, RICHMOND, TWICKENHAM, TEDDINGTON, STAINES, WINDSOR, and READING

Down	a.m.											Sundays—continued					a.m.									p.m.					
		3	3	3	3		3	3	3	3		3	3	3	3	3		3	3	3	3		3	3	3		3	3		3	3	3
Waterloo .... dep	9 54	9 56	9 59	1012	1019	..	1026	1029	1042	1049	1054	..	1056	1059	1112	1119	..	1126	1129	1142	1149	1154	..	1156	1159	..	1212	1219	..	1226	1229	1242
Vauxhall	..	9 59	10 2	..	1022	..	1029	1032	..	1052	..	..	1059	11 2	..	1122	..	1129	1132	..	1152	..	..	1159	12 2	..	..	1222	..	1229	1232	..
Queen's Road	..	10 2	..	..	1025	..	1032	1035	..	1055	..	..	11 2	..	..	1125	..	1132	1135	..	1155	..	..	12 2	..	..	..	1225	..	1232	1235	..
Clapham Junction A	..	10 5	10 8	1019	1028	..	1035	1038	1049	1058	..	..	11 5	11 8	1119	1128	..	1135	1138	1149	1158	..	..	12 5	12 8	..	1219	1228	..	1235	1238	1249
Wandsworth Town	..	10 7	1010	..	1030	..	1037	1040	..	11 0	..	..	11 7	1110	..	1130	..	1137	1140	..	12 0	..	..	12 7	1210	..	..	1230	..	1237	1240	..
Putney	..	1010	1013	..	1033	..	1040	1043	..	11 3	..	..	1110	1113	..	1133	..	1140	1143	..	12 3	..	..	1210	1213	..	..	1233	..	1240	1243	..
Barnes	..	1013	1016	..	1036	..	1043	1046	..	11 6	..	..	1113	1116	..	1136	..	1143	1146	..	12 6	..	..	1213	1216	..	..	1236	..	1243	1246	..
Barnes Bridge	..	1014	..	..	..	..	1044	..	..	..	..	..	1114	..	..	..	..	1144	..	..	..	..	..	1214	..	..	..	..	..	1244	..	..
Chiswick, for Grove Park	..	1017	..	..	..	..	1047	..	..	..	..	..	1117	..	..	..	..	1147	..	..	..	..	..	1217	..	..	..	..	..	1247	..	..
Kew Bridge	..	1019	..	..	..	..	1049	..	..	..	..	..	1119	..	..	..	..	1149	..	..	..	..	..	1219	..	..	..	..	..	1249	..	..
Brentford B	..	1022	..	..	..	..	1052	..	..	..	..	..	1122	..	..	..	..	1152	..	..	..	..	..	1222	..	..	..	..	..	1252	..	..
Syon Lane	..	1024	..	..	..	..	1054	..	..	..	..	..	1124	..	..	..	..	1154	..	..	..	..	..	1224	..	..	..	..	..	1254	..	..
Isleworth C	..	1026	..	..	..	..	1056	..	..	..	..	..	1126	..	..	..	..	1156	..	..	..	..	..	1226	..	..	..	..	..	1256	..	..
Hounslow D	..	1029	..	..	..	..	1059	..	..	..	..	..	1129	..	..	..	..	1159	..	..	..	..	..	1229	..	..	..	..	..	1259	..	..
Whitton	..	1033	..	..	..	..	11 3	..	..	..	..	..	1133	..	..	..	..	12 3	..	..	..	..	..	1233	..	..	..	..	..	1 3	..	..
Mortlake, for East Sheen	..	..	1019	..	1039	..	..	1049	..	11 9	..	..	..	1119	..	1139	..	..	1149	..	12 9	..	..	..	1219	..	..	1239	..	..	1249	..
North Sheen	..	..	1021	..	1041	..	..	1051	..	1111	..	..	..	1121	..	1141	..	..	1151	..	1211	..	..	..	1221	..	..	1241	..	..	1251	..
Richmond	..	..	1024	1029	1044	..	..	1054	1059	1114	..	..	..	1124	1129	1144	..	..	1154	1159	1214	..	..	..	1224	..	1229	1244	..	..	1254	1259
St. Margaret's	..	..	1027	..	1047	..	..	1057	..	1117	..	..	..	1127	..	1147	..	..	1157	..	1217	..	..	..	1227	..	..	1247	..	..	1257	..
Twickenham	..	1035	1029	1033	1049	..	11 5	1059	11 3	1119	..	1126	1135	1129	1133	1149	..	12 5	1159	12 3	1219	..	1226	1235	1229	..	1233	1249	..	1 5	1259	1 3
Strawberry Hill	..	..	1032	..	..	..	..	11 2	..	1122	..	..	..	1132	..	..	..	..	12 2	..	1222	..	..	..	1232	..	..	..	..	..	1 2	..
Teddington F .... arr.	..	..		..	..	..	..	11 5	..	1125	..	..	..		..	..	..	..	12 5	..	1225	..	..	..		..	..	..	..	..	1 5	..
Whitton	..	..	To Shepperton, arr. 10 48 a.m see page 413,	1035	1051	..	..	V	11 5	V	..	1128	..	To Shepperton, arr. 11 48 a.m see page 414.	1135	1151	..	..	V	12 5	V	..	1228	..	To Shepperton, arr. 12 48 p.m see page 415.	..	1235	1251	..	..	V	1 5
Hounslow D .... arr.	..	..		..	1058	..	..		..		..	1133	..		..	1158	..	..		..		..	1233	..		..	..	1258	..	..		..
Feltham	..	..		1039	..	..	..	To Waterloo via Kingston	11 9	To Waterloo, via Kingston	..	..	..		1139	..	..	..	To Waterloo via Kingston	12 9	To Waterloo via Kingston	..	..	..		..	1239	..	..	..	To Waterloo via Kington	1 9
Ashford (Middlesex)	..	..		1044	..	..	..		1114		..	..	..		1144	..	..	..		1214		..	..	..		..	1244	..	..	..		1 14
Staines J .... arr.	1022	..		1047	..	..	..		1117		1122	..	..		1147	..	..	..		1217		1222	..	..		..	1247	..	..	..		1 17
Staines .... dep.	..	..		1049	..	..	..		1119		..	..	..		1149	..	..	..		1219		..	..	..		..	1249	..	..	..		1 19
Wraysbury	..	..		1056	..	..	..		1126		..	..	..		1156	..	..	..		1226		..	..	..		..	1256	..	..	..		1 26
Sunnymeads	..	..		1059	..	..	..		1129		..	..	..		1159	..	..	..		1229		..	..	..		..	1259	..	..	..		1 29
Datchet	..	..		11 2	..	..	..		1132		..	..	..		12 2	..	..	..		1232		..	..	..		..	1 2	..	..	..		1 32
Windsor and Eton K arr.	..	..		11 8	..	..	..		1138		..	..	..		12 8	..	..	..		1238		..	..	..		..	1 8	..	..	..		1 38
Staines .... dep.	1022	..		1048	..	..	..	..	1118	..	1122	..	..		1148	..	..	..	..	1218	..	1222	..	..		..	1248	..	..	..	..	1 18
Egham L	1027	..		1053	..	..	..	..	1123	..	1127	..	..		1153	..	..	..	..	1223	..	1227	..	..		..	1253	..	..	..	..	1 23
Virginia Water M .... arr.	1031	..		1057	..	..	..	..	1127	..	1131	..	..		1157	..	..	..	..	1227	..	1231	..	..		..	1257	..	..	..	..	1 27
Virginia Water M .. dep.	..	..		1057	..	..	..	..	1127	..	..	..	..		1157	..	..	..	..	1227	..	..	..	..		..	1257	..	..	..	..	1 27
Chertsey	..	..		11 2	..	..	..	..	1132	..	..	..	..		12 2	..	..	..	..	1232	..	..	..	..		..	1 2	..	..	..	..	1 32
Addlestone	..	..		11 5	..	..	..	..	1135	..	..	..	..		12 5	..	..	..	..	1235	..	..	..	..		..	1 5	..	..	..	..	1 35
Weybridge N 394 ... arr.	..	..		11 9	..	..	..	..	1139	..	..	..	..		12 9	..	..	..	..	1239	..	..	..	..		..	1 9	..	..	..	..	1 39
Virginia Water M .... dep.	1031	..	..	..	..	..	..	..	..	..	1131	..	..	..	..	..	..	..	..	..	..	1231	..	..	..	..	..	..	..	..	..	..
Longcross Halt	1035	..	..	..	..	..	..	..	..	..	1135	..	..	..	..	..	..	..	..	..	..	1235	..	..	..	..	..	..	..	..	..	..
Sunningdale P	1038	..	..	..	..	..	..	..	..	..	1138	..	..	..	..	..	..	..	..	..	..	1238	..	..	..	..	..	..	..	..	..	..
Ascot .... arr.	1043	..	..	..	..	..	..	..	..	..	1143	..	..	..	..	..	..	..	..	..	..	1243	..	..	..	..	..	..	..	..	..	..
Ascot .... dep.	1046	..	..	..	..	..	..	..	..	..	1146	..	..	..	..	..	..	..	..	..	..	1246	..	..	..	..	..	..	..	..	..	..
Bagshot	1051	..	..	..	..	..	..	..	..	..	1151	..	..	..	..	..	..	..	..	..	..	1251	..	..	..	..	..	..	..	..	..	..
Camberley Q	1059	..	..	..	..	..	..	..	..	..	1159	..	..	..	..	..	..	..	..	..	..	1259	..	..	..	..	..	..	..	..	..	..
Frimley T	11 3	..	..	..	..	..	..	..	..	..	12 3	..	..	..	..	..	..	..	..	..	..	1 3	..	..	..	..	..	..	..	..	..	..
Ash Vale W	11 9	..	..	..	..	..	..	..	..	..	12 9	..	..	..	..	..	..	..	..	..	..	1 9	..	..	..	..	..	..	..	..	..	..
Aldershot Y .... arr.	1114	..	..	..	..	..	..	..	..	..	1214	..	..	..	..	..	..	..	..	..	..	1 14	..	..	..	..	..	..	..	..	..	..
Ascot .... dep	1044	..	..	..	..	..	..	..	..	..	1144	..	..	..	..	..	..	..	..	..	..	1244	..	..	..	..	..	..	..	..	..	..
Bracknell	1049	..	..	..	..	..	..	..	..	..	1149	..	..	..	..	..	..	..	..	..	..	1249	..	..	..	..	..	..	..	..	..	..
Wokingham 249	1056	..	..	..	..	..	..	..	..	..	1156	..	..	..	..	..	..	..	..	..	..	1256	..	..	..	..	..	..	..	..	..	..
Winnersh Halt Z	11 0	..	..	..	..	..	..	..	..	..	12 0	..	..	..	..	..	..	..	..	..	..	1 0	..	..	..	..	..	..	..	..	..	..
Earley	11 4	..	..	..	..	..	..	..	..	..	12 4	..	..	..	..	..	..	..	..	..	..	1 4	..	..	..	..	..	..	..	..	..	..
Reading .... arr.	11 9	..	..	..	..	..	..	..	..	..	12 9	..	..	..	..	..	..	..	..	..	..	1 9	..	..	..	..	..	..	..	..	..	..

FOR NOTES, SEE PAGE 475

LONDON, HOUNSLOW, RICHMOND, TWICKENHAM, TEDDINGTON, STAINES, WINDSOR, and READING

Sundays—continued (p.m)

Down	3	3		3	3	3	3		3	3	3	3	3		3	3
Waterloo .... dep	1249	..	1254	1256	1259	1 12	1 19	..	1 26	1 29	1 42	1 49	..	1 54	1 56	1 59
Vauxhall	1252	..	..	1259	1 2	..	1 22	..	1 29	1 32	..	1 52	..	..	1 59	2 2
Queen's Road	1255	..	..	1 2	..	..	1 25	..	1 32	1 35	..	1 55	..	..	2 2	..
Clapham Junction **A**	1258	..	..	1 5	1 8	1 19	1 28	..	1 35	1 38	1 49	1 58	..	..	2 5	2 8
Wandsworth Town	1 0	..	..	1 7	1 10	..	1 30	..	1 37	1 40	..	2 0	..	..	2 7	2 10
Putney	1 3	..	..	1 10	1 13	..	1 33	..	1 40	1 43	..	2 3	..	..	2 10	2 13
Barnes	1 6	..	..	1 13	1 16	..	1 36	..	1 43	1 46	..	2 6	..	..	2 13	2 16
Barnes Bridge	..	..	..	1 14	..	..	..	..	1 44	..	..	..	..	..	2 14	..
Chiswick, for Grove Park	..	..	..	1 17	..	..	..	..	1 47	..	..	..	..	..	2 17	..
Kew Bridge	..	..	..	1 19	..	..	..	..	1 49	..	..	..	..	..	2 19	..
Brentford **B**	..	..	..	1 22	..	..	..	..	1 52	..	..	..	..	..	2 22	..
Syon Lane	..	..	..	1 24	..	..	..	..	1 54	..	..	..	..	..	2 24	..
Isleworth **C**	..	..	..	1 26	..	..	..	..	1 56	..	..	..	..	..	2 26	..
Hounslow **D**	..	..	..	1 29	..	..	..	..	1 59	..	..	..	..	..	2 29	..
Whitton	..	..	..	1 33	..	..	..	..	2 3	..	..	..	..	..	2 33	..
Mortlake, for East Sheen	1 9	..	..	..	1 19	..	1 39	..	..	1 49	..	2 9	..	..	..	2 19
North Sheen	1 11	..	..	..	1 21	..	1 41	..	..	1 51	..	2 11	..	..	..	2 21
Richmond	1 14	..	..	..	1 24	1 29	1 44	..	..	1 54	1 59	2 14	..	..	..	2 24
St. Margaret's	1 17	..	..	..	1 27	..	1 47	..	..	1 57	..	2 17	..	..	..	2 27
Twickenham	1 19	1 26	..	1 35	1 29	1 33	1 49	..	2 5	1 59	2 3	2 19	2 26	..	2 35	2 29
Strawberry Hill	1 22	..	..	..	1 32	..	..	..	..	2 2	..	2 22	..	..	..	2 32
Teddington **F** ...... arr	1 25	..	..	..	..	..	..	..	..	2 5	..	2 25	..	..	..	..
Whitton	V	1 28	..	..	To Shepperton, arr. 1 48 p.m see page 415.	1 35	1 51	..	..	V	2 5	V	2 28	..	..	To Shepperton, arr. 2 48 p.m see page 416.
Hounslow **D** ...... arr		1 33	..	..		..	1 58	..	..		..		2 33	..	..	
Feltham	To Waterloo via Kingston	..	..	..		1 39	..	..	..	To Waterloo via Kingston	2 9	To Waterloo via Kingston	..	..	..	
Ashford (Middlesex)		..	..	..		1 44	..	..	..		2 14		..	..	..	
Staines **J** ...... arr		..	1 22	..		1 47	..	..	..		2 17		..	2 22	..	
Staines ...... dep		..	..	..		1 49	..	..	..		2 19		..	..	..	
Wraysbury		..	..	..		1 56	..	..	..		2 26		..	..	..	
Sunnymeads		..	..	..		1 59	..	..	..		2 29		..	..	..	
Datchet		..	..	..		2 2	..	..	..		2 32		..	..	..	
Windsor and Eton **K** arr		..	..	..		2 8	..	..	..		2 38		..	..	..	
Staines ...... dep	..	..	1 22	..		1 48	..	..	..	..	2 18	..	..	2 22	..	
Egham **L**	..	..	1 27	..		1 53	..	..	..	..	2 23	..	..	2 27	..	
Virginia Water **M** .. arr	..	..	1 31	..		1 57	..	..	..	..	2 27	..	..	2 31	..	
Virginia Water **M** .. dep	..	..	..	..		1 57	..	..	..	..	2 27	..	..	..	..	
Chertsey	..	..	..	..		2 2	..	..	..	..	2 32	..	..	..	..	
Addlestone	..	..	..	..		2 5	..	..	..	..	2 35	..	..	..	..	
Weybridge **N** 394 .... ar	..	..	..	..	..	2 9	..	..	..	..	2 39	..	..	..	..	..
Virginia Water **M** .. dep	..	..	1 31	..	..	..	..	..	..	..	..	..	..	2 31	..	..
Longcross Halt	..	..	1 35	..	..	..	..	..	..	..	..	..	..	2 35	..	..
Sunningdale **P**	..	..	1 38	..	..	..	..	..	..	..	..	..	..	2 38	..	..
Ascot ...... arr	..	..	1 43	..	..	..	..	..	..	..	..	..	..	2 43	..	..
Ascot ...... dep	..	..	1 46	..	..	..	..	..	..	..	..	..	..	2 46	..	..
Bagshot	..	..	1 51	..	..	..	..	..	..	..	..	..	..	2 51	..	..
Camberley **Q**	..	..	1 59	..	..	..	..	..	..	..	..	..	..	2 59	..	..
Frimley **T**	..	..	2 3	..	..	..	..	..	..	..	..	..	..	3 3	..	..
Ash Vale **W**	..	..	2 9	..	..	..	..	..	..	..	..	..	..	3 9	..	..
Aldershot **Y** ...... arr	..	..	2 14	..	..	..	..	..	..	..	..	..	..	3 14	..	..
Ascot ...... dep	..	..	1 44	..	..	..	..	..	..	..	..	..	..	2 44	..	..
Bracknell	..	..	1 49	..	..	..	..	..	..	..	..	..	..	2 49	..	..
Wokingham 249	..	..	1 56	..	..	..	..	..	..	..	..	..	..	2 56	..	..
Winnersh Halt **Z**	..	..	2 0	..	..	..	..	..	..	..	..	..	..	3 0	..	..
Earley	..	..	2 4	..	..	..	..	..	..	..	..	..	..	3 4	..	..
Reading ...... arr	..	..	2 9	..	..	..	..	..	..	..	..	..	..	3 9	..	..

Down	3	3		3	3	3	3		3	3	3	3	3		3	3
Waterloo .... dep	2 12	2 19	..	2 26	2 29	2 42	2 49	2 54	..	2 56	2 59	3 12	3 19	..	3 26	3 29
Vauxhall	..	2 22	..	2 29	2 32	..	2 52	..	..	2 59	3 2	..	3 22	..	3 29	3 32
Queen's Road	..	2 25	..	2 32	2 35	..	2 55	..	..	3 2	..	..	3 25	..	3 32	3 35
Clapham Junction **A**	2 19	2 28	..	2 35	2 38	2 49	2 58	..	..	3 5	3 8	3 19	3 28	..	3 35	3 38
Wandsworth Town	..	2 30	..	2 37	2 40	..	3 0	..	..	3 7	3 10	..	3 30	..	3 37	3 40
Putney	..	2 33	..	2 40	2 43	..	3 3	..	..	3 10	3 13	..	3 33	..	3 40	3 43
Barnes	..	2 36	..	2 43	2 46	..	3 6	..	..	3 13	3 16	..	3 36	..	3 43	3 46
Barnes Bridge	..	..	..	2 44	..	..	..	..	..	3 14	..	..	..	..	3 44	..
Chiswick, for Grove Park	..	..	..	2 47	..	..	..	..	..	3 17	..	..	..	..	3 47	..
Kew Bridge	..	..	..	2 49	..	..	..	..	..	3 19	..	..	..	..	3 49	..
Brentford **B**	..	..	..	2 52	..	..	..	..	..	3 22	..	..	..	..	3 52	..
Syon Lane	..	..	..	2 54	..	..	..	..	..	3 24	..	..	..	..	3 54	..
Isleworth **C**	..	..	..	2 56	..	..	..	..	..	3 26	..	..	..	..	3 56	..
Hounslow **D**	..	..	..	2 59	..	..	..	..	..	3 29	..	..	..	..	3 59	..
Whitton	..	..	..	3 3	..	..	..	..	..	3 33	..	..	..	..	4 3	..
Mortlake, for East Sheen	..	2 39	..	..	2 49	..	3 9	..	..	..	3 19	..	3 39	..	..	3 49
North Sheen	..	2 41	..	..	2 51	..	3 11	..	..	..	3 21	..	3 41	..	..	3 51
Richmond	2 29	2 44	..	..	2 54	2 59	3 14	..	..	..	3 24	3 29	3 44	..	..	3 54
St. Margaret's	..	2 47	..	..	2 57	..	3 17	..	..	..	3 27	..	3 47	..	..	3 57
Twickenham	2 33	2 49	..	3 5	2 59	3 3	3 19	..	3 26	3 35	3 29	3 33	3 49	..	4 5	3 59
Strawberry Hill	..	..	..	..	3 2	..	3 22	..	..	..	3 32	..	..	..	..	4 2
Teddington **F** ...... arr	..	..	..	..	3 5	..	3 25	..	..	..	..	..	..	..	..	4 5
Whitton	2 35	2 51	..	..	V	3 5	V	..	3 28	..	To Shepperton, arr. 3 48 p.m see page 417.	3 35	3 51	..	..	V
Hounslow **D** ...... arr	..	2 58	..	..		..		..	3 33	..		..	3 58	..	..	
Feltham	2 39	..	..	..	To Waterloo via Kingston	3 9	To Waterloo via Kingston	..	..	..		3 39	..	..	..	To Waterloo, via Kingston
Ashford (Middlesex)	2 44	..	..	..		3 14		..	..	..		3 44	..	..	..	
Staines **J** ...... arr	2 47	..	..	..		3 17		3 22	..	..		3 47	..	..	..	
Staines ...... dep	2 49	..	..	..		3 19		..	..	..		3 49	..	..	..	
Wraysbury	2 56	..	..	..		3 26		..	..	..		3 56	..	..	..	
Sunnymeads	2 59	..	..	..		3 29		..	..	..		3 59	..	..	..	
Datchet	3 2	..	..	..		3 32		..	..	..		4 2	..	..	..	
Windsor and Eton **K** arr	3 8	..	..	..		3 38		..	..	..		4 8	..	..	..	
Staines ...... dep	2 48	..	..	..	..	3 18	..	3 22	..	..		3 48	..	..	..	..
Egham **L**	2 53	..	..	..	..	3 23	..	3 27	..	..		3 53	..	..	..	..
Virginia Water **M** .. arr	2 57	..	..	..	..	3 27	..	3 31	..	..		3 57	..	..	..	..
Virginia Water **M** .. dep	2 57	..	..	..	..	3 27	..	..	..	..		3 57	..	..	..	..
Chertsey	3 2	..	..	..	..	3 32	..	..	..	..		4 2	..	..	..	..
Addlestone	3 5	..	..	..	..	3 35	..	..	..	..		4 5	..	..	..	..
Weybridge **N** 394 .... ar	3 9	..	..	..	..	3 39	..	..	..	..	..	4 9	..	..	..	..
Virginia Water **M** .. dep	..	..	..	..	..	..	..	3 31	..	..	..	..	..	..	..	..
Longcross Halt	..	..	..	..	..	..	..	3 35	..	..	..	..	..	..	..	..
Sunningdale **P**	..	..	..	..	..	..	..	3 38	..	..	..	..	..	..	..	..
Ascot ...... arr	..	..	..	..	..	..	..	3 43	..	..	..	..	..	..	..	..
Ascot ...... dep	..	..	..	..	..	..	..	3 46	..	..	..	..	..	..	..	..
Bagshot	..	..	..	..	..	..	..	3 51	..	..	..	..	..	..	..	..
Camberley **Q**	..	..	..	..	..	..	..	3 59	..	..	..	..	..	..	..	..
Frimley **T**	..	..	..	..	..	..	..	4 3	..	..	..	..	..	..	..	..
Ash Vale **W**	..	..	..	..	..	..	..	4 9	..	..	..	..	..	..	..	..
Aldershot **Y** ...... arr	..	..	..	..	..	..	..	4 14	..	..	..	..	..	..	..	..
Ascot ...... dep	..	..	..	..	..	..	..	3 44	..	..	..	..	..	..	..	..
Bracknell	..	..	..	..	..	..	..	3 49	..	..	..	..	..	..	..	..
Wokingham 249	..	..	..	..	..	..	..	3 56	..	..	..	..	..	..	..	..
Winnersh Halt **Z**	..	..	..	..	..	..	..	4 0	..	..	..	..	..	..	..	..
Earley	..	..	..	..	..	..	..	4 4	..	..	..	..	..	..	..	..
Reading ...... arr	..	..	..	..	..	..	..	4 9	..	..	..	..	..	..	..	..

LONDON, HOUNSLOW, RICHMOND, TWICKENHAM, TEDDINGTON, STAINES, WINDSOR, and READING

Sundays—*continued* (p.m)

Down	3	3	3			3	3	3	3		3	3	3	3	3		3	3	3	3		3	3	3	3	3			3	3	3	3
Waterloo dep	3 42	3 49	..	3 54	..	3 56	3 59	4 12	4 19	..	4 26	4 29	4 42	4 49	..	4 54	4 56	4 59	5 12	5 19	..	5 26	5 29	5 42	5 49	..	..	5 54	5 56	5 59	6 12	6 19
Vauxhall	..	3 52	..	..	..	3 59	4 3	..	4 22	..	4 29	4 32	..	4 52	..	..	4 59	5 2	..	5 22	..	5 29	5 32	..	5 52	..	..	..	5 59	6 2	..	6 22
Queen's Road	..	3 55	..	..	..	4 2	..	..	4 25	..	4 32	4 35	..	4 55	..	..	5 2	..	..	5 25	..	5 32	5 35	..	5 55	..	..	..	6 2	..	..	6 25
Clapham Junction A	3 49	3 58	..	..	..	4 5	4 8	4 19	4 28	..	4 35	4 38	4 49	4 58	..	..	5 5	5 8	5 19	5 28	..	5 35	5 38	5 49	5 58	..	..	..	6 5	6 8	6 19	6 28
Wandsworth Town	..	4 0	..	..	..	4 7	4 10	..	4 30	..	4 37	4 40	..	5 0	..	..	5 7	5 10	..	5 30	..	5 37	5 40	..	6 0	..	..	..	6 7	6 10	..	6 30
Putney	..	4 3	..	..	..	4 10	4 13	..	4 33	..	4 40	4 43	..	5 3	..	..	5 10	5 13	..	5 33	..	5 40	5 43	..	6 3	..	..	..	6 10	6 13	..	6 33
Barnes	..	4 6	..	..	..	4 13	4 16	..	4 36	..	4 43	4 46	..	5 6	..	..	5 13	5 16	..	5 36	..	5 43	5 46	..	6 6	..	..	..	6 13	6 16	..	6 36
Barnes Bridge	..	..	..	..	..	4 14	..	..	..	..	4 44	..	..	..	..	..	5 14	..	..	..	..	5 44	..	..	..	..	..	..	6 14	..	..	..
Chiswick, for Grove Park	..	..	..	..	..	4 17	..	..	..	..	4 47	..	..	..	..	..	5 17	..	..	..	..	5 47	..	..	..	..	..	..	6 17	..	..	..
Kew Bridge	..	..	..	..	..	4 19	..	..	..	..	4 49	..	..	..	..	..	5 19	..	..	..	..	5 49	..	..	..	..	..	..	6 19	..	..	..
Brentford B	..	..	..	..	..	4 22	..	..	..	..	4 52	..	..	..	..	..	5 22	..	..	..	..	5 52	..	..	..	..	..	..	6 22	..	..	..
Syon Lane	..	..	..	..	..	4 24	..	..	..	..	4 54	..	..	..	..	..	5 24	..	..	..	..	5 54	..	..	..	..	..	..	6 24	..	..	..
Isleworth C	..	..	..	..	..	4 26	..	..	..	..	4 56	..	..	..	..	..	5 26	..	..	..	..	5 56	..	..	..	..	..	..	6 26	..	..	..
Hounslow D	..	..	..	..	..	4 29	..	..	..	..	4 59	..	..	..	..	..	5 29	..	..	..	..	5 59	..	..	..	..	..	..	6 29	..	..	..
Whitton	..	..	..	..	..	4 33	..	..	..	..	5 3	..	..	..	..	..	5 33	..	..	..	..	6 3	..	..	..	..	..	..	6 33	..	..	..
Mortlake, for East Sheen	..	4 9	..	..	..	..	4 19	..	4 39	..	..	4 49	..	5 9	..	..	..	5 19	..	5 39	..	..	5 49	..	6 9	..	..	..	..	6 19	..	6 39
North Sheen	..	4 11	..	..	..	..	4 21	..	4 41	..	..	4 51	..	5 11	..	..	..	5 21	..	5 41	..	..	5 51	..	6 11	..	..	..	..	6 21	..	6 41
Richmond	3 59	4 14	..	..	..	..	4 24	4 29	4 44	..	..	4 54	4 59	5 14	..	..	..	5 24	5 29	5 44	..	..	5 54	5 59	6 14	..	..	..	..	6 24	6 29	6 44
St. Margaret's	..	4 17	..	..	..	..	4 27	..	4 47	..	..	4 57	..	5 17	..	..	..	5 27	..	5 47	..	..	5 57	..	6 17	..	..	..	..	6 27	..	6 47
Twickenham	4 3	4 19	4 26	..	..	4 35	4 29	4 33	4 49	..	5 5	4 59	5 3	5 19	5 26	..	5 35	5 29	5 33	5 49	..	6 5	5 59	6 3	6 19	6 26	..	..	6 35	6 29	6 33	6 49
Strawberry Hill	..	4 22	..	..	..	..	4 32	..	..	..	..	5 2	..	5 22	..	..	..	5 32	..	..	..	..	6 2	..	6 22	..	..	..	..	6 32	..	..
Teddington F arr	..	4 25	..	..	..	..	..	..	..	..	..	5 5	..	5 25	..	..	..	..	..	..	..	..	6 5	..	6 25	..	..	..	..	..	..	..
Whitton	4 5	V	4 28	..	..	..	..	4 35	4 51	..	..	V	5 5	V	5 28	..	..	..	5 35	5 51	..	..	V	6 5	V	6 28	..	..	..	..	6 35	6 51
Hounslow D arr	..	..	4 33	..	..	..	..	..	4 58	..	..	..	..	..	5 33	..	..	..	..	5 58	..	..	..	..	..	6 33	–	..	..	..	..	6 58
Feltham	4 9	To Waterloo via Kingston	..	..	..	..	To Shepperton, arr. 4 48 p.m see page 417	4 39	..	..	..	To Waterloo, via Kingston	5 9	To Waterloo via Kingston	..	..	..	To Shepperton, arr. 5 48 p.m see page 418.	5 39	..	..	..	To Waterloo, via Kingston	6 9	To Waterloo via Kingston	..	..	..	..	To Shepperton, arr. 6 48 p.m see page 418.	6 39	..
Ashford (Middlesex)	4 14	..	..	..	..	..	..	4 44	..	..	..	..	5 14	..	..	..	..	..	5 44	..	..	..	..	6 14	..	..	..	..	..	..	6 44	..
Staines J arr	4 17	..	..	4 22	..	..	..	4 47	..	..	..	..	5 17	..	..	5 22	..	..	5 47	..	..	..	..	6 17	..	..	..	6 22	..	..	6 47	..
Staines dep	4 19	..	..	..	..	..	..	4 49	..	..	..	..	5 19	..	..	..	..	..	5 49	..	..	..	..	6 19	..	..	..	..	..	..	6 49	..
Wraysbury	4 26	..	..	..	..	..	..	4 56	..	..	..	..	5 26	..	..	..	..	..	5 56	..	..	..	..	6 26	..	..	..	..	..	..	6 56	..
Sunnymeads	4 29	..	..	..	..	..	..	4 59	..	..	..	..	5 29	..	..	..	..	..	5 59	..	..	..	..	6 29	..	..	..	..	..	..	6 59	..
Datchet	4 32	..	..	..	..	..	..	5 2	..	..	..	..	5 32	..	..	..	..	..	6 2	..	..	..	..	6 32	..	..	..	..	..	..	7 2	..
Windsor and Eton K arr	4 38	..	..	..	..	..	..	5 8	..	..	..	..	5 38	..	..	..	..	..	6 8	..	..	..	..	6 38	..	..	..	..	..	..	7 8	..
Staines dep	4 18	..	..	4 22	..	..	..	4 48	..	..	..	..	5 18	..	..	5 22	..	..	5 48	..	..	..	..	6 18	..	..	..	6 22	..	..	6 48	..
Egham L	4 23	..	..	4 27	..	..	..	4 53	..	..	..	..	5 23	..	..	5 27	..	..	5 53	..	..	..	..	6 23	..	..	..	6 27	..	..	6 53	..
Virginia Water M arr	4 27	..	..	4 31	..	..	..	4 57	..	..	..	..	5 27	..	..	5 31	..	..	5 57	..	..	..	..	6 27	..	..	..	6 31	..	..	6 57	..
Virginia Water M dep	4 27	..	..	..	..	..	..	4 57	..	..	..	..	5 27	..	..	..	..	..	5 57	..	..	..	..	6 27	..	..	..	..	..	..	6 57	..
Chertsey	4 32	..	..	..	..	..	..	5 2	..	..	..	..	5 32	..	..	..	..	..	6 2	..	..	..	..	6 32	..	..	..	..	..	..	7 2	..
Addlestone	4 35	..	..	..	..	..	..	5 5	..	..	..	..	5 35	..	..	..	..	..	6 5	..	..	..	..	6 35	..	..	..	..	..	..	7 5	..
Weybridge N 394 arr	4 39	..	..	..	..	..	..	5 9	..	..	..	..	5 39	..	..	..	..	..	6 9	..	..	..	..	6 39	..	..	..	..	..	..	7 9	..
Virginia Water M dep	..	..	..	4 31	..	..	..	..	..	..	..	..	..	..	..	5 31	..	..	..	..	..	..	..	..	..	..	..	6 31	..	..	..	..
Longcross Halt	..	..	..	4 35	..	..	..	..	..	..	..	..	..	..	..	5 35	..	..	..	..	..	..	..	..	..	..	..	6 35	..	..	..	..
Sunningdale P	..	..	..	4 38	..	..	..	..	..	..	..	..	..	..	..	5 38	..	..	..	..	..	..	..	..	..	..	..	6 38	..	..	..	..
Ascot arr	..	..	..	4 43	..	..	..	..	..	..	..	..	..	..	..	5 43	..	..	..	..	..	..	..	..	..	..	..	6 43	..	..	..	..
Ascot dep	..	..	..	4 46	..	..	..	..	..	..	..	..	..	..	..	5 46	..	..	..	..	..	..	..	..	..	..	..	6 46	..	..	..	..
Bagshot	..	..	..	4 51	..	..	..	..	..	..	..	..	..	..	..	5 51	..	..	..	..	..	..	..	..	..	..	..	6 51	..	..	..	..
Camberley Q	..	..	..	4 59	..	..	..	..	..	..	..	..	..	..	..	5 59	..	..	..	..	..	..	..	..	..	..	..	6 59	..	..	..	..
Frimley T	..	..	..	5 3	..	..	..	..	..	..	..	..	..	..	..	6 3	..	..	..	..	..	..	..	..	..	..	..	7 3	..	..	..	..
Ash Vale W	..	..	..	5 9	..	..	..	..	..	..	..	..	..	..	..	6 9	..	..	..	..	..	..	..	..	..	..	..	7 9	..	..	..	..
Aldershot Y arr	..	..	..	5 14	..	..	..	..	..	..	..	..	..	..	..	6 14	..	..	..	..	..	..	..	..	..	..	..	7 14	..	..	..	..
Ascot dep	..	..	..	4 44	..	..	..	..	..	..	..	..	..	..	..	5 44	..	..	..	..	..	..	..	..	..	..	..	6 44	..	..	..	..
Bracknell	..	..	..	4 49	..	..	..	..	..	..	..	..	..	..	..	5 49	..	..	..	..	..	..	..	..	..	..	..	6 49	..	..	..	..
Wokingham 249	..	..	..	4 56	..	..	..	..	..	..	..	..	..	..	..	5 56	..	..	..	..	..	..	..	..	..	..	..	6 56	..	..	..	..
Winnersh Halt Z	..	..	..	5 0	..	..	..	..	..	..	..	..	..	..	..	6 0	..	..	..	..	..	..	..	..	..	..	..	7 0	..	..	..	..
Earley	..	..	..	5 4	..	..	..	..	..	..	..	..	..	..	..	6 4	..	..	..	..	..	..	..	..	..	..	..	7 4	..	..	..	..
Reading arr	..	..	..	5 9	..	..	..	..	..	..	..	..	..	..	..	6 9	..	..	..	..	..	..	..	..	..	..	..	7 9	..	..	..	..

FOR NOTES, SEE PAGE 475

FOR NOTES, SEE PAGE 475

LONDON, HOUNSLOW, RICHMOND, TWICKENHAM, TEDDINGTON, STAINES, WINDSOR, and READING

Sundays—continued

Down.	3	3	3		3		3	3		3	3	3		3	3	3		3		3	3	3	3	3		3	3	3	3	3		3
	p.m																									p.m						
Waterloo dep.	6 26	6 29	6 42	..	6 49	6 54	..	6 56	..	6 59	7 12	7 19	..	7 26	7 29	7 42	..	7 49	7 54	..	7 56	7 59	8 12	8 19	..	8 26	8 29	8 42	8 49	..	8 54	8 56
Vauxhall	6 29	6 32	..	..	6 52	..	..	6 59	..	7 2	..	7 22	..	7 29	7 32	..	..	7 52	..	..	7 59	8 2	..	8 22	..	8 29	8 32	..	8 52	..	..	8 59
Queen's Road	6 32	6 35	..	..	6 55	..	..	7 2	..	..	..	7 25	..	7 32	7 35	..	..	7 55	..	..	8 2	..	..	8 25	..	8 32	8 35	..	8 55	..	..	9 2
Clapham Junction A	6 35	6 38	6 49	..	6 58	..	..	7 5	..	7 8	7 19	7 28	..	7 35	7 38	7 49	..	7 58	..	..	8 5	8 8	8 19	8 28	..	8 35	8 38	8 49	8 58	..	..	9 5
Wandsworth Town	6 37	6 40	..	..	7 0	..	..	7 7	..	7 10	..	7 30	..	7 37	7 40	..	..	8 0	..	..	8 7	8 10	..	8 30	..	8 37	8 40	..	9 0	..	..	9 7
Putney	6 40	6 43	..	..	7 3	..	..	7 10	..	7 13	..	7 33	..	7 40	7 43	..	..	8 3	..	..	8 10	8 13	..	8 33	..	8 40	8 43	..	9 3	..	..	9 10
Barnes	6 43	6 46	..	..	7 6	..	..	7 13	..	7 16	..	7 36	..	7 43	7 46	..	..	8 6	..	..	8 13	8 16	..	8 36	..	8 43	8 46	..	9 6	..	..	9 13
Barnes Bridge	6 44	..	..	..	..	..	..	7 14	..	..	..	..	..	7 44	..	..	..	..	..	..	8 14	..	..	..	..	8 44	..	..	..	..	..	9 14
Chiswick, for Grove Park	6 47	..	..	..	..	..	..	7 17	..	..	..	..	..	7 47	..	..	..	..	..	..	8 17	..	..	..	..	8 47	..	..	..	..	..	9 17
Kew Bridge	6 49	..	..	..	..	..	..	7 19	..	..	..	..	..	7 49	..	..	..	..	..	..	8 19	..	..	..	..	8 49	..	..	..	..	..	9 19
Brentford B	6 52	..	..	..	..	..	..	7 22	..	..	..	..	..	7 52	..	..	..	..	..	..	8 22	..	..	..	..	8 52	..	..	..	..	..	9 22
Syon Lane	6 54	..	..	..	..	..	..	7 24	..	..	..	..	..	7 54	..	..	..	..	..	..	8 24	..	..	..	..	8 54	..	..	..	..	..	9 24
Isleworth C	6 56	..	..	..	..	..	..	7 26	..	..	..	..	..	7 56	..	..	..	..	..	..	8 26	..	..	..	..	8 56	..	..	..	..	..	9 26
Hounslow D	6 59	..	..	..	..	..	..	7 29	..	..	..	..	..	7 59	..	..	..	..	..	..	8 29	..	..	..	..	8 59	..	..	..	..	..	9 29
Whitton	7 3	..	..	..	..	..	..	7 33	..	..	..	..	..	8 3	..	..	..	..	..	..	8 33	..	..	..	..	9 3	..	..	..	..	..	9 33
Mortlake, for East Sheen	..	6 49	..	..	7 9	..	..	..	..	7 19	..	7 39	..	..	7 49	..	..	8 9	..	..	..	8 19	..	8 39	..	..	8 49	..	9 9	..	..	..
North Sheen	..	6 51	..	..	7 11	..	..	..	..	7 21	..	7 41	..	..	7 51	..	..	8 11	..	..	..	8 21	..	8 41	..	..	8 51	..	9 11	..	..	..
Richmond	..	6 54	6 59	..	7 14	..	..	..	..	7 24	7 29	7 44	..	..	7 54	7 59	..	8 14	..	..	..	8 24	8 29	8 44	..	..	8 54	8 59	9 14	..	..	..
St. Margaret's	..	6 57	..	..	7 17	..	..	..	..	7 27	..	7 47	..	..	7 57	..	..	8 17	..	..	..	8 27	..	8 47	..	..	8 57	..	9 17	..	..	..
Twickenham	7 5	6 59	7 3	..	7 19	..	7 26	7 35	..	7 29	7 33	7 49	..	8 5	7 59	8 3	..	8 19	..	8 26	8 35	8 29	8 33	8 49	..	9 5	8 59	9 3	9 19	9 26	..	9 35
Strawberry Hill	..	7 2	..	..	7 22	..	..	..	..	7 32	..	..	..	..	8 2	..	..	8 22	..	..	..	8 32	..	..	..	..	9 2	..	9·22	..	..	..
Teddington F arr.	..	7 5	..	..	7 25	..	..	..	..		..	..	..	..	8 5	..	..	8 25	..	..	..	..	..	..	..	..	9 5	..	9 25	..	..	..
Whitton	..	V	7 5	..	V	..	7 28	..	..	To Shepperton, arr. 7 48 p.m see page 419	7 35	7 51	..	..	V	8 5	..	V	..	8 28	..	To Shepperton, arr. 8 48 p.m see page 420	8 35	8 51	..	..	V	9 5	V	9 28	..	..
Hounslow D arr.	..		..	..		..	7 33	..	..		..	7 58	..	..	..	..	..		..	8 33	..		..	8 58	..	..	..	..		9 33	..	..
Feltham	..	To Waterloo via Kingston	7 9	..	To Waterloo via Kingston	..	..	..	..		7 39	..	..	..	To Waterloo, via Kingston	8 9	..	To Waterloo, via Kingston	..	..	..		8 39	..	..	..	To Waterloo, via Kingston	9 9	To Waterloo via Kingston	..	..	..
Ashford (Middlesex)	..		7 14	..		..	..	..	..		7 44	..	..	..		8 14	..		..	..	..		8 44	..	..	..		9 14		..	..	..
Staines J arr.	..		7 17	..		7 22	..	..	..		7 47	..	..	..		8 17	..		8 22	..	..		8 47	..	..	..		9 17		..	9 22	..
Staines dep.	..		7 19	..		..	..	..	..		7 49	..	..	..		8 19	..		..	..	..		8 49	..	..	..		9 19		..	..	..
Wraysbury	..		7 26	..		..	..	..	..		7 56	..	..	..		8 26	..		..	..	..		8 56	..	..	..		9 26		..	..	..
Sunnymeads	..		7 29	..		..	..	..	..		7 59	..	..	..		8 29	..		..	..	..		8 59	..	..	..		9 29		..	..	..
Datchet	..		7 32	..		..	..	..	..		8 2	..	..	..		8 32	..		..	..	..		9 2	..	..	..		9 32		..	..	..
Windsor and Eton K arr.	..		7 38	..		..	..	..	..		8 8	..	..	..		8 38	..		..	..	..		9 8	..	..	..		9 38		..	..	..
Staines dep.	..		7 18	..		7 22	..	..	..		7 48	..	..	..		8 18	..		8 22	..	..		8 48	..	..	..		9 18		..	9 22	..
Egham L	..		7 23	..		7 27	..	..	..		7 53	..	..	..		8 23	..		8 27	..	..		8 53	..	..	..		9 23		..	9 27	..
Virginia Water M arr.	..		7 27	..		7 31	..	..	..		7 57	..	..	..		8 27	..		8 31	..	..		8 57	..	..	..		9 27		..	9 31	..
Virginia Water M dep.	..	..	7 27	..	..	..	..	..	..		7 57	..	..	..	..	8 27	..	..	..	..	..		8 57	..	..	..	..	9 27	..	..	..	..
Chertsey	..	..	7 32	..	..	..	..	..	..		8 2	..	..	..	..	8 32	..	..	..	..	..		9 2	..	..	..	..	9 32	..	..	..	..
Addlestone	..	..	7 35	..	..	..	..	..	..		8 5	..	..	..	..	8 35	..	..	..	..	..		9 5	..	..	..	..	9 35	..	..	..	..
Weybridge N 394 arr.	..	..	7 39	..	..	..	..	..	..		8 9	..	..	..	..	8 39	..	..	..	..	..		9 9	..	..	..	..	9 39	..	..	..	..
Virginia Water M dep.	..	..	..	..	..	7 31	..	..	..	..	..	..	..	..	..	..	..	..	8 31	..	..	..	..	..	..	..	..	..	..	..	9 31	..
Longcross Halt	..	..	..	..	..	7 35	..	..	..	..	..	..	..	..	..	..	..	..	8 35	..	..	..	..	..	..	..	..	..	..	..	9 35	..
Sunningdale P	..	..	..	..	..	7 38	..	..	..	..	..	..	..	..	..	..	..	..	8 38	..	..	..	..	..	..	..	..	..	..	..	9 38	..
Ascot	..	..	..	..	..	7 43	..	..	..	..	..	..	..	..	..	..	..	..	8 43	..	..	..	..	..	..	..	..	..	..	..	9 43	..
Ascot dep.	..	..	..	..	..	7 46	..	..	..	..	..	..	..	..	..	..	..	..	8 46	..	..	..	..	..	..	..	..	..	..	..	9 46	..
Bagshot	..	..	..	..	..	7 51	..	..	..	..	..	..	..	..	..	..	..	..	8 51	..	..	..	..	..	..	..	..	..	..	..	9 51	..
Camberley Q	..	..	..	..	..	7 59	..	..	..	..	..	..	..	..	..	..	..	..	8 59	..	..	..	..	..	..	..	..	..	..	..	9 59	..
Frimley T	..	..	..	..	..	8 3	..	..	..	..	..	..	..	..	..	..	..	..	9 3	..	..	..	..	..	..	..	..	..	..	..	10 3	..
Ash Vale W	..	..	..	..	..	8 9	..	..	..	..	..	..	..	..	..	..	..	..	9 9	..	..	..	..	..	..	..	..	..	..	..	10 9	..
Aldershot Y arr.	..	..	..	..	..	8 14	..	..	..	..	..	..	..	..	..	..	..	..	9 14	..	..	..	..	..	..	..	..	..	..	..	1014	..
Ascot dep.	..	..	..	..	..	7 44	..	..	..	..	..	..	..	..	..	..	..	..	8 44	..	..	..	..	..	..	..	..	..	..	..	9 44	..
Bracknell	..	..	..	..	..	7 49	..	..	..	..	..	..	..	..	..	..	..	..	8 49	..	..	..	..	..	..	..	..	..	..	..	9 49	..
Wokingham 249	..	..	..	..	..	7 56	..	..	..	..	..	..	..	..	..	..	..	..	8 56	..	..	..	..	..	..	..	..	..	..	..	9 56	..
Winnersh Halt Z	..	..	..	..	..	8 0	..	..	..	..	..	..	..	..	..	..	..	..	9 0	..	..	..	..	..	..	..	..	..	..	..	10 0	..
Earley	..	..	..	..	..	8 4	..	..	..	..	..	..	..	..	..	..	..	..	9 4	..	..	..	..	..	..	..	..	..	..	..	10 4	..
Reading arr.	..	..	..	..	..	8 9	..	..	..	..	..	..	..	..	..	..	..	..	9 9	..	..	..	..	..	..	..	..	..	..	..	10 9	..

LONDON, HOUNSLOW, RICHMOND, TWICKENHAM, TEDDINGTON, STAINES, WINDSOR, and READING

Down.	Sundays—continued p.m																						
	3	3	3		3	3	3	3	3	3	3	3	3		3	3	3	3	3	3	3	3	3	3
Waterloo .... dep	8 59	9 12	9 19	9 24	9 26	9 29	9 42	9 49	..	9 56	9 59	1012	1019	1024	1026	1029	1042	1049	1056	1059	1119	112[illegible]	1149	1156
Vauxhall	9 2	..	9 22	..	9 29	9 31	..	9 52	..	9 59	10 2	..	1022	..	1029	1032	..	1052	1059	11 2	1122	1129	1152	1159
Queen's Road	..	..	9 25	..	9 32	9 35	..	9 55	..	10 2	..	..	1025	..	1032	1035	..	1055	11 2	..	1125	1132	1155	12 2
Clapham Junction **A**	9 8	9 19	9 28	..	9 35	9 38	9 49	9 58	..	10 5	10 8	1019	1028	..	1035	1038	1049	1058	11 5	11 8	1128	1135	1158	12 5
Wandsworth Town	9 10	..	9 30	..	9 37	9 40	..	10 0	..	10 7	1010	..	1030	..	1037	1040	..	11 0	11 7	1110	1130	1137	12 0	12 7
Putney	9 13	..	9 33	..	9 40	9 43	..	10 3	..	1010	1013	..	1033	..	1040	1043	..	11 3	1110	1113	1133	1140	12 3	1210
Barnes	9 16	..	9 36	..	9 43	9 46	..	10 6	..	1013	1016	..	1036	..	1043	1046	..	11 6	1113	1116	1136	1143	12 6	1213
Barnes Bridge	..	..	..	..	9 44	..	..	..	..	1014	..	..	..	..	1044	..	..	..	1114	..	..	1145	..	1215
Chiswick for Grove Park	..	..	..	..	9 47	..	..	..	..	1017	..	..	..	..	1047	..	..	..	1117	..	..	1147	..	1217
Kew Bridge	..	..	..	..	9 49	..	..	..	..	1019	..	..	..	..	1049	..	..	..	1119	..	..	1150	..	1220
Brentford **B**	..	..	..	..	9 52	..	..	..	..	1022	..	..	..	..	1052	..	..	..	1122	..	..	1153	..	1223
Syon Lane	..	..	..	..	9 54	..	..	..	..	1024	..	..	..	..	1054	..	..	..	1124	..	..	..	..	..
Isleworth **C**	..	..	..	..	9 56	..	..	..	..	1026	..	..	..	..	1056	..	..	..	1126	..	..	1157	..	1227
Hounslow **D**	..	..	..	..	9 59	..	..	..	..	1029	..	..	..	..	1059	..	..	..	1129	..	..	12 0	..	1230
Whitton	..	..	..	..	10 3	..	..	..	..	1033	..	..	..	..	11 4	..	..	..	..	..	..	..	..	..
Mortlake for East Sheen	9 19	..	9 39	..	..	9 49	..	10 9	..	..	1019	..	1039	..	..	1049	..	11 9	..	1119	1139	..	12 9	..
North Sheen	9 21	..	9 41	..	..	9 51	..	1011	..	..	1021	..	1041	..	..	1051	..	1111	..	1121	1141	..	..	..
Richmond	9 24	9 29	9 44	..	..	9 54	9 59	1014	..	..	1024	1029	1044	1038	..	1054	1059	1114	..	1124	1144	..	1214	..
St. Margaret's	9 27	..	9 47	..	..	9 57	..	1017	..	..	1027	..	1047	..	..	1057	..	1117	..	1127	1147	..	1217	..
Twickenham	9 29	9 33	9 49	..	10 5	9 59	10 3	1019	1026	1035	1029	1033	1049	..	11 6	1059	11 3	1119	..	1129	1149	..	1219	..
Strawberry Hill	9 32	..	..	..	..	10 2	..	1022	..	..	1032	..	..	..	..	11 2	..	1122	..	1132	1152	..	1222	..
Teddington F ...... arr	..	..	..	..	..	10 5	..	1025	..	..	..	..	..	..	..	11 5	..	..	..	..	1155	..	..	..
Whitton	To Shepperton, arr. 9 48 p.m see page 420.	9 35	9 51	..	..	V	10 5	V	1028	..	To Shepperton, arr. 10 48 p.m see page 421.	1035	1051	..	..	V	11 5	..		To Shepperton, arr. 11 47 p.m see page 426.	V	..	..	..
Hounslow **D** ...... arr		..	9 58	..	..	To Wimbledon	..	To Waterloo via Kingston	1033	..		..	1056	..	..	To Waterloo via Kingston	..	..	..		To Wimbledon	..	..	..
Feltham		9 39	..	..	..		10 9		..	..		1039	..	..	..		11 9	..	..			..	..	..
Ashford (Middlesex)		9 44	..	..	..		1014		..	..		1044	..	..	..		1114	..	..			..	..	..
Staines J ...... arr		9 47	..	9 52	..		1017		..	..		1047	..	1052	..		1117	..	..			..	..	..
Staines ...... dep		9 49	..	..	..		1019		..	..		1049	..	..	..		1119	..	..			..	..	..
Wraysbury		9 56	..	..	..		1026		..	..		1056	..	..	..		1126	..	..			..	..	..
Sunnymeads		9 59	..	..	..		1029		..	..		1059	..	..	..		1129	..	..			..	..	..
Datchet		10 2	..	..	..		1032		..	..		11 2	..	..	..		1132	..	..			..	..	..
Windsor and Eton K arr		10 8	..	..	..		1038		..	..		11 8	..	..	..		1138	..	..			..	..	..
Staines ...... dep		9 48	..	9 52	..		1018		..	..		1048	..	1052	..		1118	..	..			..	..	..
Egham **L**		9 53	..	9 57	..		1023		..	..		1053	..	1057	..		1123	..	..			..	..	..
Virginia Water M .. arr		9 57	..	10 1	..		1027		..	..		1057	..	11 1	..		1127	..	..			..	..	..
Virginia Water M .dep		9 57	..	..	..	..	1027	..	..	..		1057	..	..	..	..	1127	..	..		..	..	..	..
Chertsey		10 2	..	..	..	..	1032	..	..	..		11 2	..	..	..	..	1132	..	..		..	..	..	..
Addlestone		10 5	..	..	..	..	1035	..	..	..		11 5	..	..	..	..	..	..	..		..	..	..	..
Weybridge N 394 ... arr		10 9	..	..	..	..	1039	..	..	..		11 9	..	..	..	..	..	..	..		..	..	..	..
Virginia Water M ...dep	..	..	..	10 1	..	..	..	..	..	..	..	..	..	11 1	..	..	..	..	..	..	..	..	..	..
Longcross Halt	..	..	..	10 5	..	..	..	..	..	..	..	..	..	11 5	..	..	..	..	..	..	..	..	..	..
Sunningdale **P**	..	..	..	10 8	..	..	..	..	..	..	..	..	..	11 8	..	..	..	..	..	..	..	..	..	..
Ascot .... arr	..	..	..	1013	..	..	..	..	..	..	..	..	..	1113	..	..	..	..	..	..	..	..	..	..
Ascot .... dep	..	..	..	1016	..	..	..	..	..	..	..	..	..	1116	..	..	..	..	..	..	..	..	..	..
Bagshot	..	..	..	1021	..	..	..	..	..	..	..	..	..	1121	..	..	..	..	..	..	..	..	..	..
Camberley **Q**	..	..	..	1029	..	..	..	..	..	..	..	..	..	1129	..	..	..	..	..	..	..	..	..	..
Frimley **T**	..	..	..	1033	..	..	..	..	..	..	..	..	..	1133	..	..	..	..	..	..	..	..	..	..
Ash Vale **W**	..	..	..	1039	..	..	..	..	..	..	..	..	..	1139	..	..	..	..	..	..	..	..	..	..
Aldershot **Y** ...... arr	..	..	..	1044	..	..	..	..	..	..	..	..	..	1144	..	..	..	..	..	..	..	..	..	..
Ascot .... dep	..	..	..	1014	..	..	..	..	..	..	..	..	..	1114	..	..	..	..	..	..	..	..	..	..
Bracknell	..	..	..	1019	..	..	..	..	..	..	..	..	..	1119	..	..	..	..	..	..	..	..	..	..
Wokingham 249	..	..	..	1026	..	..	..	..	..	..	..	..	..	1126	..	..	..	..	..	..	..	..	..	..
Winnersh Halt **Z**	..	..	..	1030	..	..	..	..	..	..	..	..	..	..	..	..	..	..	..	..	..	..	..	..
Earley	..	..	..	1034	..	..	..	..	..	..	..	..	..	1133	..	..	..	..	..	..	..	..	..	..
Reading .... arr	..	..	..	1039	..	..	..	..	..	..	..	..	..	1138	..	..	..	..	..	..	..	..	..	..

3 Third class only

A Mid. Battersea; 1½ miles to Clapham
A Arr. 5 mins. *earlier*
B ¼ mile to G W Sta
B Arr. 7 51 p.m
C Sta for Spring Grove
C Arr 3 19 a.m
D About ¼ mile to Hounslow Central and Hounslow East Stas
F Sta for Bushy Park
J About 1 mile to G W Sta
K About ½ mile to G W Sta
L Sta for Englefield Green (1½ miles)
M Virginia Water (for Wentworth)
N Sta for Brooklands, St. George's Hill, and Oatlands Park
P Sta for Windlesham
Q Sta. for Sandhurst (1½ miles), and nearly 1½ miles to Blackwater (Hants) Station
S O or **SO** Saturdays only
S X Saturdays excepted
T About 1 mile to Farnborough North Station.
U Calls to take up only
V For Continuation of Service to Waterloo, via Kingston and Wimbledon, see pages 427 to 459
W For North Camp and South Farnborough.
Y For South Camp.
Z Halt for Sindlesham and Hurst

OTHER TRAINS
between Waterloo and Clapham Junction, see page 394—Waterloo and Teddington, 394—Waterloo and Virginia Water, 394—London & Reading 246—Wokingham and Reading, 246

FOR NOTES, SEE PAGE 489

READING, WINDSOR, STAINES, TEDDINGTON, TWICKENHAM, RICHMOND, HOUNSLOW, and LONDON

Up — Week Days — a.m.

Miles	Up	3	3	3	3	3	3	3	3	3		3	3	3	3	3	3	3	3	3	3	3	3		3	3	3	3	3		3	3
	Reading dep	..	..	..	..	..	..	..	..	..	..	..	..	..	..	..	..	..	..	..	..	..	..	..	..	..	..	..	..	6 17	..	..
3	Earley	..	..	..	..	..	..	..	..	..	..	..	..	..	..	..	..	..	..	..	..	..	..	..	..	..	..	..	..	6 22	..	..
4¾	Winnersh Halt Z	..	..	..	..	..	..	..	..	..	..	..	..	..	..	..	..	..	..	..	..	..	..	..	..	..	..	..	..	6 26	..	..
6¾	Wokingham	..	..	..	..	..	..	..	..	..	..	..	..	..	..	..	..	..	..	..	..	..	..	..	..	..	..	..	..	6 30	..	..
11	Bracknell	..	..	..	..	..	..	..	..	..	..	..	..	..	..	..	..	..	..	..	..	..	..	..	..	..	..	..	..	6 37	..	..
14½	Ascot 388 arr	..	..	..	..	..	..	..	..	..	..	..	..	..	..	..	..	..	..	..	..	..	..	..	..	..	..	..	..	6 42	..	..
—	Mls Aldershot dep	..	..	..	..	..	..	..	..	..	..	..	..	..	..	..	..	..	..	..	..	..	..	..	..	..	..	..	..	6 15	..	..
—	2½ Ash Vale W	..	..	..	..	..	..	..	..	..	..	..	..	..	..	..	..	..	..	..	..	..	..	..	..	..	..	..	..	6 19	..	..
—	5¾ Frimley T	..	..	..	..	..	..	..	..	..	..	..	..	..	..	..	..	..	..	..	..	..	..	..	..	..	..	..	..	6 25	..	..
—	8 Camberley Q	..	..	..	..	..	..	..	..	..	..	..	..	..	..	..	..	..	..	..	..	..	..	..	..	..	..	..	..	6 29	..	..
—	11½ Bagshot	..	..	..	..	..	..	..	..	..	..	..	..	..	..	..	..	..	..	..	..	..	..	..	..	..	..	..	..	6 35	..	..
—	14½ Ascot arr	..	..	..	..	..	..	..	..	..	..	..	..	..	..	..	..	..	..	..	..	..	..	..	..	..	..	..	..	6 41	..	..
—	Ascot dep	..	..	..	..	..	..	..	..	..	..	..	..	..	..	..	..	..	..	..	..	..	..	..	..	..	..	..	..	6 45	..	..
16½	Sunningdale P	..	..	..	..	..	..	..	..	..	..	..	..	..	..	..	..	..	..	..	..	..	..	..	..	..	..	..	..	6 49	..	..
18½	Longcross Halt	..	..	..	..	..	..	..	..	..	..	..	..	..	..	..	..	..	..	..	..	..	..	..	..	..	..	..	..	6 52	..	..
20½	Virginia Water M 427 arr	..	..	..	..	..	..	..	..	..	..	..	..	..	..	..	..	..	..	..	..	..	..	..	..	..	..	..	..	6 56	..	..
—	Mls Weybridge dep	From Waterloo via Kingston	From Waterloo via Kingston	From Waterloo via Kingston	..	From Waterloo via Kingston	..	..	..	..	..	..	From Wimbledon via Kingston	..	..	From Waterloo via Kingston	..	..	..	6 3	..	..	From Wimbledon via Kingston	..	..	From Waterloo via Kingston	From Shepperton, dep. 6 46 a.m., see page 428	..	6 32	..	..	6 49
—	1½ Addlestone				..		..	..	..	..	..	..		..	..		..	..	..	6 7	..	..		..	..			..	6 36	..	..	6 53
—	3½ Chertsey				..		..	..	..	..	..	..		5 39	..		..	..	..	6 10	..	..		..	..			..	6 41	..	..	7 0
—	5½ Virginia Water M arr				..		..	..	..	..	..	..		5 43	..		..	..	..	6 14	..	..		..	..			..	6 46	..	..	7 4
—	Virginia Water M dep				..		..	..	..	..	..	..		5 43	..		..	..	..	6 14	..	..		..	..			..	6 46	6 56	..	7 4
22½	Egham L				..		..	..	..	..	..	..		5 47	..		..	..	..	6 18	..	..		..	..			..	6 50	7 0	..	7 8
24½	Staines J arr				..		..	..	..	..	..	..		5 52	..		..	..	..	6 23	..	..		..	..			..	6 55	7 5	..	7 13
—	Mls Windsor and Eton dep				..		..	..	..	..	..	5 0		5 38	..		..	..	..	6 8	..	..		..	..			..	6 36	..	..	6 58
—	1½ Datchet				..		..	..	..	..	..	5 4		5 42	..		..	..	..	6 12	..	..		..	..			..	6 40	..	..	7 2
—	3 Sunnymeads				..		..	..	..	..	..	..		5 46	..		..	..	..	6 16	..	..		..	..			..	6 44	..	..	7 6
—	4½ Wraysbury				..		..	..	..	..	..	5 11		5 49	..		..	..	..	6 19	..	..		..	..			..	6 47	..	..	7 9
—	6¼ Staines J arr				..		..	..	..	..	..	5 17		5 55	..		..	..	..	6 25	..	..		..	..			..	6 53	..	..	7 15
—	Staines dep				..		..	..	..	..	..	5 19		5 57	..		..	..	..	6 27	..	..		..	..			..	6 57	7 6	..	7 17
26	Ashford (Middlesex)				..		..	..	..	..	..	5 23		6 1	..		..	..	..	6 31	..	..		..	..			..	7 1	..	..	7 21
28½	Feltham				3 47		..	5 6	..	..	..	5 27		6 5	..		..	..	..	6 35	..	..		..	..			..	7 5	..	..	7 25
—	Hounslow D dep				..		..	..	..	..	..	..		..	..		..	..	6 29	..	..	6 40		..	..			6 59	..	..	..	..
31	Whitton	V	V	V	..	V	..	5 10	..	..	..	..	V	6 9	..	V	..	..	6 33	6 39	..	6 44	V	..	..	V		7 3	7 9	..	..	..
—	Teddington F dep	1221	2 6	2 47	..	4 28	..	..	..	..	..	..	5 46	..	..	6 6	..	..	..	..	..	..	6 41	..	..	6 53	..	..	..	..	..	..
—	Strawberry Hill	1224	..	2 50	..	4 34	..	..	..	5 28	..	..	5 51	..	..	6 10	..	6 21	..	..	..	..	6 44	..	..	6 56	7 1	..	..	..	..	..
32	Twickenham	Mondays only	2 12	..	3 54	4 37	..	5 13	..	5 31	..	..	5 54	6 12	..	6 14	..	6 24	6 36	6 42	..	6 47	6 47	..	..	6 59	7 4	7 6	7 12	7 16	7 7	..
32¾	St. Margaret's		..	..	3 57	4 39	..	5 15	..	5 33	..	..	5 56	..	..	6 16	..	6 26	6 38	..	..	..	6 49	..	..	7 1	7 6	7 8	..	..	..	..
33¾	Richmond		2 16	..	4 1	4 42	..	5 18	..	5 36	..	..	5 59	6 16	..	6 19	..	6 29	6 41	6 46	..	..	6 52	..	..	7 4	7 9	7 11	7 16	7 20	..	..
34½	North Sheen		..	..	..	..	..	5 20	..	5 38	..	..	6 1	..	..	6 21	..	6 31	..	..	..	..	6 54	..	..	..	..	7 13	..	..	..	..
35½	Mortlake, for East Sheen		..	..	4 5	4 46	..	5 23	..	5 41	..	..	6 4	..	..	6 24	..	6 34	6 44	6 49	..	..	6 57	..	..	7 7	..	7 16	..	..	..	..
—	Whitton		..	..	..	..	..	..	..	..	..	..	..	..	..	..	..	..	..	..	..	..	..	..	..	..	..	..	..	..	7 10	..
—	Hounslow D		..	..	..	..	5 3	..	5 18	..	..	5 32	..	..	6 3	..	6 15	..	..	..	6 33	..	..	..	6 45	..	..	..	..	..	7 15	7 30
—	Isleworth C		..	..	..	..	5 6	..	5 21	..	..	5 35	..	..	6 6	..	6 18	..	..	..	6 36	..	..	..	6 48	..	..	..	..	..	7 18	..
—	Syon Lane		..	..	..	..	..	..	5 24	..	..	5 38	..	..	6 9	..	6 21	..	..	..	6 39	..	..	..	6 51	..	..	..	..	..	7 21	..
—	Brentford B	..	..	..	..	..	5 9	..	5 26	..	..	5 40	..	..	6 11	..	6 23	..	..	..	6 41	..	..	..	6 53	..	..	..	..	..	7 23	..
—	Kew Bridge	..	..	..	..	..	5 12	..	5 29	..	..	5 43	..	..	6 14	..	6 26	..	..	..	6 44	..	..	..	6 56	..	..	..	..	..	7 26	..
—	Chiswick, for Grove Park	..	..	..	..	..	5 15	..	5 32	..	..	5 46	..	..	6 17	..	6 29	..	..	..	6 47	..	..	..	6 59	..	..	..	..	..	7 29	..
—	Barnes Bridge	..	..	..	..	..	5 18	..	5 35	..	..	5 49	..	..	6 20	..	6 32	..	..	..	6 50	..	..	..	7 2	..	..	..	..	..	7 32	..
36½	Barnes	..	..	..	4 9	4 49	5 20	5 26	5 37	5 44	..	5 51	6 7	..	6 22	6 27	6 34	6 37	6 47	..	6 52	..	7 0	..	7 4	7 10	..	7 19	..	..	7 34	..
37½	Putney	..	2 20	..	4 13	4 53	5 23	5 29	5 40	5 47	..	5 54	6 10	6 21	6 25	6 30	6 37	6 40	6 50	..	6 55	..	7 3	..	7 7	7 13	..	7 22	..	..	7 37	..
38½	Wandsworth Town	..	..	..	..	..	5 26	5 32	5 43	5 50	..	5 57	6 13	..	6 28	6 33	6 40	6 43	..	..	6 58	..	7 6	..	7 10	7 16	..	7 25	..	..	7 40	..
39½	Clapham Junction A	..	2 23	..	4 19	4 57	5 28	5 34	5 45	5 52	..	5 59	6 15	..	6 30	6 35	6 42	6 45	6 55	6 56	7 0	..	7 8	..	7 12	7 19	..	7 27	7§25	..	7 42	..
40½	Queen's Road	..	..	..	4 22	5 0	5 31	5 37	5 48	5 55	..	6 2	6 18	..	6 33	..	6 45	..	6 58	..	7 3	..	..	..	7 15	..	..	7 30	..	..	7 45	..
42½	Vauxhall	..	2 27	..	4 25	5 3	5 34	5 40	5 51	5 58	..	6 5	6 21	..	6 36	6 39	6 48	6 49	7 1	..	7 6	..	..	..	7 18	7 24	..	7 34	..	..	7 49	..
43½	Waterloo arr	..	2 35	..	4 29	5 7	5 38	5 44	5 55	6 2	..	6 9	6 25	6 31	6 40	6 43	6 52	6 53	7 5	7 3	7 10	..	7 16	..	7 22	7 28	7 24	7 38	7 32	7 35	7 53	7 50

READING, WINDSOR, STAINES, TEDDINGTON, TWICKENHAM, RICHMOND, HOUNSLOW, and LONDON

Up — Week Days—*continued* — a.m

Up	3 From Waterloo, via Kingston	3 From Shepperton, dep. 7 16 a.m., see page 428	3	From Woking, page 389		3 From Waterloo, via Kingston	3	3	3 From Waterloo, via Kingston	3 From Shepperton, dep. 7 44 a.m., see page 430	3
Reading ....dep.	..	..	..		6 43	..	..	..	..	..	..
Earley	..	..	..		6 48	..	..	..	..	..	..
Winnersh Halt Z	..	..	..		6 52	..	..	..	..	..	..
Wokingham	..	..	..		6 56	..	..	..	..	..	..
Bracknell	..	..	..		7 3	..	..	..	..	..	..
Ascot 388 ....arr.	..	..	..		7 9	..	..	..	..	..	..
Aldershot ....dep.	..	..	..	..	..	..	..	..	..	..	..
Ash Vale W	..	..	..	..	..	..	..	..	..	..	..
Frimley T	..	..	..	6 35	..	..	..	..	..	..	..
Camberley Q	..	..	..	6H54	..	..	..	..	..	..	..
Bagshot	..	..	..	7 1	..	..	..	..	..	..	..
Ascot ....arr.	..	..	..	7 7	..	..	..	..	..	..	..
Ascot ....dep.	..	..	..	7 10	7 10	..	..	..	..	..	..
Sunningdale P	..	..	..	7 15	7 15	..	..	..	..	..	..
Longcross Halt	..	..	..	7 18	7 18	..	..	..	..	..	..
Virginia Water M 427 arr.	..	..	..	7 22	7 22	..	..	..	..	..	..
Weybridge ....dep.	..		..	..	..	..	7 11	..	..		..
Addlestone	..		..	..	..	..	7 15	..	..		..
Chertsey	..		..	..	..	..	7 22	..	..		..
Virginia Water M ..arr.	..		..	..	..	..	7 26	..	..		..
Virginia Water M ....dep.			..	7 22	7 22		7 26	..			..
Egham L			..	7 26	7 26		7 30	..			..
Staines J ....arr.			..	7 31	7 31		7 35	..			..
Windsor and Eton ..dep.			..	..	..		7 16	..			..
Datchet			..	..	..		7 20	..			..
Sunnymeads			..	..	..		7 24	..			..
Wraysbury			..	..	..		7 27	..			..
Staines J ....arr.			..	..	..		7 33	..			..
Staines ....dep.			..	7 31	7 31		7 37	..			..
Ashford (Middlesex)			..	7 34	7 34		7 41	..			..
Feltham			..	7 38	7 38		7 45	..			..
Hounslow D ....dep.			7 30	..	..		..	..			7 58
Whitton	V		7 34	..	..	V	7 49	..	V		8 1
Teddington F ....dep.	7 21		..	..	..	7 41	..	..	7 53		..
Strawberry Hill	7 24	7 31	..	..	..	7 44	..	..	7 56	7 59	..
Twickenham	7 27	7 34	7 37	..	..	7 47	7 52	7 38	7 59	8 2	8 6
St. Margaret's	7 29	7 36	7 39	..	..	7 49	..	..	8 1	8 4	8 8
Richmond	7 32	7 39	7 42	7 47	7 47	7 52	7 56	..	8 4	8 7	8 11
North Sheen	7 34	..	7 44	..	..	..	..	..	8 6	8 10	8 13
Mortlake, for East Sheen	7 37	..	7 47	..	..	7 55	..	..	8 9	..	8 16
Whitton	..	..	..	..	..	..	..	7 40	..	..	..
Hounslow D	..	..	..	..	..	..	..	7 45	..	..	..
Isleworth C	..	..	..	..	..	..	..	7 48	..	..	..
Syon Lane	..	..	..	..	..	..	..	7 51	..	..	..
Brentford B	..	..	..	..	..	..	..	7 53	..	..	..
Kew Bridge	..	..	..	..	..	..	..	7 56	..	..	..
Chiswick, for Grove Park	..	..	..	..	..	..	..	7 59	..	..	..
Barnes Bridge	..	..	..	..	..	..	..	8 2	..	..	..
Barnes	7 40	..	7 50	..	..	7 58	..	8 4	8 12	..	8 9
Putney	7 43	..	7 53	..	..	8 1	..	8 7	8 15	..	8 22
Wandsworth Town	7 46	..	..	..	..	8 4	..	8 10	8 18	..	..
Clapham Junction A	7 48	..	7 57	..	..	8 6	..	8 12	8 20	..	8 26
Queen's Road	7 51	..	8 0	..	..	..	..	8 15	..	..	8 29
Vauxhall	7 54	..	8 3	..	..	8 10	..	8 18	8 25	..	8 33
Waterloo ....arr.	7 58	7 55	8 7	8 2	8 2	8 14	8 12	8 22	8 29	8 24	8 37

Up		3		3 From Waterloo, via Kingston	3	3	3	From Woking, page 389		3 From Shepperton, dep. 8 15 a.m., see page 430	3	3	3 From Waterloo via Kingston
Reading ....dep.	..	..	7 19	..	..	..	..		7 36	..	..	..	..
Earley	..	..	7 24	..	..	..	..		7 41	..	..	..	..
Winnersh Halt Z	..	..	7 28	..	..	..	..		7 45	..	..	..	..
Wokingham	..	..	7 32	..	..	..	..		7 49	..	..	..	..
Bracknell	..	..	7 40	..	..	..	..		7 56	..	..	..	..
Ascot 388 ....arr.	..	..	7 45	..	..	..	..		8 2	..	..	..	..
Aldershot ....dep.	..	..	7 17	..	..	..	..	..	..	..	..	..	..
Ash Vale W	..	..	7 22	..	..	..	..	..	..	..	..	..	..
Frimley T	..	..	7 28	..	..	..	..	7 38	..	..	..	..	..
Camberley Q	..	..	7 32	..	..	..	..	7 46	..	..	..	..	..
Bagshot	..	..	7 38	..	..	..	..	7 54	..	..	..	..	..
Ascot ....arr.	..	..	7 43	..	..	..	..	7 59	..	..	..	..	..
Ascot ....dep.	..	..	7 48	..	..	..	..	8 4	8 4	..	..	..	..
Sunningdale P	..	..	7 52	..	..	..	..	8 8	8 8	..	..	..	..
Longcross Halt	..	..	7 55	..	..	..	..	8 11	8 11	..	..	..	..
Virginia Water M 427 arr.	..	..	7 59	..	..	..	..	8 15	8 15	..	..	..	..
Weybridge ....dep.	..	7 35	..	..	..	..	7 50	..	..		..	..	..
Addlestone	..	7 39	..	..	..	..	7 54	..	..		..	..	..
Chertsey	..	7 42	..	..	..	..	7 57	..	..		..	..	..
Virginia Water M ..arr.	..	7 46	..	..	..	..	8 1	..	..		..	..	..
Virginia Water M ....dep.	..	7 46	7 59		..	..	8 6	8 15	8 15		..	..	
Egham L	..	7 50	8 3		..	..	8 10	8 19	8 19		..	..	
Staines J ....arr.	..	7 55	8 8		..	..	8 15	8 24	8 24		..	..	
Windsor and Eton ..dep.	..	7 36	..		..	..	7 56	..	..		..	8 9	
Datchet	..	7 40	..		..	..	8 0	..	..		..	8 13	
Sunnymeads	..	7 44	..		..	..	8 4	..	..		..	8 17	
Wraysbury	..	7 47	..		..	..	8 7	..	..		..	8 20	
Staines J ....arr.	..	7 53	..		..	..	8 13	..	..		..	8 26	
Staines ....dep.	..	7 57	8 8		..	..	8 17	8 24	8 24		..	8 27	
Ashford (Middlesex)	..	8 1	..		..	..	8 21	..	..		..	8 30	
Feltham	..	8 5	..		..	..	8 25	..	..		..	8 35	
Hounslow D ....dep.	..	..	..		..	8 21	..	..	..		8 30	..	
Whitton	..	8 9	..	V	..	8 24	..	..	..		8 33	8 39	V
Teddington F ....dep.	..	..	..	8 13	..	..	..	..	..		..	..	8 41
Strawberry Hill	..	..	..	8 16	..	..	..	..	..	8 30	..	..	8 44
Twickenham	..	8 12	8 18	8 19	8 7	8 27	..	..	..	8 33	8 36	8 42	8 47
St. Margaret's	..	..	..	8 21	..	..	..	..	..	8 35	8 38	8 44	8 49
Richmond	..	8 16	8 22	8 24	..	8 31	..	..	..	8 38	8 41	8 47	8 52
North Sheen	..	..	..	..	..	..	..	..	..	..	8 43	..	8 54
Mortlake, for East Sheen	..	..	..	8 27	..	..	..	..	..	..	8 46	8 50	8 57
Whitton	..	..	..	..	8 9	..	..	..	..	..	..	..	..
Hounslow D	..	..	..	..	8 15	..	8 30	..	..	..	..	..	..
Isleworth C	..	..	..	..	8 18	..	..	..	..	..	..	..	..
Syon Lane	..	..	..	..	8 21	..	..	..	..	..	..	..	..
Brentford B	..	..	..	..	8 23	..	..	..	..	..	..	..	..
Kew Bridge	..	..	..	..	8 26	..	..	..	..	..	..	..	..
Chiswick, for Grove Park	..	..	..	..	8 29	..	..	..	..	..	..	..	..
Barnes Bridge	..	..	..	..	8 32	..	..	..	..	..	..	..	..
Barnes	..	..	..	8 30	8 35	..	..	..	..	..	8 49	..	9 0
Putney	..	..	..	8 35	8 38	..	..	..	..	..	8 52	..	9 3
Wandsworth Town	..	..	..	8 38	8 41	..	..	..	..	..	..	..	9 6
Clapham Junction A	..	..	..	8 40	8 43	..	..	..	..	..	8 56	..	9 8
Queen's Road	..	..	..	8 43	8 46	..	..	..	..	..	8 59	..	9 11
Vauxhall	..	..	..	8 46	8 49	..	..	..	..	..	9 2	..	9 14
Waterloo ....arr.	..	8 32	8 39	8 50	8 53	8 46	8 51	8 54	8 54	8 56	9 6	9 3	9 18

Up		3		3	3 From Waterloo via Kingston	3 From Shepperton dep. 8 45 a.m., see page 431.	3	3 From Waterloo via Kingston
Reading ....dep.	..	..	7 59	..	..	..	..	..
Earley	..	..	8 4	..	..	..	..	..
Winnersh Halt Z	..	..	8 8	..	..	..	..	..
Wokingham	..	..	8 12	..	..	..	..	..
Bracknell	..	..	8 20	..	..	..	..	..
Ascot 388 ....arr.	..	..	8 25	..	..	..	..	..
Aldershot ....dep.	..	..	7 52	..	..	..	..	..
Ash Vale W	..	..	7 58	..	..	..	..	..
Frimley T	..	..	8 6	..	..	..	..	..
Camberley Q	..	..	8 11	..	..	..	..	..
Bagshot	..	..	8 17	..	..	..	..	..
Ascot ....arr.	..	..	8 22	..	..	..	..	..
Ascot ....dep.	..	..	8 27	..	..	..	..	..
Sunningdale P	..	..	8 31	..	..	..	..	..
Longcross Halt	..	..	8 35	..	..	..	..	..
Virginia Water M 427 arr.	..	..	8 38	..	..	..	..	..
Weybridge ....dep.	..	8 13	..	..	..		..	..
Addlestone	..	8 17	..	..	..		..	..
Chertsey	..	8 20	..	..	..		..	..
Virginia Water M ..arr.	..	8 24	..	..	..		..	..
Virginia Water M ....dep.	..	8 24	8 38	..	..		..	
Egham L	..	8 28	8 42	..	..		..	
Staines J ....arr.	..	8 33	8 47	..	..		..	
Windsor and Eton ..dep.	..	8 18	..	..			..	
Datchet	..	8 22	..	..			..	
Sunnymeads	..	8 26	..	..			..	
Wraysbury	..	8 29	..	..			..	
Staines J ....arr.	..	8 35	..	..			..	
Staines ....dep.	..	8 37	8 47	..			..	
Ashford (Middlesex)	..	8 41	..	..			..	
Feltham	..	8 45	..	..			..	
Hounslow D ....dep.	..	..	..	..			8 59	S X
Whitton	..	8 49	..	..	V		9 3	V
Teddington F ....dep.	..	..	..	..	8 53	S X	..	9 6
Strawberry Hill	..	..	..	..	8 56	9 0	..	9 9
Twickenham	..	8 52	..	8 36	8 59	9 3	9 6	..
St. Margaret's	..	..	..	..	9 1	9 5	9 8	..
Richmond	..	8 56	..	..	9 4	9 8	9 11	..
North Sheen	..	..	..	..	9 6	9 10	..	..
Mortlake, for East Sheen	..	..	..	..	9 9	..	9 15	..
Whitton	..	..	..	8 39	..	..	..	..
Hounslow D	..	..	..	8 45	..	..	..	..
Isleworth C	..	..	..	8 48	..	..	..	..
Syon Lane	..	..	..	8 51	..	..	..	..
Brentford B	..	..	..	8 53	..	..	..	..
Kew Bridge	..	..	..	8 56	..	..	..	..
Chiswick, for Grove Park	..	..	..	8 59	..	..	..	..
Barnes Bridge	..	..	..	9 2	..	..	..	..
Barnes	..	..	..	9 5	9 12	..	9 18	..
Putney	..	..	..	9 8	9 15	..	9 21	..
Wandsworth Town	..	..	..	9 11	9 18	..	9 24	..
Clapham Junction A	..	..	..	9 13	9 20	..	9 26	..
Queen's Road	..	..	..	9 16	9 23	..	9 29	..
Vauxhall	..	..	..	9 19	9 26	..	9 32	..
Waterloo ....arr.	..	9 12	9 14	9 23	9 30	9 26	9 36	..

FOR NOTES, SEE PAGE 489

FOR NOTES, SEE PAGE 489

READING, WINDSOR, STAINES, TEDDINGTON, TWICKENHAM, RICHMOND, HOUNSLOW, and LONDON

Week Days—continued (a.m.)

Up	3		3	3	3	3		3	3	3	3	3		3	3	3		3	3	3		3	3	3		3	3	3	3	3	
Reading ... dep	..	8 28	..	..	..	..	8 48	..	..	..	..	..	..	..	..	..	9 28	..	..	..	..	..	..	..	..	..	..	..	..	..	1028
Earley	..	8 33	..	..	..	..	8 53	..	..	..	..	..	..	..	..	..	9 33	..	..	..	..	..	..	..	..	..	..	..	..	..	1032
Winnersh Halt Z	..	8 37	..	..	..	..	8 57	..	..	..	..	..	..	..	..	..	9 37	..	..	..	..	..	..	..	..	..	..	..	..	..	1037
Wokingham	..	8 41	..	..	..	..	9 1	..	..	..	..	..	..	..	..	..	9 41	..	..	..	..	..	..	..	..	..	..	..	..	..	1041
Bracknell	..	8 48	..	..	..	..	9 8	..	..	..	..	..	..	..	..	..	9 48	..	..	..	..	..	..	..	..	..	..	..	..	..	1048
Ascot 388 ... arr.	..	8 53	..	..	..	..	9 14	..	..	..	..	..	..	..	..	..	9 54	..	..	..	..	..	..	..	..	..	..	..	..	..	1054
Aldershot ... dep	..	8 24	..	..	..	..	8 41	..	..	..	..	..	..	..	..	..	9 24	..	..	..	..	..	..	..	..	..	..	..	..	..	1024
Ash Vale W	..	8 29	..	..	..	..	8 46	..	..	..	..	..	..	..	..	..	9 29	..	..	..	..	..	..	..	..	..	..	..	..	..	1029
Frimley T	..	8 35	..	..	..	..	8 52	..	..	..	..	..	..	..	..	..	9 35	..	..	..	..	..	..	..	..	..	..	..	..	..	1035
Camberley Q	..	8 40	..	..	..	..	9 K0	..	..	..	..	..	..	..	..	..	9 40	..	..	..	..	..	..	..	..	..	..	..	..	..	1040
Bagshot	..	8 46	..	..	..	..	9 6	..	..	..	..	..	..	..	..	..	9 46	..	..	..	..	..	..	..	..	..	..	..	..	..	1046
Ascot ... arr.	..	8 51	..	..	..	..	9 11	..	..	..	..	..	..	..	..	..	9 52	..	..	..	..	..	..	..	..	..	..	..	..	..	1051
Ascot ... dep.	..	8 55	..	..	..	..	9 16	..	..	..	..	..	..	..	..	..	9 56	..	..	..	..	..	..	..	..	..	..	..	..	..	1056
Sunningdale P	..	8 59	..	..	..	..	9 20	..	..	..	..	..	..	..	..	..	10 0	..	..	..	..	..	..	..	..	..	..	..	..	..	11 0
Longcross Halt	..	9 3	..	..	..	..	9 23	..	..	..	..	..	..	..	..	..	10 3	..	..	..	..	..	..	..	..	..	..	..	..	..	11 3
Virginia Water M 427 arr	..	9 6	..	..	..	..	9 27	..	..	..	..	..	..	..	..	..	10 7	..	..	..	..	..	..	..	..	..	..	..	..	..	11 7
Weybridge ... dep	8 35	..	..	..	9 1	..	..	..	..	..	..	9 20	..	..	..	9 35	..	..	..	..	..	..	..	10 5	..	..	..	..	..	1035	..
Addlestone	8 39	..	..	..	9 5	..	..	..	..	..	..	9 24	..	..	..	9 39	..	..	..	..	..	..	..	10 9	..	..	..	..	..	1039	..
Chertsey	8 42	..	..	..	9 8	..	..	..	..	..	..	9 27	..	..	..	9 42	..	..	..	..	..	..	..	1012	..	..	..	..	..	1042	..
Virginia Water M .. arr	8 46	..	..	..	9 12	..	..	..	..	..	..	9 31	..	..	..	9 46	..	..	..	..	..	..	..	1016	..	..	..	..	..	1046	..
Virginia Water M ... dep	8 46	9 6		..	9 12		9 27	..		..		9 31	..		..	9 46	10 7		..		..		..	1016	..		..		..	1046	11 7
Egham L	8 50	9 10		..	9 16		9 31	..		..		9 35	..		..	9 50	1011		..		..		..	1020	..		..		..	1050	1111
Staines J ... arr	8 55	9 15		..	9 21		9 36	..		..		9 40	..		..	9 55	1016		..		..		..	1025	..		..		..	1055	1116
Windsor and Eton .. dep	8 36	..	From Waterloo via Kingston	..	9 2	From Waterloo via Kingston	..	..	From Waterloo, via Kingston	..	From Waterloo via Kingston	9 21	..	From Waterloo via Kingston	..	9 36	..	From Waterloo, via Kingston	..	From Waterloo via Kingston	..	From Waterloo via Kingston	..	10 6	..	From Waterloo via Kingston	..	From Waterloo via Kingston	..	1036	..
Datchet	8 40	..		..	9 6		..	..		..		9 25	..		..	9 40	..		..		..		..	1010	..		..		..	1040	..
Sunnymeads	8 44	..		..	9 10		..	..		..		9 29	..		..	9 44	..		..		..		..	1014	..		..		..	1044	..
Wraysbury	8 47	..		..	9 13		..	..		..		9 32	..		..	9 47	..		..		..		..	1017	..		..		..	1047	..
Staines J ... arr	8 53	..		..	9 19		..	..		..		9 38	..		..	9 53	..		..		..		..	1023	..		..		..	1053	..
Staines ... dep	8 57	9 15		..	9 23		9 36	..		..		9 42	..		..	9 57	1016		..		..		..	1027	..		..		..	1057	1116
Ashford (Middlesex)	9 0	..		..	9 27		..	..		..		9 46	..		..	10 0	..		..		..		..	1031	..		..		..	11 1	..
Feltham	9 5	..		..	9 31		..	..		..		9 50	..		..	10 5	..		..		..		..	1035	..		..		..	11 5	..
Hounslow D ... dep	..	..	SX	..	..		..	9 29		..		..	..		9 59	..	..	SO	..	SO	..	SX	1030	..	..		..		11 0	..	..
Whitton	9 9	..	V	..	..	V	..	9 33	V	..	V	9 54	..	V	10 2	10 9	..	V	..	V	..	V	1034	1039	..	V	..	V	11 3	11 9	..
Teddington F ... dep	..	..	9 18	..	..	9 21	..	..	9 41	..	9 46	..	..	9 53	..	..	..	1013	..	1021	..	1021	..	..	..	1041	..	1053	..	..	..
Strawberry Hill	..	..	9 21	..	..	9 25	..	..	9 44	..	9 49	..	..	9 56	..	..	..	1016	..	1024	..	1026	..	..	..	1044	..	1057	..	..	..
Twickenham	9 12	..	9 24	9 7	..	9 28	..	9 35	9 47	9 37	..	9 57	..	9 59	10 5	1012	..	1019	10 7	1027	..	1029	1036	1042	..	1047	10 37	11 0	11 6	1112	..
St. Margaret's	..	..	9 26	..	..	9 30	..	9 37	9 49	..	..	..	..	10 1	10 7	..	..	1021	..	1029	..	1031	1038	..	..	1049	..	11 2	11 8	..	..
Richmond	9 16	..	9 29	..	..	9 33	..	9 40	9 52	..	..	10 1	..	10 4	1010	1016	..	1024	..	1032	..	1034	1041	1046	..	1052	..	11 5	11 11	1116	..
North Sheen	..	..	9 32	..	..	9 36	..	9 43	9 54	..	..	..	..	..	1012	..	..	..	..	1034	..	1036	1044	..	..	1054	..	..	11 13	..	..
Mortlake, for East Sheen	..	..	9 34	..	..	9 38	..	9 45	9 57	..	..	..	..	10 7	1015	..	..	1027	..	1037	..	1039	1046	..	..	1057	..	11 8	11 16	..	..
Whitton	..	..	..	9 9	..	..	..	..	..	9 39	..	..	..	..	..	..	..	..	10 9	..	..	..	..	..	..	..	10 39	..	..	..	..
Hounslow D	..	..	..	9 15	9 36	..	..	..	..	9 44	..	..	..	..	..	..	..	..	1014	..	..	..	..	..	..	..	10 44	..	..	..	..
Isleworth C	..	..	..	9 18	..	..	..	..	..	9 47	..	..	..	..	..	..	..	..	1017	..	..	..	..	..	..	..	10 47	..	..	..	..
Syon Lane	..	..	..	9 21	..	..	..	..	..	9 50	..	..	..	..	..	..	..	..	1020	..	..	..	..	..	..	..	10 50	..	..	..	..
Brentford B	..	..	..	9 23	..	..	..	..	..	9 52	..	..	..	..	..	..	..	..	1022	..	..	..	..	..	..	..	10 52	..	..	..	..
Kew Bridge	..	..	..	9 26	..	..	..	..	..	9 55	..	..	..	..	..	..	..	..	1025	..	..	..	..	..	..	..	10 55	..	..	..	..
Chiswick, for Grove Park	..	..	..	9 29	..	..	..	..	..	9 58	..	..	..	..	..	..	..	..	1028	..	..	..	..	..	..	..	10 58	..	..	..	..
Barnes Bridge	..	..	..	9 32	..	..	..	..	..	10 1	..	..	..	..	..	..	..	..	1031	..	..	..	..	..	..	..	11 1	..	..	..	..
Barnes	..	..	..	9 34	..	9 41	..	9 48	10 0	10 3	..	..	..	1010	1018	..	..	1030	1033	1040	..	1042	1049	..	..	11 0	11 3	1111	11 19	..	..
Putney	..	..	..	9 37	..	9 44	..	9 51	10 3	10 6	..	..	..	1013	1021	..	..	1033	1036	1043	..	1045	1052	..	..	11 3	11 6	1114	11 22	..	..
Wandsworth Town	..	..	..	9 40	..	9 47	..	..	10 6	10 9	..	..	..	1016	..	..	..	..	1039	1046	..	1048	..	..	..	11 6	..	1117	..	..	..
Clapham Junction A	..	..	..	9 42	..	9 49	..	9 55	10 8	1011	..	..	..	1018	1025	..	..	1037	1041	1048	..	1050	1056	..	..	11 8	11 11	1119	11 25	..	..
Queen's Road	..	..	..	9 45	..	9 52	..	9 58	1011	1014	..	..	..	..	1028	..	..	..	1044	..	..	..	1059	..	..	..	11 14	..	11 28	..	..
Vauxhall	..	..	..	9 48	..	9 55	..	10 1	1014	1017	..	..	..	1022	1031	..	..	1042	1047	1052	..	1054	11 2	..	..	1112	11 17	1123	11 31	..	..
Waterloo ... arr.	9 30	9 40	9 47	9 52	9 55	9 59	10 3	10 5	1018	1021	..	1015	..	1026	1035	1030	1042	1046	1051	1056	..	1058	11 6	11 1	..	1116	11 21	1127	11 35	1130	1142

READING, WINDSOR, STAINES, TEDDINGTON, TWICKENHAM, RICHMOND, HOUNSLOW, and LONDON

Up — Week Days—*continued* (a.m … p.m)

Station	3	3	3	3	3	3	3	3	3	3	3	3			3
Reading .... dep.	..	..	..	..	..	..	..	..	..	..	..	..	..	11 28	..
Earley	..	..	..	..	..	..	..	..	..	..	..	..	..	11 33	..
Winnersh Halt **Z**	..	..	..	..	..	..	..	..	..	..	..	..	..	11 37	..
Wokingham	..	..	..	..	..	..	..	..	..	..	..	..	..	11 41	..
Bracknell	..	..	..	..	..	..	..	..	..	..	..	..	..	11 48	..
Ascot 388 .... arr.	..	..	..	..	..	..	..	..	..	..	..	..	..	11 54	..
Aldershot .... dep.	..	..	..	..	..	..	..	..	..	..	..	..	..	11 24	..
Ash Vale **W**	..	..	..	..	..	..	..	..	..	..	..	..	..	11 29	..
Frimley **T**	..	..	..	..	..	..	..	..	..	..	..	..	..	11 35	..
Camberley **Q**	..	..	..	..	..	..	..	..	..	..	..	..	..	11 40	..
Bagshot	..	..	..	..	..	..	..	..	..	..	..	..	..	11 46	..
Ascot .... arr.	..	..	..	..	..	..	..	..	..	..	..	..	..	11 51	..
Ascot .... dep.	..	..	..	..	..	..	..	..	..	..	..	..	..	11 56	..
Sunningdale **P**	..	..	..	..	..	..	..	..	..	..	..	..	..	12 0	..
Longcross Halt	..	..	..	..	..	..	..	..	..	..	..	..	..	12 3	..
Virginia Water M 427 arr.	..	..	..	..	..	..	..	..	..	..	..	..	..	12 7	S O
Weybridge .... dep.	..	..	..	..	11 5	..	..	..	..	11 35	..	..	..	..	1155
Addlestone	..	..	..	..	11 9	..	..	..	..	11 39	..	..	..	..	1159
Chertsey	..	..	..	..	1112	..	..	..	..	11 42	..	..	..	..	12 5
Virginia Water **M** .. arr.	..	..	..	..	1116	..	..	..	..	11 46	..	..	..	..	1210
Virginia Water M ... dep.		..	..	..	1116	..	..	..	..	11 46	..	..	..	12 7	1210
Egham **L**		..	..	..	1120	..	..	..	..	11 50	..	..	..	12 11	1214
Staines J .... arr.		..	..	..	1125	..	..	..	..	11 55	..	S O	..	12 16	1219
Windsor and Eton .. dep.	From Waterloo via Kingston	..	From Waterloo via Kingston	..	11 6	From Waterloo via Kingston	..	From Waterloo via Kingston	..	11 36	From Waterloo via Kingston	1152	..	..	..
Datchet		..		..	1110		..		..	11 40		1156	..	..	..
Sunnymeads		..		..	1114		..		..	11 44		12 0	..	..	..
Wraysbury		..		..	1117		..		..	11 47		12 3	..	..	..
Staines J .... arr.		..		..	1123		..		..	11 53		12 9	..	..	..
Staines .... dep.		..		..	1127		..		..	11 57		1210	..	12 16	1219
Ashford (Middlesex)		..		..	1131		..		..	12 1		1214	..	..	1222
Feltham		..		..	1135		..		noon	12 5	p.m	1218	..	..	1227
Hounslow D .... dep.	S X	..		1130	..		..		12 0	..	S O	..	..	..	..
Whitton	**V**	..	**V**	1133	1139	**V**	..	**V**	12 3	12 9	**V**	1222	..	..	1231
Teddington F .... dep.	1113	..	1121	..	..	1141	..	11 53	..	..	1213	..	..	..	..
Strawberry Hill	1116	..	1124	..	..	1144	..	11 57	..	..	1216	..	..	..	..
Twickenham	..	11 7	1127	1136	1142	1147	11 37	12 0	12 6	12 12	1219	1225	..	..	1234
St. Margaret's	..	..	1129	1138	..	1149	..	12 2	12 8	..	1221	..	..	..	..
Richmond	..	..	1132	1141	1146	1152	..	12 5	12 11	12 16	1224	1229	..	..	1238
North Sheen	..	..	1134	1143	..	1154	..	..	12 13	..	..	..	..	..	..
Mortlake, for East Sheen	..	..	1137	1146	..	1157	..	12 8	12 16	..	1227	..	..	..	..
Whitton	..	11 9	..	..	..	..	11 39	..	..	..	..	..	..	..	..
Hounslow D	..	1114	..	..	..	..	11 44	..	..	..	..	..	..	..	..
Isleworth **C**	..	1117	..	..	..	..	11 47	..	..	..	..	..	..	..	..
Syon Lane	..	1120	..	..	..	..	11 50	..	..	..	..	..	..	..	..
Brentford **B**	..	1122	..	..	..	..	11 52	..	..	..	..	..	..	..	..
Kew Bridge	..	1125	..	..	..	..	11 55	..	..	..	..	..	..	..	..
Chiswick, for Grove Park	..	1128	..	..	..	..	11 58	..	..	..	..	..	..	..	..
Barnes Bridge	..	1131	..	..	..	..	12 1	..	..	..	..	..	..	..	..
Barnes	..	1133	1140	1149	..	12 0	12 3	12 11	12 19	..	1230	..	..	..	..
Putney	..	1136	1143	1152	..	12 3	12 6	12 14	12 22	..	1233	..	..	..	..
Wandsworth Town	..	..	1146	..	..	12 6	..	12 17	..	..	1236	..	..	..	..
Clapham Junction A	..	1140	1148	1156	..	12 8	12 10	12 19	12 26	..	1238	..	..	..	..
Queen's Road	..	1143	..	1159	..	..	12 13	..	12 29	..	..	..	..	..	..
Vauxhall	..	1146	1152	12 2	..	1212	12 16	12 23	12 32	..	1243	..	..	..	..
Waterloo .... arr.	..	1150	1156	12 6	12 0	1216	12 20	12 27	12 36	12 30	1247	1243	..	12 42	1253

Station	3	3	3	3	3		3	3	3	3	3		3	3
Reading .... dep.	..	..	..	..	..	..	..	..	..	..	..	..	..	..
Earley	..	..	..	..	..	..	..	..	..	..	..	..	..	..
Winnersh Halt **Z**	..	..	..	..	..	..	..	..	..	..	..	..	..	..
Wokingham	..	..	..	..	..	..	..	..	..	..	..	..	..	..
Bracknell	..	..	..	..	..	..	..	..	..	..	..	..	..	..
Ascot 388 .... arr.	..	..	..	..	..	..	..	..	..	..	..	..	..	..
Aldershot .... dep.	..	..	..	..	..	..	..	..	..	..	..	..	..	..
Ash Vale **W**	..	..	..	..	..	..	..	..	..	..	..	..	..	..
Frimley **T**	..	..	..	..	..	..	..	..	..	..	..	..	..	..
Camberley **Q**	..	..	..	..	..	..	..	..	..	..	..	..	..	..
Bagshot	..	..	..	..	..	..	..	..	..	..	..	..	..	..
Ascot .... arr.	..	..	..	..	..	..	..	..	..	..	..	..	..	..
Ascot .... dep.	..	..	..	..	..	..	..	..	..	..	..	..	..	..
Sunningdale **P**	..	..	..	..	..	..	..	..	..	..	..	..	..	..
Longcross Halt	..	..	..	..	..	..	..	..	..	..	..	..	..	..
Virginia Water M 427 arr.	..	..	..	S X	..	..	..	S O	..	..	S X	..	..	S O
Weybridge .... dep.	..	..	..	12 5	..	..	..	1215	..	..	12 35	..	..	12 45
Addlestone	..	..	..	12 9	..	..	..	1219	..	..	12 39	..	..	12 49
Chertsey	..	..	..	1212	..	..	..	1222	..	..	12 42	..	..	12 52
Virginia Water **M** .. arr.	..	..	..	1216	..	..	..	1226	..	..	12 46	..	..	12 56
Virginia Water M ... dep.	..	..	..	1216	..	..	..	1226	..	..	12 46	..	..	12 56
Egham **L**	..	..	..	1220	..	..	..	1230	..	..	12 50	..	..	1 0
Staines J .... arr.	..	..	..	1225	..	..	..	1235	..	..	12 55	..	..	1 5
Windsor and Eton .. dep.	..	From Waterloo via Kingston	..	12 6	From Waterloo via Kingston	..	..	1216	From Waterloo via Kingston	..	12 36	..	..	12 46
Datchet	..		..	1210		..	..	1220		..	12 40	..	..	12 50
Sunnymeads	..		..	1214		..	..	1224		..	12 44	..	..	12 54
Wraysbury	..		..	1217		..	..	1227		..	12 47	..	..	12 57
Staines J .... arr.	..		..	1223		..	..	1233		..	12 53	..	..	1 3
Staines .... dep.	..		..	1227		..	..	1237		..	12 57	..	..	1 7
Ashford (Middlesex)	..		..	1231		..	..	1241		..	1 1	..	..	1 11
Feltham	..		..	1235		..	..	1245		..	1 5	..	..	1 15
Hounslow D .... dep.	..		1229	..		..	..	..		1 0	..	..	..	..
Whitton	..	**V**	1232	1239	**V**	..	..	1249	**V**	1 3	1 9	..	..	1 19
Teddington F .... dep.	..	1221	..	..	1241	..	..	..	12 53	..	..	..	..	..
Strawberry Hill	..	1224	..	..	1244	..	..	..	12 57	..	..	..	..	..
Twickenham	12 7	1227	1235	1242	1247	..	12 37	1252	1 0	1 6	1 12	..	1 7	1 23
St. Margaret's	..	1229	1237	..	1249	..	..	..	1 2	1 8	..	..	..	..
Richmond	..	1232	1240	1246	1252	..	..	1256	1 5	1 11	1 16	..	..	1 28
North Sheen	..	1234	1242	..	1254	..	..	..	..	1 13	..	..	..	..
Mortlake, for East Sheen	..	1237	1245	.	1257	..	..	..	1 8	1 16	..	..	..	..
Whitton	12 9	..	..	..	..	..	12 39	..	..	..	..	..	1 9	..
Hounslow D	12 14	..	..	..	..	..	12 44	..	..	..	..	..	1 14	..
Isleworth **C**	12 17	..	..	..	..	..	12 47	..	..	..	..	..	1 17	..
Syon Lane	12 20	..	..	..	..	..	12 50	..	..	..	..	..	1 20	..
Brentford **B**	12 22	..	..	..	..	..	12 52	..	..	..	..	..	1 22	..
Kew Bridge	12 25	..	..	..	..	..	12 55	..	..	..	..	..	1 25	..
Chiswick, for Grove Park	12 28	..	..	..	..	..	12 58	..	..	..	..	..	1 28	..
Barnes Bridge	12 31	..	..	..	..	..	1 1	..	..	..	..	..	1 31	..
Barnes	12 33	1240	1248	..	1 0	..	1 3	..	1 11	1 19	..	..	1 33	..
Putney	12 36	1243	1251	..	1 3	..	1 6	..	1 14	1 22	..	..	1 36	..
Wandsworth Town	12 SO 39	1246	..	..	1 6	..	..	..	1 17	..	..	..	..	..
Clapham Junction A	12 41	1248	1255	..	1 8	..	1 11	..	1 20	1 26	..	..	1 40	..
Queen's Road	12 44	..	1258	..	..	..	1 14	..	..	1 29	..	..	1 43	..
Vauxhall	12 47	1252	1 1	..	1 12	..	1 17	..	1 23	1 32	..	..	1 46	..
Waterloo .... arr.	12 51	1256	1 5	1 0	1 16	..	1 21	1 12	1 27	1 36	1 30	..	1 50	1 42

FOR NOTES, SEE PAGE 489

FOR NOTES, SEE PAGE 489

READING, WINDSOR, STAINES, TEDDINGTON, TWICKENHAM, RICHMOND, HOUNSLOW, and LONDON

Up — Week Days—*continued* — p.m.

Up		3 From Waterloo via Kingston	3	3	SO	3 From Waterloo via Kingston	3	3	3 From Waterloo via Kingston	3	3		3	3		3 From Waterloo via Kingston	3	3		SO	From Waterloo, page 389	3 From Waterloo via Kingston	3	3 From Waterloo via Kingston		3	3	3		3	3 From Waterloo via Kingston
Reading ....dep.	1228	..	..	..	1258	..	..	..	..	..	..	..	..	..	1 28	..	..	..	..	1 58		..	..	..	..	..	..	..	2 28	..	..
Earley	1233	..	..	..	1 3	..	..	..	..	..	..	..	..	..	1 33	..	..	..	..	2 3		..	..	..	..	..	..	..	2 33	..	..
Winnersh Halt **Z**	1237	..	..	..	1 7	..	..	..	..	..	..	..	..	..	1 37	..	..	..	..	2 7		..	..	..	..	..	..	..	2 37	..	..
Wokingham	1241	..	..	..	1 11	..	..	..	..	..	..	..	..	..	1 41	..	..	..	..	2 11		..	..	..	..	..	..	..	2 41	..	..
Bracknell	1248	..	..	..	1 18	..	..	..	..	..	..	..	..	..	1 48	..	..	..	..	2 18		..	..	..	..	..	..	..	2 48	..	..
Ascot 388 ....arr.	1254	..	..	..	1 24	..	..	..	..	..	..	..	..	..	1 54	..	..	..	..	2 24		..	..	..	..	..	..	..	2 54	..	..
Aldershot ....dep.	1224	..	..	..	1252	..	..	..	..	..	..	..	..	..	1 24	..	..	..	..	1 54		..	..	..	..	..	..	..	2 24	..	..
Ash Vale W	1229	..	..	..	1257	..	..	..	..	..	..	..	..	..	1 29	..	..	..	..	1 59	SO	..	..	..	..	..	..	..	2 29	..	..
Frimley T	1235	..	..	..	1 3	..	..	..	..	..	..	..	..	..	1 35	..	..	..	..	2 5	2 31	..	..	..	..	..	..	..	2 35	..	..
Camberley Q	1240	..	..	..	1 10	..	..	..	..	..	..	..	..	..	1 40	..	..	..	..	2 10	2 35	..	..	..	..	..	..	..	2 40	..	..
Bagshot	1246	..	..	..	1 16	..	..	..	..	..	..	..	..	..	1 46	..	..	..	..	2 16	..	..	..	..	..	..	..	..	2 46	..	..
Ascot ....arr.	1251	..	..	..	1 21	..	..	..	..	..	..	..	..	..	1 51	..	..	..	..	2 21	2 45	..	..	..	..	..	..	..	2 51	..	..
Ascot ....dep.	1256	..	..	..	1 26	..	..	..	..	..	..	..	..	..	1 56	..	..	..	..	2 26	..	..	..	..	..	..	..	..	2 56	..	..
Sunningdale **P**	1 0	..	..	..	1 30	..	..	..	..	..	..	..	..	..	2 0	..	..	..	..	2 30	..	..	..	..	..	..	..	..	3 0	..	..
Longcross Halt	1 3	..	..	..	1 33	..	..	..	..	..	..	..	..	..	2 3	..	..	..	..	2 33	..	..	..	..	..	..	..	..	3 3	..	..
Virginia Water M 427 arr.	1 7	..	..	..	1 37	..	..	SO	..	..	SX	..	..	SO	2 7	..	..	..	..	2 37	..	..	..	..	..	..	..	SO	3 7	..	..
Weybridge ....dep.	..	..	..	1 5	..	..	..	1 25	..	..	1 35	..	..	1 45	..	..	..	2 5	..	..	..	..	..	..	..	..	2 35	2 50	..	..	..
Addlestone	..	..	..	1 9	..	..	..	1 29	..	..	1 39	..	..	1 49	..	..	..	2 9	..	..	..	..	..	..	..	..	2 39	2 54	..	..	..
Chertsey	..	..	..	1 12	..	..	..	1 35	..	..	1 42	..	..	1 52	..	..	..	2 12	..	..	..	..	..	..	..	..	2 42	2 57	..	..	..
Virginia Water M ..arr.	..	..	..	1 16	..	..	..	1 40	..	..	1 46	..	..	1 56	..	..	..	2 16	..	..	..	..	..	..	..	..	2 46	..	..	..	..
Virginia Water M ....dep.	1 7		..	1 16	1 37		..	1 40		..	1 46	..	..	1 56	2 7		..	2 16	..	2 37	..		..		..	..	2 46	..	3 7	..	
Egham **L**	1 11		..	1 20	1 41		..	1 44		..	1 50	..	..	2 0	2 11		..	2 20	..	2 41	..		..		..	..	2 50	..	3 11	..	
Staines J ....arr.	1 16		..	1 25	1 46		..	1 49		..	1 55	..	..	2 5	2 16		..	2 25	..	2 46	..		..		..	..	2 55	..	3 16	..	
Windsor and Eton ..dep.	..		..	1 6	..		..	1 31		..	1 36	..	..	1 46	..		..	2 6	..	..	..		..		..	..	2 36	..	..	..	
Datchet	..		..	1 10	..		..	1 35		..	1 40	..	..	1 50	..		..	2 10	..	..	..		..		..	..	2 40	..	..	..	
Sunnymeads	..		..	1 14	..		..	1 39		..	1 44	..	..	1 54	..		..	2 14	..	..	..		..		..	..	2 44	..	..	..	
Wraysbury	..		..	1 17	..		..	1 42		..	1 47	..	..	1 57	..		..	2 17	..	..	..		..		..	..	2 47	..	..	..	
Staines J ....arr.	..		..	1 23	..		..	1 48		..	1 53	..	..	2 3	..		..	2 23	..	..	..		..		..	..	2 53	..	..	..	
Staines ....dep.	1 16		..	1 27	1 46		..	1 51		..	1 57	..	..	2 7	2 16		..	2 27	..	2 46	..		..		..	..	2 57	..	3 16	..	
Ashford (Middlesex)	..		..	1 31	..		..	1 55		..	2 1	..	..	2 11	..		..	2 31	..	..	..		..		..	..	3 1	..	..	..	
Feltham	..		..	1 35	..		..	1 59		..	2 5	..	..	2 15	..		..	2 35	..	..	..		..		..	..	3 5	..	..	..	
Hounslow D ....dep.	..		1 29	..	..		..	..		2 0	..	..	..	..	..		2 30	..	..	..	..		..		..	3 0	..	..	..	..	
Whitton	..	V	1 32	1 39	..	V	..	..	V	2 3	2 9	..	..	2 19	..	V	2 33	2 39	..	..	..	V	..	V	..	3 3	3 9	..	..	..	V
Teddington F ....dep.	..	1 20	..	..	..	1 40	..	..	1 53	..	..	..	..	..	..	2 21	..	..	..	..	..	2 41	..	2 53	..	..	..	..	..	..	3 21
Strawberry Hill	..	1 24	..	..	..	1 44	..	..	1 57	..	..	..	..	..	..	2 24	..	..	..	..	..	2 44	..	2 57	..	..	..	..	..	..	3 26
Twickenham	..	1 27	1 35	1 42	..	1 47	1 37	..	2 0	2 6	2 12	..	2 7	2 22	..	2 27	2 36	2 42	..	..	..	2 47	2 37	3 0	..	3 6	3 12	..	..	3 7	3 29
St. Margaret's	..	1 29	1 37	..	..	1 49	..	..	2 2	2 8	..	..	..	..	..	2 29	2 38	..	..	..	..	2 49	..	3 2	..	3 8	..	..	..	..	3 31
Richmond	..	1 32	1 40	1 46	..	1 52	..	..	2 5	2 11	2 16	..	..	2 26	..	2 32	2 41	2 46	..	..	..	2 52	..	3 5	..	3 11	3 16	..	..	..	3 34
North Sheen	..	1 35	1 42	..	..	1 54	..	..	..	2 13	..	..	..	..	..	2 34	2 43	..	..	..	..	2 54	..	..	..	3 13	..	..	..	..	3 36
Mortlake, for East Sheen	..	1 37	1 45	..	..	1 57	..	..	2 8	2 16	..	..	..	..	..	2 37	2 46	..	..	..	..	2 57	..	3 8	..	3 16	..	..	..	..	3 39
Whitton	..	..	..	..	..	..	1 39	..	..	..	..	..	2 9	..	..	..	..	..	..	..	..	..	2 39	..	..	..	..	..	..	3 9	..
Hounslow D	..	..	..	..	..	..	1 44	2 4	..	..	..	..	2 14	..	..	..	..	..	..	..	..	..	2 44	..	..	..	..	..	..	3 14	..
Isleworth **C**	..	..	..	..	..	..	1 47	..	..	..	..	..	2 17	..	..	..	..	..	..	..	..	..	2 47	..	..	..	..	..	..	3 17	..
Syon Lane	..	..	..	..	..	..	1 50	..	..	..	..	..	2 20	..	..	..	..	..	..	..	..	..	2 50	..	..	..	..	..	..	3 20	..
Brentford **B**	..	..	..	..	..	..	1 52	..	..	..	..	..	2 22	..	..	..	..	..	..	..	..	..	2 52	..	..	..	..	..	..	3 22	..
Kew Bridge	..	..	..	..	..	..	1 55	..	..	..	..	..	2 25	..	..	..	..	..	..	..	..	..	2 55	..	..	..	..	..	..	3 25	..
Chiswick, for Grove Park	..	..	..	..	..	..	1 58	..	..	..	..	..	2 28	..	..	..	..	..	..	..	..	..	2 58	..	..	..	..	..	..	3 28	..
Barnes Bridge	..	..	..	..	..	..	2 1	..	..	..	..	..	2 31	..	..	..	..	..	..	..	..	..	3 1	..	..	..	..	..	..	3 31	..
Barnes	..	1 40	1 48	..	..	2 0	2 3	..	2 11	2 19	..	..	2 33	..	..	2 40	2 49	..	..	..	..	3 0	3 3	3 11	..	3 19	..	..	..	3 33	3 42
Putney	..	1 43	1 51	..	..	2 3	2 6	..	2 14	2 22	..	..	2 36	..	..	2 43	2 52	..	..	..	..	3 3	3 6	3 14	..	3 22	..	..	..	3 36	3 45
Wandsworth Town	..	1 46	..	..	..	2 6	..	..	2 17	..	..	..	..	..	..	2 46	..	..	..	..	..	3 6	..	3 17	..	..	..	..	..	..	3 48
Clapham Junction A	..	1 48	1 55	..	..	2 8	2 10	..	2 19	2 26	..	..	2 40	..	..	2 48	2 56	..	..	..	..	3 8	3 11	3 19	..	3 26	..	..	..	3 40	3 50
Queen's Road	..	..	1 58	..	..	..	2 13	..	..	2 29	..	..	2 43	..	..	..	2 59	..	..	..	..	..	3 14	..	..	3 29	..	..	..	3 43	..
Vauxhall	..	1 53	2 1	..	..	2 12	2 16	..	2 23	2 32	..	..	2 46	..	..	2 52	3 2	..	..	..	..	3 12	3 17	3 23	..	3 32	..	..	..	3 46	3 54
Waterloo ....arr.	1 42	1 57	2 5	2 0	2 12	2 16	2 20	2 24	2 27	2 36	2 30	..	2 50	2 40	2 43	2 56	3 6	3 0	..	3 12	..	3 16	3 21	3 27	..	3 36	3 30	..	3 42	3 50	3 58

READING, WINDSOR, STAINES, TEDDINGTON, TWICKENHAM, RICHMOND, HOUNSLOW, and LONDON

Week Days—*continued* (p.m.)

Station	3	3	3	SO	3	3	3	3		3 SX	3	3	3	3	
Reading dep	..	..	..	2 58	..	..	..	..	3 28	..	..	..	..	..	..
Earley	..	..	..	3 3	..	..	..	..	3 33	..	..	..	..	..	..
Winnersh Halt **Z**	..	..	..	3 7	..	..	..	..	3 37	..	..	..	..	..	..
Wokingham	..	..	..	3 11	..	..	..	..	3 41	..	..	..	..	..	..
Bracknell	..	..	..	3 18	..	..	..	..	3 48	..	..	..	..	..	..
Ascot 388 arr.	..	..	..	3 24	..	..	..	..	3 54	..	..	..	..	..	..
Aldershot dep.	..	..	..	2 54	..	..	..	..	3 24	..	..	..	..	..	..
Ash Vale **W**	..	..	..	2 59	..	..	..	..	3 29	..	..	..	..	..	..
Frimley **T**	..	..	..	3 5	..	..	..	..	3 35	..	..	..	..	..	..
Camberley **Q**	..	..	..	3 10	..	..	..	..	3 40	..	..	..	..	..	..
Bagshot	..	..	..	3 16	..	..	..	..	3 46	..	..	..	..	..	..
Ascot arr.	..	..	..	3 21	..	..	..	..	3 51	..	..	..	..	..	..
Ascot dep.	..	..	..	3 26	..	..	..	..	3 56	..	..	..	..	..	..
Sunningdale **P**	..	..	..	3 30	..	..	..	..	4 0	..	..	..	..	..	..
Longcross Halt	..	..	..	3 33	..	..	..	..	4 3	..	..	..	..	..	..
Virginia Water M 427 arr.	..	..	..	3 37	..	..	..	..	4 7	..	..	..	..	..	..
Weybridge dep.	..	3 5	..	..	..	..	..	3 35	..	..	..	..	..	4 5	..
Addlestone	..	3 9	..	..	..	..	..	3 39	..	..	..	..	..	4 9	..
Chertsey	..	3 12	..	..	..	..	..	3 42	..	..	..	..	..	4 12	..
Virginia Water M arr.	..	3 16	..	..	..	..	..	3 46	..	..	..	..	..	4 16	..
Virginia Water M dep.	..	3 16	..	3 37	..	..	..	3 46	4 7	..	..	..	..	4 16	..
Egham **L**	..	3 20	..	3 41	..	..	..	3 50	4 11	..	..	..	..	4 20	..
Staines J arr.	..	3 25	..	3 46	..	..	..	3 55	4 16	..	..	..	..	4 25	..
Windsor and Eton dep.	..	3 6	From Waterloo via Kingston	..	..	From Waterloo via Kingston	..	3 36	..	From Waterloo via Kingston	..	From Waterloo via Kingston	..	4 6	..
Datchet	..	3 10		..	..		..	3 40	..		..		..	4 10	..
Sunnymeads	..	3 14		..	..		..	3 44	..		..		..	4 14	..
Wraysbury	..	3 17		..	..		..	3 47	..		..		..	4 17	..
Staines J arr.	..	3 23		..	..		..	3 53	..		..		..	4 23	..
Staines dep	..	3 27		3 46	..		..	3 57	4 16		..		..	4 27	..
Ashford (Middlesex)	..	3 31		..	..		..	4 1	..		..		..	4 31	..
Feltham	..	3 35		..	..		..	4 5	..		..		..	4 35	..
Hounslow D dep.	3 30	..		..	..		4 0	..	..		..		4 30	..	..
Whitton	3 33	3 39	V	..	..	V	4 3	4 9	..	V	..	V	4 33	4 39	..
Teddington F dep.	..	..	3 41	..	..	3 53	..	..	..	4 13	..	4 21	..	..	..
Strawberry Hill	..	..	3 44	..	..	3 58	..	..	..	4 16	..	4 26	..	..	..
Twickenham	3 36	3 42	3 47	..	3 37	4 1	4 6	4 12	..	4 19	4 7	4 29	4 36	4 42	..
St. Margaret's	3 38	..	3 49	..	..	4 3	4 8	..	..	4 21	..	4 31	4 38	..	..
Richmond	3 41	3 46	3 52	..	..	4 6	4 11	4 16	..	4 24	..	4 34	4 41	4 46	..
North Sheen	3 43	..	3 54	..	..	..	4 13	..	..	..	..	4 37	4 43	..	..
Mortlake, for East Sheen	3 46	..	3 57	..	..	4 9	4 16	..	..	4 27	..	4 39	4 46	..	..
Whitton	..	..	..	..	3 39	..	..	..	..	..	4 9	..	..	..	..
Hounslow D	..	..	..	..	3 44	..	..	..	..	..	4 15	..	..	..	..
Isleworth **C**	..	..	..	..	3 47	..	..	..	..	..	4 18	..	..	..	..
Syon Lane	..	..	..	..	3 50	..	..	..	..	..	4 21	..	..	..	..
Brentford **B**	..	..	..	..	3 52	..	..	..	..	..	4 23	..	..	..	..
Kew Bridge	..	..	..	..	3 55	..	..	..	..	..	4 26	..	..	..	..
Chiswick, for Grove Park	..	..	..	..	3 58	..	..	..	..	..	4 29	..	..	..	..
Barnes Bridge	..	..	..	..	4 1	..	..	..	..	..	4 32	..	..	..	..
Barnes	3 49	..	4 0	..	4 3	4 12	4 19	..	..	4 30	4 34	4 42	4 49	..	..
Putney	3 52	..	4 3	..	4 6	4 15	4 22	..	..	4 33	4 37	4 45	4 52	..	..
Wandsworth Town	..	..	4 6	..	..	4 18	..	..	..	..	4 40	4 48	..	..	..
Clapham Junction A	3 56	..	4 8	..	4 11	4 20	4 26	..	..	4 38	4 42	4 30	4 56	..	..
Queen's Road	3 59	..	..	..	4 14	..	4 29	..	..	..	4 45	..	4 59	..	..
Vauxhall	4 2	..	4 12	..	4 17	4 24	4 32	..	..	4 43	4 48	4 55	5 2	..	..
Waterloo arr.	4 6	4 0	4 16	4 12	4 21	4 28	4 36	4 31	4 42	4 47	4 52	4 59	5 6	5 0	..

Station	SO	3	3	3	3		3	3 SX	3	3 SX		3 SX	3		3 SO	3
Reading dep	3 58	..	..	..	..	..	..	..	..	..	4 28	..	..	..	..	..
Earley	4 3	..	..	..	..	..	..	..	..	..	4 33	..	..	..	..	..
Winnersh Halt **Z**	4 7	..	..	..	..	..	..	..	..	..	4 37	..	..	..	..	..
Wokingham	4 11	..	..	..	..	..	..	..	..	..	4 41	..	..	..	..	..
Bracknell	4 18	..	..	..	..	..	..	..	..	..	4 48	..	..	..	..	..
Ascot 388 arr.	4 24	..	..	..	..	..	..	..	..	..	4 54	..	..	..	..	..
Aldershot dep.	..	..	..	..	..	..	..	..	..	..	4 24	..	..	..	..	..
Ash Vale **W**	..	..	..	..	..	..	..	..	..	..	4 29	..	..	..	..	..
Frimley **T**	..	..	..	..	..	..	..	..	..	..	4 35	..	..	..	..	..
Camberley **Q**	..	..	..	..	..	..	..	..	..	..	4 40	..	..	..	..	..
Bagshot	..	..	..	..	..	..	..	..	..	..	4 46	..	..	..	..	..
Ascot arr.	..	..	..	..	..	..	..	..	..	..	4 51	..	..	..	..	..
Ascot dep.	..	..	..	..	..	..	..	..	..	..	4 56	..	..	..	..	..
Sunningdale **P**	..	..	..	..	..	..	..	..	..	..	5 0	..	..	..	..	..
Longcross Halt	..	..	..	..	..	..	..	..	..	..	5 3	..	..	..	..	..
Virginia Water M 427 arr.	..	..	..	..	..	..	..	..	..	..	5 7	..	..	..	..	..
Weybridge dep.	..	..	..	..	..	..	4 32	..	..	..	..	4 55	..	..	5 5	..
Addlestone	..	..	..	..	..	..	4 36	..	..	..	..	4 59	..	..	5 9	..
Chertsey	..	..	..	..	..	..	4 41	..	..	..	..	5 5	..	..	5 12	..
Virginia Water M arr.	..	..	..	..	..	..	4 46	..	..	..	..	5 10	..	..	5 16	..
Virginia Water M dep.	..	..	..	..	..	..	4 46	..	..	..	5 7	5 10	..	..	5 16	..
Egham **L**	..	..	..	..	..	..	4 50	..	..	..	5 11	5 14	..	..	5 20	..
Staines J arr.	..	..	..	..	..	..	4 55	..	..	..	5 16	5 19	..	..	5 25	..
Windsor and Eton dep.	..	From Waterloo via Kingston	..	From Waterloo via Kingston	..	..	4 36	From Waterloo via Kingston	..	4 50	..	..	From Waterloo via Kingston	..	5 6	..
Datchet	..		..		..	..	4 40		..	4 54	..	..		..	5 10	..
Sunnymeads	..		..		..	..	4 44		..	4 58	..	..		..	5 14	..
Wraysbury	..		..		..	..	4 47		..	5 1	..	..		..	5 17	..
Staines J arr.	..		..		..	..	4 53		..	5 7	..	..		..	5 23	..
Staines dep	..		..		..	..	4 57		..	5 8	5 16	5 19		..	5 27	..
Ashford (Middlesex)	..		..		..	..	5 1		..	5 12	..	5 22		..	5 31	..
Feltham	..		..		..	..	5 5		..	5 16	..	5 27		..	5 35	..
Hounslow D dep.	..		..		5 0	..	..		..	..	..	..		..	..	5 30
Whitton	..	V	..	V	5 3	..	5 9	V	..	..	..	5 31	V	..	5 39	5 33
Teddington F dep.	..	4 41	..	4 53	..	..	..	5 13	..	..	..	..	5 21	..	..	..
Strawberry Hill	..	4 44	..	4 56	..	..	..	5 16	..	..	..	..	5 24	..	..	..
Twickenham	..	4 47	4 37	4 59	5 6	..	5 12	5 19	5 7	..	..	5 33	5 27	..	5 42	5 36
St. Margaret's	..	4 49	..	5 1	5 8	..	..	5 21	..	..	..	..	5 29	..	..	5 38
Richmond	..	4 52	..	5 4	5 11	..	5 16	5 24	..	..	..	5 37	5 32	..	5 46	5 41
North Sheen	..	4 54	..	..	5 13	..	..	..	..	..	..	..	5 34	..	..	5 43
Mortlake, for East Sheen	..	4 57	..	5 7	5 16	..	..	5 27	..	..	..	..	5 37	..	..	5 46
Whitton	..	..	4 39	..	..	..	..	..	5 9	..	..	..	..	..	..	..
Hounslow D	..	..	4 45	..	..	..	..	..	5 15	5 28	..	..	..	..	..	..
Isleworth **C**	..	..	4 48	..	..	..	..	..	5 18	..	..	..	..	..	..	..
Syon Lane	..	..	4 51	..	..	..	..	..	5 21	..	..	..	..	..	..	..
Brentford **B**	..	..	4 53	..	..	..	..	..	5 23	..	..	..	..	..	..	..
Kew Bridge	..	..	4 56	..	..	..	..	..	5 26	..	..	..	..	..	..	..
Chiswick, for Grove Park	..	..	4 59	..	..	..	..	..	5 29	..	..	..	..	..	..	..
Barnes Bridge	..	..	5 2	..	..	..	..	..	5 32	..	..	..	..	..	..	..
Barnes	..	5 0	5 4	5 10	5 19	..	..	5 30	5 34	..	..	..	5 40	..	..	5 49
Putney	..	5 3	5 7	5 13	5 22	..	..	5 33	5 37	..	..	..	5 43	..	..	5 52
Wandsworth Town	..	5 6	5 10	5 16	..	..	..	5 36	5 40	..	..	..	5 46	..	..	..
Clapham Junction A	..	5 8	5 12	5 18	5 26	..	..	5 38	5 42	..	..	..	5 48	..	..	5 56
Queen's Road	..	..	5 15	..	5 29	..	..	..	5 45	..	..	..	..	..	..	5 59
Vauxhall	..	..	5 18	5 22	5 32	..	..	5 43	5 48	..	..	..	5 52	..	..	6 2
Waterloo arr.	..	5 15	5 22	5 26	5 36	..	5 30	5 47	5 52	5 48	5 42	5 53	5 56	..	6 0	6 6

FOR NOTES. SEE PAGE 489

FOR NOTES, SEE PAGE 489

READING, WINDSOR, STAINES, TEDDINGTON, TWICKENHAM, RICHMOND, HOUNSLOW, and LONDON

Up — Week Days—continued — p.m.

Up	3	3	3	3		3	3	3		3	3	3		3	3	3
		From Waterloo via Kingston			SX	From Waterloo via Kingston					From Waterloo via Kingston				From Waterloo via Kingston	
Reading dep.	..	..	..	..	4 58	..	..	..	..	..	..	..	5 28	..	..	..
Earley	..	..	..	..	5 3	..	..	..	..	..	..	..	5 33	..	..	..
Winnersh Halt Z	..	..	..	..	5 7	..	..	..	..	..	..	..	5 37	..	..	..
Wokingham	..	..	..	..	5 11	..	..	..	..	..	..	..	5 41	..	..	..
Bracknell	..	..	..	..	5 18	..	..	..	..	..	..	..	5 48	..	..	..
Ascot 388 arr.	..	..	..	..	5 24	..	..	..	..	..	..	..	5 54	..	..	..
Aldershot dep.	..	..	..	..	4 54	..	..	..	..	..	..	..	5 24	..	..	..
Ash Vale W	..	..	..	..	4 59	..	..	..	..	..	..	..	5 29	..	..	..
Frimley T	..	..	..	..	5 5	..	..	..	..	..	..	..	5 35	..	..	..
Camberley Q	..	..	..	..	5 10	..	..	..	..	..	..	..	5 40	..	..	..
Bagshot	..	..	..	..	5 16	..	..	..	..	..	..	..	5 46	..	..	..
Ascot arr.	..	..	..	..	5 21	..	..	..	..	..	..	..	5 51	..	..	..
Ascot dep.	..	..	..	..	5 26	..	..	..	..	..	..	..	5 56	..	..	..
Sunningdale P	..	..	..	..	5 30	..	..	..	..	..	..	..	6 0	..	..	..
Longcross Halt	..	..	..	..	5 33	..	..	..	..	..	..	..	6 3	..	..	..
Virginia Water M 427 arr.	..	..	..	SX	5 37	..	..	SO	..	SX	..	SX	6 7	..	..	..
Weybridge dep.	..	..	..	5 15	..	..	..	5 35	..	5 37	..	5 45	..	..	..	..
Addlestone	..	..	..	5 19	..	..	..	5 39	..	5 41	..	5 49	..	..	..	..
Chertsey	..	..	..	5 22	..	..	..	5 42	..	5 44	..	5 52	..	..	..	..
Virginia Water M arr.	..	..	..	5 26	..	..	..	5 46	..	..	..	5 56	..	..	..	..
Virginia Water M dep.	..	..	..	5 26	5 37	..	..	5 46	..	..	..	5 56	6 7	..	..	..
Egham L	..	..	..	5 30	5 41	..	..	5 50	..	..	..	6 0	6 11	..	..	..
Staines J arr.	..	..	..	5 35	5 46	..	..	5 55	..	5 56	..	6 5	6 16	..	..	..
Windsor and Eton dep.	..	..	..	5 16	..	..	..	5 36	..	..	..	5 46	..	..	..	..
Datchet	..	..	..	5 20	..	..	..	5 40	..	..	..	5 50	..	..	..	..
Sunnymeads	..	..	..	5 24	..	..	..	5 44	..	..	..	5 54	..	..	..	..
Wraysbury	..	..	..	5 27	..	..	..	5 47	..	..	..	5 57	..	..	..	..
Staines J arr.	..	..	..	5 33	..	..	..	5 53	..	..	..	6 3	..	..	..	..
Staines dep.	..	..	..	5 37	5 47	..	..	5 57	..	5 56	..	6 7	6 16	..	..	..
Ashford (Middlesex)	..	..	..	5 41	..	..	..	6 1	..	6 0	..	6 11	..	..	..	..
Feltham	..	..	..	5 45	..	..	..	6 5	..	6 4	..	6 15	..	..	..	..
Hounslow D dep.	..	..	..	..	..	..	6 0	..	..	..	SX	..	..	..	..	6 29
Whitton	..	V	..	5 49	..	V	6 3	6 9	..	..	V	6 19	..	..	V	6 33
Teddington F dep.	..	5 41	..	..	..	5 53	..	..	..	..	6 13	..	..	..	6 21	..
Strawberry Hill	..	5 44	..	..	..	5 57	..	..	..	..	6 16	..	..	..	6 24	..
Twickenham	..	5 47	5 37	5 52	..	6 0	6 6	6 12	..	..	6 19	6 23	..	6 6	6 27	6 36
St. Margaret's	..	5 49	..	..	..	6 2	6 8	..	..	..	6 21	..	..	..	6 29	6 38
Richmond	..	5 52	..	5 57	..	6 5	6 11	6 16	..	..	6 24	6 27	..	..	6 32	6 41
North Sheen	..	5 54	..	..	..	..	6 13	..	..	..	..	..	..	..	6 34	6 43
Mortlake, for East Sheen	..	5 57	..	..	..	6 8	6 16	..	..	..	6 27	..	..	..	6 37	6 46
Whitton	SX	..	5 40	..	..	..	..	..	..	..	..	..	..	6 8	..	..
Hounslow D	5 33	..	5 44	..	..	..	..	..	..	6 9	..	..	..	6 14	..	..
Isleworth C	5 36	..	5 47	..	..	..	..	..	..	6 12	..	..	..	6 17	..	..
Syon Lane	5 39	..	5 50	..	..	..	..	..	..	6 14	..	..	..	6 20	..	..
Brentford B	5 41	..	5 52	..	..	..	..	..	..	6 17	..	..	..	6 22	..	..
Kew Bridge	5 44	..	5 55	..	..	..	..	..	..	6 19	..	..	..	6 25	..	..
Chiswick, for Grove Park	5 47	..	5 58	..	..	..	..	..	..	6 22	..	..	..	6 28	..	..
Barnes Bridge	5 50	..	6 1	..	..	..	..	..	..	6 25	..	..	..	6 31	..	..
Barnes	5 52	6 0	6 3	..	..	6 11	6 19	..	..	6 27	6 30	..	..	6 34	6 40	6 49
Putney	5 55	6 3	6 6	..	..	6 14	6 22	..	..	6 30	6 33	..	..	6 37	6 43	6 52
Wandsworth Town	5 58	6 6	6 9	..	..	6 17	..	..	..	6 33	6 36	..	..	6 40	6 46	..
Clapham Junction A	6 0	6 8	6 11	..	..	6 19	6 26	..	..	6 36	6 38	..	..	6 42	6 48	6 56
Queen's Road	..	..	6 14	..	..	..	6 29	..	..	6 39	..	..	..	6 45	..	6 59
Vauxhall	6 5	..	6 17	..	..	6 23	6 32	..	..	6 42	6 43	..	..	6 48	6 52	7 2
Waterloo arr.	6 9	6 15	6 21	6 11	6 17	6 27	6 36	6 30	..	6 46	6 47	6 42	6 44	6 52	6 56	7 6

Up	3		3	3		3	3	3	3		3	3	3			3
			From Waterloo via Kingston		SX	From Waterloo via Kingston								From Waterloo page 389		From Waterloo via Kingston
Reading dep.	..	..	..	..	5 58	..	..	..	..	..	..	..	..	..	6 28	..
Earley	..	..	..	..	6 3	..	..	..	..	..	..	..	..	..	6 33	..
Winnersh Halt Z	..	..	..	..	6 7	..	..	..	..	..	..	..	..	..	6 37	..
Wokingham	..	..	..	..	6 11	..	..	..	..	..	..	..	..	..	6 41	..
Bracknell	..	..	..	..	6 18	..	..	..	..	..	..	..	..	..	6 48	..
Ascot 388 arr.	..	..	..	..	6 24	..	..	..	..	..	..	..	..	..	6 54	..
Aldershot dep.	..	..	..	..	5 54	..	..	..	..	..	..	..	..	..	6 24	..
Ash Vale W	..	..	..	..	5 59	..	..	..	..	..	..	..	..	SX	6 29	..
Frimley T	..	..	..	..	6 5	..	..	..	..	..	..	..	..	6 39	6 35	..
Camberley Q	..	..	..	..	6 10	..	..	..	..	..	..	..	..	6 46	6 40	..
Bagshot	..	..	..	..	6 16	..	..	..	..	..	..	..	..	6 52	6 46	..
Ascot arr.	..	..	..	..	6 21	..	..	..	..	..	..	..	..	6 59	6 51	..
Ascot dep.	..	..	..	..	6 26	..	..	..	..	..	..	..	..	..	6 56	..
Sunningdale P	..	..	..	..	6 30	..	..	..	..	..	..	..	..	..	7 0	..
Longcross Halt	..	..	..	..	6 33	..	..	..	..	..	..	..	..	..	7 8	..
Virginia Water M 427 arr.	..	..	..	..	6 37	..	..	SX	SO	..	SX	..	SX	..	7 7	..
Weybridge dep.	6 5	..	..	..	..	..	..	6 25	6 35	..	6 37	..	6 50	..	..	..
Addlestone	6 9	..	..	..	..	..	..	6 29	6 39	..	6 41	..	6 54	..	..	..
Chertsey	6 12	..	..	..	..	..	..	6 32	6 42	..	6 44	..	6 57	..	..	..
Virginia Water M arr.	6 16	..	..	..	..	..	..	6 36	6 46	..	..	..	7 2	..	..	..
Virginia Water M dep.	6 16	..	..	..	6 37	..	..	6 46	6 46	..	..	..	..	..	7 7	..
Egham L	6 20	..	..	..	6 41	..	..	6 50	6 50	..	..	..	..	..	7 11	..
Staines J arr.	6 25	..	..	..	6 46	..	..	6 55	6 55	..	..	..	..	..	7 16	..
Windsor and Eton dep.	6 6	..	..	..	..	..	..	6 36	6 36	..	..	..	..	..	..	..
Datchet	6 10	..	..	..	..	..	..	6 40	6 40	..	..	..	..	..	..	..
Sunnymeads	6 14	..	..	..	..	..	..	6 44	6 44	..	..	..	..	..	..	..
Wraysbury	6 17	..	..	..	..	..	..	6 47	6 47	..	..	..	..	..	..	..
Staines J arr.	6 23	..	..	..	..	..	..	6 53	6 53	..	..	..	..	..	..	..
Staines dep.	6 27	..	..	..	6 46	..	..	6 57	6 57	..	..	..	..	..	7 16	..
Ashford (Middlesex)	6 31	..	..	..	..	..	..	7 1	7 1	..	..	..	..	..	..	..
Feltham	6 35	..	..	..	..	..	..	7 5	7 5	..	..	..	..	..	..	..
Hounslow D dep.	..	..	..	..	..	..	7 0	..	..	..	..	..	..	..	..	..
Whitton	6 39	..	V	..	..	V	7 4	7 9	7 9	..	..	..	..	..	..	V
Teddington F dep.	..	..	6 41	..	..	6 53	..	..	..	..	..	..	..	..	..	7 21
Strawberry Hill	..	..	6 44	..	..	6 58	..	..	..	..	..	..	..	..	..	7 26
Twickenham	6 42	..	6 47	6 37	..	7 1	7 7	7 12	7 12	..	..	7 7	..	..	..	7 29
St. Margaret's	..	..	6 49	..	..	7 3	7 9	..	..	..	..	..	..	..	..	7 31
Richmond	6 46	..	6 52	..	..	7 6	7 12	7 16	7 16	..	..	..	..	..	..	7 34
North Sheen	..	..	6 54	..	..	..	7 14	..	..	..	..	..	..	..	..	7 36
Mortlake, for East Sheen	..	..	6 57	..	..	7 9	7 17	..	..	..	..	..	..	..	..	7 39
Whitton	..	..	..	6 40	..	..	..	..	..	..	..	7 9	..	..	..	..
Hounslow D	..	..	..	6 45	..	..	..	..	..	..	..	7 14	..	..	..	..
Isleworth C	..	..	..	6 48	..	..	..	..	..	..	..	7 17	..	..	..	..
Syon Lane	..	..	..	6 51	..	..	..	..	..	..	..	7 20	..	..	..	..
Brentford B	..	..	..	6 53	..	..	..	..	..	..	..	7 22	..	..	..	..
Kew Bridge	..	..	..	6 56	..	..	..	..	..	..	..	7 25	..	..	..	..
Chiswick, for Grove Park	..	..	..	6 59	..	..	..	..	..	..	..	7 28	..	..	..	..
Barnes Bridge	..	..	..	7 2	..	..	..	..	..	..	..	7 31	..	..	..	..
Barnes	..	..	7 0	7 4	..	7 12	7 20	..	..	..	..	7 33	..	..	..	7 42
Putney	..	..	7 3	7 7	..	7 15	7 23	..	..	..	..	7 36	..	..	..	7 45
Wandsworth Town	..	..	7 6	7 10	..	7 18	..	..	..	..	..	7 39	..	..	..	7 48
Clapham Junction A	..	..	7 8	7 12	..	7 20	7 27	..	..	..	..	7 41	..	..	..	7 50
Queen's Road	..	..	..	7 15	..	..	7 30	..	..	..	..	7 44	..	..	..	..
Vauxhall	..	..	7 12	7 19	..	7 24	7 33	..	..	..	..	7 47	..	..	..	7 54
Waterloo arr.	7 0	..	7 16	7 22	7 12	7 28	7 37	7 31	7 31	..	..	7 51	..	..	7 42	7 58

READING, WINDSOR, STAINES, TEDDINGTON, TWICKENHAM, RICHMOND, HOUNSLOW, and LONDON

Up — Week Days—*continued* — p.m

Up	3	3	3 From Waterloo via Kingston		SX	3	3 From Waterloo via Kingston		3	3			3	3 From Waterloo via Kingston	3	
Reading ... dep.	..	..		..	6 58	..		..	..	..	7 28	..	..		..	..
Earley	..	..		..	7 3	..		..	..	..	7 33	..	..		..	..
Winnersh Halt **Z**	..	..		..	7 7	..		..	..	..	7 37	..	..		..	..
Wokingham	..	..		..	7 11	..		..	..	..	7 41	..	..		..	..
Bracknell	..	..		..	7 18	..		..	..	..	7 48	..	..		..	..
Ascot 388 ... arr.	..	..		..	7 24	..		..	..	..	7 54	..	..		..	..
Aldershot ... dep.	..	..		..	6 54	..		..	..	..	7 24	..	..		..	..
Ash Vale **W**	..	..		..	6 59	..		..	..	..	7 29	..	..		..	..
Frimley **T**	..	..		..	7 5	..		..	..	..	7 35	..	..		..	..
Camberley **Q**	..	..		..	7 10	..		..	..	..	7 40	..	..		..	..
Bagshot	..	..		..	7 16	..		..	..	..	7 46	..	..		..	..
Ascot ... arr.	..	..		..	7 21	..		..	..	..	7 51	..	..		..	..
Ascot ... dep.	..	..		..	7 26	..		..	..	..	7 56	..	..		..	..
Sunningdale **P**	..	..		..	7 30	..		..	..	..	8 0	..	..		..	..
Longcross Halt	..	..		..	7 33	..		..	..	..	8 3	..	..		..	..
Virginia Water M427 arr.	..	..		..	7 37	..		..	..	..	8 7	..	..		..	..
Weybridge ... dep.	..	7 5		..	..	..		..	..	7 35	..	..	..		..	..
Addlestone	..	7 9		..	..	..		..	..	7 39	..	..	..		..	..
Chertsey	..	7 12		..	..	..		..	..	7 42	..	..	..		..	..
Virginia Water M .. arr.	..	7 16		..	..	..		..	..	7 46	..	..	..		..	..
Virginia Water M ... dep.	..	7 16		..	7 37	..		..	..	7 46	8 7	..	..		..	..
Egham **L**	..	7 20		..	7 41	..		..	..	7 50	8 11	..	..		..	..
Staines J ... arr.	..	7 25		..	7 46	..		..	..	7 55	8 16	..	..		..	..
Windsor and Eton .. dep.	..	7 6		..	..	..		..	..	7 36	..	..	..		..	..
Datchet	..	7 10		..	..	..		..	..	7 40	..	..	..		..	..
Sunnymeads	..	7 14		..	..	..		..	..	7 44	..	..	..		..	..
Wraysbury	..	7 17		..	..	..		..	..	7 47	..	..	..		..	..
Staines J ... arr.	..	7 23		..	..	..		..	..	7 53	..	..	..		..	..
Staines ... dep.	..	7 27		..	7 46	..		..	..	7 57	8 16	..	..		..	..
Ashford (Middlesex)	..	7 31		..	..	..		..	..	8 1	..	..	..		..	..
Feltham	..	7 35		..	..	..		..	..	8 5	..	..	..		..	..
Hounslow D ... dep.	7 30	..		..	..	..		..	8 0	..	..	..	..		8 29	..
Whitton	7 33	7 39	V	..	..	..	V	..	8 3	8 9	..	..	..	V	8 32	..
Teddington F ... dep.	..	..	7 41	..	..	..	7 53	..	..	..	..	..	..	8 21	..	..
Strawberry Hill	..	..	7 44	..	..	..	7 58	..	..	..	..	..	..	8 25	..	..
Twickenham	7 36	7 42	7 47	..	..	7 37	8 1	..	8 6	8 12	..	..	8 7	8 28	8 35	..
St. Margaret's	7 38	..	7 49	..	..	..	8 3	..	8 8	..	..	..	..	8 30	8 37	..
Richmond	7 41	7 46	7 52	..	..	..	8 6	..	8 11	8 16	..	..	..	8 33	8 40	..
North Sheen	7 43	..	7 54	..	..	..	..	..	8 13	..	..	..	..	8 35	8 42	..
Mortlake, for East Sheen	7 46	..	7 57	..	..	..	8 9	..	8 16	..	..	..	..	8 38	8 45	..
Whitton	..	..	..	..	..	7 39	..	..	..	..	..	..	8 9	..	..	..
Hounslow D	..	..	..	..	..	7 44	..	..	..	..	..	..	8 14	..	..	..
Isleworth **C**	..	..	..	..	..	7 47	..	..	..	..	..	..	8 17	..	..	..
Syon Lane	..	..	..	..	..	7 50	..	..	..	..	..	..	8 20	..	..	..
Brentford **B**	..	..	..	..	..	7 52	..	..	..	..	..	..	8 22	..	..	..
Kew Bridge	..	..	..	..	..	7 55	..	..	..	..	..	..	8 25	..	..	..
Chiswick, for Grove Park	..	..	..	..	..	7 58	..	..	..	..	..	..	8 28	..	..	..
Barnes Bridge	..	..	..	..	..	8 1	..	..	..	..	..	..	8 31	..	..	..
Barnes	7 49	..	8 0	..	..	8 3	8 12	..	8 19	..	..	..	8 33	8 41	8 48	..
Putney	7 52	..	8 3	..	..	8 6	8 15	..	8 22	..	..	..	8 36	8 44	8 51	..
Wandsworth Town	..	..	8 6	..	..	8 9	8 18	..	..	..	..	..	8 39	8 47	..	..
Clapham Junction A	7 56	..	8 8	..	..	8 11	8 20	..	8 26	..	..	..	8 41	8 49	8 55	..
Queen's Road	7 59	..	..	..	..	8 14	..	..	8 29	..	..	..	8 44	..	8 58	..
Vauxhall	8 2	..	8 12	..	..	8 17	8 24	..	8 32	..	..	..	8 47	8 53	9 1	..
Waterloo ... arr.	8 6	8 1	8 16	..	8 12	8 21	8 28	..	8 36	8 30	8 42	..	8 51	8 57	9 5	..

Up	3	3 From Waterloo via Kingston	SX		3	3 From Waterloo via Kingston	3		3		3		3 From Waterloo via Kingston	3		3
Reading ... dep.	..		7 58	..	..		..	..	..	8 28	..	..		..	..	..
Earley	..		8 3	..	..		..	..	..	8 33	..	..		..	..	..
Winnersh Halt **Z**	..		8 7	..	..		..	..	..	8 37	..	..		..	..	..
Wokingham	..		8 11	..	..		..	..	..	8 41	..	..		..	..	..
Bracknell	..		8 18	..	..		..	..	..	8 48	..	..		..	..	..
Ascot 388 ... arr.	..		8 24	..	..		..	..	..	8 54	..	..		..	..	..
Aldershot ... dep.	..		..	..	..		..	..	..	8 24	..	..		..	..	..
Ash Vale **W**	..		..	..	..		..	..	..	8 29	..	..		..	..	..
Frimley **T**	..		..	..	..		..	..	..	8 35	..	..		..	..	..
Camberley **Q**	..		..	..	..		..	..	..	8 40	..	..		..	..	..
Bagshot	..		..	..	..		..	..	..	8 46	..	..		..	..	..
Ascot ... arr.	..		..	..	..		..	..	..	8 51	..	..		..	..	..
Ascot ... dep.	..		..	..	..		..	..	..	8 56	..	..		..	..	..
Sunningdale **P**	..		..	..	..		..	..	..	9 0	..	..		..	..	..
Longcross Halt	..		..	..	..		..	..	..	9 3	..	..		..	..	..
Virginia Water M427 arr.	..		..	..	..		..	..	..	9 7	..	..		..	..	..
Weybridge ... dep.	8 5		..	..	..		..	..	8 35	..	..	..		..	..	9 5
Addlestone	8 9		..	..	..		..	..	8 39	..	..	..		..	..	9 9
Chertsey	8 12		..	..	..		..	..	8 42	..	..	..		..	..	9 12
Virginia Water M .. arr.	8 16		..	..	..		..	..	8 46	..	..	..		..	..	9 16
Virginia Water M ... dep.	8 16		..	..	..		..	..	8 46	9 7	..	..		..	..	9 16
Egham **L**	8 20		..	..	..		..	..	8 50	9 11	..	..		..	..	9 20
Staines J ... arr.	8 25		..	..	..		..	..	8 55	9 16	..	..		..	..	9 25
Windsor and Eton .. dep.	8 6		..	..	..		..	..	8 36	..	..	..		..	..	9 6
Datchet	8 10		..	..	..		..	..	8 40	..	..	..		..	..	9 10
Sunnymeads	8 14		..	..	..		..	..	8 44	..	..	..		..	..	9 14
Wraysbury	8 17		..	..	..		..	..	8 47	..	..	..		..	..	9 17
Staines J ... arr.	8 23		..	..	..		..	..	8 53	..	..	..		..	..	9 23
Staines ... dep.	8 27		..	..	..		..	..	8 57	9 16	..	..		..	..	9 27
Ashford (Middlesex)	8 31		..	..	..		..	..	9 1	..	..	..		..	..	9 31
Feltham	8 35		..	..	..		..	..	9 5	..	..	..		..	..	9 35
Hounslow D ... dep.	..		..	..	..		9 0	..	..	..	..	..		9 29	..	..
Whitton	8 39	V	..	..	..	V	9 3	..	9 9	..	..	..	V	9 32	..	9 39
Teddington F ... dep.	..	8 41	..	..	..	8 53	..	..	..	..	..	..	9 21	..	..	..
Strawberry Hill	..	8 44	..	..	..	8 57	..	..	..	..	..	..	9 25	..	..	..
Twickenham	8 42	8 47	..	..	8 37	9 0	9 6	..	9 12	..	9 7	..	9 28	9 35	..	9 42
St. Margaret's	..	8 49	..	..	..	9 2	9 8	..	..	..	..	..	9 30	9 37	..	..
Richmond	8 46	8 52	..	..	..	9 5	9 11	..	9 16	..	..	..	9 33	9 40	..	9 46
North Sheen	..	8 54	..	..	..	..	9 13	..	..	..	..	..	9 35	9 42	..	..
Mortlake, for East Sheen	..	8 57	..	..	..	9 8	9 16	..	..	..	..	..	9 38	9 45	..	..
Whitton	..	..	..	..	8 39	..	..	..	..	..	9 9	..	..	..	..	..
Hounslow D	..	..	..	..	8 44	..	..	..	..	..	9 14	..	..	..	..	..
Isleworth **C**	..	..	..	..	8 47	..	..	..	..	..	9 17	..	..	..	..	..
Syon Lane	..	..	..	..	8 50	..	..	..	..	..	9 20	..	..	..	..	..
Brentford **B**	..	..	..	..	8 52	..	..	..	..	..	9 22	..	..	..	..	..
Kew Bridge	..	..	..	..	8 55	..	..	..	..	..	9 25	..	..	..	..	..
Chiswick, for Grove Park	..	..	..	..	8 58	..	..	..	..	..	9 28	..	..	..	..	..
Barnes Bridge	..	..	..	..	9 1	..	..	..	..	..	9 31	..	..	..	..	..
Barnes	..	9 0	..	..	9 3	9 11	9 19	..	..	..	9 33	..	9 41	9 48	..	..
Putney	..	9 3	..	..	9 6	9 14	9 22	..	..	..	9 36	..	9 44	9 51	..	..
Wandsworth Town	..	9 6	..	..	..	9 17	..	..	..	..	..	..	9 47	..	..	..
Clapham Junction A	..	9 8	..	..	9 11	9 19	9 26	..	..	..	9 40	..	9 49	9 55	..	..
Queen's Road	..	..	..	..	9 14	..	9 29	..	..	..	9 43	..	..	9 58	..	..
Vauxhall	..	9 12	..	..	9 17	9 23	9 32	..	..	..	9 46	..	9 53	10 1	..	..
Waterloo ... arr.	9 0	9 16	..	..	9 21	9 27	9 36	..	9 30	9 42	9 50	..	9 57	10 5	..	10 0

FOR NOTES, SEE PAGE 489

FOR NOTES, SEE PAGE 489

READING, WINDSOR, STAINES, TEDDINGTON, TWICKENHAM, RICHMOND, HOUNSLOW, and LONDON

Week Days—continued (p.m. … p.m. … ngt.)

Up	3	3	3	3		3		3	3	3		3	3	3	3	3		3		3	3	3		3	3			3	3			
Reading ....dep.							9 28												1028							1058						
Earley							9 33												1033							11 3						
Winnersh Halt **Z**							9 37												1037							11 7						
Wokingham							9 41												1041							1111						
Bracknell							9 48												1048							1118						
Ascot 388 ....arr.							9 54												1054							1124						
Aldershot ....dep.							9 24												1024							1054						
Ash Vale **W**							9 29												1029							1059						
Frimley **T**							9 35												1035							11 5						
Camberley **Q**							9 40												1040							1110						
Bagshot							9 46												1046							1116						
Ascot ....arr.							9 51												1051							1121						
Ascot ....dep.							9 56												1056							1126						
Sunningdale **P**							10 0												11 0							1130						
Longcross Halt							10 3												11 3							1133						
Virginia Water M 427 arr.							10 7												11 7							1137						
Weybridge ....dep.						9 35							10 5					1035			11 5			1135								
Addlestone						9 39							10 9					1039			11 9			1139								
Chertsey						9 42							1012					1042			1112			1142								
Virginia Water M ..arr.						9 46							1016					1046														
Virginia Water M ..dep.						9 46	10 7						1016					1046	11 7							1137						
Egham **L**						9 50	1011						1020					1050	1111							1141						
Staines J ....arr.						9 55	1016						1025					1055	1116							1146						
Windsor and Eton ..dep.	From Waterloo via Kingston		From Waterloo via Kingston			9 36			From Waterloo via Kingston				10 6	From Waterloo via Kingston	From Waterloo via Kingston			1040		From Waterloo via Kingston					From Waterloo via Kingston			From Kingston dep. 12 5 a.m see page 411	From Waterloo via Kingston			
Datchet						9 40							1010					1044														
Sunnymeads						9 44							1014					1048														
Wraysbury						9 47							1017					1051														
Staines J ....arr.						9 53							1023					1057														
Staines ....dep.						9 57	1016						1027					1059	1116							1146						
Ashford (Middlesex)						10 1							1031					11 3	1119							1149						
Feltham						10 5							1035					11 7	1124							1154						
Hounslow D ....dep.				10 0						1029																						
Whitton	V		V	10 3		10 9			V	1032			1039	V	V			1111		V					V				V			
Teddington F ....dep.	9 41		9 53						1021					1041	1053					1121					1141			1210	1241			
Strawberry Hill	9 44		9 57						1024					1044	1056					1124					1144			1214	1244			
Twickenham	9 47	9 37	10 0	10 6		1012		10 7	1027	1035		1037	1042	1047	1059	11 7		1114	1129	1130		1137				1159						
St. Margaret's	9 49		10 2	10 8					1029	1037				1049	11 1					1132												
Richmond	9 52		10 5	1011		1016			1031	1040			1046	1052	11 4			1118		1135						12 3						
North Sheen	9 54			1013					1034	1042				1054	11 7					1137												
Mortlake, for East Sheen	9 57		10 8	1016					1037	1045				1057	11 9					1140												
Whitton		9 39						10 9				1039				11 9						1139										
Hounslow D		9 44						1014				1043				1115						1144										
Isleworth **C**		9 47						1017																								
Syon Lane		9 50						1020																								
Brentford **B**		9 52						1022																								
Kew Bridge		9 55						1025																								
Chiswick, for Grove Park		9 58						1028																								
Barnes Bridge		10 1						1031																								
Barnes	10 0	10 3	1011	1019				1033	1040	1048				11 0	1112					1143												
Putney	10 3	10 6	1014	1022				1036	1043	1051				11 3	1115					1146												
Wandsworth Town	10 6	10 9	1017					1039	1046					11 6	1118					1149												
Clapham Junction A	10 8	1011	1019	1026				1041	1048	1055				11 8	1120			1127		1151												
Queen's Road		1014		1029				1044		1058					1123					1154												
Vauxhall	1012	1017	1023	1032				1047	1052	11 1				1112	1126					1157												
Waterloo ....arr.	1016	1021	1027	1036		1030	1042	1051	1056	11 5			11 0	1116	1130			1134	1145	12 1						1217						

READING, WINDSOR, STAINES, TEDDINGTON, TWICKENHAM, RICHMOND, HOUNSLOW, and LONDON

Sundays — a.m.

Up	3	3	3	3	3	3	3	3	3	3	3	3	3	3	3	3	3		3	3	3	3	3		3	3	3	3	3		3	3
Reading ... dep.	..	..	..	..	..	..	..	..	..	..	..	..	..	..	..	..	..	7 58	..	..	..	..	..	8 28	..	..	..	..	..	..	..	..
Earley	..	..	..	..	..	..	..	..	..	..	..	..	..	..	..	..	..	8 3	..	..	..	..	..	8 33	..	..	..	..	..	..	..	..
Winnersh Halt Z	..	..	..	..	..	..	..	..	..	..	..	..	..	..	..	..	..	8 7	..	..	..	..	..	8 37	..	..	..	..	..	..	..	..
Wokingham	..	..	..	..	..	..	..	..	..	..	..	..	..	..	..	..	..	8 11	..	..	..	..	..	8 41	..	..	..	..	..	..	..	..
Bracknell	..	..	..	..	..	..	..	..	..	..	..	..	..	..	..	..	..	8 19	..	..	..	..	..	8 48	..	..	..	..	..	..	..	..
Ascot 388 ... arr.	..	..	..	..	..	..	..	..	..	..	..	..	..	..	..	..	..	8 24	..	..	..	..	..	8 54	..	..	..	..	..	..	..	..
Aldershot ... dep.	..	..	..	..	..	..	..	..	..	..	..	..	..	..	..	..	..	7 54	..	..	..	..	..	8 24	..	..	..	..	..	..	..	..
Ash Vale W	..	..	..	..	..	..	..	..	..	..	..	..	..	..	..	..	..	7 59	..	..	..	..	..	8 29	..	..	..	..	..	..	..	..
Frimley T	..	..	..	..	..	..	..	..	..	..	..	..	..	..	..	..	..	8 5	..	..	..	..	..	8 35	..	..	..	..	..	..	..	..
Camberley Q	..	..	..	..	..	..	..	..	..	..	..	..	..	..	..	..	..	8 10	..	..	..	..	..	8 40	..	..	..	..	..	..	..	..
Bagshot	..	..	..	..	..	..	..	..	..	..	..	..	..	..	..	..	..	8 16	..	..	..	..	..	8 46	..	..	..	..	..	..	..	..
Ascot ... arr.	..	..	..	..	..	..	..	..	..	..	..	..	..	..	..	..	..	8 22	..	..	..	..	..	8 51	..	..	..	..	..	..	..	..
Ascot ... dep.	..	..	..	..	..	..	..	..	..	..	..	..	..	..	..	..	..	8 26	..	..	..	..	..	8 56	..	..	..	..	..	..	..	..
Sunningdale P	..	..	..	..	..	..	..	..	..	..	..	..	..	..	..	..	..	8 30	..	..	..	..	..	9 0	..	..	..	..	..	..	..	..
Longcross Halt	..	..	..	..	..	..	..	..	..	..	..	..	..	..	..	..	..	8 33	..	..	..	..	..	9 3	..	..	..	..	..	..	..	..
Virginia Water M 427 arr.	..	..	..	..	..	..	..	..	..	..	..	..	..	..	..	..	..	8 37	..	..	..	..	..	9 7	..	..	..	..	..	..	..	..
Weybridge ... dep.	From Waterloo via Kingston	..	..	..	From Waterloo via Kingston	..	..	..	..	From Waterloo via Kingston	..	..	..	From Waterloo via Kingston	..	8 5	..	..	From Wimbledon via Kingston	..	..	8 35	From Shepperton, dep. 8 58 a.m, see page 447.	..	From Waterloo via Kingston	..	9 5	..	From Waterloo via Kingston	..	..	..
Addlestone		..	..	..		..	..	..	..		..	..	..		..	8 9	..	..		..	..	8 39		..		..	9 9	..		..	..	..
Chertsey		..	..	..		..	..	..	..		..	..	7 42		..	8 12	..	..		..	..	8 42		..		..	9 12	..		..	..	..
Virginia Water M .. arr.		..	..	..		..	..	..	..		..	..	7 46		..	8 16	..	..		..	..	8 46		..		..	9 16	..		..	..	..
Virginia Water M ... dep.		..	..	..		..	..	..	..		..	..	7 46		..	8 16	..	8 37		..	..	8 46		9 7		..	9 16	..		..	..	..
Egham L		..	..	..		..	..	..	..		..	..	7 50		..	8 20	..	8 41		..	..	8 50		9 11		..	9 20	..		..	..	..
Staines J ... arr.		..	..	..		..	..	..	..		..	..	7 55		..	8 25	..	8 46		..	..	8 55		9 16		..	9 25	..		..	..	..
Windsor and Eton .. dep.		..	..	..		..	..	..	..		..	..	7 36		..	8 6	..	..		..	..	8 36		..		..	9 6	..		..	..	..
Datchet		..	..	..		..	..	..	..		..	..	7 40		..	8 10	..	..		..	..	8 40		..		..	9 10	..		..	..	..
Sunnymeads		..	..	..		..	..	..	..		..	..	7 44		..	8 14	..	..		..	..	8 44		..		..	9 14	..		..	..	..
Wraysbury		..	..	..		..	..	..	..		..	..	7 47		..	8 17	..	..		..	..	8 47		..		..	9 17	..		..	..	..
Staines J ... arr.		..	..	..		..	..	..	..		..	..	7 53		..	8 23	..	..		..	..	8 53		..		..	9 23	..		..	..	..
Staines ... dep.		..	..	..		..	..	..	..		..	..	7 57		..	8 27	..	8 46		..	..	8 57		9 16		..	9 27	..		..	..	..
Ashford (Middlesex)		..	..	..		..	..	..	..		..	..	8 1		..	8 31	..	..		..	..	9 1		..		..	9 31	..		..	..	..
Feltham		4 50	..	..		..	..	..	..		..	..	8 5		..	8 35	..	..		..	..	9 5		..		..	9 35	..		..	..	..
Hounslow D ... dep.		..	..	..		..	7 21	..	..		7 59	..	..		8 29	..	..	..		..	8 59	..		..		9 29	..	..		..	..	9 59
Whitton	V	..	..	..	V	..	7 24	..	..	V	8 3	..	8 9	V	8 33	8 39	..	..	V	..	9 3	9 9		..	V	9 33	9 39	..	V	..	..	10 3
Teddington F ... dep.	2 6	..	..	..	6 58	..	..	..	..	7 55	..	..	..	8 21	..	..	..	..	8 41	..	..	..	..	..	9 21	..	..	..	9 41	..	..	..
Strawberry Hill	..	..	..	6 44	7 4	..	..	..	7 44	7 58	..	..	..	8 24	..	..	..	..	8 44	..	..	..	9 14	..	9 24	..	..	..	9 44	..	..	..
Twickenham	2 12	4 57	..	6 47	7 7	..	7 27	..	7 47	8 1	8 5	..	8 12	8 27	8 35	8 42	8 26	..	8 47	8 49	9 5	9 12	9 17	..	9 27	9 35	9 42	9 26	9 47	..	9 49	10 5
St. Margaret's	..	..	..	6 49	7 9	..	7 29	..	7 49	8 3	..	..	..	8 29	8 37	..	..	..	8 49	..	..	..	9 19	..	9 29	9 37	..	..	9 49	..	..	..
Richmond	..	..	..	6 52	7 12	..	7 32	..	7 52	8 6	..	..	8 16	8 32	8 40	8 46	..	..	8 52	..	..	9 16	9 22	..	9 32	9 40	9 46	..	9 52	..	..	..
North Sheen	..	..	..	6 54	7 14	..	7 34	..	7 54	8 8	..	..	..	8 34	8 43	..	..	..	8 54	..	..	..	9 24	..	9 34	9 43	..	..	9 54	..	..	..
Mortlake, for East Sheen	..	..	..	6 57	7 17	..	7 37	..	7 57	8 10	..	..	..	8 37	8 45	..	..	..	8 57	..	..	..	9 27	..	9 37	9 45	..	..	9 57	..	..	..
Whitton	..	..	..	..	..	..	..	..	..	..	..	..	..	..	..	..	8 28	..	..	8 51	..	..	..	..	..	..	..	9 28	..	..	9 51	..
Hounslow D	..	..	..	..	..	7 15	..	7 33	..	..	..	7 58	..	..	..	..	8 33	..	..	8 58	..	..	..	..	..	..	..	9 33	..	..	9 58	..
Isleworth C	..	..	..	..	..	7 18	..	7 36	..	..	..	8 1	..	..	..	..	8 36	..	..	9 1	..	..	..	..	..	..	..	9 36	..	..	10 1	..
Syon Lane	..	..	..	..	..	7 21	..	7 38	..	..	..	8 3	..	..	..	..	8 38	..	..	9 3	..	..	..	..	..	..	..	9 38	..	..	10 3	..
Brentford B	..	..	..	..	..	7 23	..	7 41	..	..	..	8 6	..	..	..	..	8 41	..	..	9 6	..	..	..	..	..	..	..	9 41	..	..	10 6	..
Kew Bridge	..	..	..	..	..	7 26	..	7 43	..	..	..	8 8	..	..	..	..	8 43	..	..	9 8	..	..	..	..	..	..	..	9 43	..	..	10 8	..
Chiswick, for Grove Park	..	..	..	..	..	7 29	..	7 46	..	..	..	8 11	..	..	..	..	8 46	..	..	9 11	..	..	..	..	..	..	..	9 46	..	..	1011	..
Barnes Bridge	..	..	..	..	..	7 32	..	7 49	..	..	..	8 14	..	..	..	..	8 49	..	..	9 14	..	..	..	..	..	..	..	9 49	..	..	1014	..
Barnes	..	..	..	7 0	7 20	7 34	7 40	7 51	8 0	8 14	..	8 16	..	8 40	8 48	..	8 51	..	9 0	9 17	..	..	9 30	..	9 40	9 48	..	9 51	10 0	..	1017	..
Putney	..	..	..	7 3	7 23	7 37	7 43	7 54	8 3	8 17	..	8 19	8 22	8 43	8 51	..	8 54	..	9 3	9 21	..	..	9 33	..	9 43	9 51	..	9 54	10 3	..	1020	..
Wandsworth Town	..	..	..	7 6	7 26	7 40	7 46	7 57	8 6	8 20	..	8 22	..	8 46	8 54	..	8 57	..	9 6	9 24	..	..	9 36	..	9 46	9 54	..	9 57	10 6	..	1023	..
Clapham Junction A	..	..	..	7 8	7 28	7 42	7 48	8 0	8 8	8 22	..	8 24	8 26	8 48	8 56	8 55	9 0	..	9 8	9 26	..	9 25	9 38	..	9 48	9 56	9 55	10 0	10 8	..	1025	..
Queen's Road	..	..	5 50	7 11	7 31	7 45	7 51	8 3	8 11	8 25	..	8 27	..	..	8 59	..	9 3	..	9 11	9 29	..	..	9 41	..	..	9 59	..	10 3	1011	..	1028	..
Vauxhall	..	..	5 53	7 14	7 34	7 48	7 54	8 6	8 14	8 28	..	8 32	..	8 52	9 2	..	9 6	..	9 14	9 33	..	..	9 44	..	9 52	10 2	..	10 6	1014	..	1031	..
Waterloo ... arr.	..	..	5 57	7 18	7 38	7 52	7 58	8 10	8 18	8 32	..	8 36	8 33	8 56	9 6	9 2	9 10	9 12	9 18	9 37	..	9 32	9 48	9 42	9 56	10 6	10 2	1010	1018	..	1035	..

FOR NOTES, SEE PAGE 489

FOR NOTES, SEE PAGE 489

READING, WINDSOR, STAINES, TEDDINGTON, TWICKENHAM, RICHMOND, HOUNSLOW, and LONDON

Up — Sundays—continued (a.m. … p.m.)

Up	3		3	3	3	3	3		3	3	3	3		3	3	3	3	3	3		3	3	3		3	3	3	3	3	●	3	3
Reading dep.		9 28											1028											1128								
Earley		9 33											1033											1133								
Winnersh Halt **Z**		9 37											1037											1137								
Wokingham		9 41											1041											1141								
Bracknell		9 48											1048											1148								
Ascot 388 arr.		9 54											1054											1154								
Aldershot dep.		9 24											1024											1124								
Ash Vale **W**		9 29											1029											1129								
Frimley **T**		9 35											1035											1135								
Camberley **Q**		9 40											1040											1140								
Bagshot		9 46											1046											1146								
Ascot arr.		9 51											1051											1151								
Ascot dep.		9 56	From Shepperton dep. 9 58 a.m., see page 447										1056	From Shepperton, dep. 10 58 a.m., see page 448.										1156	From Shepperton, dep. 11 58 a.m., see page 449.							
Sunningdale **P**		10 0											11 0											12 0								
Longcross Halt		10 3											11 3											12 3								
Virginia Water M 427 arr.		10 7											11 7											12 7								
Weybridge dep.	9 35					10 5						1035					11 5						1135					12 5				
Addlestone	9 39					10 9						1039					11 9						1139					12 9				
Chertsey	9 42					1012						1042					1112						1142					1212				
Virginia Water M arr.	9 46					1016						1046					1116						1146					1216				
Virginia Water M dep.	9 46	10 7				1016						1046	11 7				1116						1146	12 7				1216				
Egham **L**	9 50	1011				1020						1050	1111				1120						1150	1211				1220				
Staines J arr.	9 55	1016				1025						1055	1116				1125						1155	1216				1225				
Windsor and Eton dep.	9 36			From Waterloo via Kingston		10 6			From Waterloo via Kingston			1036			From Waterloo via Kingston		11 6		From Waterloo via Kingston				1136			From Waterloo via Kingston		12 6			From Waterloo via Kingston	
Datchet	9 40					1010						1040					1110						1140					1210				
Sunnymeads	9 44					1014						1044					1114						1144					1214				
Wraysbury	9 47					1017						1047					1117						1147					1217				
Staines J arr.	9 53					1023						1053					1123						1153					1223				
Staines dep.	9 7	1016				1027						1057	1116				1127						1157	1216				1227				
Ashford (Middlesex)	10 1					1031						11 1					1131						12 1					1231				
Feltham	10 5					1035						11 5					1135						12 5					1235				
Hounslow D dep.					1029						1059					1129						1159					1229					
Whitton	10 9			V	1033	1039			V		11 3	11 9			V	1133	1139		V			12 3	12 9			V	1233	1239			V	
Teddington F dep.				1021					1041						1121				1141							1221					1241	
Strawberry Hill			1014	1024					1044					1114	1124				1144						1214	1224					1244	
Twickenham	1012		1017	1027	1035	1042	1026		1047	1049	11 5	1112		1117	1127	1135	1142	1126	1147		1149	12 5	1212		1217	1227	1235	1242	1226		1247	1249
St. Margaret's			1019	1029	1037				1049					1119	1129	1137			1149						1219	1229	1237				1249	
Richmond	1016		1022	1032	1040	1046			1052			1116		1122	1132	1140	1146		1152				1216		1222	1232	1240	1246			1252	
North Sheen			1024	1034	1043				1054					1124	1134	1143			1154						1224	1234	1243				1254	
Mortlake, for East Sheen			1027	1037	1045				1057					1127	1137	1145			1157						1227	1237	1245				1257	
Whitton							1028			1051								1128			1151								1228			1251
Hounslow D							1033			1058								1133			1158								1233			1258
Isleworth **C**							1036			11 1								1136			12 1								1236			1 1
Syon Lane							1038			11 3								1138			12 3								1238			1 3
Brentford **B**							1041			11 6								1141			12 6								1241			1 6
Kew Bridge							1043			11 8								1143			12 8								1243			1 8
Chiswick, for Grove Park							1046			1111								1146			1211								1246			1 11
Barnes Bridge							1049			1114								1149			1214								1249			1 14
Barnes			1030	1040	1048		1051		11 0	1117				1130	1140	1148		1151	12 0		1217				1230	1240	1248		1251		1 0	1 17
Putney			1033	1043	1051		1054		11 3	1120				1133	1143	1151		1154	12 3		1220				1233	1243	1251		1254		1 3	1 20
Wandsworth Town			1036	1046	1054		1057		11 6	1123				1136	1146	1154		1157	12 6		1223				1236	1246	1254		1257		1 6	1 23
Clapham Junction **A**	1025		1038	1048	1056	1055	11 0		11 8	1125		1125		1138	1148	1156	1155	12 0	12 8		1225		1225		1238	1248	1256	1255	1 0		1 8	1 25
Queen's Road			1041		1059		11 3		1111	1128				1141		1159		12 3	1211		1228				1241		1259		1 3		1 11	1 28
Vauxhall			1044	1052	11 2		11 6		1114	1131				1144	1152	12 2		12 6	1214		1231				1244	1252	1 2		1 6		1 14	1 31
Waterloo arr.	1032	1042	1048	1056	11 6	11 2	1110		1118	1135		1132	1142	1148	1156	12 6	12 2	1210	1218		1235		1232	1242	1248	1256	1 6	1 2	1 10		1 18	1 35

READING, WINDSOR, STAINES, TEDDINGTON, TWICKENHAM, RICHMOND, HOUNSLOW, and LONDON

Up — **Sundays**—*continued* — p.m

Up	3	3		3 (From Shepperton dep. 12 58 p.m see page 449.)	3 (From Waterloo via Kingston)	3	3	3	
Reading .... dep.	..	..	1228	..	..	..	..	..	..
Earley	..	..	1233	..	..	..	..	..	..
Winnersh Halt Z	..	..	1237	..	..	..	..	..	..
Wokingham	..	..	1241	..	..	..	..	..	..
Bracknell	..	..	1248	..	..	..	..	..	..
Ascot 388 .... arr.	..	..	1254	..	..	..	..	..	..
Aldershot .... dep.	..	..	1224	..	..	..	..	..	..
Ash Vale W	..	..	1229	..	..	..	..	..	..
Frimley T	..	..	1235	..	..	..	..	..	..
Camberley Q	..	..	1240	..	..	..	..	..	..
Bagshot	..	..	1246	..	..	..	..	..	..
Ascot .... arr.	..	..	1251	..	..	..	..	..	..
Ascot .... dep.	..	..	1256		..	..	..	..	..
Sunningdale P	..	..	1 0		..	..	..	..	..
Longcross Halt	..	..	1 3		..	..	..	..	..
Virginia Water M 427 arr.	..	..	1 7		..	..	..	..	..
Weybridge .... dep.	..	1235	..		..	..	1 5	..	..
Addlestone	..	1239	..			..	1 9	..	..
Chertsey	..	1242	..			..	1 12	..	..
Virginia Water M .. arr.	..	1246	..			..	1 16	..	..
Virginia Water M ... dep.	..	1246	1 7			..	1 16	..	..
Egham L	..	1250	1 11			..	1 20	..	..
Staines J .... arr.	..	1255	1 16			..	1 25	..	..
Windsor and Eton .. dep.	..	1236	..			..	1 6	..	..
Datchet	..	1240	..			..	1 10	..	..
Sunnymeads	..	1244	..			..	1 14	..	..
Wraysbury	..	1247	..			..	1 17	..	..
Staines J .... arr.	..	1253	..			..	1 23	..	..
Staines .... dep.	..	1257	1 16			..	1 27	..	..
Ashford (Middlesex)	..	1 1	..			..	1 31	..	..
Feltham	..	1 5	..			..	1 35	..	..
Hounslow D .... dep.	1259	..	..	..		1 29	..	..	..
Whitton	1 3	1 9	..	..	V	1 33	1 39	..	..
Teddington F .... dep.	..	..	..	..	1 21	..	..	..	..
Strawberry Hill	..	..	..	1 14	1 24	..	..	..	..
Twickenham	1 5	1 12	..	1 17	1 27	1 35	1 42	1 26	..
St. Margaret's	..	..	..	1 19	1 29	1 37	..	..	..
Richmond	..	1 16	..	1 22	1 32	1 40	1 46	..	..
North Sheen	..	..	..	1 24	1 34	1 43	..	..	..
Mortlake, for East Sheen	..	..	..	1 27	1 37	1 45	..	..	..
Whitton	..	..	..	..	..	..	..	1 28	..
Hounslow D	..	..	..	..	..	..	..	1 33	..
Isleworth C	..	..	..	..	..	..	..	1 36	..
Syon Lane	..	..	..	..	..	..	..	1 38	..
Brentford B	..	..	..	..	..	..	..	1 41	..
Kew Bridge	..	..	..	..	..	..	..	1 43	..
Chiswick, for Grove Park	..	..	..	..	..	..	..	1 46	..
Barnes Bridge	..	..	..	..	..	..	..	1 49	..
Barnes	..	..	..	1 30	1 40	1 48	..	1 51	..
Putney	..	..	..	1 33	1 43	1 51	..	1 54	..
Wandsworth Town	..	..	..	1 36	1 46	1 54	..	1 57	..
Clapham Junction A	..	1 25	..	1 38	1 48	1 56	1 55	2 0	..
Queen's Road	..	..	..	1 41	..	1 59	..	2 3	..
Vauxhall	..	..	..	1 44	1 52	2 2	..	2 6	..
Waterloo .... arr.	..	1 32	1 42	1 48	1 56	2 6	2 2	2 10	..

Up	3 (From Waterloo via Kingston)	3	3	3	3 (From Shepperton, dep. 1 58 p.m see page 450.)		3 (From Waterloo via Kingston)	3	3	3	
Reading .... dep.	..	..	..	..	..	1 28	..	..	..	..	..
Earley	..	..	..	..	..	1 33	..	..	..	..	..
Winnersh Halt Z	..	..	..	..	..	1 37	..	..	..	..	..
Wokingham	..	..	..	..	..	1 41	..	..	..	..	..
Bracknell	..	..	..	..	..	1 48	..	..	..	..	..
Ascot 388 .... arr.	..	..	..	..	..	1 54	..	..	..	..	..
Aldershot .... dep.	..	..	..	..	..	1 24	..	..	..	..	..
Ash Vale W	..	..	..	..	..	1 29	..	..	..	..	..
Frimley T	..	..	..	..	..	1 35	..	..	..	..	..
Camberley Q	..	..	..	..	..	1 40	..	..	..	..	..
Bagshot	..	..	..	..	..	1 46	..	..	..	..	..
Ascot .... arr.	..	..	..	..	..	1 51	..	..	..	..	..
Ascot .... dep.	..	..	..	..		1 56	..	..	..	..	..
Sunningdale P	..	..	..	..		2 0	..	..	..	..	..
Longcross Halt	..	..	..	..		2 3	..	..	..	..	..
Virginia Water M 427 arr.	..	..	..	..		2 7	..	..	..	..	..
Weybridge .... dep.	..	..	..	1 35		..	..	..	2 5	..	..
Addlestone		..	..	1 39		..		..	2 9	..	..
Chertsey		..	..	1 42		..		..	2 12	..	..
Virginia Water M .. arr.		..	..	1 46		..		..	2 16	..	..
Virginia Water M ... dep.		..	..	1 46		2 7		..	2 16	..	..
Egham L		..	..	1 50		2 11		..	2 20	..	..
Staines J .... arr.		..	..	1 55		2 16		..	2 25	..	..
Windsor and Eton .. dep.		..	..	1 36		..		..	2 6	..	..
Datchet		..	..	1 40		..		..	2 10	..	..
Sunnymeads		..	..	1 44		..		..	2 14	..	..
Wraysbury		..	..	1 47		..		..	2 17	..	..
Staines J .... arr.		..	..	1 53		..		..	2 23	..	..
Staines .... dep.		..	..	1 57		2 16		..	2 27	..	..
Ashford (Middlesex)		..	..	2 1		..		..	2 31	..	..
Feltham		..	..	2 5		..		..	2 35	..	..
Hounslow D .... dep.		..	1 59	..	..	..		2 29	..	..	..
Whitton	V	..	2 3	2 9	..	..	V	2 33	2 39	..	..
Teddington F .... dep.	1 41	..	..	..	..	..	2 21	..	..	..	..
Strawberry Hill	1 44	..	..	..	2 14	..	2 24	..	..	..	..
Twickenham	1 47	1 49	2 5	2 12	2 17	..	2 27	2 35	2 42	2 26	..
St. Margaret's	1 49	..	..	..	2 19	..	2 29	2 37	..	..	..
Richmond	1 52	..	..	2 16	2 22	..	2 32	2 40	2 46	..	..
North Sheen	1 54	..	..	..	2 24	..	2 34	2 43	..	..	..
Mortlake, for East Sheen	1 57	..	..	..	2 27	..	2 37	2 45	..	..	..
Whitton	..	1 51	..	..	..	..	..	..	..	2 28	..
Hounslow D	..	1 58	..	..	..	..	..	..	..	2 33	..
Isleworth C	..	2 1	..	..	..	..	..	..	..	2 36	..
Syon Lane	..	2 3	..	..	..	..	..	..	..	2 38	..
Brentford B	..	2 6	..	..	..	..	..	..	..	2 41	..
Kew Bridge	..	2 8	..	..	..	..	..	..	..	2 43	..
Chiswick, for Grove Park	..	2 11	..	..	..	..	..	..	..	2 46	..
Barnes Bridge	..	2 14	..	..	..	..	..	..	..	2 49	..
Barnes	2 0	2 17	..	..	2 30	..	2 40	2 48	..	2 51	..
Putney	2 3	2 20	..	..	2 33	..	2 43	2 51	..	2 54	..
Wandsworth Town	2 6	2 23	..	..	2 36	..	2 46	2 54	..	2 57	..
Clapham Junction A	2 8	2 25	..	2 25	2 38	..	2 48	2 56	2 55	3 0	..
Queen's Road	2 11	2 28	..	..	2 41	..	..	2 59	..	3 3	..
Vauxhall	2 14	2 31	..	..	2 44	..	2 52	3 2	..	3 6	..
Waterloo .... arr.	2 18	2 35	..	2 32	2 48	2 42	2 56	3 6	3 2	3 10	..

Up	3 (From Waterloo via Kingston)	3	3	3	3 (From Shepperton, dep. 2 58 p.m see page 451.)		3 (From Waterloo via Kingston)	3	3	3		3 (From Waterloo via Kingston)
Reading .... dep.	..	..	..	..	..	2 28	..	..	..	..	..	..
Earley	..	..	..	..	..	2 33	..	..	..	..	..	..
Winnersh Halt Z	..	..	..	..	..	2 37	..	..	..	..	..	..
Wokingham	..	..	..	..	..	2 41	..	..	..	..	..	..
Bracknell	..	..	..	..	..	2 48	..	..	..	..	..	..
Ascot 388 .... arr.	..	..	..	..	..	2 54	..	..	..	..	..	..
Aldershot .... dep.	..	..	..	..	..	2 24	..	..	..	..	..	..
Ash Vale W	..	..	..	..	..	2 29	..	..	..	..	..	..
Frimley T	..	..	..	..	..	2 35	..	..	..	..	..	..
Camberley Q	..	..	..	..	..	2 40	..	..	..	..	..	..
Bagshot	..	..	..	..	..	2 46	..	..	..	..	..	..
Ascot .... arr.	..	..	..	..	..	2 51	..	..	..	..	..	..
Ascot .... dep.	..	..	..	..	..	2 56	..	..	..	..	..	..
Sunningdale P	..	..	..	..	..	3 0	..	..	..	..	..	..
Longcross Halt	..	..	..	..	..	3 3	..	..	..	..	..	..
Virginia Water M 427 arr.	..	..	..	..		3 7	..	..	..	..	..	..
Weybridge .... dep.	..	..	..	2 35		..	..	..	3 5	..	..	..
Addlestone		..	..	2 39		..		..	3 9	..	..	
Chertsey		..	..	2 42		..		..	3 12	..	..	
Virginia Water M .. arr.		..	..	2 46		..		..	3 16	..	..	
Virginia Water M ... dep.		..	..	2 46		3 7		..	3 16	..	..	
Egham L		..	..	2 50		3 11		..	3 20	..	..	
Staines J .... arr.		..	..	2 55		3 16		..	3 25	..	..	
Windsor and Eton .. dep.		..	..	2 36		..		..	3 6	..	..	
Datchet		..	..	2 40		..		..	3 10	..	..	
Sunnymeads		..	..	2 44		..		..	3 14	..	..	
Wraysbury		..	..	2 47		..		..	3 17	..	..	
Staines J .... arr.		..	..	2 53		..		..	3 23	..	..	
Staines .... dep.		..	..	2 57		3 16		..	3 27	..	..	
Ashford (Middlesex)		..	..	3 1		..		..	3 31	..	..	
Feltham		..	..	3 5		..		..	3 35	..	..	
Hounslow D .... dep.		..	2 59	..		..		3 29	..	..	..	
Whitton	V	..	3 3	3 9		..	V	3 33	3 39	..	..	V
Teddington F .... dep.	2 41	..	..	..		..	3 21	..	..	..	..	3 41
Strawberry Hill	2 44	..	..	..	3 14	..	3 24	..	..	..	..	3 44
Twickenham	2 47	2 49	3 5	3 12	3 17	..	3 27	3 35	3 42	3 26	..	3 47
St. Margaret's	2 49	..	..	..	3 19	..	3 29	3 37	..	..	..	3 49
Richmond	2 52	..	..	3 16	3 22	..	3 32	3 40	3 46	..	..	3 52
North Sheen	2 54	..	..	..	3 24	..	3 34	3 43	..	..	..	3 54
Mortlake, for East Sheen	2 57	..	..	..	3 27	..	3 37	3 45	..	..	..	3 57
Whitton	..	2 51	..	..	..	..	..	..	..	3 28	..	..
Hounslow D	..	2 58	..	..	..	..	..	..	..	3 33	..	..
Isleworth C	..	3 1	..	..	..	..	..	..	..	3 36	..	..
Syon Lane	..	3 3	..	..	..	..	..	..	..	3 38	..	..
Brentford B	..	3 6	..	..	..	..	..	..	..	3 41	..	..
Kew Bridge	..	3 8	..	..	..	..	..	..	..	3 43	..	..
Chiswick, for Grove Park	..	3 11	..	..	..	..	..	..	..	3 46	..	..
Barnes Bridge	..	3 14	..	..	..	..	..	..	..	3 49	..	..
Barnes	3 0	3 17	..	..	3 30	..	3 40	3 48	..	3 51	..	4 0
Putney	3 3	3 20	..	..	3 33	..	3 43	3 51	..	3 54	..	4 3
Wandsworth Town	3 6	3 23	..	..	3 36	..	3 46	3 54	..	3 57	..	4 6
Clapham Junction A	3 8	3 25	..	3 25	3 38	..	3 48	3 56	3 55	4 0	..	4 8
Queen's Road	3 11	3 28	..	..	3 41	..	..	3 59	..	4 3	..	4 11
Vauxhall	3 14	3 31	..	..	3 44	..	3 52	4 2	..	4 6	..	4 14
Waterloo .... arr.	3 18	3 35	..	3 32	3 48	3 42	3 56	4 6	4 2	4 10	..	4 18

FOR NOTES, SEE PAGE 489

FOR NOTES, SEE PAGE 489

READING, WINDSOR, STAINES, TEDDINGTON, TWICKENHAM, RICHMOND, HOUNSLOW, and LONDON ●

Sundays—continued

Up (p.m.)	3	3	3	3 (From Shepperton, dep. 3 58 p.m., see page 451.)	3 (From Waterloo via Kingston)		3	3	3	
Reading ....dep.	..	..	..	..	..	3 28	..	..	..	..
Earley	..	..	..	..	..	3 33	..	..	..	..
Winnersh Halt **Z**	..	..	..	..	..	3 37	..	..	..	..
Wokingham	..	..	..	..	..	3 41	..	..	..	..
Bracknell	..	..	..	..	..	3 48	..	..	..	..
Ascot 388 ....arr.	..	..	..	..	..	3 54	..	..	..	..
Aldershot ....dep.	..	..	..	..	..	3 24	..	..	..	..
Ash Vale **W**	..	..	..	..	..	3 29	..	..	..	..
Frimley **T**	..	..	..	..	..	3 35	..	..	..	..
Camberley **Q**	..	..	..	..	..	3 40	..	..	..	..
Bagshot	..	..	..	..	..	3 46	..	..	..	..
Ascot ....arr.	..	..	..	..	..	3 51	..	..	..	..
Ascot ....dep.	..	..	..	..	..	3 56	..	..	..	..
Sunningdale **P**	..	..	..	..	..	4 0	..	..	..	..
Longcross Halt	..	..	..	..	..	4 3	..	..	..	..
Virginia Water M427 arr.	..	..	..	..	..	4 7	..	..	..	..
Weybridge ....dep.	..	..	3 35		..	..	..	4 5	..	..
Addlestone	..	..	3 39			..	..	4 9	..	..
Chertsey	..	..	3 42			..	..	4 12	..	..
Virginia Water M ..arr.	..	..	3 46			..	..	4 16	..	..
Virginia Water M ....dep.	..	..	3 46			4 7	..	4 16	..	..
Egham **L**	..	..	3 50			4 11	..	4 20	..	..
Staines J ....arr	..	..	3 55			4 16	..	4 25	..	..
Windsor and Eton ..dep.	..	..	3 36			..	..	4 6	..	..
Datchet	..	..	3 40			..	..	4 10	..	..
Sunnymeads	..	..	3 44			..	..	4 14	..	..
Wraysbury	..	..	3 47			..	..	4 17	..	..
Staines J ....arr.	..	..	3 53			..	..	4 23	..	..
Staines ....dep.	..	..	3 57			4 16	..	4 27	..	..
Ashford (Middlesex)	..	..	4 1			..	..	4 31	..	..
Feltham	..	..	4 5			..	..	4 35	..	..
Hounslow D ....dep.	..	3 59	..			..	4 29	..	..	..
Whitten	..	4 3	4 9		V	..	4 33	4 39	..	..
Teddington F ....dep.	..	..	..		4 21	..	..	..	..	..
Strawberry Hill	..	..	..	4 14	4 24	..	..	..	..	..
Twickenham	3 49	4 5	4 12	4 17	4 27	..	4 35	4 42	4 26	..
St. Margaret's	..	..	..	4 19	4 29	..	4 37	..	..	..
Richmond	..	..	4 16	4 22	4 32	..	4 40	4 46	..	..
North Sheen	..	..	..	4 24	4 34	..	4 43	..	..	..
Mortlake, for East Sheen	..	..	..	4 27	4 37	..	4 45	..	..	..
Whitten	3 51	..	..	..	..	..	..	..	4 28	..
Hounslow D	3 58	..	..	..	..	..	..	..	4 33	..
Isleworth **C**	4 1	..	..	..	..	..	..	..	4 36	..
Syon Lane	4 3	..	..	..	..	..	..	..	4 38	..
Brentford **B**	4 6	..	..	..	..	..	..	..	4 41	..
Kew Bridge	4 8	..	..	..	..	..	..	..	4 43	..
Chiswick, for Grove Park	4 11	..	..	..	..	..	..	..	4 46	..
Barnes Bridge	4 14	..	..	..	..	..	..	..	4 49	..
Barnes	4 17	..	..	4 30	4 40	..	4 48	..	4 51	..
Putney	4 20	..	..	4 33	4 43	..	4 51	..	4 54	..
Wandsworth Town	4 23	..	..	4 36	4 46	..	4 54	..	4 57	..
Clapham Junction **A**	4 25	..	4 25	4 38	4 48	..	4 56	4 55	5 0	..
Queen's Road	4 28	..	..	4 41	..	..	4 59	..	5 3	..
Vauxhall	4 31	..	..	4 44	4 52	..	5 2	..	5 6	..
Waterloo ....arr.	4 35	..	4 32	4 48	4 56	4 42	5 6	5 2	5 10	..

Up (p.m.)	3 (From Waterloo via Kingston)	3	3	3	3 (From Shepperton, dep. 4 58 p.m., see page 452)		3 (From Waterloo via Kingston)	3	3	3	
Reading ....dep.	..	..	..	..	..	4 28	..	..	..	..	..
Earley	..	..	..	..	..	4 33	..	..	..	..	..
Winnersh Halt **Z**	..	..	..	..	..	4 37	..	..	..	..	..
Wokingham	..	..	..	..	..	4 41	..	..	..	..	..
Bracknell	..	..	..	..	..	4 48	..	..	..	..	..
Ascot 388 ....arr.	..	..	..	..	..	4 54	..	..	..	..	..
Aldershot ....dep.	..	..	..	..	..	4 24	..	..	..	..	..
Ash Vale **W**	..	..	..	..	..	4 29	..	..	..	..	..
Frimley **T**	..	..	..	..	..	4 35	..	..	..	..	..
Camberley **Q**	..	..	..	..	..	4 40	..	..	..	..	..
Bagshot	..	..	..	..	..	4 46	..	..	..	..	..
Ascot ....arr.	..	..	..	..	..	4 51	..	..	..	..	..
Ascot ....dep.	..	..	..	..	..	4 56	..	..	..	..	..
Sunningdale **P**	..	..	..	..	..	5 0	..	..	..	..	..
Longcross Halt	..	..	..	..	..	5 3	..	..	..	..	..
Virginia Water M427 arr.	..	..	..	..	..	5 7	..	..	..	..	..
Weybridge ....dep.	..	..	..	4 35		..	..	..	5 5	..	..
Addlestone		..	..	4 39		..		..	5 9	..	..
Chertsey		..	..	4 42		..		..	5 12	..	..
Virginia Water M ..arr.		..	..	4 46		..		..	5 16	..	..
Virginia Water M ....dep.		..	..	4 46		5 7		..	5 16	..	..
Egham **L**		..	..	4 50		5 11		..	5 20	..	..
Staines J ....arr		..	..	4 55		5 16		..	5 25	..	..
Windsor and Eton ..dep.		..	..	4 36		..		..	5 6	..	..
Datchet		..	..	4 40		..		..	5 10	..	..
Sunnymeads		..	..	4 44		..		..	5 14	..	..
Wraysbury		..	..	4 47		..		..	5 17	..	..
Staines J ....arr.		..	..	4 53		..		..	5 23	..	..
Staines ....dep.		..	..	4 57		5 16		..	5 27	..	..
Ashford (Middlesex)		..	..	5 1		..		..	5 31	..	..
Feltham		..	..	5 5		..		..	5 35	..	..
Hounslow D ....dep.		..	4 59	..		..		5 29	..	..	..
Whitten	V	..	5 3	5 9		..	V	5 33	5 39	..	..
Teddington F ....dep.	4 41	..	..	..		..	5 21	..	..	..	..
Strawberry Hill	4 44	..	..	..	5 14	..	5 24	..	..	..	..
Twickenham	4 47	4 49	5 5	5 12	5 17	..	5 27	5 35	5 42	5 26	..
St. Margaret's	4 49	..	..	..	5 19	..	5 29	5 37	..	..	..
Richmond	4 52	..	..	5 16	5 22	..	5 32	5 40	5 46	..	..
North Sheen	4 54	..	..	..	5 24	..	5 34	5 43	..	..	..
Mortlake, for East Sheen	4 57	..	..	..	5 27	..	5 37	5 45	..	..	..
Whitten	..	4 51	..	..	..	..	..	..	..	5 28	..
Hounslow D	..	4 58	..	..	..	..	..	..	..	5 33	..
Isleworth **C**	..	5 1	..	..	..	..	..	..	..	5 36	..
Syon Lane	..	5 3	..	..	..	..	..	..	..	5 38	..
Brentford **B**	..	5 6	..	..	..	..	..	..	..	5 41	..
Kew Bridge	..	5 8	..	..	..	..	..	..	..	5 43	..
Chiswick, for Grove Park	..	5 11	..	..	..	..	..	..	..	5 46	..
Barnes Bridge	..	5 14	..	..	..	..	..	..	..	5 49	..
Barnes	5 0	5 17	..	..	5 30	..	5 40	5 48	..	5 51	..
Putney	5 3	5 20	..	..	5 33	..	5 43	5 51	..	5 54	..
Wandsworth Town	5 6	5 23	..	..	5 36	..	5 46	5 54	..	5 57	..
Clapham Junction **A**	5 8	5 25	..	5 25	5 38	..	5 48	5 56	5 55	6 0	..
Queen's Road	5 11	5 28	..	..	5 41	..	..	5 59	..	6 3	..
Vauxhall	5 14	5 31	..	..	5 44	..	5 52	6 2	..	6 6	..
Waterloo ....arr.	5 18	5 35	..	5 32	5 48	5 42	5 56	6 6	6 2	6 10	..

Up (p.m.)	3 (From Waterloo via Kingston)	3	3	3		3 (From Shepperton, dep. 5 58 p.m., see page 452)		3 (From Waterloo via Kingston)	3	3	3
Reading ....dep.	..	..	..	..	5 28	..	..	..	..	..	..
Earley	..	..	..	..	5 33	..	..	..	..	..	..
Winnersh Halt **Z**	..	..	..	..	5 37	..	..	..	..	..	..
Wokingham	..	..	..	..	5 41	..	..	..	..	..	..
Bracknell	..	..	..	..	5 48	..	..	..	..	..	..
Ascot 388 ....arr.	..	..	..	..	5 54	..	..	..	..	..	..
Aldershot ....dep.	..	..	..	..	5 24	..	..	..	..	..	..
Ash Vale **W**	..	..	..	..	5 29	..	..	..	..	..	..
Frimley **T**	..	..	..	..	5 35	..	..	..	..	..	..
Camberley **Q**	..	..	..	..	5 40	..	..	..	..	..	..
Bagshot	..	..	..	..	5 46	..	..	..	..	..	..
Ascot ....arr.	..	..	..	..	5 51	..	..	..	..	..	..
Ascot ....dep.	..	..	..	..	5 56	..	..	..	..	..	..
Sunningdale **P**	..	..	..	..	6 0	..	..	..	..	..	..
Longcross Halt	..	..	..	..	6 3	..	..	..	..	..	..
Virginia Water M427 arr.	..	..	..	..	6 7		..	..	..	..	..
Weybridge ....dep.	..	..	..	5 35	..		..	..	..	6 5	..
Addlestone		..	..	5 39	..		..		..	6 9	..
Chertsey		..	..	5 42	..		..		..	6 12	..
Virginia Water M ..arr.		..	..	5 46	..		..		..	6 16	..
Virginia Water M ....dep.		..	..	5 46	6 7		..		..	6 16	..
Egham **L**		..	..	5 50	6 11		..		..	6 20	..
Staines J ....arr		..	..	5 55	6 16		..		..	6 25	..
Windsor and Eton ..dep.		..	..	5 36	..		..		..	6 6	..
Datchet		..	..	5 40	..		..		..	6 10	..
Sunnymeads		..	..	5 44	..		..		..	6 14	..
Wraysbury		..	..	5 47	..		..		..	6 17	..
Staines J ....arr.		..	..	5 53	..		..		..	6 23	..
Staines ....dep.		..	..	5 57	6 16		..		..	6 27	..
Ashford (Middlesex)		..	..	6 1	..		..		..	6 31	..
Feltham		..	..	6 5	..		..		..	6 35	..
Hounslow D ....dep.		..	5 59	..	..		..		6 29	..	..
Whitten	V	..	6 3	6 9	..		..	V	6 33	6 39	..
Teddington F ....dep.	5 41	..	..	..	..		..	6 21	..	..	..
Strawberry Hill	5 44	..	..	..	..	6 14	..	6 24	..	..	..
Twickenham	5 47	5 49	6 5	6 12	..	6 17	..	6 27	6 35	6 42	6 26
St. Margaret's	5 49	..	..	..	..	6 19	..	6 29	6 37	..	..
Richmond	5 52	..	..	6 16	..	6 22	..	6 32	6 40	6 46	..
North Sheen	5 54	..	..	..	..	6 24	..	6 34	6 43	..	..
Mortlake, for East Sheen	5 57	..	..	..	..	6 27	..	6 37	6 45	..	..
Whitten	..	5 51	..	..	..	..	..	..	..	..	6 28
Hounslow D	..	5 58	..	..	..	..	..	..	..	..	6 33
Isleworth **C**	..	6 1	..	..	..	..	..	..	..	..	6 36
Syon Lane	..	6 3	..	..	..	..	..	..	..	..	6 38
Brentford **B**	..	6 6	..	..	..	..	..	..	..	..	6 41
Kew Bridge	..	6 8	..	..	..	..	..	..	..	..	6 43
Chiswick, for Grove Park	..	6 11	..	..	..	..	..	..	..	..	6 46
Barnes Bridge	..	6 14	..	..	..	..	..	..	..	..	6 49
Barnes	6 0	6 17	..	..	..	6 30	..	6 40	6 48	..	6 52
Putney	6 3	6 20	..	..	..	6 33	..	6 43	6 52	..	6 55
Wandsworth Town	6 6	6 23	..	..	..	6 36	..	6 46	6 55	..	6 58
Clapham Junction **A**	6 8	6 25	..	6 25	..	6 38	..	6 48	6 57	6 55	7 0
Queen's Road	6 11	6 28	..	..	..	6 41	..	..	7 0	..	7 3
Vauxhall	6 14	6 31	..	..	..	6 44	..	6 52	7 3	..	7 6
Waterloo ....arr.	6 18	6 35	..	6 32	6 42	6 48	..	6 56	7 7	7 2	7 10

READING, WINDSOR, STAINES, TEDDINGTON, TWICKENHAM, RICHMOND, HOUNSLOW, and LONDON

Sundays—continued (p.m)

Up	3	3	3	3	3	3		3	3	3		3	3	3	3	3		3	3	3	3		3	3	3	3	3		3	3	3	3
Reading ....dep.	..	..	..	..	..	..	6 28	..	..	..	..	..	..	..	..	..	7 28	..	..	..	..	..	..	..	..	..	..	8 28	..	..	..	..
Earley	..	..	..	..	..	..	6 33	..	..	..	..	..	..	..	..	..	7 33	..	..	..	..	..	..	..	..	..	..	8 33	..	..	..	..
Winnersh Halt **Z**	..	..	..	..	..	..	6 37	..	..	..	..	..	..	..	..	..	7 37	..	..	..	..	..	..	..	..	..	..	8 37	..	..	..	..
Wokingham	..	..	..	..	..	..	6 41	..	..	..	..	..	..	..	..	..	7 41	..	..	..	..	..	..	..	..	..	..	8 41	..	..	..	..
Bracknell	..	..	..	..	..	..	6 48	..	..	..	..	..	..	..	..	..	7 48	..	..	..	..	..	..	..	..	..	..	8 48	..	..	..	..
Ascot 388 ....arr.	..	..	..	..	..	..	6 54	..	..	..	..	..	..	..	..	..	7 54	..	..	..	..	..	..	..	..	..	..	8 54	..	..	..	..
Aldershot ....dep.	..	..	..	..	..	..	6 24	..	..	..	..	..	..	..	..	..	7 24	..	..	..	..	..	..	..	..	..	..	8 24	..	..	..	..
Ash Vale **W**	..	..	..	..	..	..	6 29	..	..	..	..	..	..	..	..	..	7 29	..	..	..	..	..	..	..	..	..	..	8 29	..	..	..	..
Frimley **T**	..	..	..	..	..	..	6 35	..	..	..	..	..	..	..	..	..	7 35	..	..	..	..	..	..	..	..	..	..	8 35	..	..	..	..
Camberley **Q**	..	..	..	..	..	..	6 40	..	..	..	..	..	..	..	..	..	7 40	..	..	..	..	..	..	..	..	..	..	8 40	..	..	..	..
Bagshot	..	..	..	..	..	..	6 46	..	..	..	..	..	..	..	..	..	7 46	..	..	..	..	..	..	..	..	..	..	8 46	..	..	..	..
Ascot ....arr.	..	..	..	..	..	..	6 51	..	..	..	..	..	..	..	..	..	7 51	..	..	..	..	..	..	..	..	..	..	8 51	..	..	..	..
Ascot ....dep.	..	..	..	..	..	..	6 56	..	..	..	..	..	..	..	..		7 56	..	..	..	..	..	..	..	..	..		8 56	..	..	..	..
Sunningdale **P**	..	..	..	..	..	..	7 0	..	..	..	..	..	..	..	..		8 0	..	..	..	..	..	..	..	..	..		9 0	..	..	..	..
Longcross Halt	..	..	..	..	..	..	7 3	..	..	..	..	..	..	..	..		8 3	..	..	..	..	..	..	..	..	..		9 3	..	..	..	..
Virginia Water M 427 arr.	..	..	..	..	..	..	7 7	..	..	..	..	..	..	..	..		8 7	..	..	..	..	..	..	..	..	..		9 7	..	..	..	..
Weybridge ....dep.	..	..	..	6 35		..	..	..	7 5	..	..	..	..	..	7 35		..	..	..	8 5	..	..	..	..	..	8 35		..	..	..	9 5	..
Addlestone		..	..	6 39		..	..	..	7 9	..	..	..	..	..	7 39		..	..	..	8 9	..	..	..	..	..	8 39		..	..	..	9 9	..
Chertsey		..	..	6 42		..	..	..	7 12	..	..	..	..	..	7 42		..	..	..	8 12	..	..	..	..	..	8 42		..	..	..	9 12	..
Virginia Water M ..arr.		..	..	6 46		..	..	..	7 16	..	..	..	..	..	7 46		..	..	..	8 16	..	..	..	..	..	8 46		..	..	..	9 16	..
Virginia Water M ....dep.		..	..	6 46			7 7	..	7 16	..	..		..	..	7 46		8 7		..	8 16	..	..		..	..	8 46		9 7		..	9 16	..
Egham **L**		..	..	6 50			7 11	..	7 20	..	..		..	..	7 50		8 11		..	8 20	..	..		..	..	8 50		9 11		..	9 20	..
Staines J ....arr.		..	..	6 55			7 16	..	7 25	..	..		..	..	7 55		8 16		..	8 25	..	..		..	..	8 55		9 16		..	9 25	..
Windsor and Eton ..dep.	From Waterloo via Kingston	..	..	6 36	From Shepperton, dep. 6 58 p.m, see page 453.	From Waterloo via Kingston	..	..	7 6	..	..	From Waterloo via Kingston	..	..	7 36	From Shepperton, dep. 7 58 p.m, see page 454.	..	From Waterloo via Kingston	..	8 6	..	..	From Waterloo via Kingston	..	..	8 36	From Shepperton, dep. 8 58 p.m see page 454.	..	From Waterloo via Kingston	..	9 6	..
Datchet		..	..	6 40			..	..	7 10	..	..		..	..	7 40		..		..	8 10	..	..		..	..	8 40		..		..	9 10	..
Sunnymeads		..	..	6 44			..	..	7 14	..	..		..	..	7 44		..		..	8 14	..	..		..	..	8 44		..		..	9 14	..
Wraysbury		..	..	6 47			..	..	7 17	..	..		..	..	7 47		..		..	8 17	..	..		..	..	8 47		..		..	9 17	..
Staines J ....arr.		..	..	6 53			..	..	7 23	..	..		..	..	7 53		..		..	8 23	..	..		..	..	8 53		..		..	9 23	..
Staines ....dep		..	..	6 57			7 16	..	7 27	..	..		..	..	7 57		8 16		..	8 27	..	..		..	..	8 57		9 16		..	9 27	..
Ashford (Middlesex)		..	..	7 1			..	..	7 31	..	..		..	..	8 1		..		..	8 31	..	..		..	..	9 1		..		..	9 31	..
Feltham		..	..	7 5			..	..	7 35	..	..		..	..	8 5		..		..	8 35	..	..		..	..	9 5		..		..	9 35	..
Hounslow D ....dep.		..	6 59	..			..	7 29	..	..	..		..	7 59		..	..		8 29	..		..		..	8 59	..	..	..		9 29	..	..
Whitten	V	..	7 3	7 9		V	..	7 33	7 39	..	..	V	..	8 3	8 9	..	..	V	8 33	8 39	..	..	V	..	9 3	9 9	..	..	V	9 33	9 39	..
Teddington F ......dep.	6 41	..	..	..		7 21	..	..	..	..	..	7 41	..	..	..	..	..	8 21	..	..	..	..	8 41	..	..	..	..	..	9 21	..	..	..
Strawberry Hill	6 44	..	..	..	7 14	7 24	..	..	..	..	..	7 44		..	..	8 14	..	8 24	..	..	..	..	8 44	..	..	..	9 14	..	9 24	..	..	..
Twickenham	6.47	6 49	7 5	7 12	7 17	7 27	..	7 35	7 42	7 26	..	7 47	7 49	8 5	8 12	8 17	..	8 27	8 35	8 42	8 26	..	8 47	8 49	9 5	9 12	9 17	..	9 27	9 35	9 42	9 26
St. Margaret's	6 49	..	..	..	7 19	7 29	..	7 37	..	..	..	7 49	..	..	..	8 19	..	8 29	8 37	..	..	..	8 49	..	..	..	9 19	..	9 29	9 37	..	..
Richmond	6 52	..	..	7 16	7 22	7 32	..	7 40	7 46	..	..	7 52	..	..	8 16	8 22	..	8 32	8 40	8 46	..	..	8 52	..	..	9 16	9 22	..	9 32	9 40	9 46	..
North Sheen	6 54	..	..	..	7 24	7 34	..	7 43	..	..	..	7 54	..	..	..	8 24	..	8 34	8 43	..	..	..	8 54	..	..	..	9 24	..	9 34	9 43	..	..
Mortlake, for East Sheen	6 57	..	..	..	7 27	7 37	..	7 45	..	..	..	7 57	..	..	..	8 27	..	8 37	8 45	..	..	..	8 57	..	..	..	9 27	..	9 37	9 45	..	..
Whitton	..	6 51	..	..	..	..	..	..	..	7 28	..	..	7 51	..	..	..	..	..	..	..	8 28	..	..	8 51	..	..	..	..	..	..	..	9 28
Hounslow D	..	6 58	..	..	..	..	..	..	..	7 33	..	..	7 58	..	..	..	..	..	..	..	8 33	..	..	8 58	..	..	..	..	..	..	..	9 33
Isleworth **C**	..	7 1	..	..	..	..	..	..	..	7 36	..	..	8 1	..	..	..	..	..	..	..	8 36	..	..	9 1	..	..	..	..	..	..	..	9 36
Syon Lane	..	7 3	..	..	..	..	..	..	..	7 38	..	..	8 3	..	..	..	..	..	..	..	8 38	..	..	9 3	..	..	..	..	..	..	..	9 38
Brentford **B**	..	7 6	..	..	..	..	..	..	..	7 41	..	..	8 6	..	..	..	..	..	..	..	8 41	..	..	9 6	..	..	..	..	..	..	..	9 41
Kew Bridge	..	7 8	..	..	..	..	..	..	..	7 43	..	..	8 8	..	..	..	..	..	..	..	8 43	..	..	9 8	..	..	..	..	..	..	..	9 43
Chiswick, for Grove Park	..	7 11	..	..	..	..	..	..	..	7 46	..	..	8 11	..	..	..	..	..	..	..	8 46	..	..	9 11	..	..	..	..	..	..	..	9 46
Barnes Bridge	..	7 14	..	..	..	..	..	..	..	7 49	..	..	8 14	..	..	..	..	..	..	..	8 49	..	..	9 14	..	..	..	..	..	..	..	9 49
Barnes	7 0	7 17	..	..	7 30	7 40	..	7 48	..	7 51	..	8 0	8 17	..	..	8 30	..	8 40	8 48	..	8 51	..	9 0	9 17	..	..	9 30	..	9 40	9 48	..	9 51
Putney	7 3	7 20	..	..	7 33	7 43	..	7 51	..	7 54	..	8 3	8 20	..	..	8 33	..	8 43	8 51	..	8 54	..	9 3	9 20	..	..	9 33	..	9 43	9 51	..	9 54
Wandsworth Town	7 6	7 23	..	..	7 36	7 46	..	7 54	..	7 57	..	8 6	8 23	..	..	8 36	..	8 46	8 54	..	8 57	..	9 6	9 23	..	..	9 36	..	9 46	9 54	..	9 57
Clapham Junction A	7 8	7 25	..	7 25	7 38	7 49	..	7 56	7 55	8 0	..	8 8	8 23	..	8 25	8 38	..	8 48	8 56	8 55	9 0	..	9 8	9 25	..	9 25	9 38	..	9 48	9 56	9 55	10 0
Queen's Road	7 11	7 28	..	..	7 41	..	..	7 59	..	8 3	..	8 11	8 28	..	..	8 41	..	..	8 59	..	9 3	..	9 11	9 28	..	..	9 41	..	..	9 59	..	10 3
Vauxhall	7 14	7 31	..	..	7 44	7 53	..	8 2	..	8 6	..	8 14	8 31	..	..	8 44	..	8 52	9 2	..	9 6	..	9 14	9 31	..	..	9 44	..	9 52	10 2	..	10 6
Waterloo ....arr.	7 18	7 35	..	7 32	7 48	7 57	7 42	8 6	8 2	8 10	..	8 18	8 35	..	8 32	8 48	8 42	8 56	9 6	9 2	9 10	..	9 18	9 35	..	9 32	9 48	9 42	9 56	10 6	10 2	1010

FOR NOTES, SEE PAGE 489

READING, WINDSOR, STAINES, TEDDINGTON, TWICKENHAM, RICHMOND, HOUNSLOW, and LONDON

Sundays—*continued* (p.m)

Up	3	3	3	3		3	3	3		3	3		3	3		3	3	3	3	3	3	3	3	3	3 ngt.	
Reading....dep.	..	..	..	..	9 28	..	..	..	..	..	..	9 58	..	..	..	..	..	..	..	..	..	..	..	..	..	..
Earley	..	..	..	..	9 33	..	..	..	..	..	..	10 3	..	..	..	..	..	..	..	..	..	..	..	..	..	..
Winnersh Halt Z	..	..	..	..	9 37	..	..	..	..	..	..	10 7	..	..	..	..	..	..	..	..	..	..	..	..	..	..
Wokingham	..	..	..	..	9 41	..	..	..	..	..	..	1011	..	..	..	..	..	..	..	..	..	..	..	..	..	..
Bracknell	..	..	..	..	9 48	..	..	..	..	..	..	1018	..	..	..	..	..	..	..	..	..	..	..	..	..	..
Ascot 388....arr.	..	..	..	..	9 54	..	..	..	..	..	..	1024	..	..	..	..	..	..	..	..	..	..	..	..	..	..
Aldershot....dep.	..	..	..	..	9 24	..	..	..	..	..	..	9 54	..	..	..	..	..	..	..	..	..	..	..	..	..	..
Ash Vale W	..	..	..	..	9 29	..	..	..	..	..	..	9 59	..	..	..	..	..	..	..	..	..	..	..	..	..	..
Frimley T	..	..	..	..	9 35	..	..	..	..	..	..	10 5	..	..	..	..	..	..	..	..	..	..	..	..	..	..
Camberley Q	..	..	..	..	9 40	..	..	..	..	..	..	1010	..	..	..	..	..	..	..	..	..	..	..	..	..	..
Bagshot	..	..	..	..	9 46	..	..	..	..	..	..	1016	..	..	..	..	..	..	..	..	..	..	..	..	..	..
Ascot....arr.	..	..	..	..	9 51	..	..	..	..	..	..	1021	..	..	..	..	..	..	..	..	..	..	..	..	..	..
Ascot....dep.	..	..	..	..	9 56	From Shepperton, dep. 9 58 p.m see page 455.	..	..	..	..	..	1026	..	..	..	..	..	From Kingston, dep 10 56 p.m page 421	..	From Shepperton, dep. 10 58 p.m see page 459.	..	..	..	..	..	..
Sunningdale P	..	..	..	..	10 0		..	..	..	..	..	1030	..	..	..	..	..		..		..	..	..	..	..	..
Longcross Halt	..	..	..	..	10 3		..	..	..	..	..	1033	..	..	..	..	..		..		..	..	..	..	..	..
Virginia Water M 427 arr.	..	..	..	..	10 7		..	..	..	..	..	1037	..	..	..	..	..		..		..	..	..	..	..	..
Weybridge....dep.	..	..	..	9 35	..		..	..	..	10 5	..	..	..	..	..	..	1035		1050		1135	..	..	..	..	..
Addlestone	..	..	..	9 39	..		..	..	..	10 9	..	..	..	..	..	..	1039		1054		1139	..	..	..	..	..
Chertsey	..	..	..	9 42	..		..	..	..	1012	..	..	..	..	..	..	1042		1057		1142	..	..	..	..	..
Virginia Water M..arr.	..	..	..	9 46	..		..	..	..	1016	..	..	..	..	..	..	1046		..		..	..	..	..	..	..
Virginia Water M....dep.	From Waterloo via Kingston	..	..	9 46	10 7		From Waterloo via Kingston	..	..	1016	..	1037	..	..	..	..	1046		..		..	..	..	..	..	..
Egham L		..	..	9 50	1011			..	..	1020	..	1041	..	..	..	..	1050		..		..	..	..	..	..	..
Staines J....arr.		..	..	9 55	1016			..	..	1025	..	1046		..	..	..	1055		..		..	..	..	..	..	..
Windsor and Eton...dep.		..	..	9 36	..			..	..	10 6	..	..	From Waterloo via Kingston	..	..	..	1040		..		..	From Waterloo via Kingston	From Waterloo via Kingston	From Waterloo via Kingston	From Waterloo via Kingston	..
Datchet		..	..	9 40	.			..	..	1010	..	..		..	..	..	1044		..		..					..
Sunnymeads		..	..	9 44	..			..	..	1014	..	..		..	..	..	1048		..		..					..
Wraysbury		..	..	9 47	..			..	..	1017	..	..		..	..	..	1051		..		..					..
Staines J....arr.		..	..	9 53	..			..	..	1023	..	..		..	..	..	1057		..		..					..
Staines....dep.		..	..	9 57	1016			..	..	1027	..	1046		..	..	..	1059		..		..					..
Ashford (Middlesex)		..	..	10 1	..			..	..	1031	..	..		..	..	..	11 3		..		..					..
Feltham		..	..	10 5	..			..	..	1035	..	..		..	..	..	11 7		..		..					..
Hounslow D....dep.		..	9 59	..	..	..		1029	..	..	..	..		..	.	1059	..	..	..	..	..					..
Whitton	V	..	10 3	10 9	..	..	V	1033	..	1039	..	..	V	..	..	11 4	1111	..	..	..	..	V	V	V	V	..
Teddington F....dep.	9 41	..	..	..	..	..	1021	..	..	..	..	..	1041	..	..	..	..	11 1	..	..	..	1121	1141	1155	1221	..
Strawberry Hill	9 44	..	..	..	..	1014	1024	..	..	..	..	..	1044	..	..	..	..	11 4	..	1114	..	1124	1144	1158	1224	..
Twickenham	9 47	9 49	10 5	1012	..	1017	1027	1035	..	1042	1026	..	1047	1049	..	11 6	1114	..	..	1117	..	..	..	..	..	..
St. Margaret's	9 49	..	..	..	..	1019	1029	1037	..	..	..	..	1049	..	..	..	..	..	..	1119	..	..	..	..	..	..
Richmond	9 52	..	..	1016	..	1022	1032	1040	..	1046	..	..	1052	..	..	..	1118	..	..	1122	..	..	..	..	..	..
North Sheen	9 54	..	..	..	..	1024	1034	1043	..	..	..	..	1054	..	..	..	..	..	..	1124	..	..	..	..	..	..
Mortlake, for East Sheen	9 57	..	..	..	..	1027	1037	1045	..	..	..	..	1057	..	..	..	..	..	..	1127	..	..	..	..	..	..
Whitton	..	9 51	..	..	..	..	..	..	..	..	1028	..	..	1051	..	..	..	..	..	..	..	..	..	..	..	..
Hounslow D	..	9 58	..	..	..	..	..	..	..	..	1033	..	..	1056	..	..	..	..	..	..	..	..	..	..	..	..
Isleworth C	..	10 1	.	..	..	..	..	..	..	..	1036	..	..	..	..	..	..	..	..	..	..	..	..	..	..	..
Syon Lane	..	10 3	..	..	..	..	..	..	..	..	1038	..	..	..	..	..	..	..	..	..	..	..	..	..	..	..
Brentford B	..	10 6	..	..	..	..	..	..	..	..	1041	..	..	..	..	..	..	..	..	..	..	..	..	..	..	..
Kew Bridge	..	10 8	..	..	..	..	..	..	..	..	1043	.	..	..	..	..	..	..	..	..	..	..	..	..	..	..
Chiswick, for Grove Park	..	1011	..	..	..	..	..	..	..	..	1046	..	..	..	..	..	..	..	..	..	..	..	..	..	..	..
Barnes Bridge	..	1014	..	..	..	..	..	..	..	..	1049	..	..	..	..	..	..	..	..	..	..	..	..	..	..	..
Barnes	10 0	1017	..	..	..	1030	1040	1048	..	..	1051	..	11 0	..	..	..	..	..	..	1130	..	..	..	..	..	..
Putney	10 3	1020	..	..	..	1033	1043	1051	..	..	1054	..	11 3	..	..	..	..	..	..	1133	..	..	..	..	..	..
Wandsworth Town	10 6	1023	..	..	..	1036	1046	1054	..	..	1057	..	11 6	..	..	..	..	..	..	1136	..	..	..	..	..	..
Clapham Junction A	10 8	1025	..	1025	..	1038	1048	1056	..	1055	11 0	..	11 8	..	..	..	1127	..	..	1138	..	..	..	..	..	..
Queen's Road	1011	1028	..	..	..	1041	..	1059	..	..	11 3	..	1111	..	..	..	..	..	..	1141	..	..	..	..	..	..
Vauxhall	1014	1031	..	..	..	1044	1052	11 2	..	..	11 6	..	1114	..	..	..	..	..	..	1144	..	..	..	..	..	..
Waterloo....arr	1018	1035	..	1032	1042	1048	1056	11 6	..	11 2	1110	1112	1118	..	..	..	1134	..	..	1148	..	..	..	..	..	..

NOTES.

3 Third class only
§ Stops to set down only

A Mid Battersea, 1½ miles to Clapham
B ½ mile to G.W. Sta.
B Arr. 6 mins. later on Saturdays.
C Sta. for Spring Grove
D About ½ mile to Hounslow Central & Hounslow East Stas.
F Sta. for Bushy Park.
H Arr. 6 40 a.m
J About 1 mile to G.W. Sta.
K Arr. 4 mins *earlier*
L Sta. for Englefield Green (1½ miles)
M Virginia Water (for Wentworth)
P Sta. for Windlesham
Q Station for Sandhurst (1½ miles) and nearly 1½ miles to Blackwater (Hants) Station.
SO or **S** Sats only.
SX or **X** Sats. excepted
T About 1 mile to Farnborough North Station
V For Service from Waterloo via Wimbledon & Kingston, see pages 394 to 426
W For North Camp and South Farnborough.
Z Halt for Sindlesham & Hurst.

OTHER TRAINS

BETWEEN	PAGE
Reading and Wokingham	249
Reading and London	249
Virginia Water and Waterloo	427
Teddington and Waterloo	427
Clapham Junction and Waterloo	427

DIDCOT, NEWBURY, WINCHESTER, and SOUTHAMPTON.—G.W.

Miles	Down.		Week Days. a.m	a.m	a.m	p.m	p.m	p.m (Saturdays only)	p.m	p.m	p.m (Saturdays only)	Sundays. p.m
	Didcot	dep	..	7 37	1050	..	1242	2 0	3 35	5 52	7 0	3 0
3	Upton and Blewbury		....	7 45	1056	....	1248	2 7	3 42	6 0	7 7	3 8
6¾	Churn		..	7 52	H	..	H	H	H	H	H	..
8½	Compton		....	7 58	11 7	....	1259	2 18	3 54	6 12	7 19	3 21
10¼	Hampstead Norris		..	8 3	1113	..	1 4	2 25	3 59	6 18	7 24	3 27
12¾	Pinewood Halt		....	8 9	1121	....	1 11	2 31	4 5	6 26	7 31	3 33
13½	Hermitage		..	8 12	1124	..	1 14	2 34	4 10	6 30	7 35	3 37
18	**Newbury**	arr	....	8 20	1133	....	1 25	2 50	4 18	6 41	7 43	3 45
		dep	7 45	9 5	1225	..	2 0		4 25	7 12		..
21½	Woodhay		7 53	9 16	1232	....	2 8		4 33	7 21		..
23½	Highclere		8 2	9 22	1238	..	2 14		4 39	7 27		..
25½	Burghclere **A**		8 8	9 27	1243	....	2 19		4 44	7 33		..
28	Litchfield (Hants)		8 14	9 33	1249	..	2 25		4 50	7 39		..
31½	Whitchurch **B**		8 22	9 40	1257	....	2 33		4 58	7 47		..
37½	Sutton Scotney		8 35	9 50	1 8	..	2 45		5 10	7 59		..
40½	Worthy Down Platform		8 45	9 56	1 15	....	2 55		5 20	8 7		..
42½	King's Worthy		8 50	10 2	1 20	..	3 2		5 25	8 12		..
44½	**Winchester** (Cheesehill) **C**	arr	8 55	10 8	1 26	....	3 7	....	5 30	8 17		..
		dep	9 6	10 14	..	1 27	3 20	..	5 38	8 23	..	..
47½	Shawford **D** 330	arr	9 13	10 21	....	1 34	3 29	....	5 47	8 32	....	..
51½	Eastleigh **F** 376 380		9 21	10 28	..	1 41	3 37	..	5 54	8 39	..	..
53½	Swaythling		..	10 35	....	2 10	3 44	....	6 1	8 47	....	..
55	St. Denys		9 29	10 39	..	2 14	3 48	..	6 5	8 51	..	..
56	Northam		..	10 43	....	2 19	3 52	....	6 9	8 55	....	..
56¾	Southampton Terminus **G** 324	arr	9 35	10 47	..	2 23	3 56	..	6 13	8 59	..	..

Miles	Up.		Week Days. a.m	a.m	a.m	a.m	a.m	p.m	p.m (Saturdays only)	p.m	p.m	p.m (Saturdays only)	Sundays. p.m
	Southampton Terminus G	dep	..	..	7 32	9 36	1126	1 55	..	4 55	7 35	..	..
¾	Northam		....	....	7 35	9 39	1129	1 58	....	4 58	7 38	....	....
1½	St. Denys		..	..	7 39	9 43	1133	2 2	..	5 2	7 42	..	..
3½	Swaythling		....	....	7 43	9 47	1137	2 6	....	5 5	7 46	....	....
5½	Eastleigh **F**		..	..	7 50	9 56	1145	2 20	..	5 12	7 54	..	..
9½	Shawford **D**		....	....	8 0	10 5	1153	2 29	....	5 19	8 5	....	....
12½	**Winchester** (Cheesehill) **C**	arr	..	..	8 8	1013	12 1	2 37	..	5 27	8 13	..	..
		dep	....	7 5	8 14	1025	12 7	2 45	....	5 33	....	....	....
14½	King's Worthy		..	7 10	8 20	1030	1213	2 50		5 39	..		..
16½	Worthy Down Platform		....	7 16	8 25	1036	1219	2 55		5 44	....		....
19½	Sutton Scotney		..	7 25	8 35	1043	1225	3 3		5 50	..		..
25	Whitchurch **B**		....	7 38	8 45	1054	1238	3 14		6 2	....		....
28¾	Litchfield (Hants)		..	7 48	8 55	11 4	1252	3 23		6 10	..		..
31½	Burghclere **A**		....	7 55	9 0	1110	1258	3 29		6 16	....		....
33½	Highclere		..	8 3	9 7	1115	1 3	3 34		6 22	..		..
35½	Woodhay		....	8 12	9 15	1122	1 10	3 39		6 28	....		....
38¾	**Newbury**	arr	..	8 21	9 22	1135	1 18	3 47		6 36	..	..	..
		dep	6 45	....	9 35	....	1 58	4 20	5 26	7 22	....	8 10	8 10
43½	Hermitage		6 55	..	9 45	..	2 7	4 30	5 35	7 32	..	8 20	8 20
44	Pinewood Halt		6 58	....	9 48	....	2 10	4 33	5 38	7 35	....	8 24	8 24
46½	Hampstead Norris		7 3	..	9 56	..	2 16	4 42	5 46	7 43	..	8 32	8 32
48½	Compton		7 10	....	10 3	....	2 21	4 50	5 52	7 49	....	8 40	8 40
50	Churn		..	..	T	..	T	T	T	T	..	T	..
53¾	Upton and Blewbury		7 20	....	1014	....	2 32	5 0	6 3	8 0	....	8 52	8 52
56¾	**Didcot**	arr	7 28	..	1020	..	2 38	5 8	6 9	8 10	..	9 0	9 0

3 Third class only.

A Station for Kingsclere (3½ miles).
B About 1½ miles to Southern Station.
C 1 mile from Southern Station.
D Station for Twyford.
F Station for Bishopstoke.
G Station for Docks

H Calls to pick up or set down passengers on previous notice to the Station Master at Didcot. Evening trains call during daylight only.

T Calls to pick up or set down passengers on previous notice to the Station Master at Newbury. Evening trains call during daylight only.

For Local Trains

BETWEEN	PAGE
Winchester and Southampton Terminus	384

BATH, TEMPLECOMBE and BOURNEMOUTH WEST

Somerset and Dorset—Southern and L. M. & S.

Miles from Bath	Week Days only	a.m	p.m	a.m	a.m	a.m	a.m	p.m	p.m (Thro' Train from Burnham-on-Sea)	a.m (Through Train, Manchester to Bournemouth)	p.m	p.m	a.m	p.m	p.m (Saturdays excepted)	p.m	p.m (Saturdays only)
	BRADFORD (Forster Square). dep	..	9L 0	..	..	..	..	..	..	7 35	..	..	9 20	..	..	..	1 30
	LEEDS (City) "	..	10 0	..	..	..	..	..	..	8 10	..	..	10 5	..	..	..	2 37
	YORK "	..	9 32	..	..	..	..	..	..	8 55	..	..	10 10	..	..	..	2 40
	SHEFFIELD "	..	11 17	..	..	..	..	..	..	10 10	..	..	11 35	..	..	..	3 57
	MANCHESTER (Lon. Rd.) "	..	10 25	..	..	..	..	..	..	10 20	..	..	..	..	..	..	3 0
	CREWE "	..	12 45	..	..	..	6 50	..	..	11 20	..	..	11 38	..	..	..	4 6
	NOTTINGHAM "	..	11 55	..	..	..	7 43	..	..	10 35	..	..	11 42	..	..	..	4 10
	DERBY "	..	12 45	..	..	..	8 22	..	..	11 10	..	..	12 35	..	..	..	4 58
	BURTON-ON-TRENT "	..	1 3	..	..	..	8 39	..	..	11 26	..	..	12 55	..	..	..	5 16
	LEICESTER "	..	..	..	..	..	7 45	..	..	10 10	..	..	..	..	..	..	4 8
	BIRMINGHAM (New Street) "	..	2 40	..	..	..	9 30	..	..	12 42	..	..	1 44	..	..	..	6 8
	Worcester (Shrub Hill) "	..	3 34	..	..	..	..	..	..	..	..	..	2 33	..	..	..	6 50
	CHELTENHAM SPA (Lansdown) "	..	4 9	..	..	..	10 36	..	..	1 42	..	..	3 4	..	..	..	7 37
	GLOUCESTER "	..	4 30	6 25	7 45	..	10 50	..	..	1 56	..	..	3 30	..	..	..	8 0
	BATH (L.M.S.) arr	..	6C44	8C10	9C55	..	12C20	..	..	2 50	..	..	4 25	..	..	..	9C51
	BRISTOL (Temple Meads).. dep	..	6 5	..	9 10	..	..	..	..	..	..	..	3 30	..	..	..	..
	" (St. Philips) "	..	..	7 27	..	..	12 12	..	..	1 5	..	..	..	..	4 47	5 50	9 15
	Mangotsfield "	..	6 28	7 45	9 30	..	12 27	..	..	1 19	..	..	3 47	..	5 8	6 5	9 29
	BATH (L.M.S.) arr	..	6 44	8 10	9 55	..	12 54	..	..	1 49	..	..	4 9	..	5 36	6 33	9 51
		a.m	a.m	a.m	a.m	a.m	p.m	p.m	p.m	p.m	p.m	p.m	p.m	p.m	p.m	p.m	p.m
—	**Bath** (L.M.S.) dep	..	6 55	8 15	10 5	..	1 10	..		2 55	..	3 10	4 35	4 45	6 0	7 0	10 0
4½	Midford	..	7 5	8 25	..	..	1 20	..		..	..	3 20	..	4 55	6 11	7 10	10 10
6½	Wellow	..	7 13	8 32	..	..	1 27	..		..	..	3 27	..	5 2	6 18	7 18	10 18
8½	Shoscombe and Single Hill Halt	..	7 17	8 35	..	..	1 30	..		..	..	3 30	..	5 5	6 23	7 20	10 22
10½	**Radstock**	..	7 25	8 45	1026	..	1 38	..		..	..	3 38	..	5 13	6 30	7 28	10 29
12½	Midsomer Norton and Welton	..	7 34	8 55	1035	..	1 47	..		..	..	3 47	..	5 22	6 40	7 37	10 38
14½	Chilcompton, for Downside	..	7 43	9 3	1043	..	1 56	..		..	..	3 56	..	5 31	6 48	7 46	
17	Binegar	..	7 51	9 12	..	..	2 4	..		..	..	4 4	..	5 39	6 56	7 54	
18½	Masbury Halt	..	7 55	9 17	..	..	2 9	..		..	..	4 9	..	5 44		7 58	
21½	**Shepton Mallet**	..	8 5	9 26	11 0	..	2 17	..		..	..	4 17	5 22	5 52		8 8	
25	Evercreech New	..	8 11	9 33	..	..	2 25	..		..	..	4 25	..	5 59		8 14	
26½	Evercreech Junc. C § 492.. arr	..	8 16	9 39	1110	..	2 30	..		3 49	..	4 30	5 34	6 4		8 20	
	dep	..	8 18	9 42	1112	..	2 32	..	3 30	3 50	..	4 32	5 36	6 5		8 25	
29½	Cole D §	..	8 27	9 51	..	..	2 40	..	..	..	..	4 40	..	6 13		8 35	
33½	Wincanton §	..	8 36	10 10	1125	..	2 50	..	..	..	..	4 50	5 48	6 25		8 45	
37	**Templecombe** § 340, 347 arr	..	8 45	10 20	1133	..	3 0	..	3 47	..	..	5 0	5 57	6 35		8 55	
149½	347 WATERLOO arr	..	11 46	2 29	2 29	..	6 40	..	6 40	..	..	1027	10 27	1027		3V55	..
	340 WATERLOO dep	..	..	..	..	9 0	..	1250	..	..	12 50	..	2 50	..	..	6 0	..
—	**Templecombe** dep	7 25	9 10	..	..	12 20	..	3 35	..	..	4 50	..	6 10	..	..	9 5	..
38½	Henstridge	7 34	9 18	..	..	12 28	..	..	..	..	4 58	..	..	..	..	9 14	..
40½	Stalbridge	7 43	9 23	..	..	12 35	..	3 45	..	..	5 5	..	6 19	..	..	9 20	..
44½	Sturminster Newton	8 0	9 32	..	..	12 47	..	3 53	..	..	5 16	..	6 27	..	..	9 28	..
47½	Shillingstone F	8 6	9 43	..	..	12 55	..	4 0	..	..	5 25	..	6 34	..	..	9 37	..
50½	Stourpaine and Durweston Halt	8 13	..	..	..	..	..	..	..	..	5 31	..	..	..	..	A	..
52½	**Blandford**	8 22	9 58	..	..	1 11	..	4 12	..	4 35	5 42	..	6 44	..	..	9 48	..
54½	Charlton Marshall Halt	8 27	10 3	..	..	1 15	..	..	..	..	5 46	..	..	..	..	A	..
56	Spetisbury Halt	8 32	10 8	..	..	1 20	..	..	..	..	5 51	..	..	..	..	9 55	..
59	Bailey Gate H	8D47	10 15	..	..	1 28	..	4 25	..	..	6 0	..	A	..	..	10 2	..
62	Corfe Mullen (East End) Halt	..	..	..	..	..	..	..	..	..	..	..	..	..	..	..	..
63½	Broadstone 339 arr	9 0	10 34	..	..	1 44	..	..	..	5Y44	6 14	..	7 3	..	..	10 15	..
65	Creekmoor Halt "	9 5	10 39	..	..	1 49	..	..	..	5Y39	6 18	..	8Y 3	..	..	10 21	..
64	336 WIMBORNE arr	10r31	10r48	..	..	3r 3	..	..	..	..	7r17	..	7r17	..	..	11r50	..
67	**Poole** arr	9 10	10 44	..	..	1 55	..	..	..	5 2	6 23	..	7 12	..	..	10 26	..
85	Via Poole { SWANAGE arr	10 7	12 37	..	..	3 59	..	..	..	6 0	..	..	7 59	..	..	..	..
96	Via Poole { WEYMOUTH "	10 7	12 25	..	..	4c18	..	..	..	7 18	..	..	8 3	..	..	..	..
69	Parkstone arr	9 19	10 52	..	..	2 3	..	..	..	5Y16	6r38	..	7Y34	..	..	10 33	..
70½	Branksome "	9 24	10 58	..	..	2 8	..	..	..	5Y21	6r43	..	7Y39	..	..	10 39	..
71½	**Bournemouth West** "	9 30	11 3	..	..	2 13	..	..	..	5 14	6 35	..	7 25	..	..	10 44	..
183	330 WATERLOO arr	12Y59	2r19	..	..	4Y58	..	..	..	8Y58	..	..	11r13	..	..	3Y†55	..

A Stops to set down passengers when required, Guard to be informed
C Station for Castle Cary (3 miles)
c 4 2 p.m. on Saturdays
D Station for Bruton (1½ miles) and Castle Cary (2 miles)
D Arr. 8 39 a.m.
F Station for Child Okeford (1 mile) and Okeford Fitzpaine (1½ miles)

C Change at Mangotsfield
H Station for Sturminster Marshall
L On Sunday nights depart Bradford 9.25 p.m

r Via Broadstone
V a.m. Via Eastleigh
Y Change at Poole
† Morn
§ For complete service of trains between Evercreech Junction and Templecombe, see page 492

For **LOCAL TRAINS** between Broadstone and Bournemouth West see page 337

BOURNEMOUTH WEST, TEMPLECOMBE and BATH.

Somerset and Dorset—Southern and L. M. & S.

Miles from B'mth W.	Week Days only		a.m	a.m	a.m	a.m	a.m (Through Train, Bournemouth to Manchester)	a.m (Through Train Bournemouth to Gloucester)	a.m	a.m	p.m	p.m	a.m	p.m	p.m	p.m	p.m
	324 WATERLOO	dep	..	..	..	..	5r40	8r30	..	9r30	..	..	11X30	12K30	1r30	..	5M30
	Bournemouth West	dep	..	..	6 48	8 50	9a45	11 40	..	12 55	..	..	3 30		5 15	..	10 0
1½	Branksome		..	..	6Y32	8 54	9Y 5	10Y26	..	12 59	..	..	3Yf3		5 19	..	10 4
2½	Parkstone		..	..	6Y37	8 58	9Y 9	10Y30	..	1 3	..	..	3 37		5 24	..	10 9
—	Via Poole { WEYMOUTH	dep	..	..	..	7 38	8 30	9 20	..	11 30	..	..	2 20		..	..	7 48
—	Via Poole { SWANAGE	"	..	..	..	7 47	8 58	9 26	..	11 36	..	..	2 42		..	..	6 43
4½	Poole	dep	..	..	6 59	9 4	9a54	11 49	..	1 8	..	..	3 43		5 33	..	10 17
—	337 WIMBORNE	dep	..	..	6r45	8r23	9Y20	11r42	..	12r57	..	..	2r46		4r52	..	9r33
6½	Creekmoor Halt	dep	..	..	6r48	9 9	9Y30	11Y19	..	1 13	..	..	3 48		5 39	..	9r 6
7¾	Broadstone		..	..	7 9	9 15	9Y26	11 58	..	1 19	..	..	3 52		5 46	..	10 27
9½	Corfe Mullen (East End) Halt		..	..	..	..	..	..	..	..	..	..	..		..	..	10 30
12½	Bailey Gate H		..	..	7 24	9 30	..	..	..	1 32	..	..	4 10		6 0	..	10 41
15½	Spetisbury Halt		..	..	7 30	9 35	..	..	..	1 37	..	..	..		6 5	..	10 45
17	Charlton Marshall Halt		..	..	7 35	9 40	..	..	..	1 42	..	..	..		6 10	..	10 50
18¾	Blandford		..	..	7 43	9 58	10a20	12 15	..	1 50	..	..	4 30		6 18	..	10 58
21¾	Stourpaine and Durweston Halt		..	..	7 50	..	..	..	..	..	..	..	..		..	..	11 5
24¾	Shillingstone F		..	..	8 0	10 10	..	..	..	2 2	..	..	4 43		6 35	..	11 12
27½	Sturminster Newton		..	..	8 13	10 18	..	12 30	..	2 10	..	..	4 52		6 45	..	11 19
31½	Stalbridge		..	..	8 23	10b50	10a40	..	..	2 20	..	..	5 3		6 55	..	11 27
32¾	Henstridge		..	..	8 30	11 0	..	..	..	2 26	..	..	..		7 0	..	11 32
34½	Templecombe 340, 347	arr	..	..	8 40	11 10	..	..	..	2 37	..	..	5 15		7 11	..	11a37
—	347 WATERLOO	arr	..	..	11 46	2 29	..	..	..	6 40	..	..			10 27	..	..
—	340 WATERLOO	dep	..	..	..	..	..	..	9 0	..	12 50	12 50	2 50		..	6 0	..
—	Templecombe §	dep	7 0	8 15	9 10	..	..	..	1250	..	3 55	4 30	5 30		..	8 50	
38	Wincanton §		7 7	8 27	9 20	..	..	..	1258	..	4 2	4 37	5 37		..	9 0	
42½	Cole D §		7 16	8 40	9 29	..	..	..	1 8	..	4 11	4 47	..		..	9 9	
45	Evercreech Junc. C § 492	arr	7 23	8 48	9 36	..	11 3	1 0	1 15	..	4 18	4 57	5 50		..	9 16	
		dep	7 24	..	9 38	..	11 4	1 1	1 18	..	..	5 0	5 52		..	9 18	Saturdays only
46½	Evercreech New		7 30	..	9 45	..	..	..	1 25	..	..	5 6	..		..	9 25	
49¾	Shepton Mallet		7 43	..	9 58	..	11 18	..	1 40	..	..	5 20	6 8		..	9 38	
52¾	Masbury Halt		7 54	..	10 10	..	..	..	1 52	..	..	5 30	..		..	..	
54½	Binegar		7 59	..	10 15	..	..	..	1 57	..	..	5 37	..		..	A	
57	Chilcompton, for Downside		8 5	..	10 21	..	..	..	2 3	..	..	5 43	..		..	A	
59	Midsomer Norton and Welton		8 10	..	10 26	..	..	..	2 8	..	..	5 48	6 28		..	9 59	
60¾	Radstock		8 15	..	10 35	..	..	..	2 15	..	..	5 55	6 35		..	10 5	
63	Shoscombe and Single Hill Halt		8 20	..	10 40	..	..	..	2 20	..	..	6 3	..		..	A	
64¾	Wellow		8 25	..	10 45	..	..	..	2 27	..	..	6 8	..		..	A	
67½	Midford		8 31	..	10 52	..	..	..	2 33	..	..	6 14	..		..	..	
71½	Bath (L.M.S.)	arr	8 42	..	11 5	..	11 58	1 52	2 45	..	..	6 25	6 55		..	1025	
—	BATH (L.M.S.)	dep	10 0	..	..	..	12 12	2 5	..	..	..	..	7 5		..	..	..
81½	Mangotsfield	arr	10 31	..	..	..	12 39	2 30	..	..	..	..	7 20		..	..	..
86½	BRISTOL (St. Philips)	"	10 51	..	..	..	12 54	2 44	..	..	..	..	7 44		..	..	..
86½	" (Temple Meads)	"	..	..	..	..	..	..	..	..	..	..	..		..	..	..
—	BATH (L.M.S.)	dep	10 C 0	..	..	..	12 3	1 57	..	..	..	..	7C 5		..	..	..
113½	GLOUCESTER	arr	11 11	..	..	..	12 54	2 48	..	..	..	..	8 20		..	..	..
120	CHELTENHAM SPA (Lans'wn)	"	11 31	..	..	..	1 11	3 19	..	..	..	..	8 40		..	..	..
139½	Worcester (Shrub Hill)	"	12 31	..	..	..	2 39	5 38	..	..	..	..	..		..	..	..
165½	BIRMINGHAM (New Street)	"	12 36	..	..	..	2 15	4 23	..	..	..	..	9 51		..	..	..
204½	LEICESTER	"	3 1	..	..	..	4S021	5 55	..	..	..	..	..		..	..	..
195½	BURTON-ON-TRENT	"	1 21	..	..	..	3 29	5 14	..	..	..	..	11V30		..	..	..
206½	DERBY	"	1 40	..	..	..	3 45	5 31	..	..	..	..	11V46		..	..	..
222½	NOTTINGHAM	"	2 46	..	..	..	5 13	6 34	..	..	..	..	1 43		..	..	..
217½	CREWE	"	3 20	..	..	..	3 34	7 11	..	..	..	..	11 34		..	..	..
248½	MANCHESTER (Lon. Rd.)	"	4 30	..	..	..	4L40	8 25	..	..	..	..	1 45		..	..	..
242½	SHEFFIELD	"	2 46	..	..	..	4 47	6 39	..	..	..	..	12V50		..	..	..
289	YORK	"	4 10	..	..	..	..	7 53	..	..	..	..	2 2		..	..	..
280	LEEDS (City)	"	4 27	..	..	..	6 8	8 10	..	..	..	..	2 4		..	..	..
295½	BRADFORD (Forster Square)	"	5 10	..	..	..	6 50	9 0	..	..	..	..	3B10		..	..	..

A Stops to set down passengers when required. Guard to be informed
a Passengers for Southern Railway via Templecombe, change at Stalbridge
B On Sunday mornings arrive Bradford 5 23 a.m.
b Arrive Stalbridge 10 27 a.m.
C Station for Castle Cary (3 miles)
D Station for Bruton (1½ miles) and Castle Cary (2 miles)
F Station for Child Okeford (1 mile) and Okeford Fitzpaine (1½ miles)
f 15 minutes later on Saturdays
G Change at Mangotsfield
H Station for Sturminster Marshall
K Mondays to Fridays via Bournemouth West (1st and 3rd Class Pullman Cars only, Supplementary fees charged)
L Manchester (Mayfield) Station
M Via Broadstone on Sats. On Mons. to Fris. dep. 6 30 p.m. via Poole
r Via Broadstone
SO Saturdays only
V On Fridays arrives Burton 10 55, Derby 11 13 p.m., Sheffield 12 16 a.m.
X Mondays to Fridays via Broadstone. On Saturdays only dep. 12 35 p.m. via Poole
Y Via Poole
§ For complete service of trains between Templecombe and Evercreech Junction, see page 492

For LOCAL TRAINS between Bournemouth West and Broadstone, see page 336

BURNHAM-ON-SEA, GLASTONBURY, TEMPLECOMBE, BOURNEMOUTH, and LONDON.

Somerset and Dorset—Southern and L. M. & S.

Miles	Down.		Week Days only																				
			a.m	a.m	a.m	a.m	a.m	a.m		p.m	p.m	p.m	p.m	p.m	p.m		p.m	p.m	p.m	p.m	p.m	p.m	
	Burnham-on-Sea	dep	..	..	..	9 30	..	1130	..	..	..	2 15	..	2 40	..	..	4 0	6 0	..	..	6 45	7 40	..
1¾	Highbridge C	arr	..	..	..	9 35	..	1135	..	..	..	2 20	..	2 45	..	..	4 5	6 5	..	..	6 50	7 45	..
		dep	7 0	..	..	9 53	..	..	..	..	..	2 23	..	..	..	..	4 8	..	..	..	6 57	..	..
3½	Bason Bridge	"	7 4	..	..	9 58	..	..	..	..	..	2 29	..	..	..	..	4 14	..	..	..	7 4	..	..
6¾	Edington Junction	arr	7 11	..	..	10 6	..	..	..	..	..	2 36	..	..	..	..	4 20	..	..	..	7 11	..	..
—	Mls Bridgwater H	dep	..	..	..	9 40	1035	..	..	..	..	2 10	..	..	..	..	3 55	..	..	..	6 40	..	..
—	3 Bawdrip Halt H	"	..	..	..	9 47	1043	..	..	..	..	2 15	..	..	..	..	4 0	..	..	..	6 45	..	..
—	4½ Cossington H	"	..	..	..	9 52	1048	..	..	..	..	2 20	..	..	..	..	4 5	..	..	..	6 50	..	..
—	7½ Edington Junc H	arr	..	..	..	10 0	1056	..	..	..	..	2 28	..	..	..	..	4 13	..	..	..	6 58	..	..
—	Edington Junction	dep	7 12	..	..	10 7	..	..	..	..	..	2 37	..	..	..	..	4 21	..	..	..	7 12	..	..
9	Shapwick L	"	7 18	..	..	10 13	..	..	..	..	..	2 43	..	..	..	..	4 28	..	..	..	7 19	..	..
11	Ashcott M	"	7 22	..	..	10 18	..	..	..	..	..	2 47	..	..	..	..	4 33	..	..	..	7 23	..	..
13¾	Glastonbury Q	arr	7 30	..	..	10 25	..	..	..	..	..	2 55	..	..	..	..	4 40	..	..	..	7 31	..	..
—	Mls Wells (Priory Rd) H	dep	..	8 0	..	10 10	..	..	..	1 30	..	..	..	..	..	..	4 25	..	..	6 10	7 15	..	..
—	2½ Polsham Halt H	"	..	..	..	10 15	..	..	..	1 35	..	..	..	..	..	..	4 30	..	..	6 15	7 20	..	..
—	5½ Glastonbury Q H	arr	..	8 10	..	10 23	..	..	..	1 43	..	..	..	..	..	..	4 38	..	..	6 27	7 28	..	..
—	Glastonbury Q	dep	7 33	..	..	10 28	..	..	..	..	..	2 58	..	..	..	..	4 43	..	..	..	7 37	..	..
19	West Pennard	"	7 44	..	..	10 39	..	..	..	..	..	3 9	..	..	..	..	4 54	..	..	..	7 49	..	..
22½	Pylle	"	7 54	..	..	10 50	..	..	..	..	..	3 18	..	..	..	..	5 5	..	..	..	7 58	..	..
24	Evercreech Junc. W 491a	arr	8 0	..	..	10 56	..	..	..	..	..	3 25	..	..	..	..	5 11	..	..	..	8 5	..	..
		dep	8 18	..	9 42	11 12	..	..	..	..	2 32	3 30	3 50	..	4 32	..	5 36	..	6 5	..	8 25	..	..
26¾	Cole X	"	8 27	..	9 51	..	..	..	..	..	2 40	..	..	..	4 40	..	..	..	6 13	..	8 35	..	..
31	Wincanton	"	8 36	..	1010	11 25	..	..	..	..	2 50	..	..	..	4 50	..	5 48	..	6 25	..	8 45	..	..
34½	Templecombe 491	arr	8 45	..	1020	11 33	..	..	y	..	3 0	3 47	..	..	5 0	..	5 57	..	6 35	..	8 55	..	..
146¾	347 Waterloo	arr	1146	..	2 29	2 29	..	..	..	..	6 40	6 40	..	..	1027	..	1027	..	1027	..	3y55	..	..
(9	491 Bournemouth W	arr	11 3	..	..	2 13	..	..	..	..	..	..	5 14	..	..	..	7 25	..	..	..	1044	..	..

Miles from Templecombe.	Up.		Week Days only																				
			a.m	a.m		a.m	a.m	a.m	a.m		p.m	a.m	a.m	p.m		p.m	p.m	p.m		p.m	p.m	p.m	
	491a Bournemouth W	dep	..	..	..	..	..	6 48	9 45	..	..	1140	..	..	..	1255	..	..	..	3 30	..	5 15	..
	340 Waterloo	"	..	..	..	..	..	..	..	..	..	..	9 0	..	..	1250	..	..	..	2 50	..	6 0	..
	Templecombe	dep	..	7 0	..	8 15	..	9 10	..	..	..	..	1250	..	..	3 55	4 30	..	..	5 30	..	8 50	..
3½	Wincanton	"	..	7 7	..	8 27	..	9 20	..	..	..	..	1258	..	..	4 2	4 37	..	..	5 37	..	9 0	..
7¾	Cole X	"	..	7 16	..	8 40	..	9 29	..	..	..	..	1 8	..	..	4 11	4 47	..	..	..	..	9 9	..
10½	Evercreech Junc	arr	..	7 23	..	8 48	..	9 36	11 3	..	..	1 0	1 15	..	..	4 18	4 57	..	..	5 50	..	9 16	..
		dep	..	8 25	..	..	..	10 5	..	..	..	..	1 25	..	..	4 40	..	..	..	6 15	..	9 25	..
12	Pylle	"	..	D	..	..	..	1010	..	..	..	..	1 30	..	..	4 45	..	..	..	6 20	..	..	..
15½	West Pennard	"	..	D	..	..	..	1018	..	..	..	..	1 38	..	..	4 53	..	..	..	6 28	..	9 35	..
20¾	Glastonbury Q	arr	..	8 45	..	..	..	1028	..	..	..	..	1 48	..	..	5 4	..	..	..	6 38	..	9 45	..
—	Glastonbury Q H	dep	..	9 30	..	..	..	1040	..	..	..	..	1 55	..	..	5 10	..	..	..	6 50	7 45	..	..
23¾	Polsham Halt H	"	..	9 38	..	..	..	1045	..	..	..	..	2 0	..	..	5 15	..	..	..	6 55	7 50	..	..
26½	Wells Z H	arr	..	9 48	..	..	..	1054	..	..	..	..	2 9	..	..	5 26	..	..	..	7 4	7 59	..	..
—	Glastonbury Q	dep	8 0	8 47	..	..	..	1032	..	..	..	..	1 50	..	..	5 6	..	..	..	6 42	..	9 48	..
23½	Ashcott M	"	8 6	D	..	..	..	1041	..	..	..	..	1 57	..	..	5 14	..	..	..	6 50	..	D	..
25¼	Shapwick L	"	8 14	D	..	..	..	1046	..	..	..	..	2 3	..	..	5 19	..	..	..	6 56	..	D	..
27¾	Edington Junction	arr	8 21	D	..	..	..	1052	..	..	..	..	2 9	..	..	5 25	..	..	..	7 2	..	10 5	..
—	Edington Junc. H	dep	8 22	..	..	..	1010	11 0	..	..	..	..	2 40	..	..	5 28	..	..	..	7 20	..	..	..
30¾	Cossington H	"	8 30	..	..	..	1015	11 5	..	..	..	..	2 50	..	..	5 33	..	..	..	7 25	..	..	..
32	Bawdrip Halt H	"	8 35	..	..	..	1020	1110	..	..	..	..	2 55	..	..	5 38	..	..	..	7 30	..	..	..
35	Bridgwater Y H	arr	8 45	..	..	..	1028	1118	..	..	..	..	3 5	..	..	5 46	..	..	..	7 38	..	..	..
—	Edington Junction	dep	..	..	..	..	..	1057	..	..	..	..	2 10	..	..	5 26	..	..	..	7 5	..	10 6	..
31½	Bason Bridge	"	..	D	..	..	..	11 4	..	..	..	..	2 17	..	..	5 33	..	..	..	7 15	..	D	..
32¾	Highbridge C	arr	..	9 9	..	..	..	11 9	..	..	..	..	2 22	..	..	5 38	..	..	..	7 23	..	1015	..
		dep	..	9 12	..	..	..	1113	..	..	2 0	..	2 25	3 45	..	5 41	..	6 30	..	7 26	..	..	..
34½	Burnham-on-Sea	arr	..	9 20	..	..	..	1120	..	..	2 5	..	2 32	3 50	..	5 48	..	6 35	..	7 33	..	..	..

C Adjoining G. W. Station.
D Stops to set down passengers if required, Guard to be informed

H Third class only between Bridgwater and Edington Junction and Glastonbury and Wells.
L Station for Westhay (1 mile).
M Station for Meare (1¾ miles).
Q Glastonbury and Street.

W Station for Castle Cary (3 miles).
X Station for Bruton (1½ miles), Castle Cary (2 miles).
Y Station for Spaxton; nearly ¼ mile to G. W. Station.
y Via Eastleigh
Z Priory Road; about ½ mile to Tucker Street Station.

SALISBURY, WESTBURY, TROWBRIDGE, and BATH.—G.W.

Miles from Salisbury	Up	Week Days													Sundays					
		p.m (Mondays excepted)	a.m	a.m (From Chippenham)	a.m G	a.m ③	a.m (Through Train, Portsmouth to Cardiff)	a.m G	a.m (Saturdays only. Through Train Brighton and Portsmouth to Cardiff)	p.m (Saturdays only)	p.m	p.m. G	p.m (Through Train Salisbury to Cardiff)	p.m (Thro Train, Portsmouth to Cardiff)	p.m Sat	a.m G	p.m G	p.m G	p.m ③	p.m
	159 Brighton .... dep	9 17	..	..	4 55	③	7 7	8 47	11 0	..	..	12B17	12B17	3B17	9 17	8 17	1215	5†17	③	..
	380 Portsmouth C .. "	1116	..	..	7 29	..	8 55	1034	1145		..	2 33	2 33	5 35	11 16	1015	1 55	6 33	..	..
	330 Bournemth (C) 339 "	1130	..	..	7D42	..	8 45	1030	1112		..	1 15	1 15	5 15	11 30	10 5	1 20	8 57	..	..
	380 Southampton (C.) "	1T10	..	..	8 11	..	10 0	1130	1252		..	3 18	3 18	6 38	1T10	1116	2 51	7 57	..	..
—	Salisbury .... dep	2 55	7 25	..	9 35	..	1120	1250	1 53		..	4 20	4 52	7 35	2 55	1230	3 50	9 0	..	10 0
2¼	Wilton	a.m	7 32	..	9 43	..	..	1256	..		..	..	4 59	7 41	a.m	..	..	..	..	..
5¼	Wishford		7 38		9 49	..	..	1 2	..		..	..	5 5	7 47	..	..	..	..	..	..
9¼	Wylye		7 47		9 57	..	..	1 10	..		..	..	5 14	7 56	..	1250	..	..	..	1019
13¼	Codford		7 55		10 6	..	Nn	1 17	..		..	4 39	5 22	8 4	..	1 0	..	9 20	..	1029
16	Heytesbury		8 2		1012	..	..	1 23	..		..	..	5 28	8 10	..	1 7	..	..	..	1038
19¼	Warminster		8 12		1023	1110	1150	1 33	2 25	3 12	..	4 52	5 38	8 21	..	1 17	4 20	9 35	1025	1046
—	Dilton Marsh Halt		8 20		1030	1117	..	1 40	..	3 19	..	5 0	5 46	8 29	..	1 24	..	..	1032	..
24¼	Westbury .... arr	Aa	8 25		1035	1120	12 0	1 45	2 34	3 24	..	5 3	5 50	8 36	Aa	1 27	4 28	9 45	1035	1058
	dep	..	8 33		1055	1125	12 7	1 55	2 40	..	3 28	5 8	6 12	8 45	..	1 32	4 30	9 48	..	..
28¼	Trowbridge .... arr	3 44	8 40		11 2	1133	1215	2 3	2 48	..	3 39	5 15	6 20	8 52	3 47	1 39	4 38	9 56	..	..
	dep	3 45	8 42		1110	..	1217	2 4	2 52	..	3 42	5 19	6 30	8 55	3 50	1 42	4 40	10 0	..	..
31¼	Bradford-on-Avon	..	8 50	9 4	1118	..	1227	2 12	3 2	..	3 51	5 27	6 40	..	..	1 51	..	10 9	..	..
—	Avoncliff Halt	..	..	9 7	..	..	..	2 15	..	..	..	..	..	..	..	..	..	..	..	..
34	Freshford	..	8 55	9 10	1124	..	..	2 19	..	..	..	5 32	6 47	..	..	1 56	..	Bb	..	..
34¼	Limpley Stoke	..	8 58	9 13	1127	..	..	2 23	..	..	..	5 35	6 52	..	..	2 0	..	Bb	..	..
39	Bathampton .... arr	..	..	9 21	1135	..	..	2 31	..	..	..	5 43	7 0	..	..	..	..	..	..	..
41¼	Bath .... "	4 7	9 8	9 25	1140	..	1243	2 36	3 21	..	4 10	5 49	7 5	9 18	4 15	2 11	5 2	1028	..	..
52¼	Bristol (T.M.) ... arr	4 35	9 26	9 51	12 5	..	..	3 6	..	..	4 32	6 16	..	..	4 38	2 32	5 21	1050	..	..
53¼	" (Stapleton Rd.) "	..	..	..	..	..	1 5	..	3 42	..	..	..	7 35	9 45	..	..	..	..	..	..
78¼	Newport .... "	6 39	1216	..	2 0	..	2 0	..	4 30	..	5 55	..	8 30	1038	10V17	3V51	3 25	1*47	..	..
90	Cardiff (General) "	7 0	1239	..	2 23	..	2 23	..	4 50	..	6 15	..	8 47	11 0	10V40	4V15	6 56	2*15	..	..

Miles from Bath	Down	Week Days														Sundays				
		a.m	a.m G	a.m (Through Train, Bristol to Southampton Terminus arr. 2 33 p.m.)	a.m (To Devizes and Reading)	a.m (Through Train, Cardiff to Portsmouth)	p.m	p.m (Saturdays only)	p.m (Saturdays only. Through Train Cardiff to Brighton and Portsmouth)	p.m (To Melksham)	p.m G	p.m	p.m (Through Train Cardiff to Salisbury)	p.m	p.m	a.m	a.m G	a.m	p.m G	pm
	Cardiff (Gen.) ... dep	..	6 25	8 43	..	1030	..	..	1 0	1 55	1 55	3 20	4 35	5 25	6 15	..	8 35	1025	2 40	520
	Newport .... "	..	6 45	9 8	..	1052	..	..	1 20	2 19	2 19	3 41	4 56	5 47	6 39	..	8 59	1048	3 5	544
	Bristol (Stap. Rd.) "	..	..	..	..	1139	..	..	2 5	..	..	..	5 46	..	..	..	..	..	..	..
	" (T.M.) .... "	5 45	8 10	1040	1122	..	1245	..	..	3 55	4 32	5 10	..	7 10	8 45	10 0	1120	2 30	6 5	755
—	Bath .... dep	6 10	8 37	11 0	1143	12 3	1 11		2 30	4 22	5 0	5 38	6 9	7 40	9 8	1032	1145	2 59	6 28	815
2¼	Bathampton	6 15	8 42	11 7	..	..	1 17		..	4 27	..	5 43	..	7 45	..	..	..	..	..	..
6¼	Limpley Stoke	6 23	8 50	1116	..	..	1 25		..	4 35	..	5 51	..	7 54	9 23	1043	..	3 10	..	..
7¼	Freshford	..	8 54	1121	..	..	1 29		..	4 39	..	5 55	..	7 58	9 26	1047	..	3 13	..	..
—	Avoncliff Halt	..	..	..	..	..	1 32		..	4 42	..	5 58	..	8 4	..	..	..	..	..	..
9¼	Bradford-on-Avon	6 35	9 1	1129	12 2	1218	1 37		2 48	4 47	5 17	6 1	6 27	8 9	9 32	1055	..	3 19	6 47	832
12¼	Trowbridge .... arr	6 45	9 8	1138		1228	1 44		2 56		5 25	6 8	6 34	8 16	9 40	11 4	12 8	3 27	6 55	840
	dep	6 50	9 12	1143		1230	1 48		3 0		5 27	..	6 38	8 20	9 45	1110	1212	..	6 58	842
16¼	Westbury .... arr	7 1	9 19	1153		1237	1 56		3 8		5 35	..	6 46	8 27	9 5"	1121	1220	..	7 6	850
	dep	7 20	9 25	12 0		1244	..	2 45	3 15		5 43	..	6 52	8 50	10 0	..	1232	..	7 15	856
—	Dilton Marsh Halt	7 24	9 29	12 5		..	..	2 49	..		5 48	..	..	8 55	..	..	..	..	..	..
21¼	Warminster	7 40	9 41	1216		1255	..	2 58	3 30		5 58	..	7 5	9 7	10 15	..	1248	..	7 25	9 8
25¼	Heytesbury	7 50	9 50	1223		..	..	..	..		6 8	..	..	9 17	..	..	..	..	..	..
27¼	Codford	7 55	9 55	1228		1 8	..	..	..		6 14	..	..	9 24	..	..	..	..	..	918
31¼	Wylye	8 4	10 3	1235		..	..	..	..		6 22	..	..	9 32	..	..	..	..	..	..
36	Wishford	8 13	1012	1243		..	..	..	..		6 31	..	..	9 41	..	..	..	..	..	..
38¾	Wilton ....[347, 376	8 19	1018	..		..	..	..	..		6 37	..	..	9 47	..	..	..	..	..	..
41¼	Salisbury 339, 340, arr	8 25	1024	1253		1 28	..	..	4 0		6 46	..	7 37	9 57	10 46	..	1 18	..	7 55	938
66	376 Southampton (C.) arr	10 47	1128	2A9	..	2 23	..	..	4 47	..	7 41	..	10T2	11 8	12T53	..	2 8	..	8 55	..
‡94¼	324 Bournemth (C) 339 "	10†57	1230	3 34	..	4 20	..	..	5 45	..	10H7	..	10D7	2§14	2§14	..	4 15	..	1114	..
87	376 Portsmouth C .. "	12 7	1231	..	..	3 20	..	..	5 51	..	8 59	..	1019	2§28	2§28	..	3 4	..	1012	..
130	196 Brighton .... "	1 36	2 36	..	..	5K22	..	..	6 54	..	1036	..	..	..	7Y35	..	4 36	..	..	..

③ Third class only
A Change at Romsey
Aa Stops at 3 35 a.m to set down from Southern Line.
B 30 minutes later on Saturdays
Bb Calls at Freshford and Limpley Stoke to set down from Trowbridge and beyond on notice to Guard at Trowbridge
C Portsmouth and Southsea
D Change at Salisbury

F Change at Fratton (dep 6 51 p.m) and Romsey
G Through Train between Portsmouth and Southsea and Bristol
H Change at Salisbury. On Mons. to Fris. arr. 8 51 p.m via Southampton Central
K Change at Salisbury or Southampton (Cen.)
Nn On Saturdays only calls at Codford at 11 38 a.m

T Southampton Ter. (for Docks)
V From November 2nd to December 14th, 1947, and January 4th to March 14th, 1948 inclusive, arrives one hour later
Y a.m. Arr. 7 50 a.m on Sundays
* Monday mornings
† Bournemouth West
‡ 79¾ miles via Fordingbridge
§ a.m.

For OTHER TRAINS between Salisbury and Wilton, and vice versa, pages 340 and 347.

ANDOVER JUNCTION, TIDWORTH, SWINDON, and CHELTENHAM SPA.—G.W.

Miles from Andover.	Down.	Week Days																		Sundays		
		am	am	am	a.m	a.m	a.m	a.m	a.m	p.m	p.m	p.m	p.m	p.m	p.m	p.m	p.m	pm	p.m	a.m		p.m
		Saturdays excepted	Saturdays excepted					Through Train, Southampton to Cheltenham.	Wednesdays & Saturdays only.	Saturdays only.	Saturdays excepted	Saturdays only.				Through Train Southampton to Cheltenham.						
	340London (Wat.) ..dep.	..	...	...	....	....	7 20	9 0	10 54	....	....	....	12 50	....	....	3 30	6 0	...	7 30	9 30	....	4 0
	347Salisbury ...... "	..	.	.	..	6 45	8 40	9 50	12 40	..	..	..	1 0	..	..	4 50	6 20	.	8 55	9 55	..	7 17
	330Bournemouth C. "	..	...	...	....	....	6k48	8 45	..	....	....	....	11 12	....	....	3 17	3 54	.	5 15	10 5	....	3 30
	380Portsmouth & S. "	..	.	.	..	..	6 0	8 55	..	..	..	..	11 26	..	..	2 45	3 35	...	5 35	1015	..	3 17
	380Southampton T. "	..	...	...	....	....	7 32	10 10	..	....	....	....	12 8	....	....	4 30	5 18	.	....	....	....	....
	380Southampton C. "	..	.	.	..	..	7 32	10 17	..	..	..	..	12 35	..	..	4 37	5 7	.	6 38	1116	..	4 55
—	Andover Junction ..dep.	..	...	645	7 0	8 5	9 58	11 9	p.m 1 15		..		2 35	..	..	5 36	7 45	.	9 50	p.m 1227	..	8 5
3½	Weyhill	..	...	654	. ..	8 13	10 6	11 17	1 23		....		2 43	....	....	5 44	7 52	...	9 57	1238	....	8 12
7½	Ludgershall .... arr.	..	..	7 3	7 15	8 20	10 11	11 24	1 30		..		2 50	..	..	5 53	7 59	.	10 5	1245	..	8 20
—	Ludgershall .... dep	..		7 5	....	8 30	10 18	11 30	1 35		....		2 57	....	....	6 0	8 5	...	1012	....	....	....
10	Tidworth .... arr.	..		712	..	8 37	10 25	11 37	1 45		..		3 4	..	..	6 7	8 12	.	1019	..	..	..
	Tidworth .... dep.	..		Stp	....	8 5	....	11 5			....		2 35	....	....	5 12	7 30	...	....	....	....	....
—	Ludgershall .... arr.	..			..	8 12	..	11 12			..		2 42	..	..	5 19	7 37	.	..	..	..	..
—	Ludgershall .... dep.			...	7 22	8 23	....	11 27					2 53	....	....	5 55	8 2	...	....	1248	....	8 25
10	Collingbourne ...... [Halt			.	7 29	8 29	..	..					2 59	..	..	6 1	8 7	.	..	1254	..	8 30
11¼	Collingbourne Kingston			...	7 32	8 32	....	....					3 2	....	....	..	8 10	...	....	1258	....	8 35
14¼	Grafton and Burbage			.	7 40	8 40	..	..					3 8	..	..	6 9	8 16	.	..	1 6	..	8 44
16½	Savernake (L. Level)			...	8e22	8T50	....	11T42				1 10	3 17	....	....	6T19	8 28	...	....	1T13	....	8T53
21½	Marlborough			.	8 37	9 0	..	11 52				2u10	3 27	..	..	6 29	8q42	9 5	..	1N28	..	9 3
26	Ogbourne			...	Stop	9 14	....	12 4				2 20	..	....	....	6 40	8 52	916	....	1 38	....	9 16
28¼	Chiseldon Camp Halt....			am		9 19	..	..				2 25	..	..	..	..	8 57	921	..	1 43	..	9 23
29½	Chiseldon		657	825	..	9 23	....	12 11		1257	1 35	2 29	..	....	6 26	6 50	9 2	925	....	1 49	....	9 27
32½	Swindon Town ..... arr.		7 5	835	..	9 31	..	12 19		1 5	1 43	2 37	..	.	6 34	6 57	9 10	935	..	1 56	..	9 36
—	Swindon Town ... dep.		7 8	.	..	9 52	..	12 38		Stop	1 45	2 39	..	5 22	Stop	..	9 15	Stp	..	2 0	..	9 40
35½	Swindon .... arr.		715	...	..	10 2	....	12 47			1 52	2 48	..	5 32		..	9 23		....	2 8	....	9 47
—	Swindon Town ..... dep.	550	....	....	....	9 38	....	12 23	..	....	....	....	..	6 15	....	7 0	....	....	....	....	....	....
41¼	Cricklade	6 6	.	.	..	9 53	..	12 38	..	..	..	..	..	6 30	..	7 15	..	..	..	..	..	..
44¾	South Cerney	613	....	....	....	10 0	....	12S45	..	....	....	....	..	6 39	....	7 22	....	....	....	....	....	....
47¾	Cirencester F	620	.	.	..	1010	..	12 54	..	..	..	..	..	6 45	..	7 30	..	.	..	..	..	..
54	Foss Cross	..	....	....	....	1023	....	....	..	....	....	....	..	....	....	J	....	....	....	....	....	....
55	Chedworth	..	.	.	..	1027	..	..	..	..	..	..	..	..	..	7 44	..	.	..	..	..	..
58¾	Withington (Glos.)	..	....	...	a.m	1034	....	....	..	p.m	....	....	..	....	p.m	7 50	....	pm	....	....	....	....
61¼	Andoversford Junction..	..	.	.	8 30	1042	..	..	..	1253	..	..	..	..	5 50	7 57	..	933	..	..	..	..
65¼	Charlton Kings	..	....	....	8 37	1049	....	....	..	1 0	....	....	..	....	5 58	..	....	940	....	....	....	....
66¼	Cheltenham (South) X..	..	.	.	8 40	1053	..	..	..	1 3	..	..	..	..	6 0	8 6	..	945	..	..	..	..
68¾	Cheltenham Spa H arr.	..	....	....	....	11 0	....	1 30	..	....	....	....	..	....	....	8 10	....	....	....	....	....	....

S Via Salisbury
e Arr. 7 46 a.m
F Watermoor Station; over ½ mile to Town Station
H Lansdown (L.M.S. Station); about ½ mile to Malvern Road (G.W.) Station and 1 mile to St James' (G.W.) Station

J Calls to set down passengers on notice being given by the passenger to the Guard at Cirencester (Watermoor)
k Bournemouth West Station
N Arr. Marlborough 1 23 p.m
q Arr Marlborough 8 38 p.m
S Saturdays only

T High Level Station; about 250 yards to Savernake (Low Level)
u Arr. Marlborough 1 20 p.m
X Cheltenham (South) and Leckhampton

For **OTHER TRAINS** between Tidworth and Ludgershall, see page 496.

READING and BASINGSTOKE.—G.W.

	Week Days																			Sundays					
	am	am	am	a.m		p.m	p.m SO	p.m	p.m		pm	p.m	pm		(3)	(3)	p.m			a.m	a.m	p.m	p.m	p.m	p.m
Reading .... dep	652	755	9 7	1017	..	1215	1 2	1 48	3 10	..	5 5	5 46	7 0	..	8 35	9 30	1050	..	..	9 5	1145	3 38	6 48	8 20	9 35
Reading (West)	655	758	911	1021	..	1219	1 6	1 52	3 13	..	5 9	5 50	7 4	..	8 40	9 34	..	..	..	9 8	..	3 42	6 52	8 23	9 38
Mortimer	7 8	810	922	1032	..	1229	1 17	2 3	3 22	..	519	6 1	714	..	8 52	9 47	11 7	..	..	9 18	1158	3 53	7 3	8 33	9 48
Bramley *	716	820	932	1040	..	1236	1 25	2 12	3 32	..	525	6 10	720	..	9 0	9 55	1114	..	..	9 27	12 5	4 0	7 10	8 39	9 55
Basingstoke .... arr	726	830	945	1051	..	1246	1 35	2 22	3 42	..	535	6 20	730	..	9 10	10 5	1125	..	..	9 37	1215	4 10	7 20	8 48	10 5

(3) Third class only. SO Saturdays only. * For Silchester.

CHELTENHAM SPA, SWINDON, TIDWORTH, and ANDOVER JUNCTION.—G.W.

Miles	Up.	Week Days a.m	a.m	a.m	a.m	a.m	p.m	a.m	p.m	a.m	p.m	p.m	p.m	p.m	p.m	p.m	p.m	p.m	p.m	Suns. a.m	p.m
		Saturdays excepted		Saturdays excepted			Wednesdays and Saturdays only.	Through Train, Cheltenham to Southampton	Saturdays only.		Saturdays only	Saturdays excepted	Through Train from Marlborough	Saturdays excepted							
—	Cheltenham Spa H dep	..	..		..	..	..	10 5					..	..	3 20	..	..	..	7 20	..	..
2	Cheltenham (South) X..	..	6 39		..	....	....	10 10		1044			..	2 54	3 26	..	7 14	....	7 27	....	....
3½	Charlton Kings	..	6 44		..	..	..	10 15		1049			..	2 59	3 31	..	7 19	..	7 32	..	..
7	Andoversford Junction..	..	6 53		..	....	....	10 26		1058			..	3 8	3 40	..	7 28	....	7 42	....	....
9¾	Withington (Glos.)	..	..		..	..	..	10 33		..			..	Stop	3 46	..	Stop	..	7 53	..	..
13¼	Chedworth	..	..		..	....	....	10 45		....			..		3 55	..		....	8 2	....	....
14¾	Foss Cross		..		..	..	..	10 50		..				..	3 59	..	..	..	8 6	..	..
20¾	Cirencester F		..	6 34	..	....	....	11 4		....				....	4 10	..	....	7 10	8 18	....	....
23¾	South Cerney		..	6 40	..	..	..	11 10		..				..	4 19	..	..	7 24	8 25	..	..
27¼	Cricklade		..	6 49	..	....	....	11 19		....				....	4 27	..	....	7 34	8 34	....	....
35¼	Swindon Town..... arr		..	7 3	..	..	..	11 35		..				..	4 41	..	p.m.	7 50	8 48	..	..
—	Mls Swindon ....dep		..	....	..	8 20		11 15	1224	....	1 5	1 5			4 20	6SX0	6 30	....	..	....	4 45
—	3 Swindon Town arr		..	..	..	8 30		11 23	1232	.	1 13	1 13			4 28	6SX8	6 38	..	..	..	4 53
—	Swindon Town..... dep	6 41	..	7 20	8 9	8 35		11 40	1235	....	1 14	1 14			4 45	6 10	6 40	....	8 53	1025	5 10
39	Chiseldon	6 49	..	7 30	8 17	8 44		11 50	1243	..	1 23	1 22			4 54	6 19	6 50	..	9 1	1034	5 18
40½	Chiseldon Camp Halt	....	..	7 33	Stop	8 47		....	....	....	1 26	....			4 56	..	6 54	....	9 5	1038	5 24
42½	Ogbourne	..	..	7 40		8 53		12 0	..	..	1 32	..			5 2	..	7 0	..	9 15	1044	5 29
47½	Marlborough	....	..	7 54	..	9 6		12 15	....	....	1 41	....	3 50		5 14	..	7 12	....	9 28	1054	5 40
52½	Savernake (L. Level)	..	..	8 5	..	9d35		12T26	..	..	..	..	4 T1		5T25	..	7c27	..	9 39	11T5	5T51
54½	Grafton and Burbage	....	..	....	..	9 44		d	....	....	....	....	4 7		5 33	..	7 34	....	9 47	1111	5 57
57½	Collingbourne Kingston	..	..	..	..	9 51		d	..	..	..	..	4 12		5 38	..	7 39	..	9 53	1116	6 4
58½	Collingbourne ....[Halt	....	..	....	..	9 57		d	....	....	....	....	4 15		5 42	..	7 43	....	9 57	1120	6 9
61	Ludgershall........ arr	..	..	..	..	10 2		12 42	..	..	..	..	4 20		5 48	..	7 48	..	10 2	1129	6 14
—	Ludgershall....... dep	....	..	....	..	1018		1v20	....	....	....	....	4 25		6 0	..	8 5	....	10 12	....	....
63½	Tidworth ...... arr	..	..	..	a.m	1025		1v30	..	..	..	..	4 32	p.m	6 7	..	8 12	..	10 19	..	..
	Tidworth ...... dep	....	..	....	8 45	....	12 25	12 25	....	....	....	....	3 55	5 12	5 12	..	7 30	....	....	....	....
—	Ludgershall....... arr	..	..	..	8 52	..	12 32	12 32	..	..	..	..	4 2	5 19	5 19	..	7 37	.	..	..	..
—	Ludgershall.........dep	....	..	....	8 54	10 6	12 34	12 44	....	....	....	....	4 22	5 20	5 50	..	7 52	....	10 4	1130	6 15
65	Weyhill	..	..	..	9 2	1015	12 42	..	..	..	..	..	4 30	5 28	5 58	..	8 0	..	10 12	1138	6 22
68½	Andover J. 347, 376 arr	....	..	....	9 9	1022	12 49	12 57	....	....	....	....	4 37	5 35	6 5	..	8 7	....	10 20	1145	6 30
94½	376 Southampton C.. arr	..	..	..	10 47	1 47	2 9	2 9	..	..	..	..	5 42	..	8A55	..	11 C3	..	..	2 C8	8 12
96½	376 Southampton T.. "	....	..	....	10 47	1 40	2 20	2 20	....	....	....	....	5 50	....	8 39	..	....	....	....	2b31	8 45
121	376 Portsmouth & S.. "	..	..	..	11 36	2j4	3 20	3 20	..	..	..	..	7 1	..	1019	..	2aC28	..	..	3 C4	9 27
118	324 Bournemouth C.. "	....	..	....	12 30	3h34	3 34	3 34	....	....	....	....	7 2	....	1051	..	2aC14	....	....	4C15	9 31
85½	340 Salisbury....... "	..	..	..	10 2	11 1	2 39	2 39	..	..	..	..	6 0	..	7 8	..	10 10	..	..	1257	9 26
135	347 London (Wat.)... "	....	..	....	11 13	2 29	2 29	2 29	....	....	....	....	6 40	8 0	9 14	..	10 27	....	....	3 44	9 13

A Change at Eastleigh and St. Denys
a a.m.
b Via Salisbury and Romsey
C Via Salisbury
c Arr. 7 23 p.m.
d On Fridays calls at Grafton and Burbage at 12 32 p.m. Collingbourne Kingston Halt at 12 37 p.m., and Collingbourne at 1240 p.m. to pick up passengers
d Arr. 9 17 a.m.

F Watermoor; over ¼ mile to Town Station
H Lansdown (L.M.S. Station) about ½ mile to Malvern Road (G.W.) Station and 1 mile to St. James' (G.W.) Station
h 2 55 p.m. on Sats. Passengers can arrive 2 35 p.m. by Pullman Car Train 1st and 3rd class only, from Southampton (Central) on payment of supplementary fee

j 1 49 p.m on Saturdays
SX Saturdays excepted
T High Level Station, about 250 yards to Savernake (Low Level)
v 15 minutes later on Wednesdays and Saturdays
X Cheltenham (South) and Leckhampton

For OTHER TRAINS between Ludgershall and Tidworth, see page 495.

BASINGSTOKE and READING.—G.W.

	Week Days am	am	am	a.m		a.m	non		p.m	pm	pm	pm		p.m	p.m	3	3			Sundays a.m	p.m	p.m	p.m	p.m	p.m
							S O																		
Basingstoke.... dep	7 5	738	824	9 45	..	1122	12 0	..	1 35	350	445	6 5	..	7 35	9 30	1030	1150	..	..	1010	1 20	4 58	8 0	9 25	1030
Bramley *	717	747	833	9 54	..	1132	1210	..	1 44	4 0	455	615	..	7 44	9 40	1039	..	..	..	1020	1 29	5 10	8 10	9 35	1040
Mortimer	723	754	840	10 1	..	1139	1217	..	1 51	4 7	5 2	623	..	7 51	9 47	1046	..	..	..	1028	1 36	5 16	8 18	9 45	1050
Reading (West).. ..	732	8 4	850	1011	..	1149	1227	..	2 1	416	511	633	..	8 0	9 57	..	..	..	..	1038	..	5 26	8 27	9 54	..
Reading........ arr	738	8 7	854	1015	..	1152	1234	..	2 8	425	516	638	..	8 5	10 0	11 0	1218	..	..	1042	1 50	5 30	8 32	10 0	11 5

 Third class only   S O Saturdays only   * For Silchester

ROBERTSBRIDGE, TENTERDEN TOWN, and HEADCORN.—Kent and East Sussex.

Miles from Robertsbridge.	Down.	Week Days only.																		
		a.m	a.m		a.m	a.m		a.m	a.m		a.m	a.m		p.m	p.m	p.m		p.m	p.m	
	London—																			
54	Charing Cross ......dep.	..	..	..	..	..	..	..	..	..		8 25	..	..		..	..	3 25	4 20	..
54	Cannon Street ..... "	..	..	..	..	..	..	..	..	..	Saturdays only.	..	..	..		..	..	..	..	..
54	London Bridge..... "	..	..	..	..	5 45	..	..	..	..		8 35	..	..		..	..	..	4 28	..
55	Hastings .... "	..	..	..	..	7 40	..	..		..		1040	..	..			..	5 10	5 10	..
	Robertsbridge..........dep.	..	..	..	..	8 15	..	..	Saturdays excepted	..		1120	..	..	Saturdays only.	Saturdays excepted	..	5 50	5 50	..
1½	Salehurst Halt..............	..	..	..	..	M	..	..		..		M	..	..			..	M	M	..
2½	Junction Road Halt	..	..	..	..	M	..	..		..		M	..	..			..	M	M	..
3½	Bodiam, for Staplecross	..	..	..	..	8 25	..	..		..		1135	..	..			..	6 0	6 0	..
7	Northiam W	..	..	..	..	8 35	..	..		..		1155	..	..			..	6 10	6 10	..
9½	Wittersham Road	..	..	..	..	8 42	..	..		..		1210	..	..			..	6 17	6 17	..
12	Rolvenden	6 40	7 45	..	..	8 49	..	1110		..	..	1220	..	4 45			..	6 24	6 24	..
13½	**Tenterden Town**............	6 45	7 50	..	7 55	8 54	..	1115	11 20	..	11 20	1225	..	4 50	5 0	5 10	..	6 30	6 30	..
14½	Tenterden St. Michaels.......	..	..	..	M	..	..	..	M	..	M	..	..	..	M	M	..			..
15½	High Halden Road	..	..	..	8 5	..	..	..	11 30	..	11 30	..	..	..	5 15	5 25	..	Saturdays only.	Saturdays excepted	..
18	Biddenden	..	..	..	8 15	..	..	..	11 40	..	11 40	..	..	..	5 29	5 39	..			..
19½	Frittenden Road	..	..	..	M	..	..	..	M	..	M	..	..	..	M	M	..			..
21½	**Headcorn 43**..............arr.	..	..	..	8 30	..	..	..	11 55	..	11 55	..	..	..	5 50	6 0	..			..
67½	43 London (London Bdg)..arr.	..	..	..	10 9	..	..	..	1 22	..	1 14	..	..	..	8 29	8 29	..			..
68	43 " (Cannon St.)... "	..	..	..	10 14	..	..	..	..	..	..	..	..	..	..	..	..			..
69½	43 " (Charing Crs).. "	..	..	..	..	..	..	..	1 35	..	1 24	..	..	..	8 41	8 41	..			..

Miles from Headcorn.	Up.	Week Days only.																
		a.m	a.m		a.m	a.m		p.m		p.m		p.m	p.m					
	London—																	
34	Charing Cross ......dep.	..	..	..	11 15	11 15	..	Saturdays only.	..		..	4 30	..	..	..	..	..	..
34	Cannon Street ..... "	..	6 22	..	..	..	..		..	Saturdays excepted	..	..	4 38	..	..	..	..	..
34	London Bridge ..... "	..	6 30	..	..	..	..		..		..	4 39	4 42	..	..	..	..	..
	Headcorn ....dep.	..	8 50	..	12 30	12 35	..		..		..	6 35	6 35	..	..	..	..	..
2	Frittenden Road	..	M	..	M	M	..		..		..	M	M	..	..	..	..	..
3½	Biddenden	..	9 10	..	12 43	12 48	..		..		..	6 47	6 47	..	..	..	..	..
5½	High Halden Road	..	9 20	..	12 52	12 57	..		..		..	6 56	6 56	..	..	..	..	..
7	Tenterden St. Michaels.......	..	M	..	M	M	..		..		..	M	M	..	..	..	..	..
8	**Tenterden Town**	6 55	9 40	..	1 8	1 13	..	4 20	..	4 35	..	7 12	7 12	..	..	..	..	..
9½	Rolvenden	7 0	9 48	..	1 13	1 18	..	4 25	..	4 40	..	7 18	7 18	..	..	..	..	..
12	Wittersham Road	7 7	9 55	..			..	4 35	..	4 50	..			..	..	..	..	..
14½	Northiam W	7 17	10 7	..	Saturdays excepted	Saturdays only.	..	4 45	..	5 0	..	Saturdays only.	Saturdays excepted	..	..	..	..	..
18	Bodiam, for Staplecross	7 27	10 18	..			..	4 55	..	5 10	..			..	..	..	..	..
19	Junction Road Halt	M	M	..			..	M	..	M	..			..	..	..	..	..
20½	Salehurst Halt.............	M	M	..			..	M	..	M	..			..	..	..	..	..
21½	**Robertsbridge 54, 55**...arr.	7 40	10 33	..			..	5 10	..	5 25	..			..	..	..	..	..
36½	54 Hastings ....arr.	8 25	12 46	..			..	5 51	..	6 10	..			..	..	..	..	..
71½	55 London (London Bdg).. "	..	..	..			..	..	..	[illegible] 29	..			..	..	..	..	..
72½	55 " (Cannon St.)... "	9 43	..	..	..		..	..	..	..	..		..	..	..	..	..	..
73½	55 " (Charing Crs) . "	..	12 5	..	..		..	7 38	..	7 38	..		..	..	..	..	..	..

M Stops by signal to set down or pick up passengers. W Station for Beckley and Sandhurst.

SHEPHERD'S WELL, EASTRY, and CANTERBURY ROAD, WINGHAM.—East Kent.

Miles.	Down.	Week Days only.		Saturdays excepted	Saturdays only	
		a.m		p.m	p.m	
	60 London (Victoria).....dep.	3†10	..	2 35	3 35	..
	Shepherd's Well.........dep.	7 30	..	5 0	6 3	..
1¾	Eythorne	7 37	..	5 7	6 10	..
2¾	Elvington	7 40	..	5 10	6 13	..
3¾	Knowlton	7 43	..	5 14	6 17	..
5¼	Eastry South.................	..	..	M	M	..
5¾	Eastry, for Sandwich........	7 51	..	5 22	6 23	..
6¾	Woodnesborough	7 55	..	5 26	6 27	..
8	Ash Town.....................	7 58	..	5 30	6 30	..
8¾	Staple........................	8 2	..	5 33	6 34	..
10¼	Wingham Colliery..........	8 8	..	5 38	6 39	..
10¾	Wingham Town.............	8 10	..	5 40	6 42	..
11¼	**Canterbury Road L**.....arr	8 12	..	5 42	6 44	..

Miles.	Up.	Week Days only.	Saturdays excepted	Saturdays only	
		a.m	p.m	p.m	
	Canterbury Road L.....dep.	8 40	6 20	6 50	..
½	Wingham Town.............	8 42	6 22	6 52	..
1	Wingham Colliery..........	8 45	6 25	6 55	..
2½	Staple........................	8 52	6 32	7 0	..
3½	Ash Town.....................	8 55	6 36	7 4	..
4½	Woodnesborough	8 59	6 40	7 9	..
5½	Eastry, for Sandwich........	9 5	6 45	7 13	..
6	Eastry South.................	..	M	M	..
7¼	Knowlton	9 15	M	M	..
8¼	Elvington	9 19	6 58	7 25	..
9½	Eythorne	9 23	7 2	7 28	..
11½	**Shepherd's Well 66**......arr	9 30	7 9	7 35	..
83	66 London (Victoria).....arr.	12‖20	10 28	1021	..

L Canterbury Road, Wingham.

M Stops by signal to set down or pick up passengers.

‖ Arr 1 12 p.m Sats.

† London Bridge (Third class only).

WATERLOO AND CITY RAILWAY.

QUICKEST ROUTE
BETWEEN
WATERLOO AND THE CITY.

☛ *FIVE MINUTES ON JOURNEY.* ☚

FREQUENT SERVICE OF TRAINS.
WEEKDAYS ONLY.

FROM	FIRST TRAIN	LAST TRAIN
WATERLOO To BANK	a.m. 6 46	p.m. 9 51
BANK To WATERLOO	a.m. 6 54	p.m. 10 0

FARES 3½d. SINGLE, 7d. RETURN. *** WORKMEN'S TICKETS, 3d. RETURN.**

* Issued on Weekdays until 8-0 a.m., available for return by any Train on day of issue only.

THROUGH BOOKINGS TO EUSTON, KING'S CROSS, AND LIVERPOOL STREET.

Dogs, Cycles, and Perambulators are not conveyed on the Waterloo and City Railway.

EAST LONDON LINE.

NEW CROSS AND WHITECHAPEL AND SHOREDITCH.

SHOREDITCH Station will be open ONLY BETWEEN THE FOLLOWING TIMES:—

MONDAYS TO FRIDAYS (inclusive) { 6 38 a.m and 9 50 a.m; 3 58 p.m and 8 7 p.m

SATURDAYS .. .. { 6 38 a.m and 9 48 a.m; 11 51 a.m and 2 5 p.m

SUNDAYS .. .. .. 7 36 a.m and 1 36 p.m

A Service of Trains (one class only) is run by the London Passenger Transport Board on WEEK DAYS and SUNDAYS to and from New Cross and New Cross Gate and Whitechapel (also to Shoreditch during the above-mentioned times) as under, connecting at Whitechapel with the District and Metropolitan Lines:—

From New Cross and New Cross Gate	First Trains Weekdays										Suns	
	am	am	am	am	am	am	am	am	am	am	am	am
New Cross ....dep	518	..	548	6 1	..	616	..	A	631	..	732	..
New Cross Gate "	..	533	..	..	6 8	..	623	..	..	638	..	742
Whitechapel..arr.	529	544	559	612	619	627	634	636	641	648	742	752
Shoreditch.... "	..	..	..	..	..	..	..	638	643	650	744	754

To New Cross Gate and New Cross	First Trains Weekdays										Suns	
	am	am	am	am	am	am	am	am	am	am	am	am
Shoreditch....dep	B	..	..	..	..	..	..	..	641	647	736	746
Whitechapel.. "	..	535	550	6 5	615	625	630	636	642	648	737	747
New Cross Gate arr.	531	..	6 1	616	..	636	..	647	..	659	..	758
New Cross..... "	..	546	..	..	626	..	641	..	653	..	748	..

Thence on Weekdays to and from New Cross and New Cross Gate at intervals of 12 to 18 minutes until about 8-0 p.m. Mondays to Fridays and 4 0 p.m. on Saturdays, after this time and all day on Sundays the intervals will be 20 minutes

From New Cross and New Cross Gate	Last Trains Week-days		Sundays	
	p.m	p.m	p.m	p.m
New Cross.......dep.	..	12 12	11 32	..
New Cross Gate.. "	12 2	..	..	1142
Whitechapel....arr.	1213	12 23	11 43	1153

To New Cross Gate and New Cross	Last Trains Week-days		Sundays	
	p.m	p.m	p.m	p.m
Whitechapel....dep.	12 7	12 27	11 27	1157
New Cross Gate..arr.	1218	..	11 38	..
New Cross...... "	..	12 38	..	12 8

A Starts from Surrey Docks at 6 29 a.m **B** Starts from Shadwell at 5 22 a.m

These Trains call at Surrey Docks, Rotherhithe, Wapping, and Shadwell.

EARL'S COURT, EAST PUTNEY, and WIMBLEDON.

A Service of Trains at FREQUENT intervals is run by the London Passenger Transport Board between Earl's Court, East Putney, and Wimbledon

	WEEKDAYS First		WEEKDAYS Last		SUNDAYS First		SUNDAYS Last	
	3		3		3		3	
	a.m		ngt.		a.m		ngt.	
Earl's Court .... dep	5 7	..	1251	..	7 43	..	12 7	..
West Brompton ...... "	..	..	1253	..	7 44	..	12 8	..
Walham Green .... "	5 10	..	1254	..	7 46	..	1210	..
Parsons Green .... "	5 14	..	1256	..	7 48	..	1213	..
Putney Bridge .... "	5 16	..	1258	..	7 50	..	1215	..
East Putney .... "	5 18	..	1 0	..	7 52	..	1217	..
Southfields .... "	5 20	..	1 2	..	7 54	..	1219	..
Wimbledon Park ..... "	5 22	..	1 4	..	7 56	..	1221	..
Wimbledon .... arr	5 25	..	1 7	..	7 59	..	1225	..

	WEEKDAYS First		WEEKDAYS Last		SUNDAYS First		SUNDAYS Last	
	3		3		3		3	
	a.m		ngt.		a.m		p.m	
Wimbledon .... dep	5 14	..	1241	..	8 3	..	1143	..
Wimbledon Park ...... "	5 16	..	1243	..	8 5	..	1145	..
Southfields .... "	5 18	..	1245	..	8 7	..	1147	..
East Putney .... "	5 21	..	1248	..	8 10	..	1150	..
Putney Bridge .... "	5 24	..	1250	..	8 12	..	1153	..
Parsons Green .... "	5 26	..	1252	..	8 14	..	1155	..
Walham Green .... "	5 27	..	1254	..	8 16	..	1157	..
West Brompton .... "	5 29	..	1255	..	8 17	..	1158	..
Earl's Court .... arr	5 31	..	1257	..	8 19	..	12 1	..

3 Third class only.

EARL'S COURT, WILLESDEN, GUNNERSBURY, and RICHMOND.

A Service of Trains at FREQUENT intervals is run by the London Passenger Transport Board between Earl's Court and Richmond and by London Midland and Scottish Railway Company between Willesden and Richmond.

	WEEK DAYS First				WEEK DAYS Last							SUNDAYS First					SUNDAYS Last				
	3		3		3		3		3			3		3			3		3		
	a.m		a.m		p.m		p.m		ngt.			a.m		a.m			p.m		p.m		
Earl's Court .... dep	5 47	..	..	..	Saturdays excepted	..	Saturdays only	..	1223	..	..	..	..	7 46	..	..	1126	..	..	..	..
West Kensington .... "	5 49	..	..	..		..		..	1224	..	..	..	..	7 47	..	..	1128	..	..	..	..
Barons Court .... "	5 50	..	..	..		..		..	1226	..	..	..	..	7 49	..	..	1129	..	..	..	..
Hammersmith .... "	5 52	..	..	..		..		..	1227	..	..	..	..	7 51	..	..	1131	..	..	..	..
Ravenscourt Park .... "	5 53	..	..	..		..		..	1229	..	..	..	..	7 52	..	..	1132	..	..	..	..
Stamford Brook .... "	5 55	..	..	..		..		..	1230	..	..	..	..	7 53	..	..	1133	..	..	..	..
Turnham Green .... "	5 57	..	..	..		..		..	1232	..	..	..	..	7 55	..	..	1135	..	..	..	..
Willesden (H.L.) .... dep	..	..	5 56	..	1131	..	1143	..	..	..	..	6 58	..	..	..	..	..	..	1134	..	..
Acton Central .... "	..	..	6 1	..	1136	..	1148	..		..	..	7 2	..	..	..	..	..	..	1139	..	..
South Acton .... "	..	..	6 3	..	..	..	..	..	..	..	..	7 4	..	..	..	..	..	..	1141	..	..
Gunnersbury .... dep	5 59	..	6 6	..	1142	..	1153	..	1235	..	..	7 7	..	7 58	..	..	1138	..	1145	..	..
Kew Gardens .... "	6 2	..	6 9	..	1145	..	1156	..	1237	..	..	7 10	..	8 1	..	..	1141	..	1148	..	..
Richmond .... arr	6 6	..	6 13	..	1149	..	12 0	..	1240	..	..	7 15	..	8 5	..	..	1144	..	1152	..	..

	WEEK DAYS First				WEEK DAYS Last							SUNDAYS First				SUNDAYS Last					
	3		3		3		3	3	3	3		3		3		3		3		3	
	a.m		a.m		p.m		p.m	p.m	p.m	ngt.		a.m		a.m		p.m		p.m		p.m	
Richmond .... dep	5 20	..	6 14	..	11 5	..	1110	1143	1143	1233	..	7 28	..	8 15	..	1110	..	1136	..	1150	..
Kew Gardens .... "	5 22	..	6 16	..	11 7	..	1112	1145	1145	1236	..	7 30	..	8 18	..	1112	..	1138	..	1153	..
Gunnersbury .... "	5 25	..	6 19	..	1110	..	1115	1148	1148	1239	..	7 33	..	8 21	..	1115	..	1141	..	1156	..
South Acton .... dep	5 27	..	..	..	1112	..	1117	1149	1150	..	..	7 35	..	..	..	1117	..	1143	..	..	..
Acton Central .... "	5 30	..	..	..	1114	..	1119	1151	1152	..	..	7 37	..	..	..	1119	..	1145	..	..	..
Willesden (H.L.) .... arr	5 36	..	..	..	1120	..	1125	1157	1158	..	..	7 43	..	..	..	1125	..	1152	..	..	..
Turnham Green .... dep	..	..	6 23	..	Saturdays excepted	..	Saturdays only	Saturdays excepted	Saturdays only	1241	..	..	..	8 23	..	..	..	..	..	1159	..
Stamford Brook .... "	..	..	6 24	..		..				1243	..	..	..	8 25	..	..	..	..	..	12 0	..
Ravenscourt Park .... "	..	..	6 26	..		..				1244	..	..	..	8 26	..	..	..	..	..	12 2	..
Hammersmith .... "	..	..	6 28	..		..				1246	..	..	..	8 28	..	..	..	..	..	12 3	..
Barons Court .... "	..	..	6 29	..		..				1247	..	..	..	8 29	..	..	..	..	..	12 5	..
West Kensington .... "	..	..	6 31	..		..				1249	..	..	..	8 31	..	..	..	..	..	12 6	..
Earl's Court .... arr	..	..	6 33	..		..				1251	..	..	..	8 32	..	..	..	..	..	12 9	..

3 Third class only

ISLE OF WIGHT, via SOUTHAMPTON and COWES

The Southampton, Isle of Wight, and South of England Royal Mail Steam Packet Co. Limited

Service liable to alteration

	Week Days												Sundays						
	a.m		a.m	a.m	p.m	p.m		p.m		p.m			a.m		a.m		p.m		
Waterloo .... dep	..	..	8R30	11R30	12P30	12SO35	..	1R30	..	4R35	..	..	..	..	11R30	..	2 54	..	..
Southampton Central .... arr	..	..	1026	1 19	1P55	2SO 8	..	3 20	..	6 16	..	..	..	..	1 20	..	5 25	..	..
Southampton Central .. By Bus dep	..	..	10 25		2 15		..	3 30	..	6 20	..	..	..	..	2 10	..	6 15	..	..
Southampton Royal Pier By Bus arr	..	..	1040		2 20		..	3 35	..	6 25	..	..	..	..	2 15	..	6 20	..	..
Southampton Royal Pier ...... dep	8 0	..	1045		2 30		..	3 45	..	6 30	..	..	9 30	..	2 30	..	6 30	..	..
Cowes Pier .... arr	9 0	..	1145		3 30		..	4 45	..	7 30	..	..	1030	..	3 30	..	7 30	..	..

	Week Days												Sundays.						
	a.m		a.m		p.m		p.m		p.m				a.m	a.m		p.m			
Cowes Pier .... dep	7 50	..	9 30	..	1245	..	4 15	..	5 45	..	..	..	8 0	1045	..	4 45	..	..	..
Southampton Royal Pier ...... arr	8 50	..	10 30	..	1 45	..	5 15	..	6 45	..	..	..	9 0	1145	..	5 45	..	..	..
Southampton Royal Pier By Bus dep	8 55	..	10 45	..	1 55	..	5 20	..	7 5	..	..	..	9 10	1155	..	5 50	..	..	..
Southampton Central .. By Bus arr	9 0	..	10 50	..	2 0	..	5 25	..	7 10	..	..	..	9 15	12 0	..	5 55	..	..	..
Southampton Central .... dep	9 16	..	11 20	..	2 20	..	6 20	..	7 20	..	..	..	9 51	1220	..	7 20	..	..	..
Waterloo .... arr	10R59	.	12 59	..	4 25	..	8R32	..	8R58	..	..	..	1213	2 12	..	9R21	..	..	..

P 1st and 3rd class Pullman Car Train only. Supplementary fees charged.
R Refreshment Car between Waterloo and Southampton. SO Saturdays only.

BOAT SERVICE between PORTSMOUTH HARBOUR & RYDE

Southern Company's Steam Packet Service—Weather and other circumstances permitting

	Week Days																				
	a.m	a.m	a.m		a.m	a.m	a.m	a.m	SO	p.m	p.m		p.m	p.m		p.m	p.m	p.m		p.m	
Portsmouth Harbour ..... dep	2 50	6 0	7 40	..	8 35	9 40	1035	11 35	1235	1 25	2 35	..	3 35	4 35	..	5 35	6 35	7 35	..	8 40	..
Southsea (Clarence Pier).. "	..	..	..	..	..	..	..	..	..	..	..	..	..	..	..	..	..	..	..	..	..
Ryde Pier Head .... arr	3 20	6 30	8 10	..	9 5	1010	11 5	12 5	1 5	2 5	3 5	..	4 5	5 5	..	6 5	7 5	8 5	..	9 10	..

	Sundays																				
	a.m		a.m		a.m		p.m		p.m		p.m		p.m		p.m						
Portsmouth Harbour ..... dep	6 25	..	8 25	..	1035	..	12 35	..	2 35	..	4 35	..	6 35	..	8 40	..	..	..	..	..	..
Southsea (Clarence Pier).. "	..	..	..	..	..	..	..	..	..	..	..	..	..	..	..	..	..	..	..	..	..
Ryde Pier Head .... arr	6 55	..	8 55	..	11 5	..	1 5	..	3 5	..	5 5	..	7 5	..	9 10	..	..	..	..	..	..

	Week Days																				
	a.m	a.m		a.m	a.m	a.m		p.m	SO	p.m	p.m		p.m		p.m	p.m		p.m	p.m	p.m	
Ryde Pier Head .... dep	7 30	8 35	..	9 35	10 35	1135	..	1235	1 35	2 35	3 35	..	4 35	..	5 35	6 35	..	7 35	8 35	9 35	..
Southsea (Clarence Pier).. arr	..	..	..	..	..	..	..	..	..	..	..	..	..	..	..	..	..	..	..	..	..
Portsmouth Harbour ..... "	8 0	9 5	..	10 5	11 5	12 5	..	1 5	2 5	3 5	4 5	..	5 5	..	6 5	7 5	..	8 5	9 5	10 5	..

	Sundays																				
	a.m		a.m		a.m		p.m			p.m		p.m		p.m		p.m					
Ryde Pier Head .... dep	7 30	..	9 35	..	11 35	..	1 35	..	..	3 35	..	5 35	..	7 35	..	9 35	..	..	..	..	..
Southsea Clarence Pier.. arr	..	..	..	..	..	..	..	..	..	..	..	..	..	..	..	..	..	..	..	..	..
Portsmouth Harbour ..... "	8 0	..	10 5	..	12 5	..	2 5	..	..	4 5	..	6 5	..	8 5	..	10 5	..	..	..	..	..

SO Saturdays only.

LYMINGTON and ISLE OF WIGHT

Southern Co's Steam Packet Service

	Week Days												Sundays								
	a.m F	a.m F		p.m F		p.m F	p.m F		p.m F		p.m F		a.m F		p.m F		p.m F		p.m F		p.m F
Lymington Pier .... dep	7 25	9 15	..	12 40	..	2 15	4 20	..	5 40	..	7A15	..	9 50	..	1220	..	2 35	..	4 10	..	5B35
Yarmouth Pier .... arr	..	..	..	..	..	..	..	..	..	..	..	..	..	..	..	..	..	..	..	..	..
Yarmouth Slipway ...... "	7 55	9 45	..	1 10	..	2 45	4 50	..	6 10	..	7A45	..	1020	..	1250	..	3 5	..	4 40	..	6B 5

	Week Days												Sundays								
	a.m F	a.m F		p.m F		p.m F	p.m F		p.m F		p.m F		a.m F		p.m F		p.m F		p.m F		p.m F
Yarmouth Slipway .... dep	8 20	10 40	..	1 30	..	2 55	5 0	..	6 25	..	7A55	..	1040	..	1 0	..	3 30	..	4 55	..	6B20
Yarmouth Pier .... "	..	..	..	..	..	..	..	..	..	..	..	..	..	..	..	..	..	..	..	..	..
Lymington Pier .... arr	8 50	11 10	..	2 0	..	3 25	5 30	..	6 55	..	8A25	..	1110	..	1 30	..	4 0	..	5 25	..	6B50

A Every week day to November 1st, Fridays and Saturdays only November 7th, 1947, to March 27th, 1948. Every week day commencing March 29th, 1948. B Commences April 4th 1948. F Service performed by Ferry vessel.

CONVEYANCE OF MOTOR CARS, Etc., BETWEEN MAINLAND & ISLE OF WIGHT.

PORTSMOUTH and FISHBOURNE, near Ryde, I. of W.

The Company's Ferry for the Conveyance of Motor Vehicles (which can be run on and off vessel under own power) will, weather and other circumstances permitting, run as under:—

PORTSMOUTH (Broad St. Slipway) to FISHBOURNE	FISHBOURNE (New Slipway) to PORTSMOUTH
WEEKDAYS ONLY.	
9 15 and 11 45 a.m., 2 15 p.m.	10 30 a.m., 1 0, and 3 30 p.m.

These Services are liable to alteration or cancellation without previous notice.

Motor Cars, etc., must be accompanied, and should be at the Slipways half-an-hour before the sailing times.

The Service is performed by Motor Ferry Vessels specially constructed for the conveyance of Motor Cars, etc., **which are driven on, and off, under own power, over gangways 10 feet in width.** There is a comfortable cabin for passengers on each vessel with every convenience. The journey occupies about 55 minutes.

All Traffic must be accompanied and should be at the Slipway half-an-hour before the sailing times.

It is advisable, to reserve accommodation in both directions as long in advance as possible. No charge is made for the reservation, and advance remittance is not necessary. Letters should be addressed to Divisional Marine Manager, Southern Railway, Broad Street, Portsmouth, or to Fishbourne, Wootton Bridge, I.W. Telephones, Portsmouth 4655 and Wootton Bridge 32. Telegrams—"Foremost, Portsmouth."

PORTSMOUTH AND FISHBOURNE. Rates (at Owner's Risk)

Books containing 4 Return Motor Car Tickets, at reduced rates, are obtainable. For full particulars, see page 502.	Single.		Return (A) (Available for 3 months).		Week End (A) (Friday to Tuesday).		(A) Day Return.	
	S.R. Rate	Portsmouth Corp'n Dues	S.R. Rate	Portsmouth Corp'n Dues	S.R. Rate	Portsmouth Corp'n Dues	S.R. Rate	Portsmouth Corp'n Dues
	(See Note)		(See Note)		(See Note)		(See Note)	
	£ s. d.	s. d.	£ s. d.	s. d.	£ s. d.	s. d.	£ s. d.	s. d.
Motor Cars — Not exceeding 10 feet 6 inches in length ..	1 0 2	2 2	1 16 5	4 4	1 8 8	4 4	1 6 10	3 0
Motor Cars — Over 10 feet 6 inches and not exceeding 14 feet in length ..	1 11 0	2 2	2 10 5	4 4	2 4 11	4 4	2 1 4	3 0
Motor Cars — Over 14 feet in length	2 6 6	2 2	3 17 6	4 4	3 8 2	4 4	3 2 0	3 0
Motor Tri-Car	19 5	10	1 14 11	1 8	1 7 2	1 8	1 5 10	1 1
Motor Cycle and Side Car ..	6 7	10	11 8	1 8	9 4	1 8	8 9	1 1
Motor Cycle	3 11	6½	7 0	1 1	5 5	1 1	5 2	9
Motor Car Trailers	16 3	6½	1 12 7	1 1	1 4 0	1 1	1 1 2	1 1
Caravans attached to Motor Cars	—	—	At Motor Car Rates			—	—	—
Persons Accompanying Traffic	2 5		4 10		3 7		3 7	

NOTE—These dues are levied by the Portsmouth Corporation for the use of their Slipway, and are additional to the Southern Railway Rates indicated. For the convenience of travellers the total amount (i.e., Southern Railway Rate plus the Portsmouth Corporation Dues) is collected by the Railway Company at the Booking Office.

A—The return halves of these tickets may be used, if so desired, via Yarmouth and Lymington.

A special reduced rate of a single fare and a third for the return journey is available for bona-fide **Commercial Travellers** and their Motor Cars, between any one Monday and Friday.

☞ **Senders or Owners of Motor Cars, etc., by these boats take upon themselves all risk of conveyance and of loading and unloading, as the Company will not be answerable for Accidents, Loss, or Damage done to any vehicles, accessories therein or thereon or other property therein or belonging thereto.**

Motor Car Rates and Passenger Fares on the Portsmouth-Fishbourne route will be liable to alteration at short notice.

BOOKS OF MOTOR CAR TICKETS

Books containing FOUR Return Tickets for the conveyance of Motor Cars between Portsmouth and Fishbourne, also between Lymington and Yarmouth, available for one year from date of issue, are obtainable at the following rates:—

Rates (Including all Dues)

	per book
Not exceeding 10 ft. 6 ins. in length	**£5/9/11**
Over 10 ft. 6 ins. and not exceeding 14 ft. in length	**£7/6/5**
Over 14 ft. in length	**£10/18/4**

Application for books should be made at Southern Railway Offices, Broad Street, Portsmouth, or at Fishbourne, Isle of Wight, or to the Marine Manager, Lymington, or the Station-master, Yarmouth Pier.

For rates for animals, motor lorries, etc., see other announcements.

All charges to be paid in advance, if required.

LYMINGTON and YARMOUTH.

The ferry vessel "Lymington" has been specially constructed for the conveyance of motor vehicles (which run on and off the vessel under their own power without reversing).

These will be accepted on the ferry vessel on every passage (with certain exceptions as shown in the schedule of services).

Traffic must be upon the respective slipways ready tc load half-an-hour before the advertised times. Vehicles, horses and live stock must be in charge of senders' or owners' servant, who must accompany them.

Animals, other than Dogs, are not conveyed on Sundays. The passages available for such animals are:—Lymington. dep. 7.25 a.m. and 9.15 a.m. (Mondays excepted), Yarmouth Slipway, dep. 8.20 a.m. and 1.30 p.m.

Senders or owners of motor cars, etc., by the Ferry Vessel take upon themselves all risk of conveyance and of loading and unloading, as the Company will not be responsible for loss, damage, or delay, however caused, of or to any vehicle, accessories therein or thereon, or other property therein or belonging thereto.

Alterations and additions will be made in the above services during Easter, Whitsuntide, and Christmas periods. It is advisable, especially during holiday periods and the summer months to reserve accommodation in both directions as long in advance as possible. No charge is made for the reservation, and communications should be addressed to the Marine Manager at Lymington (Telephone No. 96), or the Station Master, Yarmouth (Telephone No. 213). **For particulars of services, see page 500.**

RATES FOR MOTOR CARS, ETC.
(at Owner's Risk), via Lymington and Yarmouth.

Books containing 4 Return Motor Car Tickets, at reduced rates, are obtainable. For full particulars, see above.	Single.	Return (**A**) (Available for 3 months)	(**A**) Week End (Friday to Tuesday).	(**A**) Day Return (Week Day).
	£ s. d.	£ s. d.	£ s. d.	£ s. d.
Motor Cars: Not exceeding 10 feet 6 inches in length	1 2 4	2 0 9	1 13 0	1 9 10
Motor Cars: Over 10 feet 6 inches in length and not exceeding 14 feet in length	1 13 2	2 14 9	2 9 3	2 4 4
Motor Cars: Over 14 feet in length	2 8 8	4 1 10	3 12 6	3 5 0
Motor Tri-Car	1 0 3	1 16 7	1 8 10	1 6 11
Motor Cycle and Side Car (accompanied)..	7 5	13 4	11 0	9 10
Motor Cycle (accompanied)	4 5½	8 1	6 6	5 11
Motor Car Trailers	16 9½	1 13 8	1 5 1	1 2 3
Caravans attached to Motor Cars	—At Motor Car Rates—			
Cyc-Autos (E)	1 11	(E) 3 1	..	..
Bicycles (accompanied)	1 3	..	..	..
Persons accompanying Traffic (Third Class)	2 9	5 6	3 7	3 7

A—The return halves of these tickets may be used, if so desired, via Fishbourne and Portsmouth.
(E) Not available via Fishbourne and Portsmouth.

A special reduced rate of a single fare and a third for the return journey is available for bona-fide **Commercial Travellers** and their Motor Cars between any one Monday and Friday.

For rates for animals, furniture, etc., see other announcements.

☞ Senders or Owners of Motor Cars, &c., by the Ferry Vessel take upon themselves all risk of conveyance and of loading and unloading, as the Company will not be answerable for Accidents, Loss, or Damage done to any vehicles, accessories therein or thereon or other property therein or belonging thereto.

FIRST AND LAST  TRAINS TO LONDON MAIN LINE TERMINI.

From / To......		PADDINGTON First	PADDINGTON Last	EUSTON First	EUSTON Last	MARYLEBONE First	MARYLEBONE Last	LIVERPOOL STREET First	LIVERPOOL STREET Last	KING'S CROSS AND ST. PANCRAS First	KING'S CROSS AND ST. PANCRAS Last
WATERLOO	W	A 5 39	A 12 26	B 5 52	B 12 41	A 5 39	A 12 26	M 5 33	K 12 14	Q 5 33	C 12 25
	S	7 47	11 26	7 22	11 36	7 47	11 26	7 47	11 14	C 7 22	11 23
VICTORIA	W	H 5 58	D 12 19	F 5 43	F 12 19	G 5 30	G 12 10	L 5 30	D 12 10	L 5 30	D 12 19
	S	7 48	11 51	7 26	11 26	7 26	11 16	7 26	11 36	7 26	11 36
CHARING CROSS	W	A 5 41	A 12 28	B 5 54	B 12 43	A 5 41	A 12 28	L 5 35	K 12 16	Q 5 35	C 12 27
	S	7 49	11 28	7 24	11 38	7 49	11 28	7 31	D 11 41	C 7 24	D 11 41
LONDON BRIDGE	W	N 5 49	N 12 22	B 5 49	B 12 22	J 5 48	J 12 13	E 5 49	E 12 22	B 5 49	B 12 22
	S	7 23	11 32	7 23	11 32	7 42	11 11	7 53	11 25	7 23	11 32

W—Weekdays

NOTES

S—Sundays

A—Direct by Bakerloo Line.
B—Direct by Northern Line
C—By Northern Line to Leicester Square, thence by Piccadilly Line.
D—Direct by Inner Circle Line.
E—By Northern Line to Bank, thence by Central Line.
F—By District Line to Charing Cross, thence by Northern Line.
G—By District Line to Charing Cross, thence by Bakerloo Line.
H—By District Line to South Kensington, thence by Inner Circle Line.
J—By Northern Line to Elephant and Castle, thence by Bakerloo Line.
K—By Northern Line to Tottenham Court Road, thence by Central Line.
L—By District Line to Aldgate East, thence by Metropolitan Line.
M—By Bakerloo Line to Oxford Circus, thence by Central Line.
N—By Northern Line to Moorgate, thence by Metropolitan Line.
Q—By Bakerloo Line to Piccadilly Circus, thence by Piccadilly Line.

LONDON TERMINI INTER-STATION BUS SERVICE. DAILY (Christmas Day excepted).

		p.m.	p.m. (Not Sundays and Bank Holidays)	p.m.	p.m.	p.m.	p.m.	p.m.	p.m.	p.m.	p.m.	p.m.	p.m.	ngt.	a.m.	a.m.
WATERLOO ......dep		6 11	6 41	7 11	7 41	8 11	8 41	9 11	9 41	10 11	10 41	11 11	11 41	12 11	...	4 26
VICTORIA	arr	6 21	6 51	7 21	7 51	8 21	8 51	9 21	9 51	10 21	10 51	11 21	11 51	12 21	...	4 36
	dep	6 25	6 55	7 25	7 55	8 25	8 55	9 25	9 55	10 25	10 55	11 25	11 55	12 25	...	4 40
PADDINGTON	arr	6 38	7 8	7 38	8 8	8 38	9 8	9 38	10 8	10 38	11 8	11 38	12 8	12 38	...	4 53
	dep	6 43	7 13	7 43	8 13	8 43	9 13	9 43	10 13	10 43	11 13	11 43	12 13	12 43	...	4 58
EUSTON	arr	6 53	7 23	7 53	8 23	8 53	9 23	9 53	10 23	10 53	11 23	11 53	12 23	12 53	...	5 8
	dep	6 58	7 28	7 58	8 28	8 58	9 28	9 58	10 28	10 58	11 28	11 58	12 28	12 58	...	5 13
KING'S CROSS	arr	7 2	7 32	8 2	8 32	9 2	9 32	10 2	10 32	11 2	11 32	12 2	12 32	1 2	...	5 17
	dep	7 7	7 37	8 7	8 37	9 7	9 37	10 7	10 37	11 7	11 37	12 7	12 37	1 7	3 22	5 22
WATERLOO ......arr		7 21	7 51	8 21	8 51	9 21	9 51	10 21	10 51	11 21	11 51	12 21	12 51	1 21	3 36	5 36

		p.m.	p.m.	p.m.	p.m.	p.m.	p.m.	p.m.	p.m.	p.m.	p.m.	p.m.	p.m.	a.m.	a.m.	
WATERLOO ......dep		6 26	6 56	7 26	7 56	8 26	8 56	9 26	9 56	10 26	10 56	11 26	11 56	3 3	3 41	...
KING'S CROSS	arr	6 40	7 10	7 40	8 10	8 40	9 10	9 40	10 10	10 40	11 10	11 40	12 10	3 17	3 55	...
	dep	6 45	7 15	7 45	8 15	8 45	9 15	9 45	10 15	10 45	11 15	11 45	12 15	...	4 0	...
EUSTON	arr	6 49	7 19	7 49	8 19	8 49	9 19	9 49	10 19	10 49	11 19	11 49	12 19	...	4 4	...
	dep	6 54	7 24	7 54	8 24	8 54	9 24	9 54	10 24	10 54	11 24	11 54	12 24	...	4 9	...
PADDINGTON	arr	7 4	7 34	8 4	8 34	9 4	9 34	10 4	10 34	11 4	11 34	12 4	12 34	...	...	...
	dep	7 9	7 39	8 9	8 39	9 9	9 39	10 9	10 39	11 9	11 39	12 9	12 39	...	...	...
VICTORIA	arr	7 22	7 52	8 22	8 52	9 22	9 52	10 22	10 52	11 22	11 52	12 22	12 52	...	...	...
	dep	7 26	7 56	8 26	8 56	9 26	9 56	10 26	10 56	11 26	11 56	12 26	12 56	...	...	...
WATERLOO ......arr		7 36	8 6	8 36	9 6	9 36	10 6	10 36	11 6	11 36	12 6	12 36	1 6	...	4 21	...

OMNIBUS COMPANIES
IN ASSOCIATION WITH THE
SOUTHERN RAILWAY

Company	Head Office	Area Served
Aldershot & District Traction Co., Ltd.	Halimote Rd., Aldershot, Hants. (Aldershot 330.)	West Surrey, East and North Hants.
Devon General Omnibus and Touring Co., Ltd.	Newton Rd., Torquay. (Torquay 63226.)	East and South Devon.
East Kent Road Car Co., Ltd...	Odsal House, Harbledown, Near Canterbury. (Canterbury 3291.)	East Kent.
Hants & Dorset Motor Services, Ltd.	Royal Mews, Norwich Avenue, Bournemouth. (Bournemouth 2264.)	South Hants. and East Dorset.
Maidstone and District Motor Services, Ltd.*	Knightrider House, Knightrider Street, Maidstone. (Maidstone 2211.)	West Kent and East Sussex.
Southdown Motor Services, Ltd.	5, Steine Street, Brighton. (Brighton 4033.)	Sussex and East Hants.
Southern National Omnibus Co., Ltd.	48/50, Queen Street, Exeter. (Exeter 4191.)	Dorset, Somerset, East & North Devon, and North Cornwall.
Southern Vectis Omnibus Co., Ltd.*	Nelson Road, Newport, Isle of Wight. (Newport 2456.)	Isle of Wight.
Thames Valley Traction Co., Ltd.	83, Lower Thorn St., Reading. (Reading 4028/9.)	Berks., South Bucks, and South Oxon.
Wilts and Dorset Motor Services, Ltd.	8, Endless Street, Salisbury. (Salisbury 2255.)	Salisbury and District.

Time Tables of the above-mentioned Companies' services may be obtained at their respective Head Offices, also at their Inquiry Offices and Agencies and (except in the cases marked *) at the principal Southern Railway Stations in each Company's area.

First published 1947

ISBN 0 7110 2837 0

Published by Ian Allan Publishing

an imprint of Ian Allan Publishing Ltd, Terminal House,
Shepperton, Surrey TW17 8AS.
Printed and bound by T.J. International Ltd,
Trecerus Industrial Estate, Padstow,
Cornwall PL28 8RW.

Code: 0102/A